THOMAS JEFFERSON UNIVERSITY

A Chronological History

and

Alumni Directory

THOMAS JEFFERSON UNIVERSITY

~

A Chronological History
and
Alumni Directory

Annotated and Illustrated

1824 ~ 1990

Edited by

Frederick B. Wagner, Jr., M.D. and J. Woodrow Savacool, M.D.

Foreword by Paul C. Brucker, M.D., Sc.D
President, Thomas Jefferson University

1992

Printed in the United states of America

Print Number: 5 4 3 2 1

~ FOREWORD ~

For over a century and a half Jefferson has graduated many students. They chose to matriculate and train at Jefferson for a myriad of reasons and all with a similar goal—to become excellent health professionals. They satisfied the high Jefferson standards and eventually met the accreditation, certification, and licensure requirements of varied agencies. Jefferson is proud of them!

Fortunately, graduation from Jefferson is only the first step in their professional careers. We instill a spirit of academic curiosity in our graduates, along with a sense of professional responsibility, encouraging them to be students for life. Many of our alumni return to Jefferson for continuing education, and others contribute a great deal to various academic programs both at Jefferson and elsewhere. They perpetuate the excellent reputation for training health professionals which Thomas Jefferson University has grown to enjoy.

However, our alumni do a great deal more than just grow professionally! After graduation they continue to show gratitude to their alma mater in various ways. They remember friends and acquaintances; they have many stories about the faculty who taught them; and they are continuously inquisitive about the state and direction of the University. All of this activity is a reflection of an intense loyalty and commitment to Jefferson. The Alumni return regularly to class reunions, encourage potential students to apply, and are most generous when it comes to development campaigns. Many similar institutions would like to get a "page from our book of success."

In a more narrow sense, despite the relatively large size of the classes at Jefferson, it is unusual that so many graduates keep in touch. They maintain friendships, develop new professional ties, and are extremely proud and pleased that Jefferson has provided an important integrating focus for such relationships.

All of these considerations stimulated Drs. Wagner and Savacool to compile and edit this book. It is much more than the traditional alumni directory, which has great value in its own right. The authors have coupled a directory with an annotated and illustrated chronological history of Jefferson. That is what makes this directory so important and unique! It will make all of us more aware and proud of the Jefferson heritage, stimulate many pleasant recollections, and provide the opportunity for additional narrative. The *Chronological History and Alumni Directory* is a documentary of why Jefferson is such an esteemed University. It deals with the countless individuals who have made this possible.

Over the past several years I have had the pleasure to watch Drs. Wagner and Savacool work together in such an exacting, cooperative, and fraternal fashion. Although they had abundant support in collecting information, they themselves spent a great deal of time and meticulous effort in preferentially selecting the anecdotes and illustrations that make this directory so vibrant.

On behalf of the Jefferson community I want to thank them for all their work and also for their invitation to write the Foreword. The *Chronological History and Alumni Directory* will occupy a prominent spot in my library!

Paul C. Brucker, M.D., Sc.D.
President, Thomas Jefferson University

~ PREFACE ~

Publication of *Thomas Jefferson University: Tradition and Heritage* (1989) sparked an increased interest in the history of this institution. It served to highlight the careers of its professors along with the progress in their departments. In a sense this was a longitudinal history. The main thrust of the present book is to compile the names of those who received instruction in the Medical College, School of Nursing, College of Graduate Studies, College of Allied Health Sciences, and to include a new category of those who took training in residencies and fellowships. Another separate category lists Honorary Medical College Alumni. The names are recorded as they appear on the diplomas or certificates. In addition, this history will feature significant events on a yearly or vertical basis.

Certain individuals were selected from the various categories for special mention because of outstanding achievement. The editors acknowledge the risk of imbalance in such a policy, for which forbearance is requested. Photographs were lavishly included to enhance the vitality of this type of presentation. Search of prior historical sources such as Minutes of the Board of Trustees, all College Catalogues, Gould's *Jefferson Medical College of Philadelphia* (1904), *General Alumni Catalogue* (1917), Commencement Programs, Student Yearbooks, *Jefferson Medical College Alumni Bulletin*, *Karyon* (College of Allied Health Sciences), *Nosokomos* (School of Nursing), and especially the records of the various alumni offices, provided listings. Serial proofreadings additionally ensured the accuracy of the names.

A task of this magnitude could not have been accomplished by the editors alone. The Medical College Alumni Staff (Mary B. Montieth, Executive Director; Joan Schott, Associate Director for Annual Giving; Cynthia J.T. Clendenin, Associate Editor, Alumni Bulletin; Victoria Fullam, Associate Director for Programs and Events; Lisa M. DiCampli; Agnes Plevakas; Luann McGough; and Elizabeth Kerr) aided considerably when information was lacking or needed clarification. Faith McDowell, also from the Alumni Office, painstakingly collected and documented the names for the newly organized Postgraduate Alumni.

Nancy Braceland, Director, Office of House Staff Affairs, provided enthusiastic cooperation pertaining to the records and photographs of past residents and fellows.

The Medical Media Services (formerly Audiovisual) expertly processed the hundreds of photographs submitted, some of which were in disrepair. Pejman Makarechi, Earl J. Spangenberg and David Super carried out this work.

Claire McCurdy (Archivist), assisted by Maria Jackson and Jonathan Penders (Archival Technicians), aided in the historical searches.

Margaret L. Summers (R.N., '41) and Elizabeth Piersol (R.N., '34) from the Alumni Office of the Diploma School of Nurses Association, provided access to Alumni Bulletins, Nosokomos Yearbooks and alumni listings.

Maria C. Elfreth, Director of Alumni Programs in the College of Graduate Studies and College of Allied Health Sciences, coordinated information from both colleges.

Mr. Joseph W. Donovan, Director of Marketing and Public Relations (CAHS), acted as lead member of the team that supplied essential information and photographs for the College of Allied Health Sciences. Members of this group were: Dorothy Grieb, Health Careers Guidance Clinic; Michael J. Paquet, Registrar; and William Thygeson, Student Affairs and Services Director.

To Elaine T. Nader, Assistant to the University History Section, fell the task of computerizing the entire project, requiring prolonged concentration and persistence. Richard Chandler of Information Systems acted as a consultant in the programming.

Finally, Franklin W. Smith and Frank M. Colgan, of William J. Dornan, Inc. were outstandingly helpful in the design and typesetting of the text.

Frederick B. Wagner, Jr., M.D.
J. Woodrow Savacool, M.D.
Editors

~ CONTENTS ~

Part I

Jefferson Medical College

Jefferson Medical College (ca. 1850s)

Fig. 1.   Founders of Jefferson Medical College (1824).

2

On June 2, 1824, Dr. George McClellan, along with Dr. John Eberle, Dr. Joseph Klapp, and Mr. Jacob Green, M.A. (Fig. 1) sent a formal application to the Trustees of Jefferson College at Canonsburg, Pennsylvania, for permission to establish a medical school in Philadelphia as the Medical Department of that institution (Fig. 2). This would enable these men to form a medical faculty under the charter of a mother school located southwest of Pittsburgh, ten days distant by stagecoach. This unusual request was a strategy to circumvent the frustration owing to their inability to obtain a charter from the legislature in Harrisburg in which all previous attempts had been blocked.

Later in the same month, the Trustees at Canonsburg agreed to establish the requested medical school in Philadelphia. As a part of their institution, they were to be its legal Guardians and Directors. "Articles of Union" were submitted to the applicants and consummated on October 30, 1824 (Fig. 3). This was the founding of the Jefferson Medical College of Philadelphia as the Medical Department of Jefferson College of Canonsburg.

With vestment of authority, the skeleton faculty continued lectures without interruption in the former private facilities at George (now Sansom) and Swanwick Streets, near Independence Square. The first lecture under the charter was given by McClellan. The first faculty meeting was held December 20.

Fig. 2.   Jefferson College at Canonsburg, Pennsylvania, around 1850. (Courtesy of H.T.W. Coleman, *Banners in the Wilderness*, Univ. of Pittsburgh Press, 1956.)

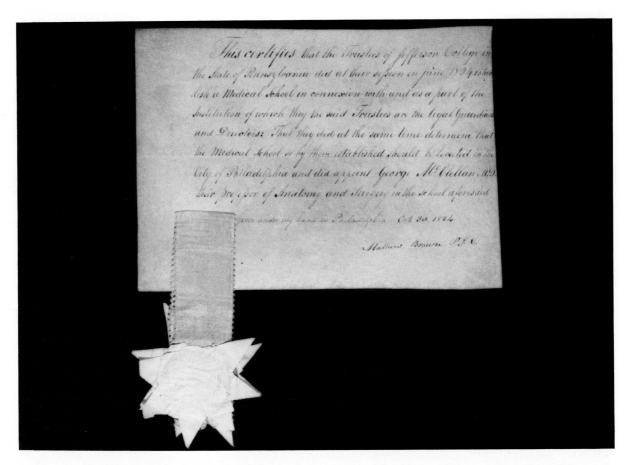

Fig. 3. The founding document states: "This certifies that the Trustees of Jefferson College in the State of Pennsylvania did at their session in June 1824 establish a Medical School in connection with and as a part of the institution of which they the said Trustees are the legal Guardians and Directors: That they did at the same time determine that the Medical School so by them established should be located in the City of Philadelphia and did appoint George McClellan, M.D. their Professor of Anatomy and Surgery in the school aforesaid."

Given under my hand in Philadelphia, Oct. 30, 1824.

Mathew Brown, P.J.C.

Fig. 4. Tivoli Theater at 518-20 Prune Street (now Locust), site of first Jefferson Medical College.

Effective January 1, 1825, a lease was signed to rent the Tivoli Theater at 518-20 Prune Street (now Locust Walk) just east of Washington Square, at an annual rate of $550 (Fig. 4 & 5). After some remodeling at a cost of $100, the "Hall of the Jefferson Medical College" was opened on March 8. An infirmary was officially started on May 16 for free medical and surgical care of out-patients as well as for the teaching of medical students. It was the first clinic established in any college in the country.

The officially designated first academic session was instituted on the last Thursday in October. Six professors lectured in the hall and provided clinical supervision in the infirmary. Tuition for this session was $78. Since the school was proprietary, the fees were paid directly to the professors, who issued tickets for their lectures.

Fig. 5.   Plaque erected in 1987 by the Alumni Association, marking site of first Jefferson Medical College.
Left to right: Robert Poole, III, M.D. (JMC, '53), Joseph S. Gonnella (Dean, JMC), Frederick B. Wagner, Jr., M.D. (JMC '41) and J. Woodrow Savacool, M.D. (JMC, '38).

On January 30, 1826, the Chairman of the Board of Trustees of the University of Pennsylvania read a protest before the Senate in Harrisburg challenging the right and power of the Jefferson Medical College to grant the M.D. degree. Dr. McClellan, who learned that a vote was to be taken in the legislature on April 7, made a legendary dash to the State Capitol and delivered an impassioned speech for the granting of the diploma. His efforts were rewarded by favorable action, representing the first state legislative recognition of the existence of Jefferson Medical College.

On April 14, the first Jefferson Medical College Commencement which had been under postponement, was held at Medical Hall (old Tivoli Theater) on Prune Street. Twenty matriculates received the M.D. diploma (Fig. 7). Among them was Nathan Lewis Hatfield, who held an A.B. degree from the University of Pennsylvania and was well prepared for the practice he established in the growing area of North Philadelphia where he became widely known as a consulting physician (Fig. 6). Active in the Northern Medical Association and in the American Medical Association following its organization in 1848, he also served as President of the Philadelphia County Medical Society in 1865. In 1870 he was elected Chairman of the organizing group for the Jefferson Alumni Association and he became the Association's President in 1874/1875. He was an active proponent of the development of the Medical College Hospital which was completed in 1877 and he also emphasized the need for innovation in premedical and medical education to adapt to medical progress. Dr. Hatfield was memorialized in 1898 by the Hatfield Memorial Fund and Lectureship at the College of Physicians of Philadelphia, and in 1946 with the Nathan Lewis Hatfield Professorship of Urology at Jefferson.

Moses L. Knapp located in the Middle West where he practiced in numerous areas becoming known as a "new schools man." Having been a founder of the Rush Medical College, Chicago, in 1835, he and colleagues established a "branch" of Madison Medical College in Rock Island, Illinois, in 1848. He became Dean and Professor of Materia Medica and Therapeutics. Dr. Knapp also served on the faculty of two new Iowa medical schools and of LaPorte Medical College in Indiana. He was always highly regarded as a teacher and man of letters but for health reasons he left his academic pursuits in 1852 and practiced in Kentucky.

Fig. 6.   Nathan Lewis Hatfield (JMC, 1826) served as President of the Alumni Association (1874/75). (Photograph courtesy of Historical Collections of College of Physicians of Philadelphia.)

The First Diploma

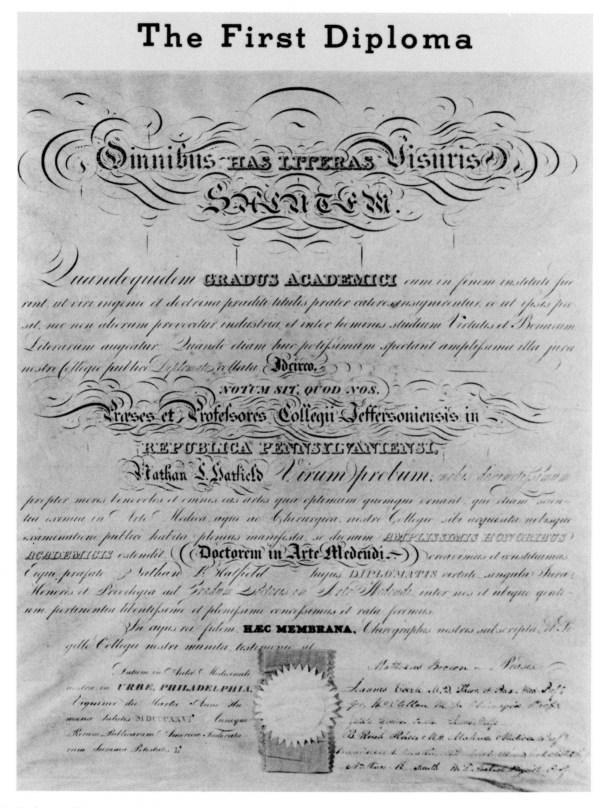

Fig. 7. Diploma of Nathan L. Hatfield, a prominent member of the first graduating class of 1826. (Translation in the text.)

Translation of the Original
Jefferson Medical College Diploma (Fig. 7)

To all who shall see these writings, greetings: For as much as academic degrees were instituted to the intent that men endowed with learning and wisdom should be distinguished from others by honors, to the end that this might be profitable to them, and also that the industry of others might be stimulated and the exercise of virtue and the liberal arts be exercised among men:

And as the fullest rights conferred publicly by diploma in our college have this end chiefly in view:

Therefore be it known, that we, the Presidents and Professors of Jefferson Medical College of Philadelphia, in the Commonwealth of Pennsylvania, have created and constituted a Doctor in the Art of Healing..........., an honorable man endeared to us by correct morals and all those virtues which adorn every good man; who, also, by his excellent knowledge of medicine as well as of surgical art acquired by him in this College, and manifested more fully in an examination publicly held by us, has shown himself worthy of the fullest academic honors.

To the one thus referred to, ..., we have by virtue of this diploma, most freely and fully granted and confirmed all the rights, honors and privileges belonging to the degree of Doctor in the Art of Medicine, among ourselves, and all nations.

In evidence of which let this diploma, signed in our handwriting, and having appended the seal of the College, be a testimonial.

Given in our medical hall, in the city of Philadelphia, on the .... day of .... in the year of human salvation..........., and in the .... year of the sovereign power of the United States of America.

CLASS OF 1826

Baldwin, George, PA
Beckman, Peter Q., NJ
Brinton, John Bowen, PA
Carll, George, PA
Coit, Benjamin B., CT
Dick, Thomas M., SC
Foster, Joel, VT
Glover, Ralph, NJ
Graff, Charles, PA
Graham, John, IRELAND

Griffiths, Charles M., PA
Griffiths, Jesse W., PA
Hatfield, Nathan L., PA
Johnson, William, PA
Knapp, M. L., NY
Maxwell, Thomas B., PA
Pelham, Atkinson, KY
Shaw, Benjamin, PA
Stadiger, J. Frederick, PA
Swan, James, MA

Among the 34 graduates of Jefferson's second class was Anson Jones from Massachusetts (Fig. 8). He was one of the first, if not the first, physician with formal medical education to practice in Texas. He founded the Medical Association of the State of Texas, was appointed Minister of the Republic of Texas (1838) to the United States by Sam Houston, served as Secretary of State (1841) of the Republic, and in 1844 was elected the fourth and last President (until 1846). He is the only American physician to have been elected President of even a portion of the present United States.

Another illustrious member of this class was Samuel S. Fitch (Fig. 9). Only two years after graduation, he published a *System of Dental Sur-gery* (Fig. 10). This book was sophisticated for its time and antedated the establishment of the first College of Dental Surgery in 1840 (Baltimore) by eleven years. He practiced as a surgeon-dentist.

Charles A. Luzenberg was notable for his part in the founding of the Medical College of Louisiana (later Tulane University School of Medicine). A controversial figure, his association with the Medical School was brief but he became well known for philanthropic and public activities including the founding of the Louisiana Medico-Chirurgical Society and an orphan asylum. Dr. Luzenberg's German birth, plus his French and German post-graduate education, contributed greatly to the moulding of his career. He died at the early age of 43.

Fig. 8. Anson Jones (JMC, 1827), last President of the Republic of Texas (1844-46).

Bitner, Abraham, PA
Carpenter, Isaac B., OH
Cullen, Patrick, VA
Cunningham, John, PA
Dingle, Edward C., DE
Donaldson, Alex C., PA
Endress, Samuel, PA
Fitch, Samuel S., VT
Hale, David, ME
Herbst, Frederick W., PA
Hubbard, Russell B., CT
Jones, Anson, PA
Kelly, Patrick PA
Kinsey, John, DE
Kline, Isaac, PA
Luzenberg, Charles A., PA
McCamant, Thomas J., PA

McCleery, William, PA
McIntosh, John P., MS
Mears, George Washington, PA
Morton, George R., PA
Murdock, John S., PA
Nichols, Benjamin R., RI
Russell, John W., CT
Shannon, Peter, PA
Sherer, Jacob, PA
Shock, Jacob G., PA
Shotwell, Randolph, NJ
Stubbs, Jeremiah B., PA
Thompson, Levis P., PA
Waldo, Frederick A., NY
Wales, Edmund L.B., NJ
Weidler, Isaac C., PA
Wray, Robert, PA

Fig. 9. Samuel Sheldon Fitch (JMC, 1827), pioneer in Dental Surgery.

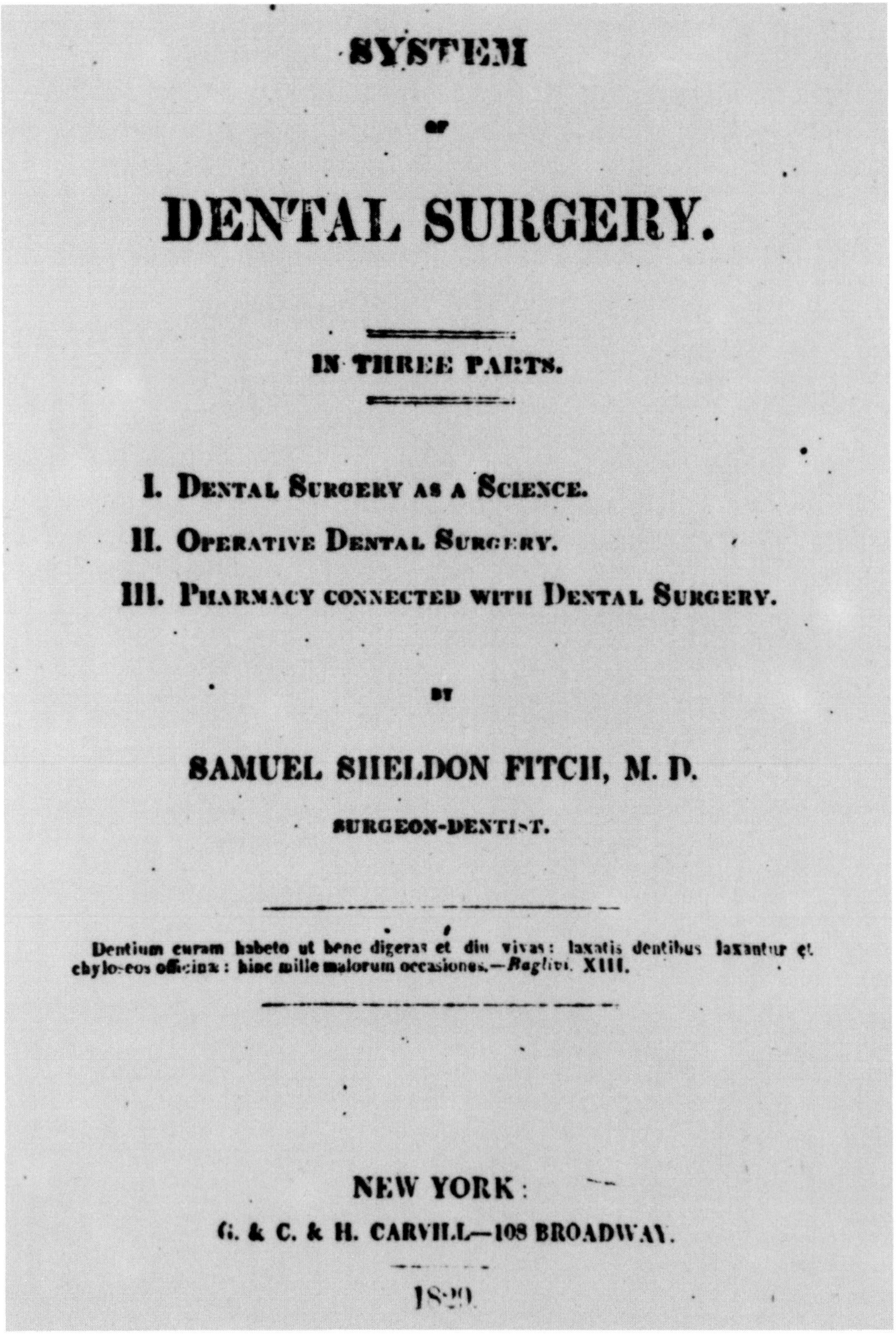

SYSTEM

OF

DENTAL SURGERY.

IN THREE PARTS.

I. DENTAL SURGERY AS A SCIENCE.

II. OPERATIVE DENTAL SURGERY.

III. PHARMACY CONNECTED WITH DENTAL SURGERY.

BY

SAMUEL SHELDON FITCH, M. D.

SURGEON-DENTIST.

Dentium curam habeto ut bene digeras et diu vivas: laxatis dentibus laxantur et chylo-eos officina: hinc mille malorum occasiones.—*Baglivi.* XIII.

NEW YORK:

G. & C. & H. CARVILL—108 BROADWAY.

1829.

Fig. 10.   Title page of Fitch's *System of Dental Surgery*.

This class was the last to graduate in Medical Hall of the old Tivoli Theater. The star of its 25 members was Samuel D. Gross (Fig. 11). He stands as tall as any in the galaxy of Jefferson alumni, and was the founding President of the Alumni Association in 1870. The embodiment of dignity and scholarship, he successfully pioneered in combining clinical surgery, teaching, and research in an academic setting. His superb attributes brought lasting fame to his alma mater and worldwide recognition to American medicine as a whole.

By August, 1828, the cornerstone of a New Medical Hall was laid at Tenth and Moravian Streets (Fig. 12). Funds for the Hall were provided by the Reverend Ezra Stiles Ely (Fig. 13), Secretary of the Board of Trustees, and the facility was rented by the Professors for $1200 annually. Lectures for the academic session were started in November, 1828. With enlargements and renovations, this building would serve until 1898 when the Jefferson Medical College moved to a new site at Tenth and Walnut Streets.

Fig. 11.   Samuel D. Gross (JMC, 1828), Professor of Surgery and Founder of the Alumni Association. (Shown in his later years.)

Bailey, Gama, PA
Bateman, Benjamin Rush, NJ
Beck, Samuel L., PA
Butler, John S., MA
Coit, Daniel T., CT
Davis, Charles, PA
Gardner, Joseph, PA
Gilbert, David, PA
Gregg, Daniel H., MA
Gross, Samuel D., PA
Higbee, Hugh H., NJ
James, David, PA
Leedom, John, PA

Maillard, Philogene P., ST. CROIX
Morgan, James, CT
O'Flaherty, Thomas J., VA
Oliver, James G., PA
Payne, George H., VA
Ream, John, PA
Seiler, Christian, PA
Slaughter, James, PA
Walker, Charles, MA
Welling, Joseph C., NJ
Welsh, John, PA
Zook, Henry, PA

Fig. 12.   New Medical Hall (1828).

Fig. 13. The Reverend Ezra Stiles Ely, Secretary of the Board of Trustees, Jefferson's first benefactor by providing funds for the new Medical Hall of 1828 at Tenth and Moravian Streets.

The fourth Commencement was held for the 25 graduates in the new Medical College (Ely Building) on Tenth Street (site of the present "Old Main Hospital"). The exercises would be held there for the next three years.

The outstanding member of this class was Washington L. Atlee (Fig. 14). He was instrumental in reviving the operation of ovariotomy (known later as oophorectomy) which had only been done occasionally since the first by Ephraim McDowell in 1809. Atlee's first ovariotomy was on March 29, 1844. During the next 34 years he performed 387. In addition, he reported the first successful abdominal myomectomy for fibroids in 1845. He was a founding member of the American Gynecologic Society and American Medical Association, and President of the Philadelphia County Medical Society in 1874.

James McClintock, a member of the graduating class, quickly became noted for anatomical demonstrations he began as a student of Professors John Eberle and George McClellan. He proceeded to several teaching posts including a private Philadelphia School of Anatomy. In 1847 he founded a medical school which was granted a charter as the Philadelphia College of Medicine, but in 1858 it merged with the Medical Department of Pennsylvania College (founder George McClellan). This institution became a casualty of the Civil War in 1861.

Fig. 14. Washington L. Atlee (JMC, 1829), pioneer in ovariotomy (oophorectomy).

Atlee, Washington L., PA
Baily, Obed, PA
Bates, Stephen, MA
Bedard, Rene, CANADA
Corbin, S. W., NY
Davis, Kendall, NH
DeHaven, Augustus A., PA
Evans, John W.C., PA
Fournier, John C., CANADA
Gallaher, William, PA
Gilbert, Jesse, PA
Goldsmith, Thomas Oliver, PA
Hickman, Joseph, PA
McClintock, James, PA
McNair, James B., PA
Mears, Benjamin Jr., PA
Oldham, William H., MD
Purdue, John H., PA
Scanlan, James William, MD
Sharpe, William, PA
Sheldon, Benjamin, MA
Sickler, John R., NJ
Sprague, Rollin, CT
Taylor, Hamilton, NC
Vastine, Thomas Jefferson, PA

No 47 MATRICULATION.

Jefferson Medical College, Philadelphia.

THIS TICKET SIGNIFIES THAT

Julius A. Keffer

is regularly matriculated in this Institution, free of any charge.

Wm P. C. Barton *Dean.*

November 9. 1829

JEFFERSON MEDICAL COLLEGE.

PRACTICAL ANATOMY,

AND

Demonstrations.

BY

SAMUEL M'CLELLAN, M. D.

For Julius A Keffer.

PHILADELPHIA, Nov. 1829

The years between 1828 and 1832 were the darkest in Jefferson's history. There were so many Faculty changes during this critical period of struggle for survival that it was referred to as "the game of musical chairs." There was personal rivalry and in-fighting among the Professors, financial instability, and continued harassment from the University of Pennsylvania.

The addition of Dr. Daniel Drake to the Faculty in 1830 as Professor of Theory and Practice of Medicine offered much promise at this time (Fig. 15). He had already been prominent in the medical history of the West and brought students with him. Dreaming of founding his own medical school in Cincinnati, he stayed at Jefferson only one year.

Jonathan Messersmith Foltz, a native of Pennsylvania, outstanding among the 35 graduates, advanced to Fleet Surgeon in the Medical Department of the United States Navy and was later named Surgeon General. He was the first Jefferson Alumnus to become a regular White House physician with an office in the White House under President James Buchanan.

In accord with the agreement with the Jefferson College Trustees (Canonsburg) that required admission of a certain number of free students, James Chamberlain of this class was the first to graduate from the Medical College under its terms.

Fig. 15. Daniel Drake, M.D., Third Chairman of Medicine (1830/31).

Barber, David, PA
Bell, Edward S., VA
Cathcart, Thomas Latimer, PA
Chamberlain, James, PA
Compton, Azel, NJ
Coverly, Thomas Z., PA
De la Puente, Eligio, CUBA
Downer, Fenno, CT
Duer, George S., PA
Dunn, Samuel, PA
Entriken, Smith, PA
Fisher, John F., PA
Foltz, Jonathan M., PA
Garrison, William P., NJ
Grosvenor, William, CT
Haller, Theodore N., PA
Hood, S. W., KY
Hudson, James A, DE

Imlay, John H., NJ
Kerfoot, George B., PA
Kilduffe, Robert, PA
Lewis, George H., CT
Martin, John, DE
Matlack, Isaiah, PA
Maull, George W., DE
McMahan, William, PA
Miller, Simon, NJ
Moran, Patrick, PA
Mulford, William C., NJ
Sailer, Thomas, PA
Salter, James W., PA
Stevens, Erastus, PA
Stewart, Robert, PA
VanKeusen, James, NY
Wistar, Richard M., PA

THE

ANATOMY,

PHYSIOLOGY, AND DISEASES

OF THE

BONES AND JOINTS.

BY SAMUEL D. GROSS, M. D.

Philadelphia:
JOHN GRIGG, NO. 9, NORTH FOURTH STREET.

1830.

This year was another low point in Jefferson's struggle for survival in which enemies had referred to it as "an institution where confusion, irregularity, and discord have prevailed from the moment of its birth." Dr. Benjamin Rush Rhees, the first Dean (1825-27) and a stellar teacher, died from tuberculosis at age 33 in October of this year (Fig. 16).

Dr. Usher Parsons accepted the vacated Chair of Midwifery, but taught for only a year. His departure was lamented by the students and was one more blow to the College.

On the positive side, two strong Professors were appointed this year who would remain for a decade. The first was Dr. John Revere (Fig. 17), son of the revolutionary patriot, Paul Revere, as Head of Theory and Practice of Medicine. The second was Dr. Granville Sharpe Pattison (Fig. 19) as Professor of Anatomy. In addition to his popularity as a teacher, he founded the Museum, enlarged the anatomical rooms, and improved the reputation of the school.

There were 32 graduates in this class.

Fig. 16.   Benjamin Rush Rhees, M.D., Professor of Materia Medica and Institutes of Medicine (1825-30) and First Dean (1825-27).

Arts, Joseph D.C., PA
Bacon, James W., KY
Beamer, George H., PA
Bye, Charles P., PA
Clinger, George, PA
Dare, George T., PA
Davis, David H., KY
DePrefontaine, Joseph R., PA
Devazac, Augustus, LA
Dodd, Robert J., PA
Egbert, Asa, OH
Gegan, John, PA
Given, James J., PA
Godwin, William P., TN
Henderson, Lorenzo N., PA
Klapp, John R., NY

Leonard, John Jr., PA
Lowrie, James A., PA
Meredith, Charles F., PA
Pearson, Seba A., PA
Pugh, John M., PA
Ramsey, Alexander, PA
Rohrer, John S., PA
Sheldon, Jonathan, PA
Steele, John, PA
Synnott, Myles, NJ
Talbot, John A., VA
Vanneman, William S., NJ
Wersler, William, PA
Willson, John J., NJ
Willson, Samuel, PA
Wily, Owen H., PA

Fig. 17. John Revere, M.D., son of revolutionary patriot Paul Revere, Professor of Medicine (1831-41) and Dean (1839-41).

This year represented another stage in Jefferson's struggle for survival, the graduating class having numbered only 23. For those who had wished the school would fail and had spread rumors to that effect, this was their golden hour and one of Jefferson's darkest. At this point it was a question of collapse or revival. This rock bottom level, however, was not the end, for the sun was soon to burst through the clouds.

The frequent Faculty changes and reconstructions had resulted in diminishing enrollment. At this juncture, stability was restored in that for the six years of 1832 to 1838 the appointed Professors kept their chairs.

CLASS OF 1832

Campbell, Joseph N., PA
Carpenter, Benoni, MA
Culbertson, Julius, KY
Diverty, James, NJ
Doggett, Perez F., MA
Forry, Samuel, PA
Gemmill, Jacob M., PA
Green, John M., PA
Griffiths, Elijah L., PA
Grossman, John, PA
Haller, Michael E., CANADA

Hutchins, Theophilus S., MA
Lazer, Edwin, MA
Leggett, Hechaliah H., NY
Maxwell, William J., PA
Mellinger, David H., PA
Morton, Francis K., PA
Nagle, Barton, PA
Palmer, Isaac S., PA
Rutherford, William W., PA
Seeger, Edwin, MA
Sinnickson, John J., NJ
Slahter, Edward, PA

HUMAN PHYSIOLOGY;

ILLUSTRATED BY

NUMEROUS ENGRAVINGS.

BY

ROBLEY DUNGLISON, M.D.

PROFESSOR OF PHYSIOLOGY, PATHOLOGY, &c. IN THE UNIVERSITY OF VIRGINIA,
MEMBER OF THE AMERICAN PHILOSOPHICAL SOCIETY, &c.

" Vastissimi studii primas quasi lineas circumscripsi."—HALLER.

VOL. I.

PHILADELPHIA:
CAREY & LEA.
1832.

The commencement Exercises were held this year, and for the next two years (1833-1835), at Masonic Hall, located on the north side of Chestnut Street between Seventh and Eighth. Although the graduates numbered only 22, the enrollment increased substantially, so the class of the succeeding year would be the largest (60) in the College's history to that date.

William Beaumont in this year published his studies on gastric digestion. Robley Dunglison, who was soon to enter Jefferson's history, had collaborated to some extent in this work.

Ninian Pinckney of Maryland, after graduating, enlisted in the Navy and went on to become Medical Director (precursor of later designation of Surgeon-General) with the rank of Commodore. During the Civil War he outfitted a captured Confederate sidewheeler on the Mississippi River, known as the *Red Rover*, as the first hospital ship in U.S. history (Figure 18). Volunteer Catholic nuns acted as nurses (untrained) and represented the first women nurses to care for patients during U.S. wartime. Pinckney improved the status of medical officers by organizing the staff to obtain rank and grade.

Joseph S. Copes, of Delaware, became active in combatting contagious diseases in the South during the mid-nineteenth century. After establishing a large medical practice in Mississippi, he authored the state's vaccination law. He introduced cotton machinery in Mississippi, helped to found Sharon College, and served as Director of Oakland College. After moving to New Orleans in 1849, he served as President of the School Board and an administrator of the University of Louisiana, the predecessor of Tulane University. He was in charge of hospital wards during epidemics of cholera, typhoid fever, and yellow fever and worked to contain the spread of yellow fever during the Civil War. His great-grandson, Mr. Collins C. Diboll, in 1987 endowed the Joseph S. Copes Chair in Epidemiology at Tulane Medical Center with a pledge of one million dollars.

CLASS OF 1833

Blanchard, Azariel, NY
Bryant, Thomas Sydenham, PA
Casey, Edwin A., RI
Copes, Joseph S., DE
Davidson, James K., PA
Fitzpatrick, John, VA
Garvey, Patrick, IRELAND
Hull, Levi, PA
Keffer, Julius A., PA
Levis, Mahlon M., PA
Loud, Watson, MA

Lyon, Thomas, PA
McCulloh, Samuel, MD
McNally, John, IRELAND
Messersmith, John S., PA
Mitchell, Joseph, PA
O'Donnell, Dominick A., PA
Pinckney, Ninian, MD
Snyder, Morgan, NY
Tebbs, Robert H., VA
Upton, George, NY
Waterman, Richard M., RI

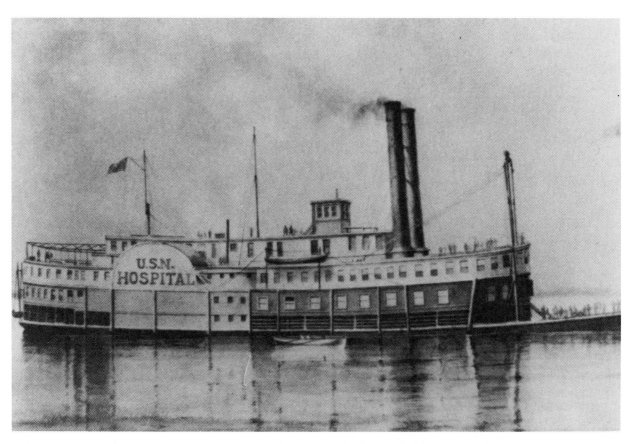

Fig. 18. *Red Rover*, the first Navy hospital ship, outfitted by Ninian Pinckney (JMC, 1833) during the Civil War.

1833

This graduating class of 60 members tripled the ones of the previous two years. It was an auspicious turn of events that boded well for the future of the fledgling school. Unfortunately, however, an unhealthy situation persisted internally in the Faculty in that the six Professors divided themselves into two factions on points of issue. George McClellan (Surgery), Samuel McClellan (Midwifery), and Samuel Colhoun (Materia Medica) were usually united against Granville Pattison (Anatomy, Fig. 19), John Re-

Fig. 19. Granville Sharpe Pattison, Professor of Anatomy (1831-41).

vere (Practice of Medicine), and Jacob Green (Chemistry). Gradually over the next six years the serious external and internal struggles of the school would be resolved.

For those students who wished the ultimate in medical education, Paris at this time was the place to go. During the reign of Louis Philippe (1830-1848) it was the undisputed center for the best organized hospitals in the world. There, likewise, were the great academies of art, conservatories of music, theological seminaries, and best schools in philosophy and science. In 1834, Jean-Baptiste Dumas in the field of chemistry obtained and named chloroform. In 1847 it would be used by Sir James Young Simpson, Professor of Obstetrics and Gynecology in Edinburgh, as a substitute for ether in deliveries.

James Platt White of this class returned to his native New York State and went on to great medical achievements. Founder of the University of Buffalo Medical School in 1846 and Professor of Obstetrics and Gynecology, he was also prominent in public affairs, President of the New York Medical Society, and a highly respected surgeon. His initiation of clinical instruction in obstetrics for medical students evoked early criticism but his principles prevailed.

Daniel Brainerd, a native of New York, proceeded to Chicago (population 7500) in 1835 and promptly founded the Rush Medical College. Early difficulties were encountered but by 1850 the school was well positioned with Brainerd, Professor of Anatomy and Surgery, Moses L. Knapp (JMC, 1826), Professor of Obstetrics and Gynecology and Austin Flint, Sr., Professor of Medicine. Dr. Brainerd achieved success in surgery, teaching, scientific medicine and writing. He was honored with membership in the Societe de Chirurgie in Paris and the Presidency of the Illinois State Medical Society. The Rush Medical College became affiliated with the University of Chicago in 1898.

Allen, Albert Gallatin, VA
Allen, George W., PA
Austin, John T., VA
Awl, William McClay, OH
Battersby, Robert, PA
Battey, Thomas W., GA
Bell, James W., NC
Bissell, William Henry, NY
Bodder, Levi D., GA
Brainard, Daniel, NY
Carpenter, Charles, VT
Cassidy, Alexander M., OH
Clarke, Henry, NY
Crawford, Conyngham, IRELAND
Crawford, James A., PA
Crossman, Thomas J., PA
Dodson, William B., PA
Eaty, Sebastian B., PA
Fawcett, Henry, NY
Field, George, PA
Ganson, Holton, NY
Glezen, Ezra W., PA
Gregg, Patrick, NY
Haden, Madison, VA
Hannay, Thomas, PA
Hays, George Washington, MD
Hereford, Thomas P., VA
Houtz, Daniel, PA
James, Robert E., PA

Jones, William Roberts, ENGLAND
King, Benjamin B., GA
King, David, RI
Lewis, Zachary, VA
Loughran, Terence, IRELAND
Matthews, Washington, PA
McMackin, Edward, PA
McNair, Alexander H., PA
Mitchell, George V., PA
Neff, Jacob K., PA
Newbill, Alexander M., VA
Nixon, Samuel, VA
Orth, Edward L., PA
Perry, George H., RI
Rex, George P., PA
Richmond, John P., MD
Simmonds, James, VA
Stansbury, Robert Mott, NY
Stevenson, J., PA
Stewart, Philander, NY
Swett, Samuel B., MA
Thatcher, Charles A., PA
Walker, John V.F., GA
Ward, David G.W., NC
Watson, D. Edward, VA
White, James P., NY
Whitney, Bradford B., NY
Wilson, Israel Kelly, NOVA SCOTIA
Woodson, Albert P., VA
Wooldridge, Beverly H., VA
Wright, Joseph J., PA

History is one of the most powerful driving forces in human development. Every situation that man has faced and every problem that he has had to solve have been the product of historical developments and processes. Furthermore, the way in which we act is, in large measure, determined by the mental image of the past that we have created. To understand our own society, to be capable of playing an intelligent role in shaping our own civilization, we must have knowledge of the actions of the past.

George Rosen (Editor, Journal of
the History of Medicine)

This graduating class of 59 members was graced by the name of James Marion Sims, a native of South Carolina. He became one of the most gifted and creative of American surgeons, which earned him the title of "Father of American Gynecology" (Fig. 20). His surgical career started immediately upon graduation in that he operated successfully for abscess of the liver in 1835 and removed both the upper and lower jaw in 1837. In the field of gynecology he discovered the Sim's position, devised the special curved speculum which bears his name, used silver wire sutures to avoid sepsis, and reported the cure for vesicovaginal fistula in 1852. In 1855 he established the Woman's Hospital in New York City which rendered the best gynecologic care of its time (Fig. 21). He was among the first to perform cholecystostomy, advocated the suture of intestinal wounds, and suggested the cleansing of the peritoneal cavity during its surgery. A statue erected to his memory in 1894 in Bryant Park, New York City, by admirers on both sides of the Atlantic was the first full length statue in the United States in honor of a physician (Fig. 135). (The one erected in 1897 in Washington, D.C. for Samuel D. Gross, now in Scott plaza, was the second).

Fig. 20.   J. Marion Sims (JMC, 1835), "Father of American Gynecology".

Fig. 21.   Stained glass window from Woman's Hospital in New York City founded by Dr. J. Marion Sims, featuring quotations from the Bible relating to gynecology and obstetrics. (Courtesy of Reynolds Historical Library of the University of Alabama at Birmingham.)

1835

Anderson, Isaac W., PA
Baker, William N., NY
Barclay, John, IRELAND
Bolling, Archibald, VA
Brooks, Jonathan W., CT
Bunting, Thomas C., PA
Chaytor, George W., MD
Cloud, Noah B., SC
Coles, Abraham, NJ
Cooper, William, PA
Crittenden, Edmund W., NY
Dabney, Thomas S., VA
Dickinson, John, MA
Dilworth, Richard B., PA
Dungan, James B., NY
Eshleman, John W., PA
Faulcon, Edward W., VA
Gegan, Richard, PA
Geoghegan, Richard, PA
Hairston, George S., VA
Hedges, Urban D., DE
Henderson, Matthew, PA
Higgs, Thomas F., GA
Hill, Charles H., PA
Hitchcock, Enos P., NY
Hort, William M.W., SC
Horton, Harry M., PA
Jenkins, William T., GA
Kirkwood, William, NY

Lockwood, Timothy T., NY
Manning, John H., MA
Martin, Thomas W., TN
McEwen, William, PA
McKelway, Alexander J., NJ
Mercer, William T., NJ
Mittower, Abraham, NY
Munger, Erastus, A., NY
Naudain, Andrew, DE
Newell, John H., VA
Parsons, James M., GA
Peniston, Thomas, AL
Petriken, William H., PA
Rees, Edwin, PA
Robarts, James, PA
Robinson, Benjamin West, NC
Rose, Erasmus T., VA
Sale, Richard A., VA
Senseny, Abraham H., PA
Sims, Marion J., SC
Sinquest, Noah C., PA
Slough, Evan, PA
Smith, Calvin Jr., MA
Stuart, John Jay, NY
Taylor, Julius S., NY
Townsend, William T., RI
Vivian, Thomas J., KY
Williams, Gustavus A., VA
Williamson, Thomas G., SC
Woodbridge, Timothy, OH

In what may be called the natural method of teaching, the student begins with the patient, continues with the patient, and ends his studies with the patient, using books and lectures as tools, as means to an end.

Sir William Osler (1849–1919)

Commencement Exercises for this class and for the next two years (1836-1838), were held at a Masonic Hall called "Washington Hall," located at Third Street above Spruce on the west side. The 135 graduates of 1836 more than doubled the largest class of any preceding year. For the first time, in a little over ten years, this number of medical graduates exceeded those of the University of Pennsylvania (123). Adding to this favorable situation was the appointment of Dr. Robley Dunglison to the Chair of Institutes of Medicine and Medical Jurisprudence (Fig. 22). The increased Faculty of seven Professors provided an all-inclusive curriculum.

Dunglison was a giant scholar who brought stability and stature to the College. He had been the private physician to Thomas Jefferson, authored a treatise on *Human Physiology* (1832) which established him as the "Father of American Physiology," and published a medical dictionary in 1833 that ultimately went through 23 editions. He became "the peacemaker" on the Faculty as a non-partisan fulcrum between the two opposed professorial factions and brought academic recognition to the school. Later as Dean (1854-1868) he signed more than 3,000 Jefferson diplomas. Dr. Dunglison died in 1869 and his gravesite in East Laurel Hill Cemetery was honored by a restoration in 1984 (Fig. 23).

John Homer Dix, a Harvard College graduate of 1834, had begun the study of medicine under the preceptorship of Dr. John Jeffries, co-founder of the Massachusetts Eye and Ear Infirmary. Following graduation from Jefferson with this class he returned to the Infirmary as the first resident to be trained there. His subsequent career led to his having been regarded by many as the first American fulltime specialist in ophthalmology and otology. In 1846 he performed the first eye operation under ether anesthesia. He was the author of three small books and many articles including the first paper about the ophthalmoscope to appear in the United States in 1854.

John Stough Bobbs, a matriculate with this class but with no record of a diploma having been awarded, is acknowledged by medical authori-

ties to have been Jefferson-trained. Dr. Bobbs on June 15, 1867, became the first in history to perform a successful cholecystotomy with removal of biliary calculi. In 1869 he became Professor of Surgery in the newly organized University of Indiana (Fig. 24).

Samuel Carswell Ely in this class was a son of the Reverend Ezra Stiles Ely, Secretary of the Board of Trustees, and Jefferson's first benefactor who financed the 1828 Medical Hall at Tenth and Sansom Streets.

Fig. 22. Robley Dunglison, M.D., Professor of Institutes of Medicine and Medical Jurisprudence (1836-68) and Dean (1854-68).

Archibald, Alexander, NJ
Bacon, A. T., GA
Barnes, John, NJ
Beach, Charles H., NJ
Beckwith, Stanley T., NC
Bell, James S., DE
Biggs, Augustine A., MD
Blakey, Yelverton C., VA
Boardman, John F., NY
Bothwell, David J., GA
Bowles, J. H., TN
Brookfield, Joseph, PA
Broom, Daniel L., PA
Carter, E. J., GA
Cheatham, William J., VA
Colby, E. L., NH
Comfort, J. W., PA
Condict, Lewis, NJ
Cornell, Theodore F., NJ
Cowan, William L., PA
Crenshaw, William M., NC

Culbertson, Edmund, PA
Culbertson, S. D., PA
Culbertson, William, PA
Davies, George W., VA
Davis, Amasa, MA
Day, Silas, NY
DeChamps, Thomas J., VA
Dix, John H., MA
Dowler, M. Morton, OH
Duffie, Washington J., PA
Ely, Horace, NC
Ely, S. Carswell, MO
Field, John W., VA
Foster, Thomas, PA
Garrish, John P., NJ
Gegan, William, PA
Gray, John, VA
Gray, John Alfred, NJ
Groff, William T., PA
Grove, George, PA
Gryder, Montgomery, PA
Hamill, Robert, PA

Fig. 23.   Grave of Robley Dunglison in East Laurel Hill Cemetery, Philadelphia, restored in 1984 under Jefferson's auspices.

Hamilton, William N., PA
Hancock, Jefferson, VA
Harris, George C., MD
Haynes, Charles E., GA
Haynes, Timothy, NH
Hereford, F. M., LA
Herriott, John V., PA
Hetick, Andrew, PA
Hine, Francis W., NY
Hobson, Richard B., VA
Holland, Lemuel C., VA
Hunter, William, NC
Iredale, Thomas A., TN
Jennings, John B., VA
Johnson, Alexander, PA
Johnson, Wesley, NY
Johnson, William H., NJ
Jones, Benjamin R., SC
Jones, Callom B., VA
Jones, John W., GA
Jordan, R. D., TN
Kean, Otho W., VA
King, Alfred T., NY
Lapham, George H., NY
Leib, Owen D., PA
Linn, Alexander, NJ
Loper, James, NJ
Marable, Henry H., TN
Marsh, Samuel B., NC
Marsh, Z. Hawley, MA
Massey, B. F., SC
Mateer, William, PA
McCallmont, Henry, PA
McClellan, John, CT
McGehee, David M., AL
McGowan, William, SC
McGrath, Robert M., PA
McKay, Isaiah R., PA
Meadows, Abraham, GA
Metzger, George S., PA
Millard, Edward M., DC
Miller, J. Witmer, PA
Mills, Charles S., VA
Mitchell, C. B., TN
Mowry, Robert B., PA
Myer, E. C., GA

Pelot, James Decatur, GA
Pollard, George F., VA
Purnell, Robert F., NC
Ragland, Joseph A., VA
Reed, George, KY
Rives, Briggs, VA
Robb, Alexander, PA
Roberts, John M., DC
Rogers, Augustine C., GA
Rohrer, Amos K., PA
Russell, George B., PA
Ryan, Thomas J., TN
Saunders, Reuben, GA
Scudder, John W., NY
Shannon, Samuel H., PA
Shipman, William, PA
Sloan, William J., PA
Smith, Alfred, PA
Smith, David S., NJ
Smith, R. K., DE
Sneed, Lewis, KY
Sweet, John Larydon, NH
Tait, G. G., GA
Talbot, Patrick, VA
Temple, Robert KY
Trego, Alfred, PA
Turner, Oliver Cromwell, RI
Vance, William N., TN
Vanhoff, Augustus H., PA
Waddle, William, OH
Wallace, William P., PA
Ward, John F., NJ
Warder, John A., OH
Wardlaw, Joseph J., SC
Ware, W. Anderson, TN
Wells, Ebenezer, MA
Wharton, Thomas J., VA
White, Martin M., NY
Wilson, R. A., VA
Wilson, William L., PA
Woodruff, Elias, NY
Wright, Isaac F., OH
Wright, William M., PA
Young, B. F., TN
Young, James A., DC
Young, Robert, PA

Fig. 24.   John Stough Bobbs, first in history to perform a successful cholecystotomy with removal of gallstones.

The success of Jefferson Medical College during this year was manifested not only by its large class of 125 graduates, but in the geographical diversification of its members. The leading state was Virginia with 26 graduates. Pennsylvania had 25. New York and Ohio each had 10, and Maryland 9. The remainder consisted of New Jersey 6, Tennessee 5, Georgia, Kentucky, and Massachusetts each 4, Delaware and District of Columbia each 3, Lower Canada 2, and Alabama, South Carolina, North Carolina, Connecticut, Rhode Island, New Hampshire, Maine, Upper Canada and Ireland each one. The classes had increased to such size that enlargement and renovation of the College building became a pressing issue.

At this time Dr. Jacob Green, Professor of Chemistry, Minerology and Pharmacy, remained popular with the students and kept aloof from the bickering of his colleagues. He was affectionately referred to as "Old Jaky Green" (Fig. 25).

CLASS OF 1837

Allen, Dudley, OH
Anderson, William J., GA
Anderson, William N., VA
Banister, Robert B., VA
Beach, Columbus, NJ
Beatty, Louis H., DE
Black, Alexander, PA
Blakey, Robert L., VA
Bronaugh, Joseph W., VA
Brooks, James L., DC
Browne, Thomas H., MA
Burnett, James W., VA
Bush, James B., KY
Cadwell, Frederick A., NY
Cassel, John M., PA
Cassidy, Patrick, OH
Chamberlain, Charles T., DE
Chapline, Hanson W., VA
Coffin, Samuel S., TN
Columbus, Beach, NJ
Conner, Phineas S., MA
Conway, Albert G., VA
Coryell, William, PA
Currie, E. A., VA
Edwards, Richard H., VA
Eldredge, James H., RI
Evans, Josiah T., AL
Ewing, Philander D., VA
Fleming, James, PA
Foster, Samuel C., MA
Garretson, Isaac W., PA
Garst, Michael, OH
Gibbs, Robert T., VA

Gilbert, Jonathan H., PA
Goheen, S.M.E., PA
Goodwin, Sherman, OH
Gray, Barzillai, NJ
Green, James M., GA
Green, William T., NY
Griffin, Edwin, NY
Hall, Robert B., VA
Harley, Levi G., OH
Harvey, F. R., NH
Hayden, H. H., MD
Henning, David M., TN
Henry, James W., MD
Hopkins, Howard H., PA
Howard, William H., MD
Hunter, William M., IRELAND
Hutchinson, James B., OH
Janney, Josiah J., VA
Johnson, Thomas J., GA
Jones, Alexander J., DE
Jones, Joseph B., PA
Jordan, John A., TN
Kain, John H., CT
Kane, Joseph C.M., PA
Kellam, Frederick C.A., VA
Kennedy, Robert F., VA
Kerr, Thomas K., NY
Key, Richard S., KY
King, Richard G., MS
Kittredge, Thomas, MA
Knight, William L., OH
Krouse, Theodore J., DC
Lachance, Gabriel, CANADA

Lawrence, William C., NY
Leaman, John, PA
Lewis, William M., VA
Marable, John H., TN
Marcy, Erastus E., MA
May, Milton R., VA
McBride, William G., GA
McClelland, James, PA
McDonald, Otis, DC
McFarland, John A., PA
McGill, Daniel NC
McIntosh, Richard, VA
McLean, Robert, CANADA
Meriwether, William H., TN
Miller, John F., VA
Morrell, William R., ME
Morrison, John A., PA
Murray, John C., PA
Muse, William H., MD
Neal, Thomas W., VA
Newell, David S., MS
Newton, Luke V., PA
Nicholson, George L., VA
Parry, Ely, PA
Phillips, B. L., MS
Pitts, Hillary, MD
Reed, James L., PA
Richardson, Ross B., PA
Robbins, George R., NJ
Salter, William H., PA

Schussler, Charles, NY
See, David, CANADA
Seiberling, John, PA
Sill, Blin S., NY
Skelton, Charles, NJ
Smith, Napoleon J.M., VA
Smith, Presley E., KY
Stackhouse, H. W., MS
Stanberry, Wellington, OH
Stearns, John W., Jr., NY
Storm, Lawrence F., NY
Stout, John S., NJ
Tebbs, Thomas C., KY
Thomas, Daniel, NY
Thomas, George S., VA
Thomas, Pernett, OH
Thompson, Robert, PA
Thruston, William S., VA
Tomkins, Gustavus A., VA
Trimble, David, MD
Turton, Thomas G., MD
Wallace, John P., SC
Webster, Samuel, PA
Wiley, Abraham D., PA
Wiley, John, NJ
Williams, James Q., MD
Wilson, James W., PA
Wootten, Lucius T., VA
Young, Elijah, OH
Zeller, Henry, MD

Fig. 25.   Jacob Green, M.D., Professor of Chemistry, Mineralogy and Pharmacy (1824-41).

In the spring of 1838 an application was made to the State Legislature for a new charter that would separate Jefferson Medical College from its parent at Canonsburg. It received prompt and favorable action not only for independence but also "the same powers and restrictions as the University of Pennsylvania." The Board of Trustees then promptly increased its number from ten to fifteen.

In this year the College building was extensively remodeled externally to include two lecture rooms each with a seating capacity for 450 students.

A unique member in this class of 103 was Emile B. Gardette who went on to become Jefferson's fourth President of the Board of Trustees from 1875 to 1888 (Fig. 26). As a celebrated surgeon-dentist he published *The Professional Education of Dentists* (1852) and belonged to numerous scientific societies including the College of Physicians of Philadelphia.

The career of Hiram Rutherford (*On the Illinois Frontier*, edited by Willene Hendrick and George Hendrick, Southern Illinois University Press, 1981) may be regarded as typical of a dedicated frontier physician (Fig. 27). Settling in Oakland, Illinois in 1840, he observed the patterns of disease as described in detail by Daniel Drake (Professor of Medicine, Jefferson Medical College, 1830/31).

Dr. Rutherford was also a participant in the evolving social and political process characteristic of the 1840s including a strong abolitionist stance. His determination to prevent return to slavery of five Negroes who had been brought to slave-free Illinois by their Kentucky master, resulted in a trial in 1843 in which Abraham Lincoln represented the slave owner after Dr. Rutherford's effort to obtain Lincoln's services for his proteges failed. The verdict for the slaves was an important victory for the cause of abolition, Lincoln's anomalous position in the case notwithstanding. Dr. Rutherford, born at Paxtang, Pennsylvania, served his preceptorship under his brother William (JMC, 1832) in Harrisburg, Pennsylvania.

Fig. 26. Emile B. Gardette (JMC, 1838) became President of the Board of Trustees (1875-88) as well as a prominent surgeon-dentist.

Agnew, Samuel, PA
Allen, Peter, OH
Andres, William S., NC
Bailey, A. H., GA
Baker, Thomas W., VA
Bass, Charles N., NY
Beamon, Richard H., VA
Bell, James, NJ
Bevier, I. D., NY
Bolling, W. M., PA
Bower, Charles, PA
Brown, William Mortimer, NJ
Burks, Jesse D., KY
Carels, Samuel, PA
Chace, John B., MA
Conry, John, PA
Copeland, W. S., VA
Cottman, Joseph B., MD
Craft, Joseph N., PA
Cramer, Benjamin, PA
Crawford, John S., PA
Cummings, S. S., PA
Dale, William W., PA
Daniel, I. M., VA
Davis, Joseph A., NJ
Davis, S. G., NH
Demuth, S. C., PA
Denig, Robert, PA
Deyo, Nathaniel, NY
Duggins, E. P., VA
Effinger, Francis A., VA
Eldridge, William H., AL
Farmer, Willis H., KY
Fleet, Benjamin, VA
Frick, Clarence H., PA
Gardette, Emile B., PA
Geddes, James Jr., NOVA SCOTIA
Gillis, Joseph I., MD
Green, George W., PA
Green, Samuel John, NY
Guerard, Augustus, GA
Hamilton, J. B., PA
Hanford, S. B., NY
Harris, James E., VA
Hayes, William Jr., PA
Hayward, W. H., MD
Henderson, A. A., PA
Hill, George, PA
Hoban, Henry, DC
Holmes, R. S., PA
Hull, Thomas R., PA

Hunt, E. K., PA
Jackson, R.M.S., PA
Jansen, John T., NY
Jones, Beverly, VA
Jones, Erasmus D., NC
Kelly, Elbridge Gerry, NH
Kerr, Mark G., PA
Langley, Samuel, SC
Lefevre, William B., NJ
Linton, Thomas P., AL
Lyon, Thomas, PA
Magruder, Archibald S., MD
Mason, E. H., PA
Mayo, Joseph A., VA
McFadyen, William, NC
Millington, John, VA
Mulhallon, J. C., PA
Musselman, Isaac, PA
Nangle, Walter, VA
Nelson, John I., VA
Nelson, Robert E., VA
Parker, Henry Clinton, NH
Parkhurst, Russel, MA
Reid, Alexander, VA
Rhodes, Samuel T., VA
Righter, William W., PA
Robeson, Jonathan, PA
Robinson, Thomas L., VA
Rutherford, Hiram, PA
Salter, H. B., NJ
Smith, Harmony A., PA
Smith, Josiah T., MD
Smith, Stokes A., KY
Smoot, S. C., DC
Sole, Sidney W., CANADA
Stees, Abiram C., PA
Stewart, George, PA
Storm, Robert B., NY
Streater, Charles, PA
Tate, Alexander C.H., MD
Ten,Brook John, PA
Thompson, Thomas H., PA
Tolson, George S., DC
Traynham, William B., SC
Treat, William, NH
Troubat, R., PA
Vanvalzah, R. F., PA
Vastine, P. B., PA
Vogely, Frederick G.L., GERMANY
Worthington, J. H., MD
Yeakel, David T., MD
Young, George D., VA

Fig. 27. Hiram Rutherford (JMC, 1838), frontier physician in Southern
Illinois (Courtesy of Southern Illinois University Press.)

During this year serious dissensions within the Faculty caused Jefferson to lose much of the prestige it had gained. Personality clashes and power struggles of George McClellan with his increasingly rebellious colleagues and with the Board of Trustees caused the temperamental founder to publicly denounce the College and its "blackguard Board."

On June 10 the Faculty was dissolved by the Board, but it was reconstituted within a month. Joseph Pancoast (Fig. 28) was elected to the Chair of Surgery by a vote of 7 to 5 against McClellan who was dismissed. McClellan retaliated by founding yet another medical school in Philadelphia (Pennsylvania Medical College) using the same strategy to obtain a charter from a parent institution (Pennsylvania College at Gettysburg) as he had with Jefferson.

Cornelius Van Allen Van Dyck pursued a remarkably varied career which included the practice of medicine. Upon graduation he became a missionary to Syria and rapidly acquired a knowledge of Arabic language and literature resulting in his preparation of Arabic texts on navigation, mathematics and geography. Ordained as a minister in 1846, he worked with other scholars on a translation of the Bible in 1857 and the work was published in 1865. In addition he became Professor of Pathology at the Syrian Protestant College as well as Professor of Astronomy in its Department of Arts and Sciences. A versatile scholar, his career related almost entirely to the Middle East.

In this year and for the next thirty, the commencement exercises were held in the Musical Fund Hall located on the south side of Locust Street between Eighth and Ninth (Fig. 29). There was a significant drop in the number of graduates to 85.

Fig. 28. Joseph Pancoast, M.D., Professor of Surgery (1839-41) and Professor of Anatomy (1841-74).

Allen, John D., MD
Allison, Robert H., PA
Allmond, Reuben J., DE
Armstrong, Daffield, DE
Aspinwall, Thomas W., CT
Atkinson, John R., ENGLAND
Bacher, John J., PA
Ballou, Newton H., VT
Bickley, William M., PA
Blankman, B.J., PA
Boyd, John J., PA
Brome, John J., MD
Calhoun, Thomas R., PA
Carmichael, Richard H., VA
Carter, Josephus, VA
Chapman, David, OH
Cline, Garner, NJ
Cochran, James H., PA
Colton, Charles E., CANADA
Coons, A. J., VA
Crane, James R., NJ
Cropp, Howard H., VA
Davis, John, SC
De La Gal, Henry H., GA
Diver, William B., PA
Donelly, Philip C., PA
Dorroh, John F., SC
Douglas, Robert, SCOTLAND
Duckett, Thomas S., MD
Engelman, E.J., PA
Fowler, Isaac D., NY
Getzendanner, Joseph D., MD
Glascock, Richard M., VA
Gouldin, Thomas W., MS
Grant, William R., NOVA SCOTIA
Guthrie, Columbus B., OH
Harding, Josiah, MD
Harker, Jesse, PA
Harnsberger, George W., VA
Hartwell, Samuel C., MA
Hine, Thomas C., VA
Hughes, Isaac, PA

Isom, Thomas D., MS
Jones, Hugh McKinsey, CANADA
Keyser, Alfred, PA
Kinsloe, Lemuel, PA
Lee, Alfred H., NY
Leedom, S. K., PA
Levering, Joseph H., PA
Mahoney, Michael, LA
Maury, Thomas, VA
McClellan, Samuel R., NY
McGinley, David B., PA
McGintie, Edward, PA
McNair, Neill, NC
McReynolds, John F., LA
Mevshon, R. B., NJ
Millard, Justin, NJ
Neal, B. T., PA
Prather, C. W., VA
Reiter, William C., PA
Riley, William H., MD
Ritchie, Joshua H., DC
Roberts, John, PA
Sample, Nathaniel W., Jr., PA
Schmoele, H. W., PRUSSIA
Scholfield, Nathan M., PA
Scoffin, Francis, IRELAND
Shackelford, John L., VA
Sledge, John G., NC
Steele, Francis J., MD
Stilwell, Thomas, PA
Stockard, William P., TN
Synott, Martin S., NJ
Taliaferro, Robert H., VA
Taylor, Charles Jr., PA
Turner, John J., OH
Upson, Francis W., OH
Van Dyck, C.V.A., NY
Weems, Richard, MD
Whitley, Albert, MD
Willetts, Reuben, NJ
Williams, Edward C., VA
Willson, James F., DE
Wolfe, William H., PA

Honour a physician with the honour due unto him for the uses which you may have of him: for the Lord hath created him.

The Bible: Apocrypha
Ecclesiasticus 38:1

Fig. 29.   Musical Fund Hall where Commencements were held from 1839 through 1869.

The strife and changes in the Faculty with dismissal of George McClellan, the founder, were reflected in the graduates of this year whose number fell to 56. This was 40 per cent below the previous class of 85 and 60 per cent below the class of 1836. In the see-saw of ups and downs, this was certainly a down year. Robert Huston, first appointed Professor of Materia Medica in 1839, added much stability at this critical time (Fig. 30).

Support for the Board of Trustees in their dismissal of the McClellan-led Faculty came from an unexpected source, the medical students themselves. The loyalty of those remaining was shown by their forming a committee which met in the Anatomical Theater of the College Building February 14, 1840. Stephen D. Mullowney was elected Chairman and James D. Cochran Secretary of the seven-man group. Their resolutions presented to the Board and the Faculty expressed appreciation for the individual former professors and their teaching but went on to declare their confidence that the new ones, especially in Surgery and Obstetrics reflected "improvements which have greatly enhanced the value of the school."

Fig. 30. Robert M. Huston, M.D., Professor of Materia Medica and Dean (1841-54).

Baldwin, Harvey, CT
Beatty, R. Coulter, PA
Beck, Morris B., VA
Brewer, Nicholas, MD
Bruce, Andrew, PA
Christie, William, NJ
Chunn, Zachariah T., VA
Cochrane, J. D., PA
Conner, Ephraim D., AL
Crosby, Edward, NY
Eldred, J. W., PA
Fassitt, O. R., NJ
Forshey, J. Madison, OH
Graydon, William, PA
Grier, J. H., PA
Hale, Albert P., ME
Houtz, Henry, OH
Ireland, John, MD
Irland, William P., PA
Irvine, John D., MI
James, Oliver P., PA
Jewett, Theodore H., ME
Jones, E. R., SC
Lambert, Jacob F., PA
Lewis, Major G., SC
Locke, W. H., MD
Masters, Holmes C., NOVA SCOTIA
Matthews, James M., PA

McIntyre, James, LA
Moore, Eli H., VA
Mortimer, John F., VA
Mullowny, Stephen D., MO
Newman, George S., VA
Nottingham C. Bell, VA
Owen, Joshua, NJ
Park, George H., CANADA
Parker, Eustace W., NC
Ramsey, Samuel J., PA
Reeve, Isaac, NY
Reid, Neville C., PA
Sellers, Charles, PA
Sheppard, William P., AL
Sims, James L., SC
Skelton, O. P., SC
Slye, Thomas B., MD
Spady, Thomas, F., VA
Stanford, H. K., GA
Stribling, W. C., VA
Stuart, John A., SC
Taliaferro, Landon, VA
Thaxton, Joseph A., VA
Towles, Thomas T., VA
Ward, Walter, MA
Wells, Charles, NH
Young, Thomas W., VA
Zevely, Augustus T., NC

LOXARTHRUS, OR CLUB FOOT.

BY

THOMAS D. MÜTTER, M. D.

LECTURER ON SURGERY, FELLOW OF THE COLLEGE OF PHYSICIANS, MEMBER OF THE
ACADEMY OF NATURAL SCIENCES OF PHILADELPHIA, HONORARY MEMBER OF
THE MEDICAL SOCIETY OF PHILADELPHIA, &c. &c.

PHILADELPHIA:

HOOKER AND CLAXTON.

1839.

~ 1841 ~

On February 1, 1841, Dr. Jacob Green ("Old Jaky") died suddenly at the age of 51. He was the last of the original Faculty. On returning from Dr. Green's funeral, Drs. John Revere and Granville Pattison tendered their resignations to join a medical Faculty in New York City. In reorganizing a new Faculty the Board of Trustees selected an illustrious team that would work in unbroken harmony for the next fifteen years and lift Jefferson to the forefront of medical schools in the United States.

In April, 1841, the Chairs were filled with Robley Dunglison in Institutes of Medicine and Medical Jurisprudence, Robert M. Huston in Materia Medica and Therapeutics (and Dean), Joseph Pancoast in Anatomy, John K. Mitchell in Medicine, Thomas D. Mutter in Surgery, Charles D. Meigs in Obstetrics and Diseases of Women and Children, and Franklin Bache in Chemistry (Fig. 31). This brought an end to the period of struggle for survival (1824-1841) and began the era of growth and development.

The graduates in this class totaled 52.

CLASS OF 1841

Adams, Henry G., NY
Anderson, Samuel, PA
Ball, John B., VA
Ball, William B., VA
Barclay, Joseph B., PA
Beemer Joseph S., NJ
Beers, Moses B., CT
Bird, Wellington, PA
Bowdoin, J. R., VA
Boyd, John C., NY
Butt, Zephaniah, PA
Chilton, John A., VA
Christy, Robert W., PA
Clark, John M., NC
Dillard, Peter F., VA
Dunklin, Irby, SC
Ellis, James E., VA
Finch, George C., NY
Grayson, John B., VA
Green, J. P., MA
Harding, Charles A., MD
Harris, William J., VA
Hays, Chaplin J., MD
Hedges, Charles H., NJ
Hepburn, Andrew, PA
Howell, A. Alexander, NJ

Hudders, James W., PA
Jones, W. Brook, DC
Lee, James C., PA
Leech, J. Stuart, PA
Lind, John Y., MD
Maupin, Richard S., VA
McCreery, John, PA
McFarland, Thomas, VA
Mulhallon, William E., PA
Muschett, James M.A., VA
Neal, Benjamin T., Jr., PA
Oyster, Joseph, PA
Smith, William J., GA
Sterret, Samuel A., PA
Tomlinson, John, PA
Tourangeau, Pierre G., CANADA
Waters, Charles O., NY
Watson, William W., PA
Wheeler, Henry H., PA
Whitney, Hamilton F., PA
Williams, A. L., CT
Wilson, John G., MD
Wilson, Myron W., NY
Winslow, Harrison G.O., MA
Woods, Josiah P., VA
Woolverton, Allen N., CANADA

Fig. 31.   Famous Faculty of 1841.

Among the members of this class was John W. Irby of Virginia whose great-grandson, Dr. Robert Irby Wise, would be the thirteenth Chairman of Medicine at Jefferson (1959-1975). Although the graduates numbered only 59, the enrollment was 229. This large attrition rate is difficult to explain. At this time it was not necessary to obtain the M.D. degree to practice as a "respectable" physician. A single course of lectures, which only would be repeated in the second year, was considered sufficient by many of the matriculants. There would be no licensing of physicians in Pennsylvania until 1893.

In this year Professor Robley Dunglison published his *Practice of Medicine* which incorporated the improvements and modifications which had occurred in the fields of pathology and therapeutics (Fig. 32).

CLASS OF 1842

Ashton, Horace D., VA
Ayer, Otis, NH
Beazley, Robert S., VA
Bell, Agrippa Nelson, VA
Bishop, William S., PA
Bringhurst, James, DE
Browder, James D., VA
Brown, Elisha, OH
Byars, William M., KY
Cooke, William E., NOVA SCOTIA
Cooper, John, NY
Craige, William Temple, PA
Crowley, Frederick, PA
Daily, James W., OH
Dennis, Welding F., PA
Ewell, Richard H.D., TN
Ford, James E., VA
Harris, Clement R., VA
Holt, Alfred C., MS
Hotchkiss, Sterne, CT
Houston, David Henry, DE
Humphrey, Henry Moore, PA
Huston, Charles, PA
Irby, John W., VA
Johnson, Henry W., VA
Jones, George C., DE
Kellog, Oliver W., CT
Lisle, James W., PA
Logue, John G., PA

Lyon, Charles L., PA
Mason, Gerrard F., VA
May, Charles, VA
McElrath, Robert, PA
McMurray, Andrew S., PA
Miller, John H., MD
Nunn, John M., VA
O'Brien, Patrick Moffit, IRELAND
Proctor, Stephen, MS
Rea, Benjamin F., GA
Richman, Elijah B., NJ
Robins, John K., PA
Rothrock, William P., PA
Schaeffer, Jackson, PA
Schrack, John Jr., PA
Scott, William H., PA
Shelton, Thomas W., VA
Smith, Benjamin, PA
Steck, Michael, PA
Stickney, Peter LeB., PA
Stubbs, Slater B., PA
Sumner, Ossian, CT
Sweat, William W., ME
Trites, David T., PA
Watson, Gillet F., VA
Weir, John H., PA
Weiser, George B., PA
Wiggin, Chase, NH
Williams, Charles F., AL
Woddrop, Robert S., SC

THE

PRACTICE OF MEDICINE;

OR,

A TREATISE

ON

SPECIAL PATHOLOGY AND THERAPEUTICS.

BY

ROBLEY DUNGLISON, M. D.,

Professor of the Institutes of Medicine, &c. in Jefferson Medical College, Philadelphia,
Lecturer on Clinical Medicine, and
Attending Physician at the Philadelphia Hospital, &c. &c.

IN TWO VOLUMES.

VOL. I.

PHILADELPHIA:

LEA & BLANCHARD.

1842.

Fig. 32.   Dunglison's *Practice of Medicine* (1842).

The outstanding member of this class was Ellerslie Wallace of Pennsylvania who was the first Jefferson graduate to obtain a teaching position in his alma mater. For 16 years he served as a Demonstrator of Anatomy (1845-1861) and for the next 20 as Chairman of Obstetrics and Diseases of Women (1862-1883). He became a founding member of the American Gynecologic Society (Fig. 33).

Up to this time, patients who underwent operations before the students in the amphitheater of the College were sent home in a carriage, with further care by an assistant or the surgeon himself. Around 1843, with realization of the dangers of removing patients after serious operations, accommodations for their care were provided by renting the upper floors of the two stores at the corner of Tenth and Sansom Streets adjacent to the College. The rooms were fitted to supply this need.

From an enrollment of 341 students there were only 41 graduates. This would improve dramatically the following year.

CLASS OF 1843

Anthony, Thomas H., VA
Bacon, John J., NY
Bierne, George W., VA
Chew, Ezekiel, NJ
Coburn, John B., PA
Core, William T., VA
Cornick, Martin L., VA
Curtis, Josiah, CT
Day, Joseph H., KY
Dix, Asa T., VA
Ducachet, Henry W., Jr., PA
Earley, Joseph R., VA
Fisler, Benjamin S., NJ
Floyd, Samuel, PA
Hall, Theophilus A., VA
Hopkins, Joseph, MD
Howard, John E., WEST INDIES
Hyett, Joseph, PA
Jones, Samuel, PA
Kerr, William R., PA

Leland, William A., AL
Mann, William B., GA
Marchand Thomas S., PA
Mason, John R., VA
Masser, Jacob B., PA
McWilliams, John C., PA
Oliver, Samuel P., SC
Parham, Frederick L., SC
Parry, Charles, IN
Paullin, Lewis, FL
Price, Thomas K., VA
Proulx, J.T. Phileas, CANADA
Rees, Frederic A., ENGLAND
Riddle, A. A. J., GA
Robison, James D., OH
Stuart, William T., VA
Taylor, Alfred, OH
Wallace, Ellerslie, PA
Watts, William W., NC
Wilkins, John T., VA
Wright, Wiley, VA

The ways in which physicians may become noteworthy are diverse and reflect uniquely the individuals whose careers are singled out as exemplary. Yet two traits seem universal among these men and women: commitment and a passion for hard work.

Appreciations Honoring John P. McGovern, M.D.,
Editorial Committee Preface.

Fig. 33. Ellerslie Wallace, Chairman of Obstetrics and Diseases of Women and Children (1862-83) and Dean (1879-83).

~ 1844 ~

The striking aspect in this year was the leap in the number of graduates to 117, an increase of almost three fold from the previous year. This could be ascribed to a maturing of the prestige of the College caused by the stellar performance of its individual Professors such as Franklin Bache in Chemistry (Fig. 34). The lag in obtaining a deserved reputation had passed and the size of the ensuing classes would reflect a growing stature of the institution.

Increased clinical demands for the rented floors above the two stores next to the College eventuated in remodeling to accommodate about fifteen patients. This constituted a miniature surgical facility which would serve until 1877, when the first new detached Jefferson Medical College Hospital was opened. The nursing care was volunteered mainly by the students. Meals were brought from a nearby restaurant.

The outstanding member of this class was William T. Howard of Virginia. He became the Professor of Diseases of Women and Children at the University of Maryland (1867-1897) and was a founding member of the American Gynecologic Society (President in 1884).

Fig. 34. Franklin Bache, M.D., Professor of Chemistry (1841-64).

CLASS OF 1844

Allen, George W., NJ
Allison, Benjamin A., IN
Anderson, James Rush, PA
Antony, William L., AL
Baily, Elisha J., PA
Baily, Samuel Gordon, NY
Baily, Wilson, PA
Barclay, James M., VA
Barcroft, John W., NJ
Bayn, John S., VA
Bertolette, Peter Grisemer, PA
Blanchard, Samuel W., ME
Bressler, Charles H., PA
Brooks, Silas S., MA
Brown, George W., PA
Buffington, Thomas J., VA
Burr, Nelson, NJ
Burr, William H., PA

Callaway, Reuben S., GA
Campbell, Archibald B., PA
Carpenter, John S., PA
Child, Henry T., PA
Clark, Courtenay J., AL
Colgan, Joseph P., DE
Conrad, John, PA
Cox, John, PA
Cronin, Edward Jr., PA
Cummings, Albert S., PA
Dana, Simeon Sessions, NH
Dawson, Plummer W., TN
Desnoyers, Edward G., MI
Dimock, Gordon Z., PA
Drake, Thomas W., PA
Durham, William W., GA
Emanuel, Samuel, MS
Esrey, William P., PA

Fisler, Samuel F., NJ
Fitch, Thomas, NY
Ford, John D., NH
Furse, William, SC
Gilman, John B., NJ
Griffing, Zachariah B. J., MS
Haines, Josiah, PA
Hanly, William H., PA
Hannon, Joseph, PA
Hardcastle, Edward M., MD
Harlow, John M., MA
Harris, Samuel, VA
Harshberger, Abraham, PA
Haskell, Joseph H., MA
Hayes, Louis W., DE
Haywood, Richard B., NC
Henderson, Daniel, PA
Hill, James S., PA
Hoskins, John R., PA
Howard, William Travis, VA
Irwin, Samuel B., PA
Johnes, Harvey C., OH
Johnston, William R., VA
Keneagy, Samuel, PA
King, Henry H., GA
Kuhn, John S., OH
Lang, Philip H., PA
Marsh, Rolph C., PA
Martin, Amzi, KY
Martin, John, PA
Maxwell, James Darwin, IN
McClure, Joseph M., PA
Miller, John F., AL
Mitchell, George H., NC
Moore, John E., VA
Moyer, Joseph, PA
Oatman, Daniel L.F., PA
Orr, Adrian V.B., PA
Owen, Thomas J., VA
Parrish, Edward, PA

Paxton, William B., VA
Pearson, Albert, PA
Phelps, Robert A., VA
Piper, William A., PA
Poley, Francis B., PA
Powell, Thomas B., NC
Prentis, William T., VA
Quinan, John R., PA
Riddle, N. Watkins, GA
Risley, James, NJ
Robie, Frederick, ME
Rodman, William W., CT
Scammon, Franklin, ME
Seabrook, Benjamin W., SC
Shipman, Azariah B., NY
Smith, George King, PA
Southwick, Edward W., ME
Spriggs, John S., PA
Steuart, James, PA
Sunderland, William P., IN
Tabb, John P., VA
Thornhill, George H., MS
Townsend, William W., PA
Ulrieh, Daniel A., PA
Upshaw, William, VA
VonBretton, Baron J. F., ST. THOMAS
Wallace, Michael, VA
Waller, Tracy E., PA
Weever, Charles S., IN
White, John D., PA
Wilcocks, Alexander, PA
Wills, Samuel E., VA
Winder, Aaron, PA
Winters, Isaac, PA
Wood, William E., NC
Woodruff, A. Dickinson, NJ
Woods, William James, SC
Woolman, Granvill S., NJ
Wright, Reginald N., MD
Ziegler, Jacob L., PA
Zullick, Samuel Morton, PA

By the neglect of the study of the humanities, which has been far too general, the profession loses a very precious quality.

Sir William Osler (1849-1919)

~ 1845 ~

At the Commencement held in Musical Fund Hall on March 20, 1845, the Degree of Doctor of Medicine was conferred on 116 graduates by the Rev. Ashbel Green, D.D.,LL.D., President of the College. The Valedictory Address was delivered by Charles Delucena Meigs, Professor of Midwifery and Diseases of Women and Children.

There is an intriguing coincidence of two members of the graduating class becoming intimately associated with the discovery of anesthesia. Edward R. Squibb of Pennsylvania became the first to manufacture pure ether (Fig. 35). This accomplishment formed the basis for the founding of the E.R. Squibb Co. which became one of the giants of the pharmaceutical industry.

In addition, Squibb's classmate, Laurence Turnbull (Fig. 36), a native of Scotland, published the first edition of his textbook *Artificial Anesthesia: A Manual of Anesthetic Agents and Their Employment in the Treatment of Disease* (Blakiston, 1878). This treatise of over 500 pages covered all known aspects of anesthetic use and went through four editions. Dr. Turnbull was appointed Aural Surgeon to the first Jefferson Hospital in 1877 after developing a career in eye and ear surgery. He edited *Defects of Sight and Hearing*, first written in London by T. Wharton Jones, for its American publication by Price & Co. of Philadelphia.

Another member, Elwood Wilson of Pennsylvania, achieved the distinction of serving on the Board of Trustees of Jefferson Medical College (1875-1889). Three of his sons graduated from Jefferson, one of whom, James Cornelius Wilson, became the Chairman of Medicine (1891-1911).

CLASS OF 1845

Andrews, James P., PA
Arbuckle, William W., VA
Bealle, Robert Oscar, AL
Bickford, Hezekiah C., NH
Birch, Solomon G., PA
Blackmon, Benjamin F., AL
Blanton, Alexander M., KY
Bond, James, PA
Boyd, William A., NC
Branham, Henry R., GA
Brown, William K., AL
Bryant, George S., VA
Cargill, Nathaniel E., VA
Carpenter, Alexander Hamilton, PA
Cary, Edward L., GA
Cates, Charles B., ME
Chapman, Edwin N., CT
Clark, Nathan H., PA
Coon, John M., PA
Cooper, George F., GA
Crawford, Francis A., PA
Cunningham, Alexander, VA
Deacon, Benjamin H., NJ
Draughon, John B., LA
Dunkum, James B., VA

Dunlap, John M., PA
Dyer, Edward C., MA
Dyott, John B., PA
Ellis, James B., MS
Evans, John F., PA
Ferguson, Thomas McKee, CANADA
Fleet, William T., VA
Foster, Charles R., NJ
Gibbons, Joseph, PA
Gordon, Thomas, PA
Graves, Thomas A., GA
Grigsby, Abner Joseph, VA
Hackedorn, Noah E., PA
Haines, Job, NJ
Hall, Richard N., VA
Harden, William P., GA
Harris, George F., VA
Harwell, John H., GA
Hazlett, Thomas Jefferson, OH
Hensley, Benjamin Jr., KY
Hill, John Edwin, MS
Hill, William Henry, NC
Hitchcock, Alfred, MA
Hoff, Alexander Henry, NY
Hottenstein, H. Percival, PA

Hughes, George W., KY
Jones, Alexander, VA
Jones, Edwin B., VA
Junkin, J. Miller, OH
Knode, Oliver B., MD
Knowlton, Charles L., MA
Kurtz, John F., VA
Landrum, Benjamin L., AL
Lefevre, Joseph H., PA
Liggett, Caleb, PA
Livezey, Abraham, PA
Mann, Joseph B., NC
Martin, Charles, NY
Martin, John, PA
Maxson, Edwin R., NY
McConaughy, James, PA
McMullen, Elias Hale, PA
Mellinger, Henry S., PA
Mendenhall, Nereus, NC
Miller, Matthew, PA
Morris, Jenkin W., OH
Moseley, George M., MS
Mott, Armistead Randolph, KY
Neves, Juan Carlos, URUGUAY
Outhit, George Edward, NOVA SCOTIA
Pancoast Richard Montgomery, NJ
Pearce, William H., SC
Pendleton, Philip Barbour, VA
Pillow, Anthony L., TN
Poitiaux, Michael Benedict, VA
Potter, Thomas R., OH
Power, R. Henry, VA
Rawlins, John W., PA

Ridgway, Charles, NJ
Roberts, Henry Jr., PA
Rogers, William P., VA
Romig, William J., PA
Rothrock, John Henry, PA
Ruffin, John M., MS
Rust, Bushrod, VA
Semple, Samuel P., VA
Silvey, James, OH
Smith, Thomas W., VA
Snowden, Benjamin C., PA
Snyder, William V., IN
Squibb, Edward R., PA
Stewart, Miller, PA
Thompson, James L., TN
Thomson, Alexander Jr., PA
Turnbull, Laurence Scotland
Tyler, Gustavus, B., KY
Van Derpoel, Samuel Oakley, NY
Vandever, John H., SC
Wall, John G., KY
Waters, George Henry, PA
Whitaker, Jonathan Sheppard, NJ
White, Samuel G., GA
Whiting, Henry, MS
Whitman, Henry L., CT
Williams, John C., NC
Wilson, Charles, PA
Wilson, Ellwood, PA
Worthington, Francis A., OH
Young, George, SC
Young, William B., VA
Ziegler, Samuel P., PA

Fig. 35. Edward R. Squibb (JMC, 1845), first manufactured pure ether.

Fig. 36. Laurence Turnbull (JMC, 1845), Aural Surgeon and Chief of Ear Clinic in the 1877 Hospital.

1845

The effectiveness of the strong Faculty of 1841 was manifested by a graduating class that numbered 170, the largest in the history of the College to that date. This is not surprising in view of the fact that the enrollment during the previous year had been 469 students, representing the largest in any institution of its kind in the United States.

On October 16, 1846, a dentist, William Morton, gave the first successful public demonstration of anesthesia in the world at the Massachusetts General Hospital. It has been considered by many to be the greatest blessing which mankind ever received. At Jefferson, the new discovery was quickly applied. On December 23, 1846, just two months later, Thomas Dent Mutter (Fig. 37) administered the first anesthetic in Philadelphia at his Jefferson Clinic for removal of a tumor of the cheek. Dr. Mutter is also remembered for having donated his private museum to the College of Physicians of Philadelphia along with an endowment of thirty thousand dollars for a Lectureship in Surgical Pathology (Fig. 38). His museum and lectureship have remained active until the present time and have so overshadowed his career that many are unaware that he was ever a Professor of Surgery at Jefferson (1841-1856).

In 1846 the Medical College building was renovated and enlarged Fig. 39). Six Corinthian columns graced the facade erected in the form of a Grecian temple. The upper and lower lecture rooms were enlarged to seat 600 students as opposed to the previous 450. The upper lecture hall was a "pit" in which surgery was performed and in which the *Gross Clinic* by Eakins would be painted in 1875. A connection was also made into the upper floor of the adjacent store as a miniature hospital, representing a precursor of the subsequent formal 1877 teaching hospital.

CLASS OF 1846

Adams, Nelson A., PA
Almand, John J., VA
Antrim, Joseph, VA
Archer, William C., VA
Ashcraft, William, PA
Baker, Dorsey Syng, IL
Banks, William A., ME
Bartolette, Charles, NJ
Baskin, George W., PA
Batte, John W., TN
Bigelow, George F., DC
Billon, Eugene, France
Boardman, Henry K. W., CT
Bold, Charles M., SC
Boyer, David P., PA
Brinker, Thomas H., PA
Brown, Edward W., SC
Bulkeley, Jonathan W., PA
Bunn, Benjamin F., PA
Burwell, George W., SC
Bythewood, Daniel H., SC
Campbell, Clark C., AL
Campbell, John A., VA

Chase, Dwight W., NY
Clements, Richard, PA
Coffman, Samuel A., VA
Cole Algernon S., FL
Copeland, Adoniram Judson, ME
Craddock, John W., VA
Crowder, John V., VA
Custis, John T., VA
Dickey, Benjamin, CANADA
Duffield, Edward, MD
Duncan, William C., MO
Duncombe, Charles, CANADA
Edge, John P., PA
Ellmaker, Thomas, PA
Evans, Dickson, NC
Everett, Azariah, OH
Ewing, William P., VA
Fant, Francis M.E., SC
Farmer, Henry H., VA
Fisher, Frederick B., VA
Fontaine, Madison R., VA
Fox, Henry Haines, PA
Frantz, Benjamin, PA

Gamble, Aaron, PA
Garner, Presley K., NC
Garrett, James R., VA
Gibson, Alexander, VA
Gill, Robert T., NY
Gilliams, James S., PA
Gorman, Charles R., PA
Graves, S. Waterman, MA
Gulley, William, AL
Hardy, George E., VA
Haynes, James H., VA
Hegins, Thomas G., PA
Hendry, Bowman, NJ
Holcombe, Hugh W., VA
Howland, David R., OH
Hoyt, John Jay, PA
Huey, James E., PA
Hughson, Walter, NY
Humphreys, Joseph D., VA
James, J. Sexton, PA
Jenkins, William H., AL
Johnston, Joseph R., NC

Jones, Edwin A., GA
Jones, John H., VA
Kern, Josiah, PA
Laird, Alexander T., VA
Lambeth, Lafayette W., VA
Lasell, Samuel M., NY
Leaming, J. Furman, NJ
Leasure, Daniel, PA
Leinaweaver, George, PA
Lenoir, Benjamin B., TN
Lewis, David William, PA
Lewis, Francis West, PA
Lewis, Magnus M., VA
Lingo, Douglass, PA
Longenecker, John Henry, PA
Longshore, Ashbel B., PA
Marable, George B., VA
Mauk, John B., PA
Mauzy, Charles K., VA
Mayes, Thomas A., SC
McClure, Samuel, PA
McClurg, John R., PA

Fig. 37.   Thomas Dent Mutter, M.D., Chairman of Surgery (1841-56).

Fig. 38.   Museum in College of Physicians of Philadelphia donated by Professor Mutter.

McConaughy, Francis M., PA
McFarland, John, PA
McKennie, Marcellus, VA
Meares, John L., NC
Meiere, William S., PA
Miller, Andrew, PA
Milner, Amor C., PA
Musser, Benjamin, PA
Negly, Eliab, PA
Nelson, Robert B., VA
Nelson, Robert William, VA
Nevin, William W., PA
Niblock, William G., PA
Nichols, Thomas G., MA
Notson, William, PA
Noyes, James, RI
Nute, William G., KY
Ord, James Lycurgus, MI
Osborne, William E., VA
Osler, Owen, PA
Otey, Paul H., TN
Palm, Philip R., PA
Patterson, James V., PA

Paul, John H., NH
Pearis, Robert A., VA
Perkins, Thomas H., VA
Phillips, Dinwiddle B., VA
Postlethwaite, Samuel, PA
Read, Albert N., OH
Reed, Thomas Sydenham, NJ
Rhees, Morgan J., PA
Richards, Buchan, VA
Rile, John H., PA
Robards, James, TN
Robertson, John H., MD
Rogers, Moses, MA
Rust, George W., VA
Scales, James T., TN
Schmeltzer, George Jr., PA
Seebold, John P., PA
Sergeant, Spencer, PA
Seymour, William J., VA
Shackelford, Edmond D., MO
Shallenberger, Aaron T., PA
Shands, Aurelius R., VA
Shelley, Benneville Y., PA

Fig. 39. The 1846 renovation of Medical Hall (Ely Building) with addition of a Grecian facade.

Shindel, Isaac N., PA
Shunk, Francis R., PA
Sides, Benjamin F., PA
Sidwell, Reuben, PA
Sifre, Santiago, WEST INDIES
Simpson, James F., NC
Sloanaker, Lewis M., PA
Smith, Edward M., PA
Spencer, H. Gordon P., NY
Spindle, Thomas G., KY
Steiner, Josephus M., MD
Stephenson, James William, VA
Stuart, James, VA
Thomas, John C., MD
Thornbury, Philip, KY
Treadwell, Robert O., PA
VanBuskirk, George, PA

Vastine, John S., PA
Wallace, John W., PA
Webb, Henry Young, AL
Webb, Samuel, TN
Wetherill, William, PA
Whaley, James E., SC
White, Wistar T., VA
Whitley, James, NY
Whitney, Marshall G., PA
Wild, Augustus Edward, MA
Williams, Sidney Hampden, NC
Williamson, Duncan, PA
Wilson, James Potter, PA
Wilson, John, PA
Wilson, Miles A., VA
Winfield, Benjamin F., VA
Winfield, John Q., VA

Morton's demonstration of ether anesthesia at Massachusetts General Hospital, October 16, 1846.
(Courtesy of Parke, Davis and Co.)

At the Commencement held in Musical Fund Hall on March 25, 1847, the degree of Doctor of Medicine was conferred on 181 graduates. The Rev. Cornelius C. Cuyler officiated in the absence of Board President, the Rev. Ashbel Green (Fig. 40), who at that time was 85 years of age and destined to die the following year. The Address was delivered by Professor Robley Dunglison.

Among the graduates was Robert Gibbon of North Carolina, the father of John Heysham

Fig. 40. The Reverend Ashbel Green, D.D., LL.D., First President of the Board of Trustees (1826-48).

Gibbon, Professor of Surgery at Jefferson (1907-1931), and grandfather of John Heysham Gibbon, Jr. (Professor of Surgery, 1946-1967, who developed the heart-lung machine). Robert Gibbon conducted a large surgical practice in Charlotte and was a Brigadier-Surgeon in the Confederate Army during the Civil War.

Of international significance was the career of John Glasgow Kerr, a native of Duncansville, Ohio. Contrary to the current lack of formal pre-medical preparation, Kerr had two years of college work at Denison University, medical apprenticeship to two Maysville, Kentucky, physicians, and a medical school course at Transylvania University. Following six years of practice in Ohio, he went to China as one of the first medical missionaries sent by the Presbyterian Board of Foreign Missions. In 1855 he became Director of the Medical Missionary Society, Canton, China, and was responsible for many innovations in Chinese medicine. These included the founding of the first hospital for the insane in China and translation of medical works into Cantonese. He trained Chinese personnel in Western medicine and continued this devotion to his career until his death in 1901. Among his medical students was Dr. Sun Yat Sen, first President of the Republic of China.

Greensville Dowell, a native of Virginia, settled in Galveston, Texas, where he became publisher of the first Texas medical periodical, *The Galveston Medical Journal*, in 1870. He was Professor of Surgery in the Texas Medical College (1865-1867) and also developed a hernia repair known as "Dowell's Operation." In 1876 he published a book on *Yellow Fever and Malarial Disease* in which he suggested that yellow fever might be related to microorganisms and mentions vector transmission. He was honored with gold medals for his work during yellow fever epidemics in Memphis and New Orleans.

Addison, Robert K., NEW BRUNSWICK
Ashley, William, GA
Atkinson, Edward C., PA
Baker, A. H., OH
Baker, Andrew J., NH
Barber, John E., PA
Barclay, Michael W., VA
Bates, Solomon A., VA
Beale, Stephen T., PA
Bell, William S., TN
Billups, Robert A., AL
Blackburn, Joseph W., PA
Boone, James, MD
Bournonville, Aug. C.H., PA
Boutelle, Nathaniel R., ME
Briceland, J. Milton, VA
Briggs, Henry C., VA
Brown, Marcus A., OH
Burton, John J., VA
Byers, William J., PA
Carter, John, VA
Chambers, William H., VA
Chapman, Charles G., CT
Clapp, William A., IN
Clarke, John E., NC
Clary, Charles S., KY
Cobb, Benjamin F., NC
Cobb, Henry, VA
Coleman, James W., VA
Craige, Thomas W., PA
Curtis, Levi, CT
Dawson, John, EAST INDIES
DeHart, John N.E., LA
Derr, Rufus M., VA
Dillard, Peter H., NC
Dowell, Greensville, TN
Dubois, John Treon, OH
Eastman, Henry, NH
Edwards, James, PA
Eichelberger, Lewis S., VA
Eliason, Talcott, VA
Few, Samuel F., VA
Flippen, Marion J., VA
Floyd, James B., VA
Folsom, Lewis A., GA
Foulke, George W., PA
Franklin, George A., MD
Fuller, Smith, PA
Funkhouser, David, VA
Gaines, James S., TN
Garlick, John W., VA
Gayle, Charles M.S., VA

Geiger, Henry, PA
Gibbon, Robert, NC
Glassell, Albert S., VA
Glentworth, William W., PA
Gosweiler, Martin H., PA
Hackett, Thomas, MD
Hancock, Francis W., VA
Harry, Benjamin F., PA
Hawkins, Alexander B., NC
Hilbish, Daniel J., PA
Hogg, Thomas D., NC
Hollinsworth, Joseph, NC
Hough, De Witt C., PA
Hunton, George W., VA
Hupp, John C., PA
Hutchinson, Thomas D., GA
Irwin, Crawford, PA
Jackson, Isaac, PA
Jackson, James C., NH
Jameson, Samuel D.M., MD
Joy, Horatio N., NY
Keene, Benjamin F., GA
Keeney, Jackson P., PA
Kerr, John G., OH
Kilby, John T., VA
Kincaid, John, SC
Kurtz, William J., VA
Lamb, William D., MA
Lewis, Joseph Addison, MO
Lindsay, Horace F., NC
Linn, Alexander E., PA
Locke, Samuel T., NJ
Lyon, Emory, MA
Marshall, John H.T., MD
Marshall, William, DE
Martin, George, VA
Martin, Robert C., NC
McChesney, William S., VA
McClenahan, Thomas J., MD
McCullough Thomas P., OH
McFerran, Joseph A., DE
McGuigan, William W., PA
McKenney, Jackson L., VA
Meeteer, William H., DE
Mehard, Samuel S., PA
Miller, James L., SC
Miller, Langdon, MS
Millner, Jesse L., VA
Moore, Bird, TN
Moore, John R., VA
Murdoch, Andrew C., IRELAND
Neff, Benjamin, OH

Nisbet, John T., GA
O'Farrell, Henry T., NY
O'Rorke, James, PA
Patterson, Ashmore P., PA
Patterson, Robert M., GA
Patton, Thomas, VA
Pendleton, Samuel H., NC
Perkins, Charles W., DE
Polk, Thomas G., TN
Pratt, Bryce M., VA
Quinby, Watson F., DE
Reading, John R., PA
Reed, Joseph A., PA
Reid, John, CANADA
Richardson, John, PA
Riely, John D., VA
Rochelle, John R., VA
Rouanet, William, LA
Royer, Franklin B., PA
Russell, William, TN
Rutter, John R., PA
Scott, Isaac, VA
Scroggs, Andrew A., Jr., NC
Shelmerdine, Robert Q., PA
Sinex, William G., IN
Smith, Elias Ely, PA
Smith, James Dickson, GA
Smith, Robert M., GA
Spears, Thomas M., VA
Spencer, James L., VA
St. Clair, Thomas, PA
Stark, Horatio, MS
Starry, John D., VA
Stephenson, Robert G., PA
Steptoe, Henry C., VA
Stith, Robert A., VA
Stokes, Josiah H., SC
Stout, Daniel M., NJ

Strong, John M., SC
Sudler, William J., MD
Thom, Allan C., VA
Tingley, William H., PA
Tinsley, Thomas, VA
Torrey, Noah, MA
Trafton, Charles T., ME
Trammell, Appling D., AL
Trenchard, Franklin J., NJ
Turner, Thomas H., NC
Turpin, Thomas J., VA
VanBuskirk, William A., PA
VanValzah, Thomas, PA
VanVoorhis, John S., PA
Walker, Calvin H., TN
Walling, Willoughby, KY
Wallop, William J.H., VA
Ward, Isaiah, PA
Wathen, Athanasius, IN
Watkins, Henry A., VA
Watson, Edward H., PA
Weaver, John, PA
Weaver, William J., IN
Wentworth, George W., NH
Wheeler, Claudius B., NC
Wheet, Thomas, NH
Whiteside, Philip S.P., PA
Wiley, George, NJ
Wilkings, William C., NC
Williams, Elisha, NC
Williams, George M., GA
Williams, James, TN
Williams, Willis A., VA
Willson, Richard T., VA
Wilson, James R., TN
Wimley, George W., PA
Wortham, Robert T., VA
Yates, La Fayeté, KY
Yerkes, Harman, PA

The successful teacher is no longer on a height, pumping knowledge at high pressure into passive receptacles. . . . he is a senior student anxious to help his juniors.

Sir William Osler (1849-1919)

In this year the Rev. Ashbel Green died (Fig. 40). This 86 year-old clergyman, first President of Jefferson's Board, had served for 22 years. The Commencement Exercises were conducted by the Rev. Ezra Stiles Ely, President pro tempore, whose benefaction had created the Medical College Building at Tenth and Sansom Streets. Professor Joseph Pancoast delivered the address.

Among the 178 graduates was Benjamin Howard Rand (Fig. 41). This alumnus was appointed to the Chair of Chemistry (1864-1877) and he also served as Jefferson's Dean (1869-1873). As a further distinction, his portrait by Thomas Eakins in 1874 preceded that of the *Gross Clinic* by one year and was the first painted by the renowned artist beyond relatives and friends. It is a gem in Jefferson's art collection.

Andrew Jackson Foard was born in Milledgeville, Georgia. Following graduation he served in the Medical Corps of the United States Army where he advanced rapidly and for nine years was Assistant Surgeon General. He resigned at the outbreak of the Civil War to enlist in the Confederacy. He organized the Medical Services of General Bragg's Army and continued in the same capacity throughout the War. In 1867 he was elected to the Chair of Anatomy at Washington University in Baltimore but died in 1868 at the early age of 39 years.

Richard J. Levis of this class became well established in ophthalmic and general surgery (Fig. 42). He was elected Surgeon to the Philadelphia General Hospital in 1859 and two years later Surgeon to the Pennsylvania Hospital

Fig. 41.   Benjamin Howard Rand (JMC, 1848), Professor of Chemistry (1864-77) and Dean (1869-73).

Fig. 42.   Richard J. Levis (JMC, 1848), Attending Surgeon to the Wills Eye Hospital and Lecturer in Ophthalmic and Clinical Surgery at Jefferson.

where his surgical clinics became popular with Jefferson students. For many years he was Lecturer on Ophthalmic and Clinical Surgery at Jefferson as well as Attending Surgeon to the Wills Eye Hospital. He was a founder and first Professor of Clinical and Operative Surgery at the new Philadelphia Polyclinic and College for Graduates in Medicine and also was active in organized medicine, including a term as President of the Pennsylvania State Medical Society in 1888. He was also a Founding Member of the Philadelphia Academy of Surgery.

William Egbert Rogers, of Tennessee, founded the Memphis Hospital Medical College in 1880 which in 1911 merged with three other medical schools in Memphis to form the Medical School of the University of Tennessee.

CLASS OF 1848

Alexander, Gerard, KY
Anderson, John B., VA
Arnold, Edmund S.F., ENGLAND
Ayer, Francis B., NH
Baer, Caleb D., MD
Bainbridge, Eusebius C., KY
Banks, William, AL
Baxley, Jabez B., SC
Bennett, Trumbull L., NY
Benson, Wirt F., TN
Bibb, William E., VA
Birch, David, IRELAND
Birdsell, Sylvester, PA
Blain, Hamilton L., VA
Bolling, Lenaeus, VA
Bolton, James N., GA
Bourn, Richard W., MO
Bournonville, A., PA
Bowen, James W., MD
Brass, Andrew J., PA
Broadnax, Robert, NC
Brookbank, John W., IA
Brown, James Henry, PA
Brown, John T., PA
Bruner, William H., PA
Buck, Jonathan, MS
Cable, Josiah C., OH
Cahall, Thomas, DE
Cameron, J. Walton, VA
Carr, William W., GA
Chambers, John M., PA
Chancellor, James E., VA
Churchman, Vincent T., VA
Clark, George W., VA
Clements, L. Morgan, AL
Collet, Mark Wilkes, PA
Connalley, Reps, VA
Crouse, George Jackson, PA
Davidson, Charles Edward, VA
Davis, John Jr., VA

Dennis, William H., VA
Deupree, William J., MS
Dice, Reuben B., VA
Dixon, Lucius, VA
Dodd, Robert J., Jr., PA
Doxey, John L., MS
Drayton, Edward F., PA
Fitzgerald, Edmund, GA
Foard, Andrew Jackson, GA
Folwell, Joseph N., KY
Fort, Moses T., GA
Frick, William S., PA
Gamble, George M., PA
Garnett, James H., VA
Gauthreaux, Joseph Justin, LA
Gilbert, Julius Caesar, GA
Glass, Samuel, OH
Green, James S., NC
Gresham, Sterling A., GA
Guild, La Fayette, AL
Gwyn, James D., NC
Habersham, Stephen Elliot, SC
Halley, Samuel H., VA
Hamilton, James, PA
Harden, Robert Raymond, GA
Harper, John P., MO
Harris, Marcus A., VA
Hayes, Pliny H., NY
Henderson, William J., PA
Herr, Henry F., PA
Hill, Alonzo A.F., GA
Hillsman, William H., VA
Hobson, Samuel A., VA
Hore, Walter, VA
Hottenstein, Cyrus D., PA
Houtz, Abraham, OH
Howard, Nelson W., NY
Howell, George H., PA
Humphreys, Benjamin W., TN
Hunter, William R., ME

Isbell, Abner C., VA
Jackson, Samuel, PA
Jenkins, Paul F., SC
Jenkins, Robert C., VA
Jessup, John J., NJ
Jeter, John W., VA
Jones, Daniel W., MD
Jones, Robert Lewis, MS
Jordan, Watson P., VA
Kendrick, Oscar C., OH
Knapp, Franklin A., NY
Koontz, George H.H., VA
Ladd, Horace, PA
Leake, Virginius, TN
Leatherbury, Edward R., VA
Levis, Richard J., PA
Lindsey, Hugh N., MS
Linn, William H., NJ
Long, John Wesley, NC
Long, Reuben K., VA
Lothrop, James E., NH
Luther, Martin, PA
Mackenzie, Thomas G., VA
Marsden, John H., PA
Marshall, Theophilus O., VA
Mason, Edmunds, AL
McClure, Henry, PA
McIlvaine, Robert H., NC
McNail, Thomas A., TN
Merinar, William H., MS
Moore, William I., NJ
Moss, George W., MO
Moultrie, Alonzo C., GA
Murphy, Cornelius T., NC
Murphy, John A., PA
Nash, John W., VA
Neblett, Sterling Jr., VA
Neff, Peter D., PA
Nicholas, John Thomas, SOUTH WALES
O'Donnell, William, PA
Oldham, Robert H., TN
Osborne, Edward A., NJ
Owen, Edward, PA
Palmer, Charles, NH
Parker, Edward H., MA
Patterson, Theophilus, NJ
Peters, Samuel Adams, MO
Pettus, Luther C., VA
Philbrick, Samuel R., MA

Phillips, Thomas A., MS
Preston, Alexander R., VA
Prince, William E., VA
Puryear, Richard R., VA
Ramsay, G. Randolph, GA
Ramsay, James Graham, NC
Rand, Howard B., PA
Reilly, Paul Jones, MO
Richardson, William L., PA
Robb, John P., VA
Robertson, Edwin I., VA
Robson, George T., VA
Rogers, William Egbert, TN
Rooke, Levi, PA
Sample, John, PA
Scott, Sameul, PA
Seltzer, John Horace, PA
Service, Lecky M., PA
Smith, Elliott Iverson, GA
Sutton, James L., PA
Sutton, Lewis, PA
Taylor, George T., NJ
Taylor, James M., PA
Taylor, Leonidas C., NC
Terhune, Archibald A., GA
Tharp, Jonathan, DE
Tharp, William H., TN
Thomas, John R., PA
Thornton, William P., MS
Timberlake, Phillip, VA
Tobias, John F., PA
Todd, Alexander H., MD
Toombs, Robert E., GA
Turner, James, PA
Urquhart, Thomas H., VA
Vaughan, Thomas B., AL
Wallace, Robert B., AL
Walsh, William F., TN
Walton, Lewis I., VA
Welsh, William A., AL
Whitaker, Benjamin F., NC
White, G. Jefferson, VA
Williams, William Jr., VA
Wilson, Andrew J., VA
Wilson, James A., PA
Wimbish, James A., VA
Womble, Pembroke, M., VA
Wright, John, PA
Zimmerman, Reuben P., MO

At this time the fee for admission to each of the seven courses in the Medical College was fifteen dollars ($105 for the session). The matriculation fee was five dollars, payable only once. A charge of thirty dollars was made for the diploma. Good boarding, including heat and light, could be had for three dollars per week.

Of the 188 graduates, one member, Jonathan Letterman, from Pennsylvania, was destined for a brilliant military career (Fig. 43). Upon graduating he entered the Army as an Assistant Surgeon. Eventually he advanced to the status of Medical Director of the Army of the Potomac under President Lincoln. His lasting contribution was the system he devised for prompt evacuation of the wounded during the course of battle (Fig. 44). The Army Medical Center, San Francisco, was named in his honor.

Charles Sutherland, a native of Pennsylvania, became a United States Army officer who from 1890 to 1893 served as Surgeon General of the Army under President Benjamin Harrison with the rank of Brigadier General.

Richard Beverly Cole proceeded to California where he was closely involved in pioneer medical activities. In accord with the times he was soon appointed Surgeon General of the Guard raised by the Vigilance Committee. Upon the founding of the Medical Department of the University of California, he was made its first Dean and Professor of Obstetrics and Diseases of Women and Children. He later served as President of the California State Medical Society and of the American Medical Association.

Fig. 43. Jonathan Letterman (JMC, 1849) devised a pioneer system to remove the wounded from the battlefield.

CLASS OF 1849

Adkins, Isaac Leonard, DE
Agard, Aurelius H., OH
Azpell, Thomas F., PA
Barksdale, Edward F., VA
Barksdale, John, VA
Bean, Cyrus Beede, NH
Bell, Addison A., GA
Bell, Aurelius A., OH
Bellamy, John T., NC
Bierer, Frederick C., PA
Bishop, George W., MD

Blackwood, William, PA
Blair, John E., MD
Bland, William F., VA
Blanton, James M., VA
Blanton, Philip S., VA
Bonifant, Benjamin, MD
Brandt, Logan, VA
Brolasky, Joseph P., PA
Butcher, Joseph Jr., NJ
Campbell, Henry H., ME
Campbell, Sidney A., PA

Carr, Thomas W., FL
Carter, John F., VA
Carter, William Lovering, MA
Challiss, William L., NJ
Chew, Robert S., Jr., VA
Clarke, William J., PA
Cole, Richard B., PA
Coues, Samuel F., NH
Cresler, Alonzo L., PA
Cresson, Charles M., PA
Croom, Platt S., AL
Crowly, Timothy S., IRELAND
Crump, William Jr., VA
Darden, David L., AL
Davis, Benjamin J.B., PA
Davis, George S., GA
Dawson, Stephen W., TN
Day, Fish Hollbrook, NY
DeLacy, John, PA
Dent, Eugene T., AL
Dickinson, Samuel T., VA
Draper, Isaac Jr., MA
Drewry, John W., GA
Durrett, Addison L., VA
Ellet, Edward C., IL
Ellis, Joseph W., ME
Elsom, James R., VA
Elsom, John W., VA

Eppes, John W., FL
Ferris, Charles E., DE
Field, Edward M., ME
Fish, James S., GA
Flint, Thomas, ME
Flournoy, Patrick H., VA
Garland, Joseph, NH
Geddes, John, PA
Graham, Henry W., NC
Graham, Neill, NC
Graham, Taylor L., PA
Groff, Jacob E., PA
Gunn, Daniel B., NC
Gunnell, William P., VA
Hackett, Robert F., NC
Hardcastle, Alexander, MD
Hardin, William N., VA
Harper, Isaac N., PA
Hatchett, Lewellyn, VA
Haynes, Robert S., VA
Heard, Falkner, GA
Henley, John B.D., TN
Henry, William S.B., VA
Hill, Ambrose B., NJ
Hillman Richard E., PA
Holt, M. Quincy, VA
Hoover, George J., PA
Hornor, Caleb W., NJ

Fig. 44.   Letterman's system for removal of wounded from the battlefield.

1849

Hosack, John P., PA
Hume., Charles E., VA
Hundley, John M., VA
Ingraham, Arthur, PA
Jackson, William F., ME
Jameson, Patrick H., IN
Jennings, John C., MO
Jennings, Lewis A., VA
Johnson, David J., PA
Jones, Charles P., MD
Jones, Luther M., VA
Joy, Henry L., NY
Kells, Louis, OH
Kimbley, John F., KY
Laidley, Thomas M., VA
Latimer, Joseph T., VA
Letterman, Jonathan, PA
Lindley, Horace S., OH
Livingood, Michael T., PA
Long, Samuel H., PA
Lyman, Joseph W., PA
Mahon, Ormsby S., PA
Marr, William P., PA
McCarty, James B., VA
McClelland, William F., OH
McElwee, Andrew, OH
McFarland, Henderson, LA
McGruder, Zachariah S., VA
McReynolds, John O., KY
Meares, William B., NC
Mendenhall, Thomas J., OH
Moody, David J., VA
Moore, James E., VA
Morrison, James, PA
Morton, William J., VA
Murdock, John N., MA
Niccolls, Robert, PA
Nofsinger, William R., IN
Northington, William H., VA
Page, James H., OH
Page, John T., NH
Palm, James P., PA
Parker, James Jr., PA
Parker, Theodore, GA
Parks, Elijah M., MS
Patterson, Cornelius D., PA
Perry, Daniel G., NY
Pitts, Francis M., GA
Presson, William F., VA
Prince, Francis M., AL
Pugh, Edward H., MD
Ragsdale, William R., MS
Reeme, Elias W., PA
Rice, Harrison J., IN
Rihl, Henry W., PA

Rives, George E., VA
Robertson, Charles, OH
Robins, Oscar M., PA
Robinson, Philemon B., VA
Rogers, George O., VA
Rohrer, Jacob M., PA
Ross, George, PA
Senseman, Hiram, PA
Sharp, Alexander Jr., PA
Shaw, Alexander, PA
Sheets, Joseph, MD
Sheridan, Campbell, PA
Shuford, Quincy A., NC
Sims, Joseph Addison, VA
Sizer, George D., VA
Sizer, James Jr., VA
Smith, Andrew K., CT
Smith, William U., VA
Spalding, Andrew J., MD
Stokes, William O., VA
Strurgeon, Eli, OH
Styer, Albanus, PA
Sutherland, Charles, PA
Sutherland, Roderick, NOVA SCOTIA
Swaby, William A., NY
Sweitzer, Lewis H., PA
Tarver, Samuel, TN
Tate, Robert H., NC
Taylor, James H., KY
Taylor, Parran, DE
Taylor, William B., VA
Thacher, James M., CT
Townsend, Charles W., PA
Trego, Joseph H., IL
Troth, Samuel N., NJ
Tulloss, Robert C., TN
Tunnicliff, Joseph Jr., MI
Waage, Charles T., PA
Walker, Bernard H., VA
Walker, William T., VA
Walton, Simeon T., VA
Webb, William, NC
Whartenby, John A., PA
White, William H., MD
Wilkinson David M., VA
Williams, Cyrenius, PA
Williams, Robert S., AL
Wilson, Alexander, NC
Wilson, Furman E., SC
Wilson, Robert V., PA
Wood, Daniel Jones, VA
Woods, Matthew, PA
Woodward, Charles, NY
Wright, Francis R., MD
Young, Thomas J., VA

The graduates of this class numbered 211, the largest total in the history of the College to that time. The Commencement Address was delivered by Professor John Kearsley Mitchell, Chairman of Medicine (1841-1858), whose son, Silas Weir Mitchell, destined for great prominence, was receiving his diploma.

S. Weir Mitchell became a pioneer in neurophysiological research but also made classic contributions in clinical neurology and psychiatry (Fig. 45). He was elected first President of the Philadelphia Neurological Society, later served as President of the American Neurological Association, and was President of the College of Physicians of Philadelphia for two different terms (1886-1888 and 1892-1894). Equally highly regarded for his novels and poetry, he received honorary degrees from Harvard and the University of Bologna. Considered a genius by his contemporaries, and abundantly gifted academically, he was disappointed in his effort to become Professor of Physiology at both Jefferson and the University of Pennsylvania.

George R. Morehouse, of this class, collaborated with S. Weir Mitchell and W.W. Keen in a significant Civil War research project entitled *Gunshot Wounds and Other Injuries of Nerves* (1864).

Addinell Hewson, another class member, was one of the ten founders (with Samuel D. Gross) of the Philadelphia Academy of Surgery in 1879 (Fig. 46). He was the private physician to General Meade from whose side he removed a bullet just before the battle of Gettysburg, when army surgeons had failed to locate the ball.

Fig. 45. Silas Weir Mitchell (JMC, 1850), pioneer in research and neuropsychiatry as well as a famed novelist.

Thomas Addis Emmett, after graduating in this class, went to New York where he subsequently collaborated with J. Marion Sims in his work at the Woman's Hospital. He published his experience with some 600 cases of vesico-vaginal fistula (1868) of which only three were incurable. Along with devising numerous gynecologic instruments, he published a text, *Principles and Practice of Gynecology* (1879), which was characterized as "the first thoroughly scientific, comprehensive work on this subject in English." In 1898 he was awarded the Laetere Medal of Notre Dame University.

Aikins, William T., CANADA
Ake, Joseph H., PA
Alcorn, James P., PA
Alexander, Richard H., KY
Anderson, Zebulon M.P., VA
Ashe, Edmund F., NC
Ashe, Richard D., AL
Ashley, Cornelius, GA
Austin, Henry O., VA
Austin, Peter, MO
Bache, Thomas Hewson, PA
Ballow, Isaac T., VA
Banks, James Oliver, AL
Barksdale, Nathaniel, VA
Barnes, Laken D., KY
Barr, Edwin W., IL
Bloodworth, Wiley W., GA
Boorse, Isaiah H.G., PA
Bott, James P., VA
Bowcock, James M., VA
Bowland, Milton J., OH
Brackenridge, Henry H., PA
Bradford, Thomas A., FL
Briggs, George W., VA
Bronson, William S., NY
Brooks, William A., MS
Brown, Neill D., MS
Brown, Robert S., PA
Brown, Solomon, CT
Brown, Spencer W., MO
Bryant, Cassander E., OH
Buckingham, E. Milton, OH
Buffington, Thomas C., VA
Buford, James S., MS
Bullock, J. Row, NY
Burnley, Hardin, MS
Burton, Daniel L., VA
Cake, William A., OH
Carithers Eli K., IL
Chamblin, Marquis R., KY
Chandler, S. Temple, VA
Chase, Charles T., NH
Chester, Samuel H., TN

Chorpenning, Frank, PA
Claiborne, J. Herbert, VA
Clark, Henry, NY
Clark, William L., PA
Cochran, William S., PA
Cockerille, Americus, VA
Coombs, David H., IN
Coover, Eli H., PA
Culbertson, Howard, OH
Cuthbertson, David H., NC
Daly, Lafayette, VA
Dameron, Robert C., MS
Dana, Marcus, OH
Daniel, Milton J., GA
Davidson, Junius, MS
Davis, Andrew J., PA
Derrickson. John B., NJ
Dickson, James T., MO
Dold, Samuel M., VA
Dorset, John Lewis, VA
Dorsey, John P., PA
Dossey, George W., VA
Drummond, John T., VA
Du Val, Lucian Spence, FL
Dunlap, Theodore, KY
Dupree, Ira E., Jr., GA
Durst, Daniel P., PA
Edwards, Americus A., MO
Elliott, Thomas Balch, NY
Emmet, Thomas Addis, VA
Ewing, George, PA
Fitts, John H., AL
Fuqua, Thomas B., VA
Gale, William H., MD
Garden, John B., VA
Gay, Neil B., VA
Gilbert, Michael M., KY
Gillam, Louis M., NC
Gillespie, William A., GA
Gilmore, William J., PA
Graham, Edward L., VA
Graham, Frederick R., NJ
Grammer, Jones M., VA

Grant, Gough W., NC
Gross, James D., PA
Haile, William J., VA
Hancock, William G., VA
Hann, John A., PA
Hardman, William B.J., GA
Hayes, Isham H., AL
Hendren, Samuel R., VA
Henry, Charlton T., PA
Heston, Abiah P., PA
Hewson, Addinell, PA
Hirst, Cyrus J., PA
Holt, Cicero, GA
Hoyt, Moses C., NH
Hudson, Robert B., VA
Hughes, Thomas I., VA
Hyde, John H., VA
Jennings, Alvan J.E., VA
Jones, John T., VA
Kelly, Charles B.P., PA
Kimmel, Edmund M., PA
Kindrick, Cyrus Jr., ME
King, James E., NC
Kreitzer, Michael C., PA
Kyle, George P., VA
Lamar, Thompson B., GA
Lamme, William H., OH
Leftwich, John W., TN
Leigh, John Randolph, VA
Lewis, James M., MA
Lewis, Richard E., VA
Lillington, George, NC
Lindley, Alfred H., NC
Lindsay, Reuben, VA
Link, William, PA
Linn, Theodore A., NJ
Logan, Matthew D., KY
Lowman, John, PA
Lugenbeel, James W., VA
Lungren, Samuel S., PA
Mackie John Howell, MA
Madison, James A., VA
Manahan, Valentine, NH
Marks, Julian C., VA
Martin, Algernon S., VA
McConaughy, Robert, PA
McCulloch, William P., PA
McDonald, Nesbit, PA
McVeigh, William H., VA
Meranda, Isaac, IN
Meriwether, John H., TN
Mettauer, Edward M., VA
Michie, John Augustus, VA
Miller, David H., PA

Mills, Samuel R., VA
Milner, James S., VA
Mitchell, S. Weir, PA
Morehouse, George R., NJ
Morrow, William, IN
Moseley, Daniel Willis, VA
Mowry, John N., PA
Neilson, Robert, PA
Nightingale, Henry B., PA
Owen, Joseph D., GA
Palmore, Charles R., VA
Parke, Clifford D., AL
Patton, Joseph C., TN
Peebles, John H.M., PA
Piggott, William M., VA
Powell, H. Brooke, VA
Prescott, Paul T., ME
Price, Jacob, PA
Quarles, Mercer W., VA
Quick, Lavington, ENGLAND
Rankin, Clarke D., PA
Rhinehart, Solomon E., OH
Ricketts, Gerard C., VA
Roberts, Benjamin F., CT
Rogers, Thomas H., VA
Ross, Samuel M., PA
Russell, William M.N., MS
Schriver, Albert, PA
Seller, Theophilus S., IN
Sharp, Alexander E., PA
Shelley, Aaron F., PA
Sherrell, Joseph L., TN
Shewalter, George William, VA
Shoyer, Charles C., WI
Smith, Frisby T., PA
Smith, George L., OH
Smith, John H., VA
Stewart, William G., PA
Stuart, Joseph G., IN
Sturdivant, Marcus, VA
Taliaferro, Philip A., VA
Taylor, Thomas W., PA
Temple, Thomas P., VA
Thorndike, Albert, ME
Todd, Louis H., KY
Trammell, Francis A., AL
Tucker, Thomas W., VA
Tuttle, Levi W., NH
Urquhart, George, PA
Voorhees, Charles H., NJ
Wakefield, Matthew F., KY
Walker, James R., VA
Wallton, James C., VA
Ward, Edward W., NC

Warfield, Milton, MD
Webber, Joseph B., ME
Weiser, Charles S., PA
Westmoreland, Willis F., GA
Whitaker, John F., AR
Wilbur, Greenleaf A., ME
Williams, Lorenzo D., VA
Wilson, Edward A., VA
Wilson, John R., PA

Woddrop, Henry, PA
Wood, Edwin N., VA
Wood, John Dean, VA
Woodbury, Jonathan, NOVA SCOTIA
Woodside, James A., SC
Worl, Eli T., PA
Wright, David D., CANADA
Young, George W., GA

Fig. 46.   Addinell Hewson (JMC, 1850) introduced the ophthalmoscope to Wills Eye Hospital.

The shining light of this class which numbered 227 was James Aitken Meigs (Fig. 47). While still an undergraduate he took notes of the lectures and debates of the Philadelphia County Medical Society, gave case reports of patients treated at Jefferson and the Pennsylvania Hospital, and presented papers on the mortuary statistics of Philadelphia which were published in the *Medical Examiner*. His long association with the Philadelphia County Medical Society led to its Presidency in 1871. Research on the *Cranial Characteristics of the Races of Man*, along with his outstanding lectures in physiology, earned him an international reputation. In 1868 he was appointed Professor of the Institutes of Medicine at Jefferson to succeed the prestigious Robley Dunglison who had been his undergraduate idol. Popular with the students and gifted as a poet, he is best remembered today because of the Meigs Medical Association, named in his honor in 1880 following his premature death at the age of 50 (Fig. 48). This Association is still active well beyond its centennial year and is one of the oldest of its kind in the country.

E. Levi Cooper Lane, a dynamic but eccentric surgeon, became the founder in 1882 of Cooper Medical College in San Francisco, which later became the medical school for Stanford University. Dr. Lane named the school for his uncle, Dr. Samuel Cooper, who was also a San Francisco physician. He contributed large sums of money to the medical school and for a hospital. His estate funded the Levi Cooper Lane Library of Medicine and Surgery in San Francisco, for a time the finest medical library west of Chicago.

CLASS OF 1851

Abbitt, William B., VA
Albright, Durant H., NC
Armistead, William B., AL
Baily, Elisha S., PA
Baily, R. Jones, PA
Barber, James K., OH
Barry, William Frederic, NC
Bateman, Ephraim, NJ
Bates, James M., ME
Battle, Lucius Lucullus, TN
Beaver, Ephraim K., PA
Black, Abraham, VA
Bly, Douglas, NY
Bobb, William H., PA
Booth, William C., VA
Boswell, John J., VA
Brannock, James M., NC
Brinker, Reuben, PA
Brooks, John G., ME
Brownrigg, John, MS
Brubaker, Henry, PA
Burnett, Elisha G., NY
Campbell, Algernon E., VA
Carnal, Reuben H., LA
Carriger, John H., TN

Carrington, Paul S., VA
Carter, Flournoy, GA
Cary, Charles W., VA
Cheney, Francis M., GA
Christian, William S., VA
Coleman, Charles T., VA
Coleman, Richard M., VA
Collins, Thomas B., NY
Conner, William H.H., NC
Cook, Columbus L., NC
Cook, George H., PA
Couse, George, CANADA
Craig, James W., NY
Crouse, William, PA
Cutliff, James S., LA
Dana, Charles H., PA
Davidson, Henry G., VA
Dickson, James G., PA
Dingee, Richard, PA
Dingley, Amasa J., ME
Duffey, John W., GA
Dulany, U. Heath, VA
Duncan, George K., TN
Edmunds, Samuel C., NJ
Eggleston, Joseph D., VA

Eshleman, Isaac S., PA
Evans, J. Mason, VA
Evans, Joshua R., PA
Fearing, Benjamin, Jr., MA
Fisher, Preston, ME
Fitts, William F., AL
Fleming, Thomas M., VA
Flewellen, Edward A., GA
Floyd, Frederic, VA
Foote, Charles C., CT
Fort, Joseph M., TX
Fox, Joseph M., KY
Friend, George W., VA
Friend, John Edward, VA
Fussell, Morris, PA
Gaddis, Elijah Franklin, AL
Gaither, Brice T., GA
Gale, Robert H., KY
Gary, Franklin F., SC
Geare, Frederic, NY
Gegan, John, Jr., PA
Gibbons, Thomas P., PA
Glenn, Lucius B., AL
Golding, Walter S., NC
Gorin, William H., KY
Griesemer, Enoch E., PA
Haggard, William D., KY
Hall, Samuel E., GA
Hall, William M., TN
Hamer, Ellis P., PA
Hamilton George S., VA
Hancock, Charles, VA
Hassenplug, Jacob H., PA
Havis, Minor W., GA
Hazlett, Robert W., PA
Henderson, Andrew J., VA
Herrick, J. Everette, NH
Hershe, Christian, IA
Heyward, James F., DE
Holbrook, William S., VA
Hood, Humphrey H., PA
Hope, Jesse P., VA
Howitt, John, CANADA
Hume, William, CANADA
Hunter, George Baxter, VA
Huntington, T. Roomeyn, NY
Huston, James M., VA
Irvine, Patrick C., VA
Jackson, Winslow, MA
James, Nathan, PA
Jenkins, William A., VA
Johnson, Emmanuel H., PA
Johnson, William M., NC
Judson, Oliver A., PA

Keenon, John G., KY
Kelly, Samuel H., VA
Keys, John, PA
Lamm, William A.B., GA
Lane, E. L.C., IL
Layton, Joseph, OH
Leinbach, Benjamin S., PA
Lemmon, William, PA
Lewis, J. Henry, TX
Line, William M., PA
Lovejoy, James W.H., DC
Luckett, Francis E., VA
Mackey, James Howard, PA
Madison, Robert L., VA
Martin, William Henry, KY
Matteson, John C., NY
McClung, John A., VA
McCorkle, John R., NC
McGrigor, Thompson L., VA

Fig. 47. James Aitken Meigs (JMC, 1851), Professor of Institutes of Medicine (Physiology) from 1868 to 1879 and namesake of the Meigs Medical Association, still flourishing after 110 years.

McGuire, John G., PA
McIntyre, De Witt C., NY
McNutt, Robert, DE
McWhinney, Arthur, PA
Meachem, Thomas G., NY
Meigs, James Aitken, PA
Meisenhelder, Samuel, PA
Mellen, George F., ME
Merritt, William, VA
Miller, William Lamech, PA
Miller, William Robards, NC
Milligan, Francis H., MO
Moodey, Joseph H., PA
Moody, Thomas H., TN
Moore, Ira L., MA
Moore, Matthew S., SC
Moore, Maurice A., SC
Morris, George W., SC
Morrison, M. Porter, PA
Mulford, Francis D., NJ
Mullins, James C., NC

Neff, Henry K., PA
Nice, Franklin B., PA
Nice, George W., PA
Oaks, Samuel, PA
Oden, J. Beverly, VA
Overton, William M., VA
Owens, Bennett G., AL
Parker, Oscar F., NY
Perkins, Joseph B., MS
Perkins, Lewis W., VA
Peterson, Bowman H., NJ
Phillips, William W.L., NJ
Piatt, William A., PA
Poindexter, Edward H., VA
Pomroy, Charles G., NY
Pratt, J. Richmond, NY
Proctor, Pelatiah R., CANADA
Rankin, E. Davidson, PA
Rankin, William M., PA
Reddick, Samuel T., PA
Reese, Beverly P., VA
Ridgill, Henry L., SC
Robinson, Frederic C., OH
Rogers, Henry R., ME
Roper, Daniel W., KY
Rose, Latinus Irvine, VA
Ruby, Cyrus B., PA
Rugh, Jacob W., PA
Russell, Preston W., PA
Sanford, Robert J., VA
Saunders, Samuel, VA
Schively, George Singer, PA
Scofield, John S., KY
Scott, A. Howard, VA
Scott, William Walter, NC
Sharpe, William R., NC
Simmons, Allen J., GA
Smith, Albert D., VT
Smith, Bart M., GA
Smith, James Gregory, KY
Smith, Pembroke, VA
Smith, Sandford F., MO
Smith, Walter R., NC
Spruill, George E., NC
Squire, William H., PA
Statler, Samuel G., PA
Stoakley, William S., VA
Stocker, Jesse, VA
Stone, Samuel A., VA
Stoner, John, PA
Suesserott, Jacob L., PA
Taylor, J. Marcus, MS
Taylor, James, PA
Taylor, Julian, VA

Fig. 48. Obelisk with urn marking gravesite of James Aitken Meigs in Woodlands Cemetery, Philadelphia.

1851

Thom, J. Pembroke, VA
Thomas, Robert W., NC
Thompson, John A., DE
Thompson, Stephen S., KY
Tipton, Richard H., OH
Tullis, Thomas Erskine, AL
Turner, Charles P., PA
Tyson, John Ambrose, TN
Umstad, Henry U., PA
Vaughn, George W., AL
Venable, Richard N., VA
Vernon, Elias, CANADA
Vollum, Edward P., NY
Wallace, James J., PA

Walser, Theodore, SWITZERLAND
Ward, Erastus B., VA
Ward, Meredith G., TN
Warren, Edward, NC
Weeks, William C., VA
Weir, John M., VA
West, William H., Jr., VA
Wilson, John W., VA
Wingfield, Alonzo C., GA
Witman, Henry O., PA
Wolf, John A., PA
Wood, Charles S., CT
Wright, Thomas E., VA
Wyker, Alfred, NJ
Young, George W., MO

The Pennsylvania Hospital (founded by Benjamin Franklin in 1751), an important clinical facility for Jefferson students through the years.

In this year the hypodermic syringe was introduced in France by Charles-Gabriel Pravaz, and in the United States the American Pharmaceutical Association was founded. There were 213 members in the graduating class, the following three of whom later became Professors in their Jefferson Alma Mater.

John Hill Brinton (Fig. 49), of Pennsylvania, served as a Brigade Surgeon of Volunteers in

Fig. 49. John Hill Brinton (JMC, 1852), Co-founder of the Army Medical Museum who also collected statistics for the *Medical and Surgical History of the War of the Rebellion*, and was Co-Chairman of the Department of Surgery (1882-1906).

which his Civil War Commission, signed by Abraham Lincoln, is in Jefferson's archives (Fig. 50). He was the personal physician to General Ulysses S. Grant, collected statistics for the *Medical and Surgical History of the War of the Rebellion*, was a co-founder of the Army Medical Museum, and wrote *Personal Memoirs* of the Civil War. At the resignation of Samuel D. Gross in 1882, he served with distinction as Co-Chairman of Surgery with Samuel W. Gross (1882-1889) and with William W. Keen (1889-1906). His portrait by Thomas Eakins (1876) is in the National Gallery of Art in Washington, D.C. Dr. Brinton is buried in Woodlands Cemetery, Philadelphia (Fig. 51).

Jacob Mendes DaCosta (Fig. 52), from Saint Thomas, was the first alumnus to occupy The Chair of Medicine (1872-1891). His textbook, *Medical Diagnosis*, went through nine editions between 1864 and 1900. His classic description of "irritable heart" (1871) marked him as a pioneer in cardiology. He received LL.D. degrees from Jefferson, the University of Pennsylvania and Harvard. Thomas Eakins painted his portrait (1893) which hangs in the Pennsylvania Hospital.

William Smith Forbes (Fig. 53), of Virginia, became the last of a continuous line of famous surgeon-anatomists at Jefferson. His greatest contribution was passage of the Anatomy Act of 1867 (amended in 1882/1883) which provided legally for equitable distribution of cadavers for teaching in Pennsylvania medical schools. He served as Chairman of Anatomy (1886-1905) and his portrait by Eakins (1905) accompanies that of Rand and Gross in the Eakins Gallery.

John McQuillan graduated while he was also studying dentistry. His D.D.S. was honorary. In his further career as a dental surgeon he founded the Philadelphia Dental College in 1863 in which he served as a professor and dean.

Fig. 50. Civil War commission of John Hill Brinton (JMC, 1852) signed by Abraham Lincoln.

Anderson, Joseph W., PA
Anderson, Philip W., PA
Anderson, William, PA
Ashley, William, GA
Atkinson, Benjamin M., VA
Baker, Moses, IN
Barksdale, William P., VA
Barton, John T., VA
Barton, Thomas F., ME
Beahan, James, NY
Bigony, Franklin W., PA
Blanchard, John H., NH
Boxley, Robert H., VA
Brelsford, James R., OH
Brinton, John H., PA
Brock Hugh W., VA
Clanton, Albert B., AL
Clements, Early C., AL
Clendaniel, William, PA
Cole, Isaac N., VA
Coleman, Robert T., VA

Collier, Abner A., MO
Cooper, Josiah C., PA
Cooper, Robert L., KY
Crawford, John W., MD
Culbertson, James, MO
Cunningham, William R., AL
DaCosta, Jacob Mendes, WEST, INDIES
Dean, Henry S., MA
Dedrick, Allen, SC
Dewitt, Benjamin, PA
Dickinson, Crispin, VA
Dillard, William D., KY
Doane, George Hobart, NJ
Dorsey, Henry A., PA
Dummer, Edward Osborne, NJ
Dunott, Thomas J., MD
Durham, Alexander F., GA
Durrett, Fountain R., MO
Eastham, John B., VA
Emmert, Andrew, MD
Eustace, James H., VA
Evans, Isaac Newton, PA
Farley, William S., MS
Farrar, William F., VA
Flack, William C.A., IN
Fletcher, Corbin D., VA
Forbes, William S., VA
Foulkes, James F., NC
Fox, Thomas G., PA
Franklin, Benjamin, TN
Gardner, Robert B., GA
Gee, Charles J., NC
Gibson, Frederick H., VA
Gooch, Allen G., TN
Goodwin, Edmund P., VA
Gordon, John N., VA
Graham, Robert H., AL
Grant, Samuel Dexter, ME
Gray, William B., VA
Green, Charles H., SC
Gulliver, Daniel F., PA
Hardy, Thomas I., VA
Harrison, James F., VA
Hart, Albert Gaillord, PA
Hart, Ira F., NY
Havens, Joseph M., IN
Hay, Randal D., NC
Hayhurst, George R., PA
Henry, Beverly A., GA
Herndon, James C., VA
Hicks, Virginius H., VA
Higday, Thompkins, IN

Fig. 51. Gravesite of John Hill Brinton (JMC 1852) in Woodlands Cemetery, Philadelphia.

Hinton, Rufus K., MS
Hogdon, Richard L., ME
Hope, John F., VA
Hoppin, Samuel B., PA
Hopping, Daniel S., GA
Hoyt, Augustus B., NH
Hudson, Clement L., MS
Huggins, George A., SC
Huggins, Hermon H., SC
James, Martin L., VA
Jarvis, James M., VA
Jones, Parrish Vernon, VA
Jordan, Richard W., PA
Keelor, Reinhard K., PA
Kelsey, Charles T., NY
Kempton, Thomas D., PA
Kendall, William S., NC
Langdon, S. Walter, NC
Larzelere, Joseph R., OH
Lathrop, Horace, Jr., NY
Lester, James D., MS
Lewellyn, John S., Jr., VA
Lineaweaver, George P., PA
Lofland, Mark Greer, DE
Lomison, Henry G., PA
Long, Andrew, IL
Lucas, George Lee, Jr., PA
Lyman, Andrew B., KY
Mabon, Thomas, PA
Mabry, James F., SC
Mairs, John C., OH
Marshall, Philip D., PA
Martin, William L., PA
Mason, J. Francis, VA
Mathews, James H., GA
Mathiot, Henry B., PA
Mayo, Thomas H., AL
McAllister, William E., MS
McChesney, Alexander G., VA
McEachin, John E., AL
McEwen, William, PA
McLean, William S., NC
McQuillen, John H., PA
Merrill, Frank B., ME
Metz, Jacob K., PA
Miles, B. Fullerton, PA
Miller, William Newlon, PA
Montague, George B., NC
Monteiro, Aristides, VA
Moore, Joseph, NJ
Moss, Obadiah C.G., AL
Nash, Shepard K., NC
Neff, Charles, PA
Nelson, Andrew J., TN

Newbaker, John B., PA
Newcomer, John, PA
Norris, James T., TX
Orr, Gabriel P.N., MO
Parker, Jabez K., VA
Parker, Thomas S., CANADA
Payne, Benjamin F., VA
Pendleton, David H., VA
Pressly, Joseph L., SC
Priest, Albert G., MO
Prince, Josiah E. Duke, AL
Pynchon, Lewis Charlton, GA
Ramsay, George M., PA
Redfield, John, PA
Revercomb, Jacob R., VA
Reynolds, Harvey M., KY
Rice, Francis E., VA
Richards, Charles A.L., OH
Richardson, George N., VA

Fig. 52. Jacob Mendes DaCosta (JMC, 1852), Professor of Medicine (1872-1891), published the classic description of functional disorders of the heart.

Richie, Robert W., OH
Richmond, John B., NJ
Riley, Samuel A., GA
Robinson, Joseph S., VA
Rose, Algernon H., VA
Rose, William W., VA
Ross, James, CANADA
Rossy, Evariste A., LA
Rundio, Peter C., PA
Sanford, James L., NC
Schofield, John L., VA
Scott, William J., VA
Shammo, Isaac R., PA
Shaw, Angus G., TX
Shields, William W., VA
Smith Daniel, NC
Smith, John C., VA

Smith, Levi H., SC
Sommers, George A., VA
Spearman, Alfred S., NY
Speir, William, GA
Spinner, Jesse F., VA
Statten, Milton, PA
Stephenson, William D., AL
Storrow, S. Appleton, VA
Strode, William R., MS
Stroud, Joseph, PA
Tallman, William, PA
Tatum, B. Harris, VA
Taylor, John Y., DE
Thomson, John A., PA
Tompkins, Samuel W., VA
Townes, Lafayette, MS
Trimble, George B., VA
Tyler, Randolph, VA
Tynes, Robert H., VA
Unseld, James T., VA
Upshur, George M., MD
Usry, Joshua F., GA
Vardeman, Thomas B., MO
Vasey, Wilson P., PA
Walker, Benjamin H., VA
Walker, George S., CA
Wallace, John R., VA
Walters, William H., IL
Watkins, Beverly S., VA
Watkins, Richard H., VA
Watson, James M., VA
Watson, Thomas E., NC
Wheeler, Alfred, OH
Whitney, John W., KY
Wiley, Oscar, VA
Wilkins, George F., Jr., VA
Willcox, William P., NC
Williams, Blewitt, GA
Williams, Henry L., AL
Williams, Orlando S., VA
Wilson, Joseph F., PA
Wilson, William C., AL
Winn, David R.E., GA
Witherspoon, John A., KY
Woodward, Abner, Jr., NJ
Woolfolk, William T., VA
Worsham, John H., VA
Wright, James I., NJ
Wyly, James G., LA
Young, Thomas S., VA

Fig. 53. William Smith Forbes (JMC, 1852) fostered the passage of the Anatomy Act of 1867 which legalized the use of cadavers for medical education in the State of Pennsylvania, and served as Professor of Anatomy (1886-1905).

1852

There were 223 graduates in this class. Many interesting titles appear among theses required from the students during most of the nineteenth century. In 1853, two graduates selected "Milk Sickness" as their subject. Special interest attaches to this illness, most notably the death in 1818 of Nancy Hanks Lincoln, the mother of Abraham Lincoln, soon after the arrival of the family in Indiana when the future President was eight years old. A frontier disease with high mortality, milk sickness attacked farm animals as well as humans. It was known for more than a century before its specific cause was acknowledged although Indians and farmers had, since early in the nineteenth century, recognized the "trembles" produced in farm animals by consumption of weeds. Ultimately the "white snake root," Eupatorium urticaefolium, was accepted as etiologic. In the 1920s the toxic principle "tremetol" was finally isolated. It is curious that nonmedical people were well in advance of medical ones in correctly identifying the cause of the illness from epidemiological observations. By the twentieth century it had become a rarity. The two graduates, Drs. William F. Boor of Indiana and Pittacus L. Richeson of Virginia, who wrote about milk sickness, came from areas where the illness was still prevalent at the time.

William Biddle Atkinson (Fig. 54), a member of the class, became important in several areas of medicine. Special interest in obstetrics and diseases of children led to publications and numerous editorial posts which developed into a lifetime pattern. As an early secretary of the Philadelphia County Medical Society (later President), he developed skills in recording and correspondence leading to his election as Secretary of the American Medical Association in 1859, its permanent secretary in 1864, and editor of its annual transactions. In 1876 he served as secretary of the "National Day" Committee of the Philadelphia County Medical Society for the Philadelphia Centennial Exposition. In 1877 he became a Lecturer on Diseases of Children at Jefferson Medical College and from 1884 to 1889 he was Professor of Sanitary Science and Pediatrics at the Medico-Chirurgical College. Probably his most important work was the first comprehensive American Medical Biography, *Physicians and Surgeons of the United States*, published by Robson in 1878 and supplemented in 1880. Also in 1880 he completed *The Therapeutics of Gynecology and Obstetrics* plus a second edition the following year. Dr. Atkinson's interests also extended into the developing field of public health.

Joseph Meredith Toner, of Pennsylvania, became the first person in the United States to en-

Fig. 54. William Biddle Atkinson (JMC, 1853) authored an important biography of *Physicians and Surgeons of the United States* (1878) and served as President of the Philadelphia County Medical Society.

dow medical lectures (the Toner Lectures of the Smithsonian Institution). An outstanding medical historian, bibliophile and librarian, he subsequently gave 30,000 medical volumes to the Library of Congress. He also published (1870) a necrology of physicians in the Civil War and served as President of the American Medical Association (1874).

David Page Smith, after studying abroad, entered the U.S. Army during the Civil War, serving as Brigade Surgeon. In 1874 he became Professor of Theory and Practice of Medicine in the Yale Medical School, and four years later took the Chair of Surgery in the same institution.

CLASS OF 1853

Abel, Lemuel F., NY
Allen, Nathaniel N., GA
Altman, William, PA
Atkinson, William B., PA
Avinger, Hamilton J., SC
Axford, Samuel M., MI
Baily, Lewis, PA
Baley, Pinckney T., MS
Ballow, W. Montgomery, VA
Batten, A. Nelson, NJ
Baylor, Joseph N., KY
Benjamin, John B., ME
Beyerle, W. George, PA
Bitting, Anthony L., NC
Blair, Alexander R., PA
Blake, E. Tucker, DC
Boatwright, John G., VA
Bombaugh, Charles C., PA
Boor, William F., IN
Bowcock, Charles S., VA
Boyett, Thomas W., AL
Brinley, Edward H., CT
Broocks, John W., VA
Brown, Robert, PA
Bryan, John C., VA
Bunn, William, GA
Burgess, Ebenezer P., MA
Butts, J. Thomas, VA
Cabell, George K., VA
Chamberlain, Joseph P., DE
Chancellor, Charles W., VA
Chapin, John B., NY
Chase, Irah E., MA
Christian, Henry B., VA
Christy, Henderson J., OH
Churchman, Henry J., VA
Closson, Lorenzo D., CANADA
Cocke, William, AL
Connelly, Joseph H., PA
Coombs, Samuel W., KY
Cox, John K., MS

Curtis, Bartlett A., VA
Czapkay, Emilius A., HUNGARY
Davis, Theodore V.L., VA
De Berry, John C., SC
De Graffeuried, William, VA
Derr, Nathaniel H., PA
Dewey, George M., MO
Dinges, George H., VA
Dirickson, James C., MD
Donnelly, Henry L., PA
Duncan, Robert, PA
Durphy, Sydenham W., VA
Earickson, James P., MO
Easton, William A., PA
Ellis, James R., MO
Eppley, George, PA
Eshleman, Abraham, PA
Evans, Faulkner H., MS
Fahrney, Jacob, PA
Farinholt, Anderson S., AL
Farrar, T. Goodridge, MS
Farrelly, James, MS
Ford, Newton S., VA
Ford, Newton S., VA
Foreman, James M., VA
Foster, Robert S., AL
Fulmer, George, PA
Galbraith, Thomas, PA
Goodman, Horace A., VA
Goodwin, William C., VA
Graham, George M., PA
Graves, J. G., NH
Gray, Tazewell M., VA
Grayson, Wray, PA
Griesemer, Hiram J., PA
Griswold, Elisha, PA
Grizzard, Theophilus D., VA
Guthrie, Guian S., OH
Hamilton, Alfred J., VA
Hamilton, Samuel M., PA
Hannan, William F., OH

Harwell, William H., VA
Henning, William H., VA
Herrmann, Francis, NJ
Hershey, Joseph H., PA
Hill, A. Chandler, GA
Hines, Andrew J., PA
Hopkins, B. Scott, TN
Hottenstein, Edward, PA
Howze, Henry Y., NC
Huey, George B., GA
Hughes, John G., MD
Hunter, John C., KY
Hunter, Samuel M., SC
Jackson, George F., ME
Jackson, Thomas H., MD
Jaudon, Benjamin A., SC
Jeffery, James C., PA
Jennings, Peter E.L., GA
Jessup, Robert B., IN
Johnson, James S., AL
Johnson, John S., NJ
Johnson, Monroe M., TN
Jones, Alexander T., GA
Jordan, David A., SC
Karsner, William C., MD
Kennedy, William B., PA
Keys, Joseph W., PA
Kimbrough, G. William, VA
King, William H., PA
Kirk, Lewis R., PA
Kirke, Henry M., PA
Lavell, Michael, CANADA
Law, Samuel B., GA
Lazier, Henry B., VA
Lessey, Davis S., NJ
Lippitt, William F., VA
Littell, Norval W., VA
Lockhart, Wilson, IN
Locuson, Joseph S., NJ
Loving, Joseph F., VA
Luckett, George T., VA
Mansfield, Richard S., DE
Marable, Joseph E., VA
Marselis, Nicholas H., PA
Marshall, David M., PA
Maull, David W., DE
McClure, James D., PA
McCollum, Ephraim J., OH
McCrary, Elisha W., SC
McCulloch, Thomas C., PA
McDonald, Donald, MO
McLeary, William T., TN
McNeil, John, PA
McNutt, Samuel D., IN

Melton, John T., VA
Miller, Benjamin F., PA
Moore, James A., DE
Morison, James H.S., TN
Musser, Philip T., PA
Myers, Jacob S., PA
Nichols, Austin W., NY
Nisbet, Richard H., GA
Norment, Benjamin C., VA
Norris, John W., NEWFOUNDLAND
Palmer, Archibald W., NC
Parker, William R., VA
Parr, Richard C., TN
Parramore, William R., VA
Parvis, George W., MD
Patterson, Arthur, PA
Pharr, Alexander F., GA
Phelps, Frederick R., CANADA
Phillips, James, IL
Porter, Gabriel Ellis, PA
Potter, Elias, OH
Powell, Alfred H., VA
Powell, Belitha, MD
Powell, Claudius W., VA
Powell, John S., VA
Price, David E., GA
Price, Richard N., VA
Quail, William, PA
Ramsay, John W., PA
Ratcliffe, Charles T., KY
Read, John T., TN
Reed, C. Richmond, OH
Reed, John, OH
Reed, William, IN
Rice, Archibald A., VA
Richardson, Nicholas D., AL
Richeson, ittacus L., VA
Robertson, Charles A., MA
Robinson, Robert R., VA
Rochelle, Thomas W., AL
Rowland, John G., GA
Sample, Joseph E., PA
Sanger, Eugene F., ME
Saylor, Obadiah L., PA
Schwenck, Samuel G., PA
Scott, Samuel B., VA
Seem, Asa K., PA
Shaw, Daniel, NC
Simpson, Robert I., VA
Sims, Frederick H., VA
Smarr, Joseph G., SC
Smith, Charles, VA
Smith, David P., MA
Smith, Duncan, NC

Smith, Ellery P., NY
Smith, Hugh C., MS
Snodgrass, James C., MS
Spears, Joseph H., GA
Speer, Alexander M., PA
Stewart, W. Walker, PA
Stoner, Andrew J., IL
Strudwick, William S., NC
Sumner, George Jr., CT
Taliaferro, David M., KY
Taliaferro, Thomas J., VA
Taylor, William C., VA
Terrell, John J., VA
Thompson, Levi H., PA
Thompson, Peter S., VA
Tompkins, Alexander C., NY

Toner, Joseph M., PA
Townsend, Morris W., NY
Turner, Orlando E., PA
Tyler, Tazewell, VA
Walker, Charles Jr., MA
Walker, William, NH
Wall, William B., MS
Walton, William D., GA
Watson, William D., NC
West, Calvin, IN
Wevill, Richard H., PA
Whitaker, Wilson C., FL
Wilkins, Edmund W., VA
Willoughby, Henry W., GA
Wolff, John S., SC
Woodson, John C., MO
Yancey, Thomas A., VA

GENERAL

THERAPEUTICS

AND

MATERIA MEDICA:

ADAPTED FOR A

MEDICAL TEXT-BOOK.

BY

ROBLEY DUNGLISON, M. D.,

PROFESSOR OF INSTITUTES OF MEDICINE, ETC., IN JEFFERSON MEDICAL COLLEGE OF PHILADELPHIA; FORMERLY
PROFESSOR OF MATERIA MEDICA AND THERAPEUTICS IN THE UNIVERSITIES OF VIRGINIA AND
MARYLAND, AND IN JEFFERSON MEDICAL COLLEGE OF PHILADELPHIA.

WITH ONE HUNDRED AND EIGHTY-SEVEN ILLUSTRATIONS.

FIFTH EDITION, REVISED AND IMPROVED.

IN TWO VOLUMES.

VOL. I.

PHILADELPHIA:
BLANCHARD AND LEA.
1853.

This class of 270 members was the largest ever to be graduated from Jefferson. Such size can only be attributed to the drawing power of "the Famous Faculty of 1841" rather than the false assumption that Jefferson was a "diploma mill," a status justifiably accorded to some other schools of the time. The Graduation Address was delivered by Dr. Franklin Bache (Fig. 34), Professor of Chemistry, who was the great grandson of Benjamin Franklin.

At this time the Washington Monument in the National Capitol was under construction. A marble plaque (Fig. 55) was donated "By the Class of 1853-54" at the 280-foot landing which bore the seal of "Jefferson Medical College of Philadelphia." This represented the first effort of Jefferson alumni to perpetuate the institution's name in a public structure.

William Goodell, born in Malta the son of missionaries, was the outstanding member of the class. In 1865 he was elected to be the first Physician-in-Charge of the newly established Preston Retreat in Philadelphia, a lying-in hospital for indigent married women. His insistence on the new principles of asepsis and antisepsis led to the amazing record of only six deaths in 2,444 deliveries. He was the first Jefferson alumnus to obtain a prominent faculty position at the University of Pennsylvania (Clinical Professor of Diseases of Women and Children, 1874-1894). A founding member of the American Gynecology Society, he was also Founder and President of the Philadelphia Obstetrical Society.

Fig. 55. Stone at 280-foot landing of Washington Monument, Washington, D.C. donated by graduating class of 1854. (Courtesy of U.S. Department of Interior, National Park Service.)

Abbott, Luther J., OH
Allison, Thomas H., PA
Archer, Edward C., VA
Armstrong, Richard, PA
Austin, William, SC
Baptist, William H., AL
Barnes, Henry F., IN
Barr, Robert, PA
Barret, L. Layton, VA
Bartleson, Samuel P., PA
Bates, Thomas B., SC
Bates, Thomas J., VA
Bell, James M., MS
Bellangee, J. Barton, NJ
Berryhill, Samuel G., PA
Bethune, Roderick A., AL
Birdsong, Miles J., TX
Bishop, J. Leander, NOVA, SCOTIA
Blake, Joseph C., NC
Bloodgood, Delavan, NY
Blount, Benjamin F., AL
Booton, John G., VA
Bosbyshell, Charles B., IL
Bosset, William C., PA
Boughan, John F., VA
Bowers, James A., TN
Bowes, George A., PA
Brandt, Jeremiah, PA
Brown, Henry T., VA
Buck, Erastus, Jr., NY
Burnell, Thomas B., VA
Burroughs, Alphonso J.L., GA
Bush, Robert H., VA
Camden, Thomas B., VA
Carlton, Benjamin F., GA
Carter, James W., VA
Cass, Edward, OH
Chancellor, Edward L., VA
Chase, Enos G., NY
Chenault, Robert C., KY
Chipman, James L., NOVA, SCOTIA
Clark, Samuel V., MS
Clarke, Rowan, PA
Clements, G. Myrick, GA
Cole, Edward C., VA
Cole, Howson W., NC
Coleman, Asa, IN
Collins, Richard T., KY
Compton, William M., MS
Conant, Oscar F., MS
Cooke, James A., SC
Corley, James A., SC

Craig, John T., SC
Crawford, William H., AL
Crow, Calvin A., AL
Daingerfield, John Elliot, VA
Davidson, William J., VA
Davis, Miranda G., MS
Dean, Richard C., NJ
Dillard, Thomas H.B., VA
Drake, William W., TN
Dugger, James M., GA
Dunham, Albright, NY
Dwinelle, James E., NY
Earl, John W., NC
Eberhard, George, GA
Eberle, Jacob K., PA
Eldridge, Erwin J., MD
Eskridge, John M., GA
Evans, Robert M., MS
Ewell, Joseph F., KY
Ewing, James P., TN
Ewing, William D., VA
Fennell, James W., Jr., AL
Fithian, Joseph, Jr., OH
Fontaine, Abraham W., VA
Foster, David W., MS
Foster, George B., MA
Fruit, Richard B., PA
Fulkerson, Putnam S., MO
Gay, W. Douglas, KY
Gilbert, Silas Terrell, NY
Gleeson, John K., LA
Goodell, William, TURKEY
Goodrich, Robert A., VA
Gregory, Oscar, VA
Griesemer, Calvin H., PA
Grimes, Franklin T., KY
Haldeman, George W., PA
Hall, A. Douglas, PA
Hall, John L., SC
Hall, William Hansell, GA
Halsey, Luther F., PA
Haring, John J., NY
Harris, Sampson H., MS
Harris, Thomas S., VA
Harrison, Marcellus T., MO
Hart, Byron, PA
Hart, William P., PA
Harter, M. Lair, PA
Haskell, Charles Henry, MA
Head, Joseph, IL
Henderson, Jophanus, ME
Hendrix, H. Walter, SC

Hezlep, William B., PA
Hicks, Edwin S., VA
Hill, Lafayette, TN
Hilleary, John W., MD
Hillyer, Eben, GA
Hitch, John W., SC
Hoffman, William F., PA
Hollifield, Horatio N., PA
Holman, William P., MS
Holmes, Henry J., MS
Homan, John C., VA
Hoover, Andrew S., SC
Hopkins, Thomas B., TX
Houston, Armstrong P., SC
Howard, William A., GA
Hoyt, William D., GA
Humphrey, William F., CT
Hunter, Duke W., MO
Hurt, Munford B., VA
Huston, Robert M., VA
Inglesby, William G., SC
Ingram, James M., TN
Ives, Charles L., CT
Jacobson, Edward H., PA
Johnson, James W., SC
Johnston, Thomas, PA
Johnston, William F., KY
Jones, William W., KY
Kennedy, Stewart, PA
Kent, John D., VA
Kerr, Boyle, PA
Kinnard, Michael C., TN
Knox, William A., IL
Kurtz, Samuel L., PA
Lacey, Daniel P., PA
Laverty, Theodore C., PA
Laws, James, PA
Lennard, Joseph M., AL
Livingood, Louis A., PA
Mason, Robert E., TN
Maxwell, John Hampden, SC
McAllister, John C., Jr., PA
McBride, Alexander, OH
McClanahan, John P., OH
McCormick, John, NC
McCormick, William H., PA
McDonald, Edward H., GA
McDonough, James B., PA
McDuffie, Hector, NC
McKay, Haden E., KY
McLatchy, Harris O., NOVA, SCOTIA
McLean, Hugh, PA
McMannen, Charles T., NC
McQuiddy, Robert S., KY

McReynolds, William T., KY
Melton, Robert D., AL
Merrill, S. Randolph, NH
Miller, George W., PA
Miller, John J., PA
Miller, Luther M., PA
Miller, William W., NY
Minor, J. Gilmer, VA
Mitchell, R. Pinckney, TN
Moore, Dunkin D., SC
Moore, John R., PA
Murchison, Kenneth B., GA
Nebinger, William P., PA
Newton, James F., KY
Nice, Curtis J., PA
Nixon, Oliver W., OH
O'Brien, John M., NC
Page, John J., KY
Paschall, Gideon W., KY
Patterson, Duncan N., NC
Patteson, Robert P., VA
Pearce, Enoch, OH
Pendleton, Edmund S., VA
Perkins, Willis M., NC
Peters, Penington L., GA
Plana, Joaquin, CUBA
Pollard, Leonidas C., VA
Pollock, William, PA
Potter, Samuel B., OH
Primrose, Harry C., PA
Pusey, David C., KY
Quesenberry, Vevion, PA
Rankin, D. Nevin, PA
Raper, Thomas J., PA
Reber, William, MS
Redd, Thomas M., KY
Reynolds, Jacob E., MD
Rice, William R., VA
Richardson, William M., NC
Ringwalt, Levi Z., PA
Robberson, Edwin T., MO
Roberts, William C., NC
Robins, Edwin S.C., PA
Rogers, James K., PA
Rogers, Orville T., VA
Sandford, Joseph K., PA
Sandford, Leonard J., CT
Saunders, William M., VA
Scales, James M.A., TN
Shepherd, Francis C., VA
Sheppard, Leander W., NJ
Shultz, B. Franklin, PA
Simpson, Joseph, DE
Sinclair, John, CANADA

Slicer, J. Edwin, VA
Smith John W.C., MS
Smith, Francis F., MD
Smith, John W., VA
Smith, Joseph T., NY
Smith, Richard E.C., AL
Smith, Robert A., VA
Smith, William T., PA
Spann, James T., MS
Spooner, Edward A., MA
Stokes, N. Newlin, NJ
Stone, Alfred B., MA
Storer, John H., PA
Strain, David E., VA
Strayer, Joseph B., VA
Stribling, Charles C., GA
Swan, Samuel M., PA
Taggart, Charles, OH
Taylor James W., VA
Teague, Thomas J., SC
Teeter, Edwin Conrad, VA
Thompson, George W., PA
Thornton, John S., PA
Todd, L. Beecher, KY
Tomb, Robert Johnson, PA
Tucker, Gustavus A.R., VA
Turner, John B., GA
Unseld, John H., VA
Vankirk, Joel K., PA

VanPelt, Joseph T.K., PA
VanValzah, Samuel B., PA
Vaughan, Bolivar H., MS
Waddle, Douglas S., NC
Walker, James, KY
Walker, Joseph R., TN
Walker, Mark, NH
Walker, Thatcher V., Jr., GA
Walker, William A., GA
Wallace, Horatio, AR
Wallace, Jonas C.B., NY
Walter, Philip S.P., PA
Walters, William L., VA
Ware, Augustus C., GA
Warner, Charles F., NY
Warren, Silas E., PA
Webb, Robert T., NC
West, Nelson G., MD
Westbrook, Ethelred E., MS
Whitaker, Jacob, NJ
White, William A., VA
Wilbur, Lloyd, NJ
Woods, William Semple, PA
Woodward, Richard H., VA
Workman, Benjamin F., MS
Wurtz, Charles Stewart, Jr., PA
Wysong, Rutherford, VA
Young, Edward, PA
Young, Wesley W., NC

The most essential part of a student's instruction is obtained, as I believe, not in the lecture room, but at the bedside. Nothing seen there is lost; the rhythms of disease are learned by frequent repetition; its unforeseen occurrences stamp themselves indelibly in the memory.

Oliver Wendell Holmes (1809-1894).
Medical Essays, "Scholastic and Bedside Teaching".

This was an important year in world medical history. Manuel Garcia first performed mirror laryngoscopy; Thomas Addison published his memoir on diseases of the suprarenal glands; J. Marion Sims founded the Woman's Hospital of New York and von Graefe introduced iridectomy.

In the large graduating class of 256 members, William Thomson of Pennsylvania was destined in 1895 to become the first Chairman of the Department of Ophthalmology at Jefferson as it is known today (Fig. 56). In 1861 he began a distinguished military career in the Union Army in which he was complimented by President Lincoln for his work at the Battle of South Mountain where he took sole charge of 2,500 wounded men. After serving as inspector of all hospitals of the Washington area, he contributed largely to the first descriptions of osteomyelitis and wounds of the joints for the newly organized Army Medical Museum of which John Hill Brinton (JMC, 1852, Fig. 51) was the first curator. He aided the establishment of a photographic bureau in the Museum which evolved into the Medical Illustration Service of the Armed Forces Institute of Pathology. He pioneered in experimental photomicrography which led to prints of microscopic fields that could be magnified 15 to 250 times. In later years he contributed to safety on railroads by developing tests for color blindness as well as acuteness of vision and hearing of the trainmen. The College of Physicians of Philadelphia houses his ophthalmoscopes, correspondence, 14 volumes of case books, and his portrait by Thomas Eakins (1907).

Another eminent graduate of 1855 was the famous Cuban, Carlos Juan Finlay, who was credited with the discovery of the mosquito transmission of yellow fever (Fig. 57). Dr. Finlay's observations on the epidemiology of the fever in his native Cuba were carried out over several decades. As early as 1881 he had proposed the conditions necessary for its propagation. He had even during the same year pointed out that the Aedes aegypti mosquito was the responsible vector. As an independent investigator his presentation before the International Sanitation Conference in Washington (February 13, 1881) elicited little response but in 1900 his observations were proven correct when the well-known experiment of the Walter Reed Yellow Fever Board in Havana, Cuba, confirmed the Aedes mosquito as the responsible vector. Finlay was honored by Jefferson with a degree of Doctor of Science in 1902 and a commemorative symposium on yellow fever was held in 1955, the centenary of his graduation.

Edward Maris, of Pennsylvania, in addition to his medical practice became a giant pioneer in

Fig. 56. William Thomson (JMC, 1855), Professor of Ophthalmology (1895-97). During the Civil War he aided the establishment of a photographic bureau that evolved into the Medical Illustration Service of the Armed Forces Institute of Pathology.

the field of numismatics. In 1869 he published *Coins of Large Cents of the U.S.* and in 1881 *Historical Sketch of Colonial Coins of New Jersey.*

Jacob C. Denise, a native of Ohio, settled in Nebraska and became one of its most prominent physicians. In 1869 he was a founder of the Omaha Medical College (with Dr. Victor F. Coffman, JMC, 1866, Fig. 75) which in 1902 became the Medical Department of the University of Nebraska. Dr. Denise was also a founder and President of the Nebraska State Medical Society.

Allen, Milton, PA
Allen, Thomas J., TN
Anawalt, James W., PA
Anthony, William, PA
Asch, Morris J., PA
Ashcraft, John H., PA
Backwell, Edward G., OH
Banner, Constantine L., NC
Barham, R. G., VA
Barr, Richard Rice, NC
Barr, W. F., VA

Bartolette, T. Miles, NJ
Bass, Robert E., VA
Basselleu, William F., SC
Beeler, Milton W., MS
Bell, Edwin R., OH
Bell, George B., AL
Bell, W. D., TX
Bennett, Edmund, NJ
Beveridge, John L., GA
Blackford, Ben, VA
Boies, Jeremich S., DE
Boswell, Lewis A., VA
Braford, Philip Spotswood, VA
Brandt, Eli Bainbridge, PA
Breed, William M., PA
Breitling, Joseph, AL
Brown, Bedford, MD
Brown, Martin L., NC
Brubaker, J. C., PA
Bryan, Cyrus P., VA
Buchanan, G. W., MO
Buffington, John F., MD
Buffington, John N., VA
Butler, Anselm B., OH
Cahall, Lawrence M., DE
Callaghan, Arthur, MO
Campbell, Westlee M., NC
Cato, James F., GA
Chew, Henry B., Jr., MD
Chrisman, Burke, VA
Clark, Hobson, VA
Cole, John P., NJ
Comfort, William A., CANADA
Cowan, George, KY
Cowell, J. George, MA
Craven, Edmund R., PA
Crothers, Robert W., IL
Curd, John R., VA
Dalton, George O., MA
Davies, William B., VA
Davis, James S., MS
Dean, Samuel Henry, GA
DeBarres, Ph., CUBA
Denise, Jacob C., OH

Fig. 57. Carlos Finlay (JMC, 1855) who in 1881 ascribed yellow fever to the bite of a mosquito.

1855

Dickerson, Robert J., AL
Dickson, Lycurgus A., TN
Diffenbacher, Philip L., IL
Dobyns, R. L.H., VA
Donnelly, Charles Henry, CANADA
Dreher, Jurias G., PA
Failor, Benjamin M., OH
Fant, Samuel F., SC
Feay, John, PA
Finlay, Carlos J., CUBA
Finlayson, William H., NC
Finley, Calvin G., SC
Fischer, W. Emil., PRUSSIA
Fisler, Jacob T., NJ
Fleming, Andrew, PA
Flournoy, David, VA
Ford, George W., PA
Freas, H. L., PA
Frederick, Edward J., SC
Gabby, R. S., OH
Garnett, O. V., KY
Garnett, Thomas N., VA
Graham, Leonidas J., AL
Gray, Alexander R., PA
Gray, John W., AL
Groome, Evan J., PA
Gross, Ferdinand H., PA
Guild, James, Jr., AL
Gwin, Robert D., TN
Hagenbuch, William A., OH
Hall, George W., IL
Hall, R. F., GA
Hamilton, John W., PA
Hamilton, Swithen N., VA
Hanley, Michael A., PA
Harding, Philander H., ME
Hardwick, J. R., GA
Harriss, Samuel G., VA
Harriss, William H., PA
Harvey, William C., MO
Haslett, John D.S., PA
Haynie, James M., AL
Hebble, Joseph, OH
Heddens, William S., Jr., PA
Herbst, William S., Jr., PA
Hill, Joseph, SC
Hinchman, B., PA
Hitt, Willis M., IN
Holman, Henry W., VA
Hopkins, Benjamin C., DE
Hopkins, Benjamin F., VA
Hoskins, William, VA
Houston, John, PA
Hudson, William M., CT

Hume, Quintus R., VA
Hunt, David G., GA
Hunt, William Henry, KY
Hunter, Samuel B., ME
Ingram, S. L., VA
Irvin, George, PA
Irvin, William, PA
Jackson, John S., VA
Jennings, Robert B., VA
Jernigan, Charles H., AL
Johnston, James, PA
Jones, Denwood T., MD
Jones, James Y., VA
Jones, Joseph Addison, VA
Jones, R. Augustus, AL
Jones, William W., GA
Kahn, Louis DeBarth, PA
Kane, John K., PA
Kay, Isaac F., PA
Kennedy, Maxwell, PA
King, John F., DC
Leitch, J. Lewis, VA
Lewis, James E., VA
Lewitt, William, MI
Lindsay, Andrew, PA
Logan, Samuel, PA
Lowman, William G., PA
Lumpkin, Samuel P., GA
Lynn, B. W., IN
Mackey, Alexander S., VA
Maddox, John Z., GA
Madill, Thomas F., PA
Magill, Thomas, PA
Maris, Edward, PA
Markle, John Gideon, PA
May, John R., VA
McClellan, Freeman, PA
McCorkle, William A., VA
McDowell, George M., GA
McEwan, Christopher, PA
McKinney, J. W., IL
McLeod, John, AL
McMullin, James, PA
McPherson, George E., PA
McPherson, John H., VA
Miller, James S., PA
Mills, Nathaniel J., KY
Milton, Harvey Oliver, AL
Moody, Milus W., MS
Moore, Alexander P., AR
Moore, John A., NC
Morgan, James, PA
Morrow, William L., PA
Moss, William, PA

Murry, John Y., MS

Myers, W. H., OH

Nash, Miles H., FL

Newman, William H., KY

Nichol, John, NY

Nicholson, John C., TN

Ogburn, John F., VA

Ohl, Josiah G., PA

Osgood, William, PA

Overton, William S., VA

Park, William H., OH

Patton, Thomas, OH

Payzant, Elias N., NOVA, SCOTIA

Peeples, P. W., MS

Pinkard, H. M., VA

Pinson, Washington S., SC

Plaisted, E. Freeman, NH

Plummer, Gardiner H., IN

Pope, Chandler M., GA

Pope, Willis, AL

Porter, Benjamin F., PA

Price, Robert A., VA

Quinn, John H., OH

Ramsey, William P., PA

Ramsey, Wilson C., NC

Ransberry, John, Jr., PA

Ranyon, Thomas H., KY

Ratliff, Charles C., MS

Rawls, Elijah H., GA

Reese, Charles E., AL

Reeve, James T., NY

Riley, John G., GA

Ringwalt, Samuel, PA

Rogers, James Henry, NY

Rowland, William A., GA

Rucker, William P., VA

Russell, Leonidas, IN

Rutledge, Jacob I., MD

Sarver, William, PA

Scott, Christopher H., MS

Scott, Daniel S., AR

Selman, David, MS

Shepherd, James B., VA

Sherrod, John I., TN

Shreve, J. Ridgway, NJ

Simmons, W. A., NC

Simms, H. C., DC

Sims, Joseph B., KY

Smith, Chauncey M., NY

Smith, Hosea H., NH

Smith, Joseph F., MS

Spears, Abraham Kellar, KY

Spencer, Cadwallader C., OH

Sproul, Samuel M., MO

Stavely, William R., PA

Stewart, David P., PA

Stewart, Samuel F., PA

Strachan, Joseph Blackmam, VA

Strother, Robert C., VA

Swift, D. D., PA

Tate, John M., VA

Thomas, David B., NC

Thomas, Robert Y.H., SC

Thompson, Kimbro, VA

Thompson, William, PA

Todd, William C., PA

Townsend, A. R.P., ME

Turner, Edward, Jr., VA

Turner, Thomas, Jr., VA

Upshaw, William T., TN

Vansant, John, VA

Wallace, R. S., PA

Warden, Jacob B., VA

Washington, H. W.M., VA

Weiser, Josiah S., PA

Welch, Samuel M., KY

Wells, J. Ralston, PA

Whalley, James G., GA

White, James L., VA

White, Walter T., MS

Wilkerson, William W., AL

Willcoxon, Levi J., GA

Willett, E. Miles., KY

Willis, George M., GA

Winsborough, Joseph W., VA

Wolfe, David E., DE

Wood, Sidney S., NC

Woodson, Philip T., GA

Woodward, William W., MO

Worthington, Thomas E., KY

Young, Alexander H., TN

Young, William P., DC

At the Commencement Exercises held in Musical Fund Hall, 215 classmates received their diplomas. Among the members was Richard J. Dunglison who had studied under his famous father, Robley Dunglison, who was presiding as Dean at this time.

Richard J. Dunglison followed in his father's footsteps by pursuing an editorial career, although he did not join a medical faculty (Fig. 58). He was one of the originators of the *Philadelphia Medical Times*, edited *Gray's Anatomy* in 1884, and continued his father's *Medical Dictionary* to its 22nd edition in 1900. (The final edition of Robley Dunglison's Dictionary was published by Thomas Stedman, A.M., M.D., in 1903.) In addition to writing many medical articles, he was assistant secretary of the American Medical Association in 1876 and its treasurer in 1877. He was assistant secretary of the International Medical Congress in 1876 and corresponding secretary of the Centennial Medical Commission the same year. Like his father, he served as President of the Musical Fund Society of Philadelphia, in the hall of which he had graduated.

Another outstanding graduate of this class was William Henry Pancoast (Fig. 59) whose father was Joseph Pancoast, the Professor of Anatomy. In pursuit of a career as surgeon-anatomist he initiated courses in visceral and surgical anatomy in Jefferson's "Summer Course" which started in 1866 and attracted students from other schools. In 1874 he succeeded his father in the Chair of Anatomy (Fig. 60). In this year (1874) Thomas Eakins studied anatomy at Jefferson under both the elder and younger Pancoasts, prior to painting the *Gross Clinic* (1875).

CLASS OF 1856

Alexander, Charles T., KY
Allen, James M., AL
Anderson, D. R., SC
Banks, John L., VA
Baxter, John S., GA
Beall, R. L., NC
Beeler, George, KY
Bennett, J. W., NC
Bloxom, John H., AL
Boucher, James H., NY
Bowen, Julius M., NY
Bower, Franklin H., PA
Bowman, John Davis, PA
Branch, John L., GA
Brawner, Lucius W., GA
Brawner, William M., GA
Brewster, T. Fort, GA
Britton, George W., NJ
Bruce, J. D., NC
Buck, Horatio B., ME
Bunting, Ross R., PA
Burroughs, Richard, GA
Burton, William H., VA
Butts, James A., GA
Byrd, W. B., SC

Cantrell, James Henry, PA
Carlton, Henry H., GA
Carpenter, A. Jackson, PA
Carswell, B. S., GA
Castleberry, Jesse R., PA
Chubb, Charles H., PA
Coad, Joseph R., PA
Cochran, Henry King, VA
Cock, J. Walter, TX
Cole, Lorenzo S., ME
Collett, W. A., NC
Cooper, Alfred M., NJ
Cotton, David B., OH
Crain, J. R., TX
Crawford, William M., VA
Cropp, J. T., VA
Crymes, A. C., AL
Cummiskey, James, PA
Cunning, Samuel R., GA
Dorsey, Frederic, MD
Dozier, Allen S., SC
Druet, John T., OH
Dulaney, Nathaniel T., TN
Dunglison, Richard J., PA
Espy, Kirk, PA

Etheridge, John H., GA
Eubank, William G., AL
Everett, P. Root., OH
Farrar, George W., GA
Fenn, M. B., AL
Fisher, William, VA
Foote, George A., NC
Foote, W. W., NC
Freeman, Ingraham B., NOVA SCOTIA
Garland, Wilson, NC
Garnett, Algernon S., VA
Ghent, Henry C., AL
Gibson, John J., IL
Good, Samuel M., MD
Goodall, C. Parke, VA
Gordon, David C., MS
Gorgas, Albert C., PA
Grant, William L., VA

Green, Bennett W., VA
Greene, J. M., AL
Gresham, Henry, VA
Griesemer, John B., PA
Haley, James, MS
Halley, H. Joseph, VA
Hammond, J. W., OH
Hanna, E. S., OH
Hardesty, J. R.L., VA
Hardy, William B., MO
Harnish, Tobias, PA
Harris, Richard M., AL
Hathaway, Joseph Cushman, MA
Herron, Levi R., TN
Hickerson, James, NC
Hildreth, Isaac F., OH
Hill, John, OH
Hill, William, IL
Hinkson, John F., BARBADOES
Hobson, George Fearn, MS
Hoey, James W., PA
Holman, J. C., GA
Homet, Volney, PA
Hooper, Philo O., AR
Hough, Thomas L., NJ
Howe, William R., PA
Hubbell, S. J., VA
Hudders, George W., PA
Humphreys, George H., PA
Humphreys, James P., TN
Hunt, J. Spofford, IL
Huntley, Oscar Hamilton, NH
James, Jesse Y., PA
Jenkins, John F., GA
Jennings, Napoleon B., NJ
Johns, Lynch D., VA
Johnson, Joe H., GA
Johnson, John D., VA
Jones, R. R., VA
Jones, U. R., AL
Jordan, William F., AL
Keating, John L., GA
Key, Thomas T., GA
Kibler, Benjamin H., VA
Lanier, I. D., AL
Laughlin, J. H., OH
Lawson, H. M., GA
Lazzell, James M., VA
LeHardy de Beaulieu, J. C., GA
Lewis, Robert S., VA
Long, Solomon, NC
Longsdorf, W. Harry, PA
Love, John S., PA
Lumpkin, James M., GA

Fig. 58.   Richard J. Dunglison (JMC, 1856), son of Professor Robley Dunglison, continued later editions of his father's medical dictionary. (Courtesy Historical Collections, College of Physicians of Philadelphia.)

Lunn, Lewis Thomas, OH
Malone, Joseph H., GA
Marbourg, J. L., PA
Mathews, Thomas P., VA
May, David G., VA
May, John W., NC
McCartney, J. S., PA
McChesney, Robert Aurel, VA
McClellan, Ely, PA
McClintic, H. D., VA
McCollester, John Q.A., NH
McGlaughlin, Charles C., PA
McKethan, J. C., NC
McKneely, J. F., LA
McLeod, Alexander, AL
McMahan, R. W., OH
McMullin, Thomas, PA
McNair, F. L., GA
McNeil, Bernard A., PA
Mease, Levi A., IL
Miller, Samuel P.H., VA
Mitchell, J. W., PA
Mobley, Samuel Goode, SC
Moffett, Charles J., GA
Moore, J. Boardman, VA
Nash, J., VA
Nebinger, A. R., PA
Nottingham, Southey S., VA
Nunn, William C., VA
Pancoast, William H., PA
Park, Frank, AL
Patterson, Samuel D., PA
Payn, Frederick G., NY
Perry, Joseph W., AL
Pfister, Benjamin, Jr., PA
Philson, C. F., SC
Pim, Louis T., MO
Prall, Claudius R., NJ
Pryor, William T., TN
Reber, Charles T., PA
Reeves, Samuel, NC
Richardson, John M., NC
Richardson, Moses, GA
Rihl, Jacob L., PA
Robertson, R. M., AL
Robertson, William S., IA
Robinson, Henry C., NC
Rutherford, Alexander D., PA
Sabine, Andrew, OH
Sankey, J. W., PA
Savidge, Aaron Raker, PA
Saxon, C. A., SC
Sayle, Robert, TN
Schively, George P., PA

Scott, J. Turner, MS
Scott, Robert, FL
Selfridge, James N., NY
Semple, James, VA
Shaw, Daniel, TX
Simpson, Thomas W., MD
Smith, G. Selden, IL
Smith, Hugh G., KY
Snead, John D., VA
Spencer, W., IN
St. Clair, W. P., KY
Stanley, Augustin O., GA
Sternberg, J. Herkimer, NY
Stevenson, W. Morton, IN
Stewart, Jordan, PA
Strudwick, James W., AL
Stuckslager, Cyrus R., TN
Sturdevant, S. Burton, PA
Sullivan, John M., PA
Taylor, Joseph Sheppard, VA

Fig. 59. William Henry Pancoast (JMC, 1856), Chairman of Anatomy 1874 to 1886), and son of Professor Joseph Pancoast.

Terrell, J. E.G., GA
Thompson, George E., PA
Torbet, George A., IN
Trout, William H., PA
Tucker, John A., GA
Tucker, William D., PA
Tupman, P. M., VA
VanHorne, Augustus K., IL
Watson, John W., SC
Watt, William, TX

Weatherly, W. E., MS
Whitmire, James S., IL
Williams, Thomas F.J., VA
Williamson, William T., DE
Wills, Alexander F., VA
Wills, James L., VA
Winchester, Edgar, IL
Yates, T. Wesley, MS
Young, Henry N., MS

Fig. 60.   Professor William Henry Pancoast with his anatomy class (ca. 1870).

1856

In the medical world at large, it was the year in which Carl Ferdinand von Graefe introduced the operation for strabismus; Eugene Bouchut performed intubation of the larynx; and the Pathological Society of Philadelphia was founded with Samuel D. Gross as a founder and first President.

Samuel W. Gross (Fig. 61), son of the world-renowned Samuel D. Gross, was the most outstanding member of this class which numbered 211. Having inherited the intellectual superiority of his father, he went on to achieve distinction in his writings, teaching, operative skill and membership in societies. He was especially in-

Fig. 61. Samuel W. Gross (JMC, 1857), son of Samuel D. Gross, served as Co-chairman of Surgery (1882-89)

terested in tumors and studied under the microscope all the ones he removed. He was one of the founders of the Philadelphia Academy of Surgery (1879) and acted as its histologist. Also, he was President of the Pathological Society of Philadelphia (1879), a fellow of the College of Physicians of Philadelphia, one of the founders of the American Genito-urinary Association and prominent fellow of the American Surgical Association which his father had founded in 1880. In 1882, upon the resignation of the elder Gross from the Professorship of Surgery, he shared the divided Chair with John Hill Brinton (JMC, 1852). In 1876 he married Grace Linzee Revere, the great-granddaughter of Paul Revere. During his last illness from pneumonia, which led to his death at the age of 52, he was seen in consultation by Dr. William Osler who later married his widow. The legacy of Grace Revere Osler endowed the Professorship of Surgery at Jefferson which bears her name.

Another member of the class who achieved prominence was Robert Battey. Following his graduation he studied in Paris for two years and then practiced in Rome, Georgia. An eminent gynecologist of his day, he was a founding member and President (1889) of the American Gynecologic Society. He served as Professor of Obstetrics in the Atlanta Medical College and was one of the most noted surgeons of the South. Other achievements were his improved operation for vesicovaginal fistula and the advocacy of iodized phenol against infection. Jefferson Medical College granted him an LL.D. degree in 1890. A monument stands to his memory in Rome, Georgia.

Austin Flint, Jr. entitled his graduation thesis *Phenomena of the Capillary Circulation* which had the merit to appear in the *American Journal of the Medical Sciences* July, 1857. For the next three years he was editor of the *Buffalo Medical Journal* which had been founded by his famous father. In 1858 he became Professor of Physiology in the Medical School of Buffalo. The following year he removed to the same position at the New York Medical College and still a year later to the same position in the New Orleans School of Medicine. He was the first physiologist in this country to operate upon the spinal cord and spinal nerves in living animals. He discovered the production of cholesterol in the physiology of the brain and nervous tissue, the elimination of cholesterol by the liver, and its discharge in the form of stercorine in the feces. He was one of the founders of the Bellevue Hospital Medical College in 1861 and held the Chair of Physiology there for more than 30 years. In 1868 he published the *Physiology of Man,* an opus of eventually five volumes of 500 pages each, of which the last volume was released in 1874. He was awarded an LL.D. degree at Jefferson in 1885.

Louis Elsberg became the founding President of the American Laryngological Association in 1878. He was among the first in the nation to demonstrate in public the use of the laryngoscope in diagnostic and treatment situations, thereby launching Jefferson's great tradition in the specialty which peaked with Chevalier Jackson (JMC, 1886) and Louis H. Clerf (JMC, 1912). He also invented a tongue depressor and sponge carrier.

CLASS OF 1857

Aikins, M. H., CANADA
Ashton, Arthur, VA
Baldridge, Alexander, TN
Banks, John, W., MO
Barbre, Jesse, IL
Barclay, Robert G., VA
Battey, Robert, GA
Bauknight, Walter J., SC
Berrien, J. Hunter, GA
Berry, George W., MD
Bibighaus, T. B., PA
Blackwell, George W., MS
Bomgardner, John E., PA
Bowen, James H., GA
Bowyer, James H., VA
Boyd, Richard, Jr., VA
Bracey, John R., VA
Branson, Jesse A., TN
Bryan, William S., NC
Buckner, Baldwin M., VA
Buhot, William J., BARBADOES
Butts, James J., GA
Camp, J. G., NC
Carleton, George E., GA
Castlen, F. G., GA
Chase, William B., VT
Chrisman, W. L., PA
Clark, Marcus A., VA
Cline, Philip M., VA
Coleman, John S., GA
Collins, William Thomas, DE
Coover, John B., PA
Coover, William H., OH
Couch, William S., VA
Crawford, William H., PA
Credille, William H., GA

Curtis, Humphrey H., Jr., VA
Dana, Robert S., PA
Daniel, A. B., GA
DeChoudens, Joseph F., CORSICA
Delano, Marcus F., MA
Delaplane, James B., MD
Dewberry, John H., GA
DeWitt, Manning F., PA
Dickson, John, PA
Dinzey, John K., WEST INDIES
Drye, William S., KY
Duval, C. A., MS
Earl, J. Madison, NC
Echols, Edward D.J., AL
Edmonds, Matthew W., NJ
Elsberg, Louis, PA
Evans, Charles H., OH
Farrell, William, GA
Fleming, Robert A., AL
Flint, Austin, Jr., NY
Fordham, John F., GA
Foster, David L., MS
Foster, A. R., AL
Fowler, A. S., GA
Freeze, Peter H., PA
Fruit, John C., PA
Frye, A. S., ME
Fuller, Daniel, PA
Gibbon, William H., NJ
Gill, Henry Z., OH
Gillespie, Zadock R., TN
Gilliam, J. P., VA
Godfrey, J. T., FL
Gray, Joseph, NY
Gross, Samuel W., PA
Halisy, Dennis J., KY

Hall, Samuel H., CT
Hambrick, Joseph M., GA
Hamilton, Robert S., VA
Hanger, John M., VA
Harrison, Eugene B., OH
Hartman, H. B., LA
Hartman, Samuel B., OH
Herndon, Thomas, VA
Hill, J. Ward, SC
Hirons, Robert S. Warren, DE
Hoke, Augustus D., SC
Holland, Thomas Walter, TN
Hollingsworth, Edwin F., NC
Holman, William A., VA
Holt, William F., GA
Houston, Joseph Willis, PA
Howard, Robert G., GA
Howerton, William H., NC
Hunt, John T., NC
Hursh, George R., PA
Jennings, William K., VA
Johns, A. Benning, Jr., NC
Johnson, William L., KY
Johnson, Jesse W., MO
Joiner, Charles J., AL
Jones, Daniel Chandler, GA
Jordan, J. C., NC
Jordan, M. D.L., TN
Juett, David P., KY
Kelly, Hiram N., PA
Kerr, Harvey, IN
Knipe, Francis M., PA
Lane, John T., GA
Lennon, John, CANADA
Lewis, Thomas M., VA
Lewis, George R., PA
Lyman, J. Baldwin, MA
Mabry, Lucien L., SC
Marr, Charles, PA
Maxwell, J. Marcellus, GA
McAden, John H., NC
McCleery, James P., PA
McConnell, William L. H., PA
McCulloch, Thomas J., VA
McFall, David M., IN
McKelvey, Charles E., IL
McLeod, James P., AL
Miller, Thomas M., VA
Miller, William H., VA
Mitchell, Benjamin W., MO
Morey, Andrew C., NY
Morrison, N. B., MD
Nagle, H. M., PA
Nesbit, Joseph A., IN

Newland, J. Oscar, KY
Nisbet, William M., AL
Nobles, William H., AL
Nowlin, John B. W., VA
Orton, Henry, CANADA
Parker, George W., NC
Parker, John R., VA
Pattishall, Daniel, GA
Payne, R. L., NC
Payne, Edward D., PA
Peake, Humphrey, AR
Pearce, James F., VA
Peebles, J. H., MS
Pepper, James R., VA
Pepper, John G., VA
Perchment, John, Jr., PA
Phillips, W. E. T., KY
Plummer, Orlando P. S., IL
Poole, R. D'Orsay, MD
Price, William B., IL
Prince, Thomas H., TN
Raine, John R., VA
Ravenscraft, William H., VA
Redden, Joseph W., DE
Reynolds, Samuel K., PA
Rhoads, Reuben B., PA
Riegel, Henry H., PA
Rieger, Francis A. A. T., MO
Rogers, J. W., TN
Roy, Gustavus G., VA
Rush, David G., PA
Ruth, Daniel G., PA
Sample, Samuel R., PA
Sanderson, E. L., AL
Sandford, James, VA
Sandford, John W., Jr., NC
Scales, Samuel W., TN
Scott, George H., IL
Scull, Benjamin F., AR
Sealy, James E., TN
Seawell, William T., VA
Shannon, T. Jefferson, OH
Sharp, Samuel C., Jr., PA
Shropshire, James W., GA
Simpson, George W., TN
Smith, W. R., GA
Smith, Jacob, CANADA
Solliday, Edwin S., OH
Spencer, Charles W., MO
Spratt, John B., KY
Stark, Edwin A., MO
Stark, Daniel P., KY
Stell, W. W., TX
Stephenson, Marcus P., NY

Stokes, James S., MS
Strudwick, Edmund, NC
Summers, Rowland T., IN
Swartz, Joseph, PA
Swiler, William E., PA
Thomas, Charles E., NJ
Thompson, Stephen B., PA
Thruston, R. Turnbull, SC
Tigner, Leander, GA
Trist, H. B., PA
Upton, William A., TN
VanArtsdalen, Frank V., PA
Vineyard, John H., MS
Walton, John J., GA
Ware, George G., TN

Watlington, Thomas J., NC
Weaver, Junius W., VA
Wilburn, John C., AL
Williams, K., MS
Williams, William A., SC
Wilson, James E., VA
Windsor, Norman, VA
Witherspoon, H. F., TX
Wolf, Jacob G., IN
Wolfe, William E., DE
Wood, Marcus M., NY
Wooding, Nathaniel H., VA
Wright, Mansur H., IN
Yarbrough, Wiley, TX
Yerkes, John D., PA
Young, Alexander, NJ

THE

AMERICAN JOURNAL

OF THE MEDICAL SCIENCES

FOR JULY 1857.

ART. I.—*Phenomena of the Capillary Circulation.*
By AUSTIN FLINT, Jr., M. D.[1]

THE statements which I shall make from my own observation concerning the capillary circulation, are based upon examinations made from time to time during the past summer, nine of which have been carefully recorded. The recorded observations were made on the web of the frog, although I have made examinations of the various other parts where the circulation can be conveniently exhibited, to which I shall refer.

The microscope used was the large instrument of Nachet, and, unless otherwise stated, with a magnifying power of 165 diameters.

I shall first point out what I have found to be the most convenient methods of conducting examinations of the circulation in the frog, and then proceed to describe the various phenomena of the circulation as viewed by means of the microscope, and then draw my deductions from these observations.

The parts of the frog which I have subjected to examination, are the web of the foot, the tongue, the peritoneum, and the lungs. All parts but the peritoneum require to be examined by transmitted light, but, in examining the circulation in the latter situation, we are compelled to use reflected light.

It is exceedingly inconvenient to make observations while the frog has the power of motion, and in securing it to the frog-plate in a proper position, we are apt to interrupt or modify the circulation by constricting the vessels with the bands which we must use. Under these circumstances, we are not able to apply medicated solutions conveniently to the entire surface, and mechanical or chemical irritation of any part occasions struggles which greatly increase

[1] An Inaugural Dissertation laid before the faculty of Jefferson Medical College in February, 1857.

No. XLVII.—JULY 1857.   2

~ 1858 ~

The emergence of the era of scientific medicine was heralded during 1858 by the publication of Rudolf Virchow's *Cellular Pathology*, a work destined to provide the basis for a new understanding of body changes incident to disease. This, together with the ferment in physiology led by Claude Bernard and Johannes Muller, would develop the background for many of the momentous biological and medical advances late in the nineteenth century.

The same year Henry Gray, age 33, a Lecturer in Anatomy at St. George's Hospital, London, and Fellow of the Royal College of Surgeons, published *Gray's Anatomy, Descriptive and Surgical*. This classic, well known to generations of medical students, was later revised by Jeffersonians Richard J. Dunglison in 1884, W.W. Keen in 1887, J. Chalmers DaCosta in 1905, and Edward A. Spitzka, Professor of Anatomy, in 1910 and 1913.

John Kearsley Mitchell (Fig. 62), Chairman of Medicine, although in failing health, held a reception for the 210 members of the graduating class at his home on Walnut Street just one month before his death. Dr. Mitchell, father of S. Weir Mitchell, had contributed greatly to the developing prestige of Jefferson Medical College as a member of the famous faculty of 1841 (Fig. 31).

CLASS OF 1858

Fig. 62. John Kearsley Mitchell, Professor of Medicine (1841-1858).

Ackley, Henry, NJ
Alexander, W. C. S., PA
Allison, James, KY
Allison, J. A., NC
Applewhite, Louis J., GA
Bacon, S. L., NJ
Barksdale, William Leigh, VA
Barrett, E. Calhoun, VA
Bass, John N., KY
Bear, Benjamin, Sr., PA
Bell, George W., PA
Bell, James Eugene, GA
Bell, J. H., SC
Bell, William, VA
Berry, A. J., SC
Bertolette, J. C., PA
Bibb, Henry B., AL
Bill, J. H., Jr., PA
Black, John, NC
Blount, T. M., Jr. DC
Bogle, R. L., GA
Bond, Francis E., MONTIVIDEO
Bowyer, Edmund F., VA
Bradford, F. Standish, RI
Branch, John H., NC
Branham, P. A., GA
Branin, Henry E., NJ
Bright, George H., SC
Briscoe, Thomas W., VA

Brooke, John B., PA
Brown, N. M., OH
Brunson, Randolph, TN
Bryant, William M., AL
Buehler, H. B., PA
Burks, Charles R. P., VA
Butcher, George E., NJ
Cade, E. W., TX
Caldwell, Samuel H., TN
Campbell, J. M., NC
Capers, LeGrand G., Jr., TX
Carson, Samuel M., TN
Cessna, B. F., OH
Christie, James, NEW BRUNSWICK
Clark, Isaac J., NJ
Clinkscales, F., SC
Combe, C. B., KY
Cook, Joseph L., PA
Cooke, William T. B., VA
Coudrick, Charles R., NJ
Crawford, John C., SC
Crawford, William, OH
Crockett, R. A., TN
Crump, Lawrence S., VA
Culler, J. P. H., GA
Cummins, J. M., PA
Cummins, Lewis C., PA
Daniels, Henry A., ENGLAND
Davis, Jesse Hudson, PA
DeYampert, T. J. L., AL
Draper, Joseph, MA
Drewrey, Henry Martyn, VA
DuPont, Charles E., SC
Eades, Upson R., GA
Epes, Algernon S., VA
Epes, J. W., AL
Evans, Edwin C., MO
Ewing, George C., PA
Figgat, William F., VA
Franklin, J. W., VA
Freyman, A. A., PA
Galt, William J., PA
Gartrell, Homer L., GA
Gilkeson, James B., VA
Gilliam, James S., VA
Gilmore, J. T., MS
Good, D. R., PA
Goodgion, W. H., SC
Gootee, Benjamin S., MD
Graham, John A., VA
Green, William, VA
Guerrant, T. D. F., VA
Hale, Peter J., VA
Haley, Argyle, VA

Harrell, Richard A., VA
Harris, William H., GA
Harvey, Granville, MO
Hauser, R. A., NC
Hayslett, A. J., VA
Heath, William H., SC
Henderson, F. B., AL
Herndon, Charles L. C., KY
Hoffman, J. M., PA
Hoffman, J. R., TN
Holman, John N., MS
Hoover, George W., PA
Hopkins, James Alfred, DE
Horner, S. H., NJ
Ingersoll, Charles J., Jr., MS
Jackson, LaFayette, VA
Kent, Joseph W., VA
Kerr, William, AL
Kimbrough, Andrew H., IL
Kindleberger, David, OH
King, A. M., MS
King, E. C., TX
King, James T., NC
King, T. Starke, MS
King, William M., PA
King, W. Norvel, OH
Kirksey, E. Jehu, AL
Lee, Paul C., AL
Legge, Josiah H., MD
Lewis, Charles I., VA
Lewis, Isaiah M., PA
Leyburn, John, VA
Lockwood, N. S., NY
Madison, Charles P., IL
Marbourg, H. W., PA
Marshall, N. S., NY
McCann Robert C., MS
McCants, W. J., SC
McCluney, J. F., SC
McConaughy, D. W., PA
McCormick, Charles, VA
McFarland, R. W., KY
McNemar, M. R., VA
McQueen, S. F., AL
Meredith, Joseph S., VA
Merriman, W. H., NY
Miller, John F., NC
Mitchell, John P., VA
Mitchell, R. V., AL
Montgomery, John, PA
Moody, J. Monroe, TN
Mooman, James P., VA
Moore, J. A., AL
Moore, E. D., MS

Morrison, A. J., KY
Nelson, John A., VA
Nordmann, L. E., PA
Oliver, James W., VA
Paine, A. B., NC
Palmer, Valentine Jackson, NC
Parberry, William, MO
Pasley, E. C., SC
Patton, George E., TN
Payne, Philander W., IN
Pelot, J. Crews, FL
Peyton, Lawrence R., KY
Phillips, P. Sanford, AL
Pomerene, Joel, OH
Pope, Sampson, SC
Randall, William, IN
Rankin, A. H., PA
Reeve, Stephen S., GA
Reiber, William F., PA
Rice, Thomas C., VA
Ricks, Fabius S., VA
Robinett, John R., MS
Rogers, James A., NC
Scarburgh, George T., VA
Scearce, J. B., KY
Scott, W. J., AL
Sears, John H., VA
Sencindiver, Lewis M., VA
Seymour, Edward W., CT
Sheets, Abraham, OH
Shotwell, C. H., MO
Shurlock, William C., PA
Sims, William B., VA
Smith, T. Albert, GA
Smith, D. M., NC
Smither, Charles G., MS

Snodgrass, William, VA
Snow, J. B., IN
Snowden, Harold, VA
Stacy, R. Q., GA
Stephenson, J. Thomas, KY
Stewart, A. E., IL
Stewart, John R., NC
Stover, John M., IN
Thatcher, John P., MO
Thomas, Jerome B., IL
Towle, Samuel Knapp, MA
Townsend, George F., ME
Tribou, N. M., Jr., MA
Trippe, Henry W., GA
Trotman, Elisha, TN
Turner, J. H., Jr., MS
Turner, J. D., VA
Vance, Thomas J., LA
Vastine, J. H., PA
Walker, T. F., GA
Walker, Delavan N., NY
Ward, Daniel O'Connell, NJ
Warnock, James T., AL
Warren, Orin, ME
Watkins, Joseph F., VA
Webb, S. V., AL
Webb, Joseph B., VA
Weever, John B., IN
West, Hilborne, PA
Wharton, John S., VA
White, Demosthenes, MO
Willetts, J. Howard, NJ
Williams, Urbane V., KY
Willis, T. Hayward, FL
Wilson, John W., VA
Wright, Astley Cooper, KY
Young, George Kemper, VA

Young men ought to come well prepared for the study of Medicine, by having their minds enriched with all the aids they can receive from the languages, and the liberal arts.

John Morgan (1735-1789).
"A Discourse Upon the Institution of Medical Schools in America".

The matriculates in the College numbered 630, exceeding all records of medical schools of any country or time. The University of Pennsylvania had 528 matriculates, also its largest enrollment to that time. Jefferson's gain in students was chiefly from the country at large, while that at the University was mainly from Pennsylvania.

An 1859 graduate, James McMaster, joined the United States Navy the same year and remained in the service until his death in 1873. He was first attached to the Naval Academy at Annapolis for one year. His career included service in the Far East and extensive experience in the Naval engagements of the Civil War. He attended Admiral David G. Farragut during the Admiral's last illness at Portsmouth, New Hampshire.

Another class member, Aaron J. Steele, became a pioneer in orthopedic surgery, serving successively as Professor of Orthopedic Surgery at Beaumont Medical College, Missouri Medical College, and Washington University, St. Louis, Missouri.

Thomas R. Dunglison (Fig. 63), another son of Professor Robley Dunglison, graduated in this class and became a well-known Philadelphia physician. His brother, Richard J., preceded him in the Class of 1856 (Fig. 58).

A major event of 1859 was the publication by Charles Darwin of his great work *On the Origin of Species by Means of Natural Selection*, a synthesis of observations and ideas destined to revolutionize scientific and philosophic thought.

On the evening of December 23 of this year, Dr. Hunter McGuire, a graduate of Winchester Medical College in Virginia, led a body of over 200 students from Jefferson and the University of Pennsylvania to Richmond, Virginia (Fig. 64). This exodus of southern medical students was triggered by the hanging of John Brown in Charles Town on December 2, 1859, and the offer of free tuition by the Medical College of Virginia. This crucial atmosphere which polarized Northern and Southern attitudes weakened Jefferson's enrollment, but the reputation of the triumvirate of Drs. Gross, Dunglison and Pancoast abetted its weathering of the storm.

CLASS OF 1859

Adams, Martin, OH
Alexander, Samuel L., PA
Alexander, Eli, MS
Almond, Andrew J., VA
Anderson, Edwin P., TN
Anderson, Peter E., VA
Bankhead, Robert A., MS
Barr, James M., VA
Baskin, Robert H., GA
Beadles. Percival, VA
Beman, Edward D., GA
Benson, Douglas B., VA
Bibb, Alexander L., MO
Bivins, Robert T., GA
Blackwell, Thomas J., NC
Blanton, William H., KY
Bledsoe, Francis M., AL
Blick, Joseph A., VA
Boggs, Charles D., VA
Boon, William C., MO

Bowers, Thomas C., CANADA
Brewer, William T., NC
Brinton, J. Bernard, PA
Brown, W. C., AR
Brown, Thomas H. B., VA
Brumby, G. McDaffie, MS
Butler, Oliver H., NY
Campbell, William, PA
Canfield, Augustus R., MS
Carn, Lewis M., FL
Caruthers, C. K., TN
Caswell, Edward T., RI
Cauthorne, A. Hart, VA
Cawood, J. C., TN
Chandler, Isaac L., GA
Cheyney, W. D., GA
Clements, William N., TN
Coard, William H., VA
Comfort, Jonathan J., MI
Cooper, Edward S., IN

Corbin, Philip S. P., VA
Cotten, James F., GA
Cox, George W., VA
Crawe, J. Mortimer, NY
Crawford, George G., GA
Crawford, James J., VA
Crews, O. L., AL
Crigler, John L., MS
Cunningham, H. Clay, KY
Davis, James F., SC
Dean, James, Jr., GA
Deloach, A. B., MS
Dickson, John H., SC
Dorset, Thomas B., Jr., VA
Drennan, Horatio, SC
Dunglison, Thomas B., PA
Dysart, Benjamin G., MO
Dysart, William P., MO
Eads, Darwin D., KY
Eckert, John N., PA
Edmonds, Nicholas C., VA
Elder, William T., VA
Fitzpatrick, William J., AL
Flagg, Samuel D., Jr., NY
Flore, Frederick B., MI
Flowers, John, PA
Foley, Thomas W., LA

Foote, Frederick, VA
Foote, George C., PA
Frame, Robert, DE
Francis, G. M., TX
Fulmore, Zachariah R., SC
Fulton, James, PA
Fussell, Benjamin L., PA
Gee, Edward C., VA
Gilkey, John H., NC
Glass, W. L., NC
Glenn, James Mallory, GA
Glover, Charles P., TN
Goodwin, Thomas W., MS
Gordan, William H., PA
Grafton, Joseph D., AR
Graham, Joseph, NC
Greene, Marshall L., MI
Gregory, Alfred B., GA
Gregory, Flavius J., VA
Gregory, Janius C., VA
Griffin, George C., GA
Grim George W., PA
Grooms, Stephen H., KY
Gunn, Silas R., MS
Gunn, William R., MS
Hall, Joseph U., CA
Happersett, John C. G., PA

Fig. 63.   Thomas R. Dunglison (JMC, 1859), son of Robley Dunglison, became a well-known Philadelphia physician. (Courtesy Historical Collections, College of Physicians of Philadelphia.)

Harper, Seborn, A., MS
Harvey, Leon F., NY
Hawthorn, Samuel W., VA
Henderson, Nat, NC
Herrington, C. P., PA
Hickman, Joseph T., VA
Higgins, William F., NC
Hillsman, John A., VA
Hines, Harvey L., NC
Hines, William H., GA
Hite, Benjamin H., VA
Hoard, Robert L., VA
Hoffman, Robert H., VA
Holloway, Thomas P., KY
Hopkins, James A., NC
Hudgens, Thomas A., SC
Hudson, Gilbert L., GA
Hull, John A., VA
Hulse, John I., FL
Hunter, Horatio D., PA
Jackson, L. D., DE

Jackson, John W., NC
Jackson, Thomas L., VA
Johnston, Thomas W., NC
Jolly, M. A., AL
Jordan, Reuben Elm, AL
Karsner, Charles, PA
Keith, N. C., VA
Kelly, John B., AL
Kimbrough, Locket M., GA
King, George M., VA
Kirkwood, H., NOVA SCOTIA
Knorr, Matthias, PA
Kuder, Joseph S., PA
Lachenour, Henry D., PA
Leary, William B., VA
Lide, William R., AL
Lindsay, James E., NC
Linthicum, Rufus, Jr., KY
Logan, John E., NC
Longnecker, Benjamin F., IL
Magruder, George W., VA
Main, Elijah W., NJ
Maney, Samuel B., TX
Marbourg, M., PA
Marlow, Nicholas P., AL
Marshall, Samuel D., DE
Matlack, William H., PA
Maurer, Jacob S., PA
McCondichie, Wiley G., AL
McCurdy, John M., OH
McEwan, Joseph W., PA
McFadyen, A. R., NC
McKinley, Charles A., GA
McLees, Joseph H., SC
McMaster, James, PA
Mechling, John, PA
Merritt, Daniel R., Jr. KY
Miller, Thomas W., MS
Mitchell, William, NOVA SCOTIA
Mitchell, William, G., KY
Monteith, William H., GA
Montfort, William J., NC
Murfree, James B., TN
Murphy, Daniel, PA
Nannelee, Virgil T., GA
Neal, Harrison, PA
Neel, James D., SC
Neff, Isaac P., PA
Newcomer, David, PA
Newell, Joseph B., GA
Newell, William L., NJ
Newton, Edwin D., GA
Nicholson, Malcolm J., GA
Norris, J. W. Stump, PA

Fig. 64. Hunter McGuire, M.D. led Philadelphia medical students to Richmond, Virginia, to aid the South in the Civil War that was imminent.

1859

Norwood, John, NC
Pancoast, George L. A., VA
Parkes, A. H., TN
Parr, William P., IN
Peacock, John L. C., GA
Perry, Turner Hunt, AL
Perry, Van Lear, MD
Peyton, Edwin O., VA
Plimpton, Albert F., ME
Potteiger, Jonathan B., PA
Powell, William J., MD
Prentiss, John Hart, ME
Prewitt, J. B., TX
Purifoy, John H., AL
Quinn, John P., DC
Randolph, Lewis C., VA
Rea, Charles T. I., MA
Read, Clement H., VA
Redd, John T., VA
Reddish, Thompson K., MO
Reed, Thomas B., PA
Richardson, David R., GA
Rigg, W. Cochrane, KY
Roberts, Rufus A., NC
Robertson, J. Royall, VA
Rodes, William R., MO
Rogers, W. F., AL
Rowe, Thomas, VA
Scott, Jesse F., KY
Scott, Robert W., TN
Scruggs, Richard F., TN
Seip, William H., PA
Shands, Thomas E., VA
Sharp, William T., OH
Sheppard, James L., NC
Slaughter, Thomas G., AL
Smith, James, PA
Smith, A. Harvey, CANADA
Snow, George W., MA
Somers, Job Braddock, NJ
Spencer, R. M., VA
Spicer, John Daniel, NC
Sprague, Albert G., Jr., RI

Stallings, C. H., NC
Steele, A. J., NY
Stevenson, Joseph M., PA
Stewart, David F., TX
Stockdell, Hugh, VA
Sudler, Arthur E., Jr., MD
Swayze, George B. H., PA
Taylor, John H., MD
Taylor, William H., KY
Thomas, Alfred N., MS
Thrush, David E., AL
Tracy, George D., PA
Triplett, W. H., VA
Vanhook, James D., KY
Waddill, John M., VA
Walker, Walter, NY
Walker, George S., VA
Walker, Charles W., VA
Walker, Z. J., VA
Walter, Barnet C., PA
Ward, Richard William, NC
Warren, A. L., AL
Waugh, James R., NC
Welborne, W. Pinckney, IN
Wells, Thomas, SC
West, Thomas S., MS
White, James A., TN
White, Thomas C., MS
Whitehead, Peter F., KY
Whitner, Hiram K., PA
Williams, John F., MS
Williamson, John H., NC
Williamson, Lea Z., MS
Wilson John B., ME
Wilson, L. James, MS
Wilson, Adolphus J., AL
Winne, Charles K., NY
Wisley, Leonard A., MO
Wood, George J., OH
Young, S. F., MS
Young, Elisha, AL
Young, Thomas R., KY
Young, Matthew H., KY

The titles of theses of the graduating students underwent gradual changes during the Civil War period. Previously, titles tended toward provincial interests or appeared to relate to subjects which might have been introduced in the lectures. The changes during the early 1860's indicated more concern with infections such as typhoid fever, pneumonia, "enteric fever", yellow fever, and tuberculosis, the latter still referred to as phthisis pulmonalis, tubercular phthisis, or consumption. During the War, more of the titles related to epidemic infections such as scarlet fever, diphtheria, dysentery, and to gunshot wounds, matters of public concern and medical ethics. An increasing number of theses related to syphilis and gonorrhea as well as to methods of clinical diagnosis. Although the work of Oliver Wendell Holmes, Ignaz Semmelweis and others had led to new concepts of the prevention of childbed fever, there were surprisingly few references to this important development. On the whole, however, there appeared to be a significant change toward involvement of physicians in public issues. It would be several decades before these interests would lead to organized action.

The number of graduates of 1860 diminished sharply from 255 of the previous year to 170, largely the result of the migration of students to aid the Southern cause in the impending conflict.

Albert W. Fischer (Fig. 65) served as an Assistant Surgeon in the Union Army and was especially commended for his services in 1862 at Harrison's Landing, Virginia. He became a member of the U.S. Pension Board of Examiners as well as Health Officer of the city of Toledo, Ohio. He served as Quarantine Officer of the port of Toledo and wrote on *The Sanitary Conditions of Cities*. For five years he was Dean of Toledo Medical College as well as Professor of Nervous Diseases and Clinical Surgery. In 1880 he served as President of the Toledo Medical Association.

CLASS OF 1860

Abercrombie, George A., AL
Adair, J. Todd, PA
Adams, Patrick H., SC
Addison, William J., MD
Andrews, A. E., GA
Arnold, A. E., LA
Atkins, William L., KY
Bache, Dallas, DC
Bailey, L. Philip, VA
Barksdale, M. S., VA
Bass, Joseph F., VA
Bass, James P., TN
Beesley, James P., MS
Bigelow, Robert J., FL
Bishop, Milton, GA
Blackwell, Nicholas, MS
Blanck, George A., PA
Blocker, John E., GA
Brinton, Daniel G., PA
Burkhalter, Charles M., SC
Buterbaugh, John, MD
Butler, Matthew M., TN

Butler, L. M., FL
Butts, Judson A., GA
Campbell, Marcus, TX
Campbell, Robert, VA
Chandler, Joseph H., DE
Childs, Benjamin F., GA
Clendenin, William G., NC
Cline, Godfrey H., PA
Coates, Benjamin F., OH
Cochran, E. C., TN
Collins, May B., MO
Comstock, Lucius L., OH
Cooper, James D., VA
Cooper, John Atchison, KY
Cowin, John H., AL
Crawford, John D., VA
Cunningham, John S., PA
Davis, William N., PA
Deane, James S., AR
Delaney, Alfred, PA
Dennis, Jacob M., VA
Dixon, John, AL

Dula, F. G., NC
Duncan, Thomas F., PA
Dunlap, B. G., NC
Dunlap, James C., VA
Elkin, Thomas B., MS
Evans, William E., MI
Fairleigh, Robert M., KY
Farnham, Horace P., MA
Ferguson, James E., VA
Fischer, Albert W., PA
Foster, Z. N., MS
Fulton, Saunders, NC
Gaines, John M., VA
Gaither, W. W., NC
Gano, R. Ewing, KY
Gibboney, S. Rush, PA
Gordon, John, MS
Graham, Daniel McL., NC
Greene, Frank M., KY

Fig. 65.   Albert Weiser Fisher (JMC, 1860) served as Dean of Toledo Medical College and Professor of Nervous Diseases and Clinical Surgery.

Hagerson, Angus C., GA
Hanks, George M., GA
Harris, Alonzo F., AL
Hatler, Morris, MI
Hedgepeth, Josiah, NC
Henderson, C. R., MS
Hendry, Bowman, NJ
Hereford, Thomas P., Jr., VA
Hinds, S. Houston, TN
Hoover, David W., PA
Hornback, William, MI
Hunter, Charles J., VA
Hunter, George W., VA
Ingalls, P. P., ME
Ingram, William A., NC
Jackson, G. A., VA
Johnson, F. F., IL
Jones, Montfort, VA
Jones, John M., PA
Judkins, George B., AL
Kelley, William I., OH
Kerns, George M., GA
King, William, Jr., GA
Knickerbocker, Boliver, PA
Lackey, Benjamin F., TN
Langenderfer, J. R., NJ
Lester, James R., TN
Lever, John D. F., SC
Lewis, Daniel W., NC
Loftin, James Merrill, GA
Mace, William G., SC
Mann, Augustine, A., MA
Mapp, John L., GA
Martin, Robert S., MI
Matthews, Fleming J., GA
Maynard, S. S., MD
McAdory, James S., AL
McCullough, Joseph, W., DE
McHatton, A. H., MI
McKinney, David, PA
McNite, William P., PA
Mitchell, G. W., PA
Moffitt, William J., TN
Morgan, Ellington J., GA
Morris, William Wade, VA
Morton, Charles B., VA
Mulholland, David, MI
Nelson, Thomas W., VA
Nelson, William W., IA
Nichols, Pennock J., PA
Nicholson, Hugh W., GA
Norris, Alonzo, NY
Owen, George A., VA
Owen, W. T., VA

Parham, R. J., MS
Perchment, Albert H., PA
Phillips, N. D., MS
Pusey, Robert B., KY
Pyles, Newton C., TN
Ralston, Robert G., PA
Roberts, George H., MD
Roberts, William H. H., GA
Robinson, L. W., NC
Rowell, E. H., AL
Rudisill, Benjamin F., GA
Rushing, Greenwood, MI
Sale, John Alexander, VA
Saunders, Samuel A., AR
Sellers, Hiram F., PA
Seydel, Arthur, NICARAGUA
Shaffer, John F., NC
Shaw, Daniel W., NC
Silvis, George W., PA
Sim, J. Thomas, MD
Spang, Frederick K., PA
Stewart, Clayton M., IL
Stewart, Elam L., IL
Stuart, Robert, KY
Taggart, John F., IN
Tate, Thomas J., AL

Taylor, Daniel W., IN
Taylor, Frederick S., NY
Thomas, William T., SC
Thompson, Davis, TN
Thompson, W. P., AL
Tilman, Joel S., IN
Tilman, J. R., IN
Van Buskirk, Joseph T., VA
Walker, Fleetwood, GA
Walker, Frank, VA
Walker, William J., AL
Wallis, Robert S., MI
Wallis, Hugh Maxwell, MD
Warren, Llewellyn P., NC
Warren, William C., VA
Watson, Andrew J., KY
Watts, David A., KY
Weldon, Andrew J., TN
Wheeler, Levi L., PA
Willcoxon, James, GA
Wingo, Thomas R., TN
Wood, Eason B., AL
Word, James C., MS
Wright, Joseph P., PA
Yantis, Robert H., KY
Yeomans, George, PA
Zacharias, J. Forney, MD

"I would wish the young practitioner, especially, to have deeply impressed on his mind, the real limits of his art, and that when the state of his patient gets beyond these, his office is to be a watchful, but quiet spectator of the operations of nature, giving them fair play by a well-regulated regimen, and by all the aid they can derive from the excitement of good spirits and hope in the patient."

Thomas Jefferson (1743-1826)

The Civil War brought about major changes at Jefferson Medical College. Southern medical students had constituted a large portion of the total enrollment. Even before the outbreak of hostilities, many of the southern students withdrew. In spite of the pressures, many Southerners did remain north. The Class of 1860 which numbered 170 still graduated 26 Virginians, 18 Georgians and 13 North Carolinians. In 1861 in a class of 187, there were 26 from Virginia, 12 from North Carolina, and 6 from Georgia. The major impact of the War occurred in 1862 when the number of graduates diminished to 77, and in 1863 when 82 graduated. The following year the total was 124 and soon thereafter enrollment stabilized.

It is of interest that Dr. Hunter Holmes McGuire, although not a Jefferson graduate, who led the withdrawal in 1859, became a prominent physician, President of the American Medical Association in 1893, and was awarded an honorary degree by Jefferson in 1888 (Fig. 64).

An outstanding member of the class was Phineas S. Connor, a native of West Chester, Pennsylvania (Fig. 66). He was raised and educated in Cincinnati, Ohio, where he began the study of medicine at the Medical College of Ohio in 1858 but came to Jefferson in 1860 to complete his medical studies. After wartime service he returned to Cincinnati as Professor of Surgery. He also held appointments in Chemistry and Anatomy and from 1900 to 1902 served as Dean. The Medical College of Ohio became the Medical Department of the University of Cincinnati in 1887.

CLASS OF 1861

Abernethy, James M., NC
Alger, Luther W., MA
Alter, David, PA
Appel, Charles H., PA
Armfield, David A., NC
Atkins, T. W., GA
Baker, John A.P., VA
Balsbaugh, George S., IL
Barclay, John, PA
Beckham, Henry C., VA
Bell, John B., VA
Bickley, Lloyd Wharton, PA
Blackburn, Cary B., MS
Blalock, N. G., NC
Bowdon, P. M., MS
Bowers, E. D., OH
Brothers, Oscar C., MS
Brown, M. A., MO
Brown, Ignatius C., TN
Brunner, Frank R., PA
Buford, Smith, MS
Burges, Richard U., VA
Bush, Dudley, KY
Bushong, Israel, PA
Chambers, William D., KY
Clark, Patrick B., TX

Cochran, John L., VA
Coe, Thomas Upham, ME
Conkwright, Allen H., MO
Conner, Phineas S., OH
Cook, George R., FL
Covington, Thomas H., KY
Crossley, George W., IL
Culver, Lucius Pitt, OH
Daniel, Thomas W., VA
Davies, William H., VA
Davis, Nicholas E., VA
Delaney, William T., TN
Duff, Edmund, PA
Duke, James E., VA
Dupuy, Joseph T., VA
Dye, Henry, TX
Earnest, J. Tate, TN
Eaves, Spencer, NC
Elder, Samuel M., PA
Embree, John W., TX
Engelman, Joseph P., PA
Eves, Abram E., DE
Ewing, W. D., VA
Farley, John C., AL
Finney, Edward B., VA
Flint, John Felix, PA

Fox, Addison C., VA
Frantz, John H., MD
Fulkerson, Albert P., MO
Gamble, Hamilton M., VA
Garrett, Lewis T., PA
Gidney, J. Chauncey, NC
Gilman, Uriah, AR
Goolrick, P., Jr., VA
Grant, John, CANADA
Greene, Lorenzo S.S., AL
Gross, Chester L., PA
Hammond, Alfred F., NC
Hanger, Cornelius, MO
Hanly, John A.C., PA
Harrill, Lawson, NC
Haughton, Richard E., IN
Haupt, Frederick L., PA
Hawkins, John W., MO
Henry, David H., IN
Herr, Ambrose J., PA
Herrick, George H., NH

Hetzell, David G., NJ
Higgins, Samuel J., GA
Hill, Lauriston H., NC
Hitch, William S., DE
Horton, Samuel M., PA
Howard, Thomas Henry, VA
Hugg, Joseph, NJ
Jones, E. W., AL
Jones, La Fayette J., VA
Keely, Thomas J., PA
Keene, Robert Wilson, KY
King, William Coffield, TN
Knott, Thomas M., KY
Kuykendall, William C., MS
Lane, Sidney W., MD
Lea, John G., NC
Lineaweaver, John K., PA
Logan, P. W., KY
Lowry, Squire M., KY
Marley, H. B., NC
Marsh, Joseph W., DE
Martin, James, OH
Massie, James W., KY
Mathis, Aylesbury, GA
McClarty, Hugh G., TX
McGee, J. P., TN
Metheny, David, PA
Michler, William H.H., PA
Miller, Victor Davis, PA
Milloy, John, MS
Miner, James, IL
Montanye, Lester de la, PA
Morley, J. R., TN
Morris, John, OH
Morrison, Joseph B., PA
Moses, Thomas Freeman, ME
Mosley, Benjamin J., GA
Munford, Samuel E., IN
Nall, Burr F., KY
Nicholson, John, PA
Noble, James D., PA
Norman, John P., PA
Notson, William Morrow, PA
Nottingham, Severn P., VA
O'Bryan, William R., KY
Oldmixon, George Scott, PA
Parker, William H.H., VA
Parker, D. Reid, NC
Pease, Loren H., CT
Picot, Mitchell H., PA
Pomerene, Peter P., OH
Powell, H. B., OH
Price, William Frederick, VA
Pulliam, John D., VA

Fig. 66. Phineas S. Conner (JMC, 1861) Professor of Surgery and Dean of Medical College of Ohio.

Pyatt, K. A., TN
Quarterman, Keith A., GA
Ragsdale, Joseph, MO
Rhinehart, Alexander K., GA
Rhoads, Thomas J. B., PA
Rice, Albert R., NY
Richey, James A., PA
Riggs, David W., PA
Ritter, Nathaniel F., PA
Robbins, Joseph, IL
Roberts, William H., IN
Robertson, A. T., AR
Robertson, T. L., AL
Roller, William C., PA
Ross, Elijah W., PA
Rugeley, Henry L., TX
Sanders, William H., AL
Satterfield, Benjamin F., MO
Saunders, John B., KY
Savage, William E.F., VA
Seargeant, Henry H., VA
Senseny, William D., PA
Shackelford, William, KY
Shackleford, James, KY
Shankle, E. A., GA
Short, Wesley, IN
Simmons, Thomas W., MD
Simpson, Joseph Hawkins, NC
Slough, G. B., PA
Smoot, John H., VA

Spencer, William Canfield, NY
Stewart, Samuel Shaw, PA
Stowe, Charles H., PA
Thomas, Richard C., KY
Thompson, Thomas C., TX
Thompson, William B., PA
Thomson, James W., PA
Totten, John Baldwin, OH
Trego, Albert, PA
Tyson, Andrew R., PA
Vaughan, Joseph H., VA
Wailes, Leonard A., MS
Wallis, Walter, MD
Warren, Francis G., ME
Washington, James S., AR
Way, William Henry, GA
Webb, Charles E., VA
Weist, J. R., OH
Welch, Stanton A., PA
White, Horace M., PA
Williams, Junius S., NC
Williams, Emmet, MS
Willson, John, PA
Wilson, Lucien Strain, GA
Wilson, W. Stockton, MD
Windle, Isaac, IA
Wood, J. Bestor, AL
Woolsey, William F., PA
Wortham, John B., AL
Wymond, Richmond, IN

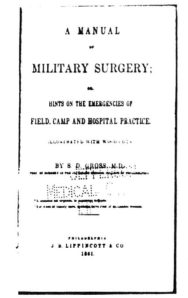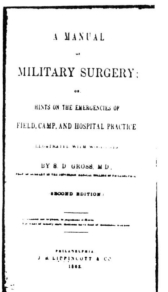

Manual of Military Surgery written by Samuel D. Gross in 1861.

William Williams Keen, Jr., in the 77 graduates of this class, was destined for the Chairmanship of Surgery at Jefferson (1889-1907). He was the most outstanding graduate of the decade (Fig. 67 & 68). His medical education was interrupted by appointment as an Acting Union Army Surgeon in July, 1861, by Dr. John Hill Brinton. He returned in time to complete graduation requirements and was immediately commissioned as an Acting Assistant Surgeon to the United States Army. His innovative approach to military hospital organization was recognized by appointments to Army Hospitals in the Philadelphia area where for a time he served with Drs. S. Weir Mitchell and George Morehouse (both JMC, 1850). Experiences there cresulted in their publication of *Gunshot Wounds and Other Injuries of*

Nerves in 1864 and stimulated Dr. Keen's interest in neurological surgery. Perhaps his most notable accomplishment was the successful removal of an intracranial tumor, the first in America, performed in 1887. He was a member of the surgical team that operated upon President Grover Cleveland in 1893. Keen was among the most decorated and honored of Jefferson's alumni. He received eleven honorary degrees and was a fellow of numerous American and foreign societies.

John Edward Owens, a native of Maryland, became a well-known surgeon in the Middle West. In 1877 he was appointed Professor of Surgery at Women's Medical College of Chicago and two years later Professor of Orthopedic Surgery at Rush Medical College. In 1891 he was named Professor of Surgery at Chicago Medical College.

Fig. 67.   William Williams Keen, Jr. (JMC, 1862), Co-chairman of Surgery (1889-1907).

Andrews, J. Charles, PA
Angle, John S., PA
Applegate, Joseph W., IN
Baldwin, Louis K., DE
Barnes, Ira Norton, NH
Barton, J. Hervey, PA
Bates, John William, MD
Beane, William H., PA
Berg, J. Frederick, Jr., PA
Blaydes, James E., TN
Bower, Henry J., PA
Brooks, Edward, NY
Burg, S. Wesley, PA
Burnett, Joshua U., NEW BRUNSWICK
Cantrell, William A., PA
Carroll, Thomas, PA
Conklin, Gustavus, PA
Cook, William Harvey, PA
Duffell, Charles L., NJ
Edwards, James L., IL
Fitch, Pelatiah, NJ
Gast, John Reynolds, PA
Girvin, Robert M., PA
Graham, Samuel, PA
Grant, John, NOVA SCOTIA
Hayes, Joseph H., PA
Healy, James, KY
Hidden, William Buffet, NH
Hoffman, Christian N., PA
Keen, William W., Jr., PA
King, Cyrus B., PA
Knipe, Jacob O., PA
Lane, Edward G., DC
Lewis, Edward C., OH
Litz, Jefferson, PA
Marchand, James I., PA
Marchand, William King, PA
Martin, Joseph R., PA

Maury, Frank F., KY
McClung, Leigh, OH
McCormick, S. Carson, PA
McGuigan, James A., PA
McHenry, Thomas, PA
Miller, Jacob M., PA
Mitchell, H. Hedge, MA
Montmollin, James M., KY
Mosser, M. Breneman, PA
Myers, Isaac N., IN
Neblett, Henry M., VA
Norris, John Clements, MD
Okie, William T., PA
Owens, John Edward, MD
Patterson, James B., IL
Perry, Marshall S., MA
Porter, George L., PA
Purcell, Wallace M., IN
Raker, Henry M., PA
Reed, J. Farley, PA
Reeves, William H., OH
Reinholdt, John B., PA
Robins, Lorenzo D., PA
Rogers, Ebenezer, PA
Rumbold, F. Frazier, WI
Seip, George W., PA
Shearer, James, PA
Smurr, Thomas A., OH
Snyder, Peter C., PA
Steckel, Edmund F., PA
Sternberg, A. Irving, NY
Stewart, Jeremiah S., PA
Strawn, Benjamin F., MO
Strode, John T., KY
Stubbs, Joseph H., PA
Taylor, Brent W., KY
Thompson, Michael, PA
Thompson, Ebenezer, NEWFOUNDLAND
Treadwell, Passmore, NH

A foreign war is like a scratch on the elbow; a civil war is an ulcer which eats away your liver.

Victor Hugo (1802-1885)

Fig. 68. Clinic of W.W. Keen in "pit" of 1877 Hospital.

1862

Jerome Keating Bauduy, in this class of 82 graduates, was educated at Georgetown College in Washington, D.C. and at the University of Louvain, Belgium. He began his three-year medical education at the University of Pennsylvania but completed it at Jefferson in 1863. After Civil War service he settled in St. Louis where he became Professor of Nervous and Mental Diseases and Medical Jurisprudence in the Missouri Medical College. He was the author of a well-known work on nervous diseases and was an early member of the American Neurological Association.

William H. Ford, whose prior education included Lawrenceville School and Princeton College, served in the Civil War (author of *Gunshot Wounds of the Chest*) but was able to complete his graduation requirements at Jefferson this year. He then studied in Europe for three years including languages in his pursuit of medical experience at Bonn, Vienna, Heidelberg, Paris and London. He established a practice in Philadelphia in 1868 and joined the Pathological Society, the College of Physicians, and in 1874 the American Public Health Association. His medical and literary erudition was promptly demonstrated with publications and studies in vital statistics, public health, and sanitation. He served as Secretary of the Board of Health of Philadelphia during a period when many new concepts in the field of public health were developing. In 1876 he was a member of the Centennial Medical Commission and a delegate to the International Medical Congress held in association with the Centennial Celebration.

William Shaw Stewart was a graduate of Jefferson College, Canonsburg, Pennsylvania, in which Jefferson Medical College was established as its Medical Department in 1824. Following service in the Civil War as Assistant Surgeon with the Army of the Potomac, he established a practice in Philadelphia and soon became involved in medical societies as well as in cultural pursuits. He was Professor of Obstetrics and Clinical Professor of Gynecology at Medico-Chirurgical College of Philadelphia for ten years, Dean for five years and later Emeritus Professor. He was a delegate to the Ninth and Tenth World Medical Congresses and presented papers at both. Dr. Stewart was a widely experienced surgeon including skills in abdominal surgery which was just in the process of development.

William T. Beach was a typical example of the excellent community general practitioner for which Jefferson Medical College had gained such a favorable reputation (Figure 69). After service in the Union Army he entered practice in Schuylkill County, Pennsylvania, a region dominated by the anthracite coal industry. He became interested in community affairs outside his profession. In later life he conducted a drug store and also served as Secretary of the Schuylkill County Medical Society.

Fig. 69. William Thomas Beach (JMC, 1863), highly respected in practice and community affairs.

Albert, David, PA
Applegate, Frederick C., OH
Barndt, Solomon K., PA
Bauduy, Jerome Keating, PA
Beach, William T., PA
Boughman, George W., DE
Boyd, George B., PA
Bradley, John, PA
Brittain, Richard James, PA
Brown, Richard E., NJ
Cadwell, Joseph W., IL
Campbell, Thomas F., PA
Canfield, Ira D., Jr., PA
Carroll, William, PA
Clark, Vachal M., TN
Clarke, George W., NOVA SCOTIA
Coles, John W., NJ
Coover, Joseph H., PA
Corbit, William B., DE
Crawford, Cornelius C.V.A., PA
Crosby, James A., KY
Dayton, Samuel W., PA
DeWitt, John Wilson, PA
Donor, William J., CANADA
Dougherty, Matthew C., VA
Eagleson, David S., PA
Etter, D. Frank, PA
Fawcett, Charles L., OH
Foote, Herschel, PA
Ford, William H., PA
Free, Jared, PA
Gale, John Witten, OH
Gerry, James, Jr., PA
Griffith, David S., PA
Handrick, Edgar L., PA
Hays, William L., MD
Huff, Isaac, PA
Huston, John M., PA
Johnson, Charles M., NY
Kelly, William R., OH
Lehr, George Y., PA

Lightner, Samuel B., PA
Loller, William B., OH
Longwill, Robert L., PA
Loper, William F., NJ
Mackey, James W., PA
Maines, Robert G., NJ
Marshall, Robert C., PA
McCandless, Jas. Newton, PA
McCandless, Josiah G., PA
McDonough, James, PA
Miller, Oliver L., PA
Morrison, John B.G., NOVA SCOTIA
Murphy, Samuel M., PA
Pigott, Charles J., PA
Pulsifer, Horatio B., PA
Reber, William M., PA
Richards, Daniel W., PA
Rittenhouse, George W., NJ
Robinson, Charles, CANADA
Sackrider, Charles H., MI
Say, Eli J., PA
Seiler, Robert H., PA
Snively, I. N., PA
Stephenson, Robert Amasa, OH
Stewart, William S., PA
Stone, Brinton, PA
Stubbs, Charles H., PA
Terry, Henry R., PA
Townsend, Ellis P., PA
Trumbauer, Henry T., PA
Tuft, Reuben H., MD
Turnbull, John, OH
Turner, Theophilus H., NJ
Vaill, Charles H., CT
Way, Walter R., PA
Whitford, Lorenzo D., OH
Wiles, C. Hamer, OH
Williams, Abraham D., OH
Willson, David B., PA
Wilson, Charles P., OH
Woods, James M.B., CANADA

~ 1864 ~

William Wallace McClure, in this class of 124, had already served for three years during the Civil War as an Assistant Surgeon. During this time he was associated with Dr. D. Hayes Agnew (later of the famous *Agnew Clinic* painted by Thomas Eakins in 1889). His residency at Philadelphia General Hospital led to acquaintance with Drs. Joseph Pancoast, Samuel D. Gross and Jacob Mendes DaCosta. This was followed by an appointment as Resident Surgeon at Wills Eye Hospital and studies in ophthalmology in London, Paris and Vienna. He became a noted ophthalmologist, and as Senior Surgeon at Wills he designed several instruments as well as teaching devices for use in the courses of lectures (Fig. 70).

Thomas Hollingsworth Andrews served as a Demonstrator of Anatomy from 1875 to 1879 under Professor William Henry Pancoast.

Abraham S. Raudenbush, in addition to more than 40 years in general practice, served as President of the Berks County Medical Society in 1877 and for 15 years as its treasurer (Fig. 71).

The wartime aspects of teaching at Jefferson were underlined by the comment in the 1864 College catalogue: "Great attention will be paid to instruction in all the departments of Medicine and Surgery, which have special relation to military and naval service." The same year marked the loss of another member of the famous 1841 faculty, Dr. Franklin Bache, great grandson of Benjamin Franklin and Professor of Chemistry (Fig. 34). His successor, Professor Benjamin Howard Rand (JMC, 1848), went on to equally important accomplishments in his long career.

CLASS OF 1864

Andrews, T. H., PA
Ashton, Asa S., OH
Barr, David Miller, MD
Bartles, William H., NJ
Bell, Joseph G., MD
Bell, James, OH
Bese, Frederick, PA
Blanton, Carter, KY
Boyer, Samuel S., PA
Brown, William A., OH
Brownfield, B. F., PA
Buckner, Garrett Davis, KY
Burden, Jesse R., PA
Butcher, Samuel, NJ
Caldwell, William Spencer, IL
Caldwell, Daniel G., PA
Campbell, William H., MO
Cary, Ezra H., PA
Case, James B., PA
Christie, William, NEW BRUNSWICK
Christopher, Howard L., KY
Clements, Christopher C., KY
Clinkinbeard, Allen K., KY
Davis, Harden A., IN
De Ford, Harry S., PA

Dean, John W., IN
Dodge, William Campbell, Jr., VT
Dougherty, J. Drake, KY
Dundor, Adam B., PA
Edwards, Thomas J., CA
Engleman, David, PA
Ferguson, Lewis L., KY
Forsythe, Matthew Leander, KY
Fress, William B., PA
Fuller, Amos B., OH
Geddes, Clarence, PA
Gemmill, Robert B., PA
Gibbs, Henry L., PA
Gibson, Lycurgus, PA
Gillespie, Robert, PA
Gray, John W., IN
Grimes, Louis A., OH
Gumbes, Charles W., PA
Hill, Walter B., KY
Hittle, Benjamin F., PA
Hogendobler, Israel, PA
Howes, Daniel L., CANADA
Jack, William, PA
Jackson, John, PA
Jones, James, MD

Jordy, George H., PA
Keeley, Jerome, PA
Krecker, Frederick, PA
Lapsley, John B., KY
Leaman, Henry, PA
Leaman, Brainerd, PA
Leighton, Walter H., MA
Lineaweaver, Simeon T., PA
Lippincott, Franklin B., NJ
Lippincott, Henry, NOVA SCOTIA
Lowndes, Charles T., WV
Martin, Edwin, PA
Massey, Isaac, PA
Maupin, William T., MO
Maxwell, J. Gordon, Jr., PA
McArthur, John A., PA
McClure, William Wallace, PA
McCormick, J. F., PA
McCoy, Henry W., IL
McIntyre, John H., IN

McKenzie, George I., NOVA SCOTIA
McLaughlin, James A., MA
Miller, Robert, KY
Miller, Lloyd T., MO
Miller, David P., PA
Millikan, Robert H., OH
Mullen, Henry, PA
Nelson, George W., MO
Newcomer, Joseph W., PA
Parker, William S., OH
Pennsyl, Philip H., PA
Phillips, Edwin, IL
Phillips, Thomas H., PA
Pitcher, Stewart C., IN
Price, William H., IN
Pritchett, James W., KY
Raudenbush, Abraham S., PA
Reed, T. J., CANADA
Richardson, Newton M., PA
Richardson, William, CANADA

Fig. 70. William W. McClure (JMC, 1864), noted Philadelphia ophthalmologist.

Fig. 71. Abraham S. Raudenbush (JMC, 1864), general practitioner for 40 years, served as President of the Berks County Medical Society.

Ridgway, Thomas Edwin, PA
Seagrave, Joseph S., NJ
Senseman, John, OH
Sharples, Abram, PA
Shew, Abraham Marvin, NJ
Simon, William I., PA
Smith, John R., IL
Smith, Henry A.M., PA
Smith, Jacob Jontz, IN
Steckel, Alfred P., PA
Stewart, Joseph F., PA
Stockton, James Clark, PA
Stokes, J. Spencer, NJ
Sudler, William T., DE
Taylor, Robert W., KY
Thompson, James F., PA
Thomson, A. Agnew, PA

Thomson, Benjamin F., KY
Tucker, James E., KY
Underwood, Warren J., PA
Van Kirk, Theophilus R., PA
Vannuys, D. H., IN
Verner, Chittick, PA
Wallace, James P., IN
Weaver, Charles H., NY
Webster, John R., IL
West, Theodore S., VA
White, Elisha M., MA
Wiley, Charles, NJ
Willis, Samuel W., KY
Witman, Harrison T., PA
Woods, William S., MO
Woodward, Charles E., NJ
Worthington, William E., MO

GUNSHOT WOUNDS

AND OTHER

INJURIES OF NERVES.

BY

S. WEIR MITCHELL, M.D.
GEORGE R. MOREHOUSE, M.D.
AND
WILLIAM W. KEEN, M.D.

PHILADELPHIA:
J. B. LIPPINCOTT & CO.
1864.

J. Ewing Mears, (Fig. 72), son of George W. Mears (JMC, 1827), a native of Indianapolis, Indiana, served as a military cadet and later as an executive officer in Civil War hospitals. Upon graduation in this class of 136 members he became an instructor in Dr. W.W. Keen's Philadelphia School of Anatomy and soon organized the new surgical laboratory at Jefferson (Fig. 73). He also lectured in gynecology. From 1870 to 1898, he occupied the Chair of Anatomy and Surgery at the Pennsylvania College of Dental Surgery. Mears was a charter member of the American Surgical Association in 1880 and later its President. He was also a founding member, Secretary and in 1898, President of the Philadelphia Academy of Surgery. As an Attending Surgeon at St. Mary's and St. Agnes Hospitals, he along with Dr. W.W. Keen were the first surgeons in Philadelphia to adopt Lister's antiseptic method, an event commemorated by a tablet at St. Mary's. His legacy to Jefferson was the establishment of the J. Ewing Mears Training and Research Fellowship. His portrait may be found in the Gross Room of the Philadelphia College of Physicians.

The first rumblings of a new era in medicine and surgery were signaled by the observation of Joseph Lister in 1865 (and introduced by him in 1867) that carbolic acid had merit in the treatment

Fig. 72.   J. Ewing Mears (JMC, 1865), gynecologist and a founder of the Philadelphia Academy of Surgery.

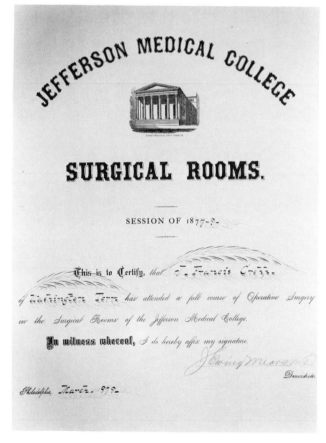

Fig. 73.   Certificate given by J. Ewing Mears for his course in operative surgery at Jefferson.

of compound fractures. This first specific approach to antisepsis and later asepsis based upon the "germ theory" of Pasteur would assure the lasting fame of its discoverer even though years would elapse before these principles would gain general acceptance.

Adoniram B. Judson received a Master of Arts degree from Brown University in 1859 and started his study of medicine in the Harvard Medical School under J.H. Bigelow and Oliver Wendell Holmes. He then entered Jefferson Medical College in 1861, but was caught up in the Civil War at which time President Lincoln commissioned him as an Assistant Surgeon in the U.S. Navy. In 1864 he was promoted to the post of Passed Assistant Surgeon and subsequently graduated from Jefferson in 1865. In 1868 he received a second M.D. degree from the College of Physicians and Surgeons of New York. In 1875 he took special training in orthopaedic surgery and devoted the rest of his professional career in that specialty. He became Assistant to the Chair of Orthopaedic Surgery in the University of New York and Orthopaedic Surgeon to the Bellevue Hospital Out-Patients, as well as Lecturer on Orthopaedic Surgery to the Woman's College of the New York Infirmary. He made significant contributions to the literature in the fields of public health and orthopaedic surgery (Fig. 74). In 1891 he delivered the President's address before the American Orthopaedic Association in Washington, D.C.

Fig. 74. Adoniram B. Judson (JMC, 1865), pioneer in orthopaedic surgery.

Alexander, Robert M., KY
Armstrong, John Maclay, IL
Bacon, James, MD
Bailey, John S., KY
Bair, John B., PA
Barbour, William, PA
Barnes, Henry R., PA
Barr, Abraham M., PA
Beidelman, Abraham C., PA
Bigler, William B., PA
Bishop, Jacques A., WV
Blount, Cyrus N., IN
Book, William P., PA
Book, James Burgess, CANADA
Bowman, John F., PA
Bradley, James, PA
Bradley, William H., PA
Budlong, William Hague, RI
Bullock, William T., RI
Burchfield, John P., PA
Burgner, Samuel H., OH
Carson, Thomas, PA
Craig, Alexander, PA
Davis, Benjamin F., MO
De Kalb, Benjamin Drew, VA
De Witt, Calvin, PA
Deal, Lemuel J., NY
Dellenbaugh, Christian W., OH
Diller, Martin H., PA
Downey, Joseph B., PA
Duerson, Charles, KY
Dunkel, Thomas A., PA
Dunmire, George B., PA

Evans, George W., KY
Finkbiner, S. Sylvanus, PA
Forster, O. Douglass, PA
French, Charles H., OH
Frick, Thomas, IL
Glanden, Andrew P., NJ
Gosling, William Eugene, TN
Grady, Robert R., KY
Greene, Willard H., RI
Grindly, Thomas R., KY
Groves, John W., KY
Gulick, Henry, PA
Gwynn, William, PA
Hall, George Henry, MD
Haller, Francis B., IL
Harralson, Benjamin F., KY
Hatfield, Nathan, PA
Herbein, Isaac S., PA
Higgins, Richard M., MO
Hill, Robert T., TN
Hoadley, Robert, OH
Hood, Richard French, KY
Hood, Joseph Turner, KY
Hoover, Nicholas M., PA
Huber, Samuel Senseny, PA
Hunt, Sylvester H., NJ
Judson, Adoniram B., U.S. NAVY
Karsner, Daniel, PA
Keith, Ezekiel, IA
Kirk, Richmond M., PA
Koch, John G., PA
Laforce, Howard C., IN
Landis, Isaac R., PA
Litch, Wilbur F., PA
Lovell, Albert G., PA
Lupfer, Samuel P., PA
Mavity, William K., IN
McClean, William J., PA
McComb, James, MO
McLanahan, Johnston, PA
Mears, James Ewing, MO
Melick, Daniel Ramsey, PA
Metcalfe, Thomas Norris, KY
Miller, John A., PA
Moore, Samuel Grant, PA
Morton, Tower D., OH
Nash, Joseph D., PA
O'Hara, Robert H., KY
Ozias, Herman W., PA
Perchment, Peter D., PA
Pilsbury, John Milton, KY

Potts, James F., IL
Raub, Michael, W., PA
Rea, Alexander M., PA
Reichard, Philip L., PA
Remondino, Peter Charles, MN
Reynolds, Samuel, PA
Richards, John C., PA
Richardson, John B., KY
Riecker, George A., NEW BRUNSWICK
Roberts, Thomas H., MD
Robinson, Lemuel A., TN
Rodman, William B., KY
Roth, Theodore, PA
Ruger, Henry H., WI
Scholfield, David Thorburn, CANADA
Schrack, David, PA
Seem, Albert A., PA
Shankland, William L., MO
Sherman, Austin B., PA
Shrawder, John S., PA
Simmons, John F., TN
Simpson, James, PA
Slack, Clarence M., NJ
Smith, Henry J., KY
Solliday, B. F., OH
Sparks, George W., NJ
Stewart, Howard P., PA
Taylor, James, PA
Throckmorton, William S., PA
Todd, Orrin D., KY
Townsend, Stephen, PA
Vansant, Joseph B., NJ
Vest, John W.H., IA
Walker, Horace, KY
Walker, James S., KY
Wallace, John S., PA
Wallingford, Alvin M., KY
Waples, Marshall H., IA
Weaver, Jacob G., PA
Wenrich, William H., PA
Wentz, William J., PA
White, Alonzo, MO
Wiley, John S., WI
Wilkins, Thomas, IL
Wilson, David H.H., KY
Wilson, Charles M., PA
Winton, Horace, IN
Wintter, William, PA
Wise, Kenneth D., IN
Witherspoon, Oran H., KY
Zarracino, Ramon D., CUBA
Zell, Amos B., PA

As the first graduating class to return entirely to civilian pursuits, the number of graduates increased this year from 136 to 165. For undergraduates, the faculty this year established the "Summer Course" which began in April and continued into October with a July-August recess. This was a demonstration-clinical program conducted at the College, at Wills Eye Hospital and at Philadelphia General Hospital. It was designed to enhance the didactic teaching since medical schools still did not have their own hospitals for practical instruction.

Robert William Long, the youngest member of the class, received the prize in obstetrics from Professor Ellerslie Wallace. He pursued graduate education at Bellevue Hospital in New York where he received an additional degree. Returning to his native Indiana, he became a busy practitioner and later a widely-known consultant. He was a contributor to medical journals and a trustee of the Central College of Physicians and Surgeons, Indianapolis, for many years.

William Henry Webb was an early convert to the "germ theory of disease." In 1878 he published a monograph, *Is phthisis pulmonalis contagious and does it belong to the zymotic group?*, supporting the infectious character of tuberculosis. While teaching at Jefferson, he persuaded Lawrence F. Flick that his views had merit. Dr. Flick (JMC, 1879) went on to prominence in efforts to control tuberculosis but little is known regarding Webb's subsequent career.

Victor F. Coffman had completed a two-year course at Chicago Medical College prior to his Jefferson experience and he had also served as a surgeon in the Civil War. Co-founder of the Omaha Medical College, he was known for community service as well as for medical accomplishment. Dr. Coffman was President of the Medical School and of the Nebraska Medical Society and was among the first to perform a successful thyroidectomy in the United States.

Oscar Huntington Allis had a great interest in problems of a mechanical nature and devised the Allis forceps which remains a widely used surgical instrument to this day. He is credited with organizing the orthopaedic outpatient clinic at Jefferson in the 1877 Hospital, and was formally named Clinical Lecturer in Orthopaedic Surgery (1888-1891). His work upon dislocation of the hip joint and lateral curvature of the spine became a classic. He was a founding member of the Philadelphia Academy of Surgery and was awarded the Samuel D. Gross Prize of this society for his monograph on *Obstacles to the Reduction of Dislocations of the Hip* (Fig. 76).

Fig. 75. Victor F. Coffman (JMC, 1866), President of Omaha Medical College.

Alexander, William J., PA
Allis, Oscar H., PA
Applegate, Charles H., IN
Arndt, Zaccheus P., PA
Bard, Cephas L., PA
Barrett, Frederick, PA
Bartholomew, William, PA
Beane, George W., PA
Berntheizel, George W., PA
Berry, Daniel, IL
Bixler, Jacob R., PA
Blackwood, Thomas J., PA
Brehm, Samuel H., PA
Brother, Ferdinand, NJ
Brown, Nathaniel W., PA
Brown, J. Alpheus, OH
Bryant, John, MO
Buck, Benjamin S., PA
Buffington, Alexander L., PA

Burke, George W., PA
Burroughs, John E., TX
Butcher, Henry B., PA
Cabanne, James S., MO
Cheeseman, George, PA
Christy, James H., PA
Clendinen, Moses W., IL
Coffman, Victor H., IA
Cogshall, Bela, Jr., MI
Conery, William B., KY
Culbertson, Samuel D., PA
Culbreth, George S., DE
Daingerfield, Joseph F., KY
Dare, George S., PA
Dick, John W., PA
Dodge, Samuel D., AR
Donnelly, John F., PA
Dundore, Adam J., PA
Easley, Andrew, VA
Ellison, L. Frank, DE
Ewing, James B., PA
Ewing, John, PA
Ferguson, James B., CANADA
Fitzgerald, J. A., IN
Flood, James Ramsay, CANADA
Foster, William S., PA
Fritts, Thomas J., IN
Fuller, Alson, NC
Gelwix, James M., PA
Gibson, William, Jr., PA
Gillespie, James L., WV
Gilpin, Fletcher, PA
Gordon, James, NY
Graham, George S., PA
Gregg, James S., IN
Gregg, Robert J., MO
Griffin, Tyler, KY
Griggs, William O., PA
Guerrant, Richard P., KY
Guss, Isaac, PA
Hamilton, Alexander P., KY
Harmon, Byron, R., PA
Hassler, William A., PA
Hill, John, OH
Hockaday, William L., KY
Hodgens, Samuel G., PA
Hoffman, Walter J., PA
Hollenbach, Theodore F., PA
Hornor, Joseph H., NJ
Huffman, D. Clark, PA
Hunter, Thomas S., OH
Huston, Joseph H., PA

Fig. 76. Oscar H. Allis (JMC, 1866) devised surgical instruments and orthopaedic appliances. (Courtesy of Historical Collections, College of Physicians of Philadelphia.)

Hutchins, Edward R., NH
Hyndman, Samuel E., OH
Jackson, William M., PA
Kennedy, Thomas J., TN
Kennedy, Robert S., PA
King, George A., PA
Klingensmith, Theodore P., PA
Knight, John, PA
Knipe, Septimus A., PA
Koch, Frederick W., MI
Landon, Hannibal, OH
Lankford, Alvin P., MO
Leech, Thomas F., IN
Levan, Daniel Henry, PA
Lindley, Henry S., PA
Long, Robert W., IN
Loughridge, Samuel O., OH
Lynde, Uri Colvin, NY
Mackie, Benjamin S., LA
Macpherson, William, PA
Madden, Edmund H., NJ
Magee, T. James, PA
Mason, Joseph Ritner, PA
Matlack, Richard B., TN
Matter, George F., PA
Maxwell, James A., PA
May, James Rundlet, NH
McCormick, A. Y., MD
McDowell, James W., IL
McElroy, James F., KY
McIntosh, John, NOVA SCOTIA
McMunn, John C., PA
McQuesten, E. Forrest, NH
McVicker, James P., PA
Mengle, Isaac L., PA
Meredith, William H., PA
Moore, Isaac H., PA
Mueller, Henry, OH
Munn, Charles W., PA
Murray, Ransom N., MI
Musser, John Henry, PA
Napheys, George H., PA
Newberry, Thomas L., KY
Newell, William M., IL
Newton, P. C., KS
O'Leary, Arthur, NY
Orvis, Charles, IL

Owens, Benjamin F., KY
Patterson, Edwin S., PA
Patton, Frederick H., WV
Peck, Alexander L., NEW BRUNSWICK
Perkins, Finis M., KY
Perry, Matthias Rizer, KY
Peterson, Henry B., KY
Peyton, John C., TN
Phillips, William D., AR
Price, Daniel T., MS
Rahauser, George G., PA
Rebman, Lawrence S., DE
Reed, Jesse J., PA
Reed, Jacob, Jr., PA
Rhoads, George W., IN
Righter, Washington, PA
Roberts, Hiram S., IL
Rodgers, David C.C., MS
Ross, James Brice, KY
Russell, Ezra R., IL
Russell, Ephraim P., KY
Sallade, Franklin L., PA
Sears, Alfred A., IL
Semans, William R., PA
Shaeffer, Brett Randolph, MS
Shurtleff, Benjamin, IL
Snodgrass, James H., PA
Stockton, Thomas C.M., PA
Thackeray, William T., PA
Townsend, Ralph M., PA
Trout, Henry S., PA
Warren, John S., NH
Way, Jacob H., PA
Weathers, Lucien V., KY
Webb, John W., NJ
Webb, William H., PA
Weber, Reinhard H., GERMANY
Wheeler, William G., KY
White, James M., WV
Whitehead, Alfred M., OH
Wilson, William M., KY
Wilson, N. M., PA
Wilson, James E., PA
Wilson, John C., PA
Witmer, Abraham H., PA
Worthington, David J., PA
Yundt, W. Scott, PA

William Joseph Hearn, pictured as the anesthetist in the Eakins *Gross Clinic*, graduated in the 1867 class of 150. He was appointed as Anesthetist by Dr. Samuel D. Gross, later advanced to Chief of the Surgical Clinic, and still later to Surgeon to Jefferson and the Philadelphia (General) Hospital (Fig. 77). Highly regarded for his surgical judgement and technique, he was appointed Professor of Clinical Surgery in 1907. His career was terminated by an accident in 1910 with head injuries resulting in blindness. He died in 1917.

C. Lester Hall, a native of Missouri, served in the Confederate Army before beginning his medical training. After graduation from Jefferson, he practiced in Marshall, Missouri, until 1890 when he relocated in Kansas City to specialize in diseases of women. He became a leader in Kansas City medicine, President of the Missouri State Medical Society, and was elected Vice President of the American Medical Association in 1903.

Richard O. Cowling, a native of Kentucky, became Professor of Surgical Pathology and Operative Surgery at the University of Louisville in 1871. In 1879 he was made Professor of Science and Art of Surgery at the same institution.

Joseph K. Weaver, of Norristown, Pennsylvania, served on the advisory board of *The Jeffersonian*, a student publication that ran from April, 1899 to 1916. He also was President of the Alumni Association (1900/01).

CLASS OF 1867

Achuff, J. Newton, PA
Adams, F. A., MD
Aikin, Perley J., TN
Allison, Samuel C., PA
Ansley, William Bailey, PA
Armstrong, John A., PA
Baker, Charles A., PA
Baker, John Wesley, PA
Barbour, Philip C.S., KY
Baskerville, Charles, Jr., MS
Beecher, Abraham C.W., PA
Bender, O. C., KS
Berry, Frank K., TN
Bliss, D. P., OH
Bollinger, Abraham D., PA
Boon, Jacob, PA
Botsford, William, NEW BRUNSWICK
Bower, Gibson W., PA
Brower, William, PA
Brown, Joseph A.C., MI
Buckley, George E., NOVA SCOTIA
Burton, John, IN
Campbell, H. F., PA
Carey, John F., DE
Carpenter, Paul D., NY
Carroll, Robert J., PA
Cassaday, Felix F., PA
Clark, Charles H., PA

Coble, Daniel W., PA
Coe, Ira E., NY
Cowling, Richard O., KY
Crockett, Samuel J., NY
Cunningham, J. Guy, PA
Davis, Thomas E., PA
DeLap, Hugh, TN
Devereaux, Robert, PA
Dobyns, William P., KY
Dunn, Samuel R., MS
Earle, Willard C., IA
Earnest, John G., TN
Ebaugh, William C., PA
Elliger, Richard A.F., PA
Embry, Gideon A., KY
Enders, F. Henry, KY
Evans, Charles R., PA
Faust, Jonathan N., PA
Fernsler, Edwin K., PA
Frank, Adam, PA
Gold, Hiram, PA
Graham, John, PA
Graham, John W., PA
Graham, James, PA
Gruel, Theodore, H.E., GERMANY
Hall, Albon Eugene, OH
Hall, C. Lester, MO
Hall, William E., PA

Harris, James Walton, MS
Hays, M. P., PA
Hearn, William Joseph, DE
Henderson, John D.W., PA
Hepburn, Charles W., PA
Heysinger, I. W., PA
Higgins, Richard T., IL
Hill, Henry Howard, MD
Hitchner, Charles F., NJ
Hollinsworth, William R., NC
Holston, John G.F., Jr., OH
Howell, William Harrison, NC
Hunsberger, William E., PA
Hurt, P. L., MO
Kennedy, David, PA
King, Charles P., OH
King, Robert M., KY
Kline, Luther B., PA
Knorr, John K., Jr., PA
Kretzer, Aaron A., MD

LeBar, Amzi, PA
Lee, James M., WV
Lloyd, David Corey, PA
Lowman, Webster B., PA
Lowry, Silvanus Todd, KY
Lyle, James Nathaniel, TN
Martin, Zachary T., KY
Maxwell, James A., KY
May, Vance W., IL
McCaa, David J., PA
McDaniel, John R., AR
McGinley, Jeremiah, PA
McKean, William, OH
McNary, Robert B., KY
Mears, Juan B.,, MEXICO
Meloy, Albert Parke, PA
Miller, Joseph W., PA
Mullen, Thomas J., PA
Mullin, John H., PA
Murray, R. J., PA
Myler, William F., IN
Newton, John Search, PA
Nichols, L. C., KY
Oatman, James J., PA
Ogden, P. B., WV
Orner, Charles T., PA
Orth, William M., IN
Otis, Ashbel R., NY
Patzki, Julius H.A., PA
Phillips, Ellis, PA
Porch, Albert, NJ
Porter, William T., PA
Purviance, George, PA
Read, Frederick B., PA
Reber, John W.H., PA
Reeser, Howard S., PA
Renfro, C. J., KY
Rex, Oliver P., AL
Richards, Milton S., PA
Rockefeller, Irvin M., PA
Rollman, William, PA
Rosser, John C., TX
Scales, Jefferson, NC
Schmalhausen, Henry, IL
Schmoele, William, Jr., PA
Scruggs, A. D., TN
Sims, Richard H., VA
Smith, J. R., NC
Smith, James I., DE
Smith, Robert B., NOVA SCOTIA
Sterling, William D., IL
Stranahan, Chester W., PA
Thomas, Andrew J., MS
Thompson, William R., PA

Fig. 77. William Joseph Hearn (JMC, 1867), Clinical Professor of Surgery and Anesthetist to Samuel D. Gross as depicted in Eakins' *Gross Clinic*.

OBSTETRICS;

THE

SCIENCE AND THE ART.

BY

CHARLES D. MEIGS, M.D.,

LATELY PROFESSOR OF MIDWIFERY AND THE DISEASES OF WOMEN AND CHILDREN IN JEFFERSON MEDI-
CAL COLLEGE AT PHILADELPHIA, AND ONE OF THE PHYSICIANS TO THE LYING-IN DEPARTMENT
OF THE PENNSYLVANIA HOSPITAL; MEMBER OF THE SOCIETY OF SWEDISH PHYSICIANS
AT STOCKHOLM, CORRESPONDING MEMBER OF THE HUNTERIAN SOCIETY OF
LONDON; MEMBER OF THE AMERICAN PHILOSOPHICAL SOCIETY; OF
THE ACADEMY OF NATURAL SCIENCES OF PHILADELPHIA;
OF THE AMERICAN MEDICAL ASSOCIATION; OF THE
LONDON OBSTETRICAL SOCIETY, ETC. ETC.

FIFTH EDITION, REVISED.

WITH ONE HUNDRED AND THIRTY ILLUSTRATIONS.

PHILADELPHIA:
HENRY C. LEA.
1867.

In this year of 159 graduates a number of important physicians were included. The most notable was James W. Holland, destined to become Dean of Jefferson Medical College with twenty-nine years of service (Fig. 78). A native of Louisville, Kentucky, Dr. Holland was trained in chemistry at the University of Louisville. After his Jefferson graduation he returned to Louisville and engaged in practice but was soon (1872) elected to the Chair of Practice of Medicine and Clinical Medicine at the University of Louisville.

Fig. 78. James W. Holland (JMC, 1868), Professor of Chemistry (1885-1912) and Dean (1887-1916).

In 1885 he was appointed to the Chair of Medical Chemistry and Toxicology at Jefferson and became Dean in 1887. His teaching in chemistry was directed toward clinical medicine and he was highly respected by the students. *The Dean's Roll Call*, a portrait of Holland, was painted by Thomas Eakins in 1899.

James M. Barton, also a member of the class, was immortalized in the Eakins *Gross Clinic* portrait as the first assistant surgeon. Barton, a private student of B. Howard Rand, Professor of Chemistry, became chief clinical assistant to Dr. Gross the year following graduation and advanced to Surgeon at Jefferson Hospital in 1882. He was also Surgeon to Philadelphia General Hospital and the German (Lankenau) Hospital. He published extensively on surgical subjects.

Thomas S. Mays, following graduation with this class, practiced in Williamsport and Upper Lehigh, Pennsylvania, until his return to Philadelphia in 1885. This followed a period of study in Europe mainly in experimental pharmacology but including time at Brompton Hospital for Consumption, London, England. He became associated with the Philadelphia Polyclinic and College for Graduates in Medicine in 1885 and was named Professor of Diseases of the Chest. He assisted in organizing the Rush Hospital for Consumption in 1890 and served as Visiting Physician. He contributed more than one hundred articles to medical literature especially with respect to physiology and the action of drugs.

The year 1868 also marked the introduction of a short clinical thermometer by Sir Clifford Allbutt, later Regius Professor of Medicine at Cambridge University, England. This instrument was the improved version of the one constructed for Professor Sir W. Audit of Netly by Casella and it added a great deal to the accuracy of clinical diagnosis. Routine use of the thermometer, however, would require several decades.

Alexander, William B., PA
Andrews, Thomas A., TX
Arms, Charles Carroll, AL
Armstrong, Robert, CANADA
Armstrong, William Gaston, GA
Bacon, Henry C., PA
Ballard, John, IN
Banes, A. V., MO
Barton, James Morrie, PA
Baxter, Louis S., IN
Beneke, George Henry, PA
Betz, Israel, PA
Blair, S. T., TN
Boggs, Samuel W., PA
Bradford, Thomas T., KY
Bradley, Robert D., IL
Brallier, Emanuel, PA
Brooking, Silas L., MO
Brooks, John G., KY
Brooks, Zachary T., NC
Brown, Gabriel A.D., KY
Brown, Alfred D., TN
Buhrman, Hiram, MD
Butcher, Thomas S., PA
Carter, Durus D., MD
Carter, John D., VA
Cassell, Martin H., Jr., IL
Chisholm, Isaac W., PA
Cooper, Joshua M., PA
Cornell, G. W., PA
Corson, Edward E.W., PA
Crawford, James L., PA
Crouse, Jerome H., IN
Davison, John B., IL
Davy, Robert B., MD
Dean, George R., SC
Dessau, S. Henry, GA
Dickson, John S., PA
Diller, John R., PA
Docker, William F., IL
Dorsett, E. Rose, NC
Dostor, Benjamin R., GA
Drake, Roger Q., KY
Dulin, John L., KY
Ekwurzel, William, SWEDEN
Evans, Cadwallader, PA
Everett, Edward, PA
Eves, William, PA
France, John K., CA
Fultz, John H., VA
Garver, Charles, PA
Gilkeson, I. W., VA

Gordon, Joseph C., OH
Graham, James Edward, MD
Green, W. Alonzo, NJ
Hartwell, Benjamin H., MA
Heckman, Samuel B., PA
Helm, Amos H., PA
Herbein, Jonathan S., PA
Hill, A. Lewis, PA
Hillis, William J., PA
Holland, James W., KY
Housekeeper, Philip B., PA
Huffman, Frederick, VA
Hughes, Brice M., AL
Hunter, John C., PA
Hunter, William L., PA
Jackson, Craven, MO
Jennings, Samuel D., PA
Johnson, Crowell W., GA
Johnson, Jacob D., PA
Johnson, William, PA
Johnston, Wirt, MS
Jones, John P., KY
Karsner, James H.M., PA
Kehoe, James S., OH
Keister, Simon W., OH
Kelly, Joseph V., PA
Kelso, Samuel M., PA
Koehl, Jeremiah, PA
Laidley, Leonidas H., PA
Lazarus, Sanderson, PA
Leach, Alonzo L., PA
Lewis, James, VT
Lewis, John S., WI
Long, H. Horace, IL
Loughlin, James Eneu, PA
Lovelace, Lemuel M., KY
Ludwig, Peter W.B., PA
Mann, C. Regulus, GA
Marsh, F. L., PA
Mathers, J. J., IN
Maxwell, Archibald, NOVA SCOTIA
Mays, Thomas J., PA
McCune, David M., PA
McFarland, John P., TN
McGuigan, Ignatius, PA
McKelvey, John N., IL
Meisenhelder, Edmund W., PA
Mensch, William H., PA
Metz, Albert H., PA
Miller, Albertus A., MD
Miller, James M., PA
Mott, Eugene K., PA

Mull, William D., IN
Musser, Milton B., PA
Myers, T. D., MD
Needham, William C.H., MA
Newman, Charles, PA
Noble, Angus, OH
North, Edward, NJ
Ogleby, James, PA
Parkison, John A., TN
Patterson, John Kinnier, VA
Peeples, James A., PA
Polk, John L., DE
Preston, Benjamin W., PA
Pryce, Richard W., PA
Quilez, Joaquin M., CUBA
Ragsdale, Edward, MO
Ramsay, Andrew M., PA
Rhea, Robert M., TN
Rhoads, Michael Albert, PA
Richards, Thomas J., IN
Ripple, John M., PA
Robinson, Thomas C., PA
Robinson, John A., SC
Sappington, John, Jr., MD
Schott, Arnold, PRUSSIA
Scott, Andrew H., AR
Seagrave, Clement S., NJ

Shannon, Richard D., MO
Shepard, W. E.W., OH
Shillito, George M., PA
Shultz, Peter H., PA
Sienknecht, Henry, TN
Silver, David R., OH
Smith, Stanley, PA
Spangler, Benjamin F., PA
Spratt, Napoleon B., MS
Statler, Emanuel J.B., IA
Steffey, John Llewellyn, MD
Stewart, John W., MO
Streeter, Henry W., NY
Todd, Edward A., MA
Underwood, William H., FL
VanBuskirk, James, PA
VanKirk, William F., VA
VanReed, Daniel R., PA
Wallace, R. Bruce, MO
Walters, John M., IL
Watkins, Claibourne, AR
West, Simeon Leslie, MD
Whann, Walter Lowrie, PA
Wheatly, Richard R., KY
White, Robert L.C., TN
Whitmer, Benjamin F., PA
Woodburn, William H., PA
Wylie, S. Moffatt, SC

MEMOIR

VALENTINE MOTT, M. D., LL. D.,

PROFESSOR OF SURGERY IN THE UNIVERSITY OF THE CITY OF NEW YORK;
MEMBER OF THE INSTITUTE OF FRANCE.

BY

S. D. GROSS, M. D., LL. D.

NEW YORK:
D. APPLETON AND CO.
PHILADELPHIA: LINDSAY AND BLAKISTON.
1868.

In this class of 127 the most famous graduate was James Cornelius Wilson, son of Ellwood Wilson (JMC, 1845). J.C. Wilson, educated at Princeton, Jefferson Medical College, and in Europe, went on to leadership in Philadelphia medicine. In 1891 he succeeded Jacob Mendes DaCosta as the eighth Chairman of the Department of Medicine at Jefferson (Fig. 79). Skilled in the teaching and practice of physical diagnosis, he was also actively involved in efforts to control tuberculosis, including the opening of a clinic at Jefferson in 1911, the forerunner of the Department for Diseases of the Chest. The J.C. Wilson Professorship of Medicine (Cardiology) at Jefferson was endowed in his honor in 1973.

The year was also marked by the death of Professor Robley Dunglison, personal physician to Presidents Jefferson and Madison, and one of Jefferson's all-time most notable scholars (Fig. 22). As Professor of the Institutes of Medicine (1836-1868) and later as Dean (1854-1868) he greatly enhanced the prestige of the College through his skilled teaching and with his medical publications, especially his *Medical Dictionary* and his *Human Physiology*. Dr. Dunglison had retired one year earlier and was named Emeritus Professor.

Joseph H. North, Jr., of New Jersey, is memorialized along with his son, Harry R. North, Class of 1904, by the late Joseph H. North and Mrs. North of St. Paul, Minnesota, in the North Scholarship Fund at Jefferson.

Upon graduation with this class, Abner Wellborn Calhoun returned to his native Georgia and established a practice. He was appointed Professor of Eye, Ear and Throat at Atlanta Medical College in 1872.

Henry Leffman, Jr. went on to a distinguished career in chemistry, culminating in his appointment as "Pathological Chemist" at Jefferson in 1889. Prior to that he was Professor of Chemistry at Wagner Free Institute of Science, Pennsylvania College of Dental Surgery, and Woman's Medical College successively. His later activities included responsibilities as Physician to the Port of Philadelphia and Chemist to the Pennsylvania Dairy and Food Commission.

CLASS OF 1869

Allison, A. S., OH
Apple, S. S., PA
Aulick, H., VA
Baxter, R. G., NOVA SCOTIA
Bigler, D. M., PA
Blanton, J. W., TX
Blanton, J. B., AR
Bliss, E. W., MO
Broidrick, J. P., MD
Caldwell, A., PA
Calhoun, A. W., GA
Chenault, W., KY
Clark, A. C., PA
Cleveland, J. F., SC
Cole, W. W., PA
Cooper, W. D., GA
Cope, Thomas, PA
Copeland, G. W., NOVA SCOTIA
Cotton, W. G., PA

Craig, G. G., PA
Cushman, A., IN
Davie, M. S., AL
Detweiler, A. C., PA
Dickson, J. N., PA
Drummond, F., VA
Fletcher, F., VA
Frantz, F. F., PA
Fulton, R. E., PA
Gandy, L. T., NJ
Garrison, J. E., PA
Gates, W. R., PA
Gay, W. S.S., MA
Gill, C. M., NJ
Glenn, J. P., PA
Gwin, W. H., PA
Hall, J. E., PA
Hammond, T. E., MO
Harrell, W. S., GA

Hechelman, H. W., PA
Heulings, J. W., Jr., NJ
Hill, W. B., PA
Holmes, J., NJ
Howard, M., VA
Hughes, M. B., PA
Hughes, R., IL
Hunter, R. P., PA
Jimenez, J. M., COSTA RICA
Johnson, F. H., TX
Jones, A. M., IN
Jones, G. P., MD
Kerley, R. M., KY
Lane, M., IN
Langrehr, H., NJ
Lavigne, A. W., CANADA
Law, H. L., CT
Leffman, H., Jr., PA
Leidy, T. H., PA
Lewis, W. H.A., KY
Linn, G. A., PA
Martin, A., PA
Mason, C. R., VA

Mayer, I. H., PA
McClain, S. W., OH
McClure, A. T., CA
McConnell, J. C., PA
McCormick, J. C., PA
Moody, B., PA
Morgan, J. C., PA
Mory, J. J., PA
Myers, B., OH
Nelson, W. H., NY
Newbaker, P. E., PA
Noble, W. P., PA
North, J. H., Jr., NJ
Oddy, J., PA
Ogle, H. O., DE
Orr, A. G., TN
Owen, A. M., PA
Owen, W. R., PA
Paschall, N. J., KY
Patterson, J. E., PA
Pepper, C. T., MO
Purvis, W. I., PA
Randle, T. S., MS

Fig. 79. James Cornelius Wilson (JMC, 1869), Professor of Medicine (1891-1911).

Reynolds, H. V.H., GA
Riddle, J. R., PA
Ridley, R. B., GA
Riggs, E. S., PA
Robinson, A. W., WV
Rockafield, A. S., PA
Santee, E. A., PA
Scanlon, M. D., NY
Schenck, J. H., Jr., PA
Schoener, F. D.H., PA
Senderling, W. H., PA
Sheets, H. W., PA
Shellenberger, J. E., OH
Shriner, Thomas, PA
Simpson, W. L., PA
Slayden, J. D., TN
Smith, J. F., MO
Smoot, J. N., TN
Snively, S. K., PA
Stafford, C. T., NC
Stevens, Mordaunt, FRANCE

Stotler, F. R., PA
Strawn, Joseph, CA
Stubbs, H. J., PA
Thomas, G. L., PA
Todd, J. S., AL
Traver, D. B., PA
Treichler, A. C., PA
Underwood, I. W., PA
VanKirk, B. H., PA
VanSickle, Lewis, PA
Wallace, I. A., PA
Weller, C. O., TX
Wiley, Eugene, NJ
Wilkins, D., F., VA
Wilkinson, C. H., TX
Wilson, J. C., PA
Winder, W. G., PA
Woodard, F. M., TN
Wright, R. S., PA
Wright, J. S., PA
Yates, Edward, NY

MANUAL

OF

HYPODERMIC MEDICATION.

BY

ROBERTS BARTHOLOW, A.M., M.D.,

Professor of Materia Medica and Therapeutics in the Medical College of Ohio;
Lecturer on Clinical Medicine and Physician to the Hospital of the
Good Samaritan; Lecturer on Morbid Anatomy and Pathologist
to the Cincinnati Hospital; Author of the Russell and
Jewett Prize Essays, of the National Medical
Association Prize Essay on Atropia, for
1869, of the Fiske Fund Prize Essay
on the Bromides, for 1869,
etc. etc.

PHILADELPHIA:
J. B. LIPPINCOTT & CO.
1869.

Roberts Bartholow, M.D., Professor of Materia Medica (1879-91)

On March 12 of this eventful year, Samuel D. Gross (JMC, 1828) brought together a five-member committee, with Nathan Hatfield, a graduate of the first Class of 1826 as Chairman, charged with the responsibility of organizing an Alumni Association. Gross, the Founder, who was aware of the power and influence that an Association of its graduates would have upon the welfare of the Medical College, also included "cultivation of good feelings among the alumni, and above all, the advancement of the interests of medical education and the diffusion of sound medical knowledge."

Also, on March 12th of this same year, Jefferson Medical College held its exercises for 160 graduates for the first time in the Academy of Music (opened in 1857). Except for rare occasions when the Academy was not available, because of renovations in progress, the Jefferson graduations have been held there ever since.

George McClellan, grandson of the Founder of Jefferson Medical College, became an important anatomist, surgeon, artist, and author. Among his publications were *Regional Anatomy* (1892) in two volumes and *Anatomy in Relation to Art* (1901). He served as Chairman of Applied and Topographic Anatomy at Jefferson from 1905 to the time of his death in 1913. His handsome portrait in the Jefferson art collection shows his hand resting on a table containing his published books and the skull of the famous Shakespearean actor, George Frederick Cooke, who lived from 1756 to 1812 (Fig. 80). McClellan obtained the skull from a physician whose father had performed the autopsy. It was subsequently given to Dean Ross V. Patterson who willed it to Jefferson. It remains a unique item in Jefferson's archives.

Thomas D. Davis, a native of Virginia, obtained a B.A. degree (1866) from Washington and Jefferson College and later honorary M.D. and Ph.D. Degrees from the same institution. After graduation from Jefferson in 1870 as president of his class, he not only practiced medicine and

surgery, but became active in academia, professional societies, and civic affairs. He lectured in ophthalmology in the Starling Medical College and for eight years was Professor and Lecturer of Physiology in the Pennsylvania College for Women (Pittsburgh). He became President of the Allegheny County Medical Society and the Pennsylvania State Medical Society (President of its Board of Trustees) and President of the Jefferson Medical College Alumni Association (1903). He

Fig. 80. George McClellan (JMC, 1870), grandson of Jefferson's Founder, Chairman of Applied and Topographic Anatomy (1905-13).

was a Trustee of the Western Theological Seminary, President of his local Young Men's Christian Association and for 20 years President of his local school board in Pittsburgh.

William H. Parish, a member of the class from Mississippi, served as Professor of Gynecology at the Philadelphia Polyclinic and College for Graduates in Medicine, Professor of Anatomy at the Woman's Medical College of Philadelphia, and Professor of Obstetrics at Dartmouth Medical College.

Morris Hale came to Jefferson in 1869 with an M.D. degree already obtained from the University of Michigan in 1864. He served on the Union side in the Civil War as an Assistant Surgeon. Among his early interests were the mineral water cures in sanitoria. He also was a founding member of the Roentgen Society of U.S.

CLASS OF 1870

Abbott, Benjamin T., NJ
Albert, John V., PA
Atlee, W. Lemuel, PA
Attaway, Thomas Mutter, TX
Barclay, John W., AL
Barnes, Robert H., PA
Bartleson, Henry C., PA
Beckwith, Frank Edwin, CT
Belo, Arthur F., NC
Betts, J. M., ID
Blachly, S. L., PA
Black, Clarence E., CANADA
Bowen, John James, PA
Brayton, E. Cullen, NY
Breneman, M. B., PA
Briggs, B. B., MI
Brown, J. Jordan, PA
Bruckart, W. Scott, PA
Buckby, Wilson, PA
Butterfield, Thomas H., PA
Campbell, Charles, PA
Chessrown, A. V., PA
Clark, E. W., VT
Collings, Posey, IN
Crenshaw, John W., KY
Crook, Joseph A., TN
Davis, John B., PA
Davis, Thomas D., PA
Dellenbaugh, Z. T., OH
Detweiler, Moses H., PA
Dickson, S. Henry, Jr., SC
Donaldson, S. J., VT
Dundore, Frank P., PA
Eberly, Alison K., PA
Edwards, Isaac L., PA
Ellis, J. Wesley, KY
Eshelman, Emory, PA
Fegley, Amandus N., PA
Ferguson, James E., MI
Franklin, M., GA
Frink, C. S., IN

Fritsch, Herman, PA
Fritzinger, Richard J., PA
Gaines, J. H., VA
Gates, Joseph M., MN
Gaut, Matthew B., PA
Gemmill, Jacob M., PA
Graham, D. M., PA
Griffith, John H., NJ
Halbert, A. C., MS
Hale, Morris, IL
Hamner, Joseph Hinton, KY
Hanna, Hugh, PA
Henderson, Henry G., GA
Hengst, D. Alfred, PA
Hickey, Eugene H., NY
Hill, George A., AL
Hittell, Randolph S., PA
Hoffman, Charles I., PA
Hopkins, Ellwood E., PA
Hopson, Joseph, KY
Howitt, William H., CANADA
Huebener, Walter A.M., PA
Huffman, John M., MO
Hullihen, M. F., WV
Hunter, W. G., PA
Irby, W. C.M., SC
Iszard, W. H., NJ
James, H. C., PA
Jarrett, George B., PA
Johnson, George F., GA
Johnston, Samuel, MD
Jones, Robert E., TX
Jones, Meredith D., MS
Keller, Henry D., PA
Kendall, Henry W., IL
Kennedy, Clempson B., KS
King, William H., PA
Kreitzer, John A., PA
Landis, Henry G., PA
Leggett, Leverett L., OH
Levy, Charles P., TN

138

Lockwood, George A., NY
Lort, Joseph, MD
Marsh, Erasmus W.W., DE
McAlerney, William M., PA
McCandless, A. W., PA
McCarthy, Samuel L., PA
McCarty, Thomas I., IL
McClellan, George, PA
McColly, Marst M., PA
McDonald, G., VA
McFadden, Will Gasten, IN
McGaughey, James D., TN
McIlwaine, R. Emmett, PA
McLean, E. P., PA
Miller, J. Edwin, PA
Miller, J. K., PA
Miller, John P., PA
Minich, A. K., PA
Mitchell, John R., VA
Moss, G. W., PA
Mosser, E. Neff, PA
Musser, F. M., PA
Neely, A. F., KS
Neff, George W., Jr., PA
Noble, John E., MS
Osgood, Hamilton, MA
Oxamendi, Pedro F., CUBA
Parish, William H., MS
Parke, Benjamin R., PA
Parker, Samuel H., AR
Patterson, John P., PA
Plank, Edward H., PA
Poley, Cyrus S., PA
Porter, Joseph Yates, FL
Powell, James, KY
Prime, Elon G., VT
Reeves, M. W., NJ
Ressler, Joel G., PA
Robbins, George R., Jr., NJ

Russell G. T., TN
Rutledge, Shallus R., PA
Schmoele, William F., PA
Schriver, Franklin, PA
Scott, John G., PA
Senseny, Edgar N., PA
Sharp, Samuel F., OH
Shultz, Abner W., PA
Smart, D. S., PA
Smith, Albert M., PA
Smith, Mark L., NJ
Smith, Frank H., NY
Smith, Robert E., MO
Snodgrass, John B., WV
Spackman, Reuben V., PA
Spencer, John E., NJ
Stokes, J. G., IL
Taxis, J. B., IL
Taylor, S. W., AL
Taylor, J. Richard, KY
Thompson, James, MO
Trabert, J. W., PA
Trenchard, Albert, PA
Trevino, Miguel,, MEXICO
Turpin, T. J., Jr., KY
Ullom, J. T., PA
Van Nuys, John D., IN
Van Valzah, Frank H., PA
Vinson, John W., GA
Voorheis, Samuel M., IN
Walker, James K., KY
Watson, Lemuel, MO
Wells, Howard, PA
White, T. H., PA
White, George A., CA
Wick, Addison J., PA
Wilson, Francis S., PA
Zimmerman, G. P., PA
Zuber, D. J., MS

To study the phenomena of disease without books is to sail an uncharted sea, while to study books without patients is not to go to sea at all.

Sir William Osler (1849-1919)

Professor Jacob M. DaCosta this year published his landmark article *On Irritable Heart; A Clinical Study of a Form of Functional Cardiac Disorder and its Consequences.* (Amer. Jour. Med. Sc., 1871, 61, 17-52). This marked him as a pioneer in the field of cardiology and constituted the first approach to the description and study of functional disorders of the heart.

The Annual Announcement (1871/72) included the introduction of supplementary lectures to be given during April, May, June and September, open to all matriculants without extra fees. These lectures antedated the extension of the normal courses beyond the traditional months of October to March.

Other notable events of the year included the publication of Darwin's *The Descent of Man*, which applied the idea of continuous development suggested earlier in his *Origin of Species by Means of Natural Selection.* Early progress in bacterial studies was stimulated by Weigert's report of the first staining of bacteria with carmine, heralding his later discovery of the use of aniline dyes. Another event of medical significance was the demonstration by Olaf Hammarsten of the role of fibrinogen in coagulation of the blood.

Professor J. Aitken Meigs, Professor of the Institutes of Medicine and Medical Jurisprudence, served as President of the Philadelphia County Medical Society.

In this class of 127, John C. Berry, of Maine, graduated with honors. He was one of the first medical missionaries to go to the Far East where in Japan it was now permissible to openly teach Christianity (Fig. 81). In 1873 he founded a Sunday school which was the first for the Japanese in the country. The following year he was the first to compile a Japanese hymnbook. Soon after arrival he was consulted because of an epidemic of beri-beri among the inmates of the city prison. He drew up a detailed outline of reforms, including better hygiene, disinfection, better care of the sick, introduction of manual labor and industrial employment, appointment of a prison chaplain, and plans for a new prison building. Another "first" to his credit was obtaining permission from the government to use unclaimed bodies of executed criminals for postmortem examinations for teaching anatomy to the hospital staff and student physicians. A facility was built which in central Japan was the first classroom for the study of human anatomy by dissection. In 1913 Dr. Berry was honored by the Emperor of Japan with the Imperial Order of the Third Class of the Sacred Treasury.

Fig. 81. John C. Berry (JMC, 1871), early medical missionary to Japan who also established its first classroom for the study of anatomy. (Courtesy of Annals Pub. Co. in Ann. Ot. Rhin. and Laryn., Vol. 90, p. 7, 1981.)

John A. Ritchey after graduation entered private practice in Oil City, Pennsylvania, which became so large that he formed a partnership which eventually required a third physician. This was a very early example of group practice. In 1890 he studied surgery in Europe with the most famous surgeons of London, Paris and Berlin, and two years later at the Postgraduate Medical College in New York City. He was a surgeon with the Erie and Pennsylvania railroads for 30 years (Fig. 82). He also became a censor of the Medico-Chirurgical College of Philadelphia and a President of the Western New York and Pennsylvania Railroad Surgeon's Society. The degree of Master of Arts was conferred upon him in 1874 by Washington and Jefferson College.

James G. Hunt grew up in a family in which his father and four uncles were physicians. In addition to a large private practice he served as President of the Oneida County Medical Society, of the Utica Medical Library Association, and of the Northern Branch of the New York State Medical Association. He was appointed by Governor A.B. Cornell as Health Commissioner of the New York State Board of Health. He contributed largely to the Annual Reports of the State Board of Health as Chairman of the Committee on Public Institutions.

CLASS OF 1871

Adams, W. Powell, PA
Adler, L. H., MD
Alden, James M., MI
Anderson, James R., CANADA
Armstrong, George M., KY
Armstrong, Leon H., OH
Armstrong, Alex H., PA
Baker, Zadoc W., AL
Beatty, Hamilton K., PA
Becker, Edward F., TX
Berry, John C., ME
Blocksom, Joseph T.V., DE
Bogman, Charles H., UT
Boughter, J. Fraser, PA
Bradford, Thomas S., KY
Brown, S. Augustine, NC
Bucher, Benedict D., PA
Burtnett, Jasper N., IL
Carson, John Alligon, PA
Cherry, James, CANADA
Christy, Robert W., PA
Clements, Franklin M., KY
Cox, Joseph J., NC
Crandall, Henry Newton, NY
Crary, Chas. W., NY
Criley, Benton H., IA
Crook, Williams J., TN
Cummings, Josephus, TX
Davison, Henry B., CA
Dial, B. F., TX
Drake, Cicero H., PA
Drescher, Joseph M., PA
Dunn, James C., NOVA SCOTIA
Eakins, Jehu, OH
Eisaman, Cyrus D.B., PA

Elliger, Arthur F., PA
Ellis, Joseph Warren, MS
English, W. T., PA
Ensminger, William H., IL
Estes, Louis P., TN
Fleming, John C., PA
Fowler, Silas W., OH
Fraser, Simon, NOVA SCOTIA
Fritch, Milton L., PA
Gates, Bruce V., CA
Getchell, Frank H., PA
Gillen, Richard H., IN
Goehring, Charles L., Jr., PA
Goodwin, Henry P., SC
Gress, H. V., PA
Harris, S. A., NY
Heilman, Salem, PA
Holbrook, Charles N., PA
Hottenstein, Austin C.L., PA
Houts, John A., PA
Howell, Samuel T., MO
Hughes, John C., PA
Hunt, L. C., VA
Hunt, James G., NY
Hunter, Cassius F., OH
Kain, John Rennett, PA
Kamerer, Joseph W.B., PA
Kehm, Henry, PA
Kerchner, Benjamin L., PA
Kissinger, A. H., PA
Lawson, T. Chalmers, PA
Lecrone, Israel Philip, PA
LeFerte, Daniel, CANADA
Madden, Charles D., PA
McBride, Thomas K., PA

McCleery, Samuel B., PA
McCord, John Price, PA
McElrath, James B., PA
McMillen, Leander, PA
McReynolds, Hugh L., TN
Meisenhelder, Robert N., PA
Miller, Joseph T., KY
Mingle, David H., PA
Moffett, Morrow M., PA
Mohr, Henry C., PA
Moreland, Isaac J.T., GA
Murray, Robert D., OH

Nipple, Henry M., PA
Oswald, C. A. Morris, PA
Palmer, Thomas Dade, MS
Parker, P. James, TX
Phillips, Edwin F., PA
Piper, Milton A., PA
Pollock, William L., IL
Porch, George B., PA
Prowell, George F., PA
Ritchey, John A., PA
Robinson, Samuel N., OH
Robinson, Christo A., AL
Robison, Morris B., PA
Rockafellow, J. Warren, PA
Rowe, J. Wesley, PA
Runcie, John W., IN
Schooley, A. Miles, PA
Seavy, Calvin, ME
Sheridan, William F., PA
Short, James W., DE
Sides, Benjamin F., PA
Simpson, J. Patillo, SC
Simpson, George B., WV
Singer, James J., PA
Small, Edwin M., ME
Smith, Chauncey H., PA
Stedman, Clarence C., NY
Sterling, Albert W., WV
Stevenson, Alfred C., PA
Stewart, William H., PA
Stoll, Joseph H., OH
Strickler, Albert William, PA
Thorley, John D., PA
Trader, J. Lindsay, PA
Van Valzah, Robert T., PA
Wallace, J. C., OH
Warder, W. H., PA
Watts, Charles W., MO
Waugh, William F., PA
Wheelock, George H., NY
Winslow, Richard Chambers, MS
Winslow, William H., ME
Woods, John F., PA
Wright, De Forest J., PA
Young, Robert C., MO

Fig. 82.   John A. Ritchey (JMC, 1871), industrial surgeon.

ART. I.—On Irritable Heart; a Clinical Study of a Form of Functional Cardiac
Disorder and its Consequences. By J. M. DA COSTA, M. D., one of the
Physicians to the Pennsylvania Hospital, etc.

IN this paper I propose to consider a form of cardiac malady common among
soldiers, but the study of which is equally interesting to the civil

Classic description of functional heart disease (see text)

~ 1872 ~

The Annual Announcement for 1872 lists statistics regarding the total number of graduates from 1826 through 1872. Of interest is the recording of the place of origin for each alumnus. In spite of the dislocations resulting from the Civil War and other factors, there were still many students from distant states and foreign countries. Of the total of 6,052 graduates, 1877 were from Pennsylvania, 947 from Virginia and many from other Eastern States. A total of 38 states, 21 foreign countries, and four Canadian Provinces were represented.

Joseph C. Hearne, a native of Kentucky, went on to a career in industrial medicine and an interest in the developing field of public health. He was secretary of the Missouri State Board of Health and an early member of the American Public Health Association. Following his move to California, he pursued similar interests and also served a term as Vice President of the National Association of Railway Surgeons.

Among the earliest of the portraits of faculty members, donated to the College during the 1870s was that of Charles Delucena Meigs, Professor of Obstetrics and Diseases of Women and Children (Fig. 83). This was the beginning of a tradition that culminated in a Jefferson art collection.

CLASS OF 1872

Abbott, John H., RI
Allison, T. D. Mutter, PA
Amos, Enos, WV
Armstrong, Harrison, OH
Badger, Emile B.G., PA
Baker, J. William, WV
Bemis, Charles A., MA
Bertolette, Daniel N., PA
Beutel, Peter, PA
Bonebrake, Andrew S., PA
Bott, Martin Luther, PA
Brush, James A., PA
Buck, Michael J., PA
Buffington, E. Stanard, WV
Bush, Lewis, PA
Byers, W. Churchman, PA
Closson, C. H., PA
Cloud, S. G., TX
Cochran, Frank T., NY
Crise, David, PA
Criswell, J. T., PA
Cummings, John B., TN
Dale, Ewing, IL
Dale, John R., AR
Dold, Harry M., VA
Driesbach, Harvey, OH
Duncan, E. M., KY

Emmert, Jos. M., MD
Eshleman, Norton A., PA
Farrar, Preston W., IL
Feick, J. F., PA
Fisher, John F., PA
Fisher, H. M., PA
Fitzpatrick, James A., PA
Fountain, T. L., AL
Fraunfelter, James, OH
Frey, Clarence, L., PA
Glenn, John B., PA
Graham, Aquila John, GA
Graham, John McK., NOVA SCOTIA
Green, Charles S., WV
Greenamyer, P. S., OH
Greene, Benj. F., PA
Greenwald, Lamartine W., OH
Gross, Jacob M., PA
Haly, J. S., OH
Handy, S. W., MD
Harrison, James Henry, SC
Harrison, Willis Benson, SC
Hearne, Joseph C., KY
Hilliard, G. Himes, PA
Ishmael, J. W., KY
Johnson, Charles W., ME
Kollock, Harry G.M., DE

Lebo, William, PA
Lenow, James H., TN
Louder, Austin J., PA
Matthews, Franklin, PA
McCallum, Donald, SCOTLAND
McClurg, Walter A., PA
McCrearey, J. K., KY
Meals, I. J., PA
Mehard, James W., PA
Miles, J. Hunter, PA
Mitchell, A. B., PA
Morris, Spencer, PA
Morrow, Francis Gayley, PA
Mundorff, E. A., PA
Nelson, Will N., KY

Norcross, J. N., VT
Orlady, George B., PA
Parry, William C., PA
Paschall, D. A., TX
Peck, Barnard S., IL
Pemberton, Harry H., NJ
Perry, Hext M., SC
Person, O. F., PA
Pettigrew, S. H., PA
Pflueger, C. F., PA
Piper, Oliver Perry, PA
Porter, William, PA
Richardson, Marcus F., VA
Ried, J. H., CO
Riggs, W. Judson, PA
Rushmore, Edward, NY
Rynard, John A., PA
Sample, George W., PA
Sanford, S. W., TN
Sawyer, Charles Milton, MA
Sellards, A. G., OH
Sharp, Francis Alex, PA
Sharpnack, T. H., PA
Shivers, C. Hendry, NJ
Siegfried, Chas. A., PA
Stone, Edward R., PA
Swartzlander, Fred, PA
Taylor, Thomas A., PA
Thompson, John M., SC
Thompson, Samuel W., IN
Tiernan, F. William, KY
Tolson, B. Franklin, DE
Tomlinson, Edwin, NJ
Topping, George G., IA
Trowbridge, F. Logan, PA
Uberroth, Adams, PA
Vanderbeck, C. C., NJ
Waggener, James R., KY
Walker, W. M., NY
Walton, G. Taylor, GA
Weaver, S. J., PA
White, J. M., WV
Williams, Thomas H., TX
Wood, George G., PA
Wynn, Ephraim S., NJ

Fig. 83. Samuel Bell Waugh portrait of Charles Delucena Meigs, Professor of Obstetrics (1841-1862).

The degree of Doctor of Medicine was conferred upon 149 graduates in the Academy of Music by the Honorable Jesse R. Burden, M.D., President of the Board of Trustees pro tempore. He was a University of Pennsylvania School of Medicine classmate of the founder of Jefferson, Dr. George McClellan. Dr. Burden had served in the Pennsylvania State Legislature for 15 years and as Speaker of the Senate during the latter part of his term. The Valedictory Address was delivered by Benjamin Howard Rand, Professor of Chemistry (Book Cover).

William Houston Greene pursued a career in chemistry after serving as Assistant to Professor of Chemistry, B. Howard Rand at Jefferson directly after graduation. In 1877 he left for two years of study in Paris and in 1879 he became a Demonstrator of Chemistry at Philadelphia Central High School where his advanced teaching methods and laboratory practice were notable. He resigned to enter business and established himself as a very skillful consulting chemist. He published his own textbook, edited others and was a member of the American Philosophical Society, the Chemical Society of London and the Societe Chemique of Paris. His bust by Samuel Murray was acquired by Jefferson in 1919 (Fig. 84).

William John Rothwell was 34 years of age upon graduation with this class. He was a native of Ottawa, Canada, and was educated in Ontario, later graduating from the University of Michigan at Ann Arbor. Upon graduation from Jefferson, he practiced in Idaho until 1887 when he moved to Denver, Colorado, and became associated with the Gross Medical College, teaching chemistry and clinical medicine. Later he was named Professor of Materia Medica, Therapeutics, and Clinical Medicine (Fig. 85). The Gross Medical College was named for Samuel D. Gross at the suggestion of Dr. Clayton Parkhill (JMC, 1883). It later merged with Denver Medical College and ultimately became a part of the University of Colorado complex. Dr. Rothwell was regarded as one of its distinguished professors.

Franklin West, Following graduation, became Prosector to the Professor of Surgery and Curator of the Museum. He is depicted as the Recorder in the *Gross Clinic* by Thomas Eakins.

W. Harvey Hartzell became prominent in professional and civic affairs in Allentown, Pennsylvania. He served as President of the Jefferson Medical College Alumni Association in 1902.

Lewis J. Picot returned to practice in his native North Carolina where he served as President of the State Medical Society in 1899.

Fig. 84. William H. Greene (JMC, 1873), internationally prominent in chemistry.

Adams, F. Percival, VA
Ake, John G., PA
Alexander, George E., PA
Austin, Alvin A., MO
Bingham, John E., OR
Black, M. F., PA
Blanck, Ephraim K., PA
Blomer, Augustus P., PA
Blyholder, C., PA
Bonsieur, Jean Paul, ENGLAND
Botsford, Le Baron, NEW BRUNSWICK
Brause, John M., PA
Brewster, William Barton, PA
Brown, Daniel Haines, GA
Brown, Robert C., VA
Brown, Thomas A., DE
Brunet, John E., CUBA

Brusstar, H. B., PA
Burris, William A., LA
Campbell, E. B., PA
Campbell, Thomas B.R., NOVA SCOTIA
Carlton, W. A., GA
Carter, W. W., MO
Cressman, Emanuel, PA
Davis, B. H., PA
Deaderick, E. L., TN
Dodge, N., PA
Downes, Bennett, MD
Dreher, George W., PA
Eberhard, J. O., PA
Eliason, John, MD
Elliott, C. B., PA
English, H. J., AR
Engram, R. O., GA
Erdman, A. J., PA
Farrow, E. W., PA
Fay, Francis Marcus, BELGIUM
Fay, Varley George, BELGIUM
Fife, J. Rowland, PA
Fisher, Charles H., CA
Floyd, John B., PA
Foster, D. Gilmore, PA
Frantz, Elias H., PA
Gaddis, L. Springer, PA
Garinger, George F., PA
Graham, Douglas, MA
Greene, W. H., PA
Halbert, J. E., MS
Hall, Chas. H.H., IL
Hancker, William H., PA
Hartzell, C. M., PA
Hartzell, W. Harvey, PA
Hatch, Fred W., Jr., CA
Henderson, Samuel, TN
Hess, J. W., PA
Hester, William Weir, IN
Howeth, V. A., TX
Hull, A. P., PA
Hurst, N. N., IL
Irwin, Jos. W., IN
Johns, S. P., PA
Jones, John W., TN
Jones, S. Willard, NY
Jones, Thomas J., GA
Jordan, W. A., KY
Keeler, William A.T., PA
Kernan, Thomas H., PA
Lamont, Robert Bruce, PA
Lane, William H., OH

Fig. 85. William John Rothwell (JMC, 1873), Professor of Materia Medica in the Gross Medical College of Denver, Colorado. This College was founded in 1887 and named in honor of Samuel D. Gross.

1873

Lawrence, Charlie W., TX
Lawyer, Fletcher C., PA
Lindley, Lutellus W., PA
Linebaugh, Joseph T., TN
Linville, Montgomery, PA
Lippincott, J. A., NOVA SCOTIA
Marlin, T. J., PA
Mateer, R. M., PA
Matthews, Abel J., PA
McCann, E. W., OH
McClelland, Cochran, IL
McCrory, W. F., CANADA
McHenry, George M., IL
McLaughlin, A. J., PA
McLean, Daniel, PA
Mindil, H. W., PA
Miner, A. G., OH
Moore, Harmar D., PA
Morrow, John W., PA
Nipple, John O., PA
Orr, Wilson J., PA
Palmer, David, PA
Park, Wesley, IL
Parson, John S., PA
Patten, Newton N., PA
Peabody, Charles A., MA
Pease, Walter C., WI
Percy, H. T., VA
Petrie, Herbert L., MS
Picot, Louis Julien, NC
Prendergast, Patrick J., IRELAND
Prettyman, G. W., DE
Red, G. J., MS
Robins, William B., PA
Ronaldson, W. D., PA
Rothwell, William J., ID
Rowland, Francis F., PA
Rush, E. W., AR
Sawyer, R. P., ME
Seaton, B. C., PA

Semans, T. B., WV
Skilling, M. J., PA
Smathers, W. J., PA
Smith, G. Albert, PA
Smith, F. A.A., ENGLAND
Spalding, Francis J., CUBA
Spencer, William Gardner, NY
Stayer, A. S., PA
Stickel, Harry L., PA
Stockbam, Alonzo, PA
Strother, Lyman, T., IN
Stubbs, Walter P., GA
Taylor, W. S., NC
Taylor, W. V.M., PA
Taylor, W. G., NJ
Tennent, John C., DE
Torrence, J. M., PA
Town, Edwin C., PA
Trenchard, C. M., NJ
Trexler, Horatio D., PA
Urtecho, J. Y., NICARAGUA
VanKirk, William Kirnan, PA
VanValzah, H. B., PA
Weaver, George W., PA
Weaver, Elijah, PA
Weaver, L. F., NY
West, Franklin, PA
Wheeler, Eno S., PA
White, Thomas J., AL
Wiggins, S. Lowry, PA
Williamson, Jesse, Jr., PA
Wilson, Clarence G., PA
Wilson, Samuel G., PA
Winter, J. W., PA
Winters, D. Nixon, PA
Wolford, W. Scott, PA
Woodbury, Frank, PA
Woolford, Joseph S., NJ
Wordin, N. E., CT
Young, Miller, IA

"The natural course of the human mind proceeds from credulity to skepticism."

Thomas Jefferson (1743-1826)

The Commencement was held at the Academy of Music on March 11, at which time the M.D. degree was awarded to 151 graduates by the Honorable Jesse R. Burden, M.D., President of the Board of Trustees pro tempore. A Valedictory Address was delivered by Professor Jacob Mendes DaCosta. During the ceremonies the portrait of Professor Samuel D. Gross by Samuel Bell Waugh was presented to the College.

It was during this year that the portrait of Benjamin Howard Rand was painted by Thomas Eakins. This was the first portrait by Eakins, then 30 years of age, of a scientific personality not a relative or friend. Dr. Rand gave this highly regarded portrait to Jefferson Medical College in 1877. It is now displayed in Jefferson's Eakins gallery and adorns the cover of this book.

Edward Emmet Montgomery was president of the class. Following 15 months as resident physician at Philadelphia General Hospital he began his practice but also taught private classes in Physiology and Anatomy at Jefferson. He joined the staff in Obstetrics at Philadelphia General Hospital in 1878 and the following year performed the first successful ovariotomy (oophorectomy) before a public clinic in Philadelphia. Dr. Montgomery in 1886 was Professor of Gynecology at Medico-Chirurgical College of Philadelphia and in 1892 he became the first Professor of Gynecology at Jefferson where he introduced the practice of having students examine patients in the clinic. He was the author of a well-known textbook, *Practical Gynecology*, and numerous papers. He was a Founding Member and later President of the American Association of Obstetrics and Gynecology, a Trustee of the American Medical Association and its Vice-President in 1910 (Fig. 86).

John Veitch Shoemaker as a student had organized the Jefferson Quiz Association and went on to become its quizmaster in Materia Medica and Therapeutics for six years. He became a Demonstrator of Anatomy at Jefferson upon graduation but soon began his pioneer work by establishing a dispensary of dermatology in 1875. This was so successful that Jefferson provided hospital space for the dispensary in 1880 and appointed him Lecturer in Skin Diseases in 1883. In 1886 he left Jefferson to become Professor of Skin and Venereal Diseases and Dean at the newly established Medico-Chirurgical College of Philadelphia where he went on to achieve power and success. He published extensively and acquired an international reputation in his special field as well as in the broader fields of medical practice, military medicine (Spanish-American War), and care of the poor and mentally ill.

John B. Roberts went on to a distinguished career in the developing field of plastic surgery (Fig. 87). He was a nephew of Jefferson surgeon Dr. Richard J. Levis (JMC, 1849) who was a pi-

Fig. 86. Edward E. Montgomery (JMC, 1874), Professor of Gynecology (1892-1920).

Fig. 87. John B. Roberts, (JMC, 1874), pioneer in plastic surgery.

oneer in that field. Roberts became a member of the Jefferson surgical staff for a few years following graduation but then transferred to Philadelphia Polyclinic Hospital. There he was President for some years and Professor of Anatomy and Surgery until its merger to form the Graduate School of Medicine of the University of Pennsylvania in which he also became Professor of Surgery. He wrote extensively and devised numerous instruments and procedures for fractures and reconstructive surgery.

John Nutting Farrar who received his Jefferson M.D. this year when he was thirty-four years of age, had a prior degree in dentistry from the Pennsylvania College of Dental Surgery and was also skillful in the mechanical arts. During his early years in Philadelphia he is stated to have invented for Robley Dunglison an embossing typewriter for the use of an institution for the blind of which Dunglison was president. Dr. Farrar went on to a career of dental surgical practice, publications and the invention of numerous dental instruments.

Daniel Hummel Coover was the son of Eli Houser Coover (JMC, 1850). He became an ophthalmologist and in 1890 settled in Denver, Colorado, developed a large consulting practice, and was appointed Professor of Ophthalmology at Gross-Denver Medical College.

CLASS OF 1874

Bachmann, G. A., PA
Baldwin, James F., OH
Barr, John W., PA
Barrett, William C., IL
Beatty, Arthur J., MD
Beaver, E. M. S., PA
Berlin, James O., PA
Bigelow, Brown A., PA
Bitting, John A., NC
Blackwood, Thomas, OH
Boland, Richard W., PA
Bradford, T. Hewson, PA
Bristol, E. L. M., MI
Brock, Luther S., WV
Brown, George C., MO
Brubaker, Albert P., PA
Brundage, Frank M., IL
Butler, James G., TN
Cahall, Thomas V., DE
Callihan, Robert, PA

Campbell, John A., WV
Carberry, P. Joseph L., PA
Carr, Edward S., TN
Chapman, George H., GA
Chase, Abner F., IL
Colley, Horace G., PA
Cooper, Joseph M., PA
Coover, David H., PA
Cresler, John M., PA
Cummings, Joseph J., PA
Cunningham, William N., PA
Dirickson, Edwin J., MD
Donehoo, R. S., PA
Duckett, James P., SC
Duff, John Milton, PA
Duffield, Harrison, PA
Eaton, Albert M., PA
Edie, James Orton, MI
Engel, Hugo, PA
Farrar, John N., MA

Fooks, John W., DE
Foster, William C., PA
Foulke, Samuel L., PA
Fulton, Archibald J., KS
Gailey, Calvin P., CA
Gale, George T., OH
Gardner, Samuel, CANADA
Getz, H. L., PA
Gilmore, A. P., PA
Goicuria, Antonio, PUERTO RICO
Goodman, Edward E., PA
Gordon, J. Crawford, PA
Gorgas, S. R., PA
Graybill, K. P., VA
Gresham, William F., GA
Hammond, T. W., MN
Hare, Thomas Dabney, AR
Hartman, Paul A., PA
Hays, Richard T.D., MS
Hays, Robert M., PA
Hildenbrand, Louis W., PA
Hines, Eben P., PA
Hollenback, Jacob S., PA
Hoover, Albert M., PA
Hosack, William, PA
Hottle, Edwin B., PA
Hudgings, John C., TN
Humphreys, George L., PA
Ivins, George, NJ
Jessop, Charles J., PA
Jones, George M., AL
Keller, Franklin B., PA
Koch, Josiah A., PA
Koogler, M. A., OH
Lamkin, Samuel R., TX
Latham, James C., PA
Lebcher, Chester, OH
Leberknight, F. B., PA
Leonard, W. L., IA
Lewis, Eugene R., MO
Lockwood, John S., IL
Loeling, Gerhard, PA
Maclay, Archibald I., IL
Mann, Charles H., PA
Mathews, Adrian, PA
McCarthy, Henry C., PA
McCormick, Horace G., PA
McCosh, Samuel A., PA
McKennon, Archibald M., AR
McLennan, Alexander, TN
McNeil, George W., PA
Meyer, L. George, PA
Miller, D. Rentch, PA
Miller, Martin L., MD
Montgomery, Edward E., OH

Moore, William J., NY
Mullan, Eugene A., PA
Nevins, John C., PA
Onan, Dennis, KY
Parker, Gilbert L., PA
Parks, Edward L., MA
Partridge, Conrad L., PA
Patterson, Howard, PA
Powell, William S., OH
Pursel, W. Wilson, PA
Ramsey, Robert W., PA
Read, Josephus D., NOVA SCOTIA
Reed, George K., PA
Reeser, T. Howard, PA
Register, H. C., PA
Rich, J. Bartlett, CT
Ritchie, M. M., PA
Ritter, J. Ellis, PA
Roberts, John B., PA
Robinson, George B., CT
Ross, Frank Marcellus, ME
Runkle, William V., PA
Sampsel, D. S., Jr., OH
Sayles, Charles E., NY
Schmidt, Henry, PA
Shoemaker, John V., PA
Silliman, James E., PA
Silvara, Joseph W., PA
Simsohn, Joseph S., GERMANY
Small, John A., NC
Snow, Emerson E., MA
Sowash, Millard, PA
Spalding, A. Eugene, MI
Spangler, Jacob R., PA
Staub, Franklin N., PA
Stehley, Martin L., PA
Strong, Charles D., GA
Stubbs, D. Alfred, PA
Taggart, Horace D., OH
Taylor, William S., PA
Taylor, Thompson J., KY
Temple, James D.W., MD
Turner, Henry H., AR
Uhler, Tobias M., PA
Venn, John Francis, PA
Walrond, Benjamin, NOVA SCOTIA
Weaver, A. S., PA
Wedge, Dudley O., IL
Wentz, Thomas H., PA
West, George W., OH
West, William L., WV
Willetts, Theodore L., PA
Wilson, Harry M., PA
Wingerd, C. Z., PA
Young, A. G., PA
Ziegler, Charles R., OH

The Commencement was held on March 11 at which time the M.D. degree was conferred upon 170 graduates by the Honorable Jesse R. Burden, M.D. The Valedictory Address was delivered by Professor Samuel D. Gross.

In retrospect, this was a momentous year in that the 31 year-old Thomas Eakins painted his uncommissioned world famous masterpiece, *The Gross Clinic*, that immortalized Professor Samuel D. Gross (Fig. 88). Daniel M. Appel of this class was depicted as a surgical assistant in the lower right foreground of the painting.

Joseph Seal Neff, son of a leading Philadelphia

Fig. 88.   The *Gross Clinic* painted by Thomas Eakins in 1875.

physician, Dr. Charles Neff (JMC, 1852), went on to signal achievements for Jefferson and Philadelphia. Able and well educated, including foreign study, he became Attending Physician at Jefferson Hospital and at Philadelphia General in 1881 to 1882. In 1889 his medical career was interrupted by impaired health and he acquired business skills with the firm of L.C. Vanuxem & Co. He capitalized on this experience in resuming his medical connections in 1895 when he was appointed Medical Director of Jefferson Hospital (Fig. 89). In this post, he made a major contribution to the planning of the 1907 Hospital Building which was constructed without a general contractor. Dr. Neff resigned in 1907 to become Director of the Department of Public Health and Charities of the City of Philadelphia. Having served also as President of the Medical Staff, he was made Emeritus by the Board of Trustees.

Jeremiah Thomas Eskridge joined the staff of the Department of Anatomy upon graduation and in 1880 became Attending Physician at Jefferson Hospital. In 1883, his interest having been stimulated in neurology, he became an instructor in nervous and mental diseases. He developed tuberculosis later that year and settled in Colorado. In 1888 he resumed practice in Denver and in 1892 became Dean of the Medical Faculty as well as Professor of Nervous Diseases and Medical Jurisprudence at the University of Colorado. He resigned in 1897 to pursue his interest in treatment of mental diseases as Commissioner of the State Asylum for the Insane and for a medico-legal career. He published numerous papers. Dr. Eskridge was the first official faculty member at Jefferson to teach nervous and mental diseases and was also one of the early professors of psychiatry in the United States.

James William Neely became a prominent and progressive Pittsburgh physician and surgeon who contributed numerous articles to medical literature and was also the inventor of the Neely fracture bed.

Abell, Amacey B., PA
Agnew, John, PA
Allen, Dixon C., NEW BRUNSWICK
Appel, Daniel M., PA
Baker, L. Jackson, PA
Baldwin, William H., CA
Balmer, Abraham, F., PA
Barr, Samuel L., DE
Bell, Edward H., PA
Bennet, Eben H., NEW BRUNSWICK
Black, Charles H., PA
Black, Henry M., PA
Bley, David L., IL
Borland, M. H., PA
Boydston, Walter J., WV
Braddock, Richard S., NJ
Bradley, Charles, PA
Brinton, William M., PA
Brown, James M., PA
Burns, Bernard, PA
Burroughs, J. J., TX
Bush, Horace, PA
Caldwell, J. J., IA
Calhoun, Albert J., PA
Caterson, William M., PA
Clark, Samuel M., PA
Coile, Henry P., TN
Cope, George W., PA
Creasey, Lloyd S., PA
Crowell, T. Alexander, NC
Crowell, George Edgar, OH
Crowell, David H., OH
Darlington, William S., PA
Davenport, Hugh H., PA
Davis, Joseph C., PA
Davis, John D., PA
Davis, Hugh L., PA
Dease, Stephen S., INDIA
Deaver, Jesse A., PA
DeGrofft, Eugene E., NJ
Derhamer, Wesley A., PA
Dickson, James W., PA
Dodds, J. Spratt, PA
Drake, Charles Mutter, TN
Dunlap, J. Francis, PA
Dwight, M. Barclay, NY
Eck, William H., PA
Edwards, C. C., NY
Eldred, Charles C., IL
Ellis, Melvin B., SC
Ellis, George S., MS
Endicott, George W., NJ

Eskridge, J. T., DE
Fisher, Frank, PA
Fulton, H. C., PA
Gaskins, J. L., FL
Gates, Albert V., OH
George, Matthew R., PA
Gladden, George, PA
Gleason, Daniel F., NY
Godfrey, E. L.B., NJ
Grady, James B., ME
Grady, John F., CA
Grant, James M., KY
Gray, Thomas D., PA
Groff, Charles A., MD
Hall, Charles F.W., MD
Hankins, John, PA
Hardeman, Samuel, TN
Harris, John B., TX
Heinitsh, Heber D., SC
Hill, T. Benton, PA
Hill, Richard J., MN
Hogue, Davis A., PA
Hoskins, Percy C., PA

Fig. 89. Joseph Seal Neff (JMC, 1875), Medical Director of the 1877 Jefferson Medical College Hospital from 1895 to 1907.

Hoss, Archibald C., TN
Houseman, William W., PA
Ingram, Thomas D., PA
Jarrell, Henry J., TX
Johnson, Edward L., OH
Johnston, Charles W., PA
Johnston, A. Warriston, PA
Johnston, J. Clark, PA
Jones, Paul, MD
Keaggy, John B., PA
Keelor, Reinard S., PA
Kelly, George M., PA
Kiester, D. Milton, PA
King, John W., MS
Kirkhuff, A. Lewis, PA
Kistler, Jacob K., PA
Klingensmith, I. Putnam, PA
Knight, Robert B., PA
Krepps, James T., PA
Limberg, F. A., PA
Lindley, Samuel H., MN
Lippincott, George C., NJ
Loder, Percival E., PA
Lord, Simon L., WI
Maloney, Richard M., TN
Mattoon, Edward A., NY
Mauger, Elam B., PA
McCarty, Rufus H., DC
McConaughy, Robert, PA
McConnell, John B., PA
McCrea, C. S. A., PA
McCreary, Henry, OH
McCrystle, John, PA
McCullough, Adam H., PA
McDonald, Charles D., GA
Mitchell, Taylor S., DE
Moffet, William, PA
Moore, William G., KY
Morrow, J. Wilson, PA
Musser, Harry E., PA
Mutchler, J. Pace, PA
Myers, Alfred, PA
Nast, Hugo, NJ
Neely, James W., PA
Neff, Joseph S., PA
Nicholls, B. Frank, SC
O'Connor, Harry R., PA

Overall, George W., TN
Painter, William P., PA
Parish, Asbury, NY
Parry, George W., OH
Pope, D. Strother, SC
Pope, J. W., PA
Potter, Thompson E., MO
Prather, Richard C., Jr., KY
Pratt, D. Leonard, PA
Proctor, David Green, OH
Quigg, Robert M., PA
Randle, Charles C., MS
Reilly, Philip, PA
Robertson, James M., KY
Robinson, Joseph F., MO
Royer, Daniel F., PA
Seibert, John P., PA
Shimwell, Benjamin T., PA
Shriver, Colley, WV
Shultz, David L., PA
Sibbald, John, PA
Sill, Thomas M., PA
Simmons, T. J., IA
Smith, John K., PA
Smith, William L., PA
Smith, Joseph E., NY
Smith, Irving W., IA
Stanger, Samuel F., NJ
Stees, John I., PA
Stone, Frank M., PA
Street, William, KS
Taliaferro, Frank, VA
Taylor, J. Zack, MD
Thompson, Charles M., ENGLAND
Thompson, Josiah M., PA
Tibbins, Joseph E., PA
Waldron, George F., OH
Ward, Eugene A., MO
Warren, Parker H., IA
Waters, John W., NV
Way, George C., OH
White, Thomas L., PA
Willits, Isaiah W., PA
Wilson, T. D. Mutter, PA
Woods, George H., PA
Woodside, John S., INDIA
Wright, Edwin W., PA
Young, Robert W., PA

In this Centennial year of the United States, celebrated in Philadelphia, Dr. Samuel D. Gross served as President of the International Medical Congress, attended by a large number of distinguished American and foreign delegates. Especially for the Centennial, he wrote *The History of American Surgery from 1776 to 1876*. Also during the exhibition, the first public demonstration of the telephone was made by Alexander Graham Bell.

On June 2, 1876, a founding meeting of the Association of American Medical Colleges was held at Jefferson with representatives of 22 Medical Colleges. Dr. John B. Biddle, Jefferson's Dean, was elected the first President.

In this class of 146 graduates, Morris Longstreth, who had already received an M.D. degree from the University of Pennsylvania in 1869, obtained a second M.D. degree from Jefferson in this year. This was a custom not uncommon in those times. In 1880/81 he gave the first laboratory course in Pathologic Anatomy and Pathologic Histology at Jefferson. In 1882 he published *Rheumatism, Gout and Some Allied Disorders*, one of the earliest pathologic treatises in rheumatology. When Pathology became a major department at Jefferson, he served as the first Professor and Department Head from 1891 to 1895 (Fig. 90).

Another outstanding member of this class was William Ward Van Valzah, a pioneer in gastroenterology (Fig. 91). From 1892 to 1902 he served as Professor of Diseases of the Digestive Organs in the New York Polyclinic College. In addition to many papers in his specialty, he was a co-author in Van Valzah and Nisbet's *Diseases of the Stomach*, published in 1889.

Louis Bazet, a native of France, proceeded to San Francisco where he became prominent in the developing field of urology (Fig. 92). He wrote extensively, translated a French textbook, and became Professor of Surgery and Genito-urinary Surgery at the San Francisco Polyclinic.

CLASS OF 1876

Akers, James W., IL
Akers, F. P.H., GA
Ayres, Samuel, IA
Bazet, Louis, FRANCE
Beale, Philip W., PA
Beaver, Abraham P., PA
Benham, R. Bruce, OH
Blake, Duncan W., NJ
Bleiler, Peter O., PA
Bonnefil, J. B. Martin, COSTA RICA
Brady, John, PA
Bringhurst, William, PA
Bryan, Thomas A., MO
Burgi, Peter, ID
Callaway, Enoch, GA
Carncross, J. Augustus, PA
Carr, L. Logan, WV
Carrell, John B., PA
Churchill, Selden A., IA
Cloak, E. Morris, DE
Collins, Stacy B., CA

Collom, Daniel L., PA
Cowden, John W., IA
Criswell, Matthew, IL
Culpepper, B. N., NC
Davis, William F., MD
Dillman, Amos F., PA
Essig, Charles J., PA
Fehrenkamp, B. J., TX
Fike, Giles A., PA
Follmer, John S., PA
Foreman, Samuel B., PA
Fraser, James W., ENGLAND
Freeman, Joseph H., GA
French, Morris Stroud, OH
Fuchs, Augustus J., Jr., MO
Garrett, E. Frank, PA
Giberson, Nelson S., CA
Gilland, John C., PA
Gilmer, Allen D., NC
Goribar, Louis G., MEXICO
Hamilton, James M., PA

Hamilton, John A., LA
Hammond, Robert A., GA
Heilman, Russell P., PA
Hill, Frank P., PA
Hindman, Charles C., PA
Hoffa, Jacob P., PA
Holland, Daniel J., IN
Horwitz, Theodore, PA
Hunter, Theophilus W., GA
Hunter, Randal R., MO
Hyer, Grainger, CA
Isett, Frederick S., PA
Jackson, Homer, PA
Jefferis, T. Norval, PA
Johnston, Robert W., NC
Johnston, W. A., IA
Kane, John J., KY
Keeton, Theodore A., MO
Kelly, M. A., ID
Kelsey, William L., CT

Kern, Palmer M., PA
Kerr, John W., PA
Kiddoo, S. R., PA
Kopetschny, Ottocar E., BOHEMIA
Kynett, L. J., IA
Linebaugh, Harry W., PA
Longanecker, William A., PA
Longenecker, David F., PA
Longstreth, Morris, PA
Lopez, Joseph H., PA
MacConnell, William G., SC
Madara, James W., PA
Madden, W. Scott, PA
Malech, Herman F., CA
Markel, Isaiah F., OH
Marshall, D. Samuel, PA
Marshall, George W., DE
Mattason, Myron J., IA
McDowell, Samuel B., PA
McFadden, William, Jr., PA

Fig. 90. Morris Longstreth (JMC, 1876), first Chairman of Pathology (1891-95).

Fig. 91. William Ward Van Valzah (JMC, 1876), pioneer in gastroenterology and Professor of Diseases of the Digestive Organs in the New York Polyclinic College.

McMillan, John D., NC
Miles, Charles A., PA
Miller, Samuel S., PA
Montelius, Ralph W., PA
Morgan, D. Porter, WV
Morris, Florance K., PA
Morris, Charles C., IN
Naugle, William M., PA
Nebeker, Henry, IN
Nightingale, Henry B., NJ
Noble, Charles M., IL
Orwig, George A., OH
Palmer, Thomas P., TN
Parker, Victor H., IL
Pierce, Amos M., PA
Pillow, Raymond H., PA

Fig. 92. Louis Bazet (JMC, 1876), early California urologist.

Plana, Guillermo Machado, CUBA
Price, Thomas H., WV
Pritchard, Enoch T., IN
Prowell, William R., PA
Purefoy, George W., Jr., NC
Race, Henry H., NJ
Ragan, Patrick J., CA
Rea, James L., PA
Reed, H. Allan, PA
Rogers, Willard H., NY
Rowe, Hezekiah J., PA
Sampsel, William H., OH
Sargent, John H., NH
Schmidt, Edgar T., IL
Seaman, Louis L., NY
Shallenberger, H. M., PA
Shuman, Jacob L., PA
Simpson, George W., PA
Sloan, George W., AR
Slocum, Charles E., OH
Smith, Albert S., PA
Smith, Lewis T., PA
Smith, George C., NJ
Somerville, Beverly R., NEW BRUNSWICK
Spratlin, William M., GA
Steans, John C., PA
Stephens, James G., VA
Stiles, Oscar, PA
Swan, John C., PA
Swartz, George W., PA
Sweringen, Hiram V., IN
Talmage, Edwin S., PA
Tenbrook, Andrew, PA
Todd, T. Erskine, SC
Trexler, William, PA
Umstad, George B.R., PA
Umstead, John R., PA
Van Valzah, William W., PA
Weddell, Oliver S., PA
Weir, Frank L., RI
Wesner, Michael A., PA
Wharton, Robert S., PA
White, Charles M., IN
Whitlock, G. E., IL
Wittkamp, Andrew L.V., PA
Woodruff, Samuel W., PA
Wright, Alfred T., OH
Young, Oscar H., NY

At the Commencement on March 10 in the Academy of Music, 198 graduates received their M.D. degrees. The diplomas were awarded by Emile B. Gardette, M.D., President of the Board of Trustees and himself a Jefferson graduate in the Class of 1838. The Valedictory Address was delivered by John Barclay Biddle, Professor of Materia Medica and Therapeutics.

This was the first year in which graduation prizes were listed in the Annual Announcements. A prize of $100 by H.C. Lea, Esq. for the best thesis was awarded to Leonardo D. Judd of Illinois, whose topic was *Periodical Asthma; Its Pathology and Its Treatment by Electricity*. A prize of $100 by Hon. H.M. Phillips for the best preparation of the cranial nerves contributed to the College's Museum was won by Samuel E. James of Kentucky. The Toner Medal presented by J.M. Toner, M.D. of Washington, D.C. for the best thesis based upon original investigation was received by A. Harper R. Guiley of Pennsylvania. His report was on *Anesthesia*.

The geographical distribution of the graduates was as follows: Pennsylvania (94), Illinois (13), Indiana (9), Arkansas (7), North Carolina (7), New York (7), Ohio (6), Kentucky (4), Missouri (4), West Virginia (4), New Jersey (3), Massachusetts (3), Maine (2), Tennessee (2), Texas (2), Wisconsin (2), and one each from Kansas, Rhode Island, Nevada, Oregon, Florida, Colorado, Maryland, Vermont, Connecticut, Delaware, Virginia, New Mexico, District of Columbia, U.S. Navy, New Brunswick, Canada, Germany and France.

Jefferson's excellent reputation, as evidenced by the large graduating class with diverse geographical representation and a strong faculty, was further augmented this year by opening on September 17 of the first detached Jefferson Medical College Hospital, the second in the nation devoted not only to patient care but to teaching of the medical students (Fig. 93). It was located on Sansom Street behind the old Tenth Street College Building where the Thompson Annex now stands. A five-story structure of Gothic design by architect Frank Furness, with 125 beds and a large clinical amphitheater (Fig. 94), it would serve Jefferson's hospital requirements until opening of "Old Main" at Tenth and Sansom Streets in 1907.

Fig. 93. First detached Jefferson Medical College Hospital of 1877, devoted to teaching of medical students as well as patient care.

Abbott, Elgin P., NY
Adams, Louis J., PA
Alexander, Martin T., GA
Allred, Edward W., NC
Anderson, George B., PA
Arment, Samuel B., PA
Augur, James T., OR
Baker, Joseph H., IN
Ballard, Silas H., IN
Barber, I. Grier, PA
Barr, John A., IL
Barton, Isaac, Jr., PA
Bean, James H., MA
Beaty, Marshal, IN
Beck, Theodore D.F., PA
Bedford, Alfred D., PA
Berlet, James F., PA
Bickford, Henry H., TN
Bickley, John G., IA
Biddle, Jonathan C., PA
Bing, Edward W., PA

Blachly, Oliver L., PA
Bley, Robert E., IL
Blue, John C., NC
Boucher, Frank H., IA
Bowman, John W., PA
Boyce, Charles S., NY
Brooks, Floyd V., PA
Burg, Horace W., PA
Burr, Evan W., PA
Bynum, John G., NC
Calhoun, Noah F., PA
Cargile, Charles H., AR
Case, Joseph W., AR
Chambers, John E., IN
Clagett, Luther S., PA
Clinkscales, Albert M., TX
Cooper, Charles A., IL
Cooper, Elias S., Jr., IL
Cornog, William E., PA
Damour, Ferdinand, KS
Davies, Charles H., OH
Davison, James, PA

Fig. 94.   Clinical amphitheater ("pit") of 1877 Hospital.

Deats, William, PA
Detweiler, Washington C., PA
Dillman, J. Walter, U.S. NAVY
Dinwoodie, William, RI
Dornsife, Daniel H., PA
Drake, Frank N., NV
Drucker, James O., AR
Duvall, Augustus W., PA
Ellery, William, MO
Elliott, Thomas, PA
Erney, Albert S., PA
Ewart, Charles R., PA
Ewing, John H., NJ
Fawcett, John W., PA
Fegley, Henry C., PA
Fisher, Claudius R.P., NJ
Fisher, Milton R., PA
Fitzmaurice, Thomas J., NEW BRUNSWICK
Frizzelle, Thomas F., TN
Geissinger, Samuel D., PA
Gibson, Lorenzo P., AR
Giese, George F., IA
Gosweiler, Augustus V., PA
Graydon, Andrew, PA
Guiley, A. Harper R., PA
Hake, Edward G., PA
Hanna, Benjamin M., PA
Hanna, William P., IN
Hardtmayer, H. R., PA
Harrison, J. Stewart, DC
Hartzell, Milton B., PA
Hays, Robert C., PA
Hepburn, Charles H., PA
Herr, Benjamin F., NY
Heston, Eber H., NY
Hewitt, George A., PA
Hinckley, Walter F., IL
Hiner, Fred T., KY
Hobaugh, David C., PA
Hoffman, Charles S., WV
Holmes, Joses B.S., GA
Holt, Mathew S., WV
Hopwood, William H., PA
Horner, James Wallace, MO
Hummel, C. Carroll, PA
Hutzell, Jacob C., IN
Hyde, Nathan D., ME
Jackson, John, Jr., PA
James, Samuel E., KY
Jones, William E., MO
Judd, Leonardo D., IL
Keesee, John J., NC
Keim, Ambrose M., PA
Kirkpatrick, Joseph T., GA

Kobler, George H., PA
Lacock, Samuel A., PA
Landis, B. F., IL
Laverty, D.W. Clinton, PA
Lawrence, William B., AR
Le Grand, Cecil W., TX
Leitzell, Charles B., PA
Lescher, Lyell J., IL
Lewis, David H., PA
Lightfoot, Gross R., KY
Little, William Seely, PA
Little, Jehu, IL
Littlepage, George C., IN
Longacre, Frederick W., PA
Lytle, George E., PA
Maddox, William R., PA
Mahan, John M., AR
Marshall, Randolph, Jr., NJ
Martin, James W., IA
Mayhew, Isaac F., MA
McCandliss, William L., PA
McCaskey, George W., OH
McClung, Samuel H., IL
McCollough, A. M.F., OH
McCulloch, James T., PA
McCurdy, Horace G., PA
McDonald, M. Gay, KY
McNary, Hugh Allison, PA
Milam, Benjamin J., MO
Minthorn, Henry J., IA
Mitchell, John William, IA
Mitchell, John A., IL
Mitchell, B. R., PA
Moyer, Adam J., PA
Mudge, William S., PA
Murray, F. Marion, FL
Nice, Benjamin H., PA
Nye, Willard W., CO
Patton, Abram B., PA
Payne, William A., NC
Perkins, Benjamin B., MD
Perkins, Henry, WI
Person, William H., PA
Poichet, Alphonse T., FRANCE
Powell, William R., CANADA
Reger, Alfred G., WV
Reynolds, Edward S., OH
Ritter, Hiram W., PA
Sahm, William K.T., PA
Sampsell, J. Vinten, OH
Sedgwick, Theodore H., PA
Shaw, Robert T., PA
Simon, T. Wallace, PA
Smith, Henry H., ME

1877

Smith, H. Rufus, VT
Smith, John W., IN
Smith, W. Harmany, PA
Snively, Joseph L., PA
Souwers, George F., PA
Speas, Julius L., NC
Sperry, Willis C., OH
Sprowls, John N., PA
Stanford, Louis W., GA
Stark, Theodore F., WI
Stehman, Harry B., PA
Sterling, Harry F., PA
Stever, John C., PA
Stewart, Joseph S., PA
Stone, Byron, MA
Strock, Daniel, NY
Sutton, Harley H., IN
Swan, Walter Sidney, IL
Swavely, Samuel B., PA
Thies, Wilhelm, GERMANY
Thompson, James R., PA
Thompson, Andrew D., PA
Throckmorton, Tom M., IA

Tipton, William R., NM
Turnbull, Frederick M., CT
Turner, Charles E., PA
Urich, Thomas K., PA
Van Buskirk, Charles, PA
Waddell, William, NY
Wagner, Jacob A., IL
Wall, Walter Z., NC
Waller, George P., PA
Wallis, James C., AR
Weikel, Charles H., PA
Wheeler, Henry C., NY
Whitworth, Richard S., PA
Williams, Roger, PA
Wilson, Harry M., PA
Wilson, Edwin K., WV
Winters, Barton M., PA
Wirgman, Charles, PA
Woods, William W., PA
Woods, Walter V., DE
Wray, James H., PA
Yeager, Edwin L., PA
Young, James W., PA
Young, Thomas J., VA

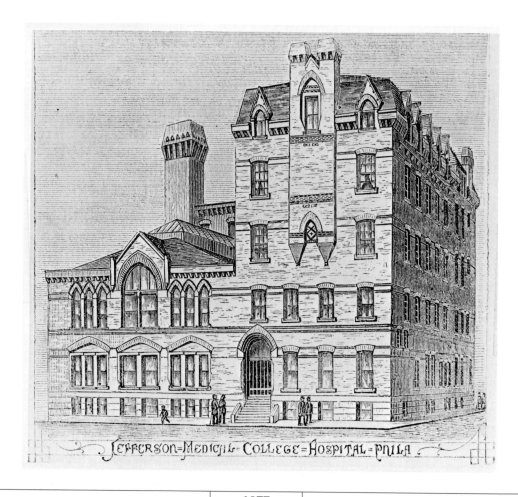

JEFFERSON-MEDICAL-COLLEGE-HOSPITAL-PHILA

1877

A little noticed event of this year, but one of later major significance, was the purchase by the Alumni Association of the portrait of Professor Samuel D. Gross from Thomas Eakins for $200. *The Gross Clinic* as it became known was donated to the Board of Trustees the following year. Time established it as the spiritual symbol of Jefferson's heritage. It was ultimately acknowledged as one of the greatest masterpieces of American art.

Charles Eucharist de Medici Sajous was the most outstanding member of this class. He took postgraduate training in France under Brown-Sequard and in 1903 published the first American textbook of endocrinology, *The Internal Secretions and the Principles of Medicine* (in two volumes of 1873 pages). Considered by some as "The Father of American Endocrinology," he held office and membership in many medical organizations such as the American Medical Editor's Association (President, 1903), American Association for the Study of Internal Secretions (President, 1917), and American Therapeutic Society (President, 1919). He authored the *Annual of the Universal Medical Sciences* (1888-96), followed by the *Sajous Analytic Cyclopaedia of Practical Medicine* (60 volumes). He became Professor of Laryngology and Dean of the Faculty of the Medico-Chirurgical College (1897-1910), Professor of Applied Therapeutics at Temple University (1910-22), and Professor of Applied Therapeutics at the Graduate School of the University of Pennsylvania (1921-29). His death in 1929 terminated the "nine hundred-year-old name" of the Medici of Florentine history (Fig. 95).

John Chalmers DaCosta graduated in this class at the age of 44 and became a gynecologist at Jefferson Hospital from 1884 to 1901 (Fig. 96). His importance is accented by his having been the father of John Chalmers DaCosta, Jr., known as "Black Jack" (JMC, 1893). "Black Jack's" cousin, John Chalmers DaCosta (JMC, 1885), became the first Samuel D. Gross Professor of Surgery in 1910. This explains the relationship of

Jefferson's three John Chalmers DaCostas, often confused.

Henry William Hermann, of Missouri, took a year of study abroad after graduation and then returned to his native state where he became a specialist in nervous diseases. He served as a Clinical Professor in the Missouri Medical College which became a part of Washington University. Active in various medical societies, he also contributed articles on neurological disorders.

Allen H. Hulshizer from this class served as President of the Alumni Association in 1899.

In this large graduating class of 203 members

Fig. 95.   Charles Eucharist de Medici Sajous (JMC, 1878), early investigator of internal secretions.

it is striking that only nine were from the South: North Carolina (4), Texas (2), Mississippi (1), Georgia (1), and South Carolina (1). More than half were from Pennsylvania (120), with many from the West and eight from outside the United States: Cuba (2), New Brunswick (2), Canada (1), Ireland (1), Sweden (1), and Central America (1). The dramatic decline in students from the South, which fortunately changed for the better in succeeding years, may be ascribed at this particular time to (1) residual antipathy to the "Northern Yankees", (2) very depressed economic conditions in the South, and (3) decreased numbers of young men by death from war injury and disease.

On September 26, 1910, G. Christopher Savage of this class, who had become Professor of Ophthalmology at Vanderbilt University, delivered the introductory address for the 86th Annual Session of Jefferson Medical College.

CLASS OF 1878

Abernethy, James W., PA
Alvord, John E., IL
Anderson, Thomas E., NC
Angney, William Muir, PA
Appel, Aaron H., PA
Arney, George F., PA
Arnold, Herbert A., PA
Bachman, Theodore S., PA
Bartholomew, Cornelius, PA
Bell, Edward S., OH
Berkey, Norman G., PA
Berliu, Wilson S., PA
Best, Austin, PA
Bickel, George V., PA
Biddle, Clement, PA
Bittinger, Joseph H., PA
Botsford, Robert L., NEW BRUNSWICK
Bowman, Robert R., PA
Boyer, Jacob H., PA
Bready, John Ely, PA
Brous, Harry A., KS
Brownfield, James H., WV
Browning, Walter C., NJ
Bryan, John S., PA
Calvin, Abner C., PA
Campbell, J. Moore, PA
Carrier, Frederic H., NY
Casanova, Juan J., CUBA
Cavitt, J. Whitley, TX
Chapman, Henry C., PA
Couard, T. Ellwood, PA
Cropp, J. Francis, WA
Cummings, M. John, PA
Curtis, Wickliffe K., WV
DaCosta, John C., PA
Davis, Frank T., KY
Day, Homer B., PA
De Wolf, J. Henry, PA
Decker, W. Frank, Jr., PA
Dillon, J. Dale, PA

Dodge, Clarence L., NY
Donnelly, Michael A., PA
Drake, Howard H., PA
Dripps, John H., PA
Ellinger, George W., IL
Emery, Boyd A., PA
Emrick, Edwin M., PA
Evans, Micaiah R., PA
Faison, William W., NC
Fink, William D., PA
Fisler, Charles F., NJ
Flagg, Urbane H., MA
Fox, L. Webster, PA
Frautz, Joseph, PA
Fuller, Smith, Jr., PA
Funk, Harry S., PA
Gale, C. Tiernan, OH
Gamble, James E., PA
Glass, Montgomery W., WV
Gontner, Aaron M., PA
Goodno, Charles F., NJ
Gordon, John W., PA
Grant, H. Horace, KY
Griffith, R. Eglesfeld, PA
Hall, Walter E., NJ
Hall, George P., TX
Hamer, Joseph R., MO
Harbison, Andrew B., PA
Hastings, John M., OH
Hengst, Milton A., PA
Henning, John D., PA
Herbst, George Edwin M., PA
Herdocia, Rodolfo F., CENTRAL AMERICA
Hermann, Henry W., MO
Hill, James W., KY
Hilliard, William D., NC
Himmelwright, Francis E., PA
Holsburg, Daniel B., PA
Hough, Charles B., PA
Hough, H. Page, NJ

At the Commencement on March 12 the Valedictory Address was delivered by James Aitken Meigs, Professor of the Institutes of Medicine (Physiology), in 534 lines of blank verse. This impressive poetry is preserved in Jefferson's Archives. A portion often quoted is his advice to the graduates.

"Shun braggart glory, crave no sounding name,
Good deeds in heaven's scale weigh more than fame.
All pomp and vain display avoid, although
The foolish world is led by empty show.
Be always what you seem, seem what you be;
With learning couple large integrity.
Through merit seek to rise, and not by dint
Of blazoning your name in public print,
Or pseudo-scientific pamphlets which
Not science, but their writers seek to enrich
Through wondrous tales of cures adroitly told,
To snare the credulous and filch their gold.
Praise not yourselves, nor others praises buy,
As men, not showmen, with each other vie.
Upon the public never seek to palm,
With face unblushing and without a qualm,
The coin of base presumptuous pretence
For sterling gold of honest excellence."

Dr. Meigs died unexpectedly on November 9 of this year at the age of 50 (Fig. 97). Joseph B. Potsdamer of this class joined with seven members of the class of 1880 to form a medical society that would honor the memory of their beloved Professor. Dr. Potsdamer became a successful pediatrician and remained active in the Meigs Medical Association until his death in 1947 at the age of 88.

William L. Rodman, of Kentucky, went on to become Professor of Surgery, Kentucky School of Medicine (1893); Professor of Surgery and Clinical Surgery, Medico-Chirurgical College, Philadelphia, Pennsylvania (1898); and Professor of Surgery and Clinical Surgery, Woman's Medical College of Pennsylvania (1900).

H. Augustus Wilson, of Pennsylvania, rose to prominence in the field of orthopaedic surgery (Fig. 98). He served as President of the American Orthopaedic Association in 1902 and became Jefferson's first Chairman of the Department of Orthopaedics (1904-18).

David D. Stewart, of Pennsylvania, served as Professor of Anatomy, Surgery, and Oral Surgery in the Philadelphia Dental College (1895).

Lawrence F. Flick became a pioneer Philadelphia crusader against tuberculosis. In 1892 he organized the first State (Pennsylvania) Society for Prevention of Tuberculosis. He founded the White Haven Sanatorium (1901) and the Henry Phipps Institute (1903). Although he never held a position on the Faculty, his portrait is in the Jefferson art collection (Fig. 99).

Howard F. Hansell, of Pennsylvania, after graduation joined the Medical Clinic of Professor Jacob Mendes DaCosta at Jefferson as well as the Ophthalmology Clinic of Professor Thomson. He took special ophthalmological training in Germany and then for more than 20 years was an Attending Ophthalmologist at the Philadelphia General Hospital. In 1895 he was appointed a Clinical Professor of Ophthalmology at Jefferson and from 1902 to 1925 served as the third Chairman of Ophthalmology in his alma mater (Fig. 100).

George Friebis following graduation, began a practice in association with William H. Pancoast, Professor of Anatomy. Later he became associated with the Laryngological Department at Jefferson and continued as Assistant in the Otological Department. He then served under Professor William Thomson in opthalmology for eleven years and became Chief of the Eye Clinic. In addition to publishing scientific articles, he was a member of the College of Physicians and American Philosophical Society.

In 1879 a new Laboratory Building was opened at the southwest corner of Tenth and Sansom Streets adjacent to the College (Ely) Building (Figure 101). It provided rooms for operative and minor surgery, practical chemistry, microscopy, and physiology. Prior to that time, the laboratory experience of the students at Jefferson had been limited to anatomy and use of the Pathology Museum.

Fig. 97.   Monument at gravesite of James Aitken Meigs (JMC, 1851) in Woodlands Cemetery, Philadelphia. (See Fig. 47 for photo of Dr. Meigs.)

1879

Armstrong, J. Stone, NY
Bair, Thomas A., PA
Bane, William C., PA
Barnes, Samuel S.P., OH
Beall, William P., NC
Beckley, Edwin L., MD
Beery, Charles C., NY
Beyer, William F., PA
Biddle, Alexander W., PA
Blunden, Boyle N., PA
Boenning, Henry C., PA
Bond, Munroe, NH
Bowcock, John W., WV
Brock, Rufus E., WV
Brower, Charles F., VA
Brown, Carlos M., CA
Brown, Page, CA
Bryson, Lewis M., PA
Buck, James P., PA
Burford, J. Edward, TX

Burgin, Herman, PA
Burroughs, Hamilton S., PA
Cahall, William Cannon, DE
Campbell, Cassius M.C., PA
Campbell, George W., PA
Carr, A. Smith, WV
Cates, Charles H., ME
Cauthorn, Franklin, OR
Chapman, Norman H., IL
Clayton, George R., TX
Cline, Lewis C., IN
Cox, Thomas B., PA
Crawford, Gustavus R.J., CANADA
Crawford, George W., PA
Criswell, John F., IN
Crump, William L., NC
Davis, Henry H., NJ
Davis, Lewis G., PA
Deemer, John T., PA
DeWolfe, Willard L., PA

Fig. 98. H. Augustus Wilson (JMC, 1879), Clinical Professor of Orthopaedic Surgery (1892-1904) and first Chairman (1904-18).

Fig. 99. Lawrence F. Flick (JMC, 1879), pioneer in tuberculosis control.

Diehl, Oliver, PA
Dillard, Richard, Jr., NC
Duggan, James R., GA
Ellenberger, J. Wesley, PA
Enos, Thos. A., DE
Entler, George F., NY
Espy, John S., PA
Feltwell, John, PA
Flick, Lawrence F., PA
Forbes, William H., IN
Forster, Charles V., PA
Fowler, Warren H., NY
Fravel, Edward H., VA
Frick, Cyrus S., PA
Friebis, George, PA
Fritz, Horace M., PA
Gandy, Charles M., NJ
Gardiner, Charles, CT
Grady, William A., MN
Guerrero, Alfonzo L., CENTRAL AMERICA
Guzman, Virgilio, CENTRAL AMERICA

Hacker, Isaac B., PA
Hale, John G., AR
Haley, George P., NJ
Hampton, John T., PA
Hankey, Wilbur H.J., PA
Hansell, Howard F., PA
Hassenplug, Galen K., PA
Hays, Peter W., PA
Hazlett, Isaac W., OH
Heddens, James W., MO
Heinitsh, George W., PA
Herbein, Milton H., PA
Herr, Francis C., PA
Herron, Charles R., FL
Hewson, Addinell, Jr., PA
Hice, Edward C., PA
Hickman, James W., PA
Holman, James A., PA
Holmes, William E., KY
Hopkins, Abram C., NC
Hopper, Harry C., IL
Horn, Harry Y., PA
Hough, Thomas A., PA
Howard, Randolph N., IN
Howell, Richard L., PA
Hoy, William S., WV
Hoyt, Theodore E., PA
Hudders, John S., PA
Ibach, Frederick G., PA
Irwin, William B., PA
Jacob, Harry, PA
Jamison, William A., PA
Jayne, Calvin K., PA
Jessup, Samuel A.S., PA
Johnson, Samuel C., PA
Johnston, John P., PA
Kilborn, Harvey B., PA
Kilburn, Frank, NEW BRUNSWICK
King, George P., PA
Kirkpatrick, M. Baldwin, IL
Kistler, James K., PA
Kneedler, William L., PA
Knox, Samuel D., OH
Koons, Philip R., PA
Kram, George W., PA
Larimer, William T., PA
Lawrance, Edward Stuart, PA
Lee, Bernard R., PA
Lichliter, David C., VA
MacCord, George Thornton, PA
MacDonald, John, PRINCE EDWARD ISLAND
Martin, Aaron, PA
McAninch, David L., PA
McCallister, Charles H., IN

Fig. 100. Howard F. Hansell (JMC, 1879), Chairman of Ophthalmology (1902-1925).

McClellan, R. Miller, PA
McClure, Frank E., VT
McComb, Samuel F., PA
McEwen, Charles M., PA
McGehee, Daniel M., MS
McGogney, Samuel, PA
McMullen, John C., PA
McNichol, Edgar, MA
Middleton, William J., PA
Mitchell, Edmund H., PA
Montgomery, James E., PA
Murray, Thomas J., TN
Musgrove, Charles W., PA
Neiman, Howard Y., PA
Nes, Henry, PA
Nicodemus, John D., MD
Nonamaker, Noah S., PA
Orr, Samuel M., SC

Otway, David B., WEST INDIES
Page, Dudley L., MA
Paine, William A., PA
Peairs, Elisha P., PA
Pershing, Frank S., PA
Pierce, George L., CA
Pigman, Samuel C., PA
Poffenberger, Albert T., PA
Potsdamer, Joseph B., PA
Pownall, Howard W., PA
Price, Allen D., PA
Price, Joseph H., PA
Pricer, William E., OH
Pringle, William W., OH
Rambo, Samuel M., PA
Reynolds, John M.C., PA
Rhoads, George H., PA
Righter, William H., DE

Fig. 101. New Laboratory Building (on right) opened in 1879 at corner of Tenth and Sansom Streets, a site previously occupied by two stores.

1879

Rinehart, Willard E., OR
Rodman, William L., KY
Rose, Archimedes, U.S. ARMY
Scates, Dan W., TN
Schaeffer, Uriah R., PA
Schellinger, Clarence M., NJ
Scroggs, Gustavus A., OH
Seaman, Dean, NY
Seibert, George W., PA
Sheardown, T. Winton, MN
Shirk, John K., PA
Shriner, Charles H., PA
Smith, Harris K., PA
Smith, Charles S., OH
Spragg, Sylvanus L.S., PA
Sprowls, Isaac Newton, PA
Stapp, James T., AL
Stewart, Francis Edward, NY
Stewart, David D., PA
Strohecker, James T., PA
Tharp, William S., MO
Throop, George S., PA

Tice, Frederic L.C., MD
Tomlinson, Thomas C., DE
Torbert, Enos G., PA
Torrence, D. Rogers, PA
Vega, Francisco, CENTRAL AMERICA
Wallace, Ellerslie, Jr., PA
Wallen, Seely, NJ
Ward, George Mason, PA
Waters, John, AR
Way, Eugene, NJ
Weiser, George B., Jr., PA
Weiss, Louis, CO
Whitaker, James S., MD
Whitney, Edward M., MA
Wiley, S. Nelson, PA
Wilson, H. Augustus, PA
Winslow, Byron, PA
Witting, Anthony P., KY
Woodruff, George, NH
Worsley, Edward A., VA
Wright, J. Edward, PA
Yard, John L., PA
Zeiner, Levi S., PA

There is no short cut, nor "royal road," to the attainment of medical knowledge. The path which we have to pursue is long, difficult, and unsafe. In our progress, we must frequently take up our abode with death and corruption; we must adopt loathsome diseases for our familiar associates, or we shall never be thoroughly acquainted with their nature and dispositions; we must risk, nay even injure, our own health in order to be able to preserve or restore that of others.

John Abernathy (1764-1831)

At the Commencement, held March 13 at the Academy of Music, 196 members of the class were awarded the M.D. degree. The Valedictory Address was delivered by Robert E. Rogers, Professor of Medical Chemistry and Toxicology. Seven of these graduates joined with Dr. Joseph Potsdamer (JMC, 1879) to honor James Aitken Meigs, their Professor of the Institutes of Medicine (Physiology), who had died suddenly on November 9 of the previous year. The J. Aitken Meigs Medical Association was founded with the purpose "to continue and strengthen the bonds of friendship formed during student life and to promote that social and intellectual condition becoming the profession." The graduates of this class who co-founded the Association were all serious students who maintained their interest in it until the time of their deaths (Fig. 102). After 110 years, the Association still flourishes as another of Jefferson's proud traditions. Brief remarks about the founders are warranted.

Edwin Rosenthal at graduation won the gold medal provided by Thomas G. Morton for his report on the Morton Surgical Clinic at the Pennsylvania Hospital. He also received honorable mention for the best graduation thesis and honorable mention for the best report of the Levis Surgical Clinic at the Pennsylvania Hospital. From 1885 to 1889 he was an Assistant Demonstrator of Chemistry at Jefferson and in 1888 opened a Skin Clinic at Jefferson along with Professor James W. Holland. He specialized in pediatrics and served as Chairman of the Section on Diseases of Children of the American Medical Association in 1900. He contributed more than 50 scientific articles to the literature and was active in the important professional societies of his time. He was the first of the founders to die (at age 54 in 1912).

Lewis W. Steinbach at graduation won the gold medal for the best report of the Levis Surgical Clinic at the Pennsylvania Hospital. Immediately after graduation he associated himself with Dr. Lawrence Turnbull at Jefferson in the Ear Clinic and rose to become the Chief of this Clinic. He aided William Smith Forbes at Jefferson in gaining passage of the amended and improved State Anatomical Law by the Legislature and continued as an active member of the State Anatomical Board. First as Chief of the Clinic in the Department of Surgery of the Philadelphia Polyclinic and College for Graduates in Medicine, he subsequently rose to the position of Professor in that institution. He also was Chief of Surgery at the old Jewish Hospital (now Einstein, Northern Division).

Max H. Bochroch became an Instructor in Electrotherapeutics at Jefferson (1885-1900) and Instructor in Diseases of the Mind and Nervous Diseases (1901-06). Specializing in neuropsychiatry, he became neurologist to St. Joseph's and the Jewish Hospital, and subsequently Professor of Psychiatry at Temple University School of Medicine.

Louis Jurist after graduation became Assistant to Professor Jacob Solis-Cohen in his Laryngological clinic at Jefferson and became Chief Clinical Assistant from 1892 to 1894. During the same years he was also Instructor in Laryngology in the regular academic session of Jefferson Medical College, as well as remaining an active member of the Philadelphia Laryngological Society.

Alexander H.S. De Young at graduation won honorable mention for the best essay on a subject pertaining to Physiology, his thesis being *Physiology of the Sympathetic Nervous System*. He remained a successful practitioner in Philadelphia along with his two other Meigs Medical Association founding classmates, Henry H. Freund (first President, 1880) and Conrad R. Bready.

Dr. Joseph Potsdamer, the eighth founder (from the Class of 1879), served as Secretary of the Association for many years (until 1941 at age 82) and died in 1947 at age 88 as the last surviving founding member.

Fig. 102.   Founders of James Aitken Meigs Medical Association in 1880.

1880

Alexander, James H., TN
Allen, Charles L., PA
Ames, Robert P.M., MA
Anderson, Edward Lane, PA
Angell, Charles E., IN
Ard, Wilson P., PA
Baird, Alexander B., KY
Baker, Harry B., MA
Baldwin, J. Marion, PA
Barclay, William H., PA
Barry, William M., TX
Barton, George C., PA
Batman, William F., IN
Beatty, Thomas J., PA
Benninger, Amandus A., PA
Bliss, Gerald C.W., NEW BRUNSWICK
Board, John C., VA
Bochroch, Max H., PA
Braden, Leroy, PA
Brainard, Medad P., OH
Bready, Conrad R., PA
Bricker, Charles E., PA
Bright, John W., PA
Brundage, Emerson K., PA
Burwell, John P., VA
Caldwell, Frank H., GA
Cameron, Norris, PA
Carroll, Edgar, OH
Caterson, William H., PA
Charlton, Alonzo P., PA
Clark, Frank A., PA
Cline, Charles H., NJ
Cline, James C., PA
Cochran, William G., IL
Coley, Andrew J., AL
Conwell, Joseph A., DE
Coulter, Benjamin F., PA
Cramer, David C., PA
Crandall, Charles R., PA
Cunningham, Dewees, PA
Cunningham, Abelard V., PA
Dalsen, Charles M., PA
Davidson, Charles C., PA
Davis, James G., PA
Decker, Corben, J., NJ
DeVore, Henry V., IN
DeWitt, John H, IL
DeYoung, A. Henriques, PA
Dock, Clifford, PA
Donnan, Edmund A., PA
Doyle, Charles F., PA
Ferguson, William A., KS

Fetherolf, James A., PA
Fiedler, Daniel W., PA
Fonseca, Antonio M., BRAZIL
Foster, Rufus M., TN
Frankhouser, Fremont W., PA
Frankish, Joseph, PA
Freund, Henry H., PA
Fulton, Thomas Chalmers, PA
Furry, Samuel E., PA
Gardner, Herbert D., PA
Garrison, Daniel, NJ
Godey, Harry, PA
Goodman, William R., PA
Gratiot, Charles C., CA
Grayson, Charles M.P., PA
Greene, Frank C., NJ
Gregg, Albert E., PA
Grim, Bladen S., PA
Groff, James E., PA
Grove, Aaron B., PA
Hafley, Lewis A., PA
Halbert, Francis M., MS
Hallowell, Charles E., PA
Halsey, Luther M., NJ
Hardister, Nathan G., AR
Harman, George G., PA
Hartman, Harry Y., PA
Hawk, William A., PA
Hecht, John P., PA
Heffner, Charles W., OH
Heiser, Edwin S., PA
Hepburn, John, Jr., NJ
Herff, Adolph C., TX
Hershey, Emanuel R., PA
Hillegass, Eugene Z., PA
Hoffman, John Y., PA
Hollingsworth, John B., NC
Hood, Thomas M., WV
Houston, Isaac N., PA
Hubbard, J. Clark, MA
Hudders, Clarence, NJ
Janney, William S., PA
Jurist, Louis, PA
Keeler, Joseph P., PA
Keelor, Vincent Z., PA
Kempton, Augustus, PA
Kennedy, James S., PA
Kimmell, Harry S., PA
King, Eugene P., RI
Kinnier, Robert Gray, VA
Klipstein, George T., VA
Knecht, Cyrus, PA

Knowles, Henry B., PA
Koontz, John W., VA
Kurtz, J. Ellis, PA
Langton, Daniel J., PA
Leberknight, Daniel C., PA
Leech, William W., PA
Lesher, David T., PA
Lockard, Daniel H., IL
Loman, Matthew F., PA
Masser, Frank B., PA
McKinley, Lucien, PA
Miller, D. Warren, IL
Mitchell, Charles L., PA
Mitchell, John T., MO
Montgomery, James R., PA
Morales, Jose M., NICARAGUA
Moser, Ira D., PA
Muelheims, Robert, IL
Musser, C. Sumner, PA
Myers, Herschel S., IN
Neale, Henry M., CT
Nelson, Frank W., VA
Nelson, H. W., OH
Newton, Frederick G., PA
Nicklin, John, OR
North, James, NJ
Odbert, Frank N., PA
Ono, Shunji, JAPAN
Ormsbee, Richard S., OH
Phillips, George S., PA
Plummer, Amos Weston, ME
Pollock, Stephen D., IL
Ramsaur, G. Alexander, NC
Reagan, Robert S., PA
Reed, Charles, PA
Reed, William E., PA
Reger, Robert A., WV
Riley, Edward W., KS
Ringwalt, Martin, PA
Robinson, Charles E., AR
Rodgers, Daniel R., WV
Rosenthal, Edwin, PA
Samuel, Edmund W., PA
Scott, James W.C., IN
Seagle, Edwin H., NC
Sharpless, B. Frank, PA

Sheaff, Charles G., PA
Sheilds, Edgar A., IN
Sherman, James S., MO
Shope, Jacob W., PA
Shriver, J. Milton, PA
Silva, Joseph C.P., BRAZIL
Smith, Jacob H., PA
Snoddy, Lot J., KS
Sockman, Henry A., OH
Steck, John M., MD
Steinbach, Lewis W., PA
Stephens, James T., TX
Sterrett, Samuel J.O., PA
Stevens, Atherton B., PA
Stevenson, Robley D., IN
Stewart, James M., PA
Stirling, Samuel R., PA
Stone, Lewis P., PA
Strayer, Jacob P., PA
Strobel, John, Jr., PA
Stuart, Richard H., Jr., VA
Swallow, Edward E., MA
Thompson, John Calvin, PA
Tobin, Hugh L., KY
Todd, Alonzo R., DE
Uhler, Sydenham P., PA
Vest, William, IA
Walter, Eyer, PA
Weatherley, T. Ogden, PA
Weeks, Albert, NJ
Weeks, Carlile B., NJ
Weisel, Adolph, NC
Welsh, Horace G., OH
Wert, John M., PA
Westcott, Frank W., NJ
Wiley, Robert B.M., NEW BRUNSWICK
Wilkinson, George W., PA
Wolff, Lawrence, PA
Wolford, M. Luther, PA
Wood, Irving C., NY
Wood, George H., PA
York, George W., CANADA
Yost, B. Myers, PA
Young, Thomas O., PA
Zieber, Edward S., PA
Ziegler, William H., PA

1880

In 1881 the Grecian facade of the College (Ely Building) was replaced by one of florid Victorian design to conform with that of the new Laboratory Building at the corner of Tenth and Sansom Streets. This allowed a frontal extension whereby the seating capacity of the lecture rooms was increased. Also, a new story was added to accommodate extra laboratory rooms (Fig. 103). The graduating class of this year numbered 205.

Jacob E. Shadle, a native of Pennsylvania, practiced in Shenandoah, Pennsylvania, for six years following graduation but soon became interested in the diseases of the nose and throat, studying with Dr. Charles E. Sajous (Fig. 95) of the Jefferson Faculty. In 1887 he relocated in St. Paul, Minnesota, where he pursued his specialty and in 1896 was appointed to the faculty in Laryngology at the University of Minnesota. He be-

came a full Professor of Rhinology and Laryngology in 1897. The same year he was Chairman of the American Laryngological, Rhinological, and Otological Association. He contributed many articles and devised several instruments for nose and throat surgery.

Isidor P. Strittmatter is well remembered for his medical and social philanthropy during his many years of practice in Philadelphia (Fig. 104). Dr. Strittmatter was a leader in organized medicine and a past President of the Philadelphia County Medical Society. In 1923 he established the Strittmatter Award providing a scroll and a gold medal for the physician selected by a committee of the County Society each year for meritorious service and a valuable contribution to the healing art. A number of Jefferson alumni have been recipients of the award.

Fig. 103.   Renovation of Medical Hall in 1881 replacing the Grecian facade with one of florid Victorian style.

Apeldorn, Ernest F., PA
Arbuthnot, Charles M., KS
Artis, Leopoldo L., CUBA
Bachman, Charles W., PA
Beers, Frank, PA
Bennett, Jacob E., NJ
Bibby, Walter E., OH
Blaine, James M., PA
Bley, George, Jr., IL
Bolin, J. Albert, IL
Botkin, Louis C., PA
Breisch, Richard R., PA
Brockway, Dudley S., AL
Brown, Robert L.P., WV
Brown, William W., PA
Brubaker, Isaac P., PA
Bruns, Henry Dickson, LA
Bullock, Lawrence M., NJ
Burwell, William N., VA
Camblos, Henry F., PA
Campbell, Harry Edgar, PA
Campbell, George N., KY
Carlton, James M., GA
Cavins, Samuel R., IN
Chance, H. Martyn, PA
Clark, Charles F., OH
Clark, Lemuel E., CANADA
Clemens, Frank L., PA
Cohen, Morris S., PA
Cole, James W., PA
Coltman, Robert, Jr., DC
Cox, Silas W., NC
Crispin, Samuel D., NJ
Daman, Charles N., PA
Davenport, William H., IN
Davis, Lewis E., PA
DeGrandchamp, F. Pinal, FRANCE
DeLannoy, Clarence W., PA
Dennis, David N., MA
Dill, Mahlon B., PA
Dodds, Archibald J., SYRIA
Dodson, William E., PA
Dowkontt, George D., ENGLAND
Doyle, William J., PA
Doyle, George W., MO
Dravo, Louis H., PA
Early, Lewis Mortimer, OH
Eastman, Thomas N., PA
Edwards, G. Hiram, KY
Edwards, John B., WI
Ellegood, Joshua A., DE
Farrow, Howard F., KY

Flagg, Herbert Horatio, MA
Frankish, John K., PA
Gaston, William F., PA
Gibson, William C., GA
Gilmer, Mauricio W., BRAZIL
Grim, F. Harvey, PA
Grimes, William J., VA
Haas, Richard P., PA
Hain, David H., PA
Hamilton, John W., PA
Harden, Benjamin F., NY
Harrington, Edwin I., NY
Hassinger, G. Edgar, PA
Hatfield, Henry R., PA
Heacock, Stacy L., PA
Heard, John H., GA
Heller, Jacob A., PA
Hickman, William H., PA

Fig. 104. Isidore Phillip Strittmatter (JMC, 1881), leader in organized medicine and a President of the Philadelphia County Medical Society. In 1923 he established the Strittmatter Award for meritorious service and valuable contribution to the healing art. (Photo courtesy of Historical Collections of College of Physicians of Philadelphia.)

Hill, J. Willis, PA
Hoffman, James A., PA
Hoffman, John Hugo, NY
Hoke, Martin, PA
Holman, Albert, PA
Howell, John T., PA
Hughes, Henry A., TX
Hurff, Joseph E., NJ
Hurlock, Frank I., PA
Husler, Edward G., PA
Johnston, A. Russell, PA
Johnston, Marion A., IN
Jones, David T., WALES
Kahn, Alexander, PA
Kalloch, Parker C., ME
Kelly, Frank P., PA
Kiernan, James O'H., PA
Kilduffe, Robert O., PA
Koons, John H., PA
Kotz, Adam L., PA
Lambking, William, PA
Lane, James A., KS
Lawrence, Henry Roscoe, NJ
Loughlin, Dennis J., PA
Love, Louis F., PA
Lowman, Alonzo, PA
Lowright, J. Harvey, PA
Luff, Jefferson M., DE
Maghee, William H., IN
Marquardt, Carl Heinrich, WI
Martin, William J., PA
Martin, J. Charles, OH
Maxwell, David P., OH
May, James C., PA
May, John F., VA
McCandless, William C., PA
McClenathan, John C., PA
McCorkle, J. Macon, NC
McCurdy, William H., PA
McKay, Alexander P., NOVA SCOTIA
McLean, John, MN
McMahon, John, CA
Meek, James A., IN
Merritt, Arthur F., MO
Midence, Juan B., NICARAGUA
Million, Edward A., IL
Moffet, David, PA
Mohr, Eugene H., PA
Moore, John C., TN
Murray, Frank, PA
Neely, Henderson J., PA
Norris, Henry L., PA
Northington, S. Sterling, VA
Oldshue, James A., PA

Oppermann, Richard F.W., PA
Palm, Howard F., PA
Papin, F. Sidney, IA
Payne, Robert Lee, Jr., NC
Pearson, Benjamin F., PA
Peat, Edward, OH
Peck, Henry T., PA
Pennington, Byron C., NY
Peter, Robert, OH
Pickford, William H., PA
Pisor, Oliver P., PA
Pitts, Francis M., Jr., TX
Pratt, Charles, MI
Purman, John, PA
Raker, Frederick D., PA
Reemsnyder, Henry G., PA
Robinson, George S., PA
Rodgers, Reuben F., PA
Rogers, L. Leonidas, PA
Rohrer, Thaddeus M., PA
Sayers, Warren A., OH
Schwarz, Louis, PA
Scott, Charles J., WV
Seybert, Frank T., PA
Shadle, Jacob E., PA
Sharp, Robert C., PA
Sheaffer, Peter F., PA
Shimmin, James, ISLE OF MAN
Sibbald, James, PA
Singer, Lewis U., OH
Singley, Charles C., PA
Slayden, William M., TN
Smiley, Edwin R., PA
Smith, Dennis F., PA
Smith, Thomas A., GA
Smith, Thomas B., VA
Sombart, John E., MO
Spangler, Charles F., PA
Spedding, Robert D., CA
Stanton, James G., PA
Stearnes, James D., VA
Stewart, William F., OH
Stewart, Samuel C., PA
Stoner, George W., U.S. MARINE HOSPITAL SERVICE
Stout, George W., PA
Strange, Warren W., PA
Strittmatter, Isidore P., PA
Suarez del Villar, Jose R., CUBA
Taylor, Edward Winslow, PA
Taylor, Hugh L., TX
Taylor, Samuel M., AR
Thatcher, Henry K., ME
Thomas, John J., PA
Thomas, Edwin R., PA

1881

177

Thompson, John O., KS
Thorington, James, Jr., IA
Torbert, John S., PA
Troxell, Thomas S., PA
Tuthill, Harry S., NY
Ullrich, Seth S., PA
VanAntwerp, Eugene H., NY
Wagner, William H., PA
Walker, Alonzo B., OH
Wallace, William Sampson, OH
Wallace, Samuel J., ME
Walter, Harry B., PA
Ward, John S., PA

Washburn, Aquila A., IN
Watt, James Smith, PA
Wetmore, George T., CT
White, James Leon, NJ
Wilhite, Joseph Oliver, SC
Williams, Howard J., GA
Wilson, Abram S., NJ
Wilson, S. Howard, PA
Witmer, Isaac M., PA
Witmer, Cassius M., IN
Woodburn, John M., KS
Wright, Henry J.B., IL
Wright, John L., GA
Yundt, Alfred M., IN

MEDICAL ELECTRICITY:

A PRACTICAL TREATISE

OF THE

APPLICATIONS OF ELECTRICITY TO MEDICINE AND SURGERY.

BY

ROBERTS BARTHOLOW, A.M., M.D., LL.D.,

PROFESSOR OF MATERIA MEDICA AND GENERAL THERAPEUTICS IN THE JEFFERSON MEDICAL
COLLEGE OF PHILADELPHIA;
FELLOW OF THE COLLEGE OF PHYSICIANS OF PHILADELPHIA;
MEMBER OF THE AMERICAN PHILOSOPHICAL SOCIETY;
HONORARY MEMBER OF THE MEDICAL AND CHIRURGICAL FACULTY OF MARYLAND,
OF THE OHIO STATE MEDICAL SOCIETY, OF THE CINCINNATI ACADEMY OF
MEDICINE, AND OF THE NEW YORK NEUROLOGICAL SOCIETY;
PRESIDENT OF THE AMERICAN NEUROLOGICAL ASSOCIATION;
AUTHOR OF "A PRACTICAL TREATISE ON MATERIA MEDICA AND THERAPEUTICS," AND OF
"A TREATISE ON THE PRACTICE OF MEDICINE," ETC.

WITH NINETY-SIX ILLUSTRATIONS.

PHILADELPHIA:
HENRY C. LEA'S SON & CO.
1881.

Roberts Bartholow, M.D., Professor of Materia Medica (1879-91).

Change in emphasis as medicine advanced is shown by gradual albeit subtle changes in the titles of theses submitted by the 247 graduates of this class. Infectious diseases are more frequently discussed as well as subjects brought to light through physiologic and metabolic discoveries. Also a number of titles indicate increasing interest in surgical procedures. The "rest cure" promoted by Dr. S. Weir Mitchell perhaps is reflected in the thesis of John K. Blanck, *Rest as a Curative Agent*. Horace G. Hill discussed *The Germ Theory in its Relation to Preventive Medicine*. A more general new departure was reflected by Herbert M. Seem's title *Scientific Medicine*. Frank E. Wilson wrote about *Lung Exercises in Certain Pulmonary Diseases*. Seem's thesis was awarded the gold medal and Wilson's received honorable mention. The increasing sophistication of the subjects of the theses became more readily apparent as the decade advanced. These forward-looking efforts were given unexpected prescience this year by the April publication of Robert Koch describing his isolation of the tubercle bacillus

The retirement of Professor Samuel D. Gross and the death of Joseph Pancoast in 1882 signaled the end of an era that had been marked by the triumvirate of Dunglison, Pancoast and Gross. The Gross retirement required "two pegs to fill one hole," namely the appointment of John Hill Brinton and Samuel W. Gross as successors in the now-divided Chair of Surgery.

The Annual Announcement for 1882 describes an increasing emphasis on the clinical aspects of medicine. It indicates the "ample material of the daily clinic" and states that "each student will be made familiar with bedside practice." Also the devotion of a number of hours to "clinical conferences" is mentioned with students being assigned to examine the patients for presentation beforehand.

Francis W. Shain, of Pennsylvania, may be singled out as a benefactor to needy students of his alma mater. He practiced successfully in Jersey City, New Jersey, and died prematurely in 1896 of heart disease at the age of 45. In his will he bequeathed $4,000 to establish and maintain two free scholarships to be competed for by graduates of any public school in Philadelphia. The examination included English composition and literature, mathematics, physics, chemistry, and any two of Latin, French or German. An additional $3,000 was left in trust for prizes at graduation for the best examinations in medicine, surgery and physiology.

John Robert Robinson in addition to his medical practice took an active interest in government and municipal affairs in Colorado Springs (Fig. 105). He served two terms as Mayor of Colorado Springs, was elected President of the League of Colorado Municipalities and Vice-President of the Colorado Good Roads Association.

James Crawford Reinhart became Professor of Anatomy in the Northwestern Ohio Medical College, Toledo, Ohio, for five years, and for two subsequent years was Professor of Materia Medica and Therapeutics in the same institution (Figure 106).

Samuel Otway Lewis Potter graduated at the head of this very large class. In 1891 he took the degree of Member of the Royal College of Physicians of London, England. As an author of international reputation he wrote and compiled many books, one of his best being the textbook on *Materia Medica, Pharmacy and Therapeutics*. For a number of years he was Professor of Medicine in Cooper Medical College, San Francisco.

Adam, George, CA
Ahbrah, BURMA
Althouse, Samuel M., PA
Ammond, Henry M., PA
Anderson, Frank T., PA
Anderson, George Randall, NJ
Atlee, Louis William, PA
Aulde, John, Jr., MI
Austin, Arthur, VA
Bailey, John A., IL
Baker, James E., WI
Ballantine, Charles H., PA
Barber, Walter, PA
Barnett, Benjamin M., OH
Barrall, Alfred, PA
Barrington, Richard C., NJ
Batton, John A., PA
Baugh, John E., TN

Bean, John W., OR
Beans, Samuel T., NJ
Becker, John N., PA
Belville, J. Edgar, PA
Bergstresser, Edwin, PA
Bigelow, Charles E., CT
Blakey, Thomas, KY
Blanck, John K., PA
Bolton, William T., CT
Bourne, George W., ME
Bowcock, Charles M., WV
Bower, John F., PA
Bower, Albert S., IN
Bowers, Moses K., PA
Boyd, John Samuel, PA
Brinton, Lewis, PA
Brobst, Daniel B., PA
Browning, Claude H., PA

Fig. 105. John Robert Robinson (JMC, 1882) took an active interest in government, leading to his becoming Mayor of Colorado Springs and President of the League of Colorado Municipalities.

Fig. 106. James Crawford Reinhart (JMC, 1882), Professor of Anatomy and subsequently Professor of Materia Medica and Therapeutics in Northwestern Ohio Medical College.

Bryan, Henry Hugh, KY
Bryan, Robert E., WV
Buckingham, John M., OH
Byles, Frederick G., PA
Byram, Claude M., KS
Cabada, Ysidoro F., CUBA
Callmann, Sallo, PA
Campbell, Taylor A., MO
Clark, Isaac E., TX
Clausen, Joseph Roberts, PA
Clifford, Edward M., PA
Cochran, Edward G., TX
Connolly, Henry, CANADA
Corbett, Vander K., PA
Costner, Thomas F., NC
Cottrell, Samuel P., RI
Crawford, John J., PA
Crowell, Godfrey M., AUSTRALIA
Dalsen, Charles W., PA
Darrow, Frank L., IA
Davidson, Samuel S., PA
Davison, Willis T., PA
Davisson, Edward Clinton, OH
De Jesi, Luigi M., ITALY
Dearth, Olie P., PA
Devine, George C., PA
Douglas, Richard, TN
Douglass, Charles E., NY
Downs, Isaac M., NJ
Drysdale, William Atlee, PA
Dyson, William W., PA
Eames, George F., ME
Eareckson, Edwin, PA
Ellis, Samuel C., NOVA SCOTIA
Ely, J. Dawes, NJ
Ely, Richard H., PA
Everett, Edward S., MA
Everett, Henry E., PA
Ewen, Warren L., NJ
Ewing, Francis M., IL
Ford, Walter A., ME
Foulkes, John Franklin, CA
Fox, C. Willard, PA
Fox, William Harkins, PA
Franklin, James S., MEXICO
Fretz, Oliver H., PA
Frye, Hamilton R., PA
Furgerson, Henry B., NC
Gardner, Edward R., PA
Gassaway, James M., U.S. MARINE HOSPITAL SERVICE
Geary, Edward P., OR
Getter, John P., PA
Giesy, Andrew J., OR
Gillingham, Harvey, PA

Glover, Lawrence L., NJ
Gordon, Eugene C., TX
Gosewisch, Charles Theodore, MO
Green, DeWitt C., IL
Green, M. Henry, PA
Gunter, John B., NC
Guzman, Horacio, NICARAGUA
Haas, John, LA
Haislip, George W., VA
Hale, William H., PA
Hallman, John S., PA
Hammond, Thomas V., MD
Harman, L. Cooper, PA
Harmer, James B., PA
Harrington, Arthur H., MA
Hartmann, John J., CUBA
Hastings, William J., PA
Hawkins, William E., LA
Hawley, Benjamin F., Jr., CT
Hazlett, Joshua D., PA
Herrero, J. Augustine, PUERTO RICO
Hill, Luther L., AL
Hill, Horace G., PA
Hirsh, A. Bern, PA
Holbert, Walter W., PA
Hollenback, David S., PA
Holmes, Thomas M., GA
Hopkins, Howard R., MD
Horwitz, Lloyd N., PA
Hunt, James Lemoin, PA
Ilyus, Edmund B., PA
Jamison, James L., PA
Jauss, Christian E., PA
Johnson, William A., ME
Jordan, H. Frank, MS
Keely, Robert N., Jr., PA
Keever, Adolphus P., NC
Kevin, Robert O., PA
Kline, Effenger R., PA
Kline, John Edward, PA
Koder, Charles A., PA
Kohler, Frederick W., PA
Lane, Dudley W., PA
Lantelme, Charles, GERMANY
Lantz, William O., PA
Lawrance, Josiah Randall, PA
Leaman, Rosh, PA
Leaming, Walter S., NJ
Lehman, Jacob R., PA
Lejarza, Jose Dolores, NICARAGUA
Lisle, Justin D., OH
Livingood, Horace F., PA
Long, Charles, PA
Longino, Thomas Dick, GA

Loux, Hiram R., PA
Lowber, Alexander, DE
Lowery, Welles James, PA
Lyle, John W., PA
Macauley, C. N.B., MA
Maclay, John, IL
Mahon, John B., PA
Mann, George Wagner, PA
Markoe, James C., MN
Marsh, James D., PA
Marsillan, Carlos J., CUBA
Mathiot, Edward B., PA
Matten, William H., PA
Mattern, William Kline, PA
McClintock, Will H., PA
McCombs, William, Jr., PA
McCormick, Daniel R., PA
McCranor, Charles D., MO
McNary, Oliver C., KS
McQueen, Charles A.S., CANADA
Mehard, George H., PA
Melchonian, A. John, ARMENIA
Melhorn, David H., PA
Mentzer, John F., PA
Miller, John W., IL
Miller, William, PA
Miller, John Sebastian, PA
Moore, Jason H., KS
Myers, John Milton, PA
Nevins, William, PA
Norris, William J., PA
O'Callaghan, Daniel, IRELAND
Ogle, William Matthews, DE
Ott, Lyman E., IN
Palmer, Thomas D., IL
Patterson, James A., NJ
Paxson, Oric H., PA
Pemberton, Charles, NJ
Person, Sylvanus, NE
Pickens, Winfield S., IN
Pollard, William M., ME
Posey, Mordecai A., PA
Post, Silas B., PA
Potter, Samuel Otway, WI
Powell, William Niles, PA
Power, Edward S., MD
Preston, William B., PA
Pursell, John C., NJ
Rainear, A. Rusling, PA
Reed, Willoughby H., PA
Reichard, V. Milton, MD

Reid, Hugh, KY
Reinhart, J. Crawford, OH
Rittenhouse, George S., PA
Rixey, Alfred S., VA
Robinson, George J., NC
Robinson, John R., NY
Roussell, Albert E., PA
Sands, J. Seldon, PA
Sawhill, William F., PA
Scott, Frederick, MA
Scott, Horace B., CT
Seem, Herbert M., PA
Seitz, John L., PA
Service, Charles A., PA
Shain, Francis W., PA
Short, James C., PA
Smith, Edward Hamilton, KY
Snowden, Charles C., NE
Sperry, Edward L., OH
Sprowls, Lee M., PA
Stealey, Jeremiah H., IL
Stevens, James A., NOVA SCOTIA
Stevenson, Andrew L., NE
Stewart, John J., PA
Stewart, Robert Reed, PA
Stidger, Samuel B., WV
Stine, John B., PA
Strickland, James T., NC
Thompson, John A., Jr., PA
Turner, John B., PA
Urich, Isaac K., PA
Usilton, C. Alfred, PA
VanBuskirk, Henry F., OH
Walker, Samuel E., PA
Ward, Stanley M., NY
Warner, Ellwood B., PA
Warren, James T., MO
Weber, Charles Z., PA
Weirich, Colin R., PA
Weldman, J. Clayton, PA
Welsh, Elmer E., OH
Whitfield, Charles L., TX
Wightman, John G., PA
Williams, Lester, OH
Willits, Charles C., PA
Wilson, Charles Meigs, PA
Wilson, Albert R., NC
Wilson, Frank E., NY
Woodburn, Samuel S., PA
Worstall, Samuel A., PA
Young, Junius D., CA
Zulch, Gustav, OH

Prominent among the 227 graduates was Solomon Solis-Cohen, a member of a distinguished Philadelphia family, who went on to a long and respected career in the teaching and practice of medicine (Fig. 107). Dr. Solis-Cohen joined the Jefferson teaching staff early and progressed to Professor of Clinical Medicine, ultimately becoming Emeritus Professor in 1927. He was a noted consultant both privately and at local hospitals but also served in many learned, cultural and scientific capacities, reflecting his superior intellectual stature. He was President of the Philadelphia County Medical Society in 1898 to 1899 and edited important medical publications. Honors included the degree of Doctor of Science from Jefferson (1933) and from Philadelphia College of Pharmacy and Science (1939), and Doctor of Hebrew Literature from the Jewish Theological Seminary of America (1928). He died at age 90 in 1948.

Orville Horwitz at the Commencement ceremonies on April 2, 1883, was awarded a gold medal for the best essay on a subject (Diphtheria) pertaining to the Practice of Medicine. Dr. Horwitz served as a Jefferson intern for a year and went on to a three-year residency at the Pennsylvania Hospital. His association with Jefferson continued through 1912, beginning in anatomy and surgery with Drs. W. W. Keen and S.W. Gross. His urological experiences began with the younger Gross, and in 1894 he was appointed Clinical Professor, advancing to full Professor and first Chairman upon the establishment of the Department of Genito-Urinary Surgery in 1904 (Fig. 108). His career ended with his death in 1913 at age 53.

Charles B. Nancrede, after serving as a surgeon on the staff of Jefferson Hospital, became a distinguished Professor of Surgery in the University of Michigan School of Medicine, Ann Arbor. Besides his reputation as a great clinician and skilled surgeon, he was scholarly in the principles of surgery, and his book on that subject remained long popular.

Fig. 107. Solomon Solis-Cohen (JMC, 1883), Professor of Clinical Medicine (1904-27) and pioneer in treatment of "rheumatic disorders."

CLASS OF 1883

Allen, Henry B., KS
Altounian Z. Melkon, TURKEY
Applegate, William S., NJ
Auffurth, William A., PA
Baldwin, Henry, Jr., OH
Bartleson, Randall N., PA
Beamensderfer, John S., PA

Beitenman, Charles A., PA
Biehl, Jefferson P., PA
Bigelow, Frederick F., MA
Black, James B., PA
Blose, George Alvin, PA
Boyers, James S., WV
Brenton, Willis, PA

Brotherlin, H. Hale, PA
Brown, J. Ewing, IA
Bush, Irvine R., PA
Butcher, Joseph, NJ
Canova, Matthew J., FL
Carothers, William H., ME
Carpenter, John Alfred, JAMAICA
Clark, Henry S., MA
Cobleigh, Bennett J., PA
Coffman, James W., AR
Cohen, Solomon-Solis, PA
Cope, Albert B., OH
Cope, Leidy L., PA
Copeland, Benjamin G., AL
Cox, Harry O., NJ
Cracraft, C. Clinton, PA
Crise, Blair F., PA
Darling, Herbert S., OH
Davis, Thomas E., PA
Dickey, John L., WV
Dodson, John Milton, WI
Donnelly, Ignatius C., MN

Dorr, Henry I., MA
Dorsey, George L., IN
Drueding, Frank F., PA
Dwyer, Charles H., PA
Ellis, Dean Samuel, MA
Epler, John William, IL
Ewen, Jonathan H., NJ
Fahey, John C., PA
Farley, Joseph, PA
Ferguson, William M., Jr., OH
Fessler, Henry H., PA
Finney, Charles Joseph, IN
Fisher, Nicholas K., PA
Flinn, Irvine Moore, DE
Flinn, Lewis Wesley, DE
Fogerty, William C., MA
Foster, B. Douglas, OH
Frank, George S., PA
Franklin, Thomas Y., MD
Frey, Robert S., PA
Fullmer, Charles L., PA
Fullton, Henry D., PA
Furey, Edward M., PA
Gabbert, Ira T., MO
Garcia, Augustine M., CUBA
Garver, A. Lincoln, PA
Gesner, Van, OR
Glass, Barney J., TX
Gray, Eb N., TX
Gregory, John A., PA
Hackett, John C., Jr., MD
Haldeman, J. Henry, KS
Hale, George V., MA
Hall, William M., PA
Hammond, J. Hill, GA
Harriman, Samuel K., MA
Harrison, James N., PA
Hartman, Marcellus T., MO
Harwood, Charles W., MA
Heagey, Henry F.C., PA
Herbert, J. Frederick, PA
Hershey, M. Landis, PA
Hertel, Emil, DE
Heysham, Stewart Charles, PA
Higbee, William S., PA
Hill, Russell S., PA
Hoffman, Ripley C., IA
Hoffmann, Joseph H., PA
Holden, Newell E., PA
Holton, Henry C., IL
Horwitz, Orville, PA
Hottenstein, Elmer K., PA
Hough, Charles L., IN
Howd, Salmon Giddings, CT

Fig. 108. Orville Horwitz (JMC, 1883), first Chairman of Urology (1904-12).

Hugg, Arthur A., OH
Hughes, Michael J., PA
Hunter, Winfield S., PA
Hurd, Michael E., PA
Irion, John W., TX
Johnson, E. Newton, PA
Johnson, Erwin T., PA
Johnson, Harris P., NJ
Johnson, Henry W., PA
Jones, William Thomas, TX
Keene, Christopher D., PA
Keller, Anthony, PA
Key, Albert Z., NEW BRUNSWICK
King, Harry B., PA
Kistler, Jonas M., PA
Klemet, John, PA
Koons, Oliver H., OH
Kraft, Frederic de, GERMANY
Kuehn, Rolando, PA
Lampen, Louis, Peale, PA
Langhorne, William H., AL
Latshaw, John H., PA
Law, George E., NY
Lawson, J. Columbus, WV
Lazarus, Solomon D., SC
Leahy, Michael M., IRELAND
Lehman, William F., PA
Lillibridge, Byron J., RI
Lincoln, James B., PA
Lippincott, DeWitt G., NY
Little, J. Warren, OH
Lock, John H., PA
Long, Lemuel L., IL
Lowerison Ellmore H., NOVA SCOTIA
Madeira, James Y. D., PA
Mahon, William T., PA
Marshall, Norman B., IL
Mauderbach, Cyrus L., PA
McCarrell, James R., PA
McCarter, Joseph D., PA
McDaniel, William J., OR
McDowell, John M., GA
McGarvey, John F., PA
Means, Charles S., PA
Means, L. Brown, PA
Melsheimer, John A., PA
Miel, George W., PA
Miller, Albert J., OH
Miller, Morrow A., PA
Milnor, Mahlon T., PA
Morrison, Robert, PA
Morrison, George W., DE
Moss, Robert E., NC
Murray, Uriah B., PA

Nancrede, Charles B., PA
Netscher, Charles Edward, PA
Newman, Louis E., MO
Nice, Harry George, PA
North, William McK., NJ
O'Neill, Rodger P., PA
Orr, Henry B., PA
Ott, Charles Henry, PA
Page, Edward J., OR
Palmer, Daniel B., PA
Parker, Henry Francis, NY
Parkhill, Clayton, PA
Parrott, Malcolm Ethan, NY
Pearce, John F., DE
Perkins, David S., OH
Phillips, Richard J., PA
Phillips, John L., PA
Pollard, Augustus T., ME
Pottberg, Charles, NJ
Pratt, Lester C., OH
Prendergast, William, NY
Preston, Robert P., PA
Rambler, Robert A., PA
Rankin, James A., IL
Rathbone, F. Wait, WV
Redman, Spence, MO
Reeves, Robert H., NJ
Rhodes, Henry F., MO
Robins, Joseph E., PA
Rodgers, Walter Ralston, PA
Ryall, Thomas M., PA
Sageser, Joseph Smiley, IL
Sayre, Jeremiah E., NJ
Scheller, Christian R., MD
Schenck, Dodson R., NC
Scherer, Thomas A., PA
Schmitt, Philip, WI
Schneideman, Theodore B., PA
Schulze, Rudolph B., PA
Scott, Joel F., PA
Sechrist, Charles J., OH
Seifert, George W., CA
Seip, Jacob W., PA
Shearer, Oliver F., PA
Shipp, Milford B., UT
Showalter Henry C.W., PA
Simpson, Moses S., OH
Slaymaker, John M., PA
Smith, W. Tyler, OR
Snowden. Arthur, VA
Sowden, Frederic D., PA
Starck, Albert A.G., IL
Stephens, Edward B., PA
Stevens, John D., PA

Stevens, John A., NC
Summy, David R., PA
Sutton, George S., PA
Sweier, William A., PA
Tenney, John A., PA
Thompson, Persifer U., PA
Timmons, John M., MD
Uhler, Henry L., OH
Unger, Camill, AUSTRIA
Up de Graff, Thad S., Jr., NY
Van Neste, George V., NJ
Velazquez Marcos E., NICARAGUA
Wallace, Nathan C., PA
Ware, Samuel F., DE

Weed, Charles L., PA
Wescoat, E. Seymour, NJ
Wescott, William A., NJ
West, Charles B., PA
Wetherill, R. Benbridge, PA
Wheaton, Joseph C., NJ
Wimpelberg, Samuel, NY
Winchester, Frank M., NC
Wishard, J. Henry, PA
Wolverton, Lewis, PA
Wormley, William, PA
Wright, Harry H., PA
Youngman, Charles W., PA
Zimmerman, Levi, PA
Zimmerman, Pius, PA

Hall of the College of Physicians of Philadelphia, Thirteenth and
Locust Streets (1863-1909)

Samuel D. Gross, a giant in Jefferson's history, died on May 6 of this year. His place of birth near Easton, Pennsylvania, may be seen to this day as a continuation of the original family farm (Fig. 109). His burial site in Woodlands Cemetery, Philadelphia, is well marked (Fig. 110).

Fayette C. Ewing, scion of an old and prominent southern professional family, had begun his medical studies at Tulane University but completed the requirements for the M.D. degree at Jefferson in 1884. He began to specialize in ear, nose, and throat diseases very early and then pursued post-graduate work in London, Vienna and New York. Locating in St. Louis, Missouri, he developed an extensive consulting practice and later was named co-editor of *Laryngoscope*, a publication with the largest circulation in its specialty in the world. He was Vice-President of the American Academy of Ophthalmology and Otolaryngology and was internationally recognized.

John M. Fisher became the private assistant to Samuel W. Gross upon conclusion of his Jefferson internship and soon was appointed to the Surgery Department. He lost two fingers following a surgical infection with almost fatal septicemia and ill health limited his activities for many months. Upon his return a chance encounter with Dr. Theophilus Parvin revealed that the loss of his fingers provided excellent facility for gynecological examination and as a result Dr. Parvin appointed him to the staff of gynecology. In 1893 he became Chief of Clinic and in 1902 Assistant Professor. He advanced to Clinical Professor in 1933 while earning the respect and admiration of his colleagues and students (Fig. 111).

S. MacCuen Smith was perhaps the most widely-known graduate in his class of 215. His commitment to the new field of otolaryngology began immediately on graduation and internship when he was appointed Clinical Chief of Otology by Dr. Turnbull, then in charge of Otology. Dr. Smith became Clinical Professor in 1894 and Chairman of Otology in 1904 (Fig. 112). He published extensively and advanced the specialty at Jefferson while promoting its interests nationally.

John W. Wade developed wide-ranging interests while practicing in Southern New Jersey. Locating in Millville, he was City Physician and Physician of the Board of Health as well as an early member of the American Public Health Association and the American Association for the Advancement of Science.

Fig. 109.   Birthplace of Samuel D. Gross near Easton, Pennsylvania, in 1912 (left) and 1990 (right).

Agque, Timothy Joseph, ITALY
Allison, John R.G., PA
Ashton, William E., PA
Bailey, Samuel DeWitt, PA
Barchfeld, Andrew J., PA
Barr, G. Walter, IL
Bauer, Charles, PA
Beckman, Oswald H., PA
Bell, James H., TX
Bigony, Franklin G., PA
Billmeyer, D. Harrison, PA
Bippus, Samuel M., PA
Bishop, S. Snively, PA
Blair, Franklin, PA
Blalock, Yancey C., WASHINGTON TERRITORY
Bollman, Henry L., PA
Brady, William F., PA
Brown, John Gilmore, PA

Brown, John Knox, PA
Bruere, John, NJ
Bruner, Harry Gilbert, PA
Bryan, Harry N., PA
Buck, Robert L., MS
Buffington, John A., MD
Calhoun, Chambers D., PA
Campbell, Osmon B., MO
Cantwell, George H., DE
Carey, Thomas H., PA
Carmichael, Daniel L., MO
Cartwright, Robert N., NC
Case, George M., PA
Casperson, Robert, PA
Casselberry, Thomas P., PA
Collins, Charles R., VA
Comstock, Andrew J., Jr., CA
Conwell, Luther Swiggett, DE

Fig. 110. Gravesite of Samuel D. Gross in Woodlands Cemetery, Philadelphia.

Fig. 111. John M. Fisher (JMC, 1884), Clinical Professor of Gynecology at Jefferson.

1884

Cook, John R., VA
Coon, John W., WI
Cooper, Joseph L., PA
Cooper, Joseph W., WV
Coskery, Thomas A., IA
Darnall, Walter M., MO
Day, George Ezra, NJ
Delker, William, PA
Derr, Fuller S., PA
Diore, Joachim, MAURITIUS
Dixon, Robert E. Lee, NC
Drabelle, Meigs J., WV
Egolf, Ephraim H., PA
Evans, Charles Henry, OH
Ewing, Fayette C., LA
Felty, John W., CT
Ferver, Wilber G., PA
Fetzer, Stanton M., PA
Fish, James C., PA
Fisher, John Monroe, PA
Flett, George H., OR
Flynn, John J., MA
Fonner, William H., PA
Foscue, Francis L., AL
Fraser, Edward Clarence, MD

Fraser, James Austin, WEST INDIES
Frazier, John R., TX
Freeman, William Snyder, NOVA SCOTIA
Frizell, James S., OH
Frost, Clifton C., TN
Garey, Henry, PA
Gerhard, Emanuel F., PA
Gibbs, Godfrey, ENGLAND
Giragosian, A. Minas, ARMENIA
Good, J. Eugene, VA
Gray, James Charles, PA
Groves, John Dowling, PA
Hagan, William James, AL
Hanna, Broderick D., PA
Hard, Addison Davis, PA
Harker, Charles, NJ
Harmonson, Charles, DE
Harris, James A., TN
Harvey, James W., PA
Hayes, Robert Goodloe, PA
Hefflin, Wyatt, AL
Herron, John Thomas, TN
Hershiser, A. Emmet, OH
Hertel, Frederick, DE
Hilt, William, PA
Hoagland, Garret G., NJ
Hood, Thomas C., IN
Hooper, John W., AL
Hoover, Albert, OH
Horning, Samuel B., PA
Hough, Frank P., PA
Huber, Levi, PA
Hull, Elmer S., PA
Hunter, Allen De Turk, PA
Huselton, Elmer C., PA
Iszard, Reeves H., NJ
Jackson, George L., MO
Janss, John, NE
Johnson, Charles H., PA
Jones, Emery G., PA
Jones, Horace L., DE
Jones, Arthur E., PA
Kane, Evan O., PA
Kappes, David A., OH
Keen, Alfred W., PA
Kinnaman, Horace A., IA
Kirkpatrick, Andrew B., IL
Konkle, W. Bastian, PA
Krause, William, PA
Kuhn, William F., OH
Kuhns, E. Augustus, PA
Kunsman, William H., PA
Lawrence, William B., PA
Lehman, Edwin F., PA

Fig. 112. Seth MacCuen Smith (JMC, 1884), first Chairman of Otology (1904-29).

Lehr, Monroe D., PA
Lindeman, Adam, PA
Loder, N. Sherman, PA
Luffbary, M. Jones, NJ
Lyon, George B., IA
MacNichol, Bernard W., NY
Marchand, Victor H., IN
Marsh, James E., MA
Marshall, William N., PA
Mason, Allen J., MD
Matlack, Granville T., PA
McCoy, William A., IN
McDowell, Samuel W., PA
McDowell, William J., PA
McGary, Robert M., PA
McKnight, William J., PA
McOscar, Edward J., IN
McWilliam, John Forsythe, NJ
McWilliams, Kimber C., PA
Meck, Pearson A., PA
Metcalf, William A., MO
Miller, Samuel Warren, PA
Miller, Charles D., PA
Miller, Albert L., PA
Miller, George W., PA
Miller, John N., PA
Muenter, Henry L., CA
Mullhaupt, Alfred, PA
Nason, Laurentius, ME
Newcomb, Charles L., NOVA SCOTIA
Numbers, William W., IN
O'Daniel, A. Allison, PA
O'Malley, John, IL
Otto, Calvin J., PA
Overend, Edmund J., CA
Palmer, William L., PA
Pancoast, George R., PA
Patton, Noah Woodrow, PA
Pendleton, Andrew L., NC
Peters, Benjamin B., DE
Pettit, Albert, PA
Phillipy, William Tell, PA
Pier, Walter B., PA
Piper, Edward W., PA
Potts, George W., KS
Reed, Eugene Lewis, NJ
Reed, Edwin B., NJ
Reed, Louis Thompson, PA
Rehm, Victor G.R.J., PA
Ressler, George W., PA

Rether, Clarence S., PA
Reutter, Harry Daniel, PA
Ritter, Newton H., PA
Roby, Thomas A., MO
Rooker, Herman S., IN
Rowley, Quintin John, MN
Schaufelberger, Frederick J., OH
Schminkey, Gurney M., PA
Schoonmaker, Irving R., PA
Searcy, James Thweatt, Jr., GA
Shafer, William, NJ
Shannon, James H., ME
Shartle, J. Miller, PA
Sinexon, Justus, PA
Skeen, Andrew M., TX
Sloan, Elmer M., PA
Smith, Charles C., NY
Smith, Charles B., PA
Smith, Seth McCuen, PA
Snyder, W. Fife, WV
Sprenkle, J. Edwin, PA
Stevens, Edmund W., NEW BRUNSWICK
Stilwagon, Philip E., PA
Stokes, Sidney A., PA
Strauss, Louis M., IL
Taylor, Daniel M., NY
Thompson, William H., PA
Thurman, J. Wilton, VA
Thurmond, John W.W., TX
Trisler, J. William, OH
Tuell, James E., ME
Turley, Hugh Grant, PA
Vallette, William H., OH
Vansant, Eugene Larue, PA
Vaughan, William Alonzo, VA
Wade, John W., NJ
Wade, Spencer S., WV
Wagner, Edward F., PA
Waln, J. Ryerss, NJ
Walter, Robley D., PA
Wamsley, Jacob E., WV
Warren, B. Harry, PA
Weiss, Lorenzo E., PA
Whitis, Rufus, TX
Wiles, D. Elmer, PA
Williams, Charles N., PA
Wills, Jesse J., NJ
Wilson, Howard A., NJ
Wortman, Frank, OR
Wright, William C., NY

This class was the last in which the thesis was a requirement for graduation. Subsequent classes were approved for the degree by a written examination. This was the first of a series of changes in educational policy dictated by the increasing complexity of the subject matter and was soon to be followed by curricular and course improvements.

The most prominent member of this class of 176 was its valedictorian , John Chalmers DaCosta, destined to become the first Gross Professor of Surgery, who would extend the tradition of the great Jefferson professors of surgery well into the twentieth century (Fig. 113). Dr. DaCosta was a resident for thirteen months at the old Blockley (Philadelphia General) Hospital and then Assistant to the Insane Department. In 1887 he became Clinical Assistant in the surgical clinic of Professor Samuel W. Gross and two years later an office assistant to W.W. Keen. His writing and literary career soon evolved and at age 31 he published his *Modern Surgery, General and Operative*. His skills as a teacher and author were soon recognized and in 1910 he was appointed to the Chair of Surgery as the Samuel D. Gross Professor. He became widely known as an orator and writer in addition to his clinical achievements. His Wednesday clinics attracted overflow audiences which frequently included famous visiting surgeons (Fig. 114). Jefferson remembers Dr. DaCosta as one of its greatest sons.

CLASS OF 1885

Able, Samuel V., PA	Cooper, James Rudolph, PA
Alexander, William H., PA	Cooper, William R., PA
Ames, James S., MA	Cornish, Percy G., AL
Bair, Philip W.O., IL	Cox, William C., WASHINGTON TERRITORY
Baldinger, William H., TX	Coyle, Robert, PA
Barr, John Chalmers, PA	Cronin, Joseph J., MA
Beatty, Franklin T., MA	Cunningham, Hugh C., TX
Beatty, Henry M., NJ	DaCosta, John Chalmers, PA
Black, William M., PA	Dahlstroem, Max, GERMANY
Bleiler, Charles Alfred, PA	Davis, Theodore G., NJ
Boardman, Walter, PA	Day, Frank B., IN
Bogle, William H., KS	Donaldson, Robert M., PA
Bolton, Mayland, NC	Dougherty, John A., PA
Bower, Collier Levis, PA	Downes, Andrew J., MA
Bower, Charles H., PA	Dunning, James H., IN
Bower, T. Charles, PA	Earley, Charles R., PA
Brandau, John, TN	Earley, Francis G., PA
Brinkey, Gasper C., PA	Endlich, William F., PA
Brown, George S., MO	Enterline, John H., PA
Burd, C. Louis, PA	Everett, Milton H., IL
Burns, Silas, PA	Fair, John F., IL
Bush, Charles B., PA	Fairchild, Courtland de N., MA
Cantrell, John Abbott, PA	Ferguson, Robert Vaughan, KY
Capp, William M., PA	Ferris, Edgar S., IN
Chapin, Samuel L., IL	Fitch, Dorsey P., WV
Collins, William W., NY	Flagg, Payson J., MA

Fuller, Harry C., PA
Garey, Jacob H., PA
German, Howard W., PA
Getchell, Albert C., ME
Gilbert, Elon B., IL
Gillespie, James S., PA
Grander, Frederick L., PA
Green, Dennis S., MN
Green, Sylvanus H., PA
Greenwald, Daniel F., PA
Griffith, Martin Edmund, PA
Hackeny, Jacob S., PA
Harding, Henry, PA
Harter, John C., IA
Hartman, George F., PA
Heffner, Oliver C., PA
Henry, George W., NJ
Henry, John, PA
Hetrich, George, PA
Hill, Jacob F., PA
Holt, Camillus I., TX
Hudson, Leonard A., DE
Huffman, Lucius D., KY
Humphries, S. Osceola, AL
Hurd, Frank H., OH
Hustead, Ashbel F., WV
Huyett, Herman J., IL

Ingram, Theodore E., PA
Ireland, Andrew B., PA
Jordan, David B., NC
Judson, Andrew Rice, NJ
Kauffman, Walter L., PA
Kent, Alfred A., NC
Kirkland, John A., IL
Kugler, George W., Jr., NJ
LaFon, Thomas F., MO
Lake, David H., PA
Lamb, Albert Victor, PA
Lang, Robert H., KY
LaRue, Franklin, OH
Lecrone, Harris R., PA
Leidy, Edwin D., PA
Marsh, George D., PA
Martin, Howard B., PA
Martin, George, PA
Martin, Ambrose H., CANADA
Maxwell, William E., AL
McCahey, Peter, PA
McCandliss, Henry M., PA
McDonald, John M., OH
McDougall, Charles S., OH
McElwee, Henry W., VA
McGlenn, J. Averill, OH
McIlhaney, William H., PA
McLaughlin, Robert J., IL
Mears, Daniel W., PA
Miller, Henry B., OH
Miller, James Calvin, PA
Millikin, Thomas N., PA
Mong, Elmer E., PA
Morton, Thomas J., PA
Moyer, John L.S., PA
Murray, Thomas Walker, PA
Mykrantz, Howard B., OH
Nance, George B., NC
Oliver, John Edward, MO
Orr, Joseph D., PA
Phillips, Lewis Oliver, PA
Porter, John, PA
Pyle, Jerome L., PA
Reading, George Evans, NJ
Reed, Anderson F., MO
Reinhard, Wilson J., PA
Rhoads, J. Neely, DE
Rich, Guy C., NY
Richardson, Davis H., MD
Richardson, James, DE
Ritter, William Elmer, PA
Riveley, Martin Pierce, PA
Rogers, Elmer H., PA
Ross, James Thweatt, GA

Fig. 113.   John Chalmers DaCosta (JMC, 1885), first Samuel
D. Gross Professor of Surgery (1910-31).

Rugh, Carroll B., PA
Sawin, Robert V., MA
Scholl, Alfred K., PA
Sheets, Everett W., PA
Sheppey, John V., DE
Shimavonian, Samuel, ARMENIA
Shollenberger, Charles F., PA
Shull, William Milton, PA
Simms, Benjamin B., AL
Simons, Arthur J., PA
Smith, H. Winchel, NJ
Sooy, John Milton, NJ
Stern, Max J., PA
Stewart, Joseph J., PA

Stewart, John C., SCOTLAND
Stoner, Harry, PA
Stoner, James Buchanan, PA
Stroud, Frank G., NJ
Stroup, J. Calvin, PA
Swygert, Sanders L., SC
Taylor, Joseph M., PA
Throckmorton, Charles M., IA
Torkington, Joseph, ENGLAND
Trumbauer, Albert H., PA
Tunison, Geoffrey Orlando, NJ
Vander Horck, Max P., MN
Walker, Benjamin Franklin, PA
Walker, Dale L., OH

Fig. 114. Surgical clinic of Professor John Chalmers DaCosta in ''pit'' of 1877 Hospital (ca.1905). Note visiting dignitaries in inner ring and the ''old operating table'' previously used by Samuel D. Gross (also depicted in the *Gross Clinic* painting by Eakins).

1885

Walker, Richard P., MO
Walton, Levi S., PA
Warder, Charles B., PA
Waterman, Francis C., PA
Way, Julius, NJ
Weaver, John D., PA
Wheeler, Walter Sewell, MO

Williams, J. Franklin, PA
Williams, Evan, PA
Wilson, James H., PA
Wright, Robert Lee, TN
Wright, Thomas Briggs, Jr., KY
Yokum, Humboldt, WV
Zauner, Robert H., PA

Lower lecture hall of Jefferson Medical College (ca 1880s)
Note *Gross Clinic* painting on side wall.

1885

William M. Sweet became the fourth chairman of the Department of Ophthalmology at Jefferson in 1925 (Fig. 115). Following graduation he studied ophthalmology at several European centers and returned to Jefferson's Eye Clinic in the next year. He developed methods of localization of intraocular foreign bodies and with the advent of x-rays in 1895 he added roentgen study to his experiments. The Sweet-Manges method soon became well known with the designing of special magnetic devices for removal. Dr. Sweet was long associated with Wills Eye Hospital first as roentgenologist and later as ophthalmic surgeon. He was also an editor and writer for ophthalmic publications and an officer of the American Ophthalmological Society for many years.

Chevalier Jackson was to become the most famous in this class of 223 (Fig. 116). A multi-talented man, he began the practice of laryngology in Pittsburgh, Pennsylvania, and then studied with Sir Morell Mackenzie in England before going on to major contributions in laryngology

Fig. 115. William M. Sweet (JMC, 1886), Chairman of Ophthalmology (1925-26).

Fig. 116. Chevalier Jackson (JMC, 1886), Chairman of Laryngology (1916-24), Chairman of Bronchoesophagology (1924-30), internationally renowned for invention and improvement of instruments for removal of foreign bodies from the air and food passages.

during the next twenty years. He was Professor of Laryngology at the University of Pittsburgh from 1912 to 1916. In 1916 after his invention of the bronchoscope and introduction of new procedures in esophagoscopy and gastroscopy he moved to Philadelphia where he became Professor of Laryngology at Jefferson. His career broadened and he progressed to academic appointments in four other Philadelphia medical schools. In 1924 he was named to the chair of the new Department of Bronchoscopy and Esophagoscopy which he held until his resignation in 1930 when he organized the Jackson Clinic at Temple University School of Medicine. Dr. Jackson was an innovator and mover, having been responsible for legislation relative to protection of children from swallowing and inhaling objects and substances which he showed to be hazardous. During his long and productive career his

publications were widely translated and he was decorated and feted throughout the world for his achievements. Skilled in drawing and painting, he illustrated most of his own publications. He was a leader in many medical organizations.

William M.L. Coplin, a native of West Virginia, began his work at Jefferson with pathological specimens as a student and after his Jefferson internship was appointed Assistant Pathologist to Philadelphia General Hospital in 1892. After a year (1895/96) as Professor of Pathology at Vanderbilt University, he returned to Jefferson as the second Professor and Chairman of Pathology and Bacteriology (Fig. 117). From 1905 to 1907 he served as Director of the Department of Public Health and Charities for the City of Philadelphia in which post he organized the Hospital for Contagious Diseases. Dr. Coplin's services to Jefferson were important and varied at a critical time in its history.

CLASS OF 1886

Alleman, L. A. Welles, NY
Allison, Robert Wilson, PA
Atlee, James Humphries, TN
Barker, T. Ridgway, PA
Barnfield, John Humes, PA
Bates, William Edgar, PA
Beach, George Brown, PA
Bickers, Alston Hubert, KY
Biesecker, James Ellsworth, PA
Blalock, Alonzo L., FL
Blanck, Joseph Elwood, PA
Bonwill, Howard G., NJ
Bossart, Harry Sherman, PA
Brady, Elliott Thomas, VA
Bricker, William Henry, PA
Brosius, William Hayes, PA
Brown, Robert Emmett, GA
Brown, Edwin, PA
Bruere, Abel T., NJ
Bucks, W. Frank, PA
Bullock, George D., RI
Bush, James H.J., DE
Butt, Abijah, PA
Butt, Virgil R., NC
Byars, Henry Tipton, TN
Cahall, Laurence M., DE
Campbell, Tobias, PA
Campbell, Charles Lawrence, PA
Care, James Roberts, PA

Carhart, Henry Osborn, NJ
Carr, Benjamin Franklin, MO
Casselberry, Harry Brundage, PA
Cato, Robert Eugene, GA
Chamberlain, John W., PA
Chilcott, Benjamin Franklin, PA
Clark, Whipple W., NC
Clayton, Joshua, DE
Coover, Harry Ross, PA
Coplin, William M. Late, WV
Courtney, David H., WV
Coyle, Henry Joseph, PA
Crowell, William David, NC
Culler, John F., OH
Davis, Nehemiah, NJ
Davis, Marshall A., PA
Deakyne, Clarence G., PA
DeFord, Moses, PA
Detwiler, Edwin Landis, VA
Dickey, Clarence Dudley, CA
Dieterich, George, Jr., PA
Dinsmore, Willard Edwin, ME
Dirmitt, Charles H., PA
Donaldson, Allen B., KY
Drumheller, Francis Edward, PA
Ellegood, Robert, DE
Ely, Harry Birney, PA
Emley, Herbert H., NJ
English, William Hope, PA

Everhart, Charles W., PA
Fackler, Lewis Henry, PA
Faison, Julius Alexander, NC
Fajans, Julian, PA
Farish, George W.T., NOVA SCOTIA
Farrell, John T., MA
Fickes, Howard C., PA
Field, William S.M., PA
Foster, Walter Ross, PA
Fountain, Henry Lilly, TX
Frank, Johnston, Jr., TX
Franklin, James Ashby, MO
Fritz, Clinton S., PA
Fruh, Ernest, PA
Gallagher, John Alexander, PA
Gans, Emanuel S., PA
Garrison, George Irwin, WV
Gauntt, Franklin Allen, NJ
Glanden, Walter Prevost, NJ
Goe, John Graham, OH
Goebel, George, PA
Good, William Taylor, CANADA
Gould, James Bennett, MN

Graham, Charles Percy, PA
Grant, William Edward, KY
Griffin, Patrick F., PA
Groom, Albert R., PA
Guss, Harry Templer, PA
Haensler, Franz. Joseph, GERMANY
Hall, William D., PA
Hard, Hanson, OH
Hassell, Starke, NC
Hawkins, Frederick Lewis, NH
Heinlein, John Andrew, OH
Hensyl, Lewis W., PA
Hepburn, James H., PA
Hepler, Albert James, PA
Hildreth, Eugenius A., WV
Holland, George, PA
Hope, Walter Geddes, PA
Horting, Levi W., PA
Hottenstein, Edward Lewis, PA
Hudders, Alva Lorraine, PA
Huebner, Dewees A.W., PA
Huntington, William Dresser, CA
Huntsman, Edwin S., PA
Husted, Francis B., NJ
Ickes, George Albert, PA
Ingraham, Samuel Cooke, PA
Ingram, Charles Braxton, NC
Irvin, John Wesley, OH
Irwin, Joseph C., PA
Ischler, George Herman, PA
Jackson, Chevalier Q., PA
Johnson, Edward Snyder, PA
Kalb, George Bigham, OH
Kane, Thomas L., PA ·
Kinnaman, Chauncey Howard, IA
Klotz, Edgar J., PA
Kurtz, Clarence M., PA
Lawhead, James H., WV
Leathers, Douglass A., IN
Lichty, Samuel M., PA
Lindsey, James W., PA
Linton, William B., MN
Lloyd, Edward Morris, PA
Lund, Oliver Pancoast, PA
Macaulay, George, Jr., GA
Malatesta, Joseph Mark, ITALY
Mattson, Charles R., PA
McBryar, William Lyle, PA
McDonald, John Angus, ME
Mettler, L. Harrison, PA
Metz, Harry William, PA
Miller, Jesse C., PA
Miller, Joseph Elias, PA
Moon, Robert Charles, ENGLAND

Fig. 117.   William M.L. Coplin (JMC, 1886), Commanding Officer of Jefferson's Base Hospital No. 38 in World War I and Chairman of Pathology (1896-1922)

Moore, Henry Boynton, ME
Moore, Brutus Caesar, NC
Morris, Joseph B., PA
Morrow, William Howard, PA
Morton, Alexander R., PA
Mosier, George W., PA
Moyer, Jacob Donelson, PA
Murphy, Henry Cloyd, TN
Murray, Bayard, PA
Nock, Thomas Oliver, DE
Norred, Charles Henry, IL
Osburn, Curran D., OR
Parker, James Pleasant, MO
Payne, John, AL
Perrine, Edmund Kirby, PA
Peters, Jacob Markwood, PA
Phillips, Charles. Montague, WEST INDIES
Plass, Charles F.W., PA
Porter, J. Elmer, PA
Preas, James Henry, VA
Purvis, William Reginald, AL
Quick, Jacques Voorhees, NJ
Rafferty, Benjamin F., KY
Ralston, George Foster, PA
Ramsay, Robert Warren, PA
Reed, I. Bebout, PA
Reeve, John Charles, OH
Rendleman, John J., IL
Richardson, William James, TX
Riggs, Edward Elder, PA
Riley, James Archer, OH
Rinehart, Milton, PA
Rinehart, William T., PA
Rockwell, William, NOVA SCOTIA
Saalfrank, Charles W., PA
Salinger, Julius Lincoln, PA
Santee, Andrew Curtin, PA
Saulsbury, James K., MD
Schlemm, Horace Edmund, PA
Scholl, Benjamin Franklin, PA
Schulze, Henry Louis, PA
Seitz, Frederick, PA
Servoss, Archibald Gooding, IL
Shastid, William Edwards, IL

Sherk, Harry Huber, NJ
Shoemaker, George Eichholtz, PA
Sidebotham, Henry Larned, PA
Siegler, Lewis Franklin, PA
Sittler, Albert Monroe, PA
Smith, William Jackson, VA
Snow, Leslie Woodruff, UTAH TERRITORY
Spangler, Jacob Benson, PA
Stevens, William Alexander, PA
Stouffer, Peter, Jr., OH
Stout, Harry A., NJ
Stratton, Robert Thompson, CA
Strock, Frederick Gelwicks, PA
Sweet, William Merrick, PA
Tantum, Percy L., DE
Tayler, Thomas George, IL
Taylor, Robert Alexander, PA
Teed, John Francis, NEW BRUNSWICK
Teters, Benjamin Franklin, OH
Thistle, Joseph Long, WV
Thorne, John Mairs, MN
Tren, Aaron, RUSSIA
Trout, William Wesley, NJ
Tullidge, George Bowler, DE
Tupper, Charles Osborne, NOVA SCOTIA
Valls, Bartholomew, TX
Vance, John Harris, PA
VanSickle, Frederick L., PA
Varrel, Frank Martin, PA
Walker, Joseph P., MO
Wallace, William C., PA
Walsh, John Joseph, PA
Weeks, Job Harry, NJ
West, Warren Finley, TX
West, John Wilson, OH
West, Samuel Albert, OH
White, William Preston, TX
Williamson, Joseph Harper, IL
Wilson, Robert Henry T., DE
Wilson, Preston, PA
Winger, Franklin, PA
Wintersteen, John Charles, PA
Wiseman, William Albert, IL
Woodruff, Charles E., PA

"Preach a crusade against ignorance."

(A motto of Thomas Jefferson)

Commencement was held at the Academy of Music on April 5, with award of the Doctor of Medicine Degree to 187 graduates by President of the College, Dr. Emile B. Gardette. The Valedictory Address was delivered by James W. Holland (JMC, 1868, Fig. 78), Professor of Medical Chemistry and Toxicology. Dr. Holland became Dean of the College the same year, a position he was to fill with distinction for the next 29 years (until 1916).

In 1887, Dr. W.W. Keen (JMC, 1862, Fig. 67) operated at St. Mary's Hospital in Philadelphia, using Lister's principles of antisepsis, on a patient with an accurately localized large meningioma of the brain. It was the first brain tumor successfully removed in America and the patient lived without recurrence for more than 30 years. Two years later (1889), Keen would take the Chair of Principles of Surgery and Practice of Surgery at Jefferson vacated by the premature death of Samuel W. Gross.

Hayward Glazier Thomas studied abroad after graduation and became Professor of Diseases of the Eye, Ear, Nose and Throat in the Oakland College of Medicine and Surgery at Oakland, California. He also served as President of the Alameda County (California) Medical Association (Fig. 118).

Henson Foster Tomb served for four years as pension examiner under President Cleveland, and he also became President of the Cambria County (Pennsylvania) Medical Society (Fig. 119).

Green Robbins Hulsizer served as Resident Physician in the Jefferson Medical College Hospital. He practiced in Philadelphia where he became Police Surgeon of the 7th District, Assistant Chief Surgeon with the Police and Fire Departments, Assistant Medical Inspector of the Bureau of Health of Philadelphia, and Commander of the Philadelphia Medical Emergency Corps (Fig. 120).

CLASS OF 1887

Adams, John William, PA
Adams, Charles Franklin, NJ
Alexander, William Brown, PA
Alkire, Herbert Lee, KS
Allen, James Franklin, IL
Applegate, John Chew, NJ
Ashby, William Gregory, VA
Austin, James Aaron, NC
Bacas, Henry, LA
Baker, Anthony George, PA
Barfoot, Albert Fremont, IA
Benerman, Louis C., PA
Bennett, John Knight, NJ
Bonnaffon, Samuel Ashton, PA
Booth, Nelson Alexander, PA
Bower, William George, PA
Boyle, Ralph Raum, PA
Boyle, George Arthur, KS
Bradfute, Champe Saunders, TX
Bradley, Alfred Eugene, NY
Bray, Walter S., ME
Bricker, Harry Reno, PA

Buckingham, Hugh W., PA
Bulis, Henry C., IA
Bull, Heman Rowley, MO
Burke, Charles Oren, IL
Cairns, Andrew A., PA
Carson, James Seymour, PA
Cato, Frank Lee, GA
Chavanne, Henry, NJ
Clifford, Charles Henry, PA
Cline, Edward W., PA
Cochran, Alvis Stafford, GA
Cox, George William, IL
Crothers, William Shrimer, PA
Daniels, Henry Manford, PA
Dengler, Robert Herman, NY
DeWitt, Moses D., PA
Diverty, Henry B., NJ
Dolan, Thomas Edward, NJ
Dollinger, Philip Julius, GERMANY
Donaldson, Elmer Ellsworth, OH
Duffau, Justus, TX
Dundore, Claude A., PA

Durham, Alexander Franklin, Jr., GA
Edmonds, Andrew, PA
Eiseman, Reuben, PA
Elliott, Washington Franklin, PA
Fahr, John William, PA
Feltwell, A. Lincoln, PA
Ferry, Franklin Forrest, PA
Fields, Alpheus, NC
Fisler, Charles Davis, NJ
Fithian, Joel W., NJ
Floyd, Charles Slocum, PA
Fockler, George W., PA
French, Edward Everett, PA
Friedel, Alexander A., TN
Garrison, William R., OH
Glass, Joseph Hoopes, PA
Goddard, Jefferson Davis, KS
Gose, John Robert, WASHINGTON TERRITORY
Graham, Norman Robert, PA

Graham, Edwin Elden, PA
Gregg, Sparrow T., OH
Grim, George Melvin, PA
Guiher, Horace Binney, PA
Haas, William David, LA
Hamilton, William Thomas, PA
Harman, Henry M., PA
Hays, Jeffeson Davis, AR
Heiser, William Henry, PA
Helm, Charles E., PA
Henlen, Benjamin Augustus, KS
Hill, John Boadley, KS
Holcomb, Charles Milo, KS
Holcomb, Guy Carleton, PA
Hoover, Andrew Jefferson, NC
Hopkins, Robert Black, DE
Howell, Andrew Rufus, AR
Howell, Aaron, NJ
Howsley, William M., KS

Fig. 118. Hayward Glazier Thomas (JMC, 1887), Professor of Diseases of the Eye, Ear, Nose and Throat in Oakland (California) College of Medicine and Surgery.

Fig. 119. Henson Foster Tomb (JMC, 1887) served as pension examiner under President Cleveland.

1887

Huffman, William Veloss, KY
Hulsizer, Green Robbins, PA
Huzza, Thomas Harry, GA
Irwin, Thaddeus S., PA
Jacoby, Aaron Peter, NJ
Jarrett Harry, PA
Johnston, George Frear, PA
Johnston, Walter, PA
Jones, William B., DE
Judge, Robert Barr, PA
Keisel, James Henry, PA
Kelley, Edward B.P., NJ
Kelly, William D., MN
Kendall, Eugene Elmer, PA
Kerling, George A., PA
Kinard, George W., PA
Kindig, Rudolph, PA
Kistler, Oliver Franklin, PA
Klein, Warren F., PA
Kohler, William Henry, PA

Krum, Astley Grant, PA
Lashelle, Charles L., PA
Leamon, George Pawling, IL
Lewis, Edmund Henry, VA
Linthicum, Richard Lee, MD
Litten, Frank, TX
Love, Frank Seymour, MO
Lowe, Clement Belton, PA
Lynch, Samuel Edward, PA
Mann, James Packard, DE
Manz, John Henry, DE
Matthews, William Edgar, PA
Mayer, Louis Henry, PA
McGuigan, John Ignatius, PA
McKee, Harry Wright, PA
Mengel, John S., PA
Miller, Allen Erskine, SC
Mink, Arthur DeWitt, PA
Moore, Henry Dare, PA
Moore, Edward E., PA
Morton, Samuel Williams, PA
Neff, Francis Felix, PA
Nesbit, Andrew David, PA
Osterhout, Paul, TX
Owens, Cleon Clinton, KY
Painter, Theodore P., PA
Peffer, Ambrose, PA
Peskind, Arnold, OH
Pittman, John H., PA
Plumstead, Matthew Woodbury, MA
Polk, Alexander, Murdoch, PA
Preston, Samuel Pleasant, VA
Red, Samuel Clark, TX
Redd, Thomas Minor, MS
Redpath, Nathaniel J., OR
Reichard, Noah W., PA
Restrepo, Delfin F., COLOMBIA
Richards, Charles Egbert, PA
Rinehart, Charles Albright, PA
Roberts, Thomas Sargent, PA
Robinson, Barzill LeDru, NY
Robinson, James, PA
Rupert, Elon, Sargent, NY
Savage, Albert Lytleton, PA
Schall, Harry Mayer, PA
Schemm, George Christoph, MI
Seymour, Stuart Howard, OH
Shannon, Daniel, IA
Shaw, Frank L., ME
Sherk, Henry Howard, PA
Shively, James Buchanan, PA
Shuttleworth, William Blair, WV
Sinne, Hans H., GERMANY
Smalley, John K., IN

Fig. 120. Green Robbins Hulsizer (JMC, 1887), physician and surgeon to Police and Fire Departments, Bureau of Health and Medical Emergency Corps of Philadelphia.

Smith, Edward Lincoln, PA
Smith, Harry Martin, PA
Smith, Henry Harrison, PA
Smith, James Edward, PA
Smith, Jeremiah Peter, PA
Souder, Lewis Reed, NJ
Stephen, John Michael, PA
Stigers, P. Ellwood, MD
Strack, David, PA
Sturges, William Warren, PA
Thomas, Hayward Glazier, CA
Thompson, John Joseph, MA
Thornley, William James, PA
Tomb, Henson, F., PA
VanBuskirk, Samuel Levick, PA

Vannort, Joseph Adams, MD
Vest, Frederick Eugene, IA
Walker, Thomas Davis, PA
Waltemeyer, John Tassey, KS
Waters, George W., PA
Watkins, David C. T., AUSTRALIA
Webb, William Ezekiel, PA
Wehner, William H.E., PA
Wells, Joseph Edgar, NEW BRUNSWICK
Wiley, Frank Hughes, PA
Williams, Martin Henry, Jr., PA
Williams, Thomas B., PA
Wood, William Alva, TX
Woods, Henry Lewis, PA
Zacherle, Otto Frank, PA
Ziegler, George William, PA

Library of College of Physicians of Philadelphia (1863-1909)

A major natural disaster occurred in Johnstown, Pennsylvania, in March 1888 with massive loss of life and property. Among the survivors who rode out the flood on a barn roof was a ten-year old boy, Victor Heiser (Fig. 139), who would graduate from Jefferson Medical College in 1897 and bring honor to the College through his pioneer exploits in international health.

In this class of 188, George M. Gould, a native of Massachusetts, received honorable mention in the prize competition for the best thesis. The prize was provided by the *Medical News*, which publication Dr. Gould later edited for five years (1891-95). Trained in ophthalmology, he developed a major interest in medical literature. He was editor of the *American Year Book of Medicine and Surgery*, a series of medical dictionaries, and the *Philadelphia Medical Journal* (1898-1900). Of most interest to Jeffersonians was his two-volume *The Jefferson Medical College of Philadelphia, A History*. Published in 1904, it was a comprehensive study of the College and many of its graduates. It constituted an important resource for future Jefferson historians (Fig. 121).

The winner of the prize for the best essay on a subject pertaining to the Practice of Medicine was Augustus A. Eshner of Pennsylvania. Dr. Eshner became well known as a clinician with many interests and hospital appointments. He was physician to the Philadelphia General Hospital, the Philadelphia Orthopaedic Hospital, the Hospital for Diseases of the Lungs in Chestnut Hill and for a time was an instructor in clinical medicine at Jefferson.

Robert L. Gibbon of North Carolina, a brother of John H. Gibbon, Sr. (Professor of Surgery at Jefferson 1907-31), also pursued a career in Surgery and in 1919 became Professor of Surgery in North Carolina Medical College.

CLASS OF 1888

Adams, Quintus L., PA
Adamsen, Hans, SIAM
Ammon, George W., PA
Anderson, Thomas S., PA
Andreas, Benjamin Adam, PA
Ashcraft, Samuel Fisler, NJ
Ashton, Thomas George, PA
Attwood, John Warren, KS
Baer, Harry George, PA
Baer, Joseph Silas, PA
Bahl, Charles Zetty, PA
Baker, William McClain, PA
Barr, Samuel Dickson, PA
Baum, William Louis, IL
Beal, Edward L., MO
Becker, Phares N., PA
Bickell, S. Ellsworth, PA
Binkley, Thomas G., PA
Blackwood, Norman Jerome, PA
Bloomfield, James Camak, GA
Bockel, Richard Martin, PA
Bower, John Lincoln, PA
Brady, Franklin, PA

Brantley, Hassell, NC
Braymer, Orange Whitney, PA
Brobst, Francis H., PA
Browder, William M., AL
Burchard, Harry H., PA
Callender, Alson B., PA
Capron, Victor James, NY
Carr, Charles Dungan, PA
Cater, Robert Lee, GA
Caveness, Isaac Wesley, NC
Chadwick, Burg, PA
Church, Clement Brooke, PA
Clark, George Campbell, PA
Conser, Thomas Curtin, PA
Davis, Edward P., PA
Dawson, Eli Lide, AR
Devenney, John C., PA
Diaz, Roman L., MEXICO
Dodson, Daniel W., PA
Downes, Clarence Eugene, MD
Dudley, Hubert W., OH
Dunbar, Thomas, Jr., PA
Elden, William McKee, PA

Ellis, J. Cannon, DE
Emrick, M. Luther, PA
Eshner, Augustus A., PA
Ewing, Charles Wesley, KS
Felder, Lawrence A., GA
Fisher, Charles W., PA
Franz, Charles H., PA
Frick, J. Howard, PA
Gaddis, Jacob Ernest, PA
Gibbon, Robert Lardner, NC
Gifford, Ulysses Grant, MD
Gillars, Alexander Liddell, PA
Goudy, Rollin Andrew, OH
Gould, George Milbury, MA
Graham, Percy Malcolm, PA
Green, Clarence Creesy, PA
Griffith, William Clark, TX
Groff, John W., PA
Haines, William Fisher, DE
Harris, Albert Beecher, DE
Hawkins, John Thomas, AR

Hershey, Edgar Parker, PA
Hickey, Stefano Joseph, PA
Hierholzer, John Charles, PA
Hilliard, Charles Eugene, NC
Hillsman, George Albert, KY
Hine, Marks Priestly, PA
Hoopingarner, George P., IN
Hoover, Daniel Henry, NC
Householder, Merchant C., PA
Hubbard, Charles Calvin, NC
Hudson, Elmer Alexander, PA
Ike, Edgar Milton, PA
Irwin, James Kennedy, PA
Jacob, Albert Nicholas, PA
Jennings, William Browning, NJ
Johnston, John Waddell, PA
Johnston, Frank Elmer, PA
Jones, Benjamin Franklin, OH
Kantner, Franklin Jacob, PA
Keily, James William, PA
Kelsey, Arthur Louis, CA
Kemble, Charles, PA
Kieffer, Charles Clifford, PA
Kirk, Edward, PA
Kline, David Frank, PA
Kring, Sylvester S., PA
Kunkle, Wesley Franklin, PA
Lane, J. Lewis, NJ
Lashell, Ralph Maclay, PA
Lenker, David Edward, PA
Lewis, Benjamin Sykes, NJ
Lewis, William H., PA
Loos, Isaac B., PA
Lovett, Henry, PA
Macfarland, Burr W., NJ
Magnus, E. R. Max, CA
Marbourg, Frank Bower, PA
Marbourg, Edgar Marcella, PA
Marbourg, Jeremiah L., PA
Maxwell, James Rea, PA
McChesney, Franklin Sayre, PA
McClellan, Robert Price, Jr., PA
McClendon, Joseph W., AL
McColgan, Robert, CANADA
McCoy, Ambrose, TN
McDonald, William Stephen, ME
McFadden, John Joseph, PA
McKnight, Adam S., PA
Meredith, Samuel Carlisle, DE
Merrick, Thomas Dudley, MD
Merrick, Frederick T., MD
Miles, William Thomas, PA
Miller, William Adam, PA
Mohr, Jacob Eugene, PA

Fig. 121. George M. Gould (JMC, 1888), opthalmologist, editor, and author of a two-volume history of Jefferson Medical College (1904).

Money, Philip Monroe, DE
Morrow, John Riddle, PA
Muller, Carl Louis, CA
Neel, George Pressley, SC
Neff, James Woodbury, PA
Newcomer, Frank Sherick, MD
Noble, Harvey Read, OH
Nusbaum, David Hamilton, IL
O'Connor, John Hugh, PA
Oliver, David H., NJ
Patterson, William Stuart, PA
Payne, Carl Forsythe, IN
Peirce, Isaac, VA
Pelham, James Wardlaw, SC
Person, John Adam, PA
Pfeiffer, Theodore P.F., PA
Pope, Irvine Clarendon, MA
Porter, Clifford Charles, PA
Pragheimer, Jacob S., PA
Reifsnyder, Joseph Calvin, PA
Ritter, F. H.S., PA
Robinson, Richard Fillmore, PA
Rocap, William Allen, PA
Rogers, Benjamin H., PA
Rosenthal, Jacob, PA
Ruch, William Starick, PA
Runkle, Stuart Calvin, PA
Ryan, Laurence Reginald, IL
Ryan, Michael C., PA
Sampsell, Charles Paul, OH
Schwartz, Frederick, PA
Shaffer, Cornelius Thaddeus, OH
Shepard, George Andrew, CT

Sherman, Henry Arthur, MA
Sherman, William Sprague, RI
Shimp, Archie Joseph, CA
Slifer, Frank Sebring, PA
Smith, Edwin Glenn, PA
Speck, George McClellan, PA
Spence, David Walter, IL
Starnes, E. Clingman, NC
Stedem, Joseph P. H., OH
Stewart, Charles B., WASHINGTON TERRITORY
Styer, Daniel Webster, PA
Swearingen, A. William, IA
Tait, Thomas Walker, PA
Talbot, Ashton Buchanan, PA
Terhune, Archibald, Alexander, TX
Tevis, Samuel, CA
Thomas, George Perce, PA
Thompson, John R. C., NJ
Thornley, Frederick Clinton, PA
Umsted, Jonathan R., PA
Van Dyke, George Marion, PA
Vaughan, Horace, DE
Wasson, James Elliot, PA
Webb, Walter, PA
West, Frederick B., PA
Wheat, Lewis Emerson, PA
White, Frederick Allen, ME
Whittington, William L., MO
Wickert, Henry Jonas, PA
Wilkinson, Chester Ambrose, PA
Willsey, Judson, T., ID
Wilson, Elmer E., NY
Wilson, William Reynolds, PA
Woods, John Franklin, Jr., PA

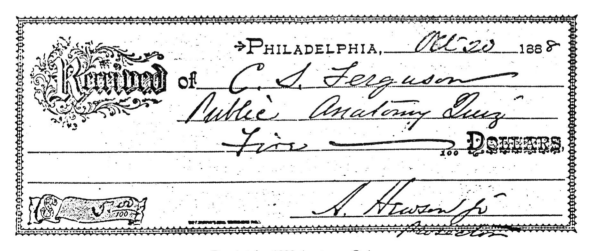

Receipt for 1888 Anatomy Quiz.

The students of this graduating class were the first to benefit from five clinical lectureships established within the Hospital to provide the latest instruction in the evolving specialties of the times. They were administered as follows: Oscar H. Allis (Orthopaedic Surgery), Charles E. de Medici Sajous (Laryngology), Oliver P. Rex (Children's Diseases), A. Van Harlingen (Dermatology), and James C. Wilson (Renal Diseases). Practical instruction was also given in the use of the laryngoscope and ophthalmoscope.

In this year the Johns Hopkins Hospital as well as the Mayo Clinic opened. Halsted at Hopkins introduced rubber gloves into surgery and devised new operations for inguinal hernia and cancer of the breast. McBurney described the topographic site of the appendix which bears his name and advised early operation for appendicitis. Von Mering and Minkowski produced experimental pancreatic diabetes. The scientific age of medicine was thus gaining momentum.

The number of graduates was 212, of which 102 were from Pennsylvania and the remainder from 28 States, Canada, New Brunswick, Brazil, Mexico, Colombia, and Spain. The Valedictory Address was delivered by Dr. William Smith Forbes, Professor of Anatomy.

Charles Frederic Pettibone established an active clinical practice in Philadelphia, but in addition was active in Jefferson Medical College and Hospital as Assistant Physician in the Medical Clinic, Chief of the Children's Clinic, and instructor in Diseases of Children (Fig. 122).

Charles George Geiger, after a year's study in Vienna, established his practice in St. Joseph, Missouri. He became Professor of Surgery and Genito-Urinary Diseases in Ensworth Medical College of St. Joseph (Fig. 123). In addition to serving as Attending Surgeon and Chief to the Ensworth Medical College Hospital, he contributed to the surgical, gynecological and urologic literature.

CLASS OF 1889

Adler, David Gilbert, PA
Antill, Joseph Vincent, PA
Apple, William Shimer, PA
Armstrong, Adam Frederick, NEW BRUNSWICK
Ball, Michael Valentine, PA
Banks, Braxton, NC
Barnes, Lewis Sherman, PA
Bastian, Charles Brown, PA
Bateman, Frank Middleton, NJ
Beach, William M., MO
Bean, Harvey F., PA
Beckler, Warren B., ME
Bennett, Francis Gurney, PA
Benton, Claude Monk, NC
Bippus, Christopher C., PA
Boston, Lemmons Peter, PA
Bowers, Herbert Roland, PA
Bracken, Joseph K.W., OH
Bricker, Samuel Reiley, PA
Britt, John Boston, SC
Brown, William Bedford, VA
Buchanan, Thomas, NJ

Buehler, William S., PA
Bullock, Charles Cevos, PA
Burd, Edwin Jasper, PA
Burke, Joseph John, PA
Butler, Edward Everett, WASHINGTON. TERRITORY
Byers, Edgar Henry, PA
Cain, Frank Monroe, PA
Carmichael, Randolph Bryan, VA
Carson, John Baxter, PA
Cason, Joseph Robert, TN
Chritzman, Harry Brant, PA
Churchman, Vincent Tapp, VA
Clifford, John James, CO
Cobb, William Henry, Jr., NC
Cox, Ross Parker, GA
Curl, Ellmer Ellsworth, OH
Danzer, William F., PA
Davis, David Dixon, PA
Denning, Ollen Lee, NC
Deupree, Albert Bush, TN
Dickson, James Alexander, OH
Dodds, Samuel, IL

Dodson, Boyd, PA
Donough, William Edgar, PA
Dougan, Robert Patten, CANADA
Dutton, Willard Oliver, PA
Eberhart, Ira A., IA
Edwards, Richard Travis, TX
Espey, John Robert, IN
Evans, Edmund Haun, PA
Everson, Malcolm Wayland, PA
Farrell, Henry William, MA
Ferguson, Charles Singleton, KS
Fitzgerald, Jesse York, NC
Flemming, Daniel William, PA
Fowler, Charles Edgar, CA
Fowlkes, Tilley, TX
Frame, Cornelius Aultman, OH
Frazier, James William, IA
Fredericks, William James, PA
Freiday, William Gustav, NE
Frist, Harry Morrison, DE

Frost, Ellis Freedom, RI
Fulper, Theodore Burd, NJ
Geiger, Charles George, MO
Giarth, David I., PA
Graham, William Turbett, PA
Greeson, George Alexander, MO
Groninger, Wilson Sherman, PA
Haines, Samuel Howard, NJ
Hall, Joseph Underwood, Jr., CA
Hamill, John Frederick, PA
Hamilton, Willis, PA
Hamilton, George Matthews, WV
Harris, John Scott, CANADA
Hart, Joseph, PA
Heintz, John P. E., CA
Hesser, Charles Le Grand, OH
Highsmith, Jacob Franklin, NC
Hopper, Thomas Thompson, PA
Hottenstein, William Jacob, PA
Howell, Elmer Ellsworth, IA

Fig. 122.   Charles Frederic Pettibone (JMC, 1889), active in Pediatrics at Jefferson Medical College and Hospital.

Fig. 123.   Charles George Geiger (JMC, 1889), Professor of Surgery and Genito-Urinary Diseases in Ensworth Medical College of St. Joseph, Missouri.

Jennings, Charles Hinchman, NJ
Johns, Jacob Rohrer, PA
Johnson, Charles Munich, PA
Judge, Hugh L., WV
Karterman, William D., PA
Kauffman, Emanuel, KS
Kendig, Jerome Stauffer, PA
Kensinger, William Henry, NJ
Kessler, Samuel Fritz, MO
King, John Wesley, PA
Kinnear, Claude Hamilton, VA
Kirk, James Newton, WV
Klapp, Joseph, PA
Kline, Edmund James, PA
Klopp, Eli Leinbach, PA
Klugh, Oliver Ringwalt, PA
Koontz, David Michael, PA
Krell, Frederick Balthazer, PA
Larendon, George W., TX
Leal, Pedro Noriega,, MEXICO
Leonhardt, Samuel Chester, VA
Leslie, LeRoy K., PA
Levengood, Brooklyn B., PA
Longfellow, Austin Harris, ME
Luckett, Charles Davis, IN
Machle, Edward Charles, OH
Maddox, John Dayton, KY
Makuen, George Hudson, NY
Manning, David Franklin, MO
Manning, Charles Jacob, PA
Marrow, Hunter, VA
Marsh, John Henry, NC
Martin, William, NJ
Mattern, Samuel Grey, PA
McColgan, James, CANADA
McCoy, Charles Wayne, OH
McLaughlin, Charles Michael, MD
McLeary, Samuel Bismarck, TX
Meigs, Joe Vincent, MA
Mickley, Howard Peter, PA
Miller, William Ischee, PA
Miller, Clinton R. DeWitt, MD
Miller, William McAlevy, PA
Miller, John Hancock, CO
Miller, Charles William, PA
Mitchell, Franklin Theodore, TX
Mitchell, John Willis, AR
Morgan, James Hamilton, DE
Nalle, William Theodore, KY
Neall, Charles H.M., PA
Newgarden, George Joseph, PA
Nixon, Warford L., NJ
O'Neill, Patrick Joseph, CA
Osmun, William Finley H., PA

Owen, William Llewellyn, PA
Oyer, William Collins, PA
Parmelee, Elmer Stuart, CT
Pennington, Charles Arthur, AR
Peters, Joel Monroe, PA
Pettibone, Charles Frederick, CT
Purviance, William Emmet, IN
Radcliffe, William Mann, PA
Ralston, Samuel Elmer, PA
Reigle, Erasmus Lear, PA
Rice, Frederick Whitney, PA
Ritchie, George Franklin, PA
Robinson, James Weir, PA
Rogan, Thomas Daniel, NJ
Ross, Matthew Wilkinson, PA
Ruiz, Jesus, COLOMBIA
Russell, Walter Judson, PA
Rutledge, Albert Thompson, PA
Salas, Juan Francisco, SPAIN
Sapp, Luther Lafayett, NC
Scott, S. Horace, PA
Seright, Thomas Clinton, OH
Serra, Arthur Alves, BRAZIL
Serra, Norberto Alves, BRAZIL
Service, John Haymaker, PA
Shelton, Edwin Bryant L., KY
Shenk, George Rigler, PA
Shields, Alexander McMakin, KY
Shope, Elias Lincoln, PA
Shumaker, Luther M., PA
Simmons, Richard Gordon, VA
Skelly, Charles Jackson, PA
Slater, George Wishart, KS
Smith, Frank Ira, PA
Snyder, Abram Elias, PA
Snyder, Emanuel Walton, PA
Southrn, Frank L., NJ
Spence, William Bayne, PA
Spencer, Boyd Cook, PA
Stapp, M. Robertson, MO
Statler, Frank B., PA
Steckman, Philip McClellan, MO
Sterner, Oliver Henry, PA
Strickland, Melville Cox, NC
Sutton, William Gordon, NC
Swayne, Howard Roeder, PA
Swiler, Robert David, PA
Taxis, Herbert John, IL
Thompson, Harry H., PA
Thompson, James Buell, PA
Thompson, Whitefield Nelson, ME
Townes, Isaac Johnson, KY
Tucker, Joseph Ellison, MO
Vincent, Thomas N., MN

1889

Walker, Harry Lewis, IA
Walter, John, PA
Ward, Richard, PA
Warg, Edwin Conner, PA
Warne, William Wilber, PA
Watt, Harry Calvin, PA
Weaver, Charles H., PA
Weida, Charles Benjamin, PA
Werley, Charles Daniel, PA
Wertman, Samuel Ellsworth, PA

Wertman, Alvin Andrew, PA
White, John Wesley, NC
Whitten, James F., NJ
Willard, Herman Frank, KS
Williamson, William S., NE
Winton, Henry Nelson, CA
Womer, Frank, PA
Woodhouse, Henry John, PA
Yarnall, Charles Wesley, PA
Zimmermann, George Luther, PA

DOCTOR AND PATIENT.

BY

S. WEIR MITCHELL, M.D., LL.D. HARV.

MEMBER OF THE UNITED STATES NATIONAL ACADEMY OF SCIENCES, PRESIDENT
OF THE COLLEGE OF PHYSICIANS OF PHILADELPHIA, PHYSICIAN
TO THE ORTHOPÆDIC HOSPITAL AND INFIRMARY
FOR NERVOUS DISEASES.

Introductory.
The Physician.
Convalescence.
Pain and its Consequences.
The Moral Management of Sick or Invalid Children.
Nervousness and its Influence on Character.
Out-Door and Camp-Life for Women.

THIRD EDITION.

PHILADELPHIA:
J. B. LIPPINCOTT COMPANY.
LONDON: 10 HENRIETTA STREET, COVENT GARDEN.
1889.

S. Weir Mitchell (JMC, 1850, Fig. 45), famed novelist and pioneer neuropsychiatrist.

On April 2, the 220 graduates of this class received their diplomas from the Honorable James Campbell, President of the Board. The Valedictory Address was delivered by Henry C. Chapman, Professor of Physiology. This large class numbered 12 from foreign countries as follows: Brazil (2), Nicaragua (2), Russia (2), and one each from Mexico, New Brunswick, France, Scotland, Germany, and China. Some of these out-of-country graduates won prizes, such as the Prize of $100 sponsored by the *Medical News* for the best Thesis embodying original research to Enrique Solorzano of Nicaragua, and a Gold Medal for the best Essay pertaining to Obstetrics to Charles S. Spivak, of Russia, with honorable mention of Jose D. Espinosa, of Nicaragua.

At a general meeting, the members of this class adopted the school colors, light blue and black, each of equal width. Louis D. Bauer of this class was present at the meeting and passed the information on to his son, Edward L. Bauer (JMC '14, Professor of Pediatrics at Jefferson, 1926 to 1954). Through the years the colors have been used on pins, badges, flags, banners and pennants. James W. Holland (Dean, 1887-1916) authorized the use of light blue and black in the cowls attached to the back of the academic gowns worn by recipients of Jefferson degrees, but the date of its inception is not recorded. The colors have been regarded as authentic, although never adopted officially by the Board of Trustees or the Faculty. The Class of 1890 acted arbitrarily in what has become one of Jefferson's entrenched traditions.

Arthur Dare, of Pennsylvania, served on Jefferson's Outpatient Medical Staff for many years and invented the Dare hemoglobinometer which remained in use in the Hospital until 1941.

E. Quinn Thornton, of Alabama, distinguished himself by collaborating with Dr. Hobart A. Hare, Professor of Therapeutics, in a *Study of the Influence of Chloroform upon the Respiration and Circulation* for the Nizam of Hyderabad (India). The silver plate he received in recognition of this work is preserved in Jefferson's Archives. Thornton (Fig. 124) went on to become Professor of Materia Medica and Therapeutics at Jefferson in 1932, following the death of Professor Hare.

CLASS OF 1890

Adams, Ellsworth Smith, NJ
Allen, Edgar, PA
Allen, Carritte Arthur, NEW BRUNSWICK
Angstadt, Thomas Miller, PA
Apple, Ammon Andrew, PA
Archibald, Charles Harvey, CA
Babcock, Franklin Elisha, MA
Backmann, Edward F., PA
Bair, George Elmer, PA
Baird, Thompson McDannold, VA
Baker, Frank Kline, PA
Barker, John Albert, PA
Barnum, Henry Weston, NY
Barr, John C., PA
Barth, James Buchanan, MD
Barton, Herbert Parks, MA
Bauer, Louis Denme, PA
Beck, Walter Milroy, KS
Beddoe, Benjamin Griffiths, PA

Beitzel, Charles Wesley, PA
Bell, John Forrest, PA
Beyer, John Jacob, PA
Bicker, Francis Joseph, PA
Blair, John A., PA
Blomer, George Davis, Jr., PA
Bold, Valentine Jacob, PA
Bolton, Joseph Peeky, PA
Bonham, James William, NY
Bortree, Thomas W., PA
Bradfield, George M., PA
Brisbin, Charles H., PA
Brown, Zalmon Kent, WV
Brown, Frederick Kendall, DE
Brugler, DeWitt, PA
Bruner, John Willet, PA
Burt, Ingram E., PA
Campbell, Ralph Rankin, PA
Chabut, Louis, FRANCE

Chambers, William James, NY
Chelf, Hugh Tucker, VA
Cobbe, Frank Edmund, RI
Cochran, John Camden, PA
Conaway, William Keith, DE
Corriher, Calvin W., NC
Courtright, Everett Peer, NJ
Creedon, William Henry, PA
Culbertson, Louis Rogers, OH
Cunningham, Daken Whitaker, PA
Curry, Thomas, PA
Dare, J. Rulon, NJ
Dare, Arthur, PA
Darnall, Carl Roger, TX
Davis, Reuben Ogden, PA
Davis, James Dudley, KY
Davis, Christian William, PA
Davis, Daniel Webster, PA
Davis, James Alexander, PA
Dean, Harry Johnson, IA
Dean, Edwin Robinson, KY
Denlinger, Maurice Musser, PA
Dennis, John, PA
Dickinson, Ernest Lincoln, NJ
Dohner, William Royer, PA
Drake, Dillon, PA
Drake, Martin Eugene, PA

Fig. 124. E. Quinn Thornton (JMC, 1890), Professor of Materia Medica and Therapeutics (1932).

Drewry, Thomas Ellis, GA
Drick, Philip, PA
Elliott, John William, PA
Emmerling, Karl August, PA
Espinosa, Jose Dolores, NICARAGUA
Estill, Andrew Davidson, VA
Etherton, William Clayton, MO
Farrar, Joseph Davidson, VA
Fegley, Oscar George, PA
Fisher, Robert Welles, DE
Fisher, Alfred Meyers, PA
Flanagan, Michael Joseph, PA
Flores, Jose Antonio, BRAZIL
Flournoy, Mathews William, MO
Frey, Robert David, PA
Garber, Jonathan Burmond, OH
Garlington, Thomas Richard, GA
Garst, Samuel Sherfey, TN
Gehring, Gustave Paul, NJ
Gillespie, William Joseph, PA
Gillespie, Peter Joseph, PA
Golding, Daniel Guedalyah, NE
Grant, Charles Longmoor, KY
Greene, Frank Nichols, PA
Gruel, Louis, Jr., PA
Hadfield, Edward John, KS
Haines, Edward Everett, NJ
Haley, John Joseph, NJ
Hanks, Jason Grant, PA
Hardie, Robert Fowler, PA
Harris, Henry F., GA
Hartman, Peter Leroy, PA
Haskins, Albert Murton, MA
Hassenplug, Frank Atwood, PA
Haymaker, Oliver Rugh, MO
Haymaker, William Jacob, PA
Hearn, Charles Sheppard, DE
Hebrank, Edmund Rock, PA
Heller, Charles Edwin, PA
Henderson, Pleasant P., OH
Hinkley, Seth Bradbury, MO
Holland, Ebe, DE
Horine, Arlington Grove, MD
Hug, John Joseph, CA
Irons, William R., PA
Jackson, Shirls Byzantine, PA
Jenkins, William Sellman, AZ
Johns, Christian Rohrer, PA
Jones, John Arthur, PA
Jones, Anderson Wilmer, KY
Keller, John Jacob, PA
Kelly, Arthur M., IL
Kitchen, Harrison Allen, PA
Klopp, Peter Paul, PA

Knipe, Jay Clarence, PA
Knox, Henry, PA
Kreider, Edwin Roger, OH
Lakin, Harry Pearce, WV
Lashells, Edward Torbett, PA
Lechner, Ralph Yahn, PA
Levan, Walter Adam, PA
Lewis, Willis Gaylord, OH
Lindsay, John, SCOTLAND
Loeb, Ludwig, GERMANY
Loughridge, Samuel Steen, PA
Lukens, Isaiah, NE
Marshall, Robert John, NJ
Mason, William Franklin, OH
Massinger, C. Jerome, PA
Maulfair, Harvey Ellsworth, PA
McCord, Eugene Woodworth, MN
McMurran, Robert Lowry, VA
McNair, Robert H., MS
McNall, James Morgan, PA
McNaul, Caleb Gleni, PA
Miller, Edwin M., PA
Miller, Harold, Baughman, NJ
Moore, John Edward, PA
Morgan, Richard J., OH
Moskievitz, Max, RUSSIA
Moy, Jin Fuey, CHINA
Mudd, John James, KY
Murry, Charles Miller, MS
Nelson, Arthur Braxton, VA
Nevin, Walter Charles, OH
O'Brien, Caleb Stanton, PA
Overton, Joe, TN
Painter, Alonzo Potter N., PA
Palmer, William Main, PA
Paules, William Rumbaugh, PA
Pettit, Joseph, PA
Pomerene, Harry Piersol, OH
Porter, George Cooper, CA
Potteiger, George Frederick, PA
Ray, Ethelbert Sheb, OH
Reilly, Peter Charles, PA
Ribeiro, Jeronymo Dias, BRAZIL
Ritter, Clement, NC
Robins, Newsom Baker, PA
Robinson, Walter Aspril, NJ
Rodgers, Robert Edward L., PA
Roehrig, George Frederick, PA
Rote, William H., PA
Ruffner, Samuel Allemong, PA

Sawyer, Waldo Fitch, NJ
Schwaemmle, Charles Henry, AL
Scott, George Barbiere, TN
Sedgwick, Henry Dean, NY
Sellew, Philip Hamilton, CT
Sharp, J. Steward, UT
Shope, Abraham Lincoln, PA
Shuman, John Clinton, PA
Siglinger, Charles Jacob, PA
Skinner, William Francis, PA
Smith, Domer Gheen, PA
Smith, John Loper, NJ
Smythe, Harry Gordon, TX
Smythe, Edward Stanhope, TX
Solorzano, Enrique, NICARAGUA
Spivak, Charles D., RUSSIA
Sprague, George Percy, PA
Steinwandel, John Anthony, PA
Stiles, Irwin A., OH
Stock, Jacob Frederick, NJ
Stone, Henry Bossinger, PA
Straub, Elmer Legrand, PA
Straughn, William David, MD
Stuart, Joseph Red, TX
Sumney, Herbert Clayton, IL
Taylor, Arthur John, PA
Taylor, James Thomas, PA
Thomas, George D., PA
Thornton, Edward Quin, AL
Thrush, Ambrose Watts, PA
Tibbins, George Hoy, PA
Tod, Alva Forman, PA
Trist, Edwin Allen, PA
Tucker, John Alfred, PA
Tuteur, Edwin B., WI
Ulmer, Charles Edward, NJ
Van Sant, Benjamin, PA
Vann, Luther Lee, NC
Veasey, Clarence Archibald, MD
Villarreal, Celso De Jesus, MEXICO
Walker, Thomas Francis, TN
Walter, William, PA
Webb, Lorenzo Lea, TN
Weiland, Carl, PA
Weitman, John Lewis, MT
White, James Taylor, CA
Wilson, Charles Wesley, NJ
Winters, John Leaman, PA
Wood, Oran Alphonso, NJ
Wright, John William, PA
Yeagy, William A., PA

With the winter session of 1890/91, a three-year graded curriculum became obligatory. Prior to this the required courses were for two years with a third year voluntary. A Training School for Nurses opened in the fall of 1891.

John Heysham Gibbon (Fig. 125) became a Co-Chairman of the Department of Surgery at Jefferson in 1907, as the successor to Dr. John Hill Brinton. He served in tandem with John Chalmers DaCosta until his retirement in 1931. Dr. Gibbon authored more than 60 articles in a diverse range of surgical subjects, including those of a historical or philosophical nature. In 1902 he reported the fourth case of a penetrating wound of the heart operated upon successfully

Fig. 125. John Heysham Gibbon (JMC, 1891), Professor of Surgery (1907-31).

in the United States. The following year he reported a painless amputation of the leg following the intraneural injection of cocaine. He served as President of the American Surgical Association, the College of Physicians of Philadelphia, and the Philadelphia Academy of Surgery. In 1948, Jefferson awarded him the Honorary Degree of Doctor of Science for his significant contributions to the medical profession, to his country in a distinguished military career, and to humanity. He was the father of John H. Gibbon, Jr., inventor of the heart-lung machine.

David Braden Kyle was awarded the gold medal by Dr. W.W. Keen at graduation for the best essay, *The Pathology and Treatment of Tetanus*. Immediately following graduation he became Assistant Demonstrator of Pathology at Jefferson. Upon beginning his practice he developed a private laboratory for instruction in clinical microscopy, bacteriology, and pathology. By 1896 he had oriented his private practice to such a degree in diseases of the ear, nose and throat that he was appointed Clinical Professor of Laryngology. In 1904 he became Jefferson's first Chairman of Laryngology and served until 1916 (Fig. 126).

Merrette W. Ireland, of Indiana, made a notable contribution to medical military history as Surgeon General of the Army from 1918 to 1931 under Presidents Wilson, Harding, Coolidge, and Hoover. He was a veteran of the Philippine and Mexican expeditions and went to France with the American Expeditionary Force in 1916. General John Pershing chose Ireland as his Chief Medical Officer in World War I (Fig. 127). Jefferson awarded him an honorary LL.D. degree in 1919, when he addressed the graduating class of that year.

Among the 188 graduates were members from British Columbia, Asia Minor, Ireland, Turkey, Mexico, Central America, India, and England.

Amon, Jesse Adolphus, KY
Anthony, Jeremiah C., MA
Bailey, Wilson Gill, NJ
Barckley, Robert George, NJ
Barcus, Adolph Ludwig, PA
Bartholow, Paul, PA
Bate, Arthur Edwin, PA
Beam, William, PA
Beatty, John James, NJ
Beck, William Franklin, PA
Behler, Jacob, PA
Bennett, Irvin Edmund, WY
Bernstein, Arthur, PA
Bevan, David, PA
Bilheimer, John Jessiah, PA
Bissell, John Robertson, PA
Bledsoe, Hugh James, TN
Bowden, Charles Prottsman, MO
Bowers, Thomas Wilson, PA

Bowes, Timothy John, DE
Boyer, I. Luther, PA
Boyle, Harlow Ashton, CA
Brown, Barton Levi, PA
Bushey, Sylvan Graham, PA
Caldwell, Euler Jones, SC
Caterson, Clarington William, PA
Coad, Theophilus John, PA
Collard, Jonathan Richard, TX
Comegys, Joseph Parsons, Jr., IA
Cooper, John S. S., PA
Coppel, Frank M., IL
Craig, Loran D., OH
Crease, Henry George, PA
Cresson, Hilborne, Thomson, PA
Cuadra, Jose Maria, NICARAGUA
Curl, Alfred Mackinnon, OH
Davis, Frederick Horace, PA
De Long, Eugene Rischel, PA

Fig. 126. David Braden Kyle (JMC, 1891), Chairman of Laryngology (1904-16).

Fig. 127. Merritte W. Ireland (JMC, 1891), Surgeon General of the Army. (Photo with Board President Robert P. Hooper (right) in 1939 on the occasion of his giving the Annual William Potter Memorial Lecture.)

1891

Derickson, Willard Porter, DE
Dittebrandt, Charles Berthol, OR
Donges, Clarence Bernard, NJ
Donnelly, Joseph Smith, TN
Dougherty, Milton Maust, PA
Eads, Benjamin Brindley, KY
Edwards, Lewis, PA
Egan, E. Winfield, MA
Eldon, Rosewell Thomas, PA
Ellershaw, Albert, PA
Emmert, Dorsey Frederick, MD
Esterly, Jacob Ritter, PA
Fahrney, Lewis Welty, MD
Farrar, John King, NY
Fiet, Harvey Jacob, PA
Fink, Ulysses S. Grant, PA
Foil, Moses Alexander, NC
Ford, Edward White, KY
Forrester, Joseph, PA
Fraser, Roderick L., BRITISH COLUMBIA
Freas, Cliffton Lewis, PA
Fries, Irvin A., PA
Garverich, Franklin Hendricks, PA
Gibbon, John Heysham, NC
Gilbert, William Leak, GA
Glasgow, George Mierley, PA
Glover, Oliver W. H., PA
Goodner, Ralph Allison, IL
Hachadoorian, Mugerditch D., ASIA MINOR
Hagen, Walter Thomas, WI
Hager, Walter Aldmond, CANADA
Hancock, Eugene Thomas, MD
Harris, Charles Hickman, OH
Harris, William, PA
Harter, George Alvin, PA
Haskin, Herbert Pliny, NY
Hawes, Albert Sidney, GA
Hazzard, Henry Draper, MO
Heider, Maurice Isaac, PA
Hewitt, Charles Ellsworth, NY
Hoffman, Olin Huntley, WV
Hofmann, Oscar Elmer, PA
Holshue, Charles Raymond, PA
Horne, John H., PA
Huston, Frank Brady, TX
Hutchison, Wilber Laurin, PA
Imhoff, Joseph Bloss, NE
Ireland, Merritte Weber, IN
Irwin, James Alexander, IRELAND
Irwin, William Underwood, PA
Jarvis, James Fletcher, MO
Jepson, Wilhelm, IA
Kaupp, Albert Theodore, PA
Kebabian, Hrand Krecor, TURKEY

Keene, Walter Bullock, RI
Kelly, William John, PA
Kieffer, Charles Ferdinand, PA
Kingsley, Charles, ME
Kirk, Grant Elmer, NJ
Klemm, Adam, PA
Kyle, David Braden, OH
Lent, Williard George, PA
Loucks, Charles Edward, OH
Lyons, Fowler, NE
Maldonado, Ferdinand Nicholas, MEXICO
Mallory, Edwin H., IA
Marvel, Charles, DE
McAdoo, Elmer Ellsworth, PA
McCleery, Edward Heber, PA
McCormick, Louis Provance, PA
McEntire, Oscar Williams, PA
McLaughlin, John Joseph, PA
Moore, Nicholas Gibbon, NC
Morison, J. Louis D., PA
Morrow, William Boyd, TN
Morton, William Thomas, PA
Moss, William Finley, OH
Newton, Francis Janvier, INDIA
Niles, John S., PA
Otis, William Henry, IA
Parramore, Edward Lyttleton, CA
Parvin, Noble Butler, PA
Patrick, Nathan Edward, IL
Perry, Warren, KS
Peter, Irvin Rue, MO
Pierce, Azel, OH
Powell, Frederick Adams, VA
Powne, Norman Groves, TX
Price, Frederick Fraley, NJ
Reith, Emil, PA
Remig, John Henry, PA
Reynolds, William Wilson, OH
Rice, Charles Samuel, PA
Robinhold, Lewis Charles, PA
Robinson, Joseph B., MO
Rosales, Nicasio, NICARAGUA
Rossiter, Henry James, CANADA
Rottner, Charles Selmar, PA
Ruch, Charles Frank, PA
Saulsberry, William, KY
Schmehl, Seymour Trout, PA
Shanks, Frederick Hastings, CA
Sherman, George Howard, MO
Shipp, Milford Bard, UT
Shook, James Curry, PA
Shoup, Jesse J., OH
Siegfried, Cyrus Sylvester, PA
Smith, John James, AR

Smith, George Calvin, IN
Smith, Matthew Mann, TX
Smith, Addison Whittaker, PA
Snowball, James William, CANADA
Sour, Stephen A.D., PA
Spence, William Edwin, MO
Spencer, William Oliver, NC
Steely, Oscar Baker, PA
Stein, George W., PA
Stem, Frank Ott, PA
Stevens, Robert W., PA
Stevens, William Bonard, PA
Stout, Amos Newton, IL
Strieby, Jacob Peter, PA
Swayze, Burton Willis, PA
Taylor, John Dempster, NY
Teagarden, James Warren, PA
Thurmond, Richard Jackson, Jr., MS
Trainor, Joseph Patrick, ENGLAND
Tule, Robert Bruce, PA
Tully, Edgar Warren, PA

Underwood, Edward Shoemaker, OH
VanKirk, Joseph, PA
Velazquez, Miguel Angel, CENTRAL AMERICA
Wales, Westley Rogers, NJ
Walker, Henry Crawford, DE
Walmer, Ephraim LeRue, PA
Walters, Edwin Campbell, PA
Ward, J. M. B., PA
Ware, James Nicholas, AR
Waters, Oren Judson, PA
Weiser, Frank Ressler, PA
Wells, William Hughes, PA
West, James Newton, GA
White, Ernest Augustus, ME
White, Frank, IN
Wickert, Victor Wilson, PA
Widder, George Haller, PA
Wiley, Harry Eugene, PA
Wilkinson, William John, PA
Williams, David, WALES
Winslow, John Lang, PA

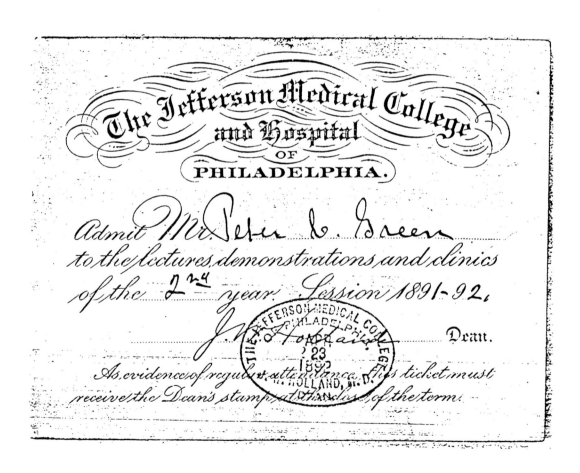

In this year the new three-year college curriculum was spelled out in the Annual Announcement. The studies of the first year included: Anatomy and Histology, Physiology, General and Medical Chemistry, and Materia Medica and Pharmacy; with laboratory work in each branch, dissection, and at the option of the student the general clinics. Studies of the second year were as follows: Anatomy and Topographical Anatomy, Physiology and Medical Jurisprudence, Toxicology and Medical Chemistry, Materia Medica and Therapeutics, Pathological Anatomy, Practice of Medicine and Clinical Medicine, Surgery and Clinical Surgery, and Didactical and Clinical Obstetrics. The third year studies were: Practice of Medicine and Clinical Medicine, Surgery and Clinical Surgery, Didactical and Clinical Pediatrics, and Hygiene and Therapeutics.

Stricker Coles, a Virginian by birth from a distinguished ancestry, became outstanding. Before his graduation from Jefferson he had devoted early studies to engineering, had two years of classical study at Roanoke College, and a year in the medical department of the University of Virginia at Charlottesville. Following graduation from Jefferson and serving as intern on the staff of Jefferson Hospital, he started a long career in obstetrics by appointment as Assistant in the Obstetrical Department at Jefferson as well as the Polyclinic (now known as the Graduate Hospital). By 1908 he rose in academic rank at Jefferson to Assistant Professor of Obstetrics. From 1902 onward he was Chief Assistant in the Department of Obstetrics and supervised the delivery of nearly every patient admitted to the 1877 Hospital. He served on the staffs in other major hospitals of Philadelphia, published many scholarly scientific papers, and was active in important professional and social societies (Fig. 128).

James Torrence Rugh (Fig. 129), a Pennsylvanian, was destined to become Jefferson's second Chairman of Orthopaedic Surgery (1918-39) and the first James Edwards Professor (1930-39). He had gained valuable experience with the surgical treatment of battle casualties during World War I and rapidly applied these lessons to patient problems at Jefferson. During his term as Department Chairman the treatment of orthopaedic disabilities generally shifted from the mechanical methods used by his predecessors to modern open surgical correction. His portrait was presented to the Medical College by the Class of 1934.

The Valedictory Address to 147 graduates was delivered by John Hill Brinton (JMC, 1852, Fig. 49), Professor of Practice of Surgery.

Fig. 128. Stricker Coles (JMC, 1892), Assistant Professor of Obstetrics and Chief Assistant in the Hospital.

Allen, Charles Leland, PA
Althouse, Albert C., PA
Anderson, John Benjamin, PA
Andreas, George R., PA
Armbrecht, Edward Louis, WV
Arnold, J. Harry, KY
Atkinson, Harry Fretts, PA
Banes, Joseph Hiram, DC
Barton, Harry Roszelle, MD
Beale, Frank Sidney, PA
Bell, James Alexander, MS
Bemis, Royal Warren, MA
Blake, Duncan W., Jr., NJ
Bloodworth, Francis Henry, GA
Brewster, Joseph Hall, PA
Brothers, William Roy, PA
Brubaker, Frank B., PA
Bruch, Elmer Clinton, PA
Bumgarner, George Leonard, PA

Fig. 129. James Torrence Rugh (JMC, 1892), Chairman of Orthopaedic Surgery (1918-39) and first James Edwards Professor.

Carnahan, William J., PA
Casey, Joseph Daniel, PA
Chapman, Charles R., MN
Chritzman, Clarence Armor, PA
Cloud, Joseph Howard, PA
Cohen, Nathan Alexander, PA
Coles, Stricker, VA
Colgan, James F. E., PA
Conkwright, Sideny Allen, MO
Conner, William, PA
Corson, Joseph Makay, PA
Craig, William Gibson, IA
Cuskaden, Albert Douglas, NJ
Dehoney, Howard, KY
Derr, James Grant, PA
Dunning, Frederick, MD
Eastman, Henry, Jr., PA
Elkin, Philip, CT
Ernest, Jacob Ellsworth, PA
Eshbach, William W., PA
Felty, Harry Bowman, PA
Ferguson, John Preston, KY
Ferree, George Perry, MN
Foster, Harry Stewart, PA
Gabrielian, Mugurdich C., ARMENIA
Goodwin, James Joseph, RI
Grime, Robert Thomas, PA
Gustin, Grant Harden, PA
Hanna, Hugh, PA
Hannan, Charles Edmund, PA
Harpel, Jesse Edward, PA
Harris, Frank P., NJ
Hartline, Charles Henry, PA
Hassenplug, William Finley, PA
Hawkes, Edwin Green, PA
Hazlett, Harry Foster, PA
Heaton, William Wright, PA
Heller, Jacob Louie, PA
Henderson, Robert James, PA
Henry, J. Malcolm, PA
Hermany, Horace David, PA
Hislop, John, PA
Hoffman, Elmer, E. M., PA
Holliday, John Wesley, IA
Hunter, Marcus Catlin, PA
Jackson, Thomas Wright, OH
Jermane, Percy Lee, MO
Jessop, Roland, PA
Johansen, Erneste Augustus, CA
Johnston, Edmund Burke, MN
Jones, Thomas Edward, PA
Jordy, Louis, PA

1892

Kane, James J., PA
Kerns, Samuel Proctor, PA
Kinsley, Edward William, PA
Krieger, Lewis William, KS
Landis, Charles Earnest, PA
Light, Lincoln Reigel, PA
Lippincott, Ahab Haines, NJ
Long, William Hillwell, Jr., KY
Marsh, Edward Brown, PA
Marshall, James Sidney, TX
McCarty, David Wilson, PA
McGrath, Francis A., PA
McLernon, John, PA
McMullin, Andrew, PA
Meek, Francis Joseph, PA
Millard, Benjamin Joshua, PA
Miller, Elmer Clare, PA
Mines, Marcus Keen, NJ
Moffet, John, PA
Monahan, Frank Henry, RI
Mullikin, Louis Wagner, NJ
Munson, Harry G., DE
Murphy, Robert Matthew, NEW BRUNSWICK
Murray, Alexander, NEW BRUNSWICK
Murray, Lewis R., NEW BRUNSWICK
Musser, William Franklin, PA
Noll, Franklin, Jr., PA
O'Reilly, Thomas W., MO
Ottinger, Samuel Joseph, PA
Page, Harlan Myron, OH
Parshall, Robert Vincent, PA
Pepper, Wilbur Lee, PA
Perry, Van Lear, WV
Pigall, Joseph Smith, MO
Pressly, George W. L., SC
Purnell, Howard Garrett, DE
Raessler, Rufus Raymond, PA
Reedy, Walter Marion, PA

Robins, William Wallace, PA
Rose, David, OH
Ross, Nathaniel, PA
Royer, Jacob Weaver, PA
Rugh, James Torrence, PA
Saunders, Robert Ritchie, PA
Schaul, Otho Daniel, PA
Seligman, Abram Pott, PA
Shannon, William A., PA
Sherman, harry Ulysses, PA
Shultz, Cameron, PA
Spencer, George Wicks, IN
Sprissler, Oscar, PA
Spruance, Henry Roche, DE
Stewart, Alonzo Hamilton, PA
Stillwagen, Charles Augustine, PA
Swartzwelder, James Sherman, PA
Swisher, David Falls, PA
Thomas, Charles Wallace, WA
Trexler, Charles Amos, PA
Trumbauer, Dalton, PA
VanBuren, Marmaduke Foster, PA
Vanneman, Walter A. R., PA
Vincent, George Walter, NY
Volz, Frederick, IL
Walker, James, DE
Ward, James H., DE
Weaver, Albert Prince, CO
Weaver, Clarence Arlington, DC
Webb, Henry McCorry, AR
West, George Henry, DE
Widmann, Louis A., AUSTRIA
Williams, Neri Barndt, PA
Winslow, Bela Henry, ME
Wootters, John Smith, TX
Work, Robert Anderson, PA
Ziegenfuss, Nathan, PA
Zuniga, Marcos, CENTRAL AMERICA

DEMONSTRATOR'S QUIZ

ANATOMY.

ADDINELL HEWSON. M.D.

Admit Mr. *O. N. Turner*

for the Session of 18*91-92*

Pub. Quiz   *A. Hewson*

Master in Anatomy

In 1893 there was instituted a fourth-year option of "advanced courses." Also offered in a voluntary fourth year was a program of special instruction at the Polyclinic Hospital where Jefferson Professors H. Augustus Wilson, E.P. Davis, Solomon Solis-Cohen, and J.A. Cantrell were affiliated.

In this class of 188, Hobart Amory Hare was the most outstanding member (Fig. 130). His first M.D. degree had been awarded by the University of Pennsylvania in 1884, at which time he won the faculty prize. During subsequent postgraduate studies both at home and abroad he received numerous other prizes and awards. In 1890 he was elected Clinical Professor of Diseases of Children at the University of Pennsylvania, but the following year he was made Professor of Therapeutics and Materia Medica at Jefferson. His 1893 Jefferson M.D. degree qualified him as an alumnus and in 1909 he served as President of the Alumni Association. National and world-wide honors accumulated during his intensely active career in teaching, medical writing and a busy consulting practice. His portrait was presented to the College by the Class of 1927.

Wilmer Krusen, a graduate pharmacist, entered Jefferson in 1891 following medical courses at Medico-Chirurgical College and the University of Pennsylvania. After Jefferson internship he served in the Department of Gynecology and became interested in the history of that specialty. In 1902 he was appointed Professor of Gynecology at Temple University School of Medicine continuing until 1927. In 1916 he became a Trustee and Vice President. Dr. Krusen was also appointed to two terms as Director of Public Health of Philadelphia.

Jesse Watson Hirst interned at Jefferson Hospital and subsequently served on the Hospital Staff in the Department of Gynecology as well as the Nose and Throat Clinic. From 1904 to 1934 he served as a medical missionary under the Presbyterian Board of Foreign Missions, stationed in Seoul, Korea with the Severance Memorial Hospital (Fig. 131).

Thomas Leidy Rhoads after graduation served under Professor W.W. Keen for four years as Assistant Demonstrator of Surgery and of Pathology. He enlisted in the Navy at the outbreak of the Spanish-American War in 1898 and was put in charge of the Naval Hospital at Washington, D.C. When the insurrection occurred in the Philippines in 1900 he switched to become an Army Surgeon. While in the Philippines he was called upon to act as the operating surgeon upon Governor Taft. When Mr. Taft was elected President of the United States, one of his first acts was to

Fig. 130.   Hobart Amory Hare (University of Pennsylvania, 1884 and JMC, 1893), Professor of Therapeutics (1891-1931).

order Dr. Rhoads from the Philippines to Washington to become his personal physician. In addition, Major Rhoads was made Chief of the Surgical Service at the Walter Reed General Hospital.

In this year the *Gross Clinic* was exhibited at the World's Fair in Chicago. The year also marked the institution of medical licensure by the Commonwealth of Pennsylvania.

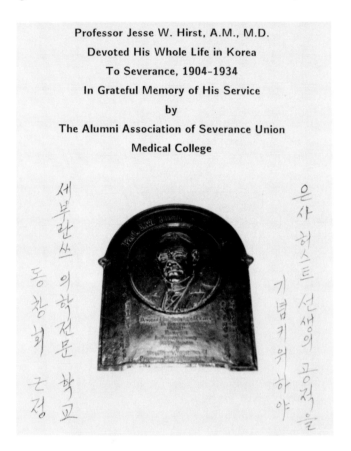

Professor Jesse W. Hirst, A.M., M.D.

Devoted His Whole Life in Korea

To Severance, 1904–1934

In Grateful Memory of His Service

by

The Alumni Association of Severance Union

Medical College

세부란쓰 의학전문 학교 동창회 근정

은사 허스트 선생의 공적을 기념키 위하야

Fig. 131. Tribute to Jesse W. Hirst (JMC, 1893) by the Severance Union Medical College.

CLASS OF 1893

Aichner, Oscar Fred, PA
Andre, Simeon Nicholas, PA
Ashburn, Percy Moreau, OH
Badeer, Sarkis, SYRIA
Baer, John Richard, PA
Baird, Howard Grant, KS
Baker, H. Hoffman, PA
Bartilson, Benjamin Matthias, PA
Baumgartner, William Jacob, PA
Bennett, William Robert, PA
Bennett, John Henry, PA
Bickell, Ulysses Grant, PA
Biehn, Andrew Clymer, PA
Birriolo, Francis Annibale, PA
Black, Judson Harmon, OH
Bodenstab, William Henry, WI
Borsch, John Louis, Jr., PA
Botkin, Amos Watts, OR
Bowman, Charles Stewart, PA

Bradshaw, Arthur Franklin, CA
Britt, Albert Jerome, PA
Brown, Harry Cox, INDIA
Bullard, John William, NE
Burton, Wilbur Darwin, DE
Busey, Charles, IN
Butterworth, Francis James, PA
Canon, Robert Taylor, TX
Carrier, Frank Nathan, PA
Carrow, Joseph, DE
Casey, Thomas Daniel, PA
Chaffin, William Wamach, VA
Chassagne, Eugene J., DC
Church, Nathan William, PA
Coburn, Charles Wilmot, PA
Cochran, Thomas Preston, Jr., PA
Cole, Thomas Porter, PA
Cole, William Gilbert, OR
Coleman, James William, PA

Corl, Harvey Elmer, OH
Corrigan, William Hilary, PA
Crabill, Thomas Voss, OH
Craig, Clark Rankin, PA
Cunningham, Daniel Henry, MN
DaCosta, John Chalmers, Jr., PA
Davis, Medus Monroe, PA
Dickel, William John, PA
Dickinson, George Standish, PA
Duke, Casper, NY
East, Albert Franklin, PA
Edwards, William J., PA
Ellis, Lyman Miles, IA
Eshleman, Edwin Franklin, PA
Farrell, Francis Albert, PA
Ferguson, Benjamin Bassett, DE
Fix, Ira Niblock, PA
Gallagher, Joseph Francis, PA
Gardiner, Sheridan Ellsworth, NY
Geisendorfer, John Alexander, OR
Gerhard, Samuel Pilgrim, PA
Gery, Alfred Oliver, PA
Geulick, Frank Wallace, PA
Goodman, Isaac, PA
Graver, Edward, PA
Green, Peter Charles, PA
Grier, Clarence Russell, DE
Hain, Leonard G., PA
Hanley, Francis Joseph, RI
Hare, Hobart Amory, PA
Harover, Samuel Richard, KY
Hassell, Howard Wesley, PA
Hassenplug, Harry Gilmore, PA
Havice, Luther Calvin, PA
Hawkins, William Henry, ME
Headings, Isaac Griffy, Jr., PA
Heiberg, Adolph Oscar, MN
Heileman, Henry, PA
Hendricks, Augustus William, PA
Hess, J. Bruce, PA
Hirst, Jesse Watson, MA
Hoopes, Charles Wilson, PA
Hubbard, John Parkinson, Jr., PA
Huebner, George William, PA
Huff, Scott M., PA
Hug, Edward Victor, OH
Humphrey, Walter Newton, PA
Hunsberger, William Henry, PA
Hunter, Joseph William, PA
Hunter, Herbert Kingsley, ENGLAND
Hutchins, Adrian Albertus, OH
Isenberg, Joseph Lloyd, PA
Jacob, James Francis, PA
Kain, William Wilkins, NJ

Kalbach, Isaac Irwin, PA
Kasten, William Henry, PA
Kiley, Frank Love, PA
King, Hiram Orville, PA
Kiteley, William Ellis, CANADA
Kleinstuber, William George, DE
Klemmer, William Nickolaus, GERMANY
Klotz, Robert Bertram, PA
Knapp, Warren A. Bickel, PA
Krusen, Wilmer, PA
Kyle, Elmer Bryan, PA
Lacey, James Henry, CO
Lewis, William H., PA
Luster, George Edgar, IL
Maddock, Louis, OR
McDaniel, Edward Bruce, OR
McGee, James McMeekin, PA
McGregor, Andrew, CANADA
McKelway, George Irvin, PA
McKenzie, William White, NC
Means, Robert Markle, PA
Meixell, Edwin Wesley, PA
Metz, John Pancoast, PA
Miller, William Haman, DE
Mitchell, William Cottonham, PA
Moore, Lynford Lardner, NC
Moukaddim, Hammoud, SYRIA
Mullen, Joseph Aloysius, PA
Muller, Rodolph Emile, SWITZERLAND
Murdoch, John Floyd, PA
Murdoch, James Hutton, PA
Murray, John Arthur, PA
O'Donnel, Hugh Boyle, IRELAND
Oyer, Harry Willrich, PA
Patty, Louis Greenlee, IA
Payne, Marshall John, VA
Pearson, Edward James, DE
Pease, Frank David, ND
Peralta, Jose Maria, CENTRAL AMERICA
Persing, Amos Vastine, PA
Piper, Charles Eugene, MO
Pope, Mardelle Yates, AR
Powell, George Perry, NE
Ramirez, Leopolde M., CENTRAL AMERICA
Ramsey, William George, PA
Reckefus, Charles Halwadt, Jr., PA
Redelin, Albert Augustus, PA
Reed, John Orlando, PA
Rentschler, Harry Fleisher, PA
Reum, Charles George, WI
Rhoads, Thomas Leidy, PA
Rich, Edward Israel, ID
Ritz, Reinhart Joseph, PA
Rogers, Asa Holt, TX

Rush, Warren Blachley, FL
Sallade, Frank Reed, PA
Sargent, Albert Alonzo, ME
Savitsky, Joseph Adam, RUSSIA
Scholl, Harvey Frederick, PA
Sedgwick, Walter Nelson, PA
Segal, Bernhard, PA
Sheeder, Benjamin Franklin, OH
Shrader, Edwin Elmer, MN
Sittler, Warren Clement, PA
Smith, Patrick Albert, CANADA
Smith, George Hartford, IA
Sommer, Henry, Jr., PA
Sorenson, Soren, WI
Speer, Henry Newton, PA
Stover, Isaac Francis, PA
Targett, Archibald Frederick, NJ
Thomas, Harry Leedon, PA
Tinker, Martin Buel, MA
Toner, Mark Ferdinand, PA
Tryon, Lewis Royer, NJ

Turner, Oliver William, ME
Walker, James W.H., PA
Wallace, William Smiley, KS
Walton, Joseph Henry, IA
Wamsley, James Winter, NJ
Ward, Percy Hall, NY
Ward, Nathan Gideon, NC
Wheeling, William Stuart, PA
White, Jonas Samuel, PA
Whitney, Walter Everett, ME
Whitten, Jarvis Adams, PA
Wilde, John R., NY
Williams, Robert J., NC
Williams, John Henry, PA
Winder, Laurence Johnson, PA
Wingender, Wendell Phillips, PA
Wintermute, George Preston, WA
Wurtele, August Herman, PA
Wyeth, Charles, IN
Yacoubi, Hazarabed Boghos, ASIA MINOR
Yenser, William Albert, PA

JEFFERSON MEDICAL COLLEGE AND HOSPITAL.

SESSION OF 1893-94.

SECOND YEAR.

Mr. *F. L. Hammond*

Is assigned to seats:

No. *230*, Lower Room.   No. *233*, Upper Room.

No. *258*, Hospital.

The above seats are reserved in the lectures on Practice of Medicine, Surgery, Obstetrics, Pathology, Therapeutics, and Hospital Clinics only.   In lectures on Anatomy, Organic Chemistry, and Physiology he is assigned to seats:

No. *20*, Lower Room.

No. *23*, Upper Room.

Section, *A*

Ticket to lectures in the Medical College.

This year was marked by the establishment of a maternity facility at 224 South Seventh Street by the Maternity Committee of the new Board of Lady Managers. It was the first major activity of the Board which had been established by the Trustees in 1890 "to aid the College and Hospital." The Lady Managers became the Women's Auxiliary of the Hospital in 1909, the title later being changed to the Women's Board which went on to increasingly meaningful accomplishments for the Hospital. "Aid" to the College was not well defined but it is clear that a group of the ladies in 1896 equipped a Reading Room and financed a Medical Library in the old College and in the new College Building when it opened in 1898.

Randle C. Rosenberger was the most widely-known among the 163 graduates. His career at Jefferson spanned 50 years during which time he was well acquainted with all Jefferson students (Figure 132). Beginning with Pathology, he quickly became attracted to the new science of Bacteriology which under Professor Coplin was a part of Pathology. In 1909 he became Professor and Head of the new Department of Bacteriology and Hygiene. He was also Pathologist to the Philadelphia General Hospital (1903-19) and later Professor of Hygiene and Preventive Medicine at Woman's Medical College of Pennsylvania. His teaching schedule at Jefferson was extensive and in 1927 his title became Professor of Preventive Medicine and Bacteriology. Another change occurred in 1941 when Dr. Rosenberger was Acting Dean following the death of Dean Mohler. Dr. Perkins, the new Dean, then became Chairman of the Department of Preventive Medicine while Dr. Rosenberger's Department was retitled the Department of Bacteriology and Immunology. He was noted for his detailed memory of the medical students and alumni who in turn accorded him affection and respect (Fig. 133). The class of 1928 presented his portrait to the College.

Ward Brinton, scion of an old Philadelphia family and son of John Hill Brinton (JMC, 1852, Fig. 49), Professor of Surgery, had interests that differed from those of his father. A member of the First City Troop, Ward Brinton served with that unit in the Spanish-American War and he later became interested in hunting and exploration. In 1903 he joined Dr. Lawrence Flick (JMC, 1879, Fig. 99) as a clinician when the Henry Phipps Institute for Tuberculosis was founded. He continued with Phipps until 1910 but he later served as Physician to the Tuberculosis Department of the Philadelphia General Hospital and as head of the Tuberculosis Division of the Department of Health of Philadelphia.

Fig. 132.   Randle C. Rosenberger (JMC, 1894), first Chairman of Bacteriology and Hygiene (1909-44).

Charles Stapler Mangum as early as five years after graduation became Professor of Materia Medica and Physiology at the University of North Carolina.

Frederick H. Mills pursued a career in the United States Army, achieving the rank of Major during World War I in 1918. In 1924 he became Professor of Military Science and Tactics at Jefferson and was later promoted to Colonel (Fig. 134).

CLASS OF 1894

Alexander, James Newton, PA
Andrews, Alonzo, MA
Austin, Lewis King, ME
Baker, Regay Leslie, IL
Barclay, John Judson, Jr., AL
Belknap, Virgil Clarence, OR
Benscoter, Perry Hubler, PA
Bouey, Neil Joseph, CANADA
Bowen, David Ralph, NY
Boyer, Charles Harvey, PA
Brand, Walter William, OH
Brick, Joseph Coles, PA
Brinton, Ward, PA
Brouwer, Frank, NJ
Brower, Charles Johnson, PA
Burke, Patrick F., PA
Carson, David James, MT

Chatterton, W.W.A., IA
Clementson, William Alexander, PA
Clewell, Clarence Henry, PA
Conboy, J. Philip, CO
Cook, Thomas Davis, DE
Coons, Samuel Gamble, PA
Cornwell, Alfred, NJ
Cover, O. Alvin, IA
Cox, Miley Edsin, WY
Crawford, John Kinnier, PA
Crawford, Herbert Pollock, PA
Cross, Otho W., PA
Cunningham, Charles, NJ
Eckert, J. Wilson, PA
Edgerton, James Ives, SC
Edwards, Edward, OH
Edwards, George Murray, PA

Fig. 134.   Colonel Frederick H. Mills (JMC, 1894), Professor of Military Science and Tactics at Jefferson.

Fig. 133.   Singing of Christmas carols by students conducted by Dr. Randle C. Rosenberger (JMC, 1894, front row to right of center).

1894

Edwards, Thomas Lewis, OH
Faddis, Thomas McClellan, PA
Faust, Albert David, PA
Fisher, John Leroy, PA
Fly, Edward Monroe, MN
Foehrenback, Julius Emmanuel, PA
Fredericks, David Patterson, PA
Frisbie, Hiram Zebulon, PA
Gaugler, Richard Sechrist, PA
Gaylord, Charles Davis, KY
Goff, Waldo Percy, WV
Good, Albert Parke, PA
Green, Edward Houghton, PA
Hagenbuch, James Hervy, PA
Hamilton, William Boyd, OR
Handrick, Frank A., PA
Harrington, George W., PA
Hartford, P. Calvin, OH
Hassler, Samuel Freeman, PA
Hazel, Thomas Harold, PA
Henyan, E. Lucas, NJ
Hertzler, William Crooks, OH
Hickey, Thomas Bernard, PA
Hirst, Levi Brook, NJ
Hoag, Harry Martin, IA
Hodgens, Isaac Walter, PA
Hoffecker, Robert Crockett, DE
Holmes, Benjamin Henry, MA
Howard, Edward W. S., PA
Huff, John Thompson, NJ
Huff, Junius K., SC
Huffman, George W., IA
Huffman, Obadiah Layton, OH
Hunt, Thomas W., KS
Irish, William Beckford, PA
Johnson, Samuel, Jr., TN
Karr, George Muster, KY
Kelly, Francis Joseph, Jr., PA
Kenyon, Charles Lewis, PA
King, Albert Hazlett, PA
King, William Howard, PA
Knipe, William Henry, PA
Kolmer, John, IN
Krape, Joseph Harman, PA
Kriebel, Elmer, PA
Lane, Leonidas Polk, GA
Lee, Frank Alexander, IA
Lethiecq, Joseph Albert, ME
Linsz, Henri Philip, PA
Lippincott, Jesse Diverty, NJ
MacElree, George Anderson, PA
Maier, Frederick Hurst, PA
Mangum, Charles Stapler, NC
Marbarger, George S., PA

Marsh, William Alfred, PA
Martin, Joseph Marsh, DE
Martindale, Joseph Watson, CANADA
McCelvey, John Samuel, TX
McKee, Frank William, WI
McMurray, Gerald Joseph, PA
McNaul, William John, PA
Mellor, Thomas, PA
Mesropian, Messiah, ASIA MINOR
Metheny, Samuel A. S., PA
Millener, Frederick Hoyer, NY
Miller, Emery, NJ
Miller, Aaron Gable, PA
Mills, Frederick Hubbell, NY
Mohn, James Oliver, PA
Moore, John W. F., PA
Moore, Maurice Gardner, IN
Morris, John Knox, KY
Muzquiz, Juan Long, MEXICO
Netherton, Samuel Oliver, PA
Noel, Joseph Roberts, IL
Nunan, William Lawrence, PA
Osmun, Milton Mackey, NJ
Painter, William Isaac, VA
Peralta, Maximiliano, CENTRAL AMERICA
Pittis, Thomas, NJ
Powell, Barton Jerome, NV
Pratt, John Lynn, DE
Prevost, Clarence Worrel, PA
Price, Frederick Kirker, OH
Rabe, John Howard, OH
Rabethge, Charles Arman, PA
Rendleman, James Walter, IL
Reynolds, Walter Forbyce, IL
Rich, Ezra Clark, ID
Robbins, Charles Pern, IA
Rosenberger, Randle Crater, PA
Rosenberger, John Ashby, CA
Ross, Joseph Herman, PA
Rothermel, Wilson H., PA
Rovno, Philip, PA
Samuel, William Charles, PA
Saulsberry, Charles Emmet, KY
Saunders, John Welcome, RI
Schaufelberger, Franklin, OH
Scribner, John King, PA
Simmons, Charles Columbus, TX
Slifer, George Baringer, PA
Smink, Alfred Harrison, PA
Smith, Delos DeWitt, MN
Smith, Joseph Isaiah, PA
Smith, Paul Crews, MO
Snyder, Alva Earl, OH
Somerville, George Wallace, CANADA

1894

Stevens, Selton Winfield, PA
Strecker, Henry Anthony, PA
Thompson, John Lemuel, PA
Thomson, Frank Frazer, PA
Timmons, Joseph McConnell, PA
Townsend, Milton Banes, MO
Trexler, Jacob Franklin, PA
Tucker, Henry, PA
Turley, John Wesley, MO
Turner, Irvine F. P., PA
VanHorn, John William, PA

Veasey, Benjamin Rammel, DE
Voss, Frederick John G., PA
Wagner, George William, Jr., MI
Wallace, William, PA
Watson, Stephen Sidney, NY
Winters, Frank Winfield, PA
Witherspoon, Ambrose Henry, KY
Wolfe, Samuel Melville, PA
Yeomans, George Ellery, PA
Zimmerman, Lorenzo Burton, PA

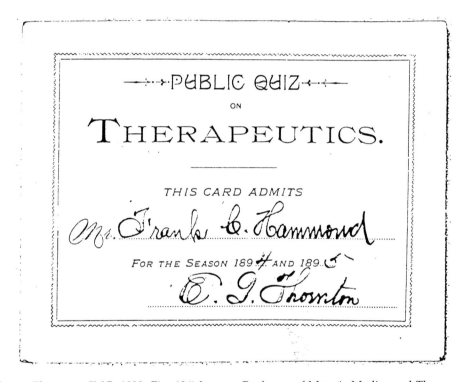

E. Quinn Thornton (JMC, 1890, Fig. 124) became Professor of Materia Medica and Therapeutics.

This year marked the end of an era for Jefferson. The proprietary status which had pertained from its founding was superseded by a change to full control by the Board of Trustees. This meant that medical education was no longer a financial interest of the professors and fees were paid directly to the administration. The prime mover in this dramatic shift was the Honorable William Potter who subsequently served as President of the Board from 1896 to 1926 (Fig. 135).

The 148 graduates of 1895 brought the total alumni number since inception of the college to 10,398. Although the stated admission requirements did not change during these years, the tendency was for matriculants to possess more than minimal qualifications. Increasingly, men with dental, pharmacy and baccalaureate degrees were admitted as well as a number who already had the M.D. degree from other institutions. In lieu of a college degree, the basic high school or academy education was still acceptable as was a "certificate from examiners of a County Medical Society." An entrance examination was also available as an option. This Class had one clerical graduate, the Rev. Howard Fisher, of India.

The medical course underwent its most important change on June 1, 1895, when the four year course became a requirement for the M.D. degree. Class instruction was spelled out in detail for each of the four years and the classes were increasingly divided into sections for laboratory and clinical teaching.

During 1894/95, funds were raised by the Alumni Association in conjunction with the American Surgical Association for erection in Smithsonian Park, Washington, D.C., of a statue of Professor Samuel D. Gross (Fig. 136). The statue was erected in 1897 and by Act of Congress was transferred to the Jefferson campus in 1970. The Gross statue was the second full-length bronze ever erected in honor of a physcian, the first having been that of J. Marion Sims (JMC, 1835) placed in Bryant Park, New York, in 1894 (Fig. 137).

CLASS OF 1895

Allen, David E., CANADA
Allman, Alfred Frederick, PA
Aufmwasser, Hugo W., PA
Avard, Charles McQueen, CANADA
Barnhardt, Charles Henry, NC
Beach, James Daniel, PA
Bermudez, Pedro Joaquin, CENTRAL AMERICA
Bicknell, Robert Cooke, NJ
Bingaman, Edwin Milton, PA
Birdsall, William George, CANADA
Bower, Ernest Ziegler, PA
Brackett, Arthur Stone, CT
Briggs, Arthur A., NH
Brobst, Daniel Reuben, PA
Brooks, Allan Colby, PA
Brooks, Frank Martin, OR
Brown, Alexander Hugh, MN
Burger, John Rudolph, IN
Burke, Richard David, PA
Carr, George W., PA

Clark, Cunningham P., PA
Clark, Oscar D. F., PA
Cleborne, Ronayne D., VA
Copp, Edgar Maitland, CANADA
Cort, Paul Lange, PA
Costello, Henry J., PA
Cox, George Rudy, MO
Craig, James Alexander, IA
Cubbage, Samuel Thomas, DE
Curry, William, PA
Davis, Alvah Ross, DE
Deweese, Cornelius Smith, MD
Dexter, Henry Leone, PA
Dickson, Richard Ensign, PA
Dixon, Charles L., CANADA
Donnelly, Peter, OH
Dostor, Benjamin Robert, Jr., GA
Duncan, Homer G., PA
Dunkel, Edwin Kilyan, PA
Fahrney, Henry Peter, MD

Farrell, George Louis, MA
Farrington, Owen Price, MO
Finley, Harry Lincoln, KS
Fisher, Rev. Howard, INDIA
Fisler, Charles Franklin, NJ
Fitzgerald, William Wesley, CA
Gearhart, Sylvester Carpenter, PA
Gilbert, John, PA
Gillette, Claudius Wesley, PA
Grim, Frank Seymour, PA
Hager, Albert Edwin, PA
Hahn, Franklin Jacob, PA
Hammond, Frank Clinch, PA
Harriman, Wilbert Eugene, IA
Hayes, Frederick Legro, NH
Hess, Louis T., PA
Hight, William Boyd, MO
Hilliard, Walter Lewis, NC
Himes, Bower Edwin, PA
Hoagland, George Bradford, NY

Hobson, William Heverin, DE
Hoffman, William Wallace, PA
Holt, William Preston, NC
Hoover, Percy Linn, PA
Horn, Wallace Lincoln, IL
Hottenstein, Charles Augustus, PA
James, John Warren, DE
Johnson, Mark E., IA
Judd, James Frederick, PA
Keenan, Isaac W., OH
King, Harry Brown, PA
Kolb, Isadore, PA
Kress, Palmer John, PA
Kurkjie, Nazareth J., ASIA MINOR
Lawson, John Alexander, IA
Lechner, LeRoy Yohn, PA
Lehnkering, Charles F., OH
Litchfield, Paul Nathan, NJ
Loeb, Louis, PA
Lowentrout, Oscar B., CA

Fig. 135. The Honorable William Potter, leader in Jefferson's change from proprietary to non-profit status in 1895. He subsequently served as Board President (1896-1926).

Fig. 136. Statue of Samuel D. Gross (JMC, 1828) in Smithsonian Park (1897).

Lowman, John Bodine, PA
Lyon, William Reynolds, PA
Manning, William J., PA
McBean, James, IL
McCreery, Rolla Lewis, CO
Meals, Charles Atlee, PA
Miles, Robert G., PA
Miller, Maurice E., DC
Milliken, William, NE
Mills, John Herman, PA
Moore, Pierre Albert, LA
Moye, Elbert Alfred, Jr., NC
Murphy, Bernard Patrick, CT
Musser, Walter Scott, PA
O'Brien, Robert Faulkner, CANADA
Pickett, William Clendenin, PA
Plant, Edgar Bossett, WV

Poust, George Alvin, PA
Province, Clarence, IN
Reed, Charles Edgar, PA
Richards, William Evans, MS
Ritter, Howard Murray, PA
Roe, William John, CANADA
Rohrs, Henry Fred, OH
Roose, Arthur Eugene, PA
Rosenberry, Edward Shimer, PA
Schultz, William Clyde, PA
Sevier, Daniel Edward, NC
Sevier, Joseph Thomas, NC
Shaffer, Charles Porter, KS
Shartle, John, PA
Shelly, Albert, ENGLAND
Shepard, Ernest Newton, PA
Simon, Lincoln G., NE
Simpson, Jonathan Chauncey, PA
Simpson, Edward Percy, MD
Smith, Frederick Forbes, CANADA
Smith, James S., PA
Smyth, Thomas Flemming, TX
Souder, Elmer Nicholas, PA
Spear, Raymond, PA
Starkey, Richard S., CANADA
Stauffer, Harry J., PA
Stevenson, Alexander M., PA
Taminosian, Timotheus, TURKEY
Taylor, Samuel Banks, PA
Taylor, Zebulon Scriven, NJ
Terry, George H. B., PA
Thompson, Oan Joshua, MN
Townsend, Charles Rees, KS
Wade, Charles Alexander, WV
Walsh, Frank Alfred, NY
Walter, Adam V., PA
Ware, James Whilldin, NJ
Ware, James Robert, SC
Waterhouse, Charles Leonard, WA
Wertz, Silas Grant, PA
Weygandt, William Wilson, PA
Williams, Philip Banatyne, PA
Wilson, Thomas Cooper, PA
Wilson, John Edwin, NY
Wolfe, Isaac Reber, PA
Wolfson, Julius, PA
Wood, Hubert, CANADA
Wood, Fred Green, PA
Wood, John William, OH
Woodhouse, Samuel William, PA
Zehner, William Henry, PA

Fig. 137.   Statue of J. Marion Sims (JMC, 1835) in Bryant Park, New York City (1894).

Francis Torrens Stewart was perhaps the most promising graduate in this class of 227. Although his premedical education was limited to Central High School, Philadelphia, he was self-taught in many areas including study of languages and literature. He received his M.D. degree at age 19 in spite of the general rule of age 21 as a graduation requirement. Following residency at the old Polyclinic Hospital and Pennsylvania Hospital, he was appointed Chief of the Outpatient Surgical Dispensary at Pennsylvania Hospital in 1900. In 1902 he became Chief Clinical Assistant to Professor W.W. Keen and Associate Attending Surgeon at Jefferson. His rise in surgical and teaching ranks was rapid, but his early death in 1920 at age 42 prevented the achievements expected of him by admiring colleagues (Figure 138). He wrote extensively on medical subjects including his highly regarded *Manual of Surgery* (1907), completed in two years, He advanced to Professor of Clinical Surgery at Jefferson in 1910, having already held the appointment as Professor of Surgery at the Philadelphia Polyclinic Hospital from 1903 to 1910. Dr. J. Chalmers DaCosta regarded him as one of the ablest men ever connected with Jefferson.

Joseph Clarence Keeler, a native of Doylestown, Pennsylvania, began his specialty of otolaryngology following Jefferson internship with his appointment as assistant to Professor S. MacCuen Smith. He later became Chief of Otology at Germantown Hospital while advancing to Chief Clinical Assistant in Otoloy at Jefferson. He succeeded Dr. Smith as Chairman of Otology in 1930, the same year as his popular textbook, *Modern Otology*, was published following a succession of scientific papers (Fig. 139). He died in 1935 at age 64.

Harvey M. Righter, following his service as a Resident Physician at Jefferson, was appointed to the staff, first in the Department of Obstetrics and later to Dr. John Chalmers DaCosta's surgical service (Fig. 140). He was a favorite among the nurses, having from 1928 presented each graduating nurse with a red rose at commencement. From this the Rose Arch tradition developed as a part of the commencement ceremony and it was continued until the Nurses Training School closed in 1982. Dr. Righter was a close associate of Dr. DaCosta and was one of a few devoted staff men who saw to the care and transportation of Dr. DaCosta following the onset of the latter's crippling arthritis.

Sherman F. Gilpin, after resident service at the Philadelphia General Hospital, went on to a career in nervous and mental diseases. He was Assistant Visiting Neurologist at the latter hospital from 1908 to 1916, Clinical Professor of Nervous and Mental Diseases at Temple University (1906-08) and Associate Professor of Nervous and Mental Diseases at Jefferson from 1908. He was also a consultant to local and regional hospitals.

CLASS OF 1896

Adams, Charles Thomas, PA
Albright, Roderick Edwin, PA
Alleman, Frank, PA
Allen, William Cline, PA
Alley, John Newton, WV
Amilon, Ivan Emil, SWEDEN
Arnold, Jesse Oglevee, PA
Bachmann, Carl Frederick, Jr., CA
Bacon, Carroll Burton, NY
Baldwin, Sanford Oscar, ME
Barker, Byron Fuller, ME

Barlett, Charles Rufus, NY
Barlow, Louis Eugene, PA
Barton, Henry Clay, PA
Bashore, Simeon David, PA
Bauer, John Nathan, PA
Becker, Alfred Nauman, PA
Bennett, Samuel Dey, NJ
Berk, John K., PA
Bertolet, John Marshall, PA
Black, Jesse Langtry, PA
Boltz, Elias Kline, PA

Boon, William M. B., KS
Borger, Joseph J., PA
Brackett, William Walker, CT
Braddock Charles Shreve, Jr., NJ
Brewer, William, NJ
Brewster, Guy Otis, NY
Brister, Frederick Elmer, PA
Brown, Michael Joseph, PA
Brown, Adolph Gustave, RI
Brunner, Henry Clay, PA
Buchanan, Joseph Hervey, NJ
Carr, John Dennis, PA
Castlebury, Frank Fulmer, PA
Catanach, Notman Guthrie, PA
Clark, Albert U. F., ME
Clauser, Harry Simon, PA
Clouting, Elmer Sherman, NJ
Cochran, Frederick Albert, Jr., VA
Coffin, Harold Leroy, ME
Cogan, James E. F., CANADA
Colhouer, Frederick Henry, PA
Collins, Howard Austin, PA

Conlin, Joseph Michael, MA .
Conn, Frederick A. W., PA
Corrigan, John Joseph, PA
Corson, George Reuben S., PA
Coyne, James Augustine, MA
Crockett, Ernest Amzi, ME
Croxall, Willard Young, UT
Crutcher, William, AR
Curley, George Frederick, MA
Dabbous, Aime Mahran, EGYPT
Dandois, George Franklin, PA
Davison, William Forester, PA
Deardorff, Benjamin M., PA
Deardorff, William Henry, PA
Decker, Van Cleft, PA
Donaldson, John Speer, PA
Doran, Charles Franklin, NJ
Dornsife, Ulysses Edward, PA
Dowling, Charles Ehrgood, PA
Dugan, William James, MA
Elliott, Andrew Henry, PA
Emerick, Martin Luther, PA

Fig. 138. Francis Torrens Stewart (JMC, 1896) Clinical Professor of Surgery (1910-20).

Fig. 139. Joseph C. Keeler (JMC, 1896), Chairman of Otology (1930-35).

Farber, William Daniel, PA
Ferguson, Edward Carlon, IL
Fischer, Gustav, MN
Fleck, Harry Willard, PA
Fry, Harvey Murrell, PA
Gahan, Patrick Francis, MA
Gallagher, Harry, GA
Garren, Albert W., PA
Gartman, Leo Noy, PA
Giberson, William Henry, PA
Giffen, John Wilson, PA
Gilpin, Sherman Fletcher, PA
Glenn, Eugene Byron, NC
Gordon, Benjamin Lee, NY
Goudiss, Archibald, RUSSIA
Graham, James Abraham, WV
Gratiot, Harry Bradley, WI
Gray, Alfred Percy, PA
Greenawalt, Albert Geary, PA
Hall, William Joseph, NJ
Harbaugh, Charles Hamilton, OH
Hare, Edgar Thomas, PA
Harman, Austin Roy, ME
Harris, James Albert, PA
Harrison, Arthur McCann, OH
Harrison, Frank Matthews, OH

Hazlett, Leslie Ramsey, PA
Henry, Clifford Elmore, MO
Hepperlen, Harry Michael, NE
Herbein, Oscar Batteiger, PA
Hickman, Thomas Elwood, PA
Hildebrand, Walter Junius, TX
Hill, John Sturgeon, PA
Hill, Anthony John, IL
Hillemeyer, William Anton, WI
Hinckle, Millard Goodrich, OR
Hirsch, Leon, PA
Hitch, Victor Elmer, DE
Hoffman, Edward Almond, PA
Holt, Hiram Allen, ME
Horner, Myers, Worman, PA
Horning, Frank, PA
Houck, Oscar, WI
Howard, Edward Stephen, CA
Hudelson, Lucius Rollin, IN
Jack, James Renwick, PA
Jackson, Robert, Jr., PA
Jennings, Joseph A., PA
John, Jacob Stacey, PA
Jolley, William Albert, KS
Jones, Ralph Richards, ME
Jones, Arthur Willis, OH
Karpeles, Maurice Joseph, OH
Kauffman, John William, PA
Kearns, William, IRELAND
Keeler, Joseph Clarence, PA
Keim, Peter Sloan, PA
Keller, Augustis Herman, PA
Kidder, Lincoln Ellsworth, PA
Koch, Alvin Adam, PA
Korhnak, August Joseph, PA
Krauss, George, PA
Krogh, Detlef M. F., PA
Lanham, Howard Meng, TX
Larson, Louis Andrew, PA
Leahy, Jeremiah Emmet, OH
LeCates, Charles Asbury, DE
Leipold, Bert Eugene, PA
Leitzell, P. Wilson, PA
Lloyd, John Hepburn, PA
Long, William Henry, Jr., PA
Malster, John Charles, OH
Mansfield, James Albert, MA
Marvin, Merton Elwood, PA
Mason, Charles Thomas, MD
McClusky, Henry Lincoln, MA
McKay, Donald MacGregor, CANADA
McKee, Joseph Allen, PA
Medd, Henry, PA
Metheny, David Gregg, PA

Fig. 140. Harvey M. Righter (JMC, 1896), member of Jefferson's Surgical Staff who initiated the "Rose Arch Tradition" at graduation in the School of Nursing.

Miller, John Harvey, PA
Miller, Edwin John, PA
Miller, Robert Hamilton, PA
Milligan, Robert, PA
Milnor, Robert Hanna, PA
Moenig, Joseph August, NY
Moore, Albert Harrison, KY
Morris, John Louis, IN
Morris, Joseph, PA
Morrison, William Francis, PA
Mountain, John Henry, CT
Nadle, Isidor M., PA
Newcomer, Irving, IL
Newman, William Harris, PA
Nichols, Henry Hessin, IA
Norris, Elmer Patterson, PA
O'Reilly, Harry Matthew, NJ
Oburn, Albert Sidney, PA
Osborne, John M., NC
Owens, Harry, PA
Paige, Harris Lee, DE
Patterson, Frank Iams, PA
Phillips, Robert H. C., NJ
Picard, Harry Leon, PA
Plank, John Ransom, PA
Pleible, Eugene Theodore, PA
Post, Albert Todd, PA
Powers, Everett, MO
Prosser, Stephen Sanford, CA
Prunk, Byron Fletcher, IN
Purdy, John, PA
Quinn, Michael Henry, PA
Ranke, John W. H., IN
Rasmussen, Hans, WI
Raub, Richard Vaux, PA
Read, William Parsons, CA
Reeser, Richard, PA
Richards, Davis Bruce, PA
Righter, Harvey Mitchell, PA
Roemermann, W. Dietrich, GERMANY

Rosenstock, Henry, PA
Rowan, Charles, PA
Salmon, James Marvin, PA
Schneider, Charles Joseph, PA
Scott, Robert Burns, PA
Sebring, John, Jr., PA
Shaffer, Orr Hilemann, PA
Sharp, Edward Smith, NJ
Shriner, Howard Martin, PA
Smith, William Alexander, PA
Smith, Stanley Sinclair, PA
Smith, Frank Quincy, PA
Smith, Benjamin Franklin, IL
Smith, Adin Louis, ME
Snyder, Marion D., PA
Spackman, James Paul, PA
Spencer, Leonard Everett, WI
Stewart, Francis Torrens, PA
Stewart, John, PA
Taggart, Thomas Dartnell, PA
Thomas, Norman A., PA
Thomas, Vernon D., PA
Thompson, Louis Levi, PA
Treible, William Henry, PA
Trout, Nicholas C., PA
Tupper, Virgil, PA
Ulmer, Stephen Edward, PA
VanHorn, Leon, PA
Walcott, Henry Joel, Jr., MA
Walz, Frank John, PA
Warner, Charles Norton, MA
Webb, Abner, AR
Welfley, Albert Jonas, PA
Wentworth, Harry Wilder, MA
White, Frederick Avery, NJ
Witmer, Peter Bachman, PA
Woodhead, Irving Henry, PA
Woodruff, John Barnaby, PA
Woods, Clarence Hubert, CO
Wright, Percy Stearns, PA
Wynn, Charles Austin, PA

"Jefferson must have tacitly recognized, although he never directly admitted the fact, that one of the important deficiencies in the course of studies which he had projected for the University was the entire absence of hospital facilities. Without those facilities, a medical school, independently of anatomy, must always remain principally an historical school, a school of theory, a descriptive rather than a practically illustrative school."

Philip A. Bruce (1856-1933)
in *History of the University of Virginia*

Victor G. Heiser, described in the year 1888, was a member of this class nine years after his experiences in the disastrous Johnstown flood during which his parents were among the three thousand persons killed. Dr. Heiser became attracted to the field of public health during his internship at Lankenau Hospital and he received an immediate appointment to the Marine Hospital Service which was to evolve into the United States Public Health Service. He was soon assigned to the Far East and became a pioneering expert in the new field of applied preventive medicine and public health administration. He was especially effective in his work in the Phil-

ippines with campaigns against smallpox, plague, cholera and leprosy. Dr. Heiser was later appointed to the Rockefeller Foundation where he continued to develop policies for world-wide health programs (Fig. 141). He was awarded the degree of Doctor of Science at Jefferson in 1911 and the Alumni Achievement Award many years later in 1968. His best-selling autobiographical work *An American Doctor's Odyssey* was published in 1936.

Henry R. M. Landis (often called Hiram because of his initials) was to become an outstanding clinician, professor and author (Fig. 142). Having developed tuberculosis as an intern at

Fig. 141. Victor Heiser (JMC, 1897), pioneer in the international approach to disease prevention.

Fig. 142. Henry R.M. Landis (JMC, 1897) a leading authority on tuberculosis control and Professor of Medicine at the University of Pennsylvania.

Philadelphia General Hospital, he devoted his career mainly to the treatment and control of this disease. In 1903 he joined the staff of the Henry Phipps Institute for Tuberculosis, beginning a relationship which endured until his death in 1937. He was known for his commitment to poor people and the management of tuberculosis among them. He was also a staff member of the White Haven Sanatorium from 1904 to 1935. His medical writing included many papers on subjects related to chest diseases and environmental dust hazards. A major textbook *Physical Diagnosis and Diseases of the Chest* with George W. Norris (1917) went through five editions, and he served on the Editorial Board of the *American Review of Tuberculosis*. Editor of *International Clinics* from 1916 to 1921, he was also active in medical organizations especially the tuberculosis societies, and advanced academically to Professor of Clinical Medicine at the University of Pennsylvania in 1926. He received an honorary degree from Amherst College, his undergraduate alma mater, in 1929.

Prominent for many years among Jefferson alumni was Leighton F. Appleman who devoted many classroom hours to the Department of Therapeutics (Fig. 143). For several decades there was a laboratory of Pharmacy in which Dr. Appleman was mainly responsible for the teaching and course material in his status as Demonstrator of Pharmacy and Materia Medica (Fig. 144). He prepared a *Working Guide* for the course which was used for a number of years until the teaching in pharmacy was superseded by the ascendancy of pharmacology in the 1930's.

Twenty-four prizes were awarded at graduation to the 161 members of this class. Of these, four were won by Charles Stewart Barnes and three by Charles W. Le Fever, both of Ohio.

On May 5th of this year Professor William Williams Keen gave the dedication address at the unveiling of the statue of Samuel D. Gross in Washington, D.C. Funds for the granite base were provided by Congress and those for the bronze figures by the Jefferson Alumni Association and the American Surgical Association (Fig. 136).

CLASS OF 1897

Appleman, Leighton Francis, PA
Ashford, John Wesson, GA
Bailey, Levi Matthew, PA
Balliet, Calvin Joseph, PA
Barkley, John Wesley, PA
Barnd, Franklin Pierce, PA
Barnes, Charles Stewart, OH
Barr, William Forse, PA
Becker, Edwin Isaac, NE
Biddle, Philip George, PA
Boehmer, George Henry, OH
Bolton, Earle William, PA
Boren, Samuel Wesley, IN
Bovard, Forrest Johnson, PA
Breneman, William Edgar, PA
Brindle, Archie Clarence, PA
Brindley, William George, OH
Brown, David Albert, PA
Brown, Elmer Ellsworth, PA
Camden, Rolla, WV
Cary, John Herschel, PA
Clark, William Pawson, CT
Clinger, Edgar Moore, PA
Colley, Brown, PA
Conway, John Baptiste, PA

Cooley, Judson Cassius, PA
Crane, Charles A., IL
Cunningham, George, NJ
Dare, Gilbert DeWitt, NY
Dawson, Byron F., CA
Deadwyler, Madison Pope, GA
Decker, Frederick Howard, NJ
Devine, Robert Hamilton, WV
Dippell, Emil Theodore, PA
Doyle, John James, PA
Dunkle, Gaily Barr, PA
Emerson, Linn, NY
Emery, Harry Smith, ME
Ericsson, Bror Otto, FINLAND
Evans, Stuart, PA
Fee, Elam Knott, PA
Fish, Clyde Milhallon, PA
Foulks, Wallace Scott, OH
Franklin, M. Burnett, GA
Fraser, Hugh Daniel, CANADA
Funk, William Warren, PA
Gilmartin, John Lawrence, IL
Gordon, Altamont Lafayette, PA
Gray, James Robinson, PA
Green, Howard Lee, PA

Groschner, Carl Braun, OH
Gutmann, Benjamin, NJ
Haines, Joseph Ridgway, NJ
Haines, Willits Parker, NJ
Halbeisen, William Joseph, NJ
Hamma, James Archibald, PA
Hamman, George Alvan, MO
Hartwell, Arthur Spear, MA
Hawkey, Richard John, CANADA
Hazlett, Silas Metz, PA
Heffner, Curtis, PA
Heflin, Ernest Lee, KY
Heiser, Victor George, PA
Hemeon, Frederick Chipman, CANADA
Henrahan, Bernard Elliot, ME
Henry, Byron, PA
Hetrick, David Joseph, PA
Hill, John Emmett, PA
Holder, Charles Adams, PA
Hopkins, Scott Bruce, IA
Irwin, William, IRELAND
Jackson, Ion A., OH
Johnson, Syvert H., ND

Jones, Leighton Wherry, PA
Jones, John Comer, NJ
Kellogg, William Ardrey, LA
Kemble, Charles Cochran, PA
Kistler, Chester K., PA
Kress, Edward Henry, PA
Kress, Frederick Charles, PA
Landis, Henry R. M., OH
Lefcowitch, Charles Henry, PA
LeFever, Charles Wesley, OH
Lewis, Norman, PA
Lockwood, George Bertrand, ME
Love, John King, PA
MacDowell, Samuel Ira, PA
Magraw, George Thomas, MD
Mahon, Alfred Neale, PA
Maloney, Maurice, CT
Many, Harry Crawford, PA
Matternes, James Gicker, PA
May, John Shepard, MA
McAdam, William Ralph, IA
McBee, John Madison, TN
McBurney, Charles Fred, PA
McConnell, Edward Fraser, CA
McCorkle, William Pyles, PA
McCormick, John Aloysius, PA
McKibben, Alpheus, KY
McMillan, William Thomas, MD
Millhoff, Clarence Beacom, PA
Mitchell, William Albert, WA
Monie, David McDonald, PA
Montgomery, James McKay, PA
Moore, Franklin Thomas, NJ
Nelson, Audley, Emmet, IA
O'Connell, Austin, PA
O'Rourke, Jeremiah Francis, CT
O'Toole, Thomas Henry, MA
Penton, Frank Vincent, CUBA
Phillips, Clarence Reynolds, PA
Pontius, Nevin Driesbach, PA
Purdon, James, CANADA
Pyfer, Howard F., PA
Ramsay, Robert Hudson, WV
Rank, Harry Phillip, PA
Raper, Thomas Walter, PA
Read, Alfred Hurst, PA
Richards, John David, MS
Risser, Ulysses Grant, PA
Roe, Byron LeRoy, PA
Rosen, Mayer, PA
Santee, George Oliver O., PA
Saunders, Robert Rogers, PA
Scheifly, John Edward, DE
Schill, Francis George, Jr., PA

Fig. 143.   Leighton F. Appleman (JMC, 1897) taught Pharmacy, Materia Medica and Therapeutics (1904-32).

Schuelke, Julius Albert, WY
Shallcross, William Gooding, MD
Shelton, Hanson Penn, OH
Shmookler, Henry Bernard, PA
Smiley, Howard Miles, PA
Smith, J. Anson, NJ
Smith, Charles Galen, PA
Spotz, Gladfelter Emanuel, PA
Spragg, Charles William, PA
Spratt, Charles Brewster, FL
Swarzlander, Joseph Rankin, PA
Taylor, Frank Herbert, PA
Thayer, Royal Westcott, WV
Thomas, Eb. W., PA
Thomas, Balorus Arby, PA
Thomason, William Paul Owen, IN
Thome, William McKee, MO

Traver, Samuel Nisley, PA
Trimmer, Luther Epeanetus, NY
Turner, Philip Percy, PA
Urmson, Allan Walker, PA
Vanneman, Albert Walter, IL
Virgin, Walter Stanley, GA
Wagner, John J., PA
Wagner, Earl Eulearn, PA
Wallace, George Sellers, PA
Watt, Robert, PA
Weever, George Slocumb, IN
Werner, Siegmund, PA
Wiggins, Edward Harvey, PA
Williams, Charles Morgan, NJ
Wolfe, William S., PA
Woods, Abraham Lincoln, NJ
Woodside, Harry Addison, PA

Fig. 144.   Laboratory of Pharmacy and Experimental Therapeutics in 1898 Medical College.

~ 1898 ~

The graduates this year numbered only 50, the smallest class for many years. The reasons for this change are not entirely clear, but the disruptions caused by the construction of the New Medical Hall (1898) probably contributed since the numbers of students of the lower classes did not diminish proportionately. Also, the increase in the number of medical schools in the middle and far west of the United States may have temporarily attracted students formerly oriented toward Jefferson.

The New Medical Hall signaled the southwesterly expansion of the Jefferson campus, later to be extended much further. The building fronted on Walnut Street and marked the decision by the Trustees to expand in the old area of the City rather than to move to a new location where property costs would be lower (Fig. 145 and 146).

Apple, William Edson, PA
Barnes, William Mitchell, OH
Bennett, Samuel, NJ
Boyer, John Clinton, PA
Bryson, Howard Russel, PA
Byars, Caspar Ralph, TX
Carpenter, Eugene R., MO
Cranmer, Carl Bernard, PA
Crawford, Walter W., MS
Crisler, Julius, MS
Curry, James Walker, GA
Daniell, Anthony Wingrove, PA
Davis, Frederick Whitney, PA
Dorsey, Rufus T., Jr., GA
Dunn, Frederick V., NJ
English, Charles Frederick, CA
Funk, Joseph, PA
Graham, Archibald Hunter, Jr., PA
Griffin, Thomas William, CANADA
Heller, James Herbert, PA
Howe, Llewellyn Oscar, PA
Howell, Park, GA
Jacoby, Charles Wesley, OH
Machete, Frank, PA
MacIntosh, James William, CANADA

Matheny, Albert Ralston, PA
McClanahan, Rice Kemper, VA
McConnell, Walker W., PA
McGhee, Saylor John, PA
McMaster, Gilbert Totten, CT
McMullen, Uriah H., PA
Metzler, Victor Wade, OH
Mintzer, Leonidas H.C., PA
Nicodemus, Edwin Arthur, PA
Nipple, Henry Newton, PA
Robison, John Isaac, PA
Saunders, Orris William, NJ
Schuster, Bruno Lyonel, WI
Sharp, Eugene B., PA
Snell, Myron Webster, IL
Snyder, Thomas, PA
Stevens, Pliny Fenimore, ME
Stock, George Andrew, PA
Tracey, George Thomas, PA
Truitt, George W., PA
Vary, Clarence Godfrey, MI
Wanner, Abram Kissinger, PA
Weaver, William Jackson, NC
Weaver, Andrew Albert, MA
Yusuf, Amin Ibrahim, SYRIA

Fig. 145.   Walnut Street entrance of 1898 Medical College Building.

Fig. 146.   New Jefferson Medical College Building (1898) at northwest corner of Tenth and Walnut Streets.

1898

The main address at the opening of the New Medical Hall on October 2, 1899, was presented by Dr. Phineas S. Connor (JMC, 1861, Fig. 61), Professor of Surgery at the Medical College of Ohio. Dr. Connor referred to the fact that his father was also a Jefferson graduate (1837), but his main theme was the status of and impending change in medical education. The description of the New Building high-lighted the Seventy-fifth Annual Announcement, and its opening marked a major forward thrust for Jefferson.

Also in 1899, a student publication, *The Jeffersonian*, was launched (Fig. 147). For some years this well-edited publication, issued monthly, provided more intimate contacts between stu-

dents and faculty as well as a very informative function in recording student life and medical events. A student government system was initiated the same year.

Among the 95 graduates, Frederick J. Kalteyer, Jr., of Texas, had previously received his M.D. degree from the University of Pennsylvania in 1895. His training also included six months at Johns Hopkins Hospital and his internship at Lankenau Hospital where he came under the teaching of Dr. James C. Wilson. He was promptly appointed as Assistant and Instructor in Hematology in the Department of Medicine at Jefferson. His rise in rank and influence in the Department was unusually rapid, with a final

Fig. 147. Title page of *The Jeffersonian*.

Fig. 148. Frederick J. Kalteyer, Jr. (JMC, 1899), Clinical Professor of Medicine at Jefferson.

promotion to Clinical Professor of Medicine in 1927 (Fig. 148). For many years he taught the second year course in Symptomatology and Physical Diagnosis. Twice he was a member of interim committees between Chairmen, in 1911 and 1935. He was a meticulous lecturer, an expert clinician, and he served as consultant in a number of regional hospitals. Dr. Kalteyer was for a time Assistant Pathologist to Philadelphia General Hospital and his teaching reflected his effort to link physical signs to pathological lesions.

James Harvey Spruance served as Coroner's Physician from New Castle County, Delaware, and also as a member of the Delaware State Legislature as the only representative from the city of Wilmington. He was a member of the Wilmington Board of Health and of the Delaware State Board of Pharmacy (Fig. 149).

CLASS OF 1899

Abrahamson, Philip, PA
Allison, Charles Edward, PA
Beggs, David B., PA
Boice, Harman Edward, MI
Bostock, Herbert Arthur, PA
Carver, Harry Franklin, PA
Cavanagh, Charles Joseph, PA
Clarke, Samuel, PA
Cleveland, Frank Mortimer, NY
Clifford, Raymond Alfred, OH
Cowgill, Solomon Macy, IN
Croft, John Walker, PA
Cushing, Herbert Howard, PA
Dollard, Edmund Charles, WI
Downs, Myron LaFayette, IL
Duffield, Elias Mortimer, NJ
Dunham, Alonzo H., CA
Ellis, Peter Clarkson, KY
Farnham, Elmer John, ME
Ferguson, George McIntire, PA
Fulton, I. M. Dudley, MI
Gross, Herbert Franklin, PA
Hayman, Edwin Henry, PA
Hearn, William P., PA
Hebsacker, William Frederick, PA
Hofer, Clarence Andreas, NJ
Holbrook, Arthur Gilbert, MI
Irvin, Edgar Harland, TX
Jackson, Charles Ellworth, TX
Joyner, Claudius Cameron, NC
Kalteyer, Frederick John, Jr., TX
Keating, William P. S., CT
Keller, Peter Martin, MI
Kennedy, James William, KS
Kennedy, Edwin Russell, OH
Kleeberg, Felix, CT
Lackey, William Nicholas, TN
Lau, Scott Wolford, PA
Lee, Alvin Craig, PA
Lewis, Estell Budd, PA
Lockett, William Robert, TN

Longfellow, Jacob Winslow, ME
Mace, Henry Fancher, NY
McCormick, John, MS
McNair, William Righter, PA
Meriweather, Tyler, IL
Merryman, John Whitfield, PA
Michener, Evan W., PA

Fig. 149. James H. Spruance (JMC, 1899) served in the Delaware Legislature and on the Wilmington Board of Health.

Moore, George Cooper, DE
Moore, Thomas Kenney, MI
Moran, Thomas Wesley, PA
Neare, Clifford Reno, OH
Nicholls, James Calvin, PA
Nicholls, Robert Delmer, PA
Nobles, Joseph Everett, NC
O'Neill, Chrysostom A., CT
Oram, Joseph Hubbhrd, NJ
Ostrander, William Alonzo, PA
Packer, Elmer Benjamin, IL
Pearce, Claude Melvin, OR
Perry, Samuel Wesley, PA
Peterson, Hirman Dewey, OH
Pollock, Raymond, NC
Post, Charles A. H., IL
Rafferty, Herbert Nowell, IL
Reese, Lewis, PA

Royce, Charles Clifton, PA
Royer, B. Franklin, PA
Shepard, Cassius Marion, OH
Smith, Henry Stephen, TX
Smith, Sydney James, TX
Smith, Willard Eugene, DE
Spruance, James Harvey, DE
Squires, Walter Howland, PA
Thomason, George W., MI
Tuers, George Edward, NJ
Tuttle, John Layton, Jr., MI
VanSciver, John E. L., NJ
Weber, Harry Friedman, OH
Williams, Chas. Henry, MI
Wimberley, Joseph Powell, NC
Windbrake, Albert Jefferson, PA
Yacub, David Elias, SYRIA
Yeager, Johnson Arthur, OH
Yeager, George Carpenter, PA

Laboratory of pathological histology in 1898 Medical College

The new century marked a period of maturity and consolidation of the changes initiated in 1895 when the proprietary years ended. Control of the College and Hospital was now unified under the Board of Trustees. Dr. William M.L. Coplin (JMC, 1886, Fig. 117) described "The New Jefferson" in the student publication *The Jeffersonian*. Relating to the proposals during the eighteen nineties to move the medical school to South Broad Street, he discussed the advantages of expanding in the present location and described the results of the first construction, the New 1898 College Building. He went on to outline plans for further expansion, all of which were to be more than fulfilled. The immediate need for enlarged hospital facilities would be addressed within the decade.

The outstanding graduate of this turn-of-the-century class which numbered 106 was Aller G. Ellis (B.S. Geneva College, 1894). During his senior year at Jefferson he was class president, President of The Academy (a student society), and Chairman of the Students' Executive Committee. Following graduation, he served a Jefferson internship (1900-02), then received an appointment in the Department of Pathology with Dr. W.M.L. Coplin. He was the first Corinna Borden Keen Fellow under the aegis of which he studied in Germany (1907/08) and later returned to Jefferson for a two-year appointment in neuropathology. He advanced to Associate Professor and became Director of the Ayer Laboratories at Pennsylvania Hospital in 1917, and also later organized the Department of Pathology at the Royal Medical College, Bangkok, Siam (Thailand). He returned to Jefferson for one year (1922/23) where he was Acting Chairman of the Department of Pathology (Fig. 150).

Clarence Scott Ramsey, a native of Springfield, Ohio, and a graduate of Wittenberg College (A.B., 1895) was one of relatively few Jefferson graduates to see service in the Spanish-American War. Dr. Ramsey was Captain and Quartermaster in the Third Ohio Volunteer Regiment.

Enhancing the prestige of the Jefferson Faculty during these years was the authorship of medical textbooks. This year alone saw the publication of *Manual of Pathology* by W.M.L. Coplin, *Modern Medicine* by Julius L. Salinger and Frederick J. Kalteyer, *Practical Gynecology* by E.E. Montgomery, and *Compend of Physiology* by Albert Brubaker.

Fig. 150. Aller G. Ellis (JMC, 1900), Acting Chairman of Pathology (1922-23). In 1917 he performed a historically significant autopsy on a patient operated upon successfully by W.W. Keen 30 years previously for a brain tumor (there was no recurrence).

Adamson, Hiram Ross, PA
Atkinson, Curtis, IN
Baer, Hermanus Ludwig, PA
Barr, Herbert Everard, PA
Beach, Oliver Jarvis, CT
Blayney, Charles Alva, PA
Bleakney, Frank, PA
Bley, Walter Clarence, IL
Brace, Robert W., NJ
Brandau, William Walker, TN
Brechemin, Louis, Jr., CO
Bremermann, Lewis Wine, PA
Brown, Pearl Hubert, SD
Brown, Swan Wilmer, OH
Brown, Allie Henry, OR
Brown, Alexander Aaron, TX
Burger, Earl Victor, IN
Cadwallader, Seth Iredell, PA
Callahan, Bernard Joseph, IN
Cecil, Edgar Thomas, KY
Chamberlain, Lowell Holbrook, IA
Culver, Charles F., MI
Dando, Elijah Tennyson, OH
Dean, Alexander Heustis, PA
Donaldson, Louis DeHaven, PA
Dougherty, Edward S., PA
Edmonds, William, NY
Eisenhardt, William George, PA
Ellis, Aller G., PA
Ewing, William Aaron, OH
Fletcher, Thomas Alfred, OH
Funkhouser, Edgar Bright, VA
Gilmore, Thomas Joseph, PA
Godfrey, Henry Granville, PA
Goodman, Sylvester J., OH
Gordon, George Jacob, MN
Grace, James Thomas, MI
Graven, Thomas Arthur, OH
Gromann, John, NY
Gulick, Arthur Cornelius, WI
Harman, William James, PA
Hatfield, George Laughead, PA
Hawkins, Charles Lewis, PA
Hayes, Randall Burrows, PA
Hedley, James Roger, PA
Henry, George, NJ
Heyde, Jacob Meyers, OH
Heysham, Horace Besson, PA
Hill, Walter de la M., PA
Hunsicker, Charles Heil, PA
Jimenez, Luis Paulino, COSTA RICA
Johnson, Frederick Charles, PA
Jones, Emlyn, PA

Keck, George Osmon, PA
Keeney, Madison J., IN
Kennedy, Joseph P., PA
Kieffer, George C., PA
Lavelle, Harry Minhern, WV
Lefevre, Rufus Eshbach, PA
Lohrmann, Henry, IN
MacOdrum, Angus, NOVA SCOTIA
Mayhew, Samuel Dixon, NJ
Mayhugh, Isaac, IN
McCay, Robert Burns, PA
Minner, Louis Augustus, IL
Morales, Marcos Delio, CUBA
Morris, William Francis, IN
Newby, George Edgar, NC
Noome, Andrew Joseph, WV
Payne, Frank Irvin, CT
Pearson, Eugene Oscar, PA
Pennington, Henry Vincent, KY
Pole, William Edward, PA
Powell, Oscar Littleton, VA
Pratt, John Perkins, OH
Price, Charles Eli, PA
Prince, Linnaeus Hodgson, PA
Ramsey, Clarence Scott, OH
Reddan, Martin W. P., NJ
Repman, Harry Joseph, PA
Richardson, Harry Tompkins, PA
Ridpath, Paul Cole, WA
Robinhold, D. Guy, PA
Robinson, Silas Edwin, NJ
Rosier, John Bruner, WV
Schwartz, George Jacob, PA
Scull, James Ireland, NJ
Small, Thomas Winn, ME
Smith, Floyd Wilbert, OH
Smith, Dudley Almonte, OH
Smith, Willard Wallace, NY
Stage, Jacob Samuel, NY
Storrs, Eckley Raynor, CT
Street, Thomas Hezekiah, AL
Stybr, Charles Joseph, PA
Swindells, Walton Creadick, PA
Tatum, Harry Erskine, MO
Taylor, Mervyn Ross F., CANADA
Taylor, Wilfred Jerrold, OH
Thigpen, William Jordan, NC
Tucker, John Davis, PA
Warren, Manley Clemont, KY
Wetherbee, Joseph Robbins, OR
White, Thomas Charles, Jr., MS
Wick, Victor Vernon, OH
Woods, Samuel Albert, PA

The Class of 1901 was notable for the number of its members among the total of 142 who became prominent in many areas of medicine, especially in the Jefferson faculty. Perhaps the best known was Pascal Brooke Bland, whose leadership qualities were shown by his election as senior class president (Fig. 151). His Jefferson internship was followed by his appointment as assistant to Dr. E. E. Montgomery, Professor of Gynecology, and as Demonstrator of Gynecology in the medical school. Studies in Europe (Paris, Freiburg, Munich) enhanced his academic position and he advanced to Assistant Professor in 1910. In 1925 he was appointed Chairman of the Department of Obstetrics which position he

held until 1937 when he became Professor Emeritus. His administration was marked by major progress in the Department and he was also widely in demand as a consultant in hospitals of Pennsylvania and New Jersey. In addition to his teaching and clinical skills he was the author of two major textbooks and many papers. His collection of books and historical works was ultimately bequeathed to Jefferson where it formed the nucleus of the Section on Historical Collections now housed in the Scott Library Archives.

One of the most popular of Jefferson teachers, also in the Department of Obstetrics, whose career somewhat paralleled that of Dr. Bland was George A. Ulrich (Fig. 152). A graduate of Leb-

Fig. 151. Pascal Brooke Bland (JMC, '01), Chairman of Obstetrics (1925-37).

Fig. 152. George A. Ulrich (JMC, '01), Clinical Professor of Obstetrics (1931).

anon Valley College (B.S., 1897, M.S., 1909), deep in "Pennsylvania Dutch" Country, Dr. Ulrich was universally loved and respected by his students as a teacher of obstetrics whose instruction included not only the "why, how, where, and when to do it" but also the "when not to do it". He joined the Department of Obstetrics following graduation and advanced to Clinical Professor in 1931. His portrait, the first of any department non-chairman, was presented to the College in 1941.

Two other members of the class also became associated with the Department of Obstetrics. Collin Foulkrod joined the Department early and advanced to Assistant Professor, serving for many years. He was also President of the Philadelphia Obstetrical Society. D. Randall MacCarroll also became a Demonstrator in the same Department and for many years was an Assistant Attending Physician in the Obstetrics Clinic.

Graduating in this class of 142 was Henry Erdman Radasch who came to Jefferson from the University of Iowa (B.Sc., M.Sc.,1897). He became Demonstrator of Histology and Embryology at Jefferson upon graduation and advanced to a final appointment in 1921 as Professor of Histology and Embryology in the Department of Anatomy (Fig. 153). He also held academic appointments in the Pennsylvania College of Dental Surgery and in the Pennsylvania Academy of the Fine Arts. Dr. Radasch was the author of numerous papers, a *Manual of Histology* and assisted in the revision of two editions of *Gray's Anatomy*.

Algernon B. Jackson of Indiana, the first identifiable black graduate of Jefferson, practiced in Philadelphia and became Chief Surgeon at Mercy Hospital. Also involved in community affairs, he was well known as a speaker, writer and bibliophile with numerous publications in the field of public policy, Negro affairs, and health education. From 1922 to 1933 he was Head of the Department of Public Health of Howard University Medical School (Fig. 154).

Elmer L. Meyers, a native of Wilkes-Barre, Pennsylvania (Princeton, A.B., 1892) was perhaps the most accomplished in literary pursuits. Dr. Meyers was editor of the 1900 yearbook *Sesamoid* as well as of the first volume of *The Jeffersonian*, the monthly student publication launched in April, 1899.

Duncan L. Despard became an Associate in Surgery at Jefferson and also ran a teaching service at the Philadelphia General Hospital. Tragically, he was shot to death in his office in 1924 at the age of 55 by an insane patient who thought his hernia had been repaired incorrectly.

Fig. 153. Henry E. Radasch (JMC, '01), Professor of Histology and Embryology (1921-42).

Altman, Owen Randolph, PA
Angle, George Burton, TX
Applewhite, Scott Carter, IN
Baldwin, Hugh Allen, OH
Banks, Philo Hamlin, PA
Barrows, Arthur Monroe, VT
Bassett, Henry Linn, PA
Beek, John Alonzo, PA
Bell, John James, IRELAND
Berberich, Herman, PA
Bland, Pascal Brooke, PA
Bossard, Harry Bardwell, PA
Bradford, Edward Burton, PA
Brown, Charles Gailey, OH
Bussey, William Joseph, IA
Cartin, Harry James, PA
Cooper, Frank Chambers, PA
Craig, John Jay, PA
Craig, Albert B., WA
Crawford, David Hutchison, NJ

Crigler, Wallace Payton, KY
Culler, Robert Martin, PA
Curtis, Ralph Gardner, CA
Davis, Robert Goode, AR
Davis, James Leslie, KY
Dean, Fred W. S., SC
Despard, Duncan Lee, WV
Diggett, Ernest William, FL
Dight, Herman Herschel, PA
Dirickson, Cyrus William, MD
Doak, Edmond, TX
Dole, William, Arthur, KS
Dolson, Frank Edgar, PA
Douglass, William Tyler, PA
Downs, Alfred Jonathan, CA
Dubbs, Robert L., PA
Duryea, Chester Ford, NY
Ellis, Edwin Milton, PA
Ellis, James Baxter, AR
Fletcher, Robert Swan, MA
Fosque, George Lee, VA
Foulkrod, Collin, PA
Freedman, Samuel Max, TX
Freeman, Walter Seip, NJ
Funke, John, PA
Gale, William Hodskin, NY
George, Henry William, PA
Gerould, Theodore Fleming, IL
Giesy, Benjamin Franklin, OR
Goddard, Francis Wayland, PA
Goheen, George Bailey, PA
Greenfield, John Claude, PA
Hale, Willis LeBaron, MA
Halpert, Louis, GA
Hamilton, Luther Hess, OR
Hamilton, Gilbert VanTassel, OH
Harkness, John Linton, PA
Harris, Alexander Everett, AR
Heysinger, James Downey, PA
Hirsch, Charles Sol, PA
Holcombe, Charles Haight, NJ
Horinstein, Joseph Benjamin, PA
Horne, Benjamin W., PA
Horne, Smith Hamill, IA
Howard, John Edgar, PA
Jackson, Algernon Brashaer, IN
Jordan, Peter Andrew, SD
Kapp, Henry Hermann, NC
Katherman, Frank Clark, PA
Keely, John, GA
Keeney, Homer Isaac, OR
Kline, Willard Daniel, PA

Fig. 154. Algernon B. Jackson (JMC, '01), Head of Department of Public Health of Howard University, and Jefferson's first known black graduate.

Kottcamp, Edward Charles, PA
Lacy, Robert Yearger, TX
LaMotte, George Althouse, MO
Langstroth, Francis Ward, Jr., NJ
Levien, David Arnold, NY
Lindley, Don Carlos, PA
Logan, Samuel Gilmore, PA
Longshaw, Thomas Elmer, PA
MacCarroll, D. Randall, PA
Macon, Roland Bain, TN
Margossian, Arshag Der, ARMENIA
McCarthy, Frank Peter, PA
McMullin, Francis Aloysius, PA
Messinger, Otis Guy, CO
Metz, Joseph Arthur, OH
Meyer, John Hermann, CA
Meyers, Elmer Llewellyn, PA
Miller, Warren Jacob, PA
Miller, John Barton, PA
Miller, James Daniel, NJ
Murphy, Felix Aloysius, PA
Murray, Harry Wallace, OH
Nice, Franklin Mickley, PA
Orr, Porter Bynum, NC
Orr, Charles Albert, PA
Palmer, Joseph Bell, WV
Patten, Robert Swift, PA
Patterson, Walter Scott, PA
Peterson, Albert Alonzo, PA
Post, Sidney Haymond, WV
Pridgen, Claude Leonard, NC
Pugh, Winfield Scott, Jr., PA
Radasch, Henry Erdman, IA
Rahn, Norman H., PA
Ralston, James Hamilton, PA

Randal, Harry Lee, WV
Rehbein, Louis William, MD
Reid, Russell Alexander, PA
Reilly, Eugene Crowell, CA
Rhea, Edwin Wilson, PA
Rich, Edward Antoine, MN
Riegel, Thomas Francis, PA
Ritter, Frederic William, PA
Rodebaugh, George Kinsman, OH
Roop, Claude Diller, PA
Schall, David Horace, Jr., PA
Shaham, Simon, PA
Solliday, Monroe Holben, IL
Stauffer, Nathan P., PA
Steele, Ernest Richmond, DE
Steiner, Edwin, NJ
Stewart, Acheson, IRELAND
Stockton, William Clark, OH
Strickler, James Porter, PA
Symmers, Douglas, SC
Trexler, Jacob Amos, PA
Ulrich, George A., PA
Vail, William Carey, IN
VanKirk, Stephen Campbell, WV
Vasey, Charles Frederick, OH
Vernon, George Von, OH
Voigt, Arno C., PA
Walters, De Forrest E., IL
Weiss, Hervey Beale, PA
Weller, Joseph Newton, OH
Weller, James Edwin, IN
Wetton, Charles, NJ
Williams, Louis Carswell, NJ
Winslow, John Hayes, NJ
Wise, Ralph C., OH

"Whoever is to acquire a competent knowledge of medicine, ought to be possessed of the following advantages: a natural disposition; instruction; a favorable position for the study; early tuition; love of labour; leisure. First of all, a natural talent is required; for, when Nature opposes, everything else is vain; but when Nature leads the way to what is most excellent, instruction in the art takes place, which the student must try to appropriate to himself by reflection, becoming an early pupil in a place well adapted for instruction. He must also bring to the task a love of labour and perseverance, so that the instruction taking root may bring forth proper and abundant fruits."

Hippocrates (460-370 B.C.)

Charles E.G. Shannon, a native of Maine (B.A., Colby College), following internship at Pottsville Hospital, Pennsylvania, went on to postgraduate study in ophthalmology at the Massachusetts Eye and Ear Infirmary. He returned to Philadelphia as assistant to Prof. Howard R. Hansell, Jefferson Chairman of Ophthalmology, and soon became Chief of the Eye Clinic. He succeeded Dr. Hansell as Attending Ophthalmologist at Philadelphia General Hospital in 1919 and then became the fifth chairman of Ophthalmology at Jefferson in 1927 (Fig. 155). Dr. Shannon resigned in 1948 and returned to Maine where he practiced for some years and received an honorary degree from Colby College in 1954. His portrait was presented to Jefferson by the Class of 1948.

Edward John Beardsley, long a favorite teacher of students in the Department of Medicine, was an intern at Philadelphia General Hospital for two years and in 1905 served as an externe at East London Hospital, England. He became a licentiate of the Royal College of Physicians the same year and developed a lifetime interest in the history of medicine. Upon return to Philadelphia he joined the Department of Medicine at Jefferson and was also a member of the staff of the Henry Phipps Institute. In World War I he served as Lieutenant-Colonel in the American Expeditionary Forces. In 1927 he was promoted to Clinical Professor of Medicine (Fig. 156). In the interim following the death of Dr. McCrae in 1935, Dr. Beardsley was one of a four-member committee to supervise the Department of Medicine until the arrival of the new Chairman, Dr. Reimann.

There were 140 graduates in this class.

CLASS OF 1902

Agnew, Fred F., IA
Albertson, Harry Walter, PA
Atkins, George Hulings, DE
Bachrach, Benjamin, IL
Barrett, Edward William, MA
Beale, Samuel Marsden, Jr., MA
Beardsley, Edward John, CT
Bell, Elliott Edwin, PA
Bellamy, Robert Hartlee, NC
Bergeron, Peirre Norbert, MA
Bertolet, Walter Melot, PA
Bice, Barrett Dedrick, WV
Bittner, Henry Edward, PA
Blackwood, James Magee, PA
Bowman, Thomas Edward, PA
Boyle, Patrick Francis, PA
Britt, Charles Carroll, PA
Brown, George C., MA
Burt, James Clark, PA
Carlin, Robert Golden, PA
Carson, Jason Wilson, PA
Chamberlin, John Leavitt, NJ
Coleman, Oscar Edwin, CO
Collins, Edward Welles, IA

Conrey, Thomas Jackson, MD
Cope, William Franklin, PA
Crowe, Frank Beresford, PA
Curley, Walter James, MA
Davis, William McKay, PA
Dexter, Charles Amory, GA
Dinkelspiel, Max Robert, NY
Doane, Samuel Newman, PA
Drick, George R., PA
Duhigg, Thomas Francis, IA
Ely, Clarence Francis, PA
Ernst, Charles Henry, PA
Ewing, Samuel Eldridge, NJ
Fitzpatrick, William Wando, TX
Fox, Francis H., PA
Freeburg, Harry Waldeen, IN
Friedman, Aaron, MN
Gasslein, Richard Joseph, PA
Gibbons, Myles Aloysius, PA
Gille, Hugo, NJ
Gillett, Omer Rand, CO
Glasgow, Luther Ellis, PA
Grimes, George Dalton, KS
Grove, Austin Millard, PA

Gyles, Edward, NY
Harris, Frederick Thomas, ID
Hartman, Milton Ellsworth, PA
Hartzell, Rein Keelor, PA
Hazlett, Edgar Marion, PA
Heacox, Frank L., CT
Hearn, Marion, MD
Heineberg, Alfred, AL
Held, Isidore William, NY
Herbein, George Winters, CA
Hollingsworth, Robert B., LA
Hoon, Anthony Wilber, PA
Horner, Earl Hartle, IL
Horning, William H., PA
Hughes, Louie B., NE
Hull, Robert Lord, ME
Ingraham, Norman Reeh, PA
Ireland, Milton Stanton, NJ
Jarvis, Cecil C., WV
Keating, Charles Albert, Jr., NJ
Kelley, Daniel Joseph, MA
Kimmelman, Simon, PA

Kirby, Frank Brennand, PA
Kirkpatrick, William Burke, PA
Kirschner, Harry Edward, PA
Kistler, Alvin Jacob, PA
Lacock, Horace Mortimer, PA
Laessle, Henry Adolph, PA
Lane, William K., NC
Lehman, Joseph Davis, PA
Lincoln, George W., PA
Linton, Jay Dever, PA
Lochhead, Harris Burton, MI
Long, William Fegely, PA
Maclay, Joseph Alan, NJ
Markel, Henry Clayton, PA
McCoy, James Edward, NY
McKinnie, Lewis Hugh, CO
Mead, Harry Burton, PA
Midgley, Harry St. John, PA
Miller, Solomon Metz, PA
Miller, James Morgan, TX
Moore, Joseph Aloysius, PA
Moore, Philip Henry, ME

Fig. 155. Charles E. G. Shannon (JMC, '02), Chairman of Ophthalmology (1927-48).

Fig. 156. Edward J. Beardsley (JMC, '02), Clinical Professor of Medicine (1927) and well regarded for his teaching.

1902

Mundhenk, Herbert Conner, OH
Newson, Albertus, MD
Nofer, George Hancock, PA
Noll, Norman Beard, PA
Outerson, Richard Ambrose, CT
Palmer, Charles Walter, PA
Patton, Gideon Harmer, PA
Pechin, Edward Charles, PA
Pelouze, Percy Starr, NJ
Poole, Louis Eben, NJ
Potter, George Walter, PA
Ralston, William James, PA
Ransom, Matthias Lent, NY
Rhoads, John, PA
Round, Frederick Lutwyche, PA
Rufe, John Johnson, PA
Saltzman, Louis Andrew, PA
Schaffner, Boyd Willamber, PA
Schoffstall, Joseph W., PA
Schultze, Frederic Pitt, IA
Scott, Robert Crawford, PA
Shannon, Charles Emery G., ME
Sharp, Norman Wallace, PA
Sharpnack, William Forrest, PA

Sheaff, Philip Atlee, PA
Shepler, Robert McMurran, PA
Sieber, Isaac Grafton, NJ
Smithgall, Melvin Harvey, PA
Snyder, Charles P., PA
Snyder, Otto Kerr, WY
Sorin, Herman Mitchell, NJ
Spitz, Louis, PA
Steele, John Ward, DE
Stewart, Ralph Waldo, OH
Stimus, Howard George, NJ
Sunstein, Noah, PA
Taylor, Herbert Leonel, NH
Trainor, Charles Edwin, MS
Verdier, John Walter, MI
Wakefield, Ralph Waldo, ME
Walker, Granville Hunt, PA
Webb, Fred Leland, IA
Webber, Edward Everett, MI
Werst, Nevin Blank, PA
Wertman, Mahlon Andrew, PA
Wherry, Calvin Norwood, PA
Woodburn, Wilton Allen, PA
Wormser, Bernard Bertram, PA

Professor Holland's chemistry recitation in West Lecture Room, fourth floor of 1898 College (ca. 1902).

Willis F. Manges (Gettysburg College, 1900), the most notable in this class of 166 and the first member of Alpha Omega Alpha at Jefferson, was immediately involved in the new science of radiology, heading the outpatient x-ray Department as early as 1904. Although his academic advancement was slow, Dr. Manges was continuously in charge. He was appointed Clinical Professor in 1918 and full Professor of Roentgenology in 1928 (Fig. 157). As a pioneer in the field he was elected President of the American Roentgen Ray Society in 1918 and was responsible for numerous innovations in the specialty. His sudden death in 1936 was a serious loss. His two

Fig. 157.   Willis F. Manges (JMC, '03), Head of Department of Radiology (1904-1936).

sons, Willis E. and W. Bosley were both Jefferson graduates. Dr. Manges was honored with the degree of Doctor of Science by Gettysburg College in 1928.

Thomas Cook Stellwagen, Jr. studied dentistry at the Philadelphia Dental College (D.D.S., 1897) but was appointed Demonstrator in Dr. W.H. Pancoast's School of Anatomy the year of graduation and entered Jefferson as a Sophomore in 1900. His residency consisted of 18 months at Jefferson Hospital and three months at Children's Hospital. His entry into urology followed his appointment to Jefferson's Department of Genito-Urinary Surgery under Dr. Orville Horwitz. He then became Attending Genito-Urinary Surgeon at Philadelphia General Hospital in 1918. Having served in World War I with the British Army and later in the United States Army, he had extensive experience at the front in France. He succeeded Dr. Hiram Loux as Chairman of the Department of Genito-Urinary Surgery at Jefferson in 1930 (Fig. 158). He died at age 56 in 1935.

Charles R. Heed became a well-known ophthalmologist. Following internship in Pottsville, Pennsylvania, he became associated with the Ophthalmology Department of the Philadelphia Polyclinic where he was soon appointed Associate Professor. He was named Assistant Attending Surgeon at Wills Eye Hospital in 1911 and later joined the staff of Jefferson's Department of Ophthalmology where he advanced to Clinical Professor in 1930 (Fig. 159).

Abraham Joseph Cohen, after establishing a practice in Philadelphia, chanced upon Dr. Lawrence Flick (Jefferson, 1879, Fig. 99) and through his influence became involved in the developing campaign against tuberculosis. He joined the staff of the recently organized Phipps Institute and the White Haven Sanatorium, then participated in the founding of Eagleville Sanatorium in 1909, going on to serve as its Medical Director for many years. Dr. Cohen became associated with the School of Medicine of Temple University soon thereafter and advanced to Clinical Professor of Medicine.

John Hume Miller of South Carolina became the second known black graduate of Jefferson. He conducted a successful general practice for many years in Chester, Pennsylvania. He was awarded Jefferson's fiftieth reunion pin in 1953 (Fig. 160).

At the commencement where 166 M.D. Degrees were awarded, the honorary degree of Doctor of Laws was conferred upon Geheimrath Johann von Mikulicz-Radecki, Professor of Surgery in the University of Breslau.

Fig. 158. Thomas C. Stellwagen (JMC, '03), Chairman of Urology (1930-1935).

Fig. 159. Charles R. Heed (JMC, '03), Clinical Professor of Ophthalmology (1930).

Adcock, Lee Campbell, KY
Akers, Andrew Franklin, PA
Allen, Charles Walker, VA
Allen, Frederick Blunt, NY
Allison, Lucian Dent, PA
Armstrong, Thomas Smith, PA
Baines, Matthew Carroll, PA
Baltz, Samuel Austin, PA
Bell, David Major, PA
Bennett, Clarence Elmer, PA
Biehn, William Milton, PA
Blankemeyer, Henry John, PA

Borneman, John Henry, NC
Boyce, Lee, PA
Bryson, John Frampton, PA
Burg, Stoddard Somers, PA
Calhoun, Howard Boyd, PA
Campbell, Walter Lowrie, PA
Carney, Samuel David, PA
Carroll, Thomas Benjamin, OH
Chamberlain, Leslie, NY
Clagett, Augustus Henry, PA
Cohen, Abraham Joseph, PA
Conger, William Watson, MI

Cooper, Herbert, MA
Corwin, James Howell, PA
Cotham, Edward Ralph, AR
Cottrell, Emile Lester, CA
Crane, Harold Hayes, ME
Crow, Arthur Everett, PA
Dana, Lawrence W., PA
Davis, George Anthony, CT
Eastwood, Edmund, NJ
Edwards, William McEwen, WI
Eisenhower, Charles Wilhelm, PA
Ellison, Thomas, PA
Farquhar, Rahleigh Claude, PA
Flatley, John Walter, PA
Fledderjohann, Ferdinand Frederick, OH
Fogarty, Charles William, MN
Foster, Wilbur Allen, PA
Garretson, William, PA
Gibson, Albert Matthew, AL
Gilmore, Wilbur Hawley, IL
Goodman, Bert Edward, OH
Gormley, James Aloysius, NJ
Green, Max, PA
Harrington, James L., CT
Harrison, John Francis, CT
Harsha, Charles Lloyd, PA
Hart, Charles Vincent, PA
Hay, George, PA
Hazlett, Frank Leslie, PA
Heed, Charles R., PA
Heim, Lyman David, PA

Heisler, Frank Joseph, PA
Henry, Albert Leon, PA
Hess, Adolph, PA
Heyser, Jonas Edward, PA
Hillard, James Pearse, MA
Hixson, George William, OH
Hoffman, Charles Wilbur, WV
Holston, John George F., Jr., OH
Howell, Samuel McKeehan, PA
Hudson, Harry, Jr., PA
Hutzel, Oliver L., PA
Hyskell, William Emory, PA
Imboden, Harry Miles, PA
Ireland, Frederick W., NY
Jones, John Bayley, PA
Kane, Clinton Austin, MD
Katz, Meyer Joseph, PA
Kerr, William Edmunds, OH
Kiefer, Raymond Arndt, NJ
King, Richard Morrison, NC
Kissinger, Walter Cealey, PA
Koser, Martin Luther, NE
Kriebel, Asher G., PA
Kunkel, Oscar Franklin, PA
Laidlaw, Frank Winfield, NY
Larkins, Clyde Raymond, OH
Loewy, Ignatz David, PA
Logan, Edward Johnson, RI
Loper, John C., NJ
Luck, Benjamin D., AR
Manges, Willis Fastnacht, PA
Manning, Charles LaForge, NJ
Mayhew, Charles Holmes, NJ
McCormick, Arthur Foster, PA
McKemy, John William, OH
Mervine, Robert Batten, PA
Miller, Henry Ernest, PA
Miller, John Hume, SC
Miller, Walter Marion, PA
Miller, Richard Oliver, PA
Mitchell, Henry Chalmers, PA
Moore, Darius Carrier, PA
Morret, Henry Eckert, PA
Moser, Raymond Anson, PA
Munroe, Henry Stokes, NC
Munsch, Augustin Philip, PA
Murphy, Francis Aloysius, PA
Myers, Edward Ralph, PA
Mylin, Walter Franklin, PA
Neil, Thomas Franklin, PA
Neptune, Norman William, OH
Newcomb, Marcus Ward, NJ
Nickel, James Edward, PA
North, Henry Urban, PA

Fig. 160. John H. Miller (JMC, '03), long term practitioner in Chester, Pennsylvania.

O'Brien, John Daniel, PA
Ogilvie, Roy K., MO
Oglevee, Thomas Edison, PA
O'Neil, Michael Joseph, RI
Patterson, Robert Mehard, PA
Peltz, Philip Malcolm, PA
Petitjean, John William, IN
Pilling, George Platt, Jr., PA
Platt, Thomas Heritage, Jr., NJ
Plymire, Isaac Swartz, PA
Prothero, Harold Ney, PA
Quiney, James J., NJ
Ralston, James Curtis, PA
Reber, Conrad Samuel, PA
Reed, Henry David, PA
Reed, Marvin Warren, PA
Reidy, John Aloysius, PA
Reser, William Marven, IN
Roberts, William Pusey, PA
Robison, Clair Edward, PA
Rodgers, William Henry, OH
Rose, Horace Lewis, NJ
Sauer, Emil, MA
Saxton, Silas Warren, PA
Schenck, Daniel Scott, IA
Schnader, Amos Bowman, PA
Schoolman, Noah, PA
Schwartz, Lorraine L., PA

Scott, Hiran C., PA
Sewall, Millard Freeman, ME
Sherger, John Adam, PA
Sheridan, Lawrence Aloysius, PA
Shimoon, Joseph, PERSIA
Slifer, Walter Levi, PA
Smith, Lawrence DeHaven, DE
Smith, Howard Sedgwick, NJ
Smith, Frederick Charles, MN
Stanton, John Joseph, PA
Stellwagen, Thomas Cook, Jr., PA
Stevenson, George, NY
Stewart, Robert Armstrong, PA
Strayer, Walter Addison, OH
Swan, James Hayes, PA
Thomas, James William, OR
Thompson, Winfield Otis, KS
Tinney, Alfred Grant, PA
Todd, Clarence Milton, NY
Tomlinson, William Hibbs, PA
Ullman, Jacob S., MS
Ullom, Frank Sellers, PA
Ward, Todd Pope, IL
Ward, William John, NY
Washabaugh, William Braham, PA
White, Francis William, RI
Whitehead, Ira Bratton, PA
Whitmore, George Byron, NY
Winship, Herring, GA

W.W. Keen Surgical Society (1903).

1903

Commencement was held on May 7 at the Academy of Music. Honorable William Potter, the President, conferred the M.D. degree upon 165 graduates and the exercises closed with an address by George F. Baer, LL.D., President of the Board of Trustees of Franklin and Marshall College. An honorary degree of Doctor of Laws was conferred upon Prof. Dr. Albert Hoffa, Medical Privy Councillor, University of Berlin.

The College announcement for 1904/05 recorded the upgrading of requirements for admission to the first year class. A college degree was stated to be preferred but certain exceptions were permitted. This step was well in advance of the policy for most American Medical Schools.

Ross Vernet Patterson won the H. Augustus Wilson Gold Medal at graduation for the best examination in orthopaedic surgery. He took his internship at the Philadelphia General Hospital until 1906, and then became a member of the Jefferson faculty in the Department of Medicine, specializing in cardiology the remainder of his life (Fig. 161). His Presidencies included the Alumni Association (1923-25), the Pennsylvania Medical Society (1930-31), and the Association of American Medical Colleges (1933-35). He was Sub-Dean at Jefferson (1906-16) and Dean from 1916 until his death in 1938. He was a strong dean who ruled Jefferson for many years with an iron hand. Dr. Patterson left his estate to Jefferson for fellowships in research. In 1939, a foundation in his memory was established for the study and treatment of diseases of the heart and circulation. The Department of Electrocardiography was named the Ross V. Patterson Heart Station.

Charles Walter Bonney, a native of Maine, won the Henry M. Phillips prize, awarded upon the recommendation of the Professor of Medicine to the graduate in his opinion most worthy, and also was elected a member of Alpha Omega Alpha Honor Medical Society. Almost continuously from the time of his graduation until his death at age 82 he was connected with Jefferson's teaching staff. His interests were in surgery, especially urologic, and the teaching of Topographic and Applied Anatomy. He contributed valuable scientific articles and was active in the important medical societies of his time (Fig. 162).

Louis Chodoff won the Francis W. Shain prize for the best examination in surgery. He taught bandaging and fracture dressing at Jefferson for many years.

Alexander Spencer Kauffman specialized in otolaryngology and served for many years as Chief Clinical Assistant in Jefferson's Otological Clinic (Fig. 163).

Orlando H. Petty of this class received the Congressional Medal of Honor for services during World War I. He was cited by Dr. J. Chalmers DaCosta in his 1920 address at the dedication of a war memorial plaque.

CLASS OF 1904

Alexander, Eben, Jr., NC
Alexander, Emory Graham, NC
Amsbry, Lewis Brownson, PA
Anderson, James Howard, PA
Apple, Clarence Elwood, PA
Bader, Walter P., PA
Barber, Raymond, PA
Barsumian, Hagop G., TURKEY
Battle, Ivan Proctor, NC
Belaval, Jose Sastrano, PUERTO RICO
Bershad, Leonard, PA

Blair, James Dana, PA
Bonney, Charles Walter, NY
Botsford, Harry Levis, WV
Briggs, Miron Luke, PA
Brody, Myer, PA
Brown, Joel Daniel, PA
Bryant, Charles Henry, MA
Buckingham, Harry Sheldon, NJ
Burwell, Howard Beirne, AL
Callan, George John, PA
Campbell, M. D., PA

Carey, Harris May, DE
Carrier, Sidney Smith, PA
Carstarphen, William Turner, NC
Charlesworth, Ralph Robert, PA
Chodoff, Louis, PA
Coll, James Patrick, PA
Condit, William Glasgow, IA
Cottom, Frank Webster, OH
Cowen, Harold David, IA
Crawford, B. Lampton, MS
Cunningham, George Aloysius, PA
Davis, William Price, Jr., PA
Davitch, David H., PA
Dean, John Henry, TX
Denman, Homer, NY
Dodge, Arthur Howard, RI
Donahoe, John Patrick, PA
Edie, Elliott Bard, PA
Elder, James Clarence, OH
Ferman, John Wesley, PA

Fleming, Edwin Rahn, PA
Forster, Andrew E., PA
Fuller, David Herman, MA
Fuller, Gaillard Botchford, OH
Gilespie, William Pounder, Jr., PA
Gillum, John Randolph, IN
Goldberg, Maurice, PA
Goodman, Lee McCluskie, PA
Gray, Stoddard Perry, NY
Grier, George W., NJ
Hall, James King, NC
Hamati, Elias Essad, SYRIA
Harper, Howard Cyrus, PA
Hartman, Gustave, SWEDEN
Hensyl, William Curtis, PA
Hoffman, George Llewellyn, PA
Hope, John Ferguson, PA
Hopwood, Lucius Locke, IA
Jefferson, James, NJ
Jones, William Thomas, MS

Fig. 161.   Ross V. Patterson (JMC, '04), Dean (1916-38).

Fig. 162.   Charles W. Bonney (JMC, '04) Assistant Professor of Topographic and Applied Anatomy (1930).

1904

Joseph, Louis, PA
Kagey, Thomas J., VA
Kaufman, Alexander Spencer, PA
Keagy, Frank, PA
Kennedy, William Morton, PA
Kesler, Byron Linzie, UT
Kilgus, Harry E., PA
King, Harry Howard, NY
Klein, Adam Raymond, IA
Lane, Harry Hamilton, NY
Larson, Edward Martin, IA
Leventhal, Nathan Lewis, PA
Lewis, Cyril Ettrick, CA
Leytze, Frank Cornelius, IA
Little, John Forsyth, PA
Longfellow, Charles Fay, IL
Luman, Clark McEwen, PA
MacCallum, Wallace Peter, MA
MacDonald, Alden B., PA
Magill, Hugh R., MA
McCormack, Condon Carleton, OR
McLaughlin, Charles Molten, PA
McLean, McCormick Earle, PA
Meisle, Frederick Aaron, PA

Melvin, Alexis Merritt, PA
Mervine, Graydon Duncan, PA
Mitchell, Atlee David, PA
Moore, Wilson McKenevy, PA
Mullison, Edwin D. S., PA
Murphy, Eugene Francis, MN
Murray, Ralph Vorhees, IN
Murrin, Connell Edward, PA
Muschlitz, Charles Henry, PA
Muta, Samuel A., NJ
Niles, William Gordon, CA
North, Harry Ross, NJ
O'Neill, Owen, CT
Oelke, Emil Heinrich, IA
Patterson, Francis Denison, PA
Patterson, Ross Vernet, IL
Paulson, Andrew James, MN
Peiffer, Charles Oscar, PA
Penrod, Harry Hartzell, PA
Petty, Orlando H., OH
Porteous, Edward Johnston, PA
Pritchard, Frederick Morris, PA
Pumphrey, Josiah Merton, OH
Ransom, Frederick Page, OH
Rea, Clarence Galleher, IN
Reinemund, Charles Adam, IA
Ridgway, William Frederick, NJ
Riter, James Foster, OH
Rogers, Jerome B., NJ
Rohrbach, James Nathan, PA
Rouse, John, Jr., PA
Rust, Emery Andrew, IA
Schaffer, Harry Abraham, PA
Schaubel, Charles Wesley, PA
Schlindwein, George William, PA
Schug, George F., IA
Segal, Julius, PA
Segal, Doyle, PA
Shenberger, William Jacob, PA
Shirey, Harlan M., IN
Shortt, William H., PA
Shrom, Ralph Edwin, PA
Smith, Owen, NC
Smith, Joseph, NY
Smith, William Francis, IL
Snyder, Howard Lincoln, KS
Sprankle, Paul Darling, PA
Spriggs, Lem Walter, CA
St. Clair, Frank Earle E., IA
Stanley, Eugene Arthur, VT
Stembler, Harry Abraham, PA
Stevenson, Eber Fortner, IA
Stevenson, Ellerslie Wallace, PA
Stokes, John Wallace, NY

Fig. 163. A. Spencer Kauffman (JMC, '04), Chief Clinical
Assistant in Otological Clinic.

Taylor, Jackson, PA
Taylor, Walter Albert, NJ
Templin, Theodore, B., IN
Thierman, Ernest Julius, IA
Thomson, John Danner, GA
Topper, John Albert, PA
Towle, Clarence Clark, MA
Treat, Ernest, PA
Trinder, John Holmes, PA
Turner, Hunter Heiner, PA
Waggoner, Leroy C., PA
Wagner, James Frederick, PA

Walter, Henry V., PA
Wellner, John Edward, PA
Westley, Martin Daniel, ND
White, J. Norman, NY
Whitehill, Ira Engler, MD
Wignall, Horace Lewis W., NJ
Williams, James Thomas, CA
Williams, Walter Edward, PA
Willis, Herbert, PA
Wingate, Otis Lee, PA
Woods, Harry Robert, PA
Woolley, Herbert, NJ
Zimmerman, Randall, PA

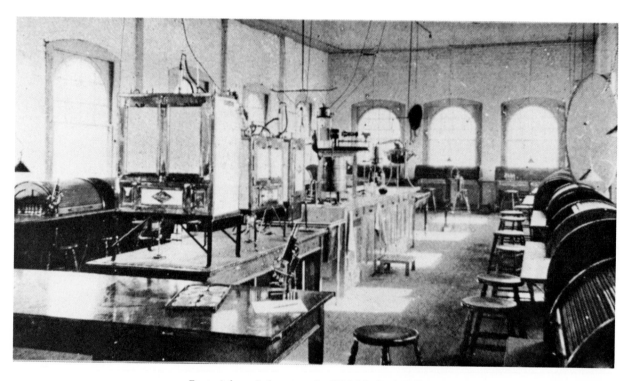

Bacteriology Laboratory in 1898 Medical College.

At the Commencement for 179 graduates held June 2 in the Academy of Music, the students presented the Thomas Eakins portrait of William Smith Forbes (JMC, 1852), Professor of Anatomy, to their alma mater. It was paid for by subscriptions from the classes of 1905, '06, '07 and '08 and "junior alumni" who requested that it hang in a prominent place in the College (currently the Eakins gallery of Jefferson Alumni Hall). The venerable 74 year-old Professor, famous for his Anatomy Act of 1867, died less than six months later (Fig. 53).

A most outstanding member of this class proved to be Alexander Jeremiah Orenstein (Fig. 164) who distinguished himself in the study and treatment of pneumoconiosis in the gold mine workers of South Africa. His organization and administration of the medical care for this disease in the mining industry was a world-wide hallmark in industrial medicine. The Alexander J. Orenstein Library of the Pneumoconiosis Research Institute was named for him as was the African Mine Workers Hospital. He was active in founding of the University of Witwatersrand Medical School which later awarded him an LL.D degree and established an annual lectureship in his name. In addition to many prestigious awards and medals, he received the Alumni Achievement Award in 1970.

James Carre Magee, of Pennsylvania, as a Major General, served as Surgeon General of the Army under President Franklin D. Roosevelt from 1939 to 1943. He thus had the responsibility for possibly the most complex medical program in any major U.S. war. At the Jefferson Commencement of 1940 he was awarded the honorary degree of Doctor of Science.

Another distinguished member of the class was Howard McCrum Snyder of Wyoming (Fig. 165). He served for more than 50 years in many parts of the world in the Army Medical Corps in which he rose to the rank of Major General. As personal physician, he took care of President Dwight Eisenhower during his heart attack.

Gabriel F. Tucker first practiced surgery in Pittsburgh but in 1919 joined Professor Chevalier Jackson in bronchoesophagology at Jefferson. He later succeeded him at the Hospital of the University of Pennsylvania and the Graduate Hospitals where in 1932 he was appointed Professor of Bronchoesophagology and Laryngeal Surgery. He was internationally known as a teacher of graduate students, inventor of numerous instruments for bronchial surgery and author of numerous articles. Dr. Tucker was also President of the American Bronchoscopic Society in 1941 and was active in many medical and specialty societies.

Tello Jaen D'Apery (Fig. 166) was listed in his Yearbook as "author traveller, student." After internship in the Philadelphia (General) Hospi-

Fig. 164. Alexander J. Orenstein (JMC, '05) international authority on industrial health and pneumonoconiosis.

tal, he conducted a successful general practice in Philadelphia. In addition, he served as Chief Clinical Assistant in the outpatient department of Clinical Medicine at Jefferson Hospital and also on the College Faculty in Clinical Medicine (Instructor in 1908 and Demonstrator from 1909 to 1920). In 1989, 40 years after his death (1949), the University received the gift of his portrait and a bequest ample to establish a Professorship in his memory.

Abbott, John George, MN
Abbott, Frank Cook, PA
Alderman, Charles G., IN
Austin, Albert Elmer, MA
Barr, John Walter, PA
Bernatz, Clarence Frank, IA
Berry, Lawrence Francis, PA
Beyer, Joseph Walter, PA
Biello, Joseph Albert, PA
Blanchard, Howard E., RI
Bloomfield, Maximilian David, MA
Borland, James Carlyle, PA
Bosworth, Robinson, VT
Boysen, Theophilius Henry, Jr., NJ
Bramble, Halsey Sandford, NY
Brandberg, Guy Alfred, PA
Brewe, Arthur Jackson, PA
Brown, Ray Clifton, ME
Brown, William Frank, IA
Bryant, Charles Page, PA
Burkholder, John Lewis, PA
Caldwell, Morris Milton, NC
Carhardt, Earl Clyde, IA
Clancy, Daniel Francis, MA
Clark, Warren Thomas, NJ
Cooner, Charles C., PA
Cooney, Sidney Alexander, MT
Cooper, Edward, MA
Cregg, Francis Aloysius, MA

d'Apery, Tello J., NY
Davenport, Frederick Marshall, PA
Davis, Frank Thomas, Jr., PA
Davison, Seward Roland, PA
Donnelly, Robert T., PA
Doyle, George Fergison, PA
Dunn, Harrison Albert, PA
Eichman, Edward Aloysius, PA
Eisenstadt, Alexander, NY
Elder, Fred Orestes, MA
Ellis, Walter Winthrop, DE
Evans, Horace Elmer, DE
Ewers, Frank Adams, OH
Eyanson, John Norbert, IN
Ferguson, Gilbert Aloysius, PA
Ferrier, William Henry, NY
Fishman, Abraham Pincos, NJ
Flemming, Major Ivy, NC
Fluke, George Thomas, PA
Fortner, Howard Garfield, PA
Fought, Edgar Newton, PA
Friedenberg, Samuel, PA
Gamble, Charles Delbert, OH
Garrett, Charles Reece, IA
Gearhart, Malcolm Zieber, PA
Glick, William Henry, PA
Goostrey, George Francis, BRITISH COLUMBIA
Griffith, Dayne Hamilton, PA
Hallett, Harley J., IL
Hanchett, Harry Bigelow, CT
Harley, John Parker, PA
Harmon, Charles Henry, NH
Harper, James Henry, NC
Harrison, Henry Hill, NC
Hayes, Charles Garfield, PA
Heimer, Louis Benjamin, PA
Heisey, William Christian, PA
Henry, Daniel Webster, PA
Herff, Ferdinand Peter, TX
Hogue, John Daniel, PA
Holbrook, Clark Bates, MA
Hoskins, John Robinson, PA
Howard, Harold Melnotte, MA
Jackson, Robert George, BRITISH COLUMBIA

Fig. 165. Howard M. Snyder (JMC, '05) with President Eisenhower for whom he was personal physician.

Jackson, Rice Robinson, TX
Johnson, Livingston Franklin, NC
Jones, Henry Orendorf, PA
Kell, Ralph Chester, PA
Killian, Frederick William, PA
Knight, Guy Augustus, PA
Larimer, Parry Bernard, PA
Lee, Thomas Benjamin, NJ
Lehman, Charles Albert, PA
Lerch, Charles Edmund, PA
Lore, Harry Elmer, NJ
Luhr, Alfred Francis, PA
Mace, Lloyd Russell, PA
MacFarlane, James P., PA
Mackenzie, Egbert Gray, NJ
Magee, James Carre, PA
Maier, Ernest George, PA
McCaffrey, Hugh Edward, MA
McCallum, Chester Harold, PA
McCanna, John Milton, PA
McCarthy, Samuel Lloyd, PA
McCready, Robert Purdon, PA
McCullough, William John L., PA
McCullough, Francis Joseph, PA

McDowell, Ralph Walker, PA
McKenna, William Bernard, PA
Miller, Oliver Joseph, FL
Milliken, Lorenzo Fremont, PA
Mitchell, Elmer Wesley, MA
Moheny, Irvin R., PA
Monahan, Thomas Aloysius, PA
Morrison, Edward Lloyd, PA
Moyar, Charles Clinton, PA
Munford, Samuel Archer, IN
Newnam, Henry Joseph E., PA
Nix, William Henry, IL
Norton, Thomas Joseph, MA
Orenstein, Alexander Jeremiah, PA
Park, Thomas Creigh, PA
Pope, Edward Sutphen, NY
Pritchard, Arthur Thomas, NC
Raff, Alexander Berkley, PA
Rains, Jesse Lewis, ID
Reichard, Morris, HUNGARY
Reynolds, Victor M., PA
Rhoads, Edward Elliott, PA
Riggs, Lindus La Rell, IA
Riker, George A., NY
Riley, Charles Allen, VT
Robinson, William Arthur, NJ
Ross, William Fay, PA
Ruhl, Levi Albertus, OH
Rumph, Sterling Price, INDIAN TERRITORY
Ryan, John Timothy, PA
Saxe, LeRoy Hallowel, PA
Scheetz, Herbert Nichols, PA
Schneider, Emil Sebastian, PA
Schwartz, Louis, PA
Severs, George Harvey, PA
Shaw, Arthur Ernest, NC
Shea, Thomas Emmet, PA
Shuttleworth, Benjamin F., WV
Siggins, George, PA
Simpson, John Reid, PA
Smathers, Frank Clifford, PA
Smith, Samuel Calvin, PA
Snyder, Howard McCrum, WY
Snyder, Wayne Lawson, PA
Sonneborn, George, PA
Spence, George Sigars, PA
Sprague, Hugh Boleyn, UT
Stanton, James Justice, IN
Stanton, James N., PA
Starr, Edison Burns, OH
Stern, Samuel, PA
Stewart, Harry Myrrel, PA
Stringfield, Samuel Lanier, NC
Strong, Francis Xavier, PA

Fig. 166. Tello Jaen D'Apery (JMC, '05), Chief of outpatient clinical medicine at Jefferson.

Sullivan, Timothy Daniel, MA
Tallmadge, William Henry, Jr., CT
Taylor, Richard F., PA
Thomssen, Herbert William, NY
Tibbins, Perry McDowell, PA
Treichler, Vere, PA
Tucker, Gabriel Fred, WV
Underwood, James Harris, NJ
VanSweringen, Garrette, IN
Vaughan, Edward Mitchell, DE
Vincent, Isaac Raymond, PA
Vosburgh, Stephen Earle, MA
Wagner, Victor Carlyle, PA
Warner, Charles Carroll, WA

Weber, Raymond Kantner, PA
Weed, Mark Dye, PA
Werner, Julius Leon, PA
Wiley, John Joseph, PA
Williams, Thomas Elmer, TX
Williams, Thomas Lamar, PA
Williams, Ernst Thornton, PA
Wilson, John Denniston, PA
Winters, William Joseph, PA
Womack, Noel Catchings, MS
Wood, James William, PA
Wood, Walter Franklin, NJ
Young, Roy Lowry, PA
Ziegler, Fred Jay, OR

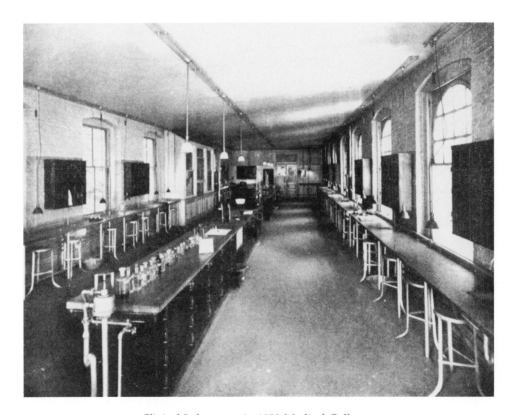

Clinical Laboratory in 1898 Medical College.

In this year, Professorships in the basic science courses of the Medical College (Anatomy, Physiology, Pathology, Bacteriology, and Chemistry) were established as fulltime teaching and research positions.

Three members of this class of 200 advanced to positions of importance on the Jefferson Faculty. Best remembered was Edward J. Klopp (Philadelphia College of Pharmacy and Science, 1901), who went on to Jefferson Hospital Internship following graduation. He was then appointed Chief Resident Physician which led to contacts with the leaders in the Department of Surgery. He began his surgical career on the staff of Dr. Francis T. Stewart and also served under Dr. John H. Gibbon, Sr., both of whom had high regard for his talents. Dr. Klopp advanced in clinical surgery at Jefferson and Pennsylvania Hospitals and acquired a large practice. In 1931 he was named Co-Chairman of the Department of Surgery (Fig. 167) and continued in that post until his early death in 1936. He delivered the first Grace Revere Osler lectures which Lady Osler had endowed in memory of her first husband, Dr. Samuel W. Gross. Dr. Klopp was also President of the Alumni Association in 1930.

Fig. 167. Edward J. Klopp (JMC, '06), Co-Chairman of Surgery (1931-36).

Fig. 168. Arthur E. Billings (JMC, '06), Clinical Professor of Surgery (1930).

Arthur E. Billings, a native of North Carolina (Davidson College), joined the Department of Surgery following Jefferson residency and progressed to the rank of Clinical Professor in 1930 (Fig. 168). He was also Surgeon to Bryn Mawr Hospital and acquired a large practice.

Willard H. Kinney (Fig. 169) joined the Department of Genito-Urinary Surgery and advanced to the rank of Clinical Professor of Urology in 1930. He was also Genito-Urinary Surgeon to the Philadelphia General Hospital. Following service in World War I he continued as Lieutenant-Commander in the United States Naval Reserve. He was author of numerous scientific papers and continued his activities at Jefferson until his resignation in June, 1942.

Among the early black graduates of Jefferson were Paul J. Taylor and Henry M. Minton of this class. Both became active in the treatment of tuberculosis. Dr. Taylor was on the staff of the Jefferson Department for Diseases of the Chest, 238 Pine Street, in addition to his private practice in Philadelphia. Dr. Minton, previously educated at the Academy of Harvard University and Phillips Exeter Academy, graduated from the Philadelphia College of Pharmacy in 1895. He practiced pharmacy for seven years but went on to Jefferson to graduate with this class after which he joined the staff of Douglass Hospital and also of the Henry Phipps Institute for the treatment of Tuberculosis. His association with Phipps continued until his death in 1946 (Fig. 170). He also became Superintendent and Director of Mercy Hospital for 24 years during which time Mercy merged with Douglass to form Mercy-Douglass Hospital.

CLASS OF 1906

Adams, Ralph Crawe, PA
Alexander, William Archibald, PA
Aydelotte, John Thomas, PA
Bachman, Milton Homer, PA
Baird, Joseph Armstrong, PA
Barnette, William Mason, CT
Barr, William Henry, CT
Beatty, Arthur William, MD
Beebe, James, DE
Benjamin, Floyd Allen, NY
Berkeley, Green Ramsey, GA
Betts, George Warren, PA
Bigley, Francis Peter, PA
Billings, Arthur Eugene, NC
Blosser, Roy, GA
Boice, James M., PA
Borzell, Francis Frank, PA
Boudwin, Charles Bacon, PA
Boyer, George Edgar, NJ
Bradley, John Aloysius, PA
Bricker, Howard Edgar, PA
Briggs, Erwin Sheridan, PA
Broadbelt, Leedom Richard, PA
Broadfield, John Augustus, PA
Brown, Arthur Aloysius, MA
Brown, Walter Henry, PA
Brundage, Robert Abner, PA
Bryan, Wallace Steele, PA
Bullock, Edwin Corlies, NJ
Campbell, John Sheridan, PA
Campbell, William Breaden, OH

Chapman, Ellis Jeakings, NJ
Clement, Edward Buehler, NC
Cogan, Richard Merwin, NJ
Compton, John Milton, NJ
Connole, John Francis, PA
Cooke, Thomas Clarence, VA
Cornwell, William Leslie, NJ
Craig, Ford B., PA
Cramp, Charles Edgar, PA
Curtis, Grant Philleo, NJ
Cutler, Franklin Earl, PA
Cutter, William W., IL
Davis, Addison Dimmitt, OH
Davis, John Hall, PA
Decker, Rudolph Frederick, IL
Dixon, Edward F., IL
Doherty, Harry Aloysius, NJ
Dwyer, Frank Philip, PA
Egly, Henry Conrad, PA
Eisenhart, Harry Picking, PA
Ellegood, Robert Edwin, DE
Ellinger, Jacob Edgar, PA
Engel, William Royal, OH
English, Samuel B., NJ
Evans, William P., PA
Evans, William Allen, PA
Evans, Clark, PA
Farwell, Frank Pierce, PA
Feldstein, George Julius, PA
Ferguson, Thomas Reed, PA
Fisher, Mulford Keene, PA

Flaherty, Michael Edward, PA
Fleming, Henry Craig, PA
Forney, Norman Nes, PA
Frost, Henry Edward, MA
Gable, Frank J., PA
Gale, George Hays, OH
Gaskill, Henry Kennedy, PA
Godfrey, James H. Mines, NE
Gonzales, Pablo Bonelli, PUERTO RICO
Gordon, Samuel, PA
Gorman, John Francis, PA
Granelli, Michael Simon, NJ
Guyot, J. DeVoine, MO
Hance, Burtis Magie, NJ
Hansel, George B., PA
Harris, Robert Edward, GA
Hempstead, Jacob, NJ
Hill, George Wright, OR
Hirsch, Henry Leon, MA
Hoffman, Clarence, MD

Hopwood, George Black, PA
Hopwood, William Hudson, PA
Horwitz, Louis, PA
Howard, LeRoy Downey, PA
Huttenlock, Robert Edelman, PA
Islenberg, Alfred Percy, PA
Jackson, James Allen, GA
Janblatte, Prince Nasib, SYRIA
Jones, Edgar Clyde, OH
Kean, Joseph Walter, NJ
Keidel, Victor, TX
Kinney, Willard Heil, PA
Kitchen, Joseph Samuel, PA
Klopp, Edward Jonathan, PA
Knight, Alfred John, SD
Koegel, William F. H., NJ
Kraemer, William Henry, WV
Lachner, Bernard Joseph, OR
Lambie, John Sioussa, Jr., PA
Lawson, Thomas Adam, PA

Fig. 169. Willard H. Kinney (JMC, '06), Clinical Professor of Urology (1930).

Fig. 170. Henry M. Minton (JMC, '06) specialized in treatment of tuberculosis and hospital administration.

1906

Levitt, Michael Lewis, PA
Lewis, Fielding Otis, KY
Lore, Andrew Provost, NJ
Lownes, John Barton, PA
Mahoney, John Edwin, PA
Martin, Daniel Webster, PA
Maxwell, George Madison, NC
McCready, James Homer, PA
McCune, Samuel R. W., PA
McKea, Carlisle Emerson, PA
McKinley, Andrew Stuart, PA
McKnight, John Roy, PA
Meek, Grover Cleveland, KY
Miller, George William, Jr., PA
Miller, Edwin Barclay, PA
Miller, Leroy Bernhardt, PA
Minton, Henry McKee, PA
Mitchell, Edward Kirkwood, PA
Molumphy, David James, CT
Moss, Harry Joseph, PA
Murphy, Edward Joseph, PA
Muthart, Lewis James, PA
Nassau, Charles Francis, PA
Neiman, Howard George, PA
Niple, Dio Maine, PA
Novack, Harry Jacob, PA
Outerson, Andrew Mansergh, CT
Parker, John L., PA
Parks, Clarence Carson, PA
Patterson, Joseph Flanner, NC
Penrose, Thomas William, PA
Penton, Jose Luis, CUBA
Phillips, Eliot Earle, PA
Prichard, Karl Campbell, WV
Prichard, William Clarence, DE
Raymond, Walter Clemens, PA
Renn, Roy Herman, PA
Rich, Lorin Farr, ID
Richter, Henry Carl, IA
Robinson, Benjamin, PA
Robinson, Heber Edward, UT
Rochester, Alexander Sands, OH
Roller, William Calvin, PA
Rose, Abraham Hewitt, NC
Ryan, Adam W. T., OH
Saleeby, Ameen Mittry, SYRIA
Sariakusi, Ibrahim Mohammed, EGYPT
Schoening, John Jacob, PA
Scott, Buckner Fairfax, WV

Scott, William Rice, OR
Secor, William Lee, OH
Shaw, Walter Corson, PA
Shelley, Jay Warren, PA
Shepherd, Richard Cotton, PA
Sheppard, Charles Woodruff, PA
Shingle, John Delroy, WY
Shoemaker, George Elmer, NJ
Shoenthal, Harry Irvin, PA
Shorkley, Thornton Moore, PA
Sibley, Edward Rufus, NY
Simkins, Daniel, PA
Smith, Russell Abbott, PA
Smith, Max Truman, NE
Spear, Owen Crow, DE
Speight, Joseph Powell, NC
Spivak, Louis Joseph, PA
Stafford, James Frederick, IA
Stayer, Morrison Clay, PA
Steel, John Mattern, PA
Steiner, John Martin, PA
Stevens, Harry Eldredge, NJ
Strousse, Leo, PA
Swallow, Frank W., PA
Tankersley, James William, NC
Taylor, Paul James, VA
Templeton, Charles Love, OR
Thomas, George Carroll, PA
Thompson, Henry Merrill, PA
Topham, Bertram Everett, PA
Uhler, Stewart Mann, PA
Vick, George Davis, NC
Wagner, Frederick Miner, Jr., PA
Wagner, William Edgar, PA
Waldner, John Louis, SD
Walson, Charles Moore, DE
Wang, Charles William, PA
Wannamaker, Theodore Elliott, Jr., SC
Weakley, William Stair, PA
Weinstein, Morris Abraham, PA
Whitall, James Dawson, PA
White, Daniel William, PA
Widdowson, Frank Ridley, PA
Williams, Robert Lloyd, WI
Willoughby, Ralph Ray, OR
Wilson, Oscar Hermon, PA
Woodbury, Malcolm Sumner, NY
Young, John Simpson, NJ
Ziegler, Alfred Henry, PA

In this year of 126 graduates, the major event was the opening on June 8 of what is now "Old Main" Hospital at Tenth and Sansom Streets (Fig. 171). Construction was started in 1903 but slowed by strikes and drawn-out attention to details. An impressive dedication ceremony was conducted by Board President, the Honorable William Potter, and enhanced by an inspired address by Dr. John Chalmers DaCosta, destined to be the first Samuel D. Gross endowed Professor in 1910. The building could vie with the best of any in the country. Eight stories tall, fireproof with ground floor and basement built of steel, concrete, brick and terra cotta; floored with tile or other nonflammable material; supplied with natural light by three streets; containing interior electric lighting; steam heated from a central outside plant; cleaned by a vacuum system; and ventilated by a noiseless exhaust system, this state-of-the-art hospital provided more than 300 beds. It remains today as Jefferson's oldest building.

Michael Anthony Burns took an early interest in neurology which at that time included psychiatry under the heading of mental and nervous diseases (Fig. 172). In 1934 he was appointed Professor of Neurology to succeed Dr. Edward A. Strecker. As the work load in psychiatry greatly increased, Dr. Burns recommended the creation of a separate Division, which led to the appointment in 1937 of Dr. Baldwin L. Keyes as Clinical Professor of Psychiatry in the Department of Neurology. Dr. Burns died suddenly in 1938 at the age of 54.

Arthur Julius Davidson was appointed Instructor of Orthopaedic Surgery in 1908 and thereafter until 1954 remained active in teaching in the orthopaedic clinic of this Department. He attained the rank of Associate Professor and was a recognized expert in the care of foot problems.

Harry Hunter Lott (Fig. 173) became an Assistant Professor of Laryngology at Jefferson and was highly regarded for his skill in tonsillectomy, which until the 1940s was performed almost as a routine.

Sidney Lessing Olsho won the prize in Otology and honorable mention in Pediatrics at graduation. He taught in the Ophthalmology Department of Jefferson for many years during which he advanced to the rank of Assistant Professor.

Benjamin Paul Weiss was awarded honorable mention for the Neurology prize at graduation. He served for many years in the Department of Mental and Nervous Diseases under Professors Dercum, Strecker, Burns and Alpers. His effective teaching led to his rise to Associate Professor of Neurology (Fig. 174).

CLASS OF 1907

Abbott, Frank Farnum, IL
Ard, George Potter, PA
Bachmann, Jean George, PA
Ballou, James Larkin, NC
Bennett, Wilford W., UT
Betts, William Williams, PA
Bitting, Numa Duncan, NC
Bliss, Gerald Douglas, NOVA SCOTIA
Blumberg, Nathan, PA
Bonelli, Victor Emmanuel, MS
Brice, Patrick Joseph, PA
Bright, James Cooper, RI

Brinson, Ed. Lane, GA
Burns, Michael Anthony, PA
Burwell, Thomas Spotuas, NC
Bushong, Frederick, PA
Chambers, William, PA
Chetwynd, Joseph Wallace, OH
Clapp, George Houghton, PA
Clark, James Cecil, UT
Cornely, J. Mossop, PA
Cox, Boaz Baxter, WV
Craig, William Clarke, NY
Crawford, James Joseph, MA

Davidson, Arthur Julius, PA
Dayton, Glenn Orville, OH
DeVore, Benjamin Franklin, OR
Dickinson, Charles Seymour, PA
Diers, Harry Edward, OH
Doster, Wade, KS
Eckhart, Godlove Grover, IN
Eulner, Elmer Harold, NJ
Everett, Shem Alfred, CT
Falk, Ralph, ID
Feild, Julian, OK

Fisher, Samuel Lloyd, PA
Follmer, George Elmer, PA
Foster, George Burgess, Jr., MA
Fox, George Timothy, MA
Gibson, George William, MA
Gillespy, Thurman, WV
Glenn, Nicholas Thomas, PA
Goldcamp, Stephen Wilfred, OH
Gonzalez, Jose, PUERTO RICO
Goodrich, Hubert John, NY
Gross, Benjamin, NY

Fig. 171.   "Old Main" Hospital opened June 8, 1907.

1907

Haines, Benjamin F., PA
Hamilton, E. Wallace, PA
Hoban, James John, MA
Hobgood, James Edward, NC
Hood, John Sidney, NC
Howe, Jesse Burket, PA
Hughes, Ephraim Georgia, UT
Hyatt, Frederick Carlyle, NC
Ives, Harold Augustus, FL
Jett, Richard Lawrence, KY
Johnson, John Huston, PA
Johnston, William McDowell, PA
Kinter, John Henry, PA
Kocher, Jacob John, CA
Kowaleski, Joseph S., PA
Krebs, Adolph, PA
Lacock, Lester Earle, PA
Laufersweiler, Leonard Frank, OH
Lott, Harry Hunter, PA
Loveren, George Stillman, CA
Mason, Willard M., NJ
Mayerberg, Israel Wallace, NC
McNerney, Aloysius Francis, PA

Meitzner, Max, PA
Mercer, Clarence Mavel, MI
Moore, Charles Edward, NC
Moorman, Albert John, OH
Morel, Henri Auguste, FRANCE
Moulton, Percy Daniel, ME
Nolan, Thomas Francis, PA
Norris, Leonard Edward, RI
Norton, Roy Roscoe, NJ
Olsho, Sidney Lessing, PA
Page, Arthur L., PA
Page, Claude Weston, PA
Patterson, Fred Lyle, PA
Phelps, George Floyd, PA
Poland, Joseph, PA
Poole, Charles Henry, PA
Powers, Marion Henderson, WV
Randles, Herbert, KS
Reed, James Craig, PA
Reiff, Rankin, PA
Ridge, Samuel LeRoy, PA
Rifat, Mansur Mustafa, EGYPT
Roddy, John A., Jr., PA

Fig. 172. Michael A. Burns (JMC, '07), Professor of Neurology (1934-38).

Fig. 173. Harry H. Lott (JMC, '07), Assistant Professor of Laryngology.

1907

271

Fig. 174. Benjamin P. Weiss (JMC, '07), Associate Professor of Neurology.

Ross, John Kirkland, NC
Ross, Daniel Curley, PA
Rozelle, Carlos C., IA
Russell, Joseph William, PA
Samuels, Bernard, NY
Sands, Charles Turner, PA
Scholl, Henry Nathaniel, PA
Schwartz, Morris R., PA
Seabold, William Franklin, NY
Seedenberg, Jesse Peightal, PA
Shick, William Binder, PA
Sloterbeck, Edgar Blackburn, PA
Smith, Wilburn H., MI
Smith, Paul Ruskin, DE
Smith, James Melvin, PA
Smith, Clarence Daniel, PA
Sprague, Frank Marion, ID
Strickler, Albert, PA
Stuckert, Harry, PA
Sweeney, Edward Joseph, MA
Talley, Lewis Robert, TX
Towler, Harold Hunt, PA
Wanner, Harry Herbert, PA
Wardle, Henry, MA
Watkins, Fonso Butler, NC
Weiss, Benjamin Paul, PA
Weiss, Harry, PA
Wells, Edgar Kennard, NJ
Wentz, Paul Roop, PA
Whiteside, Lindsay Cochrane, PA
Wills, Leon Clifford, PA
Wood, Rex, MO
Yohannan, Malcolm, NY
Zimmerman, Frank D., PA

The Jeffersonian

Editor-in-Chief
JAMES CRAIG REED, Pa., '07

General Business Manager
J. E. MACUSKER,
Address: Jefferson Medical College, Philadelphia

Associate Editors
LOUIS OTTO HEILAND, Pa., '08
EDWARD T. B. WEIDNER, Pa., '08

Athletic Editor
HARRY E. DIERS, Ohio, '07

Alumni Editor

Local Editor
Robert K. McConeghy, Pa., '08

Advisory Board
CHARLES C. TOWNSEND, ESQ., for the Board of Trustees
PROF. W. M. L. COPLIN, for the Faculty
PROF. H. AUGUSTUS WILSON, for the Faculty
HENRY LINN BASSETT, A. B., M. D., for the Alumni

Published on the tenth of each month during the college year by James Craig Reed, Philadelphia.

All matters for insertion must be in not later than the twenty-fifth of each month.

Subscription, $1 per year. Single copy, 15 cents.

Entered as second class matter at Philadelphia.

The Jeffersonian, a Student publication between 1899 and 1916.

~ 1908 ~

President William Potter awarded the M.D. degree to 170 graduates. The Commencement address was delivered by William H. Howell, Johns Hopkins Professor of Physiology and Dean.

Julius Blechschmidt, a native of Germany went on to post-graduate training in Pediatrics at Guy's Hospital, London, becoming a Licentiate of the Royal College of Physicians. He was appointed Chief Clinical Assistant in the Department for Diseases of Children at Jefferson and was also Assistant Pediatrician at the Philadelphia General Hospital while practicing pediatrics in Philadelphia for many years.

John W. Holmes also became associated with the Department for Diseases of Children at Jefferson and became a West Philadelphia pediatrician of note.

Patrick McCarthy became a respected member of the Jefferson surgical staff as well as an active Chief of Surgical service at the Philadelphia General Hospital and at St. Mary's Hospital.

Cheney M. Stimson, a native of Ohio, joined the Department of Obstetrics and Gynecology and for many years was Chief Clinical Assistant in the Gynecology Clinic.

Marshall C. Rumbaugh received honorable mention for several prizes at graduation and became a well-known physician and surgeon in Northeastern Pennsylvania as well as a leading Jefferson Alumnus. In 1952 he was President of the Alumni Association (Fig. 175).

Walter M. Bortz became a prominent internist and a leader in organized medicine in Western Pennsylvania. His son Donald W. Bortz was also a Jefferson Alumnus in the Class of 1939.

Perhaps the best known among the 1908 graduates was Elmer H. Funk. Dr. Funk's entire medical career related to Jefferson and to the Pennsylvania Hospital. Following internship he was appointed to the Department of Medicine and in 1912 Acting Medical Director of the Hospital. The same year, Dr. McCrae became Chairman of Medicine and a lifelong relationship began be-

tween these two master clinicians. Dr. Funk was made the first Medical Director (1913-26) of the new Department for Diseases of the Chest (Old Pine Street). His career broadened in Medicine and Therapeutics and he was recognized as an excellent teacher and writer (Fig. 176). On 1931 he succeeded Hobart A. Hare as Professor of Therapeutics and was President of the Alumni Association the same year. His death May 13, 1932 was a major loss. The Class of 1933 presented his portrait to the College.

Thurman D. Kitchin enhanced the prestige of Jefferson as his career broadened. After practising medicine in his native North Carolina for

Fig. 175. Marshall C. Rumbaugh (JMC, '08), well respected general surgeon. President of the Alumni Association (1952).

nine years he was called to Wake Forest College as Professor of Physiology and Pharmacology in 1918. A year later he was made Dean of the Medical School and in 1930 President of Wake Forest College. He served the State of North Carolina in many capacities including membership on a Governor's Commission to revise the State Laws and he was well known in state and national medical activities. In 1937 he was elected President of the Jefferson Medical College Alumni Association.

Wingate M. Johnson became Professor of Clinical Medicine in the Bowman Gray School of Medicine.

CLASS OF 1908

Adair, Templeton, VA
Axtell, Earl, TX
Bagshaw, David Evans, MI
Baker, Norman Clyde, NH
Baldwin, Herbert James, PA
Barnett, George Watson, PA
Basil, Aratoon, ARMENIA
Bauscher, Abner Henry, PA
Belisle, Albert Edward, NH
Berry, John, NC
Blechschmidt, Julius, GERMANY
Bornstein, Max, WI
Bortz, Walter Michael, PA
Brown, Thaddeus Clair, PA
Brown, Archie Lee, UT
Brown, Henry Ross, PA
Bugbee, Arthur Sharpe, CT
Buka, Alfred Joseph, PA
Burks, Floyd L.R., CA
Calvert, Lewis Cass, MO
Carington, Will John, MO
Clark, Clarence Merrill, UT
Clarke, Frederick George, UT
Colbert, William F., Jr., PA
Craig, Earl Burrell, PA
Crandall, Charles Perry, RI
DeLancey, William Wheelock, NY
Dengler, Henry Paul, NJ
Dougherty, James, PA
Dwyer, Richard Joseph, CT
Easley, Philip Samuel, NC
Eister, William Howard, PA
Evens, John Francis, OH
Fallon, Joseph Francis, MA
Feldman, Jacob Benjamin, NY
Fernandez, Rafael, MEXICO
Fortescue, Thomas Aloysius, PA
Freeman, Robert Herman, NC
Fritch, James Scott, PA
Frosch, Frank Joseph, PA
Funk, Elmer Hendricks, PA
George, Charles Harney, MI
Gilger, Ralph J., PA

Ginsburg, Samuel, PA
Goldfeder, Charles B., PA
Griesemer, Wellington David, PA
Haagen, David Fisk, PA
Hammond, Thomas Victor, Jr. DC
Hanlon, Edward Francis, PA
Hare, William Bathwell, OR
Harris, Harry, PA
Harris, Lorne Wilborne, MA
Hartz, Harry Jacob, PA
Heiland, Louis Otto, PA

Fig. 176. Elmer H. Funk (JMC, '08), first Medical Director of the Department for Diseases of the Chest and Professor of Therapeutics (1932).

Hemminger, Edward Franklin, PA
Herriott, Walter Hays, PA
Hewitt, Archie Edelen, OH
Hinkel, William Henry, PA
Holmberg, Carl Edward, MI
Holmes, John Williams, PA
Hull, Howard Lane, PA
Irby, Moreland R., VA
James, Richard Forrest, OR
James, William Daniel, NC
Johnson, Wingate Memory, NC
Jones, Adna Sawyer, NY
Kaufman, David, PA
Keely, Henry Edgar, PA
Kice, Luther Holden, NJ
Killips, Thomas Allen, NY
Kirk, Clair Bishop, PA
Kirkwood, Robert Carnahan, PA
Kitchin, Thurman Delna, NC
Klinzing, Henry, PA
Knoll, George Gustavus, PA
Koenig, Carl Eugene, OR
Kremens, Maxwell, PA
Krout, George Elmer, PA
Kurtz, Arthur D., PA
Lacy, Henry Clay, OR
LaGasa, James Andrew, WA
Larkin, Thomas Leo, PA
Laughrey, John Brooks, PA
Ledbetter, Penlie Briscoe, NC
Legg, Albert Neil, PA
Lenker, Robert Willis, PA
Leonard, Charles Forrest, PA
Lescher, Edwin R., IL
Levy, Jacob, PA
Leydic, Cyrus Clark, PA
Luhr, Augustine Charles, PA
MacMurdy, Carlyle Kedzie, NY
Marshall, John Peter, PA
McCarthy, Patrick Andrew, NJ
McConeghy, Robert Keating, PA
McGuire, William J., PA
McHugh, John Joseph, PA
McKee, Louis Edwin, PA
McMullin, Joseph J.A., PA
Meckstroth, Henry Louis, OH
Merrill, Horace, PA
Metzger, Carl Henry, PA
Millick, Howard Collins, PA
Montealegre, Edgar, COSTA RICA
Moore, Eugene Aloysius, PA
Morgan, David William, PA
Morse, Edwin W., OR
Moss, John T., TN

Murray, Thomas Elwin, MN
Myers, Edmund, MA
Nelson, Parley, UT
Nolan, John Thomas, PA
Orton, Henry Boylan, NJ
Patterson, John Gordon, OR
Pentecost, Milton Irving, PA
Perrault, Leo Thomas, NY
Phelan, Clause Aloysius, CA
Pherson, Frank James, NH
Phifer, Frank Marion, IL
Raken, William Elkin, PA
Rees, William Thomas, PA
Reid, James William, NC
Ricketts, George Allen, PA
Ritter, George Tilden, PA
Robinson, Alfred Andrew, UT
Roland, Marion Mansfield, OK
Rott, Otto Mathias, OH
Rumbaugh, Marshall C., PA
Rushton, Percy Hartley, RI
Russell, Thomas Hendrick, VA
Sager, Washington Budd, VA
Sayre, William Douglas, NJ
Schnorr, Alphonse Marie, PA
Schwartz, Bernard, PA
Seaton, Charles Forrest, PA
Seay, Samuel Cleveland, AL
Sells, Deshler F., WA
Shafer, Frederick William, NJ
Sherrick, Earl Cleveland, PA
Simonis, Arthur Elmer, PA
Sloop, Eustace Henry, NC
Smith, Thomas Harley, NC
Smith, John McNeill, NC
Soll, Charles Harold, CA
Stevens, John Alfred, PA
Stevenson, Frank Burton, MA
Stimson, Cheney Metcalf, OH
Streker, William Sylvester, RI
Susman, Michael, NJ
Swab, Robert Dubs, PA
Sweeney, Alvin Randolph, LA
Sweet, Paul Williams, KS
Sylvis, William Martin, PA
Timberlake, Richard E., NC
Tint, Jacob Louis, NY
Tomlinson, George Milton, PA
Upchurch, Robert Theodore, NC
Walker, Joseph, UT
Walters, Paul, Radcliffe, PA
Ward, Vernon Albert, NC
Warne, Joseph Lloyd, PA
Weidner, Edward Thomas B., PA

1908

Weiland, Carl, Jr., PA
Wood, William Charles, PA
Wood, Clark S., AR
Woodside, Horatio Linn, PA

Wurtz, John George, PA
Yoder, Mahlon Harold, PA
Zech, Harry W., PA
Zelle, Oscar Lewis, IL

Surgical Dispensary (1908).

1908

Harold L. Foss of Massachusetts was destined to become one of the leading surgeons of the United States (Fig. 177). Following graduation he was a pioneer physician in Candle, Alaska, then began formal training in surgery at the Mayo Clinic where he was elected the first president of the Mayo Alumni Association. The Mayo experience served as a model for his life-long career at the George F. Geisinger Memorial Hospital, Danville, Pennsylvania. He was Surgeon-in-Chief and Superintendent of Geisinger from its founding in 1915. He achieved renown as a skillful surgeon, able administrator, and teacher. He was President of the American College of

Fig. 177. Harold L. Foss (JMC '09), founding Surgeon-in-Chief of Geisinger Memorial Medical Center and President of the American College of Surgeons.

Surgeons in 1952/53. Under Dr. Foss' brilliant leadership, Geisinger Medical Center became influential in the medical progress of Central Pennsylvania with widespread ramifications. In 1988 an affiliation of Geisinger with Jefferson was consummated with increasing benefits to both institutions being realized. The surgical department at Geisinger bears the name of The Foss Clinic. Dr. Foss died in 1967.

Creighton H. Turner, following Jefferson internship, became a protege of Dr. James C. Wilson, Chairman of Medicine. For many years he was prominent in the teaching of physical diagnosis, going on to the rank of Associate Professor of Medicine. Dr. Turner was the physician for the Wilson family and was succeeded in this role by Dr. Robert I. Wise. Both cultivated the interest of Dr. Wilson's daughters in Jefferson so that ultimately a bequest from Miss Beatrice Wilson of $1.5 million established the Wilson Professorship of Medicine. Dr. Turner was an able clinician and a respected mentor for a generation of Jefferson students (Fig. 178).

George F. Lull, Sr. pursued a varied career. Trained in pathology at Jefferson following graduation, he joined the United States Army Medical Corps in 1912 and served until 1946. His many appointments included Panama before World War I, and the Philippines as medical advisor to the Governor General in the 1920s. From 1940 he served in the office of the Surgeon General of the United States Army, ending as Deputy Surgeon General. In 1946 he was named Secretary-General Manager of the American Medical Association. Following retirement, posts with the Illinois State Medical Society, the Cook County Department of Public Aid, and the Chicago Medical Society rounded out his career. Dr. Lull acquired a doctorate of Public Health from the University of Pennsylvania. Decorations included the Distinguished Service Medal, the French Legion of Honor, and Cuba's Finlay Order of Merit.

Harry D. Podlasky of Wisconsin returned to

his native state and took up the new specialty of roentgenology. He joined the faculty of Marquette University School of Medicine and advanced to the rank of Associate Professor before his death in 1935.

At the Commencement on June 7 for 139 graduates, the Honorary Degree of Doctor of Laws was conferred upon Colonel William Crawford Gorgas, M.D., Sc.D., who at the time was with the United States Army in Panama in connection with the construction of the Panama Canal. He delivered the address entitled *Sanitation in the Isthmus of Panama.*

Anderson, George A., UT
Baker, Carroll Royer, DE
Bakewell, Frank Smith, PA
Banes, Charles Conrad A., PA
Barker, Christopher Sylvanus, NC
Barry, William David, PA
Baxter, Milton Edwin, NJ
Bednarkiewicz, Ignatius Aloysius, PA
Betts, James Alfred, NJ
Biscoe, Gibbs, AR
Brady, Richard J., MN
Brady, Philip J., MN
Briody, Henry Edward, NJ
Brown, Carl Guille, OH
Brown, Maurice, PA
Bull, Raymond Cooley, KS
Burnside, Fred Rexford, OH
Butcher, Charles, NJ
Carter, William Stanley, PA
Cates, Thomas Herndon, AR
Cheatham, Thomas Alfred, GA
Child, Howard Tennyson, NH
Coleman, William James, MS
Collester, Charles Chapman, IA
Cowen, Brontz Luther, PA
Cranmer, Richard Raymond, MN
Davidson, Andrew Blaine, PA
Davis, Thomas Carroll, PA
Dick, Hugh Lenox H., PA
Doherty, William John, NJ
Douglas, William Elbert, DE
Dray, Edward Joseph, CT
Duvall, Frank C., PA
Eggen, Olaf K., MN
Elsinger, Lucious M., PA
Fagan, Peter Edward, PA
Faris, George Thomas, WV
Farmer, Clarence Ravenel, NC
Foss, Harold Leighton, MA
Foster, Miles Everett, AR
Frodey, Raymond J., PA
Furlong, Robert Grant, PA
Glasgow, Dan Fulkerso, PA

Glenn, Marshail Renfro, NC
Goldman, Louis Charles, PA
Goodison, William L.T., ND
Gordner, Jesse Walter, PA
Gray, Samuel Brown, PA
Grimes, Charles Henry, PA
Grow, Malcolm Cummings, PA
Guier, Luis Javier, COSTA RICA
Hall, Forest Frank, IA
Hammer, Charles M., PA
Henderlite, Aubrey Elgin, MT

Fig. 178. Creighton H. Turner (JMC, '09), Associate Professor of Medicine who taught physical diagnosis.

Hensyl, George Stanford, PA
Herbert, William Dey, NJ
Herman, Maxwell, PA
Hetherington, John, ND
Holcomb, Joel Theodore, MN
Hopkins, Frederick Miller, PA
Huber, Harry Jonas, PA
Hughes, Edgar Lee, OH
Irvan, Hardin Davenport, Jr., KY
Jackson, John Osborne, PA
Johnson, Harold Virgil, TX
Johnson, J. Thomas, IA
Jones, Harry Bradford, PA
Jordan, William Francis, AL
Keating, Charles Vincent, NY
Koplin, Nathaniel Hawthorne, PA
Kudlich, Manfred Heinrich, PA
Lambert, Henry Bertram, CT
Landry, Arthur Bernard, CT
Lau, Robert Edmund, PA
Leibold, Herbert Henry, MN
Lewis, Daniel W., TX
Leyda, Paul Leighton, CO
Loughran, James Joseph, PA
Lull, George Fairless, PA
Lyon, Richard Henry, MN
Lyons, James Chalmers, NOVA SCOTIA
Manahan, Charles Albert, IA
Marsh, Otto George, CA
McBride, James Fred, IL
McCain, Hugh White, NC
McConkey, Frank Vance, PA
McCord, James Robert, GA
Meddaugh, Fred W., PA
Miller, Hal Curtis, GA
Miller, John Charles, PA
Minford, Wilbur Henry, PA
Moss, Samuel, PA
Murphy, James F. M., MN
Orr, Adrian V., PA
Orton, George Lee, NJ
Park, Emory Robert, GA

Parmet, David Harris, PA
Pennington, George Powell, NJ
Pettigrew, James William, PA
Phillips, William Greaves, KY
Podlasky, Harry Bernard, WI
Reilly, Francis St. Clair, PA
Richardson, Waldo, WA
Rinehart, Stacy Herman, PA
Roberson, Foy, NC
Robinson, George H., PA
Rouse, William Isaac, PA
Royal, Benjamin Franklin, NC
Ruth, Edwin Z., PA
Schatz, Francis J., MN
Schilling, Francis Marion, PA
Schneyer, Julius, PA
Schonwald, John DeWitt, NC
Schramm, Francis M. B., PA
Seifriz, Alois Frank, NJ
Sender, Arthur Charles, PA
Shaffer, Phineas Jenks, PA
Shaw, John Harvey, PA
Sica, Leon Samuel, NJ
Silverstein, Nathan, PA
Smith, Etley Price, WV
Surles, Junius Boyette, NC
Thompson, Herbert Henry, MN
Throckmorton, Tom Bentley, IA
Tinker, Fay Waters, VT
Trigg, Ross Beckham, TX
Turner, Chauncey Carter, DE
Turner, Creighton Hooker, PA
Ulmer, David H. B., NJ
Vernon, James William, NC
Walker, Herman Hervey, PA
Wall, Russell Theodore, PA
Watkins, Benjamin M., PA
Weinberg, Charles Berenda, PA
Wilson, James Hamilton, PA
Withers, James Johnston, NC
Wohlwend, Fred, PA
Woodruff, James Lloyd, UT

The hardest conviction to get into the mind of a beginner is that the education upon which he is engaged is not a college course, not a medical course, but a life course, for which the work of a few years under teachers is but a preparation.

Sir William Osler (1849-1919)

Major General Malcolm Cummings Grow ('09) was appointed the first Surgeon General of the U.S. Air Force in 1949, at which time this branch had just become independent of the Army. For three years after his graduation from Jefferson he taught internal medicine and physical diagnosis in the clinic. During World War I he accepted a commission in the Russian Army (1915-17) as the Chief Surgeon attached to the First Siberian Army Corps. He then resigned to join the American Expeditionary forces to France. His awards and decorations included the U.S. Distinguished Service Medal; Legion of Merit and Bronze Star Medal; the Russian Cross of St. Stanislaus and Medal of St. George; the French Legion of Honor and Croix de Guerre; the Belgian Croix de Guerre; and Cross of Grand Officer in the order of the Crown of Italy.

General Grow pioneered in preventive medicine and developed protective equipment for airmen during his 21 years association with air forces. His research led to the development of the flak suit, electrically heated clothing and the combat ration.

1909

At the June 6 Commencement, 141 graduates received their degrees and the degree of Doctor of Laws was conferred upon S. Weir Mitchell (JMC, 1850, Fig. 45). This recognized Dr. Mitchell's status as an elder statesman of American medicine and man of letters.

The Commencement also featured a eulogy of the late Professor Samuel D. Gross (1805-84) by Dr. W.W. Keen, Emeritus Professor of Surgery. The same year the Samuel D. Gross Professorship of Surgery (the first endowed Chair at Jefferson) was inaugurated with a $60,000 gift by Gross' daughter, Maria Gross Horwitz. Dr. John Chalmers DaCosta was named the first incumbent.

The widely quoted Flexner report of 1910 in behalf of the Carnegie Foundation for the Advancement of Teaching resulted in endorsement of Jefferson Medical College relative to the quality of its medical teaching and clinical facilities. Jefferson at this time had the second largest enrollment of the nation's medical schools.

Reflecting the news this year from Germany of Ehrlich's discovery of ''606'' (Salversan), a therapeutic conference was held at Jefferson by Drs. Henry Leffman, Elmer H. Funk and Sidney L. Olsho for discussion of this first specific arsenical treatment for syphilis.

Warren B. Davis, a native of Kentucky and educated at the University of Kentucky, was elected to Alpha Omega Alpha and was awarded the Corinna Borden Keen Fellowship for foreign study. Upon return he was appointed to the Department of Surgery. After World War I service as Captain in charge of the School of Oral and Plastic Surgery at Fort Oglethorpe, Georgia, he was established as a subspecialist in plastic and reconstructive surgery. Dr. Davis was appointed Clinical Professor of Oral Surgery at Jefferson (1934) and was a founding member of the American Society of Plastic and Reconstructive Surgery in 1931, later its third president and editor of its journal. He was an innovative surgeon and

a loyal Jeffersonian, having been President of the Alumni Association in 1942 (Fig. 179).

James R. Martin (Fig. 180) was appointed to the Department of Orthopaedic Surgery in 1913, at the same time working as assistant to Dr. J. Torrance Rugh (JMC, 1892, Fig. 129), who in 1918 became Chairman of the Department. Dr. Martin remained in the Department until 1938, advancing to Assistant Professor and Chief of the Outpatient Clinic. In 1938 he was made Chief Surgeon of the State Hospital for Crippled Children at Elizabethtown, Pennsylvania, but a year later he returned to Jefferson as the James Edwards Professor of Orthopaedic Surgery, serving until 1950. From 1951 to 1956 he was Associate Dean

Fig. 179. Warren B. Davis (JMC, '10), Clinical Professor of Oral Surgery and pioneer in that field.

under Dean Bennett. The building at 11th and Walnut Streets (Southeast Corner), originally constructed as a student nurses' residence, bears his name, and the site was formally occupied by the home of Samuel D. Gross. Dr. Martin's portrait was presented to the college in 1957.

Adams, Joseph Lowrance, NC
Alexander, Isaac, UT
Alexander, Robert Mackey, PA
Andrew, David, UT
Atkinson, Thomas Herman, PA
Austin, John Watson, NC
Ayres, Wilmot, PA
Baker, Elmer, PA
Beardsley, Wayne R., ND
Beck, Homer Henry, PA
Bevis, Earle Miami, WA
Bew, Richard, NJ
Billetdoux, Chester Augustus, PA
Bingaman, Charles E., PA
Bley, Robert Etris, Jr., IL
Boden, Todd R., PA
Brain, Charles Edward, UT
Broadman, Harry, PA
Brugman, Joseph Charles, IA
Brumbaugh, Simon Clarence, PA
Cain, William Jonathan, PA
Carney, Joseph Albert, PA
Carruth, Howard Ernest, KS
Conroy, John S., NJ
Craig, Samuel Halleck, NJ
Davis, Byron Gordon, NJ
Davis, Warren B., KY
Dickerson, Orval Melcher, IL
Donahue, John Leo, PA
Dunkelberg, Elmer Irl, IA
Eberle, Walter Gilbert, AR
Ely, Reuel Abram, PA
Ernst, M. Lincoln, PA
Evans, James Lawrence, NJ
Fielden, John S.C., Jr., MA
Figueroa, Siegfried, MEXICO
Fogerty, Clement Aloysius, PA
Forcey, Charles Budd, PA
Foss, Carl Elmer, ND
Fox, Samuel Watson, DE
Fulmer, Joseph Cleveland, PA
Furman, William Haywood, NC
Gaston, Cecil Dulin, AL
Gill, George Guyer, PA
Grahn, Samuel Norman, PA
Griffin, William Ray, NC
Grim, Herman Charles, PA

Grimm, Claude Emerson, WV
Gusman, Centeno Jesus, COSTA RICA
Haney, Josiah Rowan, Jr., MS
Happel, Horace E., TN
Harding, Benjamin Milton, NJ
Harnagel, Edward John, IA
Harvey, John, PA
High, Isaac Beidler, PA
Hightower, Charley Counce, MS
Hill, John Bostwick, Jr., SC
Hilly, Joseph Francis, PA
Holmes, Andrew Byron, NC
Howard, James Harold, NY
Howard, LeRoy Spangler, NY
Howells, Thomas J., UT
Hughes, Joseph, UT

Fig. 180. James R. Martin (JMC, '10), Chairman of Orthopaedic Surgery (1939-50).

1910

Humphreys, John Charles, PA
Jackson, William Long, NY
Johnston, Russell Willhide, PA
Jones, John F.X., PA
Jones, Robert LeRoy, ME
Joss, Chester Earle, KS
Kauffman, Louis John, NJ
Keeffe, Patrick Eugene, NE
Keenan, Francis Edward, IA
Kramer, Edward Raymond, MN
LaFerte, Alfred Daniel, MI
Lea, Joseph Addison, TX
Livingston, Paul, PA
Lucas, Walter Scott, OH
Lukehart, Joseph Madison, PA
Lynch, Thomas James, MO
MacGaughey, James David, Jr., CT
Mack, Charles Beaver, PA
Mairs, Atlee, WV
Manion, James Lorne, OR
Martin, James Reid, PA
McBride, Thomas Sutch, PA
McCall, J. Harvey, IA
McCarten, Robert Emmett, MN
McConihay, Clarence William, WV
McDowell, James Edward, DE
McKay, Hamilton W., SC
McKellar, Harry Rex, GA
Mellor, John Oliver, UT
Mendelsohn, David Henry, CT
Merscher, Harry Leonard, PA
Miley, Weir Mitchell, IN
Miller, Thomas Benton, PA
Montague, Samuel Spurgeon, NC
Montgomery, Daniel Cameron, MS
Moore, William Houston, NC
Moriarty, Charles Albert, MA
Musser, Guy Musselman, PA
Newbold, William Augustus, NJ

Nothnagel, Frank Richard, NJ
Orndoff, Hersey Elroy, PA
Pershing, Paul Frederick, PA
Pilchard, Sewell Norris, DE
Pittman, Raymond Lupton, NC
Potter, Walter Hubert, RI
Pratt, Robert Boyd, OH
Prigger, Edward Reuben, NJ
Rhoads, Alfred Lawrence, PA
Rice, Wilkie Benjamin, OH
Rich, Samuel, OH
Ricketts, John G., PA
Rosenfeld, David Hiram, PA
Rosenthal, Joseph Morris, PA
Sass, Franklin Edgar, PA
Schrader, Herman Frederick, MN
Scudder, John Henry H., CA
Shepherd, Warren, UT
Shepler, Norman Bruce, PA
Shinaberry, Rollen Lemuel, OH
Siegel, Alvin Erdreich, AL
Simpson, Fred Pratt, PA
Smukler, Maximilian Edward, PA
Southwick, Harry Holmes, IL
Sprinkle, Charles Nichols, NC
Stoney, George Franklin, OH
Strauss, Abraham, PA
Stucke, Edmund Conrad, MN
Sumner, Thomas Woodfin, NC
Thomas, Charles Meade, PA
Thompson, Thomas Gotfried, SD
Treat, Albert Miller, MN
Wallace, Charles Chester, PA
Walter, Charles Arthur, PA
Wayland, Clyde, CA
Webb, Louis Harward, NC
Wolf, Frank Aloysius, PA
Wood, Chester Cameron, PA
Zahn, Samuel Finley, NJ

The successful teacher is no longer on a height, pumping knowledge at high pressure into passive receptacles. . . . he is a senior student anxious to help his juniors.

Sir William Osler (1849-1919).

At the Commencement, held June 5, the degree of Doctor of Medicine was conferred upon 117 graduates, and the honorary degree of Doctor of Science was awarded in absentia to Victor George Heiser (JMC, 1897, Fig. 141) an international pioneer in the field of public health.

The Alumni prize for highest average of the four years was won by Thomas Aloysius Shallow (Fig. 181). He became the protege and personal assistant of John Chalmers DaCosta (JMC, 1885, Fig. 113) and was made a full Professor of Surgery upon the latter's death in 1933. He was named the second Gross Professor of surgery in 1939. Shallow belonged to many societies and served as President of the Alumni Association (1938) and of the Philadelphia Academy of Surgery (1943). He pioneered in the one-stage operation for correction of pharyngeal diverticulum and excelled in gastro-intestinal surgery. His portrait was presented to the College by the class of 1950.

Edward Adam Strecker became an outstanding psychiatrist (Fig. 182). After serving as Professor of Mental and Nervous Diseases at Jefferson from 1925 to 1931, he assumed the same post in the University of Pennsylvania. He was a

Fig. 181.   Thomas A. Shallow (JMC, '11) second Gross Professor of Surgery (1939-55).

Fig. 182.   Edward A. Strecker (JMC, '11), Professor of Mental and Nervous Diseases (1925-31).

1911

scholar, brilliant teacher and skilled physician who received the honorary degrees of Sc.D, Litt. D. and LL.D. He authored many books and papers and pioneered in the treatment of alcoholism.

John DeCarlo maintained a life-long interest in anatomy and taught the course in Applied and Topical Anatomy in the Daniel Baugh Institute for many years.

The Daniel Baugh Institute of Anatomy was opened in 1911 (Fig. 183). Located at Eleventh and Clinton Streets, the building was formerly the Pennsylvania Dental College. Mr. Daniel Baugh, although never President, served on the Board of Trustees for 25 years (1896-1921). Board President William Potter characterized him as "the most valuable man ever connected with the Board." The Institute placed Jefferson's Anatomy Department in the forefront of all medical schools in the country. The Chairman's title was changed to "Professor of Anatomy, Head of the Department of Anatomy, and Director of the Daniel Baugh Institute". The Institute eventually moved to Jefferson Alumni Hall in 1968.

Mr. Baugh also donated an electrically driven ambulance to the hospital (Fig. 184).

CLASS OF 1911

Aichele, Otto Walter, PA
Alleman, George E., PA
Allison, George Kelly, PA
Allison, Harry Weamer, PA
Annealey, William Honeyford, PA
Arnold, John Loy, PA
Becker, Thomas Henry, WV
Berney, Daniel Edward, PA
Borrowes, George Henry, PA
Bowen, Charles John, PA
Boyer, Charles George, PA
Boyer, Edwin Charles, PA
Brinton, William Thomas, IA
Brockway, Charles Jesse, IN
Brown, Walter Earl, PA
Burkartmaier, John Henry, PA
Burke, Charles Perry, PA
Carbonell, Frank Arturo, PUERTO RICO
Carmelia, Francis Albion, PA
Carmichael, Daniel Lafayette, Jr., WA
Carmichael, Asa Bartholow, WA
Cary, Dale Emerson, PA
Coleman, Austin Hoffman, NJ
Collier, Martin H., PA
Cribbins, Frederick Allen, MI
Croop, James Elmer, PA
Cummings, Michael Penn, NC
Davies, Emlyn Thomas, PA
Dean, Alfred, ND
DeCarlo, John, PA
Dickson, George Blazier, PA
Donohue, John Joseph, PA
Dougherty, William Otto, PA
Dowds, Samuel Clarke, PA
Dudenhoefer, Joseph Edward, PA
Ellenberger, Jacob W. E., PA

Elliot, Francis Theodore, PA
Ewing, Leslie Hand, NJ
Feddeman, Charles Edward, VA
Feigley, Harvey P., PA
Flanagan, Edward Joseph, PA
Frankenburger, W. Sturgis, PA
Frigge, Edward Henry, IN

Fig. 183. Daniel Baugh Institute of Anatomy opened in 1911.

1911

285

Funk, Erwin Deaterly, PA
Geiger, Hugh St. Clare, FL
Gilmore, John Wesley, WV
Gross, Samuel, PA
Hagood, Rufus Hansom, Jr., AL
Halpern, Harry Samuel, Jr., PA
Hamme, Curtis J., PA
Harrigan, William Francis, ME
Harris, Benjamin Franklin, PA
Hastings, Lorne Edward, CANADA
Holt, Lloyd Mott, PA
Hubbard, Lex Walter, MS
Hustead, Frank Humbert, PA
Hynson, Garrett Lee, OR
Jacobs, Leopold, Max, CT
James, Charles Emera, DE
Johnson, Lee, NC
Jones, William Gwillym, PA
Keim, Ivan N., PA
Klein, Arno, IN
Klenk, James Monroe, PA
LaRochelle, Fred Desire, VT
Leh, Homer Deems, PA
Lovett, Joseph Cook, WA
Ludwig, David Boyd, PA
McConaghy, Edward James, NJ
McGinnis, George Edward, PA
McHugh, Patrick Francis, PA

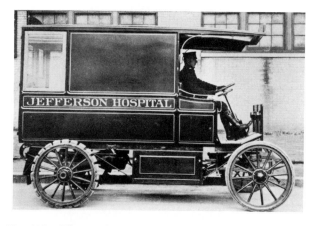

Fig. 184. Electric driven ambulance replacing horse-drawn one (ca. 1911).

McNamara, Frank Wallace, PA
Mierau, Ernest W., NJ
Moore, Edward Lane, GA
Moss, Morris Israel, PA
Mulford, Leslie Frank, NJ
Muschlitz, Frederick Allen, PA
Neilson, Clarence Jamie, UT
Oelschlegel, Herbert Charles, CT
Paul, James Hale, PA
Person, William Cortlandt, PA
Phillips, Edward Milliken, PA
Posey, Silas Robert, PA
Quinn, Sidney Augustus, PA
Reimer, Charles James, Jr., PA
Richman, Kenneth Charles, PA
Russell, Evans Dounton, PA
Ryan, William Francis, VT
Schneider, George Louis, PA
Shaffer, George Emery, PA
Shallow, Thomas Aloysius, PA
Shannon, Francis Patrick, PA
Shaw, William Alger, NC
Shelley, Penrose Herr, PA
Simmons, Howard Jackson, IA
Smith, Augustus Edwin, PA
Smith, Bernard Reid, NC
Smith, Karl Waller, PA
Smithwick, James Milton, GA
Snyder, Jacob F. M., PA
Soltz, Thomas, CT
Sosnowski, John Joseph, Jr., PA
Sowden, Edgar Lentz, PA
Steele, Willard H., TN
Strecker, Edward Adam, PA
Sweeney, Joseph John, OH
Thomas, Samuel B., PA
Toland, William Arthur, PA
Trumper, Abraham, PA
Wadsworth, William Houston, NC
Walsh, James Joseph, PA
Warnock, George Carl, PA
White, Peter Cope, PA
Whittle, Charlton Cash, GA
Wisehart, Eric Edmound, PA
Wojczynski, Leon Joseph, PA
Wolfe, R. Vincent, PA

1911

On June 3, in the Academy of Music, the M.D. degree was conferred upon 148 graduates by the President, Mr. William Potter. Dr. Thomas Mc-Crae, the new Chairman of the Department of Medicine, recently appointed from Johns Hopkins University School of Medicine, gave the address on *Postgraduate Education*. The honorary degree of Doctor of Science was conferred upon William W. Keen (JMC, 1862, Emeritus Professor of Surgery, Fig. 67) and James W. Holland (JMC, 1868, Emeritus Professor of Chemistry, Fig. 78). The honorary degree of Doctor of Laws was conferred upon Jacob Solis-Cohen (Honorary Professor of Laryngology). The honorary degree of Doctor of Public Health was conferred upon Joseph S. Neff (JMC, 1875, Fig. 88), Director of Public Health and Charities of Philadelphia, and Medical Director of Jefferson Hospital from 1895 to 1907.

Among the outstanding members of this class, no one exceeded the distinction of Louis Henry Clerf, a native of the State of Washington (Fig. 185). He trained at Jefferson as Instructor in Bronchoesophagoscopy under the great pioneer, Dr. Chevalier Jackson, and at the latters's retirement in 1930 was appointed Chairman of Bronchology and Esophagology, and additionally served as Chairman of Laryngology from 1936 until he retired in 1954. He contributed over 200 papers to the literature, gave talks in all the 48 States of the country at the time, and belonged to a host of medical organizations. He served as President of the Philadelphia County Medical Society, American Broncho-Esophageal Association, Philadelphia Laryngological Society, Triological Society and the New York Laryngological Society. Villanova University awarded him the LL.D. degree, St. Martin's College the Sc.D., and Jefferson the L.H.D. He became President of the Alumni Association, reorganized the Alumni Giving Campaign, and headed the Alumni contributions to the Foerderer Pavilion. His portrait was presented to the College (Class of 1954) and he was the first recipient of the Alumni Achieve-

ment Award (1964). Considered a member of that elite group known as "Mr. Jefferson," his loyalty continued until his death in 1989 at the age of 100.

Leon Solis-Cohen was the son of Jacob Solis-Cohen and nephew of Solomon Solis-Cohen, both outstanding members of the Jefferson Faculty. In 1920 he pioneered in radiology at Jefferson along with Dr. Willis F. Manges. He was a founding member of the "X Society" at Jefferson during the 1920s, an intimate social/scientific group that is flourishing to the present time.

Robert McDowell Lukens became an Assistant Professor of Bronchoscopy and Esophagoscopy at Jefferson and was also gifted as an artist (Fig. 186). He painted portraits of James Aitken Meigs,

Fig. 185. Louis H. Clerf (JMC, '12), second Chairman of Bronchoesophagology (1930-54) and fourth Chairman of Laryngology (1936-54).

Randle C. Rosenberger and Chevalier Jackson which are displayed in Jefferson's art collection.

Benjamin Lipshutz was the first faculty appointee at Jefferson to be identified with neuroanatomy by title as Assistant Demonstrator of Neuroanatomy in 1917. He conducted the laboratories from 1932 until 1948, when he retired at the Associate Professorial level. He was also on the surgical staff of the Hospital, in which his knowledge of anatomy served him well as a most skilled operator (Fig. 187).

Henry Keller Mohler graduated as an honor student. He became Medical Director of the Hospital from 1914 to 1938 and then succeeded Ross V. Patterson as Dean of the Medical College in 1938. He was active in cardiology and was made Professor of Therapeutics in 1938 (Fig. 188). He was prominent in many local and national societies. LaSalle College awarded him an honorary degree of Doctor of Science in 1939 and the Class of 1940 presented his portrait to the College. He died suddenly in 1941.

Roscoe L. Wall, having concluded his long career as Professor of Anesthesiology at Bowman-Gray School of Medicine, Wake Forest College in Winston-Salem, North Carolina, died in 1980 at the age of 90 years.

Following his arrival at Jefferson in June, 1912, Thomas McCrae, the new Professor of Medicine, quickly established a solid position with students and colleagues (Fig. 189). Dr. McCrae, trainee and associate of Dr. William Osler at Johns Hopkins, provided new insights in a broadening area of medical science and practice. He joined and later succeeded Osler in revisions of the classic *Principles and Practice of Medicine*, the standard textbook for a generation of American medical students.

Fig. 186.   Robert M. Lukens (JMC, '12), Assistant Professor of Bronchoesophagology, also an artist and musician.

Fig. 187.   Benjamin Lipshutz (JMC '12), skilled general surgeon who taught neuroanatomy (1917-48).

Aaronoff, Joseph, PA
Adams, Rayford Kennedy, NC
Anthony, Walter E., IA
Austin, Henry Exum, NC
Barder, Joseph John, PA
Barr, Austin Flint, AR
Barry, Rolla Grant, NJ
Bassow, Carl Frederick, OH
Baumgarten, Roy Chester, IA
Beam, Russell S., NC
Beck, Henry Allan, OH
Bertram, Albert Joseph, CT
Boord, Paul C., PA
Boring, Harold Bruce, PA
Brady, Reginald Morton, AUSTRALIA
Brady, Walter Charles, PA
Brant, Albion Earl, OH
Brindley, Arthur A., OH
Brown, Benjamin, PA
Burns, Thomas Francis, MA
Cannady, Nicholas Boddie, NC
Carroll, James Basil, PA
Childers, Robert Jefferson, TN
Ciavarelli, Constantino Nicola, ITALY
Clerf Louis H., WA
Conn, Harold Russell, IA
Connole, Joseph Vincent, PA
Cooley, Elas Earle, SC
Cox, Seth Leroy, KS
Craig, Alexander, IL
Cunningham, Jacob Metz, PA
Denny, Thomas Collins, IA
Dinnison, James Andrew, PA
Douress, Philip Charles, NJ
Doyle, William Joseph, PA
Ensminger, Samuel Hyson, PA
Esposito, Joseph Vincent, CT
Fanz, John Ignatius, PA
Fenton, Ivor David, PA
Flannery, Leo Gerald, PA
Fralinger, John Joseph, PA
Fulton, William V., WA
Garris, Frank Henry, NC
Gary, Arthur Dare, NJ
Gaston, Perry Stevenson, PA
Gordon, Abraham James, PA
Greenman, Ernest Nelson, IL
Grigg, Adrian Hansford, WV
Haines, William Henry, NJ
Hammett, Lea Jackson, SC
Hanson, Wayne Pierre, WY
Hardee, Walter Person, NC

Harris, Thomas Lewis, WV
Hartman, Morris D., TN
Hartsell, Joe Albert, NC
Henderson, David Williams, ID
Henderson, Frederick Arthur, IN
Holtz, Kenneth Jastram, NE
Hornick, Leo William, PA
Hughes, Herman Clyde, PA
Hunt, Daniel, MS
Jeffrey, Robert Harrison, PA
Jenson, James Lloyd, KS
Jones, John Paul, NC
Jones, Edward Hallaran, TX
Kain, Thomas Michael, NJ
Kaufmann, Samuel Benjamin, MA
Kealing, Otho Granville, IN
Keenan, Andrew Joseph, Jr., PA
Kirkwood, Tom, IL
Kline, Harvey Winfield, PA

Fig. 188. Henry K. Mohler (JMC, '12), cardiologist, Medical Director (1914-38) and Dean (1938-41).

Kramer, David, PA
Kraus, Gabriel Joseph, PA
Laferty, John Marshall, PA
Larkin, Edmund Peter, PA
Lashman, William Mitchel, NJ
Laverty, George Lauman, PA
Lipshutz, Benjamin, PA
Longo, James Augustus, PA
Lowe, David Earl, PA
Lukens, Robert McDowell, PA
Lytle, Ralph McKay, PA
Mann, Abraham Leon, PA
Mann, I. Thurman, NC
Manning, Harrison Martin, DE
Matta, Quinones Enrique, PUERTO RICO
Mauser, Roscoe Frederick, NC
Mayer, Willard, NE
McClellan, Wallace Roy, PA
Metz, Samuel Franklin, PA
Middlebrook, Robert, Jr., MO
Miltenberger, Arthur, PA
Mingos, Jay DePue, PA
Mitchell, Horace Erwin, IN
Mohler, Henry Keller, PA

Morian, Clarence Herbert, PA
Mullen, Thomas Francis, IL
Mullin, Charles Elmer, PA
Niebel, Benjamin Earl, PA
Nolan, Michael McCormack, AL
Pennington James F., KY
Poffenberger, Joseph Cummings, PA
Potts, Morris Leroy, NJ
Rankin, Samuel Wharton, NC
Robinson, Leigh Fowler, IN
Rose, Samuel J., KY
Ross, Hendric Arnold, AR
Rubenstone, Abraham Isadore, PA
Russell, Scott S., PA
Ryan, Charles Calvin, PA
Sanabria, Nicholas, PUERTO RICO
Schmitz, Henry Charles, IL
Sellmeyer, Bernardo Leo, MO
Shapiro, Morris Samuel, PA
Sheppard, Robert Lester, PA
Shields James M., IA
Smith, Edward Michael, NY
Smith, Lawrence Jackson, NC
Snyder, Claude Edwin, PA

Fig. 189.   Thomas McCrae in "pit" of 1877 Hospital.

Solis-Cohen, Leon, PA
Speer, William Louis, KS
St. Clair, James Roy, PA
Stephan, George Louis, PA
Streit, Ernest Hamilton, OR
Strimple, James Thurman, PA
Sullivan, Arthur James J., MA
Thomas, Llewelyn Ivor, PA
Tomlinson, Robert Williams, DE
Tunnell, Monroe Hinson, PA
Turnbull, Frederick C., NEW ZEALAND
Udinsky, Hyman Joseph, NJ
VanDuzer, William Roy, IA
VanGilder, James Emmett, PA

VanNess, Herbert Roy, NJ
Veal, William Thomas, RI
Vosburg, Harry Arthur, Jr., PA
Walker, Duncan Devane, NC
Wall, Roscoe LeGrand, NC
Wall, Joseph Amplias, KY
Waters, William Watkin, PA
West, Louis N., NC
Wilkinson, Albert Harrison, PA
Williams, Horace James, DE
Workman, William M., PA
Wrenn, Frank, NC
Ziegelman, Edward Frank, CA
Zimmerman, Edward L., KS
Zuck, Arthur C., PA

Horace J. Williams (JMC, '12), Chairman of Otology (1937-50), highly regarded for mastoid surgery.

In July, 1913, an act was passed by the State legislature requiring that candidates for licensure serve a year's internship in an accredited hospital. This represented another step in the increasing complexity of medical education and practice.

The year was also marked by plans for the Department for Diseases of the Chest at 236-238 Pine Street, a facility intended to contribute teaching material for physical diagnosis and clinical medicine as well as to forward the treatment and control of tuberculosis (Fig. 190). Dr. Elmer H. Funk was named Medical Director. Also, improvements were announced in the Daniel Baugh Institute permitting simultaneous accommodation of up to 360 students.

In this year a "Medical Preparatory Course" was started. It was a one-year liberal arts course which gave college credit in German or French, Chemistry, Physics and Biology. It started on September 24, 1913, so that students planning to matriculate at Jefferson in 1914 could fulfill the new requirement for admission of one year of college credit. This course was discontinued after three years (through the 1915/1916 session).

The Commencement exercises were again held at the Academy of Music on June 7. The degree of Doctor of Medicine was conferred on 126 graduates by Board President, the Honorable William Potter. The Address by Francis P. Venable, Ph.D., D.Sc., LL.D., President of the University of North Carolina, was titled "The Graduate of Jefferson Medical College and His Obligations".

John B. Flick, of Pennsylvania, may be re-

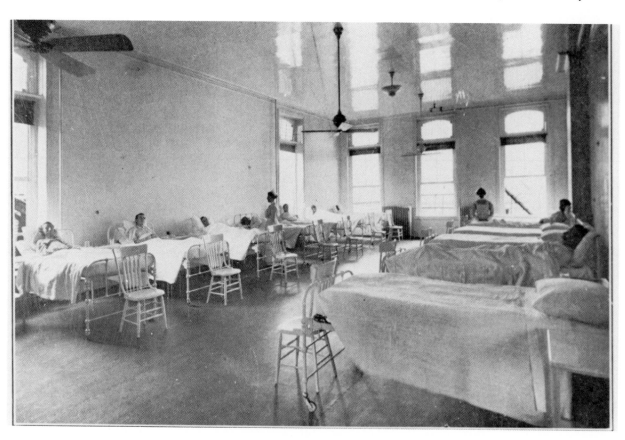

Fig. 190.   Men's ward in Pine street Department for Diseases of the Chest.

garded as Jefferson's first thoracic surgeon, and is credited with the concerted effort to develop a separate Division within the Department of Surgery. He performed the first thoracoplasty at Jefferson for tuberculosis in 1924. In the following decade he wrote extensively of techniques for treatment of lung abscess, tuberculosis and bronchiectasis. He performed the first successful pneumonectomy in Philadelphia in 1933, soon after Dr. Evarts A. Graham earlier the same year reported the first in the world. He rose through the ranks to Clinical Professor in which position he served from 1937 to 1946 (Fig. 191).

Francis Elwood Weatherby became a career military physician and was also trained in neuro-psychiatry. In 1931 he returned to Jefferson as Professor of Military Science and Tactics with the rank of Major (Fig. 192).

John Elias Livingood kept an active interest in Alumni affairs of his alma mater and served as the President in 1957 (Fig. 193).

<hr>

CLASS OF 1913

Allebach, Newton G., PA
Allen, Robert Louis, PA
Alt, Roy Colony, IA
Arnold, Herbert Leonard, MS
Ballinger, Reeve Leslie, NJ
Beck, Albert Fillmore, PA

Fig. 191. John B. Flick (JMC, '13), Clinical Professor of Surgery and pioneer in thoracic surgery.

Beebe, Richard Clarence, DE
Bibb, Clyde James, KY
Bliss, Raymond VanNess, VT
Bonnell, Frank Sumner, IA
Branon, Anthony William, VT
Brown, Harold Morris, CT
Buchanan, Luther Thomas, NC
Buckner, Hubbard Thomas, KY
Campbell, Guy Gibson, PA
Cocke, Eugene Rankin, NC
Colby, Cleon W., VT
Coles, James Garfield, PA
Cope, Roscoe Ziegler, PA
Coward, Edwin H., PA
Cressler, John Webster, PA
Cruice, Leman Dow, MI
Dapp, Gustave Adolph, PA
Davies, John Rumsey, Jr., PA
Davis, Bonaparte, KY
Degnan, Edward Joseph, CT
Dickinson, James John, MO
Doran, Benjamin Perkins, PA
Downs, Roscius Irving, NY
Dry, David Miller, PA
Dunham, Horace Garfield, NJ
Figley, Karl Dean, OH
Fisher, J. Harrison, PA
Flick, John B. L., PA
Freed, Frederick Clarence, TN
Gabrio, Max Reynold, PA
Garber, James Rhodes, AL
Gardner, Clarence Snow, UT
Garrison, Walter Sherman, NJ
Gibson, Burgess Allen, PA
Goddard, Alonzo Irie, KS
Gonzalez, Rosario Hiram, PUERTO RICO
Gottschall, Amos Wilson, PA
Greenbaum, Sigmund S., PA

Grove, William Edward, PA
Haas, Thurman Bishop, OH
Hartzell, Leo Henry, OH
Haskett, Paul Edmund, OK
Haywood, Guy Tainter, MT
Hazlett, Almon Cyrus, PA
Heady, Carlton Kellogg, CT
Heist, George David, PA
Heuler, Leo, PA
Hurff, J. Wallace, NJ
Inkrote, Warren Webster, PA
Jacobson, Nathan Barnet, NY
Johnston, Warren Herbert, PA
Kaplan, Eliah, PA
Keith, Elvin W., PA
Kessler, William Coward, PA
King, Brinsfield, LA
Kinnaird, Virgil Gibney, KY
Klingensmith, William Roger, AR
Kramer, Daniel William, PA
Krauss, Walter Raymond, PA
Livingood, John Elias, PA
Lowell, Francis Carroll, PA
Lowell, Paul, PA

Lummis, Frederick Rice, TX
Macfarlane, Menzies J., UT
Marshall, William Virden, DE
Mauger, Lee Fillmen, PA
Mayer, Louis Henry, Jr., PA
McLain, John Hillman, MS
McLelland, William Davies, NC
McNelis, Thomas, PA
Miller, Richard Hagan, RI
Moore, Carl Sinclair, OR
Moore, Harry Beaumont, OR
Murphy, Joseph T., PA
O'Brien, Theo Wallace, MD
O'Hara, Warren Thomas, PA
Palmer, Robert Maffet, PA
Quinn, Norman James, NJ
Rarig, Howard Raymond, PA
Rhea, Edwin Bruce, TN
Richards, Robert Wayne, PA
Richardson, Cleves, KY
Roberts, Nathaniel Embury, OR
Robinhold, Adam Miller, PA
Rodgers, William Daniel, Jr., NC
Rose, Clarence Atwood, NOVA SCOTIA

Fig. 192. Major Francis E. Weatherby (JMC, '13), Professor of Military Science and Tactics. (1931)

Fig. 193. John E. Livingood (JMC, '13), radiologist and Alumni President (1957).

Rosenthal, Simon Harry, VA
Ruben, Benjamin D., NY
Sage, Abner Potts H., MS
Schwarz, Paul Edgar, PA
Stone, Joseph William, WA
Storm, George Randolph, MS
Strickland, James Gardner, PA
Tempesto, Joseph Anthony, PA
Templeton, John Young, Jr., NC
Thomas, Barton Kathcart, PA
Thompson, John William, PA
Thysell, Fred August, MN
Tidball, Charles Willis, IA
Tipton, Samuel Powell, MS
Torrence, James Monroe, Jr., PA
Treacy, Edward Aloysius, PA
Tuttle, Kenneth, NY

Vernon, Charles Taylor, NC
Wagner, John George, NJ
Walker, Jacob, PA
Walter, Paul H., PA
Wayland, Raymond Theodore, CA
Weatherby, Francis Elwood, NJ
Weaver, William Amy, Jr., PA
Webster, George C., Jr., PA
Wentz, Frank Riegel, PA
Whittemore, Clarence, NY
Wiant, Roy Elson, OH
Wolfe, Robert Morton, PA
Wright, Louis W., PA
Yeakle, Walter Atwood, PA
Young, Charles Henry, SC
Young, Mason Pressly, SC
Yutski, William James, PA

College of Physicians, 19 South Twenty-Second Street. Erected 1909. (Courtesy, College of Physicians of Philadelphia.)

The 147 graduates received their M.D. degrees on June 6. The Address was delivered by Henry Harbaugh Apple, A.M., D.D., LL.D., President of Franklin and Marshall College, who spoke on "Ideals in Education for the Profession of Medicine".

The cost of tuition at this time was $180 in each of the four years. In this year the requirement for admission was increased to one year of college. Prior to this time (since 1891) the requirement had been a high school education.

The minutes of the Board of Trustees for October 18, 1914, recorded the following: "The Jefferson Medical College has finally received tardy justice from the American Medical Association in being placed, in the early part of this year, in the A plus Class of American Medical Colleges." A deciding factor in this highest rating was the Daniel Baugh institute of Anatomy which enhanced the basic science facilities.

The opening of the Department for Diseases of the Chest, planned during 1913, occurred in April of this year. The facility, located at 238 Pine Street, would add an important dimension to the teaching of physical diagnosis and chest diseases.

David Bacharach Allman (Fig. 194), of New Jersey, became a prominent surgeon in Atlantic City. Always interested in his alma mater, he served as President of the Alumni Association in 1943. Active in civic affairs and organized medicine, he also became President of the American Medical Association (1957/58).

Edward Louis Bauer was the seventh in eight generations in his family who became physicians, the last four of whom were Jefferson alumni. He led a crusade against diphtheria in the City of Philadelphia and had other major public health accomplishments. He held the position of Physician to Girard College for many years and served as Chairman of Pediatrics at Jefferson from 1926 to 1954 (Fig. 195). He was President of The Alumni Association in 1941. Dr. Bauer in later life spent six years of voluntary

fulltime research on a history of Jefferson Medical College entitled *Doctors Made in America*, published in 1963. He is credited with establishing the correct date of the founding of Jefferson Medical College in 1824 rather than the previously accepted 1825. His book brought much bypassed Jefferson history into focus and stimulated further investigation. In 1967 Dr. Bauer honored the memory of a deceased member of the Pediatric Staff, Dr. Norman MacNeill (JMC, '16, Fig. 198), in a book entitled *Profile of a Gentle Man*.

Mitchell Bernstein held a teaching medical

Fig. 194. David B. Allman (JMC, '14), Alumni Association President (1943) and American Medical Association President (1957).

service for Jefferson students at the Philadelphia General Hospital for many years and also was a Chief of Medicine at the old Jewish Hospital (now Northern Einstein Medical Center).

Alvin Meyers Struse is worthy of mention for having had the highest average for the entire four-year curriculum and wining eight prizes and one honorable mention at graduation.

Allman, David Bacharach, NJ
Armitage, George Lawrence, Jr., GA
Barnes, Albert Edmond, RI
Barsky, Joseph Mitchell, DE
Bauer, Arthur James, IN
Bauer, Edward Louis, PA
Benbow, Thomas Alex P., AUSTRALIA
Bennett, John Terrell, MS
Bennett, Earl Leslie, IL
Bentley, David Fuller, Jr., NJ
Bernstein, Mitchell, PA
Bittner, Clarence Lavan, PA
Blair, Mortimer Warren, PA
Blotz, Benjamin Franklin, NE
Bolin, Zera Exley, PA
Bowman, Kent A., PA
Boykin, Irvine Manning, SC
Braude, Bennett Arthur, PA
Brenner, Charles Raymond, PA
Bretz, Gilbert Freck, PA
Brown, George Arnold, MS
Buie, Roderick Mark, NC
Cantough, Charles Solomon, PA
Castlebury, Galen David, PA
Chesner, Frank Maurice, PA
Clancy, Leo Joseph, MA
Costello, Bernard Edward, PA
Crawford, Joseph William, PA
Crews, Numa Haden, NC
Curran, Arthur Manning, MA
Daniels, Winfred Harry, PA
Deck, Roy, PA
Dengler, Charles Rowse, PA
Dougherty, William Sylvester, PA
Dyson, Frank, PA
Edgerton, Ambrose Earl, NY
Ellis, Robert Lee, SC
Englerth, Louis Daniel, OH
Ford, William, PA
Freas, Martin Wesley, PA
Friedenwald, Gilbert A., PA
Garvey, Joseph Peter, PA
Gasser, Rolland Raymond, ID
Gilhool, Edward William, PA
Gill, Spencer Glas, VA
Gilmore, Irvin Thompson, PA

Glenn, Charles Roland, IA
Goldcamp, Edward C., OH
Gowen, Francis Vincent, PA
Griffen, Daniel Patrick, NH
Grigg, Elmer Roy, MT
Hackett, G. Clifford, NY
Haines, Charles LeRoy, PA
Harmon, Robert J. P., NY
Harris, Jack Hawley, NC
Hawkins, Harrison Morton, PA
Helff, Joseph Reuben, NH
Hicks, William Morse, OH
Hoge, Arthur Kenworthy, WV
Horn, George Frederick, PA

Fig. 195. Edward L. Bauer (JMC, '14), Alumni President (1941), Chairman of Pediatrics (1926-1954), and Historian.

Hurdle, Samuel Walker, NC
Jackson, Sumner Waldron, ME
James, Maurice Clayton, WV
Kaighn, Charles Butcher, NJ
Kane, Leo Anthony, PA
Kay, James, PA
Keath, James W., PA
Kendrick, John Fox, SC
Kerstetter, Paul Franklin, PA
Kieffer, Uldrick McLaws, GA
King, Ernest Harold, CT
Knoll, Frederick William, PA
Laughlin, Van Sanford, NY
Lavine, Barney Doibe, NJ
Leach, E. Clements, CT
Leidy, Ralph Ellis, PA
Lerner, Macy Levi, NY
Lewis, John Saunders, Jr., OH
Long, Melville Hammond, CA
MacCollum, Isaac J., DE
MacKnight, Richard Patton, MA
Marcus, Jospeh Harvey, CANADA
Martin, Charles J., NE
Mayes, Robert Lusk, SC
McConaughey, James Collier, WV
McIlvaine, William Earle, NJ
Means, Paul Barringer, NC
Metcalf, Elliott Harrison, CT
Miller, Harold Attig, PA
Mills, Arthur, RI
Montgomery, David Earl, OH
Morgan, Benjamin Franklin, OH
Morrow, James Robert, PA
Moss, John Hunton, AR
Mullahey, Leo Thomas, PA
Myers, Samuel Zigman, PA
Nesbit, Dean Abbott, PA
Nixon, Holbert James, PA
Oliver, Adlai S., NC
Pace, Karl Busbee, NC
Padilla, Alfonso, PUERTO RICO
Park, John Fish, PA
Parrish, Robert Eunice, NC
Parson, Russel Cisney, PA

Peck, Earle Curtiss, CT
Person, Russell Harrison, PA
Petree, Paul Augustus, NC
Pflug, Ferdinand James, NJ
Phillips, Charles Hayden, PA
Pratt, Malcolm Lewis, OH
Quackenbos, Harrie Maxwell, NY
Reuling, James Risley, Jr., IA
Rodman, Nathaniel Fulford, VA
Rush, Eugene, NY
Saunders, Sheldon Asa, NC
Scharmann, Frank George, PA
Schubb, Thomas, PA
Seely, Roy Brown, NJ
Sharp, Charles Edward, NJ
Sharpe, Charles Ray, NC
Slocum, Morris Abel, PA
Smith, Ernest Elmer, MA
Smith, James Davis, VA
Snow, Lawrence C., UT
Snyder, Charles Reif, PA
Speed, Joseph Anderson, NC
Sprague, Charles Henry, ID
Staub, Carl Aloysius, PA
Steadman, Henry Ree, PA
Stevens, Floyd W., PA
Stokes, Earl B., NJ
Stork, Edwin Gordon, PA
Struse, Alvin Myers, PA
Thaxton, Benjamin Adams, NC
Turley, Hubert King, MS
Valentin, August Carl, PA
Voorhees, Bert Grant, PA
Washburn, Horace Dlos, PA
Webber, Edwin Russell, CT
Webster, Jesse Grant, PA
Wheelock, Harry Elmer, NY
Whelan, William Francis, MO
White, William Francis, PA
Whitlock, Francis Elias, OH
Wickert, Howard Tilghman, PA
Williams, Victor Albert, PA
Winston, Gilbert Isaac, PA
Wolin, David, NY

The Guns of August, Barbara Tuckman's classic book title for the onset of World War I.

The Pan-European War had started in 1914 and three members of this class of 144 would serve in the Jefferson Unit, Base Hospital #38, when the United States became involved in 1917. They were Harold Stern Davidson (Lieutenant), Ralph M. Tyson (Captain) and Clifford Bell Lull (Lieutenant).

Clifford B. Lull became prominent in the Department of Obstetrics at Jefferson in which he attained the rank of Associate Professor. He also served as President of the Alumni Association in 1933 (Fig. 196).

Ralph M. Tyson during the 1920s taught Pe-

Fig. 196. Clifford B. Lull (JMC, '15), Associate Professor of Obstetrics, President of the Alumni Association (1933).

diatrics in the College and served as Chief Clinical Assistant in the pediatric outpatient department at Jefferson. He then went on to become Professor of Pediatrics at Temple University Medical School and Chief of Pediatrics at St. Christopher's and the Lying-In Hospital.

A situation of serious proportions arose in December, 1915, when Dr. Henry S. Pritchett, President of the Carnegie Foundation, urged Provost Edgar Fahs Smith of the University of Pennsylvania to open conversations with the Jefferson Board of Trustees regarding a possible union of the two institutions. This was proposed as a type of union recommended by the Flexner report of 1910. Jefferson with 650 students had become the largest medical school in the country. A possible merger was expected to gain a large financial support from the Carnegie Foundation and perhaps the Rockefeller Foundation. The following year would witness the start and end of the negotiations.

Harold Leon Goldburgh was awarded the Francis Shain Scholarship at Jefferson upon admission and he went on to graduate with honors, also being elected to Alpha Omega Alpha. Following internship at the old Jewish Hospital he served as Lieutenant in the United States Navy Medical Corps during World War I. He was appointed to the Jefferson teaching staff in the Department of Medicine as well as an attending physician at the Philadelphia General Hospital where he served for many years as Chief of Medicine. He was Senior Attending Physician at Albert Einstein Medical Center, Consultant to the Philadelphia Psychiatric Hospital, and advanced to Professor of Clinical Medicine. A generation of Jefferson students appreciated his skilled clinical teaching with special emphasis on physical diagnosis.

Hubley R. Owen became a Clinical Professor of Surgery in the Women's Medical College and Chief Surgeon of the Department of Public Safety of Philadelphia (Fig. 197).

Alexaitis, Francis Lopatto, PA
Allsop, William Kerr, PA
Aspel, Joseph, PA
Babcock, Howell Edwards, NY
Barto, Robert Edwin, PA
Baun, William Daniel, PA
Becker, Fred Charles, PA
Beidelman, Edgar Rolland, PA
Bender, Paul B., NJ
Bender, Max, CT
Benshoff Arthur M., PA
Benson, Andrew Ludwig, PA
Bernhardt, William H., PA
Berry, William Thomas, NY
Biddle, Robert M., PA
Black, Samuel Orr, SC
Blaugrand, Samuel, NJ
Bower, Franklin Townsend, MI
Brackett, William Ernest, NC
Brobst, Jacob Ralph, PA
Bunn, William Hall, OH

Burns, Joseph Vincent, PA
Cahan, Jacob M., PA
Catalano, D. Vincent, NY
Cohen, Nathan, PA
Connelly, John A., NJ
Corrigan, James A., PA
Daley, Daniel Frances, PA
Dattner, Abe, PA
Davidson, Harold Stern, PA
de la Rosa, Leander Lopez, PA
Dennis, Wilfred Sidney, PA
Dershimer, Frederick William, OH
Dobson, William Alexander, NOVA SCOTIA
Dolphin, Joseph Francis, PA
Donnelly, Francis E., PA
Durham Royal E., NJ
Fabian, Andrew A., PA
Finch, Ollie Edwin, NC
Fosselman, Don Cameron, PA
Francis, William Gifford, NC
Goldburgh, Harold Leon, PA
Goodman, Walter George, PA
Goodman, David Aaron, PA
Gorson, Samuel Francis, NJ
Graham, Vern W., PA
Granelli, H. A., NJ
Graves, Arthur Burt, NY
Gray, William Burritt, NY
Griest, Oliver Edward, IN
Griggs, Earl E., KS
Grimm, Dolmont D., PA
Haws, Ralph John, PA
Herring, George N., NY
Hill, Franklyn Chapman, PA
Horton, George Ralph, PA
House, Wooster Hassell, NC
Hoyle, Harry French, NY
Hoyt, Francis Russell, VT
Hunt, Melvin Mundy, NJ
Hydrick, John Lee, NY
Joy, Percy Clark, NJ
Kennedy, John Pressly, SC
Kinderman, Harold Wade, WV
Kirchner, Henry Stanley, PA
Knox, Harry Edward, PA
Lampe, Herman F., PA
LaRochelle, Arthur Henry, VT
Lassiter, Chester Lawrence, NC
Lavin, John Leonard, PA
Leete, Edward Don, NH
Lehman, Asa M., NE
Lineberry, William Taylor, NC
Littleton, Henry Ward, NC
Longaker, Horace G., PA
Lull, Clifford Bell, PA
Marsteller, Victor K., PA
Martsolf, Frederic, PA

Fig. 197.   Hubley R. Owen (JMC, '15), prominent in trauma surgery.

Mays, Alexis T., PA
McCoy, Clayton Lloyd, PA
McCutcheon, Royal Howard, VA
McGhee, Harrison John, PA
McHenry, Donald Barton, PA
Means, William Horace, PA
Meier, William Ulysses, NJ
Meyer, Joseph John, PA
Middlebrooks, John Raymond, GA
Miele, Michael Anthony, NJ
Miller, Paul O., PA
Milliken, James Shepard, NC
Moloney, David, MA
Montgomery, James Robert, PA
Morgan, Isaiah C., PA
Morgan, Marshall Blair, PA
Morris, Morrill Justin, IN
Morton, Charles William, PA
Murphy, Albert Thomas, PA
Parfitt, Oliver A., PA
Patton, Gordie C., WV
Pessolano, Joseph Anthony, PA
Phillips, James Wendell, PA
Poux, George Adrian, PA
Pryor, Charles Allen, PA
Rager, Samuel E., PA
Raring, Linus Maurice, PA
Ratchford, Isaac Newton, OH
Rebhoun, Earl Hert, PA
Reed, Harold R., PA
Reese, Warren Snyder, PA
Renn, Carl Grover, PA
Reynolds, Hammon, TN

Roncoviere, Louis David, CA
Roth, James, P., NY
Salisbury, Edward Irving, OH
Saylor, Melvin A., NJ
Scovern, Harold B., MO
Seidenfeld, Leon G., WA
Shalanta, Vladimir Alexis, PA
Shillott, Charles Joseph, PA
Simkins, Raymond, NJ
Singer, Samuel, PA
Smith, Harry A., PA
Smith, Ruric N., GA
Smith, Angus L., VT
Smith, Edmund Howard, NJ
Snyder, John R. T., PA
Spruance, Horace Evans, DE
Stevens, Ralph Edwin, FL
Stiles, Mitchell Porter, AL
Summey, Thomas Johnson, NC
Templeton, E. W., MO
Thomas, Herbert C., PA
Thomas, Albert M., PA
Timberlake, Claude Vernon, NC
Tolar, Julian Nolley, FL
Turner, Joseph, PA
Tyson, Ralph M., PA
Watkins, George Thomas, NC
Watson, Joseph Harry, PA
Weatherford, John Elwood, KY
Wilkinson, William Walter, PA
Wilson, Felix Brent, KY
Winter, Stanley M., PA
Wolfe, John Bloss, PA

J.C. DaCosta ("Black Jack") teaching in "pit".

~ 1916 ~

The Degree of Doctor of Medicine was conferred upon 162 graduates on June 3, at the Academy of Music, by President the Honorable William Potter. The address was delivered by William Williams Keen, M.D., Sc.D., Ph.D., LL.D., Emeritus Professor of Surgery at Jefferson and President of the American Philosophical Society (JMC, 1862, Fig. 67), on *The Doctor's Duty*. For the first time a Ph.D degree (in Physiological Chemistry) was granted under Jefferson's University privileges stipulated in 1838, to Clarence Albert Smith (M.S., JMC, '14). In this year the entrance requirement for matriculation was increased to two years of college work.

John Allan Bertolet, after serving in Jefferson's Base Hospital #38 as a Captain in World War I, took residency work at Jefferson in general surgery and otolaryngology (1919/20). He took an assistantship in otolaryngology at Jefferson and a service in this specialty at the Protestant Episcopal Hospital of Philadelphia. Likewise, he held a teaching position in otolaryngology at the Graduate School of Medicine of the University of Pennsylvania. In addition to consultant to the Medical Department of the Pennsylvania Railroad, he served as Coroner of the City of Philadelphia. Dr. Bertolet became active in organized medicine and served as a Director of the Philadelphia County Medical Society from 1938 to 1941.

Norman Merle MacNeill taught Pediatrics to two generations of Jefferson students and attained the rank of Clinical Professor (Fig. 198). He embodied the combination of ideal teacher, humanitarian, Catholic scholar and historian. During the great depression of the 1930s he often paid for the medications of his patients, supplied coal at times for heating their homes, and assisted needy medical students with tuition payments. Following his death in 1965, Dr. Edward L. Bauer, Professor Emeritus of Pediatrics, honored his memory with a book entitled *Profile of a Gentile Man* (1967).

David Reynolds Morgan achieved an outstanding record in World War I. A victim of wounds and mustard gas, he was awarded the Purple Heart. For gallantry in action he also received the Distinguished Service Cross and Croix de Guerre with Palm. After recuperation from severe war injuries, he went on to obtain a degree of Doctor of Public Health from the University of Pennsylvania and an additional degree of Master of Science in Surgery at the Graduate School. Dr. Morgan spent the remainder of his career in Pathology at Jefferson in which he attained the rank of Professor (Fig. 199). He became perhaps the most respected teacher in the basic sciences, always at his best in intimate sec-

Fig. 198. Norman M. MacNeill (JMC, '16), revered as a pediatrician, teacher and humanitarian.

tion instruction and with major interest in developing the Pathology Museum of the College. His portrait was presented to the College by the Class of 1957.

James Alexander Clarke, Jr. established the first Allergy Clinic in Philadelphia in 1921 (Fig. 200). It was organized under the Jefferson Outpatient Department with Dr. Clarke as Chief Clinical Assistant and Instructor in Medicine. The Clinic thrived and ultimately developed into one of the largest in the Outpatient Department. Dr. Clarke became a leader in all aspects of his specialty and published numerous articles, but his untimely death in 1943 at the age of 52 prevented publication of the book he had in preparation.

William T. Palchanis, experienced in tuberculosis prevention programs with the United States Army during world War I, became Professor in the Department of Preventive Medicine, Ohio State University College of Medicine.

Discussions began in January of this year for a proposed union of Jefferson and the University of Pennsylvania. In May, a joint committee of three representatives from both institutions obtained approval for a joint operation in which the combined schools would be called "The Medical School of the University of Pennsylvania and the Jefferson Medical College of Philadelphia." In June, the Boards of Jefferson and the University met separately and voted in favor of the plan. The daily press announced both "mergers." During the summer, ongoing discussions revealed more clearly that the University faction assumed that the combined school was part of the University, while the Jefferson group viewed it as a

Fig. 199.   David R. Morgan (JMC, '16), World War I hero and Professor of Pathology.

Fig. 200.   J. Alexander Clarke, Jr. (JMC, '16), pioneer who established the first Allergy Clinic in Philadelphia (1921).

new independent school. The Jefferson Trustees galvanized their stand against the University control which was fostered by the Carnegie Foundation's condition of University leadership. At a final meeting that summer it was decided that each school should proceed as in the past.

There were no further considerations of a University of Pennsylvania /Jefferson merger.

This year marked the death of Thomas Eakins, painter of Jefferson's spiritual symbol, *The Gross Clinic*. He was buried in Woodlands Cemetery, Philadelphia (Fig. 201).

Austra, Joseph John, PA
Babcock, Harold Snow, ME
Bacon, Walter Austin, DE
Bailey, John Holeman, PA
Barr, Frederick Greiner, OH
Bertolet, John Allan, PA
Boley, Henry Benjamin, NY
Bowman, Andrew John, UT
Brantley, Julian Chisolm, NC
Brenn, Chester Earle, NJ
Breslin, William Aloysius, PA
Bretzfelder, Karl Benjamin, CT
Burrus, Thomas Preston, NC
Burstan, Jacob, DE
Cantlin, Frank Hurley, PA
Carp, Israel Jay, PA
Chambers, John Howard, PA
Chernaik, Samuel Julius, CT
Clarke, James Alexander, Jr., PA
Clinton, James B., PA
Cobb, Clarence Everett, NY
Crawford, William Britton, PA
Crouch, Auley McRae, NC
Czubak, Matthew Francis, RI
Davis, Reese, PA

Dawson, Allan Wilson, PA
Derrah, Benjamin Vincent, PA
Devlin, Charles James, PA
Dunlap, Albert Knight, CA
Evans, Carroll Dandola, Jr., NE
Everlof, John Leonard, MN
Fackler, Charles Lewis, PA
Faggart, George Henry, GA
Feaster, Orion Otis, FL
Finley, Robert Kent, OH
Fishback, Hamilton Rodell, IL
Flanigan, John Louis, PA
Fleischmann, Albert Xavier, PA
Flynn, Robert Joseph, PA
Gaines, Arthur Raymond, PA
Gardner, Frank Harris, PA
Gettings, James Augustus, Jr., CT
Ginley, Frank Michael, PA
Goldberg, Maurice, PA
Goldblatt, Louis Jay, PA
Goldstein, Harry, WA
Greaves, Peyton Read, MS
Greco, Toby Anthony, PA
Green, John William, MS
Griest, Andrew Jackson, PA
Grimm, Homer Willard, WV
Grossman, Albert Allen, OR
Haines, John Bunting, PA
Hanbidge, Francis Findlay, NY
Harding, James Clayton, PA
Hebert, Arthur Winfred, LA
Heller, Edward Peter, MO
Hipps, Allen G. T., NC
Holderman, Herbert Helmuth, PA
Horger, Ulrich Peter, PA
Horrigan, Arthur Joseph, MA
Hostetter, Robert Davis, PA
Hughes, Lee Westlake, PA
Jenkins, Willaim F., GA
Jennings, Olin Henry, NC
Keating, Howard Francis, PA
Kleinstuber, William Oscar, DE
Kleintob, Freas Benjamin, PA

Fig. 201. Gravesite of Thomas Eakins in Woodlands Cemetery, Philadelphia.

1916

Knox, Robert Arthur, PA
Kupfer, Nathan Bernard, PA
Kurz, Karl John, PA
Landes, Latimer Small, PA
LaRoe, Arthur, NJ
Leigh, William Frederick, Jr., MS
Lermann, William Walsh, PA
Levine, Sidney Charles, NJ
Loftus, John Edward, PA
Logan John Adams, PA
Long, Roy Hamilton, NC
Lynn, Walter Leonard, PA
Macneill, Norman Merle, NOVA SCOTIA
Magee, Richard Samuel, PA
Mayerberg, Emil Rosenthal, NC
Mazanowski, Melchior M., PA
McCauley, Francis Joseph, NJ
McIver, Robert Boyd, GA
McKenna, Donald E., NY
McKenzie, Benjamin W., NC
Meyer, George Phillip, NJ
Miller, Ned David, KS
Mirman, Joseph M., PA
Monahan, James Joseph, PA
Moon, Alexander Charles, NJ
Moore, Allen Hoyt, NC
Morgan, David Reynolds, PA
Morgan, Thomas Rogers, PA
Mull, William Peter, NC
Mulligan, Peter Burrill, PA
Murray, Henry Joseph, Jr., CT
Musa, Agha B., PERSIA
Netzel, Charles Frederick, PA
Newhouse, John Edward, PA
Nitschke, Ernest Joseph, OR
Nittoli, Rocco Marion, PA
Norstedt, Gustaf Lewis, PA
Nutting, George Kegley, WV
O'Connor, James Joseph, PA
Owen, Richard, PA
Palchanis, William Theodore, PA
Parke, DeLos Hetrick, PA
Patten, Clarence Anderson, ME
Pennington, John, NJ
Peters, Clyde Ammon, PA
Purcell, George William, AZ
Quinones, Edgardo, PUERTO RICO

Randall, Hiram, NY
Randolph, Tucker Lucas, FL
Reade, Edwin Godwin, NC
Regester, Robert Pierson, PA
Rhode, Solon Lafayette, PA
Richard, Irving Etienne, RI
Richards, James L., PA
Robbins, William Henry, OH
Roberts, Grady Rudisill, NC
Rogers, Harold Dana, ME
Ross, Rex Lewis, WA
Santibanez, Ramon Ramirez, PUERTO RICO
Sawicki, Anthony Maryan, NY
Schless, Robert Avrom, PA
Seebert, Joseph Eldred, VA
Shaar, Camille M., SYRIA
Sharpe, Abraham Maxwell, PA
Sherrill, Wade Hampton, NC
Smith, Josiah Edward, SC
Smith, Vincent Gorman, NY
Soltero, Armando Garcia, PUERTO RICO
Spencer, William Henry, NY
Starr, Henry Frank, Jr., NC
Stauffer, Ralph Stanley, MD
Stull, Clark Deakyne, PA
Sturr, Robert Porch, NJ
Sutherland, Robert Clive, PA
Szabo, Dennis Eugene, OH
Tibbens, Clyde E., PA
Tomassene, Raymond Albert, OH
Uzzle, Edward Foy, NC
Vehrs, George Rudolph, OR
Wagnetz, John Adolph, PA
Walker, Herschel C., OH
Walker, Lynn Joseph, MN
Wallhauser, Henry Andrew, NJ
Watson, Charles James, Jr., PA
Watterson, Robert Wayne, PA
Welsby, Claude Bedford, ENGLAND
Westcott, Harold Flavell, NJ
White, Byron Dyson, MD
Williamson, Ernest Gotshall, PA
Woodhouse, Lisle William, CT
Woolridge, John Hayes, PA
Woomer, Lester Elgin, PA
Yarnall, Andra Hopkins, PA
Young, Paul Tidence, AL

In this class of 141 there was a large number of members who advanced Jefferson's prestige. Perhaps the most widely known was Henry L. Bockus who became internationally famous as a gastroenterologist (Fig. 202). Associated with the Graduate Hospital and Graduate School of Medicine of the University of Pennsylvania from 1921, he was elevated to Professor in 1931 and to Chairman of the Department of Medicine and Gastroenterology in 1949. His *Gastroenterology* became a standard world-wide reference work. Admiring students and residents formed the Bockus Society of Gastroenterology to perpetuate his teaching principles. Dr. Bockus was hon-ored by many foreign societies including Fellowship in the Royal Society of Medicine of London. He received the American Medical Association Distinguished Service Award and honorary degrees from Thomas Jefferson University, University of Pennsylvania and Dickinson College. The Jefferson Alumni Achievement Award was presented to him in 1964.

William Harvey Perkins became the seventeenth Dean of Jefferson Medical College and Professor of Preventive Medicine in 1941 (Fig. 203). His prior experience was extensive, including service in Siam (Thailand) and Tulane University School of Medicine in tropical and pre-

Fig. 202. Henry L. Bockus (JMC, '17) world famous gastroenterologist.

Fig. 203. William H. Perkins (JMC, '17), Dean and Professor of Preventive Medicine.

ventive medicine. His deanship bracketed the difficult World War II years and ended in 1950 for health reasons. Dr. Perkins was President of the Alumni Association in 1945 and the Class of 1917 presented his portrait to Jefferson in 1951.

Baldwin Longstreth Keyes had a long and distinguished career in psychiatry (Fig. 204). Following active service in World War I, he became interested in psychiatry and neurology at the Institute of the Pennsylvania Hospital. He went on to an appointment at Jefferson, first as Clinical Professor, and in 1942 as first Chairman of Psychiatry. During World War II he was Executive Officer of the Jefferson Hospital Unit #38 with the rank of Colonel. His post-war career included new approaches to the care of mentally ill persons and the teaching of medical students and residents. He received honorary degrees from

Jefferson and from Drexel University with appointment to Professor Emeritus in 1958. He was President of the Alumni Association in 1955 and received the Alumni Achievement Award in 1971. His portrait was presented to the College by the Class of 1955.

Harold W. Jones became Chief Resident Physician at Jefferson following World War I service in the Army Medical Corps. He was then appointed to the Department of Medicine and assigned to direct the course in Laboratory Medicine under Dr. McCrae. He became deeply interested in blood and blood transfusion, leading to the development of the Department of Hematology. Dr. Jones developed the support of the Cardeza family and in 1941 was named Director of the Charlotte Drake Cardeza Foundation and Professor of Clinical Medicine and He-

Fig. 204. Baldwin L. Keyes (JMC, '17), first Chairman of Psychiatry (1942-59).

Fig. 205. Harold W. Jones (JMC, '17), pioneer in blood transfusion, founding Director of Cardeza Hematology Foundation.

matology (Fig. 205). A full scale research and clinical program was developed under Dr. Jones and the Division has become a leading one in its field. Dr. Jones was also President of the Alumni Association in 1946/47.

LeRoy A. Schall pursued a career in otolaryngology from graduation and became LeCompte Professor of Otology/Laryngology at Harvard Medical School and Chief at Massachusetts General Hospital and Massachusetts Eye and Ear Infirmary. He was president of numerous societies in his field and was awarded honorary degrees by Jefferson (D.Sc., 1948) and Harvard (M.Sc., 1942). He received the Alumni Achievement Award in 1969 (Fig. 206).

Adolph A. Walkling was well known to Jefferson students for many years as a teacher of surgery (Fig. 207). He advanced to the rank of

Clinical Professor of Surgery and was also Chief of Surgery at the Pennsylvania Hospital. He was President of the Jefferson Alumni Association (1951) and of the Philadelphia Academy of Surgery (1958).

Edward Weiss joined the Department of Medicine at Jefferson, progressing to the rank of Associate in Medicine. In 1932 he was appointed Clinical Professor of Medicine at Temple University School of Medicine where he pioneered in the field of Psychosomatic Medicine, emphasizing emotional factors in disease. He became prominent as a lecturer and writer on related subjects.

Frederick E. Keller for many years operated a small private hospital in Philadelphia as a general surgeon but also oriented toward obstetrics and gynecology. His accomplishments included

Fig. 206. Leroy A. Schall (JMC, '17), outstanding in otolaryngology.

Fig. 207. Adolph A. Walking (JMC, '17), Clinical Professor of Surgery, President of the Alumni Association and Philadelphia Academy of Surgery.

1917

some literary efforts both in prose and poetry. He published a book of ballads and as an admirer of Dr. J. Chalmers DaCosta he edited a book of collected speeches and essays by DaCosta entitled *The Trials and Triumphs of the Surgeon*. Dr. Keller also edited a collection of poems by Dr. DaCosta.

The Ivycroft Farm in Wayne, Pennsylvania, was opened on May 5, 1917 (Fig. 208). A gift to Jefferson Hospital by Mr. Alba B. Johnson (Board President, 1926-35) and Mrs. Johnson, it served as a Convalescent Home for Men until 1948. It was the first scientifically conducted institution of its kind in or about Philadelphia. Patients convalescing from illness or injury were cared for, and in addition included those not sick enough to enter a hospital but to receive what was considered preventive convalescence.

CLASS OF 1917

Anderson, Horace Brockman, SC
Armao, Joseph, PA
Austin, DeWitt Ray, NC
Baer, Harry A. D., PA
Baily, Harry Wenzel, PA
Baron, Samuel Isaac, PA
Baron, Abraham Isaac, PA
Bartley, James Hugh, RI
Beals, Charles Wearne, PA
Becker, William Christian, WI
Bernstein, Abraham, PA
Bigger, David Andrew, CA
Binckley, Owen Henry, MD
Black, Hugh S., SC
Bockus, Henry LeRoy, PA
Bower, Raymond J., PA
Brown, Josiah Henry, MA
Burrows, Samuel J., IL
Campbell, Carl Bennison, PA
Carow, Fredrich G., NY
Carrell, James Fell, PA
Caso, Hilario B., PUERTO RICO
Christie, William Edgar, NJ
Clark, Rod Sidney, PA
Clovis, Oscar Ray, PA
Coleman, William Levin, PA
Comerford, Joseph F., PA
Costello, Martin Joseph, PA
Coughanour, Albert Edward, PA
Coyle, William Vincent, PA
Craven, Thomas, NC
Croop, Harry Ward, PA
Cunningham, William Louis, PA
Davis, Benjamin Shadrach, PA
Dean, Arthur Clark, ND
DeWan, Charles Henry, PA
Diebert, Irwin Elmer, NJ
Druffner, Lewis C., PA
Eiseman, Paul Claire, PA
Eshelman, Fayette Clinton, PA
Etter, Omer Rasor, CA

Evans, James North, NE
Eveland, Francis Betterly, PA
Finch, Harold, UT
Fisher, Albert W., PA
Flickinger, William Gordon, PA
Forrest, James, PA
Fromkin, Charles, NJ
Gainey, John White, NC
Golly, Harold Charles, NY
Gorman, Leo Raymond, PA
Griffin, Mark Alexander, NC
Gross, Abraham Joseph, PA
Gyles, Ronald C., SC
Hair, Wilfred Lorenz, PA
Hanks, George Wallace, UT
Hauck, William Henry, PA
Hendel, Isadore, CT
Henderson, Ira M., PA
Hensley, Charles Albert, NC
Hobbs, Harry Kane, PA
Huff, John Melville, NC
Huston, Samuel Wesley, PA
James, James Edward, PA
Jimenez, Juan Maria, COSTA RICA
Johnson, William Charles, CA

Fig. 208. Patients at Ivycroft Farm.

Jones, Harold Walter, NJ
Joyce, William Michael, CT
Keller, Frederick Eugene, WV
Keller, Paul, PA
Kemner, Edgar William, PA
Keyes, Baldwin L., PA
Kline, Oram Roscoe, NJ
Klutz, Austin Flint, NC
Langton, Daniel Joseph, PA
Latham, Joseph Roscoe, NC
Lewis, George Walter, PA
Livingood, Louis J., PA
Livingston, Walter Raleigh, PA
Mackler, Louis, NJ
McCorkle, Frank White, AL
McCorkle, Matthew Locke, NC
McTague, William Francis, NY
Meckel, Louis Oliver, PA
Meyer, Julian Erdrich, AL
Middlekauff, Casper Joseph, KN
Miller, Samuel Huston, OH
Miller, Robert Lee, FL
Moyer, Donald Grosch, PA
Mullen, Edward Andrew, PA
Noal, John Jeanette, VA
Odell, James Marge, OR
Paine, Robert, MS
Pawlikowski, Sigismond Bernard, PA
Payne, Lewis Banks, VA
Peril, Hyman Harry, PA
Perkins, William Harvey, PA
Pillmore, George Utley, NY
Platt, Michael, PA
Rawls, John Lewis, NC
Redelin, Albert Norman, PA
Robbins, James Merle, KY
Rodiquez, Calixto, PUERTO RICO

Rouse, Howard, WA
Royster, James Hunt, NC
Rozploch, Albin, NJ
Rynkiewicz, Felix S., PA
Saska, August, PA
Schall, LeRoy, PA
Segal, Morris, PA
Seibert, William Erdman, PA
Shapiro, Morris E. L., PA
Shaw, Byron Earl, PA
Shuman, George Ario, PA
Sidlich, David Mitchell, NJ
Smigelsky, Isadore Edward, PA
Smith, Barney Barr, PA
Smith, William Henley, NJ
Smoczynski, Mieczyslaw, Edward, PA
Sommers, Raymond Lock, PA
Stenberg, Edwin S., MN
Thigpen, Frank Lafayette, NC
Thigpen, Harry Gordon, NC
Thudium, William John, PA
Tilton, William Raymond, NJ
Torrey, Eugene Weiss, PA
Vann, Herbert M., VA
Vann, Julius R., Jr., NC
Wagenseller, James Kerchaer, PA
Wakefield, Clark Woodworth, PA
Walkling, Adolph Augustus, IL
Watkins, Robert Earl, NC
Weaver, Abe Kipp, PA
Weber, Francis Charles, NJ
Weber, John Malcolm, PA
Weiss, Edward, PA
Wick, Hilton Addison, PA
Wishard, Walter H., MD
Wolfe, Edward Inman, PA
Wyatt, Joseph Harrison, PA
Zwaifler, Nathan, NJ

"It is often said that to make discoveries one must be ignorant. This opinion, mistaken in itself, nevertheless conceals a truth. It means that it is better to know nothing than to keep in mind false ideas based on theories whose confirmation we constantly seek, neglecting meanwhile everything that fails to agree with them."

Claude Bernard (1813–78)

The compelling event of this year was Jefferson's involvement in World War I. Jefferson Base Hospital #38, which had been organized the year before, consisted of 35 officers, 100 registered nurses, six civilian employees, and 200 enlisted men. It provided a capacity of 1,000 beds. Contingencies sailed to France in May and June of 1918. The Hospital, established in Nantes, had 21 wards, a diet kitchen, barracks, mess hall, officers' barracks and nurses' barracks (Fig. 209). By September of 1918, one thousand patients had been admitted. The following month the daily census was up to 2,412 patients. Eventually, nearly 9,000 patients were cared for in Base Hospital #38. The primary medical problems encountered were respiratory infection, effects of gassing, diphtheria, scarlet fever, mumps and gastrointestinal disorders. There were 15 wards for surgical cases and the more than 700 active cases included fractures, gunshot wounds, hemorrhage, infection and gangrene. Seven members of the Jefferson unit died in service. By the War's end, 27 Jefferson Medical College Alumni had given their lives. In their honor, the Alumni Association presented a bronze plaque to be placed in the College building (Fig. 210).

At a meeting of the Faculty on November 25, 1918, Dr. Edward P. Davis, Professor of Obstetrics, made a motion that the Faculty of Jefferson Medical College approve of co-education. It was then voted that a Committee of the Faculty be appointed to confer with the Faculty of the Woman's Medical College to ascertain in what way and to what extent they desired to cooperate with the Jefferson Medical College in the medical education of women. Three representatives from each institution met and concluded that the interchange of teachers and teaching facilities between Woman's Medical College and Jefferson Medical College would not be advantageous or desirable. It would not occur until 1961 for women students to be admitted to Jefferson.

The Commencement was held on June 1 at which time 102 graduates received their M.D. degrees. The Address was delivered by Cheesman A. Herrick, Ph.D., LL.D., President of Girard College, on "The Physician and His Community".

Henry Kajetan Seelaus was the top honor man of the class, winning the Alumni prize for highest average of the four years plus five other prizes and one honorable mention. He was nicknamed "the shark" for his keenness and depth of knowledge. His 1918 yearbook (*Clinic*) described him as "an

Fig. 209.   Jefferson Base Hospital #38 in Nantes, France.

ordinary looking individual with the brain of a genius." His superbly organized lectures, operative skill, authorship of many papers and compassion for patients marked him as "a coming man in surgery." He had the potential to become a Chairman, but his life was cut short at age 43 by pneumonia in 1937, at which time he held the rank of Assistant Professor of Surgery (Fig. 211).

Reynold Stephen Griffith, of Pennsylvania, worked closely with Dr. Hobart A. Hare, Professor of Therapeutics at Jefferson (1891-1931), and rose in academic rank to Assistant Professor of Therapeutics. Over many years he taught classic prescription writing to thousands of Jefferson students (Fig. 212).

Henry Harris Perlman, of Pennsylvania, deserves special mention for having initiated pediatric dermatology as a subspecialty in the United States (Fig. 213). In the early 1980s he was made the first honorary member of the Pediatric Dermatology Society. At age 93 and still actively engaged in the practice of dermatology, he held the rank at Jefferson of Honorary Clinical Professor of Pediatrics and Honorary Clinical Professor of Dermatology.

Leslie O. Stone of North Carolina became Medical Officer in Command of the United States Naval Hospital at Pearl Harbor in 1944 and later Commanding Officer of the National Naval Medical Center, Bethesda. Often decorated, he retired from the Naval Medical Corps in 1955 with the rank of Rear Admiral.

Fig. 210. Bronze plaque honoring alumni who gave their lives in World War I.

1918

Andrews, James E., NC
Angel, Furman, NC
Annon, Walter Thomas, MN
Barnes, Wallace Harold, CA
Barreras-Almodovar, Jenaro, PUERTO RICO
Bellerue, Albert R., WI
Bertin, Elmer John, PA
Bethune, Charles Ward, PA
Blackmon, Stonewall Jackson, SC
Brennan, John Patrick, VT
Brewer, David Roe, NJ
Bristow, Charles Oliver, SC
Brooks, George Martin, NC
Burke, William Adam, PA
Carreras, Pedro Juan, PUERTO RICO
Chandler, Gail Ellsworth, IL
Combs, Howard Johnson, NC
Cook, Henry Lilly, Jr., NC
Cooper, William Russell, PA
Coppridge, William Maurice, VA

Dickie, Jamie William, NC
Dixon, Rufus Herbert, SC
Donnelly, Justin Matthew, OH
Dorasavage, William C., PA
Douglas, Thomas Edmund, Jr., WA
Durbin, George S., NY
Eakin, Francis Earl, PA
Epright, Paul Alonza, PA
Fairbanks, Ethelburt, UT
Favis-Frencilio, Gregory, PHILIPPINE ISLANDS
Fisher, Jacob Edgar, OH
Fisher, James Lee, OH
Fisher, Abraham, PA
Flores, Victor Manuel, COSTA RICO
Flude, John Meredith, PA
Fort, William Burnside, NJ
Fox, Charles Reuben, PA
Fox, Clyde Calvin, PA
Fullmer, John Bryan, PA

Fig. 211. Henry K. Seelaus (JMC, '18), brilliant surgeon whose promising career was cut short at the age of 43.

Fig. 212. Reynold S. Griffith (JMC, '18), Assistant Professor of Therapeutics who taught prescription writing.

Gibbon, James Wilson, NC
Griffith, Reynold, Stephen, PA
Hanson, Joel Hjaimar, WI
Harmon, James Carlisle, SC
Hawfield, James, NC
Hayworth, Ray W., NC
Heinitsh, Harry Ernest, SC
Hicks, Vonnie Monroe, NC
Highsmith, James DaCosta, NC
Hirst, Ernest Reed, NJ
Holt, Duncan Waldo, NC
Hood, Arch John, WI
Hubbard, Frederick Cecil, NC
James, Albert Warren, NC
James, Herbert Halpenny, ND
James, Jerry M., PA
Jamison, John McFarland, PA
Jaworski, Felix Andrew, PA
Jones, Florentine Barker, Jr., PA
Kelley, Harold Charles, MN
Klugh, Walter Gray, SC
Lane, John William, WI

Larson, Carl, UT
Lassiter, Henry Grady, NC
Lawrence, Benjamin Jones, NC
Leach, William Thomas, PA
Leasum, Charles, WI
Leasum, Robert Nels, WI
Limquico, Jose D., PHILIPPINE ISLANDS
Low, Chin Wen, CHINA
Mangum, Charles Preston, NC
Mason, James Henry, III., NJ
McCarthy, Justin A., MA
McCullough, Walter James, NY
McDaniel, Joseph Stites, DE
McGuire, Burruss Boyd, NC
Mendel, James Harold, WV
Milligan, Robert Sylvester, PA
Minor, Austin Joseph, PA
Molina-Castilla, Pastor, MEXICO
Mott, Edwin Leland, NY
Myers, Asa Lee, IL
Ohannesian, Frank, CA
Payne, Mosby Hale, MA
Perlman, Henry H., PA
Reisinger, Paul Bryson, PA
Rodriguez-Aviles, Juan C., PUERTO RICO
Rosenblatt, Sidney, NJ
Seelaus, Henry Kajetan, PA
Shoaff, Paris Alexander, PA
Stites, Marcus Eben, NJ
Stone, Leslie O., NC
Theriault, Louis Leo, ME
Thomison, Harry Elijah, DE
Tyson, John McClure, PA
Vaughn, Arthur Raymond, NJ
Walker, James A., PA
Wallis, Charles, AR
Werley, Walter William, PA
West, Stanley Quay, PA
Wheeler, James Hartwick, NC
Wickert, Clifford John, PA
Wolff, Denis Roscoe, NC

Fig. 213. Henry H. Perlman (JMC, '18) initiated the field of pediatric dermatology.

"Nor bring to watch me cease to live
Some Doctor, full of phrase and fame
To shake his sapient head and give
the ill he cannot cure—a name."
Matthew Arnold (1822–88)

At the Commencement in the Academy of Music on June 7, the Degree of Doctor of Medicine was conferred upon 142 graduates. Major General Merritte W. Ireland (JMC, 1891, Fig. 127) was awarded an LL.D. degree and delivered the address entitled *Progress of Medicine in the Twentieth Century*.

Burgess L. Gordon, of Spokane, Washington, spent his life in academic medicine (Fig. 214). After graduation, he became a teaching fellow in Harvard Medical School for several years and conducted clinical investigation and experiments in pulmonary physiology. In 1927 he became Director and Physician-in-Charge of Jefferson's Chest Department until 1951, ultimately rising to the rank of Clinical Professor. He then was appointed the President of Woman's Medical College. Six years later he accepted the post of Director of Education at the Lovelace Foundation

Fig. 214. Burgess L. Gordon (JMC, '19), Director of Department for Diseases of the Chest (1927-51).

in Albuquerque, New Mexico. In 1960 he joined the American Medical Association as Associate Editor, later being responsible for medical terminology and its adaptation to computers. He wrote many articles and edited four books on pulmonary disease. His article on *Pulmonary Asbestosis*, published in 1932, has achieved landmark status in pointing up the major hazards to the lungs which are now known to result from asbestos exposure.

Christian W. Nissler, of Montana, pursued a life-long interest in diseases of the chest, especially tuberculosis. As an Associate in medicine, he taught physical diagnosis at Jefferson's Pine Street Hospital for tuberculosis and later became Medical Director of White Haven Sanatorium.

Frank Weger Konzelman, of Pennsylvania, rose to Professor of Pathology at Jefferson between 1922 and 1930. He then transferred to Temple University Medical School where he remained until 1949 as Professor of Clinical Pathology. He published numerous articles on laryngeal and bronchial cancer and was a contributing editor of the *Encyclopedia of Medicine*. Active in many societies, he served as President of the American Society of Clinical Pathologists.

Lowrain E. McCrea, a native of Missouri, served his internship at St. Agnes Hospital. After a residency in Urology at Long Island College Hospital, he returned to Philadelphia for appointments at Philadelphia General and Temple University Hospitals in 1925. He progressed to Professor of Urology at Temple University School of Medicine and also served as consultant to several Delaware Valley Hospitals including the Valley Forge Army Hospital.

R. Edwin Duncan went on to a career in Naval Medicine. He was one of the physicians serving President Franklin D. Roosevelt and was later Commanding Officer of the United States Naval Hospital at Bethesda, Maryland.

Aguilu, Jorge, PUERTO RICO
Alexis, Joseph A., PA
Andrew, Lloyd Brumund, NE
Bailey, Nelson John, PA
Barbrow, Abraham L., PA
Bashore, Robert Guy, PA
Baumgart, Clarence Henry, WI
Beach, Edward W., NJ
Beck, Joseph Karl, UT
Becker, William Wendel, PA
Belgrade, Joseph T., PA
Bender, Leonard Franklin, NJ
Berman, Jacob Julius, NJ
Bittle, Stanley Edward, PA
Bossart, Merle Franklin, PA
Brewer, James Street, NC
Brinkley, Harvey Meares, NC
Brinkman, John, PA
Brody, Louis, PA
Caceres, Juan Francisco, HONDURAS
Call, Oel Facer, ID
Cannon, Douglas Launeese, SC
Cart, Julius Henry, WI
Clark, Thomas Edgar, UT
Clay, John William, PA
Codd, Alphonso Nicholas, WA
Condron, Frank M., CT
Conoly, Lacy Newton, NC
Copeland, Thomas Harold, OH
Cordonna, George, PA
Crumrine, Norman Ross, PA
DeLaney, Charles Oliver, NC
Dixon, William Harvey, NC
Doranze, Harold K., NJ
Duncan, R. Edwin, MO
Elliot, Avon Hall, NC
Emanuel, Milton Barnett, PA
Epstein, Harry Harold, NJ
Evans, James Miller, WV
Fabricant, Samuel, CT
Falconer, William George, PA
Fist, Harry S., CO
Font-Suarez, Vincente, PUERTO RICO
Foster, Howitt H., VA
Friedman, Harry Joseph, WA
Galan, Juan Jose, Jr., TX
Glass, Creed Cornelius, PA
Gordon, Burgess Lee, Jr., WA
Gozdzicki, Henry Roman, DE
Gray, Harrison, CT
Green, Ralph Dennis, NE
Gross, Donald Ammon, PA

Gross, William Adam, OH
Gross, Joseph LeRoy, PA
Gryczka, Stephen Walter, PA
Hall, Clark Homer, MO
Hanna, Dwight Corwin, Jr., PA
Happel, William Joseph, PA
Hartung, Francis Conrad, PA
Heffner, Robert Stanley, PA
Herman, Emery Cline, NC
Hermany, Solomon Lewis, PA
Hiester, William LaRoy, PA
Hill, William Adam, PA
Hirshland, Harold, ID
Holman, Charles Sherman, PA
Housman, Nathan Samuel, CA
Hunter, John Pullen, NC
Hurt, Ira Huff, VA
Jacoby, William Jerome, PA
Johnson, Theodore Martin, WI
Jones, Arthur Lane, WV
Jones, Edmund Lloyd, PA
Kanner, Harry Mitchell, FL
Kaufman, Charles, CT
Kline, Meyer A., PA
Konzelmann, Frank W., PA
Krebs, Frank Henry, PA
Lechner, Frederic Clemons, PA
Levin, Moses Jordan, PA
Levin, Louis, NJ
Long, Miguel Andres, TX
Lundberg, George A. F., MA
Lustberg, Sam R., MS
Mabey, Orson Henry, UT
Marlowe, William Anderson, NC
Marsh, Frank B., NC
Martin, Henry S., MO
McCrea, Lowrain E., NE
McGeehan, Stanley M., PA
McIlwaine, Richard, TN
Merkel, Ralph Henry, PA
Moore, Ronald Conrad, PA
Morrison, Robert Raymond, PA
Moskovich, Myer Norman, MN
Mujica-Dueno, Augustin, PUERTO RICO
Mungle, Earl William, NY
Nissler, Christian William, MT
Oaks, Lewis Weston, UT
Owens, Basil Tabor, PA
Parkes, Olyn Floyd, MS
Perry, Wendell Holmes, MS
Perry, David Russell, NC
Pfefferle, Oscar, NJ

Quinlan, John Thomas, NY
Quinn, Milton James, MO
Quinn, Thomas Ryan, PA
Redfield, J. Ralph L., NJ
Riddle, Norman Clayton, NC
Rivin, Henry A., PA
Robb, William Mayo, MO
Robinhold, Guy A., PA
Rogers, William Kingsley, NY
Ryan, Earl Francis, MA
Sanchez-Vigil, Augustin, NICARAGUA
Scouller, John Samuel, PA
Scruggs, Fred Bobo, NC
Shaw, Wilfred McLaurin, SC
Simpson, Eugene Robbins, PA
Smith, Gerald Barcroft, NJ
Smith, Morris, PA
Sonda, Lewis Paul, PA
Speck, Julius Caesar, OH

Squires, Claude Babington, NC
Stroup, Paul Eugene, PA
Suseri, Caesar William, PA
Tatum, Roy C., NC
Trimmer, Ralph Waldo, PA
Walsh, Thomas Joseph, PA
Weaver, Oscar Montague, PA
Weest, Harry Wolfgang, Jr., PA
Weil, Burton A., PA
Welsh, William Andrew, OH
West, Gordon Fitzhugh, NC
West, Hans Peter, WV
Williams, Gomer Thomas, PA
Williams, Royal William, PA
Wilson, James Alfred, PA
Woody, William Sterling, VA
Wrang, William Emil, CT
Wyatt, Arthur Thomas, NC
Zimmerman, Cyrus Becker, PA

Bacteriology Laboratory in 1898 Medical College Building

An outstanding member in this class of 165 was Thaddeus Lemert Montgomery, from Missouri. He was an honor student in his sophomore and senior years. Following internship at Jefferson, he became an assistant to Dr. E.E. Montgomery, his uncle, who was then Professor Emeritus of Gynecology. During that period (1922-25) he held appointments as Instructor in Anatomy and Instructor in Surgery. In the Department of Obstetrics from 1925 to 1940 he rose to Clinical Professor of Obstetrics. He then resigned to become Professor of Obstetrics and Gynecology and Head of the Department at Temple University School of Medicine. This appointment witnessed the combination of the Departments of Obstetrics and Gynecology into a single entity, the first so constituted in Philadelphia. Dr. Montgomery in 1946 returned to Jefferson as Professor of Obstetrics and Gynecology and Director of the Division of Obstetrics, and from 1955 to 1961 he served as Chairman (Fig. 215). He was an early proponent of "natural childbirth" and "rooming in" of newborn infants with their mothers. He was active in all the important societies of his field and co-authored a *Textbook of Practical Obstetrics*. He served as President of the Alumni Association in 1948, was honored by presentation of his portrait to the College in 1961, and was awarded an honorary LL.D. degree at Jefferson's Commencement Exercises in 1963. As a talented artist, Dr. Montgomery exhibited his paintings under his middle name of Lemert.

Lewis Cass Scheffey, of Pennsylvania, took his internship at Jefferson Hospital and joined the Faculty as Assistant Demonstrator of Gynecology. He rose to Clinical Professor by 1938. From 1940 to 1946 he served as Chairman of Gynecology, and from 1946 to 1955 as Chairman of Obstetrics and Gynecology and Director of the Division of Gynecology (Fig. 216). Dr. Scheffey had a life-long interest in pelvic cancer which led him to establish a Pelvic Cancer Clinic in the Gynecology Outpatient Department in 1928. As Director of the clinic until 1955, he conducted a

remarkable follow-up study of nearly 100 percent of treated patients over thirty years. He was an early advocate of cervical and vaginal cytology and collaborated with George N. Papanicolaou in developing the Inter-Society Cytology Council, serving as its President in 1956. He was active in the American Cancer Society and President of the Philadelphia Division in 1957. He served as President of the American Gynecologic Society, the Philadelphia County Medical Society, the Obstetrical Society of Philadelphia, and the College of Physicians of Philadelphia.

Martin J. Sokoloff joined the Jefferson Department for Diseases of the Chest in 1924 and became a stalwart in the teaching of physical

Fig. 215.   Thaddeus L. Montgomery (JMC, '20), Chairman of Obstetrics and Gynecology (1956-61).

diagnosis and chest diseases (Fig. 217). Serving as Acting Medical Director of the Chest Department during World War II, he succeeded Dr. Burgess Gordon as Director in 1951. Dr. Sokoloff also was Attending Physician at White Haven Sanatorium from 1924 until its takeover by Jefferson in 1946. He was Chief of the Division of Tuberculosis Control in the Philadelphia Department of Health for many years.

Maxwell Cherner taught for many years as a prosector of anatomy in the Daniel Baugh Institute.

Figure 218 depicts the Resident House Staff in 1920 with the Medical Director, Henry K. Mohler.

Fig. 216.   Lewis C. Scheffey (JMC, '20), Chairman of Obstetrics and Gynecology (1946-55).

Fig. 217.   Martin J. Sokoloff (JMC, '20), Director of Department for Diseases of the Chest (1951-62).

CLASS OF 1920

Ambler, Arthur Chase, NC
Amshel, Jesse L., PA
Anderson, Guy B., IA
Balph, James, Jr., PA
Banner, Allan Carithers, NC
Barsby, John Edward, PA
Beaumont, Dudley Hanss, WV
Bertrand, Elmer, DE
Bishop, Paul Arthur, IN
Bories, Henry Villard, WA
Bradley, Robert Aloysius, WA

Brayshaw, James Ellis, DE
Brooks, Ralph Elbert, NC
Brossman, Martin W., PA
Brownson, Hollis Lee, NE
Bulger, Kenneth Scott, PA
Burkley, Louis F., Jr., PA
Byron, Harold J., MA
Cahall, Walter Lawrence, PA
Campbell, James Truan, TN
Cherner, Maxwell, PA
Clark, Eugene E., NE
Clendenning, William Burdette, PA

Collins, George, NC
Collins, Harold J., NY
Conklin, Stanley DeWitt, PA
Conway, John Joseph, PA
Cook, Thomas William, PA
Cozzolino, James Anthony, CT
Crain, Carroll Francis, SD
Cryder, Millard, PA
Curran, John Harrison, PA
Dalrymple, Richard Ray, PA
Davenport, Irwin Pattison, PA
Davidow, Samuel H., OH
Dawson, William Earl, NC
Decker, Henry Bristol, NJ
Dembo, Leon Haskins, PA
Ditto, Edward Wilson, Jr., MD
Dominguez-Conde, Cesar, PUERTO RICO
Duling, Milton Stone, WV
Durgin, Lawrence Newton, MA
Duttenhofer, Charles Spindler, PA
Ellis, Lyle Gaffney, NC
Evans, Harlem Irvin, PA

Ewens, Frederic, PA
Farmakis, Leonidas John, PA
Fickel, Creedin Spencer, PA
Fishel, Linnaeus Wayne, PA
Fitzgerald, John Herbert, NC
Flannelly, George John, PA
Flannery, James Joseph, PA
Fleck, Roland F., PA
Flock, Herman F. W., PA
Funch, Hans Christian, DENMARK
Garner, Vaughn Clifton, CT
Goldbacher, Lawrence, PA
Goldstein, Eli Whitney, PA
Grier, Robert Martin, PA
Guardia, Jaime de la, PANAMA
Hamilton, Lloyd Alexander, PA
Harper, William Troy, NC
Harris, Edwin Anderson, NJ
Harris, Cary Fletcher, NC
Hawn, William Seymour, OH
Heckman, Ira Dietrich, PA
Hodgson, Michael Aloysius, PA

Fig. 218.   Resident House Staff in 1920 with Medical Director Henry K. Mohler.

1920

Hough, Ralph C., PA
Howard, James David, PA
Hurwitz, Isadore, PA
Israel, George Irving, MA
Jacobson, Harry Jacob, TN
Johnson, Vivian Earl, NC
Johnson, Charles Thomas, NC
Jones, Z. B. Vance, NC
Jones, Carey Celester, NC
Kahler, John Alexander, PA
Keane, John F. M., MA
Keck, William Frederick, PA
Keller, Roy L. G., TX
Kershaw, George Henry, MA
Kielar, Joseph Romuald, PA
Kowal, Vladimir, AUSTRIA
Learn, Blair George, PA
Leiby, Raymond Aaron, PA
Lentz, John Amandus, PA
Lober, William N., MO
Luschinskey, Walter, PA
Mallek, Anthony Stephen, PA
Mantz, Herbert Leslie, MO
Martin, Lester P., NC
Martinez, Jose Marie, HONDURAS
Mattas, Clyde Leslie, PA
McConnell, Thomas William, PA
McElhinney, P. P. Bliss, WA
McGuinness, Robert Jones, PA
McLaughlin, James Stephen, Jr., PA
McWilliams, Charles Earle, NJ
Mercado, Heriberto, BOLIVIA
Messmer, Anthony Conrad, PA
Metzger, Harry, PA
Monahan, Stanley Theobald, PA
Montgomery, Thaddeus L., PA
Moore, Henry Blanchard, NC
Murray, William John, PA
Nall, Joseph A. F., PA
Navas-Torres, Antonio, PUERTO RICO
Neel, Vern Arguile, OH
Nelson, John, PA
Nolte, Harry Frederick, WV
Noss, John Cyrus, PA
O'Brasky, George Harry, CT
O'Briant, Albert Lee, NC
O'Brien, Joseph Elmer, PA
O'Donnell, John Anthony, PA
O'Malley, Eugene John, IA

Ott, Charles Henry, NY
Owen, John Fletcher, NC
Owens, Creston Linwood, DE
Palmieri, Julio, PUERTO RICO
Parsons, Willard Herring, MS
Peacock, Howell, GA
Pons, Carlos A., PUERTO RICO
Price, Thomas Horner, PA
Ralston, Hugh Evans, PA
Rambo, Harold Shaner, PA
Reed, James Madison, Jr., WV
Reed, Leo Buckley, PA
Reyes, Salvador, NICARAGUA
Roberts, Charles Kingsley, NY
Rogers, Charles Henry, OR
Ryder, William Harold, CT
Sargent, Willard Snow, UT
Scheffey, Lewis Cass, PA
Schoenheit, Edward William, NC
Schwartz, Abraham Irving, CT
Searle, Maurice James, PA
Sokoloff, Martin Joseph, PA
Sonne, Clarence Melvin, PA
Speck, Moses Henry, OH
Spencer, George Francis, PA
Stoler, George W., PA
Sturgeon, John D., Jr., PA
Summers, William Herbert, PA
Sweeney, Joseph Patrick, MA
Thompson, Samuel Alcott, SC
Thompson, Paul Francis, SC
Tulsky, Harry, PA
Turner, Arthur L., WV
Victor, Simon Leonard, NY
Wallace, William Alexander, PA
Wallace, William Davies, PA
Wallace, William Earl, MO
Watkins, Harold Ryburn, IL
Weimar, Russell Conwell, PA
Weise, Ellwood Carl, CT
Wentz, Irl Ziegler, PA
Wharton, Louis Earl, OH
Williams, Jabez Herring, NC
Wilson, Joseph S., PA
Winston, Maurice Joseph, PA
Woodson, Lewis Green, Jr., AL
Wooten, William Isler, NC
Wooten, Floyd Pugh, NC
Worster, Vere K., PA

Commencement exercises were held in the Academy of Music on June 4 at which time 114 graduates received their degrees. The Address was delivered and an honorary LL.D. conferred upon the Rev. Samuel Charles Black, D.D., LL.D., President of Washington and Jefferson College. It was entitled "The Release of Power."

Frank H. Krusen (Fig. 219) received the prize in Therapeutics at Commencement but his projected career in surgery was interrupted by tuberculosis requiring sanatorium treatment. This led to a concern for the handicapped and he went on to a distinguished pioneering career in physical medicine and rehabilitation. He organized

Fig. 219. Frank H. Krusen (JMC, '21), pioneer in Rehabilitation Medicine.

the first Department of Physical Medicine in the United States at Temple University Medical School in 1928 and quickly became known as a persuasive speaker, writer and planner. In 1935 he founded the Department of Physical Medicine and Rehabilitation at the Mayo Clinic where he served until retirement in 1963. He then returned as Coordinator in the Department he had founded at Temple and also became research director at Tufts-New England Rehabilitation Institute in Boston. Dr. Krusen was a motivator, founder and first Chairman of the American Board of Physical Medicine and Rehabilitation, editor of the *Yearbook of Physical Medicine* and a consultant in great demand. He was Chairman of the Baruch Committee on Rehabilitation of the American Medical Association and Consultant to the Surgeon General of the United States Army. Honors included the 1953 Physician's Award for contributions to employment of the handicapped signed by President Eisenhower, the Distinguished Service Award of the American Medical Association in 1958, and the Dwight D. Eisenhower People-to-People Award in 1959. The Frank H. Krusen Center at Temple University was dedicated in his honor in 1966.

William T. Lemmon of South Carolina received training at Jefferson through internship, teaching anatomy at the Daniel Baugh Institute, and surgery under the preceptorship of Professor Thomas A. Shallow. He pursued an active career in the teaching and practice of surgery. Dr. Lemmon devised the new technique of continuous spinal anesthesia and described it in a presentation to the Philadelphia Academy of Surgery in 1939. This was a commonly used anesthetic procedure which underwent subsequent modifications. He rose to the rank of Professor of Surgery (Fig. 220).

Roy W. Mohler served his internship at Bryn Mawr Hospital and then became associated with Jefferson's Professor of Gynecology, Brooke M. Anspach. He was active clinically and in teaching, advancing through the ranks to Clinical Professor of Obstetrics and Gynecology. He also joined the staff of Philadelphia Lying-in Hospital under Professor Norris W. Vaux where he saw intense activity during the years of World War II. In 1947 he became chief of Obstetrics and Gynecology at Methodist Hospital of Philadelphia until his retirement in 1957. Dr. Mohler was active in Philadelphia and State medical affairs, President of the Obstetrical Society of Philadelphia, and a long-time director of the Medical Service Association of Pennsylvania. He was a trustee of his alma mater, Dickinson College, and received its honorary degree (D.Sc.) in 1943.

Adams, Paul Risley, OH
Atkinson, William Burr, KY
Baker, Maurice Edward, NC
Barrows, Victor Ira, VT
Bell, George Erick, NC
Berman, Jacob Kohn, IN
Binkowitz, Joseph, PA
Britt, Tilman Carlyle, NC
Brunson, Edward Porcher, SC
Bucher, Albert Herman, PA
Bucher, Robert Leon, PA
Caviness, Verne S., NC
Clark, Stanley M., UT
Corpening, Sherrill Gaither, NC
Corson, Joseph Alan, PA
Crowe, Aldrich Clements, AL
Daniel, Doff D., WV
DelMarco, Benjamin Aloysius, PA
Dennis, Foster Leonard, KS
Dodson, Hobart W., PA
Douglas, Julius Judson, Jr., TN
Erpelding, John Kenneth, MN
Farthing, Fred Robert, NC
Fenimore, William Nolan, DE
Fleming, Bruce L., PA
Flythe, Allen Grant, NC
Frye, Glenn Raymer, NC
Futrell, Walter Edward, NC
Gamette, Douglas Leon, UT
Geddie, Kenneth B., NC
Gift, Weldon Armean, IN
Ginsburg, Macy, PA
Green, Morris Beryl, MN
Gregersen, Orman, UT
Hadley, William Sampson, NC
Halloran, Edward J., MA
Hansell, Henry Lewis, PA
Haussmann, David Spotkin, PA
Heckert, Emerson Monroe, PA
Heins, Lawrence Gustavus, MO
Hill, Ben Spalding, KY
Hinckley, Livingston S., NJ
Holzman, Jerome Leopold, OR

Horine, Dewey Grove, MD
Hurst, Lloyd, ID
Katzman, Samuel Sidney, CT
Kennedy, David Ross, SC
Kessel, Charles Royall, WV
Koerth, Charles John, TX
Kopelman, Nathan Austin, PA
Krusen, Frank Hammond, PA
Lafferty, Howard George, PA

Fig. 220. William T. Lemmon (JMC, '21), Professor of Surgery and inventor of continuous spinal anesthesia.

Lambert, Critz Fred, NC
Lambert, Waite Leonidas, NC
Lane, Martin Edgar, NC
Langan, Paul Conway, NY
Lemmon, William Thomas, SC
LeVan, Gerald W., PA
Lide, Lewis Maxwell, SC
Love, Walter Standlee, MO
Lutterloh, Isaac Hayden, NC
Maeso, Manuel M., PUERTO RICO
Matzger, Edward, WA
May, Karl Joseph, OR
McCahey, James Francis, PA
McCullough, William Earl, UT
McGinnis, Russell Smith, WV
Miller, Charles Robert, Jr., PA
Mohler, Roy W., PA
Mohney, Fred Curtis, PA
Morgan, Louis Schubert, KS
Morrison, George Brooks, MO
Neupauer, M. G. Adolph, PA
Newman, Philip Floyd, NE
Nolan, James Onslow, NC
Nye, Howard Holland, OH
O'Donnell, Leo Day, PA
Park, Cecil Richard, PA
Parks, Hugh, NC
Pastor, Jose Rodriguez, PUERTO RICO
Perri, Ernest L., PA
Pittman, Malory Alfred, NC
Post, William Glenn, Jr., GA

Proctor, Francis Edward, DE
Rankin, Lynn M., TN
Reese, Lewis Samuel, Jr., PA
Rile, Walter Bright, PA
Ross, Earl Blan, KS
Rusling, Robert S., NJ
Seed, Raymond Charles, MA
Shapera, William, PA
Sheridan, William Martin, SC
Singleton, William McCormick, WV
Slater, Ralph Lewis, OH
Small, Edward Lester, NJ
Smith, Matthew Mann, Jr., TX
Smith, Franklin Calton, NC
Smith, Bernard Herman, OH
Smith, Clyde Francis, PA
Spindler, Alva Reed, OH
Stinson, John Wesley, ME
Stout, Benjamin Mortimer, WV
Strawn, Leo Stacy, PA
Swisher, Kyle Young, WV
Tally, Bailey T., NC
Thorn, Druery Rodgers, KS
van der Bie, Roscoe, WI
Vanderbeek, Stuart Ward, NJ
Walsh, Harry A., PA
Warden, Paul Pelley, WV
White, Edgar Hartley, UT
Whitehead, Seba L., NC
Wilson, William Gilliam Jr., NC
Winger, Ira Bitzer, PA

Verne S. Caviness (JMC, '21), Professor Emeritus of Medicine at the University of North Carolina, started the first practice of internal medicine in Raleigh in 1923. He conducted clinical research in diabetes and later in hypertension, continuing his practice until nearly the age of 90.

An unusual number of the 88 members in the Class of 1922 became involved with academic medicine. Among them was John T. Farrell, Jr., his father also a Jefferson alumnus (1866). Dr. Farrell interned at Rhode Island Hospital but returned to Jefferson's Department of Roentgenology in 1924. He was roentgenologist to Jefferson's Chest Department and to White Haven Sanatorium. In 1936, upon the death of Willis F. Manges (JMC, '03, Fig. 157), Professor of Roentgenology, he became Acting Chairman of the Department, but resigned the next year to join the staff of the Graduate Hospital. He published *Roentgen Diagnosis of Diseases of the Gastrointestinal Tract*. In 1944 he was Vice-President of the Radiological Society of North America. Dr. Farrell became involved in organized medicine and served as President of the Philadelphia County Medical Society in 1956 and the Pennsylvania State Medical Society in 1958 (Fig. 221).

Austin T. Smith, following internship at Pennsylvania Hospital, became a prominent laryngologist, maintaining his accociation with Pennsylvania Hospital and receiving an appointment at Jefferson where he advanced to Assistant Professor of Laryngology. During World War II he was a naval surgeon in the Pacific Theater. He was generally acknowledged as a leading clinician in the area of nose and throat medicine (Fig. 222).

S. Dale Spotts, who was awarded eight prizes at graduation, joined the Department of Surgery where he was known for his technical skills. He was Attending Surgeon at the Philadelphia General Hospital and at St. Joseph's Hospital, but his career ended in 1952 from a malignancy acquired by early unprotected fluoroscopy for fracture reductions. Dr. Spotts, a native of Lewisburg, Pennsylvania, was honored with the degree of Doctor of Science by his alma mater, Bucknell University, in 1949. In 1950 he was elected a Trustee of Bucknell (Fig. 223).

J. Bernard Bernstine, following internship at the old Jewish Hospital, joined the Department of Obstetrics and Gynecology. Known as a skilled operator and respected as a teacher, Dr. Bernstine also had a broad background in the arts, especially opera. He contributed numerous articles to medical literature (Fig. 224).

John F. Coppolino became associated with the Department of Pediatrics and for many years was a stalwart in the Pediatric Clinic. As a leading pediatrician in South Philadelphia, he loyally promoted the interests of Jefferson and was advanced to Clinical Professor of Pediatrics.

Eli R. Saleeby, a native of Lebanon, joined the Department of Surgery after internship at

Fig. 221. John T. Farrell, Jr. (JMC, '22), radiologist involved in organized medicine.

Cooper Hospital, Camden, New Jersey, and obtained an appointment in the Jefferson Department of Pathology. He became interested in student life and teaching. Remembered for his sponsorship of Kappa Beta Phi fraternity and its annual Black and Blue Ball, he initiated the student scholarship fund (Fig. 225).

Lawrence S. Carey was an intern at Pennsylvania Hospital where he joined the clinical staff in the Department of Medicine under Dr. Thomas McCrae and later Dr. Garfield Duncan. He was an able clinical teacher and advanced to Assistant Professor of Medicine at Jefferson.

Ralph Hand was appointed to the Department of Orthopaedic Surgery, relating especially to the Outpatient Department and advanced to the rank of Associate.

Fig. 222. Austin T. Smith (JMC, '22), prominent otolaryngologist.

Fig. 223. S. Dale Spotts (JMC, '22), surgical martyr to pioneer unprotected use of x-rays.

CLASS OF 1922

Albright, William John, PA
Amerise, Anthony Daniel, PA
Bastian, William Clair, PA
Bernstine, J. Bernard, PA
Blackmon, Heyward James, SC
Bridger, Dewey Herbert, NC
Cain, Norman Hugh, PA

Carey, Lawrence Sherwood, DE
Carpenter, Uri Alonzo, NY
Carroll, Joseph Herbert, PA
Chaplin, Steenie C., NC
Chee, Ching Hsin, CHINA
Coppolino, John Frank, NJ
Crandall, Harry Franklin, RI

1922

Crist, Guy Charles, PA
Danisawich, Anthony Bernard, PA
Eley, Vernon Lyndon, NC
Etter, Harry Havelock, CA
Everhart, Lysle Rogers, WV
Farrell, John Thompson, Jr., RI
Feibus, Arthur, OH
Folger, Paul Bernays, NC
Franklin, Earl Alexander, ND
Gallagher, Herbert Kelley, AL
Gibbs, Albert Gabriel, PA
Goldbloom, Abraham Allen, PA
Goldman, Max Robert, PA
Gordon, George, NY
Hand, Ralph Carlisle, NJ
Harrison, Francis Murphy, CT
Hays, Robert Reeves, TN
Hecht, Joseph Jerome, PA
Hennemuth, John Henry, MN
Holley, Chesterfield James, OH

Ingram, Frank Welton, NY
Ivey, Hubert Turner, NC
Jimenez, Jose Miguel, COSTA RICA
Johnson, David Morrison, WV
Ketchie, James Meredith, NC
Kibbe, John Halbert, MO
Kinnard, George Potts, GA
Lancaster, Forrest Jackson, NC
Latham, Claude Aubra, WV
Lavelle, Paul Edmund, PA
Lee, Harry Wooten, NC
Li, Min Hin, HAWAII
McCallum, Arthur Storey, GA
McCormick, Donald John, WI
McElroy, Ervin, NJ
Megna, Salvatore, WI
Meikle, Grover Andrew, PA
Metzgar, Marshall Rinker, PA
Miller, Wesley Shaffer, PA
Morrison, William Byrne, WV

Fig. 224. J. Bernard Bernstine (JMC, '22), Clinical Professor of Obstetrics.

Fig. 225. Eli R. Saleeby (JMC, '22) sponsored the Black and Blue Ball and student scholarship fund.

Newcomb, Andrew Purefoy, Jr., NC
Nisbett, James Menior, AR
Norment, William Blount, NC
O'Brasky, Louis, CT
O'Donnell, Francis T., PA
Ours, Lester, WV
Penta, Michael, PA
Pfost, Donald Monroe, WV
Porter, John Henning, SC
Poston, James Lewis, NC
Quinn, William Russell, MO
Rankin, John Oliver, OH
Reisman, Henry Allen, NY
Riffle, George Newcomer, PA
Saleeby, Eli Richard, NC
Saltzman, Maurice, PA
Shapiro, Leonard, NY

Sharp, Oliver Ledbetter, SC
Shope, Charles Edgar, PA
Sippel, George Richard, PA
Smith, Austin Thomas, PA
Solomon, Henry Doyle, GA
Spotts, Samuel Dale, PA
Strathearn, Hugh John, CA
Strittmatter, Louis Edward, PA
Swern, Nathan, NJ
Tandowsky, Ralph Myron, UT
Tatum, Walter Low, NC
Tice, Raymond Deily, PA
Wallace, Hugh Stanley, PA
Walsh, Gerald Girard, PA
Weber, Edgar H., IN
Whalen, H. Edward, ME
Zeve, Herman Sigmund, OH

Physiological Chemistry Laboratory in 1898 Medical College Building.

At the Commencement on June 1, the 147 graduates received their M.D. degrees from President, the Honorable William Potter. Dr. Edward H. Hume, Dean of the Hunan-Yale College of Medicine, Changha, China, spoke on "The Contributions of Eastern Asia to the Science and Art of Medicine."

George J. Willauer served his internship at Jefferson, beginning an association of lifelong duration. Early interest in the developing field of thoracic surgery led to postgraduate study in Europe after which he returned to establish a practice and become affiliated with the Departments of Surgery and Anatomy at Jefferson. His activities were many including operating at the main hospital and at the Pine Street Chest Department as well as being responsible for anesthesia for a number of years. He advanced to Professor of Surgery all the while serving as Chief of Surgery at Eagleville Sanatorium and from 1948 to 1966 as Director of Surgery at Methodist Hospital, Philadelphia. Dr. Willauer was President of the Alumni Association (1962), an Alumni member of the Board of Trustees (1968-71), and an important fund raiser (Fig. 226). His portrait was presented to the College in 1965 (Fig. 227) and he was the 1972 recipient of the Alumni Achievement Award.

W. Emory Burnett (Fig. 228), a close friend of Dr. Willauer, likewise became a pioneer in tho-

Fig. 226.   George J. Willauer (JMC, '23) with President Peter A. Herbut (left) at plaque honoring donors to the Founders Association.

racic surgery. Following Jefferson internship, he was appointed to the Department of Surgery at Temple University where he reached the post of Professor and Chairman. He became Vice-President of the American College of Surgeons (1954/55) and President of the Philadelphia Academy of Surgery (1960/61).

Benjamin F. Haskell (Fig. 229), a native of Virginia, also was associated with Jefferson throughout his medical career. His Jefferson internship was followed by appointment to the Department of Surgery where he became involved with the developing specialty of proctology. His teaching and clinical skills were accompanied by concern for the poor and disadvantaged. He advanced in academic rank to Clinical Professor of Surgery (Proctology). In 1963 he was President of the Alumni Association and was responsible for the institution of the annual Parents' Day for sophomore medical students. In 1975 his portrait was presented to the College and in 1978 he received the Alumni Achievement award.

David Metheny served his internship at Jefferson but went on to residency at the Mayo Clinic and a surgical career in Seattle, Washington. He was Chief of Surgery at Kings County Hospital and was an acknowledged leader in organized medicine. Dr. Metheny was the major

Fig. 227. Portrait of George J. Willauer (JMC, '23), pioneer in thoracic surgery.

Fig. 228. W. Emory Burnett (JMC, '23), chairman of Surgery at Temple University.

1923

force in the organization of the School of Medicine of the University of Washington, serving as Chairman of the Founding Committee and overcoming bitter opposition both medically and politically.

Hilton S. Read served internship at the Philadelphia General Hospital and for several years was Clinical Assistant in the Diabetic Clinic at Jefferson. This was followed by further experience at Graduate Hospital while establishing himself as a leading internist in Atlantic City, New Jersey. During World War II he was Chief of Medicine at Finney General Hospital with the rank of Lieutenant Colonel. He later organized post-graduate seminars for Atlantic City Hospital.

Frank M. Keiser returned to his native Illinois where he became a prominent urologist. In 1975 the Urology Department of Jefferson received a bequest of $50,000 for urological research from his estate.

<hr>

CLASS OF 1923

Adams, Edward Everard, NC
Amateau, Morris, NY
Antupitzky, Louis, CT
Ayer, Philip Edward, UT
Bair, George Elmer, Jr., PA
Ball, Charles Edward, TX
Barefoot, Graham Ballard, NC
Barnd, Guy Henry, PA
Bauman, Harvey R., PA
Bausch, Mark Adolph, PA
Beauchamp, Eugene Wilfrid, MA
Berson, George Jarcho, NY
Blair, George Dewey, PA
Blair, James Albert, PA
Bonatti, Anthony C., PA
Boone, William Waldo, NC
Brewster, John M., WV
Bronaugh, Wayne, OK
Brostrom, Frank, PA
Burnett, Wilbur Emory, SC
Burton, William Preston, WV
Byrd, William Carey, NC
Caudy, Daniel Gilbert, WV
Ceraso, Thomas, PA
Chiang, Yu Ying, CHINA
Churchman, Vincent Tapp, Jr., WV
Clark, O. Dwight, MO
Cofrances, Louis William, CT
Colgan, William Shockey, PA
Cooperman, William, NJ
Corrado, Cataldo, PA
Crist, Walter Allen, NJ
Croyle, Reuben Woods, PA
Delaney, William Eugene, Jr., PA
Dress, Robert William, PA
Drummond, Ainslie H., ME
Dumbauld, Carl Matthews, PA
Eagle, James Carr, NC

Enfield, George Stuart, PA
Finn, Adolph, PA
Fisher, Ivan Edgar, PA
Flax, Jacob Louis, NJ
Fletcher, Elmer Gordon, OR
Freed, Morris Albert, PA
Furr, William Charles, NC
Gardner, Robert Edward, PA
Gauthier, Henri Edouard, MA
Gennaria, Charles Reed, PA
German, George Burton, DE
Giambra, Samuel Murray, NJ
Gledhill, Horace, CT
Gocke, Thomas Vincent, WV
Goodwin, Oscar Sexton, NC
Gordy, Samuel Tobias, PA
Grahn, Henry Victor, PA
Gross, Moses, NY
Hackett, Leon William, NJ
Haggerty, Francis Ignatius, MA
Halporn, Benjamin, PA
Hangen, Russell Jonas, PA
Hannigan, Martin James, PA
Hartman, Jerome, OH
Haskell, Benjamin, VA
Hays, James Franklin, WV
Heatter, Max William, PA
Heikes, Francis Luther C., PA
Hendrickson, Frank Oscar, PA
Herff, Augustus F., TX
Herman, Charles Bernard, NC
Hetrich, George Roberts, PA
Himes, Ralph Francis, PA
Hoge, Thomas Rogers, WV
Holman, Wilgus Alexander, NJ
Hostetter, Herman H., PA
Hursh, Alexander Miller W., PA
Hutchison, Wilber Laurin, PA

Jacobson, Joseph, NY
Jeppson, John Rufus, UT
Keiser, Frank Martin, IL
Keiser, Roland Roderic, PA
Larkin, Walter J., PA
Lebovitz, Edward, PA
Lindquist, Charles Ariel, UT
Lutz, Francis Creveling, PA
Lyon, Thayer Claude, PA
Mackie, John Alfred, PA
Massey, Charles Caswell, NC
Matthews, William, NJ
McDonnel, Gerald Ellsworth, UT
McLaughlin, Howard Elliott, PA
Mendenhall, Elliott Marion, TX
Meredith, Guy Irving, MO
Metheny, David, PA
Miksch, Carl Edward, PA
Miller, James Wesley, PA
Millhon, Myron Eli, OH
Musante, Adloph Joseph, CT
Nelms, Homer Leroy, PA
Noone, Ernest L., PA
Oppermann, Ralph Clifford, PA

Owings, Capers Baxter, SC
Parker, Alan Phares, NC
Peck, Franklin Bruce, IN
Pedlow, Edward B., OH
Perkins, Arthur H., MA
Pohl, Henry, PA
Pohl, William Frederick, PA
Pool, Bennette Baucom, NC
Pressly, James Lowry, NC
Prioletti, Giovanni P., PA
Read, Hilton Shreve, NJ
Restaino, Charles Frederick, NJ
Richardson, George A., NC
Rosati, Vincent Fortunato, NY
Rosenzweig, Maurice, PA
Roth, Theodore Irving, PA
Rubenstein, Myer W., PA
Rumbaugh, Ulrich David, PA
Serafin, Frank J., NY
Sherk, Abraham Lincoln, NJ
Shulman, Nathan L., NJ
Silvis, Charles Harrold, PA
Simons, John Shirk, PA
Simons, Samuel Shirk, PA

Fig. 229. Benjamin F. Haskell (JMC, '23), Clinical Professor of Surgery (Proctology).

1923

Smith, Andrew Milliken, MD
Smith, Randall Collins, NC
Springer, Joseph Vincent, OR
Stenger, Leo E., WV
Sullivan, John James, MA
Syracuse, Victor R., NY
Thomas, George Norfleet, NC
Thomas, Howard Jones, PA
Tilghman, Brenton Alfred, VA
Tyler, Earl Runyon, NC
Ward, Donald Slusher, PA
Ward, Edward Patrick, WA

Wassman, Charles Weyman, OH
Watkins, William Merritt, NC
Wheeling, George F., PA
White, Carl Wilma, VA
Whyte, Kenneth Griffith, ID
Wilentz, William Crane, NJ
Willauer, George Jacob, PA
Wilson, Lester Ramon, NJ
Young, Clifton A., PA
Youseberg, Louis Israel, NY
Zeller, Theodore Cyril, PA

Pathology Laboratory in 1898 Medical College Building.

This was the Centennial of the founding of Jefferson Medical College (in 1824). Mr. Alba B. Johnson, Chairman of the Hospital Committee, spearheaded the Jefferson Centennial Campaign to raise funds for a New Hospital Annex. Mr. William Thompson in a legacy of $200,000, stipulated that the Annex be named in memory of his brother, Samuel Gustine Thompson, who had been a Trustee on Jefferson's Board from 1895 to 1909. The Thompson Annex was dedicated on October 30, 1924, and opened for patients the following day (Fig. 230). It occupied the site of the former 1877 Hospital located on Sansom Street between Tenth and Eleventh. With its sixteen floors, it was the tallest such hospital in the world. It connected with the first seven floors of the 1907 Main Hospital at Tenth and Sansom Streets and contained a clinical amphitheater ("pit") with a seating capacity of 500. This third and last "pit" in Jefferson's history would be replaced in 1968 by the Thompson Auditorium and New Emergency Room.

Abraham Cantarow, of Connecticut, was an honor graduate in this class of 145. His interest in biochemical research was stimulated during his undergraduate years by his Professor of Physiological Chemistry, Philip B. Hawk. Cantarow spent his entire professional career at Jefferson. He served as Resident Chemist of Jefferson Hospital (1925-27), following which he rose by 1945 to Associate Professor of Medicine. From 1945 to 1966 he was Professor of Biochemistry and Chairman of the Department (Fig. 231). Among the many honors bestowed on him, those most closely related to Jefferson were the two issues of the Clinic (1943 and 1959), presentation of his portrait to the College by the class of 1960, Presidency of the Alumni Association (1964), recipient of the Alumni Achievement Award (1968), Honorary Doctor of Science conferred by his alma mater (1969), and appointment as Alumni Representative on the Board of Trustees (1970). In addition to numerous articles, he authored or co-authored six books in biochemistry. After retirement in 1966, he accepted a post as Research Planning Officer at the National Cancer Institute.

Aaron Capper won top honors in this class for highest average in the entire curriculum as well as the surgery prize. As a scholarly clinically oriented member of the Pediatric Staff for many years, he advanced to Professor of Clinical Pediatrics. He was the author of a complete book of pediatrics which unfortunately was never published.

Oliver Spurgeon English, of Maine, another honor graduate, went on to outstanding prominence in the field of psychiatry. He wrote a book on psychoanalytic psychiatry as well as another on psychosomatic disorders, in which fields he became recognized as authoritative. For many years he served as Chairman of Psychiatry at Temple University School of Medicine. He represented his class with a talk at its 50th reunion in 1974. He remained very active in the professional societies of his field as well as other academic circles well beyond the usual retirement years.

Dale Woods Garber spent his life as a devoted and compassionate general practitioner of medicine at the community level. He became a major benefactor to his alma mater in a bequest, following his death in 1981, which endowed a Chair in Family Medicine in Dr. and Mrs. Garber's name.

CLASS OF **1924**

Altemus, Leard Reed, PA
Anderson, Evon Lucian, OR
Androsky, Bernard Stanley, PA
Arrasmith, Thomas Milton, Jr., NC

Bacon, Lewis Heisler, DE
Baluta, Victor John, PA
Baxter, Oscar Dixon, NC
Bitner, Charles Hilaire, PA

Boudreau, William Joseph, MA
Brennan, Charles Lewis S., NJ
Brindamour, Jean Louis E., MA
Brodkin, Henry Andrew, NJ
Burns, John Joseph, PA
Cantarow, Abraham, CT
Capper, Aaron, DC
Carlet, Louis Anthony, PA
Carney, Francis Thomas, PA
Chandlee, Benjamin Herbert, PA
Cloud, Milton Harlan, PA
Cooper, Thomas Franklin, MO

Corrigan, Harry Bernard, IA
Costner, Walter Vance, NC
Curran, Edwin Russell, CT
Cush, Thomas James, PA
Dalton, Simon Eugene, Jr., UT
Davila, Jose Antonio, PUERTO RICO
DeRosa, Sylvester Frank, CT
Dininger, William Straughn, OH
Drake, Paul Frederick, NJ
Dusinberre, Robert K. Y., NY
Duster, Amil Martin, PA
English, O. Spurgeon, ME

Fig. 230. Thompson Annex, dedicated October 30, 1924, at site of original 1877 Hospital.

Faries, George Bonnell, PA
Feher, Ladislas A. M., NJ
Feinberg, Albert Robins, PA
Fernandez-Lopez, Mario C., PUERTO RICO
Fish, Sylvan M., PA
Frame, Ray Ira, WV
Frazier, John Wesley, Jr., NC
Friedman, Alfred William, PA
Gagliardi, Joseph Matthews, PA
Garber, Dale Woods, PA
Gibson, Jesse Merrill, VT
Gladney, James Clifford, AL
Haas, Albert Carl, PA
Headings, Donald Moore, PA
Hendricks, Francis Royal, WA
Hess, Joseph Carbaugh, PA
Hickey, Francis Solano, PA
Hill, Edward Roland, CT
Holm, Alf Justin, IL
Houston, Vernon Frederick, UT
Hudacek, Albert Andrew, PA
Hughes, Vincent C., NY
Jacobs, Donald Ray, PA
Jarka, Casimir Joseph, PA
John, Brinley, WV
Johnson, Walter Frederick, CT
Jubelirer, Isaac Harold, PA
Judge, Francis Patrick, PA
Jumblatt, Albert Fuad, PA
Katz, Harry Kolman, PA
Kauffman, Lyman Greenleaf, OH
King, Alden P., NJ
Kuldoshes, John Patrick, NJ

Lape, Irwin Samuel, PA
Larkin, Thomas Edward J., NY
LeFavor, Dean Hart, OH
Leivy, Frank Edward, NJ
Levin, Israel, PA
Lewis, Arthur Kenneth, PA
Lippy, George Dewey, MD
Markowitz, Harry, PA
Mazaleski, Stanley Charles, PA
McDonald, Lester Bowman, PA
Mench, John Rishel, PA
Moore, Merle Wayland, OR
Moriarty, John Francis, MA
Nale, Thomas William, Jr., WV
Noble, Ellis Leo, OH
Olsen, Norman Alma, UT
Orris, John Andrew, MO
Paluso, Arthur Albert, PA
Parent, John Wilfrid, ME
Paul, Artie Blair, OR
Perry, Frank Leslie, NC
Peter, Alexander Monroe, PA
Phillips, Earl S., WV
Range, Irving, NY
Riggins, Hazel McLeod, NC
Ritchie, DeVere, PA
Roark, Jesse Lawrence, MS
Rogers, George Gaillard, NJ
Romano, Anthony, RI
Rose, David, PA
Rosenfeld, Maurice Harry, PA
Rothenberger, Marvin K., PA
Rourk, William Asbury, Jr., NC
Rubin, Harry, PA
Rudisill, Hillyer, Jr., GA
Russo, Joseph Romeo, DE
Sala-Diaz, Miguel E., PUERTO RICO
Savage, Nephi Henry, UT
Sawyer, Blackwell, NC
Scherma, Angelo Salvatore, NY
Schlachter, Frank, PA
Schwartz, Henry Clay, PA
Scott, Parry Mason, WV
Scott, Samuel Gerald, NJ
Sell, Byron Monroe, PA
Shapiro, Samuel S., PA
Shinabery, Lawerence, OH
Shrom, Howard Kenneth, MI
Silverman, Maurice, PA
Silvis, John Steele, Jr., PA
Skurkay, John Bernard, PA
Slagle, William Lister, OH
Smith, James Willard, OH
Snow, William J., UT

Fig. 231. Abraham Cantarow (JMC, '24), Chairman of Biochemistry (1945-66).

1924

Solo, David Howard, PA
Spagna, Francis, PA
Spikes, Norman Owen, NC
Stadulis, I. Martin, PA
Stein, David, PA
Steinberg, William, NJ
Stern, Samuel Molver, PA
Stewart, Walter King, OH
Streker, Edward T., RI
Strittmatter, Isidor Thomas, PA
Subin, Harry, NJ
Szlachetka, Vincent Edward, PA
Taylor, Claude L., ID

Thomas, George Clair, PA
Thornton, John Lemuel, VA
Tonrey, Francis G., PA
Toth, George, PA
Traugh, John Calvin, PA
Truscott, David Walton, PA
Wallace, Ray B., PA
Warner, Harold Ritter, PA
Weber, Henry Meyer, MD
Wharton, Ray H., WV
Wilson, Lawrence Addison, NC
Wilson, William Clarence, SC
Zemp, Francis Eugene, SC

New (Third) Clinical Amphitheater ("pit"), Thompson Annex.

This was the last year that Mr. William Potter, President of the Board of Trustees for 30 years, would confer the degrees. A great benefactor to Jefferson with his time and means, he died the following Spring from a ruptured appendix. His magnificent portrait is on permanent display in the Board room of the Scott Library/Administration building (Fig. 232).

Samuel Bellett, after completing his internship, joined the staff of the newly formed Division of Cardiology of the Philadelphia General Hospital in which he rose to become the Chief. His research investigations in this field resulted in 275 published papers and three editions of his authoritative textbook, *Clinical Disorders of the Heart Beat*. His later researches dealt with tobacco, caffeine and diet in relation to heart disease and the development of electronic devices for study of the heart.

Nine other members of this class, most of whom were honor graduates, went on to serve in various Departments of the Jefferson Faculty. These included Alfred E. Brunswick in Surgery, Abraham Cohen in Rheumatology, John H. Dugger and Charles I. Lintgen in Obstetrics/Gynecology, Jacob Hoffman in Gynecologic Endocri-

Fig. 232.   Portrait of Mr. William Potter, President of the Board of Trustees for 30 years, responsible for change to non-profit status of Jefferson Medical College in 1895.

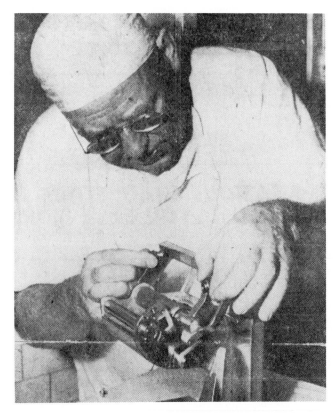

Fig. 233.   John D. Reese (JMC, '25) with his invention of the Reese Dermatome.

nology, Gulden M. Mackmull in Preventive Medicine, John D. Reese in Plastic Surgery (inventor of the Reese dermatome, (Fig. 233), Robert H. Robertson in Operative Surgery, and Clyde M. Spangler in Obstetrics/Gynecology.

The addition of 142 graduates in this class brought the grand total of Alumni to 14,625. The sophomore class of this year is depicted in Figure 234.

Fig. 234.   Sophomore class outside of the Daniel Baugh Institute (1925).

1925

Diebel, Alfred Hoffman, PA
Donoghue, John Joseph, PA
Dorris, Thomas Raymond, PA
Dougherty, Russell James, NJ
Dugger, John Halbert, TN
Evans, Winborne Dewey, NC
Faulkner, George Edward, IL
Findlay, Robert Tower, MA
Finnerty, William Joseph, PA
Flanders, Elwood Phares, PA
Fluegel, Gerald N., PA
Froggatt, John Wesley, WV
Goff, Harry Louis, PA
Gombar, Emil Frank, PA
Hadley, Carl M., CA
Haines, Harlan Fisher, DE
Hanlon, Frank Robert, PA
Harrell, William Horace, NC
Hartman, Luther Monroe, PA
Harvey, Dean Alexander, UT
Heckman, George Bowers, PA
Hepner, Herman S., OH
Hoffman, Jacob, PA
Hummel, Merwin Lester, NJ
Hurwitz, Nathaniel, PA
Jodzis, Frank Joseph, PA
Johnson, Alf Cornelius, ND
Kelly, Herbert T., NC
Kessel, Russel, WV
Kielty, John Thomas, PA
Kleinbart, Morris, PA
Lecklitner, Paul R., IN
LeFever, Harry Everett, OH
Lilla, Robert Stephen, MA
Lintgen, Isidor Charles, IA
Little, Lonnie M., NC
Mackmull, M. Gulden, OH
Mather, Clayton Black, PA
McBride, Thomas Elliott, MO
McFadden, Patrick John, PA
McNeal, Samuel W., PA
Millberg, William, OH
Miller, Horace G., NE
Mitchell, James Aloysius, NJ
Moore, D. Forrest, NC
Morosini, Charles Joseph, PA
Morrison, Archibald, PA
Mountain, Walter S., Jr., PA
Moyer, George Alfred F., PA
Murray, Roger, DE
Nelson, Lyle Milton, Jr., MO
Novicki, Zenon Francis, MA
Noyes, Franklin L., UT
Nunn, Leslie L., OR

O'Brien, David William, PA
O'Brien, Michael Gerald, PA
Pearah, Jeremiah Baba, IL
Pegau, Paul McDowell, VA
Perri, Angelo Marco, PA
Pietaro, Michael James, NY
Poland, George Alec, OH
Poole, Ernest Frederick, MD
Porterfield, Hubert Lester, MD
Purificato, Alfred Thomas, NY
Radom, Myron M., CT
Reese, John Davies, PA
Robertson, Robert Hugh, PA
Roddy, Henry Justin, Jr., PA
Roseman, Milo A. J., NC
Rosenblatt, Harold S., PA
Rossien, Ahbrohm Xerxes, PA
Saenz-Cuadra, Rafael, NICARAGUA
Sanford, Karl Thomas, NY
Schaffner, Meade Daniel, PA
Schisler, Milton Moody, NJ
Schooley, Sherman Richards, PA
Schultz, Robert Richie, PA
Scofield, Paul Drury, OH
Scruggs, William Joseph, NC
Senor, Samuel Earl, MO
Shafer, Albert Henry, PA
Shaffer, Foster Clarke, PA
Shapiro, A. Alver, NJ
Shapiro, Sigmond Joseph, PA
Shore, Ernest Luke, WV
Slonimsky, I. Paul, PA
Slotkin, Herman Bennett, PA
Spangler, Clyde Mitchell, PA
Speacht, Clarence Franklin, PA
Stark, Jesse D., NY
Stec, Michael John, PA
Stedge, Rodney Luther, PA
Stewart, Irving Jaggard, NJ
Stillman, Eugene Hitch, PA
Stillwell, Harry Clifford, NC
Stolfo, Michael, PA
Swett, Chester Parker, OH
Trevaskis, John Davis, PA
Vaccaro, Philip F., PA
VerNooy, Stewart Anderson, NY
Walen, Jacob, PA
Walsh, James A., PA
Weaver, Harold Johnson, NC
Weaver, William Abbott, PA
Whalen, Edward William, PA
White, Roscoe Rostin, WV
Wilkinson, Ralph W. E., PA
Wise, Emery D., WV

At Commencement for the 144 graduates, the address *Consecratio Medici* (Devotion of the Doctor) was delivered by the distinguished Harvard Professor of Surgery, Dr. Harvey C. Cushing, who was a close associate of Professor Thomas McCrae during their early careers at Johns Hopkins School of Medicine.

The Jefferson Society for Clinical Investigation was organized in this year with eleven founders and thirty charter members from the faculty. Dr. Harold W. Jones was the first President and Dr. Thaddeus L. Montgomery the Vice President. Most of these participants achieved prominence in Academic Medicine.

John B. Montgomery's lifelong association with Jefferson began with his internship, followed by association with Professor Brooke M. Anspach. This began his advancement in the Department of Gynecology leading to Co-Chairmanship of Obstetrics and Gynecology in 1955 (Fig. 235). He became Chairman in 1961. He was a popular teacher and also served as President of the Philadelphia Obstetrical Society as well as a founding member of the American College of Obstetricians and Gynecologists. Upon retirement from the Chairmanship in 1965 he became Chief of the Department of Obstetrics and Gynecology at Methodist Hospital. He was President of the Alumni Association in 1961 and his portrait was presented to the College in 1965. In 1951 he was awarded the honorary degree of Doctor of Science by his alma mater, Juniata College, where he was also a trustee. In 1972 Jefferson honored him with the degree of Doctor of Pedagogy and he received its Alumni Achievement award in 1979.

Theodore R. Fetter, student leader and editor of the year book, served his internship at Jefferson and was then appointed to the staff of genitourinary surgery. He became assistant to Professor Loux and later to Professor Stellwagen. Under Professor Davis he advanced rapidly and absorbed the new teachings leading to an extensive practice. In 1951 he succeeded Dr. Davis as Chairman of Urology. Dr. Fetter was a forceful person, technically skilled, and a frequent contributor to medical literature. He served as President of the Alumni Association in 1950 and of the Philadelphia County Medical Society, the Pennsylvania State Medical Society, and the Mid-Atlantic Section of the American Urological Association. Lebanon Valley College honored him with the degree of Doctor of Science (Fig. 236).

Harold L. Stewart, Senior Class President and winner of the Surgery Prize, pursued post-graduate study at the United States Army Medical School. He returned to Jefferson as a research fellow in 1929 and advanced in the Department of Pathology until he joined a new research group at Harvard University in 1937 which in

Fig. 235. John B. Montgomery (JMC, '26), Chairman of Obstetrics and Gynecology (1961-65).

1939 moved to Bethesda, Maryland as the nucleus of the National Cancer Institute. In 1954 he became Chief of the Department of Pathological Anatomy of the Clinical Center of the National Institutes of Health. He served as a member of the National Research Council and on the World Health Organization Advisory Panel on Cancer. Dr. Stewart was also President of the American Society for Cancer Research, the American Society for Experimental Pathology, Society of Pathologists, and the International Council of Societies of Pathologists. In 1966 he received the Jefferson Alumni Achievement Award (Fig. 237).

Leandro M. Tocantins, a native of Brazil, became an internationally recognized hematologist. Beginning in 1930 as J. Ewing Mears Fellow, his clinical and research skills were quickly ap-

parent and he advanced in the Department of Medicine to Director of the Cardeza Foundation for Hematologic Research in 1954. In 1959 he achieved the position of Cardeza Professor of Clinical Medicine and Hematology. He was Vice-President of the International Society of Hematology and President (1956/57) of the National Blood Club while also doing extensive writing, speaking and editing (Fig. 238). The portrait of Dr. Tocantins was presented to the College in the Tocantins Memorial Library of the Charlotte Drake Cardeza Foundation in 1964.

George C. Griffith's evolving career was heralded by his winning the Alumni Prize at graduation. His progress in academic medicine was rapid and distinguished, leading to his Professorship of Medicine, School of Medicine, Uni-

Fig. 236. Theodore R. Fetter (JMC, '26), Chairman of Urology (1951-67).

Fig. 237. Harold L. Stewart (JMC, '26), prominent in cancer research.

versity of Southern California. A master clinician and teacher, he became one of the nation's leading cardiologists. He held many important posts, including Presidency of the American College of Cardiology and the American Therapeutic Society. He received numerous awards including the Cummings Humanitarian Award for Distinguished Teaching, Merit Awards from Los Angeles County and California Heart Associations and the Gold Heart Award from the American Heart Association. In 1969 he received the Jefferson Alumni Achievement Award (Fig. 239).

Pascal F. Lucchesi, following internship at the Philadelphia General Hospital, went on to the Philadelphia Hospital for Contagious Diseases, soon becoming Medical Director. During World War II he advanced in multinational public health posts as Lieutenant Colonel in the United States Army and was cited for meritorious service. In 1946 he was appointed Medical Director of the Philadelphia General Hospital and in 1952 he accepted the post of administrator of the newly merged Albert Einstein Medical Center. He was President of the Hospital Association of Pennsylvania and of the Philadelphia County Medical Society. From 1949 to 1960 he was Professor and Head of the Section of Public Health and Preventive Medicine at Hahnemann Medical College. He received the Strittmatter Award in 1947 and a Doctor of Science degree from LaSalle College in 1954.

Arno E. Town pursued training in Ophthalmology, receiving an M.Sc. degree in Ophthalmology at Graduate School of Medicine of the University of Pennsylvania in 1929, and served a residency at Bellevue Hospital in New York. He was then appointed to several New York hospitals advancing to Acting Chief of Ophthal-

Fig. 238. Leandro M. Tocantins (JMC, '26), internationally recognized hematologist.

Fig. 239. George C. Griffith (JMC, '26), one of the nation's leading cardiologists.

mology at Bellevue and Acting Head of the Department at New York University College of Medicine. After wartime Naval service he returned to New York but in 1948 he was appointed Professor and Chairman of Ophthalmology at Jefferson where he established a research program in his specialty allied with the Department of Physiology (Fig. 240).

Fig. 240. Arno E. Town (JMC, '26), Chairman of Ophthalmology (1948-56).

Carroll R. Mullen followed his internship at the Philadelphia General Hospital with direct appointment to its ophthalmology staff, advancing to its chief in 1936. He became associated with Jefferson and Wills Eye Hospitals and advanced in the latter to become Executive Surgeon in 1949. A popular and energetic person, he was elected President of the Jefferson Alumni Association in 1953 and succeeded classmate Arno Town as Chairman and Professor of Ophthalmology at Jefferson in 1956. In 1959 he was elected to the Board of City Trusts. He was also consultant to numerous regional hospitals (Fig. 241).

John T. Eads, following Jefferson internship, became associated with Dr. Martin E. Rehfuss in the organization of the Gastrointestinal Clinic. He advanced to Assistant Professor of Medicine. He was consultant to numerous hospitals and during World War II served as Commander in the United States Navy Medical Corps.

Pyn Noyes Muangman returned to his native Thailand (Siam) to teach medicine and establish the first Radiology Department there. He served as Under Secretary of Health in the Ministry of Public Health from 1958 to 1960. In 1961 he was awarded the degree of Doctor of Science by Grinnell College and the Doctor of Laws by Jefferson Medical College.

Kelvin A. Kaspar became widely known for tear duct surgery on which he published numerous articles. He became affiliated with several Philadelphia hospitals and went on to Chief of Otolaryngology at Wills Eye Hospital. His Jefferson association was followed by advancement to Clinical Professor of Otolaryngology.

CLASS OF 1926

Atkinson, Harold C., GA
Baker, Eugene Manigault, Jr., GA
Baker, George Iverson, TN
Baker, John Cushing, PA
Baldauf, Leonard Clair, PA
Barr, William Bryce, PA
Beckley, James Harold, PA
Beeghley, Jesse Wirt, WV
Belknap, Harold Porter, NY
Bloemendaal, Gerrit J., SD
Bloom, D. George, PA
Brooks, David Marshall, PA
Buechele, Modestus William, PA
Carlyle, John Bethune, NC

Charles, Roland Keith, Jr., SC
Chritzman, Henry G., PA
Ciliberti, Frank John, Jr., NJ
Clair, Philip S., PA
Cleland, J. Wallace, PA
Cohen, Morton Reese, PA
Conly, Leonard Hudson, NY
Corrin, Kenneth Matthew, CO
Crowl, Edward Cleaver, PA
Davis, Adrian Eugene, OH
Davis, Philip B., NC
Doster, James Thomas, Jr., AL
Drake, Ralph L., KS
Dwyer, Charles Raymond, PA

Eads, John Trimble, IL
Ericson, Russell Waldo, MN
Fahrney, Henry Laurence, MD
Fetter, Theodore Roosevelt, PA
Fox, William, NY
Franco-Guerra, Rodrigo, PERU
Fresoli, Michael, PA
Gemmill, Norman Hamilton, PA
George, Melbourne E. W., MO
Glinsky, George Clement, PA
Glover, Lewis Pellman, PA
Goldman, Sidney Sanders, PA
Goodwin, Harold Isaac, UT
Gordon, John Wood, Jr., PA
Griffith, George Cupp, PA
Grone, Robert Yocum, PA
Gross, Harry, NY
Grove, Bruce A., PA
Gusman, Harry Arnold, OH
Hackler, Robert Hardin, Jr., NC
Hamner, Benjamin Harold, Jr., PA
Hannon, James Augustus, PA

Harwitz, Morris, DE
Hester, William Shepherd, NC
Hirschfield, Bernard, A., NJ
Holt, William Preston, Jr., NC
Hopkins, Maurice Albert, CA
Humphrey, Isaac, PA
Hyman, Isaac Charles, NJ
Jackson, Thomas, Jr., PA
Johnson, Joseph Lewis, NC
Jones, Emmett Lee, Jr., MD
Kasper, Kelvin A., MN
Kinsey, Irwin Zepp, PA
Kirk, Marvin Edward, CA
Kline, Luther Henry, PA
Langston, William C., MO
Lentz, Edmund Tutay, PA
Linard, Donald Herbert, OH
Lorry, Ralph W., PA
Lucchesi, Pascal Francis, PA
Luckey, Paul David, WV
Mainzer, Francis S., PA
Mainzer, Peter George, PA
Manley, John Gerard, PA
Marcil, George Edward, MA
Marshall, Louis Richard, OH
Martin, John Allen, PA
Matheson, Robert Arthur, Jr., NC
McDermott, Vincent Thomas, NJ
McDonald, Edward Paul, NY
McGeary, Francis J., PA
Meikle, Thomas Harry, PA
Menard, Oliver Joseph, NY
Mengel, Sterling Frederic, PA
Mensch, Harvey George, PA
Miller, Armand Jones, PA
Miller, Wilbur Hobson, PA
Montgomery, John Barrick, PA
Moore, Neal Richard, MI
Mowry, Harry Dale, PA
Muangman, Pyn Noyes, SIAM
Mullen, Carroll Richard, NE
Murdock, John Robinson, UT
Murphy, Charles Michael, AL
Nesbit, William Wesley, PA
Nichols, Harold, PA
Oesau, Harold Thomas, CT
Parent, Fernand Noel, PA
Parris, Herman Morris, PA
Pick, Theodore, NY
Pratt, Gerald Edward, NE
Purcell, James Bernard, PA
Pyles, John Wylie, WV
Rankin, Charles Albert, PA
Rappaccioli, Buenaventura, NICARAGUA

Fig. 241.   Carroll R. Mullen (JMC, '26), Chairman of Ophthalmology (1956-61).

Redland, Arthur John, PA
Reed, Thomas Godfrey, WV
Richards, Thomas, PA
Rivers, Thurston Donnell, AL
Robinson, Joseph LeRoi, UT
Roderer, Louis J. F., PA
Roeder, Paul Herbert, PA
Rosenberg, Louis, NJ
Rowe, Daniel Mannix, ME
Rush, George Blackmore, WV
Sandler, Isadore Lewis, DC
Schultz, William Clyde, Jr., PA
Shapiro, Jacob, DE
Shipps, Hammell Pierce, NJ
Smith, Richard Mays, TX
Snyder, Harry Minis, PA
Sterner, Robert Fulton, PA
Stewart, Harold L., PA
Stomberg, Dwight William, MN
Stone, Alvord Lovell, FL

Stubenrauch, Walter Herman, NJ
Sumner, Howard Leon, NC
Sussman, Walter, NY
Swindell, Orval Fisher, MO
Tate, James H., PA
Thomas, Carlyle Milton, PA
Thomas, Edward L. C., PA
Tocantins, Leandro Maues, BRAZIL
Touhey, J. Manning, PA
Town, Arno Emerson, FL
Trexler, Clifford Hertzog, PA
Ulloa, Angel Augusto, HONDURAS
Uttal, Joseph, NY
Vesell, Morton, NY
Watkins, Joseph Conrad, Jr., NC
Weimann, Max Ludwig, NJ
White, Joseph William, PA
Winston, Julius, PA
Wolfrom, Carlos Eugene, NY
Young, James L., SC

Entrance to Thompson Annex, 1020 Sansom Street.

1926

At the Commencement of June 3, in the Academy of Music, the honorary degree of Doctor of Science was awarded by Board President, Mr. Alba B. Johnson, to Francis Xavier Dercum, Emeritus Professor of Nervous and Mental Diseases at Jefferson Medical College. Degrees were awarded to 138 graduates.

John Heysham Gibbon, Jr. was destined to become world-renowned for his perfection of the heart-lung machine and successful performance of the first intracardiac operation with its aid on May 6, 1953 (Fig. 242). He was a fifth generation physician whose father (JMC, 1891, Fig. 125) was a Professor of Surgery at Jefferson from 1907 to 1931. Dr. Gibbon went on to become the third

Samuel D. Gross Professor of Surgery (1956-67) and to receive innumerable honors both at home and abroad. In addition to a distinguished military career in World War II, he was active in matters relating to teaching, training, research, writing and editing, public health, community affairs, and presidency of many professional organizations. His name was engraved on Jefferson's Winged Ox Column; he served as President of the Alumni Association in 1960; the Class of 1963 presented his portrait to the College; and a room in the Kellow Conference Area was named in his honor in 1979 (Fig. 243).

Howard Holt Bradshaw, of Tennessee, became a pioneer in thoracic surgery (Fig. 244). He pub-

Fig. 242. John H. Gibbon, Jr. (JMC, '27) with his heart-lung machine.

Fig. 243. John H. Gibbon, Jr. (JMC, '27), Samuel D. Gross Professor of Surgery (1956-67).

lished numerous papers pertaining to basic research in anesthesia and pulmonary physiology. After special training in Boston, he activated the thoracic surgical service at Jefferson's Pine Street Hospital, maintained an active role in clinical thoracic surgery at Jefferson Hospital, and lectured to the medical students. In 1940 his international reputation led to an invitation to the Bowman Gray School of Medicine as Professor of Surgery, where he continued to contribute to the development of thoracic surgery.

Robert Bruce Nye, as a bright youthful clinician in Jefferson's Department of Medicine, became Director of the Curtis Clinic at its opening in 1931. His success in administrative duties led to his appointment to succeed Dr. Henry K. Mohler as Director of Jefferson Hospital in 1938 when the latter became Dean. Dr. Nye's tenure was interrupted by World War II in which he served as a Lieutenant Colonel with Jefferson's 38th General Hospital (1941-45). He returned to his teaching post in the Department of Medicine in 1946 and became Assistant Dean in 1951 and Associate Dean in 1960. Until his sudden death in 1966 he was intimately involved with Jefferson Medical College admissions (Fig. 245).

Fig. 244. Howard H. Bradshaw (JMC, '27), pioneer in thoracic surgery and research.

Fig. 245. Robert B. Nye (JMC, '27), Director of Jefferson Hospital and Assistant Dean.

1927

Samuel M. Dodek became Professor of Clinical Obstetrics/Gynecology at George Washington School of Medicine. As Professor Emeritus his portrait was presented to the library of the School of Health Sciences at George Washington University in 1976.

Members of this class who subsequently taught at Jefferson were: David Raymond Mer-anze in Bacteriology, William Taylor Hunt, Jr. in Ophthalmology, John Cornelius McNerney in Neurosurgery, Richard Manges Smith in Roent-genology, and Herbert Andrew Widing in Surgery. Orville Carrier King became a well known Philadelphia surgeon and Chief of Surgery at the Pennsylvania Hospital.

CLASS OF 1927

Allen, Robert E., PA
Alley, Ralph Martin, ID
Anderson, Claude, FL
Bache, William, Jr., PA
Bauer, Henry Paul, PA
Beckley, Daniel William, PA
Bell, Benjamin Tertius, PA
Berlin, Allison Janis, PA
Bertolet, Charles Boileau, PA
Bigelow, Samuel Irvin, PA
Bloemendaal, Dirk Cornelius, SD
Bonner, William Richard, PA
Bowman, James E., PA
Boylan, Peter Clement, CT
Boyle, Peter Leo, IL
Bradshaw, Howard Holt, TN
Brophy, John Robert, CANADA
Brown, Kermit English, NC
Bryant, Frank Leytze, IA
Callahan, Peter Alfonso, PA
Canby, Joseph Edward, PA
Carter, Thomas Jerrell, KS
Cippes, Isaac Benjamin, PA
Conrad, Robert Parlett, MD
Crawford, Lewis Gething, PA
Crothers, W. Gifford, MD
Cunningham, George Norman, WV
Dankmyer, Edward Charles, PA
Derr, Raymond Kiesling, PA
Diehl, William Harold, IN
Dinge, Ferdinand Charles, NJ
Dinnison, Charles Clarence, NJ
Dodek, Samuel Mayer, DC
Dougherty, Joseph Francis, PA
Elicker, Charles Robert, NJ
Epstein, Isadore Leslie, PA
Etheridge, Charles Henry, PA
Fischl, Arthur Allyn, NY
Fisher, Luther Irvin, PA
Fockler, Hubert Haymond, WV
Fooks, Carleton Cannon, NJ
Fox, William F., PA

Foxe, Arthur Norman, NY
Gasteiger, Ernest Sipe, PA
Gelpi, William Rosario, PUERTO RICO
George, Arnold Phillips, MA
Gibbon, John Heysham, Jr., PA
Gibson, Arnold L., PA
Gifford, Roy William, PA
Glenn, Herbert Ross, PA
Green, Joseph Sidney, PA
Griffith, Jo Crownover, PA
Hanlon, Edmund Francis, PA
Hannon, John W. G., PA
Hawkins, William Raymond, RI
Heise, Herbert vonRohr, MN
Hogsett, Robert Fuller, PA
Hughes, Brady Alexander, MS
Hunt, William T., Jr., PA
Imhoff, Robert Ernst, NJ
Imler, Daniel Canning, PA
King, Edward Sandling, NC
King, Orville Carrier, PA
Klein, Isadore, CT
Kneibert, Fred Louis, MO
Koppisch de Cardona, Enrique, PUERTO RICO
Landau, James Hard, PA
Leventhal, Gottlieb Samuel, NY
Levi, Leo Meyer, OH
Logan, Thomas Megowan, PA
Lucas, Robert Sloan, PA
Magrath, Joseph Leo, PA
Matter, Ralph P., PA
McGourty, David Philip, CT
McMahon, James Jerome, PA
McMahon, James Joseph, PA
McNerney, John C., CT
Meranze, David Raymond, PA
Miceli, Silvio, PA
Michelson, Joseph Percy, NY
Milham, Claude Gilbert, Jr., NC
Miller, Fred John, PA
Mitchell, Gurney Talmage, NC
Mobilio, Joseph A., PA

Moore, John Burleson, Jr., TX
Morris, Truman Nicholas, AR
Nicodemus, Roy Elvin, PA
Noyes, Kenneth Eugene, UT
Nye, Robert Bruce, NC
Ogden, Andrew Edman, OH
Pell, Edward N., Jr., WV
Phillips, John D., PA
Promin, David, PA
Purnell, John Straw, PA
Purpura, Anthony J., WV
Quinn, Everett Roy, MO
Ralph, Leland Paul, WI
Ringawa, Peter E., PA
Robart, Wilbur C., OH
Ross, Donald Price, NC
Ross, Thomas Wallace, NC
Ruth, Chauncey Elwood, PA
Scicchitano, Romualdo Riccardo, PA
Seltzer, Mitchell, TX
Shanno, Ralph Leopold, PA
Smith, Richard Manges, PA
Sneddon, Alexander Hamilton, OH
Snyder, Howard Errol, KS
Somers, Myer, VA
Sparks, Samuel M., PA
Stambaugh, Ervin Luther, PA

Stein, Bernard Benjamin, PA
Stephenson, John Edward, WV
Surkosky, John Joseph, PA
Sweterlitsch, Louis Henry, PA
Thomas, Irving Oakley, PA
Tice, Walter Thomas, NC
Tomlinson, J. Wesley, PA
Tracy, Henry Miron, PA
Turchik, Frank, CT
Tushim, John Andrew, PA
Van Sciver, Cecil B., NJ
Vance, John Clair, PA
Wall, James H., SC
Walsh, William Joseph, Jr., PA
Weidenmier, Carl Henry, OH
Weiler, Howard George, WV
Weiss, Edward Hervey, PA
Whalen, John Francis, PA
Whims, Clarence Bernard, NC
Whitehouse, Alfred Edmund, Jr., NJ
Widing, Herbert Andrew, PA
Witt, Eric William, OR
Yarbrough, James Elmo, NC
Yoshida, Yasohichi, JAPAN
Zehner, George D., PA
Zeller, Raymond Bryant, MS
Zimskind, Joshua Norman, NJ

The Commencement was held on June 1 for 144 graduates at which time the Address was delivered by Henry A. Christian, M.D., Hersey Professor of Medicine at Harvard, on "The Lure of Medicine." He was awarded an honorary degree of Doctor of Science by the President of the Board, Mr. Alba B. Johnson.

In this illustrious class, no one would exceed Jo Ono, of Japan, in world acclaim (Fig. 246). He came to the United States at the age of 16 and worked his way through high school, Lafayette College, and Jefferson Medical College. After internship at Jefferson, he took special training in diseases of the chest and continued with the study of bronchoesophagology under Professor Louis H. Clerf (JMC, '12, Fig. 183) from 1932 to 1934. He then returned to Tokyo where he was instrumental in organizing the Japanese Bronchoesophagological Society and the International Federation of Oto-Rhino-Laryngological Societies in which he served as Chairman from 1965 to 1973. He was instrumental in organizing the Japan Chapter and became Regent of the American College of Chest Physicians. He also organized the Society for Promotion of International Otolaryngology in which he held the position of Director for a number of years. An Official Delegate of Japan to meetings in foreign countries 15 times, an officer in 15 medical societies, author of eight books and at least 100 medical papers, he was a recipient of the Alumni Achievement Award in 1976.

Robert Archibald Matthews, of Pennsylvania, won four prizes at graduation. After internship (1930) he was appointed Instructor in Nervous and Mental Diseases at Jefferson, which marked the beginning of a distinguished career in psychiatry. During the next 20 years he rose to Clinical Professor of Psychiatry and served as Acting Head of the Department during World War II. In 1950 he accepted the position of Head of Psychiatry and Neurology at the Louisiana State University School of Medicine. In 1956 he returned to Jefferson as Chairman of Psychiatry as well as the first Commissioner of Mental Health for the State of Pennsylvania (Fig. 247). He also became the first Chairman of a clinical department to be fully salaried by the institution. At the height of his career as teacher, author, commissioner and as lecturer to numerous professional and lay groups, he was tragically killed in an automobile accident in 1961 at the age of 58.

David Mendel Farrell spent his entire professional career at Jefferson as a model clinician and teacher in which he rose to the rank of Professor of Obstetrics and Gynecology. He pioneered in a method to obtain pre-natal electrocardiograms.

Guy Maurice Nelson developed an early interest in gastroenterology at Jefferson and participated with Dr. Martin E. Rehfuss in research in this specialty. Together in 1935 they co-au-

Fig. 246. Jo Ono (JMC, '28), internationally renowned otolaryngologist and bronchoesophagologist.

thored a book on *The Medical Treatment of Gall-bladder Disease*. Dr. Nelson was prominent as a clinician and teacher in the Department of Medicine for many years (Fig. 248).

Other members of this class who served on the Jefferson Faculty were Robert Smith Book-hammer in Psychiatry, Mahlon Carlton Hine-baugh in Obstetrics, and William Joseph Tourish in Surgery. Ignatius Stanley Hneleski went on to become Medical Director of the Philadelphia General Hospital for many years.

CLASS OF 1928

Angel, Edgar, NC
Applestein, Robert, NJ
Auslander, Milton Manuel, PA
Bailey, Desmond Mark, PA
Baker, Leslie Earl, PA
Barr, John Franklin, MO
Beaumont, Fred Higgins, IA
Benner, Norman Ray, PA
Blanchard, Charles Lester, NJ
Bohlender, John Frederick, PA
Bolman, Harold Robert, UT
Bookhammer, Robert S., PA

Bowersox, Clarence Allen, PA
Boyle, James William, PA
Bray, Russell Stanton, RI
Briglia, Frank Joseph, PA
Brock, Ernest, PA
Burnett, George Warren, PA
Carroll, Walter James E., MA
Cashman, William M., PA
Cason, William Martin, GA
Chenowith, Robert F., MD
Clay, Harry A., PA
Collett, Harry Downing, PA
Corpening, Flave Hart, NC
Custer, Richard Philip, PA
Daugherty, John Arthur, PA
Davidson, Henry A., NJ
Deardorff, Charles Leedom, PA
DeWitt, Virgil Barzillai, NY
Duffy, Thomas Ambrose, PA
Earp, Halburt Hale, MO
Elias, Elmer John, NJ
Ellrich, David L., CT
Eschbach, Joseph William, PA
Farrell, David Mendel, VA
Fetter, E. Minton, NC
Fliegel, William Milton, PA
Gallagher, Charles Michael, PA
Gates, Lionel, PA
George, Forney Philip, PA
Givhan, Edgar Gilmore, Jr., AL
Gleitz, Allen August, PA
Goldstein, Samuel, NJ
Grundfast, Theodore Harvey, NY
Haire, Robert Donnell, Jr., MO
Hatch, Lerleen Clement, ID
Hedde, Eugene Lee, IN
Hermanutz, William Henry, PA
High, Carl Milton, PA
Hinebaugh, Mahlon Carleton, Jr., MD
Hneleski, Ignatius Stanley, NY
Hofer, Clarence John M., NJ
Hoffman, Richards Holmes, PA
Hoge, Vane Morgan, PA
Holsinger, Paul G., PA

Fig. 247. Robert A. Matthews (JMC, '28), Chairman of Psychiatry (1958-61).

Jackson, Clarence Cecil R., CANADA
Jacobson, Frank Jay, RI
Jamack, John August, PA
Johnston, David Anderson, PA
Kalett, Joseph, CT
Kalez, Marion Michael, WA
Kapp, Carl Gailard, PA
Kennedy, William McLane, NC
Kinney, Albert Girton, NJ
Knappenberger, Fred Charles, PA
Koppel, Alexander, DE
Laauwe, Harold William, NJ
Lampe, William Thomas, PA
Lauster, Carl Franz, OH
Lavell, Meyer Quintin, PA
Lazzaro, Orlando Anthony, PA
Lehman, James Alphonsus, PA
Leonard, Jacob C., Jr., NC
Levy, Charles, DE
Levy, Jacob Julius, PA

Lighthizer, Charles William, OH
Luckett, Charles Luther, IN
Lungerhausen, Carl Oscar, MI
Mancoll, Morris Max, CT
Maness, Archibald Kelly, NC
Manley, John Edward, PA
Marquand, Edgar Allen, OH
Matthews, Robert Archibald, PA
McCandless, Garrett C., PA
McCarthy, George Logan, RI
McCuskey, William Cecil D., WV
McGovern, Leonard F., PA
McIntyre, Stephen, NC
Mecca, James John, PA
Metzgar, Thomas I., PA
Metzler, Gottfried, Jr., PA
Mhley, Cornelius Michael, PA
Millard, Joseph Delcamp, PA
Millard, Oscar Benjamin, PA
Moll, Francis Keiter, PA
Moretti, John Joseph, NJ
Morgan, Philip John, PA
Murphy, Herschel Stratton, TX
Nelson, Guy Maurice, SC
Niemtzow, Frank, NJ
Ogburn, Lundie C., NC
Ono, Jo, JAPAN
Ornston, Darius Gray, PA
Osterhout, Franklin Farnham, PA
Park, George, WV
Pinner, Warren Elias, NJ
Pollock, James Kells, PA
Pons, Juan Antonio, PUERTO RICO
Pulliam, Benjamin E., NC
Purser, Thomas, Jr., MS
Rafferty, Francis Brai, CT
Ranck, John Milton, PA
Reyes de los, Joseph M., CUBA
Ringwalt, John David, PA
Roberts, Allison Hardee, FL
Rudolph, Jack Arthur, OH
Russo, Joseph, PA
Salvin, Monte, NY
Sample, Adrian Moore, FL
Scarano, Joseph Albert, PA
Schildnecht, Page Milburn, MD
Schloss, C. Kenneth, OH
Schloss, Eugene Mathias, OH
Sekerak, Albert John, NJ
Selen, Swen Gideon, PA
Shaub, A. Paul, PA
Shellman, Alexander, NY
Snyder, George A., PA
Staats, Roydice, WV

Fig. 248. Guy M. Nelson (JMC, '28), a clinician and researcher in gastroenterology.

Strauch, Henry Jacob, PA
Strause, Harold Luther, PA
Tai, En Shui, CHINA
Tarrant, James Wyatte, Jr., SC
Thomas, James Anthony, PA
Timberlake, Baxter Hall, NC
Tiracchia, Joseph, PA

Tourish, William Joseph, PA
Warren, Jacob, NJ
Weigel, Charles F. B., PA
Welcher, Howard Alfred, PA
White, William Whitney, PA
Wiley, Norman Hyde, PA
Wood, George Thomas, Jr., NC

Architect's Drawing for the new College (1929) and Curtis Clinic (1931) Buildings.

At the Commencement held at the Academy of Music on June 7, the honorary LL.D. degree was conferred upon Lawrence F. Flick, M.D. (JMC, 1879, Fig. 99) by Board President Mr. Alba B. Johnson. Dr. Flick was a pioneer in promoting measures to more effectively prevent and control pulmonary tuberculosis.

This year marked the completion of the new Medical College Building at 1025 Walnut Street, a major milestone in Jefferson's progress (Fig. 249). This replaced the 1898 Medical College Building previously located at the Northwest Corner of 10th and Walnut Streets.

Anthony Frederick DePalma, of Pennsylvania, became the James Edwards Professor and Chairman of Orthopaedics at Jefferson in 1950. He was a forceful teacher, skillful surgical technician, and prolific writer. His textbooks became classics and included: *Surgery of the Shoulder* (1950), *Diseases of the Knee* (1954), *Degenerative Changes in the Sternoclavicular and Acromioclavicular Joints in Various Decades* (1957), *The Management of Fractures*

Fig. 249.   College Building at 1025 Walnut Street under construction in 1928 (left) and completed in 1929 (right).

and Dislocations (1959), and *The Intervertebral Disc* (co-authored with Dr. Richard H. Rothman, 1970). He also edited *Clinical Orthopaedics*, a series of volumes in symposium form produced under the auspices of the Association of Bone and Joint Surgeons. The Class of 1962 presented his portrait to the College and he received the Alumni Achievement Award in 1975 (Fig. 250). The Thompson auditorium was named in his honor in 1990.

Mario Alberto Castallo, of Rhode Island, took residency training in obstetrics and gynecology in New York. He joined the Jefferson Faculty in 1933 and maintained an active practice for almost 50 years. Rising to the rank of Clinical Professor of Obstetrics and Gynecology by 1952, he authored numerous contributions to the medical literature, published more than ten books, and served as Alumni Association President in 1966. He was never seen on campus without a fresh carnation in his lapel (Fig. 251).

Sherman Alfred Eger, of Pennsylvania, took a surgical residency at the Crile Clinic, working under the influence of its founder, the elder George Crile. On his return to Philadelphia he joined Jefferson's Faculty in the Department of Surgery, rising to Clinical Professor. He was the author of many articles on a broad spectrum of surgical disorders and prepared exhibits for local and national meetings. His particular interest, which had been stimulated initially by Dr. Crile, was in surgery for hypertension by denervation of the adrenal glands (Fig. 252).

James Miller Surver, of Pennsylvania, after serving as intern and chief resident physician at Jefferson Hospital, went abroad to visit many of the outstanding clinics. On return to Jefferson's Department of Surgery, he lectured on basic principles of surgery in the sophomore year and on oncology during the junior year. For many years he conducted the weekly tumor conferences. In addition to general surgery, Dr. Surver

Fig. 250.   Anthony F. DePalma (JMC, '29), James Edwards Professor and Chairman of Orthopaedics (1950-70).

Fig. 251.   Mario A. Castallo (JMC, '29), Clinical Professor of Obstetrics and Gynecology.

356

1929

played an important role in the early phases of chest surgery at Jefferson. The senior class of 1954 dedicated its year book to him (Fig. 253).

Paul Owen Blake, of North Carolina, for more than 60 years kept his association with the Department of Surgery and rarely missed any event connected with his alma mater.

Aaron, Francis A., PA
Adams, John M., NC
Bartlett, Lester Lawson, PA
Bauer, William Andrew, PA
Baylor, Robert Stewart, Jr., PA
Bisbing, John Hoover, PA
Blake, Paul O., NC
Boines, George James, DE
Bolich, John Albert, PA
Boyer, Ivan Norman, PA
Bridges, Edward, NJ
Brown, Joseph Donald, PA
Browning, William John, II., NJ
Castallo, Mario Alberto, RI
Chambers, Paul Jones, Jr., AL

Chang, Yen Pui, HAWAII
Cohen, Louis Benjamin, PA
Cox, Ralph L., PA
Davis, Reuben, Jr., TX
DeCato, Alfred A., OH
Delicate, William Ernest, IL
DePalma, Anthony F., PA
Dieker, Howard E., NJ
Eger, Sherman Alfred, PA
Evans, Archie Paul, AL
Floyd, William R., SC
Freeman, Alton Brooks, NC
Gahan, John Winthrop, MA
Garcia-Estrada, Manuel, PUERTO RICO
Geetter, Isidore S., CT

Fig. 252. Sherman A. Eger (JMC, '29), Clinical Professor of Surgery.

Fig. 253. James M. Surver (JMC, '29) lectured on basic principles of surgery.

Gehret, Andrew Martin, PA
Goehring, Donald E., PA
Graham, Charles Macgirt, NC
Gregersen, Leo Delbert, UT
Griffith, Alexander Hamilton, II, CA
Grossman, Samuel Linn, PA
Hahn, Karl William, PA
Harrison, Milton, MD
Hart, Vincent Paul, PA
Hartley, Colin Hays, PA
Hauck, Samuel Melvin, PA
Hawes, Vernon Lee, NC
Heberling, Jacob Zern, PA
Henry, John Cotton, OH
Hess, Paul Richard, PA
Hoberman, Louis Karl, PA
Holland, Eugene Amos, WV
Hollywood, James Leonard, PA
Houston, Robert Alexander, PA
Hudson, Joseph Charles, PA
Hume, Evan Borroum, TX
Hutchinson, William James, PA
Hymovich, Leo, CT
Izenberg, David, NJ
Izlar, William H., GA
Johnson, John Samuel, NC
Johnson, Lawrence Carl, CA
Jones, Eurfryn, PA
Jordan, John Brogan, Jr., PA
Keating, John Francis, NJ
Kegaries, Donald Luther, PA
Kelley, Eugene Michael, PA
Kennedy, Finley A., SC
Kerry, Marshall, GA
Kirk, David John, PA
Kirk, Norris Jacob, PA
Kleinman, Herman, PA
Krug, Edgar S., PA
Le Winn, Edward Bernard, CT
Leahy, John Francis, NY
Li, Benjamin Luka, HAWAII
Lindsay, Thomas Edgar, PA
Majeski, Henry John, NJ
Markel, Maurice, PA
Matheson, Joe Gaddy, NC
Matternes, Lawrence A., PA
McCain, Walkup Kennard, NC
McCauley, Francis P., PA
McDade, Robert E., NC
McNair, Stirling Sharp, MS
McNicholas, Edward Thomas, PA
Merendino, Anthony Girard, NJ
Metz, Charles Oliver, MO
Meyers, Max Irving, PA
Miller, Francis Grove, MD
Miller, Frank Henry, PA

Minier, Carl Louis, NJ
Mogan, Christopher Joseph, PA
Morgan, Arthur Elwood, NC
Morris, Rae H., NC
Murray, William Archibald, PA
Narducci, Anthony E., PA
Nebinger, Rankin A., PA
Nichols, Ace Elliott, TX
Oreamuno-Flores, Alberto, COSTA RICA
Parrish, Joseph Andrew, PA
Pasquariello, Patrick S., PA
Penta, John Joseph, PA
Petrucci, Ralph Joseph, RI
Pollock, Isador Ira, CT
Ralston, James G., WV
Rampona, James Raymond, OH
Repa, Joseph John, PA
Riddle, Alfonso Ricardo, TX
Riggins, John Carlton, VA
Romesberg, Earl Clinton, PA
Rose, Thurman Hubert, NC
Rummell, Russell William, OH
Schellenger, Edward A. Y., NJ
Seaman, Stephen Francis, PA
Sentner, Charles Sylvester, PA
Shaw, Ernest Irwin, AR
Shipley, John Thomas, PA
Smith, Isaac Robert, PA
Smith, Lewis Aaron, PA
Snyder, Cecil Dawson, KS
Sommer, Ferdinand Comfort, PA
Staats, Enoch Dwight, WV
Stamps, George Ruffin, NC
Stecher, William A. R., PA
Stewart, James Kennedy, WV
Stump, Wayne George, PA
Sullivan, William Martin, Jr., NJ
Surver, James Miller, PA
Szabo, Ladislas Thomas, OH
Taylor, Francis I., PA
Thomas, Harry Burger, PA
Tolan, Edward Vincent, PA
Troncelliti, Alfred E., PA
Uchiyama, Hoichiro, HAWAII
Vick, Charles Lovell, NC
Villegas, A. Juan, COLOMBIA
Walsh, Joseph Michael, PA
Ward, James Purnell, MS
Ward, Maurice John, PA
Ware, Marvin Brister, MS
Weed, Melrose Edmund, PA
Whitsell, Fay Merrill, MO
Williams, Harry, PA
Yinger, Starling Cisco, OH
Zavod, William Abraham, PA
Zielinski, Edmund John, MA

On February 22, 1930, the new 1025 Walnut Street College was dedicated. The speaker on this occasion was George B. McClellan, Ph.D., Professor of Economic History at Princeton University, the great-grandson of Jefferson's Founder (Fig. 254).

Among the 140 graduates, Francis J. Braceland was destined to become the most famous member of the Class (Fig. 255). His prize in obstetrics, however, was not prophetic since he went directly into psychiatry following residency, beginning at the Institute of the Pennsylvania Hospital. Upon his return from a year of study in Europe in 1936, he was named Clinical Director at Pennsylvania. Advancing quickly he was also Assistant Professor at the Graduate School of Medicine of the University of Pennsylvania and Associate Professor at Woman's Medical College.

In 1941 he was made Professor of Psychiatry and Dean of Loyola University School of Medicine, Chicago. During World War II he advanced to the rank of Captain in the United States Navy Medical Corps, serving as Special Assistant in Psychiatry to the Surgeon General. He was awarded the Legion of Merit by the Secretary of the Navy for outstanding services which included duty as Chief of Neuropsychiatry, Bureau of Medicine and Surgery. In 1946 Dr. Braceland established the section of psychiatry at the Mayo Clinic as Consulting Psychiatrist as well as Professor of Psychiatry at the Graduate School, University of Minnesota. He was President of the American Psychiatric Association (1956/57) in addition to many activities in other organizations. Upon retirement from Mayo, he became Psychiatrist-in-Chief at the institute of Living at

Fig. 254. Dedication of new 1025 Walnut Street College Building on February 22, 1930. Dean Patterson, Dr. George B. Mclellan, and Board President Alba B. Johnson (left to right).

Hartford, Connecticut and Clinical Professor at Yale University. He received seven honorary degrees, was named Knight of St. Gregory the Great by Pope Pius XII in 1951, and was awarded the Laetare Medal from Notre Dame University as America's Outstanding Catholic Layman. In 1967 he was the recipient of the Jefferson Alumni Achievement award.

A number of 1930 graduates were prominent in Philadelphia medical circles. George W. Bland

Fig. 255. Francis J. Braceland (JMC, '29), renowned psychiatrist.

became an instructor in the Department of Obstetrics; Patrick J. Kennedy was a prominent ophthalmologist for many years associated with the Wills Eye Hospital; Edward H. Kotin joined the Department of Medicine and for many years contributed clinical and teaching services; Marshall M. Lieber, after two years of European study, became a devoted teacher and researcher in the Department of Pathology, advancing to Associate Professor; Joseph Waldman went on to major achievements in ophthalmology, treating the King of Saudi Arabia during World War II while a major in the U.S. Army for which he received the Legion of Merit Award, and in civilian life specializing in neuro-ophthalmology with promotion at Jefferson to Professor of Ophthalmology.

Leon L. Berns, an honor graduate, after completing his internship, joined the Department of Anatomy at Jefferson and continued his teaching for more than 55 years, even after achieving the rank of Honorary Clinical Professor (Fig. 256).

At the fiftieth Reunion of the Class of 1930, three retired Rear Admirals in the United States Navy were in attendance. They were Drs. Francis J. Braceland, Cecil H. Coggins, and Charles W. Letcher (Fig. 257).

CLASS OF 1930

Aukstakalnis, Frank Joseph, PA
Baker, Thomas Harding, DE
Beasley, William DeFord, NC
Beatty, Gerald Aloysius, PA
Berns, Leon L., PA
Biglan, Albert Manley, PA
Bland, George Willis, PA
Blatt, John Frederick, PA
Bluestone, George Gabriel, PA
Bolton, William Worden, PA
Bowerhan, Robert Leroy, NY
Boyd, David A., Jr., MI
Boyer, John Lott, PA
Braceland, Francis James, PA
Brettell, Howard W., OH
Brown, Robert Hyatt, NC
Brown, William Lewis, OH
Buchman, David Hyman, PA
Burns, Francis L., MA
Cammarata, Joseph Anthony, PA
Candel, Samuel, NY
Carl, Robert Delroy, PA

Caulfield, Walter Harry, RI
Chylack, Leo T., PA
Cimochowski, Alexander, Bernard, PA
Cobots, Joseph Charles, PA
Cocke, Joseph G., AL
Coggins, Cecil Hengy, MO
Cohen, Samuel, NY
Coleman, Ernest H., PA
Colley, Arthur Truman, PA
Cornely, James Lemoyne, PA
Cox, Percy Evans, MD
Cravotta, Charles Angelo, PA
Crothers, Kenneth Janney, MD
Cyr, Gerald A., ME
Daugherty, Earl Alfred, PA
Davis, Elbert Vernon, NC
DeFrancois, Walter, PA
Donald, Robert Lavalle, MS
Duffy, Charles, NC
Eason, Jack B., AZ
Eberly, Albert Dunn, PA
Ehrig, Philip Frederick, PA

Fabian, John Paul, PA
Findley, David Pressly, NE
Fogel, Roland Harwood, PA
Foy, James Henry, PA
Fritts, Lewis Caufield, PA
Garman, Russell Arthur, PA
Goldfarb, Abraham, NJ
Golub, Leib J., PA
Goss, Louis, PA
Gough, Edward John, PA
Gunnet, Oren W., PA
Guyer, Edward Cecil, WA
Haentze, Frederick Edward, PA
Hair, Joseph Tracey, SC
Hammond, Newton Keith, PA
Harmon, Walter H., NC
Hartman, Russell Milton, PA
Helmick, John Pierpont, WV
Holmes, William Frederick,Jr., TX
Hopkins, Wallace Eckley, PA
Hubbard, Charles Crow, PA

Hudson, William Evans, OH
Hutchison, Lloyd Snyder, PA
Jordan, James Shannon, PA
Karr, David Bernard, TN
Kendig, Harry Charles, PA
Kennedy, Patrick J., PA
Kesilman, Morris, PA
Ketchum, Robert Dickerson, WV
Kilborn, Melville Graves, NJ
Kotin, Edward Howard, PA
Kramer, Frederick Herman, WV
Kuhn, John Raymond, Jr., MO
Lasky, Lester, MS
Ledden, John V., PA
Lemmon, Junius Mayes, SC
Lentz, Sylvester Eugene, PA
Letcher, Charles W., PA
Lieber, Marshall Max, CT
Lucas, William Frederick, PA
Makowski, Israel, RI
Marcks, Kerwin Mathias, PA
Marvil, James E., DE
Mattas, Joseph Charles, PA
Mattas, Oliver E., PA
McHugh, Thomas Francis, PA
Meagher, Angus Campbell, MT
Miller, Merle Middour, PA
Munson, Charles Leith, DE
Nicholls, Richard B., VA
Nightingale, Louis M., NH
O'Donnell, Alan Edward, RI
Oaks, Lloyd Edress, UT
Ormond, Allison Lee, NC
Padgett, Charles King, NC
Peede, Alvin Wortham, NC
Peoples, Harry Joseph, PA
Powell, Raymond Knight, PA
Rankin, Stewart L., PA
Reeves, Julius Norman, NC
Reigart, Paul M., PA
Ricchiuti, Joseph F., PA
Richardson, Claude Ervin, TN
Riggle, Paul Phillips, PA
Saslaw, Lewis Benjamin, FL
Schell, Donald Edmond, PA
Schultz, Merritt Campbell, PA
Shemanski, Henry Leopold, PA
Sherman, Fuller G., NJ
Shirk, Paul Kuhlmann, PA
Silbernagel, Wynne Metcalf, OH
Smith, Ernest Gerard, PA
Sorrell, Furman Yates, NC
Stailey, Henry David, CA
Stein, Irvin, NC

Fig. 256.   Leon L. Berns (JMC, '30), Clinical Professor of Anatomy who taught for more than 55 years.

Streker, John Francis, RI
Swartz, Edward Philip, PA
Tong, Fook Hing, HAWAII
Urbaitis, John Charles, PA
Wagner, Edward Joseph, NY
Waldman, Joseph, PA
Wander, Maurice Carlyle, PA
Warnock, Charles Harry, OH
Wayman, Bernard Ralph, NJ
Weakley, Virgil William, OH
Weems, Don Bright, TN

Weinstein, Sydney, OR
White, Norman W., PA
Williams, Arnold Herbert, PA
Wilson, Dwight Elliott, FL
Woehrle, Nelson Christian, PA
Woodruff, Marston True, PA
Woodruff, Ralph G., FL
Wright, Herman Wilder, NC
York, James Lawrence, PA
Zipin, David, PA

Fig. 257.   Three Rear Admirals from Class of 1930 at their 50th reunion. (Left to right Francis J. Braceland, Cecil H. Coggins and Charles W. Letcher.)

"And to this thought I hold with firm persistence
The last result of wisdom stamps it true:
He only earns his freedom and existence
Who daily conquers them anew."
        Johann Wolfgang von Goethe (1749–1842).

At the Academy of Music on June 5, the degree of Doctor of Medicine was conferred upon the 141 members of the class. This brought 15,474 names to the total list of graduates.

The Curtis Clinic, constructed at the Tenth and Walnut Street site of the 1898 Medical College building was dedicated on December 17, 1931. This facility greatly enhanced patient care and student teaching (Fig. 258).

Kenneth Evans Fry won the gold medal surgery prize for the best essay on a subject pertaining to surgery and the gold medal for general excellence in clinical surgery. This marked the beginning of his career in the Surgery Depart-

ment in which he remained a role model to students and residents alike in his well organized lectures, his operative technique, his surgical judgment and his keen knowledge of the surgical literature. He served throughout World War II in the Middle East and was most active in Alumni affairs such as Chairman of Annual Giving and President (1965). He was the first member of the Surgical Department to become Board Certified (1939) through taking the examinations (Fig. 259).

Robert Kyun Hyun Charr was an honor graduate whose appointment in the Department of Medicine was interrupted by tuberculosis. Upon

Fig. 258.   Cyrus H. K. Curtis, benefactor of the Curtis Clinic. Curtis Clinic dedicated December 17, 1931.

recovery he taught in Jefferson's Pine Street Department for Diseases of the Chest and carried out research with Dr. J. Woodrow Savacool (JMC, '38, Fig. 280) in basic science and clinical aspects of pulmonary disease. He was a most effective instructor in physical diagnosis and much admired by the students as a superb and compassionate clinician (Fig. 260). His brilliant career was cut short by premature death.

Antis, Max Abram, PA
Ball, Charles Lightfoot, Jr., NC
Banks, Roland W., PA
Bartho, Blaine F., PA
Berger, Morley, PA
Berrillo, Anacleto, RI
Bishko, Samuel J., OH
Bonham, Dwight Turney, IL
Borbonus, John Norbert, PA
Brown, Albert Wheatland, PA
Brunner, Austin Franklin, PA
Burdick, Bingley Lyman, NY
Butler, Claude Henry, NJ
Charr, Robert Kyun Hyun, KOREA
Cohen, Milton H., PA
Cokely, Harold Jay, MO
Collett, William Rich, MT
Conlan, James Adrian, PA
Corman, Paul M., PA
Crellin, William Nathan, PA
Danielson, Carl Leon, PA
Davis, Raymond C., NJ
de Prophetis, Rocco I., PA
Deutel, Oscar R., NJ
Dichter, Irving Samuel, CT
Dietz, Henry W., NC

Donnelly, Edward John J., PA
Driscoll, Charles Dennis, RI
Dubbs, Alfred W., PA
Edson, Reginald C., PA
Emery James W., PA
Farace, Joseph L., PA
Fisher, Edward J., PA
Fry, Kenneth E., WA
Giering, John F., PA
Gillen, Dennis Ryan, OH
Gingrich, Rife, PA
Gipstein, Edward, CT

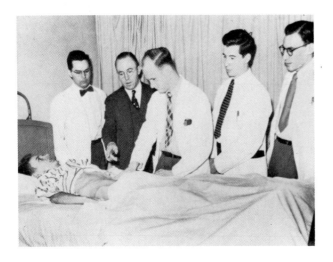

Fig. 259. Kenneth E. Fry (JMC, '31), Clinical Professor of Surgery, teaching at the bedside.

Fig. 260. Robert K. H. Charr (JMC, '31), researcher in pulmonary diseases and popular lecturer in physical diagnosis.

Glenn, Eugene Byron, NC
Goldman, Joel, PA
Grazier, Clark Gilson, PA
Green, Southgate Jones, NC
Grossman, Maurice, NC
Hager, Henry George, Jr., MD
Haight, Warne Lowell, PA
Halpern, Samuel, NJ
Hauver, Richard V., MD
Hemphill, Stuart Price, KY
Hendricks, Walter Jacob, PA
Henstell, Philip, CT
Hobbs, Robert E., PA
Hodges, Wyllys Royce, Jr., MD
Horwell, Richard J., PA
Hurley, Michael Joseph, Jr., PA
Ishler, Harold L., PA
Jacobs, Louis C., PA
Jahnig, Richard Paul, PA
Johnson, Howard A., NJ
Justin, Peter A., PA
Kahn, Leo, NJ
Kaplan, Herbert, PA
Katz, Martin Edwin, PA
Kaufman, Abraham, PA
Keller, Eli Jeremiah, PA
Kent, Alfred Abraham, Jr., NC
Kessler, Harry Tay, PA
Knox, Earl Ross, PA
Kough, Othello S., PA
Krauss, Maurice Daniel, PA
Latzo, John, PA
Lesnow, Jack M., CT
Lewis, John E., PA
Lowry, Forrest Ellsworth, OH
Lupo, Deonis M., CT
Lyerly, James Miller, VA
Lynch, Edward Thomas, NC
Maddrey, Milner Crocker, NC
Markel, Joseph, PA
Markley, Ralph, PA
Marks, Myer, PA
Matta, Amar Dass, INDIA
McClain, Harry C., PA
McCormick, William Milton, PA
McDowell, Harold Clyde, NC
McDowell, William K., NC
McMartin, William Joseph, NE
Miller, John Veil, PA
Morgan, Leslie Emanuel, PA
Moser, George P., PA

Murphy, John Thomas, PA
Murray, John Allen, PA
Newman, William Harris, Jr., PA
Nipple, Vincent Clayton, PA
Noble, Nathan Morton, PA
O'Leary, Thomas Francis, PA
Oliver, Andres Gilberto, PUERTO RICO
Parks, Harold Darby, TX
Paschal, George W., Jr., NC
Patella, Eugene Michael, NY
Peacock, Arthur Bigelow, NC
Pepper, Max, FL
Praver, Louis L., OH
Prunty, Francis Crandall, WV
Quinn, John Lawrence, OH
Ralph, Nathan, PA
Rathmell, Thomas Kessinger, PA
Ravit, George Jonathan, MA
Reis, Paul B., PA
Riley, Frederick Raymond, RI
Rintz, Norman Charles, PA
Roccapriore, Benjamin Anthony, CT
Schuster, Lawrence E., NY
Shapiro, Jacob, PA
Shue, Spurgeon Theodore, PA
Sica, Paul Anthony, PA
Sikes, Charles Henry, NC
Smith Donald C., PA
Smith, Rollin H., MO
Smyth, Jack Flemming, OH
Sprenkel, Vaughan Leroy, PA
Steinberg, Saul, PA
Stoner, Donald Dudley, PA
Suffoletta, Daniel Benedict, PA
Suter, Harry F., PA
Taylor, Raymond A., NJ
Tisherman, Robert Carl, PA
Todd, Myron Andrew, PA
Tompkins, Donald R., ND
Tornay, Anthony Stephen, PA
Turner, Wayne Edward, PA
Tyau, George K. F., HAWAII
Van Loon, Lawrence Gwyn, PA
Vatter, Leonard George, Jr., IL
Wagner, Ira Garfield, Jr., PA
White, Hilary Francis, MA
Wiant, Herman Ernest, NJ
Williams, James Thomas, PA
Wolverton, Giles, OH
Zangrilli, Alfred A., PA
Zimmerman, Coler, NJ
Zugerman, Isadore, PA

The Commencement was held on June 3 for 143 graduates in the Academy of Music. The address was delivered by George Barton Cutten, D.D., Ph.D., LL.D., President of Colgate University, on "A Layman's Advice to Doctors."

C. Earl Albrecht, class historian with a prior degree in theology from Moravian College and Seminary, became a pioneer in the Matanuska Valley of Alaska. He progressed to appointment as the first Alaskan Commissioner of Health. In 1961 as Assistant Secretary of Health for Pennsylvania, he was named Visiting Professor of Public Health at Jefferson. In 1963 he became fulltime Professor of Preventive Medicine, conducting several important regional surveys. He also advanced in the United States Army Medical Corps to the rank of Brigadier General. Following retirement from Jefferson, he became involved with the Trans-Arctic Medical Association and participated in its symposia on Circumpolar Health (Fig. 261).

Nathan S. Schlezinger, following Jefferson internship, pursued the study of neurology and psychiatry at Columbia University where he received the degree of Doctor of Science in 1938. Returning to Jefferson as Ross V. Patterson Fellow in Neurology, he soon joined the staff of Wills Eye Hospital where he developed the new specialty of neuro-ophthalmology. He progressed to Chief of Neurology at Wills, serving until retirement in 1976. Dr. Schlezinger advanced to Professor of Neurology at Jefferson where he also organized the Myasthenia Gravis Clinic (Fig. 262).

Howard C. Leopold, winner of the Saunders Prize, trained under Bela Schick and at the Cooke Clinic in New York in the emerging field of allergy. He was appointed to the Jefferson Allergy Clinic under Dr. J. Alexander Clarke in 1936. He became Chief of the Clinic in 1959 in addition to serving as consultant to numerous regional hospitals.

G. Henry Katz became a psychiatrist, for many years Director of the Devereux School. He was also affiliated with the Graduate School of the University of Pennsylvania and was elected the first President of the Philadelphia Association for Psychoanalysis.

Several class members became associated with the teaching staff following Jefferson internship. John J. Cheleden was trained in proctology and was a loyal alumnus throughout his career which he later pursued in Florida. Frederick W. Deardorff was appointed to the Department of Surgery, also briefly serving in thoracic surgery at the Department for Diseases of the Chest. Lewis C. Manges, Jr. was on the surgical staff of Jefferson as well as of the Philadelphia General Hospital. George A. Porreca became Clinical Assistant Professor of Obstetrics and Gynecology.

Fig. 261. C. Earl Albrecht (JMC, '32), first Alaskan Commissoner of Health.

Adlin, Albert, PA
Albrecht, C. Earl, MN
Allen, Homer Richard, PA
Allen, Reginald A., RI
Ashley, Claude Wilber, MO
Averbach, Bertram Frederick, OH
Ayers, James S., NC
Bair, Charles William, PA
Bakunin, Maurice Irving, CT
Barthold, Joseph Leo, PA
Baver, George A., PA
Benson, Kenneth Haworth, IN
Berrettini, Achilles Alfred, PA
Bittrich, Norbert Martin, PA
Boland, Francis Patrick, PA
Brandwan, Samuel, Jr., PA
Bronk, Henry N., PA
Brown, Augustus W. H., OH
Brown, Louis Emmitt, Jr., OH
Buonato, Sebastian James, PA
Cacia, John Joseph, PA
Chapnick, Morton Herman, CT
Cheleden, John Joseph, PA
Claffey, John Bernard, PA
Costello, Thomas Joseph, PA

Curtis, Morris Williams, PA
Darnall, Carl Robert, DC
Deardorff, Frederick W., PA
Deich, Samuel, NJ
Deitz, Aaron, MD
Dodson, Claude Cordray, PA
Doyle, William Joseph, PA
Durante, Raphael Henry, PA
Endres, Warren H., PA
Ezell, Stiles Dean, SC
Fales, Robert M., NC
Ferguson, George B., OH
Fine, Barnet, CT
Finkelstein, Herman, PA
Flaig, Julian Vincent, PA
Fortin, Francis Frederick, MA
Gelfand, David, PA
Gerber, Morris Jean, PA
Gillespie, Patrick Joseph, PA
Gillis, Alfred George, PA
Goodman, Francis Eugene, PA
Grace, James J., PA
Grim, Earl Henry, PA
Haar, Frederick B., NC
Haimes, Solomon Manuel, PA
Hawley, Charles F., NY
Hegarty, Francis A., PA
Hershey, Joseph Ivan, PA
Hinkson, William James, PA
Hoffman, David, NJ
Hoffman, Joseph Francis, PA
Hohman, George Charles, PA
Holleman, Charles Edward, Jr., NC
Horn, Leonard, NY
Horovitz, Morris Thomas, PA
Horton, Park Martin, PA
Howell, William Murdock, PA
Hudson, Floyd Isaac, PA
Hughes, William Lloyd, PA
James, Alfred Elmore, PA
Karr, Howard Harris, TN
Katz, Gabriel Henry, PA
Kaufman, Samuel Russel, PA
Kehres, Henry Nathan, PA
Klempner, Paul, NJ
Kredel, Thomas W., PA
LaClair, Charles Huston, Jr., PA
Ladden, John Joseph, PA
Layton, Robert Reese, Jr., DE
Lechman, Joseph Francis, PA
Leopold, Howard Charles, PA
Lesh, Vincent O., NJ

Fig. 262. Nathan S. Schlezinger (JMC, '32), pioneer in neuro-ophthalmology.

Liberace, Ettore Valentino, PA
Lichstein, Jacob, PA
Lomax, Joseph, PA
Lyons, Ralph, PA
Lytle, Carl S., FL
Maloney, Francis Dunn, CT
Manges, Lewis C., Jr., PA
Martin, John T., SC
McClintock, Walter Lowrie, MA
McGlade, Thomas Henry, NJ
McLaughlin, Thomas Finley, PA
Meckstroth, Herman Franklin, PA
Megowan, Robert, PA
Meranse, Theodore, PA
Moore, Thomas Scott, OH
Morrison, Donald Allan R., HAWAII
Moscarella, Alfred Savino, NY
Murphy, Myles Joseph, PA
Murray, William J. C., RI
Neff, Walter S., PA
Nightingale, Arthur B., NH
Northrop, Robert Arthur, CT
Pace, Samuel Eugene, NC
Pearson, Julius R., NJ
Pentz, Clarence Rolland, PA
Perrine, Cornelius C., NJ
Phelps, John Mahlon, NC
Pious, William L., CT
Podboy, August J., PA
Porreca, George A., PA
Pratt, Arthur G., NJ
Provisor, Benjamin, NJ
Ricchiuti, A. George, PA

Rice, William Thomas, OH
Rogers, Herman C., PA
Rosenberry, Benjamin F. L., PA
Rosenbluth, Sidney B., NY
Rothermel, John Keim, PA
Runkle, Stuart Calvin, Jr., PA
Saylor, Lloyd Elwood, PA
Schlezinger, Nathan S., OH
Schreiner, Herman Michael, PA
Schwebel, Samuel, OH
Scott, Michael Milton, NJ
Serino, Gerard S., PA
Shoun, Alexander Nelson, TN
Silver, Morris Alvin, PA
Spalletta, Camillus Henry, PA
Stahl, Lloyd Alva, PA
Stiller, David, NY
Thorner, Melvin Wilfred, NJ
Tomaseski, William Henry, PA
Ullery, John Calvin, OH
Ungar, John, Jr., PA
Vastine, J. Robert, PA
Viener, Bernard, PA
Wade, James Lowrance, WV
Weintraub, Sydney Edward, PA
Weres, James, NJ
West, William B., PA
Wetzel, Roy James, PA
Weymouth, Raymond Eugene, ME
Windley, William Hays, NC
Wolfe, Eugene Fink, PA
Wright, Burchard E., Jr., FL
Young, Herbert Keith, SC

Do not stop to think about the reasons for what you are doing, about why you are questioning. Curiosity has its own reason for existence. One cannot help but be in awe when he contemplates the mysteries of eternity, of life, of the marvelous structure of reality. It is enough if one tries merely to comprehend a little of this mystery each day. Never lose a holy curiosity.

Albert Einstein (1879–1955)

Class of 1932, Commencement June 3, Academy of Music.

The Oath of Hippocrates

I swear by Apollo, the physician, and Asclepius and Health and All-Heal and all the gods and goddesses that, according to my ability and judgment, I will keep this oath and stipulation:

To reckon him who taught me his art equally dear to me as my parents, to share my substance with him and relieve his necessities if required; to regard his offspring as on the same footing with my own brothers, and to teach them this art if they should wish to learn it, without fee or stipulation, and that by precept, lecture and every other mode of instruction, I will impart a knowledge of the art to my own sons and to those of my teachers, and to disciples bound by a stipulation and oath, according to the law of medicine, but to none others.

I will follow that method of treatment which, according to my ability and judgment, I consider for the benefit of my patients, and abstain from whatever is deleterious and mischievous, I will give no deadly medicine to anyone if asked, nor suggest any such counsel; furthermore, I will not give to a woman an instrument to produce abortion.

With purity and with holiness I will pass my life and practice my art, I will not cut a person who is suffering from a stone, but will leave this to be done by practitioners of this work. Into whatever houses I enter I will go into them for the benefit of the sick and will abstain from every voluntary act of mischief and corruption; and further from the seduction of females or males, bond or free.

Whatever, in connection with my professional practice, or not in connection with it, I may see or hear in the lives of men which ought not to be spoken abroad I will not divulge, as reckoning that all such should be kept secret.

While I continue to keep this oath unviolated may it be granted to me to enjoy life and the practice of the art, respected by all men at all times, but should I trespass and violate this oath, may the reverse be my lot.

1932

Four years of the 1929 depression had changed many aspects of the Jefferson experience. Austerity was the order of the period and many ambitious programs had to be deferred or cancelled. Generally, however, morale was well maintained although many graduates were compelled to alter their career goals and hopes. The members of this class numbered 140.

Daniel C. Baker, Jr., after his Jefferson internship, went on to a career in otolaryngology, stimulated in the specialty by admiration for Professor Louis H. Clerf (JMC, '12, Fig. 183). Dr. Baker served in the U.S. Navy during World War II and was appointed Assistant Professor of Otolaryngology at Columbia University School of Medicine in 1946. He became full Professor in 1964 (Fig. 263). He was Director of the Otolaryngological service at Presbyterian Hospital, New York, and consultant at many regional hospitals. He was President of the American Broncho-esophagological Association and at the time of his death he was President-elect of the American Laryngological Association. He was much in demand as a lecturer. He delivered the Chevalier Jackson Memorial Lectureship of the Philadelphia Laryngological Society. Selected to receive the Jefferson Alumni Achievement Award for 1974, Dr. Baker died a few days prior to the event. The Award was received in his behalf by his son, Daniel C. Baker, III, M.D.

Jacob J. Kirshner was appointed to the Department of Medicine and served for many years in the Pulmonary Division (Fig. 264). He advanced to Clinical Assistant Professor of Medicine. Dr. Kirshner also served for some years as Medical Director of the Eagleville Sanatorium and as Consultant to the Philadelphia Department of Health.

Other class members who were appointed to Jefferson teaching posts included Charles W. Semisch, III, Assistant Professor of Medicine, Leon N. Prince and Arnold Goldberger, both Clinical Assistant Professors of Obstetrics and Gynecology.

CLASS OF 1933

Alexander, Gilbert H., NY
Baker, Daniel Clifton, Jr., PA
Baker, Theodore, Jr., PA
Barner, John L., IA
Barnett, Thomas, PA
Barstow, Richard I., MA
Bell, Dudley Philip, CA
Bobes, Solomon Subere, WV
Boland, Francis Bernard, PA
Bond, Jesse H., OH
Borthwick, Malcolm James, PA
Bower, John R., PA
Britt, Edward Charles, PA
Brown, Joseph Mark, ND
Burn, John F., PA
Cantor, Max, PA
Cassone, Vincent James, PA
Chodoff, Richard Joseph, PA
Cleaver, C. Perry, PA
Cook, Norman Lyle, PA
Copleman, Benjamin, NJ

Crandall, Noble Franklin, OH
Crow, Morton Jay, OH
Cuden, Nathan Joseph, PA
Custer, Edward William, PA
Dacus, Robert Mabry, Jr., SC
Davis, John Evan, Jr., PA
Deibert, Glenn Aneas H., PA
Denbo, Elic A., NJ
Denny, Michael Richard, PA
Detar, David Dewey, PA
Dye, Franklin Foster, OH
Eddy, Lester R., OH
Elkins, Murray, NY
Ellin, Victor Blewett, PA
Elliott, Frazier Jackson, PA
Evans, Thomas Russell, PA
Feissner, Herman, Jr., PA
Feldser, Oscar Benjamin, PA
Fennell, Ralph Elmer, PA
Fescina, Joseph Vincent, PA
Finlayson, Bliss L., UT

Flaherty, James Aloysius, PA
Frick, Willis Gilbert, PA
Fuerst, Harold T., NY
Gadomski, Casimir Francis, NJ
Gartman, Edward, PA
Geibel, Frank Baum, PA
Gibbons, Charles Aloysius, Jr., PA
Gilbert, Philip D., PA
Glocker, Rudolph Karl, PA
Goldberger, Arnold, PA
Gordon, Jacob, PA
Habel, Karl, PA
Hamilton, Francis J., PA
Harris, Harold Byron, PA
Harris, Isaac Emeron, Jr., NC
Hawkins, Wilbur James, Jr., PA
Heiligman, Nathan H., PA
Hersohn, William Wolf, NJ
Hipple, Percy L., Jr., PA
Holmes, Arthur E., PA
Hoyt, Ralph c., PA
Irwin, George Middleton, PA
Jenkins, Edward John, PA

Kavanaugh, Myles Thomas, PA
Kemble, John W., PA
Kemble, Robert Penn, PA
Kessel, Clark, WV
Kieffer, Jesse, PA
Kirshner, Jacob J., PA
Kitchin, Jesse Walton, NC
Kniseley, Joseph Harry, PA
Koretsky, Leo, MA
Kotanchik, Walter E., PA
Lamberson, Harry Henry, CO
Leach, John Edward, NJ
Leath, MacLean Bacon, Jr., NC
Leiby, Lewis James, PA
Leichner, Thomas Joseph, PA
Levick, Alfred David, MA
Loder, Earl Samuel, PA
Lyman, James Francis, PA
Mackowski, Herbert William, NY
Matys, Edmund Vincent, PA
McCorkle, William Pyles, Jr., PA
McKnight, William Patton, PA
Mermon, Michael S., PA

Fig. 263.   Daniel C. Baker, Jr. (JMC, '33), noted otolaryngologist.

Fig. 264.   Jacob J. Kirshner (JMC, '33) pictured (left) with Burgess L. Gordon (JMC, '14) and Peter A. Theodos (JMC, '35) in Jefferson Unit of World War II.

Miller, Connell Hutchison, PA
Miller, Leon, PA
Morgan, Richard William, PA
Murphy, Thomas Francis, CT
Murray, Edwin N., PA
Myers, Norman VanSant, NJ
Pandolfo, Harry, PA
Patton, Howard R., Jr., PA
Pellicane, Anthony J., NJ
Pewterbaugh, David Chester, PA
Pezzuti, Hamil Ralph, PA
Phillips, Clarence Eugene, PA
Prince, Leon Nathaniel, PA
Raymond, Eugene Edward, PA
Reedy, Walter Joseph, PA
Reeves, Raymond W., NC
Reynolds, Kenneth Earl, PA
Ricker, Charles Thorne, NJ
Ridgway, Eli Chester, Jr., NJ
Ruppersberg, Anthony, Jr., OH
Sabatino, Nathan Andrew, NY
Schaub, John J., PA
Schlossbach, Theodore, NJ
Schwartz, Charles E., PA
Schwartz, George Jacob, Jr., PA
Seidelman, Sidney Elias, NJ

Sellitto, Anthony M., NJ
Semisch, Charles William, III, PA
Sharp, William Thomas, OH
Shellenberger, Lewis C., PA
Shields, Marshall Francis, PA
Shivelhood, David Kalbach, PA
Smith, J. Stanley, PA
Smith, Raymond Francis, NY
Stapinski, Stanley Michael, PA
Steele, James McLeod, PA
Steele, Robert, PA
Stein, Samuel H., PA
Sutula, John Vincent, PA
Taggart, William Graham, OH
Thompson, Thomas Ewing, Jr., PA
Urban, Joseph T., PA
Vaughan, Walter Weddle, NC
Vincent, Nicholas F. K., NJ
Walter, Henry, Jr., PA
Warfield, Robert B., PA
Weaver, Andrew Jackson, NC
Wilson, George Brinton, Jr., PA
Windham, John Evans, MS
Wolf, Edward T., OK
Wong, James Sin Fook, HAWAII
Zakrzewski, Matthew Joseph, PA

College Auditorium, named "Herbut Auditorium" in 1979.

1933

At the Commencement held on June 1 at the Academy of Music, the M.D. degree was conferred upon 143 graduates.

Charles Wilmer Wirts, Jr., of Pennsylvania, took residency training in medicine at the American Hospital in Paris. Upon returning to Jefferson he was appointed the first Ross V. Patterson Fellow in Gastroenterology (1940-42). He introduced the use of the Schindler gastroscope at Jefferson, and in 1946 became the Head of the Gastrointestinal Clinic as well as developing the first Division of Gastroenterology in the Department of Medicine (Fig. 265). He carried out significant research in gastroenterology along with an active clinical practice and served as President of the American College of Gastroenterology (1957) and of the American Gastroscopic Society (1959). His portrait was presented to the University in 1978.

Harold L. Israel, of Massachusetts, interned at the Philadelphia General Hospital where he received the Research Prize in 1936. He developed an interest in sarcoidosis which continued for more than 50 years during which he achieved a national and international reputation, attaining the rank of full professor at Jefferson. In recognition of his outstanding qualities as teacher, researcher and pulmonary clinician his portrait was presented to the University in 1984 (Fig. 266).

Joe Henry Coley practiced obstetrics and gynecology for more than 40 years in his native Oklahoma City and served as Clinical Assistant Professor in that specialty in the University of Oklahoma (Fig. 267). He served as an Alumni Representative on Jefferson's Board of Trustees (1972-79) and as Chairman of the Alumni Division of the Sesquicentennial Fund (1974). He was awarded an honorary degree of Doctor of Science by Jefferson in 1980, the Alumni Achievement

Fig. 265. Charles W. Wirts, Jr. (JMC, '34) developed the first Division of Gastroenterology in the Department of Medicine (1946).

Fig. 266. Harold L. Israel (JMC, '34), internationally known for his work in sarcoidosis.

Fig. 267. John H. Coley (JMC, '34), Alumni Trustee and Recipient of Alumni Achievment Award.

Award in 1982, and the President's Cornerstone Award in 1984 (Fig. 461). His father was a Jefferson graduate in the Class of 1880 and had attended the lectures of Samuel D. Gross.

Members of the class who subsequently taught on the Jefferson Faculty were Louis Keeler Collins in Surgery (Proctology), Edward Joseph Moore, Jr. in Pediatrics, Floyd Johnson Putney in Bronchoesophagology, and Oscar Thompson Wood, Jr. in Medicine.

CLASS OF 1934

Andrews, Raymond W., PA
Angle, William D., PA
Bar, Samuel, PA
Barrett, Sterling Archie, NC
Bloom, Charles Henry, PA
Bolus, Michael, NC
Bower, Harry B., PA
Bowie, George W. R., ME
Braun, William, NJ
Carbonetta, Reno Raymond, PA
Cassano, William Thomas, NY
Cinberg, Leonard A., PA
Clark, Ralph Elden, WA
Cole, Richard S., PA

Coley, Joe H., OK
Collins, Louis Keeler, NJ
Conahan, Thomas Joseph, Jr., PA
Conole, Frank D., NY
Cooch, Joseph Wilkins, DE
Cook, Aaron, ME
Dantini, Daniel, C., PA
Dawe, George Griffith, AZ
de Diego, Manuel, PUERTO RICO
Desantes, Francis August, PA
Emery, Clarence, Jr., ME
Eshelman, Carl Bushman, PA
Failmezger, Theodore Richard, NJ
Falcone, Nicholas A., PA

Ferer, Walter C., PA
Frank, David, PA
Freeman, Eliot N., Jr., KS
Freeman, Joseph T., PA
Fronduti, Lucian J., PA
Funke, Alvin H., PA
Gallagher, John P. J., PA
Gallo, Frank, CT
Gidding, Samuel S., NJ
Gillespie, Harry, CT
Glenn, James A., Jr., NY
Goldcamp, John S., OH
Grady, Hugh Gerard, PA
Grieco, Anthony Leonard, NJ
Grim, Mark D., PA
Grunt, Louis, NJ
Halpern, Gilbert M., HAWAII
Hammond, Alfred F., Jr., NC
Hanks, William Harvey, DE
Harrer, William J., Jr., PA
Hart, Alonzo Winfield, Jr., PA
Hawk, Malcolm Henry, OH
Hebble, Howard Miller, OH
Hesch, Joseph Anthony, PA
Hoberman, Edward, PA
Hofer, William Robb, NJ
Houser, Benjamin P., PA
Hoyt, Dorsey Raymond, PA
Hyman, Jacob George, PA
Ingham, John L., PA
Isenberg, Chester L., PA
Ishii, Clyde H., HAWAII
Israel, Harold L., MA
Johnson, Gaston Frank, NC
Johnson, George D., SC
Jonas, Stephen Alphonse, PA
Kandle, Roscoe Peacock, NJ
Keever, Kenneth William, WV
Keithan, John F., PA
Kenworthy, William Parke, Jr., PA
Kerstein, Louis Norton, NY
Kessler, William Frederic, NY
Kosanovic, Frederick, PA
Larkin, Frank Loftus, PA
Lawrence, Charles Thomas, Jr., NC
Lecklitner, Myron DeVoy, IN
Lerner, Joseph, PA
Lim, John P., CA
Liu Foo-Sen, Arthur, HAWAII
Lohmann, John, Jr., PA
Lohnes, James T., Jr., NY
Lohr, Dermot, NC
MacConkey, Harmar Hendrix, OH
Mansmann, James Andrew, PA

March, Linton Ellsworth, PA
McConnell, Irvin Waldo, NJ
McCool, Stanley Gaylord, NJ
McFadden, John Francis, PA
McMullin, John Francis, PA
McSteen, Arthur Joseph, PA
Miller, C. Joseph, PA
Miller, Lawson E., Jr., MO
Moore, Edward John, PA
Moore, Edward Joseph, Jr., PA
Newmark, Abe A., PA
Phillips, Warren Charles, PA
Place, E. Raymond, PA
Pomerleau, Ovid Felix, ME
Powers, Bruce R., TN
Pumphrey, Gordon H., OH
Putnam, William Frederick, NJ
Putney, F. Johnson, SC
Quinlan, James William, NJ
Rabinovitz, Isaac, PA
Ramsey, Russell Wiest, PA
Redfield, Ronald Laverne, PA
Robinson, Joseph Patrick, Jr., PA
Rosenberg, Edward Frank, DE
Rush, Irving Arnold, PA
Ryan, James John, PA
Sales, Phoenix M., PA
Santoro, Thomas Amerigo, NJ
Sapiro, Howard Marshall, ME
Saxe, Earl I., PA
Schultz, Samuel Karl, PA
Schwartz, Edward, ME
Shanks, Harold Jackson, CA
Shields, William Peter, RI
Shovlin, John Patrick, PA
Silver, Israel Oscar, PA
Singh-Janda, Gurbachan, INDIA
Smith, Harold C., PA
Sollenberger, Franklin Samuel, PA
Stabnick, Joseph Sigmund, MI
Steele, Frederic Hohman, PA
Stewart, Harry Lawrence, Jr., PA
Strong, Paul T., NJ
Sutula, Stanley Joseph, PA
Swanker, Wilson A., NY
Swearingen, Robert Goodwin, TX
Taylor, Thomas J., NC
Vaccaro, Michael, PA
Wagner, Charles Andrew, OH
Wallace, Clarence MacNair, PA
Wallen, Albert D., PA
Walsh, John J., PA
Weggenmann, Edward Earle, DE
Westcott, William I., NJ

Whitken, Albert Irving, NJ
Williams, Charles F., NC
Willis, Carroll Vance, NC

Wirts, C. Wilmer, Jr., PA
Wood, Oscar T., Jr., PA
Woods, William S., PA
Zielinski, John B., MA

Board of Trustees Room in College Building

The 142 members of this class received their M.D. degrees on June 7 in the Academy of Music. It was destined to be the only occasion on which the new Board President Mr. Wilfred W. Fry would award diplomas, since his term of office was only eight months, limited by his death at age 60 of complications of pneumonia.

The top honor graduate of this class was John Aloysius McCormick, of Pennsylvania, who won six prizes in addition to the Alumni prize for the highest four-year academic average. After his internship, he shared the first Ross V. Patterson Fellowship in Obstetrics and Gynecology with his classmate Joseph Lawrence Finn. Both subsequently taught in the Department at Jefferson,

but devoted their main energies to private practice (Fig. 268).

Hayward Russell Hamrick, of West Virginia, was promptly appointed to administrative posts at Jefferson. He served as Director of the Curtis Clinic from 1938 to 1957, but also as Medical Director from 1942 to 1957. His familiarity with all aspects of Jefferson affairs led to his appointment as Secretary of the Board of Trustees in 1943 and to the newly created position of Vice President of the Corporation in 1948. His clinical interest in the Department of Medicine was in cardiology (Fig. 269).

Peter Andrew Theodos, of Pennsylvania, became prominent in research and treatment of

Fig. 268. John A. McCormick and Joseph L. Finn (JMC, '35) the first Ross V. Patterson Fellows in Obstetrics/Gynecology.

lung diseases in miners. He participated at the Barton Division of Jefferson Hospital in studies of relationships among lesions of silicosis, anthracosis, tuberculosis, and emphysema and described cavitating silicotic masses exclusive of the effects of tuberculosis. These studies made a significant contribution to preventive measures in all industries associated with dust inhalation (Fig. 270).

Charley J. Smyth, Alpha Omega Alpha at Jefferson, achieved national distinction in rheumatology and medical education (Fig. 271). He received the Jefferson Alumni Achievement Award for 1985, being cited for teaching, organizational and clinical skills, and publications. He was Professor of Internal Medicine at the University of Colorado and co-editor of five editions of *Arthritis* with Dr. Joseph Hollander. He was President of the American Rheumatism Association and the National Society of Clinical Rheumatology. He received numerous awards and citations including the prestigious Harding Medal of the Arthritis Foundation. He was made a Master of the American College of Physicians.

Edmund Llewellyn Housel, of Pennsylvania, won the prize in therapeutics at graduation and became a pioneer in geriatrics and hypertension at Jefferson. He served as a President of the Philadelphia County Medical Society and on the Board of Directors of Blue Cross and Blue Shield. The endowed Annual Edmund L. Housel Lectureship in Hypertension was initiated in 1981.

Ned Tyson Raker, of Pennsylvania, was an honor graduate who served as the first Resident in Surgery in Jefferson Hospital on the "A" service of Professor Thomas A. Shallow. He then went on to a successful clinical practice in South America.

Fig. 269.   Hayward R. Hamrick (JMC, '35) Curtis Clinic Director (1938-57) and Medical Director (1942-57).

Fig. 270.   Peter A. Theodos (JMC, '35), Prominent in pulmonary diseases.

1935

Hyman Yaskin, of Pennsylvania, also an honor graduate, became a Clinical Professor of Neurology at Jefferson, and John Edward Lynch, of Pennsylvania, became a Professor of Obstetrics and Gynecology in his alma mater.

Abell, Charles F., IN
Alexander, Maurice H., NJ
Angstadt, Norman George, PA
Assante, Mario Hugo, PA
Banick, Vincent William, PA
Barroway, James N., NJ
Bender, Charles E., OH
Berlin, Irvin I., DE
Biddle, William Earl, PA
Bishko, Maurice J., OH
Blair, Albert J., PA
Brandon, Thomas Campbell, PA
Brindle, Harry Robert, PA
Brownstein, Samuel R., WV

Fig. 271. Charles J. Smyth (JMC, '35), noted rheumatologist.

Bull, Heman R., Jr., CO
Burden, Samuel S., PA
Camp, Glenn Curtis, PA
Carr, James V., PA
Chappel, Merwin R., OH
Clark, John Craig, TN
Coleman, Donald K., PA
Corwin, James Douglas, PA
Craddock, George Barksdale, VA
Crittenden, Donald W., PA
Cronlund, Philip Robert, PA
Cushing, Jean G. N., PA
Dembinski, T. Henry, NJ
DeSantis, Archie Joseph, PA
DeTroia, Frederick Carl, NJ
Dickson, Glenn Simmons, NC
Dickson, T. Bruce, PA
Donnelly, Kenneth Lawrence, PA
Dunham, Malcolm Melville, NJ
Eames, William N., PA
Eisenberg, Milton, PA
Ericksen, Arthur N., PA
Fenichel, Benjamin, NJ
Finkle, Lester Jules, NJ
Finn, Joseph L., PA
Fleming, Frank Reavis, NC
Force, Elwood Brower, PA
Forcey, Clarke M., PA
Furlong, Lawrence Roy, PA
Gehris, Leroy A., PA
Glaudel, Stanley Francis, PA
Goldweber, Josef Koppelman, NJ
Goodman, David Henry, DE
Gordon, George R., PA
Guckavan, Martin Francis, PA
Hammond, Charles P., PA
Hamrick, Hayward Russell, WV
Hanning, William Holman, OH
Hatfield, Nicholas William, IN
Hearn, William Prettyman, Jr., PA
Heim, Hugh Wilson, PA
Hoerner, Ralph W., PA
Hoffman, Charles W., NJ
Horhovitz, George Isaac, NJ
Housel, Edmund Llewellyn, PA
Hughes, Joseph F., NJ
Jacob, S. Sprigg, III, WV

Jones, Richard Wayland, OH
Karshmer, Ernest Emil, NJ
Kaufman, Irwin Leonard, PA
Keagy, R. Marvel, PA
Kennedy, Leon Toland, NC
Kernish, Alexander I., PA
Kerr, Joseph T., NC
Kilmer, John H., WV
Kirk, Albert Charles, VA
Kline, Edgar W., PA
Kochenderfer, Thomas Taylor, PA
Kraemer, Richard Joseph, RI
Kredel, Richard A., PA
Kreeger, Morris Harold, NJ
Lanahan, Francis B., PA
Laskin, Isadore, PA
Lehman, John Foster, PA
Lesse, S. Michael, PA
Leymeister, Martin Luther, PA
Luders, John Amandus, PA
Lussier, Raphael Andre, RI
Lynch, John Edward, RI
Mansker, Joseph Solomon, NY
Martin, Thomas Anthony, Jr., RI
McClements, William M., PA
McCloy, Merritt J., PA
McCluskey, Harry B., NJ
McCormick, John Aloysius, PA
McHale, Donald Gareth, PA
McKim, Charles Palmer, OR
McLane, Charles Francis, Jr., PA
McLane, Robert A., Jr., DE
Meiser, Edgar William, PA
Menegas, Jacinto John, PA
Meyers, Melvin Miller, PA
Mozes, Edward, MA
Murphy, James Paul, PA
Murphy, Leo J., NY
Nicodemus, Bryce Elton, PA
Nutter, Phosa David, WV
O'Brien, John Patrick, PA

Oblazney, Ludwig John, PA
Patterson, Robert Lewis, PA
Phalen, Thomas H., NY
Plummer, Harold B., DE
Purvine, Ralph Emerson, OR
Raker, Ned T., PA
Randell, Asher, OH
Redpath, Nathaniel James, WA
Revere, Seth Dustin, NJ
Richardson, Fred MacDonald, NJ
Riddle, Ransford, John, PA
Riffert, Paul M., PA
Roath, Clinton A., CA
Rotko, Bernard Benjamin, PA
Rudolph, Herman Louis, PA
Sage, Bernard, MI
Sherger, John Chalmers, PA
Sherman, Bernard Israel, RI
Smith, Forrest Fullerton, PA
Smith, Kenneth M., ME
Smyth, Charley J., OH
Snesavage, Bernard Anthony, PA
Snyder, Charles P., Jr., PA
Sowers, John W., PA
Starcher, Richard Camden, WV
Stephenson, Daniel H., NJ
Sufrin, Emanuel, PA
Sussman, Nathan, PA
Theodos, Peter A., PA
Thomas, John Henry, FL
Toll, William G., PA
Tucker, Harry Earle, PA
Tulin, Philip, PA
Tunick, George Louis, CT
Velardi, Martin Julius, NY
Wiest, Philip Ray, PA
Williams, John Scott, PA
Winick, William, PA
Wright, James Franklin, Jr., MD
Yaskin, H. Edward, PA
Young, Ellis William, PA

Education is the best provision for old age.

Aristotle (384-322 B.C.)

The degree of Doctor of Medicine was conferred upon 133 graduates by Mr. Robert P. Hooper, the new President of the Board of Trustees who would serve until 1949 and with change of title would be the first Board Chairman (1949/50).

J. Edward Berk, Distinguished Professor of Medicine and Chairman of the Department of Medicine at the University of California, received the Jefferson Alumni Achievement Award in 1977. His leadership in the field of gastroenterology was nationally recognized through his research accomplishments, authorship of medical publications and as a member of four editorial boards. He was President of the American College of Gastroenterology and the Bockus International Society of Gastroenterology. In 1989 he received the Clinical Achievement Award of the American College of Gastroenterology (Fig. 272).

Leonard W. Parkhurst began a lifetime rela-

tionship with Pennsylvania Hospital with his internship. He became a Founder and for 23 years Director of the Benjamin Franklin Clinic at Pennsylvania.

John T. Millington, Jr. became a public health physician and in later years served as Regional Health Commissioner with the Department of Health of Pennsylvania. For a time he was on the teaching staff at Jefferson as Visiting Professor of Preventive Medicine.

Four members of this class, in addition to private practice, taught on the Jefferson Faculty as follows: David Naidoff in Ophthalmology, Marcel Sussman in Obstetrics and Gynecology, and both Nicholas Raphael Varano (Fig. 273) and Max Rosensweig in Urology.

Paul Regis Davidson became the first Surgical Resident in Jefferson Hospital on the "B" service of Professor George P. Muller. His further career was in community surgery in Pennsylvania.

CLASS OF 1936

Amsterdam, Julius, PA
Andrews, P. Joseph, PA
Arey, Donald L., VA
Bell, Benjamin, MA
Berger, I. Robert, PA
Berk J. Edward, CA
Brandmiller, Barclay M., OH
Breisacher, Carl Frederick, PA
Brogan, Edmund J., PA
Buchert, Joseph Gerard, PA
Burke, James F., PA
Byrd, Allen Leet, NC
Cameron, Richard Ray, WV
Carr, Chalmers Rankin, NC
Catanzaro, Santino J., NY
Chesnick, Reuben Bernard, PA
Clancy, John, MT
Clime, Gilbert Newpher, PA
Clough, Joseph Messer, NH
Cohen, Oscar H., NJ
Conlon, William Linas, RI
Conrad, Roy Garman, PA
Cope, J. Hallam, Jr., CA

Counts, Richard L., OH
Crystal, Harry, PA
Davidson, Paul R., PA
DeCicco, Gabriel E., OH
DeNote, Anthony Paul, PA
Devers, Patrick Joseph, PA
Doe, Harvey Franklin, NJ
Durham, James Richard, Jr., PA
Duzmati, Paul Peter, CT
Dziob, Joseph M., RI
Ebner, Paul G., NJ
Erdman, George L., PA
Farmer, John L., PA
Feild, William M., VA
Fetter, John Sylvester, PA
Fogarty, Thomas Francis, RI
Forsberg, Philip M. L., NH
Fortunato, Samuel J., NJ
Fox, Jackson Leland, PA
Freeman, Albert W., PA
Gabriele, August A., OH
Gatti, Joseph W., PA
Ginsberg, Joseph E., PA

Glass, Frederic A., WI
Goldman, Leo Lawrence, NJ
Gompertz, John L., CA
Grobman, Irving Leonard, PA
Gunter, June U., NC
Hanlon, Clement Richard, PA
Hanna, Charles Marcus, PA
Hartman, Henry Raymond, PA
Heiligman, Raymond, NY
Helms, David Orville, PA
Hepler, Thomas Robert, PA
Hodas, Sidney M., NJ
Hoffmaster, Alfred L., PA
Hulick, Peter Vaughn, PA
Ishler, H. Richard, PA
Jacobs, Louis, PA
Jacobson, Milton B., NJ
Jacobson, Robert Morris, PA
Keveney, John Joseph, PA
Koffler, Arthur, CT
Kottcamp, Edward Charles, Jr., PA

Kramen, S. Victor, PA
Krieger, Arthur, PA
Lancione, Peter, OH
Law, Harold William, OH
Leland, John Augustine,Jr., CA
Leone, Peter Pascal, PA
Lutz, Edgar H., PA
Lutz, William Miller, PA
Manges, John P., PA
Marnell, Joseph Vincente, PA
Martin, Benjamin F., NC
Mason, Bernard, NJ
McCall, Robert E., NC
McCoy, James Edward, Jr., NY
McFarland, Paul E., PA
Meikle, George Charles, PA
Mervine, Ned Dewar, PA
Millington, J. Thomas, Jr., PA
Moore, Davis Lee, NC
Morehead, Robert P., NC
Moyer, LeRoy M., PA

Fig. 272.   J. Edward Berk (JMC, '36), nationally prominent gastroenterologist.

Fig. 273.   Nicholas R. Varano (JMC, '36), Assistant Professor of Urology.

Naidoff, David, PA
Nayfield, Romald Cornelius, PA
Nicolo, Anthony, PA
Nimoityn, Benjamin Solomon, PA
Nirosky, Joseph Anthony, PA
O'Neill, James F., PA
Parkhurst, Leonard Woods, PA
Pearl, Morton S., PA
Pearson, Manuel Malcolm, CT
Pennes, Alexander E., PA
Phoebus, Clifford Preston, NY
Rachunis, Michael Lewis, PA
Ramos-Oller Antonio, PUERTO RICO
Reed, Elmer M., PA
Reynolds, Oscar Lloyd, PA
Rinker, William H. S., PA
Rongaus, Walter Ferdinand, PA
Rosenzweig, Max, PA
Samuels, Sidney Solomon, PA
Sandhaus, Julius L., PA
Schwartz, Albert Morton, PA
Schwartzman, Joel J., PA

Share, William Lionel, WI
Singley, Harry Paul, NJ
Slasor, William Johnson, PA
Small, Louis, NJ
Smith, John A., NJ
Smith, Joseph A., PA
Soloman, Milton Bennet, NJ
Sortman, Harold P., DE
Suenaga, Howard James, CA
Sugint, Felix Peter, PA
Supowitz, Saul, PA
Sussman, Marcel S., PA
Suter, Stanley C., PA
Thornbury, James Harvey, WV
Tracey, Martin L., RI
Troy, William Daniel, CT
Turner, Oliver E., PA
Varano, Nicholas R., PA
Wagner, Philip Vincent, NY
Walter, Paul James, PA
Weinstein, Rayford Lee, NC
Wolff, Herbert M., NJ
Wong, Robert T., HAWAII

Student Lounge in College Building

The 138 graduates of this class brought the total number to 16,313. Although outstanding members could be singled out in every graduating class since 1826, this one ranked high in the number attracted to academic medicine and prominence in later professional activities.

Abraham Edward Rakoff, of Pennsylvania, an honor graduate, became interested in gynecologic endocrinology in his student years. As early as 1940 he joined with Drs. Cantarow and Paschkis to form an endocrine outpatient facility, an endocrine laboratory, and an informal research group at Jefferson. With these associates he developed procedures for increasing the sensitivity of the pregnancy test, for the bioassay of pituitary and chorionic gonadotropins, and for the assessment of the pituitary-ovarian-adrenal function in infertility and hirsutism. Dr. Rakoff's academic and clinical reputation became world wide (Fig. 274). His portrait was presented to the College by the Class of 1964 and he received the Alumni Achievement Award posthumously in 1984.

Paul Applegate Bowers, of Pennsylvania, after specialty training at Chicago Lying-In Hospital and serving in World War II as Colonel, rose academically at Jefferson to Professor of Obstetrics and Gynecology. As a respected teacher, author of many papers, and devoted Alumnus (President, 1973), his portrait was presented to the University in 1982. He was elected to two terms as Alumni Member of the Board of Trustees in 1984 and among many other honors received the Winged Ox Award of Thomas Jefferson University in 1985 (Fig. 275).

John Joseph O'Keefe, of Pennsylvania, after his internship at Jefferson Hospital, received the Ross V. Patterson Fellowship in Bronchoesophagology. After World War II service he continued through the academic ranks until appointed Chairman of Otolaryngology in 1973. His organizational memberships were legion and he authored many papers, including the development of bronchoscopy at Jefferson (Fig. 276).

Members of the class who became respected teachers and clinicians at Jefferson were: John Francis Wilson (Dermatology, Fig. 277), John Joseph Duncan (Plastic Surgery), Basil Giletto (Obstetrics and Gynecology), John Molyneux Flumerfelt (first Resident in Psychiatry), Louis Merves (Cardiology), Daniel Wilner (Radiology), and Irwin Jack Pincus (Physiology).

Bernard Benjamin Zamostein, of Pennsylvania, became a Charter Diplomate of the American Board of Family Practice. He served for over 50 years as a practitioner, teacher (Family Medicine at Jefferson), researcher, and humanitarian. He received the first Practitioner of the Year Award

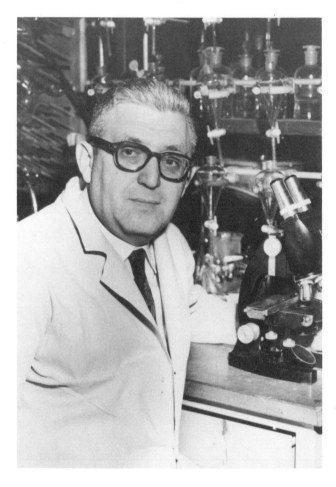

Fig. 274. Abraham E. Rakoff (JMC, '37), pioneer in gynecologic endocrinology.

Fig. 275. Paul A. Bowers (JMC, '37), Professor of Obstetrics and Gynecology.

of the Philadelphia County Medical Society in 1974 and its 1988 Cristol Award for significant contributions to the goals of organized medicine.

Everett Julius Gordon, of Washington, D.C., served as Clinical Associate Professor of Orthopaedic Surgery in Georgetown University School of Medicine as well as Chief of Orthopaedic Surgery in several of the leading hospitals. He was awarded the Maimonides Medal of the Antidefamation League in Washington, D.C. in 1987.

Robert Clifton McElroy, of West Virginia, was a Clinical Associate Professor of Obstetrics at the University of Pennsylvania School of Medicine and was prominent on the staff of the Pennsylvania Hospital.

Robert S. Garber became a widely-known New Jersey psychiatrist following his war-time service as Lieutenant Colonel in the United States Army. He went on to a career in clinical psychiatry and later was named Visiting Associate Professor at Rutgers University School of Medicine and at Jefferson Medical College. He received numerous awards including the first Mt. Airy Foundation Award, Denver, Colorado in 1971.

CLASS OF 1937

Abramson, Maurice, NJ
Ackerman, William E., Jr., WV
Allyn, Russell E., PA
Anchors, Eugene Louis, PA
Atwell, Floyd C., PA
Axelrod, Bernard Manuel, PA
Beamer, William Dale, PA
Bendix, Paul Alexander, NY
Bixler, Lester George, PA
Blanch, Joseph J., PA
Bowers, Paul A., PA
Boyd, Thomas Scott, PA
Bromberg, Norbert, NY
Bush, William M., PA
Campbell, James M., Jr., PA
Chang, Hon C., HAWAII
Ciaccia, Nicholas Louis, PA
Citta, James Philip, NJ
Conner, Loren, PA
Crevello, Albert James, PA
Currie, Daniel Smith, Jr., NC
Davis, Lindon Lee, NY
Dellinger, Woodrow Strayer, PA
Dickerson, Thomas Henry, DE
Dobson, Leslie, DE

Domaleski, Alfred Frank, PA
Donnelly, John Henry, NJ
Douglass, William T., Jr., PA
Duncan, John Joseph, PA
Evans, J. Lawrence, Jr., NJ
Ewan, John R., NJ
Fenstermacher, Richard Henry, PA
Fisher, Arthur A., OR
Flumerfelt, John M., PA
Focht, William Weinhold, PA
Garber, Robert S., PA
Geise, Ralph W., PA
Giletto, Basil, PA
Gollub, Ernest, PA
Gordon, Everett J., DC
Gordon, Milton H., NJ
Goyne, James Bevan, PA
Halpern, Sidney, FL
Henderson, Allen W., NY
Hermann, Irvin F., PA
Hieber, G. Frederick, PA
Hindle, Frank Lawton, Jr., NJ
Hooper, Fred Badman, PA
Howell, Thomas W., NJ
Iannuzzi, Peter J., NY

James, Joseph M., CT
Jones, Carl White, NC
Jones, Frank Allen, NC
Jones, Robert Turner, PA
Kenan, Frederick M., OH
Kimmelman, David B., PA
Klemmer, Herbert, NJ
Koplin, A. Herman, NJ
Korns, Charles Byron, Jr., PA
Kunz, Harold George, NJ
Laigon, Albert William, PA
Law, Kenneth Alexander, OH
LeFevre, John Daniel, OH
Leisawitz, Paul A., PA
Lenehan, J. Richard, RI
Lerch, Thomas Van Reed, PA
Levenson, Morton W., NJ
Levine, Arnold Sidney, NJ
LeWinn, Emmanuel Sigmund, PA
Lipinski, Joseph Floyd, PA
Marten, Milton Lewis, OH

McElroy, Robert Clifton, WV
Meehan, William Francis, Jr., NY
Merritt, Thomas Edwin, AL
Merves, Louis, NJ
Miller, Alfred Benjamin, PA
Minner, Roger Jonas, PA
Mirbach, Sidney Hershel, PA
Moser, Howard F. D., PA
Murray, Henry D., DE
Muschlitz, Robert Roper, PA
Neary, Edward R., NJ
O'Keefe, John Joseph, PA
Paradowski, Frank W., PA
Parks, Richard Hill, PA
Picciochi, Joseph Michael, PA
Pincus, Irwin J., PA
Poole, Charles H., Jr., PA
Potter, Leonard LeGrande, PA
Powell, Sydney Joseph, Jr., PA
Rader, George Andrew, NC
Rakoff, Abraham Edward, PA

Fig. 276.   John J. O'Keefe (JMC, '37), Chairman of Otolaryngology (1973-75).

Fig. 277.   John F. Wilson (JMC, '37), Associate Professor of Dermatology and Alumni Officer.

Ralston, Joseph Alexander, OH
Reardon, James J., NY
Reath, Joseph Pancoast, PA
Robinson, William Patrick, PA
Roos, Leon, PA
Rosenberg, Leon, NJ
Saylor, Clyde Llewellyn, PA
Scholl, Harvey W., PA
Scholten, Roger A., MI
Seltzer, Joseph P., ME
Shuster, Samuel A., NJ
Siddall, John Richard, NJ
Siegfried, Edward G., OH
Silverman, Daniel, PA
Skreczko, Charles K., CT
Slease, Cyrus B., PA
Smith, Lloyd Francis, CT
Snyder, M. Wilson, PA
Stanton, Edward Vincent, PA
Starz, Walter Earl, PA
Stein, Samuel Charles, PA
Stephens, James T., CA
Swift, Coe T., CA
Thaimann, William Gregory, Jr., PA

Thomas, Densmore, OH
Thompson, Thomas M., II, OH
Walters, John Dulany, PA
Washburn, C. Yulan, NC
Waterhouse, Robert Parkins, NE
Webb, E. Burton, PA
Weintrob, Joseph R., NJ
Weniger, Frederick L., PA
Wentzell, James Earl, NJ
Whitaker, Henry James, PA
Whitbeck, Carl G., NY
Wikler, Louis A., PA
Wilner, Daniel, PA
Wilson, John F., PA
Wilson, Walter Howard, NC
Wise, Robert Eric, PA
Woldow, Irving, PA
Wolfinger, Walter L., PA
Wotchko, John, PA
Wright, John E., NC
Zamostien, Bernard B., PA
Zelt, Leo George, PA
Ziccardi, Anthony Vincent, NJ
Zionts, Martin Arnold, PA

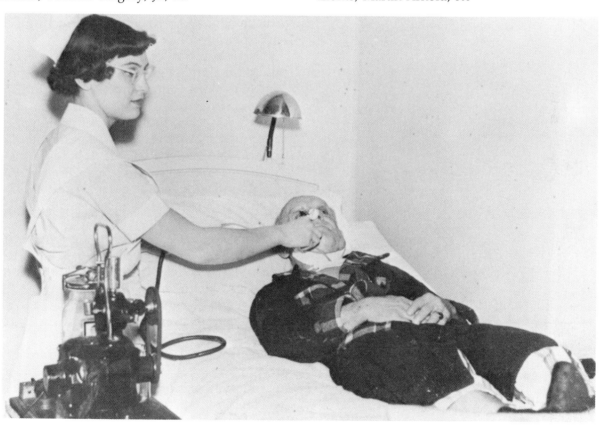

Bronchoscopic Ward care in Thompson Annex.

1937

Among the 134 graduates a major prize winner, William W. L. Glenn, pursued an academic career in surgery. Following World War II he completed residency at Jefferson and went on to appointment at Yale University School of Medicine where he progressed to Professor of Surgery with many publications and research activities in cardiothoracic surgery. He was President of the American Heart Association in 1971 and received the Jefferson Alumni Achievement Award in 1973. On retirement he was named Charles S. Ohse Professor Emeritus and Senior Research Scientist at Yale (Fig. 278).

R. Howard Lackay trained at Walter Reed Hospital, Jefferson, and at Graduate School of Medicine of University of Pennsylvania. As a career officer, he served in Preventive Medicine and Aviation Medicine. During the immediate postwar period he was assigned to Jefferson as Professor of Military Science and Tactics.

John J. DeTuerk, following wartime service, returned to Jefferson to complete his surgical residency, then joined the staff in surgery. He succeeded his mentor, Dr. George Willauer (JMC, '23, Fig. 227) as Director of Surgery at Methodist Hospital, Philadelphia, while advancing to Clinical Professor of Surgery at Jefferson (Fig. 279).

Victor P. Satinsky practiced cardiothoracic surgery at Hahnemann Medical College Hospital with numerous research accomplishments. At retirement he organized the Satinsky Institute for Human Resource Development for educational achievement and rehabilitation of young people with special problems.

J. Woodrow Savacool became associated with the Pulmonary Division at Jefferson, first as Joseph V. Horn Fellow and advanced to Clinical Associate Professor of Medicine. He was also appointed Associate Professor of Preventive Medicine and directed the Health Maintenance Clinic for ten years. He was a consultant in pulmonary diseases for the Philadelphia Department of Health. In later years he aided in editing *Thomas Jefferson University: Tradition and Heritage* (Fig. 280).

Alison H. Price, an early resident in medicine at Jefferson, joined the staff as Ross V. Patterson Fellow. He was closely associated with Professor Hobart A. Reimann in major clinical and academic work. He advanced to Associate Professor of Medicine but resigned in the early 1960's to establish the Price Clinic (Fig. 281).

Woodrow W. Lindenmuth, trained in surgery at Pennsylvania Hospital, then went on to an appointment as Chief of Surgery at New Haven Veterans Administration Hospital and as Professor of Surgery at Yale University School of Medicine.

George A. Silver was with the United States Public Health Service and was affiliated academ-

Fig. 278. William W. L. Glenn (JMC, '38), Professor of Surgery at Yale University School of Medicine.

ically with Johns Hopkins and Columbia Universities with final location at Yale University as Professor of Public Health (International Health).

Wilfred I. Carney, longtime surgeon in Providence, Rhode Island, also served as Clinical Assistant Professor of Surgery at Brown University School of Medicine.

Morris J. Shapiro went on to a career in surgery, associated with Strong Memorial Hospital and the University of Rochester, New York, as Associate Professor of Surgery. His many community activities in Upstate New York were especially notable.

Paul Chodoff was trained in psychiatry at St. Elizabeth's Hospital, Washington, D.C. and remained there to practice psychiatry and psychoanalysis. He became Clinical Professor of Psychiatry at Georgetown University School of

Medicine and was also President of the American Academy of Psychoanalysis.

Albert M. Biele was for many years a practicing psychiatrist affiliated with Jefferson and numerous other Philadelphia institutions. He advanced to Clinical Professor of Psychiatry and Human Behavior at Jefferson.

Victor Mayer proceeded to a full career in orthopaedic surgery with many associated consulting posts in the New York area. He was for many years Assistant Professor of Orthopaedic Surgery at Cornell University School of Medicine and Associate Attending Surgeon at New York Hospital and the Hospital for Special Surgery.

Norman W. Henry, Jr. was Pathologist to St. Joseph's Hospital and for many years Assistant Professor of Pathology at Jefferson.

Martin Green was trained in pediatrics and

Fig. 279.   John J. DeTuerk (JMC, '38), Clinical Professor of Surgery.

Fig. 280.   J. Woodrow Savacool (JMC, '38), pulmonary specialist and historian.

allergy. He became Chairman of Pediatrics at Atlantic City Medical Center, also holding an appointment in Pediatrics at Jefferson with the rank of Assistant Professor.

William I. Heine, cardiologist and Senior Attending Physician at Einstein Medical Center was also Clinical Professor of Medicine at Temple University School of Medicine.

Fig. 281. Alison H. Price (JMC, '38), Associate Professor of Medicine.

Albert, Perry, NJ
Anzinger, Robert J., OH
Armalavage, Leon J., PA
Axelrod, Solomon Jacob, PA
Bancroft, Charles March, PA
Barrett, Arthur Miller, KS
Berg Philip Jr., PA
Berger, Simon Melvin, DE
Biele, Albert Melvin, PA
Blumberg, Leon David, PA
Boquist, Walter A., NJ
Brickley, Kenneth S., PA
Brown, Thomas Paul, PA
Canter, Harold, PA
Carney, Wilfred, OH
Chaimovitz, Jerome, PA
Chandler, Harold L., MA
Cherashore, Ralph Raub, PA
Chodoff, Paul E., PA

Cohn, Clarence, PA
Cole, Seymour L., NY
Colosi, Nicholas A., PA
Connole, John F., Jr., PA
Cooperman, Martin, NY
Coverdale, Edward James, PA
DeLeo, Caesar A., PA
DeTuerk, John J., PA
Devlin, Joseph Thomas, Jr., PA
Dougherty, Charles Joseph, DE
Eckstein, David, NJ
Eisner, Joseph Harold, PA
English, Harrison Force, III, NJ
Fish, Henry, PA
Frediani, Alexander W., VA
Gabreski, Thaddeus S., PA
Gardner, Everett W., WY
Gehl, Sidney Hersh, NJ
Georgetson, James Michael, PA

1938

Gershman, Isadore, RI
Gladsden, Eugene S., DC
Glenn, William L., NC
Gonzalez-Flores, Jose R. PUERTO RICO
Green Martin, NJ
Greenberg, Mortimer, NJ
Halton, Edward J., MA
Hause, Welland Angel, PA
Hazlett, James C., WV
Heine, William I., NJ
Henning, Curtis Fisher, PA
Henry, Norman W., PA
Hinman, Louis Franklin, PA
Houck, Earl E., Jr., PA
Houston, Bernard John, PA
Hurwitz, Abraham, PA
Iannone, Angelo B., NJ
Jacques, Richard H., OH
Johnson, Tillman D., UT
Judson, G. Vernon, Jr., NJ
Kaczynski, Stanley Bernard, PA
Kane, James A., PA
Kaplan, Albert Jordan, PA
Kaplan, Louis, PA
Keesal, Solomon, PA
Kline, Joseph J., NJ
Kostyla, Edward Andrew, RI
Kravitz, Morton Atherton, PA
Krosnick, Gerald, CT
Kurfees, James G., NC
Lackay, R. Howard, NC
Langdon, Benjamin Bruce, NC
Lihn, Henry, NJ
Lindenmuth, Woodrow Wilson, PA
Longaker, George M., Jr., PA
Luckner, Wendelin George, CT
Lustig, Melvin, NJ
Lynch, Vincent Aloysius, NY
Marenus, Edward Benjamin, PA
Marsh, William Edward, PA
Mayer, Victor, NY
McClintock, John Laughlin, OH
McCullough, Alexander Roscoe, TN
Miller, Elmer Harry, PA
Miller, Horatio Brown, PA
Morton, Paul Harry, UT
Motsay, Dominic Sylvester, PA
Nishijima, Satoru, HI

Noel, George Thompson, Jr., NC
Phillips, Edward Stephens, WV
Pitone, A. Joseph, PA
Platt, Edward V., NJ
Pobirs, Frederick Walter, RI
Potelunas, Clement B., PA
Price, Henry S., NJ
Price, Alison Howe, PA
Rednor, Daniel Jay, NJ
Remley, Luke Kinsel, PA
Richlin, Padie, NY
Rinaldi, Lucian Louis, PA
Robbins, Jacob J., PA
Romejko, Walter J., Jr., PA
Roscoe, Constantine R., PA
Rosset, Ephriam Manuel, PA
Satinsky, Victor P., PA
Savacool, J. Woodrow, PA
Schlesinger, Samuel, PA
Schwab, John E., PA
Seigal, Harold Leonard, ME
Shapiro, Morris J., NY
Shepherd, Warren S., UT
Shoenthal, W. James, PA
Siegel, Joseph F., PA
Siegel, John Morris, PA
Silver, George A., PA
Skloff, Samuel Harry, PA
Snyder, Gordon Elias, PA
Sobie, Pincus, NY
Spilka, George Martin, PA
Stankard, William F., CT
Stevens, Hamilton Wright, Jr., NC
Stevens, Herman D., VA
Supple, Leonard Keating, NY
Taylor, Vernon W. Jr., NC
Tripp, Edwin P. Jr., MA
Ulrich, Samuel D., PA
Underwood, Harry Burnham, PA
Vance, Ralph B., PA
Wachtel, Leo Michael, Jr., GA
Watkin, Walter Brown, PA
Weiss, William Anthony, PA
Wentzel, George Robert, PA
Wentzel, John H. C., PA
Wiener, Jacob S., PA
Wildmann, George Alexander, NJ
Yost, Howard A., PA
Zielinski, Joseph Francis, MA

At the Commencement held June 2 at the Academy of Music, Mr. Robert P. Hooper conferred the M.D. degree upon 122 graduates. The Honorable Arthur H. James, Governor of the Commonwealth of Pennsylvania, gave the Address and received an honorary LL.D. degree.

John Hendricks Hodges, of West Virginia, an honor graduate, went on to a distinguished career at Jefferson in teaching, research and clinical practice. From 1944 to 1972 he directed the student course in Clinical Laboratory Medicine. He worked with Professor Hobart A. Reimann in the first elucidation of a viral etiology for both pneumonia and gastroenteritis. In 1964 he was appointed the first Ludwig A. Kind Professor of Medicine and from 1968 to 1978 was Director of the Division of Internal (General) Medicine. He was also an Associate in the Division of Hematology (Fig. 282). On two occasions the students dedicated their *Clinic Yearbook* (1951 and 1962) to him. Dr. Hodges served for two terms as Alumni Member on the Board of Trustees (1978 to 1984) and was selected by the Board to continue in an emeritus status as the only Alumnus ever to be so honored. He served as President of the Alumni Association (1972), Acting Chairman of the Department of Medicine (1976), and his portrait was presented to the University in 1981. The Alumni Association honored him with its Achievement Award in 1990.

Joseph Medoff, of Pennsylvania, another honor graduate, became an outstanding teacher and clinician in gastroenterology at Jefferson, rising to the rank of Clinical Professor (Fig. 283). He was twice the recipient of the Lindback Award for distinguished teaching (1967 and 1971) and was Faculty Advisor to the Hare Medical Society for 16 years (1960-76). In appreciation the Hare Society members presented his portrait to the University in 1976.

Three other members of this class subsequently became prominent on the Jefferson Faculty, namely Joseph Pote Long, Clinical Professor of Obstetrics and Gynecology (Fig. 284), Paul Fried (Obstetrics and Gynecology), and James Byron Carty (Surgery).

Donald Worcester Bortz became Regional Chairman of the American College of Physicians; Frederick Lee Byerly rose to Professor of Surgery at the University of Pittsburgh; Henry Arnold Shenkin was Head of Neurosurgery at the Episcopal Hospital of Philadelphia; William Luther White became Professor of Plastic Surgery at the University of Pittsburgh; and Claude Nash Herndon, Jr. was Chairman of Preventive Medicine and Genetics at the Bowman Gray School of Medicine, North Carolina.

Fig. 282. John H. Hodges (JMC, '39), first Ludwig A. Kind Professor of Medicine.

Leonard Philip Lang, an early Fellow in Pulmonary Physiology at Jefferson's Chest Department, went on to a leading role in pulmonary medicine in Wilmington, Delaware. He was later named Clinical Professor of Medicine at Jefferson through its affiliated hospital program.

Fig. 283. Joseph Medoff (JMC, '39), Clinical Professor of Medicine (Gastroenterology).

Alexander, John B., PA
Arms, Arnold V., KS
Badman, Fred S., PA
Beardsley, Wayne Peter, MI
Bers, Sol N., PA
Block, Louis Henry, PA
Bortz, Donald W., PA
Brady, Fred Charles, PA
Burry, William C., PA
Bush, William M., NY
Butler, Fred A., FL
Byerly, Frederick Lee, NC
Campbell, Vernon W. H., PA
Carty, James Byron, NJ
Chain, William Thomas, PA
Clunan, Ambrose P., NJ
Cochran, James Edward, PA
Cohen, Isadore Sacks, PA

Coll, James J., PA
Cornwell, Robert A., NY
Covington, Furman Payne, NC
Crane, Morris, PA
Deininger, John T., PA
Delehanty, John Thomas, PA
DePersio, John D., PA
Dineen, Francis A., PA
Dunn, David D., PA
Engle, J. Harold, PA
Evashwick, George, PA
Falker, John Michael, PA
Faux, Frederick J., NJ
Fish, David Joseph, RI
Fitzpatrick, James Joseph, PA
Fried, Paul, PA
Garner, Blaine R., PA
Geib, Wayne A., MI

Goldberg, Louis, PA
Greaser, George Lewis, PA
Grimes, James Thomas, PA
Hale, Raymond M., Jr., PA
Hanley, J. B., CT
Herndon, Claude N., Jr., NC
Hodges, John H., WV
Hollander, George, PA
Hood, George B., PA
Jastram, George Berlin, MA
Joseph, Lester George, CT
Keller, William McConkey, OH
Kelly, James J., Jr., PA
Kennedy, Paul A., PA
Kilker, John J. B., PA
Kistler, William S., PA
Knoll, George M., PA
Kurtz, C. Roger, PA
Labenski, Alfred, PA
Lang, Leonard P., PA
Lawlor, John Martin, PA
Lee, Robert Edward, NJ
Lehrer, Lewis, PA
Leventhal, Louis, NY
Levin, Raphael A., PA
Lippman, Nathan Louis, NJ
Long, Joseph P., PA
Lupton, Albert Marsee, DE
Maguda, Thomas A., PA
Maisel, Albert Lloyd, NM

McCarron, Joseph Patrick, PA
McDaniel, Joseph Stites, Jr., DE
McNally, John B., PA
Medoff, Joseph, PA
Miller, George William, III, PA
Mira, Joseph Anthony, PA
Monroe, Daniel Geddie, NC
Norton, Joseph Glen, DC
Nussbaum, Herman, NJ
O'Donnell, Charles Hugh, PA
Page, William G., MT
Parmet, Morris, PA
Patrick, Nicholas Emil, PA
Perlmutter, Irving Kenneth, NJ
Perrl, Frank Adrian, PA
Podolnick, Nelson, VA
Pottash, Ruben R., PA
Powell, Thurston G., NC
Price, Walter Samuel, NJ
Quiney, James J., Jr., PA
Repici, Anthony J., NJ
Repta, Stephen, Jr., NJ
Riegert, Louis C., NJ
Rudolph, John P., NJ
Ruetschlin, James H., PA
Salvatore, Joseph Thomas, NJ
Scharadin, Nelson S., PA
Schinfeld, Louis H., DE
Schiowitz, Albert, PA
Schlechter, Charles Francis, PA
Shaen, Edward, NJ
Shenkin, Henry A., PA
Shirey, John L., NC
Shoenfelt, James Whitaker, Jr., PA
Simmons, Alexander Wingate, NC
Sims, Arthur I., VA
Skversky, Norman J., FL
Slovin, Isadore, DE
Sniscak, John Michael, PA
Somers, Lewis F., VA
Steele, R. Edward, PA
Stein, Hymen D., RI
Stroud, Henry H., DE
Sullivan, Frederick Jeremiah, Jr., MA
Tallant, Edward James, PA
Thomas, Nathanael Ross, PA
Tursi, Joseph John, PA
Violetti, Raffaole Lombardo, PA
Wagner, William Joseph, NY
Watkins, Evan Lloyd, PA
Weiner, Simon, DC
Wennersten, Jack R., PA
Wertheim, Arthur Robert, NJ
White, George S., PA
White, William L., NC
Williams, Glenn L., PA

Fig. 284.   Joseph P. Long (JMC, '39), Clinical Professor of Obstetrics and Gynecology.

At the Commencement for 125 graduates on June 7 at the Academy of Music, four honorary degrees were awarded. William Lyon Phelps, Ph.D., LL.D., Orator of Yale University, received a Doctorate of Civil Law and gave the Address entitled "The Art of Living." Other awards were the LL.D. to Thomas Sovereign Gates, Ph.D, LL.D., President of the University of Pennsylvania; the Sc.D. to James Carre Magee, M.D. (JMC, '05), Surgeon General of the United States Army; and LL.D. to Robert Poole Hooper, President of the Board of Trustees of the Jefferson Medical College.

Herbert Alfred Luscombe, Jr., of Pennsylvania, an honor graduate, served his internship at Jefferson Hospital, and, after returning from service in World War II, devoted the rest of his professional life to dermatology at Jefferson. In 1959 he was appointed to the Chairmanship of the Department. Under his direction a modern Department evolved with a fully accredited three-year residency program. By 1986, 35 residents had been trained and the Luscombe Club was formed. Dr. Luscombe served as President of the Alumni Association in 1971 and his portrait was presented to the University in 1977. His excellence in teaching was recognized nationally when he received the Clark W. Finnerud Award

Fig. 285.   Herbert A. Luscombe (JMC, '40), Chairman of Dermatology (1959-86).

Fig. 286.   Thomas B. Mervine (JMC, '40), Clinical Professor of Surgery.

for Teaching from the Dermatology Foundation in 1981. In 1983, the Herbert A. Luscombe Lectureship was established to bring distinguished dermatologists to Jefferson, emphasizing the role of progress in other institutions. At his retirement from the Chairmanship in 1986, Dr. Luscombe had served for 27 years for the longest term of leadership of any Dermatology Department in the United States (Fig. 285).

Thomas Burritt Mervine, another honor graduate, was appointed Instructor in Anesthesiology in the Department of Surgery at Jefferson in 1944 and served in that capacity until 1953. He was the first to use intravenous pentothal at Jefferson, to institute routine intravenous infusion at the start of surgery, and he performed many of the early endotracheal intubations. He also worked closely with Dr. William T. Lemmon in the early use of continuous spinal anesthesia. In the Surgery Department, Dr. Mervine was outstanding in his knowledge of the surgical literature and rose through the academic ranks to Clinical Professor. He served as President of the Alumni Association in 1980 (Fig. 286).

Ray Winfield Kehm went on to surgical training at the Cleveland Clinic. He established his practice in York, Pennsylvania, where in 1965 he became Chairman of the Department of Surgery at York Hospital. In 1982 he published an autobiography entitled *The Birth of a Surgeon*.

William John Snape, of New Jersey, taught in Jefferson's Department of Physiology and carried out research in gastroenterology. In later years he conducted an active clinical practice in New Jersey.

Gaetano Brindisi, taught in Jefferson's Department of Medicine and became Chief of Medicine in Saint Mary's Hospital, Philadelphia.

CLASS OF 1940

Allison, Olaf W., IL
Aughinbaugh, Thomas H., PA
Bauer, Francis Xavier, PA
Bauer, Walter David, Jr., PA
Berger, Melvin Martin, PA
Bernhard, Joel Augustin, NJ
Biggar, Raymond Whitney, MI
Bigley, Joseph R., PA
Boysen, Theophilus Henry, III, NJ
Brady, John C., NY
Brindisi, Gaetano, PA
Brogan, John J., PA
Browne, E. Westbrook, OH
Byrne, Philip Joseph, PA
Cappiello, William A., NJ
Clements, Harry Henry, PA
Cohen, Ben, PA
Collins, Clyde A., PA
Cotter, John Joseph, PA
Covey, John Knox, PA
Crawford, Walter W., MS
Cubberley, Charles L., Jr., NJ
Derr, Russell H., PA
Dickerman, Frederick A., PA
Eisner, Abraham G., PA
Ellis, William A., RI
Ferrier, Melvin C., PA
Fetter, Franklin Clayton, PA
Fletcher, Henry Bennett, Jr., RI
Forbes, Thomas E., NC

Forte, Joseph Anthony, Jr., PA
Frank, Lewis P., PA
Gabriel, Frederick Raphael, PA
Gabriel, Louis Thomas, Jr., PA
Glass, William J., Jr., WV
Goodman, Leo M., OH
Goodman, William Edward, OH
Grem, Frank M., PA
Grier, John C., Jr., NC
Hanlon, Paul Adrian, PA
Hanson, Wayne Pierre, CA
Herron, James Robert, Jr., NJ
High, John David, PA
Hindle, Joseph A., RI
Horn, Edward T., PA
Hudson, Robert J., PA
Johnson, Paul Churchill, PA
Kaar, Richard C., ID
Kaneshiro, Francis T., HI
Kehm, Ray W., PA
Kelly, Rupert Emery, PA
Kessler, Carl Conrad, PA
King, John F. W., DE
Kitchin, William W., NC
Knowles, Willard E., PA
Kornfield, Harry, PA
Langston, John D., PA
Lasichak, Andrew Gregory, PA
Lauria, Michael H., PA
Lessey, Arthur Gerald, DE

Lindsay, Robert Boyd, NC
Long, Robert Schofield, DE
Lull, George Fairless, Jr., PA
Luscombe, Herbert A., Jr., PA
Malia, Joseph Eugene, PA
Mangus, Julian Edward, WV
Markunas, Francis B., PA
Matsko, Stephen Edmund, PA
Matta, Enrique L., Jr., PUERTO RICO
McCoy, Edwin Richard, SC
McTear, Thomas Francis, Jr., PA
Mechanik, Harvey Kenneth, NJ
Mellor, Wendell John, ID
Mervine, Thomas B., PA
Messmore, Isaac Lindsey, PA
Mikowski, I. Edmund, PA
Miller, Charles William, PA
Moir, John A., PA
Morrison, John Huff, MD
Moy, James Thomas, PA
O'Leary, James J., MA
Oliver, Adlai Stevenson, Jr., NC
Osborn, Edward George, NJ
Pechin, Sergius, PA
Poteat, Robert M., Jr., NC
Quinn, James Joseph, PA
Rich, Richard Innis, WA
Riddle, Lindsay R., PA
Robinson, William H., III, PA
Sales, Irving J., PA
Saunders, Richard Hoskins, PA
Saylor, Blair W., PA

Scalera, John F., NJ
Scanlon, James Patrick, PA
Schaeffer, Alan M., NJ
Seligman, Randolph V., NM
Sewall, Arthur D., NJ
Shaffer, Irvin G., PA
Shaffer, John F., PA
Silenskey, John J., PA
Simon, John L., PA
Sites, Charles J., WV
Smith, H. Lawrence, PA
Snape, William J., NJ
Stancil, James R., NC
Starr, Robert R., OH
Stein, Gerald Bernard, PA
Taft, William C., PA
Tattersall, Harold A., FL
Thomas, Roger B., DE
Treat, Michael E., PA
Trippe, Morton Fitch, NJ
Wagner, Richard Lawrence, OH
Walker, Robert Latshaw, III, PA
Wall, Roscoe L., Jr., NC
Webster, David K., NH
Welsh, Albert Eugene, Jr., PA
Wenger, Christian Showalter, PA
Whiteman, John Richard, IL
Willis, John Mitchell, Jr., PA
Wilson, Dale Sloan, FL
Winkler, Louis H., Jr., PA
Wood, Rowland Emery, FL
Wyker, Albertus Cleon, OH
Yap, Peter T. J., HAWAII

The heights by great men reached and kept
Were not attained by sudden flight.
But they, while their companions slept,
Were toiling upward in the night.

Henry Wadsworth Longfellow
(1807–82)

This year marked the entry of the United States into World War II with the bombing of Pearl Harbor by the Japanese on December 7. Forty-three members of this class of 120 had taken training in the Reserve Officers training corps during their four years and at graduation, in addition to their M.D. degrees, also received a certificate of Lieutenancy in the Reserve. Four out of the 102 class members who served would make the supreme sacrifice of their lives in the global conflict.

A stirring address was delivered by John M.T. Finney, M.D., LL.D. who spoke on *The True Province of the Doctor.* He had been a protege of Dr. William Stewart Halsted at Johns Hopkins, was Emeritus Professor of Surgery at Hopkins, and was awarded the honorary degree of Doctor of Letters by Mr. Robert P. Hooper, President of the Board.

John Y. Templeton, III, an honor graduate, was the first surgical resident to work with Dr. John H. Gibbon, Jr. in the laboratory at Jefferson. Following appointment to the Faculty in 1950 his academic rise was meteoric to Samuel D. Gross Professor of Surgery and Chairman of the Department (1967). He was a pioneer in the establishment of clinical cardiac surgery at Jefferson. He published more than 80 articles on a wide spectrum of surgical subjects and held membership in 50 professional organizations, serving in official positions in 14 of these. He became President of the Laennec Society, Pennsylvania Association for Thoracic Surgery, Philadelphia Academy of Surgery, Philadelphia County and Pennsylvania State Medical Societies, and Meigs Medical Association. At Jefferson he served as President of the Medical Staff and of the Alumni Association (1976). The Templeton Lectureship was established in 1980 and in the same year his portrait was presented to the University. He received the Jefferson Alumni Achievement Award in 1981. In 1987 Davidson College, his undergraduate alma mater, awarded him the Sc.D. degree and Jefferson later that year the LL.D. He was elected to serve on Jefferson's Board of Trus-

tees as Alumni Representative (1989), and became "a legend in his own time" (Fig. 287).

Frederick B. Wagner, Jr., also an honor graduate, taught Anatomy at the Daniel Baugh Institute (1942-46) and served as a Ross V. Patterson Fellow in Surgery. Following service as a private assistant to Thomas A. Shallow, the Samuel D. Gross Professor of Surgery, he rose to Clinical Professor of Surgery by 1955, served as acting Chairman of Surgery in 1977, and became the Grace Revere Osler Professor of Surgery in 1978. In the latter year his portrait was presented to the University. He was a founding member of the International Society for Cardiovascular Sur-

Fig. 287. John Y. Templeton, III (JMC, '41), Gross Professor of Surgery and prominent alumnus.

gery, and among his many professional organizations served as President of the Philadelphia Academy of Surgery (1986). In addition to more than 50 scientific articles Dr. Wagner co-authored a textbook on *Preoperative and Postoperative Care* (1947) and published *The Twilight Years of Lady Osler* (1985). A surgical library in the University Hospital was named in his honor by the residents, and in 1987 he received the Dean's Medal for dedicated service to the College. He served as President of the Alumni Association (1975) and was elected an Alumni Representative to the Board of Trustees in 1985. Appointed the University Historian in 1984, he edited *Thomas Jefferson University: Tradition and Heritage* published in 1989. He received the Alumni Achievement Award in 1990 (Fig. 288).

Paul J. Poinsard served in World War II in the South Pacific as a Flight Surgeon and received five battle stars. He then pursued a distinguished career devoted to both general psychiatry and psychoanalysis at Jefferson, where he served as Acting Chairman (1961-1962). Dr. Poinsard was the first psychiatrist to be elected as President of the Thomas Jefferson University Hospital Staff (1979-1981) and he served for many years on its Executive Committee. He became President of

the Philadelphia Psychiatric Society, the Pennsylvania Psychiatric Society, the Medical Club of Philadelphia, the Jefferson Alumni Association during the Centennial (1970) of its founding, the Meigs Medical Association, and as the 120th President of the Philadelphia County Medical Society. After achieving Emeritus status in 1983, he continued as an active member of the Psychiatry Department, the Hospital, and the Alumni Association (Fig. 289).

Oscar Creech, Jr., of North Carolina, an honor graduate, became associated with the world-renowned Dr. Michael E. DeBakey in vascular surgery and made notable contributions in this field (Fig. 290). He also was a pioneer in the perfusion of malignant tumors of the lower extremities with chemotherapeutic agents. He went on to become Chairman of Surgery at the Tulane School of Medicine and also its Dean. His brilliant career was cut short by premature death at the height of his career.

Clyde C. Greene, Jr., of North Carolina, became a founding member of the American Society of Internal Medicine in 1956, its President in 1969/70, Editor of its National Magazine (1981-84), and co-author of its history, *Aspirations and Achievements* (1981).

Fig. 288.   Frederick B. Wagner, Jr. (JMC, '41) Grace Revere Osler Professor of Surgery and University Historian.

1941

399

Fig. 289.   Paul J. Poinsard (JMC, '41), Professor of Psychiatry and Acting Chairman.

Fig. 290.   Oscar Creech, Jr. (JMC, '41), Chairman of Surgery and Dean, Tulane University School of Medicine.

Adams, Winford C., ME
Appel, Charles F., MA
Appel, John F., MA
Armstrong, Thomas Smith, Jr., PA
Ballenberger, Louis Porter, NC
Beasely, Norris Morey, OH
Bell, Ralph M., NC
Blaum, Louis C., PA
Boylston, Bedford Forrest, SC
Brown, Samuel H., MO
Bruno, John Robert, PA
Burnett, Lawrence F., NJ
Burns, Charles N., PA
Campbell, John Hugh, PA
Campbell, Walter Edmund, RI
Carapella, John D., PA
Carmona, Manuel G., PUERTO RICO

Carroll, Irvin Norwood, DE
Catlett, George F., NJ
Collins, James Anthony, Jr., PA
Crawford, Joseph Benjamin, NC
Creech, Oscar, Jr., NC
Cressler, John C., PA
DeLawter, Dewitt E., MD
Derr, Frederick S., PA
Drake, Willard M., Jr., NJ
Dunn, Paul Fallon, RI
Ealy, David Lawrence, WV
Eckhart, William Vincent, IN
Farmer, Rodney Arnold, PA
Fehr, John U., PA
Fetter, Donald Evans, PA
Flanagan, James Francis, Jr., NJ
Flanigan, Edward Anthony, Jr., PA

1941

Flood, Richard Edward, WV
Forcey, L. Ralph, PA
Forejt, Joseph M., PA
Forgiel, Ferdinand Stephen, RI
Forse, David P., Jr., PA
Fortune, Benjamin F., NC
Fotouhi, Abol H., IRAN
Gardner, James L., PA
Garnet, James D., NJ
Geraghty, John Francis, PA
Gill, John Joseph, PA
Gormley, James B., PA
Greene, Clyde C., Jr., NC
Griffin, Leslie W., NC
Gruber, Charles Michael, Jr., PA
Halbeisen, William A. C., NJ
Hanlon, George Henry, PA
Hepler, Thomas K., PA
Hoffman, Arthur F., IN
Johnson, Albert Sidney, Jr., GA
Kim, Chang H., KOREA
Kreger, Oliver Judson, Jr., PA
Kubek, John Anthony, PA
Leydic, Cyrus Clark, Jr., PA
Lightcap, Clement A., AL
Lockwood, James Harrison, MA
Longshore, William Allen, Jr., PA
Malley, William L., PA
Marx, Halvey Edward, PA
Mazur, Edward Frank, NJ
McEvilly, James Patrick, PA
McKinley, Oscar Vincent, PA
McMahan, Joseph N., PA
McNickle, Jerry Hal, KS
Mihalick, Peter John, PA
Miller, James Henry, PA
Mumford, Ander M., NC
Murray, Kenneth Joseph, MA
Nishijima, Randal A., HAWAII
Nosal, Joseph Louis, PA
O'Brien, John R., NY
Over, Stuart B., Jr., PA
Paden, Norton Crane, PA

Palmer, Rufus Edward, III, PA
Palmisano, Vincent S., PA
Patton, Thomas Bustard, PA
Peoples, Samuel Sterrett, PA
Peters, Robert H., Jr., PA
Pettit, Paul H., NJ
Poinsard, Paul J., PA
Possner, Howard Edmond, Jr., RI
Powell, Grover Cleveland, Jr., PA
Ratke, Henry V., PA
Regan, Joseph James, PA
Repman, Harry Joseph, Jr., PA
Ricketts, Edward A., PA
Robinson, Frederick A., Jr., PA
Sams, James M., TN
Schadt, Oliver S., Jr., PA
Schafer, Earl W., Jr., WV
Schaffer, Edward D., PA
Schucker, Charles L., PA
Sloss, James Olson, PA
Smith, Richard Thomas, PA
Smith, William C. F., PA
Snyder, Albert Joseph, PA
Somerville, William Joseph, PA
Sprecher, Omer D., Jr., MD
Stevens, Raymond T., RI
Stotler, Charles Wilbur, PA
Swan, James R., PA
Taft, George H., RI
Tallman, Edwin H., PA
Taylor, William I., Jr., NC
Templeton, John Y., III, NC
Troncelliti, Mario V., PA
Tucker, James Martin, PA
Vick, Edward Hoge, NC
Wagner, Frederick B., Jr., PA
Washburn, Hubert Horace, PA
Webster, Harry N., Jr., AL
Welch, William Lee, PA
White, Wesley R., PA
Wiggins, Walter S., PA
Wolford, Robert W., OH
Youngman, George Andrew, MO

As a war measure, President Robert P. Hooper in January of this year announced the decision of the Board to place Jefferson on an accelerated curriculum to provide 500 to 600 new doctors by 1945. At this time Dean Perkins confirmed that four academic years would be compressed to three chronologic years. The internship in Jefferson Hospital was concomitantly reduced from 27 to 12 months.

John Wallace Davis in this class of 131 won multiple prizes at graduation and followed in the footsteps of his illustrious father (Professor Warren B. Davis, JMC, '10, Fig. 179) in plastic surgery at Jefferson. After spending the years 1943 to 1946 as a Major in the Medical Corps in the China-Burma-India Theater during World War II, he returned to Jefferson for training under his father. As one of the pioneers in cosmetic surgery, he was one of the original proponents of psychologic good health (Fig. 291). He gained national recognition in his specialty and served as a Director and Board Trustee of the American Society of Plastic and Reconstructive Surgery. In addition to service as Chairman of Alumni Annual Giving at Jefferson for more than 27 years he received Jefferson's prestigious Cornerstone Award in 1978 (Fig. 443).

Willis Edmund Manges, an honor student, joined Jefferson's Radiology Staff in 1945, following the family tradition initiated by his father, Willis F. Manges (JMC, '03, Fig. 157), who had been the First Head of the Department of Roentgenology (1904-36). He subsequently went on to become Head of Radiology at the Methodist Hospital in Philadelphia and completed his professional career there.

Joseph John Rupp devoted his academic career at Jefferson to the field of endocrinology and oncology, rising to the rank of Professor of Medicine (Fig. 292). In 1961 he became Director of the Division of Endocrine and Cancer Research. His most intense area of interest was in disorders of the thyroid gland. Also in 1961, he, along with associates, initiated continuing medical educa-

tion programs which led to a position in the Dean's office (1969) to further sponsor these programs. Dr. Rupp's portrait was presented to the College by the Class of 1969.

Joseph Webster Stayman, Jr., of West Virginia, took his Fellowship in thoracic surgery at Jefferson (1947/48) and became an Associate of Dr. John H. Gibbon, Jr. the following year. He played an important role in the teaching of Jefferson surgical residents who were assigned to Germantown Hospital and still later at Chestnut Hill

Fig. 291. J. Wallace Davis (JMC, '42), a pioneer in cosmetic surgery.

Fig. 292. Joseph J. Rupp (JMC, '42), Professor of Medicine (Endocrinology).

Hospital where he became Chief of Surgery. He achieved the position of Clinical Professor of Surgery and subsequent Emeritus status.

Thomas M. Scotti, a maxima cum laude graduate of LaSalle College, was awarded the Alumni and Potter Memorial prizes. Following internship and pathology fellowship he joined the teaching staff of the Department of Pathology. He subsequently served at the Medical College of Virginia, the Armed Forces Institute of Pathology, and the University of Miami School of Medicine where he advanced to Professor of Pathology in 1957. Research in cardiovascular pathology and later in environmental toxicology led to his many publications. He was repeatedly honored at Miami for distinguished teaching.

George N. Stein became Professor of Radiology at the School of Medicine, University of Pennsylvania.

Three other members of this class joined the Jefferson Faculty: Chester Brinley Bland in Obstetrics, Paul Kramer Perilstein in Medicine and Edward Kiefer Yantes in Medicine.

CLASS OF 1942

Alden, John W., Jr., DE
Anstine, Dale T., PA
Bailey, Abbott Kenyon, NC
Bantly, Harry C., PA
Barnes, Everett Beck, Jr., AL
Barringer, Phil L., NC
Bausch, Richard D., PA
Bland, C. Brinley, PA
Bowman, Thomas E., Jr., PA
Braden, Robert G., PA
Brandon, M. Boyd, PA
Brown, Harold E., PA
Brubaker, Jacob H., PA
Callaghan, Philip James, PA
Cavalieri, Rinaldo J., CT
Cheffey, John Howard, PA
Christ, Nicholas J., PA
Ciacci, Vincent W., PA
Cochrane, Fred Richard, Jr., NC
Connell, James Vincent, NJ
Connelly, Edward W., KY
Conroy, Edward George, PA
Crissey, Robert R., MI

Davis, J. Wallace, PA
Deily, Raymond E., PA
Deitmaring, Francis A., NJ
Dineen, Thomas Gerard, PA
Doherty, Joseph C., PA
Eckley, Robert, PA
Ehrgott, William August, PA
Emery, Frederick C., ME
Federowicz, Joseph Anthony, PA
Feigley, Harvey P., Jr., PA
Flick, Lawrence Francis, III, PA
Fox, Robert T., OH
Galson, John W., PA
Gibson, Edgar T., PA
Goble, Garvin G., CA
Gocke, Jack T., WV
Gold, David Albert, PA
Goldcamp, Richard Renner, OH
Graff, John Joseph, PA
Grendal, Michael Francis, MA
Grisinger, George Floyd, Jr., WV
Grubbs, William E., OH
Hackman, Edmund T., RI

1942

Hanlon, David G., PA
Healey, Joseph Thomas, PA
Heaton, Vincent Warner, PA
Heckman, James A., PA
Hegarty, William M., IN
Heinbach, Robert A., PA
Hetrick, Matthew Adam, PA
Higgins, Eugene Victor, NJ
Hilderman, Walter C., Jr., NC
Ho, Albert Kam Tai, HAWAII
Horan, Austin Joseph, PA
Houston, Robert R., PA
Hughes, Roger Lott, PA
Hussey, Howard S., Jr., NC
Johnson, David O., PA
Johnson, Edgar N., NH
Keyes, John W., PA
Knopf, Carl Ludwig, PA
Knorr, John K., III, PA
Knowles, Harry J., PA
Krzywicki, Stanley B., PA
Lau, Robert E., PA
Leach, Edwin M., ME
Liggett, John S., OH
Little, Joseph Rice, NC
Manges, Willis Edmund, PA
Marino, Joseph N., PA
Marthouse, Stephen J., PA
McCallion, Luther Layton, NJ
McCarter, Robert H., NJ
McKeigue, John E., MA
McLean, David William, MS
McNicholas, Edward Martin, PA
Miller, John E., MD
Min, Thomas S., HAWAII
Moog, Charles R., NJ
Murray, Edward Francis, NJ
Murray, Richard C., PA
Nelson, William J., SC
Neves, Edmund Fraga, MA
O'Brien, Frank Thomas, PA
O'Connor, John P., NY

Oliver, Richard Loomis, NC
Orton, Stuart, NJ
Parker, Philip John, NJ
Patterson, John C., NJ
Perilstein, Paul K., PA
Pfister, John A., PA
Phillips, Vernon R., PA
Pohowsky, Alex, Jr., PA
Polischuk, Wasyl James, PA
Pressly, David L., NC
Ranson, John L., Jr., NC
Reed, Harry Wilson, PA
Rentschler, John Horace, PA
Ressetar, Michael J., NJ
Rhodes, John Frederick, PA
Richards, Charles F., DE
Ridgway, William G., NJ
Rupp, Joseph J., PA
Ryan, James Joseph, PA
Schaefer, William L., Jr., PA
Scotti, Thomas M., PA
Smith, Jay L., Jr., NC
Stapinski, Cyril Charles, PA
Stayman, Joseph W., Jr., WV
Stein, George N., PA
Steitz, J. Arthur, NJ
Steward, Robert Excel, NJ
Stone, John Samuel, NC
Strunk, Charles F., PA
Sullivan, Arthur F., Jr., MA
Troncelliti, Edward A., PA
Ulrich, Robert P., OH
Uram, Irving Emanuel, PA
Veve, Frank J., PUERTO RICO
Warakomski, Alphonse Stanley, PA
Warren, Thomas N., DE
Warshaw, Harold, PA
Weeks, John Francis, Jr., NC
Williams, Burton L., PA
Winham, Arthur Jerome, Jr., PA
Yantes, Edmond K., OH
Zale, Anthony G., PA
Zukoski, Frank Joseph, PA

Work as if you were to live a hundred years,
Pray as if you were to die tomorrow.

Benjamin Franklin (1706–90)

Due to the accelerated curriculum as a result of the War, the members of this class graduated in three years instead of the previous four. The Jefferson Hospital internship was further shortened to ten months. The Dean stated in the Circular of Information of this year that "Personnel and college procedures may require alterations almost from day to day. Commitments in the future as to opening and closing of sessions, holidays, length and makeup of courses, admission requirements, etc., must be tentative and subject to whatever the present war emergency may dictate." The graduates this year numbered 142, bringing the grand total of alumni to 17,087.

Warren Reichert Lang graduated at the top of the class, and after internship (1943/44) served in the U.S. Army (1945-47). He returned to Jefferson and was academically advanced to Professor of Obstetrics and Gynecology by 1963. He cooperated with Drs. Lewis C. Scheffey and Abraham Rakoff in the early development of gynecologic cytology and served for four years as President of the American Society of Colposcopy. In 1968 he made a career switch to pathology and served a residency under Dr. Gonzalo Aponte (1968-70) and a third year (1970/71) at Case-Western Reserve. He returned to Jefferson in 1971 as Assistant Professor of Pathology. He served as Acting Chairman of Pathology from 1979 to 1983, and in the latter year was appointed the first Gonzalo Enrique Aponte Professor of Pathology and Chairman of the Department (Fig. 293). A prolific writer, Dr. Lang published 147 scientific articles, with his work most highly regarded in cytopathology. In 1984 he received the prestigious Papanicolau Award of the American Society of Cytology and was the Society's President in 1984/85. The Class of 1985 presented his portrait to the University. Dr. Lang bequeathed his entire estate to Jefferson.

John Norman Lindquist, another honor graduate, pursued an outstanding teaching career at Jefferson as Director of the General Medical Clinic and the Geriatric Clinic from 1951 to 1975 during which time he rose to Clinical Associate Professor of Medicine (Fig. 294). His undergraduate alma mater, Washington and Jefferson College, bestowed upon him its Alumni Achievement Award in 1967. He became a recognized expert in subjects relating to geratrics and nursing home problems in which he was a delegate to numerous committees and councils on aging, including the White House Conferences. The 1956 Jefferson Yearbook was dedicated to him; he received the Lindback Award for Distinguished Teaching (1964); and the John N. Lindquist, M.D. Hall in the Philadelphia Center for Older People, at which he was a Trustee and had

Fig. 293.   Warren R. Lang (JMC, '43), first Gonzalo Enrique Aponte Professor of Pathology.

been Chairman of the Board, was dedicated to him. He served as President of the Alumni Association in 1978 and became its representative on Jefferson's Board of Trustees in 1990.

Bernard Joseph Miller, yet another honor graduate, became outstanding in teaching, clinical practice, and research at Jefferson, culminating in appointment as Clinical Associate Professor of Surgery and Professor of Anatomy (Fig. 295). After internship and residency at Jefferson, interrupted by War service (1945-47), he was appointed the Research Associate to Dr. John H. Gibbon, Jr. in 1950 and spearheaded a team that improved the experimental heart-lung machine by electronic and other components that moved it into use for patients by 1953. Dr. Miller additionally maintained an active interest in the teaching of anatomy that persisted throughout his life. He also developed an extracorporeal cir-

cuit for perfusion of chemotherapeutic agents for inoperable malignant tumors of the extremities. Among his other contributions was his demonstration of the important role of expiratory assistance during anesthesia and the method for avoidance of air embolization during open cardiotomy and total cardio-pulmonary by-pass. In addition to his scientific articles, procurement of five patents for medical electronic devices, and activities in professional societies, he was honored by the Samuel D. Gross Distinguished Service Award of the Department of Surgery and an Honorary Degree of Doctor of Science by his undergraduate alma mater, Villanova University, in 1982.

William Henry Whiteley, III, an honor graduate, became the first neurosurgical resident at Jefferson under Dr. Rudolph I. Jaeger (1944). After service in World War II (1945/46), he took

Fig. 294. John N. Lindquist (JMC, '43), an expert in problems of the elderly.

Fig. 295. Bernard J. Miller (JMC, '43) aided Dr. John H. Gibbon, Jr. in the development of the heart-lung machine.

1943

postgraduate work in neurosurgery and rose in academic rank to Clinical Professor (Fig. 296). For a time he was the personal assistant to Dr. Jaeger and aided in preparation of color motion pictures of neurosurgical operations that were shown at national meetings. He contributed to the neurosurgical literature, produced many scientific exhibits, and was active in the societies of his specialty. In the Christian Medical Society he served as National President in 1948 and 1961.

Winslow Joseph Borkowski took his residency in neurology at Jefferson, rose to Associate Professor in the Department and was active in the establishment of electroencephalography (Fig. 297).

Other members of the class who served faithfully on the Jefferson Faculty were: Gerald Edward Callery (Orthopaedics), Leonard Samuel Davitch (Medicine), Kalman Frankel (Neurology), Joseph Francis McCloskey (Pathology), Frank Robb Kinsey (Roentgenology), and James S.D. Eisenhower, Jr. (Medicine).

Harry VanGorder Armitage became Chief of Surgery at two community hospitals in Chester, Pennsylvania. He served as a member for 22 years on the Board of Directors of Blue Shield of Pennsylvania, eventually becoming the Chairman. At Hahnemann University he became Professor of Surgery.

| CLASS OF 1943 |

Adam, Stewart Inglis, NJ
Aitken, Douglas Harold, PA
Alderfer, Henry Harr, PA
Ambrose, John Francis, Jr., PA
Appleby, George Stephen, WV
Armitage, Harry V., PA
Bender, John A., PA
Berry, Theodore J., PA
Borkowski, Winslow J., DE
Bush, Louis G., PA
Byrum, Clifford C., NC
Callery, Gerald E., PA
Campbell, Robert C., PA
Carman, Harry E., NY
Ceraso, Samuel Thomas, PA
Cessna, Gerald H., PA
Clader, Stanley C., DC
Conrady, William E., PA
Cooper, Leonard Selby, MD
Costello, Patrick Joseph, PA
Crawford, Robert A., Jr., WV
Cresson, Samuel Lukens, PA
Crouch, Auley McRae, Jr., NC
Davitch, Leonard S., PA
Deardorff, John E., PA
Derickson, Philip G., DE
Diamon, Richard Charles, PA
DiCecco, Frank J., DE
Dore, Clarence E., ME
Dorman, Gordon, PA
Durham, Davis G., DE
Durr, Theodore H., Jr., PA
Earnest, Franklin, III, NJ
Eisenhower, James S. D., Jr., PA

Elwell, Hildreth B., Jr., PA
Erwin, Evan Alexander, Jr., NC
Faris, Samuel Sheets, II, PA
Fisher, H. Logan, PA
Fornwalt, George R., PA
Fox, J. Robert, PA
Fox, John Lincoln, PA
Frankel, Kalman, PA
Friedman, Adolph, PA
Fulton, William O., PA
Funk, Vance Anderson, Jr., IN
Furlong, John H., Jr., PA
Garcia Castillo, Armando, PUERTO RICO
Gibbons, Robert J., PA
Gillis, John Angus, PA
Goode, Norman Johnson, Jr., MI
Goodin, William L., NV
Grady, William Francis, PA
Greaney, Edward M., Jr., CT
Groff, Harvey Deily, PA
Grugan, Hartford Ernest, PA
Hager, George W., Jr., PA
Hamburg, Allen E., PA
Harnagel, Edward E., IA
Hawkins, Charles Franklin, PA
Headrick, Elmer Oscar, Jr., NJ
Hecksher, Rudolph H., Jr., PA
Helden, Gerard Oscar, NJ
Henson, Edward Vale, PA
Hile, Harry Eugene, Jr., NJ
Hilferty, Daniel Joseph, Jr., PA
Hoffman, Lewis Albert, Jr., PA
Hosay, John J., PA
Houck, George William, PA

Howe, Robert Gerard, PA
Jackson, Richard Stuart, NJ
Johnston, Frank B., PA
Kain, Thomas Michael, Jr., NJ
Kareha, Louis G., PA
Kearney, Paul A., NJ
Kidney, James Jordan, CT
Kinsey, Frank Robb, PA
Kolarsick, Albert J., NJ
Ladden, Paul A., PA
Lang, Warren Reichert, PA
Langan, Thomas Joseph, PA
Leslie, Warren Deck, PA
Levy, Edwin J., PA
Light, John H., PA
Lindquist, John N., NY
McCafferty, John P., PA
McCloskey, Joseph Francis, PA
McDonald, Brown, Jr., WV
McElree, James, PA
McGee, Leonard Joseph, PA

McGinty, John Francis, Jr., PA
McHugh, Joseph John, PA
McKee, Edward Thomas, Jr., AL
Miller, Bernard J., PA
Miller, Stanley, PA
Milson, Thomas J., PA
Nelson, Francis B., NJ
Nifong, Frank M., NC
Norton, Edward A., PA
O'Brien, William R., PA
Owen, John J., PA
Palmer, Louis H., Jr., PA
Parry, Rhinard D., PA
Payne, Walter A., Jr., KY
Pennington, Howard L. J., PA
Reed, Franklin L., Jr., NJ
Reinhart, Harry A., NJ
Rich, Joseph R., OH
Richards, Arthur Charles, Jr., PA
Richardson, Ernest C., Jr., NC
Rodham, Russell David, PA

Fig. 296.   William H. Whiteley, III (JMC, '43), Clinical Professor of Neurosurgery.

Fig. 297.   Winslow J. Borkowski (JMC, '43) established electroencephalography at Jefferson.

Rodman, Clark, NC
Rogers, Lewis Leonidas, III, PA
Rose, Francis Leland, NJ
Rossman, Bernard Schecter, NJ
Rouse, Paul V., PA
Rumer, George Francis, PA
Ruof, Andrew C., III, NJ
Ruth, John Francis, PA
Saul, Robert J., PA
Schackleton, John Henry, Jr., PA
Schlosser, David E., PA
Shaffrey, Thomas A., NJ
Smith, Howard B., PA
Smith, Philip Allen, MT
Stanton, John J., Jr., PA
Suter, William B., PA

Tananis, Anthony Adam, PA
Tobias, Carl Adam, PA
Uhler, Walter M., PA
Valerio, James Vincent, Jr., PA
Wagner, Henry Sherman, PA
Washburn, W. Wyan, NC
Wenger, Alvin P., Jr., PA
West, William J., OH
White, Robert Emerson, IN
Whiteley, William H., III, PA
Williamson, Robert G., WV
Willis, George G., NJ
Wilson, John K., VA
Wright, James Thurman, NC
Zimmer, Louis E., NJ
Zimmerman, Franklin D., Jr., PA

Colonel Baldwin L. Keyes (JMC, '17), Executive Officer for Medical Affairs in Base Hospital #38, demonstrates x-ray equipment to Muhammed Ali, uncle of King Farouk of Egypt.

JANUARY, 1944

The Commencement of this war-time class in January was held in the Academy of Music on the 6th of the month. Its 133 members brought the total graduates to 17,220. Archbishop of New York and Vicar of the Armed Forces, The Most Reverend Francis Joseph Spellman, D.D, spoke on "Medicine as a Pillar of Peace".

Many of the students in this year were in uniform (Fig. 298) since their tuition was being paid by the government. Figure 299 shows a part of the Jefferson Unit, Base Hospital #38 during their stay in Camp Bowie, Texas.

Daniel William Lewis, an honor graduate, taught physical diagnosis and was active in cardiology in the Department of Medicine for many years (Fig. 300). Later, he became Director of Cardiology at St. Agnes Hospital in Philadelphia.

Burton Leonard Wellenbach joined the Jefferson staff in Obstetrics and Gynecology shortly after World War II and advanced to Clinical Professor (Fig. 301). In 1983 he served as President of the Alumni Association and in 1988 received the Leon A. Peris Award for Distinguished Teaching and Patient Care.

Stacy Linton Rollins, Jr. took his neurosurgical residency at Jefferson and then joined the teaching staff. He helped to devise a method of cerebral angiography by percutaneous carotid puncture. In 1972, after having left Jefferson, he removed the bullet from the spinal canal of Alabama's Governor George Wallace, following an assassination attempt.

Robert Loftus Breckenridge, a prize winner at graduation, went on to a distinguished career in pathology, much of which was devoted to service at Jefferson, culminating in his final title of Honorary Professor of Pathology (Fig. 302). He served as President of the College of American Pathologists (1987) and in 1988 was named "Pathologist of the Year" by that organization. Among many chairmanships and committee activities he also participated in the AIDS Task Force of the College of American Pathologists.

Fig. 298. Students in uniform (1944).

Paul Cutler won many honors at graduation, including the Alumni prize. He traveled internationally as a teacher, including presentation of a course in pathology in Afghanistan. In addition to a private practice of cardiology in Atlantic City he achieved the position of Honorary Clinical Professor of Medicine at Jefferson (Fig. 303).

Members of this class who served on the Jefferson Faculty were: John Dwight Allen (Proctology), Irvin Mayo Gerson (Psychiatry and Human Behavior), Frank Joseph Gilday, Jr. (Medicine), and Edward Joseph Murphy, Jr. (Obstetrics and Gynecology).

Prince Drummond Beach became Professor of Urology at Baylor University College of Medicine, Houston, Texas, and John H. Scott served as Associate Professor of Family Practice at Texas Tech University Health Services Center, Lubbock, Texas.

SEPTEMBER, 1944

This was the second senior class to graduate during this war year as a result of the accelerated curriculum. Commencement took place on September 22 in the Academy of Music for 135 graduates. Franklyn B. Snyder, LL.D., Ph.D., President of Northwestern University, spoke on "An Incident in the History of Fort Ticonderoga."

Samuel Stinger Conly, Jr., like the other members of the class, entered in September, 1941, as

the United States was about to enter World War II. The class graduated in September, 1944, rather than June of 1945. Among most of the members of the class, he entered the Army Student Training Program as a private. In the mornings before class, a drill was held in a field at Lombard Street between Tenth and Eleventh. After an internship shortened to nine months at Bryn Mawr Hospital, he entered the Army for two years as a First Lieutenant. Upon his return he joined the Department of Physiology for teaching and research. After a period of private practice (1950-53) he re-joined the Department of Physiology as Assistant Professor and shortly thereafter accepted an appointment in the Office of Dean George Bennett as an Assistant (Fig. 304). Later as Associate Dean under Dean William A. Sodeman he aided in the implementation of the Jefferson-Penn State accelerated plan for cooperative College and Medical School degrees in a total of five years. From 1967 to 1982 he served with distinction in the exacting position of Director of Admissions under Deans William F. Kellow and Leah Lowenstein. Friends and Colleagues presented his portrait to the University in 1983.

John Joseph Gartland, Jr. joined the Department of Orthopaedics in 1952 after completing his residency at the Columbia-Presbyterian Medical Center. For the following year and a half he

Fig. 299. Portion of Jefferson Unit, Base Hospital #38, in Camp Bowie, Texas.

was Professor Anthony F. DePalma's Associate in practice. By 1968 he rose to Associate Professor. Gartland had a deep interest in orthopaedic education which led to his authorship of "Fundamentals of Orthopaedics" (1965) and which by 1986 was in its fourth edition. In 1966 he became a co-editor of the *Journal of Bone and Joint Surgery*. In 1970 he was appointed the James Edwards Professor of Orthopaedics and Chairman of the Department, and as such was the first full-time Professor of Orthopaedic Surgery at Jefferson (Fig. 305). Gartland was elected President of the Pennsylvania Orthopaedic Society in 1961 and of the Philadelphia Orthopaedic Society in 1970. he served as President of the Alumni Association in 1974. In 1979 he was elected President of the American Academy of Orthopaedic Surgeons, the largest orthopaedic organization in the world. In 1981 his portrait was presented to the University by friends and associates. After achieving Emeritus Status in 1985, he continued his academic career at Jefferson as Director in the Office of Departmental Review. In 1989 he received the Alumni Achievement Award.

Thomas Francis Nealon, Jr., after service in the U.S. Naval Hospital, took his surgical residency at Jefferson in 1950. He participated in the research activities of Professor John H. Gibbon, Jr. and taught in the Department of Surgery in which by 1963 he achieved the position of Professor (Fig. 306). In 1968 he was appointed Director of Surgery at the St. Vincent's Hospital in New York City and Professor of Surgery at the New York University School of Medicine. A prolific writer, in addition to numerous scientific articles, he contributed chapters to Dr. John H. Gibbon, Jr.'s *Surgery of the Chest*, and authored *Fundamental Skills in Surgery* (1963) and *Manage-*

Fig. 300.   Daniel W. Lewis (JMC, J'44) taught physical diagnosis and cardiology at Jefferson.

Fig. 301.   Burton L. Wellenbach (JMC, J'44) Clinical Professor of Obstetrics and Gynecology.

1944

ment of the Patient with Cancer (1965). He was active in many societies, served as President of the New York Surgical Society, and was an Alumni Trustee on Jefferson's Board.

William Bosley Manges, whose father was Professor Willis F. Manges (JMC, '03, Fig. 157), first Head of Roentgenology at Jefferson won top honors at graduation with award of the Alumni and other prizes. After war-time service, internship and surgical residency at Jefferson, he remained active on the Faculty and Hospital throughout the remainder of his professional career. Despite a physical disability which forced his early retirement as Honorary Associate Professor of Surgery, he contributed to the literature, participated in the important societies of his field and was highly respected for his teach-

ing, surgical skill, and compassionate care of patients.

Felix Edmund Karpinski, Jr., another prize winner, achieved distinction in the Department of Pediatrics at the rank of Clinical Professor. He became the first to espouse modern pediatric teaching at Jefferson as a master of bedside grand rounds. His full teaching load, marked by innovation, evoked the loyalty and admiration alike of students and house staff (Fig. 307).

Charles L. Liggett served for many years as State Vice-President of the Alumni Association for Texas and was a significant fund raiser (Fig. 308).

Herbert Lipshutz served on the Jefferson staff in the Department of Surgery and Edmund Lockhart McConnell, Jr. in Obstetrics and Gynecology.

Fig. 302. Robert L. Breckenridge (JMC, J'44), Honorary Professor of Pathology.

Fig. 303. Paul Cutler (JMC, J'44), cardiologist, pathologist and international teacher.

Acree, Page Waddill, SC
Alberstadt, Norbert F., PA
Allen, John Dwight, PA
Anderson, Carl Victor, RI
Balin, Benjamin R., PA
Balin, Robert W., PA
Bartoshesky, Stephen W., DE
Beach, Prince D., MA
Beard, John C., Jr., MS
Bertsch, A. Monroe, PA
Bibighaus, Warren Y., NJ
Blake, William Bradford, Jr., IN
Bland, John H., IN
Boyle, William F., PA
Boysen, Otto T., NJ
Brantley, Julian C., Jr., NC
Braveman, Bernard L., NJ
Breckenridge, Robert L., PA
Butscher, William C., Jr., PA
Butt, Frank H., Jr., PA
Carrera, Manuel Enrique, PUERTO RICO
Cattie, Vincent J., PA
Cavender, John C., PA
Chun, Lin T., HAWAII
Clark, Frank, NJ
Cohen, Harry, PA
Cole, Benjamin E., Jr., NJ
Cooper, Harry F., WV
Cooper, Ray C., PA
Cramp, Lloyd L., PA
Cutler, Paul, PA
Davis, Harry A., Jr., SC
Day, Harold Ellsworth, NJ
De Carlo, John, Jr., PA
Donlan, Francis Albert, NJ
Doroshow, Herbert Samuel, PA
Duncan, James R., Jr., PA
Edwards, Charles H., Jr., NJ
Filipek, Walter J., PA
Filmyer, Edward A., Jr., PA
Flynn, John B., CT
Frohner, Richard Norman, PA
Gaines, John L., AL
Gaughn, Joseph Francis, PA
Gehron, William H., Jr., PA
Gerson, Irvin M., PA
Gilday, Frank J., Jr., PA
Glick, Melvin Ira, PA
Gorsuch, Paul L., PA
Gragg, Wilford H., Jr., TN

Hamill, John Paterson, PA
Heath, Robert D., PA
Hewitt, Clarence B., CA
Hoskins, John R., III, PA
Jacobson, Bert P., WA
Johnson, Gale D., NC
Jones, George Howard, Jr, PA
Karlik, Paul, Jr., PA
Kavanagh, John J., NJ
Kehm, Vincent A., PA
Kelleher, John C., OH
Knerr, Edgar D., Jr., PA
Krall, Robert P., PA
Kron, Samuel D., PA
Lamp, J. Curtis, NJ
Lenahan, Paul John, PA
Leonard, James B., WV
LeStrange, Thomas A., PA
Lewis, Daniel W., PA
Loftus, Thomas M., PA
Lynch, John F., Jr., NC
Martin, John A., PA
Martsolf, John, II, PA
McCabe, Edward Burnard, PA
McCormack, Raymond A., Jr., NJ
McLane, William Leonard, DE
McLaughlin, F. Wendle, PA
McLemore, Robert A., NC
McPherson, Sidney R., CT
Meals, Melvin John, PA
Miller, Carl S., PA
Mills, William L., PA
Moore, James L., NC
Moore, Richard Dixon, PA
Movelle, John B., NJ
Murphy, Edward J., Jr., PA
Nicklas, Floyd W., PA
O'Hanlan, J. Treacy, PA
Oliver, Howard M., MA
Oliver, John G., WV
Packer, George L., CA
Palmer, U. Grant, III, PA
Pierson, Howard Wilson, Jr., NJ
Plonk, George W., NC
Porter, Richard Arnold, PA
Porterfield, Robert Allen, OH
Putzel, Charles L., Jr., NC
Radcliffe, Glen J., IA
Rawley, Clarence G., Jr., DE
Reber, Howard F., PA

Refowich, Richard S., PA
Revelli, Robert J., WA
Ricks, Henry C., Jr., MS
Rollins, Stacy L., Jr., AL
Rongaus, William J., PA
Russo, James, PA
Scott, John H., MO
Shafer, Edward A., PA
Shoff, John Frank, PA
Shull, William H., NC
Southard, Durward W., OR
Sproch, Thomas M., PA
Steel, Maxwell W., Jr., PA
Storer, Alexander, Jr., NJ
Sumner, Robert Ernest, SC
Suttles, Charles M., OH

Taylor, Charles Fleming, PA
Tice, George A., PA
Tobin, Thomas Joseph, DE
Truxal, Albert C., ID
Turley, Hubert K., TN
Tymeson, Glenn W., NY
Van Gundy, Arthur B., OH
VanBuskirk, Gordon Parker, OH
Ward, Hugh John, PA
Wasnick, William, PA
Wellenbach, Burton L., PA
Wetmore, Stephen Reading, PA
Wilfong, Thomas L., PA
Witmer, Donald B., PA
Wong, James T. S., HAWAII
Wright, Alfred E., PA
Young, Marion M., SC

Fig. 304.   Samuel S. Conly, Jr. (JMC, S'44), associate Dean for College admissions.

Fig. 305.   John J. Gartland, Jr. (JMC, S'44), James Edwards Professor of Orthopaedic Surgery.

Fig. 306. Thomas F. Nealon, Jr. (JMC, S'44), Professor of Surgery and Alumni Trustee.

Fig. 307. Felix E. Karpinski (JMC, S'44), Clinical Professor of Pediatrics.

Anderson, William R., PA
Arrington, Robert Glenn, WV
Barto, Robert E., Jr., PA
Beebe, James, Jr., DE
Beittel, Charles R., Jr., PA
Bennett, Ivan F., CT
Bernardin, Ronald Maurice, PA
Bernstein, Melvin L., PA
Berry, James D., AL
Blair, Frank W., PA
Brennan, Walter J., NY
Brenner, Angus L., PA
Brewer, David R., Jr., NJ
Brower, Francis Marion, III, PA
Burros, Harry M., PA
Chase, David W., PA
Chomko, Martin, PA

Clark, Stanely N., UT
Conly, Samuel S., Jr., PA
Cramer, Harry R., PA
Cross, Charles J., OH
Culp, David A., PA
de Andino, Agustin M., PUERTO RICO
Derham, Robert J., PA
Dick, H. Lenox H., Jr., PA
Dickensheets, James G., PA
Dickson, Brice T., Jr., NC
Dix, Robert C., Jr., PA
Dolan, Charles V., PA
Donovan, John J., PA
Douglass, Frederick Melvin, Jr., OH
Dowdell, William F., PA
Dumeyer, William Henry, PA
Dunavant, W. David, MS

1944

Eichman, Eugene, Jr., PA
Falcone, Albert M., PA
Feeney, Edward J., NJ
Flory, Ray H., PA
Foley, James G., NJ
Fortnum, Walter George, PA
Foster, John T., NJ
Frantz, Robert C., PA
Froelich, Jerome J., NJ
Gallagher, John E., PA
Gartland, John J., Jr., PA
Goldstone, Sheldon B., PA
Grantham, Edwin S., MS
Griffin, William R., Jr., NC
Hagarty, John J., Jr., PA
Hanford, Kenneth K., ID
Heise, Carl V., MN
Herrold, Warren C., PA
Holland, Robert H., PA
Hough, Charles E., PA
Howanitz, Emil, PA

Hunter, Herbert S., PA
Hussong, Wallace B., NJ
Johnson, Melford I., PA
Johnson, William G., IN
Jones, Paul Erastus, Jr., NC
Kain, Eugene H., NJ
Kapcar, Albert D., PA
Kapeghian, Edward, PA
Karpinski, Felix E., Jr., PA
Kerr, Robert M., PA
Kiebler, George M., PA
Kiley, Robert William, PA
Kitei, Milton N., PA
Konhaus, Carol H., PA
Kraus, Theodore J., PA
Lamb, Robert H., AL
Lanman, Ben Marr, OH
Lempke, Richard Joseph, NJ
Leute, William R., Jr., PA
Lewis, Robert Edward, Jr., NC
Liggett, Charles L., OH
Lipshutz, Herbert, PA
Manges, W. Bosley, PA
Mann, Hillard, PA
Matthews, John W., PA
McConnell, Edward L., Jr., PA
McConville, Edward B., PA
McGaughey, J. David, III, CT
McGeehan, John T., PA
Merrill, Byrd Farmer, AL
Midura, Peter P., NJ
Minnich, Philip H., PA
Monk, John S., PA
Morton, William A., Jr., PA
Mourat, Stephen, WV
Murry, Charles M., MS
Nealon, Thomas F., Jr., PA
Osterberg, Eric Runo, NJ
Owen, George F., NC
Packer, Robert M., SC
Pashuck, Eugene T., PA
Pass, James H., PA
Pilla, Thomas E., PA
Pophal, Mahlon J., NC
Potter, Charles Wilbur, Jr., PA
Pulliam, John M., Jr., NJ
Reedy, William J., PA
Reganis, John C., PA
Relfe, Conyers Blakely, AL
Resch, Frederick A., OH
Rich, Robert E., NJ
Robertson, Frank O'Neil, Jr., ME
Rosch, Julius C., PA
Rosenbaum, Leon, Jr., PA

Fig. 308. Charles L. Liggett (JMC, S'44), prominent Texas Alumnus.

Ross, Richard Hawthorne, WA
Rothermel, William S., PA
Ryan, Eugene J., PA
Salasin, Robert, NJ
Schopbach, Robert R., NJ
Schuessler, Paul W., PA
Shaffer, Jerome D., PA
Shields, Daniel R., Jr., NC
Soronkanich, Stephen, PA
Spencer, James T., VA
Stashak, Frank J., Jr., PA
Stinson, Roy F., AL
Trilla, Emilio F., PUERTO RICO

Underwood, Grant, PA
Updegrove, Robert A., PA
Wannemacher, Paul H., NJ
Watson, John S., OH
Webster, James Weldon, ID
Weiland, T. Frederick, Jr., PA
Wentz, Henry S., PA
Wichern, Homer Elton, OH
Wilf, Harold, PA
Williams, Kenan B., NC
Williams, Raymond Matthew, NY
Wilson, William M., Jr., PA
Yankevitch, John James, Jr., PA

Wartime instruction for students in uniform.

Dominating the list of prize-winners in this class of 154 was William C. Gaventa who had the highest average for the four years. Dr. Gaventa went on to a long career in missionary medicine in Nigeria and in 1984 was appointed Director of Medical Services for the Foreign Mission Board of the Southern Baptist Convention.

Edward H. McGehee was primarily trained in internal medicine and hematology, serving for a time as Hematologist to Pennsylvania Hospital and Chairman of Medicine at Chestnut Hill Hospital. In 1974 he shifted careers to join the new Jefferson Department of Family Medicine where he promptly became one of its best known and respected teachers and role models. His portrait was presented to the College in 1976 and he was named Ellen M. and Dale W. Garber Professor of Family Medicine in 1984 (Fig. 309).

James H. Lee, Jr. pursued a career in the United States Navy until his retirement in 1966 with the rank of Captain, his last assignment having been that of Chief of Obstetrics and Gynecology at United States Naval Hospital, Philadelphia. He then joined the faculty of Hahnemann Medical College as Professor and Co-Chairman until his appointment as Chairman of Obstetrics and Gynecology at Jefferson in 1973. He retired from the Chairmanship in 1987 but continued to practice at Jefferson (Fig. 310).

Raymond C. Grandon, became Clinical Associate Professor of Medicine at the Milton S. Hershey School of Medicine. Active in organized medicine, he was a Trustee of the American Society of Internal Medicine and in 1982 was President of the Pennsylvania State Medical Society.

Claude W. Barrick, Jr. went on to a career in radiology and from 1955 to 1958 served as Associate Professor of Radiology at Jefferson during the Chairmanship of Dr. Russell L. Nichols.

Several class members were academically oriented. Robert E. DuPrey practiced ophthalmology in Washington, D.C. and was Clinical Pro-

Fig. 309. Edward H. McGehee (JMC, '45), Ellen M. and Dale W. Garber Professor of Family Medicine.

Fig. 310. James H. Lee, Jr. (JMC '45), Chairman of Obstetrics and Gynecology (1973-87).

fessor of Ophthalmology at George Washington University School of Medicine. Ralph J. Veenema was trained in urology and became Professor of Clinical Urology at Columbia University College of Physicians and Surgeons. F. Albert Olash, became Clinical Professor of Medicine at the University of Louisville School of Medicine. Stanley

Leese served as President of the Association for Advancement of Psychotherapy and became Editor-in-Chief of the *American Journal of Psychotherapy*.

Desmond S. O'Doherty became Professor of Neurology at Georgetown University School of Medicine, Washington, D.C.

CLASS OF 1945

Anthony, John J., Jr., NJ
Apt, Leonard, PA
Ayres, John A., PA
Baldock, William E., WV
Balshi, Stephen F., PA
Barrick, Claude W., Jr., OR
Bauer, Richard D., PA
Bear, John M., PA
Bicknell, Frank J., MO
Birch, William Benjamin, PA
Blair, Joseph R., NC
Boggs, Joseph D., OH
Brannen, Daniel Edwin, OH
Brant, Earl E., OH
Brown, Joseph S., Jr., PA
Bryan, J. Elder, Jr., PA
Burkett, Donald E., PA
Caddy, James A., PA
Call, Lloyd S., ID
Cameron, George F., Jr., TX
Carlisle, Dyer, Jr., AL
Carmichael, Herbert N., AL
Carrigan, Paul T., PA
Casey, E. Allan, RI
Cavett, James R., Jr., MS
Clements, C. Glenn, PA
Coleman, Daniel H., MT
Collinson, Daniel J., NJ
Cooper, Kent P., NJ
Costa, Eugene E., PA
Cox, John J., Jr., NJ
Cubler, Edward W., PA
Culbertson, John Smith, Jr., PA
Cunningham, Merrill Duffield, PA
Davis, William Lovell, PA
duPrey, Robert E., CT
Durning, Clifton M., PA
Eckert, Robert T., NJ
Eichman, Joseph Cornelius, PA
Eister, Donald H., PA
Ellis, W. Pierce, Jr., PA
Elwell, Robert W., NJ
Forsberg, Roy T., NJ

Fullerton, Harry W., Jr., PA
Garcia-Oller, Jose L., PUERTO RICO
Gaventa, William C., FL
Gold, Paul Allen, PA
Grabiak, Charles F., PA
Graham, Thomas Francis, PA
Grandon, Raymond C., PA
Gress, Frank A., PA
Grove, Russell E., PA
Hagedorn, Maxwell Ernest, CT
Hain, Raymond F., OK
Hamill, Robert W., PA
Harrelson, Rose Cranse, NC
Hauck, Herbert Harry, NJ
Hayman, H. Blake, PA
Helden, Rudolph A., NJ
Holden, William Benjamin, NC
Holman, Theodore Long, PA
Imler, Robert L., Jr., OK
Jeffrey, Robert Brooke, PA
Johnson, Robert Mandis, OH
Johnston, George B., NC
Keenan, Paul C., PA
Kelly, Richard Sterling, Jr., NC
Kennamer, Samuel R., AL
Kilduff, Charles J., Jr., PA
King, Jack Austin C., NJ
Kline, Oram R., Jr., NJ
Knapp, Thomas Sheridan, WV
Knupp, Melvin L., PA
Koch, Joseph C., PA
Kocot, Wenceslaus V., MA
Krieger, Benson, PA
Kwong, Mon Q., CA
Laggner, Harold J., PA
Larkin, Joseph E., PA
Laughlin, Herbert A., NY
Lavelle, Patrick J., Jr., PA
Leaming, Robert H., NJ
Lee, James H., Jr., DE
Lesse, Stanley, PA
Levinson, William D., PA
Lewis, Albert Gamaliel, Jr., GA

Lineberry, William T., Jr., NC
Loftus, Joseph A., PA
MacAndrew, Vincent I., RI
MacKelcan, Douglas W., NJ
Madara, John S., NJ
Marnie, James G., HAWAII
Martin, William P., PA
Masson, Newton L., PA
Mattei, Frank A., PA
Mazzeo, Albert Anthony, NY
McAdams, Charles R., Jr., NC
McDonnell, Robert R., CT
McGehee, Edward H., AL
McKeever, John Beaumont, PA
McLelland, John Rockwell, NC
McMurry, Avery W., NC
McNelis, Francis L., RI
McStravog, Joseph Lawrence, PA
Murphy, Franics John, PA
Nelson, Joseph Eugene, PA
Norton, James F., NY
O'Doherty, Desmond S., PA
O'Looney, John Joseph, Jr., CT
Olash, F. Albert, PA
Olley, James Francis, PA
Parkinson, Edwin B., SC
Parks, L. Raymond, Jr., PA
Pechstein, Henry, PA
Peoples, Claude Theodore, NC
Phillips, Howard Troy, Jr., WV
Puff, Robert C., NJ
Ramel, William Joseph, NJ
Rangatore, Joseph Samuel, NY
Reiter, Martin D., PA

Rosenheim, Gustav E., ID
Ross, William L., Jr., NC
Rowand, Robert E., PA
Ruby, Victor Mordecai, OH
Sanner, John C., PA
Savage, Peter J., PA
Schulman, Jesse, NJ
Sciubba, Rocco P., Jr., PA
Seely, Richard Henry, PA
Shuman, Bernard J., PA
Sieber, Paul Eugene, PA
Smith, Robert W., PA
Snoddy, Claude C., AL
Sprinkle, Lawrence T., NC
Stewart, H. William, PA
Stockdale, Robert Howard, PA
Suermann, John E., PA
Sweetser, Arthur Atkins, Jr., PA
Thompson, Harvey Johnston, Jr., WV
Tomassetti, Bernard A., PA
Tozer, Richard C., PA
Tyson, Russell Ray, Jr., PA
Unterberger, Herbert, PA
Van Valzah, Henry J., PA
Veenema, Ralph J., NJ
Vesey, John M., RI
Wakefield, John R., AL
Warga, William P., PA
Werley, Charles W., PA
White, John B., Jr., WV
White, Stanley Eugene, PA
Widdowson, Harold R., PA
Wong, Sau Ki, HAWAII
Wydrzynski, John Joseph, PA
Ziemba, Joseph F., PA

To teach is to learn twice.

Joseph Joubert (1754–1824)

The first post-World War II graduating class reflected a return to the annual curriculum of nine months, later to be modified as the education process continued to expand. Commencement was held on March 27 in the Academy of Music at which time 155 graduates received their degrees from Board President Robert P. Hooper. The address was delivered by Brooke M. Anspach, Professor Emeritus of Gynecology, who spoke on "Life, Liberty, and the Pursuit of Happiness."

This year marked the relocation of the Department for Diseases of the Chest from 238 Pine Street to a renovated 90-bed building at Broad and Fitzwater Streets designated the Barton Memorial Division (Fig. 311). The same year, Jefferson acquired the White Haven Sanatorium (Fig. 312). The two facilities provided acute and chronic care for tuberculosis, anthracosilicosis, and the burgeoning lung problems of carcinoma and emphysema. Dr. Burgess Gordon continued as Director.

In this year Jefferson Medical College received a Mark of Commendation for effective training of naval personnel during World War II (Fig. 313). Jefferson also received from the War Department a Certificate of Distinction for the training of soldiers in the Army Specialized Training Program (Fig. 314).

The winner of the major prizes at commence-

Fig. 311. Barton Memorial Division, Department for Diseases of the Chest.

ment was John Paul Decker, who went to Pennsylvania Hospital for internship and remained there for his lifetime career, advancing to Chairman of Pathology and Director of the Ayer Laboratory. His portrait was presented to the hospital's historical collection upon his retirement.

William H. Baltzell, IV, following Jefferson internship became associated with Dr. Louis Clerf's Department of Laryngology and Broncho-Esophagology, advancing to the rank of Clinical Professor. In 1988 he served as President of the Jefferson Alumni Association (Fig. 315).

Ralph A. Carabasi, Jr., after internship at Fitzgerald-Mercy Hospital, was trained in endocrinology and oncology at Tulane University School of Medicine (Fig. 316). In 1950 he returned to Jefferson's Department of Medicine where he pursued the same interests, but gradually his skills in oncology led to specialization in breast carcinoma. He advanced to Clinical Associate Professor of Medicine.

John R. Griffith served his internship at Jef-

ferson. Following a fellowship he became a respected cardiologist, practicing at Jefferson with an appointment on the volunteer faculty as Clinical Assistant Professor of Medicine (Fig. 317). He was a role model in this endeavor and was commonly regarded as a phycician's physician among members of the staff. In 1990 he received the Leon A. Peris Memorial Award for excellence in clinical teaching and superior patient care.

James V. Mackell, also a Jefferson intern, was for many years associated with the Department of Pediatrics as Clinical Assistant Professor. As founding Chairman of the Department of Pediatrics at Holy Redeemer Hospital, his outstanding services over a period of 26 years redounded to the credit of his alma mater.

Frederick Urbach, following Jefferson internship, began his career in dermatology at the University of Pennsylvania School of Medicine, then became Chief Cancer Research Dermatologist at Roswell Park Memorial Institute, Buffalo, New York. He returned to Philadelphia in 1958 with

Fig. 312.   White Haven Sanitorium acquired by Jefferson in 1946.

appointments at Temple University School of Medicine and at the Skin and Cancer Hospital, becoming Chairman of Dermatology in 1967.

Other graduates with academic associations included Joseph P. Gadomski, who became a physiatrist affiliated with the Graduate and Philadelphia General Hospitals and Einstein Medical Center. He served on the board of the American College of Physical Medicine and Rehabilitation. David G. Simons was Clinical Professor of Phys-ical Medicine and Rehabilitation at the University of California, Irvine. Henry A. Seidenberg became Clinical Professor of Psychiatry at Pritzker School of Medicine, Chicago and Bruce M. Wimer, Associate Professor of Internal Medicine at Texas Tech University Health Sciences Center, Lubbock, Texas. Leon Levintow was Professor of Microbiology at the University of California Medical Center, San Francisco.

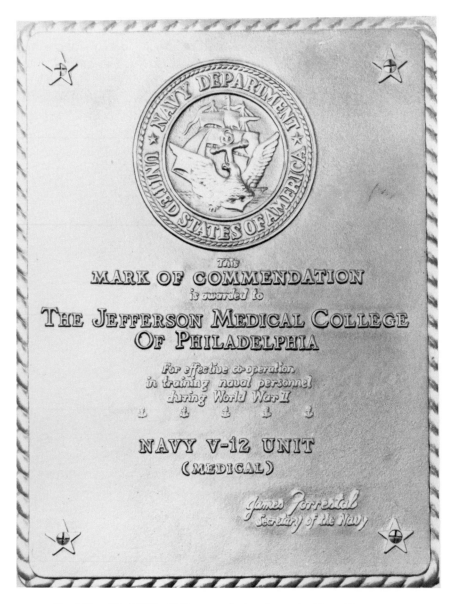

Fig. 313.   World War II Commendation from the Navy Department.

1946

BE IT KNOWN THAT THIS

CERTIFICATE OF DISTINCTION

HAS BEEN AWARDED BY THE

WAR DEPARTMENT

TO

Jefferson Medical College

FOR THE TRAINING OF SOLDIERS IN THE

ARMY SPECIALIZED TRAINING PROGRAM

DURING WORLD WAR II

Robt P Patt

SECRETARY OF WAR

Fig. 314.   World War II Certificate of Distinction from the War Department.

Alderfer, Harold H., PA
Anderson, Gustav W., CT
Ashbey, Dwight, Jr., PA
Austin, Claude L., MS
Babcock, Edward B., ME
Bacharach, Herbert Joseph, Jr., PA
Baldwin, Clifford A., Jr., NJ
Baltzell, William H. IV, PA
Bannett, Aaron D., PA
Barringer, Charles C., NC
Bash, Myron, NJ
Bickham, Charles E., Jr., AL
Bierly, Mahlon Z., Jr., PA
Blake, Hu A., SC
Bongiovanni, John James, PA
Boysen, Homer W., NJ
Brandon, William Douglas, PA
Burbridge, I. Ralph, Jr., PA
Cappelletti, A. Joseph, CT
Carabasi, Ralph A., Jr., PA
Carberry, George August, IN
Carrabba, Salvatore R., CT
Carter, William S., Jr., PA
Catanzaro, Charles, PA

Chmelewski, Anthony E., PA
Cohen, Abraham L., PA
Collins, Harry L., Jr., FL
Cone, Theodore S., AL
Coppa, Vito L., RI
Cramer, Bernard, PA
Curry, William Oliver, Jr., PA
Daly, Thomas W., RI
Davis, John W., NC
Decker, John P., WA
Devenney, Joseph Francis, PA
Dietel, Robert Charles, MA
Dolphin, J. Murray, PA
Dowdell, Paul J., PA
Dugan, Charles C., PA
Eriksen, George N., Jr., DE
Fidler, Harry Earl, PA
Fiedler, James J., PA
Flotte, Camille Thomas, PA
Gadomski, Joseph Peter, NJ
Gallagher, Henry G., PA
Gallagher, James J., PA
Gaudielle, Andrew W., NJ
Gelb, Jack, PA

1946

Fig. 315. William H. Baltzell, IV (JMC, '46), Clinical Professor of Otolaryngology.

Fig. 316. Ralph A. Carabasi, Jr. (JMC, '46), Associate Professor of Medicine with specialization in breast cancer.

Fig. 317. John R. Griffith (JMC, '46), recipient of Leon A. Peris Award for excellence in clinical teaching and superior patient care.

Gilbert, James B., PA
Gliwa, Edward F., PA
Gosztonyi, Rudolph E., Jr., PA
Greble, Edwin S., III, CA
Griffith, John R., PA
Grugan, Robert A., PA
Haines, Robert A., NJ
Haines, Robert William, NJ
Hanlon, John Joseph, Jr., PA
Hannan, Charles E., PA
Hargreaves, William James, PA
Harrop, Daniel S., Jr., RI
Hawkins, James H., NC
Henderson, F. William, PA
Heuston, Paul B., WA
Hogan, Henry William, Jr., OH
Isaacson, Howard, NJ
Jenkins, John R., Jr., NY
Johnson, James Joseph, PA
Jones, Allen W., PA
Jordan, Herbert V., Jr., PA
Jordan, John Alfred, Jr., PA
Kane, William M., PA
Keller, John M., PA
Kennedy, Thomas J., PA
Knowles, Charles Arthur, PA
Knox Kenneth R., WV
Korbonits, Charles W., NJ
Koretsky, Sidney, MA
Krevsky, Seymour, PA
Krisanda, Joseph B., PA
Kujda, Domenic A., PA
Lacock, Robert R., PA
Lanich, Oscar K., Jr., PA
LaNoce, Louis F., PA
Lechner, Frederic C., PA
Lee, Allen H., NC
Lemmon, Gamewell A., Jr., SC
Levick, Leonard J., PA
Levintow, Leon, PA
Lewis, Marvin O., PA
Lindes, DeArmond, PA
Luhr, John Paul, NY
Lumpkin, Forrest E., Jr., TX
Mackell, James V., PA
Matteucci, Walter V., PA
Mazmanian, Joseph, MA
McAndrew, Michael J., Jr., IL
McCormick, John, PA
McGovern, Edwin Andrew, RI
McLaughlin, Randall M., PA
Melnick, Joseph L., PA
Meyer, Harold, PA

Miller, Clarence M., Jr., NC
Minde, George Francis, NJ
Mudd, Joseph P., Jr., AL
Muehlhauser, William O., PA
Murphy, Robert A., NJ
Nelson, Robert M., NJ
O'Connell, William Aloysius, PA
O'Leary, James Michael, PA
Orr, Sidney H., PA
Palmer, Frank Cameron, PA
Pastras, Thomas, NJ
Patrick, Thomas E., PA
Perkins, Benjamin S., PA
Petre, John H., Jr., PA
Puleo, Joseph Salvatore, PA
Raban, Reginald J., NJ
Reberdy, George Kanter, MI
Redmond, John L., NY
Reitz, Melvin L., PA
Rose, Isadore, PA
Rowley, Samuel D., CT
Roy, Robert H., PA
Ruht, Joseph C., PA
Saleeby, Richard G., NC
Sass, Robert E., PA
Scarborough, Charles F., Jr., NC
Schramm, Frank E., Jr., PA
Scott, Norman M., Jr., NJ
Seidenberg, Henry A., PA
Senita, G. Robert, PA
Shannon, Frank J., Jr., PA
Shaub, Howard G., PA
Sherer, Bernard D., PA
Shugart, Richard Tatum, NC
Silliman, Warren B., CT
Simoncelli, Leonard Robert, PA
Simons, David G., PA
Sipes, Earl K., PA
Smith, Harry C., PA
Stevens, Robert G., PA
Stone, Harry A., MS
Sullivan, Robert J., MA
Tobia, Enio W., PA
Urbach, Fredrick, PA
Walker, Duncan D., Jr., GA
Walker, John S., NC
Walter, Herbert L., PA
Weber, George L., PA
Wentzler, J. Donald, PA
Wiley, Thomas M., Jr., AL
Wimer, Bruce M., NJ
Woodward, William M., NJ
Worsham, Richard A., FL
Zehner, Richard Franklin, PA

At the Commencement held in the Academy of Music on May 23 the 151 graduates received their M.D. degrees from Board Chairman Robert P. Hooper. The Address was delivered by Ralph Cooper Hutchison, Ph.D., D.D., LL.D., L.H.D., President of Lafayette College who spoke on "The Professional Man."

Gerald D. Dodd, Jr. served a Jefferson residency in radiology and progressed to a faculty appointment. He soon manifested exceptional skills in diagnostic roentgenology. After a sojourn at M.D. Anderson Hospital, Houston, Texas, he returned to Jefferson as Clinical Professor of Radiology. In 1966 he left Jefferson once more for professorial appointments in Houston, the principal one being Head of the Division of Diagnostic Imaging at the University of Texas Medical Center. National honors included a year as President of the American College of Radiology and Trustee of the American Board of Radiology. He received the Alumni Achievement Award in 1986 (Fig. 318).

John A. Koltes, winner of the Psychiatry Prize, fulfilled his early interest with a career in clinical psychiatry. Trained at Jefferson, Friends' Hospital and the Hospital of the University of Pennsylvania, he was active in the institutional care of mentally ill people. He became the first Director of the Psychiatric Unit at Jefferson which opened in 1957, one of the first such units to be installed in a general hospital. He advanced to Clinical Professor of Psychiatry and became head of psychiatry at Chestnut Hill Hospital (Fig. 319).

John J. McKeown, Jr., following military service and Jefferson residency, joined the Department of Surgery as Research Associate investigating extracorporeal circulation in the surgical treatment of heart disease (1954-59). He was also Consulting Surgeon to the Henry Landis State Tuberculosis Hospital. Later Dr. McKeown was appointed Chairman of Surgery at Mercy Catholic Medical Center and promoted to Clinical Professor of Surgery at Jefferson. In 1988 he became

head of surgery at Wilmington Veterans Administration Hospital (Fig. 320).

Nathan M. Smukler pursued training in internal medicine and rheumatology at the Hospital of the University of Pennsylvania and joined the staff there under Dr. Joseph Hollander. He returned to Jefferson as its first rheumatologist and went on to organize the Division of Rheumatology in 1959 (Fig. 321). The Division prospered and Dr. Smukler was later promoted to Professor of Medicine. He served until his retirement to private practice in 1980.

John J. Dowling, who was trained in orthopaedic surgery at Jefferson, progressed in the

Fig. 318. Gerald D. Dodd, Jr. (JMC, '47), distinguished radiologist who won the 1986 Alumni Achievement Award.

Department to the rank of Professor of Orthopaedic Surgery (Fig. 322). He also became attending physician at St. Edmund's Home for crippled children, Rosemont, where Jefferson students received instruction. In 1970 he became Chief of Orthopaedics at Lankenau Hospital and in 1971 received the Lindback Award for distinguished teaching. Dr. Dowling was knighted in the Order of St. Gregory the Great by Pope John Paul in 1982 and was President of the Jefferson Alumni Association in 1984.

Elmer H. Funk, Jr. was a Bryn Mawr Hospital intern and a resident in internal medicine at Pennsylvania Hospital. Beginning as coordinator of Clinical Research with Dr. Leandro M. Tocantins (Fig. 238), he went on to a career in Research and Administration in the pharmaceutical industry, advancing to Director of Clinical Research, (Cardiovascular Renal) Merck Sharp & Dohme Research Laboratories. He held an appointment as Clinical Assistant Professor of Medicine at Jefferson for many years and in 1968 was President of the Alumni Association (Fig. 323).

William B. Abrams pursued graduate training in clinical pharmacology. His career broadened in administration and research with pharmaceutical corporations culminating in his appointment as Executive Director of Clinical Research at Merck Sharp & Dohme Laboratories. He was President of the American Society for Clinical Pharmacology and Therapeutics and since 1977 Adjunct Professor of Medicine at Jefferson (Fig. 324).

Herbert S. Bowman, following training in hematology at Jefferson, practiced in Harrisburg and became Director of the Blood bank and Co-director of Hematology at Harrisburg Hospital.

Fig. 319. John A. Koltes (JMC, '47), Clinical Professor of Psychiatry.

Fig. 320. John J. McKeown, Jr. (JMC, '47), Clinical Professor of Surgery.

1947

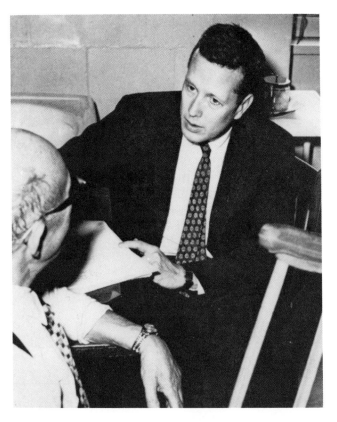

Fig. 321.   Nathan M. Smukler (JMC, '47), organized the Division of Rheumtaology at Jefferson.

Fig. 322.   John J. Dowling (JMC, '47) Professor of Orthopaedic Surgery.

Fig. 323.   Elmer H. Funk, Jr. (JMC, '47), Alumni President and a Director of Research in the pharmaceutical industry.

Fig. 324.   William B. Abrams (JMC, '47), Executive Director of Research in the pharmaceutical industry.

1947

In 1976 he was appointed Professor of Medicine (Hematology) at Milton S. Hershey School of Medicine of Pennsylvania State University.

Paul H. Jernstrom, trained in pathology and advanced to Assistant Professor at Jefferson. He moved to the West Coast in the late 1950s and became Director of Laboratories at California Medical Center. He later became prominent for his practice and promotion of marathon running for physical training and rehabilitation.

Edward J. Klopp, Jr., after a career in cardiothoracic surgery in Michigan, served for many years as a mission surgeon in Tanzania (Fig. 325).

Numerous 1947 graduates were notable. They included Martin M. Mandel with appointments at Einstein Medical Center, Temple University School of Medicine and as Chief of Neurology at Germantown Hospital; Edwin Boyle, Jr., Clinical Professor of Medicine at the University of South Carolina, formerly Senior Clinical investigator at the National Institutes of Health; Edgar C. Hanks who became Professor of Clinical Anesthesiology at Columbia University College of Physicians and Surgeons; Joseph M. Corson, Professor of Pathology at Massachusetts General Hospital; Ray Korson, Professor of Pathology at the Medical Center of Vermont, Burlington; Harold A. Wurzel, Professor of Pathology at the Hospital of the University of Pennsylvania; and William A. Cull, Associate Professor of Anesthesiology at Case Western Reserve University, Cleveland, Ohio.

CLASS OF 1947

Abrams, William B., NJ
Aceto, Joseph N., PA
Allan, John Purcell, NC
Babskie, Robert F., PA
Baker, Robert H., PA
Barsky, Joseph M., Jr., DE
Bashore, Sidney M., PA
Blumberg, Alan I., PA
Bode, Frederick W., Jr., PA
Bostian, David W., PA
Bowen, John R., Jr., NJ
Bowman, Herbert S., PA
Boyle, Edwin, Jr., SC
Brockunier, Alfred, Jr., PA
Browning, William J., Jr., NJ
Bucan, Michael, PA
Burkley, Louis Franklin, III, PA
Burns, Benjamin F., PA
Cahall, W. Lawrence, Jr., PA
Casale, Lawrence F., PA
Coghlan, William Patrick, PA
Cook, Alfred S., Jr., NJ
Corazza, Leo J., PA
Corley, Luther F., Jr., AL
Corson, Joseph M., PA
Cox, William Franklin, III, PA
Cull, William A., PA
Danyliw, Joseph M., CT
Davies, W. Clayton, PA
De Wan, Charles Joseph, PA
Diorio, Joseph Alfred, PA
Dodd, Gerald D., Jr., PA
Dowling, John J., PA
Eberly, Byron Thomas, PA

Feldstein, Leonard Charles, PA
Fidler, W. Larch, III, NJ
Fister, Harris G., NJ
Foster, Charles Goddard, CT
Foushee, J. Henry S., Jr., NC
Funch, Robert B., PA
Funch, Ross S., PA
Funk, Elmer H., Jr., PA
Gaffney, John J., PA
Gensemer, George John, PA
Goeckler, John E., PA
Greeley, Joseph P., PA
Groblewski, John D., PA
Gross, William H., OH
Haas, Melvin E., PA
Hanes, Charles Benjamin, PA
Hanks, Edgar C., PA
Hastings, Richard A., PA
Haupt, Lamar Emerson, PA
Hausman, David H., PA
Helff, John R., NJ
Heller, David B., PA
Helsper, James T., NJ
Herrick, William C., PA
Hickman, Charles N., MS
Jaslow, Robert I., PA
Jernstrom, Paul H., PA
Jones, Albert R., Jr., PA
Jones, Lewis Edward, VA
Kelly, Edward A., PA
King, S. Victor, Jr., PA
Kirchner, Richard G., PA
Klopp, Edward J., Jr., PA
Koltes, John A., Jr., PA

Korson, Roy, PA
Koval, John M., PA
Kraft, Albert J., Jr., PA
Kramer, Herbert, NJ
Krevsky, David A., PA
LaFia, David J., PA
Lam, Pritchard T., HAWAII
Lawrence, Benjamin J., Jr., NC
Lee, Jeremiah F., PA
Lerner, Sidney Simon, PA
Levin, David W., PA
Li, Gail Gar Lyai, HAWAII
Lussy, William J., PA
MacAndrew, Raymond N., RI
Mandel, Martin M., PA
Mann, Lester, PA
Marino, Dante E., PA
Mayock, Peter P., Jr., PA
McChesney, C. Thomas, Jr., PA
McCurdy, Robert S., NJ

McDonnell, William V., PA
McGee, Donald H., PA
McGee, Joseph P., Jr., PA
McKeown, John J., Jr., PA
McKim, Menzie, Jr., OR
Meehan, Edward Joseph, MA
Meehan, John J., PA
Miller, Charles E., PA
Miller, Warren A., PA
Mintz, Alfred M., PA
Moore, Walter W., PA
Moran, Thomas W., Jr., PA
Mosier, Laurance A., MD
Mszanowski, Edwin M., PA
Oliver, Jim Upton, NC
Pace, Karl B., Jr., NC
Pender, John R., III, NC
Phillips, William A., WV
Reidt, William U., PA
Reinhardt, George Robert, MO
Ressler, Vincent Roland, PA
Reynolds, John R., NJ
Rhoda, Robert Gordon, PA
Rhode, Marvin C., PA
Rodgers, Charles J., PA
Roque, Richard M., PA
Rosen, Leonard P., PA
Samuels, Melvin L., PA
Schneider, Chester L., PA
Schran, Albert G., PA
Shaar, Richard Thomas, FL
Shershin, Peter H., NJ
Smigelsky, Richard G., PA
Smith, Clyde F.B., PA
Smith, Edgar C., PA
Smukler, Nathan M., PA
Sproch, Richard M., PA
Stokes, T. Lane, VA
Strauss, Richard E., PA
Strong, Leonell C., Jr., CT
Struve, John F., PA
Surmonte, John A., NJ
Swartley, Robert Norman, PA
Terheyden, William A., Jr., PA
Thomas, Francis Xavier, PA
Tibbens, George F., PA
Topp, Edwin Mitchell, Jr., MS
Trossman, Chester M., PA
Van Vranken, Bruce, CA
Vaughn, Arthur R., Jr., PA
Watkins, Donald Riegel, PA
Wehler, Andrew J., PA
Weinstein, Stanley, PA
Weise, Ellwood C., Jr., CT

Fig. 325.   Edward J. Klopp, Jr. (left, JMC, '47) with colleagues in Tanzania.

1947

Wolfe, Sidney Maurice, PA
Womack, Noel C., Jr., MS
Woodward, William John, NJ
Wurzel, Harold A., PA

Yannaccone, Robert, PA
Yingling, Nathaniel D., PA
Younger, Samuel, PA
Zukoski, Joseph T., PA

Gross Clinic at top of College Stairway.

At the Commencement held June 4 at the Academy of Music, 152 graduates received their degrees. Fred Pierce Corson, D.D., Bishop of the Methodist Church, spoke on "The Instincts of the American Mind."

This year marked the beginning of Alumni Annual Giving, a program which would prove the unique loyalty of Jefferson Alumni and a major source of funds for the Medical College. Under the Chairmanship of Dr. Louis H. Clerf, a sum in excess of $62,800 was raised, encouraging the committee to set a goal of $125,000 for the next year.

George J. Haupt received surgical training at Jefferson following Korean War Service. His career in clinical surgery was supplemented by his research in cardiothoracic physiology and he was the principal inventor of the "Jefferson Ventilator" for respiratory assistance during surgery (Fig. 326). He was advanced to Clinical Professor of Surgery and became Chief of Cardiothoracic Surgery at Lankenau Hospital where he was also active in research in aerospace science.

Ellsworth R. Browneller became the first academically trained Medical Director of Jefferson Hospital in 1957 (Fig. 327). After administrative experience in the United States Navy from 1948 to 1954, he received the degree of Master of Science from the Columbia University School of Public Health and Administrative Medicine. He resigned in 1962 to become Administrator of Geisinger Medical Center Danville, Pennsylvania.

Charles G. Steinmetz, III, (Fig. 328) pursued residency at Wills Eye Hospital following Jefferson internship. Joining the Wills Staff as well as an appointment at Jefferson, he advanced to Clinical Associate Professor of Ophthalmology and Attending Physician at Wills. He served as Interim Chairman of Opthalmology in 1961 following the death of Dr. Carroll R. Mullen (Fig. 241).

C. Jules Rominger took up the specialty of radiology. He became Chairman of the Department of Radiology at Mercy-Catholic Medical Center and retained his appointment as Research Professor of Radiation Oncology and Nuclear Medicine at Jefferson.

James W. Daly and John B. Atkinson, both Jefferson interns, went on to parallel careers in internal medicine, Dr. Daly in cardiology and Dr. Atkinson in hematology. Both were advanced to the rank of Clinical Associate Professor of Medicine at Jefferson.

John E. Healey, Jr., after his Jefferson internship, taught anatomy at Jefferson. He then went on to Houston, Texas, where he was Professor of Anatomy and was also associated with the

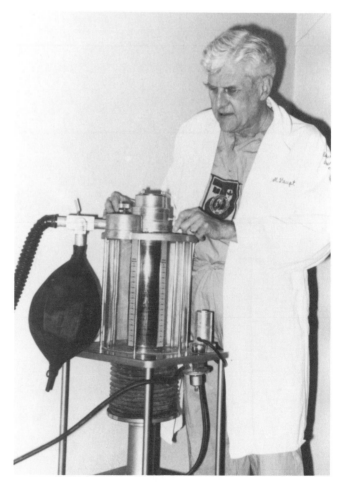

Fig. 326.   George J. Haupt (JMC, '48), Clinical Professor of Surgery and inventor of the "Jefferson Ventilator."

M.D. Anderson Hospital Rehabilitation Center. Also involved with research in liver transplantation, he later joined the Comprehensive Cancer Center at the University of Miami, Florida, School of Medicine.

Robert K. Finley Jr., following Lankenau internship and Jefferson residency in surgery became Chief of Surgery at the United States Naval Submarine Base, New London, Connecticut. He later practiced in Dayton, Ohio and was appointed Clinical Professor of Surgery at Wright State University School of Medicine.

David S. Masland became the youngest President of the Medical Society of Pennsylvania at the time of his election in 1976 (Fig. 329). He served for many years as Chairman of the Board of the Pennsylvania Medical Society Liability Insurance Company.

R. William Alexander, Director of Radiology at Reading Hospital, was also President of the Pennsylvania State Medical Society in 1988 and was honored at a dinner by the Jefferson Alumni Association.

Norman J. Quinn, Jr. became an important leader in the Jefferson Alumni Association. A major accomplishment was his chairmanship of the Committee for Celebration of the Centennial of the Association in 1970. He was at the same time involved in the effort to acquire the Samuel D. Gross statue from the federal government. Dr. Quinn also organized the Travel Seminars for the Association and in 1982 was elected President (Fig. 330).

Daniel L. Shaw, Jr. became Vice-President of Medical Affairs for Wyeth-Ayerst Laboratories and was elected to serve as President of the College of Physicians of Philadelphia for the term 1990-92.

Other notables of 1948 included R.C. Laning, Director of Surgical Services at the Veterans Administration; Leonard F. Bender, Professor of Physical Medicine and Rehabilitation at the University of Michigan and later Chairman of the same department at Wayne State University; William B. Annesley, Jr., Professor of Ophthalmology at Jefferson and Director of Wills Eye Hospital Retina Service, who received the honor award of the American Academy of Ophthal-

Fig. 327.   Ellsworth R. Browneller (JMC, '48), Medical Director of Jefferson Hospital (1957-62).

Fig. 328.   Charles G. Steinmetz, III, (JMC, '48), Interim Chairman of Opthalamology.

1948

mology; Richard L. Bernstine, Professor of Obstetrics/Gynecology at Northeastern Ohio School of Medicine; Bent G. Boving, Professor of Obstetrics/Gynecology at Wayne State University;

Donald A. Cornely, Associate Professor of Medicine at Johns Hopkins University; and Daniel S. Rowe, Professor of Pediatrics at Yale University.

Fig. 329. David Masland (JMC, '48), President of the Pennsylvania Medical Society.

CLASS OF 1948

Alexander, R. William, PA
Alexander, Richard P., CA
Amadio, Julio J., PA
Anderson, Charles W., VA
Annesley, William H., Jr., PA
Atkinson, John Bond, NJ
Balis, Sol, PA
Barton, Charles R., Jr., PA
Bartos, Joseph E., PA
Bealer, John D., PA
Bender, Leonard Franklin, PA
Berardis, Velio Eliseo, PA
Berger, Robert A., PA
Bernstine, Richard L., PA
Birrell, Donald G., PA
Blake, Thomas F., DC

Blatchley, Donald M., PA
Boving, Bent G., PA
Boyle, Denis A., PA
Brenneman, Paul G., KS
Brooks, Thomas R., PA
Brown, Robert Gaylord, OH
Browneller, Ellsworth Russell, PA
Cable, Sydney R., NY
Carabasi, Robert J., PA
Carroll, Joseph Leo, PA
Carson, Charles P., PA
Cassidy, William Joseph, PA
Cerne, Andrew J., PA
Clark, R. Craig, UT
Cohn, C. Harold, PA
Conroy, Joseph V., Jr., PA

1948

Cornely, Donald A., PA
Croll, Millard N., PA
Cullen, Chester F., PA
Daly, James Wilton, NY
Datz, Thomas Arthur E., PA
DePersia, Rudolph T., NJ
Douglas, Thomas E., WA
Edelman, Meyer, PA
Eiseman, Paul C., Jr., PA
Evans, James H., Jr., PA
Federici, Valerio J., PA
Feigley, Donald M., PA
Felder, Edward A., CT
Fingo, Albert J., PA
Finley, Robert K., Jr., OH
Flacco, Albert J., PA
Foster, Charles D., III, NJ
Francos, Charles G., PA
Frank, Patrick Joseph, PA
Gale, Larrey Bernard, OH
Gatski, Robert L., PA

Gearren, John Bernard, NJ
Goodman, Charles Clarke, RI
Gordy, Edwin, PA
Goulard, Alexander, Jr., NJ
Griffin, John H., Jr., NJ
Harrold, Bruce Durston, OH
Hastedt, Robert C., PA
Haupt, George J., PA
Healey, John Edward, Jr., PA
Heckler, G. Barrett, PA
Hill, J. Mark, MS
Hoffman, Gilbert M., PA
Huber, Richard Lumley, PA
Hughes, Eugene P., PA
Hughes, John Edward, NJ
Hughes, William F., NJ
Humes, James J., PA
Jahnke, Edward J., Jr., PA
Jones, John Gulick, PA
Kahn, Murray, NJ
Kenna, Joseph P., PA
Kessel, James S., WV
Kittleberger, William C., Jr., PA
Kleckner, James F., PA
Kohl, John Michael, PA
Kress, James W., PA
Lackey, Robert S., NC
Lancaster, Edward L., Jr., PA
Landis, Richard M., PA
Lane, Paul J., PA
Laning, Robert C., NY
Lev, Ralph, NJ
Liss, Henry R., NJ
Liu, Gordon Foo-Hin, HAWAII
Loftus, James B., PA
Logan, John Bronson, DC
Loomis, Charles Hepford, PA
Lull, Clifford Bell, Jr., PA
Lytle, Creighton L., PA
Masland, David S., PA
McBride, Thomas J., PA
McCormack, John L., ID
McCoy, Robert W., Jr., PA
McDonald, Donald J., PA
McGettigan, Manus John, PA
McKinney, J. Edward, GA
Michelson, Alan L., MA
Moyer, Earl S., PA
Nassef, George J., NC
O'Connor, James J., Jr., PA
O'Donnell, George J., PA
Pascucci, Stephen E., PA
Patrick, Theodore E., PA
Pechstein, George R., PA

Fig. 330. Norman J. Quinn (JMC, '48), President of the Alumni Association (1982).

Peterson, William Elmer, PA
Pfister, Joseph Charles, PA
Potter, Richard Joseph, PA
Powell, Clermont S., PA
Quinn, Norman J., Jr., NJ
Ranson, William A., NC
Rector, Robert D., PA
Risi, George F., NJ
Rodriquez, Roberto C., PUERTO RICO
Rominger, C. Jules, PA
Rowe, Daniel S., PA
Rushton, John R., III, NJ
Ryan, Charles S., PA
Schimmel, Nelson H., PA
Schlosser, Ralph J., WA
Schofield, R. Alan, PA
Schwartz, Francis R., PA
Schwartz, Melvin Leslie, PA
Scull, Edward, PA
Serfas, Lee S., PA
Shaffer, Howard L., PA
Shander, Ernest G., PA

Shaw, Daniel L., Jr., PA
Sheely, William E., NC
Shope, William B., PA
Silberman, Ellis L., PA
Silk, Raymond E., PA
Skinner, Richard W., PA
Smythe, John W., PA
Starr, Henry F., Jr., NC
Steinmetz, Charles G., III, PA
Stenhouse, Henry M., Jr., NC
Sturr, Robert Porch, Jr., NJ
Swartz, Curtis H., PA
Thomas, David W., Jr., PA
Tulsky, Emanuel G., PA
Turner, Thomas C., AL
Vassalotti, Stephen B., PA
Weaver, Oscar M., PA
Webb, Edwin L., GA
Weyher, John E., Jr., NC
Willie, Roy C., Jr., TX
Wright, Robert B., PA
Zeeman, Stanley E., PA
Zutz, Harry M., NJ

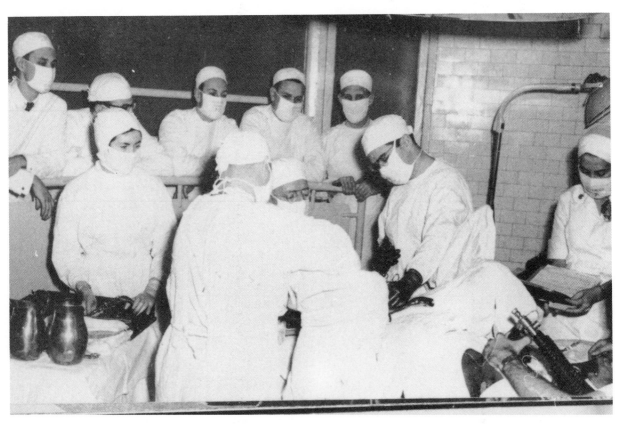

Students observe surgery by Kenneth E. Fry (JMC, '31), Old Main Hospital.

Post-War readjustments continued, including military service obligations which related to the recent war and new threats of the "Cold War." It was in this year that Robert P. Hooper, LL.D., who had been President of the Board of Trustees for the past decade, changed title to Chairman of the Board, with creation of a new post in the College, namely that of President. The first President duly appointed was James Laurence Kauffman, Vice Admiral, U.S. Navy (Ret.), who awarded the degrees to the 150 members of the class.

Gerald J. Marks was an enlisted man who proceeded through Villanova University and Jefferson. Following internship at Jefferson he was on active military duty, after which he returned for completion of his residency in surgery, subsequently joining the staff. Dr. Marks developed a major interest in colorectal surgery which was further stimulated by the development of fiberoptic endoscopy. He became the founding President of the Society of American Gastrointestinal Endoscopic Surgeons, and advanced to Professor of Surgery and Director of the new Division of Colorectal Surgery at Jefferson in 1984 (Fig. 331). He also headed the Colorectal Section at Pennsylvania Hospital. His innovative treatment of lower rectal carcinoma with preoperative radiation and sphincter conservation constituted a major advance.

Carl Zenz became a leader in occupational medicine. He earned a Doctor of Science degree at the University of Cincinnati in 1956 and became Director of Medical Services of Allis-Chalmers Corporation. He was Editor of the *Journal of Occupational Health and Safety*, author of two books and Clinical Professor at the Medical College of Wisconsin. He was also President of the American Academy of Occupational Medicine and in 1977 was elected Alumni Trustee of Thomas Jefferson University. He later served as a consultant in Occupational Medicine in various industries as well as for the State of Wisconsin Division of Health (Fig. 332).

W. Bernard Kinlaw, trained in internal medicine and cardiology, served as Assistant Professor of Preventive Medicine at Jefferson prior to his appointment as Chairman of the Department of Medicine and Co-Chief of Cardiology at Abington Memorial Hospital. The latter position led to his association with Temple University School of Medicine as Associate Clinical Professor of Medicine.

Harold Rovner joined the staff of the Jefferson Department of Surgery following his internship at Mt. Sinai Hospital. He specialized in proctology and advanced in rank to Assistant Professor of Surgery.

Fig. 331. Gerald J. Marks (JMC, '49), Professor of Surgery and Director of the Colorectal Division.

Richard A. Ellis, trained in ophthalmology, became associated with Wills Eye Hospital and in 1983 was promoted to Clinical Professor at Jefferson. He has been one of the "Flying Doctors", providing medical care to Third World Countries.

A number of class members were academically oriented. A partial list included Stewart W. Hamburger, Clinical Professor of Surgery at the School of Medicine of the University of Michigan; Edward J. Saltzman, Clinical Professor of Pediatrics at the University of Miami (Florida) School of Medicine; Scott J. Boley, Professor of Surgery at Einstein College of Medicine, New York; Gerald M. Shannon, Attending Surgeon and Director of Oculoplastic Service at Wills Eye Hospital and Professor of Ophthalmology at Jefferson; George A. Winich, Clinical Professor of Obstetrics and Gynecology at the School of Medicine, University of California, San Francisco; Peter L. Eichmann, Professor of Neurology and former Dean at the University of Wisconsin School of Medicine; and Erwin R. Smarr, Professor of Psychiatry, Medical Center of Central Georgia, Macon.

CLASS OF 1949

Anderson, Robert V., NJ
Apple, John Matthew, PA
Au, Francis T., HAWAII
Avonda, Richard P., NY
Bascove, S. Jack, NJ
Beers, Ray F. Jr., PA
Biser, David Isaac, PA
Blumfield, Irvin H., PA
Boggs, Lawrence K., AL
Boley, Scott J., NY
Booher, David O., KY
Boyer, Walter E. Jr., PA
Breneman, Gerald M., PA
Brennan, Robert S., DE
Bressler, Victor A., NJ
Bryson, Richard L., PA
Callis, Charles Alton, PA
Carlson, Richard A., PA
Chmelewski, Edward J., PA
Clelan, George M., PA
Cleveland, Samuel Mortimer, PA
Crosby, William V., MI
Crowder, Richard Brent, MO
De Villers, Paul Romeo, MA
Deck, Roy Jr., PA
Deck, Frederick Webster, Jr. DC
Easling, Howard DeWitt, PA
Eichman, Peter L., PA
Ellis, Richard A., PA
Eskey, Chester W., CT
Farrell, George R., PA
Feddeman, Frederick A., PA
Felderman, Eugene S., PA
Fields, Joshua, PA
Finley, John G., PA
Fisher, Norman J., PA
Frey, Charles D., PA

Gelb, Albert, PA
Gilbertson, Francis E., NJ
Giuliucci, Canzio E., CA
Goodman, Sanford M., PA
Gormley, Joseph J., PA
Gusciora, Stanley J., NJ
Hamburger, Stuart W., FL
Hamilton, Charles R. Jr., MA
Hart, Rinard Z., PA
Hart, William E., CT
Hartstein, Paul, PA
Head, Thomas Francis, RI
Healy, John R., WI
Hopen, Joseph M., PA
Huff, Charles W., WY
Huntington, Park W. Jr., DE
Hurley, Harry J. Jr., PA
Iozzi, Louis, PA
Johnkins, Roland, NJ
Johnson, Matthew E., NJ
Johnson, Robert G., PA
Jordan, W. Edward Jr., PA
Joselson, Howard, NJ
Keck, David John, PA
Kesselman, Russell H., PA
Kidder, Richard Francis, PA
Kinlaw, W. Bernard Jr., PA
Kutz, Paul Jacob, PA
Kuzman, William J., PA
Larkin, Duane Rhodes, MI
Larsen, Lawrence Louis, WI
Lilien, Otto M., NY
Lincoff, Milton H., PA
Lincoff, William, PA
Lindell, Marvin M., PA
Longenecker, Benjamin E., PA
Ma Koon Tuck, HAWAII

Macbeth, L. Craig, NJ
Mally, S. Stuart, NJ
March, Conrad Francis, CA
Markind, Simon, PA
Marks, Gerald, PA
May, Carl J., PA
Mazer, Howard, PA
McWilliams, Fred D., PA
Michael, Robert L., OH
Michael, Thomas D., MD
Miller, Charles Alexander, Jr., PA
Mills, John E., WA
Mitchener, Calvin C., NC
Moffitt, John S., PA
Moseley, Dan Parrott, NC
Mourat, Constantine, WV
Nabity, Stanley F., NE
Nelson, Mortimer T., NY
Newitt, Thomas R., NY
Newman, L. Roy, PA
O'Neill, John J., PA
Orlidge, Arthur E., PA

Fig. 332. Carl Zenz (JMC, '49), outstanding in the field of occupational medicine.

Pace, Charles T., NC
Paul, John D. Jr., PA
Perlman, Abraham, PA
Perry, Henry M., NY
Piekenbrock, Thomas C., WI
Popp, George, PA
Potter, H. Phelps Jr., DE
Powers, Northern Leslie, Jr., VA
Purcell, Edward Francis, MI
Rafter, James J., NY
Robinson Edward H., NH
Rodriguez, Hector F., PUERTO RICO
Roman, Henry A., MA
Rovner, Harold, NJ
Rudansky, Sheldon, NY
Sallee, William T., IN
Saltzman, Edward J., PA
Schauer, Edward A., PA
Schulz, Robert E., PA
Shannon, Gerard Michael, PA
Shoemaker, Henry Keen, NJ
Silberg, Samuel J., PA
Smarr, Erwin R., PA
Smith, Burgess A., PA
Smith, Edward C., PA
Smith, Irwin S., PA
Snyder, Allen M., PA
Spangler, Ford C., PA
Spong, George R., PA
Stark, Robert E., IA
Strause, Harold L. Jr., PA
Swan, Reyer O., PA
Sweeney, Edgar C., NC
Tanner, Leonard M., OH
Taylor, Robert Watson, IL
Teufen, Henry J. Jr., PA
Tinsley, Jack Byrd, MS
Ulmer, George B. IV, NJ
Valloti, Joseph M., PA
Vetto, R. Mark, WA
Veve, Juan E., PUERTO RICO
Voigt, George B., PA
Von Dedenroth, Edward A., PA
Walrath, Martin H. III, PA
Weaver, John Louis, KS
Weinstein, Jack H., NY
Wells, Mortimer H. Jr., MA
Whittington, Richard M., NY
Williams, Neil Saxton, NJ
Winch, George A., IL
Woodside, Jack R., VA
Zagory, Conrad, NY
Zenz, Carl, WI
Zientek, Leon T., PA

The year 1950 ushered in a decade of dynamic change. Dean William Harvey Perkins resigned for reasons of health and was succeeded by Dr. George Allen Bennett. The Honorable Alfred E. Driscoll, Governor of New Jersey, addressed the 153 graduates at Commencement on June 9.

Richard Lee Rovit, winner of the prize in Clinical Surgery, pursued a career in neurosurgery with postgraduate experience in Boston, London, and Montreal. He was appointed Associate Professor of Surgery (Neurosurgery) at Jefferson in 1961 and headed the Division of Neurosurgery. Dr. Rovit left Jefferson in 1965 to become Chairman of the Department of Neurosurgery at New York's St Vincent's Hospital and Professor of Clinical Neurosurgery at New York University School of Medicine (Fig. 333).

Hal E. Snedden, following his Jefferson internship, received training in orthopaedic surgery under Jefferson's new department head, Dr. Anthony F. DePalma (Fig. 250). He later joined the staff of Bryn Mawr Hospital where he advanced to Chief of Orthopaedic Surgery and to Clinical Professor at Jefferson (Fig. 334).

William J. Jacoby, Jr. went on to a career in Naval Medicine. After many experiences, his last naval assignment was as Chairman of Internal Medicine and Director of Education and Research at the National Naval Medical Center, Bethesda, Maryland, with the rank of Rear Admiral. In 1980 he retired and joined the Veterans Administration in Washington D.C. as Director of Medical Services.

Jay W. MacMoran served his internship at Geisinger Memorial Medical Center, Danville, Pennsylvania. His career in radiology evolved at Germantown Hospital where in 1977 he became Chairman of the Department. He was also appointed Clinical Professor of Radiology at Temple University School of Medicine. In addition to his skills in chest x-ray diagnosis he became interested in the ancient problem of leprosy. On two occasions he served as Visiting Professor of Radiology at Christian Medical College, Vellore, South India. His studies of leprosy in Nepal, India, and Pakistan from the radiological aspect have continued including publication of papers on the subject. He has also been consultant to the United States Public Health Service Hospital, Carville, Louisiana.

James R. Hodge became prominent in the field of psychiatry with many national relationships. In 1981 he was appointed Chairman of Psychiatry at Akron (Ohio) City Hospital and Professor of Psychiatry at Northeastern Ohio Universities College of Medicine.

Irwin N. Perr, winner of the Alumni Prize, was outstanding in psychiatric circles in New Jersey.

Fig. 333. Richard L. Rovit (JMC, '50), headed the Division of Neurosurgey at Jefferson (1961-65).

He was Professor of Psychiatry at Robert Wood Johnson Medical School and in 1987 received the Golden Merit Award of the New Jersey Psychiatry Association.

Herbert A. Yantes, following Frankford Hospital internship, returned to Jefferson as a resident in medicine and Rehfuss Fellow in Gastroenterology. He was appointed to the teaching staff and advanced to Clinical Assistant Professor of Medicine.

Numerous class members were involved in academic pursuits. Frank R. Hendrickson in 1977 was President of the Department of Therapeutic Radiology at Rush-Presbyterian- St. Luke's Hospital, Chicago, and Director of the Rush Medical College Cancer Center. Murray A. Kessler was Associate Clinical Professor of Medicine at Hahnemann Medical College. Martin Goldberg was Director of the Marriage Council of Philadelphia and Head of the Division of Family Study at the University of Pennsylvania. William B. McNamee was Clinical Assistant Professor of Orthopaedic Surgery at Jefferson and in 1979 was made Medical Director of the Greater Delaware Health Plan. Erich A. Everts-Suarez, winner of the Saunders Prize, became Adjunct Clinical Associate Professor of Pathology and Cell Biology at Jefferson. Maurice R. Turcotte was Assistant Professor of Anesthesiology, Emory University School of Medicine.

CLASS OF 1950

Backenstose, Daniel Lee, PA
Bair, Robert C., PA
Ball, J. Robert, MD
Barba, William M., PA
Barbor, Linus Andrews, PA
Barnes, James D., PA
Beauchamp, Eugene W., Jr, MA
Bechtel, Harry B., PA
Besse, Byron E., Jr., PA
Blake, Joseph John, PA
Brown, Frank Elliott, Jr., PA
Callista, Richard L., PA
Camp, Mark O., WV
Cantafio, Ralph, PA
Capito, Emil, WV
Childers, Eugene L., CA
Clark, Edward J., PA
Clark, William Roy, PA
Cleveland, Edwin I., PA
Clevenger, Marshall Lewis, NM
Coffroth, Leroy Ward, PA
Colcher, Robert E., PA
Cort, Carter F., WV
Courtney, Drew E., PA
Crews, Louis M., NJ
Critchlow, Robert J., PA
DeAugustine, Vincent P., PA
DelVecchio, Leonard M., PA
Derrickson, Charles R., DC
DeValinger, Henry Clay, III, NJ
Donaghue, George Lewis, PA
Dougherty, Thomas J., PA
Duffey, Richard V., ME
Englehart, William P., PA

Erdman, Leonard A., PA
Evans, John R., UT
Everts-Suarez, Erich A., PUERTO RICO
Farrell, Francis X., PA
Fay, Frederick Justin, RI
Forker, Thomas, NJ
Foster, Albert, RI
Franks, Donald P., OH
Frederickson, Victor J., MA
Frommelt, J. Calvin, NJ
Gazowski, Thomas E., PA
Goldberg, Martin, PA
Goldstein, Marvin, NY
Grandon, Eugene L., PA
Grant, Albert J., PA
Greenberg, Milton Sidney, PA
Grunthal, Leonard H., Jr., FL
Haas, Albert Cottrell, AL
Hall, Laurence B., PA
Haney, Joseph S., Jr., MS
Harley, Wilbur J., PA
Harper, Harry L., PA
Helm, Albert H., NJ
Hendrickson, Frank R., PA
Henkelmann, Charles R., PA
Hill, Franklyn C., Jr., CA
Hodge, James R., OH
Holman, William B., OH
Hunter, Robert G., MN
Hyland, Bernard V., Jr., PA
Jacoby, William J., Jr., PA
Jaffe, David, PA
Jamison, James Braden, II, PA
Jensen, Ernest Harry, PA

John, Joseph James, PA
Joy, William A., NJ
Kanner, Harry Hamilton, CA
Karns, Robert Earl, PA
Kaufman, Kimball C., Jr., OR
Keiser, Lester, PA
Kermon, Louis T., NC
Kessler, Murray A., NJ
Kienhofer, Robert F., MD
King, Weir L., RI
Kirshbaum, Bernard A., PA
Kraft, William F., MD
Layden, Paul W., PA
Lesse, Henry, PA
Lewis, Donald Burns, PA
Lewis, Milton L., PA
Lieberman, David J., PA
Limeres-Jimenez, Jose Rafael, PUERTO RICO
Lopes, John David, CA
Lychak, John C., PA
MacMoran, Jay W., PA

Fig. 334.   Hal E. Snedden (JMC, '50), Clinical Professor of Orthopaedic Surgery.

Malia, Edward Regis, PA
Matta, Joseph Samuel, PA
Maynard, Eugene V., NC
Mazza, Patrick A., Jr., PA
McCraw, Ernest Joseph, MS
McElree, Frank E., Jr, PA
McGuigan, John D., Jr., RI
McLavery, Bernard J., PA
McNamee, William B., PA
Meyers, Donald Irwin, NJ
Milligan, James R., FL
Monaghan, James M., III, NJ
Moyer, Ralph D., Jr., NJ
Murtland, Albert M., PA
Murtland, Richard L., PA
Nardi, Michael Emil, NJ
O'Brien, George W., PA
Painter, Robert H., NY
Paxson, Chauncey G., Jr., PA
Pennes, Edward Lewis, PA
Perr, Irwin N., NJ
Peters, Gerard Joseph, PA
Pierce, Carl G., Jr., PA
Powell, W. Ernest, Jr., NC
Ripepi, James D., Jr., PA
Rogers, Alan S., PA
Rosenthal, Aaron, PA
Rovit, Richard L., MA
Rowe, Joseph J., Jr., NJ
Samms, V. William, Jr., PA
Sargent, John P., UT
Sass, Donald K., PA
Saunders, Charles L., Jr., NC
Schmidt, H. William, PA
Sear, Hubert S., NY
Seidenberg, Leonard, PA
Shafer, James A., PA
Silberman, Charles G., FL
Simmermon, Gerald Fletcher, PA
Smith, Amos Vastine, Jr., PA
Smith, Richard H., RI
Snedden, Hal E., OH
Sophocles, Aris M., NJ
Stein, Robert S., PA
Steinberg, Arthur, PA
Stoddard, Darrel C., ID
Strawcutter, Howard E., PA
Sullivan, Andrew A., PA
Tabasco, Joseph F., PA
Tenn, Richard S., HAWAII
Thoma, Theodore Benjamin, PA
Thompson, John F., PA
Titus, J. Richard, OH
Turcotte, Maurice R., RI

1950

Vossenberg, Frans J., PA
Watkins, Thomas W., NJ
West, George William, WV
Wiland, Olin K., PA
Williams, J. Harold, PA

Winchell, William H., CA
Wood, Sherrod N., NC
Woodward, Hugh B., NJ
Worman, Robert K., PA
Yantes, Herbert A., PA

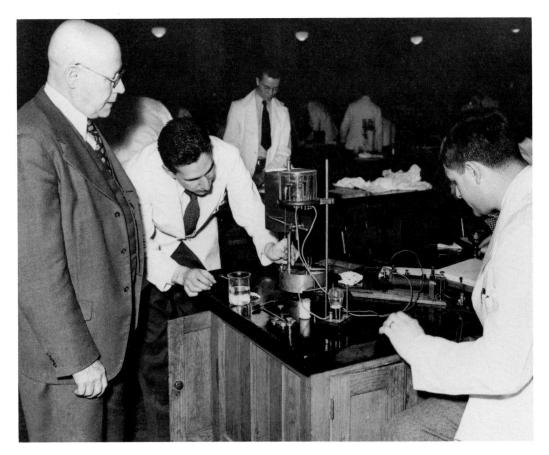

Dr. J.O. Crider in physiology laboratory.

Changes in medicine continued apace during the early 1950s. Post-war discoveries included new antibiotics, corticosteroid preparations and technological advances. Numerous 1951 graduates would participate actively in the progress of this decade.

Milton S. Eisenhower, President of Pennsylvania State College and brother of General Dwight D. Eisenhower, addressed the 161 graduates assembled in the Academy of Music.

Francis J. Sweeney, Jr. (Fig. 335) achieved an important place in Jefferson's growth. From intern, resident, and fellow, he proceeded to major teaching and clinical responsibilities for the Department of Medicine at Jefferson and at Phila-

Fig. 335. Francis J. Sweeney, Jr. (JMC, '51), Vice President for Health Services at Jefferson.

delphia General Hospital. In 1968 he was appointed Hospital Director at Jefferson and in 1972 Vice President for Health Services. He served until his resignation in 1984 to become Vice President for the Health Services Center at Temple University. Dr. Sweeney was prominent in the affairs of the American College of Physicians for many years, serving as Chairman of its Board of Regents and as its Governor for Pennsylvania. He was elected a Master of the latter organization and the recipient of its Stengel Award. His portrait was presented to Jefferson in 1978. Other Jefferson honors bestowed upon him were the Alumni Achievement award in 1983 and the Winged Ox Award in 1984.

Herbert C. Mansmann, Jr. pursued a career in pediatrics and allergy, beginning with internship and residency in Pittsburgh, then a fellowship at Massachusetts General Hospital. He returned to Jefferson in 1968 as Professor of Pediatrics and Director of its Division of Allergy and Immunology, and as Associate Professor of Medicine. An authority on childhood asthma, he has been active in national societies and editor of the journal *Pediatric Asthma, Allergy and Immunology* (Fig. 336).

Peter Chodoff pursued a varied career. In addition to his basic appointment as Professor of Anesthesiology at Jefferson, he went on to a Master of Public Health degree from Johns Hopkins University in 1979 and became Director of Education and Research Medicine at the Medical Center of Delaware. In 1987 he was appointed Assistant Dean at Jefferson.

Irwin L. Stoloff, following Jefferson internship and residency, joined the staff in Medicine and advanced to Associate Professor. He also became Director of the Health Maintenance Clinic and Assistant Professor of Preventive Medicine in 1965 and served until the Department was absorbed into the Department of Medicine in 1979.

Victor F. Greco after residency training at Jefferson, became a power in Northeastern Pennsylvania, beginning as a general and thoracic surgeon. He was a founding member of the Pennsylvania Society of Thoracic Surgeons and became Chief of Surgery at Hazleton State Hospital and at St. Joseph's Hospital. He was Chairman of the Board of the White Haven Center for some years and in 1986 was named Deputy Secretary for Community Health for the State of Pennsylvania by Governor Robert Casey. He also served on the Advisory Committee of the National Institutes of Health (Fig. 337).

Leonard Girsh served a Jefferson internship following which he was trained in allergy. He was later affiliated with the teaching staff at Temple University Hospital and still later became Director of Allergy and Clinical Immunology at the Medical College of Pennsylvania. In 1980 he was elected to the Board of Regents of the American College of Allergists.

Jasper G. Chen-See, following residency in pathology, joined the teaching staff at Jefferson. He later moved to Reading, Pennsylvania where he was Chief Pathologist at St. Joseph's Hospital. In 1979 he was appointed Vice-Chairman of the Board of Directors of the National Council on Alcoholism.

Bernard W. Mayer pursued training in anesthesiology and was Director of Anesthesia at St. Christopher's Hospital for Children. In 1981 he was appointed Professor of Anesthesiology at the Medical College of Pennsylvania. He published a textbook, *A Clinical Guide to Pediatric Anesthesia.*

Other 1951 graduates who were academically connected included Howard C. Mofenson, Professor of Clinical Pediatrics, New York State College of Medicine, Stony Brook; Simon C. Brumbaugh, Jr., Assistant Clinical Professor of Family Medicine, University of California at San Diego;

Fig. 336. Herbert C. Mansmann, Jr. (JMC, '51), prominent nationally in allergy and immunology.

Fig. 337. Victor F. Greco (JMC, '51), a leading general and thoracic surgeon in Northeastern Pennsylvania.

Vincent J. McPeak, Clinical Professor of Obstetrics and Gynecology at Jefferson; Harry H. Steinmeyer, Jr., Clinical Associate Professor of Radiology, also at Jefferson; James C. McLaughlin, Clinical Assistant Professor of Obstetrics and Gynecology at Bowman-Gray School of Medicine, Wake Forest University and Chairman of Obstetrics and Gynecology at Winston-Salem Health Care Facility; Arthur H. Auerbach, Assistant Professor of Psychiatry, University of Pennsylvania School of Medicine; Daniel T. Berney, Assistant Professor of Anesthesiology, Los Angeles County, U.S.C. Medical Center; David M. Carberry, Associate Professor of Surgery, Presbyterian Hospital, New York; and Calbert T. Seebert, Assistant Professor of Anesthesiology at Johns Hopkins.

Dean B. Olewiler served as a missionary physician to Nigeria for fourteen years.

CLASS OF 1951

Abelove, William A., PA
Abrahamsen, Edwin H., NY
Allgair, William A., NJ
Anderson, George W., NJ
Anderson, Robert V., MI
Auerbach, Arthur H., PA
Barger, Andrew J., PA
Beer, Louis, PA
Berney, Daniel T., PA
Bertolette, Richard D., PA
Blair, Willis Thomas, PA
Boretsky, Harry, PA
Borman, John O., PA
Bower, Robert J., PA
Brabson, Howard W., PA
Brady, Douglas F., PA
Brandfass, Robert T., WV
Brumbaugh, Simon C., Jr., CA
Call, Dean E., ID
Capper, Stanley A., PA
Carberry, David M., NY
Carroll, Frank A., Jr., PA
Carter, James Vincent, WY
Chen-See Jasper, JAMAICA
Cheyney, J. Barton, II, PA
Chodoff, Peter, PA
Cimoch, Paul Joseph, PA
Clark, Richard S., UT
Clauss, Thomas F., PA
Cox, James B., MS
Crutchlow, Paul F., NJ
Cwik, John C., PA
Dandrea, Raymond L., PA
Dannenberg, Stanley, NY
Deam, John H., PA
DeBonis, Charles S., PA
DeMeo, Daniel R., NJ
Deschler, Paul A., Jr., PA
Dobridge, Michael R., Jr., NJ
Dodge, Herbert C., NJ

Doherty, Ernest F., Jr., NJ
Douglas, John T., WA
Ebersole, Glen M., PA
Engel, Herbert Walter, NJ
Erhard, Daniel T., PA
Escoll, Philip J., PA
Farr, Joseph Louis, WV
Field, William G., NJ
Fishman, Harold, NJ
Flynn, Joseph C., NJ
Gallagher, Eugene Joseph, PA
Geneczko, John Theodore, PA
Gerhart, Robert Pemberton, Jr., PA
Gibson, Joseph V., Jr., WV
Gilmore, Irvin W., PA
Gingrich, Russell L., Jr., PA
Girsh, Leonard S., PA
Glickman, Murray, PA
Grab, David S., FL
Greco, Victor F., PA
Groblewski, Benjamin Gordon, PA
Grubb, Willard Y., PA
Guillard, Peter M., PA
Hale, Robert G., PA
Hauser, Charles F., NY
Hickey, John Solano, PA
Hitchner, James C., NJ
Homer, Robert W., NJ
Huffman, Charles R., PA
Inghram, John Garrett, PA
Jackson John R., PA
Jamison, Alfred R., Jr., PA
Jernstrom, Charles L., PA
Johnkins, Edmund A., NJ
Kanter, Earl I., NJ
Kaplan, Harry Aaron, PA
Kardos, Joseph A., PA
Kester, Richard Joseph, PA
Kitrinos, Nicholas Peter, PA
Kremens Jack B., PA

Langley, John W., NJ
Lantos, Raymond J., PA
LaVoice, H. Edward, Jr., PA
Lehman, Edward Dennis, PA
Leicht, Paul Franklin, PA
Lentini, Joseph A. , PA
Leonard, Glenn R., PA
Levitsky, David A., NJ
Lupin, Gordon W., PA
Lutz, R. Bruce, Jr., PA
Mabey, Orson H., Jr., ID
Maerz, John C., PA
Mann, Harold J., PA
Mansmann, Herbert C., Jr., PA
Masterson, James F., Jr., PA
Mayer, Bernard W., PA
McBride, William W., PA
McCloskey, Edwin Michael, PA
McClowry, James T., PA
McDonnel, Gerald E., NJ
McGeary, Lester E., PA
McKinley, Robert A., PA
McLaughlin, James C., PA
McLaughlin, Robert W., PA
McPeak, Vincent J., Jr., PA
Meier, George M., NJ
Mofenson, Howard C., NY
Mulligan, Robert L., PA
Murphy, Robert M. J., NJ
Olewiler, Dean B., PA
Oliver, James E., PA
Owen, Richard D., PA
Paradee, Benjamin R., NJ
Parker, Talbot F., Jr., NC
Perrige, John Joseph, PA
Peter, Walter P., Jr., NJ
Peters, David A., PA
Peters, Harold E., PA
Piovanetti, Simon, PUERTO RICO
Potter, Lloyd G., Jr., PA

Quesada-Guardia, Roberto A., COSTA RICA
Radin, Sherwin S., NY
Rados, Walter T., NJ
Raffensperger, Bruce W., PA
Rahter, Paul D., PA
Reifsnyder, William H., III, PA
Reinhard, Warren J., CT
Reinhardt, David Jones, III, DE
Richardson, George B., PA
Richardson, Ross E., PA
Riegel, George E., III, PA
Robinson, David Morton, WV
Rosenblatt, Morton A., NJ
Rowland, N. Dean, Jr., PA
Sanchez-Longo, Luis P., PUERTO RICO
Sattel, Leonard, PA
Schwimmer, Morton, NY
Seebert, Calbert Trent, VA
Shields, Hubert L., IN
Shmokler, Leon, PA
Shoemaker, David M., PA
Simpson, Roy W., PA
Small, Richard H., NJ
Smith, Verne L., Jr., NJ
Starer, Larry J., PA
Stein, Louis H., PA
Steinmeyer, Harry H., Jr., PA
Stillings, Samuel L., WV
Stoloff, Irwin L., PA
Stringfield, James K., NC
Sweeney, Frank J., Jr., PA
Vetto, Roy R., WA
Wachtel, Fred W., NJ
Wallace, William E., FL
Wallack, Armand, PA
Wang, Charles Nathaniel, PA
Ward, Cameron S., WA
Webster, Lane H., PA
White, Charles G., PA
Wofford, Jesse Lucius, MS
Young, Keith R., PA

For the things we have to learn before we can do them, we learn by doing them.

Aristotle (384–322 B.C.)

On June 12, the M.D. degree was awarded in the Academy of Music by President of the College, James L. Kauffman, to 160 graduates. This brought the grand total in the College history to 18,590.

Gonzalo Enrique Aponte, a native of Puerto Rico, won many of the prizes at graduation, and pursued a brilliant career in pathology at Jefferson (Fig. 338). After residency and duty in the U.S. Navy he returned as a full-time teacher and researcher. He was the first Jeffersonian to receive the prestigious Markle Scholarship in Medical Science (1960-65). In 1967 he succeeded Peter A. Herbut as Chairman of the Department of Pathology and Director of the Clinical Labora-

tories. Winner of the Lindback Award for distinguished teaching, he was also consistently chosen to administer the Hippocratic Oath to each year's graduating class. His portrait was commissioned by the Class of 1971 when he was only 41 years of age, the youngest Professor ever so honored. In 1967 he was named Clinical Scientist of the Year by the Association of Clinical Scientists and in 1977 he served as President of the Alumni Association. Tragically, Aponte died suddenly in 1979 at age 49, shortly after having been named the first Peter A. Herbut Professor of Pathology. His memory was honored by creation of the Gonzalo Enrique Aponte endowed Professorship of Pathology of which Warren Reichert Lang (JMC, '43, Fig. 293) was the first incumbent.

Jerome Marvin Cotler finished his residency in orthopaedics at Jefferson in 1957 and conducted a highly successful practice in New Jersey. In 1973 he became a fulltime member of the orthopaedic faculty in which he rose to Professorship and Vice-Chairman of the Department. In 1979 he became a Co-Director of the Regional Spinal Cord Injury Center at Jefferson in which he was responsible for the orthopaedic aspects of the patient care program. He served as Chairman of the Board of Councilors of the American Academy of Orthopaedic Surgeons in 1975 and as President of the American Board of Orthopaedic Surgery in 1982. He contributed frequently to the literature in orthopaedics and received the Lindback Award for Distinguished Teaching (Fig. 339).

Warren Pearlman Goldburgh became an outstanding clinician and teacher in cardiology at Jefferson in which he rose in rank to Clinical Professor (Fig. 340). He served as Director of the Cardiac Outpatient Clinic from 1965 until its closing in 1975. A recipient of the Lindback Award for Distinguished Teaching, he also served as President of the Medical Staff and of the Volunteer Faculty Association. In 1987 his portrait

Fig. 338. Gonzalo E. Aponte (JMC, '52), Chairman of Pathology at Jefferson.

was presented to the University by colleagues and friends.

James Edward Clark became a pioneer in nephrology and started hemodialysis at Jefferson in 1959 after he had trained with Dr. Lewis W. Bluemle at the University of Pennsylvania. He continued as the major renal clinician and researcher in dialysis until he left in 1968 to become the Chief of Medicine at Crozer-Chester Hospital. This led to his appointment as Professor of Medicine and Associate Dean at Hahnemann University. He served as President of the Alumni Association 1990/1991 (Fig. 341).

Other members of this class who joined the teaching staff at Jefferson were: Jose Heraclio Amadeo (Surgery, later Chief of Surgery in Veterans Hospital in Puerto Rico, also Governor of the American College of Surgeons for Puerto Rico); Robert Thomas Carroll (Hematology, and Director of Jefferson Hospital's Blood Bank); George Francis Gowen (Surgery, with special interest in gastroscopy); Wesley W. Bare (Obstetrics/Gynecology), Associate Professor; and Elmer J. Taylor, Jr., Clinical Associate Professor of Family Medicine and Clinical Assistant Professor of Medicine.

Joseph Hodge became a prominent surgeon in his native Spartanburg, South Carolina, and carried on research that led to the development of an improved tube for decompression of the bowel in cases of intestinal obstruction. Along with John E. Healey (JMC, '48) he published the textbook, *Surgical Anatomy*.

Other members of this class who became academically associated were: Albert H. Wilkinson, Jr., Clinical Professor of Pediatric Surgery at the

Fig. 339. Jerome M. Cotler (JMC, '52), Professor of Orthopaedic Surgery and Vice Chairman of the Department at Jefferson.

Fig. 340. Warren P. Goldburgh (JMC, '52), Clinical Professor of Medicine (Cardiology).

University of Florida College of Medicine, Jacksonville; Jerome I. Brody, Professor of Medicine, Medical College of Pennsylvania; Alan B. Gould, Jr., Professor of Anesthesiology, Mayo Graduate School of Medicine, Rochester; Herbert A. Saltzman, Professor of Internal Medicine, Duke University School of Medicine; and Nathan J. Zweifler, Professor of Internal Medicine, University of California Medical Center, San Diego.

Fig. 341. James E. Clark (JMC, '52), pioneer in renal dialysis research.

CLASS OF 1952

Abbott, R. Roderic, IL
Amadeo, Jose H., PUERTO RICO
Amshel, Albert L., PA
Aponte, Gonzalo E., Jr., PUERTO RICO
Aspen, Nelson P., PA
Avella, Arthur N., NJ
Babcock, Albert L., ME
Baird, Harry L., NJ
Bakewell, Frank S., Jr., PA
Bare, Wesley W., PA
Barry, David M., RI
Bashore, Robert M., Jr., PA
Berner, Jerome J., NJ
Bittner, Donald L., CA

Bond, Jess F., OH
Bonin, Lawrence I., NJ
Bricker, Glenn W., PA
Brinton, William T., Jr., CO
Brody, Jerome I., NY
Brooks, Bert Watson, NJ
Brown, Matthew G., PA
Brown, Richard Stewart, PA
Carlile, William K., PA
Carper, John Mark, PA
Carroll, James Freed, CA
Carroll, Robert T., NH
Chappen, Edward P., PA
Chinn, Franklin J., CA

Christianson, Kjell H., PA
Cicchino, Joseph Raymond, NJ
Clark, James E., WV
Cloud, Laurence P., PA
Clouser, William F., PA
Collier, John Martin, NJ
Comerford, James P., PA
Cooper, Harold B., PA
Cornfeld, Joseph, PA
Costanza, Louis Carmine, NJ
Cotler, Jerome M., NJ
Counts, Robert W., WV
Crawford, William Robert, NJ
Cunneff, Raymond Leo, Jr., PA
Dabback, DeWitt T., PA
Davidson, Donald C., NJ
Davis, William S., PA
Davison, William R., PA
Ditto, Edward W., III, MD
Dollinger, Kenneth, NJ
Dooley, Michael B., PA
Duhigg, William J., OH
Dunn, Philip F., PA
Early, Robert F., PA
Ebersole, Robert A., CO
Eney, Irving P., PA
Evans, Robert L., PA
Eyerly, Robert C., PA
Finnesey, Robert Van D., NJ
Fiorello, Joseph Michael, NJ
Fitzpatrick, James J., Jr., NJ
Fong, Bernard Wah Doung, HAWAII
Fugate, Howard, Jr., PA
Gardner, Thomas A., PA
Gibson, Jesse Merrill, Jr., RI
Godfrey, George C., II, NJ
Goldburgh, Warren P., PA
Gould, Allan B., Jr., OH
Gowen, George F., PA
Graff, Louis G., PA
Grasse, John M., Jr., PA
Gregersen, James O., NY
Hansell, Howard W., PA
Harriger, Miles D., PA
Hermany, Paul L., PA
Hicks, Vonnie Monroe, Jr., NC
Hill, William Reed, PA
Hodge, Joseph, SC
Hoerner, Oscar G., PA
Hoffman, Harry H., Jr., PA
Hofford, James M., PA
Houck, Virgil Lydic, PA
Hutchison, James C., PA
Huxster, Howard Knight, PA

Jaffurs, William J., PA
Katz, Robert Edward, PA
Kegel, Eugene E., PA
Kelley, Thomas J., Jr., PA
Kennedy, Burwell M., PA
Kirkland, Matt L., Jr., WV
Krevsky, Harold, PA
Kron, Kenneth M., PA
Kubiak, Richard Victor, PA
Kurman, Martin, NJ
Lauer, Kurt E., PA
Lebovitz, Jerome J., PA
Leute, Millard S., PA
Lumpkin, Bryan H., SC
Lutterloh, I. Hayden, NC
Lynch, Thomas Sturgis, PA
Lynch, William F., CT
Madura, Joseph R., PA
Maguire, Leo J., Jr., PA
Mahoney, Jack L., ND
Martinez, William V., PA
Matthews, Joseph G., WV
McAndrew, Joseph R., IL
McAninch, Edward M., PA
McGehee, John M., AL
McIlvaine, Paul William, PA
McLoone, John Cornelius, PA
Mears, Elmer E., PA
Merkin, Alvin, PA
Meyer, Maurice Mark, Jr., PA
Mimm, Charles Oliver, PA
Moran, John J., PA
Mullen, Andrew J., AL
O'Hurley, John George, CT
O'Toole, Thomas F., PA
Owens, Thomas Charles, PA
Partyka, Leo C., PA
Paulus, George Ervin, Jr., PA
Peck, F. Bruce, Jr., IN
Pedrotty, Francis W., Jr., PA
Perloff, Milton Max, PA
Phillips, Robert Lewis, WV
Potocki, Peter P., DE
Raymond, Joseph C., CA
Rosen, Leonard E., NJ
Saltzman, Herbert A., PA
Sanabria, Arturo E., PUERTO RICO
Sanabria, John F., PUERTO RICO
Schmidt, William Clark, PA
Sencindiver, Paige Victor, WV
Shaw, John W., FL
Sloss, Joseph H., PA
Smith, Alvin H., PA
Smith, William H., Jr., PA

Stack, William T., PA
Stadulis, Jerome M., PA
Stepansky, William, PA
Stout, Benjamin Mortimer, Jr., PA
Stout, Robert E., PA
Stoy, Robert P., PA
Strimel, William H., Jr., NJ
Stroup, Paul E., PA
Syms, Charles A., Jr., PA
Tatarian, Gabriel, PA
Taylor, Elmer J., Jr., PA
Thompson, James M., PA

Tribit, Charles Burns, Jr., PA
Trostle, Henry Stuart, PA
Turner, Kenneth Wayne, OH
Vincent, Lyle Dustin, Jr., WV
Wagner, Louis Joseph, NY
Wagner, Robert Anthony, NY
West, Stanley Q., PA
Wiedmann, Francis Edward, PA
Wilkinson, Albert H., Jr., FL
Wolff, George T., NC
Woolridge, John Hayes, Jr., PA
Zweifler, Nathan J., NJ
Zweig, Robert M., PA

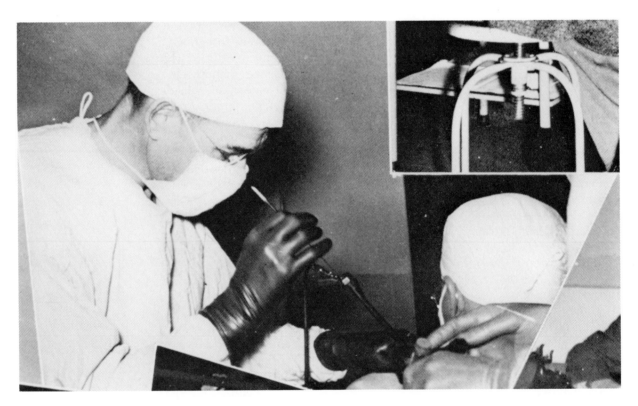

Professor Louis H. Clerf (JMC, '12) performs bronchoscopy.

The M.D. degrees were conferred by President James L. Kauffman on June 12 in the Academy of Music upon 160 graduates. Governor of the Commonwealth of Pennsylvania, John S. Fine, LL.B., LL.D., L.H.D., gave the Address.

On May 6 of this year, the first successful open heart surgery was performed by John H. Gibbon, Jr., (JMC, '27, Fig. 242)) at Jefferson. This dramatic event marked the culmination of more than twenty years of his research in the development of the heart-lung machine and inaugurated the era of definitive surgical correction of congenital and acquired cardiac defects (Fig. 342).

Franz Goldstein won top honors for highest average as well as other prizes. After completing training in gastroenterology at the Graduate Hospital under the prestigious Henry L. Bockus (JMC, '17, Fig. 202) he was appointed at Jefferson as the first fulltime member of the Division of Gastroenterology. He conducted significant research in his field and succeeded in collaboration with Dr. Charles W. Wirts, (JMC, '34, Fig. 265) in obtaining the first National Institutes of Health gastrointestinal research and training grant at Jefferson. This permitted the establishment of offices, research laboratories and stipends for the trainees. His many scientific contributions led to his rank of Professor of Medicine in 1970. At that time he transferred his activities to Lankenau Hospital where he became Chief of the newly created Department of Gastroenterology and developed a training program. He served as President of the American College of Gastroenterology in 1981/82 (Fig. 343).

Russell William Schaedler, an Alpha Omega Alpha honor student, went on to a distinguished career in microbiology. After an internship at Jefferson he received an appointment to the Rockefeller Institute for Medical Research where he advanced to Physician to its Hospital in 1962. He became well known in the field of gastrointestinal microecology in which he developed a cul-

Fig. 342.   John H. Gibbon, Jr. (JMC, '27) with his heart-lung machine.

ture medium that carries his name and is widely used for isolation and identification of anaerobes. Appointed Chairman of Microbiology at Jefferson in 1968, he became the first Plimpton-Pugh Professor in 1985 (Fig. 344). His portrait was presented to the University in 1990.

Jay A. Nadel pursued a career in clinical and research pulmonary medicine. His accomplishments included the presidency of the American Thoracic Society (1973/74) and publication of a textbook of respiratory medicine. He became Chief of the Section of Pulmonary Diseases and Professor of Medicine, Physiology and Radiology as well as Director of the Multidisciplinary Research Training Program on Pulmonary Diseases at the University of California, San Francisco (Fig. 345).

James M. Hunter completed his orthopaedic residency under Anthony F. DePalma at Jefferson and took a fellowship in hand surgery at Columbia-Presbyterian Medical Center in New York. On returning to Jefferson he became the first Philadelphia orthopaedic surgeon to practice totally in surgery of the hand. His research led to development of the "Hunter tendon" in 1965, the first successful artificial tendon for use in reconstructing severely damaged hands. He became recognized internationally and co-authored *Rehabilitation of the Hand* in 1978. He established the Hand Rehabilitation Center which became the Division of Hand Surgery of the Department of Orthopaedics and he advanced to the rank of Professor (Fig. 346). His portrait was presented to Jefferson in 1990.

William Eugene Delaney, III, another honor student, went on to become Professor of Medicine and Associate Professor of Pathology at Jefferson. He became highly respected as a clinician, teacher, general pathologist, and medical oncologist (Fig. 347).

Vernon Watson Pugh became a successful pediatrician in his native Raleigh, North Carolina. In 1985, he and Mrs. Frances Plimpton-Pugh es-

Fig. 343. Franz Goldstein (JMC, '53), Professor of Medicine (Gastroenterology).

Fig. 344. Russell W. Schaedler (JMC, '53), Plimpton-Pugh Professor of Microbiology and Immunology and Chairman of the Department.

1953

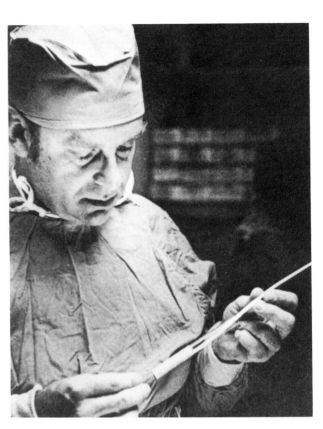

Fig. 345. Jay A. Nadel (JMC, '53), Professor of Medicine, Physiology and Radiology, University of California, San Francisco.

Fig. 346. James M. Hunter (JMC, '53), innovative orthopaedic surgeon who developed the "Hunter Tendon."

Fig. 347. William E. Delaney, III (JMC, '53), pathologist and medical oncologist.

Fig. 348. Robert Poole, III, (JMC, '53), Alumni President (1987).

1953

457

ferson in which his classmate, Dr. Russell W. Schaedler, became the first incumbent.

Henry A. Kane specialized in pediatric cardiology and was a respected teacher at Jefferson.

Robert Poole, III, remained active in the affairs of the Alumni Association and served as its President in 1987. He became a model for family practice in his community (Fig. 348).

John Milton Levinson, of New Jersey, took an American Cancer Society Clinical Fellowship in gynecology at Jefferson and rose in the Faculty to Associate Professor in the Department of Obstetrics and Gynecology. Between 1961 and 1980 he made eleven trips as a consultant, practicing physician, ship's surgeon and visiting professor to Africa, Antarctica, Europe, People's Republic of China, Southeast Asia and St. Lucia. Also, on the international level, he was the President and Founder of Aid for International Medicine, Inc., a charitable organization registered with the Advisory Committee on Voluntary Foreign Aid in the U.S. Department of State. He has contributed many scientific articles and served prominently in civic and governmental agencies.

Other class members in academic pursuits included Gerhard H. Fromm, Professor of Neurology, Presbyterian- University Hospital, Pittsburgh; John H. Harris, Jr., Professor of Radiology, Memorial Medical Center, Houston, Texas; Richard W. Hill, Associate Professor of Internal Medicine, Mayo Graduate School of Medicine, Rochester; and Lindsay L. Pratt, Professor of Otolaryngology at Jefferson and from 1975 to 1977 Chairman of the Department (Fig. 349).

CLASS OF 1953

Abrams, Jerome, NJ
Allen, Harold Y., PA
Anthony, Luther L., Jr., NC
Armao, Joseph J., PA
Bailey, Lloyd W., NC
Barr, Richard G., PA
Becker, Charles Frederick,III, NJ
Belgrade, Joseph E., DE
Bennett, Lansing H., PA
Berry, Bradley D., MS
Bittner, William E., CA
Boyer, David Joseph, Jr., PA
Brandfass, Carl F., Jr., WV
Brennan, James E., NJ
Brodsky, Leonard, PA
Carter, Joseph H., PA
Cawley, Thomas Patrick, PA
Chambers, Joseph Edward, WV
Chaplin, Charles Hal, NC
Coffey, William F. X., PA
Cook, T. William, PA
Corson, Hampton P., PA
Crill, Norman C., PA
Dalrymple, Richard E., PA
Dalsimer, Walter D., II, PA
Dauerty, Charles V. R., FL
Davis, Edwin D., WV
Delaney, William E., III, PA
Dettor, Vernon B., MD

Dorman, Frank L., PA
Doyle, Robert, PA
Dudeck, Carl R., PA
Dudek, William C., PA
Duke, Grady F., AL
Duling, W. Edward, WV
Dunkle, Donald D., PA
Fahringer, Robert R., PA
Fernandez, Manuel C., PUERTO RICO
Finkbiner, Rodman B., PA
Folker, Charles Warren, CA
Frank, Robert L., PA
Fromm, Gerhard H., PUERTO RICO
Furman, Harold B., PA
Gaither, Edwin Stanton, PA
Gillespy, Thurman, Jr., WV
Gingrich, Ralph Max, PA
Gladsden, Norman, PA
Goldstein, Franz, PA
Hand, Roy H., PA
Harris, John H., Jr., PA
Heil, Charles G., Jr., PA
Hekking, Robert J., PA
Herff, August F., Jr., TX
Hering, Norton, PA
Herrman, John C., PA
Hickey, Daniel, Jr., PA
Hicks, William Wynne, Jr., WA
Hill, Richard W., PA

Holland, Edward F., PA
Hollendonner, Werner J., PA
Holverson, Harmon E., ID
Hunter, James M., PA
Jacobs, Irvin, PA
Jacobs, Irwin Seymour, PA
Jaeger, Eugene A., PA
Jenson, William K., KS
Johns, Milton W., PA
Johnson, Charles T., Jr., NC
Kane, Henry A., PA
Kelleher, Robert C., OH
Kennedy, David Francis, PA
Killian, Caleb L., III, PA
Klinghoffer, Leonard, PA
Koury, James Solomon, Jr., PA
Krabill, Willard S., OH
Krasney, Robert Louis, NJ
Kulp, David W., PA
Larkin, Walter J., Jr., PA
Lassiter, James Alexander, NC

Levinson, John M., NJ
Lindemuth, Edmund K., Jr., PA
Lovelace, Roger David, NJ
Lundberg, George A. F., Jr., CT
Lynn, John T., PA
Marine, Robert M., DE
May, Lewis H. V., WV
McAndrew, James Alfred, IL
McFadden, James Andrew, Jr., PA
McLaughlin, William J., PA
Mead, Robert M., PA
Meredith, J. Rodney, PA
Metheny, John E., PA
Mettler, Dallas E., PA
Millberg, William Burkley, OH
Moore, Donald B., OH
Morehead, John Ellwood, PA
Morris, James Aloysius, Jr., PA
Muffly, Harry Mac, WV
Murphy, Michael Joseph, PA
Murray, William E., NC
Musser, Guy R., PA
Myers, Carl B., PA
Nadel, Jay A., PA
Naden, Randall Stedman, Jr., MA
Naef, Richard W., MS
Nierle, Richard Hugh, PA
Oliver-Smith, Richard W., CA
Orlick, Arnold H., DE
Owens, Joseph L., Jr., GA
Perrige, William Michael, PA
Pisula, Vincent Paul, Jr., PA
Poole, Robert, III, PA
Potash, Irwin M., PA
Pratt, Lindsay L., NJ
Pugh, V. Watson, NC
Rank, Dale C., PA
Reinhard, Harold J., CT
Remley, Stuart K., PA
Robinson, Richard F., PA
Roland, Frederick H., PA
Rubin, Robert J., NY
Rudolph, Burton M., FL
Rushton, Harold W., NJ
Sampsel, John J., PA
Schaedler, Russell W., PA
Schneider, Stanley S., NY
Seckinger, Raymond P., PA
Sexton, George L., Jr., PA
Shore, Dean C., WV
Simpson, Joseph W., PA
Smith, Claude A., NC
Smith, John Waddell, PA
Snyder, Marvin C. G., PA

Fig. 349. Lindsay L. Pratt (JMC, '53), Chairman of Otolaryngology (1975-77).

Stader, Richard Otto, PA
Staub, Carl Aloysius, Jr., PA
Stauffer, Stanely Sell, PA
Stein, Donald Beuchler, Jr., PA
Stierstorfer, Max Joseph, PA
Stockdale, Earl McAninch, PA
Stoner, Robert E., PA
Sugg, William C., NC
Tedesco, Orlando P., PA
Thomas, James H., PA
Thomson, Alvernon H., PA
Tice, Walter Ruhl, PA
Ullmann, Thomas M., PA

Vorys, Nichols, OH
Walker, William J., III, PA
Wallace, William D., Jr., PA
Ward, Jack L., NJ
Watkins, Jack G., PA
Wertz, Robert R., PA
West, Edward, PA
Wharton, Earl W., OH
Wheelock, Dana McKinstry, NY
Wilkie, Louis J., PA
Williams, Gomer Thomas, Jr., PA
Wilson, Frederick S., NJ
Wilton, Edward Andrew, PA
Wolf, Frank A., Jr., NJ

Surgical Clinic of Professor Thomas A. Shallow (JMC, '11).

The construction of a new hospital building on Eleventh Street between Walnut and Sansom, later (1962) to be designated the "Foerderer Pavilion," was the major event of the year (Fig. 350). It won a prize for the architect, Mr. Vincent Kling, but rapidly changing needs would require frequent modifications and renovations.

The 163 graduates were awarded their degrees at the Academy of Music on June 18. Thomas B. McCabe, a prominent industrialist, gave the Commencement Address.

Howard L. Field went from his Jefferson internship to training in psychiatry and progressed in that Department at Jefferson to a major role. For a number of years he was Director of Resident Training and Director of the In-Patient Unit,

Fig. 350. "New Pavilion" (1954) given the name Foerderer in 1962.

as well as Medical Director of Friends Hospital. He was later Director of the Division of Consultation and Liaison and of Psychosomatic Medicine with the rank of Clinical Professor of Psychiatry and Human Behavior (Fig. 351).

Rudolph C. Camishion was trained in surgery at Jefferson and held an appointment as National Cancer Institute Fellow until 1962. He later advanced to Professor of Surgery (Fig. 352). In 1978 he was appointed Professor of Surgery and Head of the Department of Surgery at Rutgers Medical School, Camden. In 1990 he served as President of the Philadelphia Academy of Surgery.

John W. Goldschmidt was attracted to Rehabilitation Medicine. Following training at the Hospital of the University of Pennsylvania he returned to Jefferson in 1959 and soon became Director of Rehabilitation Medicine. He had major responsibility for developing the new Rehabilitation Unit in the Thompson Building. In 1961 he received the Lindback Award for Distinguished Teaching. He became the first Dean of Allied Health Sciences in 1967 (Fig. 353) but returned to Rehabilitation Medicine with his appointment to Northwestern University School of Medicine, Chicago, in 1971. In 1983 he became

Vice-President and Medical Director of the National Rehabilitation Hospital, Washington, D.C.

John R. Patterson, winner of the Practice Prize in Medicine, served his residency at Jefferson. Following training in rheumatology, he joined the Department of Medicine where he became a leading member of the Division of Rheumatology and advanced to Clinical Associate Professor of Medicine. He also served a term as President of the Philadelphia Rheumatism Society (Fig. 354).

John J. Kelly served his internship, residency and Fellowship in Cardiology at Jefferson and then joined the staff of Lankenau Hospital where he progressed to Chief of Medicine and Co-Director of Cardiology. Since 1979 he has been Clinical Professor of Medicine through the Lankenau-Jefferson affiliation.

Warren W. Nichols in 1980 was the winner of the Jefferson Alumni Achievement Award. He served as Senior Director, Genetic and Cellular Toxicology for Merck, Sharp and Dohme Laboratories. He was also Professor of Pediatrics and Human Genetics at the University of Pennsylvania School of Medicine.

Numerous members of the Class of 1954 were prominent in their special fields. Charles H.

Fig. 351. Howard L. Field (JMC, '54), Clinical Professor of Psychiatry.

Fig. 352. Rudolph C. Camishion (JMC, '54), Professor of Surgery.

Greenbaum, trained in dermatology at the University of Pennsylvania and the Philadelphia General Hospital, went on to the rank of Clinical Professor of Dermatology at Jefferson. Thomas Aceto, Jr. became Professor and Chairman of the Department of Pediatrics and Adolescent Medicine at St. Louis University School of Medicine. Edward M. Podgorski joined the Department of Obstetrics and Gynecology at Jefferson and advanced to Clinical Assistant Professor. John J. Blizzard became prominent in the Department of Medicine at the Lankenau Hospital and advanced to Clinical Professor of Medicine at Jefferson. Philip Woolcott, Jr., trained in psychiatry at the Menninger Clinic in Topeka, Kansas, was Psychiatrist-in-Chief and Professor at the University of Illinois Medical Center. Martin D. Shickman was Assistant Dean for Post-Graduate Medical Education and Clinical Professor in the Department of Medicine and Cardiology at the University of Los Angeles School of Medicine. Paul Griesmer, major prize winner at graduation, became Chief of Obstetrics and Gynecology

at Wilkes-Barre General Hospital and at Nesbitt Memorial Hospital, Kingston, Pennsylvania. Howard E. Sullivan, Jr. was Chief of Allergy at Bryn Mawr Hospital and Associate Professor of Medicine at the University of Pennsylvania School of Medicine. Joseph B. Green in 1982 was named Chairman of the Department of Psychiatry and Neurology at Tulane University School of Medicine. Stanley R. Kern in 1980 was President of the New Jersey Psychoanalytic Society and in 1987 President of the New Jersey Psychiatric Association. Jack W. Fink, very active in Alumni affairs, became Clinical Assistant Professor of Obstetrics and Gynecology at Jefferson. Robert B. Cahan, trained in psychiatry in the Philadelphia area, became Associate Clinical Professor of Psychiatry at the University of California at San Francisco. Alfred P. Spivak was trained in cardiology and advanced to Clinical Professor at Stanford University School of Medicine. Thornton A. Vandersall, prior to retirement in 1988, was Professor of Clinical Psychiatry at Cornell University School of Medicine. Lewis P.

Fig. 353. John W. Goldschmidt, First Dean, School of Allied Health Sciences (1967-69), then College of Allied Health Sciences (1969-75).

Fig. 354. John R. Patterson (JMC, '54), Clinical Associate Professor of Medicine (Rheumatology).

1954

Scott was Professor of Pediatrics at George Washington School of Medicine, Washington, D.C. Murray N. Silverstein was Professor of Internal Medicine at Mayo Graduate School, Rochester. George D. Sorenson served as Professor of Pathology at Dartmouth-Hitchcock Medical Center, Hanover. Andrew J. Zweifler was Professor of Internal Medicine at the University of Michigan, Ann Arbor. Charles J. Beauchamp was Associate Professor of Pediatrics, University of California, Davis, and G. Richard Dickersin, Associate Professor of Pathology, Massachusetts General Hospital.

CLASS OF 1954

Abbott, Joseph L., PA
Aceto, Thomas, Jr., PA
Albright, William J., III, PA
Allen, Robert M., PA
Allshouse, Richard Reaser, PA
Amer, Norman S., NY
Atkinson, G. Russell, PA
Baisden, Carl Francis, PA
Beasley, Frank J., PA
Beauchamp, Charles J., MA
Biedlingmaier, Gerard Joseph, PA
Blizzard, John J., PA
Borkowski, Bernard B., DE
Boyle, Playford, Jr., PA
Breslin, Harvey Jerome, NY
Brubaker, Warren W., PA
Bucher, Robert G., PA
Byron, Harold Joseph, PA
Cahan, Robert B., PA
Camishion, Rudolph C., NJ
Carroll, Edward A., PA
Chesen, David, PA
Cheslock, William B., PA
Clarke, Frank R., PA
Colon-Bonet, Cesar H., PUERTO RICO
Cook, Jerome I., NJ
Coyne, Charles T. B., PA
Croft, David W., PA
Culp, Robert T., PA
Dannenberg, Marvin, NY
Davis, Dwight G., Jr., NY
Dersh, Jerome, PA
Dickersin, G. Richard, PA
Dougherty, Malvin J., PA
Eichner, Lambert G., PA
Evans, Carl T., PA
Field, Howard Lawrence, NJ
Fink, Jack W., PA
Flanigan, John L., Jr., PA
Forte, Anthony L., PA
Foster, Donald H., NJ
Freeman, Donald H., PA
Fryczynski, Thaddeus P., PA

Gamon, Robert Speer, Jr., NJ
Garcia, Theodore A., PA
Gerner, Paul Calvin, PA
Gill, Patrick H., MS
Glowacki, Peter, PA
Goldschmidt, John W., PA
Goodwin, John J., PA
Gordon, John William, II, PA
Green, Joseph B., PA
Greenbaum, Charles Hirsch, PA
Griesmer, Paul Dalton, PA
Groves, Norris B., WV
Halpern, Barry R., NJ
Hamilton, John S., AL
Harriger, Clyde Everett, PA
Hassel, C. Walter, Jr., PA
Himes, Ralph F., Jr., PA
Hinrichs, Robert A., NY
Hodge, Thomas Ashton, OH
Hoffman, Glen H., PA
Hood, Christopher K., NC
Hunsicker, Philip M., PA
Iames, William P., PA
Ivker, Miton, PA
Jacob, Thomas Charles, PA
Jacobs, William Robert, NJ
Kaigh, Irvin, PA
Katzman, Merle H., CT
Kelly, John J., PA
Kendig, Newton Emerson, PA
Kern, Stanley R., NJ
Kopack, Francis M., PA
Koretsky, Irving Bennett, MA
Ladika, Joseph Albert, PA
Lauricella, John P., NJ
Laurie, Robert Edward, FL
Lavine, Harris, NJ
Leasum, Robert N., WI
Lee, Robert C., HAWAII
Levick, Stanley Nelson, PA
Lewis, Earl T., MS
Lipschutz, Harold, PA
Loughead, John R., Jr., PA

Luongo, Romeo A., PA
Martin, Gilbert A., Jr., WV
McGowan, John Patrick, PA
McKeon, Frank Anthony, Jr., PA
McMorris, David L., PA
Millberg, Richard S., OH
Minter, Donald L., PA
Moury, Nelson F., Jr., PA
Nash, Francis J., MA
Nelson, John B., III, NJ
Nichols, Warren W., NJ
O'Connor, Dennis Stephen, PA
Okun, Milton R., PA
Oschell, William J., PA
Patterson, John M., MS
Patterson, John R., PA
Paul, Carey B., Jr., OH
Paxson, Edwin M., PA
Peoples, Richard B., PA
Phifer, Joe Carl, IL
Pletcher, Henry William, II, NY
Podgorski, Edward M., NJ
Powell, Charles H., NC
Purnell, John S., Jr., PA
Putman, Billie H., MS
Randall, Thomas Anthony, PA
Rankin, Charles A., Jr., PA
Rawls, John E., MS
Renquest, Edward Allan, PA
Rodgers, William Leitch, WV
Rosenberg, Jack N., PA
Rumbaugh, James O., Jr., PA
Salisbury, Edward M., NY
Samuels, Pierce D., PA
Schonholz, David H., NJ
Scott, Lewis P., II, NJ
Scottolini, Alfred G., PA
Shickman, Martin D., PA

Shively, Wyant J., OH
Silverstein, Murray N., PA
Smith, H. Alexander,Jr., PA
Solomon, Macy B., PA
Sorensen, Robert J., PA
Sorenson, George D., Jr., PA
Southwick, Samuel G., IL
Spivack, Alfred P., MA
Stacks, Jacob C., Jr., PA
Stec, Eugene G., PA
Stone, Edgar Franklin, Jr., RI
Sullivan, Howard E., Jr., PA
Sunada, Kayo, WY
Tananis, Leonard J., PA
Tannenbaum, Gerald, PA
Taylor, William H., PA
Tippetts, Charles S., Jr., PA
Tober, Edward, NH
Tocantins, Ronald, PA
Vandersall, Thornton A., PA
Wapner, John M., PA
Wargovich, Raymond Michael, PA
Webb, Lawrence Clayton, PA
Weidaw, Harold R., PA
Weinberg, Jerome A., PA
Weis, Paul R., PA
Weller, Harry W., PA
Welsh, James F., PA
Werley, John D., PA
West, William A., NJ
Weylman, Walther T., NJ
Whitcomb, John F., NH
White, Joseph C., AR
Williams, Ralph H., PA
Winston, Joseph M., PA
Wofford, John D., MS
Woollcott, Phillip, Jr., NC
Yenney, Matthew F., PA
Zweifler, Andrew J., NJ

Where there is much desire to learn, there of necessity will be much arguing, much writing, many opinions, for opinion in good men is but knowledge in the making.

John Milton (1608–76)

The Commencement Address for the 169 graduates of 1955 was delivered by Norman Vincent Peale, D.D., then at the height of his popularity. Dr. Peale was Minister of the Marble Collegiate Church, New York.

Herbert E. Cohn was the major awards recipient. Among these he received the Alumni, Potter Memorial, and Einstein prizes for the highest academic performance. He was trained in surgery at Jefferson and joined the surgical staff with an interest in organ transplantation. He performed the first successful renal transplant at Jefferson in 1972. Dr. Cohn went on to academic and clinical accomplishments resulting in his ultimate promotion to Professor of Surgery and Vice-Chairman of the Department (Fig. 355). He also received the Lindback Award for teaching excellence and in 1984 was President of the Medical Staff. In 1988 he was honored by the Jewish National Fund as Man of the Year. His portrait was presented to the University in 1990.

Leon A. Peris, also a prize winner, became an important member of the Department of Obstetrics and Gynecology at Jefferson. When Dr. Laird Jackson organized the Division of Medical Genetics, Dr. Peris represented the Department of Obstetrics and Gynecology in investigation and clinical genetic counseling. He advanced to Clinical Associate Professor and in 1987 was elected President of the Medical Staff (Fig. 356). Following his early death, the Leon A. Peris Memorial Award was established in 1988 for that member of the Volunteer Faculty showing excellence in clinical teaching and superior patient care.

Edward C. Bradley, S.J. was trained in internal medicine and cardiology and joined the staff of the Department of Medicine. He later became a priest of the Society of Jesus but continued his clinical teaching and advanced to Clinical Associate Professor. In 1988 he was appointed to the post of Special Counselor in Residence, available for student consultation (Fig. 357).

F. William Sunderman, Jr., also a winner of five prizes at graduation, became a clinical pathologist of note. An officer of the Association of Clinical Scientists, he has been Professor of Laboratory Medicine and Pharmacology at the University of Connecticut School of Medicine.

Rachmel Cherner, following internship at Graduate Hospital, joined the Department of Medicine at Jefferson and advanced to Clinical Associate Professor. His major interest was endocrinology and diseases of metabolism.

H. William Porterfield entered the expanding field of plastic surgery and served as an officer of several associations including the Presidency of the American Society of Plastic and Recon-

Fig. 355. Herbert E. Cohn (JMC, '55), Professor of Surgery and Vice-Chairman of the Department.

structive Surgeons in 1981. He was Associate Clinical Professor of Surgery at Ohio State University School of Medicine.

Richard H. Schwartz, after internship at Philadelphia General Hospital, was trained in obstetrics and gynecology. He went on to appointment as Professor and Chairman of the Department at State University of New York Downstate Medical Center and also Dean of the College of Medicine and Vice President for Medical Affairs at the same institution. In 1989 he was Vice President of the American College of Obstetrics/Gynecology.

Robert I. Fraser entered the field of public health after his Pennsylvania Hospital internship. He was involved in the study and control of tuberculosis in Alaska. From 1969 he served as Chief of Communicable Disease Control and was later named Director of the Division of Public Health for the State of Alaska.

Thomas W. Georges, Jr. was trained in Public Health (M.P.H) and became an administrator in the Philadelphia Health Department. He served a term as Commissioner of Health for the State of Pennsylvania, was Professor of Public Health at Temple University School of Medicine, and later Professor of Preventive Medicine at Howard University School of Medicine.

A number of 1955 graduates were notable in various careers. Robert J. Senior was a charter member of the Society for Adolescent Medicine and in 1981 was a member of the Editorial Board of the *Journal of Current Adolescent Medicine*. Guy L. Schless, trained at the Pennsylvania Hospital and in London in endocrinology and metabolic diseases, was Assistant Clinical Professor of Medicine at the University of Pennsylvania School of Medicine. Robert E. Berry, after a tour of duty in Nepal where he performed the first thoracic surgery in that country's history, practiced in Roanoke, Virginia, and held an appointment as Professor of Surgery at the University

Fig. 356. Leon A. Peris (JMC, '55), Clinical Associate Professor of Medicine and President of the Medical Staff.

Fig. 357. Edward C. Bradley, S.J. (JMC, '55), Clinical Associate Professor of Medicine and Jesuit Priest!

Fig. 358. Leonard J. Graziani (JMC, '55), Professor of Pediatrics and Neurology.

of Virginia. Arthur C. Huntley was Associate Clinical and Research Professor at the Medical College of Pennsylvania and Coordinator of Group Psychotherapy Training at Eastern Pennsylvania Psychiatric Institute. Frederick Lytel was a Clinical Assistant Professor of Family Medicine in Jefferson's preceptor program. William D. Millhon was Associate Clinical Professor of Medicine at Ohio State University College of Medicine. Harry G. Light, a surgeon in Bethlehem, Pennsylvania, was a Governor of the American College of Surgeons. Bernard W. Godwin was Clinical Assistant Professor of Medicine at Jefferson in the Division of Allergy and Immunology. Thomas N. Gates, after experience in private practice, became associated with pharmaceutical medical research. He progressed to Director of Clinical Renal Research at Merck, Sharp and Dohme Laboratories and later was appointed Vice President of the Medical Department of McNeil Laboratories and a member of the Management Board. Leonard J. Graziani served at Jefferson as Professor of Pediatrics, Director of Child Development, and Professor of Neurology (Fig. 358). Richard E. Hicks was Associate Professor of Psychiatry and Joseph A. Miller Professor of Obstetrics/Gynecology at Hahnemann University.

CLASS OF 1955

Anthony, William A., Jr., PA
Arsht, Edwin D., PA
Aspiote, John George, PA
Bailey, Dewey J., Jr., WV
Baron, Bernard W., PA
Bauer, H. Paul, Jr., PA
Becker, Edward F., PA
Beggs, David W., NJ
Benovitz, Burton S., PA
Bernstine, Earl L., PA
Berry, Robert E., PA
Blackburn, Joseph M., PA
Bloemendaal, John W., SD
Boyer, Carl W., Jr., PA
Bradley, Rev. Edward C.,S.J. PA
Brahen, Louis, PA
Brams, Richard F., NJ
Brandfass, W. Taylor, WV
Braun, Frederick C., Jr., NJ
Broderick, John R., Jr., GA
Brown, Marion Havard, MS

Brown, Richard, IN
Brown, Robert A., PA
Capper, Robert, PA
Carlin, Elwin S., PA
Carter, W. Neal, PA
Castiglia, Eugene A., PA
Centrone, Joseph F., PA
Cherner, Rachmel, PA
Christy, Michael G., PA
Cleland, William O., MS
Coccia, S. Paul, NY
Cohen, Richard A., NY
Cohn, Herbert E., NJ
Coletta, Domenic F., PA
Condefer, William Thomas, PA
Conley, Paul J., MA
Conner, J. Hubert, MD
Cordier, Robert D., PA
Cornfeld, Edward, PA
Cravetz, Howard, PA
Curran, Francis J., RI

Curtin, Eugene A., PA
Donald, Delmar J., PA
Duncan, Theodore G., PA
Elmer, Alfred Cornwell, NJ
Eppley, Robert D., PA
Fishter, Michael F., PA
Fraser, Robert I., PA
Gates, Thomas N., PA
Geisler, Philip Howard, PA
Gemmill, Reginal B., PA
Georges, Thomas W., Jr., PA
Godwin, Bernard Whitehead,Jr., VA
Goodman, Bruce, NJ
Gould, R. John, NJ
Graziani, Leonard J., PA
Groblewski, Edward A., PA
Harun, Joseph S., PA
Hastings, Leo J., Jr., PA
Heaney, Joseph A., PA
Henderson, William P., IL
Hewlett, John O., PA
Hicks, Richard E., NJ
Hoch, John J., PA
Holland, William T., Jr., PA
Huntley, Arthur C., Jr., FL
Ivker, Milton, PA
Jeffrey, William L., MS
Jenkins, Cecil G., MS
John, Joseph R., PA
Jones, Robert E., PA
Joyce, Michael F., PA
Kanenson, William L., PA
Kapcar, Andrew J., Jr., PA
Kessel, Ray M., WV
Kline, Ben, PA
Kline, Robert M., PA
Klinges, Henry George, Jr., PA
Laauwe, Roger C., NJ
Lape, I. Samuel, Jr., PA
Lenyo, George E., PA
Light, Harry G., NJ
Lissner, Arthur Bart, NJ
Lista, William A., PA
Long, Delbert L., Jr., PA
Lukens, Robert W., Jr., WV
Lytel, Frederick, PA
Mackey, James G., Jr., PA
Maguire, Joseph I., PA
Mandel, Harvey I., NY
Mann, Joseph Jacob, NJ
Manz, Donald J., PA
Marchesani, John A., NJ
Markowitz, Julius Leonard, PA
Mazur, John H., PA

McCarthy, John A., PA
McCuskey, Bradford M., PA
McKenna, Ernest L., Jr., PA
McNally, Michael J., PA
Miller, Donald G., IN
Miller, Joseph A., PA
Miller, Wilbur H., Jr., PA
Millhon, Judson S., OH
Millhon, William A., OH
Montgomery, George A., Jr., PA
Moore, LeRoy E., PA
Moore, William R., Jr., WV
Morrow, Robert E., FL
Murray, James A., PA
Murray, Joseph Edward, RI
Nagle, John A., CT
Nolan, J. Philip, PA
O'Connell, Joseph P., PA
Parenteau, Roger E., MA
Pathroff, Robert, PA
Perch, Robert B., PA
Peris, Leon Abraham, PA
Pershing, Hugh S., NY
Pierucci, Louis, Jr., PA
Pohl, Donald Robert, PA
Porterfield, H. William, MD
Potts, Donald E., PA
Powers, Donald V., PA
Raiford, John W., NJ
Rannels, Darwin W., PA
Rappaport, Myron E., NY
Rightmyer, Eugene R., PA
Roddy, Lewis Ralph, OK
Rosenblatt, Alfred A., NJ
Rosenblatt, Elwood C., NJ
Schaffer, Burton, PA
Schauer, Joseph W., Jr., PA
Schelpert, John W., III, NY
Schless, Guy L., PA
Schorn, Victor G., PA
Schultz, J. Donald, NJ
Schultze, Charles F., WV
Schwartz, John T., PA
Schwarz, Richard H., PA
Selfon, Paul M., PA
Senior, Robert J., NY
Shoaff, Paris A., III, PA
Shoener, John A., PA
Shuptar, Daniel, PA
Singer, Alvin, NJ
Singleton, James A., WV
Sourbeer, John N., FL
Spagnoli, Robert C., PA
Speirs, Harold Archer, NJ

Steck, Charles G., PA
Steele, John T., WV
Stillwell, John Clifford, NJ
Stoker, John W., PA
Storm, Charles T. H., PA
Stoudt, Donald E., PA
Sunderman, F. William, Jr., PA
Taylor, Philip H., WV
Templeton, Thomas B., NC
Turco, John D., PA

Vallow, Morton J., PA
Vanderlin, Robert L., PA
Voshell, Thomas H., Jr., PA
Weintraub, William C., DC
Wiss, Raymond J., PA
Yurick, Bernard S., PA
Zangrilli, Alfred George, PA
Zenker, David O., PA
Zuch, Robert F., NJ

North Lecture Room in College Building.

The M.D. degrees were conferred on June 15 in the Academy of Music by President Kauffman on 171 graduates, which brought the total number to 19,255. The Address was delivered by Frank Brown Berry, M.D., Assistant Secretary of Defense.

Benjamin Bacharach, of New Jersey, devoted his career to surgery and to administration at Jefferson. During his surgical residency he worked in the research laboratory under the auspices of Professor John H. Gibbon, Jr. From 1962 to 1965 he operated on cases of complicated tuberculosis and continued his research in cardiothoracic problems. He served as President of the Alumni Association in 1981. In 1987 he became a Clinical Professor of Surgery and also the Associate Dean for Admissions of Jefferson Medical College. The following year he was appointed Vice Chairman of the Department of Surgery. As a fund raiser for Jefferson for many years he has acted as leader for the President's Club contributors and was the first to be awarded the Gold-Headed Cane of that organization (Fig. 359).

Sheldon Gerald Gilgore took residency training at Jefferson in endocrine and metabolic diseases in which he conducted important research in carbohydrate metabolism. He went on to become President of Pfizer Pharmaceuticals and then Chairman of the Board and Chief Executive Officer of G.D. Searle and Company. He served as Chairman of the Board at Clark University and a six-year term as Alumni Representative on the Board of Thomas Jefferson University. In 1988 he was the recipient of Jefferson's prestigious Alumni Achievement Award (Fig. 360).

David Charles Schechter won many of the prizes at graduation. He interned at Jefferson and took his residency training under Professor John H. Gibbon, Jr., with participation in the research laboratory. After a tour of military duty he was the recipient of a Fellowship Award for postgraduate study under Sir Russel Brock at the Institute for Diseases of the Chest at Brompton Hospital in London and with Professor Charles Dubost in Paris at the Hospital Broussais. He then continued his surgical career at the New York Medical College where he became a Clinical Professor of Surgery.

Wallace T. Miller, Professor of Radiology, University of Pennsylvania School of Medicine, received numerous awards for excellence in teaching of medical students and residents. In 1989 he was selected as editor of *Seminars in Roentgenology*.

James P. Boland, Professor and Chairman of the Department of Surgery at West Virginia Uni-

Fig. 359. Benjamin Bacharach (JMC, '56), Clinical Professor of Surgery, Vice-Chairman of the Department, and Associate Dean for Admissions.

versity Health Sciences Center, Charleston, became notable as a medical writer and frequent visiting professor.

Leopold Samuel Loewenberg joined Jefferson's Department of Obstetrics/Gynecology and advanced to Clinical Associate Professor. He was President of the Medical Staff in 1990 (Fig. 361).

Edward David McLaughlin augmented his surgical residency at Jefferson with research at the National Cancer Institute. He served for many years as Chief of Surgery at Misericordia Hospital, Philadelphia, in which capacity he trained Jefferson students on rotation (Fig. 362).

Other members of the class who were highly respected on Jefferson's Faculty were George Manuel Arnas and Stewart E. First (both in Ob-

stetrics/Gynecology), and Joel David Hoffman (Orthopaedics).

Class members with academic appointments elsewhere included: William E. Clendenning, Professor of Internal Medicine, Dartmouth-Hitchcock Medical Center, Hanover; Ernest R. Griffith, Professor of Physical Medicine and Rehabilitation, University of Illinois; James B. Lee, Professor of Internal Medicine, University of Buffalo; Paul G. McDonough, Professor of Obstetrics/Gynecology, Medical College of Georgia, Augusta; Patrick S. Pasquariello, Associate Professor of Pediatrics at the University of Pennsylvania; Kenneth N. Beers, Associate Professor of Internal Medicine, and Charles J. Stahl, III, Associate Professor of Pathology, both at Wright State University, Dayton, Ohio.

Fig. 360. Sheldon G. Gilgore (JMC, '56), Alumni Member of the Board of Trustees and recipient of the Alumni Achievement Award (1988).

Fig. 361. Leopold S. Loewenberg (JMC, '56), Clinical Associate Professor of Obstetrics and Gynecology and President of the Medical Staff (1990).

1956

Abell, Charles F., Jr., IN
Adams, Arland A., PA
Alexander, William Newton, AZ
Andracchio, Vincent C., PA
Arnas, George M., WV
Arouh, Albert, NJ
Ashmore, Hugh W., NJ
Bacharach, Benjamin, NJ
Bacon, Wm. Dudson, PA
Bailey, Carl H., Jr., PA
Baker, Richard P., Jr., PA
Baldi, Frederick V., PA
Bard, Joseph L., PA
Barr, William Bryce, Jr., PA
Beers, Kenneth N., PA
Bell, Thomas G., PA
Bering, Joseph P., PA

Fig. 362.   Edward D. McLaughlin (JMC, '56), Chief of Surgery at Misericordia Hospital who taught Jefferson medical students on rotation in this affiliated hospital.

Berne, Bernard, IL
Boland, James P., PA
Bonacci, Eugene F., NJ
Brennan, Charles L., Jr., NJ
Brust, Raymond W., Jr., PA
Carson, John C., WV
Carter, Thomas L., PA
Chang, Owen A., JAMAICA
Chitterling, Nelson M., NJ
Christie, Alfred Douglas, PA
Clair, Gerald F., PA
Clendenning, William E., PA
Cole, Charles E., PA
Corwin, James H., II, PA
Cottone, Robert N., NJ
Coyle, William A., PA
Daniel, John M., WV
Danishanko, Albert G., PA
Davies, John B., PA
Davis, John Mostyn, Jr., PA
Davis, Thomas Gale, Jr., PA
Demmy, Merlyn R., PA
Doneker, Thomas G., NJ
Drucker, Paul, NJ
Dugan, Paul J., PA
Edalatpour, Nasrola, IRAN
Feigelson, Charles I., AL
First, Stewart E., PA
Fisch, Irwin R., PA
Fisher, Peter B., PA
Flaharty, William James, MI
Flickinger, Haviland, PA
Frank, Paul E., PA
Gersten, Hilliard Clive, NJ
Gibson, Theodore K., RI
Gilgore, Sheldon G., PA
Given, George Gordon, Jr., PA
Glick, Eugene, PA
Goldblatt, Seymour Z., NJ
Gorszyca, Casimir A., PA
Gostigian, John J., PA
Green, Philip S., NJ
Green, Rex W., Jr., PA
Griffith, Ernest R., NJ
Grollman, Albert H., PA
Grove, Dale A., Jr., PA
Hagopian, Edward R., PA
Harris, Russell H., SD
Harrold, Brian S., OH
Hemminger, Charles H., NJ

Hobbs, Joseph H., PA
Hoffman, J. David, PA
Holdcraft, John W., NJ
Horn, Paul C., MS
Housman, J. Harold, PA
Howe, William L., PA
Jackson, C. Robert, MN
Jacobs, William Harold, MS
Johnson, James H., OH
Kahn, Hyman R., PA
Kane, Wilton R., FL
Kastner, Richard H., PA
Kessler, Frank J., PA
Klinges, Karl G., NJ
Koehl, C. Warren, Jr., NY
Kostrzewa, Raymond M., NJ
Kushner, Bertrand, PA
Kuzmishin, George, PA
Landry, Arthur B., Jr., CT
Lee, James B., MA
LeRoy, Pierre L., PA
Levin, Warren M., PA
Levitt, Donald G., PA
Lipson, Richard L., PA
Loewenberg, Leopold S., PA
Loomis, James W., PA
Loucks, James Howe, NJ
Luczynski, Edward W., Jr., NJ
Lundgren, Wilbert G., PA
Mabey, Rex G., ID
Magley, Robert C., NJ
Magrath, Joseph L., Jr., PA
Malfara, Joseph Francis, PA
Maro, Robert J., PA
Marshall, Theodore J., DE
Martin, Neil Douglas, PA
Mayhew, Cliford L., NJ
McCadden, Joseph A., PA
McCaughan, James S., Jr., PA
McDonough, Paul G., PA
McGrath, Kenneth J., NY
McLaughlin, Edward D., PA
Meckelnburg, Robert L., PA
Mele, Frank E., Jr., PA
Mella, Gordon W., PA
Melmed, Ronald M., CT
Merlino, Anthony F., RI
Mervine, Charles K., III, PA
Meyerson, Sheldon B., FL
Miller, Wallace T., PA
Minier, Edward L., NJ

Mokychic, Walter E., PA
Moyer, Rodney D., PA
Nellas, Constantine L., PA
Nestor, Hubert Richard, PA
Niklewski, Edmund V., PA
Nix, James Elmer, MS
O'Brien, Thomas Gore, PA
Oliva, Vincent S., NJ
Paoletti, Michael A., NJ
Pasquariello, Patrick S., PA
Pearl, Robert M., PA
Peril, Jack Jerome, PA
Price, Richard Taylor, PA
Raiber, Richard, PA
Ramos-Barroso, Antonio R., PUERTO RICO
Ravin, Joseph P., PA
Regan, James R., PA
Rosenthal, Herbert A., PA
Rothfeld, Edwin L., NJ
Rubin, Jack D., NJ
Sawyer, Blackwell, Jr., NJ
Schechter, David C., PA
Schwartz, Robert R., PA
Senn, Francis E., Jr., PA
Shapiro, Bertram H., PA
Sherk, Henry H., NJ
Sitkoff, Malcolm, PA
Skloff, David Samuel, PA
Smith, Joseph Francis, Jr., NJ
Smith, Robert William, PA
Snyder, H. Martin, KS
Soll, Kenneth H., PA
Stahl, Charles J., III, PA
Stennis, William Hardy, Jr., MS
Stettler, Wayne D., Jr., PA
Stine, Thomas D., PA
Stone, James L., FL
Swartz, Harry M., NJ
Thomas, Carlyle Milton, Jr., PA
Vitosky, Stanley, PA
Weimann, Robert B., NJ
Weissman, William K., NY
Whitmore, John T., PA
Whitsell, David Clark, IL
Wilhelm, Frederick H., NY
Williams, Claude M., Jr., PA
Williams, Stephen K., PA
Wong, Wallace Bow On, HAWAII
Woutersz, Theodore B., PA
Yale, Noyes E., Jr., NJ
Yim, Henry L., HAWAII
Zangrilli, James G., PA

Although the graduation exercises had been held without interruption in the Academy of Music since 1870, this year marked the Centennial of the opening (1857) of the Academy, and because of renovations to the building the Commencement was held in the Forrest Theater. President Kauffman awarded the degrees to 165 graduates, which brought the grand total to 19,420. The Most Reverend Fulton J. Sheen, Ph.D.,D.D., Director, The Society for the Propagation of the Faith, gave the Address.

Paul Donald Zimskind, of New Jersey, an honor graduate, son of Joshua N. Zimskind (JMC, '27), pursued an academic career at Jefferson devoted to teaching and research in urology. After internship and residency at Jefferson, he was awarded a Postdoctoral Fellowship by the National Institutes of Health in which he earned a Ph.D. degree in the Department of Physiology in 1964. While functioning as Assistant Professor of Urology and in charge of the Urology Research Laboratories, he was selected in 1966 as a Markle Scholar in Academic Medicine. In 1967, during his second year in this capacity, at the age of 36, he was appointed Chairman of the Department of Urology (Fig. 363). His Urodynamics Laboratory at Jefferson attained an international reputation for productivity and excellence. Tragically, Dr. Zimskind died suddenly in 1976. Family, colleagues and friends presented his portrait to the University in 1983.

Joseph Francis Rodgers completed a Residency in Internal Medicine and a Fellowship in Infectious Diseases at Jefferson. In 1962 he joined the Faculty and rose to Clinical Professor of Medicine (Fig. 364). In addition, he became Director of the new Division of Home Care (1964) while maintaining his teaching activities in the Division of Infectious Diseases. In 1984 he was appointed Associate Dean for Affiliations and Residency Programs in the Medical College.

John Richard Prehatny completed his residency training in surgery at Jefferson in 1964. He was involved in the on-going research in the lab-

oratory of Professor John H. Gibbon, Jr. Prehatny rose to Clinical Professor of Surgery at Jefferson, Chairman of Surgery of the Methodist Hospital in Philadelphia, and served as President of the Alumni Association in 1985 (Fig. 365).

Phillip Joseph Marone, after taking his residency in orthopaedics at Jefferson under Professor Anthony F. DePalma (Fig. 250), became Chief at Methodist Hospital. At Jefferson he rose to Clinical Professor of Orthopaedic Surgery, Clinical Professor of Rehabilitation Medicine, and Director of the Sports Medicine Program (Fig. 366).

John T. Magee became Clinical Professor of Medicine at Jefferson. Three other members of

Fig. 363. Paul D. Zimskind (JMC, '57), Nathan Lewis Hatfield Chairman of Urology (1967-76).

the class became Clinical Associate Professors on the Jefferson Faculty, namely: Robert H. Schwab (Medicine), Ronald Edwin Traum (Obstetrics/Gynecology), and William Albert Rutter (Psychiatry).

Alfred Oswald Heath took his Residency in Surgery at Jefferson. He returned to his native St. Thomas in the Virgin Islands where he became Director of Hospitals and Medical Services, and in 1973 the Commissioner of Health.

Paul Carl Schroy won high honors at graduation and became the first Ph.D. in Anatomy in the Graduate School. His research on delineation of the lobes of the liver led to improvements in the surgery of this organ. He subsequently joined the Department of Surgery.

Serving in academic posts in other medical schools were: Robert M. Allman, Professor of Radiology, George Washington University School of Medicine, Washington, D.C.; Francis F. Bartone, Professor of Surgery, University of Nebraska; Morton J. Robinson, Professor of Pathology and Marvin A. Sackner, Professor of Medicine both at the University of Miami School of Medicine; and George F. Unger, Professor of Radiology at the Medical College of Wisconsin, Milwaukee.

Fig. 364. Joseph F. Rodgers (JMC, '57), Clinical Professor of Medicine and Associate Dean for Affiliations and Residency Programs.

Fig. 365. John R. Prehatny (JMC, '57), Clinical Professor of Surgery.

1957

Aaronson, Herbert G., PA
Alderfer, Kenneth G., PA
Allen, Herbert V., Jr., PA
Allman, Robert M., NJ
Antoniacci, Cesare R., PA
Au, Otto Y. T., CHINA
Ayres, Robert D., ID
Baird, Robert M., OH
Baker, Louis Reed, PA
Banks, Henry C., NY
Bartone, Francis F., PA
Bastian, Robert Cronwell, Jr., PA
Bedford, Richard A., PA
Bellus, John J., PA
Bender, John M., PA
Bennett, Gaylord W., OH
Berger, Norman, PA
Black, David Harold, PA
Blechman, Martin G., NJ
Boring, Robert S., PA

Boron, Robert J., PA
Boulis, Gust, PA
Brennan, Martin T., PA
Brillman, Nathan, PA
Brodar, Franc, PA
Brodstein, Robert S., PA
Brotman, Robert K., NJ
Bryan, Frank S., PA
Cahn, Michael S., PA
Centrone, Anthony L., PA
Cionni, Joseph, WV
Coleman, Ernest H., Jr., PA
Colliver, Ronald Robinson, PA
Cooper, Edward I., PA
Cooperman, Lawrence R., PA
Corson, T. Clark, III, PA
Cousounis, Gerry T., PA
Cuddy, Vincent D., WV
Culbert, James Edward, PA
DiNicola, Arthur N., PA
Dooley, John Thomas, NJ
Easler, Richard E., PA
Elliott, Donald P., TX
Farfel, Gilbert S., NY
Fee, Eugene A., PA
Ferri, John Peter, Jr., PA
Flanagan, John C., PA
Freeman, Richard B., PA
Frohman, Bertram Herbert, NJ
Galligan, William J., PA
Gigliotti, Anthony C., PA
Glick, Joseph A., DE
Green, Edward Russell, PA
Gruszka, Francis Anthony, PA
Haines, William Fisher, II, PA
Halenda, J. Ronald, PA
Halicke, Philip V., PA
Hansell, John R., PA
Hassel, Harold J., PA
Hassler, Ralph Walter, PA
Hastings, Charles D., CA
Heath, Alfred O., ST. THOMAS
Herceg, Stephen J., PA
Hess, Joseph B., PA
Hester, John E., III, PA
Hill, David I., CA
Hostetter, Abram M., PA
Inglis, William D., OH
Kashoff, Robert Leonard, PA
Kaufman, James Nelson, NJ
Keates, Edwin U., PA
Keates, Richard H., PA

Fig. 366. Phillip J. Marone (JMC, '57), Clinical Professor of Orthopaedic Surgery.

Kendra, Stephen J., PA
Kennard, John F., PA
Kessler, Paul Rudolph, PA
Kirschner, Robert J., PA
Knecht, Charles L., III, PA
Knox, H. Donald, PA
Kocot, Stanley L., MA
Koppel, Max M., PA
Kravitz, Simon, PA
Krawczun, Alex J., NJ
Krepps, Arthur C., II, PA
Kuensell, Sidney Lee, NJ
Labriola, Gerald, CT
Lampe, William Thomas, II, PA
Landes, Ivan Cramer, PA
Lazar, Allan W., PA
Lee, Arthur B., HAWAII
LePar, Edwin, PA
Lewbart, Marvin L., NJ
Lowry, Welles Norwood, Jr., PA
Lucarella, Joseph Anthony, NJ
Lynch, Robert E., PA
Mackrell, William P., PA
Maddux, James Tolbert, Jr., MS
Magee, John T., PA
Mainzer, Thomas R., PA
Mann, Lowell D., OH
Marone, Phillip J., PA
Match, Ronald M., NY
McNierney, Bronson J., PA
Messori, Divo A., PA
Mest, John S., PA
Miller, Sanford M., PA
Millrood, Bernard, PA
Moll, Joseph H., PA
Morgan, Walter R., PA
Morgese, Albert Nicholas, NJ
Murray, John P., PA
Newton, James C., NY
Orchow, Harold S., PA
Oriente, Michael A., PA
Paddock, Richard Bolles, CA
Parent, Fernand N., Jr., PA
Pavich, Rudolph William, PA
Posatko, Robert J., PA
Powers, John C., PA

Prehatny, John Richard, PA
Priebe, Carl William, Jr., PA
Reichling, George H., PA
Reno, Joseph David, PA
Richter, Howard S., NJ
Robinson, Morton J., PA
Rodgers, Joseph F., PA
Rosenzweig, Stanley C., PA
Rotz, C. Theodore, Jr., PA
Rutter, William Albert, PA
Sabol, John R., PA
Sackner, Marvin A., PA
Salverian, George A., PA
Schaebler, M. Lee, PA
Schroy, Paul C., NJ
Schwab, Robert H., PA
Scrobola, Charles C., PA
Shelley, Penn P., PA
Sherwood, Norman S., NY
Sieber, Grafton F., OH
Singley, Thomas L., III, PA
Sinks, Lucius F., OH
Skutches, Joseph M., PA
Smith, Richard N., PA
Smith, Robert A., PA
Spelsberg, Walter T., WV
Spock, Nicholas, PA
Stief, Kirwin H., MI
Stull, James R., PA
Swenson, John A., PA
Thomas, Charles Daniel, PA
Thomas, Frank B., III, PA
Totino, Joseph A., PA
Traum, Ronald E., NJ
Trellis, Emil S., PA
Tronzo, Raymond G., PA
Unger, George F., Jr., PA
Weibel, David C., PA
Wickstrom, Otto W., Jr., IN
Williams, Langdon T., Jr., OH
Willwerth, James W., PA
Wilson, George M., NJ
Witthoff, E. Milton, Jr., IL
Wolfe, William Franklin, PA
Yadusky, Donald P., PA
Yadusky, Ronald J., PA
Zimskind, Paul Donald, NJ

Because of continuing renovations in the Academy of Music, the Commencement Exercises on June 12 were held once more in the Forrest Theater. The Degrees of Doctor of Medicine were conferred upon 159 graduates by President Kauffman and the Address was delivered by the Honorable Walter H. Judd, M.D., Member of the House of Representatives of the United States.

Joseph Thomas English won the prize for excellence in Psychiatry and went on to a distinguished career in this field (Fig. 367). He became a Senior Psychiatric Consultant to the Peace

Fig. 367. Joseph T. English (JMC, '58), Chief of Health Services in the Department of Health, Education, and Welfare.

Corps and served as Assistant Director of Economic Opportunity for Health Affairs where he was responsible for planning and implementation of programs. In 1968 he received an Arthur S. Flemming Award as one of the ten outstanding men in the Federal Government of that year. (Flemming was Former Secretary of Health, Education and Welfare). From 1968 to 1970 he was Chief of Health Services and Mental Health Administration in the Department of Health, Education and Welfare. In 1970 he was appointed President of New York City's Health and Hospital Corporation.

Peter Amadio, Jr. won several prizes at graduation and during the 1960s served in the Division of Clinical Pharmacology at Jefferson. In 1976 he joined the newly formed Department of Family Medicine in which he achieved the rank of Clinical Professor. In 1989 he received the Lindback Award for Distinguished Teaching (Fig. 368).

Austin Paul Murray took his residency in ophthalmology at Jefferson and became prominent clinically in the Department at Jefferson and Wills Eye Hospital in which he served as Clinical Assistant Professor (Fig. 369). He contributed the chapter on the Department of Ophthalmology for the history of *Thomas Jefferson University: Tradition and Heritage* (1989).

Richard Anthony Cautilli took residency training in orthopaedics at Jefferson under Professor Anthony F. DePalma (Fig. 250). He then served on the Staff of the Department and rose to the rank of Clinical Assistant Professor.

William Eliades, an Alpha Omega Alpha honor student, rose to prominence in the Department of Medicine at Jefferson in the Division of Cardiology. From 1967 to 1969 the cardiac catheterizations were under his direction. A Clinical Assistant Professor of Medicine, he became one of the most respected clinicians on the Jefferson Hospital Staff (Fig. 370).

Class members serving on medical faculties included: Robert A. Cooper, Professor of Pathology, Strong Memorial Hospital of the University of Rochester; David B. Propert, Professor of Medicine, and George A. Griggs, Associate Professor of Medicine, both at Eastern Virginia Graduate School of Medicine, Norfolk; Vernon G. Wong, Professor of Ophthalmology at Georgetown University Hospital, Washington, D.C.; John L.

Dunn, Associate Professor of Pathology, Darmouth-Hitchcock Medical Center, Hanover; George A. Jack, Assistant Professor of Pathology, Emory University School of Medicine, Atlanta; and Donald L. Clark, Associate Professor of Anesthesiology, University of Pennsylvania Hospital.

Fig. 368. Peter Amadio, Jr. (JMC, '58) Clinical Professor of Family Medicine.

Fig. 369. Austin P. Murray (JMC, '58), prominent ophthalmologist at Wills Eye Hospital.

CLASS OF 1958

Altman, Barry L., NJ
Amadio, Peter, Jr., PA
Antolik, John T., PA
Arden, Sidney H., PA
Aronica, Michael J., PA
Barrett, Warren M., PA
Bauer, William F., PA
Beetel, Christopher J., PA
Bemiller, Carl R., PA

Berkebile, Paul E., PA
Bernstine, Richard T., PA
Blechschmidt, George F., PA
Bloemendaal, Robert D., SD
Bock, Martin O., NY
Bortner, Donald L., PA
Bowman, John H., PA
Bradley, Vernon F., PA
Brock, Richard R., PA

Brodkin, Roger H., NJ
Brown, Charles C., WA
Brown, Garland R., IN
Brown, Sheldon C., PA
Bucko, Matthew I., Jr., PA
Carnabuci, Guy J., PA
Carney, Frank T., PA
Caulfield, Frank J., PA
Cautilli, Richard A., PA
Clair, Henry S., PA
Clark, Donald L., PA
Clements, William W., Jr., PA
Cohen, Jerome I., NJ
Concors, Edwin R., PA
Coniff, Robert F., PA
Cooper, Robert A., Jr., CA
Cowen, Malcolm L., PA
Cox, Jay S., PA
Cozzolino, H. Jay, CT
Craig, John A., PA

Crouse, Farrell R., NJ
Davison, Carter Nichols, PA
DeCato, Alfred R., OH
DeCurtis, George M., PA
DiGiacobbe, F. Paul, PA
Dill, Donald M., OH
Dillon, Thomas E., PA
Dubrow, Donald N., PA
Dunn, John L., PA
Eisenstein, Mark C., NY
Eliades, William, PA
English, Joseph T., PA
Epstein, Howard N., NJ
Eshbach, Richard E., PA
Feldman, Julian D., PA
Fessler, Robert Henry, PA
Feudale, Richard F., PA
Fine, Edward, NJ
Floyd, Frederick W., Jr., NJ
Fogel, Norman Allen, PA
Fonde, Edgar C., AL
Gerhart, George R., PA
Glorioso, Joseph J., PA
Goodman, Bernard, PA
Greenburg, Morren J., PA
Greenwood, Henry J., PA
Griggs, George Albert, DE
Gross, Robert E., NE
Hadlock, Harold William, Jr., PA
Hankin, Melvin, PA
Hanratty, Richard J., NY
Hedges, Richard C., PA
Herr, David R., PA
Hewson, George F., Jr., NJ
Hopwood, Herbert G., Jr., PA
Hudock, George E., Jr., PA
Hughes, Jay M., PA
Hughes, Philip C., NJ
Hurowitz, Bertram D., NJ
Jack, George A., CT
Johnson, Howard K., Jr., RI
Jones, David J., III, PA
Kallick, Charles J., PA
Kallish, Marvin, PA
Kaufman, H. Calvin, MD
Kern, Jay A., PA
Kipp, Charles M., PA
Kostelnik, Francis V., PA
Kostinas, John E., NJ
Kreider, John K., PA
Kruper, John S., PA
LaBraico, James M., PA
Lane, John D., PA
Lederman, Ivan I., PA
LeDonne, Anthony T., PA

Fig. 370. William Eliades (JMC, 58), highly respected cardiologist at Jefferson who directed the cardiac catheterizations from 1967 to 1969.

LeFever, Harry E., Jr., OH
Lilli, Elmo J., PA
Lushbough, Bruce C., SD
Mancino, Peter J., PA
Mayro, Julian, PA
McGarry, Thomas F., CT
McGrath, James E., PA
McKenna, Patrick J., Jr., NJ
McMicken, William H., WV
Moll, Francis K., Jr., PA
Monaco, Dean D., NY
Montague, James W., PA
Mori, Gino, PA
Murray, Austin P., PA
Nappi, Dominic F., PA
Nies, Gerald F., PA
O'Brien, Richard Francis, PA
Oskin, Hilbert E., PA
Panitch, Victor, NJ
Pellicane, Anthony J., Jr., NJ
Plummer, Lloyd G., PA
Pompey, Daniel T., PA
Popowich, John G., PA
Porter, Samuel C., NJ
Prahar, Temple F., PA
Praiss, Donald E., NJ
Propert, David B., VA
Radomski, Theodore J., PA
Reef, James S., OH
Reese, Charles Lee, III, DE
Rightor, John T., PA
Roediger, Paul M., NJ
Rothrock, Gilmore M., PA

Rotman, Marvin Z., PA
Rudolph, Samuel F., Jr., PA
Ruffini, John A., PA
Ryder, Blair L., PA
Sandler, Jerome L., DC
Scarcella, James V., PA
Schloss, C. David, OH
Schneeberg, J. Myron, PA
Scicchitano, Leon P., PA
Seidel, Henry E., PA
Seres, Joel L., DE
Shillingford, Robert P., PA
Singer, Arnold, PA
Smith, Donald L., PA
Snyder, Harry D., PA
Somers, Robert G., PA
Spiegleman, Arthur M., PA
Stecher, William A., MD
Stern, James M., PA
Thomas, John E., PA
Thomas, William J., PA
Turchi, Joseph J., PA
Vaccaro, V. Michael, PA
Vanderbeek, Richard R., NJ
Vanoni, Frank R., CT
VerNooy, Stewart A., Jr., NY
Walker, James M., PA
Warren, William J., NJ
Weems, Don B., Jr., NJ
Welton, John Seymour, WV
Willard, Donald E., Jr., PA
Wolbach, Albert Bogh, Jr., PA
Wong, Vernon Genkin, PA

Look to your health; and if you have it, praise God and value it next to a good conscience; for health is the second blessing that we mortals are capable of—a blessing that money cannot buy; therefore value it, and be thankful for it.

Isaak Walton (1593–1683)

In 1959 Jefferson made a major move beyond the boundaries of the block from Sansom to Walnut between Tenth and Eleventh Streets by building a new student nurses' residence across Walnut on the Southwest corner at Eleventh (Fig. 371). This was historic ground, since it was the site of the home of Professor Thomas Dent Mutter in the 1840s to the mid 1850s, and from 1856 to 1884 was occupied by Samuel D. Gross. Built at a cost of $2 million, aided by a bequest in the will of James R. Martin, Professor of Orthopaedics (1939-50) after whom it was named, it was a significant addition to Jefferson's physical plant and an attraction to qualified women interested in nursing careers at Jefferson. When the Diploma School of Nursing was disbanded

in 1982 and carried on as a Baccalaureate Program in the College of Allied Health Sciences, the Martin Nurses' Residence was used for administrative offices and additional student housing within the University.

The Commencement was held on June 12 at the Academy of Music. M.D. Degrees were presented to 166 graduates by President Kauffman, bringing the grand total to 19,745. The Honorable David Leo Lawrence, Governor of the Commonwealth of Pennsylvania, gave the Address.

Kenneth Peter Johnson, Jr., of New York, went on to become Chairman of Neurology in the School of Medicine of the University of Maryland.

Harris R. Clearfield pursued his training at the

Fig. 371.   James R. Martin Nurses' Residence (1959).

Graduate Hospital of the University of Pennsylvania. Specializing in gastrointestinal diseases, he became Professor of Medicine and Director of the Division of Gastroenterology at Hahnemann University.

John Joseph Danyo (Fig. 372) became President of the Medical Society of Pennsylvania in 1989.

William C. Sherwood, a resident in hematology and later Associate Professor of Medicine at Jefferson, became Director of its Blood Bank. He was later the head of the Red Cross Regional Blood Bank (Fig. 373).

Members of the class who served on the Faculty at Jefferson included: Malcolm Kates, Clinical Assistant Professor of Medicine; Guy William McLaughlin, Jr., Instructor in Pediatrics; Lawrence J. Mellon, Adjunct Clinical Assistant Professor of Medicine; and Saul Glasner, Clinical Associate Professor of Psychiatry and Human Behavior.

Those serving on other medical faculties included: Siamak A. Adibi, Professor of Internal Medicine, Presbyterian-University Hospital, Pittsburgh; Francis J. Kazmier, Professor of Internal Medicine, Mayo Graduate School of Medicine, Rochester; Samuel L. Stover, Professor of Internal Medicine, Georgetown University School of Medicine, Washington, D.C.; George Pappas, Associate Professor of Surgery, University of Colorado School of Medicine; Burritt L. Haag, Associate Professor of Pathology, University of Miami Affiliated Hospitals; Paul L. Flicker, Assistant Professor of Surgery, Parkland Memorial Hospital, Dallas; and Nathaniel P. Ching, Associate Professor of Surgery, University of Hawaii.

Fig. 372. John J. Danyo (JMC, '59), President of the Medical Society of Pennsylvania.

Fig. 373. William C. Sherwood (JMC, '59), Associate Professor of Medicine and Head of the Red Cross Regional Blood Bank.

1959

Adibi, Siamak, IRAN
Altemus, L. Reed, Jr., PA
Andrews, Peter J., PA
Armstrong, Robert B., WV
Ashbaugh, William H., PA
Aucoin, Jean P., MA
Baka, Joseph, OH
Baldauf, James A., PA
Baldauf, Leonard Clair, Jr., PA
Balotin, Nahum M., NY
Baranski, Edward J., PA
Barr, Samuel J., PA
Bauer, Harold E., NJ
Baumm, N. Craig, PA
Beauchamp, David T., MA
Besecker, Joseph Albert, PA
Bixler, Lester George, Jr., PA
Blanc, Kenneth M., PA
Blizard, Eugene B., PA
Bloes, Walter S., PA
Blue, Vincent P., PA
Blumenthal, Harold L., WV
Boffa, Felix J., PA
Bonatti, William D., PA
Borska, Henry Benjamin, NY
Bowers, K. Douglas, Jr., WV
Brodhead, Charles L., Jr., PA
Broscius, Benjamin Michael, PA
Brown, Stuart B., PA
Callan, John J., Jr., RI
Caplan, Murray S., PA
Carroll, William J., PA
Castellano, Patrick V., NY
Centrone, Ronald J., PA
Ching, Nathaniel P., HAWAII
Chmielewski, Robert E., PA
Clearfield, Harris R., PA
Cocco, Arthur E., MD
Cohn, Ronald E., PA
Cook, Howell E., Jr., NJ
Corliss, Robert J., PA
Corwin, Douglas T., PA
Coughlin, John J., RI
Crawford, William O., Jr., PA
Daley, Marvin C., PA
Danyo, John Joseph, PA
Davis, Robert V., Jr., PA
Delp, James R., PA
DelSordo, Joseph Louis, NJ
DiMaio, Anthony J., DE
Druffner, Lewis C., Jr., PA
English, Thomas Odie, Jr., PA

Eschbach, Joseph W., MI
Farrell, Aloysius W., PA
Feingold, Murray, PA
Ferraro, Patrick J., PA
First, Steven E., PA
Fisher, Ronald M., PA
Flicker, Paul L., PA
Frank, James H., PA
Freedman, Howard H., PA
Furey, Sandy A., PA
Gainer, James V., Jr., WV
Gallagher, Donald I., PA
Geetter, David M., PA
Gigliotti, Lawrence G., PA
Gillespy, William G., WV
Girsh, Sidney, PA
Glasner, Saul, PA
Glenn, Trevor D., PA
Godshall, Richard W., PA
Goldstein, Louis Marshall, NJ
Gorby, Charles K., PA
Greenawald, Henry A., PA
Greenberg, Leonard F., PA
Greenwood, Lawrence, PA
Gumina, Thomas F., Jr., PA
Haag, Burritt L., PA
Halliday, Tom Dunbar, OH
Halpern, Arnold J., NJ
Harnish, David M., PA
Heisey, William G., PA
Hernberg, Joseph Gerald, PA
Howard, James T., Jr., PA
Ioffreda, Pasqualino, NJ
Jablon, Norman C., PA
Johnson, Kenneth P., Jr., NY
Jones, Archbold M., Jr., WV
Kates, Malcolm, PA
Katzman, Harold, CT
Kauffman, Mark S., NJ
Kazmier, Francis J., PA
Kelly, John E., NEWFOUNDLAND
Kolchins, Milton L., PA
Kolecki, Richard S., PA
Kong, Albert Y. Tau, Jr. HAWAII
Kutney, Francis G., PA
Larson, William F., PA
Leister, Howard A., PA
Liddy, Thomas J., NJ
Lodise, Raymond J., PA
Lubin, Jack, PA
Magenheim, Herbert G., NJ
Malcolm, John A., Jr., PA

Marcus, Edwin Murray, PA
Maurer, Roger Earl, PA
McCabe, James L., Jr., PA
McCallum, James A., NJ
McConnell, Walter L., NJ
McDonough, Gerard A., Jr., PA
McDowell, Charles L., NC
McLaughlin, Guy W., Jr., PA
Meckler, David, PA
Mellon, Lawrence J., Jr., PA
Meloy, Thomas R., PA
Mika, John J., Jr., PA
Milani, Frank A., PA
Miller, Claude J., PA
Molina, Ramon B., PA
Morrow, Thomas F., PA
Murray, Stephen R., PA
Nelson, Paul I., NJ
Nicholson, Charles E., Jr., PA
Paluso, Arthur K., PA
Pappas, George, PA
Parks, Colby R., TX
Pepper, Marshall A., FL
Perch, Gerald A., PA
Phillips, Frederic A., WV
Poole, Edward K., PA
Powell, Philip, PA
Price, Albert C., PA
Romisher, Gary P., PA
Rose, Walter C., Jr., PA
Rubel, Martin, PA

Ryan, William E., NJ
Scarano, Joseph J., PA
Schiffman, Raymond Jack, PA
Schubert, John J., PA
Schultheis, Carl F., Jr., PA
Schwartz, Marvin N., PA
Scott, Jackson V., PA
Shelly, Walter M., PA
Sherwood, William C., NJ
Shilen, Thomas, PA
Simons, Carl I., PA
Sirotnak, John J., Jr., PA
Snyder, Alan I., PA
Somers, Herbert J., PA
Speirs, Alfred C., NJ
Spielman, Stanley L., NJ
Steinbach, William Alexander, PA
Stose, Willis G., PA
Stover, Samuel L., PA
Swisher, Louis Bush, Jr., WV
Tambascia, John Joseph, NJ
Thomas, Terrence J., PA
Vance, John C., Jr., OH
Vanston, Gerald Edward, PA
Venditti, Michael Carmon, NJ
Walker, L. Brooke, Jr., PA
Wanczyk, Casimir J., NJ
Weigand, Alan H., NY
Wiant, James R., NJ
Wilt, John W., PA
Zaleznik, Elliot, PA

As knowledge with regard to the effects of food upon man increases, it is more than conceivable that the races that first avail themselves of the new values of nutrition may decrease the handicaps of disease, lengthen their lives, and so become the leaders of the future.

Victor G. Heiser (JMC, 1897)

For the third and last time, Commencement Exercises were held in the Forrest Theater on June 17. Degrees were conferred upon 164 graduates by the new President of the College, William W. Bodine, Jr. (Fig. 374). The total number of graduates was now 19,909. The address was delivered by Dr. Eric Arthur Walker, President of the Pennsylvania State University.

Gary G. Carpenter pursued a career in pediatrics. After training and research at St. Christopher's Hospital he returned to Jefferson in 1968 as Associate Professor of Pediatrics. In addition to his post as Director of the Endocrine and Metabolic Division, he was also involved in Child neurology and neonatology as well as serving as consultant to numerous regional hospitals. A gifted artist, his art works, especially water colors, have been widely exhibited (Fig. 375).

William R. Fair, winner of the 1987 Jefferson Alumni Achievement Award, had a distinguished career in urology. He advanced to Professor of Urology at Washington University School of Medicine until his removal to New York as Chief of Urology at Sloan-Kettering Institute, Memorial Hospital, and Professor of Surgery at Cornell University School of Medicine (Fig. 376).

Marvin E. Jaffe became associated with Merck, Sharp and Dohme Laboratories as Vice President for Clinical Research and advanced to Senior Vice President for Medical Affairs. In 1988 he became President of the Robert Wood Johnson Pharmaceutical Research Institute.

Richard R. Soricelli, after Jefferson residency, joined the staff of Crozer-Chester Hospital, Chester, Pennsylvania, where his developing skills in renal diseases led to his direction of the dialysis unit in 1968. In 1985 he was appointed Director of the Division of Nephrology and in 1988 he became Senior Vice-President for Medical Affairs at Crozer-Chester. Dr. Soricelli also held an appointment as Associate Professor of Medicine at Hahnemann Medical College.

William T. Lemmon, Jr. was a major prize winner at graduation, his awards including highest honors for the four-year curriculum. Dr. Lemmon served his residency in surgery at Jefferson and joined the teaching staff.

Bruce B. Montgomery followed in his father's (John B. Montgomery, JMC, '26, Fig. 235) footsteps with a career in obstetrics and gynecology. He was trained at Jefferson, joined the teaching staff and was appointed to the staff of Byrn Mawr Hospital. He advanced to Director of the Department of Obstetrics and Gynecology at Bryn Mawr and to Clinical Assistant Professor at Jefferson.

Herbert D. Kleber became active in psychiatric programs in the Yale-New Haven area and Professor of Psychiatry at Yale University. He wrote extensively in professional journals and served as Director of the Substance Abuse Treatment Unit at the Connecticut Mental Health Unit. He later served as Deputy Director for Demand Reduction, Office of Drug Control Policy, U.S. Government (Fig. 377).

Among the 1960 graduates, a number were notable for academic and other accomplishments. Luke G. Tedeschi went on to training in pathology at Massachusetts Memorial Hospitals and became Director of Pathology at Framingham Union Hospital. He was also Associate Professor of Pathology at Boston University School of Medicine. Vincent T. McDermott, Jr. served as Clinical Assistant Professor of Medicine at Jefferson in its affiliation with Our Lady of Lourdes Hospital, Camden. Sherman W. Everlof became Clinical Professor of Obstetrics and Gynecology at Jefferson and Director of Reproductive Surgery at Mercy-Catholic Medical Center, a Jefferson affiliate. Gordon R. Cohen was Clinical Associate Professor of Psychiatry at Stanford University School of Medicine. Paul J. Schneider was Clinical Assistant Professor of Medicine at Jefferson. William H. Mahood, winner of the Practice Prize at Commencement, headed the Gastroenterology Section at Abington Memorial Hospital and held an affiliated academic appointment at Temple University School of Medicine. Robert A. Senft was named Director of Alcohol and Drug Recovery for the Northeast Region of Kaiser-Permanente.

David Green became Professor of Medicine, Northwestern University School of Medicine, Chicago. Edward Kaufman was Professor of Psychiatry at the University of California, Irvine. Francis H. Sterling served as Associate Professor of Internal Medicine at the Hospital of the University of Pennsylvania. Bruce L. Johnson was Associate Professor of Pathology at Presbyterian-University Hospital, Pittsburgh, and John N. Giacobbo was Instructor of Pathology at Jefferson. Donald Hooper became Chairman of the Department of Anesthesiology at the Ochsner Clinic, Baton Rouge, Louisiana.

Fig. 374.   William W. Bodine, Jr., L.H.D., Second Medical College President (1959-66) and Fourth Board Chairman (1970-77).

1960

Abell, Torrance Bryson, IN
Adams, Gene R., PA
Alley, Richard A., PA
Angstadt, Paul N., Jr., PA
Balaicuis, Charles W., PA
Barkett, Robert E., OH
Barr, Gavin C., PA
Bastian, James R., PA
Bee, Rudolf W., PA
Bhatt, Jitendra R., PA
Blecker, David, PA
Bocher, Jack, PA
Brennan, John P., PA
Bridenbaugh, Robert P., PA
Brubaker, James D., PA
Campanella, Joseph A., PA
Capozzi, Joseph A., PA
Carpenter, Gary G., PA
Chernaik, Richard B., NY
Cohen, Gordon R., PA

Cohen, Ronald A., PA
Collins, Gerald P., PA
Connor, Robert W., PA
Constable, G. Robert, PA
Coyle, John J., PA
Cristofori, Fred C., PA
DeCato, Richard L., OH
Dongell, Robert John, Jr., PA
Downing, Samuel W., IV, CO
Druffner, Charles R., PA
Dunkelberger, Richard H., PA
Dunn, Ernest C., PA
Elicker, John E., PA
Epstein, Herbert M., FL
Everlof, Sherman W., PA
Fair, William R., PA
Feins, Neil R., NJ
Finn, Alfred J., Jr., CT
Finnen, Karl Francis, OH
Fleckner, Alan N., PA

Fig. 375. Gary G. Carpenter (JMC, '60), Director of Endocrine and Metabolic Division in Department of Pediatrics.

Fig. 376. William R. Fair (JMC, '60), prominent urologist and winner of 1987 Jefferson Alumni Achievement Award.

1960

Friedman, Milton L., PA
Gagliardi, Joseph M., Jr., PA
Galgon, John P., PA
German, Terry M., PA
Giacobbo, John N., PA
Ginns, David A., PA
Goldman, Arnold M., PA
Gordon, Ernest M., PA
Green, David, PA
Haacker, Lee P., NJ
Haberern, Edward J., PA
Hadden, Michael J., PA
Hagg, Doyle D., SD
Hannemann, J. Howard, CO
Hartley, Robert A., NY
Haskell, David S., PA
Hebert, Peter W., PA
Hellman, Barry H., NY
Hemsley, Hubert L., PA
Hertzog, Francis J., PA
Hess, John M., PA
Hetherington, John, Jr., NJ

Hiehle, J. Frederick, WV
Hoberman, Maury, PA
Hock, Howard E., NJ
Hooper, Donald, PA
Hostetter, H. Glenn, PA
Howard, Thomas K., NY
Howden, Richard F., PA
Hresko, Michael B., PA
Hughes, James T., WV
Hushion, William F., PA
Jaffe, Marvin E., PA
Johnson, Bruce L., PA
Katchman, Jerome J., PA
Kaufman, Edward, PA
Keenan, Gerald R., NJ
Kelso, Thomas, PA
Kleber, Herbert David, PA
Kobb, Harold J., PA
Korn, Laurence, PA
Larkin, Robert Morgan, PA
Lautt, Marvin E., PA
Leivy, David M., PA
Lemmon, William T., Jr., PA
Lentz, Conrad L., PA
Levin, Harvey M., PA
Lipp, Edward B., Jr., PA
Mackall, James I., PA
Mahood, William H., WV
Mancoll, William, CT
Marva, Donald J., PA
Mauler, G. Gregg, PA
Mays, Richard R., PA
McDermott, Vincent T., Jr., NJ
McDonough, Gilbert L., PA
Mears, William W., NJ
Meikle, Charles E., PA
Melnick, Irving, PA
Meredith, Arch F., Jr., WV
Mergenthaler, Dean D., OH
Meyer, Carl A., Jr., PA
Mitchell, Paul L., NY
Montgomery, Bruce B., PA
Morosco, Samuel G., PA
Morosini, Charles J., PA
Murray, John Thomas, PA
Nevara, John B., PA
Newton, Charles T., PA
Nichols, Robert A., PA
Nordberg, E. David, PA
O'Brien, James J., PA
O'Brien, William H., NJ
O'Rourke, Terence L., PA
Oshrin, Harvey W., NJ
Pearlman, Samuel, NJ

Fig. 377. Herbert D. Kleber (JMC, '60), Professor of Psychiatry, Yale University.

Peditto, Joseph J., PA
Peters, Thomas G., PA
Philson, John R., PA
Pintimalli, Joseph T., PA
Ramser, James Richard, OH
Riffle, George N., II, PA
Ringawa, Peter E., PA
Rizzo, Frank D., PA
Rogowski, Raymond A., PA
Rosenfeld, Myron E., PA
Rutstein, Harvey R., PA
Rutt, Wilmer M., PA
Rykiel, Frank K., NJ
Schneider, Bernard, NJ
Schneider, Paul J., NJ
Seigle, Walter E., PA
Senft, Robert A., PA
Shaw, Joseph Bowen, AR
Shea, Peter Champ, NY
Shisler, Frederick H., PA
Shlomchik, Seymour, PA
Silver, Harvey D., NJ
Soricelli, Richard R., PA
Sterling, Francis H., PA

Stine, Robert H., PA
Straus, Neil Baer, PA
Sutton, Roger D., PA
Swartz, Edward F., PA
Sweterlitsch, Louis H., Jr., PA
Tedeschi, Luke G., MA
Temple, Joel R., WV
Thomas, James A., Jr., PA
Thompkins, Leonard Joseph, PA
Trimber, Connell James, PA
Vinnick, Leonard, NJ
Vivacqua, Raymond J., PA
Volk, Philip D., PA
Wachter, Francis W., PA
Wadewitz, Peter, NC
Wankmuller, Robert T., PA
Watson, Ulysses Edward, PA
Weinstein, Arnold H., PA
Weiss, Robert A., PA
Wentzel, Harvey E., Jr., PA
West, William J., PA
Wiza, Edward Joseph, Jr., PA
Young, Walter K. W., HAWAII
Ziegler, Maurice L., Jr., PA

Abraham Cantarow (JMC, '24), Chairman of Biochenistry with students.

Commencement took place on June 16 in the Academy of Music where the M.D. degrees were conferred upon 167 graduates by President William W. Bodine, Jr. The grand total was now 20,076. The Address was delivered by General Alfred M. Gruenther, U.S. Army (Ret.), President of the American National Red Cross.

A tradition of 137 years was broken by the matriculation in September of this year of nine women medical students, eight of whom went on to graduate (Fig. 378). Jefferson was thereby the last all-male medical school to become co-educational.

A faculty Wives Club also was founded in this year by Agnes Wagner Sodeman, wife of Dean William A. Sodeman.

Stanton N. Smullens, following internship at Presbyterian Hospital, served as Fellow in Cardiothoracic Surgery at Pennsylvania Hospital. He was an investigator funded by the National Institutes of Health in vascular research. Joining the staff in surgery at Jefferson, he advanced to Associate Professor of Surgery and of Radiology (Fig. 379). In 1989 he served as President of the Volunteer Faculty Association.

Allen E. Chandler was an army reserve officer for many years and in 1988 advanced to the rank of Brigadier General in the Pennsylvania National Guard. A Clinical Instructor in Pediatrics at Jefferson, he also served as Director of Pediatrics for the Philadelphia Department of Health.

John V. Bennett, winner of several prizes at Commencement, went on to appointments in the Centers for Disease Control. He advanced to

Fig. 378.   First women medical students attend lectures in Daniel Baugh Institute of Anatomy (1961).

Medical Director of the Bacterial Disease Division, Bureau of Epidemiology. In 1981 he received its Gold Medal.

Warren A. Katz was trained in rheumatology after his internship at Albert Einstein Medical Center. In 1977 he published the first edition of his *Rheumatic Diseases, Diagnosis and Management* (Lippincott). He was also Clinical Professor of Medicine and Chief of Rheumatology at the Medical College of Pennsylvania.

Gerald Salen, who was awarded the Henry Keller Mohler Prize, became Professor of Medicine and Director of the Division of Gastroenterology at the College of Medicine and Dentistry, New Jersey Medical Center at Newark.

Kenneth M.Given, whose major prizes included those for best academic achievement, after a 15-year career with Merck, Sharp and Dohme Research Laboratories, was appointed

Senior Vice-President for World-Wide Medical and Regulatory Affairs, Squibb Institute for Medical Research in 1988.

Other members of the class who achieved prominence included Robert W. Solit who joined the Department of Surgery at Jefferson and advanced to Clinical Associate Professor (Fig. 380); William A. Browne, who following practice in Ohio became Director of Student Health Services at Miami University, Oxford, Ohio; Eugene Shuster, Clinical Professor of Obstetrics and gynecology at Hahnemann Medical College in 1981 received the Award for Excellence in Teaching; Harold L. McWilliams, who became Assistant Professor of Surgery at Johns Hopkins University School of Medicine; Jay S. Barnhart, Jr., who in 1979 discontinued his practice in Maryland, went on to residency in Pathology at Jefferson and later became Assistant Medical Examiner for

Fig. 379.   Stanton M. Smullens (JMC, '61), vascular surgeon, Associate Professor of Surgery and Radiology.

Fig. 380.   Robert W. Solit (JMC, '61), Clinical Associate Professor of Surgery.

Dade County, Florida; Martin G. Durkin, Professor of Internal Medicine, Loyola University Medical Center, Chicago; Robert E. McLaughlin, Associate Professor of Psychiatry, Medical College of Pennsylvania; Louis A. Wilson, Professor of Ophthalmology, Emory University School of Medicine, Atlanta; Sheldon Amsel, Associate Professor of Internal Medicine, University of Maryland Hospital, Baltimore; Arthur S. Besser, Associate Professor of Surgery, University of Chicago Hospital and Clinics; Robert B. Tesh, Associate Professor of Public Health, Yale-New Haven Hospitals; and Joel B. Goldstein, Associate Professor of Psychiatry, Medical College of Pennsylvania.

CLASS OF 1961

Amsel, Sheldon, PA
Anderson, Arlo C., PA
Anderson, Willaim T., NJ
Anthony, Lewis G., PA
Antognoli, William J., PA
Avellino, Joseph D., PA
Barnhart, Jay S., Jr., PA
Bendy, Robert H., Jr., NJ
Bennett, John V., PA
Besser, Arthur S., OH
Boxer, Arthur D., NJ
Brecht, James A., PA
Brown, Louis, CT
Browne, William A., IV, OH
Buterbaugh, John C., PA
Butler, Herbert H., Jr., PA
Carey, Edward D., PA
Cavoto, Michale J., PA
Cera, Peter J., Jr., PA
Cerrato, Walter A., NY
Chandler, Allen E., PA
Chyatte, Samuel B., D.C.
Cirotti, Joseph J., PA
Cohen, J. Jerome, PA
Colarusso, Calvin A., PA
Conte, Robert R., PA
Corrin, Kenneth M., Jr., DE
Crane, Jeffrey S., PA
Davies, Allen L., PA
Deardorff, Charles L., Jr., PA
DeFelice, Stephen L., PA
Dennis, Lewis H., PA
DiMeo, Richard A., NJ
Dodge, Frederick A., NJ
Durkin, Martin G., PA
Eddy, Richard L., NJ
Emanuel, E. Stephen, PA
Eppley, Samuel M., PA
Evans, James L., III, NJ
Fanfera, Francis J., PA
Farrell, William J., PA
Fleck, Roland F., Jr., PA

Forman, Harris, PA
Fox, Richard W., PA
Fresoli, Rocco P., PA
Given, Kenneth M., PA
Goldstein, Joel B., PA
Gordon, Bruce, NJ
Gould, John H., PA
Graubard, David J., PA
Greenawald, Kenneth A., PA
Grosky, Murray B., PA
Grossman, Marvin, PA
Harrell, Jerry D., Jr., PA
Harrop, James S., RI
Heister, Joseph Baker, III, PA
Herlocher, James E., PA
Herwig, Karl R., PA
Homel, Steven R., PA
Hook, William F., ND
Horewitz, James S., PA
Huddell, Benjamin Raymond, PA
Huffnagle, Frederic T., PA
Kahn, Eric M., PA
Katz, Warren A., PA
Keefe, John P., OH
Kessler, Carl P., PA
Kieffer, Robert A., PA
Kilfeather, John E., VA
Klein, Jack J., PA
Kline, Richard J., NJ
Klinman, Jerome J., PA
Knepley, David W., PA
Kostello, Robert T., WV
Kotler, Barry M., NJ
Krain, Samuel, PA
Krauss, Jack, PA
Kravatz, Arnold S., PA
Lehman, James A., Jr., PA
Lentz, Ronald J., PA
Lesniak, John P., PA
Lewis, Maurice J., PA
Liebman, Irvin M., PA

Longacre, Aaron M., PA
Lutton, Charles E., PA
Maraskco, Richard M., PA
McCann, William D., PA
McLaughlin, Robert E., MA
McWilliams, Harold L., Jr., PA
Mendelssohn, Saul, PA
Meyer, Arthur N., PA
Mironoff, Leon, PA
Monihan, Richard M., PA
Montgomery, Ernest J., PA
Moretti, Everett A., NJ
Morgan, Philip J., Jr., PA
Moselle, Herbert I., PA
Mulligan, Wallace J., PA
Newman, William H., III, PA
Nitzberg, Jerome, PA
O'Brien, Thomas E., NY
O'Neil, Jack D., PA
Oesterling, Everett F., Jr., PA
Padula, Richard T., PA
Parsons, Sidney Alfred, Jr., PA
Pentz, Paul G., PA
Perlin, Elliott, NJ
Platt, Howard A., PA
Polin, Gerald M., PA
Pratt, William B., NJ
Promin, Richard E., PA
Racho, George J., PA
Reef, Thomas Cline, OH
Riley, George R., PA
Robbins, Terrance J., PA
Robinson, Norman R., NJ
Roeder, Donald K., NJ
Rogers, Albert K., PA
Roncace, Emilio A., PA
Rosen, Joseph H., PA
Sabo, Jack C., NJ
Sakulsky, Stephen Barry, PA
Salen, Gerald, PA
Salvo, John P., NJ
Scarano, Victor R., PA

Sheaffer, Harold Clement, PA
Shue, William M., PA
Shuster, Eugene, PA
Silver, Frank, PA
Skeel, David A., PA
Small, Michael L., NJ
Smullens, Stanton N., PA
Snyder, James L., WV
Solit, Robert W., PA
Sphar, Raymond L., Jr., PA
Spielman, Ronald L., NJ
Spivack, Jerome, DE
Sponaugle, H. Dale, WV
Starr, John G., PA
Stevenson, Walter D., PA
Stone, Ronald K., PA
Storazzi, J. Jordan, Jr., PA
Subin, David K., NJ
Sugden, William A., PA
Sweterlitsch, Paul R., PA
Taylor, W. Scott, PA
Tesh, Robert B., DE
Titus, Bruce M., CA
Updike, Furman T., Jr., NJ
Vassallo, Enrique M., PUERTO RICO
Vigario, Gordon D., CA
Vorosmarti, James, Jr., PA
Wadler, Dennis M., NY
Walsh, James A., PA
Wamsley, Richard C., OH
Wanger, William H., WV
Ward, Thomas A., PA
Wasserman, Theodore W., PA
Webster, James Weldon, Jr., UT
Weintraub, Harvey, PA
Whalen, Edward W., Jr., PA
Wilson, James L., PA
Wilson, Louis A., PA
Wimsatt, William Anthony, VA
Wolfson, Benjamin, NJ
Zankman, Nathan, PA
Ziegenfus, William D., PA

Health is so necessary to all the duties, as well as pleasures of life, that the crime of squandering it is equal to the folly.

Samuel Johnson (1709–84)

The Commencement was held at the Academy of Music on June 15, and the M.D. degrees were conferred upon 146 graduates by President William W. Bodine, Jr. The members of this class brought the total Medical College Alumni to 20,222. The Address was delivered by Luther L. Terry, M.D., Surgeon General of the U.S. Public Health Service.

William Emil Staas, Jr., after two years of military service trained in Rehabilitation Medicine and joined the staff at Jefferson in this specialty, advancing to full Professor. In 1977 he was appointed Medical Director and President of Magee Rehabilitation Hospital, which had become an affiliate of Jefferson in 1975 (Fig. 381). Dr. Staas' unique abilities as a clinician, administrator, and teacher were responsible for the accelerated growth of Magee and the refinement of its relationship with Jefferson.

Jerome Jay Vernick won the Clinical Surgery prize at graduation and went on to a distinguished surgical career at Jefferson, with the ultimate rank of Clinical Professor (Fig. 382). After extensive surgical experience in the Vietnam War, he joined Jefferson's first kidney transplant team and in 1982 he headed the Division of Emergency Medicine which led to Jefferson's designation as a Level One Trauma Center in 1987.

Joseph William Sokolowski, Jr., of New York, another honor student, trained in pulmonary diseases in the Navy. He became a Clinical Professor of Medicine at Jefferson, Director of Pulmonary Diseases at Our Lady of Lourdes Hospital, President of the New Jersey Thoracic Society and President of the Camden County Medical Society (Fig. 383).

Melvin L. Moses became a Clinical Professor of Surgery at Jefferson, later the Chief of Surgery at Jefferson Park Hospital and in 1990 Chief of Surgery at the Methodist Hospital (Fig. 384).

John Placido Capelli, another honor student, served his residency in medicine at Jefferson and became a pioneer in nephrology as well as full-time Director of the Division of Clinical Phar-

macology. He subsequently transferred to Our Lady of Lourdes Hospital to head the Division of Nephrology.

Other members of the class who joined the Jefferson Faculty were: Courtney Malcolm Malcarney (Obstetrics and Gynecology), George Stephens Nicoll (Surgery), and Stephen Gosin (Surgery, awarded the Alumni Prize at graduation).

Robert C. Nuss served in the Medical Corps of the United States Naval Reserve and was promoted to Rear Admiral in 1989. He was Professor of Obstetrics/Gynecology at the University of Florida Affiliated Hospitals, Gainesville.

Fig. 381. William E. Staas, Jr. (JMC, '62), Medical Director and President of Magee Rehabilitation Hospital, Professor of Rehabilitative Medicine.

Other class members with academic affiliations included Richard J. Hamburger, Professor of Internal Medicine at Indiana University Hospitals, Indianapolis; Henry A. Gelband, Professor of Pediatrics at University of Miami Affiliated Hospitals; Robert J. Neviaser, Professor of Orthopedic Surgery, George Washington University Hospital, Washington, D.C.; Joseph Honigman, Associate Professor of Internal Medicine, University of Florida Affiliated Hospitals, Gainesville; Ronald F. Green, Assistant Professor of Surgery, New York Hospital; George E. McCarthy, Jr., Associate Professor of Radiology; and Jerome Rudnitsky, Associate Professor of Medicine at Hahnemann University.

Fig. 382. Jerome J. Vernick (JMC, '62), Clinical Professor of Surgery and Director of the Division of Trauma.

Fig. 383. Joseph W. Sokolowski, Jr. (JMC, '62), Clinical Professor of Medicine (Pulmonary Diseases).

CLASS OF 1962

Addington, Donald Barrett, AZ
Aikey, Barry R., PA
Altaker, Lawrence L., PA
Anderson, Charles W., FL
Bannon, Charles J., NJ
Becker, Irwin, PA
Bernstein, Stanley, NJ
Billstein, Stephan Anthony, PA

Bisset, James F., Jr., PA
Blewitt, George A., PA
Bloom, Michael A., PA
Boland, Francis B., Jr., PA
Bonn, Jerrold C., PA
Brennan, William J., Jr., PA
Brodie, Donald E., DE
Cahn, Edward Laurence, PA

Candela, Harry J., NJ
Capelli, John P., NJ
Carmany, Thomas B., PA
Cashatt, Wesley Lewis, PA
Cefaratti, Michael D., PA
Chalick, Morris J., PA
Clayton, Walter B., Jr., MA
Courogen, William P., PA
Craig, Michael W., OH
Crumrine, Richard S., PA
Currie, Richard Jay, PA
D'Orazio, Edward A., PA
DeBenedictis, Kenneth J., PA
DeNaples, Mark A., NJ
Dennison, W. Landon, Jr., NJ
Diehl, William H., Jr., PA
Doorly, Thomas J., NJ
Drew, W. Lawrence, NY
Estlow, Bert R., NJ
Farrell, Robert E., PA
Feldman, Martin, PA

Fetkenhour, Carl L., PA
Fiegenberg, Donald Saul, PA
Fisher, Norman F., PA
Forchetti, John A., PA
Freedman, Alan Reinald, PA
Gailliot, Robert V., VA
Gelband, Henry, NJ
Giampetro, Anthony M., PA
Gilroy, Robert C., PA
Glazer, Robert M., PA
Glickman, Joseph M., NJ
Gold, Allan, PA
Goldberg, Richard E., PA
Goldstein, Norman Arnold, PA
Goosenberg, Jerry, PA
Gosin, Stephen, PA
Gottfried, William G., PA
Graham, Robert H., PA
Green, Ronald F., PA
Hamburger, Richard J., PA
Hamilton, Richard, WV
Harrer, William V., PA
Harriman, Ben B., PA
Hassler, Carl W., PA
Haughwout, Peter J., PA
Haynicz, Peter, NJ
Helmick, Nathaniel David, II, WV
Hillig, John Edward, Jr., PA
Hollander, Arnold I., PA
Honigman, Joseph, PA
Hyman, Paul S., PA
Kauders, James T., PA
Kienzle, G. Edward, PA
Klinman, Norman R., PA
Kornblith, Paul L., PA
Kratzinger, Stephen Francis, Jr., PA
LaRuffa, Paschal J., PA
Lasota, George L., PA
Leavitt, Richard M., PA
Levinson, Louis E., PA
Lindenheim, Norman, Jr., PA
Love, Jack W., Jr., PA
Lozman, Harvey, NY
Macom, Vorrie B., NJ
Macri, Anthony J., NJ
Malcarney, Courtney M., NJ
Marvel, James P., Jr., DE
Mason, Joel A., NJ
Matthews, Robert B., NJ
Matzelle, Donald W., PA
McCall, Douglas S., NC
McCarthy, George E., Jr., PA
McKeever, Clark D., TX
McKeever, Grant R., TX

Fig. 384. Melvin L. Moses (JMC, '62) Clinical Professor of Surgery.

498

McLaughlin, David B., PA
Mielcarek, Leon M., Jr., PA
Miller, John W., Jr., PA
Mineo, Cyrus Louis, PA
Mori, Hugo, PA
Morita, Eugene T., NJ
Morris, Sheldon L., PA
Moses George P., PA
Moses, Melvin L., PA
Muangman, Debhanom, THIALAND
Neviaser, Robert J., DC
Newton, Zachariah B., III, PA
Nicoll, G. Stephens, NJ
Nuss, Robert C., PA
Oesau, Harold Thomas, Jr., CT
Orbock, Jacob A., PA
Park, Richard C., PA
Pelczar, Eugene W., PA
Pepino, Alfred T., PA
Perlman, Herbert Charles, PA
Peters, Stanley F., PA
Phillips, Herman P., PA
Pittelli, Joseph J., PA
Pliskin, Mark, PA
Prendergast, Michael J., WV
Price, Raphael I. M., PA
Quinn, Frank M., PA

Quinn, Gerald J., PA
Rapaport, Marvin J., PA
Richter, Julius S., PA
Robbins, Michael S., FL
Robins, Sander J., PA
Rosenbaum, Jerald Manuel, NJ
Rosenblatt, Stanley A., PA
Rosenthal, David E., PA
Rubens, Alan Bruce, PA
Rudnitzky, Jerome, PA
Scott, Norman R., NJ
Sebastianelli, Mario J., PA
Segal, A. Carl, PA
Snyder, Joseph, PA
Sokolowski, Joseph W., Jr., NY
Sponsler, Rodney L., PA
Staas, William E., Jr., PA
Steinberg, Harvey, PA
Steinberg, Stanford M., PA
Stirna, John M., Jr., PA
Tawil, Albert, FL
Tomlinson, John W., PA
Vasso, Stephen G., PA
Vernick, Jerome J., PA
Weissman, Burton E., PA
White, Hobart, Jones, UT
Willard, Willis W., III, PA
Zemo, Peter L., III, PA

Standing, left to right: Philip Hodes, Floyd Cornelison, Bernard Alpers, Abraham Cantarow, Fred Harbert, Robert Wise, Louis Hampton, Julius Coon, Thomas Duane, M. H. F. Friedman.
Seated: Kenneth Goodner, John Gibbon, Theodore Fetter, William Sodeman, Peter Herbut, Hans Keitel, Anthony DePalma, William Bodine, Andrew Ramsay, Herbert Luscombe.

Executive Faculty of Medical College.

In 1963, under the Deanship of William A. Sodeman (Fig. 385), a cooperative program between Jefferson Medical College and the Pennsylvania State University was established in which selected students could earn both the Bachelor of Science and Doctor of Medicine degrees in five calendar years after graduating from high school. These students were required to be in the highest fifth of their classes and have combined Scholastic Aptitude Test scores totaling 1300 or higher. The B.S. degree was granted by Penn State after completion of the second year at Jefferson. This program was eventually (1983) extended to six years.

Pioneered by Jefferson, this type of arrangement has been adopted by several other medical schools.

The Commencement was held on June 14 in the Academy of Music, with award of the M.D. degrees to 148 graduates by President William

Fig. 385.   William A. Sodeman, M.D., Sc.D., L.H.D., Dean of Jefferson Medical College (1956-67).

W. Bodine, Jr. Included in the total were graduates from China, Egypt, and Vietnam. This brought the graduate total to 20,370. The Address was delivered by the Honorable William W. Scranton, Governor of the Commonwealth of Pennsylvania.

Robert Charles Gallo, of Connecticut, was a prize winner at graduation and went on to a most distinguished career of research in microbiology. He became Chief of the Laboratory of Tumor Cell Biology at the National Cancer Institute in Bethesda and achieved major credit in the discovery of the AIDS virus (Fig. 386). In 1988 he received the Sword of Ignatius Loyola Award of St. Louis University.

John Major Fenlin, Jr. won the Orthopaedic Surgery prize and went on to a residency in this specialty under Professor Anthony F. DePalma (Fig. 250) at Jefferson. On the teaching staff he rose to Associate Clinical Professor of Orthopaedic Surgery and served as President of the Medical Staff of the Hospital as well as the Volunteer Faculty (Fig. 387).

Joseph C. Flanagan, Professor of Ophthalmology, became Head of the Department of Ophthalmology at Lankenau Hospital and Director of Oculoplastics at Wills Eye Hospital (Fig. 388).

Manfred Wilhelm Lichtmann took his internship and residency at Walter Reed Army Hospital, starting in surgery and switching to anesthesiology. As part of the trauma unit at George Washington University Hospital with the rank of professor, he was one of the physicians who administered anesthesia to President Ron-

Fig. 386.   Robert C. Gallo (JMC, '63), discoverer of HIV virus.

Fig. 387.   John M. Fenlin, Jr. (JMC, '63), orthopaedic surgeon and President of Jefferson's Medical Staff.

1963

ald Regan at the time of the assassination attempt on March 30, 1981.

Edward Albert Teitelman was editor of the Class Yearbook. He interned in the U.S. Public Health Service and became assigned to the Federal Correctional Institution in Danbury, Connecticut. After residency in Psychiatry at Jefferson he became successful in clinical practice in his native New Jersey. An interest in architectural history led to his study of Jefferson's buildings (past, present and future) which he published in the *Alumni Bulletin* (Fall and Winter issue of 1966).

Marvin Ronald Hyett, of New Jersey, became

Clinical Associate Professor of Obstetrics and Gynecology at Jefferson.

Academically associated class members included Michael J. Pitt, Professor of Radiology at the University of Arizona Medical Center, Tucson; James Price, Professor of Ophthalmology, Texas Tech University Health Sciences Center, Lubbock; William B. Lorentz, Jr., Professor of Pediatrics, North Carolina Baptist Hospital, Winston-Salem; Paul C. Rodenhauser, Jr., Professor of Psychiatry, Wright State University, Dayton; and Rugh A. Henderson, Associate Professor of Family Practice, Milton S. Hershey Medical Center.

CLASS OF 1963

Agre, Rodger S., PA	Farber, Joseph M., PA
Anrode, Harry G., PA	Favino, James C., PA
Aronow, Phillip Z., NJ	Feinberg, Richard I., DE
Aspel, Bennett D., PA	Feldman, Philip M., PA
Atkinson, William W., KY	Fenlin, John M., Jr., NJ
Bagley, Marshall Thomas, VA	Fitzpatrick, Francis T., NY
Barefoot, James Earl, PA	Flanagan, Joseph C., PA
Bauer, Fredric B., PA	Forde, David L., PA
Beebe, D. Blair, PA	Fost, Arthur F., NJ
Besley, Richard N., NJ	Friday, Daniel M., PA
Bevan, James L., PA	Gallo, Robert C., CT
Binder, Charles A., NJ	Gehman, Linford K., PA
Blinn, Nathan, PA	Gilcher, Ronald O., PA
Boissevain, Andre R., PA	Glad, Robert M., PA
Borman, David G., OH	Glow, David E., OH
Boulis, Matthew N., PA	Goldstein, David P., PA
Breen, Francis A., Jr., PA	Gryczko, Gerald A., PA
Brentlinger, Dale C., PA	Haddad, Nickie J., WV
Breza, George M., PA	Heiman, Elliott M., PA
Burak, William E., PA	Henderson, Rugh A., PA
Burns, Joseph P., Jr., NJ	Hentosh, John P., PA
Butcofski, James S., PA	Hohl, Joseph C., PA
Carrozza, Harry D., PA	Horner, Daniel W., Jr., PA
Chodroff, Paul H., NJ	Houser, Ben P., Jr., PA
Cohen, George H., PA	Hull, Paul J., MA
Colokathis, Bernard Peter, NH	Hyett, Marvin R., NJ
Curti, Joseph T., PA	Johnson, Joseph M., PA
Dankmyer, Frederick L., PA	Kahn, Charles B., PA
Davis, Robert Morris, PA	Klump, Thomas E., PA
Deitz, Robert D., PA	Kotchick, E. Donald, PA
Delp, Richard U., PA	Kreider, H. Dale, PA
DePasquale, Salvatore C., PA	Kricun, Morrison E., PA
Devine, Peter J., Jr., PA	Leinweber, Bruce K., PA
Dick, John M., PA	Lemp, Rolf W., NJ
Drapiewski, Vincent A., PA	Leschey, William H., Jr., PA
Dulaney, David D., PA	Levitt, Robert S., PA

Lichtmann, Manfred W., NJ
Lippe, Richard D., PA
Lipschultz, Sandor F., PA
Longo, Santo, PA
Lorentz, William B., Jr., WV
Lovrinic, William S., PA
Magilner, Arthur D., PA
Mainker, William S., NJ
Markosi, Charles, Jr., PA
Marlier, Bertrand Joseph, Jr., PA
Martella, Arthur, Jr., PA
McMicken, Thomas E., FL
McNutt, James R., PA
Merlino, William A., NJ
Meunier, Paul A., MA
Miller, Roger M., OH
Miller, William E., PA
Moliken, Murray H., PA
Morioka, Wilfred T., HAWAII
Munzer, Steven J., PA

Fig. 388. Joseph C. Flanagan (JMC, '63), Professor of Ophthalmology.

Nellas, Alex L., PA
Nobel, Joel J., PA
Ostrow, Arnold, PA
Otto, Ralph N., PA
Palena, Peter V., PA
Patricoski, Thomas S., PA
Pellegrini, Ronald V., PA
Petrovich, Frank P., PA
Pitt, Michael Jerome, PA
Preletz, Rudolph J., Jr., PA
Price, James, PA
Prince, Robert L., PA
Prorok, Joseph J., PA
Rader, Major H. C., NJ
Ratner, Irving P., PA
Reier, Charles E., OH
Rightmyer, John N., PA
Roberts, Keith Arnold, PA
Rodenhauser, Paul C., Jr., PA
Rosania, B. Hoagland, NJ
Rothfeld, Donald, NJ
Rudolph, Eugene, PA
Salwen, Jay K., NY
Santaella, Luis R., PUERTO RICO
Santiago-Rivera, Fernando, PUERTO RICO
Saxanoff, Seymour, PA
Scrak, Michael J., PA
Scuderi, Richard A., NY
Serota, Roger Gene, PA
Shearer, Donald E., PA
Shinbach, Kent D., IL
Shoemaker, B. Dawson, PA
Sims, W. Caldwell, PA
Slezak, Joseph A., PA
Smith, Henry F., PA
Stehlik, John M., PA
Suckow, Lowell C., OR
Swank, Ralph L., II, FL
Taraska, John J., PA
Teitelman, Edward A., NJ
Thomas, Daniel J., PA
Toreki, William, NJ
Ushinski, Stanley C., PA
Vassalluzzo, Julio E., PA
Verbinski, Ted, PA
Ward, Maurice J., Jr., PA
Wasilewski, Charles L., Jr., NJ
Wayman, B. Ralph, Jr., PA
Weller, Michael H., PA
Wermuth, Charles R., NJ
Williams, J. Thomas, Jr., PA
Wilson, John S., Jr., PA
Winn, Rodger J., NJ
Wishnev, Martin A., PA
Yudis, Melvin, PA
Zavod, Robert, NY

The Commencement was held on June 12 at the Academy of Music. The M.D. degree was awarded to 164 graduates, which brought the total number of alumni to 20,524. The Address was delivered by William B. Castle, M.D., Professor of Medicine, Harvard Medical School.

In order to shorten the graduation exercises, which had become unduly long, the prizes were awarded the day before. Class Day was thus first instituted in 1964 with presentation of the Lindback Awards for Distinguished Teaching to John B. Montgomery, M.D., Sc.D., Chairman of Obstetrics and Gynecology (Fig. 235), and to John N. Lindquist, M.D., Clinical Associate Professor of Medicine (Fig. 294). Twenty-one prizes were awarded to the graduating students. The number of prizes to be awarded on Class Day would increase to 33 by 1989.

In this year the scattered programs in cardiology throughout the Hospital and College were formally integrated into a Division of Cardiology. The appointments of professional personnel and the standards of quality for education, medical practice and research came under the unified aegis of the Medical Department. Cardiac clinics and conferences were extended into a weekly graphic records conference; a clinical medical, pediatric and surgical cardiology conference; daily instruction of students and residents in interpretation of electrocardiograms; and instruction in cardiac catheterization, vectorcardiography, phonocardiography, and apexcardiography was instituted. Introduction to electrocardiography for students was offered in an elective series of ten lectures.

Robert Carl Mackowiak, an honor graduate, specialized in cardiology and rose to the rank of Clinical Professor of Medicine at Jefferson. From 1972 to 1983 he served as an Associate of the Dean as Director of Student Affairs. He also participated in teaching the sophomore course "Introduction to Clinical Medicine." The senior class of 1980 presented his portrait to the University.

This beloved and highly respected Jeffersonian died suddenly in 1983 (Fig. 389).

Robert Morris Steiner rose in Faculty rank at Jefferson to Professor of Radiology and Associate Professor of Medicine. He became Co-Director of General Diagnostic Radiology and Chief of Thoracic Radiology (Fig. 390). His sabbatical period at the University of Leiden (1983/84) in magnetic resonance imaging introduced this new technology to the Department. Interest in Jefferson history led to his suggestion of placing an Alumni plaque at the site of the First Jefferson Medical Hall at 518-520 Prune Street (now Locust Walk) in 1987 (Fig. 5 & 467). Also, he contributed the chapter on the Department of Radiology in *Thomas Jefferson University: Tradition and Heritage* (1989).

David M. Capuzzi (also Ph.D.) served as Ad-

Fig. 389. Robert C. Mackowiak (JMC, '64), Associate Dean, Director of Student Affairs.

junct Professor of Medicine and of Molecular Biology at Jefferson. He was also Professor of Medicine and Biochemistry at Medical College of Pennsylvania.

Alfred J. Martin, Jr. became a career surgeon in the United States Navy. Having entered military service during the Vietnam War, he served a surgical residency at Jefferson, then a transplantation fellowship at the University of Colorado under Thomas Starzl, M.D.. Having seen sea duty in all parts of the world, he was intimately involved in the care of casualties from the bombing of the United States Embassy in Beirut in April, 1983. Dr. Martin was later appointed Chief of Vascular Surgery at the Naval Medical Center in Bethesda with the rank of Captain (Fig. 391).

Ignatius Stanley Hneleski, Jr., whose father (JMC, '28) was Medical Director of the Philadelphia General Hospital, became a Clinical Assistant Professor of Ophthalmology at Jefferson (Wills Eye).

Class members with academic connections included Joseph A. Lieberman, III, Professor of Internal Medicine at Robert Wood Johnson Medical School, Piscataway, New Jersey; Milton J. Sands, Jr., Professor of Medicine at the University of Connecticut Affiliated Hospitals, Farmington; George B. Segal, Professor of Pediatrics at Strong Memorial Hospital of the University of Rochester, New York; Bennett M. Shapiro, Professor of Medicine, University of Washington Hospitals, Seattle; David P. Schreiner, Associate Professor of Internal Medicine at Presbyterian-University Hospital, Pittsburgh; John W. Yunginger, Associate Professor of Internal Medicine, Mayo Graduate School of Medicine, Rochester; Carl M. Pinsky, Associate Professor of Internal Medicine, New York Hospital; Charles W. Nichols, Associate Professor of Ophthalmology, Hospital of the University of Pennsylvania; Charles R. Kelley, Associate Professor of Internal Medicine, Indiana University Hospitals, Indianapolis; Donald F. Eipper, Associate Professor of Internal Medicine and Thomas J. Jackson, Assistant Professor of Radiology, both of Akron, Ohio; and Thomas M. Bender, Assistant Professor of Radiology, Presbyterian-University Hospital, Pittsburgh.

Fig. 390. Robert M. Steiner (JMC, '64), Professor of Radiology.

CLASS OF 1964

Abrams, Steven L., PA
Alan, Robert L., PA
Amuso, Samuel J., MA
Ascolese, Vincent Raymond, PA
Babitt, Henry I., PA
Baer, Kenneth A., PA
Baker, Joseph H., PA
Barndt, Robert, Jr., PA

Barroway, Robert P., NJ
Barton, James C., PA
Bayer, Joel S., NJ
Beauchamp, Joseph O., MA
Behling, Helmut H., NJ
Bender, Thomas M., PA
Bennett, Richard L., OH
Bingham, William F., PA

Boben, William R., Jr., PA
Brandau, A. Gordon, Jr., MD
Brian, David A., PA
Browning, Jim R., PA
Bullock, Robert A., NJ
Burde, Ronald M., CT
Burns, Robert B., PA
Buyalos, Richard P., KY
Capuzzi, David M., PA
Chang, Sherman S., PA
Clark, Leroy S., PA
Cohen, Ronald H., PA
Cooke, Alfred J., Jr., PA
Cosgrove, Martin J., PA
Davies, Joseph A., III, PA
Dawson, John T., Jr., PA
Delaplane, James M., OH
DiDonato, Richard R., NJ
Donnelly, John M., CT
Downing, Edwin L., OH
Ebert, Richard T., NJ
Eidenberg, Peter J., III, PA
Eipper, Donald F., NJ
Eisenberg, Harvey C., PA

Fabricant, Michael S., NJ
Fahrney, Peter M., MD
Fisher, Herbert M., PA
Fleming, George E., PA
Fogel, William M., PA
Foster, Stanley C., PA
Fox, James M., PA
Freeman, William A., PA
Friedman, Robert C., PA
Gnau, Charles R., PA
Goodritz, Paul Stephan, PA
Graves, Stephen R., OH
Green, Lawrence, NJ
Grim, James S., PA
Harrison, Anthony M., PA
Heilman, John P., Jr., PA
Herdelin, Nils G., Jr., NJ
Hirschy, James C., HAWAII
Hirsh, Philip R., Jr., VA
Hneleski, Ignatius S., Jr., PA
Horton, Vern H., PA
Horvath, Ronald J., PA
Houser, Cyrus G., PA
Houser, James J., PA

Fig. 391. Alfred J. Martin, Jr. (JMC, '64), Captain, U.S. Navy.

Howe, John K., Jr., PA
Isaacs, Herman R., PA
Jackson, Thomas J., PA
Kalish, Robert W., PA
Kauffman, Stephen C., PA
Keesal, Richard W., PA
Keller, I. Basil, FL
Kelley, Charles R., PA
Klein, Arthur L., PA
Knapp, Don B., II, PA
Kosoy, Jerome, PA
Krizman, David J., IN
Krosnoff, Michael, PA
Leavitt, Thomas J., CA
Lehman, Robert F., NY
Leonard, Arthur, PA
Leonard, Edward C., Jr., MA
Levin, Harvey A., PA
Levy, Alan B., PA
Lieberman, Joseph A., III, PA
Lussier, George A., RI
Mackowiak, Robert Carl, PA
Magargee, Edward M., PA
Maioriello, Richard P., PA
Marchand, Gilles A., CT
Mariotti, Joseph R., PA
Martin, Alfred J., Jr., NE
Martincheck, Louis Andrew, PA
Mayer, Robert G., PA
Maylock, John H., PA
McBride, Robert E., WV
McGroarty, Raymond J., PA
McKim, Robert M., OR
Meltzer, Eli O., PA
Metzger, Walter S., PA
Miller, Joseph H., PA
Milroth, William L., PA
Mintell, David F., CT
Mooney, Charles S., CA
Mucha, Theodore F., PA
Murata, James J., HAWAII
Nichols, Charles W., DE
O'Donnell, Michael P., PA
Oscar, Alvin D., MD
Ostrow, David E., PA

Parsons, John M., NJ
Paskin, David L., PA
Pepper, James J., PA
Pinsky, Carl M., PA
Rees, Jerome R., ID
Rhode, Solon L., III, PA
Riffle, John E., PA
Rosenberg, Paul E., PA
Rubin, S. Bruce, PA
Rumbaugh, James Howard, PA
Safir, Donald, PA
Salerno, Nicholas R., PA
Sanderson, Vincent R. A., PA
Sands, Milton J., PA
Sarnowski, Robert J., PA
Schiffer, Stanton, PA
Seda, Hector J., PA
Segel, George, PA
Shapiro, Bennett M., PA
Shapiro, Richard D., OH
Shreiner, David P., PA
Silverman, Stephen D., PA
Soss, Sheldon B., DE
Steele, John E., PA
Steffens, Arnold O., PA
Stein, Elliott M., PA
Steiner, Robert M., PA
Stewart, J. Bartley, Jr., DE
Tenaglia, Nicholas C., FL
Thompson, Charles O., PA
Tisherman, Darryl B., CA
Todd, Curtis Thomas, IN
Toy, Frederick J., NJ
Trabulsi, L. Richard, NJ
Trachtenberg, Stanford B., PA
Traiman, Harris I., PA
Tucker, Harvey M., PA
Varner, L. Robert, PA
Watterson, Samuel G., PA
Weisman, Barrie L., PA
White, Robert A., PA
Whitecar, John P., Jr., PA
Woldorf, Norman M., PA
Yoder, Marion K., IN
Yoder, Stanley J., IN
Yunginger, John W., PA

The Commencement was held at the Academy of Music on June 12 (Fig. 392). The M.D. degrees were conferred upon 157 graduates by President William W. Bodine, Jr. and the Address was delivered by James A. Shannon, Ph.D., Director of the National Institutes of Health.

Percival E. Foerderer, Emeritus Chairman of the Board of Trustees, this year was honored by the Alumni Association with its Annual Achievement Award for his outstanding services to Jefferson over a period of 33 years (Fig. 393). On only one other occasion was a non-alumnus accorded this distinction (George M. Norwood, Jr. in 1978, Fig. 442).

A basic research arm of the Department of Radiology was developed in 1965 as the Stein Radiation Biology Research Center. It was named for Louis Stein who spearheaded the project. The center was located on grounds at Tenth and Locust Streets that would later (1991) accomodate a much larger facility (The Bluemle Life Sciences Building). The mission of the Stein Center was to explore new research frontiers in chromosomes, genetics, tissue culture, intrauterine life, electron microscopy, radiation physics, and immunity (Fig. 394).

In this year the Trustees approved the yearly appointment of two Alumni Representatives, each to serve on the Board for a period of three years. Drs. Henry L. Bockus (JMC, '17, Fig. 202) and Francis Braceland (JMC, '30, Fig. 255) were the first to serve in this capacity.

Fig. 392.   Commencement Exercises at Academy of Music.

This was the first class to have women graduates, of which there were eight (Fig. 395). Nancy Szwec Czarnecki was the first alumna to receive a diploma from Jefferson Medical College and in addition won a C.V. Mosby Prize as a "worthy graduate." She conducted a highly successful family practice and served as the first woman President of the Alumni Association in 1989 (Fig. 396).

Joyce Evaline Price became the first woman medical graduate from the ranks of Jefferson R.N. diploma nurses. After serving as operating room nurse, she completed the pre-medical requirements and matriculated in 1961. Her Pennsylvania Hospital internship was followed by a career in surgery in New Mexico (Fig. 397).

Ronald L. Poland became Professor of Pediatrics at Wayne State University and Director of Neonatal Services at Detroit Medical Center Affiliated Hospitals. In 1989 he was named Profes-

Fig. 393. Percival E. Foerderer, LL.D., Board of Trustees Chairman (1950-62).

1965

sor and Chairman of the Department of Pediatrics at Hershey Medical Center, Hershey, Pennsylvania.

Arthur Norris Triester became a Clinical Assistant Professor of Medicine at Jefferson and in 1989 was made President-elect of the Volunteer Faculty Association.

Ernest Edward Flegel specialized in cardiovascular diseases. He became prominent on the staff of Our Lady of Lourdes Hospital, Camden, and a Clinical Assistant Professor of Medicine at Jefferson.

Other class members who were academically associated included Mark D. Brown, Professor of Orthopaedic Surgery at University of Miami Affiliated Hospitals; Richard P. Wenzel, Professor of Internal Medicine at University of Iowa, Iowa City; Lionel W. Rosen, Professor of Psychiatry at Michigan State University Clinical Center, East Lansing; Louis A. Leaff, Professor of Psychiatry, Hospital of the Medical College of Pennsylvania; Ronald C. Kim, Associate Professor of Pathology, University of California, Irvine Medical Center; Joseph P. Leddy, Associate Professor of Orthopaedic Surgery, Robert Wood Johnson Medical School, Piscataway, New Jersey; Carol A. Miller, Associate Professor of Medicine, Los Angeles County USC Medical Center; Joseph W. Smiley, Clinical Associate Professor of Medicine at Jefferson; Kevin Parent, Assistant Professor of Medicine, Mayo Graduate School of Medicine, Rochester; and Joseph X. Grasso, Assistant Professor of Psychiatry, University of Medicine and Dentistry, Newark, New Jersey.

Fig. 394.   Stein Radiation Biology Research Center (1965).

510

1965

Abrams, Edward, PA
Adler, Jon S., PA
Anderson, Merrill A., PA
Baker, Dole P., PA
Baroff, Sheldon, NJ
Bauer, Thomas L., PA
Beggs, Robert A., PA
Bellin, Harvey J., PA
Berwind, Robert T., PA
Bigley, Elmer C., Jr., PA
Boriosi, Guido D., PA
Bost, Frederic W., CA
Bradley, Martin R., PA
Brown, Mark D., DE
Brunswick, Richard A., PA
Bubeck, Robert C., PA
Casel, Bernard S., NJ
Cashman, John, PA
Chaplin, Stanley S., PA
Cohen, Edwin E., PA
Cohen, Richard W., PA
Cohen, Robert M., PA
Conrad, James L., OR
Copeland, James E., Jr., FL
Corcoran, Edward R., Jr., PA
Crawford, Ralph W., Jr., PA
Criden, Louis E., PA

Czarnecki, Nancy S., PA
Davidson, Robert, PA
Decker, Carolyn P., PA
Dingfelder, James R., PA
Doo, Gene W., HI
Dresner, Martin L., PA
Dubin, Albert A., PA
Dwoskin Joseph Y., MA
Eash, Galen J., IN
Echenberg, Robert J., PA
Elkins, Robert W., NY
Federico, Frank N., CT
Fiscus, William Patrick, PA
Fitchett, David F., DE
Fleegler, Earl J., PA
Flegel, Ernest E., PA
Francis, Charles K., Jr., NJ
Gallo, Erly P., CT
Gillespie, John B., PA
Grodin, Jay M., NY
Grosso, Joseph X., PA
Halpren, Benjamin A., PA
Hamilton, George L., PA
Harwitz, Daniel G., DE
Hildreth, John A., DE
Hirsch, Nathan B., PA
Hopper, Bruce D., NY
Jenofsky, Jack, PA

Fig. 395.   First women graduates (1965).

John, Harry N., PA
Jones, David G., PA
Jones, Paul B., PA
Jones, Ward L., CA
Karp, Louis A., NJ
Kim, Ronald C., MD
King, Richard A., PA
Kirshner, Lewis A., PA
Knepp, Mary E., PA
Kramer, Norman J., CT
Kuehnle, John C., PA
Kutell, Michael A., NY
Lally, James F., PA
Lanard, Bruce J., PA
Laub, Allen S., PA
Laurelli, Henry E., RI
Leaff, Louis A., PA
Leddy, Joseph P., NJ
Leeds, William Stuart, Jr., PA
Leichner, Thomas J., Jr., PA
Levine, Raphael K., NY
Levinson, Stuart A., VA
Levitt, Richard L., PA
Libonati, Margaret M., PA
Lipkin, Philip, PA

Lizerbram, Martin H., PA
Lohman, James W., PA
Longnecker, Robert E., NJ
MacDonald, Gerard L., PA
Mahoney, John T., PA
Maleson, Franklin G., PA
Malin, Thomas H., PA
Martin, Amilu S., CO
McGovern, Lawrence O., PA
McKeever, John D., TX
McLellan, J. Densmore, TX
Mellk, Harlan M., NJ
Miller, Carol A., OH
Miller, Robert V., NJ
Minicozzi, William P., PA
Mutschler, Louis H., Jr., PA
Naide, William, PA
Osgood, Carroll P., Jr., CT
Ousler, George W., Jr., PA
Parent, Kevin, ME
Parry, Carolyn E., PA
Paul, David B., PA
Pearl, Burton W., NJ
Pharr, William F., WV
Pilewski, Robert M., PA
Polan, William S., PA

Fig. 396. Nancy S. Czarnecki (JMC, '65), first alumna to receive a diploma (1965).

Fig. 397. Joyce E. Price (JMC, '65), first Jefferson R.N. to receive the M.D. degree (1965).

Poland, Ronald L., PA
Post, Donald Francis, PA
Price, Joyce E., PA
Quinn, Edward J., CT
Ramos-Umpierre, Antonio, PUERTO RICO
Reiber, E. William, II, PA
Renzulli, William F., NJ
Roe, Thomos C., Jr., MD
Rogers, William H., IL
Rosen, Lionel W., PA
Rosenblatt, Stanley G., NJ
Salen, Samuel, PA
Salerno, Merle S., PA
Sandberg, Ronald K., PA
Sandler, Steven C., DC
Schall, Robert S., NJ
Schlein, Allen P., NJ
Schneider, Thomas J., PA
Seipel, Wayne D., NJ
Senape, Saverio J., PA
Sheppard, Thomas D., PA
Sherrod, John H., PA
Slater, Harvey, PA
Slotnick, Victor B., PA
Smiley, Joseph W., PA
Smith, Donald H., PA

Smith, George William, PA
Smith, Harry F., NC
Smith, Kent K., PA
Steen, J. Dennis, NY
Steiner, John C., PA
Stewart, Paul F., Jr., PA
Sutula, Stanley J., Jr., CT
Taylor, John O., Jr., PA
Thompson, Robert R., IA
Tisherman, Sanford A., PA
To, William T. M., HONG KONG
Toney, David M., PA
Triester, Arthur N., PA
Varano, Lottie A., PA
Wachtel, Garry H., PA
Warden, James R., PA
Weissman, Bruce W., PA
Wenzel, Richard P., PA
Wilkins, Charles E., Jr., NJ
Wilson, Richard C., NJ
Winslow, Phillip H., PA
Wood, William B., PA
Woodruff, Ralph D., NJ
Yates, Barry C., PA
Zemel, Norman P., NJ
Zweig, Charles H., PA

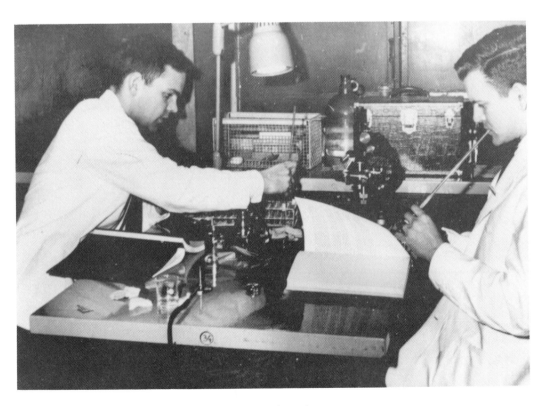

Students in physiology.

1965

At the Academy of Music Commencement on June 10 the M.D. degree was conferred upon 154 graduates by President William W. Bodine, Jr. The Address was delivered by the Honorable Lister Hill, distinguished Senator from Alabama and author of the important Hill-Burton Act for construction of Hospitals.

Harvey Jay Sugarman won prizes for highest average and clinical excellence. He became prominent in academia as the Davis M. Hume Professor of Surgery at the Medical College of Virginia (Fig. 398).

James Francis Burke, Jr. served his internship and residency in medicine at Jefferson. He joined the Division of Nephrology in the dialysis program in 1971 and later became nephrologist for the transplantation program. A gifted teacher and investigator, he advanced rapidly to the rank of Professor of Medicine (Fig. 399).

Susan Joan Gordon, winner of the William Potter Memorial Prize, was appointed to the staff in 1971 following residency and undertook clinical research and teaching in the Division of Gastro-enterology during a period of rapid increase in the application of endoscopic techniques. She advanced to the rank of Clinical Professor of Medicine (Fig. 400).

Warren D. Lambright served as a medical officer in Ghana, West Africa, from 1968 to 1970. Returning to Jefferson for medical residency (1971-73), followed by a year as Chief Resident in Medicine, he was then appointed Assistant Hospital Director for Medical Care Programs. In 1975 he became Director of the Family Practice Residency Program at Chestnut Hill Hospital and in 1985 Chairman of the Department of Ambulatory Care at Abington Memorial Hospital. He continued as Clinical Assistant Professor of Family Medicine and Instructor in Medicine at Jefferson. Dr. Lambright's contributions in clinical research and community service have been notable.

John E. Stambaugh, Jr. went on to the Jefferson Graduate School and was awarded the Ph.D. in

Fig. 398. Harvey J. Sugarman (JMC, '66), Professor of Surgery at Medical College of Virginia.

Fig. 399. James F. Burke, Jr. (JMC, '66), Professor of Medicine (Nephrology).

Pharmacology in 1968. He served his residency in Medicine and a fellowship in Oncology while teaching in the Department of Pharmacology. In 1975 he was appointed full Professor of Pharmacology. Dr. Stambaugh has published more than 100 papers on pharmacological and oncological subjects, especially respecting relief of pain. He continued the practice of oncology and hematology in Camden area hospitals.

Joseph Benjamin Doto, Jr. took a residency in anesthesiology at Jefferson. As Clinical Assistant Professor he specialized in anesthesia for cardiac surgery (Fig. 401). In 1985 he became Chief of Anesthesiology at St. Luke's Hospital in Bethlehem, Pennsylvania.

Michael D. Strong, serving in the U.S. Army Reserve, was promoted to the rank of Brigadier General in 1988. He also served as Assistant Pro-

Fig. 400.   Susan J. Gordon (JMC, '66), Clinical Professor of Medicine (Gastroenterology).

fessor of cardiothoracic surgery at Hahnemann University.

Other 1966 graduates whose careers were of interest included Edward T. Carden, a Jefferson intern who went on to training in otolaryngology and was later appointed Clinical Associate Professor of Otolaryngology at Jefferson. Gwen K. Kaplow specialized in obstetrics and gynecology and became Clinical Assistant Professor also at Jefferson. Howard Silberman, winner of the Phillips Surgery Prize, was appointed Associate Professor of Surgery at the School of Medicine, University of Southern California. He was co-author of the book *Parenteral and Enteral Nutrition for the Hospitalized Patient* published in 1982. Arthur D. Schatz became Assistant Professor of Obstetrics and Gynecology at the University of Miami School of Medicine. Michael C. Coplon and Timothy J. Michals were both appointed Clinical Assistant Professor of Psychiatry and Human Behavior at Jefferson. Michael C. Snyder held an appointment as Clinical Associate Professor of Radiology at Southern Illinios School of Medicine. Laurence R. Lewinn became Chief of Reconstructive Surgery at Geisinger Medical Center, Danville, Pennsylvania, a Jefferson affiliate. Lynn G. Cranmer served as Associate Clinical Professor of Dermatology at the University of California School of Medicine, Irvine. Barton L. Hodes, formerly Professor of Surgery and Chief of Ophthalmology at Hershey Medical Center, was in 1985 appointed Professor and Head of the Department of Ophthalmology at the University of Arizona, Tucson.

Additional graduates with academic careers were: James V. Snyder, Professor of Anesthesiology at Presbyterian University Hospital, Pittsburgh; William D. Lerner, Professor of Internal Medicine at the University of Alabama, Birmingham; Elethea Hitchens Caldwell, Associate Professor of Plastic Surgery at the University of Rochester, New York; Robert A. Greenstein, Associate Professor of Psychiatry at the University of Pennsylvania School of Medicine; Joseph F. Lipinski, Associate Professor of Psychiatry at Massachusetts General Hospital; Paul L. Schraeder, Associate Professor of Internal Medicine at Robert Wood Johnson Medical School, Piscataway; Jerome Singer, Assistant Professor of Pediatrics at Jefferson; Carter M. Becker, Assistant Professor of Pathology at the University of Cincinnati; David S. Colville, Assistant Professor of Internal Medicine at Mayo Graduate School of Medicine, Rochester; Robert H. Lerman, Assistant Professor of Internal Medicine at Boston University School of Medicine; and Thomas W. Muhlfelder, Assistant Professor of Internal Medicine at Mount Sinai Hospital, New York.

Fig. 401.   Joseph B. Doto, Jr. (JMC, '66) teaching anesthesiology to Jefferson students.

<hr />

CLASS OF 1966

Adams, George L., PA
Barrett, John P., Jr., MD
Becker, Carter M., PA
Bender, Andrew L., PA
Benjamin, James J., NJ
Bishop, David E., PA
Blood, Joseph Belton, Jr., PA
Booth, Donald M., PA
Bosniak, Jay B., PA
Bower, John R., PA
Brodey, James F., PA
Burke, James F., Jr., PA

Carden, Edward Thomas, PA
Centrella, Louis John, PA
Chase, William V., PA
Chudnow, I. Paul, PA
Clark, Allen M., PA
Clarke, G. Donald, NJ
Cohen, Merrill J., PA
Cohen, Nathan N., NJ
Collini, William R., NY
Colville, David S., PA
Cook, Franklyn R., NJ
Coplon, Michael Carl, NY

Cranmer, Lynn G., NJ
Curtin, Charles T., PA
Cutler, Robert S., PA
Davis, Murray C., III, PA
DePalma, Walter Patrick, NJ
Dickson, Charles M., NJ
Dolan, Michael P., FL
Doto, Joseph B., Jr., PA
Dyer, James S., PA
Erdman, Robert L., NJ
Fisher, Robert, PA
Flynn, Paul G., NE
Friedman, Barton Jay, PA
Friedman, Steven A., PA
Fronduti, Robert L., PA
Getz, Donald D., PA
Gibbon, Robert, Jr., PA
Girone, Joseph A. C., DE
Goldstein, Robert A., PA
Gordon, Susan J., NJ
Gosnell, Kermit B., PA
Grant, Stuart R., PA
Green, Thomas J., PA
Greenstein, Robert A., PA
Hammond, N. LeRoy, III, NJ
Heaps, Kenneth P., PA
Hegarty, Thomas J., Jr., PA
Hitchens, Elethea Marion, PA
Hodes, Barton L., PA
Hodges, Wyllys Royce, III, MD
Hood, Henry H., Jr., PA
Hooper, Joseph Roberts, PA
Howard, Stephen, PA
Jenkin, Michael A., DE
Jenkins, David W., NJ
Jones, William D., III, PA
Judson, James N., NJ
Kaplow, Gwen H. K., PA
Kearney, Donald Joseph, NY
Kelly, Daniel J., PA
Kinstlick, Emanuel, PA
Kirschner, Robert H., PA
Klein, Sheldon, PA
Kozlek, Thomas F., PA
Kushner, Gary Gerald, PA
Lable, Ira, NY
Lambright, Warren D., IN
Leach, Gary R., PA
LerMan, Robert H., NJ
Lerner, William D., PA
Letson, James A., Jr., PA
LeWinn, Laurence R., PA
Lintgen, Arthur B., PA
Lipinski, Joseph F., Jr., PA

Lloyd, Thomas V., III, PA
Love, Harry M. P., PA
Lovrinic, Daniel F., PA
Maher, Paul J., CT
Manashil, Gordon B., PA
Manfredi, John A., PA
Mass, Burton, PA
Matzelle, Wayne J., PA
Mayes, Richard L., PA
Messersmith, John K., PA
Michals, Timothy J., PA
Miller, Bernard J., NJ
Mlynarczyk, Francis A., DE
Moll, Thomas B., PA
Muhlfelder, Thomas William, PA
Newman, Henry E., PA
Nosheny, Stanley Z., PA
Nowicki, Edward Richard, PA
Pacanowski, John P., PA
Padnes, Stephen C., NY
Paolino, James S., NY
Pazner, Sherman S., PA
Pell, Edward N., III, WV
Perrine, Robert Gordon, NJ
Phillips, Edward B., WV
Pincus, Frances Ellen, PA
Popolow, Michael L., PA
Porter, Charles A., Jr., NC
Pupi, Paul A., PA
Raymond, Roger D., MA
Reams, Carl L., PA
Rich, Robert D., WA
Rising, David C., NJ
Roberts, Alan S., AR
Rosenbaum, Arnold S., PA
Rothman, Gerson B., PA
Ruggiero, Nicholas J., PA
Sack, John T., PA
Schatz, Arthur J., PA
Schecter, Benjamin C., PA
Schilling, Jane, PA
Schonauer, Thomas D., MI
Schraeder, Paul Louis, PA
Shaw, Jonathan K., OH
Shorb, Stanley R., PA
Silberman, Howard, PA
Silver, Lawrence B., PA
Singer, Jerome, PA
Singer, Ronald, NJ
Snyder, James Victor, PA
Snyder, Michael C., PA
Stambaugh, John E., Jr., PA
Steindel, Carl R., PA
Strong, Michael D., PA

Sugerman, Harvey J., PA
Szarko, Frank J., PA
Tai, George M., PA
Timmons, Robert G., PA
Tober, Robert L., MA
Tressan, Elliott R., PA
Tull, John W., DE
Turco, Ronald N., PA
Ulrich, Richard A., IA
Vannucci, Robert C., PA
Vastine, David W., PA

Viozzi, Francis J., PA
Warren, Sara A., PA
Weis, Walter F., Jr., PA
Wetter, Marvin S., NJ
Williams, W. Scott, NJ
Wiswesser, George A., PA
Wolff, Theodore, NJ
Woodruff, Charles L., PA
Yim, Donald W. S., HI
Zavod, William S., PA
Zeitlin, Mark H., PA

Robert I. Wise, Magee Professor of Medicine, in "pit" of Thompson Annex.

Peter A. Herbut succeeded William W. Bodine, Jr. as the Third President of Jefferson Medical College in an impressive ceremony held May 3 at the Academy of Music. In 1969 he would become the First President of Thomas Jefferson University. Dr. Herbut, formerly Chairman of Pathology at Jefferson, was the first faculty member to become a President of the institution (Fig. 402).

The graduation exercises were held on June 2 at the Academy of Music. Peter A. Herbut, the new President of the College, conferred the M.D. degrees upon 161 graduates. The Address was delivered by Honorable Raymond P. Shafer, LL.B., Governor of Pennsylvnia.

In this year a School of Allied Health Sciences was established, which in two years would become the College of Allied Health Sciences within the newly formed Thomas Jefferson University. John W. Goldschmidt (JMC, '54, Fig. 353) became its first Dean.

In December, 1967, under the initiative of President Peter A. Herbut, the Graduate School became more formally organized. Two years later it would become the College of Graduate Studies of Thomas Jefferson University.

In 1967 the Louis B. and Ida K. Orlowitz Residence Hall for students and house staff was opened at the southwest corner of Tenth and Walnut Streets. This 20-floor, 239- apartment building at a cost of $4.7 million also provided for social and professional gatherings (Fig. 403).

Joseph Martin Giordano, after internship and residency at George Washington University, worked at Walter Reed Army Hospital for three years and then joined the surgical staff at George Washington University Hospital in 1976, advancing to Professor of Surgery (Fig. 404). He headed the trauma unit that received President Ronald Regan on March 30, 1981, at the time of the assassination attempt. Dr. Giordano performed the chest surgery that saved the President's life. The President required 3 1/2 units of blood in the emergency room and 4 1/2 units during the operation.

Ralph Riddall Dobelbower, Jr. became an Assistant Professor of Radiation Therapy and Nuclear Medicine at Jefferson. He pioneered in improved techniques for radiation therapy of pancreatic cancer.

Joseph Frederick Laucius, of Delaware, entered the field of medical oncology and became prominent at Jefferson Hospital and in the College as Assistant Professor of Medicine (Fig. 405).

Elliott James Rayfield went on to become Professor of Medicine and Chief of the Diabetes Section, Mount Sinai School of Medicine.

Anthony Michael Padula took his surgery residency at Jefferson and became a member of the Jefferson affiliate staff at Chestnut Hill Hospital.

Other academically affiliated members of the class included Charles B. Higgins, Professor of Radiology at the University of California, San Francisco; Jonathan L. Williams, Professor of Radiology, University of Florida Affiliated Hospitals, Gainesville; John S. Wills, Associate Professor of Radiology at Jefferson; Isabel C. Yoder, Assistant Professor of Radiology at Massachusetts General Hospital; Marc A. Shuman, Associate Professor of Internal Medicine at University of California, San Francisco; Charles A. Meyer, Jr., Associate Professor of Psychiatry, Medical College of Georgia, Augusta; Claire Langston, Associate Professor of Pathology, Baylor College of Medicine, Houston; Clifford C. Kuhn, Associate Professor of Psychiatry, University of Louisville; Stephen Frytak, Associate Professor of Oncology at Mayo Graduate School of Medicine, Rochester; and Elliott M. Badder, Associate Professor of Surgery, University of Maryland, Baltimore.

Fig. 402. Peter A. Herbut, Third President of Jefferson Medical College (1967), and First President of Thomas Jefferson University (1969).

Adams, D. Leslie, PA
Altschuler, Robert G., PA
Anderson, William H., PA
Arbeter, Allan M., PA
Badder, Elliott M., PA
Balling, David Anderson, PA
Balsbaugh, G. Thomas, PA
Baumgarner, Gene T., NJ

Bieber, James R., NY
Block, Robert A., PA
Boris, Michael Z., PA
Brait, Kenneth A., PA
Brodsky, Stuart L., PA
Byrne, Stephen, PA
Caruso, Vincent George, PA
Chiurco, Anthony A., PA

1967

Fig. 403.   Orlowitz Residence Hall (1967).

Chollak, Joseph P., Jr., PA
Cimochowski, George E., PA
Clements, Harry Michael, PA
Coverdale, Edward J., PA
Crutchlow, William P., NJ
Culp, Larry H., OH
Cutler, Neil C., PA
Davis, Campbell M., CT
Dellevigne, William M., PA
Dobelbower, Ralph R., Jr., PA
Docktor, John W., PA
Donnon, Henry P., Jr., NJ
Dorn, Barry C., NJ
Druckman, Stephen M., PA
Evans, Charles H., PA
Faries, George B., Jr., PA
Ferguson, William D., PA
Fischer, Steven William, PA
Flynn, Richard J., PA
Fox, Richard D., PA
Franger, Joseph E., IL
Fraunfelder, John P., PA
Freshman, J. Rodney, PA

Friedenberg, William R., NJ
Friedlander, Robert M., NJ
Friedman, Sheldon A., PA
Frytak, Stephen, PA
Gangloff, Michael A., PA
Gentsch Goldin, Alice L., PA
Gilgore, Gary Steven, PA
Giombetti, Joseph John, PA
Giordano, Joseph Martin, PA
Gordon, Mark W., PA
Grabias, Stanley L., Jr., PA
Greenberg, Steven J., PA
Grossman, Joel S., PA
Hall, Robert F., II, PA
Harrer, Daniel C., PA
Hawksley, Vaughan C., PA
Higgins, Charles B., PA
Hinkle, James E., PA
Holstein, James J., PA
Holsten, Steven B., PA
Horner, William R., ME
Hughes, George H., CT

Fig. 404. Joseph M. Giordano (JMC, '67) performed life-saving surgery on President Ronald Regan on March 30, 1981.

Fig. 405. J. Frederick Laucius (JMC, '67) prominent oncologist at Jefferson.

Ishler, Harold L., Jr., PA
Jurnovoy, Joel B., PA
Karabell, Sheldon I., PA
Karp, Robert J., PA
Karsch, Daniel N., PA
Keohane, Richard B., PA
Kershbaum, Kenneth L., PA
Klemek, Joseph S., PA
Klieman, Charles H., PA
Kodroff, Michael B., PA
Koutcher, Martin E., PA
Kuhn, Clifford C., PA
Labunetz, William H., PA
Langston, Claire, MI
Laucius, J. Frederick, DE
Leone, Michael R., NY
Levin, Gene D., PA
Levin, Stephen A., PA
Little, Robert G., Jr., PA
Madden, Francis P., PA
Madigan, Robert R., PA
Mahan, Robert G., PA
March, Noreen Marie, PA
Martin, Fredric W., KS
Meloy, John Harold, PA
Meyer, Charles A., Jr., PA
Meyer, Fred H., III, PA
Mikuliak, Helen J., PA
Miller, David H., PA
Moldovan, Stanton I., PA
Moseley, Lloyd W., PA
Mulveny, Carl P., PA
O'Connell, Brent J., DE
O'Hara, James P., PA
Olsen, Jean E., PA
Padula, Anthony M., PA
Peterson, Gary Ragner, PA
Pinsk, Stephen H., PA
Pryharski, Andrew J., MA
Rayfield, Elliot J., PA
Reynolds, Walter J., III, PA
Rosenfeld, Philip A., PA
Rothermel, Franklin J., PA
Rubin, Allen W., PA
Rubin, Morton L., PA
Sabow, J. David, PA
Salgado, Edward M., NJ
Sall, David L., PA
Samuels, Bruce Steven, DE
Schaffzin, Elliott A., NJ

Scholl, Harvey W., Jr., PA
Schwartz, Burton W., PA
Schwartz, Louis Winn, PA
Seda, Russell P., PA
Seltzer, Leonard H., PA
Shapiro, Stephen J., NY
Shuman, Marc A., PA
Sica, Paul A., Jr., PA
Silver, Barry A., PA
Silverman, Paul B., PA
Slawek, Paul P., PA
Slogoff, Stephen, PA
Sorr, Edward M., NJ
Stanitski, Carl L., PA
Stein, Scott C., PA
Stouffer, Vance R., Jr., PA
Sumerson, James M., PA
Tartaglia, Louis, Jr., PA
Tenn, Gordon K., PA
Thomas, F. Ardell, PA
Thompson, Anne M., PA
Traiman, Richard G., PA
Varano, Vincent J., PA
Venuto, Ralph J., PA
Verlin, Michael, PA
Vernick, Richard T., PA
Walker, L. Reed, Jr., PA
Warren, Jonathan, NJ
Watkin, Walter B., Jr., PA
Weiner, Michael D., PA
Weiser, Don Coleman, PA
Wells, Allan B., CT
White, Alan F., PA
White, Matthew, PA
Wilf, Theodore J., PA
Williams, David E., PA
Williams, Jonathan L., DE
Wills, John S., PA
Winters, Lewis, PA
Woldoff, Herbert S., PA
Wolf, Melvyn A., PA
Wolfgang, Gary L., PA
Wolson, Alan H., PA
Wong, James, PA
Yauch, John A., PA
Yoder, Isabel Cecilia Saldana, PUERTO RICO
Young, Lockwood Se-Joong, HI
Zeok, John V., PA
Ziegenfuss, Jay F., Jr., PA
Zieziula, Ronald F., NY

Commencement was held on May 31 in the Academy of Music. The M.D. degrees were conferred by President Peter A. Herbut upon 156 graduates, which brought the grand total of alumni to 21,152. The Address was delivered by Keith Spalding, B.A.,LL.D., President of Franklin and Marshall College.

Ira Roy Tannebaum, in the joint Penn State-Jefferson five-year program, won the Alumni prize for highest average and several other clinical awards. He took his residency in general surgery at Jefferson and entered private practice in Potomac, Maryland.

Raphael Joseph DeHoratius took a residency in internal medicine and a fellowship in rheumatology at the University of New Mexico. He joined the faculty of the New Mexico University School of Medicine and conducted research in pathogenetic immune mechanisms in connective tissue diseases. In 1974 he joined the Division of Rheumatology at Jefferson and continued his studies of defects in immune regulation in systemic lupus erythematosus (Fig. 406). He rose to the rank of full Professor of Medicine in 1982, at which time he accepted a position as Director of Immunology and Rheumatology in the Department of Medicine at Hahnemann University.

Noble Thompson, Jr., an honor graduate, after training in radiology transferred from the Martin Luther King, Jr. Hospital in Los Angeles to Jefferson in 1976. He then progressed to the rank of Clinical Associate Professor of Radiology.

Several class members joined the teaching staff at Jefferson: Robert E. Bellet, Associate Professor of Medicine (Cardiology); David A. Berd, also Associate Professor of Medicine; Donald D. Serota, winner of the Potter Prize, Clinical Assistant Professor of Psychiatry and Human Behavior; and John C. Baylis, Instructor in Pathology and Cell Biology.

Class members serving in other institutions included: Thomas J. Gal, Professor of Anesthesiology, Hospital of the University of Virginia, Charlottesville; Friedrich C. Luft, Professor of Internal Medicine, Indiana University Hospitals, Indianapolis; Robert C. Kurtz, Associate Professor of Medicine, New York Hospital; Joel A. Kaplan, Professor of Anesthesiology, Mount Sinai Hospital, New York; John Lazarchick, Associate Professor of Pathology, Medical University of South Carolina, Charleston; Charles E. Sparks, Associate Professor of Pathology, Strong Memorial Hospital of University of Rochester, New York; Stephen J. Thomas, Associate Professor of Anesthesiology, New York Hospital; Philip E. Donahue, Associate Professor of Surgery, University of Illinois Hospital, Chicago; Robert A. Jacobs, Associate Professor of Pediatrics, Los An-

Fig. 406.   Raphael J. DeHoratius (JMC, '68), Professor of Medicine (Rheumatology).

geles County USC Medical Center, Los Angeles; John A. Jeffries, Assistant Professor of Obstetrics/Gynecology, Mayo Graduate School of Medicine, Rochester; Robert J. Risimini, Assistant Professor of Family Practice, Robert Wood Johnson Medical School, Piscataway; Gill R. Alderfer, Assistant Professor of Obstetrics/Gynecology, and Charles M. Brooks, Assistant Professor of Internal Medicine, both at Hahnemann University.

Alderfer, Gill R., PA
Ashby, Bonnie L., NJ
Barish, Joel M., PA
Barnaby, William H., NJ
Baylis, John C., DE
Beekey, Cyrus E., Jr., PA
Bell, George S., PA
Bellet, Robert E., PA
Berardinelli, John L., NJ
Berd, David A., PA
Berger, Jay B., PA
Binns, Carl B., Jr., PA
Bosanac, Paul Robert, PA
Braverman, Wayne H., PA
Brooks, Charles M., NJ
Campbell, Virginia Johnston, PA
Carney, Wilfred I., Jr., RI
Casper, William J., Jr., PA
Chase, Jeffrey S., PA
Cohen, Richard I., NJ
Colcher, Irving S., PA
Comperatore, Dominic F., PA
Cooperman, Elliot M., PA
Copulsky, Robert H., NY
Corson, Barry, PA
Davies, Richard L., CA
Deglin, Edward A., PA
DeHoratius, Raphael J., PA
Dennis, William J., PA
DiCuccio, Nicholas W., PA
Donahue, Philip E., PA
Eboch, William Maynard, Jr., PA
Ellin, Stephen R., NY
Epple, Walter D., PA
Ezerman, Robert H., PA
Feen, Alan E., NJ
Fitzpatrick, Marcia A., PA
Flanigan, Richard J., PA
Fletcher, Thomas G., CA
Francesconi, Albert R., NJ
Frost, John D., PA
Funkhouser, Laura Belle, PA
Gal, Thomas J., PA
Gelfond, Stephen D., PA

Gerry, Hubert W., NJ
Glasberg, Mark R., PA
Glaser, Joseph P., PA
Gordon, Clifford A., NJ
Green, Carl M., PA
Grossman, William K., PA
Hershey, Stephen L., PA
Hiatt, Gerald A., HAWAII
Hofmann, Lawrence V., PA
Holman, Paul D., SC
Holmes, William F., NY
Humphrey, John B., Jr., NJ
Jacobs, Robert A., NY
Jacoby, James H., PA
Jefferies, George E., III, PA
Jefferies, John A., PA
Kaplan, Gerald F., PA
Kaplan, Joel A., PA
Kaufman, Jerold, PA
Kestner, Joseph F., Jr., PA
Kimmel, Judson Howard, PA
Klein, Jacob, PA
Kniazer, Barry, PA
Koch, Frederick J., PA
Koniver, Garth A., PA
Kozloff, Stephen R., PA
Kravis, Thomas C., NY
Kun, Larry E., PA
Kurtz, Robert C., PA
Label, Norman, PA
Lazarchick, John, PA
Lefrak, Steven L., NY
Lev, Ian M., PA
Loder, John L., PA
Logan, William E., PA
Luft, Friedrich C., NM
Luscombe, Herbert J., PA
Malyk, Bohdan, NJ
Manges, John P., Jr., PA
Mannes, Harvey A., NJ
Mansfield, Lyndon E., PA
Marone, Michael L., PA
Meadowcroft, James A., PA
Mech, John J., NJ

Medford, William L., Jr., PA
Metz, Glen W., PA
Metzger, Carl D., PA
Mizak, Daniel J., CT
Mockaitis, Martina M., PA
Molinari, William J., Jr., PA
Mullin, William J., PA
Orocofsky, Morris L., PA
Palascak, Joseph E., PA
Pergam, Carl J., NY
Phillips, Warren C., Jr., NJ
Probst, Charles E., Jr., PA
Ramsey, Harry E., Jr., PA
Reisman, Barry M., NJ
Reynard, Kenneth B., NJ
Richman, Alan V., PA
Risimini, Robert J., NJ
Roberge, Leo A., CT
Robinson, John H., WV
Rockfeld, Robert D., NY
Rofman, Barry A., PA
Rosenman, David E., PA
Russo, James M., Jr., NJ
Ryan, Charles H., NJ
Sabarra, Howard N., NY
Salazar, Andres M., PUERTO RICO
Savran, Stephen V., PA
Schwartz, Martin, NJ
Scott, Thomas S., PA
Serota, Ronald D., PA
Shawaluk, Paul D., Jr., PA
Shull, Stewart D., PA
Sirlin, Nelson, PA
Skowronski, Theodore J., PA

Skrenta, Allan W., MA
Slachta, Gregory A., MA
Snyder, Charles W., PA
Snyder, Lawrence K., PA
Sparks, Charles E., NJ
Spurgeon, Lincoln, NJ
Stack, John M., PA
Stein, Mark R., PA
Stein, Robert M., PA
Stevens, Bruce L., NY
Stock, Donald H., PA
Stumacher, Russell J., PA
Syrek, Susan J., PA
Tannebaum, Ira R., PA
Thomas, Stephen Jay, DC
Thompson, Noble L., Jr., PA
Townsend, Jay A., PA
Turchik, James B., CT
Urban, Donald G., PA
Vaccaro, Vincent M., PA
Vagley, Richard T., PA
Venier, Leon H., NJ
von der Heyde, Sarah Jennings, CT
Walchak, Frank R., PA
Webber, Charles E., Jr., PA
Weinberg, Robert M., PA
Weiss, Malcolm S., PA
Werner, Stephen E., OH
Williams, J. Stewart, PA
Wilson, Jacquelyn J., NY
Wroblewski, Edward A., PA
Yocum, Harold A., PA
Zemel, Walter G., NJ
Zengerle, Frances Susan, PA
Zwerling, Charles J., PA

"Seeming failures are often just the threads of a larger tapestry. . . . A willingness to accept the risk of failure is the price of all success."

Howard Shapiro (Science: 250, 609, 1990)

Through the efforts of Peter A. Herbut, President of the Medical College, University Status was achieved for Jefferson by a Charter received in City Hall on May 20, 1969 (Fig. 407). At this juncture the new members of the Board were no longer required to be sworn into Trusteeship. On a reference date of July 1, 1969, the four divisions of Thomas Jefferson University were established as (1) Jefferson Medical College, (2) College of Graduate Studies, (3) College of Allied Health Sciences, and (4) Thomas Jefferson University Hospital. It was created as a totally health re-lated, medically oriented University. Dr. Herbut thus became the first President of the University.

The M.D. degree was conferred by President Herbut upon 166 graduates. The Address was delivered by Frederic K. Miller, Ph.D., Commissioner for Higher Education of the Commonwealth of Pennsylvania.

Among the members of the class who obtained academic appointments at Jefferson were: Robert Abel, Jr., Clinical Associate Professor of Ophthalmology; Salvatore P. Girardo, Clinical Assistant Professor of Medicine and Chairman of the

Fig. 407.   Reception of Thomas Jefferson University Charter at City Hall, May 20, 1969. Left to right: John W. Goldschmidt, M.D., (Dean of College of Allied Health Sciences); Francis J. Sweeney, Jr., M.D. (Hospital Director); James M. Large (Board Chairman); Judge Vincent Carroll; Peter A. Herbut, M.D. (President); N. Ramsay Pennypacker (Vice President for Development); George M. Norwood (Vice-President for Planning); and William F. Kellow, M.D. (Dean).

Department of Medicine at Methodist Hospital, a teaching affiliate; William G. Chodoff, Clinical Assistant Professor of Pediatrics; Linda L. Weinberg, Clinical Assistant Professor of Pediatrics; Donald L. Tomasello, Clinical Assistant Professor of Surgery; Anthony J. Del Rossi (Fig. 408), Clinical Assistant Professor of Surgery; and Richard L. Allman, Clinical Assistant Professor of Medicine.

A large number in the class obtained academic teaching appointments in institutions other than Jefferson. Among these were: Lawrence S. Berman, Associate Professor in the Departments of Anesthesiology and Pediatrics at the University of Florida; James D. Heckman. Professor and Deputy Chairman in the Department of Orthopaedics at the University of Texas Health Science Center at San Antonio; Jay S. Skyler, Professor of Medicine and Associate Professor of Pediatrics

Fig. 408. Anthony J. DelRossi (JMC, '69), Clinical Assistant Professor of Surgery (Cardiothoracic).

at Miami University School of Medicine and the recipient of the 1985 Distinguished Achievement Award of the American Society of Contemporary Medicine and Surgery; Barry S. Smith, Assistant Professor in the Department of Physical Medicine and Rehabilitation at Baylor College of Medicine, Houston, Texas; Kenneth L. Wible, Associate Professor of Pediatrics at the West Virginia University School of Medicine and Vice-Chairman of the West Virginia Chapter of the American Academy of Pediatrics; Benjamin P. Seltzer, Professor of Neurology and Psychiatry, Tulane University School of Medicine; Harold R. Hansen, Associate Professor in the Department of Psychiatry and Behavioral Science of the University of Louisville School of Medicine, given the "Golden Apple Award" for outstanding teaching by the class of 1980; Robert A. Lustig, Assistant Professor of Radiation Therapy and Nuclear Medicine at Cooper Medical Center, Camden; Richard A. Insel, Assistant Professor of Pediatrics at the University of Rochester Medical Center where he carried out research for developing a vaccine for prevention of infections by Hemophilus influenza, Type B; Sander J. Levinson, Assistant Professor of Medicine at Temple University with special orientation in pulmonary diseases; and John F. Frantz, Instructor in Ophthalmology at Eastern Virginia Medical School, Norfolk.

Other members of the class with academic appointments were: Jesse H. Wright, III, Professor of Psychiatry, University of Louisville, Kentucky; James Winter, Associate Professor of Radiology at U.C.L.A. Medical Center, Los Angeles; William J. Snape, Professor of Medicine, U.C.L.A. Medical Center, Los Angeles; Robert M. MacMillan, Jr., Associate Professor of Medicine, Gerald A. Mandell, Associate Professor of Radiology, and Peter M. Anson, Associate Professor Surgery, all at Hahnemann University; John H. Bauer, Associate Professor of Medicine, University of Missouri, Columbia; Garret E. Bergman, Professor of Pediatrics, Medical College of Pennsylvania; Donna L. Cooper, Associate Professor of Obstetrics/Gynecology, U.S.C. Medical Center, Los Angeles; Judith M. Cooper, Associate Professor of Internal Medicine, Wayne State University, Detroit; Peter M. Farmer, Assistant Professor of Pathology, S.U.N.Y. Downstate Medical Center, New York; Kay Ellen Frank, Assistant Professor of Surgery, Case Western Reserve University, Cleveland; James E. Goodrick, Associate Professor of Anesthesiology, University of California, Irvine; Truvor V. Kuzmowych, Assistant Professor of Medicine, George Washington University, Washington, D.C.; Thomas A. Lane, Associate Professor of Pathology, University of California, San Diego; John H. MacIndoe, II, Associate Professor of Medicine, University of Iowa; Thomas J. McGlynn, Associate Professor of Medicine, Milton S. Hershey Medical Center, Hershey; William G. Negendank, III, Associate Professor of Medicine, Wayne State University, Detroit; William H. Sherman, Assistant Professor of Medicine, Presbyterian Hospital, New York; John W. Shigeoka, Associate Professor of Medicine, University of Utah, Salt Lake City; and Paul M. Weinberg, Assistant Professor of Pediatrics, Hospital of the University of Pennsylvania.

CLASS OF 1969

Abel, Robert, Jr., PA
Addis, David J., NJ
Allman, Richard L., PA
Anderson, John B., PA
Anson, Peter M., PA
Arkus, Robert L., NJ
Balizet, Louis B., PA
Baron, Alan L., PA
Batchis, Van S., NJ
Bauer, John H., PA
Benzel, Stanley, CT
Bergman, Garrett E., PA
Berman, Lawrence S., PA
Bockner, Andrew C., NY
Bonafide, Peter Robert, NY
Brand, Stanley N., NY
Bricklin, Alan S., PA
Briggs, C. Christian, III, PANAMA
Busenkell, Gary L., PA
Bussard, John R., PA
Carrig, Thomas F., Jr., NJ
Chodoff, William G., PA
Clement, John A., PA
Cline, Charles T., Jr., WV
Coleman, Linda L., PA
Cooper, Donna L., PA
Cooper, James R., PA
Cooper, Judith M., PA
Coren, Gary S., PA
Cotton, Paul E., PA
Coverdale, Paul J., PA
Cramer, Marvin E., PA
Cuomo, Thomas J., Jr., NY
DeFrance, John H., NJ
Del Rossi, Anthony J., PA
Del Giorno, John T., PA
Diakun, Robert G., NY
Donoho, Christopher R., Jr., DE

Drasin, Edward, PA
Dudenhoefer, Frederick J., PA
Durkin, Martin J., PA
Dziob, Edward F., NY
Ebel, Marc S., PA
Edwards, Gary Allen, PA
Egdell, Robert W., NY
Essick, David J., PA
Farmer, Peter M., PA
Finkle, Howard I., NJ
Finnegan, Walter J., NJ
Fireman, Richard L., PA
Forkin, Daniel, NJ
Frank, Kay E., WV
Frantz, John F., II, WV
Freedman, S. Robert, PA
Friedman, Jules M., PA
Friedman, Robert Hilton, PA
Gadkowski, Walter J., NJ
Geetter, Philip H., CT
Gehret, Peter A., DE
Gellman, Alexander C., NJ
Ginieczki, Michael J., PA
Girardo, Salvatore P., PA
Glassman, Leonard M., PA
Goldin, Michael R., NY
Goodman, Harris M., PA
Goodrick, James E., PA
Gouger, Dale B., NY
Gross, Barry Charles, PA
Gross, Richard C., PA
Grunau, Charles F., PA
Grunt, Richard F., NJ
Hansen, H. Roger, NJ
Heckman, James D., WV
Heim, William J., NJ
Henderson, David F., ME

Hersh, Carol B., NJ
Heym, Herbert H., PA
Ifft, F. Nicholas, PA
Insel, Richard A., MD
Jacobson, Robert E., PA
Kain, Thomas M., III, NJ
Kaplan, Jonathan S., PA
Katz, David J., PA
Kavalier, Morton A., CT
Keveney, John J., Jr., PA
Kinsey, M. Dean, NJ
Kleiman, M. Leonard, PA
Kravitz, Alan E., NJ
Krebs, Alfred G., PA
Kuzmowych, Truvor V., PA
Lane, Linda K., PA
Lane, Thomas A., PA
Lepie, Richard M., MA
Lerro, Furey A., PA
Levinson, Sander J., PA
Lustig, Robert A., NJ
MacIndoe, John H., VA
Mackell, James V., Jr., PA
MacMillan, Robert M., NJ
Malit, Lee A., PA
Mandell, Gerald A., PA
Mang, Justin, HONG KONG
Maurer, Alan R., NY
Mauriello, Alfred J., II, PA
McConnell, David B., OH
McGlynn, Thomas J., Jr., PA
McGovern, Edward W., Jr., DE
McMahon, Thomas P., PA
McSwiggan, Kathleen C., PA
Meringolo, Robert D., NY
Metz, Albert V., Jr., NJ
Millington, J. Thomas, Jr., PA
Mlynarczyk, Peter J., NJ
Negendank, William G., III, DE
Nelson, Leroy John, PA
Nissenbaum, Mark, PA
Okie, Allen, PA
Okulski, Thomas A., NJ
O'Neil, Ann, PA
Pang, Meredith K. L., HI
Penta, John M., PA

Pollock, Morris A., PA
Poupko, Gary G., PA
Randazzo, Vincent T., NJ
Raynak, Jan T., PA
Raynes, Stanton M., PA
Ricketts, Edward A., Jr., CA
Rizzo, Thomas A., Jr., PA
Robinson, Earl W., NJ
Rokui, Carole Yukimi, HI
Rosenberg, Paul J., NJ
Schein, Alan L., PA
Schickling, Leonard F., PA
Schiro, John C., PA
Schroeder, Elizabeth Ann, CT
Schwalb, Neil S., PA
Schwartz, Stephen M., PA
Seibert, S. Neitz, PA
Seltzer, Benjamin P., PA
Shack, Robert P., NJ
Sherman, Fred P., PA
Sherman, William H., PA
Shigeoka, John W., PA
Skyler, Jay S., PA
Smith, Barry S., PA
Snape, William J., Jr., NJ
Sokoloff, Norman F., PA
Spahr, Robert C., PA
Springer, Suzanne R., PA
Stabinski, Elizabeth Marie, PA
Stockman, James A., PA
Strong, Wilson W., Jr., CA
Sullivan, Thomas E., MA
Terkelsen, Kenneth G., MA
Timins, Eugene Lawrence, NJ
Tomasello, Donald N., NJ
Tornay, Anthony S., Jr., PA
Townsend, James W., Jr., PA
Tuma, Victor B., NJ
Walker, Andrew B., NJ
Weinberg, Linda L., PA
Weinberg, Paul M., PA
Weinstein, Mitchell A., PA
Wible, Kenneth L., PA
Winter, James, NY
Wirth, John C., Jr., PA
Wright, Jesse H., III, PA
Yellig, Edward B., PA

This year marked the Centennial of the founding of the Alumni Association. The event was celebrated by a performance of the London Philharmonic Orchestra at the Academy of Music which over 2,000 alumni, faculty and guests attended. A preceding dinner was held with the Governor as guest, and a reception followed at Jefferson Alumni Hall (Fig. 409). The statue of Samuel D. Gross, the founder, was moved from Smithsonian Park in Washington, D.C. to Jefferson's Scott Plaza and rededicated for the Centennial (Fig. 410).

The Scott Library/Administration Building was dedicated in 1970. In September of this year the library collection was moved from the 1025 Walnut Street Medical College. A spacious 53,000 square-foot area contrasted to the former 9,000. At the time of moving the collection comprised over 68,000 volumes with subscriptions to over 1,200 journals. The new building was an architectural gem and the library itself one of the best of its kind in the country (Fig. 411).

Exercises were held at the Academy of Music on June 5 at which time the M.D. degree was conferred by President Peter A. Herbut upon 166 graduates. The Address was delivered by the Honorable Hugh Scott, A.B., LL.B., U.S. Senator, Commonwealth of Pennsylvania.

The Alumni Prize for highest cumulative average was won for the first time by a woman, Marie Vincenza Olivieri Russell, who went on to become Associate Professor of Pediatrics and Di-

Fig. 409.   Alumni Centennial (1970). Reception in Jefferson Alumni Hall after London Philharmonic Concert at the Academy of Music.

rector of the Division of Pediatric Hematology at Hahnemann University (Fig. 412).

Among other members of the class who achieved academic affiliation in teaching institutions other than Jefferson were: William C. Lambert, Assistant Professor of Pathology at the College of Medicine and Dentistry of New Jersey, and member of the editorial staff of the *Journal of the American Academy of Dermatology*; Harvey B. Lefton, Clinical Professor of Medicine at the Medical College of Pennsylvania, who contributed a book chapter on *Inflammatory Bowel Disease*; Ronald A. Leff, Assistant Professor of Anesthesiology at the New York Hospital and Cornell Medical Center; Frederick E. Hampf, Assistant Professor of Radiology at Tufts Medical School; Theodore Lo, Chairman of the Department of Radiotherapy at the Lahey Clinic; James

Fig. 410. Rededication of Gross Statue on Scott Plaza (1970). Left to right: Dean William F. Kellow, President Peter A. Herbut, and Alumni President Paul J. Poinsard.

1970

M. Gerson, Assistant Professor of Pediatrics and Director of Pediatric Hematology at the Milton S. Hershey Medical Center; Sarah S. Long, Associate Professor of Pediatrics and Chief of Infectious Diseases at St. Christopher's Hospital for Children, Temple University, who received the "Golden Apple Award" for outstanding teaching; Michael K. Farrell, Associate Professor of Pediatric Gastroenterology at the University of Cincinnati College of Medicine; Fred A. Mettler, Jr., Professor of Radiology in the University of New Mexico; John A. Kline, Staff of University of Medicine and Dentistry of New Jersey and Chief of Orthopaedics at the Rahway Hospital; Lawrence L. Miller, Clinical Associate Professor of Medicine at the University of California, Los Angeles; Louis Vignate, Director of the Fellowship Program and Patient Care of the Joslin Diabetes Center in Boston, on teaching staff of Harvard Medical School; Steven A. Kline, Assistant Professor of Obstetrics and Gynecology at the State University of New York, Stonybrook; Barry

J. Make, Associate Professor of Medicine in the Pulmonary Section at the Boston University School of Medicine; Leonard J. Cerullo, received invitations to lecture on use of the laser in neurosurgery in Taiwan, Saudi Arabia, Spain and Switzerland; William J. Peters, Adjunct Professor of Obstetrics and Gynecology at the Montana State University and Chairman of Obstetrics at Bozeman Deaconess Hospital; Christopher C. Rose, Assistant Professor of Medicine at the University of Pennsylvania School of Medicine; Howard D. Toff, Staff Psychiatrist at the Cedars Sinai Medical Center; William D. Bloomer, Associate Professor of Radiation Therapy at Harvard Medical School and Associate Editor of *Radiation Research*; Allan P. Freedman, Assistant Professor of Medicine at Hahnemann University; Steven A. Klein, Director of Maternal Fetal Medicine at Winthrop University Hospital in Long Island; Stephen E. Abram, Professor of Anesthesiology, Medical College of Wisconsin Affiliated Hospitals, Milwaukee; Michael Clancy, As-

Fig. 411. Scott Library/Administration Building (1970).

1970

Fig. 412. Marie Oliveri Russell (JMC, '70), Alumni Prize winner, Associate Professor of Pediatrics, Hahnemann University.

sociate Professor of Orthopaedic Surgery, Temple University Hospital, Philadelphia; James M. Kendig, Assistant Professor of Pediatrics, Strong Memorial Hospital, Rochester, New York; Paul C. Marshall, Associate Professor of Pediatrics, University of Massachusetts Hospital, Worcester; Milton Rossman, Assistant Professor of Medicine, Hospital of the University of Pennsylvania; and Peter V. Scoles, Assistant Professor of Orthopaedic Surgery, Case Western Reserve University, Cleveland.

Some members who obtained teaching appointments at Jefferson were: Peter D. Pizzutillo, Clinical Associate Professor of Orthopaedics and Director of Pediatric Orthopaedics; Jacquelyn Zavodnick, Clinical Associate Professor of Psychiatry and Human Behavior; Charles R. Schleifer, Clinical Assistant Professor of Medicine; William J. Bainbridge, Instructor in Family Medicine at Jefferson's affiliate, Bryn Mawr; Seth A. Malin, Clinical Assistant Professor of Surgery; and John W. Breckenridge, Clinical Assistant Professor of Radiology and President of the Greater Delaware Valley Ultrasound Society.

Neil O. Thompson served for some years at Manorom Christian Hospital, Thailand, experiencing all the stresses of frontier medicine during the turbulent years of Southeast Asian wars.

William E. Whiteman of this class was killed in the Vietnam War on October 19, 1971. A plaque in his memory and also honoring other alumni who served in the conflict was erected at Jefferson (Fig. 413).

CLASS OF 1970

Abram, Stephen E., OH
Anderson, Arlene J., PA
Anstadt, George W., PA
Azzato, John A., PA
Bainbridge, William J., PA
Barylak, Edward J., PA
Baxter, Thomas L., III, PA
Berger, Bruce A., PA
Berley, Lawrence F., PA
Bernini, Richard L., PA
Besses, Gerald S., PA
Biddle, David, PA
Blofstein, Barbara, PA
Bloomer, William D., PA
Blum, Ronald I., PA
Bower, Edward B., PA

Breckenridge, John W., PA
Breslin, Joseph A., Jr., PA
Brown, Harvey N., NY
Cacchione, Robert J., PA
Carlton, John W., PA
Carty, James B., Jr., PA
Cerullo, Leonard J., PA
Charney, Richard Howard, PA
Chatfield-Taylor, Robert F., Jr., MA
Clancy, Michael, PA
Cohen, Larry S., PA
Comfort, Joseph A., Jr., NJ
Connelly, Thomas Rowan, PA
Cox, Robert W., MD
Davenport, Richard D., IL
Davis, Allen B., NY

Devers, Thomas J., PA
Dmochowski, John F., NJ
Douglass, Paul H., PA
Dovnarsky, James H., PA
Ellis, Michael D., PA
Farrell, Michael K., PA
Feldman, Richard M., IL
Fisher, Joseph S., PA
Fox, James W., IV, PA
Freedman, Allan P., PA
Freeman, Louis A., CT
Furr, Charles M., PA
Gardner, Alan M., PA
Gerson, James M., PA
Gingold, Bruce S., NY
Glassberg, Stephen C., NY
Goeggel, Christia Bracken, ST. THOMAS
Gold, Alan M., PA
Goldman, Howard, NY
Goldstein, Laurence, PA
Goodwin, Richard H., Jr., NJ
Green, Alan J., NY
Hagen, Douglas Beriah, CT
Hampf, Frederick E., Jr., PA
Ingwer, Irwin, NY
Isajiw, George, PA
Johnson, Bertram L., Jr., PA
Johnson, Robert P., PA
Judson, William W., PA
Kane, Robert C., PA
Kautz, Paul D., PA
Kay, Thomas R., NJ
Keel, Willaim A., Jr., PA
Keiserman, Wayne M., PA
Kendig, James W., PA
Kenny, Rose M., PA
Kern, George W., IV, PA

Kershner, George H., PA
Kershner, Marilyn S. P., NJ
Klein, Steven A., NY
Klick, James M., PA
Kline, John A., NJ
Lambert, W. Clark, KY
LaMorgese, James R., NJ
Laska, Edward M., PA
Lauria, Michael David, PA
Leff, Ronald A., NJ
Lefton, Harvey B., OH
Lewis, William J., PA
Liekweg, William G., Jr., VA
Lintz, David I., NJ
Lo, Theodore C. M., HONG KONG
Loberant, Norman G., NY
Long, Sarah S., DC
Lumish, Robert M., PA
Make, Barry J., PA
Malin, Seth A., CT
Malovany, Robert John, PA
Marshall, Paul C., PA
Martin, Richard E., PA
Martsolf, John T., PA
McCloskey, John R., PA
McCormick, John F., MA
McGovern, James B., Jr., PA
McLane, Rogers D., PA
Mersky, Steven A., PA
Mettler, Fred A., Jr., NJ
Miller, Joseph A., NJ
Miller, Lawrence S., PA
Miner, Philip T., PA
Monkowski, Alfred M., NJ
Monroe, John B., CT
Murray, William M., PA
Myers, Larry S., PA
Nemiroff, Richard L., NJ
Neubeck, James M., PA
Noller, William E., NJ
Nutt, James N., III, PA
Olivieri, Marie V., PA
Palmieri, Ronald J., NJ
Pashman, David R., NJ
Perry, John F., PA
Peters, William J., PA
Pizzutillo, Peter D., NJ
Polsky, Harry S., PA
Quaglieri, Charles E., NJ
Randell, David J., OH
Reichel, John, III, PA
Richmond, Allen C., NJ
Rose, Christopher C., PA
Rossman, Milton O., NJ

IN MEMORY OF
WILLIAM E. WHITEMAN, M.D. '70
KILLED OCTOBER 19, 1971
AND TO ALL ALUMNI WHO SERVED IN
THE VIET NAM CONFLICT

Fig. 413. Plaque honoring William E. Whiteman (JMC, '70), killed in Vietnam War.

Salasin, Robert I., NJ
Schleifer, Charles R., PA
Schneider, Glenn D., PA
Schwartz, Judith P., PA
Scoles, Peter V., NJ
Selinkoff, Paul M., DE
Seymour, Parker M., OH
Shovlin, J. Michael, PA
Skoloff, Joseph, NJ
Skvara, Frederick C., NJ
Smoyer, Phyllis M., DE
Sophocles, Aris M., Jr., NJ
Sowden, Richard G., Jr., NY
Spiegelman, David M., PA
Starz, Kenneth E., PA
Stayman, J. Webster, III, PA
Stein, Robert A., PA
Steinberg, Michael B., PA
Streltz, Patricia M.C., PA
Szawlewicz, Stephen A., PA
Taylor, Robert F. C., Jr., MA

Terry, Roger L., OH
Terzis, Julia K., GREECE
Thomas, Nathan O., PA
Thompson, Neil O., NJ
Tobey, Martin A., TX
Toff, Howard D., PA
Tolley, Douglas G., Jr., PA
Tomlinson, Charles O., PA
Vignati, Louis, CT
Voron, Stephen C., PA
Wakefield, Frank G., DE
Walheim, Jon P., PA
Walters, Charles Albert, PA
Weisberger, Calvin L., PA
Wetterholt, David G., NJ
Whitbeck, John V., NY
Whiteman, William Earl, II, TX
Wolfer, Carl F., PA
Woodley, Bruce L., NJ
Woodruff, Stephen M., PA
Zavodnick, Jacquelyn M., PA
Ziegler, Virginia Flory, PA

Study area in Scott Library.

1970

President Peter A. Herbut conferred the M.D. degree upon 186 graduates at the Academy of Music Commencement on June 11. Governor of Pennsylvania Milton J. Shapp gave the Address.

Joseph Louis Seltzer served a residency in surgery at Geisinger Medical Center following which he changed his career to anesthesiology with a residency at Jefferson (1973-75). After appointments at Wright-Patterson Air Force Base, Dayton, Ohio, and State University Hospital, Syracuse, New York, he returned to Jefferson as a Staff Anesthesiologist. Upon the retirement of Dr. Jay Jacoby in 1984, he succeeded him as Professor and Chairman of the Department. Dr. Seltzer has published widely in the fields of physiologic and pharmacologic research in anesthesiology while continuing to build upon the clinical excellence of his department (Fig. 414).

Virginia Brodhead Clemmer, winner of the Phillips Prize in Surgery, served her residency in surgery at Jefferson and went on to appointment in the Department of Surgery at Wilmington Veterans Administration Hospital.

Cora L. Christian became established in the United States Virgin Islands. In 1975 she received an M.P.H. degree from Johns Hopkins University School of Public Health and went on to become Executive Director of the Virgin Islands Medical Institute and Assistant Commissioner of Health for the Islands. In 1985 she was elected President of the Virgin Islands Medical Society.

Arthur E. Brown became prominent in the field of oncology. Following training in medicine with special interest in infections, he advanced to Associate Professor of Medicine and Pediatrics, Cornell University School of Medicine on the infectious disease service at Memorial Sloan-Kettering Cancer Center. His publications were numerous and he served as Editorial Consultant for the *American Journal of Medicine*.

William C. Hamilton was trained in Jefferson's Department of Orthopaedic Surgery and was selected by the American Orthopaedic Association as a North American Traveling Fellow. He re-

turned as Assistant Professor, later becoming associated with Lankenau Hospital. Richard I. Clemmer also became Clinical Assistant Professor of Orthopaedic Surgery at Jefferson.

Among numerous other class members who achieved prominence in their various specialties may be mentioned Jeffrey C. Weiss, Professor of Pediatrics and Director of the Division of General Pediatrics at Jefferson. John L. Nosher in 1985 served as Acting Chairman, Department of Radiology at Rutgers Medical School with the rank of Clinical Assistant Professor of Radiology and Obstetrics/Gynecology. Lowell E. Kobrin was in

Fig. 414. Joseph L. Seltzer (JMC, '71), Professor of Anesthesiology and Chairman of the Department.

private practice of Obstetrics/Gynecology with an appointment as Clinical Professor at Oregon Health Services University, Portland. Terrence S. Carden, Editor of both 1970 and 1971 Clinic Yearbooks, served for a time as Editorial Assistant for the *Journal of the American Medical Association*. Edwin P. Ewing, Jr. was Staff Pathologist, Center for Disease Control, Atlanta, Georgia, with special responsibilities relative to studies of the Acquired Immune Deficiency Syndrome. Allen E. Summers was Clinical Assistant Professor of Psychiatry and Human Behavior at Jefferson. George W. Dennish, III, was Assistant Clinical Professor of Medicine at the University of California School of Medicine, San Diego, while also Director of Special Care Units at Scripps Memorial Hospital, La Jolla. Francisco J. Garcia-Torres was Clinical Assistant Professor of Medicine at Baylor University College of Medicine, Houston, Texas. Richard W. Bagge was Assistant Professor of Psychiatry, Medical College of Georgia. Arthur S. Tischler in 1986 was advanced to Associate Professor of Pathology, Tufts University School of Medicine. Gregory P. Borkowski was named Chairman of Diagnostic Radiology, Cleveland Clinic Foundation. Ronald H. Hirokawa was Vice-Chairman of Otolaryngology at Naval Medical Center and Assistant Professor of Surgery at Uniformed Services University of Health Sciences. Edward B. Ruby was Assistant Professor of Medicine at Jefferson in the Division of Endocrinology. Paul M. Fernhoff was Assistant Professor of Pediatrics, Emory University.

Other academically associated members of the Class of 1971 included: John A. Belis, Professor of Surgery, Milton S. Hershey Medical Center, Hershey; John W. Bloom, Assistant Professor of Medicine, University of Arizona, Tucson; Thomas A. Brasitus, Professor of Medicine, University of Chicago Hospital; Judith R. Derasse, Assistant Professor of Medicine, Hahnemann University; Henry M. Feder, Jr., Professor of Family Practice, University of Connecticut Hospitals, Farmington; Erwin S. Fleishman, Assistant Professor of Medicine at Jefferson; Robert L. Hellman, Assistant Professor of Pathology at University of Miami Affiliated Hospitals; James J. Nocon, Assistant Professor of Obstetrics/Gynecology, Indiana University Hospitals, Indianapolis; Jay Nogi, Associate Professor of Surgery, Medical College of Virginia, Richmond; Frank R. Reale, Associate Professor of Pathology, University of Massachusetts, Worcester; Elizabeth A. London Rogers, Associate Professor of Internal Medicine, University of Maryland Hospital, Baltimore; Ronald J. Rosenberg, Assistant Professor of Nuclear Medicine, University of Connecticut, Farmington; Harvey F. Sasken, Assistant Professor of Pathology at Brown University Affiliated Hospitals, Providence; Arthur M. Segal, Assistant Professor of Psychiatry, Westchester County Medical Center, Valhalla, New York; J. Stanley Smith, Jr., Assistant Professor of Surgery, Milton S. Hershey Medical Center, Hershey; William H. Topper, Associate Professor of Pediatrics, University of Kansas Medical Center, Kansas City; and David J. Weber, Associate Professor of Psychiatry at Medical College of Virginia, Richmond.

CLASS OF 1971

Altreuter, Richard W., NJ
Appleman, Warren, NY
Atkinson, Alvan W., NJ
Bagge, Richard W., NJ
Balkany, Christopher K., PA
Banner, Marc P., PA
Barone, James E., WV
Baskous, Alexander T., NY
Becker, Gary L., PA
Belis, John A., PA
Bergman, Donald A., NJ
Bescher, R. Anthony, PA
Blecker, Michael J., NJ

Bloom, John W., MO
Blumberg, Michael Zangwill, PA
Borkowski, Gregory Peter, PA
Borthwick, Thomas R., PA
Borucki, Louis J., NJ
Braid, Byron S., PA
Brasitus, Thomas A., CT
Brodhead, Virginia S., PA
Brown, Arthur E., NJ
Brown, Sylvan, PA
Brundage, Gertrude B., NJ
Bryan, Thomas M., PA
Buffington, Gary K., PA
Callahan, Daniel J., PA

Caravello, Peter M., PA
Carden, Terrence S., Jr., PA
Casaday, Floyd M., III, PA
Case, Delvyn C., Jr., CT
Chandlee, Robert E., PA
Chase, Lawrence J., PA
Chepko, Milan D., PA
Chollak, William L., PA
Christian, Cora L., ST. THOMAS
Clemmer, Richard I., Jr., PA
Cooper, David R., NY
Craddock, Mary K., LA
Cramer, Harry R., Jr., PA
Crawford, Carolyn S., PA
Danoff, David M., NY
Davidson, Robert, PA
Davison, William C., NJ
Dennish, George W., III, NJ
Derasse, Judith R., PA
Dmochowski, T. Jeffrey, NJ
Dolinskas, Carol A., NJ
Donnelly, Brian, NJ
Dooley, James R., NJ
Doyle, Harry A., PA
Duffy, Scott S., PA
Eccleston, Joan B., PA
Edwards, Lin-Sey Nancy W., PA
Evitts, Mary Lou, PA
Ewing, Edwin Paul, Jr., PA
Falk, Robert B., Jr., PA
Feder, Henry Morton, Jr., PA
Fell, William F., Jr., NJ
Ferguson, John B., III, PA
Fernhoff, Paul Martin, NJ
Fetter, Theodore W., PA
Fishbane, Bruce M., NY
Fiss, Thomas W., Jr., PA
Fleischman, Ervin Saphir, PA
Forrest, Bruce Alan, NJ
Freeland, George R., PA
Frost, Stephen S., PA
Garcia-Torres, Francisco J., PUERTO RICO
Geha, Michael A., PA
Glaser, Arthur H., PA
Glass, Phillip, NJ
Goldstein, Robert W., PA
Goodwillie, Walter F., PA
Gormally, Eric P., PA
Gould, Daniel B., NJ
Gray, Stephen R., NY
Grossman, Ronald D., PA
Guralnik, Jack M., PA
Guzzardi, Lawrence J., PA
Hamilton, William C., PA

Heller, Alvin G., PA
Hellman, Robert Lewis, NJ
Hennessey, David H., PA
Henrick, William Robert, PA
Hirokawa, Ronald H., PA
Hoffman, Ronald A., NJ
Holzsager, David J., NY
Iacuzzo, John C., NJ
Jambro, Robert D., PA
Johnston, Russell G., PA
Jones, David W., PA
Jordan, Jerome W., PA
Julian, Joseph, Jr., PA
Kale, Milton P., PA
Kambe, Joseph C., PA
Keene, Richard R., NJ
Klein, Barry R., PA
Klein, Gerald M., PA
Klinman, Steven W., PA
Kobrin, Lowell E., PA
Kontrick, Andrew J., PA
Kozielski, Joseph W., PA
Langan, E. Lawrence, III, PA
Lechman, Michael J., PA
Lehr, Cynthia D., NY
Light, Wilma C., PA
Lombardi, Anthony C., DE
London, Elizabeth Ann, FL
Lynd, Clifford W., Jr., PA
Maas, James C., PA
Macy, Philip A., III, PA
Mandel, Sheldon R., PA
Margolis, Stephen H., PA
Margulies, Michael C., PA
McBrearty, Francis X., Jr., PA
McBride, James G., NJ
Mebane, Thomas S., III, PA
Monk, Susan Marie, PA
Motley, John F., PA
Mullins, Thomas F., III, MA
Nocon, James J., PA
Nogi, Jay, PA
Noone, James P., PA
Nosher, John L., NJ
O'Conner, Nancy K., PA
Orvald, Todd Busse, PA
Penchansky, Barry H., NJ
Place, Robert A., PA
Pomerantz, Philip A., PA
Posner, Mark A., NJ
Probst, Theodore G., NJ
Pryor, Wilbur Michael, CO

1971

Rakoff, Jeffrey S., PA
Ratchford, W. Buckley, PA
Raymond, Paul A., PA
Read, J. Harleston, PA
Read, Randolph Alexander, PA
Reale, Frank R., NJ
Riff, Dennis S., PA
Ritter, William S., PA
Robin, Howard S., PA
Rosenberg, Ronald J., PA
Rosof, Edward, NY
Rubin, Jeffry F., PA
Ruby, Edward B., NJ
Salko, Gregory J., PA
Sasken, Harvey F., NY
Scherr, Stuart A., PA
Schneider, Myles S., NY
Schwartz, Augustin J., III, PA
Schwimmer, Richard P., NJ
Segal, Arthur M., PA
Seltzer, Joseph L., NJ
Shepp, Margaret A., NJ
Silbert, Paul J., NJ
Silver, Stephen C., PA
Smith, Arthur K., PA

Smith, J. Stanley, Jr., PA
Snyder, Robert C., PA
Sommer, Daniel G., NY
Spears, Brent Wood, PA
Spechler, Floyd F., NJ
Spigel, G. Thomas, NJ
Starrels, Michael E., PA
Starz, Terence W., PA
Stock, Merril, PA
Summers, Alan L., PA
Sussman, Robert L., PA
Tenney, Barbara L., MA
Timins, Julie E. K., NY
Tischler, Arthur S., PA
Topper, William H., PA
Trachtenberg, Jacob, NY
Urbanski, Timothy E., PA
Van Bavel, James O., NJ
Vizer, Mark B., PA
Waterhouse, Robert B., PA
Weber, David J., NJ
Weiss, Jeffrey C., PA
Wilson, Norman E., MA
Winans, Lewis E., PA
Wineburgh, George S., MD
Zeligman, Harvey D., PA

Student examinations in McClellan Hall.

On January 18, at the Second Session of the Ninety-second Congress of the United States, a resolution was passed by the Senate and House of Representatives recognizing the Thomas Jefferson University of Philadelphia as the first university in the United States to bear the full name of the third President (Fig. 415).

Commencement Exercises were held at the Academy of Music on June 9, and 194 M.D. degrees were conferred by President Peter A. Herbut. The address was delivered by George Alexander Heard, Chancellor of Vanderbilt University.

First honors were won by Fred David Lublin. These included the Alumni Prize, the Potter Prize and the Phillips Prize for academic excellence. Dr. Lublin proceeded to special training in neurology and biochemistry in New York and returned to Jefferson with appointments in both departments. He was promoted in 1986 to full Professor of Neurology. As Vice-Chairman of the Department and Director of the Division of Neuroimmunology he continued as Associate Professor of Biochemistry and Molecular Biology. His special interest was the clinical investigation of multiple sclerosis (Co-Director) with emphasis on its immunological aspects (Fig. 416).

Stanley R. Jacobs served his residency in Jefferson's Department of Rehabilitation Medicine and remained on its staff. He was the Department's representative on the staff of the Arthritis Center, advancing to Clinical Associate Professor (Fig. 417).

Ronald J. Wapner, following his training in obstetrics and gynecology, went on to the position of Director of the Division of Maternal-Fetal Medicine in Jefferson's Department, advancing to Associate Professor of both Obstetrics/Gynecology and Radiology. His studies in genetics and fetal diagnosis using ultrasound and chorionic villus sampling gained widespread recognition (Fig. 418).

Academically oriented graduates in the 1972 class included Michael L. Eisenmann who became Associate Clinical Professor of Plastic and Reconstructive Surgery at Baylor University College of Medicine, Houston, Texas. Larry H. Klein was Associate Professor of Pathology and Director of Pathology residency at Northeastern Ohio Universities College of Medicine. Arlen D. Meyers became Associate Professor of Otolaryngology at the University of Colorado Health Science Center. Joseph P. Horstmann was Adjunct Clinical Assistant Professor of Pathology and Cell Biology at Jefferson. Bruce L. Gewertz was Associate Professor of Cardiovascular Surgery at the University of Chicago. Stephen P. Flynn served as Clinical Assistant Professor of Family Medicine at Case Western Reserve University. Stephen W. Wong was Assistant Professor of Ophthalmology and Vice-Chairman of the Department at Temple University School of Medicine. William C. Boswell, Jr. was Vice-Chairman of the Department of Radioogy at the University of Southern California. Richard E. Brennan served as a Professor of Radiology at Jefferson. Lawrence R. Schiller was Assistant Professor of Medicine (Gastroenterology) at the University of Texas Southwestern Medical School, Dallas. Thomas E. Zukowski was Clinical Assiciate Professor of Medicine at Temple University School of Medicine. Irwin J. Hollander was Adjunct Clinical Assistant Professor of Pathology and Cell Biology at Jefferson while serving as Director of Pathology for Grand View Hospital, Sellersville. Paul A. Dainer became Assistant Professor of Medicine, University of Florida and hematologist-oncologist at its University Hospital, Jacksonville. Anthony A. Rooklin served as Director of Allergy and Immunology at Crozer-Chester Hospital and Assistant Professor of Pediatrics at Jefferson. James R. Roberts in 1981 was appointed Director of the University of New Mexico Emergency Medical Services and Assistant Professor of Emergency Medicine at the University's School of Medicine, Albuquerque. Philip C. Hoffman was Assistant Professor of Medicine

Ninety-second Congress of the United States of America

AT THE SECOND SESSION

*Begun and held at the City of Washington on Tuesday, the eighteenth day of January,
one thousand nine hundred and seventy-two*

Joint Resolution

To recognize Thomas Jefferson University, Philadelphia, Pennsylvania, as the
first university in the United States to bear the full name of the third President
of the United States.

Whereas the Jefferson Medical College of Philadelphia was founded
in 1824 during the lifetime of its namesake, Thomas Jefferson;
Whereas the Jefferson Medical College of Philadelphia was given a
university charter in 1838 by the State of Pennsylvania;
Whereas the Jefferson Medical College of Philadelphia has long represented and promoted the principles for which Thomas Jefferson
stood;
Whereas the Jefferson Medical College of Philadelphia officially
changed its name to the Thomas Jefferson University on July 1,
1969: Now, therefore, be it

*Resolved by the Senate and House of Representatives of the United
States of America in Congress assembled,* That the Thomas Jefferson
University, Philadelphia, Pennsylvania, be and is hereby recognized
as the first university in the United States to bear the full name of the
third President of the United States.

Carl Albert

Speaker of the House of Representatives.

Vice President of the United States and
President of the Senate.

Fig. 415.   Congressional Resolution recognizing the full name of Thomas Jefferson University (1972).

1972

(Hematology-Oncology) at the University of Chicago School of Medicine.

Beverly C. Borlandoe, trained in Boston and at the Hospital of the University of Pennsylvania, went on to the specialized practice of dermatopathology. She has been an active participant on the Executive Committee of the Jefferson Alumni Association.

Other graduates with academic appointments were: Robert C. Beckerman, Associate Professor of Pediatrics, Tulane Medical Center, New Orleans; Carolyn E. Bekes, Assistant Professor of Medicine, Robert Wood Johnson Medical School, Piscataway; Harry S. Cooper, Professor of Pathology, Gene H. Ginsberg and Charles A. Gordon, both Assistant Professors of Medicine, all at Hahnemann University; Barbara F. Danoff, Associate Professor of Radiology, Hospital of the University of Pennsylvania; Richard M. Donner, Associate Professor of Pediatrics, Temple University Hospital, Philadelphia; Norman Lindenmuth, Assistant Professor of Medicine, George Washington University Hospital, Washington; Robert McKay, Associate Professor of Anesthesiology, University of Alabama Medical Center, Birmingham; Cheryl M. Naulty, Assistant Professor of Pediatrics and John S. Naulty, Associate Professor of Anesthesiology at George Washington University Hospital, Washington, D.C.; Herbert N. Ochitill, Assistant Professor of Psychiatry, University of California Medical Center, San Francisco; Theodore R. Sunder, Associate Professor of Pediatrics, East Carolina School of Medicine, Greensboro; Martin Weisberg, Associate Professor of Obstetrics/Gynecology at Jefferson; and Rosemary E. Zuna, Assistant Professor of Pathology, S.U.N.Y., Stony Brook, New York.

CLASS OF 1972

Abelow, Gerald G., NJ	Caplan, Howard J., PA
Ackerman, Samuel K., NY	Carson, John N., III, PA
Ager, Steven A., NY	Caskey, Herbert T., PA
Andrias, Rosemary, PA	Castle, Jay I., PA
Andrulonis, Paul A., PA	Catanzaro, Robert J., FL
Bancks, Nicholas H., PA	Cleri, Dennis J., NY
Baron, Michael B., NJ	Cohen, Paul S., NJ
Baskoff, Joel D., PA	Connelly, Mary E., MA
Beckerman, Robert C., PA	Cooper, Harry S., PA
Behrend, A. James, PA	Cossrow, Joel I., PA
Bekes, Carolyn E., NJ	Crissinger, Howard P., PA
Bell, Richard T., NJ	D'Amico, Anna M., PA
Benjaminm, Wallace F., PA	D'Amico, Joseph J., DE
Berger, Gary W., NJ	Dainer, Paul M., NJ
Bernstein, Lawrence D., PA	Danoff, Barbara F., MD
Blaum, Louis C., Jr., PA	David, Cynthia L., NY
Blore, James P., Jr., PA	Deglin, Stuart M., PA
Bonanno, Richard J., NJ	DeNoia, Anthony P., NJ
Borlandoe, Beverly C., PA	DiGiacomo, Philip J., Jr., PA
Boswell, William D., Jr., PA	Doering, Richard A., NJ
Braconaro, Francis J., PA	Donner, Richard M., DE
Braverman, Gerald L., PA	Dorand, Rodney D., PA
Brennan, Richard E., PA	Dotsey, Michael T., PA
Bressler, William L., PA	Dowshen, Steven A., PA
Brooks, James A., Jr., PA	DuPont, Philip J., Jr., CT
Brown, Christopher L., NJ	Edinger, Gregory J., PA
Brubaker, William H., PA	Edwards, Rubin A., NY
Buechler, Mary F., NH	Ehrlich, Alexander E., NY
Burket, David G., OH	Eisemann, Michael L., NJ
Calabrese, Anthony J., NJ	Fenster, Martin M., PA

Fieo, Richard L., PA
Fiorelli, Richard C., MA
Fishbane, Marsha J., NY
Fitzgerald, Paul A., OH
Fitzig, Sanford, NJ
Flanigan, D. Preston, PA
Fleishman, Martin J., PA
Fliegelman, Martin J., PA
Flynn, Stephen P., CT
Fornace, Albert J., Jr., PA
Fremer, Stephen, PA
Friedman, Alan S., PA
Fticsar, James E., PA
Gardner, James L., II, PA
Garnet, Richard F., Jr., PA
Gauvin, Gregory P., NJ
Gewertz, Bruce L., PA
Ginsberg, Gene H., PA
Goeltsch, Robert E., PA
Goldberg, Stanley J., NJ
Golden, Michael P., PA

Goodman, Richard M., PA
Gordon, Charles A., NY
Grumet, Bernard A., PA
Hager, George W., III, NJ
Hay, James T., PA
Haytmanek, Craig T., PA
Hoffman, Philip C., PA
Hollander, Irwin J., NJ
Horstmann, Joseph P., PA
Howard, Lawrence J., PA
Hryshko, Frank G., PA
Hughes, David P., PA
Huhn, Wolfgang A., PA
Hyde, William J., PA
Interdonato, Anthony M., NJ
Jacobs, Robert A., NY
Jacobs, Stanley R., PA
Jaeger, Scott H., NJ
Jarmoszuk, Nicholas, NJ
Johnson, David S., SD
Josephs, Mark, PA

Fig. 416.   Fred D. Lublin (JMC '72), Professor of Neurology with special interest in multiple sclerosis.

Fig. 417.   Stanley R. Jacobs (JMC, '72), Clinical Associate Professor of Rehabilitation medicine.

1972

Judson, Susan C., PA
Juhasz, Alex B., PA
Kabler, Ronald L., PA
Klein, Larry H., PA
Krieger, Myles K., PA
Kunkle, Arthur A., III, PA
Laskas, John J., Jr., PA
Leibowitz, Helen A., PA
Lenetsky, Allan M., PA
Levinsky, Joseph J., NJ
Lewis, Michael R., PA
Lewkowicz, Charles John, PA
Lichtenfeld, Karen M., PA
Lindenmuth, Norman W., PA
Locke, Charles J., NC
Lublin, Fred D., PA
MacDonald, Warren F., Jr., PA
Mackell, Thomas E., PA
Mahoney, James W., PA
Marder, Carey M., PA

Marinari, Rosalie K., PA
Mattes, Jeffrey A., MI
McCoy, William H., III, PA
McCurdy, Richard R. P., PA
McKay, Robert D., NJ
Meyers, Arlen D., PA
Milander, John H., PA
Miller, John J., Jr., CA
Moss, Steven H., NJ
Mossbrook, Sandra Slade, PA
Naulty, Cheryl M., PA
Naulty, John S., PA
Nespoli, Anthony M., PA
Niemeyer, Richard, NJ
Nye, Glenn C., PA
O'Shaughnessy, Nicholas J., Jr., PA
Ochitill, Herbert N., PA
Olsen, Lawrence C., PUERTO RICO
Pfupajena, Howard T., RHODESIA
Pietragallo, Louis D., PA
Pitchon, Howard E., PA
Rayfield, Morton M., PA
Redka, James Wilson, PA
Redo, Frank L., PA
Rensimer, Wayne T., PA
Rhodes, Charles E., CT
Riley, Christopher S., PA
Rinaldi, Robert E., NJ
Roberts, James R., PA
Rodzvilla, John P., Jr., PA
Rooklin, Anthony R., PA
Rosch, Jeffrey M., PA
Roth, Michael S., PA
Russell, Edward R., PA
Ryan, James M., PA
Salkin, Marshall A., PA
Saltzman, Bruce S., PA
Schaffzin, Lawrence S., PA
Schiller, Lawrence R., PA
Schneyer, Barton L., PA
Schwartz, Richard P., MA
Seiler, C. Richard, NY
Shapiro, Joan H., PA
Shapiro, Marc Wells, NJ
Shiroff, Robert A., PA
Silberman, Carl M., PA
Skeist, Barry P., NY
Smith, Robin Edwards, NY
Smith, Stephen H., PA
Sonstein, Allen, PA
Speace, George F., II, PA
Staniels, Susan Edwards, NJ
Steward, Robert E., Jr., PA
Strum, Steven Charles, PA

Fig. 418. Ronald J. Wapner (JMC, '72), Associate Professor of Obstetrics/Gynecology and Radiology with special interest in genetics.

Sunder, Theodore R., PA
Szydlowski, Thaddeus R., PA
Talacki, Carol Ann, PA
Tenikat, Gail A., IL
Thomas, William J., Jr., PA
Tyler, John R., PA
Volk, Stephen A., NJ
Wall, James R., PA
Wapner, Ronald J., PA
Weiner, Fredric R., NJ

Weisberg, Martin, PA
Wixted, William M., NJ
Wolfgang, Timothy C., PA
Wong, Stephen W., HI
Wynne, Ernest C., III, NJ
Zabielski, Gerald C., PA
Zaret, Cheryl R., PA
Zlupko, George M., PA
Zukoski, Thomas E., PA
Zuna, Rosemary E., PA

Solis-Cohen Auditorium, Jefferson Alumni Hall.

~ 1973 ~

President Herbut conferred the M.D. degree on 182 graduates on June 8 at the Academy of Music. David E. Rogers, President of the Robert Wood Johnson Foundation, delivered the Address. Milton Packer, of the Pennsylvania State University Joint Program, received highest academic honors.

Bruce Evans Jarrell served his residency and fellowship at the Medical College of Virginia where he gained experience in dialysis procedures and transplantation surgery. He returned to Jefferson in 1980 as Director of the Transplant Program in the Department of Surgery. Within a few years, Jefferson's transplantation program was one of the largest in the United States. Dr. Jarrell advanced to Professor of Surgery and in 1988 was elected to the Society of University Surgeons (Fig. 419).

Eric John Bergquist, Ph.D. (University of Maryland) was appointed to the staff of the Department of Medicine following his residency with special research in infectious diseases. An effective and meticulous teacher, he quickly advanced to Clinical Associate Professor of Medicine and Assistant Professor of Microbiology. In 1987 he became Director of Infectious Diseases at Latrobe Hospital, Latrobe, Pennsylvania, a Jefferson affiliate (Fig. 420).

Anton Peter Kemps, winner of the Phillips Prize, embarked on a career in internal medicine and was Clinical Assistant Professor of Medicine at Rutgers University School of Medicine.

The increasing diversity of careers relative to the technological age of medicine was distinctly evident in this class. Benjamin Gerson, trained in pathology, advanced to Associate Professor at Harvard University and conducted sophisticated studies on Alzheimer's Disease; he later became Professor of Pathology at Boston University School of Medicine. Richard M. Sostowski was Associate Professor of Psychiatry, University of Medicine and Dentistry of New Jersey, Newark. Paul A. Bialas was Clinical Assistant Professor of Medicine, University of Pittsburgh School of

Medicine, while also Chief of Medicine at Warren General Hospital, Warren, Pennsylvania. Robert P. Good became Assistant Professor of Orthopaedic Surgery at Jefferson. Gary R. Fleisher was Director of the Emergency Laboratory at Children's Hospital of Philadelphia and Associate Professor of Pediatrics at the University of Pennsylvania School of Medicine. Frederick L. Kramer served for a time as Clinical Assistant Professor in the Departments of Radiology and Urology at Jefferson. David Shore became Chief of Biological and Chemical Factors Research Program in the Schizophrenic Research Branch of the National Institute of Mental Health. Jerry D. Glenn,

Fig. 419. Bruce E. Jarrell (JMC, '73), Professor of Surgery (Transplantation).

after a fellowship in surgery at National Cancer Institute, Bethesda, Maryland, became Professor in the Departments of Surgery and Microbiology at Milton S. Hershey Medical Center; he also edited the *Accident and Poison Prevention Newsletter* for the American Academy of Pediatrics. Kathleen W. McNicholas, winner of the Glasgow Award for Clinical Proficiency, was later appointed Assistant Professor of Cardiothoracic Surgery at the College of Medicine and Dentistry of New Jersey. Eric W. Blomain was appointed Assistant Professor of Surgery at Hershey Medical Center and Clinical Professor of Plastic and Maxillofacial Surgery at the University of Vir-

Fig. 420. Eric J. Bergquist (JMC, '73), Clinical Associate Professor of Medicine and Assistant Professor of Microbiology.

ginia Medical Center. Arthur W. Colbourn served as Clinical Assistant Professor of Medicine at Jefferson. Jeffrey J. Dekret became Clinical Associate Professor of Psychiatry and Human Behavior and Director of Inpatient Units at Jefferson. Joseph W. Sassani was Assistant Professor of Ophthalmology and Pathology at Hershey Medical Center. Norman H. Braslow was Clinical Assistant Professor of Medicine at Jefferson. Rodney A. Appell served as Assistant Professor of Urology and Director of the Urodynamics Unit at Louisiana State University School of Medicine, New Orleans. Peter C. Amadio became Assistant Professor of Orthopaedic Surgery at Mayo Graduate School of Medicine, Rochester; in 1988 he was elected to the Board of Directors of the American Association for Hand Surgery. Frank M. Taylor, III, became Clinical Assistant Professor of Pathology, University of South Florida, Tampa.

Other graduates with academic appointments included Robert G. Lahita, Associate Professor at Rockefeller University in Rheumatic and Immunologic Diseases; Philip M. Bernini, Associate Professor of Surgery, Dartmouth-Hitchcock Medical Center, Hanover; Susan Uhrmann Campbell, Assistant Professor of Pediatrics, University of Mississippi; Christopher M. Clark, Assistant Professor of Medicine, Duke University Medical Center, Durham; Frank Fromowitz, Assistant Professor of Pathology, S.U.N.Y. at Stony Brook; Marc R. Goldenberg, Instructor in Surgery at Jefferson; Roberta C. Kahn, Assistant Professor of Anesthesiology, New York University Medical Center; Harry R. Katz, Assistant Professor of Radiology, Hospital of the University of Pennsylvania; Paul D. Manganiello, Assistant Professor of Obstetrics/Gynecology, Dartmouth-Hitchcock Medical Center, Hanover; Milton Packer, Associate Professor of Internal Medicine, Mount Sinai Hospital, New York; Robert D. Rafal, Assistant Professor of Medicine, Brown University Affiliated Hospitals, Providence; Mary A. Resnik, Assistant Professor of Anesthesiology at Jefferson; and Fred A. Rosenblum, Instructor in Anesthesiology, also at Jefferson.

Abraham, Barry B., PA

Altman, Gary, PA

Altschuler, Edwin M., PA

Amadio, Peter C., NJ

Appell, Rodney A., PA

Bagby, Ramon H., PA

Banes, Dean Marie, PA

Barmach, Kenneth R., PA

Benner, John H., IV, PA

Bergquist, Erick J., PA

Berkel, Boyce N., CURACAO

Bernini, Philip M., NY

Bernstein, Marc L., NJ

Bialas, Paul A., PA

Binnick, Alan N., PA

Blanch, John J., PA

Bleiman, Bruce S., PA

Blomain, Eric W., PA

Borgia, Frank A., PA

Bradenham, Ben P., VA

Braslow, Norman H., PA

Brosof, Alan B., PA

Brown, Daniel J., PA

Brown, Earl H., PA

Brownstein, Gary M., PA

Bryant, Michael H., CO

Burger, Steven A., NJ

Car, Joseph R., NJ

Casdonte, Paul P., NJ

Cassel, John J., PA

Celani, Victor J., PA

Cerza, Paul F., NJ

Chain, William T., Jr., PA

Chalfant, Richard S., PA

Cianfrani, Peter M., PA

Clark, Christopher M., PA

Clemens, Thomas M., PA

Cochran, John W., IL

Cohen, Michael M., PA

Colatrella, Anthony M., NJ

Colbourn, Arthur W., DE

Constant, Fred G., NY

Cropper, Leland D., Jr., PA

Cunningham Thomas P., III, PA

Dekret, Jeffrey J., PA

DelVecchio, Leonard M., Jr., PA

DeMaria, Louis C., Jr., NJ

DiMarco, Ross F., Jr., PA

Dumin, Robert N., PA

Edeiken, Beth S., PA

Egan, Charles Frederick, Jr., DE

Engel, Steven M., PA

Falker, John M., PA

Feinstein, Michael A., PA

Ferroni, Joseph S., PA

Firth, Joanna R., PA

Fleisher, Gary R., PA

Forbes, William I., III, PA

Frazer, Joseph F., III, PA

Fromowitz, Frank B., NJ

Fuller, Philip S. B., MD

Gerson, Benjamin, PA

Gerstein, Gary, PA

Glenn, Jerry D., PA

Gold, Gordon R., PA

Goldenberg, Marc R., OH

Goldsmith, Charles L., PA

Goldstein, Larry E., PA

Good, Robert P., PA

Goore, Myrtle E., AL

Gordon, Barry, PA

Gordon, Richard S., PA

Gordon, Robert A., PA

Gorrie, Edward P., PA

Gottlieb, Fredric R., NJ

Gray, Lewis W., NJ

Greenberg, Richard D., PA

Greenhawt, Michael H., NJ

Grossman, Jerry J., PA

Gustainis, George J., PA

Hilton, E. Bruce, PA

Hoover, Alan D., PA

Hulick, Peter R., WI

Isaacson, Steven R., PA

Jacobs, Ivan H., NJ

Jacobs, Joseph A., PA

Jacoby, David A., PA

Jarrell, Bruce E., MD

Josselson, Alan S., NJ

Kahn, Roberta C., NY

Katz, Harry R., PA

Katz, Richard B., NY

Kelly, Edward A., Jr., PA

Kemps, Anton P., NJ

King, Joseph J., NJ

Kistler, Priscilla J., PA

Koizumi, Bradley H., HI

Korbonits, C. William, Jr., PA

Kramer, Frederick L., PA

Kuhn, Joseph A., DE

Kunsman, William E., PA
Lahita, Robert G., NJ
Layton, Thomas R., PA
Leach, Christopher L., NJ
Leis, Dean J., PA
Leisawitz, Elliott G., PA
Levin, Gary J., PA
Liggett, Charles L., Jr., TX
Mambu, Joseph F., PA
Manganiello, Paul D., NJ
Mann, Stephen C., PA
McCorvey, Roosevelt, FL
McGraw, James J., Jr., PA
McKeag, Kathleen A., PA
McLean, Lois G., PA
McNicholas, Kathleen W., PA
Meyers, Michael B., NY
Miller, Eugenia M., NJ
Miller, Laurence J., PA
Mullen, Joseph P., III, PA
Muller, Stephen P., NJ
Nicklas, Donald A., PA
Packer, Milton, PA
Palermo, Louis M., PA
Parks, Gilbert R., OK
Pascal, Mark S., NJ
Paul, David H., PA
Perry, Russell E., PA
Perzley, Richard I., NY
Porter, Lynne E., NY
Puhalla, Cyril M. J., PA
Quinlan, Michael F., PA
Rafal, Robert D., DE
Ratico, Helen L., PA
Resnik, Alan M., PA
Reuben, Mark S., PA
Reuss, Mary Lynne, PA
Robinson, Leslie S., PA
Rogers, Jean C., CT
Rogovitz, David M., PA
Rosen, Barry A., NY

Rosen, Jay S., PA
Rosenblum, Fred A., PA
Rosenshein, Marc S., PA
Ruggeri, Anthony Joseph, PA
Sabatini, John R., PA
Sassani, Joseph W., PA
Saylor, Richard F., PA
Schmerin, Michael J., PA
Schwartz, Daniel J., PA
Schwartz, David S., NY
Scotti, Daniel M., PA
Sebastianelli, John R., PA
Shaffer, Eugene M., PA
Shanfeld, Norman M., PA
Shore, David, PA
Smallwood, John T., PA
Smey, Paul, PA
Snead-Poellnitz, Stephanie Eileen, PA
Solow, Edward A., PA
Sostowski, Richard M., NJ
Souder, Ronald L., PA
Starks, Gregory C., MS
Starsnic-Resnik, Mary Ann, PA
Stelzer, Leo, Jr., NJ
Stern, Alan L., PA
Strout, Charles Denny, PA
Sullum, Stanford N., PA
Sundheim, John M., PA
Tatnall, Phillip R., Jr., DE
Taylor, Frank M., III, PA
Thomas, Joseph R., Jr., NJ
Tibone, James E., NY
Tracey, Kevin T., MA
Traupman, Arnold F., TX
Urmann, Susan B., DE
Wasserman, Emilian J. L., NY
Widome, Mark D., MD
Wisneski, Leonard A., PA
Wrigley, Michael S., PA
Zamostien, Paul S., PA
Zavodnick, Steven, PA

If you would not be forgotten, as soon as you are dead and rotten, either write things worth reading, or do things worth the writing.

Benjamin Franklin (1706–1790)

The year 1974 marked the Sesqui-Centennial of the founding of Jefferson Medical College. The event was observed in all University activities and the Alumni Bulletin carried articles summarizing Jefferson's history. On March 1 the Alumni Association celebrated with a Sesquicentennial Dinner at the Union Leaque (Fig. 421).

The Sesquicentennial focused on Jefferson's present and future including articles in the student yearbook, *The Clinic*, discussing plans for a new hospital building and teaching center as well as a description of the new Health Sciences Center just opened this year. The Center occupied the twenty-two story building at Ninth and Sansom Streets recently acquired from the Philadelphia Electric Company. Intended mainly as an ambulatory care center and medical office build-

ing, it was quickly fully functional. Its uses gradually changed as other office space was developed for the rapidly increasing number of staff physicians. The facility was later largely given over to the College of Allied Health Sciences and became popularly known as the Edison Building (Fig. 422).

As a Sesquicentennial Gift to Jefferson, the Alumni Association commissioned a processional composed by Burle Marx to be played on all ceremonial occasions.

At the Commencement held June 8 at the Academy of Music, 192 graduates were awarded M.D. degrees by President Peter A. Herbut. Highest honors were won by Steven R. Peikin who served his internship and residency in medicine at the University of California, San Fran-

Fig. 421.   Sesquicentennial Alumni Dinner at Union League, March 1, 1974.

cisco. From 1976 to 1978 he was a Clinical Associate in Digestive Diseases at the National Institutes of Health, Bethesda, Maryland. He returned to Jefferson as Assistant Professor of Medicine in 1979, became Associate Professor in 1982, and carried on important research and teaching in gstroenterology. Dr. Peikin also served a term on the Board of Trustees of Thomas Jefferson University from 1977 to 1979 (Fig. 423).

Barbara F. Atkinson, trained in Pathology at the Hospital of the University of Pennsylvania, became Professor and Chairman of the Department of Pathology at Medical College of Pennsylvania. In 1989 she was elected to its Board of Directors (Fig. 424).

Kathleen F. Cheyney received the prize in anesthesiology but went on to surgical training. She was in the fortuitous position of first assistant surgeon at George Washington University Hospital for the emergency surgery on President

Fig. 422.   Edison Building (1974).

1974

Ronald Reagan on March 30, 1981. The operating surgeon was Joseph M. Giordano (JMC, '67, Fig. 404).

Bartley P. Griffith prepared for a career in transplantation surgery with six years of residency and an American Heart Association Research Fellowship. He joined the surgical staff of the University of Pittsburgh School of Medicine, becoming Associate Professor and proceeding to develop new techniques for the handling of organs for transplantation which contributed signally to the success of one of the most active programs in the United States (Fig. 425).

The increasing diversity of medical progress was evidenced by the numerous 1974 graduates who went on to academic associations. James A. Kenning, who won the Potter Prize, was trained in neurosurgery and became Clinical Assistant Professor at Temple University School of Medi-

cine. John H. Brown became Assistant Professor of Surgery, Uniformed Services University of Health Sciences and Chief of the Maxillofacial Stabilization Team; he later engaged in private practice. Michael A. Kutcher in 1988 was appointed Associate Professor of Medicine (Cardiology) in the Bowman-Gray School of Medicine, Winston-Salem, North Carolina. Also in 1988, John P. Lubicky was appointed Chief of Shriner's Hospital for Crippled Children, Chicago, and Associate Professor of Orthopaedic Surgery at Rush Medical College. Stephen B. Lichtenstein, who won the Prize in Ophthalmology, became Assistant Professor of Ophthalmology at Jefferson and Co-Director of Emergency Services at Wills Eye Hospital. Marilyn Manco McDonald (Manco-Johnson), a participant in the Pennsylvania State University—Jefferson accelerated program and winner of the

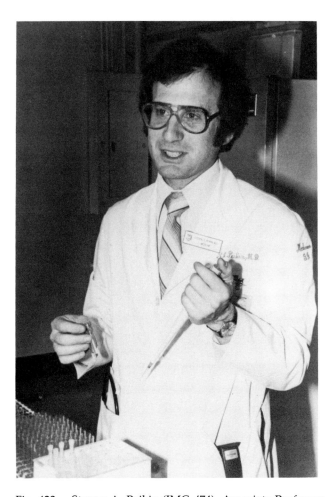

Fig. 423.   Steven A. Peikin (JMC, '74), Associate Professor of Medicine (Gastroenterology).

Fig. 424.   Barbara F. Atkinson (JMC, '74), Chairman of Pathology, Medical College of Pennsylvania.

1974

Pediatrics Prize, became Associate Professor of Pediatrics at the University of Colorado School of Medicine. John J. Brooks developed skills in immunohistochemistry and advanced to Associate Professor of Pathology at the University of Pennsylvania School of Medicine. Bruce C. Berger, trained in cardiology, became Assistant Professor of Medicine at the University of Pennsylvania School of Medicine. Lee D. Griffith was Assistant Professor of Surgery at the University of California Medical Center, San Diego. Thomas L. Matulewski was appointed Chief of Surgery at Haverford Hospital and Assistant Professor at Hahnemann University. Jay D. Amsterdam was Adjunct Associate Professor of Psychiatry and Human Behavior at Jefferson, and Thomas J. Phelan became Clinical Assistant Professor of Surgery also at Jefferson. Barry S. Stein was appointed Director of Oncology in the Department

Fig. 425. Bartley P. Griffith (JMC, '74), Associate Professor of Surgery (transplantation) at University of Pittsburgh.

of Urology at Brown University School of Medicine, Providence. Jay G. Weisberg was Clinical Assistant Professor of Psychiatry and Human Behavior and Louis T. Broad, Clinical Assistant Professor of Medicine, both at Jefferson. John Hermanovich, Jr. became Assistant Professor of Medicine at Hershey Medical Center. Bruce P. Meinhard was Associate Professor of Orthopaedics, State University of New York at Stonybrook. David A. Brent received a Career Development Award from the National Institutes of Health and was Assistant Professor of Psychiatry at the University of Pittsburgh School of Medicine. Arnold J. Wills became Associate Professor of Urology at George Washington Medical Center. R. Brooke Jeffrey, Jr. was serving as Associate Professor of Radiology at the University of California School of Medicine, San Francisco. Robert J. Wasnick was Director of Pediatric Urology, Hospital of the State University of New York, Stonybrook and Assistant Professor at New York University. James D. Plumb, trained in Family Medicine at Jefferson, joined the staff and advanced to Assistant Professor. Stephen H. Whitenack also trained at Jefferson and went on to serve as Attending Surgeon in charge of Thoracic Surgery at Chestnut Hill Hospital and Assistant Professor at Jefferson. Joseph R. Berger became Associate Professor of Neurology and Internal Medicine at the University of Miami (Florida) School of Medicine; in 1985 he received the Puff Award for Teaching Excellence. Howard G. Hughes was made President of the Geisinger Health Plan, Geisinger Medical Center in Danville, Pennsylvania, in 1987; he was a Past President of the Pennsylvania Chapter of the American College of Emergency Medicine. Jay S. Schinfeld, winner of the Obstetrics/Gynecology Prize, was Chief of Endocrinology/Infertility at Abington Memorial Hospital and Associate Professor at Temple University School of Medicine. Thomas J.A. Lehman was Chief of the Division of Pediatric Rheumatology at the Hospital for Special Surgery, New York, and Associate Professor of Medicine at Cornell University School of Medicine. Robert L. Breckenridge, Jr., having completed training in Pathology at Mayo Clinic, became a member of a group of pathologists in

Kansas City, serving ten hospitals in Northwestern Missouri.

Other graduates with academic connections included: Stanley J. Geyer, Associate Professor of Pathology, University of Washington Hospitals, Seattle; Ann P. Guillot, Assistant Professor of Pediatrics, Medical Center Hospital of Vermont, Burlington; Kenneth E. Jaffe, Assistant Professor of Psychiatry, Tufts University School of Medicine; David Karasick and his brother Stephen, both Associate Professors of Radiology at Jefferson; Thomas A. Klotz, Associate Professor of Medicine, Los Angeles County USC Medical Center; William D. Lawrence, Assistant Professor of Medicine, S.U.N.Y. at Buffalo; Mark A. Pearlman, Assistant Professor of Pediatrics, University of Medicine and Dentistry, Newark; Anna T. Sasaki, Assistant Professor of Medicine, University of Oregon Medical School, Portland; Linda M. Sundt, Assistant Professor of Anesthesiology at Jefferson; and Michael L. Podolsky, Professor of Obstetrics/Gynecology at Jefferson.

CLASS OF 1974

Agnello, Joseph S., Jr., NY
Amsterdam, Jay D., PA
Angelo, Alice A., DE
Atkinson, Barbara F., PA
Baez, Steve A., PA
Becker, Ward G., PA
Berger, Bruce C., PA
Berger, Joseph R., PA
Blumberg, Albert L., PA
Breckenridge, Robert L., Jr., PA
Brent, David A., PA
Broad, Louis T., PA
Brooks, John J., Jr., PA
Brown, Joel Martin, OH
Brown, John H., PA
Burt, Theresa A., PA
Campbell, Tom E., PA
Caputo, Larry A., PA
Carunchio, Michael J., Jr., PA
Cattie, John V., PA
Chadwick, Neal C., PA
Cheyney, Kathleen F., MD
Clark, David G., UT
Cochran, Thomas P., III, PA
Cornish, James W., PA
Crispino, Richard D., PA
Crowley, Kevin D., DE
Danoff, Burton H., NY
Decker, Steven E., IN
DeHart, Scott M., PA
Dekutoski, John T., PA
Denlinger, Lee E., PA
Dershaw, D. David, PA
Devereux, Linda, PA
DiCuccio, William A., II, PA
DiPhillips, Raymond P., PA
Dougherty, Anthony C., DE
Drass, Edward F., PA
Ellsweig, Bruce A., PA
Ennis, Len E., PA
Evans, Richard A., TX

Falcone, Domenico, PA
Figgs, Barbara L., DE
Filstein, Allen B., PA
Forsyth, Alice J., PA
Forsyth, Thomas, Jr., PA
Freedman, Samuel P., PA
Freeman, Tiyi R., NY
Fried, Stanley M., PA
Gardner, Robert W., PA
Gaspari, Raymond J., PA
Gersh, Douglas B., NY
Geyer, Stanley J., PA
Gibbons, William J., PA
Gillis, Victoria A., PA
Glenn, John F., III, DE
Godfrey, Michael Paul, PA
Gordin, Stephen J., PA
Granda, Antonio M., DE
Greenspan, Mitchell M., PA
Griffith, Bartley P., PA
Griffith, Lee D., PA
Griger, Christine A., PA
Guidon, Mariotta F., PA
Guillot, Ann P., GA
Gullotti, Michael J., PA
Habecker, Elizabeth T., PA
Hamsher, C. David, PA
Harding, David B., PA
Harrold, Leslie S., OH
Hauser, Raymond J., PA
Heiser, Mark S., PA
Hermanovich, John, Jr., PA
Hobbs, Robert E., PA
Hoch, Bradley R., PA
Horst, H. Mathilda, PA
Hughes, Howard G., PA
Hunt, Clifton H., DE
Jaffe, Kenneth E., PA
Jaffe, Richard L., PA
Jeffrey, R. Brooke, Jr., PA
Jeryan, Edward M., PA

Johnson, Robert M., DE
Kanofsky, Jacob D., PA
Kaplan, Bertram D., FL
Karasick, David, PA
Karasick, Stephen, PA
Karlavage, John J., PA
Kaskey, Gary B., PA
Kelton, Franklin C., Jr., PA
Kenning, James A., PA
Kessel, James W., WV
Klotz, Thomas A., PA
Kluchinski, Barbara J., PA
Kobialka, Walter M., PA
Kohn, Jeffrey K., PA
Kucer, Frank T., PA
Kuchler, Joseph A., NJ
Kuhlmann, Elizabeth, NJ
Kutcher, Michael A., NC
Lampert, Scott I., PA
Laury, William L., PA
Lawrence, William D., PA
Lehman, Thomas J. A., CA
Leichter, Larry R., NJ
Leo, Michael C., PA
Lewis, Kenneth S., NY
LeWitt, Michael H., CT
Lichtenstein, Stephen B., PA
Lindes, Conrad, PA
Lubicky, John P., PA
Lupold, Georgetta D., PA
Mapow, Larry S., PA
Marencik, James G., PA
Martell, Stephen P., PA
Matulewski, Thomas J., PA
Maxin, Charles W., PA
McClinton, Cedric W., PA
McDonald, Marilyn Manco, PA
Meinhard, Bruce P., NJ
Merrell, Raymond W., PA
Meyer, Allen E., NJ
Meyer, Willaim A., Jr., DE
Meyer, William H., PA
Miller, William I., PA
Mitchell, Perry L., DE
Molinaro, Anthony D., Jr., PA
Mollen, Martin D., PA
Morton, John P., CA
Nardella, Guy M., Jr., PA
Nielsen, Marvin E., Jr., AK
Olney, William Bert, FL
Patterson, Ronald J., GUYANA
Pearl, Frank J., PA
Pearlman, Mark A., PA
Peikin, Steven R., PA
Pellegrini, Vincent A., PA

Peruzzi, Robert V., Jr., PA
Phelan, Thomas I., PA
Pholeric, John F., Jr., PA
Plumb, James D., PA
Podolsky, Michael L., DE
Roberts, Alan K., PA
Robinson, C. Anita, MD
Rogers, Jonathan J., PA
Rosenfeld, Joel C., PA
Sasaki, Anna W., DE
Savage, Kenneth L., PA
Schinfeld, Jay S., PA
Schulman, William M., NJ
Schwartz, Ira, PA
Seaver, Philip R., Jr., NJ
Shapiro, Jeryl R., PA
Share, Edward J., NY
Shrom, Stanley H., PA
Shugar, Gary L., PA
Silver, Bruce G., PA
Sklaroff, Robert B., PA
Smoyer, Ronald L., PA
Soraruf, L. Peter, IV, PA
St. John, Thomas Arthur, Jr., NJ
Stein, Barry S., PA
Stevenson, Susan M., PA
Stotler, Charles W., PA
Suchman, James Frederick, PA
Sundt, Linda M., PA
Thorpe, George E., NJ
Tomichek, Richard C., PA
Trabin, Jay R., PA
Vanett, Bruce B., PA
Vasta, Alfred G., PA
Vazquez, Guillermo J., PUERTO RICO
Venit, Bethany A., PA
Vickerman, Charles E., Jr., PA
Wallace, Richard P., PA
Wasnick, Robert J., PA
Weidner, Donald R., PA
Weinstein, Steven L., NY
Weisberg, Jay G., PA
Wenner, Steven M., PA
Wenof, Michael, PA
Whitenack, Stephan H., NY
Wighton, Harold B., NJ
Williams, Donald B., PA
Willis, Arnold J., PA
Wills, Reginald D., PA
Wirts, Steven B., PA
Worhacz, Walter, PA
Wrenn, Walter F., III, PA
Yim, Ernie M. S., HI
Young, Dennis M., DE
Zamore, Steven M., NY
Zaret, Bruce S., PA

In the Senate of the United States

November 18, 1974

——————

Whereas *Thomas Jefferson University of Philadelphia, Pennsylvania, celebrates its one hundred and fiftieth anniversary in 1974 and is a totally health-related, medically-oriented university, comprising three colleges and a teaching hospital; and*

Whereas *the University's Jefferson Medical College, founded in 1824, is the largest private medical college in the Nation; and*

Whereas *Jefferson encouraged graduate studies in the basic medical sciences as early as 1941 and consolidated these into a College of Graduate Studies in 1969; and*

Whereas *in 1967 Jefferson chartered a College of Allied Health Sciences to provide both academic and clinical education in the health professions and occupations; and*

Whereas *Thomas Jefferson University has committed its resources and the talents of its faculty to care of the sick and injured through an infirmary that opened in May 1825 and subsequently through Thomas Jefferson University Hospital that first opened its doors in 1877: Now, therefore, be it*

Resolved, *That the Senate congratulates Thomas Jefferson University on its one hundred and fiftieth anniversary, commends the faculty, staff, employees, and graduates of its colleges and hospital on their dedication, vision, and exemplary professionalism, and extends to them every good wish for continued growth and impact on the health care needs of this Nation.*

Sec. 2. That a certified and enrolled copy of this resolution introduced by Mr. Hugh Scott be transmitted to Dr. Peter A. Herbut, President of Thomas Jefferson University, Philadelphia, Pennsylvania.

Attest:

Secretary.

This year saw completion of a 400-car University parking facility on the north side of Locust Street between Tenth and Eleventh. The architecture was artfully designed to be unobtrusive, with two low-level buildings divided by a wide elevated walkway. It preserved an open area (Scott Plaza) for trees and the Gross Statue (Fig. 426). Together with the Martin Nurses' Residence, Scott Library and Orlowitz Hall it completed Jefferson's buildings on the city block between Walnut and Locust and Tenth and Eleventh Streets.

On June 6, the M.D. degree was conferred in the Academy of Music upon 218 graduates by President Peter A. Herbut. Dr. Herbut also delivered the Address that year, which ironically was his last to attend because of his sudden death the following March.

Geno J. Merli, Clinical Associate Professor of Medicine, became Director of the Division of Internal Medicine at Jefferson in 1987. He conducted significant studies on the prevention and treatment of venous thrombosis. Also, as Associate Professor of Rehabilitation Medicine, he developed workshops on spinal cord injury (Fig. 427).

Robert T. Sataloff became a Professor of Otolaryngology. Holding a Doctor of Musical Arts degree, he specialized in vocal therapy with innovative care for professional singers. He also became outstanding in his concerts at Jefferson featuring orchestral and choral groups (Fig. 428).

Fig. 426.   Scott Plaza and University Parking Facility (1975).

Donald L. Myers took his neurological surgery residency at Jefferson, with additional training in the use of the laser, surgery of the ear and skull base, and advanced trauma life support. He became an Assistant Professor in the Department of Neurological Surgery and Director of the Neurosensory Intensive Care Unit from 1980 to 1985 (Fig. 429).

Among the graduates the trend into academic appointments increased. Some of the positions occupied in institutions other than Jefferson were as follows: Winslow J. Borkowski, Jr. (son of W.J. Borkowski, Honorary Associate Professor of Neurology at Jefferson, JMC, '43, Fig. 297) who followed in his father's footsteps to become a neurologist at the Alfred I. DuPont Institute in Wilmington and subsequently Assistant Professor of Pediatric Neurology at the University of

Nebraska; Robert E. Wall, Chairman of the Department of Obstetrics and Gynecology at an affiliate of the University of Colorado Health Science Center; Jonathan Kay, Assistant Professor of Surgery in the Department of Anesthesiology at the Medical College of Wisconsin; Marilyn Kay, Assistant Professor in the Department of Ophthalmology at the Medical College of Wisconsin; Bradley D. Wong, Assistant Professor of Surgery at the University of Hawaii School of Medicine; David P. Mayer, Clinical Assistant Professor of Radiology at Temple University School of Medicine; Richard S. Jackson, Assistant Professor of Surgery in the University of Vermont Medical School; Gary S. Clark, Associate Professor of Clinical Rehabilitation Medicine at the University of Rochester; Donald E. Schepps, Assistant Clinical Professor of Surgery at the Uni-

Fig. 427. Geno J. Merli (JMC, '75), Clinical Associate Professor of Medicine and Director of the Division of Internal Medicine.

Fig. 428. Robert T. Sataloff (JMC, '75), Professor of Otolaryngology and Doctor of Musical Arts.

versity of California, Davis; Edward S. Schulman, Assistant Professor of Medicine at Hahnemann University; Ellis R. Levin Assistant Professor of Medicine at the University of California, Irvine; John R. Hain, Clinical Instructor in Pathology, University of Pittsburgh; Laurence R. Plumb, faculty member in Family Practice Department of the University of Buffalo Medical School; John H. Kavanagh, Jr., Assistant Professor in the Department of Developmental Therapeutics and Gynecology at the University of Nebraska Medical School; Richard H. Bennett, Associate Professor of Neurology at Temple University; Robert H. Gordon, Staff of the Medical College of Pennsylvania, with specialty in rheumatology; Paul J. Ruschak, Clinical Assistant Professor of Dermatology at the University of Pittsburgh; Anne P. Hench, Clinical Activities Coordinator for the National Health Service

Fig. 429. Donald L. Myers (JMC, '75), Assistant Professor of Neurosurgery and Instructor in Radiology.

Corps in Health Region II, encompassing New York, New Jersey, Puerto Rico and the Virgin Islands; Craig F. LaForce, Director of Pediatric Allergy in the Department of Pediatrics, University of North Carolina; Victor L. Woo, Clinical Assistant Professor of Radiology at the University of California, San Diego; Jerry M. Belsh, Assistant Professor of Neurology at the College of Medicine and Dentistry of New Jersey; Robert R. Houston, Assistant Professor of Pathology at the University of Cincinnati; and William A. Spahn, Assistant Professor of Medicine at Wright State University in Dayton.

Some members who obtained academic appointments at Jefferson were: William A. Bierman, Clinical Assistant Professor of Medicine; Howard E. Goody, Instructor in Dermatology; Eugene P. Hughes, Jr., Clinical Assistant Professor of Surgery; John E. Hocutt, Jr., Clinical Assistant Professor in Family Medicine at Jefferson affiliate, Wilmington Medical Center; William A. Auritt, Instructor in Pediatrics (Our Lady of Lourdes affiliate); Theodore A. Feinstein, Instructor in Obstetrics and Gynecology; Craig L. Muetterties, Instructor in Anesthesiology; Alexander G. Paterson, Instructor in Family Medicine; John T. Santarlas, Instructor in Family Medicine (Latrobe Hospital affiliate); John F. Nansted, Jr., Clinical Assistant Professor of Medicine at Jefferson's affiliate, Lankenau; Irena O. Stolar, Instructor in Medicine; and Randall F. Maguire, Adjunct Clinical Assistant Professor of Pathology and Cell Biology.

Additional members in academic medicine were: Paul D. Berguson, Assistant Professor of Anesthesiology, New York University Medical Center; Gerard T. Berry, Assistant Professor of Pediatrics and Robert Y. Gumnit, Assistant Professor of Anesthesiology, both at the Hospital of the University of Pennsylvania; Lawrence J. Gibel, Assistant Professor of Surgery, University of New Mexico Affiliated Hospitals, Albuquerque; Alan Goldberg, Assistant Professor of Internal Medicine, Leonard Grossman, Assistant Professor of Obstetrics/Gynecology, and Mark J. Pello, Assistant Professor of Surgery, all at Robert Wood Johnson Medical School, Piscataway; Gail Goldstein, Assistant Professor of Anesthesiology, U.C.L.A. Hospital Medical Center, Los An-

1975

geles; Samuel C. Hughes, Assistant Professor of Anesthesiology, University of California Medical Center, San Francisco; Jeanne M. Pelensky, Assistant Professor of Physical Medicine and Rehabilitation, Temple University Hospital; and Mark Weissmann, Assistant Professor of Pediatrics, George Washington University Hospital, Washington.

CLASS OF 1975

Agro, Angelo S., PA
Anthony, Christopher H., PA
Auritt, William A., PA
Azar, David J., PA
Bader, William, PA
Baker, Robert B., NJ
Barger, Geoffrey R., PA
Beatty, Lawrence T., PA
Belsh, Jerry M., PA
Bennett, Richard H., PA
Berger, Stuart M., PA
Bergum, Allen Anton, PA
Berguson, Paul D., PA
Berlin, Howard F., PA
Berry, Gerard T., PA
Besozzi, Michael J., TX
Bierlein, Alan H., PA
Bierman, William A., PA
Blutstein, Richard N., PA
Borgelt, Bruce B., PA
Borkowski, Winslow J., Jr., PA
Branconi, Joseph M., PA
Brodie, Gordon L., NY
Browning, Clifford, PA
Brunt, Margaret Jean, NJ
Cain, Robert A., NJ
Caruso, Anthony P., NY
Catherwood, Edward, PA
Clark, Gary S., PA
Clinton, David L., DE
Coghlan, William P., Jr., PA
Cohen, Terry B., PA
Conrad, Stephen D., DE
Cook, Lawrence J., PA
Daniels, Warren C., NJ
Delehanty, James C., PA
Dembert, Mark L., PA
Detrick, Kenneth J., PA
DiSaverio, Joseph, PA
Doherty, John H., Jr., PA
Domanski, John D., NJ
Durkan, Gerald P., PA
Ekman, Linda M., NJ
Ellenberger, Thomas R., Jr., PA
England, Kent B., PA
Engle, Edward A., PA

Etter, Mark S., PA
Evans, Bradley D., PA
Factor, Mitchell L., PA
Feinstein, Theodore A., PA
Fields, Robert S., NJ
Flacco, Michael P., PA
Gellerman, Douglas R., NY
Gibel, Lawrence J., NY
Gibson, Barbara B., NJ
Giletto, Joseph Basil, PA
Ginsberg, Lawrence W., PA
Glinka, Steven J., PA
Gold, Alan C., PA
Goldberg, Alan C., PA
Goldberg, Paul E., PA
Goldstein, Gail S., PA
Goldstein, Irwin S., PA
Good, Vance A., PA
Goody, Howard E., PA
Gordon, Richard D., PA
Gordon, Robert H., PA
Gray, Herbert E., III, CT
Griffin, Michael J., MI
Griggs, John E., Jr., DE
Grossman, Leonard, PA
Gumnit, Robert Y., PA
Hain, John R., PA
Hall, Kathryn L., PA
Hall, Robert H., PA
Hallock, Geoffrey G., PA
Harden, Wesley R., III, PA
Harris, Robert A., PA
Hayes, Arthur C., PA
Hench, Anne P., PA
Hocutt, John E., Jr., DE
Horowitz, Steven L., NY
Houston, Robert R., Jr., PA
Hughes, Eugene P., Jr., PA
Hughes, Samuel C., Jr., DE
Hurvitz, Lawrence M., PA
Jackson, Richard S., Jr., NH
Jacobson, Nathan A., PA
Jezyk, David S., DE
Johnson, Steven C., DE
Jones, James M., DE
Kamsler, David M., PA

Kates, Jonathan L., PA
Kavanagh, John J., Jr., CO
Kay, Jonathan, DE
Kay, Marilyn C., NJ
Kerschbaum, Wesley E., PA
Kilcullen, Michael J., PA
Kitei, William J., PA
Klacsmann, Peter G., DE
Kolker, Steven A., PA
Korey, Joseph J., Jr., PA
Kuhns, Karen F., PA
Kundrat, Mary Louise, PA
LaForce, Craig F., PA
Levin, Ellis R., PA
Lewis, Gregory L., PA
Linton, Dale, PA
Lipsitz, Hyman David, PA
Lowenstein, Edward Howard, NJ
Luscombe, Susan, PA
Maguire, Randall F., NJ
Malachesky, Thomas Michael, PA
Mandell, Herbert E., PA
Manser, Jeannne I., PA
Marcello, Richard P., DE
Martin, Gerald B., MD
Matsko, Janine A., PA
Maxwell, Thomas J., DE
Mayer, David P., NY
McGeary, James E., PA
McGowan, John M., PA
McJunkin, Cheryl L., DE
Merli, Geno J., PA
Mersky, Martin R., DE
Miller, Fred H., PA
Mirenda, William M., Jr, PA
Mizianty, Thomas J., PA
Moore, David H., PA
Morningstar, Carol A., PA
Morningstar, Phyllis Jane, PA
Morris, Wayne S., PA
Mory, Stephen C., PA
Muetterties, Craig L., DE
Myers, Donald L., PA
Nansteel, John F., Jr., PA
Nasca, Thomas J., NY
Neff, Allan J., PA
Oddi, Bernard D., PA
Owens, Gary M., DE
Paist, Stanley S., III, PA
Palace, William G., NJ
Pancerev, C. Paul, PA
Parr, Shelley J., NJ
Paterson, Alexander G., PA
Pedicino, Alexander R., PA

Pelensky, Jeanne M., PA
Pello, Mark J., NJ
Penater, Frank R., NJ
Pepper, L. Douglas, PA
Perilstein, Michael D., PA
Piccini, Paul A., NJ
Pirigyi, Paul R., PA
Pitone, Randall E., FL
Plumb, Laurence R., NJ
Pratt, Stephen G., PA
Rauth, John D., Jr., PA
Rayner, Mark E., NJ
Rogers, John P., PA
Romanzo, George M., PA
Rominger, John M., PA
Rosenthal, Gary I., PA
Rosner, William F., PA
Ruschak, Paul J., PA
Rutenberg, Joel M., NJ
Salkowe, Jerry, PA
Santarlas, John T., NJ
Sataloff, Robert T., PA
Scharff, Norbert D., NJ
Schepps, Donald E., PA
Schlaff, Zachary, PA
Schlechter, William G., PA
Schulman, Edward S., PA
Seelaus, Jere F., NY
Sexton, Darryl M., NJ
Sharps, Lewis S., PA
Sherman, Virica J., KY
Silfen, Sheryl L., NJ
Simpson, Joan W., PA
Sitelman, Arthur, PA
Smith, Crawford C., PA
Sokol, Joel H., PA
Spohn, William A., PA
Sprague, Thomas H., PA
St. Andre, Arthur C., NJ
Staiman, Keith M., PA
Sternberg, Marc E., PA
Stewart, Michael P., PA
Stolar, Irena O., PA
Stratt, Bruce J., PA
Strehle, Kenneth R., PA
Thayer, David O., PA
Thompson, Kennith, DE
Townend, Stephen C., PA
Turner, Bruce C., DE
Valentine, Lee S., PA
Van Bolden, Vernon, II, TX
Van Summern, John M., PA
Van Vranken, Bruce H., CA
Vander Hulst, John C., PA

Veve, R. Theodore, PUERTO RICO
Vlasca, Gladi E., PA
Wall, Paul M., PA
Wall, Robert E., PA
Wei, Nathan, PA
Weiner, Michael Z., PA
Weiss, David L., NY
Weiss, Justin F., PA
Weissman, Mark I., PA

Wertheimer, Marc J., PA
West, C. Forrest, III, PA
West, Douglas H., OH
Williams, Edward S., DE
Wong, Bradley D., HAWAII
Woo, Victor L., PA
Zager, Mark A., PA
Zegel, Harry G., PA

William F. Kellow, M.D., D.Sc., L.H.D., Dean of Medical College (1967–81)

Jefferson's increasing size for education and health care required additional convenient and comfortable living accommodations at reasonable rents for the University's students and personnel. This was met by opening of the Barringer Residence Hall in this year at the southeast corner of Tenth and Walnut Streets (Fig. 430). It contained 138 apartments for approximately 420 occupants with layouts based upon those in the Orlowitz Residence. This project honored two generations of Jefferson Trustees. The first was the late Daniel Moreau Barringer who had served on the Board from 1902 to 1936. The second was his son, Brandon Barringer, who had been a Life Trustee succeeding his father in 1936. The latter as Chairman of the Finance Committee had kept Jefferson on a sound financial basis for several decades.

In 1976 the Winged Ox Column was erected on the south side of Walnut Street between Orlowitz Hall and the Scott Library (Fig. 431). The winged ox, the ancient symbol for both physicians and sculptors, was erected as a 1,400-pound bronze statue on a platform subtended by a Trajan Column on which a spiral contained names of 50 personages who had made outstanding contributions to medicine. Five of these were Jefferson Alumni (J. Marion Sims, Samuel D. Gross, Carlos Finlay, Chevalier Jackson and John H. Gibbon, Jr.).

At the Commencement on June 11 in the Academy of Music the M.D. degree was conferred upon 217 graduates by the interim President, Mr. George M. Norwood (Fig. 442).

Among the many graduates who subsequently

Fig. 430.   Barringer Residence Hall (1976).

obtained academic appointments on the Jefferson Faculty were: John R. Cohn, Clinical Assistant Professor of Medicine and Clinical Assistant Professor of Pediatrics (pulmonary medicine, allergy and immunology); Gary A. Emmett, Clinical Assistant Professor of Pediatrics; Linda D. Green, Clinical Assistant Professor of Pediatrics (at Jefferson affiliate, Mercy Catholic Medical Center); John D. Blannett, Clinical Assistant Professor of Medicine (also at Mercy Catholic); Robert S. Zibelman, Clinical Assistant Professor of

Psychiatry and Human Behavior; Christopher M. Frauenhoffer, Adjunct Clinical Assistant Professor of Pathology and Cell Biology; Amy N. Sukati, Instructor in Obstetrics and Gynecology; Dean L. Winslow, Clinical Associate Professor of Medicine; Michael E. Stillabower, Instructor in Medicine; David E. Nutter, Clinical Assistant Professor of Psychiatry and Human Behavior; Valerie A. West (Urian), Instructor in Medicine; Joanna Miller, Instructor in Obstetrics and Gynecology; Philip Nimoityn (Fig. 432), Instructor

Fig. 431.   Winged Ox Column (1976).

in Medicine (Cardiology); Steven J. Glass, Adjunct Clinical Assistant Professor of Psychiatry and Human Behavior; Richard A. Jacoby, Clinical Associate Professor of Dermatology as well as Pathology and Cell Biology; Andrew J. Levin, Instructor in Ophthalmology; Paul J. Hoyer, Instructor in Pathology and Cell Biology; Frederic B. Kremer, Clinical Assistant Professor of Ophthalmology; Robert G. McCairns Jr. (Fig. 433), Instructor in Surgery (Cardiothoracic); David A. Allan, Instructor in Medicine; Ted M. Parris, Clinical Assistant Professor of Medicine; and Gordon J. Ostrum, Jr., Instructor in Obstetrics and Gynecology.

Some of the graduates who obtained academic appointments other than at Jefferson were: Monica Morrow, Chief of Surgical Oncology at SUNY, Downstate Medical Center and Kings County Hospital; Marjorie A. Williamson (Bowman), Associate Dean for Continuing Medical Education and Assistant Professor of Community and Family Medicine at Georgetown University School of Medicine; George J. Heymach, III, Clinical Assistant Professor of Medicine at the University of Pittsburgh (Pulmonary Medicine); Eugene E. Wolfel, Assistant Professor of Medicine at the University of Colorado Health Services Center (Cardiology); John S. Liggett, Jr., Assistant Professor of Clinical Pulmonary Pediatrics in the University of Texas Health Center at Tyler; James H. Garvin, Jr., Assistant Professor of Pediatrics at Columbia University; Thomas S. Kilcheski, Clinical Professor of Radiology at the University of California, San Diego; Robert R. Farquharson, Assistant Professor of Family Practice, the University of Nebraska College of Medicine; Scott M. Goldman, Assistant Professor of Surgery (Cardiothoracic) at Hahnemann University (Fig.

Fig. 432.   Philip Nimoityn (JMC, '76), Instructor in Medicine (Cardiology).

Fig. 433.   Robert G. McCairns Jr. (JMC, '76), Instructor in Surgery.

434); Michael R. Treat, member of the faculty in colorectal surgery at Columbia-Presbyterian Medical Center; Kenneth W. Sommerville, Associate Professor of Neurology at Hershey Medical Center; Johannes D. Weltin, Clinical Instructor in Family Medicine at New York Medical College; Gary F. Purdue, after Fellowship in brain surgery joined the faculty of the University of Texas at Dallas; Manuel R. Morman, Instructor in Dermatology at Mount Sinai Medical Center in New York City; and Francis A. Chervenak, Associate Professor of Obstetrics/Gynecology at New York Hospital—Cornell Medical Center.

Additional graduates with academic appointments were: Richard C. Cherkis, Assistant Professor of Obstetrics/Gynecology, New York Hospital; Joanna Connolly, Instructor in Obstetrics/Gynecology, Hospital of Medical College of Pennsylvania; Paul T. Cullen, Instructor in Medicine, Hahnemann University; Brad M. Dworkin, Associate Professor of Medicine, Westchester County Medical Center, New York; Charles S. Finch, Assistant Professor of Preventive Medicine, Grady Memorial Hospital, Atlanta; Sandra Horowitz, Associate Professor of Radiology, Loyola University Medical Center, Illinois; Michael C. Kallay, Associate Professor of Medicine, Strong Memorial Hospital of University of Rochester; Donald E. Martin, Associate Professor of Anesthesiology, Milton S. Hershey Medical Center, Hershey; Melissa J. Riedy, Assistant Professor of Radiology, University of Massachusetts Hospital, Worcester; Steven E. Ross, Assistant Professor of Surgery, Robert Wood Johnson Medical School, Piscataway; Nancy M. Satur, Instructor in Dermatology, Case Western Reserve Affiliated Hospitals, Cleveland; William F. Tatu, Assistant Professor of Radiology, University of Virginia Hospital, Charlottesville; Richard C. Wasserman, Assistant Professor of Pediatrics, Medical Center Hospital of Vermont, Burlington; Sno White, Assistant Professor of Anesthesiology, University of Florida Affiliated Hospitals, Gainesville; and Richard Whittington, Assistant Professor of Radiology, Hospital of the University of Pennsylvania.

Fig. 434.   Scott M. Goldman (JMC, '76).

Allan, David A., PA
Ashley, Ann Ava, FL
Bade, Harry A., III, CT
Baraldi, Raymond L., Jr., PA
Batt, David S., PA
Bearoff, Richard J., PA
Beebe, J. Kirk, DE
Belmont, Jonathan B., PA
Bender, Joseph M., NJ
Bernett, Gary B., PA

Berry, David G., PA
Bielawski, Donald M., PA
Blaker, Mark E., PA
Blannett, John D., Jr., PA
Boerner, Carol F., PA
Bonner, Dennis J., PA
Bonner, Robert E., PA
Bowman, Scott W., PA
Boyd, Robert L., PA
Bradfield, James E., PA

Brener, Harry M., PA
Brenner, Barry S., PA
Brenner, Ira, DE
Brenner, Robert R., PA
Brock, David C., DE
Broff, Martin D., PA
Brownstein, Richard E., PA
Buechler, Elizabeth J., NH
Burns, Charles N., Jr., PA
Cappiello, Wiliam F., PA
Carter, William S., III, PA
Chalfin, Lenn Jay, PA
Charlton, Glenn B., PA
Cherkis, Richard C., PA
Chervenak, Francis A., NJ
Ciano, Michael C., PA
Clark, Mark A., DE
Cohn, John R., PA
Coleman, Raymond L., PA
Conti, Joseph D., PA
Cullen, Paul T., PA
Daly, William J., PA
DeAndino, Richard M., PUERTO RICO
Deeney, Vincent F., PA
Denny, Edward C., PA
Dobson, James J., DE
Donahue, John R., PA
Dougherty, Miriam T., PA
Dworkin, Brad M., PA
Ecker, Herbert A., Jr., PA
Eilers, Robert P., NJ
Eisen, Richard F., PA
Emmett, Gary A., PA
English, Richard B., PA
Ergas, Sanders S., PA
Farquharson, Robert R., PA
Faust, Halley S., PA
Finch, Charles S., PA
Flomenberg, Neal, PA
Foster, David C., PA
Franton, Barry, PA
Frauenhoffer, Christopher M., PA
Fuller, Garry L., PA
Garber, Edward H., Jr., PA
Garrett, Robert Charles, PA
Garvin, James H., Jr., DE
Gernerd, Mark D., PA
Gilman, Paul B., OH
Glass, Steven J., PA
Glazerman, Larry R., PA
Goldberg, Robert L., PA
Goldman, Arthur J., PA
Goldman, Scott M., PA
Goodman, Michael S., PA

Gottlieb, Marc E., PA
Gottstein-Eidelson, Stewart G., PA
Grant, Kathleen J., PA
Green, Linda D., PA
Grem, Judith F., PA
Grem, Philip C., IL
Groll, Jerome E., DE
Groomes, Roderick, PA
Grossman, Roy, CA
Hagedorn, Mark D., CT
Harrison, Theodore J., PA
Heffron, Timothy J., PA
Hetrick, Thomas J., DE
Heymach, George J., III, PA
High, Bertrand J., II, PA
Hilaman, Brad L., NJ
Horowitz, Sandra W., NY
Hoyer, Paul J., DE
Jacoby, Richard A., PA
Jens, Kurtis D., IL
Johnson, Sally A., PA
Jordan, W. Edward, III, ME
Kalin, Ned H., PA
Kallay, Michael C., PA
Kao, Yi How, PA
Kastner, Scott Meyers, PA
Katz, Barbara L., PA
Katz, Stephen K., PA
Kehm, Robert F., PA
Kernish, Richard C., FL
Kilcheski, Thomas S., PA
Klein, Kenneth I., NY
Klein, Raymond A., PA
Kline, Kathy T., PA
Kloss, Robert A., NJ
Kradin, Richard L., PA
Krall, Robert A., PA
Kreiser, Joseph R., Jr., PA
Kremer, Frederic B., PA
Kribbs, John B., PA
Kucer, Kathleen B., PA
Kushner, Stuart F., PA
LaFever, Marianne, NJ
Lammie, John J., GA
Lamparter, Robert W., PA
Lasichak, Lydia M., MI
Leipold, Robert A., PA
Lenox, Robert J., PA
Levin, Andrew J., PA
Levin, Norman P., PA
Levy, Michael H., DE
Lewis, Ivor F., PA
Lichtenstein, Mark D., PA
Liggett, John S., Jr., PA

1976

Long, Paul R., PA
Lyons, Lawrence H., Jr., DE
Lytle, Nelson K., PA
Malone, G. Dwight, DE
Mandel, Richard J., PA
Marsh, Peter K., PA
Martin, Donald E., PA
Martsolf, Robert H., PA
McCairns, Robert G., Jr., PA
McCann, James P., PA
McConnell, Edward J., III, DE
McCunney, Robert J., PA
McElwain, Guy E., Jr., PA
McGraw, Patrick J., PA
McLaughlin, Mark A., PA
Meloni, Michael A., Jr., PA
Michaelson, Robert I., PA
Miller, Joanna, PA
Montique, Frank, Jr., PA
Morman, Manuel R., PA
Morris, A. Jesse, III, DE
Morrow, Monica, PA
Myers, Virginia C., PA
Nahirniak-Kaufman, Laryssa, WI
Nessa, William T., PA
Nevulis, John J., PA
Nimoityn, Philip, PA
Noreika, Joseph C., PA
Nutter, David E., PA
Olson, David A., DE
Ostrum, Gordon J., Jr., NJ
Parris, Ted M., PA
Paul, Stuart R., PA
Peterson, Robert D., CT
Pierotti, Richard J., PA
Plastino, John E., PA
Polan, Ruth L., PA
Porter, I. Stanley, PA
Punderson, John O., Jr., DE
Purdue, Gary F., NJ
Purvis, Joseph D., PA
Ralph, Jonathan D., PA
Riedy, Melissa Jane, PA
Roberts, Nancy S., PA

Rosen, Bruce J., PA
Rosenschein, Serl E., PA
Ross, Steven E., PA
Ruby, Samuel R., NJ
Russell, B. Royce, Jr., PA
Sallee, Kent A., DE
Sands, Jeffrey J., PA
Sanstead, John K., PA
Satur, Nancy M., PA
Schwartz, Myron E., PA
Shucker, Mark A., PA
Smith, Mark A., PA
Sobelman, Paul B., PA
Solomon, Dean, PA
Sommerville, Kenneth W., NJ
Spotts, Ricke L., PA
Stauber, Gerson, PA
Steel, Maxwell W., III, PA
Stick, Michael O., PA
Stillabower, Michael E., DE
Sukati, Amy M., PA
Sullivan, Daniel R., PA
Tatu, William F., PA
Thilo, Elizabeth H., PA
Thomas, L. Martha A., PA
Thompson, John W., PA
Treat, Michael R., PA
Udell, Brian D., PA
Urian West, Valerie A., DE
Waples, Charles H., Jr., DE
Ward, Michael J., PA
Wasserman, Richard C., NY
Weisel, William M., PA
Weltin, Johannes D., DE
Wenner, Nadine P., PA
White, Sno E., PA
Whittington, Richard, MD
Williamson, Marjorie Ann, PA
Willis, David W., DE
Winslow, Dean L., DE
Wolfel, Eugene E., PA
Ytterberg, Steven R., TX
Zamore, Michael S., NY
Zazow, Paul L., PA
Zibelman, Robert S., PA

Interim President George M. Norwood, Jr. (Fig. 443) presided over the Commencement ceremonies and conferred M.D. degrees upon 212 graduates at the Academy of Music on June 10. This was his last official act prior to the arrival of the new President, Lewis W. Bluemle, Jr., M.D.

Dr. Bluemle, the second President of the University, was inaugurated on September 7 at the Walnut Street Theater (Fig. 435). For this occasion a Presidential Badge was created, consisting of four official corporate seals of the institution (Fig. 436). President Bluemle's 13-year tenure until 1990 would mark a golden era in Jefferson's history.

Achieving notoriety early in his career was James P. Bagian. Holding a prior degree in Electrical Engineering from Drexel University, he embarked on a course leading to participation in the National Aeronautics and Space Administration program in 1978. Although having planned for orthopaedic surgery, his acceptance into the space program was followed by training as a flight surgeon and continued with a residency in anesthesiology in 1979. Dr. Bagian's long preparation culminated in his flight aboard the Spaceship Discovery in March, 1989 (Fig. 437 & 438). Dr. Bagian carried into space a bronze Jefferson medallion to be presented to President Bluemle for permanent display.

R. Anthony Carabasi, III, won the Surgery Prize at graduation and went on to training in surgery with special emphasis on vascular surgery and organ transplantation. He advanced to Associate Professor in the Departments of Surgery and Radiology in 1987 (Fig. 439). In 1986 he was co-author with Dr. Bruce Jarrell (JMC, '73, Fig. 419) of *Surgery*, published by Wiley, New York.

Herbert Patrick was trained in pulmonary and critical care medicine at Jefferson and in 1984 joined the fulltime staff of the Department of Medicine as Assistant Professor. He also received a five-year Clinical Investigator Award from the National Heart, Lung and Blood Institute for advanced studies in pulmonary diseases (Fig. 440).

A number of graduates received academic appointments. John W. Peters was Clinical Assistant Professor of Medicine at Temple University School of Medicine. Margaret M. Dunn was Assistant Professor of Surgery at Wright State University School of Medicine, Dayton, Ohio. Virginia Chalfant Wood became Assistant Clinical Professor of Medicine, also at Wright State; in 1988 she received the Teaching Excellence Award. James F. Burke was Clinical Assistant Professor of Medicine at Jefferson and Thomas C. Benfield, Clinical Assistant Professor of Psychiatry and Human Behavior, also at Jefferson. David M. Rodgers served as Assistant Professor of Medicine at Medical College of Pennsylvania. Alan M. Sugar was Assistant Professor of Medicine at Boston University School of Medicine, Section on Infectious Diseases. Mary E. O'Connor was Clinical Assistant Professor of Pediatrics at the University of California School of Medicine, San Francisco. Cynthia B. Altman, trained in Clinical Pharmacology, was for a time Director of World Wide Clinical Research Management for Smith, Kline, French Laboratories; she was later Executive Director of Strategic Planning for Grand View Hospital, Sellersville, Pennsylvania. Joseph J. Evans became Director of the Clinical Electrophysiology Laboratory and Pacemaker Service, Marshfield, Wisconsin, and Clinical Assistant Professor of Medicine at the University of Wisconsin School of Medicine, Madison.

Other appointments included James C. Folk, Professor of Ophthalmology and Director of Vitreoretinal Service, University of Iowa Hospitals, Iowa City; Randy V. Campo, winner of the Potter Prize, Instructor in Ophthalmology at Mayo Graduate School of Medicine, Rochester; Blair Ardman, Assistant Professor of Medicine, Tufts University School of Medicine, Boston; Michael T. Brady, Assistant Professor of Pediatrics, Ohio State University School of Medicine, Columbus; Jeffrey B. Gross, winner of the Alumni Prize,

Assistant Professor of Anesthesiology, Hospital of the University of Pennsylvania; Murali J. Jasty, Instructor in Orthopaedics at Massachusetts General Hospital; Samuel M. Lasko, Assistant Professor of Public Health, Boston University Affiliated Hospitals; Kenneth Levin, Assistant Professor of Radiology, Hahnemann University; Bruce D. Lindsay, Instructor in Medicine at Barnes Hospital, St. Louis; David C.S. Nikeson, Assistant Professor of Internal Medicine, Baylor College of Medicine, Houston; Sandra M. Wolf, Assistant Professor of Obstetrics/Gynecology at Hahnemann University; Warren B. Matthews, Instructor in Family Medicine and William B. McNamee, Jr., Instructor in Medicine, both at Jefferson Medical College.

Fig. 435. Lewis W. Bluemle, Jr., M.D., L.H.D., Sc.D., F.R.C.P., second University President (1977-90).

Adam, Anne Wynn W., DE
Adam, Jeffrey S., OH
Adelson, Leonard J., PA
Alteveer, Janet G., NJ
Altman, Cynthia B., PA
Anselmi, Lanning A., PA
Ardman, Blair, PA
Armstrong, Donald J., PA
Armstrong, Ned B., PA
Atkinson, Robert E., PA
Bagian, James P., PA
Baltuch, Leigh, PA
Barbee, Carl A., DE
Barnes, Glen D., PA
Bartges, John D., PA
Batten, George B., PA
Bauman, David C., PA
Beimfohr, Sylvia L., PA
Bender, Bruce R., PA
Benfield, Thomas C., PA
Berger, Barbara J., NJ
Berrittini, Wade H., PA

Bodenstab, Alanna F., DE
Bodenstab, Alex B., DE
Bodenstab, William E., DE
Bogner, Edward W., PA
Boova, Robert S., PA
Bowen, J. Hartley, III, NJ
Brady, Michael T., PA
Brown, Sarah C., PA
Burbridge, Geoffrey R., PA
Burke, James F., PA
Camas, John M., PA
Campfield, Thomas J., PA
Campo, Randy V., PA
Carabasi, R. Anthony, III, PA
Carey, Kent V., CA
Carim, Moiz M., PA
Cassidy, Harvey D., PA
Chalfant, Virginia Ann, PA
Cherry, Scott M., PA
Cobert, Howard S., PA
Colletta, Joseph A., DE
Connerton, George E., NJ

Fig. 436. Presidential Badge.

Cooper, Mark W., PA
Cornish, Juanita S., PA
Cowan, Kathryn G., PA
Craig, Richard A., PA
Crampton, Ronald W., PA
Cummings, Curtis E., PA
Davis, William Charles, PA
DeBiasse, Timothy A., NJ
Delehanty, Thomas J., PA
DeLone, Francis X., Jr., PA
Delucca, Leopoldo E., PUERTO RICO
Diamond, Mark S., NJ
Dietz, John R., DE
Doll, Robert B., Jr., PA
Doroshow, Carol A., CA
Dubin, Elyse C., PA
Dulcey, John J., Jr., PA
Dunn, Margaret Mary, NY
Eggebroten, William E., MD
Eisenhower, E. Susanna, NJ
Eisner, Davis S., PA
Elkind, Jeffrey Howard, NY
Evans, Joseph J., PA

Fairman, Ronald M., PA
Fehnel, Stephen H., PA
Ferraris, Victor A., PA
Ferriss, John A., III, NJ
Fine, Robert, CT
Fischer, Jerome S., PA
Fischer, Michael E., PA
Flanagan, Richard A., Jr., PA
Fogley, Anees R., PA
Folk, James C., PA
Fornadel, Richard M., PA
Foster, Bruce A., DE
Freedman, Sheldon J., PA
Fronduti, Ronald A., PA
Funk, William B., DE
Fuste, Rosa M., DE
Gerard, Joseph A., DE
Gilbert, Bruce, CA
Ginsberg, Fredric L., PA
Ginsberg, Jay, PA
Glowacki, Jan S., NJ
Golkow, Russell S., PA
Goode, Dale N., MI

Fig. 437. James P. Bagian (JMC, '77) Astronaut in U.S. Space Program.

Fig. 438. Dr. Bagian floating in space.

Graves, Walter G., PA
Gross, Jeffrey B., PA
Halpern, Jean A., NY
Hauser, Sally J., DE
Hayward, R. Bradley, PA
Heller, Bruce, NY
Hensal, Frederick J., PA
Herman, Dennis, PA
Herrmann, William J., NY
Hiltz, Deborah J., PA
Hodge, Beth Orringer, PA

Hoffman, Gregory A., IN
Hofmann, Michael P., DE
Hopen, Gary R., FL
Isserman, Mark S., PA
Janerich, Albert D., PA
Jasty, Murali J., PA
Jaxheimer, Eric C., PA
Johnson, Eric G., NJ
Jones, Russell C., CT
Kelleman, John J., NJ
Klinger, Frank A., PA

Fig. 439.   R. Anthony Carabasi, III (JMC, '77).

Fig. 440.   Herbert Patrick (JMC, '77), Assistant Professor of Medicine (Pulmonary Diseases).

Knowles, Harry J., Jr., PA
Koffler, Jeffrey M., CT
Kogut, Kathleen Marie, PA
Konchar, William C., PA
Korneluk-Reilly, Theresa, PA
Kruger, Eric N., PA
Krywicki, William Joseph, PA
LaManna, John V., PA
Laub, Ronald M., PA
Laubach, Sherri J., PA
Lawlor, Robert J., PA
Lawrence, Gary W., PA
Lechmanick, Eugene A., PA
Lepoff, Norman J., PA
Lesko, Samuel M., PA
Levin, Kenneth, PA
Levin, Robert M., PA
Ligato, Vincent Anthony, NJ
Liggett, Scott P., TX
Lindsay, Bruce D., NJ
Loftus, Thomas J., PA
Margolis, Mitchell L., PA
Marten, Lawrence A., MI
Massimino, F. Anthony, CA
Matthews, Warren B., PA
Maxwell, Mark W., PA
McCloskey, Sister Ann M., PA
McDonald, David R., PA
McLaughlin, Thomas W., PA
McNamee, William B., Jr., PA
Medway, Marc J., PA
Mendelsohn, Jay S., PA
Miller, G. Geoffrey, PA
Miller, Gary A., PA
Miller, Robert J., NJ
Minteer, Jeffrey F., PA
Mintek, Rian D. C., IL
Mintzer, David M., PA
Morrow, Thomas J., PA
Naples, Anthony F., PA
Nickeson, David C., PA
Novinger, Q. Thomas, PA
O'Connor, Mary E., PA
Olivere, Robert F., DE
Patrick, Herbert, PA
Peacock, Jay A., DE
Peck, William J., PA
Pergola, Richard M., NY
Peters, John W., PA
Piatt, John E., III, PA

Playfoot, Donald E., PA
Read, Edward J., Jr., DE
Robinson, John H., PA
Robinson, Kevin G., PA
Rodgers, David M., PA
Rogers, Brad S., NY
Roman, Vincent T., PA
Roumm, Alan D., PA
Runowicz, Carolyn D., FL
Ruzbarsky, Joseph J., PA
Samms, John M., OR
Savage, Donald J., PA
Savage, Robert C., PA
Schaefer, Patricia K., DE
Schoenburn, Marc J., PA
Schoenfeld, Larry, PA
Scott, S. David, Jr., PA
Sears, Cynthia Louise, PA
Sharkey, Thomas G., PA
Shea, David S., PA
Simmons, Agnes H., PA
Smoger, Barry R., PA
Smyth, Lawrence T., Jr., PA
Solinsky, Stanley P., PA
Steinberg, William J., PA
Storer, Joan N., NJ
Sugar, Alan M., NJ
Tems, Sandra J., PA
Tenn, Patricia F., PA
Thompson, Kenneth W., FL
Urban, Paul L., PA
Van Uitert, Bonnie L., NJ
Wagner, K. Thomas, Jr., PA
Wasserbly, Pamela J., PA
Weber, Paul R., PA
Weinberg, Michael G., PA
Weiss, Joan, PA
Wessell, Rosalie W., PA
Williams, Gary J., PA
Williams, Robert H., Jr., PA
Wisniewski, Robert E., DE
Wolf, Sandra M., PA
Wolfe, Dwight D., PA
Wolitz, Richard A., PA
Woodhouse, Robert J., PA
Woodside, Jack R., Jr., VA
Wright, Frank J., PA
Ytterberg, Karen L., PA
Zubrow, Marc T., PA
Zukoski, Robert M., CT

Commencement exercises were held June 9 and the M.D. degree was conferred upon 230 graduates by the new President, Lewis W. Bluemle, Jr. (Fig. 435 and 441). The sharp increase in the number of medical graduates was in part a reflection of the alarm sounded during the past decade that a physician shortage was imminent.

The afternoon of Commencement Day was marked by the dedication of the New Thomas Jefferson University Hospital, a century after the construction of the first Jefferson Medical College

Fig. 441. President Bluemle at the Alumni Gate of Eakins Gallery.

Hospital (1877). Appropriate ceremonies were held in the West Atrium with Jefferson officials and civic leaders in the forefront. Innovations in design along functional lines characterized the new structure, incorporating offices for staff physicians, outpatient services and improved access for inpatients to hospital facilities (Fig. 442). It was named the Gibbon Building in 1990 in honor of John H. Gibbon, Jr. (JMC, '27, Fig. 243), inventor of the heart-lung machine.

An Alumni Achievement Award was presented at the Winter dinner meeting of the Alumni Association to Mr. George M. Norwood, Jr. (Fig. 443), recognizing his services as interim President of the University during the critical period following the unexpected death of President Herbut.

For almost three decades, J. Wallace Davis (JMC, '42, Fig. 291) served as Chairman of Alumni Annual Giving. In appreciation, the President's Club honored him with the prestigious 1978 Cornerstone Award (Fig. 444).

Numerous 1978 graduates joined the Jefferson teaching staff. Among them, George C. Francos was trained in the Department of Medicine's Nephrology Section and was appointed Assistant Professor and Director of the Chronic Dialysis Program. Norman G. Rosenblum was Assistant Professor of Obstetrics/Gynecology. Howard H. Weitz, following his residency, was a Chief Resident in the Department of Medicine and later was appointed Clinical Associate Professor of Medicine. Kenneth C. Rosenberg became an Instructor in Medicine (Cardiology). Christine A. Byrnes was appointed Clinical Assistant Professor of Medicine. Eric J. Michael, Clinical Assistant Professor of Pediatrics, was on the fulltime staff in Neonatology. David G. Schutzman was also Clinical Professor of Pediatrics. Instructors included Daniel B. DiCola (Family Medicine), Gerald L. Gary (Pediatrics), George R. Kenner, Jr. (Ophthalmology), and Charles L. Reese (Surgery).

Other alumni were appointed to various aca-

Fig. 442. 1978 New Hospital, named the Gibbon Building in 1990.

demic positions. David S. Ginsburg, winner of the Obstetrics/Gynecology Prize, became Assistant Professor of Obstetrics/Gynecology at Hahnemann University. Marilee H. Frazer was appointed Assistant Medical Examiner for Wayne County (Michigan), Detroit; in 1989 she received the degree of Doctor of Jurisprudence from Wayne State University Law School. William G. Ellien became Director of Ambulatory services (Psychiatry) at Pennsylvania Hospital, and Clinical Assistant Professor at the University of Pennsylvania School of Medicine after having previously held a similar position at Georgetown University. Stephen I. Kramer, winner of the Psychiatry Prize, was Assistant Professor of Psychiatry and Behavior, Bowman-Gray School of Medicine and Chief of Psychiatry at Forsyth Memorial Hospital, Winston-Salem, North Carolina. Gaylin Li-Ma served as Assistant Professor of Obstetrics/Gynecology, University of Hawaii School of Medicine and Medical Director of Obstetrics/Gynecology at the Outpatient Clinic, Kaprolane Medical Center. David F. Flynn, following fellowship training at Massachusetts General Hospital, was named Director of Radiation Oncology at the University of Texas Southwestern

Fig. 443. George W. Norwood, Interim President (1976/77).

1978

Medical School. Raymond B. Leidich was Assistant Chairman of the Urology Department at Naval Regional Medical Center, Oakland, California. Alexander C. Mamourian was Assistant Professor of Radiology at Milton S. Hershey Medical Center. Howard S. Klein became Chief of the Pulmonary Disease Section at Philadelphia Geriatric Center and Assistant Professor of Medicine at Medical College of Pennsylvania. Patricia Harper Petrozza was Assistant Professor of Anesthesiology at Bowman-Gray School of Medi-

cine, Winston-Salem. Victor A. Zachian became Clinical Instructor in Obstetrics/Gynecology at the University of Pennsylvania School of Medicine. David M. Reed, trained in surgical oncology at Roswell Park Memorial Institute, Buffalo, New York, and was appointed Clinical Professor of Surgery at New York Medical College. Nancy H. Sherman was Assistant Professor of Radiology at the University of Pennsylvania and a staff radiologist at Children's Hospital of Philadelphia. Katherine C. Krause was Assistant Professor of Family medicine at Case Western Reserve School of Medicine, Cleveland, Ohio. Maria O. Uberti in 1983 was named Chief of Dermatology at Presbyterian-University of Pennsylvania Hospital. Neil H. Shusterman was Assistant Professor of Medicine in the Renal-Electrolyte Section of the University of Pennsylvania School of Medicine.

Other appointments included Robert J. Mead, Jr., Associate Professor of Anesthesiology, Duke University Medical Center, Durham; Gerald L. Andriole, Assistant Professor of Surgery, Barnes Hospital of Washington University School of Medicine, St. Louis; Anthony R. Dal Nogare, Assistant Professor of Medicine, Parkland Hospital, Dallas; Patricia G. Fitzgerald, Assistant Professor of Medicine, Strong Memorial Hospital, University of Rochester, New York; Robert S. Finkelhor, Instructor in Medicine, Case Western Reserve School of Medicine, Cleveland; E. Paul Howanitz, Assistant Professor of Surgery, Ohio State University Hospital, Columbus; John B. Kneeland, Assistant Professor of Radiology, Medical College of Wisconsin Affiliated Hospitals, Milwaukee; Bruce Z. Morgenstern, Assistant Professor of Pediatrics, Mayo Graduate School of Medicine, Rochester; Jeffrey B. Robin, Assistant Professor of Ophthalmology, Los Angeles County USC Medical Center; Eric J. Werner, Assistant Professor of Pediatrics, Eastern Virginia Graduate Medical School, Norfolk; and Keith R. Young, Jr., Assistant Professor of Internal Medicine, University of Alabama Medical Center, Birmingham.

Fig. 444. J. Wallace Davis (JMC, '42) receives Cornerstone Award of President's Club (1978) on behalf of fund raising for the Alumni Association.

CLASS OF 1978

Abramowitz, Richard P., PA
Allawi, Diane C., PA
Allen, Gregg P., PA
Anagnost, John W., CA

Andrews, Ronald W., PA
Andriole, Gerald L., Jr., PA
Armao, Francis B., PA
Austin, Charles B., Jr., PA

Baron, Andrew J., Jr., PA
Benecki, Theresa R., DE
Benz, Robert L., PA
Berger, Robert B., NJ
Bonanni, Loretta D., PA
Boran, Robert P., Jr., PA
Border, Michael W., PA
Brillman, David A., PA
Bronstein, Jeffrey B., PA
Brozell, Douglas P., PA
Busillo, Barbara Maria M., PA
Busillo, Nicholas A., PA
Buza, Richard S., PA
Byrnes, Christine A., NJ
Camp, John F., NJ
Carey, Asher B., III, DE
Cassel, Gary H., NJ
Chaikin, Harry L., NJ
Chiu, Arthur O., PA
Cofer, Harold A., Jr., PA
Cohen, Stanley A., PA
Colangelo, Anthony B., PA
Corwin, James Howell, III, FL
Coyle, Johnson G., PA
Crake, Roger F., PA
Cregan, Gregg E., PA
Dal Nogare, Anthony R., DE
Dalzell, Frederick G., NJ
Danyliw, Thomas J., CT
Davis, Allan S., PA
Davis, Harold J., PA
Dethoff, John C., PA
DiCola, Daniel B., PA
Dietz, Jeffrey W., PA
Dove, Otto E., PA
Edson, Steven B., PA
Egel, James W., PA
Eisner, Steven B., PA
Ellien, William G., PA
Everts, Deborah, PA
Feiner, Larry A., PA
Filippone, Marciana D., DE
Finder, Marc J., PA
Finkelhor, Robert S., PA
Fitzpatrick, Patricia G., DE
Fleites, Rafael A., OH
Flinn, Margaret S. M., PA
Flynn, Daniel F., MA
Foulsham, Charles K., II, NJ
Francos, George C., PA
Frankel, Harry A., PA
Frazer, Marilee H., DE
Frederick, James E., PA
Freedman, Ellen Penny, PA
Friedman, Erica Sue, PA
Garcia, Jose R., PA

Gary, Gerald L., PA
Geisler, Cheryl Hirsch, NY
Geisler, Edward, PA
Ginsberg, Susan M., PA
Ginsburg, David S., PA
Gkonos, Peter J., DE
Glasofer, Eric D., NJ
Gold, Barbara W., PA
Goodman, David M., PA
Grad, L. Christine, PA
Graybeal, Glenn E., DE
Griffin, Gregory C., PA
Guillard, Frank, PA
Gutbezahl, Cary D., PA
Haibach, Raymond A., PA
Hall, Bruce C., CA
Hammerman, Louis, NJ
Hankey, John C., PA
Hanna, Edward S., VA
Harper, Patricia, M., PA
Hart, Marilyn M., PA
Heller, Arthur D., NY
Henderson, Valerie G., OH
Herbets, Steven S., PA
Herman, Leonard Y., PA
Herpst, Sally L., PA
Hoellein, Kenneth D., PA
Howanitz, E. Paul, PA
Hunker, Susan L., CO
Hutchinson, Thomas A., PA
Huxster, Robert H., PA
Hyatt, Glenn A., PA
Ishii, Cylde H., Jr., HI
Jahnke, Eric W., CA
Johnston, Sjanna, PA
Jones, Raymond R., PA
Jones, Thomas K., PA
Josephs, Allen S., PA
Kegel, Daniel P., PA
Kenner, George R., Jr., PA
King, Joyce R., PA
Kittle, Chris A., DE
Klein, Howard S., PA
Klepser, Marian B., PA
Kmonicek, Joseph M., NY
Kneeland, John B., PA
Kovalsky, Kenneth, PA
Krafft, Rudolph M., PA
Kramer, Stephen I., PA
Krause, Katherine C., PA
Kreider, Kathleen A., PA
Krupa, Robert, PA
Kuklinski, Lawrence M., PA
Lauter, M. David, DE
Lavin, David M., DE
Lazar, Richard J., PA

Leidich, Raymond B., PA
Levinson, Nat E., PA
Levy, Alfred E., PA
Li-Ma, Gaylyn G. L., HI
Lintz, Robert M., NJ
Liu, Curtis R., HI
Lombardo, Joseph A., CA
Long, Kimberly R., PA
Love, Carol A., PA
Lupu, Janice, PA
Lynch, George Michael, PA
Maletz, Frank W., PA
Mamourian, Alexander C., PA
Marro, Francis A., PA
Martin, Richard A., PA
Matthews, Joseph G., II, FL
Mayer, Stephen A., PA
McArthur, Alexander, III, PA
Mead, Robert J., Jr., DE
Metkus, Francis M., PA
Metkus, Thomas S., PA
Michael, Eric J., DE
Miller, William D., PA
Mogul, Robert S., PA
Molino, Robert D., NJ
Montigney, Paul W., DE
Morgenstern, Bruce Z., NY
Muffly, James T., CO
Nayowith, Bruce E., PA
Nee, Martin P., Jr., PA
Neifeld, Kenneth A., PA
Noyes, Brent R., DE
Packman, Barry E., PA
Pansick, Bob Lee, NY
Parks, Donald B., PA
Patterson, Arthur J., Jr., PA
Patterson, John W., NJ
Pavlikowski, Fred Lewis, Jr., PA
Pekala, Raymond T., PA
Pemberton, Clifford H., PA
Peters, Robert H., III, PA
Peters, Stanley W., PA
Petrozza, Joseph A., PA
Pilgram, Paul E., PA
Portfolio, Almerindo G., Jr., NJ
Puleo, Samuel M., PA
Reed, David M., PA
Reese, Charles L., IV, PA
Reilly, Ann E., PA
Riley, Jean G., PA
Rizzo, Albert A., PA
Robin, Jeffrey B., PA
Robinson, Richard W., PA
Robinson, Warren L., Jr., PA
Romisher, Marc K., PA

Rosenberg, Kenneth C., PA
Rosenblum, Harry M., NJ
Rosenblum, Norman G., PA
Rosenthal, Norman R., PA
Rowand, Randall W., PA
Russo, Michael P., MD
Ryan, Timothy M., PA
Salmon, Duncan, DE
Sawula, Boris J., NJ
Scavone, Jerome G., PA
Schell, Roxie Ann, DE
Schiowitz, Mark F., PA
Schutzman, David L., DE
Scott, Thomas B., PA
Sears, Alan J., PA
Sherman, Nancy H., PA
Shumaker, Scott D., PA
Shusterman, Neil H., PA
Sipple, Katharyn Marie, PA
Smith, Ellen K., PA
Smith, George J., PA
Smith, Ira U., NJ
Smolow, Craig R., PA
Springel, Ronald D., PA
Starsnic, Janice, PA
Stepansky, David W., PA
Stutzman, Charles D., PA
Sumfest, Jill M., PA
Summersgill, R. Blair, PA
Surkin, Marc Ivan, PA
Talamo, Thomas S., PA
Teichman, Fred, PA
Ting, Helen P., PA
Topilow, Edmund C., NJ
Trump, David H., PA
Tucker, Dale C., PA
Uberti, Marie O., PA
Ullman, Bernard L., CA
Van Gundy, Gregory A., PA
Wang, Chi-Lun Charles, DE
Weitz, Howard H., PA
Wendel, Christopher H., DE
Werner, Eric J., CT
Wiley, Michael J., MI
Williams, Burton J., PA
Wilson, Linda C., NJ
Witte, Eric H., PA
Wofford, John D., Jr., MS
Yingling, Douglas B., PA
Yohe, Frank J., PA
Young, Keith R., Jr., NJ
Younger, Joel B., CA
Zachian, Victor A., PA
Zenz, Carl N., WI
Zimmerman, Neal J., NJ

President Bluemle conferred the M.D. degree upon 215 graduates at the annual Commencement held at the Academy of Music June 8. On this occasion the honorary degree of Doctor of Literature was awarded to one of the leading figures in American Medicine, Jonathan Edward Rhoads, M.D., longtime Professor and Chairman of the Department of Surgery at the School of Medicine, University of Pennsylvania. Dr. Rhoads' national and international achievements both in medicine and academic affairs were widely acclaimed. It was appropriate that one of his distinguished proteges, Francis Ernest Rosato, M.D., Jefferson's new Samuel D. Gross Professor and Chairman of Surgery presented the citation.

The Alumni Prize and the Potter Memorial Prize were both won by Kevin Robert Harris.

In September, Jefferson signally honored Mr. William W. Bodine, Jr. (Fig. 374), by dedication of the Bodine Fountain, which consisted of five frolicking otters on a stone playground (Fig. 445). The sculptor was Henry Mitchell who had also created Jefferson's Winged Ox Column. Mr. Bodine had served as President of Jefferson Medical College (1959-66) and as Chairman of the Board of Trustees (1970-77).

Some of the class members early in their careers received academic appointments at Jefferson Medical College. Anthony V. Coletta became Instructor in Surgery in connection with his appointment as Assistant Attending Surgeon at the

Fig. 445. Bodine Fountain (1979).

affiliated Bryn Mawr Hospital (Fig. 446). Robert S. Marcello and Kenneth M. Certa were Instructors in Psychiatry and Human Behavior. John V. Cunningham, Jr. was made Instructor in Otolaryngology and Richard W. Ziegler Instructor in Orthopedic Surgery. Philip J. Dzwonczyk became Clinical Assistant Professor of Surgery. Richard A. Carapellotti was Instructor in Obstetrics/Gynecology. Joseph R. Spiegel was appointed Instructor in Otolaryngology following completion of his service as Chief Resident in the Department at the University of Michigan. Lawrence S. Miller was Clinical Assistant Professor of Orthopaedic Surgery through the Lankenau Hospital affiliation. At the Medical Center of Delaware affiliate, Michael J. Guarino and Stephen S. Grubbs were appointed Instructors in Medicine.

William H. Messerschmidt, following residency at Jefferson, became Assistant Professor and Director of Cardiothoracic Surgery at the College of Medicine of East Tennesee, Johnson City.

Sandra F. Schnall joined the Faculty of Yale University School of Medicine in Hematology-Oncology in 1987. Douglas R. Hough served as Chief of the Rheumatology and Clinical Immunology Service at William Beaumont Medical Center, El Paso, Texas. Richard S. Blumberg joined the Faculty of Harvard University Medical School in the Department of Medicine's Gastroenterology Division at Brigham and Women's Hospital.

Dennis R. Witmer and his wife Diana Dickson-Witmer (University of Florida School of Medicine), of Wilmington, Delaware, joined the Dooley Intermed Foundation and participated in medical missions in Africa and Latin America. Dr. Dennis Witmer was later Instructor in Surgery at Jefferson.

Other graduates with teaching associations were: Adam S. Asch, Assistant Professor of Medicine, New York Hospital; Scott D. Berkowitz, Assistant Professor of Medicine, S.U.N.Y. at Stony Brook; Lawrence H. Brent, Instructor and Gaetano J. Capone, Assistant Professor of Medicine at Hahnemann University; Peter L. Choyke, Assistant Professor of Radiology, and Joan S. DiPalma, Assistant Professor of Pediatrics, Georgetown University Hospital, Washington, D.C.; Warren E. Cohen, Assistant Professor of Pediatrics, Los Angeles County USC Medical Center; Kathleen C. Dougherty, Assistant Professor of Psychiatry, Case Western Reserve University Affiliated Hospitals, Cleveland; Catherine Z. Hayward, Instructor in Surgery, the Medical College of Pennsylvania; Natalie C. Klein, Assistant Professor of Internal Medicine, Westchester County Medical Center, New York; Michael E. Mahla, Assistant Professor of Anesthesiology, University of Florida Affiliated Hospitals, Gainesville; Patricia M. Maguire, Assistant Professor of Psychiatry, Presbyterian-University Hospital, Pittsburgh; Steven G. Meranze, Assistant Professor of Radiology, University of Pennsylvania; Vikki Ann Stefans, Instructor in Physical Medicine and Rehabilitation, University of Michigan Affiliated Hospitals, Ann Arbor; and James W. Vick, Instructor in Family Practice, Robert Wood Johnson Medical School, Piscataway.

Fig. 446. Anthony V. Coletta (JMC, '79), Instructor in Surgery.

Abrahamsen, Robert B., PA
Ajello, Robert R., PA
Algeo, James H., Jr., PA
Ambrus, Julian L., NY
Asch, Adam S., NY
Au, Victor K., HONG KONG
Axe, Michael J., PA
Babins, Noah A., PA
Bachow, Terry B., NJ
Baer, David G., PA
Bagian, Robert G., PA
Balick, Howard N., NY
Bartos, Paul B., PA
Basara, Bruno E., Jr., DE
Bashore, Robert L., PA
Baugh, Wilfreta G., PA
Berardis, John M., PA
Berk, Theodore F., PA
Berkowitz, Scott D., DE
Berley, Robert M., PA
Bickerton, Michael W., PA
Blumberg, Richard S., PA
Brackbill, Elizabeth W., PA
Brackbill, Robert M., Jr., PA
Brandon, Jeffrey C., PA
Brent, Lawrence H., PA
Brest, Norman A., PA
Bridenbaugh, G. Alan, PA
Brown, Diana, PA
Burdumy, Theodore J., PA
Burke, Bernard S., PA
Burnham, Marie Robb, PA
Burnham, William D., PA
Campbell, Janis P., PA
Capone, Gaetano J., PA
Carapellotti, Richard A., PA
Certa, Kenneth M., AZ
Cetrone, Anthony C., NJ
Cherry, Steven B., PA
Childress, Deborra Kim, PA
Choyke, Peter L., PA
Christ, Peter J., PA
Coblentz, Jeanette B., PA
Coblentz, Robert H., PA
Cohen, Warren E., PA
Coletta, Anthony V., PA
Colombo, John M., Jr., PA
Comissiong, Thelma W., ST. THOMAS
Corley, Luther F., III, AL
Cotler, Howard B., NJ
Cruz, Richard L., NJ
Cunningham, J. David, NJ
Davidson, Gail, NJ
DeWire, Thomas M., PA
DiPalma, Joan S., PA

Ditto, Allen W., PA
Djergaian, Robert S., PA
Dotterer, Christine E. S., PA
Dougherty, Kathleen C., PA
Dunn, Geoffrey P., PA
Dzwonczyk, Philip J., PA
Ellis, Paul S., PA
Elston, A. Storm L., PA
Elston, Jan E., PA
Erickson, Alan R., DE
Everts, Erich A., Jr., NJ
Facciolo, Mary A., DE
Faris, Mary Rachel, PA
Farquhar, Scott D., PA
Fellin, Fredrick M., PA
Fields, Richard T., MD
Fiorello, Anthony W., FL
Foreman, Steven A., PA
Frei, Timothy E., PA
Freilich, Ira W., PA
Gabor, Gary T., PA
Gardner, Stuart A., PA
Gardner, Thomas W., PA
Genz-Remshard, Bernadette, PA
Gilson, Allen J., PA
Glick, David, PA
Glick, Robert P., CA
Goldberg, Alan H., PA
Goldberg, Bruce A., PA
Goldberg, Marc B., PA
Grasberger, Robert Cook, Jr., PA
Graybeal, Michael L., DE
Greenberg, Richard H., PA
Grubbs, Stephen S., DE
Guarino, Michael J., PA
Haag, Jeffrey R., PA
Hamburger, Harry A., MI
Harris, Kevin R., PA
Hayward, Catherine Z., PA
Herman, Robert L., NY
Herold, Creston C., Jr., PA
Herold, Kevan C., PA
Hobbs, Barbara A., PA
Holland, Timothy W., PA
Horowitz, Glenn D., PA
Hough, Douglas R., PA
Jewell, Kathleen T., NJ
Johnston, Dale E., PA
Kaan, Kenneth T., RI
Kachik, Larry J., PA
Kahng, Kim U., NJ
Kavchok, Jospeh, Jr., PA
Kazenoff, Steven, NY
Kennedy, Kathleen Ann, CA
Kesselring, William T., Jr., PA

Kibelbek, Michael J., PA
Klein, Natalie C., NY
Kovatich, Audrey M. W., PA
Lam, James B., PA
Lamperski, Curtis R., PA
Laskin, William B., PA
Lavelle, James P., PA
Lebovitz, Mark A., PA
Leidich, Barbara Pittner, PA
Levenberg, Steven, PA
Leventhal, Janet B., CA
Liberman, Miryam, CA
Lindsey, Beth H., PA
Maerz, John C., Jr., PA
Mahla, Michael E., DE
Marcello, Robert S., DE
Marshall, Thomas J., Jr., NY
May, Stanley C., Jr., PA
McGlaughlin, Michael J., PA
McGuire, Patricia M., PA
Mendelsohn, Steven L., PA
Meranze, Steven G., PA
Messerschmidt, William H., PA
Michael, Douglas W., PA
Miller, Lawrence S., PA
Miller, William S., PA
Mitchell, Robert J., PA
Mohr, Gary A., PA
Narkevic, Carol A., PA
Nealon, William H., CT
Neifeld, Lise Moore, DE
O'Brien, John S., II, DE
O'Byrne, Brian E., PA
Ott, Brian R., PA
Overbeck, Michael D., PA
Pachtman, Allen H., PA
Parlavecchio, Joseph G., NJ
Patlovich, Mark F., FL
Pennisi, Alfio K., NJ
Petrone, Carol T., PA
Phiambolis, Thomas P., PA
Potter, Jeffrey N., PA
Reeves, W. Brian, PA
Reichman, Robert T., PA
Remington, Neil D., DE
Repka, Michael X., DE
Robinson, Mark K., PA
Robinson, Thomas A., PA
Rooney, Steven J., PA
Rose, Robert M., NJ
Rowe, Daniel S., Jr., CT
Rudansky, Max C., NY
Sacoolidge, John C., PA

Sarmousakis, Constance G., DE
Sastic, Jonathan W., NJ
Sastic, Lois M., MA
Schnall, Sandra F., PA
Scholl, Catherine M., PA
Schwarcz, Harriet B., PA
Schweizer, Robert A., DE
Scott, Martin E., PA
Seely, Richard B., HI
Senecal, Keith E., DE
Shaffer, Lawrence A., PA
Sharp, Ira R., PA
Sherman, Linda Ann, PA
Shmokler, Mitchell F., PA
Shoemaker, Michael Elias, PA
Silverstine, Randy J., PA
Smethers, Gary D., PA
Smith, Gail B., PA
Smith, Kenneth J., PA
Snedden, Michael H., PA
Snyder, Herbert D., PA
Snyder, Mark H., PA
Solan, James A., PA
Spiegel, Joseph R., PA
St. Clair, Jesse W., III, PA
Stefans, Vikki A., PA
Steinour, William J., PA
Stern, Sheva Merle, PA
Strimel, Kathleen M., PA
Stulpin, Michael D., PA
Sunshine, Jeffrey A., PA
Thomas, Victor J., PA
Tokairin, Donn S., HI
Trumbore, David J., PA
Tyler, Allen E., PA
Vick, James W., PA
Vilogi, Joseph P., PA
Vincent, Michael B., DE
Wagner, Katherine M., NJ
Walsh, Joseph A., PA
Walters, Virginia L., NJ
Weinstein, Steven H., PA
Weiss, Janet S., NY
Williams, Thomas M., PA
Willingmyre, Phyllis Sandra, PA
Wilson, Donald F., PA
Wilt, Jeffrey A., PA
Witmer, Dennis R., PA
Wong, Edwin H., PA
Yindra, John M., DE
Young, Wesley W. H., HI
Zavanelli, Barbara Ann, CA
Zenz, Sonja J., WI
Ziegler, Richard W., NJ

The Commencement spearheading the eventful decade of the 1980s was held on June 6 at the Academy of Music. The M.D. degree was conferred upon 221 graduates by President Bluemle. The highest honors for academic achievement were won by John Jacob Woog of the Penn State-Jefferson accelerated program.

A "Strategic Plan for the 1980s," deliberated by a Task Force led by Chairman of the Board, Frederic L. Ballard, Esq. (Fig. 447), for almost two years, gave direction for building upon the strengths of Jefferson as an academic health center but emphasized an improved balance between patient care, education and research. The results far exceeded in magnitude those anticipated in the report. It was realized that large-scale giving was more essential than ever. Funds were needed to attract the best possible new faculty leadership, to encourage research and to offset imminent declining external support by government and third party payers. Additional endowments for titled professorships and funds for student aid were envisioned. A goal of $65 million for the 1980s was deemed appropriate

Fig. 447. Frederic L. Ballard

and attainable. Subsequent years would enfold annual contributions in excess of $10 million, so that by 1986 a $60 million mark was reached. The remaining years of the decade would see the same scale of giving, aided substantially by foundations and corporations.

The John Y. Templeton, III, Annual Lecture in Surgery was first given in May of this year by internationally known Denton A. Cooley, M.D. (Fig. 448). Dr. Templeton (JMC, '41, Fig. 287) was a pioneer in cardiac surgery and had served as the Samuel D. Gross Professor.

Warren W. Nichols (JMC '54) received the alumni Achievement Award (Fig. 449). As Professor of Human Genetics and Pediatrics at the University of Pennsylvania he had conducted research on viruses as a cause of cancer.

As in previous years, many of the graduates pursued academic careers. Jean L. Grem, following a fellowship in oncology at the University of Wisconsin, joined the National Cancer Institute in Bethesda where she advanced to Senior Investigator in the Clinical Oncology Program, Medicine Branch, Division of Cancer Treatment.

John A. Friedline, combining medicine and theology, received his Master of Arts in Theology

and served with the United Methodist Church in Costa Rica for a time. He later settled in Jenkins, Kentucky, where in 1989 he was Chief of Staff at Jenkins Community Hospital.

Terrence J. Wilson was trained in physical medicine and served as Chief Resident in the Department of Rehabilitation Medicine at the Hospital of the University of Pennsylvania. In 1986 he was appointed Assistant Professor of Physical Medicine and Rehabilitation at Eastern Virginia Medical School, Norfolk.

Arthur H. Shedden was trained in ophthalmology including a fellowship in neuroophthalmology at Bascum-Palmer Eye Institute, Miami, Florida. In 1988 he was named Associate Director of Clinical Research at Merck, Sharp, & Dohme Laboratories in relation to ophthalmological projects. Leo J. Maguire, also an ophthalmologist, was appointed to the Staff of the Department at Mayo Clinic.

James D. Balshi, Chief Resident in Surgery at the Hospital of the University of Pennsylvania, went on to a fellowship in vascular surgery at Boston University and later entered private practice. Paul E. Stander became Chairman of the Department of Medicine at Maricopa Medical

Fig. 448. John Y. Templeton, III, M.D., and Denton A. Cooley, M.D. at first annual Templeton Lectureship (1980).

Fig. 449. Warren W. Nichols (JMC, '54) receives the 1980 Alumni Achievement Award.

Center, Phoenix, Arizona, and later moved to Milwaukee. Shahab S. Minassian, who completed a Jefferson Fellowship in Reproductive Endocrinology and Fertility, was appointed Assistant Professor of Obstetrics/Gynecology at Medical College of Pennsylvania in 1987. Matthew H. Carabasi was Instructor in Internal Medicine at Hahnemann University. David R. Gastfriend was Assistant Professor of Psychiatry at Massachusetts General Hospital. Thurman Gillespy, III, advanced to Assistant Professor of Radiology at the University of Florida Affiliated Hospital, Gainesville. Beverly L. Hershey was Assistant Professor of Radiology at Medical College of Pennsylvania. Hu Da-Shih became Assistant Professor of Psychiatry at Dartmouth-Hitchcock Medical Center, Hanover, New Hampshire. Paul A. Kearney was appointed Assistant Professor of Surgery at the University of Kentucky Medical Center, Lexington. Robert J. Snyder was Instructor in Obstetrics/Gynecology at Hahnemann University. Joseph G. Sodroski was Instructor in Pathology at Massachusetts General Hospital. Raymond Wargowich was Assistant Professor of Anesthesiology at Robert Wood Johnson Medical School, Piscataway, New Jersey. Carol Anne Wheeler was Assistant Professor of Obstetrics/Gynecology at Tulane University Medical Center.

Appointments of 1980 graduates to the teaching staff at Jefferson included Thomas S. Nowicki who was named Clinical Assistant Professor of Ophthalmology in the Department of Oculoplastics at Wills Eye Hospital. Gail S. Greenspan became Clinical Assistant Professor of Psychiatry and Human Behavior. Michael P. Savage became Clinical Assistant Professor of Medicine in 1987 and John F. Reinhardt Instructor in Medicine at the Medical Center of Delaware affiliate. Anne E. Connor was Instructor in Rehabilitation Medicine also at the Medical Center of Delaware. Barbara G. Frieman was Instructor in Orthopaedic Surgery and Joseph G. Grover Instructor in Ob-

stetrics/Gynecology. Michael S. Kornhauser and Eric J. Margolis became Instructors in Pediatrics. Mark C. Norris was named Assistant Professor of Anesthesiology and Edward H. Jasper Instructor in Surgery (Emergency Surgery). Paul L. Gorsuch, Jr. was appointed Instructor in Neurosurgery in 1988 but resigned the next year to enter private practice in Montana. Haynes B. Cates, Jr. and Thomas P. Lehman were Instructors in Urology. Regina M. Cudemo was appointed Instructor and Karl Doghramji Assistant Professor of Psychiatry and Human Behavior. The latter (Fig. 450) was Director of the Sleep Disorders Center.

At ceremonies in McClellan Hall on September 17, Dr. Andrew J. Ramsay (Fig. 451) was named Daniel Baugh Professor of Anatomy. On this occasion Dr. Joe Henry Coley (JMC, '34, Fig. 267) presented to the Alumni Association a painting of the Daniel Baugh Institute of Anatomy executed by Hobart A. Reimann, M.D., former Chairman of Medicine at Jefferson.

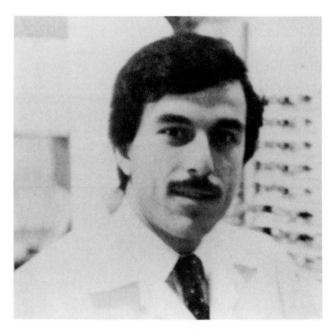

Fig. 450. Karl Doghramji (JMC, '80), Director of the Sleep Disorders Center in Department of Psychiatry and Human Behavior.

Abrahamsen, Charles E., PA
Adelman, Seth S., PA
Allen, Robert B., DE
Anderson, Mark E., NY
Andrews, Willard G., MD
Andries, Raymond C., PA
Au, Lee K. W., HI
Babb, John D., NY
Balshi, James D., PA
Becker, Andrea J., PA
Becker, Frederick L., Jr., PA
Bell, Stephen T., PA
Beste, Gary A., DE
Bills, Thomas K., PA
Bonner, John J., PA
Boyd, Willis S., PA
Boyle, Kevin M., PA
Boylston, Bedford F., TX
Bressler, Lawrence P., PA
Brownstein, Arthur H., CA
Cambridge, William R., MA
Capparuccini, Mario D., Jr., DE

Carabasi, Matthew H., PA
Carlin, Hugh M., PA
Carney, Martin J., RI
Cates, Haynes B., Jr., DE
Chilton, Mark D., PA
Clancy, Patricia E., PA
Clayton, J. Wesley, III, DE
Clements, William T., PA
Clifford, Frank D., PA
Codispoti, Joseph R., PA
Cohn, Jeffrey B., PA
Collingwood, John C., PA
Conly, Frank L., PA
Connor, Anne E., PA
Conroy, Joseph V., III, PA
Corley, Thomas R., AL
Corrado, Gail C., PA
Corse, Steven K., PA
Cox, Jonathan M., NJ
Cudemo, Regina M., PA
Curtis, Paul F., NJ
DeCaro, Matthew V., Jr., PA
DeGaeta, Linda R., PA
DeLorenzo, Donald P., Jr., PA
Devlin, Joseph M., PA
Dickensheets, David L., SC
Doenlen, Henry A., III, PA
Doghramji, Karl, PA
Dooley, Bruce R., PA
Dukart, Gary, DE
Dunn, William F., PA
Dunton, Charles J., PA
Eister, Ronald N., PA
Epsten, Robert M., Jr., CA
Erdman, John P., FL
Fallor, Martin K., NY
Fetzer, Jean Hamilton, DE
Finegold, Richard N., PA
Fisher, Daniel L., IL
Fisher, Madeleine R., MD
Fishman, David J., CA
Flanagan-DeLorenzo, Margaret M., PA
Flashner, Gary M., PA
Fong, Jeffrey S., HI
Friedline, John A., PA
Frieman, Barbara G., MA
Gastfriend, David R., PA
Gebert, Harry F., PA
Geletka, Susan M., PA
Geraci, Stephen A., NJ
Gerber, Richard M., PA
Gill, Kevin J., PA

Fig. 451. Andrew J. Ramsay, Ph.D., Daniel Baugh Professor of Anatomy.

Gill, Lewis M., PA
Gillespy, Thurman, III, FL
Gorsuch, Paul L., Jr., TX
Grabiak, Thomas A., NJ
Graham, Alan D., MI
Greenspan, Gail S., PA
Grem, Jean L., IL
Griffin, Thomas D., PA
Grimes, Michael J., PA
Grover, Joseph G., NJ
Heald, James I., PA
Hershey, Beverly L., PA
Hill, Robert G., Jr., PA
Hiller, Tyrie L. J., DE
Holdsworth, Charles M., PA
Hopkins, James T., PA
Hu, Da-Shih, PA
Hume, Douglas P., CA
Hyde, Patrice, M., DE
Jacobson, Barry J., PA
Jahnke, Edward J., CA
Jasper, Edward H., PA
Joselson, Rae A., NJ
Kanwal, Neeraj K., PA
Kaplan, Eliot F., PA
Kaplan, Susan G., NY
Kearney, Paul A., Jr., NJ
Kiefner, Robert S., PA
Kipa, S. George, PA
Klinzing, Gerard F., PA
Korinchak, Jerome L., PA
Kornhauser, Michael S., PA
Korvick, Joyce A., PA
Krall, Michael L., CT
Krawitz, Mark J., PA
Kuhnle, Christine Margrethe, PA
Kushner, Mitchell S., NY
Lamb, Charles J., PA
Lawler, Robert A., OH
Lehman, Robert D., Jr., PA
Lehman, Thomas P., PA
Leisner, William R., PA
Lim, Nyok K., PA
Lin, Angela E., PA
Little, Edwin P., NJ
Lockard, James W., Jr., PA
Loeliger, William N., PA
Loh, Gary T., IN
Loken, Susan C., DE
Lovett, William J., DE
Lubin, Jeffrey H., FL
Lynch, Marjorie P., PA
Maguire, Leo J., III, PA
Maliver, Leonard E., NY

Malleus, Stephanie, DE
Marcelli, Gene A., Jr., PA
Marchlewski, Walter F., Jr., DE
Margolies, Richard P., PA
Margolis, Eric J., PA
Maro, Robert J., Jr., NJ
Martin, H. Frederick,III, PA
Matthews, Barbara G., PA
Matthews, Lawrence M., Jr., PA
Maxwell, Henry L., Jr., DE
McCall, Jane, SC
McCready, Paul J., DE
McGinnis, Edward J., PA
McGuire, Elizabeth A., PA
McLaughlin, Margaret L., NJ
McLaughlin, Raymond S., PA
McLemore, William E., OH
McManigle, John E., PA
Mellen, Arthur W., IV, PA
Metzger, M. Diana, DE
Millard, Frederick E., PA
Miller, Stanton B., PA
Minassian, Shahab S., PA
Mingle, Daniel B., PA
Mooney, Jane M., PA
Morrow, Nancy B., DE
Murphy, Margaret G., DE
Murphy, Michael A., PA
Nagel, David B., PA
Norris, Mark C., PA
Nowinski, Thaddeus S., PA
Nungesser, Raymond F., PA
O'Brien, Jeremiah F., PA
Owens, Thomas A., PA
Packer, Susan B., PA
Paskert, James P., PA
Perry, Richard J., PA
Pfaff, Donna M., PA
Podrasky, David F., PA
Polacheck, William J., Jr., PA
Proy, Bernard C., Jr., PA
Raczkowski, Wanda T., NJ
Reinhardt, John F., PA
Risi, George F., FL
Ritchie, Marianne T., PA
Robinson, David M., II, WV
Rommel, Catherine T., PA
Ross, D. Gwendolyn, DE
Rovner, Barry W., NJ
Rozycki, Grace F., PA
Rucker, Ellis D., CA
Rupp, James P., PA
Sandrowicz, Richard R., PA
Savage, Michael P., PA

Scariato, Albert F., PA
Schaefer, Robert M., PA
Scherer, Bernard C., PA
Schwartz, Stephen M., PA
Schweich, Daniel P., PA
Sechler, James L., PA
Shedden, Arthur H., PA
Siegel, Everett R., PA
Silko, Gary J., PA
Simpkins, Albert, Jr., PA
Snyder, Barry J., PA
Snyder, Robert J., PA
Sodroski, Joseph G., PA
Sokas, Patrick, MD
Spagnoli, Marie V., NJ
Spigel, James H., PA
Squadrito, James F., Jr., PA
Stander, Paul E., PA
Starynski, John R., PA

Tepe, Nicholas A., DE
Thomas, Robert F., Jr., PA
Toof, Richard S., PA
Trichtinger, Martin D., PA
Udofa, Daniel E., PA
Vanderlin, Robert L., II, PA
Verbeck, Stephen R., PA
Wagner, Jere L., PA
Wain, John C., Jr., PA
Wargovich, Raymond M., PA
Weisman, Kenneth M., NY
Werkman, Robert F., PA
Westgate, Randy R., PA
Wheeler, Carol A., PA
Widger, John E., PA
Williams, Clara D., TN
Wilson, James A., II, PA
Wilson, Terrence J., PA
Woog, John J., NY
Zerby, Glenn A., PA

Herbut Auditorium in College basement.

At the Commencement on June 5 in the Academy of Music the M.D. degree was conferred upon 222 graduates by President Bluemle. Thirty-two members of the class had fathers who were alumni. The Alumni Prize was won by John S. Radomski.

Dean William F. Kellow (Fig. 452) died on December 4th of this year and Frank W. Gray, Jr., M.D. (Fig. 453) was appointed Interim Dean. Dr. Kellow's accomplishments for Jefferson were recognized by the Alumni Association's Achievement Award and by the naming of the recently renovated College Building's second floor as the Kellow Conference Center.

The portraits of Drs. Carla E. Goepp, John H. Hodges (JMC, '39) and John J. Gartland (JMC, S'44) were presented to the University. John Y. Templeton, III (JMC, '41 Fig. 287) received the Alumni Achievement Award.

The *Gross Clinic* was exhibited at the Birmingham Museum of Art from February 7 to March 29.

Members of the class who obtained academic appointments at Jefferson were: John D. Angstadt and Diane R. Gillum (Instructors in Surgery); John S. Radomski and Anne L. Rosenberg (Asstistant Professors of Surgery); Linda M. D'Andrea (Instructor in Medicine); Stephen J. Schuster (Assistant Professor of Medicine); Terry Ann Estner (Instructor in Emergency Medicine); Stephen P. Gadomski (Instructor in Otolaryngology); David A. High (Instructor in Dermatology); Andrea G. Jordan (Assistant Professor of Psychiatry); William D. Kocher (Instructor in Pathology and Cell Biology); and John F. Schilling (Instructor in Radiology).

Graduates who obtained academic appointments in other institutions were: Bruce Hart (Instructor in Medicine, Temple University, Fig. 454); Karen A. Johnson (Assistant Professor of Medicine, Georgetown University); Gregory A. Kujala (Instructor in Medicine, West Virginia University); Frederic J. Matlin (Instructor in Anesthesiology, Medical College of Pennsylvania); Hilary Anne Perr (Assistant Professor of Pediatrics, Medical College of Virginia); Barry D. Rinker (Instructor in Medicine, Columbia-Presbyterian Medical Center); Diana A. Watts (Assistant Professor of Obstetrics/Gynecology, University of Washington); and Elizabeth T. Young (Assistant Professor of Anesthesiology, Tulane Medical Center).

CLASS OF 1981

Acton, Kelly J., CA
Adams, Jonathan D., PA
Allcroft, Roger A., NJ
Amer, Jeffrey A., NY
Angstadt, John D., PA
Bacon, Alfred E., III, DE
Bartlett, Frederick H., III, PA
Bercaw, David M., DE
Biles, Daniel T., PA
Billys, James B., IN
Bippart, Peter E., NJ
Blasetto, James W., NJ
Boerner, David A., PA
Brenman, Scott A., NJ
Bryner, Charles L., Jr., PA
Buckwalter, Kenneth A., PA
Cairns, Michael R., DE

Campanella, Stephen D., PA
Chan, Sophia, PA
Coar, George R., PA
Cook, Richard A., PA
Correnti, Lawrence M., PA
Cramer, Arnold J., PA
Crollick, Jill S., PA
Crosby, Victor A., II, GA
D'Andrea, Linda Maria, PA
Day, Francis P., PA
DeGroat, Thomas S., PA
Dennis, Lee M., DE
DePersia, Rudolph T., Jr., PA
Desjardins, Christine Carol, PA
Diehl, Daniel L., PA
DiIenno, Donald A., PA
DiMattia, Ralph R., PA

DonDiego, Frank R., Jr., NJ
Eckenbrecht, Paul D., DE
Edmondson, G. Mitchell, DE
Ellis, David J., PA
Emery, Donald L., DE
Estner, Terry Ann, PA
Farkas, Andrew A., PA
Feduska, Richard G., PA
Feldstein, Brad, PA
Fink, Gary E., PA
Finley, Robert K., III, OH
Fishbein, Donn S., NJ
Fluellen, Judith H., PA

Fraser, E. Kenneth, PA
Freas, Glenn C., PA
Frei, Steven P., PA
Froehlich, Hervey W., Jr., DE
Fulchiero, Randall M., PA
Gadomski, Stephen P., NJ
Gamburg, Steven J., PA
Garrett, Paul R., PA
Gaspari, Anthony A., PA
Gillum, Diane R., PA
Gilman, Philip B., PA
Gilmore, Ina M., PA
Gingrich, David N., PA

Fig. 452. William F. Kellow, M.D., Dean (1967-81).

Giordano, Guy A., PA
Goll, Stephen R., PA
Gordon, Stuart L., DC
Grant, Jeanne Olivia L., PA
Grizos, Willaim T., PA
Guardiani, Mary J., DE
Guarino, Julius M., PA
Guillard, Paul, PA
Gula-West, Cynthia L., PA
Harner, Jeffrey D., PA
Hart, Bruce, PA
Hart, Geoffrey A., DE
Heckert, Richard R., DE

Herbst, Vincent P., PA
Herrick, Wayne C., DE
Hershberger, David G., PA
High, David A., PA
Hiller, W. D. B., HI
Hillyard, Raymond W., Jr., DE
Hoffman, Jamie L., PA
Hood, Renwick C., NC
Hopkins, Benjamin T., PA
Hulkower, Stephen D., NY
Hurtt, Mark R., PA
Illions, Edward H., PA
Ingerman, Mark J., PA

Fig. 453.   Frank W. Gray, Jr., Interim Dean (1981/82).

Ishman, Raymond M., PA
Jack, Gregory M., WA
Johnson, Karen A., DE
Jordan, Andrea G., PA
Jordan, Marshall C., ME
Katz, James K., PA
Kenagy, David N., OH
Kennedy, George W., PA
Kennedy, Scott M., CA
Kester, Robert R., DE
Kirschbaum, Jodi Ann, NJ
Kocher, William D., PA
Kolker, James D., PA
Korman, Michael J., NJ
Korn, Scott H., PA
Kramer, Donald L., PA
Kress, Marc M., PA
Kruger, Mark S., PA
Kujala, Gregory A., DE
Kuranda, David J., PA
Labota, Dolores B., PA
Lamon, Kim D., PA
Langston, Gordon M., PA
Lasner, Jay E., NJ
Laucks, Samuel S., II, PA
Lawless, Stephen J., DE
Lawson, Scott R., PA
Layton, Bradley W., PA
Lehman, Matthew H., PA
Leib, Pamela L., PA
Leicht, John P., PA
Lerner, Helen B., PA
Longenbach, Eric W., PA
Mandel, Harold, PA
Mann, Robert J., PA

Mannino, David M., III, PA
Mansmann, Kevin A., PA
Marcum, Stephen C., PA
Martell, John R., Jr., PA
Mateer, Harry O., Jr., PA
Matlin, Fredric J., PA
Matthews, Martha L. S., NY
Maynard, Roy C., PA
McAninch, Malcolm L., WA
McCloskey, Michael D., CT
McKee, Violet J., CA
McWeeney, James M., CA
Mihalick, Ann L., PA
Miller, Matthew C., PA
Mirabile, Robert J., PA
Mohan, Francis P., PA
Monteiro, Dennis T., PA
Morris, Kathryn E., NJ
Myrick, Steven R., DE
Newell, Paul M., PA
O'Leary, Michael P., PA
O'Malley, Thomas F., Jr., PA
Onufrey, Victor G., PA
Pai, Eun Chan S., PA
Paul, Seth B., NY
Pennings, Simon P., PA
Perr, Hilary A., NJ
Peters, Johna H., NJ
Peterson, Albert H., NY
Pronko, Cynthia M., PA
Radomski, John S., PA
Ranish, Deborah A., PA
Remetz, Michael S., PA
Repka, Mark L., DE
Rinker, Barry D., PA
Rittenberg, Michael H., PA
Robb, Stephen S., PA
Rommel, F. Michael, PA
Rosenberg, Anne L., NJ
Rosenstein, Jerome H., PA
Rosko, Christopher J., PA
Ross, Terence C., DE
Rothstein, Marianne S., PA
Rubin, Mark G., NJ
Ruth, Corey K., WA
Rybarczyk, Richard M., PA
Sack, David M., PA
Saleeby, Eli R., PA
Schaudt, Deborah A., PA
Schauer, Joseph W., III, NJ
Schilling, John F., PA
Schroy, Paul C., III, NJ
Schuster, Stephen J., PA
Sewell, Myron L., NJ

Fig. 454. Bruce Hart (JMC, '81), engineer, lawyer, physician.

Sherard, Jerome A., PA
Shusman, Robert S., PA
Siegel, Dolores A., NJ
Siegle, John C., Jr., DE
Silver, Richard C., PA
Silverman, Edward J., PA
Skibber, John M., PA
Slagle, David C., OH
Slick, Gregory D., PA
Smith, John W., II, PA
Smith, Mark Andrew, PA
Somers, Russell E., PA
Sorokanich, Stephen, PA
Spaide, Richard F., PA
Squires, Leslie S., PA
Stabler, Craig L., PA
Staffaroni, Mark A., PA
Stanilla, Joseph K., PA
Stiner, Allan E., Jr., PA
Suarez, Paul A., NY
Sudler, Stephen A., PA
Sutter, Frederick T., PA
Swan, Barbara E., PA
Swan, David M., PA

Tam, Felix K., HONG KONG
Thompson, Charles E., PA
Ventriglia, Warren J., PA
Viscomi, Vincent A., PA
Viscusi, Eugene R., PA
Wagner, John E., Jr., DE
Watts, D. Heather, PA
Weeks, Ruthellen D., PA
Wehner, Daniel R., PA
Welch, J. Patrick, PA
West, Max L., WV
Westphal, Thomas R., PA
Wigfall, Preston A., PA
Williams, Delores J., AL
Williams, Ulysses, Jr., PA
Wilson, Thomas S., PA
Winch, George A., Jr., CA
Witt, Robert L., DE
Wofford, Emily, MS
Woynarowski, John Joseph, PA
Wugofski, Leon P., PA
Yelovich, Maureen L., PA
Yelovich, Richard M., PA
Young, Elizabeth T., PA
Zajac, Andrej J., PA

Robert T. Sataloff ('75) conducts the Jefferson choir which he founded in 1970, and also the symphony orchestra.

At the Commencement held on June 11 at the Academy of Music the M.D. degree was conferred upon 221 graduates by President Bluemle. The Alumni Prize was won by Craig H. Sherman.

In the spring of this year The Eakins Gallery in Jefferson Alumni Hall was opened (Fig. 455). This housed the world-renowned *Gross Clinic* and also two other masterpieces by Thomas Eakins,—the portraits of Benjamin Howard Rand and William Smith Forbes. Funds were supplied by the Connelly Foundation, the William Penn Foundation and Trustees. The specially designed wrought iron "Alumni Gate" was provided by the Alumni Association (Fig. 456).

The Samuel D. Gross Conference Room of the Department of Surgery on the sixth floor of the College Building was dedicated on September 10. It was constructed through voluntary funding and declared available for use by all the divisions of the University. With seating capacity for 75 persons, it provided the latest in audiovisual aids including simultaneous closed circuit television transmission from four operating rooms. The surgical heritage of Jefferson was represented with portraits, plaques, archival material and the "old operating table" used by Samuel D. Gross and others of Jefferson surgical fame (Fig. 457).

Graduates who obtained academic appointments at Jefferson were: Anthony Billas, Jr. and

Fig. 455.   Eakins Gallery.

Russell S. Breish (Instructors in Family Practice); Michael E. Goldberg (Assistant Professor of Anesthesiology); David P. Maguire (Instructor in Anesthesiology); Ralph J. Marino (Instructor in Physical Medicine and Rehabilitation); Leonard A. Nitowski (Instructor in Emergency Medicine); and Lorraine C. Palos (Instructor in Pediatrics).

Graduates who obtained academic appointments in other institutions were: Robert H. Boretsky (Assistant Professor of Anesthesiology, University of Pittsburgh); John R. Evans (Instruc-

tor in Medicine, Loma Linda University); Richard E. Hawkins (Instructor in Medicine, Eastern Virginia Medical School); James S. Lewis (Assistant Professor of Ophthalmology, Hahnemann University); Edward Lubat (Instructor in Radiology, New York University); Cary L. Lubkin (Associate Professor of Medicine, Robert Wood Johnson Medical School); Robert McNamara (Instructor in Emergency Medicine, Medical College of Pennsylvania); David L. Reich (Assistant Professor of Anesthesiology, Mount Sinai Hospital, New

Fig. 456.   Alumni Gate.

York); Devereux N. Saller (Instructor in Obstetrics/Gynecology, University of Maryland); Steven A. Scott (Instructor in Medicine, Hahnemann University); Thomas J. Wargovich (Assistant Professor of Medicine, University of Florida); and Mark L. Zwanger (Assistant Professor of Surgery, Wayne State University).

Altadonna, Victor F., NJ
Amadee, Charles M., PA
Antinozzi, Rex D., PA
Armenti, Vincent T., NJ
Armstrong, Robert W., Jr., PA
Avedissian, Michael G., PA
Banyas, Jeffrey B., PA
Bartlett, Richard A., PA
Bash, Evan K., NJ
Bashore, Randall T., PA
Biester, Robert J., PA
Bikle, Jeffrey M., PA
Billas, Anthony, Jr., PA
Blasko, Edward C., PA
Bloss, Jeffrey D., PA
Blumenthal, Sherry L., PA
Boretsky, Robert H., PA
Brantley, Kenneth M., PA
Breish, Russell S., PA
Breslow, Michael F., PA
Broad, Todd H., PA
Brockman, Ronald J., PA
Bruehlman, Richard D., DE
Carpenter, Kim L., PA
Chinn, Franklin J., Jr., CA
Chiosi, Christine, MD
Cienki, John J., PA
Clare, Timothy P., PA
Clyman, Jeffrey I., PA
Clyman, Stephen G., PA
Cohen, Alan Jay, PA
Cohen, Steven W., PA
Cohick, Bruce S., PA
Collette, Cora J., DE
Cummings, Allan H., NY
D'Amour, James E., DE
Dearolf, Walter W., III, PA
DeNunzio, Neil L., NY
Depman, Stanley T., PA
DiGerolamo, Albert, PA
Doghramji, Paul P., PA
Doherty, Eileen M., PA
Downey, Mark P., PA
Dozier, Lance C., PA
Edwards, David B., DE
Elston, Dirk M., PA

Eriksen, Christopher M., DE
Estner, Michael J., PA
Estock, David S., DE
Evans, J. Robert, CA
Evans, Robert J., PA
Feinberg, Gary L., PA
Fenton, Drew E., PA
Flashner, Steven C., PA
Fowler, Dale E., PA
Franchetti, Michael A., PA
Freed, Melanie, PA
Galdini, Angela M., PA
Gall, Janice R., PA
Gamble, Wm Bryan, CT
Gardner, John C., PA
Gersten, Larry M., NJ
Gillespy, Albert W., FL
Gilmore, Bruce S., PA
Gittlen, Stanford D., PA
Goldberg, Michael E., PA
Goldstein, Richard E., PA
Gorsen, Robert M., NJ
Greb, David C., PA
Groves, Claudia I., PA
Hagerty, Michael F., PA
Halista, Scott M., PA
Hardisky, Jo-Anne M., PA
Hawkins, Richard E., PA
Hess, Deborah K., PA
Hessen, Margaret T., PA
Hessen, Scott E., PA
Hinks, Robert P., PA
Hoidal, Charles R., DE
Horvick, David, PA
Howe, William L., PA
Huang, Marian M., DE
Iobst, William F., PA
Jackson, Edward A., PA
Jahnle, Richard L., PA
Jurkowski, Paul M., CA
Kegel, Mary F., PA
Kenna, Denise M., PA
Kine, Garrett D., PA
Kivell, Howard N., CT
Koch, Gary D., PA
Kovach, Richard C., PA

Krespan, Charles B., DE
Landin, Peter D., PA
Larkin, Gail G., DE
Laurence, William R., Jr., PA
Lauter, O. Scott, DE
Lawlis, John F., III, PA
Lefkowitz, Ilene B., PA
Levin, Alex V., PA
Lewis, James S., PA
Liberman, Orlin M., CA
Lorraine, Richard S., PA
Lubat, Edward, NY
Lubkin, Cary L., NY
Lutz, R. Bruce, III, PA
Lystash, John C., NJ
MacFarlane, A. Radford, DE
Magley, R. Scott, PA
Maguire, David P., PA
Mandelberg, Charles A., DE
Marino, Ralph J., PA
Massey, David B., NJ
McFadden, Denise C., NJ
McGeehan, Paul A., PA
McGuire, Thomas E., PA

McGurrin, Mark A., PA
McNamara, Kevin P., PA
McNamara, Robert M., PA
Midura, Alan T., NY
Monk, John S., Jr., PA
Monte, Steven A., PA
Moore, David K., DE
Moritz, Howard A., PA
Moul, Judd W., PA
Navarrete, Ricardo J., CA
Nesbitt, Richard A., PA
Nitowski, Leonard A., PA
Nogueras, Juan J., NJ
Nolan, John P., Jr., PA
Norton, Andrew J., NY
Pacropis, Richard F., PA
Palos, Lorraine C., CA
Panasuk, David B., NJ
Parent, F. Noel, III, PA
Park, Pauline K., PA
Paronish, William J., PA
Paterson, William D., PA
Pearson, Steven W., DE
Pezzi, Christpher M., PA

Fig. 457.   Samuel D. Gross conference room in Department of Surgery.

Pilla, Timothy S., PA
Platko, William P., Jr., PA
Ponchak, Stephen F., Jr., PA
Powell, James R., PA
Reich, David L., PA
Rivitz, S. Mitchell, PA
Robinson, Cynthia B., PA
Robinson, James W., WV
Robinson, Jay A., PA
Rohrer, George R., Jr., PA
Roman, Nina M., PA
Roth, Jerry M., PA
Ryan, Randall W., NJ
Saller, Deveraux N., Jr., PA
Schaefgen, Madalyn, DE
Schiowitz, Robert F., PA
Schlesinger, Robert B., PA
Schorr, Neal A., PA
Scott, Daniel A., DE
Scott, Steven A., NJ
Seeger, A. Randall, DE
Setzkorn, Ronald K., PA
Shelley, Mark H., PA
Sherman, Craig H., NY
Sidor, Carolyn F., DE
Signorella, Albert M., MA
Singer, Stuart J., PA
Slompak, Carol A., PA
Smith, George F., Jr., NJ
Smith, Gregory T., PA
Smith, Tina M., PA
Sobie, Stephen R., NY
Solomon, Ira S., NY
Songer, John E., PA
Sorensen, Maryanne, NJ
Sorenson, Julie D., NH
Springer, James C., PA
Stauffer, Daniel J., PA
Stella, Joseph H., NJ

Strauser, Walter W., PA
Strittmatter, John M., PA
Stuck, Craig A., PA
Stull, Mark W., PA
Sumfest, Joel M., PA
Szucs, Richard A., PA
Tenn, David T., CA
Thistlethwaite, Alan J., PA
Thomas, Cynthia, PA
Tilley, John W., Jr., PA
Tompkins, Kenneth J., PA
Tressler, Allene M., PA
Trujillo, Lloyd L., CO
Turchin, Louise H., NY
Turissini, Thomas J., PA
Uniacke, Brian M., DE
Vause, Sandra E., PA
Vernace, Joseph V., PA
vonCleff, Julius S., III, PA
Vorys, Ann S., OH
Vossenberg, Frans A., III, PA
Walker, Lise C., NV
Wallick, Peter G., PA
Walls, Joseph P., PA
Wargovich, Thomas J., PA
Weaverling, Eric R., PA
Whetzel, Thomas P., PA
Wilson, John A., Jr., PA
Wilson-King, Genester S., PA
Wolf, Marie Bush, PA
Woods, Essie J., TN
Woods, Kathleen J., PA
Yamamoto, Kenneth A., PA
Yaros, Mark F., PA
Yee, Jerry, PA
Zolnick, Mark R., DE
Zorch, Michael J., PA
Zorch, Paul M., PA
Zurad, Edward G., PA
Zwanger, Mark L., NJ

A wise man should consider that health is the greatest of human blessings, and learn by his own thought to derive benefit from his illnesses.

Hippocrates (460-370 B.C.)

At the Commencement held in the Academy of Music on June 10, President Bluemle conferred M.D. degrees upon 211 graduates. Honorary degrees, reflecting the increasing emphasis on basic medical sciences, were awarded to Baruch S. Blumberg, winner of the Nobel Prize in Medicine and Physiology (1976); Robert Charles Gallo (JMC, '63, Fig. 386 & 458), noted researcher and Chief of the Laboratory of Tumor Cell Biology at the National Cancer Institute; Isaac Asimov, prolific writer and biochemist with emphasis on popular interpretation of scientific data; and Ruth Patrick, former Curator and later Chairman of the Board of the Academy of Natural Sciences of Philadelphia and recipient of many awards for scientific accomplishments.

For the second time highest honors were awarded to a woman graduate, Mary Frances Boyle (Fig. 459). She was appointed to Massachusetts General Hospital.

After only one year Dean Leah Lowenstein resigned September 1, 1983, because of failing health (Fig. 460). She was succeeded by Dr. Joseph S. Gonnella who served as Acting Dean until his unanimous election as Dean the following year.

Professor of Anatomy John Raymond Shea, Ph.D. was selected for the honor of the annual senior class portrait which was presented May 26. On June 22, the portrait of Dr. Samuel S. Conly (JMC, S'44, Fig. 304) was presented by friends and colleagues at the time of his retirement as Associate Dean for Admissions.

The annual Alumni Achievement Award was presented to Francis J. Sweeney, Jr. (JMC, '51, Fig. 335), Hospital Director and Vice President for Health Services.

Early career appointments were received by a number of graduates in academic posts. Among those joining the Jefferson Faculty were Irene Phillips Raisis, Leonidas W. Raisis and Edward M. Podgorski, Jr., all Instructors in Radiology. Joseph M. Henry was appointed Instructor in Surgery. Anthony J. Prestipino became Assistant

Professor of Pathology and Cell Biology. Paul F. Mansfield was appointed to the Board of Trustees of Thomas Jefferson University in June, 1983, and served a three-year term (Fig. 461).

Appointments to other medical faculties included Fred Caroll, winner of the Prize in Pediatrics, who was appointed Assistant Professor of Pediatrics affiliated with Westchester County Medical Center, Valhalla, New York. Stephen A. Edmundowicz in 1988 joined the faculty of Washington University School of Medicine, St. Louis, as Assistant Professor of Internal Medicine (Gastroenterology); he was speaker for his class at its fifth reunion in 1988, discussing biliary stone dis-

Fig. 458. Robert C. Gallo (JMC, '63), receives an honorary degree from his alma mater.

ease. Peter R. Bergethon was Instructor in Internal medicine at Boston University Affiliated Hospitals. Margaret Mary Corboy was Assistant Professor of Pediatrics at Robert Wood Johnson Medical School, Piscataway, New Jersey. David J. Kramer became Assistant Professor of Anesthesiology at Presbyterian-University Hospital, Pittsburgh and Craig M. Palmer served in the same capacity at the University of Arizona Medical Center, Tucson. Wayne K. Ross was Instructor in Pathology at Emory University School of Medicine, Atlanta.

Albertson, Keith S., PA
Allen, Brian D., NJ
Andersen, James S., DE
Arthur, Kenneth R., PA
Ashcom, Thomas L., PA
Baker, Richard P., III, PA
Baum, Neil B., PA
Bergethon, Peter R., PA
Bertolino, John G., PA
Bitterman, Stuart R., NY
Blair, Ellen K., PA
Blazek, F. Douglas, PA

Fig. 459. Mary F. Boyle (JMC,'83), awarded the highest honors at graduation.

Bleznak, Aaron D., PA
Blinn, Lawrence A., NJ
Bowers, Jeffery J., PA
Boyajian, James G., PA
Boyer, Debra, PA
Boyle, Mary F., PA
Brenner, Lawrence D., PA
Buonanno, Susan M., PA
Buyalos, Richard P., Jr., MD
Cacciola, Thomas A., NJ
Campbell, Kevin M., PA
Carnevale, Thomas A., DE
Carney, James J., DE
Carroll, Fred, PA
Carter, Debbie Rene, NY
Chain, Jeffrey R., PA
Chang, Robert M., NJ
Chasteney, Mark E., PA
Chauhan, Suneet B., PA
Chen, George T., PA
Chesen, Neil, PA
Choi, Hin Sing, PA
Christian, Dean A., PA
Clemson, Barry S., PA
Clinch, Thomas E., PA
Cognetti, Peter A., PA
Cohen, Joel R., PA
Colavita, Mauro A., PA
Corboy, Margaret Mary, PA
Cullen, Michael H., CT
Curtin, Andrew J., PA
D'Amelio, Louis F., PA
Daly, Theodore J., NY
Davies, Barbara Lea, PA
Davis, Paul K., PA
Demmy, Todd L., PA
Drabick, Joseph J., PA
Durkan, William J., PA
Edmundowicz, Steven A., PA
Edwards, Mark, PA
Feinstein, Alex, PA
Feldman, Ellen K., PA
Fetterolf, Michael L., PA
Freed, Jeffrey A., NJ
Freeman, Richard B., Jr., NY
Fugate, Howard, III, PA

Fig. 460. Leah Lowenstein, M.D., D. Phil., Dean (1982/83).

Fig. 461. Paul F. Mansfield (JMC, '83) served a three-year term on Jefferson's Board of Trustees.

Little, Nancy A., PA
Long, Ronald A., PA
Lucarella, Vanessa J., PA
Mackin, Glenn A., PA
Madara, Glenn S., NJ
Maguire, Joseph I., PA
Manning, Richard G., PA
Mansfield, Paul F., PA
Markind, Samuel H., PA
Maslin, Stuart J., PA
Massari, Ferdinand E., MD
Matheson, Donald S., NY
Mathias, Brad T., PA
Maurer, Philip M., PA
Mazanek, Gregory J., PA
McCrone, Elcinda L., PA
McDonald, Michael M., PA
McDonnel, James K., CO
McShane, Elizabeth, DE
Meade, Thomas D., PA
Michelson, Peter H., MA
Miller, Wayne, DE
Naegele, Karl Theodore, PA
Nasca, Leonardo S., Jr., PA
Niehls, Beverly, NJ
Norelli, Charles C., PA
O'Brien, Lynn Murphy, NY
O'Brien, Walter M., PA
O'Neil, Kevin, DE
Olewnik, Ann B., DE
Orr, Daniel G., PA
Osenbach, Richard K., PA
Ott, Gary Y., PA
Palmer, Craig M., DE
Pascucci, Stephen E., Jr., PA
Pearcy, Cornell, PA
Philbrick, Kemuel L., MN
Phillips, Irene, DE
Piercy, Elizabeth A., PA
Podgorski, Edward M., Jr., NJ
Prata, James M., PA
Prestipino, Anthony J., PA
Price, Donna B., DE
Rach, Joel F., PA
Raisis, Leonidas W., NJ
Rees, Glenys S., DE
Reid, James H., III, PA
Ritter, James M., DE
Rogers, Susan L., PA
Romanic, Bruce M., PA
Roscoe, Diane L., PA
Ross, Wayne K., PA
Rozick, Mark S., PA
Rubinstein, Mark I., PA

Ruffini, John J., PA
Russell, W. Randall, PA
Ruthardt, Frederick W., Jr., PA
Sailer, Dale W., PA
Sariego, Joaquin, Jr., PA
Sattel, Andrew B., NJ
Sayre, Rodger C., PA
Schneider, Lynda C., PA
Seaford, John W., PA
Shanholtz, Carl B., PA
Sheehe, Dennis M., PA
Shelman, Keith B., PA
Shoupe, Branden A., DE
Shrader, W. Eric, PA
Silverman, Howard S., PA
Sims, Amy Louise, PA
Singh, Ajay B., PA
Sipski, Marca Leonise, NJ
Slenker, Kevin F., PA
Sloan, Dean A., PA
Smith, Henry Francis, Jr., PA
Spielman, Sheryl B., PA
Spinuzza, Thomas J., PA
Squiers, Elizabeth C., MI
Stang, Robert B., NJ
Sunnergren, Kenneth P., PA
Sutyak, John P., PA
Sygenda, James Thomas, PA
Talamo, Robert J., PA
Thatcher, Jeffrey D., PA
Thornsley, Susan L., PA
Thornton, Lauren E., PA
Trezza, Scott A., PA
Tripp, Warren H., Jr., PA
Tuke, Kessi Moses O., NJ
Usala, Anton-Lewis, DE
Varga, Jeffrey M., PA
Vossler, David G., NJ
Waciega, Mark, PA
Wagner, James D., PA
Waldron, Peter E., PA
Walker, Stephen R., PA
Walsh, Timothy P., PA
Walton, Paul L., PA
Weiss, Steven J., PA
Weissberger, Ruth E., NJ
Welsh, Theresa M., PA
Werhun, Anthony T., PA
Whiteman, Mitchell S., DE
Willet, Andrew A., PA
Wilson, Thomas G., PA
Yingling, Bryan L., PA
Zeller, Donald J., PA
Zon, Leonard I., PA
Zumsteg, Thomas A., DE

1983

~ 1984 ~

The annual Commencement was held June 8 at the Academy of Music. President Bluemle conferred the M.D. degree upon 212 graduates. Honorary degrees were awarded to Sidney Weinhouse, Ph.D., Emeritus Professor of Biochemistry and Director of the Fels Research Institute at Temple University School of Medicine, who was nationally recognized for advances in cancer research; Francis Clark Wood, M.D., Emeritus Professor and former Chairman of the Department of Medicine, University of Pennsylvania School of Medicine and a distinguished teacher; and John A.D. Cooper, M.D., President of the Association of American Medical Colleges, a medical statesman, scholar and educator. Dr. Cooper presented the commencement address.

The Alumni Prize for the highest cumulative average was won by John Wesley Spurlock who went on for his further training to Walter Reed Hospital.

Joseph S. Gonnella, M.D. (Fig. 462) was unanimously elected Dean to succeed the late Leah Lowenstein (Fig. 460).

An outstanding alumnus, Joe Henry Coley (JMC, '34, Fig. 267) received the Cornerstone Award of the President's Club (Fig. 463) for his fund raising and personal contributions.

The Alumni Achievement Award for the year was made posthumously to Abraham E. Rakoff, M.D. (JMC, '37, Fig. 274), Professor of Obstetrics/Gynecology, whose many scientific contributions to the field of infertility and gynecologic endocrinology were nationally acclaimed.

On April 27 the Herbert A. Luscombe Visiting Lectureship was inaugurated with a presentation by Irwin M. Braverman, M.D., Professor of Dermatology at Yale University School of Medicine. Dr. Luscombe continued to serve as Professor and Chairman of Dermatology at Jefferson until his Emeritus status in 1986.

The Class of 1984 selected Robert J. Mandle, Ph.D., Professor of Microbiology, for its Senior Class Portrait. Dr. Mandle's teaching skills had previously been recognized by his receipt of the Lindback Award in 1979. Harold L. Israel (JMC, '34, Fig. 266), Emeritus Professor of Medicine, was honored with the presentation of his portrait September 14. His accomplishments in pulmonary medicine and his pioneering in the study of sarcoidosis were thus recognized.

Jefferson faculty appointments were achieved by several 1984 graduates. Peter A. DeMaria, Jr. was made Medical Director of the Narcotic Addict Rehabilitation Program and Instructor in Psychiatry and Human Behavior in 1989. Kathleen Shander Guarneri was appointed Instructor in Anesthesiology also in 1989. Bruce I. Blatt was an Instructor in Medicine and Michael J. Rupp Instructor in Pathology and Cell Biology.

Appointments to other medical schools included James P. Daubert, Associate Professor of Internal Medicine, Duke University Medical Center, Durham; Richard T. Cook, Assistant Professor of Emergency Medicine at Hershey Medical Center; Mary C. Martini, Assistant Professor of Dermatology, Presbyterian-University of Pennsylvania Hospital; Michael J. Stewart, Instructor in Internal Medicine, Northwestern University Medical School, Chicago; and Marijo Ann Zelinka, Instructor in Pediatrics at West Virginia University Medical Center, Morgantown.

CLASS OF 1984

Allen, James E., PA
Angeloni, Vincent L., PA
Bakewell, Brock K., PA
Bartlow, William P., PA
Bartman, Barbara A., PA
Basista, Michael H., OH

Beers, Richard A., PA
Beneski, Daniel A., PA
Berman, Claudia G., WA
Blatt, Bruce I., PA
Boyle, Sean P., PA
Briggs, Roberto E., MD

Carter, Thomas L., Jr., CA
Celestine, Gerald T., PA
Chen, Steve T., NJ
Chow, Joseph W., PA
Christie, C. Michele, PA
Clair, David L., PA
Clark, Maureen D., PA
Cohen, Herbert T., PA
Colangelo, Francis R., PA
Cole, Daniel J., PA
Collier, William E., PA
Collins, Deirdre M., PA
Cook, Frederick J., DE
Cook, James A., DE
Cook, Richard T., Jr., NJ
Cooley, Susan L., PA

Cox, John F., PA
Dabney, Kirk W., PA
Daitch, Jonathan S., NJ
Daniel, John C., PA
Daubert, James P., NJ
Davoli, Robert L., PA
DeAntonio, Angela M., PA
DeCandis, Francis X., PA
DellaCroce, Joseph M., PA
DeMaria, Peter A., Jr., PA
Dennen, Timothy J., PA
Devlin, Charlie W., SC
Dietz, Bernhard E., PA
DiNicola, Maribeth M., PA
Doherty, Michael J., DE
Dolphin, Basil, PA

Fig. 462.   Joseph S. Gonnella, M.D., Dean (1984-).

Duer, Nathan B., PA
Duker, Jay S., PA
Early, Robert F., Jr., PA
Eberts, Paul M., II, PA
Edwards, Karen A., NY
Edwards, Terry L., PA
Egan, Richard J., Jr., PA
Eisenman, Jesse H., DE
Ellis, Christina E., PA
Escoll, Andrew J., PA
Evans, Richard C., CA
Flick, Pamela A., PA
Forsyth, Kyle L., PA
Fox, Elisabeth A., PA
Furnary, Anthony P., PA
Gillan, Ernest F., PA
Glick, Andrew J., DE
Gold, Howard S., PA
Goldbach, Norman J., PA
Gordon, Gregory R., PA
Grabiak, Charles F., Jr., NJ
Grimm, Ian S., NJ
Grindlinger, Jonathan L., PA
Guarnieri, Kathleen S., PA

Halenda, Gregory, PA
Hardy, Kevin R., PA
Harvey, W. Frederic, PA
Heffner, George W., Jr., PA
Hellerman, Pamela E., PA
Henrickson, Michael, DE
Hill, David W., CA
Hlavac, Cheryl A., PA
Hoerner, Kathleen M., PA
Hoover, Todd A., PA
Hosford-Skapof, Martha A., PA
Houston, William M., Jr., PA
Huffard, Robert S., PA
Hufnal-Miller, Carrie A., DE
Hultsch-Smith, Sara E., PA
Hurowitz, Gerald I., PA
Hutchinson, Douglas T., DE
Inverso-Kirkland, Michele R., PA
Jaffe, Jonathan S., PA
Kane, Michael A. C., PA
Kapoor, Deepak A., NY
Kates, Michael B., PA
Katz, Steven A., PA
Kavanagh, James K., TX

Fig. 463.   President Bluemle presents the Cornerstone Award to Joe Henry Coley (JMC, '34), accompanied by Mrs. Coley.

608   1984

Kazal, Louis A., Jr., PA
Kelly, John J., III, PA
Kendig, Newton E., II, PA
Kerrigan, James J., DE
King, Douglas R., PA
Kiproff, Paul M., PA
Kirshner, Drew L., PA
Klimowicz, Maryida, DE
Kravitz, Daniel B., PA
Kubiak, Joseph S., Jr., PA
Kushner, Jonathan D., PA
Lantos, Thomas J., PA
Leach, Lois Marie, MA
Leinberry, Charles F., Jr., PA
Leopold, Ronald S., PA
Lerner, Lori A., PA
Lien, Jean M., PA
Lindner, Henry H., PA
Lisehora, George B., DE
Liu, Evan Y., PA
Lynch, David J., PA
MacAndrew, Vincent I., Jr., RI
Macones, Alexnader J., Jr., PA
Magill, Ian D., PA
Mansmann, Paris T., PA
Markowitz, Laurie E., CA
Martin, James J., PA
Martin, Robert A., PA
Martini, Mary C., PA
Maslow, Joel N., PA
McGee, Michael J., PA
Megivern, Daniel G., PA
Meikle, Robert W., PA
Michael, Herman J., Jr., PA
Miller, Randolph J., DE
Mizes, Craig B., CA
Mock, Gregory D., PA
Monihan, James M., DE
Montella, Joseph M., PA
Moore, Thomas A., II, WV
Moyer, Robert A., PA
Nair, Suresh G., PA
Nard, James A., III, PA
Nguyenpho, Hoa T., VA
Oberholtzer, John C., PA
Orlick, Martin E., FL
Osei-Tutu, Ernest P., DE
Palermo, Francis A., DE
Panitch, Deborah, MA
Pastor, Larry H., PA
Pedrotty, John C., PA
Penny, Stephen F., PA
Petrillo, Raymond J., PA
Phillips, Eric D., PA

Pickett, Clifford, Jr., NJ
Pihoker, Catherine M., PA
Polin, David G., PA
Possanza, Carl J., PA
Prosperi, Aldo J., PA
Rappaport, Steven H., MD
Reedman, Gail A., PA
Rehfuss, Kathleen Louise, PA
Reynolds, Bradley P., PA
Reynolds, V. Karen A., PA
Rhee, John W., PA
Rivas, David A., PA
Rogalski, Cynthia, NJ
Rosenblatt, Michael S., NJ
Rosenblum, Benjamin A., PA
Ross, Ellen I., PA
Ruffini, Robert A., PA
Rupp, Michael J., PA
Ruth, John A., Jr., DE
Ruzbarsky, Philip J., PA
Sahelian, Ray R., PA
Saxe, Jonathan C., PA
Schmouder, Robert L., PA
Schoen, Michael I., PA
Schuman, Robert J., NY
Schwabe, Karl G., NJ
Schwartz, Steven R., PA
Sell, Ronald J., PA
Seller, Michael S., NY
Seltzer, Alan M., DE
Shirey, Pamela S., PA
Siegel, Ayn D., PA
Sieger, David D., PA
Silver, Joel S., CA
Slack, James W., NJ
Slimak, Randall E., PA
Smith, David A., PA
Smith, Ruth E., NY
Snipes, Edward R., PA
Snyder, Lincoln M., CA
Sostok, Michael A., PA
Spellman, James E., Jr., PA
Spikol, Louis E., PA
Spurlock, John W., PA
Stevens, Charles K., FL
Stewart, Michael J., PA
Stofman, Guy M., PA
Stoner, Mary F., NJ
Stoner, Richard S., PA
Storm, Randle H., PA
Stroz, Margaret M., DE
Tabas, Janet H., PA
Tobin, Richard W., Jr., DE
Trubilla, Susan J., PA

1984

609

Uhl, Richard L., NJ
Wallace, Robert D., PA
Wargovich, James P., PA
Wenzel, David R., IL
White, Mary B., ME
Wilson, Brian D., PA

Winter, Robert D., PA
Wolf, Lisa C., NJ
Wolfert, Irwin H., PA
Xenophon, James C., NY
Yonemura, Kenneth S., CA
Zelinka, Marijo A., PA

For the first time, Annual Alumni Giving exceeded $1,000,000 (1983/84).

At the Commencement held at the Academy of Music June 7, President Bluemle conferred the M.D. degree upon 210 graduates. The honorary degree of Doctor of Humane Letters was awarded to William B. Bean, M.D., longtime Professor and Chairman of Internal Medicine at the University of Iowa School of Medicine. Author, editor, historian and teacher, Dr. Bean's accomplishments, especially his literary skills, were widely acclaimed. W. Paul Havens, Jr., M.D., Professor of Medicine and Microbiology at Jefferson, was awarded the honorary degree of Doctor of Science, recognizing his research achievements in viral hepatitis as well as his writing and teaching contributions.

The Alumni Prize was won by Kenneth James Arnold (Fig. 464). The Mohler Prize and the Kellow Prize were both awarded to Mary Elizabeth Rueckel.

The 1985 Alumni Achievement Award was presented to Charley J. Smythe, M.D. (JMC, '35, Fig. 271), Professor of Medicine, University of Colorado. Dr. Smythe, an early rheumatologist, was formerly President of the American Rheumatism Association and the National Society of Rheumatology. A noted teacher, clinician and author, he received many awards including a Commendation from President Gerald Ford.

The Senior Class Portrait honored Jefferson's Warren R. Lang, M.D. (JMC '43, Fig. 293), Professor of Obstetrics/Gynecology and later the first Aponte Professor and Chairman of the Department of Pathology. Dr. Lang was long a favorite teacher and his research in gynecologic cytology was widely recognized including the Papanicolau Award of the American Society of Cytology.

Susan Bullitt Ward (Fig. 465) of this class was the great-great-great granddaughter of Samuel D. Gross (JMC, 1828, Fig. 11), founder of the Alumni Association in 1870. From her family heirlooms she generously donated to Jefferson a copy of the Samuel Bell Waugh portrait of her famous ancestor as well as a scrap book of news-

paper clippings and correspondence relating to his death in 1884. Dr. Ward trained in rheumatology and joined the Jefferson faculty.

Early academic appointments were acquired by a few class members as careers were evolving. Mary Lisa Gunning, after a period of training at Duke University Medical Center, returned to Family Medicine at Jefferson as Instructor. Gayle Ann Hopper was named Assistant Professor of Family Practice at the University of Maryland, and Mary E. Rueckel Patti Instructor in Internal Medicine at Eastern Virginia Graduate Medical School, Norfolk.

Fig. 464. Kenneth J. Arnold (JMC, '85), Alumni Prize winner.

Albright, William J., PA
Allen, Amy J., NY
Altman, David S., PA
Amrick, Thomas J., PA
Andrews, Peter J., Jr., PA
Androkites, Arthur T., PA
Arnold, Kenneth J., PA
Ball, Robert A., PA
Baran, James J., PA
Barna, Nicholas J., PA
Baseman, Alan S., PA
Baylor, Richard D., PA
Belgrade, Joseph M., DE

Bennett, Paula R., PA
Berlin, Paul J., DE
Bertsch, David J., PA
Boos, Lauren M., NY
Borkowski, Teresa A., PA
Boyle, Brian F., PA
Bregman, Daniel K., DE
Bubenheim, Daniel M., PA
Buinewicz, Brian R., PA
Camerota, Andrew M., PA
Camishion, Germaine M., PA
Canty, Thomas P., NJ
Carney, Mary D., RI

Fig. 465. Susan Bullitt Ward (JMC, '85) stands before the portrait of Samuel D. Gross, her great-great-great-grandfather.

Cautilli, Richard A., Jr., PA
Chaputa, Melanie M., PA
Chernoff, David B., PA
Cherry, Kenneth L., Jr., PA
Clemente, Joseph A., DE
Columbus, Michael J., PA
Coughlin, Cynthia Marie, RI
Dalton, Matthew L., PA
Dankoff, Joseph S., PA
Dashow, Larry J., PA
Daubert, Jack G., PA
David, Richard D., CA
DeLaurentis, Mark, NJ
Deliyannides, Deborah A., PA
Devlin, James E., PA
DiCenzo, Donna M., PA
Edmonds, Lee C., PA
Ellis, Scott J., DE
Fabi, Mark B., PA
Fahy, Brenda G., PA
Felmly, William T., NY
Field, Bonni S., DE
Fink, David L., PA
Fink, David M., PA
Fishbein, Gary E., PA
Fiss, Michael-Dennis Anthony, CA
Flynn, Karin, NJ
Fromuth, Thomas E., PA
Fusia, Tod J., PA
Gallagher, Michael D., PA
Gansner, Robyn K., PA
George, Bradley A., PA
Georgetson, Michael J., PA
Gest, Steven A., CA
Gibbons, Mary Stull, DC
Gillis, Angus T., PA
Gilman, Andrew L., OH
Gilman, Gary R., PA
Girdhar-Gopal, Harsha V., NY
Glauser, Tracy A., PA
Goldfine, Carole S., PA
Goldschmidt, Joseph C., Jr., PA
Goldstone, Andrew C., PA
Goyal, Amit, NJ
Greco, Robert M., PA
Grubbs, David S., DE
Gunning, Mary Lisa, PA
Gzesh, Dan J., PA
Haimowitz, Bernard, PA
Harned, E. Michael, PA
Harvey, William J., PA
Hassel, Mark H., PA
Helinek, Thomas G., PA
Herbert, Lawrence G., NY

Herring, Steven J., PA
Hewlett, Guy S., VI
Hickey, Joseph J., PA
Hickey, Robert W., PA
Hoobler, Randall J., PA
Hopper, Gayle A., DE
Hummel, Mark J., DE
Isaac, Leon A. C., VI
Jacob, Thomas C., Jr., PA
Jacobs, Jeffrey M., DE
Jacobs, Jill E., NJ
Jalali, Shailen, MD
Kalchman, Steven H., PA
Kane, Anthony M., PA
Kelly, Mark F., PA
Kern, Robert C., NJ
Kesselring, Joseph J., PA
Krohn, Jonathan S., NY
Kruger, Mitchel, PA
Kruger, Scott, PA
Kuchar, John J., Jr., PA
Lane, John I., PA
LaNeve, Ralph J., PA
Larson, John R., NJ
Lasker, Halette, R., PA
Lehrman, Bruce J., PA
Lentz, Mark R., PA
Levin, Matthew W., PA
Long, J. Stephen, PA
Lorah, Kevin N., PA
Loughran, James P., PA
Mabey, Rex G., Jr., ID
Machiko, Gregory G., PA
MacKay, Gregory D., PA
Madonick, Harvey L., PA
Maholtz, Michele S., PA
Mailman, Wendy R., PA
Mandalaskas, Nicholas J., PA
Mannella, Randall G., PA
Marchant, DeForrest W., PA
Maroney, Jane W., DE
Martin, John A., Jr., VA
Massari, Luisa F., MD
Maus, Marlon T.,, MEXICO
McAninch, Gregg W., WA
McConnell, Jeffrey R., NJ
McGarry, Thomas F., Jr., PA
McLaughlin, Elgie R., PA
McMorris, Marc S., AZ
Meikle, George C., PA
Mendez, Armando A., DE
Meyers, Joel S., PA
Meza, Manuel P., MI
Michalski, John A., PA

Milewski, Julia A., DE
Miller, Celeste June, PA
Mingey, John R., PA
Mitchell, Carol G., PA
Motley, Robert J., PA
Nardi, David A., NJ
Nardone, Donald T., PA
Newman, Schuyler, PA
O'Brien, Thomas M., PA
Orndorf, Thomas P., PA
Patti, Michael J., PA
Patti, Richard B., PA
Philip, George, PA
Plotzker, Edward D., PA
Pompey, Daniel T., Jr., PA
Prabhu, Sumanth D., PA
Priem, Robert W., PA
Pronesti, George R., PA
Ramos, Theodore, FL
Reihard, Kathryn A., PA
Ricciardi, Susan L., PA
Robertson, Carol F., DE
Robertson, Frank M., DE
Rosenberg, Dale J., PA
Rosner, Michael S., PA
Rowland, Robert B., Jr., PA
Rueckel, Mary E., NJ
Sajer, Susan A., PA
Saukkonen, Jussi J., PA
Schadt, Mark E., PA
Schaeffer, Scott J., PA
Scimeca, Gregory H., NJ
Scott, Richard D., PA
Sebastian, Linda Andrea, PA
Seifert, Carol Lee, PA
Seres, David S., OR
Sigal, Robert K., PA
Skibber, Sharon A., PA

Skypala, Patricia L., PA
Slimak, Grace G., NJ
Smith, Spurgeon S., VT
Smith, Thomas C., PA
Snyder, Jeffrey C., PA
Sonsini, Gregg A., PA
Sourbeer, Jay C., FL
Spiegel, Richard H., PA
Stefanelli, James L., PA
Stern, David E., PA
Stern, Debora Lynn, PA
Stoloff, Amy C., PA
Syms, Charles A., III, PA
Szgalsky, Joseph B., PA
Tedesco, Louis J., PA
Tran, Michael S., PA
Tran, Nho Van, PA
Travitz, Ronald P., PA
Truscott, Kenneth D., Jr., PA
Versland, Mark R., NJ
Wagner, Brent J., PA
Wainstein, Jeffrey L., PA
Walker, Robert B., PA
Wang, Lawrence C. M., NJ
Ward, Susan B., PA
Weaver, Amy L., PA
Weber, Susan L., PA
Wein, Barry K., DE
Welkie, John F., PA
Welty, Katherine K., PA
Whiting, Donald M., PA
Wilk, Richard M., DE
Winkler, Jeffrey R., PA
Yavorek, Henry G., Jr., PA
Zeeman, Beth A., PA
Zorn, Burkhardt H., PA
Zuch, Robert H., AZ
Zucker, Miriam S., PA

Life is short, and the Art long; the occasion fleeting; experience fallacious, and judgment difficult. The physician must do what is right himself, but also make the patient, the attendants, and externals co-operate.

Hippocrates (460-370 B.C.)

~ 1986 ~

The Commencement was held on June 6 at the Academy of Music, at which time the M.D. degree was conferred upon 222 graduates by President Bluemle. Honorary degrees were awarded to Hilary Koprowski, M.D., Director of the Wistar Institute of Anatomy and Biology, and to Carol M. McCarthy, Ph.D., President of the American Hospital Association. The Alumni Prize was won by Eliav Barr (Fig. 466).

The University Mace (Fig. 467) was carried for the first time in the 1986 Commencement. It was the noble emblem of the University's heritage, for use at all formal academic processions.

Fig. 466.   Eliav Barr (JMC, '85), winner of Alumni Prize.

The Christian R. and Mary F. Lindback Award for Distinguished Teaching was given to George C. Brainard, Ph.D., Associate Professor of Neurology (Basic Sciences) and to Willis C. Maddrey, M.D., the Magee Professor of Medicine and Chairman of the Department (Clinical Sciences). The Burlington Northern Foundation Faculty Achievement Award for excellence in teaching and research productivity was given to Marion J. Siegman, Ph.D., Professor of Physiology (Basic Sciences) and to Laird G. Jackson, M.D., Professor of Medicine and Director of the Division of Genetics (Clinical Sciences).

The Alumni Achievement Award was bestowed upon Gerald D. Dodd (JMC, '47, Fig. 318), a national leader in the field of radiology. He served as President of the American College of Radiology, a Trustee of the American Board of Radiology, and Vice President of the American Roentgen Ray Society.

In this year, the Jefferson campus was extended farther by the dedication on July 29 of the new Medical Office Building (Fig. 468) on the southwest corner of Eleventh and Walnut Streets, adjacent to the Forrest Theater. This eight-story building constructed at a cost of $12 million contained an organized variety of outpatient departments, along with physicians' offices supplementing those in the Edison Building of 1974 and the Thomas Jefferson University Hospital of 1978.

The "Decade Fund of the Eighties" reached $60 million and would soon thereafter exceed the goal of $65 million in four years less than projected.

John C. Cardone became an Instructor in General Surgery at the University of Medicine and Dentistry (N.J.), Newark. At this time the graduates became dispersed in residencies that included Family Medicine, which, since becoming a formally organized specialty, attracted increasing numbers of trainees. Many of these would pursue their careers in academic medicine while others would ultimately become leaders in the practice of their communities.

Adler, Lawrence M., IL
Alman, Benjamin A., PA
Austin, David K., NY
Auteri, Joseph S., PA
Bailey, James L., PA
Baka, Joseph J., OH
Baker, Karen S., PA
Barr, Eliav, MI
Bautista, Alejandro A., CA
Bayo, Alexis J., Jr., NY
Bell, Joseph G., PA
Belles, William J., PA
Berger, Mitchell R., NY
Beyer, John C., PA
Birnbaum, Glenn A., NY
Bluestine, Steven J., PA
Boerner, Thomas F., PA
Boreen, Stuart M., PA
Boring, Steele D., FL
Bowker, Beverly L., NJ
Bradbury, Andrew R., PA

Bradley, Timothy M., PA
Brotman, David N., NY
Brown-Gibson, Elizabeth L., PA
Brown, Melissa C. M., PA
Brown, Michael T., PA
Brown, Patti J. S., PA
Buinewicz, Anna M., PA
Bunnell, Eugene, PA
Burge, Daniel J., DE
Campbell, Glenn C., PA
Cardone, John C., PA
Carey, Andrew B., DE
Carter, W. Bradford, CA
Cautilli, George P., PA
Chase, Jeffrey M., DE
Chen, Lin H., PA
Clark, Anthony J., CT
Clark, Francis J., PA
Coar, Daniel N., DE
Cohen, David M., PA
Cohen, Ellen M., NY
Cohn, David B., PA

Fig. 467.   With the University Mace, first carried in 1986, are Grand Marshall Robert J. Mandle, Ph.D. and President of the Board, Edward C. Driscoll.

Comiter, Scott L., NY
Cook, Philip I., PA
Cooper, Paul S., NJ
Corson, Gail R., MA
Cortina, Gary J., PA
Costa, Ralph F., PA
Cox, Walter R., PA
Coyle, Denise E. G., PA
Coyle, Walter J. E., DE
Cummings, Hugh B., NY
Czajkowski, Thomas J., PA
Daghir, John N., PA
Danella, John F., PA
Davis, Richard G., PA
Davis, Timothy A., PA
Dawson, Bessann, DE
DeBias, Dennis A., PA
Deguchi, Mario, PA
DeLago, Cynthia W., PA
Dowling, Richard J., DE
Dragon, Greg R., PA

Durinzi, Karen L., PA
Dwyer, Boyd A., NJ
Earle, Linda A., NJ
Eschelman, David J., PA
Famiglio, Gregory, PA
Farrell, Melanie A., CA
Fechtner, Lawrence M., NJ
Fineman, Jay S., PA
Fisch, Paul J., CA
Freimuth, Loren M., PA
Fulginiti, John, III, PA
Gallivan, William R., Jr., CA
Gibson, Joseph M., PA
Gibson, Keith, PA
Gibson, Ken, PA
Gillespy, Mark C., FL
Gohsler, Steven P., PA
Gould, John H., NJ
Grasso, Michael, III, PA
Graziani, Virginia, PA
Greco-Hunt, Valerie T., PA

Fig. 468. Medical Office Building (1986).

Grossman, Sheila S., PA
Haas, David R., PA
Hackman, H. Holly, RI
Haimowitz, Marcia D., PA
Halista, Kevin D., PA
Hammond, Michele J., PA
Haupt, Hans M., PA
Heim-Rivers, Kathleen, NJ
Heldman, Irene K., PA
Hoff, William S., PA
Hofmann, Kurt P., PA
Holloway, Anita M., DE
Howe, Barbara Joanne, NJ
Huang, Janice, MI
Ito, Mari B., PA
Izes, Joseph K., PA
Johnson, Cherie J., DE
Jones, Seth M., PA
Kanefield, Jeffrey K., PA
Keeler, Louis L., III, NJ
Keeney, Gilbert, MI
Kessler, Dan D., NJ
Kester, Kent E., PA
Keyser, Bruce J., NJ
Kints, Geertruida, PA
Kistler, Sarah E., CA
Kline, Antonie D., PA
Knox, James D., Jr., DE
Kohl, Sarah Elizabeth, PA
Krebs, Thomas A., PA
Krepps, Bryan K., GA
Kuo, Jeffrey V., MD
Kuric, Kevin M., PA
Lamper, Kathlyn, DE
Lavanier, Jeffrey A., PA
Lawrence, Steven P., PA
LeDonne, Karen A., PA
Lehrer, Luisa E., NJ
Levin, Steven P., PA
Lewis, Joseph G., PA
Ling, Henry T., PA
Long, Richard H., Jr., PA
Lopez, Bernard L., PA
Loprest, Lorraine Jo, PA
Lundgren, Eric C., PA
Lybbert, Glen D., WA
Lynott, Paul J., PA
Magargee, Edward R., NJ
Magen, Andrea B., PA
Mamo, George J., PA
Manley, James S., PA
Margulies, Kenneth B., NY
Mark, James B., PA
Maroney, John W., Jr., DE

Martinez, William V., Jr., PA
Matunis, Suzanne F., PA
McCandlish, Mitch, OH
McCormack, Patricia A., PA
McDevitt, Gordon R., Jr., PA
McGettigan, Marie C., KY
McGrail, William T., Jr., PA
McTiernan, Eugene J., PA
Mead, Michelle A., NY
Melton, Susan M., PA
Meyer, Thomas J., PA
Mihalsky, Stephen W., PA
Mike, Joseph J., Jr., PA
Mike, Margaret E., MA
Minehan, Kathryn Ann, DE
Mokrynski, Gregory, PA
Montella, Michael K., PA
Montini, John, PA
Morrow, Todd A., PA
Mozdy, Lauren M., PA
Mueller, Thomas C., PA
Mulvey, John R., PA
Murdoch, Winslow W., PA
Noble, S. Ross, PA
Nurkiewicz, Stephen A., PA
O'Connor, Robert L., III, DE
O'Donnell, Michael J., PA
Oh, Min C., MD
Overmiller, Carl L., DE
Paluzzi, Michael W., PA
Peek-Ball, Cheryl E., PA
Pepe, Rosalie, PA
Phifer, William F., IL
Phillips, Gordon R., III, NJ
Powell, Craig C., NY
Prosapio, Philip L., NY
Pugh, Holly P., NC
Pugh, Vernon W., NC
Putnam, Samuel G., III, PA
Ream, Robert S., NJ
Robles, Robert L., AZ
Roche, James J., PA
Rothenberger, Rodger F., PA
Rumbaugh, William P., PA
Schetman, William R., DE
Scorza, Leslie B., NJ
Shelly, Mark A., OH
Shen, Jane, PA
Shuster, Patricia A., CA
Simonian, Thomas M., PA
Slemmer, J. Ross, NJ
Smith, Brian S., PA
Smith, James A., FL
Snell, John A., PA

Snyderman, Deborah A., PA
Sokoloff, Bruce H., DE
Solnick, Bennett L., PA
Solomon, Lynn, PA
Solomon, Robert A., PA
Spikol, Lorraine C., PA
Spitko, Jane A., PA
Strohmayer, Paul N., PA
Superdock, Keith R., PA
Swift, Joanne, Hummel, DE
Tachmes, Leonard, FL
Taddonio, William S., PA
Tandy, Thomas K., III, DE
Temple, H. Thomas, PA
Tingley, Stephen T., PA

Trauffer, Patrice Lamb, PA
Valko, George P., PA
Voss, Philip J., PA
Wagner, J. Kent L., PA
Wawrose, Stephen F., PA
Weinman, David S., DE
Welgoss, Jeffrey A., NY
West, William J., Jr., PA
Wiesen, Scott L., DE
Williams, Douglass K., CA
Williams, Mark L., PA
Wills, JoAnne K., PA
Winheld, Rebecca J., PA
Zukoff, Paul B., DE
Zuurbier, Rebecca A., PA

Dean's Luncheon for Alumni, June 4, 1986.

At the Commencement held at the Academy of Music June 5, President Bluemle conferred the M.D. degree upon 207 graduates. The honorary degree of Doctor of Literature was bestowed upon John Phillip McGovern, M.D., Sc.D., medical scholar, writer, editor and teacher. Having held various professorships, he served as President of the John P. McGovern foundation and Chairman of the Texas Allergy Research Foundation. The degree of Doctor of Laws was awarded to Tai Joon Moon, M.D., former Founding Chairman of the Department of Neurosurgery at Yonsei University College of Medicine, Seoul, Korea, and a one-time Jefferson resident. Dr. Moon served in international medical organizations, including the presidency of the World Medical Association (1985/86) and in his own country as a member of the Korean National Assembly. He was awarded its highest civilian honor by the Korean Government in 1987.

A majority of the prizes were won by women. The Alumni Prize went to Alexandra Helene Simkovich. Two prizes each were won by Janice Elizabeth Nevin, Christine Elaine Puschak, Paul O. Moon and Charles Andrew Pohl.

The Alumni Achievement Award for 1987 was presented to William R. Fair, M.D. (JMC, '60, Fig. 376). Dr. Fair was Chief of Urology and Vice-Chairman of the Department of Surgery at Memorial Sloan-Kettering Cancer Center and Professor of Surgery at Cornell University School of Medicine. His previous experiences had included appointments at Washington University School of Medicine, St. Louis, Visiting Fellow at the Chester Beatty Cancer Research Institute in London and at Stanford University School of Medicine. His many publications, research in urologic oncology, and teaching accomplishments were recognized with memberships in many prestigious societies, domestic and foreign.

The hospital appointments of the 1987 graduates reflected the great diversity of background of Jefferson students as well as their varied career plans. Included in the students' selection were the most prestigious teaching hospitals and the excellent community hospitals which have kept pace with medical developments. A distinct contribution was made by the Alumni Association which established a program whereby individual alumni hosted students during visits to prospective hospitals.

On October 22 the Alumni Association sponsored a ceremony (Fig. 5) for placing a bronze plaque (Fig. 469) at 518-520 Locust Walk. This marked the site of the Tivoli Theater which was the first home of Jefferson Medical College.

This year marked the Bicentennial not only of the Constitution of the United States but also the founding of the College of Physicians of Philadelphia. On April 1, President Ronald Reagan was the honored guest of the College at which occasion President Bluemle presided (Fig. 470).

CLASS OF 1987

Abboud, Semaan M., DE	Bannon, Joseph P., PA
Abrams, David B., NJ	Barnum, Rachel I., PA
Addiego, Raffaello, NJ	Bateman, Joseph N., PA
Aksu, Errol M., PA	Bebb, Gregory G., PA
Andreychik, David A., PA	Beckhard, Sharon A., PA
Atlas, Robert O., MD	Bender, David B., PA
Auffarth, Bradley R., DE	Berkowitz, Kathleen M., NJ
Baer, Susan C., NJ	Beyth, Rebecca J., PA
Bagley, Ann S., FL	Bilyk, Jurij R., PA
Bahler, Eileen, PA	Bowen, Elizabeth L., DE
Bailey, Dewey J., III, VA	Bozentka, David J., DE

Breslin, Kenneth S., NY
Brodstein, David E., UT
Brown, Alan S., NJ
Brundage, William J., PA
Brzezienski, Mark A., PA
Burak, William E., Jr., PA
Callan, Donna J., MA
Caplan, Amy B., PA
Carpenter, Matthew T., OH
Carson, Teresa C., PA
Carter, John M., NJ
Case, Brad A., PA
Chang, Catherine A., CA
Chasteney, Edward A., IV, PA
Chattha, Geetinder K., WV
Chen, Morgan Y., CA
Chinn, Bertram T., CA
Chung, Linda C., PA
Cirone, Maria C., PA
Clyman, Robert F., PA
Clymer, David G., PA
Cohan, Michael L., PA
Cook, David J., PA
Cosgarea, Andrew J., VA
Cromo, Sandra A., PA
Crossan, Laurence T., PA

DeLeo, Caesar A., III, PA
Dennis, Judith J., PA
Dickter, Steven J., PA
DiPaolo, Jeffrey C., PA
Dragelin, Joel B., PA
Duarte, Luis E., DE
Dunstone, Joan Marie, PA
Edinger, Andrew M., PA
Eisenman, Richard E., DE
Elener, Valerie A., DE
Falkenberg, Thomas, PA
Falls, Mark D., VA
Ferrante, Maurice A., NJ
Ferry, James A., CA
Finesmith, Tina H., DE
Finnegan, Mark O., PA
Fishman, Alan, PA
Fitzpatrick, Anne M., PA
Fong, Jonathan C., PA
Fox, Carol W., PA
Fraser, Douglas H., FL
Gabuzda, George M., PA
Gallagher, Michael R., PA
Gelb, Daniel J., DE
Geller, Joyce G., PA
Ginsberg, Gregory G., PA

Fig. 469. Bronze plaque marking first site of Jefferson Medical College (1825-28) at 518-20 Locust Walk.

Goldman, David L., NY
Gordon, Jean S., ME
Green, Phillip A., PA
Greenspan, Stephen S., PA
Grugan, Scott S., PA
Hamilton, Glenn D., NJ
Harpster, Lewis E., PA
Hawkins, Millard, MD
Henzes, John F., III, PA
Herrine, Gail M., PA
Hill, Cynthia A., PA
Horgan, Kelly A., MA
Horton, Terry L., DE
Hughes, Harry F., PA
Hunter, Terry W., NJ
Hutchinson, Howard G., PA
Ioffreda, Richard E., NJ
Izes, Betsy A., PA
Jenson, James J., CA
Johnson, David M., DE
Kahn, Joel A., PA
Kane, Gregory C., CT
Karam, Joseph A., PA

Kasarda, Lynnanne, DE
Katz, David A., VA
Keenan, Lynn M., PA
Kegel, Jeffrey G., CA
Kingma, Douglas W., NY
Kramer, Naomi R., PA
Kropp, William E., NY
Kurtz, James W., PA
Lackovic, Michelle F., PA
Lapinski, Brenda J., PA
Larkin, Jeffrey J., NJ
LaVan, Marthe Adler, PA
Lavanier, Gregory L., PA
Lawrence, Steven J., PA
Leenay, Mark, NY
Leivy, Sander W., NY
Lenahan, Terrence P., PA
Leschingski, Robert F., PA
Li, John C., NJ
Liao, Jeanne, Min-Li, NY
Liebreich, Mark E., PA
Lin, Dennis S., PA
Lipton, Jeffrey F., PA

Fig. 470. President Bluemle presides at Bicentennial Celebration of College of Physicians (founded 1787). Left to right: Lewis Coriell, current College President, President Reagan and President Bluemle.

622   1987

Liu, Ellen A., PA
Liu, Jeffrey E., HI
Liu, Randal J., HI
Maletta, Karen A., PA
Margiotta, Michael S., NJ
Martin, Scott D., PA
Maser, Steven A., PA
Maunus, Howard B., PA
Mayer, William D., PA
McBride, Mark J., PA
McCabe, Paul H., PA
McLaughlin, Catherine, PA
Melanson, Scott W., PA
Memolo, Mark W., PA
Mitchell, Bradford K., DE
Montgomery, Karyn, NJ
Monzon, Gary R., NY
Moon, Paul O., OH
Moses, Brett L., PA
Mullen, Mark J., NJ
Nedeljkovic, Srdjan S., FL
Nevin, Janice E., DE
Novielli, Karen D., PA
O'Riordan, Martin J., PA
Odorisio, Lynne A., NJ
Ott, Susan E. Werhun, PA
Perlmutter, Mark N., NJ
Petrone, Louis R., PA
Plotnick, Marc P., PA
Pohl, Charles A., PA
Pollack, Lee S., PA
Portz, Robert A., DE
Pressman, Mark J., PA
Przybylski, Gregory J., PA
Puschak, Christine E., PA
Ramani, Tushar M., NJ
Rayner, Richard M., PA
Rehr, Eric L., NY
Reilly, Patrick M., PA
Robinson, Alyn, PA
Rooney, David G., NY
Root, Douglas C., PA
Rosenfeld, Edward J., PA
Rothfeld, Laura N., NJ

Rothong, Carole L., PA
Rubenfeld, Gordon D., PA
Ruzich, Andrew H., PA
Sable, Carole A., PA
Sackner, Jonathan D., FL
Sartschev, Caroline A., PA
Schlitt, Michael T., NJ
Schneider, Peter J., PA
Schultz-Ross, Roy A., PA
Schwartzkopf, Paul B., DE
Scott, David G., PA
Sernyak, Michael J., Jr., PA
Sheehy, Eileen T., DE
Sheppard, Lisa M., PA
Siatkowski, Raymond M., PA
Sigler, Allison J., PA
Silver, Harris S., NJ
Simkovich, Alexandra H., PA
Simmons, Cheston, Jr., PA
Singer, Jodi S., NJ
Sivalingam, Jocelyn J., PA
Slater, Lindsey M., DE
Spagnoli, Bernita M., PA
Spar, Ellen, PA
Starke, Richard T., DE
Stoddard, Bradley K., ID
Takash, Thomas J., AZ
Thompson, William O., PA
Tuckey, Corinne N., PA
VanDerwerken, Suzanne, Wanlass, CA
Vujic, Dragomir M., NJ
Walker, Kathleen A., NJ
Walsh, Arthur W., VA
Watts, David C., PA
Weyn, David C., PA
Whitley, Amy B., FL
Wilson, John F., NJ
Woloshin, Jeffrey, PA
Yablonski, Thomas E., PA
Yao, Michael J., PA
Yavorek, George A., PA
Zale, Gregory J. P., PA
Zapolin, Carrie J., MA
Zaragoza, Michael R., DE

At the Commencement held June 5 at the Academy of Music, President Bluemle conferred the M.D. degree upon 219 graduates. The Alumni Prize and three others were won by Lynn Ryan Williams, already a holder of an M.P.H. degree from the University of Michigan. Two prizes each were won by three graduates, Greg Francis Burke, Eileen Theresa McGlynn, and James Leo McCabe.

The one honorary degree was awarded this year to Bernard Lown, M.D., founder and first President of Physicians for Social Responsibility. Dr. Lown, Professor of Cardiology at the Harvard School of Public Health, in 1985 accepted the Nobel Peace Prize along with Dr. Evgueni Chazov of the Soviet Union on behalf of the International Physicians for the Prevention of Nuclear War. His achievements in cardiac research and his hundreds of publications were widely recognized.

The Alumni Achievement Award for 1988 went to Sheldon Gilgore, M.D. (JMC, '56, Fig. 360), Chairman of the Board, President and Chief Executive Officer of G.D. Searle Company. Dr. Gilgore's early training in the Department of Medicine at Jefferson was followed by an appointment as Associate Director of Clinical Research at Pfizer Pharmaceuticals where he advanced to President of the Company in 1971. He served as a member of Jefferson's Board of Trustees for six years.

Patricia M. Curtin (Fig. 471), an outstanding student leader and prize winner at graduation, was elected to serve on Jefferson's Board of Trustees for a three-year term (1988-91).

The year 1988 marked exchange visits between Jefferson Professors and their counterparts at "La Sapienza" University of Rome (Fig. 472). Regular annual visits were planned. Robert M. Steiner (JMC '64, Fig. 390), Professor of Radiology, was Visiting Professor in Rome while Professor of Surgery Alberto Montori visited Jefferson, and his resident worked during the fall with

Gerald Marks, Professor of Surgery at Jefferson (JMC, '49, Fig. 331).

Providing further international flavor to the teaching at Jefferson was the appointment in January, 1988, of a native of Scotland, David M. Macfadyen, M.D. as Associate Dean for Health Policy. Dr. Macfadyen had extensive experiences world-wide as teacher, researcher and clinician in problems of aging and access to health care information. He was on a two-year leave from his duties as Chief of the World Health Organization's Program for the Health of Older Persons. At Jefferson he would serve in the Department of Family Medicine in addition to his

Fig. 471. Patricia M. Curtin (JMC, '88) a Board of Trustees member (1988-91).

principal duties in epidemiology and technology assessment.

In this year Mary B. Monteith was selected as the new Executive Director of the Alumni Association to succeed Nancy S. Groseclose. The latter (Fig. 473), who was greatly admired and beloved by all alumni, had served since 1966 and was forced to resign because of illness. The new Director was well qualified to fill this responsible position (Fig. 474).

Abreu, Jose J., FL
Acker, Brett L., PA
Ahlswede, Karl M., CO
Albert, Jeffrey J., PA
Alden, Mark E., PA
Alessandrini, Evaline A., DE
Alfano, Alan, NY
Alfond, Steven M., NY
Ashley, Kenneth B., CA
Auletta, Ann G., PA
Baldauf, John M., AZ
Battaglia, David R., PA
Belardi, Albert A., PA
Benge, Bruce N., DE
Bering, Joseph P., Jr., PA
Berkebile, Brenda L., PA
Bianchini, Adam A., RI
Bierman-Dear, Nancy A., NJ
Bothwell, William N., NJ
Brezinski, Mark E., PA
Broscius, Michael B., PA
Brumbaugh, Patricia A., CA
Burge, John R., DE
Burke, Greg F., PA
Byers, Ruth A., PA

Carney, William M., PA
Carroll, William J., PA
Caruso, Richard F., PA
Casteel, Linda L., PA
Catalano, John B., NJ
Cautilli, David A., PA
Clark, Richard R., PA
Cohn, Gregory S., PA
Cohn, Neil R., PA
Cole, Timothy J., DE
Cooper, Glenn S., PA
Copit, Steven E., PA
Craft, David V., PA
Crochelt, Robert F., Jr., NY
Curtin, Patricia M., DE
Cwik, Jason C., PA
Dallara, Charles A., PA
Dankmyer, Christopher C., PA
Davila, Virgil A., FL
Davis, Jeffrey A., PA
Decter, Bruce M., NY
DelGrippo, Gerard A., Jr., PA
Deshmukh, Ravi M., NY
DiCassimirro, John A., PA
Dodge, John M., PA
Dorazio, Stephen E., PA
Dvorak, Mary D., PA
Elgart, Richard L., PA
Elston, Scott C., PA
Erdman, Daniel E., PA
Esham, Charles A., DE
Etzi, Susan, NJ
Evans, Douglas J., NJ
Fendrick, Jeffrey S., NJ
Fireman, Andrew S., PA
Firouzbakhsh, Sima, CA
Flynn, Diane M., NJ
Fox, Michael A., PA
Fusman, Benjamin, BRAZIL
Gailliot, Robert V., Jr., VA
Garber, Donna A., PA
Gelmann, Gregory F., NJ
Gentile, Frances E., PA
Gill, Brian D., CO
Gillen, William S., PA

Fig. 472. The medal of "La Sapienza" University of Rome and a special citation are presented (left to right) by Dr. Montori and Dr. DeCarlo to President Bluemle, Professor Marks and Dean Gonnella.

Glasgold, Mark J., NJ
Gokcen, Eric C., NJ
Goldberg, Fredric H., PA
Goldberg, Steven E., PA
Gottlieb, Ron D., NY
Goyal, Maheep K., PA
Greenbarg, Jeffrey B., PA
Grieco, William M., PA
Gunn, Pamela R., KY
Gustafson, Thomas R., NY
Hale, John E., DE
Hammers, Karen R., NC
Harrell, David D., III, FL
Harvey, Steven S., PA
Herman, Gregory E., PA
Hoopes, Timothy G., DE

Horton, David J., MA
Hudock, Jude A., PA
Hudson, Mark E., PA
Hurwitz, Herbert I., PA
Ise, Charleen L., PA
Jackson, Darryl B., PA
Kairys, John C., MA
Kaiser, Paul K., NJ
Karl, Laurie A., CA
Katzen, Brett W., MD
Kaulback, Kyle R., NJ
Kessler, Eileen S., NJ
Kim, Edward, CA
Klufas, Roman A., RI
Kolecki, Richard S., NJ
Kostianovsky, Deborah J., NJ

Fig. 473.   Nancy S. Groseclose, Executive Secretary of Alumni Association (1966-73) and Executive Director (1973-88).

Kostianovsky, Deborah J., NJ
Kotalik, Frederick, PA
Kreider, Mary A., PA
Kresge, Carrie L., PA
Kulp-Hugues, Deborah A., PA
Langer, Carolyn S., NJ
Lederman, Jeffrey A., NY
Lees, Michael E., NJ
Londergan, Thomas A., DE
Lopez-Garcia, Ana Maria, AZ
Macones, George A., PA
Magee, John C., PA
Maiese, Russell L., NJ
Manges, Krista A., PA
Marino, Kathleen M., PA
Markowski, William J., PA
Marks, Richard M., PA
Marrazzo, Jeanne M., PA
Marsili, Mark A., PA
Matflerd, Carolynn A., NJ
Matsko, Jane R., PA
McCabe, James L., III, PA
McGlynn, Eileen T., PA
Mechem, C. Crawford, PA

Metzler, Erich G., DE
Miller, Pamela J., DE
Moffitt, John J., PA
Mujica, Jorge A., GA
Mummaw, Lisa A., PA
Munin, Michael C., PA
Murphy, Michael F., PA
Mustin, Andrew J., PA
Narzikul, Gregory T., PA
Nelson, Jean M., DE
Nelson, William H., NJ
Nowotarski, Peter J., PA
O'Connor, James J., III, PA
O'Connor, Stefan S., PA
O'Donnell, Philip H., MI
O'Donnell, Ward J., PA
O'Hara, Brian J., NJ
Olitsky, Scott E., PA
Olivieri, Suzanne P., PA
Parente, Maria G., CA
Parker, Gerald B., III, PA
Pasquarette, Mark M., PA
Pelczar, Brian T., PA

Fig. 474.   Paul A. Bowers (JMC, '37) welcomes Mary B. Monteith as the new Alumni Association Executive Director (1988).

1988

Peters, Barbara D., PA
Phillips, Todd E., PA
Pinizzotto, Marie E., PA
Pollack, Robert B., NJ
Prebola, William R., Jr., PA
Rabinowitch, Bonnie L., PA
Reiss, Suzanne E., PA
Remsburg, Stacia T., DE
Reynolds, John W., PA
Rich, John T., Jr., PA
Richman, Craig G., PA
Richman, Suzanne, IA
Robbins, Inga H., NH
Rodgers, Margaret L., WV
Rollman, Bruce L., NJ
Ruffini, Christopher P., PA
Russo, Marc S., PA
Sacharok, Cynthia A., PA
Sasso, Philip J., PA
Saukkonen, Kai D. J., PA
Saunders, Christopher J., PA
Schaebler, David L., PA
Schaffer, Michael A., NY
Schauer, Andrea J., NJ
Schrager, Randall E., NY
Shepard, Harvey E., MA
Shih, Richard D., DE
Siegel, Eric J., PA
Silverman, Lee D., PA
Sinha, Christopher K., NJ
Sirotnak, John J., PA
Slavens, Timothy E., DE
Siiwkowski, Joseph J., Jr., DE
Slota, Paul A., PA
Small, George A., NY

Sohn, Sae H., DE
Sprague, William L., PA
Staffen, Robert N., PA
Stanley, Christine L., PA
Stello, Brian, PA
Sterling, Richard K., FL
Stock, Robert R., DE
Stokes, Gordon K., VA
Sugarman, Kate S., MD
Sunday, Michael L., PA
Sundheim, Suzanne T., PA
Tan, Clinson B., SINGAPORE
Tonken, Heidi P., PA
Toy, Stephanie M., CA
Travaline, John M., Jr., PA
Viti, Craig G., PA
Walker, Michael J., PA
Warning, William J., II, PA
Weaver, Martin D., PA
Wiggill, Sharon J., DE
Williams, David A., PA
Williams, Lynn Ryan, PA
Winton, Carol J., CA
Wong, Randall V., PA
Wong, Randolph W., CA
Worman, Scott L., GA
Yanez, Brenda A., AZ
Yavorek, Amy, PA
Yim, Gregory K., HI
Zajaczkowski, Marie, PA
Zakrzewski, Kevin M., PA
Zangrilli, James G., PA
Zeitzer, Kenneth L., PA
Zelkovic, Mark A., PA
Zilber, Claire S., CA
Zorn, Gunnar W., III, PA

Of all the causes of failure I doubt if any is more potent than vanity. The proper attitude toward all scientific questions is one of humility. When one can no longer wonder at nature, he can no longer progress.

John Chalmers DaCosta (1863-1933)

The Commencement was held on June 9 in the Academy of Music at which time the M.D. degree was conferred upon 223 graduates by President Bluemle. The Alumni Prize was awarded to Madeline Sandra Wood-Wagemaker. Honorary degrees were bestowed upon William H. Gray, III, a prominent Congressman, and Allan J. Erslev for his work in the discovery of a red cell regulating hormone, erythropoietin.

The Alumni Achievement Award was bestowed upon John J. Gartland (JMC, S'44, Fig. 305), The James Edwards Professor Emeritus of Orthopaedic Surgery, who had distinguished himself as Chairman of Orthopaedics (1970-1985), author of authoritative textbooks in his field, and President of National organizations.

In this year Nancy S. Czarnecki (JMC, '65, Fig. 396), who was the first woman graduate of Jefferson Medical College, was also the first woman to serve as President of the Alumni Association (Fig. 475).

Ground breaking ceremonies took place on July 24 for construction by the University of a Life Sciences Building for medical and scientific research on a site at the northeast corner of Tenth and Locust Streets. This eleven-story structure, named in honor of President Bluemle, was projected to alleviate the latest critical need for space in the basic sciences and to accommodate the increasing number of full-time research faculty in the burgeoning field of molecular biology. Entirely devoted to research, the building was to house the work in biochemistry, pathology, microbiology, and the Stein Research Center (Fig. 476).

The need for additional space for clinical facilities was also implemented in this year by start of construction of a "Clinical Office Building" on the north side of Walnut Street between Ninth and Tenth. This three-story structure with basement would house two magnetic resonance imaging machines and provide supplementary office space (Fig. 477).

Portraits presented to the University in this year were those of Paul C. Brucker, M.D., the Alumni Professor of Family Medicine and Chairman of the Department and George C. Brainard, Ph.D., Associate Professor of Neurology.

This class, like others before it, had been selectively recruited from the best applicants from diverse areas of the United States. They all secured residency positions of their choice from among the best academic institutions and hospitals in a widely scattered geographic area. They entered to learn and went forth to serve in the Jefferson tradition of 165 years.

CLASS OF 1989

Ackerman, Bruce M., PA
Alicea, Ariel A., PA
Alicea, Susan Adamitis, PA
Amadio, Patricia B., PA
Andersen, Donald H., DE
Anderson, David C., NJ
Arlis-Mayor, Stephanie Lynn, NY
Bade, Steven C., PA
Barry, Kevin P., PA
Benton, Lisa D., NJ
Berman, Joel E., PA
Berna, Ronald A., NJ
Birenbaum, Dale S., PA
Blinn, Randall D., FL

Borkowski, Raymond G., PA
Bough, Irvin D., Jr., NJ
Braccia, Gregory M., PA
Bush, Todd A., PA
Cahn, David A., CA
Carlough, Martha C., PA
Carroll, William L., PA
Chen, Jennifer Chen-Hui, PA
Chiesa, Nicolette E., PA
Classen, Carolyn F., PA
Cohen, David M., VA
Colcher, Amy, PA
Conaway, Herbert C., Jr., NJ
Conway, Michael K., DE

Coombe, Raymond P., PA
Coslett, Douglas S., PA
Coyle, Bonnie S., PA
Craft, Jeanne A., DE
Cummings, Peter Dean, PA
Cutler, Lori R., MI
Davis, Michele D., MD
DelGaudio, John M., PA
Demangone, Michael J., PA
Dhaliwal, Avninder Singh, NJ
DiBello, Joseph N., Jr., PA
DiNicola, Arturo N., PA
Dinwiddie, David Wayne, PA
Doghramji, James, PA
Dolphin, Kip W., PA
Dombrowski, Jan, PA
Drapcho-Foti, Connie S., PA
Duffy, Margaret H., MI
Eichman, Margaret J., PA
Ellis, Frank D., DE
Erhard, Michael J., PA
Eschbach, Jeffrey C., PA
Fang, Jane Yi-Jen, PA
Farabaugh, Alan A., PA

Field, Douglas G., NJ
Figueroa, Cynthia A., NY
Fleming, George E., Jr., PA
Folkman, Michele G., PA
Fowler, Eric K., PA
Frankel, Linda K., CA
Furlong, Christopher B., PA
Ganong, Kevin D., PA
Garcia, Mark J., DE
Gelman-Weidman, Debra M., PA
Gobetz, Deborah Troth, CT
Gombeda, Maria A., PA
Gordon, Joel P., NJ
Gorman, Richard E., DE
Gosin, Jeffrey S., NJ
Greenberg, Caroline M., PA
Greenblatt, Dana B., MA
Griscom, Andrew H., RI
Guion, Tamara L., PA
Hallstrom, Laun R., PA
Hanau, Cheryl A., PA
Hardiman, Edward R., PA
Harrer, William V., NJ
Hart, Carol Ann C., PA

Fig. 475.   Nine Past Presidents congratulate Dr. Czarnecki.

1989

Heckert, Jeffrey J., DE
Hickey, Denise M., PA
Hoffman, Susan D., PA
Honsberg, Angelica E., DE
Huffnagle, Milford J., II, CA
Huffnagle, Vera Hentosh, PA
Hummer, Charles D., III, PA
Hursh, Dale K., PA
Iannotta, Patricia N., PA
Imbesi, Steven G., PA
Inman, Mark G., MI
Josloff, Robert K., PA
Kahn, Harry A., NJ
Kalinowski, Joseph E., Jr., PA
Kamerling, Joseph M., NJ
Kaplan, Seth A., PA
Katzman, Scott S., CA
Kent, Jeffrey D., NJ
Kessler, David J., PA
Khalil, Cindy L., PA
Kim, Edward C., DE
Kim, John H., NJ
Kistler, Dominick A., PA
Kitei, Robert A., PA

Kline, Gerard L., PA
Kodroff, Kurt S., PA
Kolecki, Robert V., NJ
Konlian, Donna M., NY
Korn, Robert L., PA
Kosar, Erol M., PA
Kreider-Voloshin, Denise G., PA
Laporte, Patrick J., III, PA
Lau, Mark T., HI
Le, Daniel Dung Quoc, CA
Lee, Jaeho, CA
Leh, David W., Jr., PA
Lin, Sheldon S., PA
Livesay, Susan, DE
Livingston, Elizabeth R., DE
Lizerbram, Frances W., CA
Lowry, Jonathan C., DE
Luongo, Peter A., NJ
Maitin, Ian B., NJ
Mancini, Joseph A., NY
Maravich, Nick, Jr., PA
Markiewitz, Andrew D., DE
Marks, John H., PA
Martella, Arthur Thomas, PA

Fig. 476.   Architect's model of the Bluemle Life Sciences Building.

Martella, Arthur Thomas, PA
Mattiace, William Joseph, PA
May, Carl J., Jr., CT
McCann, Julia A., NY
McGarvey, William C., PA
Medve, Robert A., PA
Meihofer, Mary A., PA
Meyer, Kathryn J., PA
Mezey, Alan L., PA
Monath, James R., PA
Montemuro, Anthony J., PA
Morales, Thomas G., CA
Morley, Wynne A., PA
Nukes, Theodore A., OH
O'Connor, Carolyn B., PA
O'Neill, Daniel K., DE
Ogrodnick, John P., PA
Paffrath, Jeffrey A., PA
Palmer, Kathleen M., NJ
Patchen, Patrick N., Jr., PA
Pavlinko-Ghosh, Jody, PA
Pluto, Christine M., PA
Pontell, Jonathan, NJ
Pretell, Judith O., PA

Reed, Crystal D., PA
Reid, Christopher J., DE
Reilly, James F., PA
Richter, Douglas M., NJ
Ridilla, Leonard V., Jr., PA
Rizzo, Richard J., DE
Rodgers, John C., PA
Rollo, Vincent J., DE
Rosen, Harel D., NJ
Russ, Heidi R., NY
Salvati, Catherine R., NJ
Sarfati, Mark R., MD
Sauerwine, Scott A., PA
Savopoulos, Sotiere E., DE
Sawyer, David T., NJ
Schlitt, Mark G., NJ
Schwartz, Philip S., PA
Shih, Henry Han-Liang, NJ
Shotwell, Barbara A., PA
Siegel, Christopher T., PA
Sinha, Raj K., PA
Sirotnak, Andrew P., PA
Smeal, Brian C., PA
Smith, Timothy C., PA

Fig. 477.   Clinical Office Building, 909 Walnut St. (1990).

1989

Somers, Debra Lynn, PA
Somers, Debra Lynne, PA
Spandorfer, John M., PA
Spanich, Christopher G., DE
Sperandio, Peter G., NJ
Steward, Donna L., PA
Stoffa, Robert J., PA
Sutton, Douglas C., PA
Sweterlitsch, Eric M., PA
Swisher, John W., PA
Szeremeta, Wasyl, DE
Taggart, Tina S., PA
Tananis, Leonard J., Jr., PA
Taraska, Gregory J., IL
Tatarko, Michael, PA
Tolberg, Mary Ellen, CA
Trachtenberg, Eric L., CA
Trachtman, William M., DE
Triano, Marla R., PA
Triolo, Joseph, PA
Triolo, Paul, PA
Tsai, John Y., CA
Tsatalis, James T., PA
Tullius, Charles D., PA

Venkatesula, Sunder, PA
Verno, Lisa C., PA
Ververeli, Kathleen O., PA
Ververeli, Prodromos, PA
Vinnick, Deborah M., CT
Viola, John J., Jr., PA
Walsh, Eugenia S., DE
Walsh, John J., IV, PA
Wasserman, Andrew P., PA
Wayman, Bernard R., III, PA
Weber, Cynthia Elinor, PA
Weber, Robert C., II, PA
Wetzel, Michael H., PA
Whitcomb, Winthrop F., MA
Willard, Brian M., PA
Wilson, Jonathan M., PA
Wolf, Kathleen M., CT
Wonnell, Diane M., DE
Wood-Wagemaker, Madeline S., PA
Wright, Deborah S., PA
Yanez, Daria C., NJ
Yim, Robyn S.L., HI
Young, Linda L., PA
Zimmer, Michael A., PA
Zurmuhl, Martin A., PA

The 50th Reunion of Class of 1939 at Union League.

Commencement was held on June 8 at the Academy of Music, at which time President Bluemle awarded M.D. degrees to 202 graduates. This was Dr. Bluemle's last appearance in this capacity before retirement after his 13 years of Presidency for which he was given accolades by Board President, Edward C. Driscoll. The latter himself was about to conclude six years of distinguished service (1984-90). The Honorary Degree of Doctor of Humane Letters was conferred upon Lewis W. Sullivan, Secretary of Health and Human Services.

On Class Day the Alumni Prize was awarded along with several others to Niti Goel. The Lindback Award for Distinguished Teaching in the Basic Sciences went to Richard Ralph Schmidt, Ph.D., Associate Professor of Anatomy and that for Clinical Sciences to Eric Lynn Hume, M.D., Assistant Professor of Orthopaedic Surgery. Robert L. Brent, M.D., Ph.D., the Louis and Bess Stein Professor of Pediatrics, received the Burlington Northern Foundation Faculty Achievement Award for excellence in teaching and research productivity. The Blockley-Osler Award for Excellence in Teaching of Clinical Medicine to a faculty member of Jefferson-Affiliated Hospitals went to Laurence H. Beck, M.D., Professor of Medicine in the Geisinger Medical Center. John R. Griffith (JMC, '46, Fig. 317), won the Leon A. Peris Award for excellence in clinical teaching and superior patient care.

In this year Willis C. Maddrey, the Magee Professor of Medicine, was selected for the Class Portrait. Other portraits accepted by the University were those of Russell W. Schaedler (JMC, '53, Fig. 344), the Plimpton-Pugh Chairman of Microbiology and Immunology; James M. Hunter (JMC, '53, Fig. 346), Professor of Orthopaedic Surgery; Lewis W. Bluemle, Jr., President of Thomas Jefferson University and Herbert E. Cohn (JMC, '55, Fig. 355), Professor of Surgery.

Alumni Achievement Awards were presented to John H. Hodges (JMC, '39, Fig. 282) the Ludwig A. Kind Professor of Medicine, and to Frederick B. Wagner, Jr. (JMC, '41, Fig. 286), the Grace Revere Osler Professor Emeritus of Surgery.

Dean Joseph Gonnella became interested in developing educational relationships in the Orient, especially in Korea and China. With the collaboration of Jefferson's Professor of Medicine (Cardiology), Edward D. Chung, there was established an association in 1988 with the Gil General Hospital in Inchon, Korea. This was followed in 1989 by a similar connection with the Pusan National University College of Medicine, and in 1990 with the Soon Chun Hyang University Hospital in Seoul. Dean Gonnella also received an Honorary Professorship from Tianjin University in China in 1990. This type of honor in China is regarded more highly than an honorary degree.

A new Level I Emergency and Trauma Center under construction for two years, occupying the first floor of Old Main Hospital and Thompson Annex, was opened this year at a cost of approximatley $40 million (Fig. 478). A distinctive feature in addition to the operating rooms and other sophisticated facilities was the transfer of patients by elevator from the heliport atop the Foerderer Pavilion directly to the Emergency Room.

A special event in the final decade of the 20th Century was the Inauguration on September 5 of Paul C. Brucker, M.D., as the new President of Thomas Jefferson University. Dr. Brucker had attained national recognition as Jefferson's Alumni Professor of Family Medicine since 1973. In a team approach, Mr. James W. Stratton, the newly elected Chairman of the Board of Trustees, joined the administrative forces. He had been a Jefferson Trustee since 1970 (Fig. 479).

At no time in the history of Jefferson did the future appear more promising.

Acker, Matthew Carl, III, PA
Ada, Frances Perez, GUAM
Aguas, Joy Ann Ma. A., NJ
Alaimo-Dinwiddie, Maria, CA
Aldrete, Andres Martin, CO
Allardyce, Thomas James, PA
Arai, Taro, PA
Arch, Ellen Michele, PA
Arenson, Christine Ann, DE
Armao, Diane Mary, PA
Badiavas, Evangelos Van, NJ
Baker, Dole Parker, Jr., MD
Baldassano, Vincent Francis, PA
Bamberger, Peter Kurt, PA
Baram, Daniel, PA
Baram, Lena Diane, NY
Barkett, Robert Edward, Jr., OH
Bates, Andrea Rose, CA
Bauer, Andrew William, PA
Beilis, Heidi, NY
Bennett, Nathan Louis, PA
Berger, Alan Keith, MD

Berghella, Vincenzo, ITALY
Berne, Ronald Stuart, IL
Bigatel, David Alfred, PA
Brasacchio, Ralph Anthony, NY
Brennan, Mark David, Jr., PA
Burke, John Kilgallen, PA
Butz, Todd Michael, PA
Byron, Mary Christine, PA
Cardelia, James Marc, NJ
Carroll, Leslie Seton, PA
Carter, Stephen Lindsay, CA
Case, Mark Edward, PA
Chan, Jane Wor, CA
Chao, Wen, DE
Chern, Sandra, VA
Cole, Scott C., PA
Curran, Thomas Patrick, PA
D'Amato, Thomas Andrew, PA
Dalessandro, David Arthur, PA
Dannenberg, Michael James, NY
Davis, Neville, NJ
Delcore, Randy George, NY

Fig. 478.   Trauma Center, 10th & Sansom.

Dick, Alice Ruth, CA
DiFlorio, Roberta Maria, NJ
Donati, Theresa Ann V., PA
Draper, Randall Richard, PA
Driban, David Ezra, PA
Duffy, Rosemary Ann, NJ
Dunfee, Robin Ann, PA
Eisen, Deborah Ida, NJ
Elfman, Karen Sue, PA
Ellis, Jennifer Lynn, NY
Everts, Leslie Elizabeth, NJ
Fales, William Dana, PA
Fantaski, Mark Robert, PA
Farrell, Timothy Jude, PA
Florio, Catherine Marie, NJ
Frattali, Mary J. Boland, PA
Freedman, Noah David, PA
Furness, Peter Donald, III., DE
Gabor, Howard, MA
Gallagher, Terence James, PA
Gallivan, Mary Elizabeth, CA
Gannon, Catherine M., PA
Garazo-Lorente, Henry Fernando, MD
Gavin, Thomas Joseph, PA

Gilliam, Bruce Lawrence, CA
Ginn, Karen Ruth, PA
Ginsberg, Susan Beth, PA
Glorioso, David Vaughn, PA
Glowacki, Keith Adam, PA
Goel, Niti, NY
Gohel, Mira Manhar, CA
Grillo, Angelo, DE
Guilday, Robert E., PA
Herrine, Steven Kenneth, PA
Hoffman, David F., PA
Hoffman, Jeffrey Mark, FL
Hogue, Rebecca Manning, CA
Horvath, David Addis, PA
Houser, Angela Grace, PA
Hunn, Richard Hayes, PA
Huntington, Christopher Fell, DE
Inguito, Galicano Fernando, Jr., DE
Inverso, Nicholas Anthony, PA
Ioffreda, Michael David, NJ
James, Carol Jean, DE
Jayson, Maury Alan, NJ
Johnson, Margaret Mary, DE
Jones, Ernest Price, Jr., PA

Fig. 479.   Chairman James Stratton and President Paul Brucker.

1990

Josephson, Lisa Dawn, CA
Jovanovich, Veda Louise, PA
Kashyap, Vikram Shantaram, IL
Katlan, Michael George, NY
Kearney, James John, PA
Keeley, Ellen Catherine, NJ
Kelton, Melanie Sharon, NY
Kennedy, Susan Lucille, NJ
Kim, Sanghoon, PA
Kline, Michael A., PA
Kottenhahn, Renee Kathrin, DE
Kozak, John Matthew, MA
Kramer, Sherri Lynn, PA
Krupnick, Matthew Eric, PA
Kuo, Cindy Peilun, PA
Kupas, Douglas Frank, PA
Lamberts, Robert John, NY
Leighton, Barbara Mary, PA
Lekawa, Michael Edward, CA
Leonard, Daniel James, III., PA
Levine, Marc Jason, NJ
Lin, Rosina P., PA
Liu, Donald Chua, MD
Lo, Alan Yung-Tsu, PA
Mackle, Edward Joseph, PA
Manin, Gordon Charles, PA
Markmann, Daniel Paul, PA
Martino, James Vincent, PA
McDyer, John Francis, NJ
Meade, Theresa A., PA
Meyer, Monica Ann, PA
Miller, Michael Kenneth, PA
Mitchell, Edmund Mansfield, DE
Monroe, John Joseph, Jr., PA
Monteleone, Gaetano P., Jr., PA
Montgomery, Catherine J. Piecyk, PA
Moore, Daniel Paul, DE
Morrison, William Brian, NJ
Nichols, Bradley Gibson, PA
Noyes, Willard Stover, PA
O'Brien, Timothy James, PA
O'Reilly, Robert Carlos, PA
O'Rourke, Terence Leonard, PA
Osborne, John Andrew, PA
Ost, David Edward, PA
Pacifico, Daniel Scott, NJ
Parente, John Peter, Jr., PA
Park, Grace Eunhye, PA
Parker, Pamela Dorothea, OH
Peck, Ronald Alan, NJ
Pellegrini, Daniel P., PA
Perlman, Claire Bertha, PA
Reardon, Lawrence Craig, PA

Reich, Alice, MA
Rooney, John Edward, NJ
Roperti, Karen Ann, PA
Rorabaugh, James Douglas, PA
Rosato, Ernest Lancelot, PA
Rosenblum, Bret Abraham, PA
Ross, Helen L., PA
Rutstein, Eric Stephen, NY
Sabo, Robert Alan, NJ
Sabol, Jennifer Lane, PA
Sangimino, Mark Joseph, MD
Sangimino, Ursula Ripepi, PA
Schapiro, Gregory David, MA
Schoedler, Scott James, DE
Schwam, Brian Lewis, PA
Schwartzstein, Robert, PA
Sepich, Rodney Milan, PA
Seraly, Mark Patrick, NJ
Shafritz, Randy, PA
Siegel, Linda Beth, NY
Silodor, Scott Wayne, NJ
Singh, Amitabh, PA
Sklar, Leslie Ann, DE
Slovin, Susan Faith, PA
Smith, Scott Douglas, NJ
Smith, Staci Jill, PA
Soble, Toby Kleiner, NJ
Spalding, Jennifer Anne, PA
Stafford, Marshall William, PA
Stampien, Ted Michael, PA
Steinberg, Amber Lynne B., NJ
Sterling, Sara Ange, PA
Stevenson, Alan Jay, PA
Stewart, Geoffrey, DE
Summerville, Gregg Paul, PA
Suntharalingam, Mohan, NJ
Thomas, Carole Ellen, PA
Tietjens-Grillo, Lenore M., PA
Torna, Patricia Ann, PA
Treiman, Arthur Mark, PA
Trott, Edward Ashley, BERMUDA
Tse, K. Edmund, HONG KONG
Uppal, Arvinder Singh, WA
VanCleeff, Sander, VA
Wagner, Kathleen Therese, PA
Watson, Maria Jeanette, WA
Weaver, Gayle Joelene, PA
Wheelock, Dana Whitham, NY
Whelan, John William, PA
Whitehead, Deborah Anne, CA
Whitney, Charles Candee, II., DE
Wilson, John David, MD
Yap, Englok, SINGAPORE
Yee, Emily L., PA

The last lecture in the third "pit," May 27, 1966.

Former Thompson Auditorium, designated the Anthony F. DePalma Auditorium on November 15, 1990. Prior to 1966 it was the site of Jefferson's third clinical amphitheater ("pit").

THE ALUMNI ASSOCIATION
OF JEFFERSON MEDICAL COLLEGE
Achievement Award

1964 LOUIS H. CLERF, M.D. CLASS OF 1912	1969 LEROY A. SCHALL, M.D. CLASS OF 1913	1973 WILLIAM W. L. GLENN, M.D. CLASS OF 1938	1979 JOHN B. MONTGOMERY, M.D. CLASS OF 1926	1985 CHARLEY J. SMYTH, M.D. CLASS OF 1935
1964 HENRY L. BOCKUS, M.D. CLASS OF 1917	1969 GEORGE C. GRIFFITH, M.D. CLASS OF 1926	1974 DANIEL C. BAKER, JR., M.D. CLASS OF 1933	1980 WARREN W. NICHOLS, M.D. CLASS OF 1954	1986 GERALD D. DODD, M.D. CLASS OF 1947
1965 PERCIVAL E. FOERDERER TRUSTEE	1970 THADDEUS L. MONTGOMERY, M.D. CLASS OF 1920	1975 ANTHONY F. DePALMA, M.D. CLASS OF 1929	1981 JOHN Y. TEMPLETON, III, M.D. CLASS OF 1941	1987 WILLIAM R. FAIR, M.D. CLASS OF 1960
1966 HAROLD L. STEWART, M.D. CLASS OF 1926	1970 JOHN H. GIBBON, JR., M.D. CLASS OF 1927	1976 JO ONO, M.D. CLASS OF 1928	1981 WILLIAM F. KELLOW, M.D. DEAN, 1967–1981	1988 SHELDON G. GILGORE, M.D. CLASS OF 1956
1967 FRANCIS J. BRACELAND, M.D. CLASS OF 1930	1970 ALEXANDER J. ORENSTEIN, M.D. CLASS OF 1905	1977 J. EDWARD BERK, M.D. CLASS OF 1936	1982 JOE HENRY COLEY, M.D. CLASS OF 1934	1989 JOHN J. GARTLAND, M.D. CLASS OF 1944S
1968 VICTOR G. HEISER, M.D. CLASS OF 1897	1971 BALDWIN L. KEYES, M.D. CLASS OF 1917	1978 GEORGE M. NORWOOD, JR. INTERIM PRESIDENT, TJU	1983 FRANCIS J. SWEENEY, JR., M.D. CLASS OF 1951	1990 JOHN H. HODGES, M.D. CLASS OF 1939
1968 ABRAHAM CANTAROW, M.D. CLASS OF 1924	1972 GEORGE J. WILLAUER, M.D. CLASS OF 1923	1978 BENJAMIN HASKELL, M.D. CLASS OF 1923	1984 ABRAHAM E. RAKOFF, M.D. CLASS OF 1937	1990 FREDERICK B. WAGNER, JR., M.D. CLASS OF 1941

~ A ~

Aaron, Francis A., 1929
Aaronoff, Joseph, 1912
Aaronson, Herbert G., 1957
Abbitt, William B., 1851
Abbott, Benjamin T., 1870
Abbott, Elgin P., 1877
Abbott, Frank Cook, 1905
Abbott, Frank Farnum, 1907
Abbott, John George, 1905
Abbott, John H., 1872
Abbott, Joseph L., 1954
Abbott, Luther J., 1854
Abbott, R. Roderic, 1952
Abboud, Semaan M., 1987
Abel, Lemuel F., 1853
Abel, Robert, Jr., 1969
Abell, Amacey B., 1875
Abell, Charles F., 1935
Abell, Charles F., Jr., 1956
Abell, Torrance Bryson, 1960
Abelove, William A., 1951
Abelow, Gerald G., 1972
Abercrombie, George A., 1860
Abernethy, James M., 1861
Abernethy, James W., 1878
Able, Samuel V., 1885
Abolofia, David Joseph, 1947
Abraham, Barry B., 1973
Abrahamsen, Charles E., 1980
Abrahamsen, Edwin H., 1951
Abrahamsen, Robert B., 1979
Abrahamson, Philip, 1899
Abram, Stephen E., 1970
Abramowitz, Richard P., 1978
Abrams, David B., 1987
Abrams, Edward, 1965
Abrams, Jerome, 1953
Abrams, Steven L., 1964
Abrams, William B., 1947
Abramson, Maurice, 1937
Abreu, Jose J., 1988
Aceto, Joseph N., 1947
Aceto, Thomas, Jr., 1954
Achuff, J. Newton, 1867
Acker, Brett L., 1988
Acker, Matthew Carl, III, 1990
Ackerman, Bruce M., 1989
Ackerman, Samuel K., 1972
Ackerman, William E., Jr., 1937
Ackley, Henry, 1858

Acree, Page Waddill, J1944
Acton, Kelly J., 1981
Ada, Frances Perez, 1990
Adair, J. Todd, 1860
Adair, Templeton, 1908
Adam, Anne Wynn W., 1977
Adam, George, 1882
Adam, Jeffrey S., 1977
Adam, Stewart Inglis, 1943
Adams, Arland A., 1956
Adams, Charles Franklin, 1887
Adams, Charles Thomas, 1896
Adams, D. Leslie, 1967
Adams, Edward Everard, 1923
Adams, Ellsworth Smith, 1890
Adams, F. A., 1867
Adams, F. Percival, 1873
Adams, Gene R., 1960
Adams, George L., 1966
Adams, Henry G., 1841
Adams, John M., 1929
Adams, John Quincy W., 1925
Adams, John William, 1887
Adams, Jonathan D., 1981
Adams, Joseph Lowrance, 1910
Adams, Louis J., 1877
Adams, Martin, 1859
Adams, Nelson A., 1846
Adams, Patrick H., 1860
Adams, Paul Risley, 1921
Adams, Quintus L., 1888
Adams, Ralph Crawe, 1906
Adams, Rayford Kennedy, 1912
Adams, W. Powell, 1871
Adams, Winford C., 1941
Adamsen, Hans, 1888
Adamson, Hiram Ross, 1900
Adcock, Lee Campbell, 1903
Addiego, Raffaello, 1987
Addington, Donald Barrett, 1962
Addis, David J., 1969
Addison, Robert K., 1847
Addison, William J., 1860
Adelman, Seth S., 1980
Adelson, Leonard J., 1977
Adibi, Siamak, 1959
Adkins, Isaac Leonard, 1849
Adler, David Gilbert, 1889
Adler, Jon S., 1965
Adler, L. H., 1871
Adler, Lawrence M., 1986
Adlin, Albert, 1932

Agard, Aurelius H., 1849
Ager, Steven A., 1972
Agnello, Joseph S., Jr., 1974
Agnew, Fred F., 1902
Agnew, John, 1875
Agnew, Samuel 1838
Agque, Timothy Joseph, 1884
Agre, Rodger S., 1963
Agro, Angelo S., 1975
Aguas, Joy Ann Ma. A., 1990
Ahbrah, 1882
Ahlswede, Karl M., 1988
Aichele, Otto Walter, 1911
Aichner, Oscar Fred, 1893
Aikey, Barry R., 1962
Aikin, Perley J., 1867
Aikins, M. H., 1857
Aikins, William T., 1850
Aitken, Douglas Harold, 1943
Ajello, Robert R., 1979
Ake, John G., 1873
Ake, Joseph H., 1850
Akers, Andrew Franklin, 1903
Akers, F. P.H., 1876
Akers, James W., 1876
Aksu, Errol M., 1987
Alaimo-Dinwiddie, Maria, 1990
Alan, Robert L., 1964
Alberstadt, Norbert F., J1944
Albert, David, 1863
Albert, Jeffrey J., 1988
Albert, John V., 1870
Albert, Perry, 1938
Albertson, Harry Walter, 1902
Albertson, Keith S., 1983
Albrecht, C. Earl, 1932
Albright, Durant H., 1851
Albright, Roderick Edwin, 1896
Albright, William J., 1985
Albright, William J., III, 1954
Albright, William John, 1922
Alcorn, James P., 1850
Alden, James M., 1871
Alden, John M., 1942
Alden, Mark E., 1988
Alderfer, Gill R., 1968
Alderfer, Harold H., 1946
Alderfer, Henry Harr, 1943
Alderfer, Kenneth G., 1957
Alderman, Charles G., 1905
Aldrete, Andres Martin, 1990
Alessandrini, Evaline A., 1988

Alexaitis, Francis Lopatto, 1915
Alexander, Cassidy, M., 1834
Alexander, Charles T., 1856
Alexander, Eben, Jr., 1904
Alexander, Eli, 1859
Alexander, Emory Graham, 1904
Alexander, George E., 1873
Alexander, Gerard 1848
Alexander, Gilbert, 1933
Alexander, Isaac, 1910
Alexander, James H., 1880
Alexander, James Newton, 1894
Alexander, John B., 1939
Alexander, Martin T., 1877
Alexander, Maurice H., 1935
Alexander, R. William, 1948
Alexander, Richard H., 1850
Alexander, Richard P., 1948
Alexander, Robert M., 1865
Alexander, Robert Mackey, 1910
Alexander, Samuel L., 1859
Alexander, W. C. S., 1858
Alexander, William Archibald, 1906
Alexander, William B., 1868
Alexander, William Brown, 1887
Alexander, William H., 1885
Alexander, William J., 1866
Alexander, William Newton, 1956
Alexis, Joseph A., 1919
Alfano, Alan, 1988
Alfond, Steven M., 1988
Algeo, James H., Jr., 1979
Alger, Luther W., 1861
Alicea, Ariel A., 1989
Alicea, Susan Adamitis, 1989
Alkire, Herbert Lee, 1887
Allan, David A., 1976
Allan, John Purcell, 1947
Allardyce, Thomas James, 1990
Allawi, Diane C., 1978
Allcroft, Roger A., 1981
Allebach, Newton G., 1913
Alleman, Frank, 1896
Alleman, George E., 1911
Alleman, L. A. Welles, 1886
Allen, Albert Gallatin, 1834
Allen, Amy J., 1985
Allen, Brian D., 1983
Allen, C. Dixon, 1875
Allen, Carritte Arthur, 1890
Allen, Charles L., 1880
Allen, Charles Leland, 1892
Allen, Charles Walker, 1903
Allen, David E., 1895
Allen, Dudley 1837
Allen, Edgar, 1890
Allen, Frederick Blunt, 1903
Allen, George W., 1834

Allen, George W., 1844
Allen, Gregg P., 1978
Allen, Harold Y., 1953
Allen, Henry B., 1883
Allen, Herbert V., Jr., 1957
Allen, Homer Richard, 1932
Allen, James E., 1984
Allen, James Franklin, 1887
Allen, James M., 1856
Allen, John D., 1839
Allen, John Dwight, J1944
Allen, Milton, 1855
Allen, Nathaniel N., 1853
Allen, Peter, 1838
Allen, Reginald A., 1932
Allen, Robert B., 1980
Allen, Robert E., 1927
Allen, Robert Louis, 1913
Allen, Robert M., 1954
Allen, Thomas J., 1855
Allen, William Cline, 1896
Alley, John Newton, 1896
Alley, Ralph Martin, 1927
Alley, Richard A., 1960
Allgair, William A., 1951
Allis, Oscar H., 1866
Allison, A. S., 1869
Allison, Benjamin A., 1844
Allison, Charles Edward, 1899
Allison, George Kelly, 1911
Allison, Harry Weamer, 1911
Allison, J. A., 1858
Allison, James, 1858
Allison, John R.G., 1884
Allison, Lucian Dent, 1903
Allison, Olaf W., 1940
Allison, Robert H., 1839
Allison, Robert Wilson, 1886
Allison, Samuel C., 1867
Allison, T. D. Mutter, 1872
Allison, Thomas H., 1854
Allman, Alfred Frederick, 1895
Allman, David Bacharach, 1914
Allman, Richard L., 1969
Allman, Robert M., 1957
Allmond, Reuben J., 1839
Allred, Edward W., 1877
Allshouse, Richard Reaser, 1954
Allsop, William Kerr, 1915
Allyn, Russell E., 1937
Alman, Benjamin A., 1986
Almand, John J., 1846
Almond, Andrew J., 1859
Alt, Roy Colony, 1913
Altadonna, Victor F., 1982
Altaker, Lawrence L., 1962
Altemus, L. Reed, Jr.,,1959
Altemus, Leard Reed, 1924

Alter, David, 1861
Alter, Samuel, 1925
Alteveer, Janet G., 1977
Althouse, Albert C., 1892
Althouse, Samuel M., 1882
Altman, Barry L., 1958
Altman, Cynthia B., 1977
Altman, David S., 1985
Altman, Gary, 1973
Altman, Owen Randolph, 1901
Altman, William, 1853
Altounian Z. Melkon, 1883
Altreuter, Richard W., 1971
Altschuler, Edwin M., 1973
Altschuler, Robert G., 1967
Alvord, John E., 1878
Amadee, Charles M., 1982
Amadeo, Jose H., 1952
Amadio, Julio J., 1948
Amadio, Patricia B., 1989
Amadio, Peter C., 1973
Amadio, Peter, Jr., 1958
Amateau, Morris, 1923
Ambler, Arthur Chase, 1920
Ambrose, John Francis, 1943
Ambrus, Julian L., 1979
Amer, Jeffrey A., 1981
Amer, Norman S., 1954
Amerise, Anthony Daniel, 1922
Ames, James S., 1885
Ames, Robert P.M., 1880
Amilon, Ivan Emil, 1896
Ammon, George W., 1888
Ammond, Henry M., 1882
Amon, Jesse Adolphus, 1891
Amos, Enos, 1872
Amrick, Thomas J., 1985
Amsbry, Lewis Brownson, 1904
Amsel, Sheldon, 1961
Amshel, Albert L., 1952
Amshel, Jesse L., 1920
Amsterdam, Jay D., 1974
Amsterdam, Julius, 1936
Amuso, Samuel J., 1964
Anagnost, John W., 1978
Anawalt, James W., 1855
Anchors, Eugene Louis, 1937
Andersen, Donald H., 1989
Andersen, James S., 1983
Anderson Robert V. 1949
Anderson, Arlene J., 1970
Anderson, Arlo C., 1961
Anderson, Carl Victor, J1944
Anderson, Charles W., 1948
Anderson, Charles W., 1962
Anderson, Claude, 1927
Anderson, D. R. 1856
Anderson, David C., 1989

Anderson, Edward Lane, 1880
Anderson, Edwin P., 1859
Anderson, Evon Lucian, 1924
Anderson, Frank T., 1882
Anderson, George A., 1909
Anderson, George B., 1877
Anderson, George Randall, 1882
Anderson, George W., 1951
Anderson, Gustav W., 1946
Anderson, Guy B., 1920
Anderson, Horace Brockman, 1917
Anderson, Isaac W., 1835
Anderson, James Howard, 1904
Anderson, James R., 1871
Anderson, James Rush, 1844
Anderson, John B., 1848
Anderson, John B., 1969
Anderson, John Benjamin, 1892
Anderson, Joseph W., 1852
Anderson, Mark E., 1980
Anderson, Merrill A., 1965
Anderson, Peter E., 1859
Anderson, Philip W., 1852
Anderson, Robert V., 1951
Anderson, Samuel, 1841
Anderson, Thomas E., 1878
Anderson, Thomas S., 1888
Anderson, Willaim T., 1961
Anderson, William H., 1967
Anderson, William J., 1837
Anderson, William N., 1837
Anderson, William R., S1944
Anderson, William, 1852
Anderson, Zebulon M.P., 1850
Andracchio, Vincent C., 1956
Andre, Simeon Nicholas, 1893
Andreas, Benjamin Adam, 1888
Andreas, George R., 1892
Andres, William S., 1838
Andrew, David, 1910
Andrew, Lloyd Brumund, 1919
Andrews, A. E., 1860
Andrews, Alonzo, 1894
Andrews, J. Charles, 1862
Andrews, James E., 1918
Andrews, James P., 1845
Andrews, P. Joseph, 1936
Andrews, Peter J., 1959
Andrews, Peter J., Jr., 1985
Andrews, Raymond, 1934
Andrews, Ronald W., 1978
Andrews, T. H., 1864
Andrews, Thomas A., 1868
Andrews, Willard G., 1980
Andreychik, David A., 1987
Andrias, Rosemary, 1972
Andries, Raymond C., 1980
Andriole, Gerald L., Jr., 1978

Andriole, Vincent Anthony, 1925
Androkites, Arthur T., 1985
Androsky, Bernard Stanley, 1924
Andrulonis, Paul A., 1972
Angel, Edgar, 1928
Angel, Furman, 1918
Angell, Charles E., 1880
Angelo, Alice A., 1974
Angeloni, Vincent L., 1984
Angle, George Burton, 1901
Angle, John S., 1862
Angle, William, 1934
Angney, William Muir, 1878
Angstadt, John D., 1981
Angstadt, Norman George, 1935
Angstadt, Paul N., Jr., 1960
Angstadt, Thomas Miller, 1890
Anlick, H., 1869
Annealey, William Honeyford, 1911
Annesley, William H., Jr., 1948
Annon, Walter Thomas, 1918
Anrode, Harry G., 1963
Anselmi, Lanning A., 1977
Ansley, William Bailey, 1867
Anson, Peter M., 1969
Anstadt, George W., 1970
Anstine, Dale T., 1942
Anthony, Christopher H., 1975
Anthony, Jeremiah C., 1891
Anthony, John J., Jr., 1945
Anthony, Lewis G., 1961
Anthony, Luther L., Jr., 1953
Anthony, Thomas H., 1843
Anthony, Walter E., 1912
Anthony, William A., Jr., 1955
Anthony, William, 1855
Antill, Joseph Vincent, 1889
Antinozzi, Rex D., 1982
Antis, Max Abram, 1931
Antognoli, William J., 1961
Antolik, John T., 1958
Antoniacci, Cesare R., 1957
Antony, William L., 1844
Antrim, Joseph 1846
Antupitzky, Louis, 1923
Anzinger, Robert J., 1938
Apeldorn, Ernest F., 1881
Aponte, Gonzalo, Jr., 1952
Appel, Aaron H., 1878
Appel, Charles F., 1941
Appel, Charles H., 1861
Appel, Daniel M., 1875
Appel, John F., 1941
Appell, Rodney A., 1973
Apple, Ammon Andrew, 1890
Apple, Clarence Elwood, 1904
Apple, John Matthew, 1949
Apple, S. S., 1869

Apple, William Edson, 1898
Apple, William Shimer, 1889
Appleby, George Stephen, 1943
Applegate, Charles H., 1866
Applegate, Frederick C., 1863
Applegate, John Chew, 1887
Applegate, Joseph W., 1862
Applegate, William S., 1883
Appleman, Leighton Francis, 1897
Appleman, Warren, 1971
Applestein, Robert, 1928
Applewhite, Louis J., 1858
Applewhite, Scott Carter, 1901
Apt, Leonard, 1945
Arai, Taro, 1990
Arbeter, Allan M., 1967
Arbuckle, William W., 1845
Arbuthnot, Charles M., 1881
Arch, Ellen Michele, 1990
Archer, Edward C., 1854
Archer, William C., 1846
Archibald, Alexander 1836
Archibald, Charles Harvey, 1890
Ard, George Potter, 1907
Ard, Wilson P., 1880
Arden, Sidney H., 1958
Ardman, Blair, 1977
Arenson, Christine Ann, 1990
Arey, Donald L., 1936
Arguilu, Jorge, 1919
Arkus, Robert L., 1969
Arlis-Mayor, Stephanie Lynn, 1989
Armalavage, Leon J., 1938
Armao, Diane Mary, 1990
Armao, Francis B., 1978
Armao, Joseph J., 1953
Armao, Joseph, 1917
Armbrecht, Edward Louis, 1892
Arment, Samuel B., 1877
Armenti, Vincent T., 1982
Armfield, David A., 1861
Armistead, William B., 1851
Armitage, George Lawrence, Jr., 1914
Armitage, Harry V., 1943
Arms, Arnold V., 1939
Arms, Charles Carroll, 1868
Armstrong, Adam Frederick, 1889
Armstrong, Alex H., 1871
Armstrong, Daffield 1839
Armstrong, Donald J., 1977
Armstrong, George M., 1871
Armstrong, Harrison, 1872
Armstrong, J. Stone, 1879
Armstrong, John A., 1867
Armstrong, John Maclay, 1865
Armstrong, Leon H., 1871
Armstrong, Ned B., 1977
Armstrong, Richard, 1854

Armstrong, Robert B., 1959
Armstrong, Robert W., Jr., 1982
Armstrong, Robert, 1868
Armstrong, Thomas Smith, 1903
Armstrong, Thomas Smith, Jr., 1941
Armstrong, William Gaston, 1868
Arnas, George M., 1956
Arndt, Zaccheus P., 1866
Arney, George F., 1878
Arnold, A. E., 1860
Arnold, Edmund S.F., 1848
Arnold, Herbert A., 1878
Arnold, Herbert Leonard, 1913
Arnold, J. Harry, 1892
Arnold, Jesse Oglevee, 1896
Arnold, John Loy, 1911
Arnold, Kenneth J., 1985
Aronica, Michael J., 1958
Aronow, Phillip Z., 1963
Arouh, Albert, 1956
Arrasmith, Thomas Milton, Jr., 1924
Arrington, Robert Glenn, S1944
Arsht, Edwin D., 1955
Arthur, Kenneth R., 1983
Artis, Leopoldo L., 1881
Arts, Joseph D.C., 1831
Asch, Adam S., 1979
Asch, Morris J., 1855
Ascolese, Vincent Raymond, 1964
Ashbaugh, William H., 1959
Ashbey, Dwight, Jr., 1946
Ashburn, Percy Moreau, 1893
Ashby, Bonnie L., 1968
Ashby, William Gregory, 1887
Ashcom, Thomas L., 1983
Ashcraft, John H., 1855
Ashcraft, Samuel Fisler, 1888
Ashcraft, William 1846
Ashe, Edmund F., 1850
Ashe, Richard D., 1850
Ashford, John Wesson, 1897
Ashley, Ann Ava, 1976
Ashley, Claude Wilber, 1932
Ashley, Cornelius 1850
Ashley, Kenneth B., 1988
Ashley, William, 1847
Ashley, William, 1852
Ashmore, Hugh W., 1956
Ashton, Arthur, 1857
Ashton, Asa S., 1864
Ashton, Horace D., 1842
Ashton, Thomas George, 1888
Ashton, William E., 1884
Aspel, Bennett D., 1963
Aspel, Joseph, 1915
Aspen, Nelson P., 1952
Aspinwall, Thomas W., 1839
Aspiote, John George, 1955

Assante, Mario Hugo, 1935
Atkins, George Hulings, 1902
Atkins, T. W., 1861
Atkins, William L., 1860
Atkinson, Alvan W., 1971
Atkinson, Barbara F., 1974
Atkinson, Benjamin M., 1852
Atkinson, Curtis, 1900
Atkinson, Edward C., 1847
Atkinson, G. Russell, 1954
Atkinson, Harold C., 1926
Atkinson, Harry Fretts, 1892
Atkinson, John Bond, 1948
Atkinson, John R., 1839
Atkinson, Robert E., 1977
Atkinson, Thomas Herman, 1910
Atkinson, William B., 1853
Atkinson, William Burr, 1921
Atkinson, William W., 1963
Atlas, Robert O., 1987
Atlee, James Humphries, 1886
Atlee, Louis William, 1882
Atlee, W. Lemuel, 1870
Atlee, Washington L., 1829
Attaway, Thomas Mutter, 1870
Attwood, John Warren, 1888
Atwell, Floyd C., 1937
Atwell, Loyal Porter, 1925
Au Francis T. 1949
Au, Lee K. W., 1980
Au, Otto Y. T., 1957
Au, Victor K., 1979
Aucoin, Jean P., 1959
Auerbach, Arthur H., 1951
Auffarth, Bradley R., 1987
Auffurth, William A., 1883
Aufmwasser, Hugo W., 1895
Aughinbaugh, Thomas H., 1940
Augur, James T., 1877
Aukstakalnis, Frank Joseph, 1930
Aulde, John, Jr., 1882
Auletta, Ann G., 1988
Auritt, William A., 1975
Auslander, Milton Manuel, 1928
Austin, Albert Elmer, 1905
Austin, Alvin A., 1873
Austin, Arthur, 1882
Austin, Charles B., Jr., 1978
Austin, Claude L., 1946
Austin, David K., 1986
Austin, DeWitt Ray, 1917
Austin, Henry Exum, 1912
Austin, Henry O., 1850
Austin, James Aaron, 1887
Austin, John T., 1834
Austin, John Watson, 1910
Austin, Lewis King, 1894
Austin, Peter, 1850

Austin, William, 1854
Austra, Joseph John, 1916
Auteri, Joseph S., 1986
Avard, Charles McQueen, 1895
Avedissian, Michael G., 1982
Avella, Arthur N., 1952
Avellino, Joseph D., 1961
Averbach, Bertram Frederick, 1932
Avinger, Hamilton J., 1853
Avonda, Richard, 1949
Awl, William McClay, 1834
Axe, Michael J., 1979
Axelrod, Bernard Manuel, 1937
Axelrod, Solomon Jacob, 1938
Axford, Samuel M., 1853
Axtell, Earl, 1908
Aydelotte, John Thomas, 1906
Ayer, Francis B., 1848
Ayer, Otis 1842
Ayer, Philip Edward, 1923
Ayers, James S., 1932
Ayres, John A., 1945
Ayres, Robert D., 1957
Ayres, Samuel, 1876
Ayres, Wilmot, 1910
Azar, David J., 1975
Azpell, Thomas F., 1849
Azzato, John A., 1970

~ B ~

Babb, John D., 1980
Babcock, Albert L., 1952
Babcock, Edward B., 1946
Babcock, Franklin Elisha, 1890
Babcock, Harold Snow, 1916
Babcock, Howell Edwards, 1915
Babins, Noah A., 1979
Babitt, Henry I., 1964
Babskie, Robert F., 1947
Bacas, Henry, 1887
Bacharach, Benjamin, 1956
Bacharach, Herbert Joseph, Jr., 1946
Bache, Dallas, 1860
Bache, Thomas Hewson, 1850
Bache, William, Jr., 1927
Bacher, John J., 1839
Bachman, Charles W., 1881
Bachman, Milton Homer, 1906
Bachman, Theodore S., 1878
Bachmann, Carl Frederick, Jr., 1896
Bachmann, G. A., 1874
Bachmann, Jean George, 1907
Bachow, Terry B., 1979
Bachrach, Benjamin, 1902
Backenstose, Daniel Lee, 1950
Backmann, Edward F., 1890
Backwell, Edward G., 1855

Backwell, Edward G., 1855
Bacon, A. T., 1836
Bacon, Alfred E., III, 1981
Bacon, Carroll Burton, 1896
Bacon, Henry C., 1868
Bacon, James W., 1831
Bacon, James, 1865
Bacon, John J., 1843
Bacon, Lewis Heisler, 1924
Bacon, S. L., 1858
Bacon, Walter Austin, 1916
Bacon, Wm. Dudson, 1956
Badder, Elliott M., 1967
Bade, Harry A., III, 1976
Bade, Steven C., 1989
Badeer, Sarkis, 1893
Bader, Walter P., 1904
Bader, William, 1975
Badger, Emile B.G., 1872
Badiavas, Evangelos Van, 1990
Badman, Fred S., 1939
Baer, Caleb D., 1848
Baer, David G., 1979
Baer, Harry A. D., 1917
Baer, Harry George, 1888
Baer, Hermanus Ludwig, 1900
Baer, John Richard, 1893
Baer, Joseph Silas, 1888
Baer, Kenneth A., 1964
Baer, Susan C., 1987
Baez, Steve A., 1974
Bagby, Ramon H., 1973
Bagge, Richard W., 1971
Bagian, James P., 1977
Bagian, Robert G., 1979
Bagley, Ann S., 1987
Bagley, Marshall Thomas, 1963
Bagshaw, David Evans, 1908
Bahl, Charles Zetty, 1888
Bahler, Eileen, 1987
Bailey, A. H., 1838
Bailey, Abbott Kenyon, 1942
Bailey, Carl H., Jr., 1956
Bailey, Clarence Whitfield, 1925
Bailey, Desmond Mark, 1928
Bailey, Dewey J., III, 1987
Bailey, Dewey J., Jr., 1955
Bailey, Gama 1828
Bailey, James L., 1986
Bailey, John A., 1882
Bailey, John Holeman, 1916
Bailey, John S., 1865
Bailey, L. Philip, 1860
Bailey, Levi Matthew, 1897
Bailey, Lloyd W., 1953
Bailey, Nelson John, 1919
Bailey, Samuel DeWitt, 1884
Bailey, Wilson Gill, 1891

Baily, Elisha J., 1844
Baily, Elisha S., 1851
Baily, Harry Wenzel, 1917
Baily, Lewis, 1853
Baily, Obed, 1829
Baily, R. Jones, 1851
Baily, Samuel Gordon, 1844
Baily, Wilson, 1844
Bainbridge, Eusebius C., 1848
Bainbridge, William J., 1970
Baines, Matthew Carroll, 1903
Bair, Charles William, 1932
Bair, George Elmer, 1890
Bair, George Elmer, Jr., 1923
Bair, John B., 1865
Bair, Philip W.O., 1885
Bair, Robert C., 1950
Bair, Thomas A., 1879
Baird, Alexander B., 1880
Baird, Harry L., 1952
Baird, Howard Grant, 1893
Baird, Joseph Armstrong, 1906
Baird, Robert M., 1957
Baird, Thompson McDannold, 1890
Baisden, Carl Francis, 1954
Baka, Joseph J., 1986
Baka, Joseph, 1959
Baker, A. H., 1847
Baker, Andrew J., 1847
Baker, Anthony George, 1887
Baker, Carroll Royer, 1909
Baker, Charles A., 1867
Baker, Daniel Clifton, Jr., 1933
Baker, Dole P., 1965
Baker, Dole Parker, Jr., 1990
Baker, Dorsey Syng, 1846
Baker, Elmer, 1910
Baker, Eugene Manigault, Jr., 1926
Baker, Frank Kline, 1890
Baker, George Iverson, 1926
Baker, H. Hoffman, 1893
Baker, Harry B., 1880
Baker, J. William, 1872
Baker, James E., 1882
Baker, John A.P., 1861
Baker, John Cushing, 1926
Baker, John Wesley, 1867
Baker, Joseph H., 1877
Baker, Joseph H., 1964
Baker, Karen S., 1986
Baker, L. Jackson, 1875
Baker, Leslie Earl, 1928
Baker, Louis Reed, 1957
Baker, Maurice Edward, 1921
Baker, Moses, 1852
Baker, Norman Clyde, 1908
Baker, Regay Leslie, 1894
Baker, Richard P., III, 1983

Baker, Richard P., Jr., 1956
Baker, Robert B., 1975
Baker, Robert H., 1947
Baker, Theodore, Jr., 1933
Baker, Thomas Harding, 1930
Baker, Thomas W., 1838
Baker, William McClain, 1888
Baker, William N., 1835
Baker, Zadoc W., 1871
Bakewell, Brock K., 1984
Bakewell, Frank S., Jr., 1952
Bakewell, Frank Smith, 1909
Bakunin, Maurice Irving, 1932
Balaicuis, Charles W., 1960
Baldassano, Vincent Francis, 1990
Baldauf, James A., 1959
Baldauf, John M., 1988
Baldauf, Leonard Clair, 1926
Baldauf, Leonard Clair, Jr., 1959
Baldi, Frederick V., 1956
Baldinger, William H., 1885
Baldock, William E., 1945
Baldridge, Alexander, 1857
Baldwin, Clifford A., Jr., 1946
Baldwin, George, 1826
Baldwin, Harvey, 1840
Baldwin, Henry, Jr., 1883
Baldwin, Herbert James, 1908
Baldwin, Hugh Allen, 1901
Baldwin, J. Marion, 1880
Baldwin, James F., 1874
Baldwin, Louis K., 1862
Baldwin, Sanford Oscar, 1896
Baldwin, William H., 1875
Baley, Pinckney T., 1853
Balick, Howard N., 1979
Balin, Benjamin R., J1944
Balin, Robert W., J1944
Balis, Sol, 1948
Balizet, Louis B., 1969
Balkany, Christopher K., 1971
Ball, Charles Edward, 1923
Ball, Charles Lightfoot, Jr., 1931
Ball, J. Robert, 1950
Ball, John B., 1841
Ball, Michael Valentine, 1889
Ball, Robert A., 1985
Ball, William B., 1841
Ballantine, Charles H., 1882
Ballard, John, 1868
Ballard, Silas H., 1877
Ballenberger, Louis Porter, 1941
Balliet, Calvin Joseph, 1897
Balling, David Anderson, 1967
Ballinger, Reeve Leslie, 1913
Ballou, James Larkin, 1907
Ballou, Newton H., 1839
Ballow, Isaac T., 1850

Ballow, W. Montgomery, 1853
Balmer, Abraham, F., 1875
Balotin, Nahum M., 1959
Balph, James, Jr., 1920
Balsbaugh, G. Thomas, 1967
Balsbaugh, George S., 1861
Balshi, James D., 1980
Balshi, Stephen F., 1945
Baltuch, Leigh, 1977
Baltz, Samuel Austin, 1903
Baltzell, William H., 1946
Baluta, Victor John, 1924
Bamberger, Peter Kurt, 1990
Bancks, Nicholas H., 1972
Bancroft, Charles March, 1938
Bane, William C., 1879
Banes, Charles Conrad A., 1909
Banes, Dean Marie, 1973
Banes, Joseph Hiram, 1892
Banick, Vincent William, 1935
Banister, Robert B., 1837
Bankhead, Robert A., 1859
Banks, Braxton, 1889
Banks, Henry C., 1957
Banks, James Oliver, 1850
Banks, John L., 1856
Banks, John W., 1857
Banks, Philo Hamlin, 1901
Banks, Roland W., 1931
Banks, William, 1848
Banks, William A., 1846
Banner, Allan Carithers, 1920
Banner, Constantine L., 1855
Banner, Marc P., 1971
Bannett, Aaron D., 1946
Bannon, Charles J., 1962
Bannon, Joseph P., 1987
Bantly, Harry C., 1942
Banyas, Jeffrey B., 1982
Baptist, William H., 1854
Bar, Samuel, 1934
Baraldi, Raymond L., Jr., 1976
Baram, Daniel, 1990
Baram, Lena Diane, 1990
Baran, James J., 1985
Baranski, Edward J., 1959
Barba, William M., 1950
Barbee, Carl A., 1977
Barber, David, 1830
Barber, I. Grier, 1877
Barber, James K., 1851
Barber, John E., 1847
Barber, Raymond, 1904
Barber, Walter, 1882
Barbor, Linus Andrews, 1950
Barbour, Philip C.S., 1867
Barbour, William, 1865
Barbre, Jesse, 1857

Barbrow, Abraham L., 1919
Barchfeld, Andrew J., 1884
Barckley, Robert George, 1891
Barclay, James M., 1844
Barclay, John, 1835
Barclay, John Judson, Jr., 1894
Barclay, John W., 1870
Barclay, John, 1861
Barclay, Joseph B., 1841
Barclay, Michael W., 1847
Barclay, Robert G., 1857
Barclay, William H., 1880
Barcroft, John W., 1844
Barcus, Adolph Ludwig, 1891
Bard, Cephas L., 1866
Bard, Joseph L., 1956
Barder, Joseph John, 1912
Bare, Wesley W., 1952
Barefoot, Graham Ballard, 1923
Barefoot, James Earl, 1963
Barfoot, Albert Fremont, 1887
Barger, Andrew J., 1951
Barger, Geoffrey R., 1975
Barham, R. G., 1855
Barish, Joel M., 1968
Barker, Byron Fuller, 1896
Barker, Christopher Sylvanus, 1909
Barker, John Albert, 1890
Barker, T. Ridgway, 1886
Barkett, Robert E., 1960
Barkett, Robert Edward, Jr., 1990
Barkley, John Wesley, 1897
Barksdale, Edward F., 1849
Barksdale, John, 1849
Barksdale, M. S., 1860
Barksdale, Nathaniel, 1850
Barksdale, William Leigh, 1858
Barksdale, William P., 1852
Barlett, Charles Rufus, 1896
Barlow, Louis Eugene, 1896
Barmach, Kenneth R., 1973
Barna, Nicholas J., 1985
Barnaby, William H., 1968
Barnd, Franklin Pierce, 1897
Barnd, Guy Henry, 1923
Barndt, Robert, Jr., 1964
Barndt, Solomon K., 1863
Barner, John, 1933
Barnes, A. V., 1868
Barnes, Albert Edmond, 1914
Barnes, Charles Stewart, 1897
Barnes, Everett Beck, Jr., 1942
Barnes, Glen D., 1977
Barnes, Henry F., 1854
Barnes, Henry R., 1865
Barnes, Ira Norton, 1862
Barnes, James D., 1950
Barnes, John, 1836

Barnes, Laken D., 1850
Barnes, Lewis Sherman, 1889
Barnes, Robert H., 1870
Barnes, Samuel S.P., 1879
Barnes, Wallace Harold, 1918
Barnes, William Mitchell, 1898
Barnett, Benjamin M., 1882
Barnett, George Watson, 1908
Barnett, Thomas, 1933
Barnette, William Mason, 1906
Barnfield, John Humes, 1886
Barnhardt, Charles Henry, 1895
Barnhart, Jay S., Jr., 1961
Barnum, Henry Weston, 1890
Barnum, Rachel I., 1987
Baroff, Sheldon, 1965
Baron, Abraham Isaac, 1917
Baron, Alan L., 1969
Baron, Andrew J., Jr., 1978
Baron, Bernard W., 1955
Baron, Michael B., 1972
Baron, Samuel Isaac, 1917
Barone, James E., 1971
Barr, Abraham M., 1865
Barr, Austin Flint, 1912
Barr, David Miller, 1864
Barr, Edwin W., 1850
Barr, Eliav, 1986
Barr, Frederick Greiner, 1916
Barr, G. Walter, 1884
Barr, Gavin C., 1960
Barr, Herbert Everard, 1900
Barr, James M., 1859
Barr, John A., 1877
Barr, John C., 1890
Barr, John Chalmers, 1885
Barr, John Franklin, 1928
Barr, John W., 1874
Barr, John Walter, 1905
Barr, Richard G., 1953
Barr, Richard Rice, 1855
Barr, Robert, 1854
Barr, Samuel Dickson, 1888
Barr, Samuel J., 1959
Barr, Samuel L., 1875
Barr, W. F., 1855
Barr, William Bryce, 1926
Barr, William Bryce, Jr., 1956
Barr, William Forse, 1897
Barr, William Henry, 1906
Barrall, Alfred, 1882
Barreras-Almodovar, Jenaro, 1918
Barret, L. Layton, 1854
Barrett, Arthur Miller, 1938
Barrett, E. Calhoun, 1858
Barrett, Edward William, 1902
Barrett, Frederick, 1866
Barrett, John P., Jr., 1966

Barrett, Sterling Archie, 1934
Barrett, Warren M., 1958
Barrett, William C., 1874
Barrick, Claude W., Jr., 1945
Barringer, Charles C., 1946
Barringer, Phil L., 1942
Barrington, Richard C., 1882
Barroway, James N., 1935
Barroway, Robert P., 1964
Barrows, Arthur Monroe, 1901
Barrows, Victor Ira, 1921
Barry, David M., 1952
Barry, Kevin P., 1989
Barry, Rolla Grant, 1912
Barry, William David, 1909
Barry, William Frederic, 1851
Barry, William M., 1880
Barsby, John Edward, 1920
Barsky, Joseph M., Jr., 1947
Barsky, Joseph Mitchell, 1914
Barstow, Richard I., 1933
Barsumian, Hagop G., 1904
Bartges, John D., 1977
Barth, James Buchanan, 1890
Bartho, Blaine F., 1931
Barthold, Joseph Leo, 1932
Bartholomew, Cornelius, 1878
Bartholomew, William, 1866
Bartholow, Paul, 1891
Bartilson, Benjamin Matthias, 1893
Bartles, William H., 1864
Bartleson, Henry C., 1870
Bartleson, Randall N., 1883
Bartleson, Samuel P., 1854
Bartlett, Frederick H., III, 1981
Bartlett, Lester Lawson, 1929
Bartlett, Richard A., 1982
Bartley, James Hugh, 1917
Bartlow, William P., 1984
Bartman, Barbara A., 1984
Barto, Robert E., Jr., S1944
Barto, Robert Edwin, 1915
Bartolette, Charles, 1846
Bartolette, T. Miles, 1855
Barton, Charles R., Jr., 1948
Barton, George C., 1880
Barton, Harry Roszelle, 1892
Barton, Henry Clay, 1896
Barton, Herbert Parks, 1890
Barton, Isaac, Jr., 1877
Barton, J. Hervey, 1862
Barton, James C., 1964
Barton, James Morrie, 1868
Barton, John T., 1852
Barton, Thomas F., 1852
Bartone, Francis F., 1957
Bartos, Joseph E., 1948
Bartos, Paul B., 1979

Bartoshesky, Stephen W., J1944
Barylak, Edward J., 1970
Basara, Bruno E., Jr., 1979
Bascove, S. Jack, 1949
Baseman, Alan S., 1985
Bash, Evan K., 1982
Bash, Myron, 1946
Bashore, Randall T., 1982
Bashore, Robert Guy, 1919
Bashore, Robert L., 1979
Bashore, Robert M., Jr., 1952
Bashore, Sidney M., 1947
Bashore, Simeon David, 1896
Basil, Aratoon, 1908
Basista, Michael H., 1984
Baskerville, Charles, Jr., 1867
Baskin, George W., 1846
Baskin, Robert H., 1859
Baskoff, Joel D., 1972
Baskous, Alexander T., 1971
Bass, Charles N., 1838
Bass, James P., 1860
Bass, John N., 1858
Bass, Joseph F., 1860
Bass, Robert E., 1855
Basselleu, William F., 1855
Bassett, Henry Linn, 1901
Bassow, Carl Frederick, 1912
Bastian, Charles Brown, 1889
Bastian, James R., 1960
Bastian, Robert Cromwell, 1925
Bastian, Robert Cronwell, Jr., 1957
Bastian, William Clair, 1922
Batchis, Van S., 1969
Bate, Arthur Edwin, 1891
Bateman, Benjamin Rush, 1828
Bateman, Ephraim, 1851
Bateman, Frank Middleton, 1889
Bateman, Joseph N., 1987
Bates, Andrea Rose, 1990
Bates, James M., 1851
Bates, John William, 1862
Bates, Solomon A., 1847
Bates, Stephen, 1829
Bates, Thomas B., 1854
Bates, Thomas J., 1854
Bates, William Edgar, 1886
Batman, William F., 1880
Batt, David S., 1976
Battaglia, David R., 1988
Batte, John W., 1846
Batten, A. Nelson, 1853
Batten, George B., 1977
Battersby, Robert, 1834
Battey, Robert, 1857
Battey, Thomas W., 1834
Battle, Ivan Proctor, 1904
Battle, Lucius Lucullus, 1851

Batton, John A., 1882
Bauduy, Jerome Keating, 1863
Bauer, Andrew William, 1990
Bauer, Arthur James, 1914
Bauer, Charles, 1884
Bauer, Edward Louis, 1914
Bauer, Francis Xavier, 1940
Bauer, Fredric B., 1963
Bauer, H. Paul, Jr., 1955
Bauer, Harold E., 1959
Bauer, Henry Paul, 1927
Bauer, John H., 1969
Bauer, John Nathan, 1896
Bauer, Louis Denme, 1890
Bauer, Richard D., 1945
Bauer, Thomas L., 1965
Bauer, Walter David, Jr., 1940
Bauer, William Andrew, 1929
Bauer, William F., 1958
Baugh, John E., 1882
Baugh, Wilfreta G., 1979
Bauknight, Walter J., 1857
Baum, Neil B., 1983
Baum, William Louis, 1888
Bauman, David C., 1977
Bauman, Harvey R., 1923
Baumgarner, Gene T., 1967
Baumgart, Clarence Henry, 1919
Baumgarten, Roy Chester, 1912
Baumgartner, William Jacob, 1893
Baumm, N. Craig, 1959
Baun, William Daniel, 1915
Bausch, Mark Adolph, 1923
Bausch, Richard D., 1942
Bauscher, Abner Henry, 1908
Bautista, Alejandro A., 1986
Baver, George A., 1932
Baxley, Jabez B., 1848
Baxter, John S., 1856
Baxter, Louis S., 1868
Baxter, Milton Edwin, 1909
Baxter, Oscar Dixon, 1924
Baxter, R. G., 1869
Baxter, Thomas L., III, 1970
Bayer, Joel S., 1964
Baylis, John C., 1968
Baylor, Joseph N., 1853
Baylor, Richard D., 1985
Baylor, Robert Stewart, Jr., 1929
Bayn, John S., 1844
Bayo, Alexis J., Jr., 1986
Bazanson, Almira, 1904
Bazet, Louis, 1876
Beach, Charles H., 1836
Beach, Columbus, 1837
Beach, Edward W., 1919
Beach, George Brown, 1886
Beach, James Daniel, 1895

Bell, James W., 1834
Bell, James, 1864
Bell, John B., 1861
Bell, John Forrest, 1890
Bell, John James, 1901
Bell, Joseph G., 1864
Bell, Joseph G., 1986
Bell, Ralph M., 1941
Bell, Richard T., 1972
Bell, Stephen T., 1980
Bell, Thomas G., 1956
Bell, W. D., 1855
Bell, William S., 1847
Bell, William, 1858
Bellamy, John T., 1849
Bellamy, Robert Hartlee, 1902
Bellangee, J. Barton, 1854
Bellerue, Albert R., 1918
Belles, William J., 1986
Bellet, Robert E., 1968
Bellet, Samuel, 1925
Bellin, Harvey J., 1965
Bellus, John J., 1957
Belmont, Jonathan B., 1976
Belo, Arthur F., 1870
Belsh, Jerry M., 1975
Belville, J. Edgar, 1882
Beman, Edward D., 1859
Bemiller, Carl R., 1958
Bemis, Charles A., 1872
Bemis, Royal Warren, 1892
Benbow, Edgar Vernon, 1925
Benbow, Thomas Alex P., 1914
Bender, Andrew L., 1966
Bender, Bruce R., 1977
Bender, Charles E., 1935
Bender, David B., 1987
Bender, John A., 1943
Bender, John M., 1957
Bender, Joseph M., 1976
Bender, Leonard Franklin, 1919
Bender, Leonard Franklin, 1948
Bender, Max, 1915
Bender, O. C., 1867
Bender, Paul B., 1915
Bender, Thomas M., 1964
Bendix, Paul Alexander, 1937
Bendy, Robert H., Jr., 1961
Benecki, Theresa R., 1978
Beneke, George Henry, 1868
Benerman, Louis C., 1887
Beneski, Daniel A., 1984
Benfield, Thomas C., 1977
Benge, Bruce N., 1988
Benham, R. Bruce, 1876
Benjamin, Floyd Allen, 1906
Benjamin, James J., 1966
Benjamin, John B., 1853

Benjamin, Wallace F., 1972
Benner, John H., IV, 1973
Benner, Norman Ray, 1928
Bennet, Eben H., 1875
Bennett, Clarence Elmer, 1903
Bennett, Earl Leslie, 1914
Bennett, Edmund, 1855
Bennett, Francis Gurney, 1889
Bennett, Gaylord W., 1957
Bennett, Irvin Edmund, 1891
Bennett, Ivan F., S1944
Bennett, J. W., 1856
Bennett, Jacob E., 1881
Bennett, John Henry, 1893
Bennett, John Knight, 1887
Bennett, John Terrell, 1914
Bennett, John V., 1961
Bennett, Lansing H., 1953
Bennett, Nathan Louis, 1990
Bennett, Paula R., 1985
Bennett, Richard H., 1975
Bennett, Richard L., 1964
Bennett, Samuel Dey, 1896
Bennett, Samuel, 1898
Bennett, Trumbull L., 1848
Bennett, Wilford W., 1907
Bennett, William Robert, 1893
Benninger, Amandus, A., 1880
Benovitz, Burton S., 1955
Benscoter, Perry Hubler, 1894
Benshoff Arthur M., 1915
Benson, Andrew Ludwig, 1915
Benson, Douglas B., 1859
Benson, Kenneth Haworth, 1932
Benson, Wirt F., 1848
Bentley, David Fuller, Jr., 1914
Benton, Claude Monk, 1889
Benton, Lisa D., 1989
Benz, Robert L., 1978
Benzel, Stanley, 1969
Beppler, Paul Hazen, 1925
Berardinelli, John L., 1968
Berardis, John M., 1979
Berardis, Velio Eliseo, 1948
Berberich, Herman, 1901
Bercaw, David M., 1981
Berd, David A., 1968
Berg, J. Frederick, Jr., 1862
Berg, Philip, Jr., 1938
Berger, Alan Keith, 1990
Berger, Barbara J., 1977
Berger, Bruce A., 1970
Berger, Bruce C., 1974
Berger, Gary W., 1972
Berger, I. Robert, 1936
Berger, Jay B., 1968
Berger, Joseph R., 1974
Berger, Melvin Martin, 1940

Berger, Mitchell R., 1986
Berger, Morley, 1931
Berger, Norman, 1957
Berger, Robert A., 1948
Berger, Robert B., 1978
Berger, Simon Melvin, 1938
Berger, Stuart M., 1975
Bergeron, Pierre Norbert, 1902
Bergethon, Peter R., 1983
Berghella, Vincenzo, 1990
Bergman, Donald A., 1971
Bergman, Garrett E., 1969
Bergquist, Erick J., 1973
Bergstresser, Edwin, 1882
Bergum, Allen Anton, 1975
Berguson, Paul D., 1975
Bering, Joseph P., 1956
Bering, Joseph P., Jr., 1988
Berk J. Edward, 1936
Berk, John K., 1896
Berk, Theodore F., 1979
Berkebile, Brenda L., 1988
Berkebile, Paul E., 1958
Berkel, Boyce N., 1973
Berkeley, Green Ramsey, 1906
Berkey, Norman G., 1878
Berkheimer, Park, 1925
Berkowitz, Kathleen M., 1987
Berkowitz, Scott D., 1979
Berlet, James F., 1877
Berley, Lawrence F., 1970
Berley, Robert M., 1979
Berlin, Allison Janis, 1927
Berlin, Howard F., 1975
Berlin, Irvin I., 1935
Berlin, James O., 1874
Berlin, Paul J., 1985
Berliu, Wilson S., 1878
Berman, Claudia G., 1984
Berman, Jacob Julius, 1919
Berman, Jacob Kohn, 1921
Berman, Joel E., 1989
Berman, Lawrence S., 1969
Bermudez, Pedro Joaquin, 1895
Berna, Ronald A., 1989
Bernardin, Ronald Maurice, S1944
Bernatz, Clarence Frank, 1905
Berne, Bernard, 1956
Berne, Ronald Stuart, 1990
Berner, Jerome J., 1952
Bernett, Gary B., 1976
Berney, Daniel Edward, 1911
Berney, Daniel T., 1951
Bernhard, Joel Augustin, 1940
Bernhardt, William H., 1915
Bernini, Philip M., 1973
Bernini, Richard L., 1970
Berns, Leon L., 1930

Bernstein, Abraham, 1917
Bernstein, Arthur, 1891
Bernstein, Lawrence D., 1972
Bernstein, Marc L., 1973
Bernstein, Melvin L., S1944
Bernstein, Mitchell, 1914
Bernstein, Stanley, 1962
Bernstine, Earl L., 1955
Bernstine, J. Bernard, 1922
Bernstine, Richard L., 1948
Bernstine, Richard T., 1958
Berntheizel, George W., 1866
Berrettini, Achilles Alfred, 1932
Berrien, J. Hunter, 1857
Berrillo, Anacleto, 1931
Berrittini, Wade H., 1977
Berry, A. J., 1858
Berry, Bradley D., 1953
Berry, Daniel, 1866
Berry, David G., 1976
Berry, Frank K., 1867
Berry, George W., 1857
Berry, Gerard T., 1975
Berry, James D., S1944
Berry, John C., 1871
Berry, John, 1908
Berry, Lawrence Francis, 1905
Berry, Robert E., 1955
Berry, Theodore J., 1943
Berry, William Thomas, 1915
Berryhill, Samuel G., 1854
Bers, Sol N., 1939
Bershad, Leonard, 1904
Berson, George Jarcho, 1923
Bertin, Elmer John, 1918
Bertolet, Charles Boileau, 1927
Bertolet, John Allan, 1916
Bertolet, John Marshall, 1896
Bertolet, Walter Melot, 1902
Bertolette, Daniel N., 1872
Bertolette, J. C., 1858
Bertolette, Peter Grisemer, 1844
Bertolette, Richard D., 1951
Bertolino, John G., 1983
Bertram, Albert Joseph, 1912
Bertrand, Elmer, 1920
Bertsch, A. Monroe, J1944
Bertsch, David J., 1985
Berwind, Robert T., 1965
Bescher, R. Anthony, 1971
Bese, Frederick, 1864
Besecker, Joseph Albert, 1959
Besley, Richard N., 1963
Besozzi, Michael J., 1975
Besse, Byron E., Jr., 1950
Besser, Arthur S., 1961
Besses, Gerald S., 1970
Best, Austin, 1878

Beste, Gary A., 1980
Bethune, Charles Ward, 1918
Bethune, Roderick A., 1854
Betta, J. M., 1870
Betts, George Warren, 1906
Betts, James Alfred, 1909
Betts, William Williams, 1907
Betz, Israel, 1868
Beutel, Peter, 1872
Bevan, David, 1891
Bevan, James L., 1963
Beveridge, John L., 1855
Bevier, I. D., 1838
Bevis, Earle Miami, 1910
Bew, Richard, 1910
Beyer, John C., 1986
Beyer, John Jacob, 1890
Beyer, Joseph Walter, 1905
Beyer, William F., 1879
Beyerle, W. George, 1853
Beyth, Rebecca J., 1987
Bhatt, Jitendra R., 1960
Bialas, Paul A., 1973
Bianchini, Adam A., 1988
Bibb, Alexander L., 1859
Bibb, Clyde James, 1913
Bibb, Henry B., 1858
Bibb, William E., 1848
Bibby, Walter E., 1881
Bibighaus, T. B., 1857
Bibighaus, Warren Y., J1944
Bice, Barrett Dedrick, 1902
Bickel, George V., 1878
Bickell, S. Ellsworth, 1888
Bickell, Ulysses Grant, 1893
Bicker, Francis Joseph, 1890
Bickers, Alston Hubert, 1886
Bickerton, Michael W., 1979
Bickford, Henry H., 1877
Bickford, Hezekiah C., 1845
Bickham, Charles E., Jr., 1946
Bickley, John G., 1877
Bickley, Lloyd Wharton, 1861
Bickley, William M., 1839
Bicknell, Frank J., 1945
Bicknell, Robert Cooke, 1895
Biddle, Alexander W., 1879
Biddle, Clement, 1878
Biddle, David, 1970
Biddle, Jonathan C., 1877
Biddle, Philip George, 1897
Biddle, Robert M., 1915
Biddle, William Earl, 1935
Bieber, James R., 1967
Biedlingmaier, Gerard Joseph, 1954
Biehl, Jefferson P., 1883
Biehn, Andrew Clymer, 1893
Biehn, William Milton, 1903

Bielawski, Donald M., 1976
Biele, Albert Melvin, 1938
Biello, Joseph Albert, 1905
Bierer, Frederick C., 1849
Bierlein, Alan H., 1975
Bierly, Mahlon Z., Jr., 1946
Bierman, William A., 1975
Bierman-Dear, Nancy A., 1988
Bierne, George W., 1843
Biesecker, James Ellsworth, 1886
Biester, Robert J., 1982
Bigatel, David Alfred, 1990
Bigelow, Brown A., 1874
Bigelow, Charles E., 1882
Bigelow, Frederick F., 1883
Bigelow, George F., 1846
Bigelow, Robert J., 1860
Bigelow, Samuel Irvin, 1927
Biggar, Raymond Whitney, 1940
Bigger, David Andrew, 1917
Biggs, Augustine A., 1836
Biglan, Albert Manley, 1930
Bigler, D. M., 1869
Bigler, William B., 1865
Bigley, Elmer C., Jr., 1965
Bigley, Francis Peter, 1906
Bigley, Joseph R., 1940
Bigony, Franklin G., 1884
Bigony, Franklin W., 1852
Bikle, Jeffrey M., 1982
Biles, Daniel T., 1981
Bilheimer, John Jessiah, 1891
Bill, J. H., Jr., 1858
Billas, Anthony, Jr., 1982
Billetdoux, Chester Augustus, 1910
Billings, Arthur Eugene, 1906
Billmeyer, D. Harrison, 1884
Billon, Eugene, 1846
Bills, Thomas K., 1980
Billstein, Stephan Anthony, 1962
Billups, Robert A., 1847
Billys, James B., 1981
Bilyk, Jurij R., 1987
Binckley, Owen Henry, 1917
Binder, Charles A., 1963
Bing, Edward W., 1877
Bingaman, Charles E., 1910
Bingaman, Edwin Milton, 1895
Bingham, John E., 1873
Bingham, William F., 1964
Binkley, Thomas G., 1888
Binkowitz, Joseph, 1921
Binnick, Alan N., 1973
Binns, Carl B., Jr., 1968
Bippart, Peter E., 1981
Bippus, Christopher C., 1889
Bippus, Samuel M., 1884
Birch, David, 1848

Birch, Solomon G., 1845
Birch, William Benjamin, 1945
Bird, Wellington, 1841
Birdsall, William George, 1895
Birdsell, Sylvester, 1848
Birdsong, Miles J., 1854
Birenbaum, Dale S., 1989
Birnbaum, Glenn A., 1986
Birrell, Donald G., 1948
Birriolo, Francis Annibale, 1893
Bisbing, John Hoover, 1929
Biscoe, Gibbs, 1909
Biser, David Isaac, 1949
Bishko, Maurice J., 1935
Bishko, Samuel J., 1931
Bishop, David E., 1966
Bishop, George W., 1849
Bishop, J. Leander, 1854
Bishop, Jacques A., 1865
Bishop, Milton, 1860
Bishop, Paul Arthur, 1920
Bishop, S. Snively, 1884
Bishop, William S., 1842
Bissell, John Robertson, 1891
Bissell, William Henry, 1834
Bisset, James F., Jr., 1962
Bitner, Abraham, 1827
Bitner, Charles Hilaire, 1924
Bitterman, Stuart R., 1983
Bitting, Anthony L., 1853
Bitting, John A., 1874
Bitting, Numa Duncan, 1907
Bittinger, Joseph H., 1878
Bittle, Stanley Edward, 1919
Bittner, Clarence Lavan, 1914
Bittner, Donald L., 1952
Bittner, Henry Edward, 1902
Bittner, William E., 1953
Bittrich, Norbert Martin, 1932
Bivins, Robert T., 1859
Bixler, Jacob R., 1866
Bixler, Lester George, 1937
Bixler, Lester George, Jr., 1959
Blachly, Oliver L., 1877
Blachly, S. L., 1870
Black, Abraham, 1851
Black, Alexander, 1837
Black, Charles H., 1875
Black, Clarence E., 1870
Black, David Harold, 1957
Black, Henry M., 1875
Black, Hugh S., 1917
Black, James B., 1883
Black, Jesse Langtry, 1896
Black, John, 1858
Black, Judson Harmon, 1893
Black, M. F., 1873
Black, Samuel Orr, 1915

Black, William M., 1885
Blackburn, Cary B., 1861
Blackburn, Joseph M., 1955
Blackburn, Joseph W., 1847
Blackford, Ben, 1855
Blackmon, Benjamin F., 1845
Blackmon, Heyward James, 1922
Blackmon, Stonewall Jackson, 1918
Blackwell, George W., 1857
Blackwell, Nicholas, 1860
Blackwell, Thomas J., 1859
Blackwood, James Magee, 1902
Blackwood, Norman Jerome, 1888
Blackwood, Thomas J., 1866
Blackwood, Thomas, 1874
Blackwood, William, 1849
Blain, Hamilton L., 1848
Blaine, James M., 1881
Blair, Albert J., 1935
Blair, Alexander R., 1853
Blair, Ellen K., 1983
Blair, Frank W., S1944
Blair, Franklin, 1884
Blair, George Dewey, 1923
Blair, James Albert, 1923
Blair, James Dana, 1904
Blair, John A., 1890
Blair, John E., 1849
Blair, Joseph R., 1945
Blair, Mortimer Warren, 1914
Blair, S. T., 1868
Blair, Willis Thomas, 1951
Blake, Duncan W., 1876
Blake, Duncan W., Jr., 1892
Blake, E. Tucker, 1853
Blake, Hu A., 1946
Blake, Joseph C., 1854
Blake, Joseph John, 1950
Blake, Paul O., 1929
Blake, Thomas F., 1948
Blake, William Bradford, Jr., J1944
Blaker, Mark E., 1976
Blakey, Robert L., 1837
Blakey, Thomas, 1882
Blakey, Yelverton C., 1836
Blalock, Alonzo L., 1886
Blalock, N. G., 1861
Blalock, Yancey C., 1884
Blanc, Kenneth M., 1959
Blanch, John J., 1973
Blanch, Joseph J., 1937
Blanchard, Azariel 1833
Blanchard, Charles Lester, 1928
Blanchard, Howard E., 1905
Blanchard, John H., 1852
Blanchard, Samuel W., 1844
Blanck, Ephraim K., 1873
Blanck, George A., 1860

Blanck, John K., 1882
Blanck, Joseph Elwood, 1886
Bland, C. Brinley, 1942
Bland, George Willis, 1930
Bland, John H., J1944
Bland, Pascal Brooke, 1901
Bland, William F., 1849
Blankemeyer, Henry John, 1903
Blankman, B.J. 1839
Blannett, John D., Jr., 1976
Blanton, Alexander M., 1845
Blanton, Carter, 1864
Blanton, J. B., 1869
Blanton, J. W., 1869
Blanton, James M., 1849
Blanton, Philip S., 1849
Blanton, William H., 1859
Blasetto, James W., 1981
Blasko, Edward C., 1982
Blatchley, Donald M., 1948
Blatt, Bruce I., 1984
Blatt, John Frederick, 1930
Blaugrand, Samuel, 1915
Blaum, Louis C., 1941
Blaum, Louis C., Jr., 1972
Blaydes, James E., 1862
Blayney, Charles Alva, 1900
Blazek, F. Douglas, 1983
Bleakney, Frank, 1900
Blechman, Martin G., 1957
Blechschmidt, George F., 1958
Blechschmidt, Julius, 1908
Blecker, David, 1960
Blecker, Michael J., 1971
Bledsoe, Francis M., 1859
Bledsoe, Hugh James, 1891
Bleiler, Charles Alfred, 1885
Bleiler, Peter O., 1876
Bleiman, Bruce S., 1973
Blewitt, George A., 1962
Bley, David L., 1875
Bley, George, Jr., 1881
Bley, Robert E., 1877
Bley, Robert Etris, Jr., 1910
Bley, Walter Clarence, 1900
Bleznak, Aaron D., 1983
Blick, Joseph A., 1859
Blinn, Lawrence A., 1983
Blinn, Nathan, 1963
Blinn, Randall D., 1989
Bliss, D. P., 1867
Bliss, E. W., 1869
Bliss, Gerald C.W., 1880
Bliss, Gerald Douglas, 1907
Bliss, Raymond VanNess, 1913
Blizard, Eugene B., 1959
Blizzard, John J., 1954
Block, Louis Henry, 1939

Block, Robert A., 1967
Blocker, John E., 1860
Blocksom, Joseph T.V., 1871
Bloemendaal, Dirk Cornelius, 1927
Bloemendaal, Gerrit J., 1926
Bloemendaal, John W., 1955
Bloemendaal, Robert D., 1958
Bloes, Walter S., 1959
Blofstein, Barbara, 1970
Blomain, Eric W., 1973
Blomer, Augustus P., 1873
Blomer, George Davis, Jr., 1890
Blood, Joseph Belton, Jr., 1966
Bloodgood, Delavan, 1854
Bloodworth, Francis Henry, 1892
Bloodworth, Wiley W., 1850
Bloom, Charles Henry, 1934
Bloom, D. George, 1926
Bloom, John W., 1971
Bloom, Michael A., 1962
Bloomer, William D., 1970
Bloomfield, James Camak, 1888
Bloomfield, Maximilian David, 1905
Blore, James P., Jr., 1972
Blose, George Alvin, 1883
Bloss, Jeffrey D., 1982
Blosser, Roy, 1906
Blotz, Benjamin Franklin, 1914
Blount, Benjamin F., 1854
Blount, Cyrus N., 1865
Blount, T. M., Jr., 1858
Bloxom, John H., 1856
Blue, John C., 1877
Blue, Vincent P., 1959
Bluestine, Steven J., 1986
Bluestone, George Gabriel, 1930
Blum, Ronald I., 1970
Blumberg, Alan I., 1947
Blumberg, Albert L., 1974
Blumberg, Leon David, 1938
Blumberg, Michael Zangwill, 1971
Blumberg, Nathan, 1907
Blumberg, Richard S., 1979
Blumenthal, Harold L., 1959
Blumenthal, Sherry L., 1982
Blumfield Irvin H. 1949
Blunden, Boyle N., 1879
Blutstein, Richard N., 1975
Bly, Douglas, 1851
Blyholder, C., 1873
Board, John C., 1880
Boardman, Henry K. W., 1846
Boardman, John F., 1836
Boardman, Walter, 1885
Boatwright, John G., 1853
Bobb, William H., 1851
Boben, William R., Jr., 1964
Bobes, Solomon Subere, 1933

Bocher, Jack, 1960
Bochroch, Max H., 1880
Bock, Martin O., 1958
Bockel, Richard Martin, 1888
Bockner, Andrew C., 1969
Bockus, Henry LeRoy, 1917
Bodder, Levi D., 1834
Bode, Frederick W., Jr., 1947
Boden, Todd R., 1910
Bodenstab, Alanna F., 1977
Bodenstab, Alex B., 1977
Bodenstab, William E., 1977
Bodenstab, William Henry, 1893
Boehmer, George Henry, 1897
Boenning, Henry C., 1879
Boerner, Carol F., 1976
Boerner, David A., 1981
Boerner, Thomas F., 1986
Boffa, Felix J., 1959
Boggs Lawrence K., 1949
Boggs, Charles D., 1859
Boggs, Joseph D., 1945
Boggs, Samuel W., 1868
Bogle, R. L., 1858
Bogle, William H., 1885
Bogman, Charles H., 1871
Bogner, Edward W., 1977
Bohlender, John Frederick, 1928
Boice, Harman Edward, 1899
Boice, James M., 1906
Boies, Jeremich S., 1855
Boines, George James, 1929
Boissevain, Andre R., 1963
Boland, Francis B., Jr., 1962
Boland, Francis Bernard, 1933
Boland, Francis Patrick, 1932
Boland, James P., 1956
Boland, Richard W., 1874
Bold, Charles M., 1846
Bold, Valentine Jacob, 1890
Boley, Scott J., 1949
Boley, Henry Benjamin, 1916
Bolich, John Albert, 1929
Bolin, J. Albert, 1881
Bolin, Zera Exley, 1914
Bolling, Archibald, 1835
Bolling, Lenaeus, 1848
Bolling, W. M., 1838
Bollinger, Abraham D., 1867
Bollman, Henry L., 1884
Bolman, Harold Robert, 1928
Bolton, Earle William, 1897
Bolton, James N., 1848
Bolton, Joseph Peeky, 1890
Bolton, Mayland, 1885
Bolton, William T., 1882
Bolton, William Worden, 1930
Boltz, Elias Kline, 1896

Bolus, Michael, 1934
Bombaugh, Charles C., 1853
Bomgardner, John E., 1857
Bonacci, Eugene F., 1956
Bonafide, Peter Robert, 1969
Bonanni, Loretta D., 1978
Bonanno, Richard J., 1972
Bonatti, Anthony C., 1923
Bonatti, William D., 1959
Bond, Francis E., 1858
Bond, James, 1845
Bond, Jess F., 1952
Bond, Jesse H., 1933
Bond, Munroe, 1879
Bonebrake, Andrew S., 1872
Bonelli, Victor Emmanuel, 1907
Bongiovanni, John James, 1946
Bonham, Dwight Turney, 1931
Bonham, James William, 1890
Bonifant, Benjamin 1849
Bonin, Lawrence I., 1952
Bonn, Jerrold C., 1962
Bonnaffon, Samuel Ashton, 1887
Bonnefil, J. B. Martin, 1876
Bonnell, Frank Sumner, 1913
Bonner, Dennis J., 1976
Bonner, John J., 1980
Bonner, Robert E., 1976
Bonner, William Richard, 1927
Bonney, Charles Walter, 1904
Bonsieur, Jean Paul, 1873
Bonwill, Howard G., 1886
Booher David O., 1949
Book, James Burgess, 1865
Book, William P., 1865
Bookhammer, Robert S., 1928
Boon, Jacob, 1867
Boon, William C., 1859
Boon, William M. B., 1896
Boone, James, 1847
Boone, William Waldo, 1923
Boor, William F., 1853
Boord, Paul C., 1912
Boorse, Isaiah H.G., 1850
Boos, Lauren M., 1985
Booth, Donald M., 1966
Booth, Nelson Alexander, 1887
Booth, William C., 1851
Booton, John G., 1854
Boova, Robert S., 1977
Boquist, Walter A., 1938
Boran, Robert P., Jr., 1978
Borbonus, John Norbert, 1931
Border, Michael W., 1978
Boreen, Stuart M., 1986
Boren, Samuel Wesley, 1897
Boretsky, Harry, 1951
Boretsky, Robert H., 1982

Boyer, Samuel S., 1864
Boyers, James S., 1883
Boyett, Thomas W., 1853
Boykin, Irvine Manning, 1914
Boylan, Peter Clement, 1927
Boyle, Brian F., 1985
Boyle, Denis A., 1948
Boyle, Edwin, Jr., 1947
Boyle, George Arthur, 1887
Boyle, Harlow Ashton, 1891
Boyle, James William, 1928
Boyle, Kevin M., 1980
Boyle, Mary F., 1983
Boyle, Patrick Francis, 1902
Boyle, Peter Leo, 1927
Boyle, Playford, Jr., 1954
Boyle, Ralph Raum, 1887
Boyle, Sean P., 1984
Boyle, William F., J1944
Boylston, Bedford F., 1980
Boylston, Bedford Forrest, 1941
Boysen, Homer W., 1946
Boysen, Otto T., J1944
Boysen, Theophilius Henry, Jr., 1905
Boysen, Theophilus Henry, III, 1940
Bozentka, David J., 1987
Brabson, Howard W., 1951
Braccia, Gregory M., 1989
Brace, Robert W., 1900
Braceland, Francis James, 1930
Bracey, John R., 1857
Brackbill, Elizabeth W., 1979
Brackbill, Robert M., Jr., 1979
Bracken, Joseph K.W., 1889
Brackenridge, Henry H., 1850
Brackett, Arthur Stone, 1895
Brackett, William Ernest, 1915
Brackett, William Walker, 1896
Braconaro, Francis J., 1972
Bradbury, Andrew R., 1986
Braddock Charles Shreve, Jr., 1896
Braddock, Richard S., 1875
Braden, Leroy, 1880
Braden, Robert G., 1942
Bradenham, Ben P., 1973
Bradfield, George M., 1890
Bradfield, James E., 1976
Bradford, Edward Burton, 1901
Bradford, F. Standish, 1858
Bradford, T. Hewson, 1874
Bradford, Thomas A., 1850
Bradford, Thomas S., 1871
Bradford, Thomas T., 1868
Bradfute, Champe Saunders, 1887
Bradley, Alfred Eugene, 1887
Bradley, Charles, 1875
Bradley, James, 1865
Bradley, John Aloysius, 1906

Bradley, John, 1863
Bradley, Martin R., 1965
Bradley, Rev. Edward C., S.J., 1955
Bradley, Robert Aloysius, 1920
Bradley, Robert D., 1868
Bradley, Timothy M., 1986
Bradley, Vernon F., 1958
Bradley, William H., 1865
Bradshaw, Arthur Franklin, 1893
Bradshaw, Howard Holt, 1927
Brady, Douglas F., 1951
Brady, Elliott Thomas, 1886
Brady, Franklin, 1888
Brady, Fred Charles, 1939
Brady, John C., 1940
Brady, John, 1876
Brady, Michael T., 1977
Brady, Philip J., 1909
Brady, Reginald Morton, 1912
Brady, Richard J., 1909
Brady, Walter Charles, 1912
Brady, William F., 1884
Braford, Philip Spotswood, 1855
Brahen, Louis, 1955
Braid, Byron S., 1971
Brain, Charles Edward, 1910
Brainard, Daniel 1834
Brainard, Medad P., 1880
Brait, Kenneth A., 1967
Brallier, Emanuel, 1868
Bramble, Halsey Sandford, 1905
Brams, Richard F., 1955
Branch, John H., 1858
Branch, John L., 1856
Branconi, Joseph M., 1975
Brand, Stanley N., 1969
Brand, Walter William, 1894
Brandau, A. Gordon, Jr., 1964
Brandau, John, 1885
Brandau, William Walker, 1900
Brandberg, Guy Alfred, 1905
Brandfass, Carl F., Jr., 1953
Brandfass, Robert T., 1951
Brandfass, W. Taylor, 1955
Brandmiller, Barclay M., 1936
Brandon, Jeffrey C., 1979
Brandon, M. Boyd, 1942
Brandon, Thomas Campbell, 1935
Brandon, William Douglas, 1946
Brandt, Eli Bainbridge, 1855
Brandt, Jeremiah, 1854
Brandt, Logan, 1849
Brandwan, Samuel, Jr., 1932
Branham, Henry R., 1845
Branham, P. A., 1858
Branin, Henry E., 1858
Brannen, Daniel Edwin, 1945
Brannock, James M., 1851

Branon, Anthony William, 1913
Branson, Jesse A., 1857
Brant, Albion Earl, 1912
Brant, Earl E., 1945
Brantley Hassell, 1888
Brantley, Julian C., Jr., J1944
Brantley, Julian Chisolm, 1916
Brantley, Kenneth M., 1982
Brasacchio, Ralph Anthony, 1990
Brasitus, Thomas A., 1971
Braslow, Norman H., 1973
Brass, Andrew J., 1848
Braude, Bennett Arthur, 1914
Braun, Frederick C., Jr., 1955
Braun, William, 1934
Brause, John M., 1873
Braveman, Bernard L., J1944
Braverman, Gerald L., 1972
Braverman, Wayne H., 1968
Brawner, Lucius W., 1856
Brawner, William M., 1856
Bray, Russell Stanton, 1928
Bray, Walter S., 1887
Braymer, Orange Whitney, 1888
Brayshaw, James Ellis, 1920
Brayton, E. Cullen, 1870
Bready, Conrad R., 1880
Bready, John Ely, 1878
Brechemin, Louis, Jr., 1900
Brecht, James A., 1961
Breckenridge, John W., 1970
Breckenridge, Robert L., J1944
Breckenridge, Robert L., Jr., 1974
Breed, William M., 1855
Breen, Francis A., Jr., 1963
Bregman, Daniel K., 1985
Brehm, Samuel H., 1866
Breisacher, Carl Frederick, 1936
Breisch, Richard R., 1881
Breish, Russell S., 1982
Breitling, Joseph, 1855
Brelsford, James R., 1852
Bremermann, Lewis Wine, 1900
Breneman Gerald M., 1949
Breneman, M. B., 1870
Breneman, William Edgar, 1897
Brener, Harry M., 1976
Brenman, Scott A., 1981
Brenn, Chester Earle, 1916
Brennan Robert S., 1949
Brennan, Charles L., Jr., 1956
Brennan, Charles Lewis S., 1924
Brennan, James E., 1953
Brennan, John P., 1960
Brennan, John Patrick, 1918
Brennan, Mark David, Jr., 1990
Brennan, Martin T., 1957
Brennan, Richard E., 1972

Brennan, Walter J., S1944
Brennan, William J., Jr., 1962
Brenneman, Paul G., 1948
Brenner, Angus L., S1944
Brenner, Barry S., 1976
Brenner, Charles Raymond, 1914
Brenner, Ira, 1976
Brenner, Lawrence D., 1983
Brenner, Robert R., 1976
Brent, David A., 1974
Brent, Lawrence H., 1979
Brentlinger, Dale C., 1963
Brenton, Willis, 1883
Breslin, Harvey Jerome, 1954
Breslin, Joseph A., Jr., 1970
Breslin, Kenneth S., 1987
Breslin, William Aloysius, 1916
Breslow, Michael F., 1982
Bressler Victor A., 1949
Bressler, Charles H., 1844
Bressler, Lawrence P., 1980
Bressler, William L., 1972
Brest, Norman A., 1979
Brettell, Howard W., 1930
Bretz, Gilbert Freck, 1914
Bretzfelder, Karl Benjamin, 1916
Brewe, Arthur Jackson, 1905
Brewer, David R., Jr., S1944
Brewer, David Roe, 1918
Brewer, James Street, 1919
Brewer, Nicholas 1840
Brewer, William T., 1859
Brewer, William, 1896
Brewster, Guy Otis, 1896
Brewster, John M., 1923
Brewster, Joseph Hall, 1892
Brewster, T. Fort, 1856
Brewster, William Barton, 1873
Breza, George M., 1963
Brezinski, Mark E., 1988
Brian, David A., 1964
Brice, Patrick Joseph, 1907
Briceland, J. Milton, 1847
Brick, Joseph Coles, 1894
Bricker, Charles E., 1880
Bricker, Glenn W., 1952
Bricker, Harry Reno, 1887
Bricker, Howard Edgar, 1906
Bricker, Samuel Reiley, 1889
Bricker, William Henry, 1886
Brickley, Kenneth S., 1938
Bricklin, Alan S., 1969
Bridenbaugh, G. Alan, 1979
Bridenbaugh, Robert P., 1960
Bridger, Dewey Herbert, 1922
Bridges, Edward, 1929
Briggs, Arthur A., 1895
Briggs, B. B., 1870

Briggs, C. Christian,III, 1969
Briggs, Erwin Sheridan, 1906
Briggs, George W., 1850
Briggs, Henry C., 1847
Briggs, Miron Luke, 1904
Briggs, Roberto E., 1984
Bright, George H., 1858
Bright, James Cooper, 1907
Bright, John W., 1880
Briglia, Frank Joseph, 1928
Brillman, David A., 1978
Brillman, Nathan, 1957
Brindamour, Jean Louis E., 1924
Brindisi, Gaetano, 1940
Brindle, Archie Clarence, 1897
Brindle, Harry Robert, 1935
Brindley, Arthur A., 1912
Brindley, William George, 1897
Bringhurst, James, 1842
Bringhurst, William, 1876
Brinker, Reuben, 1851
Brinker, Thomas H., 1846
Brinkey, Gasper C., 1885
Brinkley, Harvey Meares, 1919
Brinkman, John, 1919
Brinley, Edward H., 1853
Brinson, Ed. Lane, 1907
Brinton, Daniel G., 1860
Brinton, J. Bernard, 1859
Brinton, John Bowen, 1826
Brinton, John H., 1852
Brinton, Lewis, 1882
Brinton, Ward, 1894
Brinton, William M., 1875
Brinton, William T., Jr., 1952
Brinton, William Thomas, 1911
Briody, Henry Edward, 1909
Brisbin, Charles H., 1890
Briscoe, Thomas W., 1858
Brister, Frederick Elmer, 1896
Bristol, E. L. M., 1874
Bristow, Charles Oliver, 1918
Britt, Albert Jerome, 1893
Britt, Charles Carroll, 1902
Britt, Edward Charles, 1933
Britt, John Boston, 1889
Britt, Tilman Carlyle, 1921
Brittain, Richard James, 1863
Britton, George W., 1856
Broad, Louis T., 1974
Broad, Todd H., 1982
Broadbelt, Leedom Richard, 1906
Broadfield, John Augustus, 1906
Broadman, Harry, 1910
Broadnax, Robert, 1848
Brobst, Daniel B., 1882
Brobst, Daniel Reuben, 1895
Brobst, Francis H., 1888

Brobst, Jacob Ralph, 1915
Brock Hugh W., 1852
Brock, David C., 1976
Brock, Ernest, 1928
Brock, Luther S., 1874
Brock, Richard R., 1958
Brock, Rufus E., 1879
Brockman, Ronald J., 1982
Brockunier, Alfred, Jr., 1947
Brockway, Charles Jesse, 1911
Brockway, Dudley S., 1881
Brodar, Franc, 1957
Broderick, John R., Jr., 1955
Broderick, John Reid, 1925
Brodey, James F., 1966
Brodhead, Charles L., Jr.,,1959
Brodhead, Virginia S., 1971
Brodie, Donald E., 1962
Brodie, Gordon L., 1975
Brodkin, Henry Andrew, 1924
Brodkin, Roger H., 1958
Brodsky, Leonard, 1953
Brodsky, Stuart L., 1967
Brodstein, David E., 1987
Brodstein, Robert S., 1957
Brody, Jerome I., 1952
Brody, Louis, 1919
Brody, Myer, 1904
Broff, Martin D., 1976
Brogan, Edmund J., 1936
Brogan, John J., 1940
Broidrick, J. P., 1869
Brolasky, Joseph P., 1849
Bromberg, Norbert, 1937
Brome, John J., 1839
Bronaugh, Joseph W., 1837
Bronaugh, Wayne, 1923
Bronk, Henry N., 1932
Bronson, William S., 1850
Bronstein, Jeffrey B., 1978
Broocks, John W., 1853
Brookbank, John W., 1848
Brooke Smith, C. F., 1947
Brooke, John B., 1858
Brookfield, Joseph, 1836
Brooking, Silas L., 1868
Brooks, Allan Colby, 1895
Brooks, Bert Watson, 1952
Brooks, Charles M., 1968
Brooks, David Marshall, 1926
Brooks, Edward, 1862
Brooks, Floyd V., 1877
Brooks, Frank Martin, 1895
Brooks, George Martin, 1918
Brooks, James A., Jr., 1972
Brooks, James L., 1837
Brooks, John G., 1851
Brooks, John G., 1868

Brubaker, William H., 1972
Bruce, Andrew, 1840
Bruce, J. D., 1856
Bruch, Elmer Clinton, 1892
Bruckart, W. Scott, 1870
Bruehlman, Richard D., 1982
Bruere, Abel T., 1886
Bruere, John, 1884
Brugler, DeWitt, 1890
Brugman, Joseph Charles, 1910
Brumbaugh, Patricia A., 1988
Brumbaugh, Simon C., Jr., 1951
Brumbaugh, Simon Clarence, 1910
Brumby, G. McDaffie, 1859
Brundage, Emerson K., 1880
Brundage, Frank M., 1874
Brundage, Gertrude B., 1971
Brundage, Robert Abner, 1906
Brundage, William J., 1987
Bruner, Harry Gilbert, 1884
Bruner, John Willet, 1890
Bruner, William H., 1848
Brunet, John E., 1873
Brunner, Austin Franklin, 1931
Brunner, Frank R., 1861
Brunner, Henry Clay, 1896
Bruno, John Robert, 1941
Bruns, Henry Dickson, 1881
Brunson, Edward Porcher, 1921
Brunson, Randolph, 1858
Brunswick, Alfred E., 1925
Brunswick, Richard A., 1965
Brunt, Margaret Jean, 1975
Brush, James A., 1872
Brusstar, H. B., 1873
Brust, Raymond W., Jr., 1956
Bryan, Cyrus P., 1855
Bryan, Frank S., 1957
Bryan, Harry N., 1884
Bryan, Henry Hugh, 1882
Bryan, J. Elder, Jr., 1945
Bryan, John C., 1853
Bryan, John S., 1878
Bryan, Robert E., 1882
Bryan, Thomas A., 1876
Bryan, Thomas M., 1971
Bryan, Wallace Steele, 1906
Bryan, William S., 1857
Bryant, Cassander E., 1850
Bryant, Charles Henry, 1904
Bryant, Charles Page, 1905
Bryant, Frank Leytze, 1927
Bryant, George S., 1845
Bryant, John, 1866
Bryant, Michael H., 1973
Bryant, Thomas Sydenham, 1833
Bryant, William M., 1858
Bryner, Charles L., Jr., 1981

Bryson Richard L., 1949
Bryson, Howard Russel, 1898
Bryson, John Frampton, 1903
Bryson, Lewis M., 1879
Brzezienski, Mark A., 1987
Bubeck, Robert C., 1965
Bubenheim, Daniel M., 1985
Bucan, Michael, 1947
Buchanan, G. W., 1855
Buchanan, Joseph Hervey, 1896
Buchanan, Luther Thomas, 1913
Buchanan, Thomas, 1889
Bucher, Albert Herman, 1921
Bucher, Robert G., 1954
Bucher, Robert Leon, 1921
Buchert, Joseph Gerard, 1936
Buchman, David Hyman, 1930
Buck, Benjamin S., 1866
Buck, Erastus, Jr., 1854
Buck, Horatio B., 1856
Buck, James P., 1879
Buck, Jonathan, 1848
Buck, Michael J., 1872
Buck, Robert L., 1884
Buckby, Wilson, 1870
Buckingham, E. Milton, 1850
Buckingham, Harry Sheldon, 1904
Buckingham, Hugh W., 1887
Buckingham, John M., 1882
Buckley, George E., 1867
Buckner, Baldwin M., 1857
Buckner, Garrett Davis, 1864
Buckner, Hubbard Thomas, 1913
Bucko, Matthew I., Jr., 1958
Bucks, W. Frank, 1886
Buckwalter, Kenneth A., 1981
Budlong, William Hague, 1865
Buechele, Modestus William, 1926
Buechler, Elizabeth J., 1976
Buechler, Mary F., 1972
Buehler, H. B., 1858
Buehler, William S., 1889
Buffington, Alexander L., 1866
Buffington, E. Stanard, 1872
Buffington, Gary K., 1971
Buffington, John A., 1884
Buffington, John F., 1855
Buffington, John N., 1855
Buffington, Thomas C., 1850
Buffington, Thomas J., 1844
Buford, James S., 1850
Buford, Smith, 1861
Bugbee, Arthur Sharpe, 1908
Bugbee, Frederick Calhoun, 1925
Buhot, William J., 1857
Buhrman, Hiram, 1868
Buie, Roderick Mark, 1914
Buinewicz, Anna M., 1986

Buinewicz, Brian R., 1985
Buka, Alfred Joseph, 1908
Bulger, Kenneth Scott, 1920
Bulis, Henry C., 1887
Bulkeley, Jonathan W., 1846
Bull, Heman R., Jr., 1935
Bull, Herman Rowlee, 1887
Bull, Raymond Cooley, 1909
Bullard, John William, 1893
Bullock, Charles Cevos, 1889
Bullock, Edwin Corlies, 1906
Bullock, George D., 1886
Bullock, J. Row, 1850
Bullock, Lawrence M., 1881
Bullock, Robert A., 1964
Bullock, William T., 1865
Bumgarner, George Leonard, 1892
Bunn, Benjamin F., 1846
Bunn, William, 1853
Bunn, William Hall, 1915
Bunnell, Eugene, 1986
Bunting, Ross R., 1856
Bunting, Thomas C., 1835
Buonanno, Susan M., 1983
Buonato, Sebastian James, 1932
Burak, William E., 1963
Burak, William E., Jr., 1987
Burbridge, Geoffrey R., 1977
Burbridge, I. Ralph, Jr., 1946
Burchard, Harry H., 1888
Burchfield, John P., 1865
Burd, C. Louis, 1885
Burd, Edwin Jasper, 1889
Burde, Ronald M., 1964
Burden, Jesse R., 1864
Burden, Samuel S., 1935
Burdick, Bingley Lyman, 1931
Burdumy, Theodore J., 1979
Burford, J. Edward, 1879
Burg, Horace W., 1877
Burg, S. Wesley, 1862
Burg, Stoddard Somers, 1903
Burge, Daniel J., 1986
Burge, John R., 1988
Burger, Earl Victor, 1900
Burger, John Rudolph, 1895
Burger, Steven A., 1973
Burges, Richard U., 1861
Burgess, Ebenezer P., 1853
Burgi, Peter, 1876
Burgin, Herman, 1879
Burgner, Samuel H., 1865
Burkartmaier, John Henry, 1911
Burke, Bernard S., 1979
Burke, Charles Oren, 1887
Burke, Charles Perry, 1911
Burke, Clemens Stanley, 1925
Burke, George W., 1866

Burke, Greg F., 1988
Burke, James F., 1936
Burke, James F., 1977
Burke, James F., Jr., 1966
Burke, John Kilgallen, 1990
Burke, Joseph John, 1889
Burke, Patrick F., 1894
Burke, Richard David, 1895
Burke, William Adam, 1918
Burket, David G., 1972
Burkett, Donald E., 1945
Burkhalter, Charles M., 1860
Burkholder, John Lewis, 1905
Burkley, Louis F., Jr., 1920
Burkley, Louis Franklin, III, 1947
Burks, Charles R. P., 1858
Burks, Floyd L.R., 1908
Burks, Jesse D., 1838
Burn, John F., 1933
Burnell, Thomas B., 1854
Burnett, Elisha G., 1851
Burnett, George Warren, 1928
Burnett, James W., 1837
Burnett, Joshua U., 1862
Burnett, Lawrence F., 1941
Burnett, Wilbur Emory, 1923
Burnham, Marie Robb, 1979
Burnham, William D., 1979
Burnley, Hardin, 1850
Burns, Benjamin F., 1947
Burns, Bernard, 1875
Burns, Charles N., 1941
Burns, Charles N., Jr., 1976
Burns, Francis L., 1930
Burns, John Joseph, 1924
Burns, Joseph P., Jr., 1963
Burns, Joseph Vincent, 1915
Burns, Michael Anthony, 1907
Burns, Robert B., 1964
Burns, Silas, 1885
Burns, Thomas Francis, 1912
Burnside, Fred Rexford, 1909
Burr, Evan W., 1877
Burr, Nelson, 1844
Burr, William H., 1844
Burris, William A., 1873
Burros, Harry M., S1944
Burroughs, Alphonso J.L., 1854
Burroughs, Hamilton S., 1879
Burroughs, J. J., 1875
Burroughs, John E., 1866
Burroughs, Richard, 1856
Burrows, Samuel J., 1917
Burrus, Thomas Preston, 1916
Burry, William C., 1939
Burstan, Jacob, 1916
Burt, Ingram E., 1890
Burt, James Clark, 1902

Burt, Theresa A., 1974
Burtnett, Jasper N., 1871
Burton, Daniel L., 1850
Burton, John J., 1847
Burton, John, 1867
Burton, Wilbur Darwin, 1893
Burton, William H., 1856
Burton, William Preston, 1923
Burwell, George W., 1846
Burwell, Howard Beirne, 1904
Burwell, John P., 1880
Burwell, Thomas Spotuas, 1907
Burwell, William N., 1881
Busenkell, Gary L., 1969
Busey, Charles, 1893
Bush, Charles B., 1885
Bush, Dudley, 1861
Bush, Horace, 1875
Bush, Irvine R., 1883
Bush, James B., 1837
Bush, James H.J., 1886
Bush, Lewis, 1872
Bush, Louis G., 1943
Bush, Robert H., 1854
Bush, Todd A., 1989
Bush, William M., 1937
Bush, William M., 1939
Bushey, Sylvan Graham, 1891
Bushong, Frederick, 1907
Bushong, Israel, 1861
Busillo, Barbara Maria M., 1978
Busillo, Nicholas A., 1978
Bussard, John R., 1969
Bussey, William Joseph, 1901
Butcher, Benedict D., 1871
Butcher, Charles, 1909
Butcher, George E., 1858
Butcher, Henry B., 1866
Butcher, Joseph Jr., 1849
Butcher, Joseph, 1883
Butcher, Samuel, 1864
Butcher, Thomas S., 1868
Butcofski, James S., 1963
Buterbaugh, John C., 1961
Buterbaugh, John, 1860
Butler, Anselm B., 1855
Butler, Claude Henry, 1931
Butler, Edward Everett, 1889
Butler, Fred A., 1939
Butler, Herbert H., Jr., 1961
Butler, James G., 1874
Butler, John S., 1828
Butler, L. M., 1860
Butler, Matthew M., 1860
Butler, Oliver H., 1859
Butscher, William C., J1944
Butt, Abijah, 1886
Butt, Frank H., Jr., J1944

Butt, Virgil R., 1886
Butt, Zephaniah, 1841
Butterfield, Thomas H., 1870
Butterworth, Francis James, 1893
Butts, J. Thomas, 1853
Butts, James A., 1856
Butts, James J., 1857
Butts, Judson A., 1860
Butz, Todd Michael, 1990
Buyalos, Richard P., 1964
Buyalos, Richard P., Jr., 1983
Buza, Richard S., 1978
Byars, Caspar Ralph, 1898
Byars, Henry Tipton, 1886
Byars, William M., 1842
Bye, Charles P., 1831
Byerly, Frederick Lee, 1939
Byers, Edgar Henry, 1889
Byers, Ruth A., 1988
Byers, W. Churchman, 1872
Byers, William J., 1847
Byles, Frederick G., 1882
Bynum, John G., 1877
Byram, Claude M., 1882
Byrd, Allen Leet, 1936
Byrd, W. B., 1856
Byrd, William Carey, 1923
Byrne, Philip Joseph, 1940
Byrne, Stephen, 1967
Byrnes, Christine A., 1978
Byron, Harold J., 1920
Byron, Harold Joseph, 1954
Byron, Mary Christine, 1990
Byrum, Clifford C., 1943
Bythewood, Daniel H., 1846

~ C ~

Cabada, Ysidoro F., 1882
Cabanne, James S., 1866
Cabell, George K., 1853
Cable, Josiah C., 1848
Cable, Sydney R., 1948
Cacchione, Robert J., 1970
Cacciola, Thomas A., 1983
Caceres, Juan Francisco, 1919
Cacia, John Joseph, 1932
Cadden, Joseph Thomas, 1925
Caddy, James A., 1945
Cade, E. W., 1858
Cadwallader, Seth Iredell, 1900
Cadwell, Frederick A., 1837
Cadwell, Joseph W., 1863
Cahall, Laurence M., 1886
Cahall, Lawrence M., 1855
Cahall, Thomas, 1848
Cahall, Thomas V., 1874
Cahall, W. Lawrence, Jr., 1947

Cahall, Walter Lawrence, 1920
Cahall, William Cannon, 1879
Cahan, Robert B., 1954
Cahn, David A., 1989
Cahn, Edward Laurence, 1962
Cahn, Michael S., 1957
Cain, Frank Monroe, 1889
Cain, Norman Hugh, 1922
Cain, Robert A., 1975
Cain, William Jonathan, 1910
Cairns, Andrew A., 1887
Cairns, Michael R., 1981
Cake, William A., 1850
Calabrese, Anthony J., 1972
Caldwell, A., 1869
Caldwell, Daniel G., 1864
Caldwell, Euler Jones, 1891
Caldwell, Frank H., 1880
Caldwell, J. J., 1875
Caldwell, Morris Milton, 1905
Caldwell, Samuel H., 1858
Caldwell, William Spencer, 1864
Calhoun, A. W., 1869
Calhoun, Albert J., 1875
Calhoun, Chambers D., 1884
Calhoun, Howard Boyd, 1903
Calhoun, Noah F., 1877
Calhoun, Thomas R., 1839
Call, Dean E., 1951
Call, Lloyd S., 1945
Call, Oel Facer, 1919
Callaghan, Arthur, 1855
Callaghan, Philip James, 1942
Callahan, Bernard Joseph, 1900
Callahan, Daniel J., 1971
Callahan, Peter Alfonso, 1927
Callan, Donna J., 1987
Callan, George John, 1904
Callan, John J., Jr., 1959
Callaway, Enoch, 1876
Callaway, Reuben S., 1844
Callen, H. Samuel, 1925
Callender, Alson B., 1888
Callery, Gerald E., 1943
Callihan, Robert, 1874
Callis, Charles Alton, 1949
Callista, Richard L., 1950
Callmann, Sallo, 1882
Calvert, Lewis Cass, 1908
Calvin, Abner C., 1878
Camas, John M., 1977
Camblos, Henry F., 1881
Cambridge, William R., 1980
Camden, Rolla, 1897
Camden, Thomas B., 1854
Cameron, George F., Jr., 1945
Cameron, J. Walton, 1848
Cameron, Norris, 1880

Cameron, Richard Ray, 1936
Camerota, Andrew M., 1985
Camishion, Germaine M., 1985
Camishion, Rudolph C., 1954
Cammarata, Joseph Anthony, 1930
Camp, Glenn Curtis, 1935
Camp, J. G., 1857
Camp, John F., 1978
Camp, Mark O., 1950
Campanella, Joseph A., 1960
Campanella, Stephen D., 1981
Campbell, Algernon E., 1851
Campbell, Archibald B., 1844
Campbell, Carl Bennison, 1917
Campbell, Cassius M.C., 1879
Campbell, Charles Lawrence, 1886
Campbell, Charles, 1870
Campbell, Clark C., 1846
Campbell, E. B., 1873
Campbell, George N., 1881
Campbell, George W., 1879
Campbell, Glenn C., 1986
Campbell, Guy Gibson, 1913
Campbell, H. F., 1867
Campbell, Harry Edgar, 1881
Campbell, Henry H., 1849
Campbell, J. M., 1858
Campbell, J. Moore, 1878
Campbell, James M., Jr., 1937
Campbell, James Truan, 1920
Campbell, Janis P., 1979
Campbell, John A., 1846
Campbell, John A., 1874
Campbell, John Hugh, 1941
Campbell, John Sheridan, 1906
Campbell, Joseph N., 1832
Campbell, Kevin M., 1983
Campbell, M. D., 1904
Campbell, Marcus, 1860
Campbell, Osmon B., 1884
Campbell, Ralph Rankin, 1890
Campbell, Robert C., 1943
Campbell, Robert, 1860
Campbell, Sidney A., 1849
Campbell, Taylor A., 1882
Campbell, Thomas B.R., 1873
Campbell, Thomas F., 1863
Campbell, Tobias, 1886
Campbell, Tom E., 1974
Campbell, Vernon W. H., 1939
Campbell, Virginia Johnston, 1968
Campbell, Walter Edmund, 1941
Campbell, Walter Lowrie, 1903
Campbell, Westlee M., 1855
Campbell, William, 1859
Campbell, William Breaden, 1906
Campbell, William H., 1864
Campfield, Thomas J., 1977

Campo, Randy V., 1977
Canby, Joseph Edward, 1927
Candel, Samuel, 1930
Candela, Harry J., 1962
Canfield, Augustus R., 1859
Canfield, Ira D., Jr., 1863
Cannady, Nicholas Boddie, 1912
Cannon, Douglas Launeese, 1919
Cannon, Nellie, 1904
Canon, Robert Taylor, 1893
Canova, Matthew J., 1883
Cantafio, Ralph, 1950
Cantarow, Abraham, 1924
Canter, Harold, 1938
Cantlin, Frank Hurley, 1916
Cantor, Max, 1933
Cantough, Charles Solomon, 1914
Cantrell, James Henry, 1856
Cantrell, John Abbott, 1885
Cantrell, William A., 1862
Cantwell, George H., 1884
Canty, Thomas P., 1985
Capelli, John P., 1962
Capers, LeGrand G., Jr., 1858
Capito, Emil, 1950
Caplan, Amy B., 1987
Caplan, Howard J., 1972
Caplan, Murray S., 1959
Capone, Gaetano J., 1979
Capozzi, Joseph A., 1960
Capp, William M., 1885
Capparuccini, Mario D., Jr., 1980
Cappelletti, A. Joseph, 1946
Capper, Aaron, 1924
Capper, Robert, 1955
Capper, Stanley A., 1951
Cappiello, Wiliam F., 1976
Cappiello, William A., 1940
Capron, Victor James, 1888
Caputo, Larry A., 1974
Capuzzi, David M., 1964
Car, Joseph R., 1973
Carabasi, Matthew H., 1980
Carabasi, R. Anthony, III, 1977
Carabasi, Ralph A., Jr., 1946
Carabasi, Robert J., 1948
Carapella, John D., 1941
Carapellotti, Richard A., 1979
Caravello, Peter M., 1971
Carberry, David M., 1951
Carberry, George August, 1946
Carberry, P. Joseph L., 1874
Carbonell, Frank Arturo, 1911
Carbonetta, Reno Raymond, 1934
Cardelia, James Marc, 1990
Carden, Edward Thomas, 1966
Carden, Terrence S., Jr., 1971
Cardone, John C., 1986

Care, James Roberts, 1886
Carels, Samuel, 1838
Carey, Andrew B., 1986
Carey, Asher B., III, 1978
Carey, Edward D., 1961
Carey, Harris May, 1904
Carey, John F., 1867
Carey, Kent V., 1977
Carey, Lawrence Sherwood, 1922
Carey, Thomas H., 1884
Cargile, Charles H., 1877
Cargill, Nathaniel E., 1845
Carhardt, Earl Clyde, 1905
Carhart, Henry Osborn, 1886
Carim, Moiz M., 1977
Carington, Will John, 1908
Carithers Eli K., 1850
Carl, Robert Delroy, 1930
Carlander, Oswald Rudolph, 1925
Carlet, Louis Anthony, 1924
Carleton, George E., 1857
Carlile, William K., 1952
Carlin, Elwin S., 1955
Carlin, Hugh M., 1980
Carlin, Robert Golden, 1902
Carlisle, Dyer, Jr., 1945
Carll, George, 1826
Carlough, Martha C., 1989
Carlson Richard A., 1949
Carlton, Benjamin F., 1854
Carlton, Henry H., 1856
Carlton, James M., 1881
Carlton, John W., 1970
Carlton, W. A., 1873
Carlyle, John Bethune, 1926
Carman, Harry E., 1943
Carmany, Thomas B., 1962
Carmelia, Francis Albion, 1911
Carmichael, Asa Bartholow, 1911
Carmichael, Daniel L., 1884
Carmichael, Daniel Lafayette, Jr., 1911
Carmichael, Herbert N., 1945
Carmichael, Randolph Bryan, 1889
Carmichael, Richard H., 1839
Carmona, Manuel G., 1941
Carn, Lewis M., 1859
Carnabuci, Guy J., 1958
Carnahan, William J., 1892
Carnal, Reuben H., 1851
Carncross, J. Augustus, 1876
Carnevale, Thomas, A., 1983
Carney, Francis Thomas, 1924
Carney, Frank T., 1958
Carney, James J., 1983
Carney, Joseph Albert, 1910
Carney, Martin J., 1980
Carney, Mary D., 1985
Carney, Samuel David, 1903

Carney, Wilfred I., Jr., 1968
Carney, Wilfred, 1938
Carney, William M., 1988
Carothers, William H., 1883
Carow, Fredrich G., 1917
Carp, Israel Jay, 1916
Carpenter, A. Jackson, 1856
Carpenter, Alexander Hamilton, 1845
Carpenter, Benoni, 1832
Carpenter, Charles, 1834
Carpenter, Eugene R., 1898
Carpenter, Gary G., 1960
Carpenter, Isaac B., 1827
Carpenter, John Alfred, 1883
Carpenter, John S., 1844
Carpenter, Kim L., 1982
Carpenter, Matthew T., 1987
Carpenter, Paul D., 1867
Carpenter, Uri Alonzo, 1922
Carper, John Mark, 1952
Carr, A. Smith, 1879
Carr, Benjamin Franklin, 1886
Carr, Chalmers Rankin, 1936
Carr, Charles Dungan, 1888
Carr, Edward S., 1874
Carr, George W., 1895
Carr, James V., 1935
Carr, John Dennis, 1896
Carr, L. Logan, 1876
Carr, Thomas W., 1849
Carr, William W., 1848
Carrabba, Salvatore R., 1946
Carrell, James Fell, 1917
Carrell, John B., 1876
Carrera, Manuel Enrique, J1944
Carreras, Pedro Juan, 1918
Carrier, Frank Nathan, 1893
Carrier, Frederic H., 1878
Carrier, Sidney Smith, 1904
Carrig, Thomas F., Jr., 1969
Carrigan, Paul T., 1945
Carriger, John H., 1851
Carrington, Paul S., 1851
Carroll, Edgar, 1880
Carroll, Edward A., 1954
Carroll, Frank A., Jr., 1951
Carroll, Fred, 1983
Carroll, Irvin Norwood, 1941
Carroll, James Basil, 1912
Carroll, James Freed, 1952
Carroll, Joseph Herbert, 1922
Carroll, Joseph Leo, 1948
Carroll, Leslie Seton, 1990
Carroll, Robert J., 1867
Carroll, Robert T., 1952
Carroll, Thomas Benjamin, 1903
Carroll, Thomas, 1862
Carroll, Walter James E., 1928

Carroll, William J., 1959
Carroll, William J., 1988
Carroll, William L., 1989
Carroll, William, 1863
Carrow, Joseph, 1893
Carrozza, Harry D., 1963
Carruth, Howard Ernest, 1910
Carson, Charles P., 1948
Carson, Clayton Calvin E., 1925
Carson, David James, 1894
Carson, James Seymour, 1887
Carson, Jason Wilson, 1902
Carson, John Alligon, 1871
Carson, John Baxter, 1889
Carson, John C., 1956
Carson, John N., III, 1972
Carson, Samuel M., 1858
Carson, Teresa C., 1987
Carson, Thomas, 1865
Carstarphen, William Turner, 1904
Carswell, B. S., 1856
Cart, Julius Henry, 1919
Carter, Debbie Rene, 1983
Carter, Durus D., 1868
Carter, E. J., 1836
Carter, Flournoy, 1851
Carter, James Vincent, 1951
Carter, James W., 1854
Carter, John, 1847
Carter, John D., 1868
Carter, John F., 1849
Carter, John M., 1987
Carter, Joseph H., 1953
Carter, Josephus, 1839
Carter, Stephen Lindsay, 1990
Carter, Thomas Jerrell, 1927
Carter, Thomas L., 1956
Carter, Thomas L., Jr., 1984
Carter, W. Bradford, 1986
Carter, W. Neal, 1955
Carter, W. W., 1873
Carter, William Lovering, 1849
Carter, William S., III, 1976
Carter, William S., Jr., 1946
Carter, William Stanley, 1909
Cartin, Harry James, 1901
Cartwright, Robert N., 1884
Carty, James B., Jr., 1970
Carty, James Byron, 1939
Carunchio, Michael J., Jr., 1974
Caruso, Anthony P., 1975
Caruso, Richard F., 1988
Caruso, Vincent George, 1967
Caruthers, C. K., 1859
Carver, Harry Franklin, 1899
Cary, Charles W., 1851
Cary, Dale Emerson, 1911
Cary, Edward L., 1845

Cirotti, Joseph J., 1961
Citta, James Philip, 1937
Clader, Stanley C., 1943
Claffey, John Bernard, 1932
Clagett, Augustus Henry, 1903
Clagett, Luther S., 1877
Claiborne, J. Herbert, 1850
Clair, David L., 1984
Clair, Gerald F., 1956
Clair, Henry S., 1958
Clair, Philip S., 1926
Clancy, Daniel Francis, 1905
Clancy, John, 1936
Clancy, Leo Joseph, 1914
Clancy, Michael, 1970
Clancy, Patricia E., 1980
Clanton, Albert B., 1852
Clapp, George Houghton, 1907
Clapp, William A., 1847
Clare, Timothy P., 1982
Clark, A. C., 1869
Clark, Albert U. F., 1896
Clark, Allen M., 1966
Clark, Anthony J., 1986
Clark, Charles F., 1881
Clark, Charles H., 1867
Clark, Christopher M., 1973
Clark, Clarence Merrill, 1908
Clark, Courtenay J., 1844
Clark, Cunningham P., 1895
Clark, David G., 1974
Clark, Donald L., 1958
Clark, E. W., 1870
Clark, Edward J., 1950
Clark, Eugene E., 1920
Clark, Francis J., 1986
Clark, Frank A., 1880
Clark, Frank, J1944
Clark, Gary S., 1975
Clark, George Campbell, 1888
Clark, George W., 1848
Clark, Henry, 1850
Clark, Henry S., 1883
Clark, Hobson, 1855
Clark, Isaac E., 1882
Clark, Isaac J., 1858
Clark, James Cecil, 1907
Clark, James E., 1952
Clark, John Craig, 1935
Clark, John M., 1841
Clark, Lemuel E., 1881
Clark, Leroy S., 1964
Clark, Marcus A., 1857
Clark, Mark A., 1976
Clark, Maureen D., 1984
Clark, Nathan H., 1845
Clark, O. Dwight, 1923
Clark, Oscar D. F., 1895

Clark, Patrick B., 1861
Clark, R. Craig, 1948
Clark, Ralph Elden, 1934
Clark, Richard R., 1988
Clark, Richard S., 1951
Clark, Rod Sidney, 1917
Clark, Samuel M., 1875
Clark, Samuel V., 1854
Clark, Stanely N., S1944
Clark, Stanley M., 1921
Clark, Thomas Edgar, 1919
Clark, Vachal M., 1863
Clark, Warren Thomas, 1905
Clark, Whipple W., 1886
Clark, William L., 1850
Clark, William Pawson, 1897
Clark, William Roy, 1950
Clarke, Frank R., 1954
Clarke, Frederick George, 1908
Clarke, G. Donald, 1966
Clarke, George W., 1863
Clarke, Henry, 1834
Clarke, James Alexander, Jr., 1916
Clarke, John E., 1847
Clarke, Rowan, 1854
Clarke, Samuel, 1899
Clarke, William J., 1849
Clary, Charles S., 1847
Classen, Carolyn F., 1989
Clausen, Joseph Roberts, 1882
Clauser, Harry Simon, 1896
Clauss, Thomas F., 1951
Clay, Harry A., 1928
Clay, John William, 1919
Clayton, George R., 1879
Clayton, J. Wesley, III, 1980
Clayton, Joshua, 1886
Clayton, Walter B., Jr., 1962
Clearfield, Harris R., 1959
Cleaver, C. Perry, 1933
Cleborne, Ronayne D., 1895
Clelan George M., 1949
Cleland, J. Wallace, 1926
Cleland, William O., 1955
Clemens, Frank L., 1881
Clemens, Thomas M., 1973
Clement, Edward Buehler, 1906
Clement, John A., 1969
Clemente, Joseph A., 1985
Clements, C. Glenn, 1945
Clements, Christopher C., 1864
Clements, Early C., 1852
Clements, Franklin M., 1871
Clements, G. Myrick, 1854
Clements, Harry Henry, 1940
Clements, Harry Michael, 1967
Clements, L. Morgan, 1848
Clements, Richard, 1846

Clements, William zN., 1859
Clements, William T., 1980
Clements, William W., Jr., 1958
Clementson, William Alexande, 1894
Clemmer, Richard I., Jr., 1971
Clemson, Barry S., 1983
Clendaniel, William, 1852
Clendenin, William G., 1860
Clendenning, William Burdette, 1920
Clendenning, William E., 1956
Clendinen, Moses W., 1866
Clerf Louis H. 1912
Cleri, Dennis J., 1972
Cleveland, Edwin I., 1950
Cleveland, Frank Mortimer, 1899
Cleveland, J. F., 1869
Cleveland, Robert Bryan, 1925
Cleveland, Samuel Mortimer, 1949
Clevenger, Marshall Lewis, 1950
Clewell, Clarence Henry, 1894
Clifford, Charles Henry, 1887
Clifford, Edward M., 1882
Clifford, Frank D., 1980
Clifford, John James, 1889
Clifford, Raymond Alfred, 1899
Clime, Gilbert Newpher, 1936
Clinch, Thomas E., 1983
Cline, Charles H., 1880
Cline, Charles T., Jr., 1969
Cline, Edward W., 1887
Cline, Garner 1839
Cline, Godfrey H., 1860
Cline, James C., 1880
Cline, Lewis C., 1879
Cline, Philip M., 1857
Clinger, Edgar Moore, 1897
Clinger, George 1831
Clinkinbeard, Allen K., 1864
Clinkscales, Albert M., 1877
Clinkscales, F., 1858
Clinton, David L., 1975
Clinton, James B., 1916
Cloak, E. Morris, 1876
Closson, C. H., 1872
Closson, Lorenzo D., 1853
Cloud, Joseph Howard, 1892
Cloud, Laurence P., 1952
Cloud, Milton Harlan, 1924
Cloud, Noah B., 1835
Cloud, S. G., 1872
Clough, Joseph Messer, 1936
Clouser, William F., 1952
Clouting, Elmer Sherman, 1896
Clovis, Oscar Ray, 1917
Clunan, Ambrose P., 1939
Clyman, Jeffrey I., 1982
Clyman, Robert F., 1987
Clyman, Stephen G., 1982

Clymer, David G., 1987
Coad, Joseph R., 1856
Coad, Theophilus John, 1891
Coar, Daniel N., 1986
Coar, George R., 1981
Coard, William H., 1859
Coates, Benjamin F., 1860
Cobb, Benjamin F., 1847
Cobb, Clarence Everett, 1916
Cobb, Henry, 1847
Cobb, William Henry, Jr., 1889
Cobbe, Frank Edmund, 1890
Cobert, Howard S., 1977
Coble, Daniel W., 1867
Cobleigh, Bennett J., 1883
Coblentz, Jeanette B., 1979
Coblentz, Robert H., 1979
Cobots, Joseph Charles, 1930
Coburn, Charles Wilmot, 1893
Coburn, John B., 1843
Coccia, S. Paul, 1955
Cocco, Arthur E., 1959
Cochran, Alvis Stafford, 1887
Cochran, E. C., 1860
Cochran, Edward G., 1882
Cochran, Frank T., 1872
Cochran, Frederick Albert, Jr., 1896
Cochran, Henry King, 1856
Cochran, James Edward, 1939
Cochran, James H., 1839
Cochran, John Camden, 1890
Cochran, John L., 1861
Cochran, John W., 1973
Cochran, Thomas P., III, 1974
Cochran, Thomas Preston, Jr., 1893
Cochran, William G., 1880
Cochran, William S., 1850
Cochrane, Fred Richard, Jr., 1942
Cochrane, J. D., 1840
Cock, J. Walter, 1856
Cocke, Eugene Rankin, 1913
Cocke, Joseph G., 1930
Cocke, William, 1853
Cockerille, Americus, 1850
Codd, Alphonso Nicholas, 1919
Codispoti, Joseph R., 1980
Coe, Ira E., 1867
Coe, Thomas Upham, 1861
Cofer, Harold A., Jr., 1978
Coffey, William F. X., 1953
Coffin, Harold Leroy, 1896
Coffin, Samuel S., 1837
Coffman, James W., 1883
Coffman, Samuel A., 1846
Coffman, Victor H., 1866
Coffroth, Leroy Ward, 1950
Cofrances, Louis William, 1923
Cogan, James E. F., 1896

Cogan, Richard Merwin, 1906
Coggins, Cecil Hengy, 1930
Coghlan, William P., Jr., 1975
Coghlan, William Patrick, 1947
Cognetti, Peter A., 1983
Cogshall, Bela, Jr., 1866
Cohan, Michael L., 1987
Cohen, Abraham Joseph, 1903
Cohen, Abraham L., 1946
Cohen, Abraham, 1925
Cohen, Alan Jay, 1982
Cohen, Ben, 1940
Cohen, David M., 1986
Cohen, David M., 1989
Cohen, Edwin E., 1965
Cohen, Ellen M., 1986
Cohen, George H., 1963
Cohen, Gordon R., 1960
Cohen, Harry, J1944
Cohen, Herbert T., 1984
Cohen, Isadore Sacks, 1939
Cohen, J. Jerome, 1961
Cohen, Jacob M., 1915
Cohen, Jerome I., 1958
Cohen, Joel R., 1983
Cohen, Larry S., 1970
Cohen, Louis Benjamin, 1929
Cohen, Merrill J., 1966
Cohen, Michael M., 1973
Cohen, Milton H., 1931
Cohen, Morris S., 1881
Cohen, Morton Reese, 1926
Cohen, Nathan Alexander, 1892
Cohen, Nathan N., 1966
Cohen, Nathan, 1915
Cohen, Oscar H., 1936
Cohen, Paul S., 1972
Cohen, Richard A., 1955
Cohen, Richard I., 1968
Cohen, Richard W., 1965
Cohen, Robert M., 1965
Cohen, Ronald A., 1960
Cohen, Ronald H., 1964
Cohen, Samuel, 1930
Cohen, Solomon-Solis, 1883
Cohen, Stanley A., 1978
Cohen, Steven W., 1982
Cohen, Terry B., 1975
Cohen, Warren E., 1979
Cohick, Bruce S., 1982
Cohn, C. Harold, 1948
Cohn, Clarence, 1938
Cohn, David B., 1986
Cohn, Gregory S., 1988
Cohn, Herbert E., 1955
Cohn, Jeffrey B., 1980
Cohn, John R., 1976
Cohn, Neil R., 1988

Cohn, Ronald E., 1959
Coile, Henry P., 1875
Coit, Benjamin B., 1826
Coit, Daniel T., 1828
Cokely, Harold Jay, 1931
Colangelo, Anthony B., 1978
Colangelo, Francis R., 1984
Colarusso, Calvin A., 1961
Colatrella, Anthony M., 1973
Colavita, Mauro A., 1983
Colbert, William F., Jr., 1908
Colbourn, Arthur W., 1973
Colby, Cleon W., 1913
Colby, E. L., 1836
Colcher, Amy, 1989
Colcher, Irving S., 1968
Colcher, Robert E., 1950
Cole Algernon S., 1846
Cole, Benjamin E., Jr., J1944
Cole, Charles E., 1956
Cole, Daniel J., 1984
Cole, Edward C., 1854
Cole, Howson W., 1854
Cole, Isaac N., 1852
Cole, James W., 1881
Cole, John P., 1855
Cole, Lorenzo S., 1856
Cole, Richard B., 1849
Cole, Richard S., 1934
Cole, Scott C., 1990
Cole, Seymour L., 1938
Cole, Thomas Porter, 1893
Cole, Timothy J., 1988
Cole, W. W., 1869
Cole, William Gilbert, 1893
Coleman, Asa, 1854
Coleman, Austin Hoffman, 1911
Coleman, Charles T., 1851
Coleman, Daniel H., 1945
Coleman, Donald K., 1935
Coleman, Ernest H., 1930
Coleman, Ernest H., Jr., 1957
Coleman, James W., 1847
Coleman, James William, 1893
Coleman, John S., 1857
Coleman, Linda L., 1969
Coleman, Marion W., 1925
Coleman, Oscar Edwin, 1902
Coleman, Raymond L., 1976
Coleman, Richard M., 1851
Coleman, Robert T., 1852
Coleman, William James, 1909
Coleman, William Levin, 1917
Coles, Abraham, 1835
Coles, James Garfield, 1913
Coles, John W., 1863
Coles, Stricker, 1892
Coletta, Anthony V., 1979

Coletta, Domenic F., 1955
Coley, Andrew J., 1880
Coley, Joe H., 1934
Colgan, James F. E., 1892
Colgan, Joseph P., 1844
Colgan, William Shockey, 1923
Colhouer, Frederick Henry, 1896
Coll, James J., 1939
Coll, James Patrick, 1904
Collard, Jonathan Richard, 1891
Collester, Charles Chapman, 1909
Collet, Mark Wilkes, 1848
Collett, Harry Downing, 1928
Collett, W. A., 1856
Collett, William Rich, 1931
Colletta, Joseph A., 1977
Collette, Cora J., 1982
Collette, Laura, 1905
Colley, Arthur Truman, 1930
Colley, Brown, 1897
Colley, Horace G., 1874
Collier, Abner A., 1852
Collier, John Martin, 1952
Collier, Martin H., 1911
Collier, William E., 1984
Collings, Posey, 1870
Collingwood, John C., 1980
Collini, William R., 1966
Collins, Charles R., 1884
Collins, Clyde A., 1940
Collins, Deirdre M., 1984
Collins, Edward Welles, 1902
Collins, George, 1920
Collins, Gerald P., 1960
Collins, Harold J., 1920
Collins, Harry L., Jr., 1946
Collins, Howard Austin, 1896
Collins, James Anthony, Jr., 1941
Collins, Louis Keeler, 1934
Collins, May B., 1860
Collins, Richard T., 1854
Collins, Stacy B., 1876
Collins, Thomas B., 1851
Collins, William Thomas, 1857
Collins, William W., 1885
Collinson, Daniel J., 1945
Colliver, Ronald Robinson, 1957
Collom, Daniel L., 1876
Colokathis, Bernard Peter, 1963
Colombo, John M., Jr., 1979
Colon-Bonet, Cesar H., 1954
Colosi, Nicholas A., 1938
Coltman, Robert, Jr., 1881
Colton, Charles E., 1839
Columbus, Beach, 1837
Columbus, Michael J., 1985
Colville, David S., 1966
Combe, C. B., 1858

Combs, Howard Johnson, 1918
Comegys, Joseph Parsons, Jr., 1891
Comerford, James P., 1952
Comerford, Joseph F., 1917
Comfort, J. W., 1836
Comfort, Jonathan J., 1859
Comfort, Joseph A., Jr., 1970
Comfort, William A., 1855
Comissiong, Thelma W., 1979
Comiter, Scott L., 1986
Comperatore, Dominic F., 1968
Compton, Azel, 1830
Compton, John Milton, 1906
Compton, William M., 1854
Comstock, Andrew J., Jr., 1884
Comstock, Lucius L., 1860
Conahan, Thomas Joseph, Jr., 1934
Conant, Oscar F., 1854
Conaway, Herbert C., Jr., 1989
Conaway, William Keith, 1890
Conboy, J. Philip, 1894
Concors, Edwin R., 1958
Condefer, William Thomas, 1955
Condict, Lewis, 1836
Condit, William Glasgow, 1904
Condron, Frank M., 1919
Cone, Theodore S., 1946
Conery, William B., 1866
Conger, William Watson, 1903
Coniff, Robert F., 1958
Conklin, Gustavus, 1862
Conklin, Stanley DeWitt, 1920
Conkwright, Allen H., 1861
Conkwright, Sidney Allen, 1892
Conlan, James Adrian, 1931
Conley, Paul J., 1955
Conlin, Joseph Michael, 1896
Conlon, William Linas, 1936
Conly, Frank L., 1980
Conly, Leonard Hudson, 1926
Conly, Samuel S., Jr., S1944
Conn, Frederick A. W., 1896
Conn, Harold Russell, 1912
Connalley, Reps 1848
Connell, James Vincent, 1942
Connelly, Edward W., 1942
Connelly, John A., 1915
Connelly, Joseph H., 1853
Connelly, Mary E., 1972
Connelly, Thomas Rowan, 1970
Conner, Ephraim D., 1840
Conner, J. Hubert, 1955
Conner, Loren, 1937
Conner, Phineas S., 1837
Conner, Phineas S., 1861
Conner, William H.H., 1851
Conner, William, 1892
Connerton, George E., 1977

Connole, John F., 1938
Connole, John Francis, 1906
Connole, Joseph Vincent, 1912
Connolly, Henry, 1882
Connor, Anne E., 1980
Connor, Joseph Francis, 1925
Connor, Robert W., 1960
Conole, Frank D., 1934
Conoly, Lacy Newton, 1919
Conrad, James L., 1965
Conrad, John, 1844
Conrad, Robert Parlett, 1927
Conrad, Roy Garman, 1936
Conrad, Stephen D., 1975
Conrady, William E., 1943
Conrey, Thomas Jackson, 1902
Conroy, Edward George, 1942
Conroy, John S., 1910
Conroy, Joseph V., 1948
Conroy, Joseph V., III, 1980
Conry, John, 1838
Conser, Thomas Curtin, 1888
Constable, G. Robert, 1960
Constant, Fred G., 1973
Conte, Robert R., 1961
Conti, Joseph D., 1976
Conway, Albert G., 1837
Conway, John Baptiste, 1897
Conway, John Joseph, 1920
Conway, Michael K., 1989
Conwell, Joseph A., 1880
Conwell, Luther Swiggett, 1884
Cooch, Joseph Wilkins, 1934
Cook, Aaron, 1934
Cook, Alfred S., Jr., 1947
Cook, Columbus L., 1851
Cook, David J., 1987
Cook, Franklyn R., 1966
Cook, Frederick J., 1984
Cook, George H., 1851
Cook, George R., 1861
Cook, Henry Lilly, Jr., 1918
Cook, Howell E., Jr., 1959
Cook, James A., 1984
Cook, Jerome I., 1954
Cook, John R., 1884
Cook, Joseph L., 1858
Cook, Lawrence J., 1975
Cook, Norman Lyle, 1933
Cook, Philip I., 1986
Cook, Richard A., 1981
Cook, Richard T., Jr., 1984
Cook, T. William, 1953
Cook, Thomas Davis, 1894
Cook, Thomas William, 1920
Cook, William Harvey, 1862
Cooke, Alfred J., Jr., 1964
Cooke, James A., 1854

Cottman, Joseph B., 1838
Cottom, Frank Webster, 1904
Cotton, David B., 1856
Cotton, Paul E., 1969
Cotton, W. G., 1869
Cottone, Robert N., 1956
Cottrell, Emile Lester, 1903
Cottrell, Samuel P., 1882
Couard, T. Ellwood, 1878
Couch, William S., 1857
Coudrick, Charles R., 1858
Coues, Samuel F., 1849
Coughanour, Albert Edward, 1917
Coughlin, Cynthia Marie, 1985
Coughlin, John J., 1959
Coulter, Benjamin F., 1880
Counts, Robert W., 1952
Courogen, William P., 1962
Courtney, David H., 1886
Courtney, Drew E., 1950
Courtright, Everett Peer, 1890
Couse, George, 1851
Cousounis, Gerry T., 1957
Cover, O. Alvin, 1894
Coverdale, Edward J., 1967
Coverdale, Edward James, 1938
Coverdale, Paul J., 1969
Coverly, Thomas Z., 1830
Covey, John Knox, 1940
Covington, Furman Payne, 1939
Covington, Thomas H., 1861
Cowan, George, 1855
Cowan, Kathryn G., 1977
Cowan, William L., 1836
Coward, Edwin H., 1913
Cowden, John W., 1876
Cowell, J. George, 1855
Cowen, Brontz Luther, 1909
Cowen, Harold David, 1904
Cowen, Malcolm L., 1958
Cowgill, Solomon Macy, 1899
Cowin, John H., 1860
Cowling, Richard O., 1867
Cox, Boaz Baxter, 1907
Cox, George Rudy, 1895
Cox, George W., 1859
Cox, George William, 1887
Cox, Harry O., 1883
Cox, James B., 1951
Cox, Jay S., 1958
Cox, John, 1844
Cox, John F., 1984
Cox, John J., Jr., 1945
Cox, John K., 1853
Cox, Jonathan M., 1980
Cox, Joseph J., 1871
Cox, Miley Edsin, 1894
Cox, Percy Evans, 1930

Cox, Ralph L., 1929
Cox, Robert W., 1970
Cox, Ross Parker, 1889
Cox, Seth Leroy, 1912
Cox, Silas W., 1881
Cox, Thomas B., 1879
Cox, Walter R., 1986
Cox, William C., 1885
Cox, William Franklin, III, 1947
Coyle, Bonnie S., 1989
Coyle, Denise E. G., 1986
Coyle, Henry Joseph, 1886
Coyle, John J., 1960
Coyle, Johnson G., 1978
Coyle, Robert, 1885
Coyle, Walter J. E., 1986
Coyle, William A., 1956
Coyle, William Vincent, 1917
Coyne, Charles T. B., 1954
Coyne, James Augustine, 1896
Cozzolino, H. Jay, 1958
Cozzolino, James Anthony, 1920
Crabill, Thomas Voss, 1893
Cracraft, C. Clinton, 1883
Craddock, George Barksdale, 1935
Craddock, John W., 1846
Craddock, Mary K., 1971
Craft, David V., 1988
Craft, Jeanne A., 1989
Craft, Joseph N., 1838
Craig, Albert B., 1901
Craig, Alexander, 1865
Craig, Alexander, 1912
Craig, Clark Rankin, 1893
Craig, Earl Burrell, 1908
Craig, Ford B., 1906
Craig, G. G., 1869
Craig, James Alexander, 1895
Craig, James W., 1851
Craig, John A., 1958
Craig, John Jay, 1901
Craig, John T., 1854
Craig, Loran D., 1891
Craig, Michael W., 1962
Craig, Richard A., 1977
Craig, Samuel Halleck, 1910
Craig, William Clarke, 1907
Craig, William Gibson, 1892
Craige, Thomas W., 1847
Craige, William Temple, 1842
Crain, Carroll Francis, 1920
Crain, J. R., 1856
Crake, Roger F., 1978
Cramer, Arnold J., 1981
Cramer, Benjamin 1838
Cramer, Bernard, 1946
Cramer, David C., 1880
Cramer, Harry R., S1944

Cramer, Harry R., Jr., 1971
Cramer, Marvin E., 1969
Cramp, Charles Edgar, 1906
Cramp, Lloyd L., J1944
Crampton, Ronald W., 1977
Crandall, Charles Perry, 1908
Crandall, Charles R., 1880
Crandall, Harry Franklin, 1922
Crandall, Henry Newton, 1871
Crandall, Noble Franklin, 1933
Crane, Charles A., 1897
Crane, Harold Hayes, 1903
Crane, James R., 1839
Crane, Jeffrey S., 1961
Crane, Morris, 1939
Cranmer, Carl Bernard, 1898
Cranmer, Lynn G., 1966
Cranmer, Richard Raymond, 1909
Crary, Chas. W., 1871
Craven, Edmund R., 1855
Craven, Thomas, 1917
Cravetz, Howard, 1955
Cravotta, Charles Angelo, 1930
Crawe, J. Mortimer, 1859
Crawford, B. Lampton, 1904
Crawford, Carolyn S., 1971
Crawford, Conyngham, 1834
Crawford, Cornelius C.V.A., 1863
Crawford, David Hutchison, 1901
Crawford, Francis A., 1845
Crawford, George G., 1859
Crawford, George W., 1879
Crawford, Gustavus R.J., 1879
Crawford, Herbert Pollock, 1894
Crawford, James A., 1834
Crawford, James J., 1859
Crawford, James Joseph, 1907
Crawford, James L., 1868
Crawford, John C., 1858
Crawford, John D., 1860
Crawford, John J., 1882
Crawford, John Kinnier, 1894
Crawford, John S., 1838
Crawford, John W., 1852
Crawford, Joseph Benjamin, 1941
Crawford, Joseph William, 1914
Crawford, Lewis Gething, 1927
Crawford, Norbert P., 1925
Crawford, Ralph W., Jr., 1965
Crawford, Robert A., Jr., 1943
Crawford, Walter W., 1898
Crawford, Walter W., 1940
Crawford, William Britton, 1916
Crawford, William H., 1854
Crawford, William H., 1857
Crawford, William M., 1856
Crawford, William O., Jr., 1959
Crawford, William Robert, 1952

Crawford, William, 1858
Crease, Henry George, 1891
Creasey, Lloyd S., 1875
Credille, William H., 1857
Creech, Oscar, Jr., 1941
Creedon, William Henry, 1890
Cregan, Gregg E., 1978
Cregg, Francis Aloysius, 1905
Crellin, William Nathan, 1931
Crenshaw, John W., 1870
Crenshaw, William M., 1836
Cresler, Alonzo L., 1849
Cresler, John M., 1874
Cressler, John C., 1941
Cressler, John Webster, 1913
Cressman, Emanuel, 1873
Cresson, Charles M., 1849
Cresson, Hilborne Thomson, 1891
Cresson, Samuel Lukens, 1943
Crevello, Albert James, 1937
Crews, Louis M., 1950
Crews, Numa Haden, 1914
Crews, O. L., 1859
Cribbins, Frederick Allen, 1911
Criden, Louis E., 1965
Crigler, John L., 1859
Crigler, Wallace Payton, 1901
Criley, Benton H., 1871
Crill, Norman C., 1953
Crise, Blair F., 1883
Crise, David, 1872
Crisler, Julius, 1898
Crispin, Samuel D., 1881
Crispino, Richard D., 1974
Crissey, Robert R., 1942
Crissinger, Howard P., 1972
Crist, Guy Charles, 1922
Crist, Walter Allen, 1923
Cristofori, Fred C., 1960
Criswell, J. T., 1872
Criswell, John F., 1879
Criswell, Matthew, 1876
Critchlow, Robert J., 1950
Crittenden, Donald W., 1935
Crittenden, Edmund W., 1835
Crochelt, Robert F., Jr., 1988
Crockett, Ernest Amzi, 1896
Crockett, R. A., 1858
Crockett, Samuel J., 1867
Croft, David W., 1954
Croft, John Walker, 1899
Croll, Millard N., 1948
Crollick, Jill S., 1981
Cromo, Sandra A., 1987
Cromwell, John Seymour, Jr., 1910
Cronin, Edward Jr., 1844
Cronin, Joseph J., 1885
Cronlund, Philip Robert, 1935

Crook, Joseph A., 1870
Crook, Williams J., 1871
Croom, Platt S., 1849
Croop, Harry Ward, 1917
Croop, James Elmer, 1911
Cropp, Howard H., 1839
Cropp, J. Francis, 1878
Cropp, J. T., 1856
Cropper, Leland D., Jr., 1973
Crosby William V., 1949
Crosby, Edward, 1840
Crosby, James A., 1863
Crosby, Victor A., II, 1981
Cross, Charles J., S1944
Cross, Otho W., 1894
Crossan, Laurence T., 1987
Crossley, George W., 1861
Crossman, Thomas J., 1834
Crothers, Kenneth Janney, 1930
Crothers, Robert W., 1855
Crothers, W. Gifford, 1927
Crothers, William Shrimer, 1887
Crouch, Auley McRae, 1916
Crouch, Auley McRae, Jr., 1943
Crouse, Farrell R., 1958
Crouse, George Jackson, 1848
Crouse, Jerome H., 1868
Crouse, William, 1851
Crow, Arthur Everett, 1903
Crow, Calvin A., 1854
Crow, Morton Jay, 1933
Crowder, John V., 1846
Crowder, Richard Brent, 1949
Crowe, Aldrich Clements, 1921
Crowe, Frank Beresford, 1902
Crowell, David H., 1875
Crowell, George Edgar, 1875
Crowell, Godfrey M., 1882
Crowell, T. Alexander, 1875
Crowell, William David, 1886
Crowl, Edward Cleaver, 1926
Crowley, Frederick, 1842
Crowley, Kevin D., 1974
Crowly, Timothy S., 1849
Croxall, Willard Young, 1896
Croyle, Reuben Woods, 1923
Cruice, Leman Dow, 1913
Crump, Lawrence S., 1858
Crump, William Jr., 1849
Crump, William L., 1879
Crumrine, Norman Ross, 1919
Crumrine, Richard S., 1962
Crutcher, William, 1896
Crutchlow, Paul F., 1951
Crutchlow, William P., 1967
Cruz, Richard L., 1979
Cryder, Millard, 1920
Crymes, A. C., 1856

Crystal, Harry, 1936
Cuadra, Jose Maria, 1891
Cubbage, Samuel Thomas, 1895
Cubberley, Charles L., Jr., 1940
Cubler, Edward W., 1945
Cuddy, Vincent D., 1957
Cudemo, Regina M., 1980
Cuden, Nathan Joseph, 1933
Culbert, James Edward, 1957
Culbertson, Edmund, 1836
Culbertson, Howard, 1850
Culbertson, James, 1852
Culbertson, John Smith, Jr., 1945
Culbertson, Julius, 1832
Culbertson, Louis Rogers, 1890
Culbertson, S. D., 1836
Culbertson, Samuel D., 1866
Culbertson, William, 1836
Culbreth, George S., 1866
Cull, William A., 1947
Cullen, Chester F., 1948
Cullen, Michael H., 1983
Cullen, Patrick, 1827
Cullen, Paul T., 1976
Culler, J. P. H., 1858
Culler, John F., 1886
Culler, Robert Martin, 1901
Culp, Charles Thomas B., 1954
Culp, David A., S1944
Culp, Larry H., 1967
Culpepper, B. N., 1876
Culver, Charles F., 1900
Culver, Lucius Pitt, 1861
Cummings, Albert S., 1844
Cummings, Allan H., 1982
Cummings, Curtis E., 1977
Cummings, Hugh B., 1986
Cummings, John B., 1872
Cummings, Joseph J., 1874
Cummings, Josephus, 1871
Cummings, M. John, 1878
Cummings, Michael Penn, 1911
Cummings, Peter Dean, 1989
Cummings, S. S., 1838
Cummins, J. M., 1858
Cummins, Lewis C., 1858
Cummiskey, James, 1856
Cunneff, Raymond Leo, Jr., 1952
Cunning, Samuel R., 1856
Cunningham, Abelard V., 1880
Cunningham, Alexander, 1845
Cunningham, Charles, 1894
Cunningham, Daken Whitaker, 1890
Cunningham, Daniel Henry, 1893
Cunningham, Dewees, 1880
Cunningham, George Aloysius, 1904
Cunningham, George Norman, 1927
Cunningham, George, 1897

Cunningham, H. Clay, 1859
Cunningham, Hugh C., 1885
Cunningham, J. David, 1979
Cunningham, J. Guy, 1867
Cunningham, Jacob Metz, 1912
Cunningham, John, 1827
Cunningham, John S., 1860
Cunningham, Merrill Duffield, 1945
Cunningham, Thomas P., III, 1973
Cunningham, William Louis, 1917
Cunningham, William N., 1874
Cunningham, William R., 1852
Cuomo, Thomas J., Jr., 1969
Curd, John R., 1855
Curl, Alfred Mackinnon, 1891
Curl, Ellmer Ellsworth 1889
Curley, George Frederick, 1896
Curley, Walter James, 1902
Curran, Arthur Manning, 1914
Curran, Edwin Russell, 1924
Curran, Francis J., Jr., 1955
Curran, John Harrison, 1920
Curran, Thomas Patrick, 1990
Current, Howard Wesley, 1925
Currie, Daniel Smith, Jr., 1937
Currie, E. A., 1837
Currie, Richard Jay, 1962
Curry, James Walker, 1898
Curry, Thomas, 1890
Curry, William Oliver, Jr., 1946
Curry, William, 1895
Curti, Joseph T., 1963
Curtin, Andrew J., 1983
Curtin, Charles T., 1966
Curtin, Eugene A., 1955
Curtin, Patricia M., 1988
Curtin, Vincent Timothy, 1925
Curtis, Bartlett A., 1853
Curtis, Grant Philleo, 1906
Curtis, Humphrey H., Jr., 1857
Curtis, Josiah, 1843
Curtis, Levi, 1847
Curtis, Morris Williams, 1932
Curtis, Paul F., 1980
Curtis, Ralph Gardner, 1901
Curtis, Wickliffe K., 1878
Cush, Thomas James, 1924
Cushing, Herbert Howard, 1899
Cushing, Jean G. N., 1935
Cushman, A., 1869
Cuskaden, Albert Douglas, 1892
Custer, Edward William, 1933
Custer, Richard Philip, 1928
Custis, John T., 1846
Cuthbertson, David H., 1850
Cutler, Franklin Earl, 1906
Cutler, Lori R., 1989
Cutler, Neil C., 1967

Cutler, Paul, J1944
Cutler, Robert S., 1966
Cutliff, James S., 1851
Cutter, William W., 1906
Cwik, Jason C., 1988
Cwik, John C., 1951
Cyr, Gerald A., 1930
Czajkowski, Thomas J., 1986
Czapkay, Emilius A., 1853
Czarnecki, Nancy S., 1965
Czubak, Matthew Francis, 1916

~ D ~

D'Alessandro, Michael Adam, 1925
D'Amato, Thomas Andrew, 1990
D'Amelio, Louis F., 1983
D'Amico, Anna M., 1972
D'Amico, Joseph J., 1972
D'Amour, James E., 1982
D'Andrea, Linda Maria, 1981
d'Apery, Tello J., 1905
D'Orazio, Edward A., 1962
da Fonseca Antonia M., 1880
Dabback, DeWitt T., 1952
Dabbous, Aime Mahran, 1896
Dabney, Kirk W., 1984
Dabney, Thomas S., 1835
DaCosta, Jacob, 1852
DaCosta, John C., 1878
DaCosta, John Chalmers, 1885
DaCosta, John Chalmers, Jr., 1893
Dacus, Robert Mabry, Jr., 1933
Daghir, John N., 1986
Dahlstroem, Max, 1885
Daily, James W., 1842
Dainer, Paul M., 1972
Daingerfield, John Elliot, 1854
Daingerfield, Joseph F., 1866
Daitch, Jonathan S., 1984
Dal Nogare, Anthony R., 1978
Dale, Ewing, 1872
Dale, John R., 1872
Dale, William W., 1838
Dalessandro, David Arthur, 1990
Daley, Daniel Frances, 1915
Daley, Marvin C., 1959
Dallara, Charles A., 1988
Dalrymple, Richard E., 1953
Dalrymple, Richard Ray, 1920
Dalsen, Charles M., 1880
Dalsen, Charles W., 1882
Dalsimer, Walter D., II, 1953
Dalton, George O., 1855
Dalton, Matthew L., 1985
Dalton, Simon Eugene, Jr., 1924
Daly, James Wilton, 1948
Daly, Lafayette, 1850

Daly, Theodore J., 1983
Daly, Thomas W., 1946
Daly, William J., 1976
Dalzell, Frederick G., 1978
Daman, Charles N., 1881
Dameron, Robert C., 1850
Damour, Ferdinand, 1877
Dana, Charles H., 1851
Dana, Lawrence W., 1903
Dana, Marcus, 1850
Dana, Robert S., 1857
Dana, Simeon Sessions, 1844
Dando, Elijah Tennyson, 1900
Dandois, George Franklin, 1896
Dandrea, Raymond L., 1951
Danella, John F., 1986
Daniel, A. B., 1857
Daniel, Doff D., 1921
Daniel, I. M., 1838
Daniel, John C., 1984
Daniel, John M., 1956
Daniel, Milton J., 1850
Daniel, Thomas W., 1861
Daniell, Anthony Wingrove, 1898
Daniels, Henry A., 1858
Daniels, Henry Manford, 1887
Daniels, Warren C., 1975
Daniels, Winfred Harry, 1914
Danielson, Carl Leon, 1931
Danisawich, Anthony Bernard, 1922
Danishanko, Albert G., 1956
Dankmyer, Christopher C., 1988
Dankmyer, Edward Charles, 1927
Dankmyer, Frederick L., 1963
Dankoff, Joseph S., 1985
Dannenberg, Marvin, 1954
Dannenberg, Michael James, 1990
Dannenberg, Stanley, 1951
Danoff, Barbara F., 1972
Danoff, Burton H., 1974
Danoff, David M., 1971
Dantini, Daniel, C., 1934
Danyliw, Joseph M., 1947
Danyliw, Thomas J., 1978
Danyo, John Joseph, 1959
Danzer, William F., 1889
Dapp, Gustave Adolph, 1913
Darden, David L., 1849
Dare, Arthur, 1890
Dare, George S., 1866
Dare, George T., 1831
Dare, Gilbert DeWitt, 1897
Dare, J. Rulon, 1890
Darling, Herbert S., 1883
Darlington, William S., 1875
Darnall, Carl Robert, 1932
Darnall, Carl Roger, 1890
Darnall, Walter M., 1884

Dayton, Glenn Orville, 1907
Dayton, Samuel W., 1863
de Andino, Agustin M., S1944
De Berry, John C., 1853
De Carlo, John, Jr., J194
de Diego, Manuel, 1934
De Ford, Harry S., 1864
de Graffeuried, William, 1853
De Jesi, Luigi M., 1882
De Kalb, Benjamin Drew, 1865
de Kraft, Frederic, 1883
De La Gal, Henry H., 1839
de la Montanye, Lester, 1861
De la Puente, Eligio, 1830
de la Rosa, Leander Lopez, 1915
De Long, Eugene Rischel, 1891
de Prophetis, Rocco I., 1931
De Villers, Paul Romeo, 1949
De Wan, Charles Joseph, 1947
De Witt, Calvin, 1865
De Wolf, J. Henry, 1878
Deacon, Benjamin H., 1845
Deaderick, E. L., 1873
Deadwyler, Madison Pope, 1897
Deakyne, Clarence G., 1886
Deal, Lemuel J., 1865
Deam, John H., 1951
Dean, Alexander Heustis, 1900
Dean, Alfred, 1911
Dean, Arthur Clark, 1917
Dean, Edwin Robinson, 1890
Dean, Fred W. S., 1901
Dean, George R., 1868
Dean, Harry Johnson, 1890
Dean, Henry S., 1852
Dean, James, Jr., 1859
Dean, John Henry, 1904
Dean, John W., 1864
Dean, Richard C., 1854
Dean, Samuel Henry, 1855
DeAndino, Richard M., 1976
Deane, James S., 1860
DeAntonio, Angela M., 1984
Deardorff, Benjamin M., 1896
Deardorff, Charles L., Jr., 1961
Deardorff, Charles Leedom, 1928
Deardorff, Frederick W., 1932
Deardorff, John E., 1943
Deardorff, William Henry, 1896
Dearolf, Walter W., III, 1982
Dearth, Olie P., 1882
Dease, Stephen S., 1875
Deats, William, 1877
DeAugustine, Vincent P., 1950
Deaver, Jesse A., 1875
DeBarres, Ph., 1855
DeBenedictis, Kenneth J., 1962
DeBias, Dennis A., 1986

DeBiasse, Timothy A., 1977
DeBonis, Charles S., 1951
DeCandis, Francis X., 1984
DeCarlo, John, 1911
DeCaro, Matthew V., Jr., 1980
DeCato, Alfred A., 1929
DeCato, Alfred R., 1958
DeCato, Richard L., 1960
DeChamps, Thomas J., 1836
DeChoudens, Joseph F., 1857
DeCicco, Gabriel E., 1936
Deck Roy Jr., 1949
Deck, Frederick Webster, Jr., 1949
Deck, Roy, 1914
Decker, Carolyn P. 1965
Decker, Corben, J., 1880
Decker, Frederick Howard, 1897
Decker, Henry Bristol, 1920
Decker, John P., 1946
Decker, Rudolph Frederick, 1906
Decker, Steven E., 1974
Decker, Van Cleft, 1896
Decker, W. Frank, Jr., 1878
Decter, Bruce M., 1988
DeCurtis, George M., 1958
Dedrick, Allen, 1852
Deemer, John T., 1879
Deeney, Vincent F., 1976
DeFelice, Stephen L., 1961
DeFord, Moses, 1886
DeFrance, John H., 1969
DeFrancois, Walter, 1930
DeGaeta, Linda R., 1980
Deglin, Edward A., 1968
Deglin, Stuart M., 1972
Degnan, Edward Joseph, 1913
DeGrandchamp, F. Pinal, 1881
DeGroat, Thomas S., 1981
DeGrofft, Eugene E., 1875
Deguchi, Mario, 1986
DeHart, John N.E., 1847
DeHart, Scott M., 1974
DeHaven, Augustus A., 1829
Dehoney, Howard, 1892
DeHoratius, Raphael J., 1968
Deibert, Glenn Aneas H., 1933
Deich, Aaron, 1932
Deich, Samuel, 1932
Deily, Raymond E., 1942
Deininger, John T., 1939
Deitmaring, Francis A., 1942
Deitz, Robert D., 1963
Dekret, Jeffrey J., 1973
Dekutoski, John T., 1974
Del Giorno, John T., 1969
Del Rossi, Anthony J., 1969
DeLacy, John, 1849
DeLago, Cynthia W., 1986

DeLancey, William Wheelock, 1908
Delaney, Alfred, 1860
DeLaney, Charles Oliver, 1919
Delaney, William E., III, 1953
Delaney, William Eugene, Jr., 1923
Delaney, William T., 1861
DeLannoy, Clarence W., 1881
Delano, Marcus F., 1857
DeLap, Hugh, 1867
Delaplane, James B., 1857
Delaplane, James M., 1964
DeLaurentis, Mark, 1985
DeLawter, Dewitt E., 1941
Delcore, Randy George, 1990
Delehanty, James C., 1975
Delehanty, John Thomas, 1939
Delehanty, Thomas J., 1977
DeLeo, Caesar A., 1938
DeLeo, Caesar A., III, 1987
DelGaudio, John M., 1989
DelGrippo, Gerard A., Jr., 1988
Delicate, William Ernest, 1929
Deliyannides, Deborah A., 1985
Delker, William, 1884
DellaCroce, Joseph M., 1984
Dellenbaugh, Christian W., 1865
Dellenbaugh, Z. T., 1870
Dellevigne, William M., 1967
Dellinger, Woodrow Strayer, 1937
DelMarco, Benjamin Aloysius, 1921
Deloach, A. B., 1859
DeLone, Francis X., Jr., 1977
DeLorenzo, Donald P., Jr., 1980
Delp, James R., 1959
Delp, Richard U., 1963
DelSordo, Joseph Louis, 1959
Delucca, Leopoldo E., 1977
DelVecchio, Leonard M., 1950
DelVecchio, Leonard M., Jr., 1973
Demangone, Michael J., 1989
DeMara, Stephanie Lee, 1990
DeMaria, Louis C., Jr., 1973
DeMaria, Peter A., Jr., 1984
Dembert, Mark L., 1975
Dembinski, T. Henry, 1935
Dembo, Leon Haskins, 1920
DeMeo, Daniel R., 1951
Demmy, Merlyn R., 1956
Demmy, Todd L., 1983
Demuth, S. C., 1838
DeNaples, Mark A., 1962
Denbo, Elic, 1933
Dengler, Charles Rowse, 1914
Dengler, Henry Paul, 1908
Dengler, Robert Herman, 1887
Denig, Robert, 1838
Denise, Jacob C., 1855
Denlinger, Lee E., 1974

Denlinger, Maurice Musser, 1890
Denman, Homer, 1904
Dennen, Timothy J., 1984
Denning, Ollen Lee, 1889
Dennis, David N., 1881
Dennis, Foster Leonard, 1921
Dennis, Jacob M., 1860
Dennis, John, 1890
Dennis, Judith J., 1987
Dennis, Lee M., 1981
Dennis, Lewis H., 1961
Dennis, Welding F., 1842
Dennis, Wilfred Sidney, 1915
Dennis, William H., 1848
Dennis, William J., 1968
Dennish, George W., III, 1971
Dennison, James Andrew, 1912
Dennison, W. Landon, Jr., 1962
Denny, Edward C., 1976
Denny, Michael Richard, 1933
Denny, Thomas Collins, 1912
DeNoia, Anthony P., 1972
DeNote, Anthony Paul, 1936
Dent, Eugene T., 1849
DeNunzio, Neil L., 1982
DePalma, Anthony F., 1929
DePalma, Walter Patrick, 1966
DePasquale, Salvatore C., 1963
DePersia, Rudolph T., 1948
DePersia, Rudolph T., Jr., 1981
DePersio, John D., 1939
Depman, Stanley T., 1982
DePrefontaine, Joseph R., 1831
Derasse, Judith R., 1971
Derham, Robert J., S1944
Derhamer, Wesley A., 1875
Derickson, Philip G., 1943
Derickson, Willard Porter, 1891
DeRosa, Sylvester Frank, 1924
Derr, Frederick S., 1941
Derr, Fuller S., 1884
Derr, James Grant, 1892
Derr, Nathaniel H., 1853
Derr, Raymond Kiesling, 1927
Derr, Rufus M., 1847
Derr, Russell H., 1940
Derrah, Benjamin Vincent, 1916
Derrickson, Charles R., 1950
Derrickson. John B., 1850
Dersh, Jerome, 1954
Dershaw, D. David, 1974
Dershimer, Frederick William, 1915
Desantes, Francis August, 1934
DeSantis, Archie Joseph, 1935
DeSanto, Emelia, 1902
Deschler, Paul, Jr., 1951
Deshmukh, Ravi M., 1988
Desjardins, Christine Carol, 1981

Desman, Eric, 1990
Desnoyers, Edward G., 1844
Despard, Duncan Lee, 1901
Dessau, S. Henry, 1868
Detar, David Dewey, 1933
Dethoff, John C., 1978
Detrick, Kenneth J., 1975
DeTroia, Frederick Carl, 1935
Detterer, Nellie, 1904
Dettor, Vernon B., 1953
DeTuerk, John J., 1938
Detweiler, A. C., 1869
Detweiler, Moses H., 1870
Detweiler, Washington C., 1877
Detwiler, Edwin Landis, 1886
Detwiler, Elizabeth, 1905
Deupree, Albert Bush, 1889
Deupree, William J., 1848
Deutel, Oscar R., 1931
DeValinger, Henry Clay, III, 1950
Devazac, Augustus, 1831
Devenney, John C., 1888
Devenney, Joseph Francis, 1946
Devereaux, Robert, 1867
Devereux, Linda, 1974
Devers, Patrick Joseph, 1936
Devers, Thomas J., 1970
Devine, George C., 1882
Devine, Peter J., Jr., 1963
Devine, Robert Hamilton, 1897
Devlin, Charles James, 1916
Devlin, Charlie W., 1984
Devlin, James E., 1985
Devlin, Joseph M., 1980
Devlin, Joseph Thomas, Jr., 1938
DeVore, Benjamin Franklin, 1907
DeVore, Henry V., 1880
DeWan, Charles Henry, 1917
Dewberry, John H., 1857
Deweese, Cornelius Smith, 1895
Dewey, George M., 1853
DeWire, Thomas M., 1979
Dewitt, Benjamin, 1852
DeWitt, John Wilson, 1863
DeWitt, Manning F., 1857
DeWitt, Moses D., 1887
DeWitt, Virgil Barzillai, 1928
DeWolfe, Willard L., 1879
Dexter, Charles Amory, 1902
Dexter, Henry Leone, 1895
DeYampert, T. J. L., 1858
Deyo, Nathaniel, 1838
DeYoung, A. Henriques 1880
Dhaliwal, Avinder Singh, 1989
Diakun, Robert G., 1969
Dial, B. F., 1871
Diamon, Richard Charles, 1943
Diamond, Mark S., 1977

Diaz, Roman L., 1888
DiBello, Joseph N., Jr., 1989
DiCassimirro, John A., 1988
Dice, Reuben B., 1848
DiCecco, Frank J., 1943
DiCenzo, Donna M., 1985
Dichter, Irving Samuel, 1931
Dick, Alice Ruth, 1990
Dick, H. Lenox H., Jr., S1944
Dick, Hugh Lenox H., 1909
Dick, John M., 1963
Dick, John W., 1866
Dick, Thomas M., 1826
Dickel, William John, 1893
Dickensheets, David L., 1980
Dickensheets, James G., S1944
Dickerman, Frederick A., 1940
Dickersin, G. Richard, 1954
Dickerson, Orval Melcher, 1910
Dickerson, Robert J., 1855
Dickerson, Thomas Henry, 1937
Dickey, Benjamin 1846
Dickey, Clarence Dudley, 1886
Dickey, John L., 1883
Dickie, Jamie William, 1918
Dickinson, Charles Seymour, 1907
Dickinson, Crispin, 1852
Dickinson, Ernest Lincoln, 1890
Dickinson, George Standish, 1893
Dickinson, James John, 1913
Dickinson, John, 1835
Dickinson, Samuel T., 1849
Dickson, Brice T., Jr., S1944
Dickson, Charles M., 1966
Dickson, George Blazier, 1911
Dickson, Glenn Simmons, 1935
Dickson, J. N., 1869
Dickson, James Alexander, 1889
Dickson, James G., 1851
Dickson, James T., 1850
Dickson, James W., 1875
Dickson, John H., 1859
Dickson, John S., 1868
Dickson, John, 1857
Dickson, Lycurgus A., 1855
Dickson, Richard Ensign, 1895
Dickson, Robert Lee, 1925
Dickson, S. Henry, Jr., 1870
Dickson, T. Bruce, 1935
Dickter, Steven J., 1987
DiCola, Daniel B., 1978
DiCuccio, Nicholas W., 1968
DiCuccio, William A., II, 1974
DiDonato, Richard R., 1964
Diebel, Alfred Hoffman, 1925
Diebert, Irwin Elmer, 1917
Diehl, Daniel L., 1981
Diehl, Oliver, 1879

Drick, George R., 1902
Drick, Philip, 1890
Driesbach, Harvey, 1872
Dripps, John H., 1878
Driscoll, Charles Dennis, 1931
Drucker, James O., 1877
Drucker, Paul, 1956
Druckman, Stephen M., 1967
Drueding, Frank F., 1883
Druet, John T., 1856
Druffner, Charles R., 1960
Druffner, Lewis C., 1917
Druffner, Lewis C., Jr., 1959
Drumheller, Francis Edward, 1886
Drummond, Ainsie H., 1923
Drummond, F., 1869
Drummond, John T., 1850
Dry, David Miller, 1913
Drye, William S., 1857
Drysdale, William Atlee, 1882
Du Val, Lucian Spence, 1850
Duarte, Luis E., 1987
Dubbs, Alfred W., 1931
Dubbs, Robert L., 1901
Dubin, Albert A., 1965
Dubin, Elyse C., 1977
Dubois, John Treon, 1847
Dubrow, Donald N., 1958
Ducachet, Henry W., Jr., 1843
Duckett, James P., 1874
Duckett, Thomas S., 1839
Dudeck, Carl R., 1953
Dudek, William C., 1953
Dudenhoefer, Frederick J., 1969
Dudenhoefer, Joseph Edward, 1911
Dudley, Hubert W., 1888
Duer, George S., 1830
Duer, Nathan B., 1984
Duerson, Charles, 1865
Duff, Edmund, 1861
Duff, John Milton, 1874
Duffau, Justus, 1887
Duffell, Charles L., 1862
Duffey, John W., 1851
Duffey, Richard V., 1950
Duffie, Washington J., 1836
Duffield, Edward, 1846
Duffield, Elias Mortimer, 1899
Duffield, Harrison, 1874
Duffy, Charles, Sr. 1930
Duffy, Margaret H., 1989
Duffy, Rosemary Ann, 1990
Duffy, Scott S., 1971
Duffy, Thomas Ambrose, 1928
Dugan, Charles C., 1946
Dugan, Paul J., 1956
Dugan, William James, 1896
Duggan, James R., 1879

Dugger, James M., 1854
Dugger, John Halbert, 1925
Duggins, E. P., 1838
Duhigg, Thomas Francis, 1902
Duhigg, William J., 1952
Dukart, Gary, 1980
Duke, Casper, 1893
Duke, Grady F., 1953
Duke, James E., 1861
Duker, Jay S., 1984
Dula, F. G., 1860
Dulaney, David D., 1963
Dulaney, Nathaniel T., 1856
Dulany, U. Heath, 1851
Dulcey, John J., Jr., 1977
Dulin, John L., 1868
Duling, Milton Stone, 1920
Duling, W. Edward, 1953
Dumbauld, Carl Matthews, 1923
Dumeyer, William Henry, S1944
Dumin, Robert N., 1973
Dummer, Edward Osborne, 1852
Dunavant, W. David, S1944
Dunbar, Thomas, Jr., 1888
Duncan, E. M., 1872
Duncan, George K., 1851
Duncan, Homer G., 1895
Duncan, James R., Jr., J1944
Duncan, John Joseph, 1937
Duncan, R. Edwin, 1919
Duncan, Robert, 1853
Duncan, Theodore G., 1955
Duncan, Thomas F., 1860
Duncan, William C., 1846
Duncombe, Charles, 1846
Dundor, Adam B., 1864
Dundore, Adam J., 1866
Dundore, Claude A., 1887
Dundore, Frank P., 1870
Dunfee, Robin Ann, 1990
Dungan, James B., 1835
Dunglison, Richard J., 1856
Dunglison, Thomas B., Jr., 1859
Dunham, Albright, 1854
Dunham, Alonzo H., 1899
Dunham, Horace Garfield, 1913
Dunham, Malcolm Melville, 1935
Dunkel, Edwin Kilyan, 1895
Dunkel, Thomas A., 1865
Dunkelberg, Elmer Irl, 1910
Dunkelberger, Richard H., 1960
Dunkle, Donald D., 1953
Dunkle, Gaily Barr, 1897
Dunklin, Irby 1841
Dunkum, James B., 1845
Dunlap, Albert Knight, 1916
Dunlap, B. G., 1860
Dunlap, J. Francis, 1875

Dunlap, James C., 1860
Dunlap, John M., 1845
Dunlap, Theodore, 1850
Dunmire, George B., 1865
Dunn, David D., 1939
Dunn, Ernest C., 1960
Dunn, Frederick V., 1898
Dunn, Geoffrey P., 1979
Dunn, Harrison Albert, 1905
Dunn, James C., 1871
Dunn, John L., 1958
Dunn, Margaret Mary, 1977
Dunn, Paul Fallon, 1941
Dunn, Philip F., 1952
Dunn, Samuel, 1830
Dunn, Samuel R., 1867
Dunn, William F., 1980
Dunning, Frederick, 1892
Dunning, James H., 1885
Dunott, Thomas J., 1852
Dunstone, Joan Marie, 1987
Dunton, Charles J., 1980
DuPont, Charles E., 1858
DuPont, Philip J., Jr., 1972
Dupree, Ira E., Jr., 1850
duPrey, Robert E., 1945
Dupuy, Joseph T., 1861
Durante, Raphael Henry, 1932
Durbin, George S., 1918
Durgin, Lawrence Newton, 1920
Durham, Royal E., 1915
Durham, Alexander F., 1852
Durham, Alexander Franklin, Jr., 1887
Durham, Davis G., 1943
Durham, James Richard, Jr., 1936
Durham, William W., 1844
Durinzi, Karen L., 1986
Durkan, Gerald P., 1975
Durkan, William J., 1983
Durkin, Martin G., 1961
Durkin, Martin J., 1969
Durning, Clifton M., 1945
Durphy, Sydenham W., 1853
Durr, Theodore H., Jr., 1943
Durrett, Addison L., 1849
Durrett, Fountain R., 1852
Durst, Daniel P., 1850
Duryea, Chester Ford, 1901
Dusinberre, Robert K. Y., 1924
Duster, Amil Martin, 1924
Duttenhofer, Charles Spindler, 1920
Dutton, Willard Oliver, 1889
Duval, C. A., 1857
Duvall, Augustus W., 1877
Duvall, Frank C., 1909
Duzmati, Paul Peter, 1936
Dvorak, Mary D., 1988
Dwight, M. Barclay, 1875

Dwinelle, James E., 1854
Dworkin, Brad M., 1976
Dwoskin, Joseph Y., 1965
Dwyer, Boyd A., 1986
Dwyer, Charles H., 1883
Dwyer, Charles Raymond, 1926
Dwyer, Frank Philip, 1906
Dwyer, Richard Joseph, 1908
Dye, Franklin Foster, 1933
Dye, Henry, 1861
Dyer, Edward C., 1845
Dyer, James S., 1966
Dyott, John B., 1845
Dysart, Benjamin G., 1859
Dysart, William P., 1859
Dyson, Frank, 1914
Dyson, William W., 1882
Dziob, Edward F., 1969
Dziob, Joseph M., 1936
Dzwonczyk, Philip J., 1979

~ E ~

Eades, Upson R., 1858
Eads, Benjamin Brindley, 1891
Eads, Darwin D., 1859
Eads, John Trimble, 1926
Eagle, James Carr, 1923
Eagleson, David S., 1863
Eakin, Francis Earl, 1918
Eakins, Jehu, 1871
Ealy, David Lawrence, 1941
Eames, George F., 1882
Eames, William N., 1935
Eareckson, Edwin, 1882
Earickson, James P., 1853
Earl, J. Madison, 1857
Earl, John W., 1854
Earle, Linda A., 1986
Earle, Willard C., 1867
Earley, Charles R., 1885
Earley, Francis G., 1885
Earley, Joseph R., 1843
Early, Lewis Mortimer, 1881
Early, Robert F., 1952
Early, Robert F., Jr., 1984
Earnest, Franklin, III, 1943
Earnest, J. Tate, 1861
Earnest, John G., 1867
Earp, Halburt Hale, 1928
Eash, Galen J., 1965
Easler, Richard E., 1957
Easley, Andrew, 1866
Easley, Philip Samuel, 1908
Easling Howard DeWitt, 1949
Eason, Jack B., 1930
East, Albert Franklin, 1893
Eastham, John B., 1852

Eastman, Henry, 1847
Eastman, Henry, Jr., 1892
Eastman, Thomas N., 1881
Easton, William A., 1853
Eastwood, Edmund, 1903
Eaton, Albert M., 1874
Eaty, Sebastian B., 1834
Eaves, Spencer, 1861
Ebaugh, William C., 1867
Ebel, Marc S., 1969
Eberhard, George, 1854
Eberhard, J. O., 1873
Eberhart, Ira A., 1889
Eberle, Jacob K., 1854
Eberle, Walter Gilbert, 1910
Eberly, Albert Dunn, 1930
Eberly, Alison K., 1870
Eberly, Byron Thomas, 1947
Ebersole, Glen, 1951
Ebersole, Robert A., 1952
Ebert, Richard T., 1964
Eberts, Paul M., II, 1984
Ebner, Paul G., 1936
Eboch, William Maynard, Jr., 1968
Eccleston, Joan B., 1971
Echenberg, Robert J., 1965
Echols, Edward D.J., 1857
Eck, William H., 1875
Eckenbrecht, Paul D., 1981
Ecker, Herbert A., Jr., 1976
Eckert, J. Wilson, 1894
Eckert, John N., 1859
Eckert, Robert T., 1945
Eckhart, Godlove Grover, 1907
Eckhart, William Vincent, 1941
Eckley, Robert, 1942
Eckstein, David, 1938
Edalatpour, Nasrola, 1956
Eddy, Lester R., 1933
Eddy, Richard L., 1961
Edeiken, Beth S., 1973
Edelman, Meyer, 1948
Edge, John P., 1846
Edgerton, Ambrose Earl, 1914
Edgerton, James Ives, 1894
Edie, Elliott Bard, 1904
Edie, James Orton, 1874
Edinger, Andrew M., 1987
Edinger, Gregory J., 1972
Edmonds, Andrew, 1887
Edmonds, Lee C., 1985
Edmonds, Matthew W., 1857
Edmonds, Nicholas C., 1859
Edmonds, William, 1900
Edmondson, G. Mitchell, 1981
Edmundowicz, Steven A., 1983
Edmunds, Samuel C., 1851
Edson, Reginald C., 1931

Edson, Steven B., 1978
Edwards, Americus A., 1850
Edwards, C. C., 1875
Edwards, Charles H., Jr., J1944
Edwards, David B., 1982
Edwards, Edward, 1894
Edwards, G. Hiram, 1881
Edwards, Gary Allen, 1969
Edwards, George Murray, 1894
Edwards, Isaac L., 1870
Edwards, James, 1847
Edwards, James L., 1862
Edwards, John B., 1881
Edwards, Karen A., 1984
Edwards, Lewis, 1891
Edwards, Lin-Sey Nancy W., 1971
Edwards, Mark, 1983
Edwards, Richard H., 1837
Edwards, Richard Travis, 1889
Edwards, Robin A., 1972
Edwards, Terry L., 1984
Edwards, Thomas J., 1864
Edwards, Thomas Lewis, 1894
Edwards, William J., 1893
Edwards, William McEwen, 1903
Effinger, Francis A., 1838
Egan, Charles Frederick, Jr., 1973
Egan, E. Winfield, 1891
Egan, Richard J., Jr., 1984
Egbert, Asa, 1831
Egdell, Robert W., 1969
Egel, James W., 1978
Eger, Sherman Alfred, 1929
Eggebroten, William E., 1977
Eggen, Olaf K., 1909
Eggleston, Joseph D., 1851
Egly, Henry Conrad, 1906
Egolf, Ephraim H., 1884
Ehrgott, William August, 1942
Ehrig, Philip Frederick, 1930
Ehrlich, Alexander E., 1972
Eichelberger, Lewis S., 1847
Eichman Peter L. 1949
Eichman, Edward Aloysius, 1905
Eichman, Eugene, Jr., S1944
Eichman, Joseph Cornelius, 1945
Eichman, Margaret J., 1989
Eichner, Lambert G., 1954
Eidenberg, Peter J., III, 1964
Eilers, Robert P., 1976
Eipper, Donald F., 1964
Eisaman, Cyrus D.B., 1871
Eiseman, Paul C., Jr., 1948
Eiseman, Paul Claire, 1917
Eiseman, Reuben, 1887
Eisemann, Michael L., 1972
Eisen, Deborah Ida, 1990
Eisen, Richard F., 1976

Eisenberg, Harvey C., 1964
Eisenberg, Milton, 1935
Eisenhardt, William George, 1900
Eisenhart, Harry Picking, 1906
Eisenhower, Charles Wilhelm, 1903
Eisenhower, E. Susanna, 1977
Eisenhower, James S. D., Jr., 1943
Eisenman, Jesse H., 1984
Eisenman, Richard E., 1987
Eisenstadt, Alexander, 1905
Eisenstein, Mark C., 1958
Eisner, Abraham G., 1940
Eisner, Davis S., 1977
Eisner, Joseph Harold, 1938
Eisner, Steven B., 1978
Eister, Donald H., 1945
Eister, Ronald N., 1980
Eister, William Howard, 1908
Ekman, Linda M., 1975
Ekwurzel, William, 1868
Elden, William McKee, 1888
Elder, Fred Orestes, 1905
Elder, James Clarence, 1904
Elder, Samuel M., 1861
Elder, William T., 1859
Eldon, Rosewell Thomas, 1891
Eldred, Charles C., 1875
Eldred, J. W., 1840
Eldredge, James H., 1837
Eldridge, Erwin J., 1854
Eldridge, William H., 1838
Elener, Valerie A., 1987
Eley, Vernon Lyndon, 1922
Elfman, Karen Sue, 1990
Elgart, Richard L., 1988
Eliades, William, 1958
Elias, Elmer John, 1928
Eliason, John, 1873
Eliason, Talcott, 1847
Elicker, Charles Robert, 1927
Elicker, John E., 1960
Elkin, Philip, 1892
Elkin, Thomas B., 1860
Elkind, Jeffrey Howard, 1977
Elkins, Murray, 1933
Elkins, Robert W., 1965
Ellegood, Joshua A., 1881
Ellegood, Robert Edwin, 1906
Ellegood, Robert, 1886
Ellenberger, J. Wesley, 1879
Ellenberger, Jacob W. E., 1911
Ellenberger, Thomas R., Jr., 1975
Ellershaw, Albert, 1891
Ellery, William, 1877
Ellet, Edward C., 1849
Ellien, William G., 1978
Elliger, Arthur F., 1871
Elliger, Richard A.F., 1867

Ellin, Stephen R., 1968
Ellin, Victor Blewett, 1933
Ellinger, George W., 1878
Ellinger, Jacob Edgar, 1906
Elliot, Avon Hall, 1919
Elliot, Francis Theodore, 1911
Elliott, Andrew Henry, 1896
Elliott, C. B., 1873
Elliott, Donald P., 1957
Elliott, Frazier Jackson, 1933
Elliott, John William, 1890
Elliott, Thomas Balch, 1850
Elliott, Thomas, 1877
Elliott, Washington Franklin, 1887
Ellis, Aller G., 1900
Ellis, Christina E., 1984
Ellis, David J., 1981
Ellis, Dean Samuel, 1883
Ellis, Edwin Milton, 1901
Ellis, Frank D., 1989
Ellis, George S., 1875
Ellis, J. Cannon, 1888
Ellis, J. Wesley, 1870
Ellis, James B., 1845
Ellis, James Baxter, 1901
Ellis, James E., 1841
Ellis, James R., 1853
Ellis, Jennifer Lynn, 1990
Ellis, Joseph W., 1849
Ellis, Joseph Warren, 1871
Ellis, Lyle Gaffney, 1920
Ellis, Lyman Miles, 1893
Ellis, Melvin B., 1875
Ellis, Michael D., 1970
Ellis, Paul S., 1979
Ellis, Peter Clarkson, 1899
Ellis, Richard A., 1949
Ellis, Robert Lee, 1914
Ellis, Samuel C., 1882
Ellis, Scott J., 1985
Ellis, W. Pierce, Jr., 1945
Ellis, Walter Winthrop, 1905
Ellis, William A., 1940
Ellison, L. Frank, 1866
Ellison, Thomas, 1903
Ellmaker, Thomas 1846
Ellrich, David L., 1928
Ellsweig, Bruce A., 1974
Elmer, Alfred Cornwell, 1955
Elsberg, Louis, 1857
Elsinger, Lucious M., 1909
Elsom, James R., 1849
Elsom, John W., 1849
Elston, A. Storm L., 1979
Elston, Dirk M., 1982
Elston, Jan E., 1979
Elston, Scott C., 1988
Elwell, Hildreth B., Jr., 1943

Elwell, Robert W., 1945
Ely, Clarence Francis, 1902
Ely, Harry Birney, 1886
Ely, Horace 1836
Ely, J. Dawes, 1882
Ely, Reuel Abram, 1910
Ely, Richard H., 1882
Ely, S. Carswell, 1836
Emanuel, E. Stephen, 1961
Emanuel, Milton Barnett, 1919
Emanuel, Samuel, 1844
Embree, John W., 1861
Embry, Gideon A., 1867
Emerick, Martin Luther, 1896
Emerson, Linn, 1897
Emery James W. 1931
Emery, Boyd A., 1878
Emery, Clarence, Jr., 1934
Emery, Donald L., 1981
Emery, Frederick C., 1942
Emery, Harry Smith, 1897
Emley, Herbert H., 1886
Emmerling, Karl August, 1890
Emmert, Andrew, 1852
Emmert, Dorsey Frederick, 1891
Emmert, Jos. M., 1872
Emmet, Thomas Addis, 1850
Emmett, Gary A., 1976
Emrick, Edwin M., 1878
Emrick, M. Luther, 1888
Enders, F. Henry, 1867
Endicott, George W., 1875
Endlich, William F., 1885
Endres, Warren H., 1932
Endress, Samuel, 1827
Eney, Irving P., 1952
Enfield, George, 1923
Engel, Herbert Walter, 1951
Engel, Hugo, 1874
Engel, Steven M., 1973
Engel, William Royal, 1906
Engelman, E.J., 1839
Engelman, Joseph P., 1861
England, Kent B., 1975
Engle, Edward A., 1975
Engle, J. Harold, 1939
Englehart, William P., 1950
Engleman, David, 1864
Englerth, Louis Daniel, 1914
English, Charles Frederick, 1898
English, H. J., 1873
English, Harrison Force, III, 1938
English, Joseph T., 1958
English, O. Spurgeon, 1924
English, Richard B., 1976
English, Samuel B., 1906
English, Thomas Odie, Jr., 1959
English, W. T., 1871

English, William Hope, 1886
Engram, R. O., 1873
Ennis, Len E., 1974
Enos, Thos. A., 1879
Ensminger, Samuel Hyson, 1912
Ensminger, William H., 1871
Enterline, John H., 1885
Entler, George F., 1879
Entriken, Smith, 1830
Epes, Algernon S., 1858
Epes, J. W., 1858
Epler, John William, 1883
Eppes, John W., 1849
Epple, Walter D., 1968
Eppley, George, 1853
Eppley, Robert D., 1955
Eppley, Samuel M., 1961
Epright, Paul Alonza, 1918
Epstein, Harry Harold, 1919
Epstein, Herbert M., 1960
Epstein, Howard N., 1958
Epstein, Isadore Leslie, 1927
Epsten, Robert M., Jr., 1980
Erdman, A. J., 1873
Erdman, Daniel E., 1988
Erdman, George L., 1936
Erdman, John P., 1980
Erdman, Leonard A., 1950
Erdman, Robert L., 1966
Ergas, Sanders S., 1976
Erhard, Daniel T., 1951
Erhard, Michael J., 1989
Ericksen, Arthur N., 1935
Erickson, Alan R., 1979
Ericson, Russell Waldo, 1926
Ericsson, Bror Otto, 1897
Eriksen, Christopher M., 1982
Eriksen, George N., 1946
Ernest, Jacob Ellsworth, 1892
Erney, Albert S., 1877
Ernst, Charles Henry, 1902
Ernst, M. Lincoln, 1910
Erpelding, John Kenneth, 1921
Erwin, Evan Alexander, Jr., 1943
Eschbach, Jeffrey C., 1989
Eschbach, Joseph W., 1959
Eschbach, Joseph William, 1928
Eschelman, David J., 1986
Escoll, Andrew J., 1984
Escoll, Philip J., 1951
Esham, Charles A., 1988
Eshbach, Richard E., 1958
Eshbach, William W., 1892
Eshelman, Carl Bushman, 1934
Eshelman, Emory, 1870
Eshelman, Fayette Clinton, 1917
Eshleman, Abraham, 1853
Eshleman, Edwin Franklin, 1893

Eshleman, Isaac S., 1851
Eshleman, John W., 1835
Eshleman, Norton A., 1872
Eshner, Augustus A., 1888
Eskey Chester W., 1949
Eskridge, J. T., 1875
Eskridge, John M., 1854
Espey, John Robert, 1889
Espinosa, Jose Dolores, 1890
Esposito, Joseph Vincent, 1912
Espy, John S., 1879
Espy, Kirk, 1856
Esrey, William P., 1844
Essick, David J., 1969
Essig, Charles J., 1876
Esterly, Jacob Ritter, 1891
Estes, Louis P., 1871
Estill, Andrew Davidson, 1890
Estlow, Bert R., 1962
Estner, Michael J., 1982
Estner, Terry Ann, 1981
Estock, David S., 1982
Etheridge, Charles Henry, 1927
Etheridge, John H., 1856
Etherton, William Clayton, 1890
Etter, D. Frank, 1863
Etter, Harry Havelock, 1922
Etter, Mark S., 1975
Etter, Omer Rasor, 1917
Etzi, Susan, 1988
Eubank, William G., 1856
Eulner, Elmer Harold, 1907
Eustace, James H., 1852
Evans, Archie Paul, 1929
Evans, Bradley D., 1975
Evans, Cadwallader, 1868
Evans, Carl T., 1954
Evans, Carroll Dandola, Jr., 1916
Evans, Charles H., 1857
Evans, Charles H., 1967
Evans, Charles Henry, 1884
Evans, Charles R., 1867
Evans, Clark, 1906
Evans, Dickson, 1846
Evans, Douglas J., 1988
Evans, Edmund Haun, 1889
Evans, Edwin C., 1858
Evans, Faulkner H., 1853
Evans, George W., 1865
Evans, Harlem Irvin, 1920
Evans, Horace Elmer, 1905
Evans, Isaac Newton, 1852
Evans, J. Lawrence, Jr., 1937
Evans, J. Mason, 1851
Evans, J. Robert, 1982
Evans, James H., 1948
Evans, James L., III, 1961
Evans, James Lawrence, 1910

Evans, James Miller, 1919
Evans, James North, 1917
Evans, John F., 1845
Evans, John R., 1950
Evans, John W.C., 1829
Evans, Joseph J., 1977
Evans, Joshua R., 1851
Evans, Josiah T., 1837
Evans, Micaiah R., 1878
Evans, Richard A., 1974
Evans, Richard C., 1984
Evans, Robert J., 1982
Evans, Robert L., 1952
Evans, Robert M., 1854
Evans, Stuart, 1897
Evans, Thomas Russell, 1933
Evans, William Allen, 1906
Evans, William E., 1860
Evans, William P., 1906
Evans, Winborne Dewey, 1925
Evashwick, George, 1939
Eveland, Francis Betterly, 1917
Evens, John Francis, 1908
Everett, Azariah, 1846
Everett, Edward S., 1882
Everett, Edward, 1868
Everett, Henry E., 1882
Everett, Milton H., 1885
Everett, P. Root., 1856
Everett, Shem Alfred, 1907
Everhart, Charles W., 1886
Everhart, Lysle Rogers, 1922
Everlof, John Leonard, 1916
Everlof, Sherman W., 1960
Everson, Malcolm Wayland, 1889
Everts, Deborah, 1978
Everts, Erich A., Jr., 1979
Everts, Leslie Elizabeth, 1990
Everts-Suarez, Erich A., 1950
Eves, Abram E., 1861
Eves, William, 1868
Evitts, Mary Lou, 1971
Ewan, John R., 1937
Ewart, Charles R., 1877
Ewell, Joseph F., 1854
Ewell, Richard H.D., 1842
Ewen, Jonathan H., 1883
Ewen, Warren L., 1882
Ewens, Frederic, 1920
Ewers, Frank Adams, 1905
Ewing, Charles Wesley, 1888
Ewing, Edwin Paul, Jr., 1971
Ewing, Fayette C., 1884
Ewing, Francis M., 1882
Ewing, George, 1850
Ewing, George C., 1858
Ewing, James B., 1866
Ewing, James P., 1854

Ewing, John H., 1877
Ewing, John, 1866
Ewing, Leslie Hand, 1911
Ewing, Philander D., 1837
Ewing, Samuel Eldridge, 1902
Ewing, W. D., 1861
Ewing, William Aaron, 1900
Ewing, William D., 1854
Ewing, William P., 1846
Eyanson, John Norbert, 1905
Eyerly, Robert C., 1952
Ezell, Stiles Dean, 1932
Ezerman, Robert H., 1968

~ F ~

Fabi, Mark B., 1985
Fabian, Andrew A., 1915
Fabian, John Paul, 1930
Fabricant, Michael S., 1964
Fabricant, Samuel, 1919
Facciolo, Mary A., 1979
Fackler, Charles Lewis, 1916
Fackler, Lewis Henry, 1886
Factor, Mitchell L., 1975
Faddis, Thomas McClellan, 1894
Fagan, Peter Edward, 1909
Faggart, George Henry, 1916
Fahey, John C., 1883
Fahr, John William, 1887
Fahringer, Robert R., 1953
Fahrney, Henry Laurence, 1926
Fahrney, Henry Peter, 1895
Fahrney, Jacob 1853
Fahrney, Lewis Welty, 1891
Fahrney, Peter M., 1964
Fahy, Brenda G., 1985
Failmezger, Theodore Richard, 1934
Failor, Benjamin M., 1855
Fair, John F., 1885
Fair, William R., 1960
Fairbanks, Ethelburt, 1918
Fairchild, Courtland de N., 1885
Fairleigh, Robert M., 1860
Fairman, Ronald M., 1977
Faison, Julius Alexander, 1886
Faison, William W., 1878
Fajans, Julian, 1886
Falcone, Albert M., S1944
Falcone, Domenico, 1974
Falcone, Nicholas A., 1934
Falconer, William George, 1919
Fales, Robert M., 1932
Fales, William Dana, 1990
Falk, Ralph, 1907
Falk, Robert B., Jr., 1971
Falkenberg, Thomas, 1987
Falker, John M., 1973

Falker, John Michael, 1939
Fallon, Joseph Francis, 1908
Fallor, Martin K., 1980
Falls, Mark D., 1987
Famiglio, Gregory, 1986
Fanfera, Francis J., 1961
Fang, Jane Yi-Jen, 1989
Fant, Francis M.E., 1846
Fant, Samuel F., 1855
Fantaski, Mark Robert, 1990
Fanz, John Ignatius, 1912
Farabaugh, Alan A., 1989
Farace, Joseph L., 1931
Farber, Joseph M., 1963
Farber, William Daniel, 1896
Farfel, Gilbert S., 1957
Faries, George B., Jr., 1967
Faries, George Bonnell, 1924
Farinholt, Anderson S., 1853
Faris, George Thomas, 1909
Faris, Mary Rachel, 1979
Faris, Samuel Sheets, II, 1943
Farish, George W.T., 1886
Farkas, Andrew A., 1981
Farley, John C., 1861
Farley, Joseph, 1883
Farley, William S., 1852
Farmakis, Leonidas John, 1920
Farmer, Clarence Ravenel, 1909
Farmer, Henry H., 1846
Farmer, John L., 1936
Farmer, Peter M., 1969
Farmer, Rodney Arnold, 1941
Farmer, Willis H., 1838
Farnham, Elmer John, 1899
Farnham, Horace P., 1860
Farquhar, Rahleigh Claude, 1903
Farquhar, Scott D., 1979
Farquharson, Robert R., 1976
Farr, Joseph Louis, 1951
Farrar, George W., 1856
Farrar, John King, 1891
Farrar, John N., 1874
Farrar, Joseph Davidson, 1890
Farrar, Preston W., 1872
Farrar, T. Goodridge, 1853
Farrar, William F., 1852
Farrell, George R. 1949
Farrell, Aloysius W., 1959
Farrell, David Mendel, 1928
Farrell, Francis Albert, 1893
Farrell, Francis X., 1950
Farrell, George Louis, 1895
Farrell, Henry William, 1889
Farrell, John T., 1886
Farrell, John Thompson, Jr., 1922
Farrell, Melanie A., 1986
Farrell, Michael K., 1970

Farrell, Robert E., 1962
Farrell, Timothy Jude, 1990
Farrell, William J., 1961
Farrell, William, 1857
Farrelly, James, 1853
Farrington, Owen Price, 1895
Farrow, E. W., 1873
Farrow, Howard F., 1881
Farthing, Fred Robert, 1921
Farwell, Frank Pierce, 1906
Fassitt, O. R., 1840
Faulcon, Edward W., 1835
Faulkner, George Edward, 1925
Faust, Albert David, 1894
Faust, Halley S., 1976
Faust, Jonathan N., 1867
Faux, Frederick J., 1939
Favino, James C., 1963
Favis-Francilio, Gregory, 1918
Fawcett, Charles L., 1863
Fawcett, Henry, 1834
Fawcett, John W., 1877
Fay, Francis Marcus, 1873
Fay, Frederick Justin, 1950
Fay, Varley George, 1873
Fearing, Benjamin, Jr., 1851
Feaster, Orion Otis, 1916
Feay, John, 1855
Fechtner, Lawrence M., 1986
Feddeman, Frederick A., 1949
Feddeman, Charles Edward, 1911
Feder, Henry Morton, Jr., 1971
Federici, Valerio J., 1948
Federico, Frank N., 1965
Federowicz, Joseph Anthony, 1942
Feduska, Richard G., 1981
Fee, Elam Knott, 1897
Fee, Eugene A., 1957
Feen, Alan E., 1968
Feeney, Edward J., S1944
Fegley, Amandus N., 1870
Fegley, Henry C., 1877
Fegley, Oscar George, 1890
Feher, Ladislas A. M., 1924
Fehnel, Stephen H., 1977
Fehr, John U., 1941
Fehrenkamp, B. J., 1876
Feibus, Arthur, 1922
Feick, J. F., 1872
Feigelson, Charles I., 1956
Feigley, Donald M., 1948
Feigley, Harvey P., 1911
Feigley, Harvey P., Jr., 1942
Feild, Julian, 1907
Feild, William M., 1936
Feinberg, Albert Robins, 1924
Feinberg, Gary L., 1982
Feinberg, Richard I., 1963

Feiner, Larry A., 1978
Feingold, Murray, 1959
Feins, Neil R., 1960
Feinstein, Alex, 1983
Feinstein, Michael A., 1973
Feinstein, Theodore A., 1975
Feissner, Herman, Jr., 1933
Felder, Edward A., 1948
Felder, Lawrence A., 1888
Felderman Eugene S., 1949
Feldman, Ellen K., 1983
Feldman, Jacob Benjamin, 1908
Feldman, Julian D., 1958
Feldman, Martin, 1962
Feldman, Philip M., 1963
Feldman, Richard M., 1970
Feldser, Oscar Benjamin, 1933
Feldstein, Brad, 1981
Feldstein, George Julius, 1906
Feldstein, Leonard Charles, 1947
Fell, William F., Jr., 1971
Fellin, Fredrick M., 1979
Felmly, William T., 1985
Feltwell, A. Lincoln, 1887
Feltwell, John, 1879
Felty, Harry Bowman, 1892
Felty, John W., 1884
Fendrick, Jeffrey S., 1988
Fenichel, Benjamin, 1935
Fenimore, William Nolan, 1921
Fenlin, John M., Jr., 1963
Fenn, M. B., 1856
Fennell, James W., Jr., 1854
Fennell, Ralph Elmer, 1933
Fenster, Martin M., 1972
Fenstermacher, Richard Henry, 1937
Fenton, Drew E., 1982
Fenton, Ivor David, 1912
Ferer, Walter C., 1934
Ferguson, Benjamin Bassett, 1893
Ferguson, Charles Singleton, 1889
Ferguson, Edward Carlon, 1896
Ferguson, George B., 1932
Ferguson, George McIntire, 1899
Ferguson, Gilbert Aloysius, 1905
Ferguson, James B., 1866
Ferguson, James E., 1860
Ferguson, James E., 1870
Ferguson, John B., III, 1971
Ferguson, John Preston, 1892
Ferguson, Lewis L., 1864
Ferguson, Robert Vaughan, 1885
Ferguson, Thomas McKee, 1845
Ferguson, Thomas Reed, 1906
Ferguson, William A., 1880
Ferguson, William D., 1967
Ferguson, William M., Jr., 1883
Ferman, John Wesley, 1904

Fernandez, Manuel C., 1953
Fernandez, Rafael, 1908
Fernandez-Lopez, Mario C., 1924
Fernhoff, Paul Martin, 1971
Fernsler, Edwin K., 1867
Ferrante, Maurice A., 1987
Ferraris, Victor A., 1977
Ferraro, Patrick J., 1959
Ferree, George Perry, 1892
Ferri, John Peter, Jr., 1957
Ferrier, Melvin C., 1940
Ferrier, William Henry, 1905
Ferris, Charles E., 1849
Ferris, Edgar S., 1885
Ferriss, John A., III, 1977
Ferroni, Joseph S., 1973
Ferry, Franklin Forrest, 1887
Ferry, James A., 1987
Ferver, Wilber G., 1884
Fescina, Joseph Vincent, 1933
Fessler, Henry H., 1883
Fessler, Robert Henry, 1958
Fetherolf, James A., 1880
Fetkenhour, Carl L., 1962
Fetter, Donald Evans, 1941
Fetter, E. Minton, 1928
Fetter, Franklin Clayton, 1940
Fetter, John Sylvester, 1936
Fetter, Theodore Roosevelt, 1926
Fetter, Theodore W., 1971
Fetterolf, Michael L., 1983
Fetzer, Jean Hamilton, 1980
Fetzer, Stanton M., 1884
Feudale, Richard F., 1958
Few, Samuel F., 1847
Fickel, Creedin Spencer, 1920
Fickes, Howard C., 1886
Fidler, Harry Earl, 1946
Fidler, W. Larch, III, 1947
Fiedler, Daniel W., 1880
Fiedler, James J., 1946
Fiegenberg, Donald Saul, 1962
Field, Bonni S., 1985
Field, Douglas G., 1989
Field, Edward M., 1849
Field, George, 1834
Field, Howard Lawrence, 1954
Field, John W., 1836
Field, William G., 1951
Field, William S.M., 1886
Fields Joshua, 1949
Fields, Alpheus, 1887
Fields, Richard T., 1979
Fields, Robert S., 1975
Fieo, Richard L., 1972
Fiet, Harvey Jacob, 1891
Fife, J. Rowland, 1873
Figgat, William F., 1858

Figgs, Barbara L., 1974
Figley, Karl Dean, 1913
Figueroa, Cynthia A., 1989
Figueroa, Siegfried, 1910
Fike, Giles A., 1876
Filipek, Walter J., J1944
Filippone, Marciana D., 1978
Filmyer, Edward A., Jr., J1944
Filstein, Allen B., 1974
Finch, Charles S., 1976
Finch, George C., 1841
Finch, Harold, 1917
Finch, Ollie Edwin, 1915
Finder, Marc J., 1978
Findlay, Robert Tower, 1925
Findley, David Pressly, 1930
Fine, Barnet, 1932
Fine, Edward, 1958
Fine, Robert, 1977
Finegold, Richard N., 1980
Fineman, Jay S., 1986
Finesmith, Tina H., 1987
Fingo, Albert J., 1948
Fink, David L., 1985
Fink, David M., 1985
Fink, Gary E., 1981
Fink, Jack W., 1954
Fink, Ulysses S. Grant, 1891
Fink, William D., 1878
Finkbiner, Rodman B., 1953
Finkbiner, S. Sylvanus, 1865
Finkelhor, Robert S., 1978
Finkelstein, Herman, 1932
Finkle, Howard I., 1969
Finkle, Lester Jules, 1935
Finlay, Carlos J., 1855
Finlayson, Bliss L., 1933
Finlayson, William H., 1855
Finley John G., 1949
Finley, Calvin G., 1855
Finley, Harry Lincoln, 1895
Finley, Robert K., III, 1981
Finley, Robert K., Jr., 1948
Finley, Robert Kent, 1916
Finn, Adolph, 1923
Finn, Alfred J., Jr., 1960
Finn, Joseph L., 1935
Finnegan, Mark O., 1987
Finnegan, Walter J., 1969
Finnen, Karl Francis, 1960
Finnerty, William Joseph, 1925
Finnesey, Robert Van D., 1952
Finney, Charles Joseph, 1883
Finney, Edward B., 1861
Fiorelli, Richard C., 1972
Fiorello, Anthony W., 1979
Fiorello, Joseph Michael, 1952
Fireman, Andrew S., 1988

INDEX

Foster, Harry Stewart, 1892
Foster, Howitt H., 1919
Foster, Joel, 1826
Foster, John T., S1944
Foster, Miles Everett, 1909
Foster, Robert S., 1853
Foster, Rufus M., 1880
Foster, Samuel C., 1837
Foster, Stanley C., 1964
Foster, Thomas, 1836
Foster, Walter Ross, 1886
Foster, Wilbur Allen, 1903
Foster, William C., 1874
Foster, William S., 1866
Foster, Z. N., 1860
Fotouhi, Abol H., 1941
Fought, Edgar Newton, 1905
Foulke, George W., 1847
Foulke, Samuel L., 1874
Foulkes, James F., 1852
Foulkes, John Franklin, 1882
Foulkrod, Collin, 1901
Foulks, Wallace Scott, 1897
Foulsham, Charles K., II, 1978
Fountain, Henry Lilly, 1886
Fountain, T. L., 1872
Fournier, John C., 1829
Foushee, J. Henry S., Jr., 1947
Fowler, A. S., 1857
Fowler, Charles Edgar, 1889
Fowler, Dale E., 1982
Fowler, Eric K., 1989
Fowler, Isaac D., 1839
Fowler, Silas W., 1871
Fowler, Warren H., 1879
Fowlkes, Tilley, 1889
Fox, Addison C., 1861
Fox, C. Willard, 1882
Fox, Carol W., 1987
Fox, Charles Reuben, 1918
Fox, Clyde Calvin, 1918
Fox, Elisabeth A., 1984
Fox, Francis H., 1902
Fox, George Timothy, 1907
Fox, Henry Haines, 1846
Fox, J. Robert, 1943
Fox, Jackson Leland, 1936
Fox, James M., 1964
Fox, James W., IV, 1970
Fox, John Lincoln, 1943
Fox, Joseph M., 1851
Fox, L. Webster, 1878
Fox, Michael A., 1988
Fox, Richard D., 1967
Fox, Richard W., 1961
Fox, Robert T., 1942
Fox, Samuel Watson, 1910
Fox, Thomas G., 1852

Fox, William F., 1927
Fox, William Harkins, 1882
Fox, William, 1926
Foxe, Arthur Norman, 1927
Foy, James Henry, 1930
Fralinger, John Joseph, 1912
Frame, Cornelius Aultman, 1889
Frame, Ray Ira, 1924
Frame, Robert, 1859
France, John K., 1868
Francesconi, Albert R., 1968
Franchetti, Michael A., 1982
Francis, Charles K., Jr.,,1965
Francis, G. M., 1859
Francis, William Gifford, 1915
Franco-Guerra, Rodrigo, 1926
Francos, Charles G., 1948
Francos, George C., 1978
Franger, Joseph E., 1967
Frank, Adam, 1867
Frank, David, 1934
Frank, George S., 1883
Frank, James H., 1959
Frank, Johnston, Jr., 1886
Frank, Kay E., 1969
Frank, Lewis P., 1940
Frank, Patrick Joseph, 1948
Frank, Paul E., 1956
Frank, Robert L., 1953
Frankel, Harry A., 1978
Frankel, Kalman, 1943
Frankel, Linda K., 1989
Frankenburger, W. Sturgis, 1911
Frankhouser, Fremont W., 1880
Frankish, John K., 1881
Frankish, Joseph, 1880
Franklin, Benjamin, 1852
Franklin, Earl Alexander, 1922
Franklin, George A., 1847
Franklin, J. W., 1858
Franklin, James Ashby, 1886
Franklin, James S., 1882
Franklin, M. Burnett, 1897
Franklin, M., 1870
Franklin, Thomas Y., 1883
Franks, Donald P., 1950
Franton, Barry, 1976
Frantz, Benjamin, 1846
Frantz, Elias H., 1873
Frantz, F. F., 1869
Frantz, John F., II, 1969
Frantz, John H., 1861
Frantz, Robert C., S1944
Franz, Charles H., 1888
Fraser, Douglas H., 1987
Fraser, E. Kenneth, 1981
Fraser, Edward Clarence, 1884
Fraser, Hugh Daniel, 1897

Fraser, James Austin, 1884
Fraser, James W., 1876
Fraser, Robert I., 1955
Fraser, Roderick L., 1891
Fraser, Simon, 1871
Frattali, Mary J. Boland, 1990
Frauenhoffer, Christopher M., 1976
Fraunfelder, John P., 1967
Fraunfelter, Jas., 1872
Frautz, Joseph, 1878
Fravel, Edward H., 1879
Frazer, Joseph F., III,,1973
Frazer, Marilee H., 1978
Frazier, James William, 1889
Frazier, John R., 1884
Frazier, John Wesley, Jr., 1924
Freas, Cliffton Lewis, 1891
Freas, Glenn C., 1981
Freas, H. L., 1855
Freas, Martin Wesley, 1914
Frederick, Edward J., 1855
Frederick, James E., 1978
Fredericks, David Patterson, 1894
Fredericks, William James, 1889
Frederickson, Victor J., 1950
Frediani, Alexander W., 1938
Free, Jared, 1863
Freeburg, Harry Waldeen, 1902
Freed, Frederick Clarence, 1913
Freed, Jeffrey A., 1983
Freed, Melanie, 1982
Freed, Morris Albert, 1923
Freedman, Alan Reinald, 1962
Freedman, Allan P., 1970
Freedman, Ellen Penny, 1978
Freedman, Howard H., 1959
Freedman, Noah David, 1990
Freedman, S. Robert, 1969
Freedman, Samuel Max, 1901
Freedman, Samuel P., 1974
Freedman, Sheldon J., 1977
Freeland, George R., 1971
Freeman, Albert W., 1936
Freeman, Alton Brooks, 1929
Freeman, Donald H., 1954
Freeman, Eliot N., Jr., 1934
Freeman, Ingraham B., 1856
Freeman, Joseph H., 1876
Freeman, Joseph T., 1934
Freeman, Louis A., 1970
Freeman, Richard B., 1957
Freeman, Richard B., Jr., 1983
Freeman, Robert Herman, 1908
Freeman, Tiyi R., 1974
Freeman, Walter Seip, 1901
Freeman, William A., 1964
Freeman, William Snyder, 1884
Freeze, Peter H., 1857

Gabor, Gary T., 1979
Gabor, Howard, 1990
Gabreski, Thaddeus S., 1938
Gabriel, Frederick Raphael, 1940
Gabriel, Louis Thomas, Jr., 1940
Gabriele, August A., 1936
Gabrielian, Mugurdich C., 1892
Gabrio, Max Reynold, 1913
Gabuzda, George M., 1987
Gaddis, Elijah Franklin, 1851
Gaddis, Jacob Ernest, 1888
Gaddis, L. Springer, 1873
Gadkowski, Walter J., 1969
Gadomski, Casimir Francis, 1933
Gadomski, Joseph Peter, 1946
Gadomski, Stephen P., 1981
Gaffney, John J., 1947
Gagliardi, Joseph M., Jr., 1960
Gagliardi, Joseph Matthews, 1924
Gahan, John Winthrop, 1929
Gahan, Patrick Francis, 1896
Gailey, Calvin P., 1874
Gailliot, Robert V., 1962
Gailliot, Robert V., Jr., 1988
Gainer, James V., Jr., 1959
Gaines, Arthur Raymond, 1916
Gaines, J. H., 1870
Gaines, James S., 1847
Gaines, John L., J1944
Gaines, John M., 1860
Gainey, John White, 1917
Gaither, Brice T., 1851
Gaither, Edwin Stanton, 1953
Gaither, W. W., 1860
Gal, Thomas J., 1968
Galan, Juan Jose, Jr., 1919
Galbraith, Thomas, 1853
Galdini, Angela M., 1982
Gale, C. Tiernan, 1878
Gale, George Hays, 1906
Gale, George T., 1874
Gale, John Witten, 1863
Gale, Larrey Bernard, 1948
Gale, Robert H., 1851
Gale, William H., 1850
Gale, William Hodskin, 1901
Galgon, John P., 1960
Gall, Janice R., 1982
Gallagher, Charles Michael, 1928
Gallagher, Donald I., 1959
Gallagher, Eugene Joseph, 1951
Gallagher, Harry, 1896
Gallagher, Henry G., 1946
Gallagher, Herbert Kelley, 1922
Gallagher, James J., 1946
Gallagher, John Alexander, 1886
Gallagher, John E., S1944
Gallagher, John P. J., 1934

Gallagher, Joseph Francis, 1893
Gallagher, Michael D., 1985
Gallagher, Michael R., 1987
Gallagher, Terence James, 1990
Gallaher, William, 1829
Galligan, William J., 1957
Gallivan, Mary Elizabeth, 1990
Gallivan, William R., Jr., 1986
Gallo, Erly P., 1965
Gallo, Frank, 1934
Gallo, Robert C., 1963
Galson, John W., 1942
Galt, William J., 1858
Gamble, Aaron, 1846
Gamble, Charles Delbert, 1905
Gamble, George M., 1848
Gamble, Hamilton M., 1861
Gamble, James E., 1878
Gamble, Wm Bryan, 1982
Gamburg, Steven J., 1981
Gamette, Douglas Leon, 1921
Gamon, Robert Speer, Jr., 1954
Gandy, Charles M., 1879
Gandy, L. T., 1869
Gangloff, Michael A., 1967
Gannon, Catherine M., 1990
Gano, R. Ewing, 1860
Ganong, Kevin D., 1989
Gans, Emanuel S., 1886
Gansner, Robyn K., 1985
Ganson, Holton, 1834
Garazo-Lorente, Henry Fernando, 1990
Garber, Dale Woods, 1924
Garber, Donna A., 1988
Garber, Edward H., Jr., 1976
Garber, James Rhodes, 1913
Garber, Jonathan Burmond, 1890
Garber, Robert S., 1937
Garcia Castillo, Armando, 1943
Garcia, Augustine M., 1883
Garcia, Jose R., 1978
Garcia, Mark J., 1989
Garcia, Theodore A., 1954
Garcia-Estrada, Manuel, 1929
Garcia-Oller, Jose L., 1945
Garcia-Torres, Francisco J., 1971
Garden, John B., 1850
Gardette, Emile, 1838
Gardiner, Charles, 1879
Gardiner, Sheridan Ellsworth, 1893
Gardner, Alan M., 1970
Gardner, Clarence Snow, 1913
Gardner, Edward R., 1882
Gardner, Everett W., 1938
Gardner, Frank Harris, 1916
Gardner, Herbert D., 1880
Gardner, James L., 1941
Gardner, James L., II, 1972

Gardner, John C., 1982
Gardner, Joseph, 1828
Gardner, Robert B., 1852
Gardner, Robert Edward, 1923
Gardner, Robert W., 1974
Gardner, Samuel, 1874
Gardner, Stuart A., 1979
Gardner, Thomas A., 1952
Gardner, Thomas W., 1979
Garey, Henry, 1884
Garey, Jacob H., 1885
Garinger, George F., 1873
Garland, Joseph 1849
Garland, Wilson, 1856
Garlick, John W., 1847
Garlington, Thomas Richard, 1890
Garman, Russell Arthur, 1930
Garner, Blaine R., 1939
Garner, Presley K., 1846
Garner, Vaughn Clifton, 1920
Garnet, James D., 1941
Garnet, Richard F., Jr., 1972
Garnett, Algernon S., 1856
Garnett, James H., 1848
Garnett, O. V., 1855
Garnett, Thomas N., 1855
Garren, Albert W., 1896
Garretson, Isaac W., 1837
Garretson, William, 1903
Garrett, Charles Reece, 1905
Garrett, E. Frank, 1876
Garrett, James R., 1846
Garrett, Lewis T., 1861
Garrett, Paul R., 1981
Garrett, Robert Charles, 1976
Garris, Frank Henry, 1912
Garrish, John P., 1836
Garrison, Daniel, 1880
Garrison, George Irwin, 1886
Garrison, J. E., 1869
Garrison, Walter Sherman, 1913
Garrison, William P., 1830
Garrison, William R., 1887
Garst, Michael, 1837
Garst, Samuel Sherfey, 1890
Gartland, John J., Jr., S1944
Gartman, Edward, 1933
Gartman, Leo Noy, 1896
Gartrell, Homer L., 1858
Garver, A. Lincoln, 1883
Garver, Charles, 1868
Garverich, Franklin Hendricks, 1891
Garvey, Joseph Peter, 1914
Garvey, Patrick, 1833
Garvin, James H., Jr., 1976
Gary, Arthur Dare, 1912
Gary, Franklin F., 1851
Gary, Gerald L., 1978

Gaskill, Henry Kennedy, 1906
Gaskins, J. L., 1875
Gaspari, Anthony A., 1981
Gaspari, Raymond J., 1974
Gassaway, James M., 1882
Gasser, Rolland Raymond, 1914
Gasslein, Richard Joseph, 1902
Gast, John Reynolds, 1862
Gasteiger, Ernest Sipe, 1927
Gastfriend, David R., 1980
Gaston, Cecil Dulin, 1910
Gaston, Perry Stevenson, 1912
Gaston, William F., 1881
Gates, Albert V., 1875
Gates, Bruce V., 1871
Gates, Joseph M., 1870
Gates, Lionel, 1928
Gates, Thomas N., 1955
Gates, W. R., 1869
Gatski, Robert L., 1948
Gatti, Joseph W., 1936
Gaudielle, Andrew W., 1946
Gaughn, Joseph Francis, J1944
Gaugler, Richard Sechrist, 1894
Gauntt, Franklin Allen, 1886
Gaut, Matthew B., 1870
Gauthier, Henri Edouard, 1923
Gauthreaux, Joseph Justin, 1848
Gauvin, Gregory P., 1972
Gaventa, William C., 1945
Gavin, Thomas Joseph, 1990
Gay, Neil B., 1850
Gay, W. Douglas, 1854
Gay, W. S.S., 1869
Gayle, Charles M.S., 1847
Gaylord, Charles Davis, 1894
Gazowski, Thomas E., 1950
Geare, Frederic, 1851
Gearhart, Malcolm Zieber, 1905
Gearhart, Sylvester Carpenter, 1895
Gearren, John Bernard, 1948
Geary, Edward P., 1882
Gebert, Harry F., 1980
Geddes, Clarence, 1864
Geddes, James Jr., 1838
Geddes, John, 1849
Geddie, Kenneth B., 1921
Gee, Charles J., 1852
Gee, Edward C., 1859
Geetter, David M., 1959
Geetter, Isidore S., 1929
Geetter, Philip H., 1969
Gegan, John, 1831
Gegan, John, Jr., 1851
Gegan, Richard, 1835
Gegan, William, 1836
Geha, Michael A., 1971
Gehl, Sidney Hersh, 1938

Gehman, Linford K., 1963
Gehret, Andrew Martin, 1929
Gehret, Peter A., 1969
Gehring, Gustave Paul, 1890
Gehris, Leroy A., 1935
Gehron, William H., Jr., J1944
Geib, Wayne A., 1939
Geibel, Frank Baum, 1933
Geiger, Charles George, 1889
Geiger, Henry, 1847
Geiger, Hugh St. Clare, 1911
Geise, Ralph W., 1937
Geisendorfer, John Alexander, 1893
Geisler, Cheryl Hirsch, 1978
Geisler, Edward, 1978
Geisler, Philip Howard, 1955
Geissinger, Samuel D., 1877
Gelabert, Hugh A., 1983
Gelb, Albert, 1949
Gelb, Daniel J., 1987
Gelb, Jack, 1946
Gelband, Henry, 1962
Geletka, Susan M., 1980
Gelfand, David, 1932
Gelfond, Stephen D., 1968
Geller, Joyce G., 1987
Gellerman, Douglas R., 1975
Gellman, Alexander C., 1969
Gelman-Weidman, Debra M., 1989
Gelmann, Gregory F., 1988
Gelpi, William Rosario, 1927
Gelwix, James M., 1866
Gemmill, Jacob M., 1832
Gemmill, Jacob M., 1870
Gemmill, Norman Hamilton, 1926
Gemmill, Reginal B., 1955
Gemmill, Robert B., 1864
Geneczko, John Theodore, 1951
Gennaria, Charles, 1923
Gensemer, George John, 1947
Gentile, Frances E., 1988
Gentsch Goldin, Alice L., 1967
Genz-Remshard, Bernadette, 1979
Geoghegan, Richard, 1835
George, Arnold Phillips, 1927
George, Bertha H., 1903
George, Bradley A., 1985
George, Charles Harney, 1908
George, Forney Philip, 1928
George, Henry William, 1901
George, Matthew R., 1875
George, Melbourne E. W., 1926
Georges, Thomas W., Jr., 1955
Georgetson, James Michael, 1938
Georgetson, Michael J., 1985
Geraci, Stephen A., 1980
Geraghty, John Francis, 1941
Gerard, Joseph A., 1977

Gerber, Morris Jean, 1932
Gerber, Richard M., 1980
Gerhard, Emanuel F., 1884
Gerhard, Samuel Pilgrim, 1893
Gerhart, George R., 1958
Gerhart, Robert Pemberton, Jr., 1951
German, George Burton, 1923
German, Howard W., 1885
German, Terry M., 1960
Gerner, Paul Calvin, 1954
Gernerd, Mark D., 1976
Gerould, Theodore Fleming, 1901
Gerry, Hubert W., 1968
Gerry, James, Jr., 1863
Gersh, Douglas B., 1974
Gershman, Isadore, 1938
Gerson, Benjamin, 1973
Gerson, Irvin M., J1944
Gerson, James M., 1970
Gerstein, Gary, 1973
Gersten, Hilliard Clive, 1956
Gersten, Larry M., 1982
Gerulick, Frank Wallace, 1893
Gery, Alfred Oliver, 1893
Gesner, Van, 1883
Gessner, Harlen W., 1983
Gest, Steven A., 1985
Getchell, Albert C., 1885
Getchell, Frank H., 1871
Getter, John P., 1882
Gettings, James Augustus, Jr., 1916
Getz, Donald D., 1966
Getz, H. L., 1874
Getzendanner, Joseph D., 1839
Getzow, Martin Brian, 1983
Gewertz, Bruce L., 1972
Geyer, Stanley J., 1974
Ghent, Henry C., 1856
Giacobbo, John N., 1960
Giambra, Samuel Murray, 1923
Giampetro, Anthony M., 1962
Giarth, David I., 1889
Gibbon, James Wilson, 1918
Gibbon, John Heysham, 1891
Gibbon, John Heysham, Jr., 1927
Gibbon, Robert, 1847
Gibbon, Robert Lardner, 1888
Gibbon, Robert, Jr., 1966
Gibbon, William H., 1857
Gibboney, S. Rush, 1860
Gibbons, Charles Aloysius, Jr., 1933
Gibbons, Joseph, 1845
Gibbons, Mary Stull, 1985
Gibbons, Myles Aloysius, 1902
Gibbons, Robert J., 1943
Gibbons, Thomas P., 1851
Gibbons, William J., 1974
Gibbs, Albert Gabriel, 1922

Gibbs, Godfrey, 1884
Gibbs, Henry L., 1864
Gibbs, Robert T., 1837
Gibel, Lawrence J., 1975
Giberson, Nelson S., 1876
Giberson, William Henry, 1896
Gibson, Albert Matthew, 1903
Gibson, Alexander, 1846
Gibson, Arnold L., 1927
Gibson, Barbara B., 1975
Gibson, Burgess Allen, 1913
Gibson, Edgar T., 1942
Gibson, Frederick H., 1852
Gibson, George William, 1907
Gibson, Jesse Merrill, 1924
Gibson, Jesse Merrill, Jr., 1952
Gibson, John J., 1856
Gibson, Joseph M., 1986
Gibson, Joseph V., Jr., 1951
Gibson, Keith, 1986
Gibson, Ken, 1986
Gibson, Lorenzo P., 1877
Gibson, Lycurgus, 1864
Gibson, Theodore K., 1956
Gibson, William C., 1881
Gibson, William, Jr., 1866
Gidding, Samuel S., 1934
Gidney, J. Chauncey, 1861
Giering, John F., 1931
Giese, George F., 1877
Giesy, Andrew J., 1882
Giesy, Benjamin Franklin, 1901
Giffen, John Wilson, 1896
Gifford, Roy William, 1927
Gifford, Ulysses Grant, 1888
Gift, Weldon Armean, 1921
Gigliotti, Anthony C., 1957
Gigliotti, Lawrence G., 1959
Gilbert, Bruce, 1977
Gilbert, David, 1828
Gilbert, Elon B., 1885
Gilbert, James B., 1946
Gilbert, Jesse, 1829
Gilbert, John, 1895
Gilbert, Jonathan H., 1837
Gilbert, Julius Caesar, 1848
Gilbert, Mary, 1983
Gilbert, Michael M., 1850
Gilbert, Philip, 1933
Gilbert, Silas Terrell, 1854
Gilbert, William Leak, 1891
Gilbertson, Francis E., 1949
Gilcher, Ronald O., 1963
Gilday, Frank J., Jr., J1944
Gilespie, William Pounder, Jr., 1904
Giletto, Basil, 1937
Giletto, Joseph Basil, 1975
Gilger, Ralph J., 1908

Gilgore, Gary Steven, 1967
Gilgore, Sheldon G., 1956
Gilhool, Edward William, 1914
Gilkeson, I. W., 1868
Gilkeson, James B., 1858
Gilkey, John H., 1859
Gill, Brian D., 1988
Gill, C. M., 1869
Gill, George Guyer, 1910
Gill, Henry Z., 1857
Gill, John Joseph, 1941
Gill, Kevin J., 1980
Gill, Lewis M., 1980
Gill, Patrick H., 1954
Gill, Robert T., 1846
Gill, Spencer Glas, 1914
Gillam, Louis M., 1850
Gillan, Ernest F., 1984
Gilland, John C., 1876
Gillars, Alexander Liddell, 1888
Gille, Hugo, 1902
Gillen, Dennis Ryan, 1931
Gillen, Richard H., 1871
Gillen, William S., 1988
Gillespie, Harry, 1934
Gillespie, James L., 1866
Gillespie, James S., 1885
Gillespie, John B., 1965
Gillespie, Patrick Joseph, 1932
Gillespie, Peter Joseph, 1890
Gillespie, Robert, 1864
Gillespie, William A., 1850
Gillespie, William Joseph, 1890
Gillespie, Zadock R., 1857
Gillespy, Albert W., 1982
Gillespy, Mark C., 1986
Gillespy, Thurman, 1907
Gillespy, Thurman, III, 1980
Gillespy, Thurman, Jr., 1953
Gillespy, William G., 1959
Gillett, Omer, Rand, 1902
Gillette, Claudius Wesley, 1895
Gilliam, Bruce Lawrence, 1990
Gilliam, J. P., 1857
Gilliam, James S., 1858
Gilliams, James S., 1846
Gillingham, Harvey, 1882
Gillis, Alfred George, 1932
Gillis, Angus T., 1985
Gillis, John Angus, 1943
Gillis, Joseph I., 1838
Gillis, Victoria A., 1974
Gillum, Diane R., 1981
Gillum, John Randolph, 1904
Gilman, Andrew L., 1985
Gilman, Gary R., 1985
Gilman, John B., 1844
Gilman, Paul B., 1976

Gilman, Philip B., 1981
Gilman, Uriah, 1861
Gilmartin, John Lawrence, 1897
Gilmer, Allen D., 1876
Gilmer, Mauricio W., 1881
Gilmore, A. P., 1874
Gilmore, Bruce S., 1982
Gilmore, Ina M., 1981
Gilmore, Irvin Thompson, 1914
Gilmore, Irvin W., 1951
Gilmore, J. T., 1858
Gilmore, John Wesley, 1911
Gilmore, Thomas Joseph, 1900
Gilmore, Wilbur Hawley, 1903
Gilmore, William J., 1850
Gilpin, Fletcher, 1866
Gilpin, Sherman Fletcher, 1896
Gilroy, Robert C., 1962
Gilson, Allen J., 1979
Gingold, Bruce S., 1970
Gingrich, David N., 1981
Gingrich, Ralph Max, 1953
Gingrich, Rife, 1931
Gingrich, Russell L., Jr., 1951
Ginieczki, Michael J., 1969
Ginley, Frank Michael, 1916
Ginn, Karen Ruth, 1990
Ginns, David A., 1960
Ginsberg, Fredric L., 1977
Ginsberg, Gene H., 1972
Ginsberg, Gregory G., 1987
Ginsberg, Jay, 1977
Ginsberg, Joseph E., 1936
Ginsberg, Lawrence W., 1975
Ginsberg, Susan Beth, 1990
Ginsberg, Susan M., 1978
Ginsburg, David S., 1978
Ginsburg, Macy, 1921
Ginsburg, Samuel, 1908
Giombetti, Joseph John, 1967
Giordano, Guy A., 1981
Giordano, Joseph Martin, 1967
Gipstein, Edward, 1931
Giragosian, A. Minas, 1884
Girardo, Salvatore P., 1969
Girdhar-Gopal, Harsha V., 1985
Girone, Joseph A. C., 1966
Girsh, Leonard S., 1951
Girsh, Sidney, 1959
Girvin, Robert M., 1862
Gittlen, Stanford D., 1982
Giuliucci, Canzio E., 1949
Given, George Gordon, Jr., 1956
Given, James J., 1831
Given, Kenneth M., 1961
Givhan, Edgar Gilmore, Jr., 1928
Gkonos, Peter J., 1978
Glad, Robert M., 1963

Gladden, George, 1875
Gladney, James Clifford, 1924
Gladsden, Eugene S., 1938
Gladsden, Norman, 1953
Glanden, Andrew P., 1865
Glanden, Walter Prevost, 1886
Glasberg, Mark R., 1968
Glascock, Richard M., 1839
Glaser, Arthur H., 1971
Glaser, Joseph P., 1968
Glasgold, Mark J., 1988
Glasgow, Dan Fulkerso, 1909
Glasgow, George Mierley, 1891
Glasgow, Luther Ellis, 1902
Glasner, Saul, 1959
Glasofer, Eric D., 1978
Glass, Barney J., 1883
Glass, Creed Cornelius, 1919
Glass, Frederic A., 1936
Glass, Joseph Hoopes, 1887
Glass, Montgomery W., 1878
Glass, Phillip, 1971
Glass, Samuel, 1848
Glass, Steven J., 1976
Glass, W. L., 1859
Glass, William J., Jr., 1940
Glassberg, Stephen C., 1970
Glassell, Albert S., 1847
Glassman, Leonard M., 1969
Glaudel, Stanley Francis, 1935
Glauser, Tracy A., 1985
Glazer, Robert M., 1962
Glazerman, Larry R., 1976
Gleason, Daniel F., 1875
Gledhill, Horace, 1923
Gleeson, John K., 1854
Gleitz, Allen August, 1928
Glenn, Charles Roland, 1914
Glenn, Eugene Byron, 1896
Glenn, Eugene Byron, 1931
Glenn, Herbert Ross, 1927
Glenn, J. P., 1869
Glenn, James A., Jr., 1934
Glenn, James Mallory, 1859
Glenn, Jerry D., 1973
Glenn, John B., 1872
Glenn, John F., III, 1974
Glenn, Lucius B., 1851
Glenn, Marshail Renfro, 1909
Glenn, Nicholas Thomas, 1907
Glenn, Trevor D., 1959
Glenn, W. L., 1938
Glentworth, William W., 1847
Glezen, Ezra W., 1834
Glick, Andrew J., 1984
Glick, David, 1979
Glick, Eugene, 1956
Glick, Joseph A., 1957

Glick, Melvin Ira, J1944
Glick, Robert P., 1979
Glick, William Henry, 1905
Glickman, Joseph M., 1962
Glickman, Murray, 1951
Glinka, Steven J., 1975
Glinsky, George Clement, 1926
Gliwa, Edward F., 1946
Glocker, Rudolph Karl, 1933
Glorioso, David Vaughn, 1990
Glorioso, Joseph J., 1958
Glouner, Anna, 1902
Glover, Charles P., 1859
Glover, Lawrence L., 1882
Glover, Lewis Pellman, 1926
Glover, Oliver W. H., 1891
Glover, Ralph, 1826
Glow, David E., 1963
Glowacki, Jan S., 1977
Glowacki, Keith Adam, 1990
Glowacki, Peter, 1954
Gnau, Charles R., 1964
Gobetz, Deborah Troth, 1989
Goble, Garvin G., 1942
Gocke, Jack T., 1942
Gocke, Thomas Vincent, 1923
Goddard, Alonzo Irie, 1913
Goddard, Francis Wayland, 1901
Goddard, Jefferson Davis, 1887
Godey, Harry, 1880
Godfrey, E. L.B., 1875
Godfrey, George C., 1952
Godfrey, Henry Granville, 1900
Godfrey, J. T., 1857
Godfrey, James H. Mines, 1905
Godfrey, Michael Paul, 1974
Godshall, Richard W., 1959
Godwin, Bernard Whitehead, Jr., 1955
Godwin, William P., 1831
Goe, John Graham, 1886
Goebel, George, 1886
Goeckler, John E., 1947
Goeggel, Christia Bracken, 1970
Goehring, Charles L., Jr., 1871
Goehring, Donald E., 1929
Goel, Niti, 1990
Goeltsch, Robert E., 1972
Goff, Harry Louis, 1925
Goff, Waldo Percy, 1894
Goheen, George Bailey, 1901
Goheen, S.M.E., 1837
Gohel, Mira Manhar, 1990
Gohsler, Steven P., 1986
Goicuria, Antonio, 1874
Gokcen, Eric C., 1988
Gold, Alan C., 1975
Gold, Alan M., 1970
Gold, Allan, 1962

Gold, Barbara W., 1978
Gold, David Albert, 1942
Gold, Gordon R., 1973
Gold, Hiram, 1867
Gold, Howard S., 1984
Gold, Paul Allen, 1945
Goldbach, Norman J., 1984
Goldbacher, Lawrence, 1920
Goldberg, Alan C., 1975
Goldberg, Alan H., 1979
Goldberg, Bruce A., 1979
Goldberg, Fredric H., 1988
Goldberg, Louis, 1939
Goldberg, Marc B., 1979
Goldberg, Martin, 1950
Goldberg, Maurice, 1904
Goldberg, Maurice, 1916
Goldberg, Michael E., 1982
Goldberg, Paul E., 1975
Goldberg, Richard E., 1962
Goldberg, Robert L., 1976
Goldberg, Stanley J., 1972
Goldberg, Steven E., 1988
Goldberger, Arnold, 1933
Goldblatt, Louis Jay, 1916
Goldblatt, Seymour Z., 1956
Goldbloom, Abraham Allen, 1922
Goldburgh, Harold Leon, 1915
Goldburgh, Warren P., 1952
Goldcamp, Edward C., 1914
Goldcamp, John S., 1934
Goldcamp, Richard Renner, 1942
Goldcamp, Stephen Wilfred, 1907
Golden, Michael P., 1972
Goldenberg, Marc R., 1973
Goldfarb, Abraham, 1930
Goldfeder, Charles B., 1908
Goldfine, Carole S., 1985
Goldin, Michael R., 1969
Golding, Daniel Guedalyah, 1890
Golding, Walter S., 1851
Goldman, Arnold M., 1960
Goldman, Arthur J., 1976
Goldman, David L., 1987
Goldman, Howard, 1970
Goldman, Joel, 1931
Goldman, Leo Lawrence, 1936
Goldman, Louis Charles, 1909
Goldman, Max Robert, 1922
Goldman, Scott M., 1976
Goldman, Sidney Sanders, 1926
Goldschmidt, John W., 1954
Goldschmidt, Joseph C., Jr., 1985
Goldsmith, Charles L., 1973
Goldsmith, Thomas Oliver, 1829
Goldstein, David P., 1963
Goldstein, Eli Whitney, 1920
Goldstein, Franz, 1953

Goldstein, Gail S., 1975
Goldstein, Harry, 1916
Goldstein, Irwin S., 1975
Goldstein, Joel B., 1961
Goldstein, Larry E., 1973
Goldstein, Laurence, 1970
Goldstein, Louis Marshall, 1959
Goldstein, Marvin, 1950
Goldstein, Norman Arnold, 1962
Goldstein, Richard E., 1982
Goldstein, Robert A., 1966
Goldstein, Robert W., 1971
Goldstein, Samuel, 1928
Goldstone, Andrew C., 1985
Goldstone, Sheldon B., S1944
Goldweber, Josef Koppelman, 1935
Golkow, Russell S., 1977
Goll, Stephen R., 1981
Gollub, Ernest, 1937
Golly, Harold Charles, 1917
Golub, Leib, 1930
Gombar, Emil Frank, 1925
Gombeda, Maria A., 1989
Gompertz, John L., 1936
Gontner, Aaron M., 1878
Gonzales, Pablo Bonelli, 1906
Gonzalez, Eric H., 1983
Gonzalez, Jose, 1907
Gonzalez, Rosario Hiram, 1913
Gonzalez-Flores, Jose R., 1938
Gooch, Allen G., 1852
Good, Albert Parke, 1894
Good, D. R., 1858
Good, J. Eugene, 1884
Good, Robert P., 1973
Good, Samuel M., 1856
Good, Vance A., 1975
Good, William Taylor, 1886
Goodall, C. Parke, 1856
Goode, Dale N., 1977
Goode, Norman Johnson, Jr., 1943
Goodell, William, 1854
Goodgion, W. H., 1858
Goodin, William L., 1943
Goodison, William L.T., 1909
Goodman, Bernard, 1958
Goodman, Bert Edward, 1903
Goodman, Bruce, 1955
Goodman, Charles Clarke, 1948
Goodman, David A., 1983
Goodman, David Aaron, 1915
Goodman, David Henry, 1935
Goodman, David M., 1978
Goodman, Edward E., 1874
Goodman, Francis Eugene, 1932
Goodman, Harris M., 1969
Goodman, Horace A., 1853
Goodman, Isaac, 1893

Goodman, Lee McCluskie, 1904
Goodman, Leo M., 1940
Goodman, Michael S., 1976
Goodman, Richard M., 1972
Goodman, Sanford M., 1949
Goodman, Sylvester J., 1900
Goodman, Walter George, 1915
Goodman, William Edward, 1940
Goodman, William R., 1880
Goodner, Ralph Allison, 1891
Goodno, Charles F., 1878
Goodrich, Hubert John, 1907
Goodrich, Robert A., 1854
Goodrick, James E., 1969
Goodritz, Paul Stephan, 1964
Goodwillie, Walter F., 1971
Goodwin, Edmund P., 1852
Goodwin, Harold Isaac, 1926
Goodwin, Henry P., 1871
Goodwin, James Joseph, 1892
Goodwin, John J., 1954
Goodwin, Oscar Sexton, 1923
Goodwin, Richard H., Jr., 1970
Goodwin, Sherman, 1837
Goodwin, Thomas W., 1859
Goodwin, William C., 1853
Goody, Howard E., 1975
Goolrick, P., Jr., 1861
Goore, Myrtle E., 1973
Goosenberg, Jerry, 1962
Goostrey, George Francis, 1905
Gootee, Benjamin S., 1858
Gorby, Charles K., 1959
Gordan, William H., 1859
Gordin, Stephen J., 1974
Gordner, Jesse Walter, 1909
Gordon, Abraham James, 1912
Gordon, Altamont Lafayette, 1897
Gordon, Barry, 1973
Gordon, Benjamin Lee, 1896
Gordon, Bruce, 1961
Gordon, Burgess Lee, Jr., 1919
Gordon, Charles A., 1972
Gordon, Clifford A., 1968
Gordon, David C., 1856
Gordon, Ernest M., 1960
Gordon, Eugene C., 1882
Gordon, Everett J., 1937
Gordon, George Jacob, 1900
Gordon, George R., 1935
Gordon, George, 1922
Gordon, Gregory R., 1984
Gordon, J. Crawford, 1874
Gordon, Jacob, 1933
Gordon, James, 1866
Gordon, Jean S., 1987
Gordon, Joel P., 1989
Gordon, John N., 1852

Gordon, John W., 1878
Gordon, John William, II, 1954
Gordon, John Wood, Jr., 1926
Gordon, John, 1860
Gordon, Joseph C., 1868
Gordon, Mark W., 1967
Gordon, Milton H., 1937
Gordon, Richard D., 1975
Gordon, Richard S., 1973
Gordon, Robert A., 1973
Gordon, Robert H., 1975
Gordon, Samuel, 1906
Gordon, Stuart L., 1981
Gordon, Susan J., 1966
Gordon, Thomas, 1845
Gordy, Edwin, 1948
Gordy, Samuel Tobias, 1923
Gorgas, Albert C., 1856
Gorgas, S. R., 1874
Goribar, Louis G., 1876
Gorin, William H., 1851
Gormally, Eric P., 1971
Gorman, Charles R., 1846
Gorman, John Francis, 1906
Gorman, Leo Raymond, 1917
Gorman, Richard E., 1989
Gormley Joseph J., 1949
Gormley, James Aloysius, 1903
Gormley, James B., 1941
Gorrie, Edward P., 1973
Gorsen, Robert M., 1982
Gorson, Samuel Francis, 1915
Gorsuch, Paul L., J1944
Gorsuch, Paul L., Jr., 1980
Gorszyca, Casimir A., 1956
Gose, John Robert, 1887
Gosewisch, Charles Theodore, 1882
Gosin, Jeffrey S., 1989
Gosin, Stephen, 1962
Gosling, William Eugene, 1865
Gosnell, Kermit B., 1966
Goss, Louis, 1930
Gostigian, John J., 1956
Gosweiler, Augustus V., 1877
Gosweiler, Martin H., 1847
Gosztonyi, Rudolph E., Jr., 1946
Gottfried, William G., 1962
Gottlieb, Fredric R., 1973
Gottlieb, Marc E., 1976
Gottlieb, Ron D., 1988
Gottschall, Amos Wilson, 1913
Gottstein-Eidelson, Stewart G., 1976
Goudiss, Archibald, 1896
Goudy, Rollin Andrew, 1888
Gouger, Dale B., 1969
Gough, Edward John, 1930
Goulard, Alexander, Jr., 1948
Gould, Allan B., Jr., 1952

Gould, Bruce J., 1983
Gould, Daniel B., 1971
Gould, George Milbury, 1888
Gould, James Bennett, 1886
Gould, John H., 1961
Gould, John H., 1986
Gould, R. John, 1955
Gouldin, Thomas W., 1839
Gowen, Francis Vincent, 1914
Gowen, George F., 1952
Goyal, Amit, 1985
Goyal, Maheep K., 1988
Goyne, James Bevan, 1937
Gozdzicki, Henry Roman, 1919
Grab, David S., 1951
Grabiak, Charles F., 1945
Grabiak, Charles F., Jr., 1984
Grabiak, Thomas A., 1980
Grabias, Stanley L., Jr.,,1967
Grace, James J., 1932
Grace, James Thomas, 1900
Grad, L. Christine, 1978
Grady, Hugh Gerard, 1934
Grady, James B., 1875
Grady, John F., 1875
Grady, Robert R., 1865
Grady, William A., 1879
Grady, William Francis, 1943
Graff, Charles, 1826
Graff, John Joseph, 1942
Graff, Louis G., 1952
Grafton, Joseph D., 1859
Gragg, Wilford H., Jr., J1944
Graham, Alan D., 1980
Graham, Aquila John, 1872
Graham, Archibald Hunter, Jr., 1898
Graham, Charles Macgirt, 1929
Graham, Charles Percy, 1886
Graham, D. M., 1870
Graham, Daniel McL., 1860
Graham, Douglas, 1873
Graham, Edward L., 1850
Graham, Edwin Elden, 1887
Graham, Frederick R., 1850
Graham, George M., 1853
Graham, George S., 1866
Graham, Henry W., 1849
Graham, James Abraham, 1896
Graham, James Edward, 1868
Graham, James, 1867
Graham, John, 1826
Graham, John A., 1858
Graham, John McK., 1872
Graham, John W., 1867
Graham, John, 1867
Graham, Joseph, 1859
Graham, Leonidas J., 1855
Graham, Neill, 1849

Graham, Norman Robert, 1887
Graham, Percy Malcolm, 1888
Graham, Robert H., 1852
Graham, Robert H., 1962
Graham, Samuel, 1862
Graham, Taylor L., 1849
Graham, Thomas Francis, 1945
Graham, Vern W., 1915
Graham, William Turbett, 1889
Grahn, Henry Victor, 1923
Grahn, Samuel Norman, 1910
Grammer, Jones M., 1850
Granda, Antonio M., 1974
Grander, Frederick L., 1885
Grandon, Eugene L., 1950
Grandon, Raymond C., 1945
Granelli, H. A., 1915
Granelli, Michael Simon, 1906
Granger, Marilyn, 1983
Grant, Albert J., 1950
Grant, Charles Longmoor, 1890
Grant, Gough W., 1850
Grant, H. Horace, 1878
Grant, James M., 1875
Grant, Jeanne Olivia L., 1981
Grant, John, 1861
Grant, John, 1862
Grant, Kathleen J., 1976
Grant, Samuel Dexter, 1852
Grant, Stuart R., 1966
Grant, William Edward, 1886
Grant, William L., 1856
Grant, William R., 1839
Grantham, Edwin S., S1944
Grasberger, Robert Cook, Jr., 1979
Grasse, John M., Jr., 1952
Grasso, Michael, III, 1986
Gratiot, Charles C., 1880
Gratiot, Harry Bradley, 1896
Graubard, David J., 1961
Graven, Thomas Arthur, 1900
Graver, Edward, 1893
Graves, Arthur Burt, 1915
Graves, J. G., 1853
Graves, S. Waterman, 1846
Graves, Stephen R., 1964
Graves, Thomas A., 1845
Graves, Walter G., 1977
Gray, Alexander R., 1855
Gray, Alfred Percy, 1896
Gray, Barzillai, 1837
Gray, Eb. N., 1883
Gray, Harrison, 1919
Gray, Herbert E., III, 1975
Gray, James Charles, 1884
Gray, James Robinson, 1897
Gray, John, 1836
Gray, John Alfred, 1836

Gray, John W., 1855
Gray, John W., 1864
Gray, Joseph, 1857
Gray, Lewis W., 1973
Gray, Samuel Brown, 1909
Gray, Stephen R., 1971
Gray, Stoddard Perry, 1904
Gray, Tazewell M., 1853
Gray, Thomas D., 1875
Gray, William B., 1852
Gray, William Burritt, 1915
Graybeal, Glenn E., 1978
Graybeal, Michael L., 1979
Graybill, K. P., 1874
Graydon, Andrew, 1877
Graydon, William, 1840
Grayson, Charles M.P., 1880
Grayson, John B., 1841
Grayson, Wray, 1853
Graziani, Leonard J., 1955
Graziani, Virginia, 1986
Grazier, Clark Gilson, 1931
Greaney, Edward M., Jr., 1943
Greaser, George Lewis, 1939
Greaves, Peyton Read, 1916
Greb, David C., 1982
Greble, Edwin S., III, 1946
Greco, Richard J., 1983
Greco, Robert M., 1985
Greco, Toby Anthony, 1916
Greco, Victor F., 1951
Greco-Hunt, Valerie T., 1986
Greeley, Joseph P., 1947
Green, Alan J., 1970
Green, Bennett W., 1856
Green, Carl M., 1968
Green, Charles H., 1852
Green, Charles S., 1872
Green, Clarence Creesy, 1888
Green, David, 1960
Green, Dennis S., 1885
Green, DeWitt C., 1882
Green, Edward Houghton, 1894
Green, Edward Russell, 1957
Green, George W., 1838
Green, Howard Lee, 1897
Green, J. P., 1841
Green, James M., 1837
Green, James S., 1848
Green, John M., 1832
Green, John William, 1916
Green, Joseph B., 1954
Green, Joseph Sidney, 1927
Green, Lawrence, 1964
Green, Linda D., 1976
Green, M. Henry, 1882
Green, Martin, 1938
Green, Max, 1903

Green, Morris Beryl, 1921
Green, Peter Charles, 1893
Green, Philip S., 1956
Green, Phillip A., 1987
Green, Ralph Dennis, 1919
Green, Rex W., Jr.,,1956
Green, Ronald F., 1962
Green, Samuel John, 1838
Green, Southgate Jones, 1931
Green, Sylvanus H., 1885
Green, Thomas J., 1966
Green, W. Alonzo, 1868
Green, William T., 1837
Green, William, 1858
Greenamyer, P. S., 1872
Greenawald, Henry A., 1959
Greenawald, Kenneth A., 1961
Greenawalt, Albert Geary, 1896
Greenbarg, Jeffrey B., 1988
Greenbaum, Charles Hirsch, 1954
Greenbaum, Sigmund S., 1913
Greenberg, Caroline M., 1989
Greenberg, Leonard F., 1959
Greenberg, Milton Sidney, 1950
Greenberg, Mortimer, 1938
Greenberg, Richard D., 1973
Greenberg, Richard H., 1979
Greenberg, Steven J., 1967
Greenblatt, Dana B., 1989
Greenblatt, Marc S., 1983
Greenburg, Morren J., 1958
Greene, Benj. F., 1872
Greene, Clyde C., Jr., 1941
Greene, Frank C., 1880
Greene, Frank M., 1860
Greene, Frank Nichols, 1890
Greene, J. M., 1856
Greene, Lorenzo S.S., 1861
Greene, Marshall L., 1859
Greene, W. H., 1873
Greene, Willard H., 1865
Greenfield, John Claude, 1901
Greenhawt, Michael H., 1973
Greenman, Ernest Nelson, 1912
Greenspan, Gail S., 1980
Greenspan, Mitchell M., 1974
Greenspan, Stephen S., 1987
Greenstein, Robert A., 1966
Greenwald, Daniel F., 1885
Greenwald, Jeffrey R., 1983
Greenwald, Lamartine W., 1872
Greenwood, Henry J., 1958
Greenwood, Lawrence, 1959
Greeson, George Alexander, 1889
Gregersen, James O., 1952
Gregersen, Leo Delbert, 1929
Gregersen, Orman, 1921
Gregg, Albert E., 1880

Gregg, Daniel H., 1828
Gregg, James S., 1866
Gregg, Patrick, 1834
Gregg, Robert J., 1866
Gregg, Sparrow T., 1887
Gregory, Alfred B., 1859
Gregory, Flavius J., 1859
Gregory, Janius C., 1859
Gregory, John A., 1883
Gregory, Oscar, 1854
Grem, Frank M., 1940
Grem, Jean L., 1980
Grem, Judith F., 1976
Grem, Philip C., 1976
Grendal, Michael Francis, 1942
Gresham, Henry, 1856
Gresham, Sterling A., 1848
Gresham, William F., 1874
Gress, Frank A., 1945
Gress, H. V., 1871
Grieco, Anthony Leonard, 1934
Grieco, William M., 1988
Grier, Clarence Russell, 1893
Grier, George W., 1904
Grier, J. H., 1840
Grier, John C., Jr., 1940
Grier, Robert Martin, 1920
Griesemer, Calvin H., 1854
Griesemer, Enoch E., 1851
Griesemer, Hiram J., 1853
Griesemer, John B., 1856
Griesemer, Wellington David, 1908
Griesmer, Paul Dalton, 1954
Griest, Andrew Jackson, 1916
Griest, Oliver Edward, 1915
Griffen, Daniel Patrick, 1914
Griffin, Edwin, 1837
Griffin, George C., 1859
Griffin, Gregory C., 1978
Griffin, John H., Jr., 1948
Griffin, Leslie W., 1941
Griffin, Mark Alexander, 1917
Griffin, Michael J., 1975
Griffin, Patrick F., 1886
Griffin, Thomas D., 1980
Griffin, Thomas William, 1898
Griffin, Tyler, 1866
Griffin, William R., Jr., S1944
Griffin, William Ray, 1910
Griffing, Zachariah B. J., 1844
Griffith, Alexander Hamilton, II, 1929
Griffith, Bartley P., 1974
Griffith, David S., 1863
Griffith, Dayne Hamilton, 1905
Griffith, Ernest R., 1956
Griffith, George Cupp, 1926
Griffith, Jo Crownover, 1927
Griffith, John H., 1870

Griffith, John R., 1946
Griffith, Lee D., 1974
Griffith, Martin Edmund, 1885
Griffith, R. Eglesfeld, 1878
Griffith, Reynold, Stephen, 1918
Griffith, William Clark, 1888
Griffiths, Charles M., 1826
Griffiths, Elijah L., 1832
Griffiths, Jesse W., 1826
Griger, Christine A., 1974
Grigg, Adrian Hansford, 1912
Grigg, Elmer Roy, 1914
Griggs, Earl E., 1915
Griggs, George Albert, 1958
Griggs, John E., Jr., 1975
Griggs, William O., 1866
Grigsby, Abner Joseph, 1845
Grillo, Angelo, 1990
Grim George W., 1859
Grim, Bladen S., 1880
Grim, Earl Henry, 1932
Grim, F. Harvey, 1881
Grim, Frank Seymour, 1895
Grim, George Melvin, 1887
Grim, Herman Charles, 1910
Grim, James S., 1964
Grim, Mark D., 1934
Grime, Robert Thomas, 1892
Grimes, Charles Henry, 1909
Grimes, Franklin T., 1854
Grimes, George Dalton, 1902
Grimes, James Thomas, 1939
Grimes, Louis A., 1864
Grimes, Michael J., 1980
Grimes, William J., 1881
Grimm, Claude Emerson, 1910
Grimm, Dolmont D., 1915
Grimm, Homer Willard, 1916
Grimm, Ian S., 1984
Grindlinger, Jonathan L., 1984
Grindly, Thomas R., 1865
Griscom, Andrew H., 1989
Grisinger, George Floyd, Jr., 1942
Griswold, Elisha, 1853
Grizos, Willaim T., 1981
Grizzard, Theophilus D., 1853
Groblewski, Benjamin Gordon, 1951
Groblewski, Edward A., 1955
Groblewski, John D., 1947
Grobman, Irving Leonard, 1936
Grodin, Jay M., 1965
Groff, Charles A., 1875
Groff, Harvey Deily, 1943
Groff, Jacob E., 1849
Groff, James E., 1880
Groff, John W., 1888
Groff, William T., 1836
Groll, Jerome E., 1976

Grollman, Albert H., 1956
Gromann, John, 1900
Grone, Robert Yocum, 1926
Groninger, Wilson Sherman, 1889
Groom, Albert R., 1886
Groome, Evan J., 1855
Groomes, Roderick, 1976
Grooms, Stephen H., 1859
Groschner, Carl Braun, 1897
Grosky, Murray B., 1961
Gross, Abraham Joseph, 1917
Gross, Barry Charles, 1969
Gross, Benjamin, 1907
Gross, Chester L., 1861
Gross, Donald Ammon, 1919
Gross, Ferdinand H., 1855
Gross, Harry, 1926
Gross, Herbert Franklin, 1899
Gross, Jacob M., 1872
Gross, James D., 1850
Gross, Jeffrey B., 1977
Gross, Joseph LeRoy, 1919
Gross, Moses, 1923
Gross, Richard C., 1969
Gross, Robert E., 1958
Gross, Samuel D., 1828
Gross, Samuel W., 1857
Gross, Samuel, 1911
Gross, William Adam, 1919
Gross, William H., 1947
Grossman, Albert Allen, 1916
Grossman, Jerry J., 1973
Grossman, Joel S., 1967
Grossman, John, 1832
Grossman, Leonard, 1975
Grossman, Marvin, 1961
Grossman, Maurice, 1931
Grossman, Ronald D., 1971
Grossman, Roy, 1976
Grossman, Samuel Linn, 1929
Grossman, Sheila S., 1986
Grossman, William K., 1968
Grosso, Joseph X., 1965
Grosvenor, William, 1830
Grove, Aaron B., 1880
Grove, Austin Millard, 1902
Grove, Bruce A., 1926
Grove, Dale A., Jr., 1956
Grove, George, 1836
Grove, Russell E., 1945
Grove, William Edward, 1913
Grover, Joseph G., 1980
Groves, Claudia I., 1982
Groves, John Dowling, 1884
Groves, John W., 1865
Groves, Norris B., 1954
Grow, Malcolm Cummings, 1909
Grubb, Willard Y., 1951

Grubbs, David S., 1985
Grubbs, Stephen S., 1979
Grubbs, William E., 1942
Gruber, Charles Michael, Jr., 1941
Gruel, Louis, Jr., 1890
Gruel, Theodore, H.E., 1867
Grugan, Hartford Ernest, 1943
Grugan, Robert A., 1946
Grugan, Scott S., 1987
Grumet, Bernard A., 1972
Grunau, Charles F., 1969
Grundfast, Theodore Harvey, 1928
Grunt, Louis, 1934
Grunt, Richard F., 1969
Grunthal, Leonard H., Jr., 1950
Gruszka, Francis Anthony, 1957
Gryczka, Stephen Walter, 1919
Gryczko, Gerald A., 1963
Gryder, Montgomery, 1836
Guardia, Jaime de la, 1920
Guardiani, Mary J., 1981
Guarino, Julius M., 1981
Guarino, Michael J., 1979
Guarnieri, Kathleen S., 1984
Guckavan, Martin Francis, 1935
Guerhard, Augustus, 1838
Guerrant, Richard P., 1866
Guerrant, T. D. F., 1858
Guerrero, Alfonzo L., 1879
Guidon, Marietta F., 1974
Guier, Luis Javier, 1909
Guiher, Horace Binney, 1887
Guild, James, Jr., 1855
Guild, La Fayette, 1848
Guilday, Robert E., 1990
Guiley, A. Harper R., 1877
Guillard, Frank, 1978
Guillard, Paul, 1981
Guillard, Peter M., 1951
Guillot, Ann P., 1974
Guion, Tamara L., 1989
Gula-West, Cynthia L., 1981
Gulick, Arthur Cornelius, 1900
Gulick, Henry, 1865
Gulley, William, 1846
Gulliver, Daniel F., 1852
Gullotti, Michael J., 1974
Gumbes, Charles W., 1864
Gumina, Thomas F., Jr., 1959
Gumnit, Robert Y., 1975
Gunn, Daniel B., 1849
Gunn, Pamela R., 1988
Gunn, Silas R., 1859
Gunn, William R., 1859
Gunnell, William P., 1849
Gunnet, Oren W., 1930
Gunning, Mary Lisa, 1985
Gunter, John B., 1882

Gunter, June U., 1936
Guralnik, Jack M., 1971
Gusciora, Stanley J. 1949
Gusman, Centeno Jesus, 1910
Gusman, Harry Arnold, 1926
Guss, Harry Templer, 1886
Guss, Isaac, 1866
Gustafson, Thomas R., 1988
Gustainis, George J., 1973
Gustin, Grant Harden, 1892
Gutbezahl, Cary D., 1978
Guthrie, Columbus B., 1839
Guthrie, Guian S., 1853
Gutmann, Benjamin, 1897
Guyer, Edward Cecil, 1930
Guyot, J. DeVoine, 1906
Guzman, Horacio, 1882
Guzman, Virgilio, 1879
Guzzardi, Lawrence J., 1971
Gwin, Robert D., 1855
Gwin, W. H., 1869
Gwyn, James D., 1848
Gwynn, William, 1865
Gyles, Edward, 1902
Gyles, Ronald C., 1917
Gzesh, Dan J., 1985

~ H ~

Haacker, Lee P., 1960
Haag, Burritt L., 1959
Haag, Jeffrey R., 1979
Haagen, David Fisk, 1908
Haar, Frederick B., 1932
Haas, Albert Carl, 1924
Haas, Albert Cottrell, 1950
Haas, David R., 1986
Haas, John, 1882
Haas, Melvin E., 1947
Haas, Richard P., 1881
Haas, Thurman Bishop, 1913
Haas, William David, 1887
Habecker, Elizabeth T., 1974
Habel, Karl, 1933
Haberern, Edward J., 1960
Habersham, Stephen Elliot, 1848
Habig, Joseph A., II, , 1983
Hachadoorian, Mugerditch D., 1891
Hackedorn, Noah E., 1845
Hackeny, Jacob S., 1885
Hacker, Isaac B., 1879
Hackett, G. Clifford, 1914
Hackett, John C., Jr., 1883
Hackett, Leon William, 1923
Hackett, Robert F., 1849
Hackett, Thomas, 1847
Hackler, Robert Hardin, Jr., 1926
Hackman, Edmund T., 1942

Hackman, H. Holly, 1986
Haddad, Nickie J., 1963
Hadden, Michael J., 1960
Haden, Madison, 1834
Hadfield, Edward John, 1890
Hadley, Carl M., 1925
Hadley, William Sampson, 1921
Hadlock, Harold William, Jr., 1958
Haensler, Franz. Joseph, 1886
Haentze, Frederick Edward, 1930
Hafley, Lewis A., 1880
Hagan, William James, 1884
Hagarty, John J., Jr., S1944
Hagedorn, Mark D., 1976
Hagedorn, Maxwell Ernest, 1945
Hagemann, Timothy W., 1983
Hagen, Douglas Beriah, 1970
Hagen, Walter Thomas, 1891
Hagenbuch, James Hervy, 1894
Hagenbuch, William A., 1855
Hager, Albert Edwin, 1895
Hager, George W., III, 1972
Hager, George W., Jr., 1943
Hager, Henry George, Jr., 1931
Hager, Walter Aldmond, 1891
Hagerson, Angus C., 1860
Hagerty, Michael F., 1982
Hagg, Doyle D., 1960
Haggard, William D., 1851
Haggerty, Francis Ignatius, 1923
Hagood, Rufus Hansom, Jr., 1911
Hagopian, Edward R., 1956
Hahn, Franklin Jacob, 1895
Hahn, Karl William, 1929
Haibach, Raymond A., 1978
Haight, Warne Lowell, 1931
Haile, William J., 1850
Haimes, Solomon Manuel, 1932
Haimowitz, Bernard, 1985
Haimowitz, Daniel, 1983
Haimowitz, Marcia D., 1986
Hain, David H., 1881
Hain, John R., 1975
Hain, Leonard G., 1893
Hain, Raymond F., 1945
Haines, Benjamin F., 1907
Haines, Charles LeRoy, 1914
Haines, Edward Everett, 1890
Haines, Harlan Fisher, 1925
Haines, Job, 1845
Haines, John Bunting, 1916
Haines, Joseph Ridgway, 1897
Haines, Josiah, 1844
Haines, Robert A., 1946
Haines, Robert William, 1946
Haines, Samuel Howard, 1889
Haines, William Fisher, 1888
Haines, William Fisher, II, 1957

Haines, William Henry, 1912
Haines, Willits Parker, 1897
Hair, Joseph Tracey, 1930
Hair, Wilfred Lorenz, 1917
Haire, Robert Donnell, Jr., 1928
Hairston, George S., 1835
Haislip, George W., 1882
Hake, Edward G., 1877
Halbeisen, William A. C., 1941
Halbeisen, William Joseph, 1897
Halbert, A. C., 1870
Halbert, Francis M., 1880
Halbert, J. E., 1873
Haldeman, George W., 1854
Haldeman, J. Henry, 1883
Hale, Albert P., 1840
Hale, David, 1827
Hale, George V., 1883
Hale, John E., 1988
Hale, John G., 1879
Hale, Morris, 1870
Hale, Peter J., 1858
Hale, Raymond M., Jr., 1939
Hale, Robert G., 1951
Hale, William H., 1882
Hale, Willis LeBaron, 1901
Halenda, Gregory, 1984
Halenda, J. Ronald, 1957
Haley, Argyle, 1858
Haley, George P., 1879
Haley, James, 1856
Haley, John Joseph, 1890
Halicke, Philip V., 1957
Halista, Kevin D., 1986
Halista, Scott M., 1982
Halisy, Dennis J., 1857
Hall, A. Douglas, 1854
Hall, Albon Eugene, 1867
Hall, Bruce C., 1978
Hall, C. Lester, 1867
Hall, Charles F.W., 1875
Hall, Chas. H.H., 1873
Hall, Clark Homer, 1919
Hall, Forest Frank, 1909
Hall, George Henry, 1865
Hall, George P., 1878
Hall, George W., 1855
Hall, J. E., 1869
Hall, James King, 1904
Hall, John L., 1854
Hall, Joseph U., 1859
Hall, Joseph Underwood, Jr., 1889
Hall, Kathryn L., 1975
Hall, Laurence B., 1950
Hall, R. F., 1855
Hall, Richard N., 1845
Hall, Robert B., 1837
Hall, Robert F., II, 1967

Hall, Robert H., 1975
Hall, Samuel E., 1851
Hall, Samuel H., 1857
Hall, Theophilus A., 1843
Hall, Walter E., 1878
Hall, William D., 1886
Hall, William E., 1867
Hall, William Hansell, 1854
Hall, William Joseph, 1896
Hall, William M., 1851
Hall, William M., 1883
Haller, Francis B., 1865
Haller, Michael E., 1832
Haller, Theodore N., 1830
Hallett, Harley J., 1905
Halley, H. Joseph, 1856
Halley, Samuel H., 1848
Halliday, Tom Dunbar, 1959
Hallman, John S., 1882
Hallock, Geoffrey G., 1975
Halloran, Edward J., 1921
Hallowell, Charles E., 1880
Hallstrom, Laun R., 1989
Halpern, Arnold J., 1959
Halpern, Barry R., 1954
Halpern, Gilbert M., 1934
Halpern, Harry Samuel, Jr., 1911
Halpern, Jean A., 1977
Halpern, Samuel, 1931
Halpern, Sidney, 1937
Halpert, Louis, 1901
Halporn, Benjamin, 1923
Halpren, Benjamin A., 1965
Halsey, Luther F., 1854
Halsey, Luther M., 1880
Halton, Edward J., 1938
Haly, J. S., 1872
Hamati, Elias Essad, 1904
Hambrick, Joseph M., 1857
Hamburg, Allen E., 1943
Hamburger, Stuart W., 1949
Hamburger, Harry A., 1979
Hamburger, Richard J., 1962
Hamer, Ellis P., 1851
Hamer, Joseph R., 1878
Hamill, John Frederick, 1889
Hamill, John Paterson, J1944
Hamill, Robert, 1836
Hamill, Robert W., 1945
Hamilton, Alexander P., 1866
Hamilton, Alfred J., 1853
Hamilton, Charles R., 1949
Hamilton, E. Wallace, 1907
Hamilton, Francis, 1933
Hamilton, George L., 1965
Hamilton, George Matthews, 1889
Hamilton, George S., 1851
Hamilton, Gilbert VanTassel, 1901

Hamilton, Glenn D., 1987
Hamilton, J. B., 1838
Hamilton, James, 1848
Hamilton, James M., 1876
Hamilton, John A., 1876
Hamilton, John S., 1954
Hamilton, John W., 1855
Hamilton, John W., 1881
Hamilton, Lloyd Alexander, 1920
Hamilton, Luther Hess, 1901
Hamilton, Richard, 1962
Hamilton, Robert S., 1857
Hamilton, Samuel M., 1853
Hamilton, Swithen N., 1855
Hamilton, William Boyd, 1894
Hamilton, William C., 1971
Hamilton, William N., 1836
Hamilton, William Thomas, 1887
Hamilton, Willis, 1889
Hamma, James Archibald, 1897
Hamman, George Alvan, 1897
Hamme, Curtis J., 1911
Hammell, Eugene J., Jr., 1983
Hammer, Charles M., 1909
Hammerman, Louis, 1978
Hammers, Karen R., 1988
Hammett, Lea Jackson, 1912
Hammond, Alfred F., 1861
Hammond, Alfred F., Jr., 1934
Hammond, Charles P., 1935
Hammond, Frank Clinch, 1895
Hammond, J. Hill, 1883
Hammond, J. W., 1856
Hammond, Michele J., 1986
Hammond, N. LeRoy, III, 1966
Hammond, Newton Keith, 1930
Hammond, Robert A., 1876
Hammond, T. E., 1869
Hammond, T. W., 1874
Hammond, Thomas V., 1882
Hammond, Thomas Victor, Jr., 1908
Hamner, Benjamin Harold, 1926
Hampf, Frederick E., Jr., 1970
Hampton, John T., 1879
Hamrick, Hayward Russell, 1935
Hamsher, C. David, 1974
Hanau, Cheryl A., 1989
Hanbidge, Francis Findlay, 1916
Hanchett, Harry Bigelow, 1905
Hancker, William H., 1873
Hancock, Charles, 1851
Hancock, Eugene Thomas, 1891
Hancock, Francis W., 1847
Hancock, Jefferson 1836
Hancock, William G., 1850
Hand, Ralph Carlisle, 1922
Hand, Roy H., 1953
Handrick, Edgar L., 1863

Handrick, Frank A., 1894
Handy, S. W., 1872
Hanes, Charles Benjamin, 1947
Haney, Joseph S., Jr., 1950
Haney, Josiah Rowan, Jr., 1910
Hanford, Kenneth K., S1944
Hanford, S. B., 1838
Hangen, Russell Jonas, 1923
Hanger, Cornelius, 1861
Hanger, John M., 1857
Hankey, John C., 1978
Hankey, Wilbur H.J., 1879
Hankin, Melvin, 1958
Hankins, John, 1875
Hanks, Edgar C., 1947
Hanks, George M., 1860
Hanks, George Wallace, 1917
Hanks, Jason Grant, 1890
Hanks, William Harvey, 1934
Hanley, Francis Joseph, 1893
Hanley, J. B., 1939
Hanley, Michael A., 1855
Hanlon, Clement Richard, 1936
Hanlon, David G., 1942
Hanlon, Edmund Francis, 1927
Hanlon, Edward Francis, 1908
Hanlon, Frank Robert, 1925
Hanlon, George Henry, 1941
Hanlon, John Joseph, Jr., 1946
Hanlon, Paul Adrian, 1940
Hanly, John A.C., 1861
Hanly, William H., 1844
Hann, John A., 1850
Hanna, Benjamin M., 1877
Hanna, Broderick D., 1884
Hanna, Charles Marcus, 1936
Hanna, Dwight Corwin, Jr., 1919
Hanna, E. S., 1856
Hanna, Edward S., 1978
Hanna, Hugh, 1870
Hanna, Hugh, 1892
Hanna, William P., 1877
Hannan, Charles E., 1946
Hannan, Charles Edmund, 1892
Hannan, William F., 1853
Hannay, Thomas 1834
Hannemann, J. Howard, 1960
Hanner, Joseph Hinton, 1870
Hannigan, Martin James, 1923
Hanning, William Holman, 1935
Hannon, James Augustus, 1926
Hannon, John W. G., 1927
Hannon, Joseph 1844
Hanratty, Richard J., 1958
Hansel, George B., 1906
Hansell, Henry Lewis, 1921
Hansell, Howard F., 1879
Hansell, Howard W., 1952

Hansell, John R., 1957
Hansen, H. Roger, 1969
Hanson, Joel Hjaimar, 1918
Hanson, Wayne Pierre 1912
Hanson, Wayne Pierre, 1940
Happel, Horace E., 1910
Happel, William Joseph, 1919
Happersett, John C. G., 1859
Harbaugh, Charles Hamilton, 1896
Harbison, Andrew B., 1878
Hard, Addison Davis, 1884
Hard, Hanson, 1886
Hardcastle, Alexander, 1849
Hardcastle, Edward M., 1844
Hardee, Walter Person, 1912
Hardeman, Samuel, 1875
Harden, Benjamin F., 1881
Harden, Robert Raymond, 1848
Harden, Wesley R., III, 1975
Harden, William P., 1845
Hardesty, J. R.L., 1856
Hardie, Robert Fowler, 1890
Hardiman, Edward R., 1989
Hardin, William N., 1849
Harding, Benjamin Milton, 1910
Harding, Charles A., 1841
Harding, David B., 1974
Harding, Henry, 1885
Harding, James Clayton, 1916
Harding, Josiah, 1839
Harding, Philander H., 1855
Hardisky, Jo-Anne M., 1982
Hardister, Nathan G., 1880
Hardman, William B.J., 1850
Hardtmayer, H. R., 1877
Hardwick, J. R., 1855
Hardy, George E., 1846
Hardy, Kevin R., 1984
Hardy, Thomas I., 1852
Hardy, William B., 1856
Hare, Edgar Thomas, 1896
Hare, Hobart Amory, 1893
Hare, Thomas Dabney, 1874
Hare, William Bathwell, 1908
Hargreaves, William James, 1946
Haring, John J., 1854
Harker, Charles, 1884
Harker, Jesse, 1839
Harkness, John Linton, 1901
Harley, John Parker, 1905
Harley, Levi G., 1837
Harley, Wilbur J., 1950
Harlow, John M., 1844
Harman, Austin Roy, 1896
Harman, George G., 1880
Harman, Henry M., 1887
Harman, L. Cooper, 1882
Harman, William James, 1900

Harmer, James B., 1882
Harmon, Byron, R., 1866
Harmon, Charles Henry, 1905
Harmon, James Carlisle, 1918
Harmon, Robert J. P., 1914
Harmon, Walter H., 1930
Harmonson, Charles, 1884
Harnagel, Edward E., 1943
Harnagel, Edward John, 1910
Harned, E. Michael, 1985
Harner, Jeffrey D., 1981
Harnish, David M., 1959
Harnish, Tobias, 1856
Harnsberger, George W., 1839
Harover, Samuel Richard, 1893
Harpel, Jesse Edward, 1892
Harper, Harry L., 1950
Harper, Howard Cyrus, 1904
Harper, Isaac N., 1849
Harper, James Henry, 1905
Harper, John P., 1848
Harper, Patricia, M., 1978
Harper, Seborn, A., 1859
Harper, William Troy, 1920
Harpster, Lewis E., 1987
Harralson, Benjamin F., 1865
Harrell, David D., III, 1988
Harrell, Jerry D., Jr., 1961
Harrell, Richard A., 1858
Harrell, W. S., 1869
Harrell, William Horace, 1925
Harrelson, Rose Cranse, 1945
Harrer, Daniel C., 1967
Harrer, William J., Jr., 1934
Harrer, William V., 1962
Harrer, William V., 1989
Harrigan, William Francis, 1911
Harriger, Clyde Everett, 1954
Harriger, Miles D., 1952
Harrill, Lawson, 1861
Harriman, Ben B., 1962
Harriman, Samuel K., 1883
Harriman, Wilbert Eugene, 1895
Harrington, Arthur H., 1882
Harrington, Edwin I., 1881
Harrington, George W., 1894
Harrington, James L., 1903
Harris, Albert Beecher, 1888
Harris, Alexander Everett, 1901
Harris, Alonzo F., 1860
Harris, Benjamin Franklin, 1911
Harris, Cary Fletcher, 1920
Harris, Charles Hickman, 1891
Harris, Clement R., 1842
Harris, Edwin Anderson, 1920
Harris, Frank P., 1892
Harris, Frederick Thomas, 1902
Harris, George C., 1836

Harris, George F., 1845
Harris, Harold Byron, 1933
Harris, Harry, 1908
Harris, Henry F., 1890
Harris, Isaac Emeron, Jr., 1933
Harris, Jack Hawley, 1914
Harris, James A., 1884
Harris, James Albert, 1896
Harris, James E., 1838
Harris, James Watson, 1867
Harris, John B., 1875
Harris, John H., Jr., 1953
Harris, John Scott, 1889
Harris, Kevin R., 1979
Harris, Lorne Wilborne, 1908
Harris, Marcus A., 1848
Harris, Richard M., 1856
Harris, Robert A., 1975
Harris, Robert Edward, 1906
Harris, Russell H., 1956
Harris, S. A., 1871
Harris, Sampson H., 1854
Harris, Samuel, 1844
Harris, Thomas Lewis, 1912
Harris, Thomas S., 1854
Harris, William H., 1858
Harris, William J., 1841
Harris, William, 1891
Harrison, Anthony M., 1964
Harrison, Arthur McCann, 1896
Harrison, Eugene B., 1857
Harrison, Francis Murphy, 1922
Harrison, Frank Matthews, 1896
Harrison, Henry Hill, 1905
Harrison, J. Stewart, 1877
Harrison, James F., 1852
Harrison, James N., 1883
Harrison, Jas. Henry, 1872
Harrison, John Francis, 1903
Harrison, Marcellus T., 1854
Harrison, Milton, 1929
Harrison, Theodore J., 1976
Harrison, Willis Benson, 1872
Harriss, Samuel G., 1855
Harriss, William H., 1855
Harrold, Brian S., 1956
Harrold, Bruce Durston, 1948
Harrold, Leslie S., 1974
Harrop, Daniel S., Jr., 1946
Harrop, James S., 1961
Harry, Benjamin F., 1847
Harsha, Charles Lloyd, 1903
Harshberger, Abraham, 1844
Hart, Rinard Z., 1949
Hart, William E., 1949
Hart, Albert Gaillord, 1852
Hart, Alonzo Winfield, Jr., 1934
Hart, Bruce, 1981

Hart, Byron, 1854
Hart, Carol Ann C., 1989
Hart, Charles Vincent, 1903
Hart, Geoffrey A., 1981
Hart, Ira F., 1852
Hart, Joseph, 1889
Hart, Marilyn M., 1978
Hart, Vincent Paul, 1929
Hart, William P., 1854
Harter, George Alvin, 1891
Harter, John C., 1885
Harter, M. Lair, 1854
Hartford, P. Calvin, 1894
Hartley, Colin Hays, 1929
Hartley, Robert A., 1960
Hartline, Charles Henry, 1892
Hartman, George F., 1885
Hartman, Gustave, 1904
Hartman, H. B., 1857
Hartman, Harry Y., 1880
Hartman, Henry Raymond, 1936
Hartman, Jerome, 1923
Hartman, Luther Monroe, 1925
Hartman, Marcellus T., 1883
Hartman, Milton Ellsworth, 1902
Hartman, Morris D., 1912
Hartman, Paul A., 1874
Hartman, Peter Leroy, 1890
Hartman, Russell Milton, 1930
Hartman, Samuel B., 1857
Hartmann, John J., 1882
Hartsell, Joe Albert, 1912
Hartstein, Paul, 1949
Hartung, Francis Conrad, 1919
Hartwell, Arthur Spear, 1897
Hartwell, Benjamin H., 1868
Hartwell, Samuel C., 1839
Hartz, Harry Jacob, 1908
Hartzell, C. M., 1873
Hartzell, Leo Henry, 1913
Hartzell, Milton B., 1877
Hartzell, Rein Keelor, 1902
Hartzell, W. Harvey, 1873
Harun, Joseph S., 1955
Harvey, Dean Alexander, 1925
Harvey, F. R., 1837
Harvey, Granville, 1858
Harvey, James W., 1884
Harvey, John, 1910
Harvey, Leon F., 1859
Harvey, Steven S., 1988
Harvey, W. Frederic, 1984
Harvey, William C., 1855
Harvey, William J., 1985
Harwell, John H., 1845
Harwell, William H., 1853
Harwitz, Daniel G., 1965
Harwitz, Morris, 1926

Harwood, Charles W., 1883
Haskell, Benjamin, 1923
Haskell, Charles Henry, 1854
Haskell, David S., 1960
Haskell, Joseph H., 1844
Haskett, Paul Edmund, 1913
Haskin, Herbert Pliny, 1891
Haskins, Albert Murton, 1890
Haslett, John D.S., 1855
Hassel, C. Walter, Jr., 1954
Hassel, Harold J., 1957
Hassel, Mark H., 1985
Hassell, Howard Wesley, 1893
Hassell, Starke, 1886
Hassenplug, Frank Atwood, 1890
Hassenplug, Galen K., 1879
Hassenplug, Harry Gilmore, 1893
Hassenplug, Jacob H., 1851
Hassenplug, William Finley, 1892
Hassinger, G. Edgar, 1881
Hassler, Carl W., 1962
Hassler, Ralph Walter, 1957
Hassler, Samuel Freeman, 1894
Hassler, William A., 1866
Hastedt, Robert C., 1948
Hastings, Charles D., 1957
Hastings, John M., 1878
Hastings, Leo J., Jr., 1955
Hastings, Lorne Edward, 1911
Hastings, Richard A., 1947
Hastings, William J., 1882
Hatch, Fred W., Jr., 1873
Hatch, Lerlenn Clement, 1928
Hatchett, Lewellyn, 1849
Hatfield, George Laughead, 1900
Hatfield, Henry R., 1881
Hatfield, Nathan L., 1826
Hatfield, Nathan, 1865
Hatfield, Nicholas William, 1935
Hathaway, Joseph Cushman, 1856
Hatler, Morris, 1860
Hauck, Herbert Harry, 1945
Hauck, Samuel Melvin, 1929
Hauck, William Henry, 1917
Haughton, Richard E., 1861
Haughwout, Peter J., 1962
Haupt, Frederick L., 1861
Haupt, George J., 1948
Haupt, Hans M., 1986
Haupt, Lamar Emerson, 1947
Hause, Welland Angel, 1938
Hauser, Charles F., 1951
Hauser, R. A., 1858
Hauser, Raymond J., 1974
Hauser, Sally J., 1977
Hausman, David H., 1947
Haussmann, David Spotkin, 1921
Hauver, Richard V., 1931

Havens, Joseph M., 1852
Havice, Luther Calvin, 1893
Havis, Minor W., 1851
Hawes, Albert Sidney, 1891
Hawes, Vernon Lee, 1929
Hawfield, James, 1918
Hawk, Malcolm Henry, 1934
Hawk, William A., 1880
Hawkes, Edwin Green, 1892
Hawkey, Richard John, 1897
Hawkins, Alexander B., 1847
Hawkins, Charles Franklin, 1943
Hawkins, Charles Lewis, 1900
Hawkins, Frederick Lewis, 1886
Hawkins, Harrison Morton, 1914
Hawkins, James H., 1946
Hawkins, John Thomas, 1888
Hawkins, John W., 1861
Hawkins, Millard, 1987
Hawkins, Richard E., 1982
Hawkins, Wilbur James, Jr., 1933
Hawkins, William E., 1882
Hawkins, William Henry, 1893
Hawkins, William Raymond, 1927
Hawksley, Vaughan C., 1967
Hawley, Benjamin F., Jr., 1882
Hawley, Charles F., 1932
Hawn, William Seymour, 1920
Haws, Ralph John, 1915
Hawthorn, Samuel W., 1859
Hay, George, 1903
Hay, James T., 1972
Hay, Randal D., 1852
Hayden, H. H., 1837
Hayes, Arthur C., 1975
Hayes, Charles Garfield, 1905
Hayes, Frederick Legro, 1895
Hayes, Isham H., 1850
Hayes, Joseph H., 1862
Hayes, Louis W., 1844
Hayes, Pliny H., 1848
Hayes, Randall Burrows, 1900
Hayes, Robert Goodloe, 1884
Hayes, William Jr., 1838
Hayhurst, George R., 1852
Haymaker, Oliver Rugh, 1890
Haymaker, William Jacob, 1890
Hayman, Edwin Henry, 1899
Hayman, H. Blake, 1945
Haynes, Charles E., 1836
Haynes, James H., 1846
Haynes, Robert S., 1849
Haynes, Timothy, 1836
Haynicz, Peter, 1962
Haynie, James M., 1855
Hays, Chaplin J., 1841
Hays, George Washington, 1834
Hays, James Franklin, 1923

Hays, Jefferson Davis, 1887
Hays, M. P., 1867
Hays, Peter W., 1879
Hays, Richard T.D., 1874
Hays, Robert C., 1877
Hays, Robert M., 1874
Hays, Robert Reeves, 1922
Hays, William L., 1863
Hayslett, A. J., 1858
Haytmanek, Craig T., 1972
Hayward, Catherine Z., 1979
Hayward, R. Bradley, 1977
Hayward, W. H., 1838
Haywood, Guy Tainter, 1913
Haywood, Richard B., 1844
Hayworth, Ray W., 1918
Hazel, Thomas Harold, 1894
Hazlett, Almon Cyrus, 1913
Hazlett, Edgar Marion, 1902
Hazlett, Frank Leslie, 1903
Hazlett, Harry Foster, 1892
Hazlett, Isaac W., 1879
Hazlett, James C., 1938
Hazlett, Joshua D., 1882
Hazlett, Leslie Ramsey, 1896
Hazlett, Robert W., 1851
Hazlett, Silas Metz, 1897
Hazlett, Thomas Jefferson, 1845
Hazzard, Henry Draper, 1891
Heacock, Stacy L., 1881
Heacox, Frank L., 1902
Head, Joseph, 1854
Head, Thomas Francis, 1949
Headings, Donald Moore, 1924
Headings, Isaac Griffy, Jr., 1893
Headrick, Elmer Oscar, Jr., 1943
Heady, Carlton Kellogg, 1913
Heagey, Henry F.C., 1883
Heald, James I., 1980
Healey, John Edward, Jr., 1948
Healey, Joseph Thomas, 1942
Healy John R., 1949
Healy, James, 1862
Heaney, Joseph A., 1955
Heaps, Kenneth P., 1966
Heard, Falkner, 1849
Heard, John H., 1881
Hearn, Charles Sheppard, 1890
Hearn, Marion, 1902
Hearn, William Joseph, 1867
Hearn, William P., 1899
Hearn, William Prettyman, Jr., 1935
Hearne, Jos. C., 1872
Heath, Alfred O., 1957
Heath, Robert D., J1944
Heath, William H., 1858
Heaton, Vincent Warner, 1942
Heaton, William Wright, 1892

Heatter, Max William, 1923
Hebble, Howard Miller, 1934
Hebble, Joseph, 1855
Heberling, Jacob Zern, 1929
Hebert, Arthur Winfred, 1916
Hebert, Peter W., 1960
Hebrank, Edmund Rock, 1890
Hebsacker, William Frederick, 1899
Hechelman, H. W., 1869
Hecht, John P., 1880
Hecht, Joseph Jerome, 1922
Heckert, Emerson Monroe, 1921
Heckert, Jeffrey J., 1989
Heckert, Richard R., 1981
Heckler, G. Barrett, 1948
Heckman, George Bowers, 1925
Heckman, Ira Dietrich, 1920
Heckman, James A., 1942
Heckman, James D., 1969
Heckman, Samuel B., 1868
Hecksher, Rudolph H., Jr., 1943
Hedde, Eugene Lee, 1928
Heddens, James W., 1879
Heddens, William S., Jr., 1855
Hedgepeth, Josiah, 1860
Hedges, Charles H., 1841
Hedges, Richard C., 1958
Hedges, Urban D., 1835
Hedley, James Roger, 1900
Heed, Charles R., 1903
Hefflin, Wyatt, 1884
Heffner, Charles W., 1880
Heffner, Curtis, 1897
Heffner, George W., Jr., 1984
Heffner, Oliver C., 1885
Heffner, Robert Stanley, 1919
Heffron, Timothy J., 1976
Heflin, Ernest Lee, 1897
Hegarty, Francis A., 1932
Hegarty, Thomas J., Jr., 1966
Hegarty, William W., 1942
Hegins, Thomas G., 1846
Heiberg, Adolph Oscar, 1893
Heider, Maurice Isaac, 1891
Heikes, Francis Luther C., 1923
Heil, Charles G., Jr., 1953
Heiland, Louis Otto, 1908
Heileman, Henry, 1893
Heiligman, Nathan, 1933
Heiligman, Raymond, 1936
Heilman, John P., Jr., 1964
Heilman, Russell P., 1876
Heilman, Salem, 1871
Heilmann, Timothy M., 1983
Heim, Hugh Wilson, 1935
Heim, Lyman David, 1903
Heim, William J., 1969
Heim-Rivers, Kathleen, 1986

Heiman, Elliott M., 1963
Heimer, Louis Benjamin, 1905
Heinbach, Robert A., 1942
Heine, William I., 1938
Heineberg, Alfred, 1902
Heinitsh, George W., 1879
Heinitsh, Harry Ernest, 1918
Heinitsh, Heber D., 1875
Heinlein, John Andrew, 1886
Heins, Lawrence Gustavus, 1921
Heintz, John P. E., 1889
Heise, Carl V., S1944
Heise, Herbert vonRohr, 1927
Heiser, Edwin S., 1880
Heiser, Mark S., 1974
Heiser, Victor George, 1897
Heiser, William Henry, 1887
Heisey, William Christian, 1905
Heisey, William G., 1959
Heisler, Frank Joseph, 1903
Heist, George David, 1913
Heister, Joseph Baker, III, 1961
Hekking, Robert J., 1953
Held, Isidore William, 1902
Helden, Gerard Oscar, 1943
Helden, Rudolph A., 1945
Heldman, Irene K., 1986
Heldt, Cynthia A., 1983
Helff, John R., 1947
Helff, Joseph Reuben, 1914
Helfing, Saul H., 1983
Helinek, Thomas G., 1985
Heller, Alvin G., 1971
Heller, Arthur D., 1978
Heller, Bruce, 1977
Heller, Charles Edwin, 1890
Heller, David B., 1947
Heller, Edward Peter, 1916
Heller, Jacob A., 1881
Heller, Jacob Louie, 1892
Heller, James Herbert, 1898
Hellerman, Pamela E., 1984
Hellman, Barry H., 1960
Hellman, Robert Lewis, 1971
Helm, Albert H., 1950
Helm, Amos H., 1868
Helm, Charles E., 1887
Helmick, John Pierpont, 1930
Helmick, Nathaniel David, II, 1962
Helms, David Orville, 1936
Helsper, James T., 1947
Hemeon, Frederick Chipman, 1897
Hemminger, Charles H., 1956
Hemminger, Edward Franklin, 1908
Hemphill, Stuart Price, 1931
Hempstead, Jacob, 1906
Hemsley, Hubert L., 1960
Hench, Anne P., 1975

Hendel, Isadore, 1917
Henderlite, Aubrey Elgin, 1909
Henderson, A. A., 1838
Henderson, Allen W., 1937
Henderson, Andrew J., 1851
Henderson, C. R., 1860
Henderson, Daniel, 1844
Henderson, David F., 1969
Henderson, David Williams, 1912
Henderson, F. B., 1858
Henderson, F. William, 1946
Henderson, Frederick Arthur, 1912
Henderson, Henry G., 1870
Henderson, Ira M., 1917
Henderson, John D.W., 1867
Henderson, Jophanus, 1854
Henderson, Lorenzo N., 1831
Henderson, Matthew, 1835
Henderson, Nat, 1859
Henderson, Pleasant P., 1890
Henderson, Robert James, 1892
Henderson, Rugh A., 1963
Henderson, Samuel, 1873
Henderson, Valerie G., 1978
Henderson, William J., 1848
Henderson, William P., 1955
Hendren, Samuel R., 1850
Hendricks, Augustus William, 1893
Hendricks, Francis Royal, 1924
Hendricks, Walter Jacob, 1931
Hendrickson, Frank Oscar, 1923
Hendrickson, Frank R., 1950
Hendrix, H. Walter, 1854
Hendry, Bowman, 1846
Hendry, Bowman, 1860
Hengst, D. Alfred, 1870
Hengst, Milton A., 1878
Henkelmann, Charles R., 1950
Henlen, Benjamin Augustus, 1887
Henley, John B.D., 1849
Hennemuth, John Henry, 1922
Hennessey, David H., 1971
Henning, Curtis Fisher, 1938
Henning, David M., 1837
Henning, John D., 1878
Henning, William H., 1853
Henrahan, Bernard Elliot, 1897
Henrick, William Robert, 1971
Henrickson, Michael, 1984
Henry, Albert Leon, 1903
Henry, Beverly A., 1852
Henry, Byron, 1897
Henry, Charlton T., 1850
Henry, Clifford Elmore, 1896
Henry, Daniel Webster, 1905
Henry, David H., 1861
Henry, George W., 1885
Henry, George, 1900

Henry, J. Malcolm, 1892
Henry, James W., 1837
Henry, John Cotton, 1929
Henry, John, 1885
Henry, Joseph M., 1983
Henry, Norman W., 1938
Henry, William S.B., 1849
Hensal, Frederick J., 1977
Hensley, Benjamin Jr., 1845
Hensley, Charles Albert, 1917
Henson, Edward Vale, 1943
Henstell, Philip, 1931
Hensyl, George Stanford, 1909
Hensyl, Lewis W., 1886
Hensyl, William Curtis, 1904
Hentosh, John P., 1963
Henyan, E. Lucas, 1894
Henzes, John F., III, 1987
Hepburn, Andrew, 1841
Hepburn, Charles H., 1877
Hepburn, Charles W., 1867
Hepburn, James H., 1886
Hepburn, John, Jr., 1880
Hepler, Albert James, 1886
Hepler, Thomas K., 1941
Hepler, Thomas Robert, 1936
Hepner, Herman S., 1925
Hepperlen, Harry Michael, 1896
Herbein, George Winters, 1902
Herbein, Isaac S., 1865
Herbein, Jonathan S., 1868
Herbein, Milton H., 1879
Herbein, Oscar Batteiger, 1896
Herbert, J. Frederick, 1883
Herbert, Lawrence G., 1985
Herbert, William Dey, 1909
Herbets, Steven S., 1978
Herbst, Frederick W., 1827
Herbst, George Edwin M., 1878
Herbst, Vincent P., 1981
Herbst, William S., Jr., 1855
Herceg, Stephen J., 1957
Herdelin, Nils G., Jr., 1964
Herdocia, Rodolfo F., 1878
Hereford, F. M., 1836
Hereford, Thomas P., 1834
Hereford, Thomas P., Jr., 1860
Herff, Adolph C., 1880
Herff, August F., Jr., 1953
Herff, Augustus F., 1923
Herff, Ferdinand Peter, 1905
Hering, Norton, 1953
Herlocher, James E., 1961
Herman, Charles Bernard, 1923
Herman, Dennis, 1977
Herman, Emery Cline, 1919
Herman, Gregory E., 1988
Herman, Leonard Y., 1978

Herman, Maxwell, 1909
Herman, Robert L., 1979
Hermann, Henry W., 1878
Hermann, Irvin F., 1937
Hermanovich, John, Jr., 1974
Hermanutz, William Henry, 1928
Hermany, Horace David, 1892
Hermany, Paul L., 1952
Hermany, Solomon Lewis, 1919
Hernberg, Joseph Gerald, 1959
Herndon, Charles L. C., 1858
Herndon, Claude N., Jr., 1939
Herndon, James C., 1852
Herndon, Thomas, 1857
Herold, Creston C., Jr., 1979
Herold, Kevan C., 1979
Herpst, Sally L., 1978
Herr, Ambrose J., 1861
Herr, Benjamin F., 1877
Herr, David R., 1958
Herr, Francis C., 1879
Herr, Henry F., 1848
Herrero, J. Augustine, 1882
Herrick, George H., 1861
Herrick, J. Everette, 1851
Herrick, Wayne C., 1981
Herrick, William C., 1947
Herrine, Gail M., 1987
Herrine, Steven Kenneth, 1990
Herring, George N., 1915
Herring, Steven J., 1985
Herrington, C. P., 1859
Herriott, John V., 1836
Herriott, Walter Hays, 1908
Herrman, John C., 1953
Herrmann, Francis, 1853
Herrmann, William J., 1977
Herrold, Warren C., S1944
Herron, Charles R., 1879
Herron, James Robert, Jr., 1940
Herron, John Thomas, 1884
Herron, Levi R., 1856
Hersh, Carol B., 1969
Hershberger, David G., 1981
Hershe, Christian, 1851
Hershey, Beverly L., 1980
Hershey, Edgar Parker, 1888
Hershey, Emanuel R., 1880
Hershey, Joseph H., 1853
Hershey, Joseph Ivan, 1932
Hershey, M. Landis, 1883
Hershey, Stephen L., 1968
Hershiser, A. Emmet, 1884
Hersohn, William Wolf, 1933
Hertel, Emil, 1883
Hertel, Frederick, 1884
Hertzler, William Crooks, 1894
Hertzog, Francis J., 1960

Herwig, Karl R., 1961
Hesch, Joseph Anthony, 1934
Hess, Adolph, 1903
Hess, Deborah K., 1982
Hess, J. Bruce, 1893
Hess, J. Clair, 1983
Hess, J. W., 1873
Hess, John M., 1960
Hess, Joseph B., 1957
Hess, Joseph Carbaugh, 1924
Hess, Louis T., 1895
Hess, Paul Richard, 1929
Hessen, Margaret T., 1982
Hessen, Scott E., 1982
Hesser, Charles Le Grand, 1889
Hester, John E., III, 1957
Hester, William Shepherd, 1926
Hester, William Weir, 1873
Heston, Abiah P., 1850
Heston, Eber H., 1877
Hetherington, John, 1909
Hetherington, John, Jr., 1960
Hetick, Andrew, 1836
Hetrich, George Roberts, 1923
Hetrich, George, 1885
Hetrick, David Joseph, 1897
Hetrick, Matthew Adam, 1942
Hetrick, Thomas J., 1976
Hetzell, David G., 1861
Heuler, Leo, 1913
Heulings, J. W., Jr., 1869
Heuston, Paul B., 1946
Hewitt, Archie Edelen, 1908
Hewitt, Charles Ellsworth, 1891
Hewitt, Clarence B., J1944
Hewitt, George A., 1877
Hewlett, Guy S., 1985
Hewlett, John O., 1955
Hewson, Addinell, 1850
Hewson, Addinell, Jr., 1879
Hewson, George F., Jr., 1958
Heyde, Jacob Meyers, 1900
Heym, Herbert H., 1969
Heymach, George J., III, 1976
Heyser, Jonas Edward, 1903
Heysham, Horace Besson, 1900
Heysham, Stewart Chas., 1883
Heysinger, I. W., 1867
Heysinger, James Downey, 1901
Heyward, James F., 1851
Hezlep, William B., 1854
Hiatt, Gerald A., 1968
Hice, Edward C., 1879
Hickerson, James, 1856
Hickey, Daniel, Jr., 1953
Hickey, Denise M., 1989
Hickey, Eugene H., 1870
Hickey, Francis Solano, 1924

Hickey, John Solano, 1951
Hickey, Joseph J., 1985
Hickey, Robert W., 1985
Hickey, Stefano Joseph, 1888
Hickey, Thomas Bernard, 1894
Hickman, Charles N., 1947
Hickman, James W., 1879
Hickman, Joseph, 1829
Hickman, Joseph T., 1859
Hickman, Thomas Elwood, 1896
Hickman, William H., 1881
Hicks, Edwin S., 1854
Hicks, Margaret, 1905
Hicks, Richard E., 1955
Hicks, Virginius H., 1852
Hicks, Vonnie Monroe, 1918
Hicks, Vonnie Monroe, Jr., 1952
Hicks, William Morse, 1914
Hicks, William Wynne, Jr., 1953
Hidden, William Buffet, 1862
Hieber, G. Frederick, 1937
Hiehle, J. Frederick, 1960
Hierholzer, John Charles, 1888
Hiester, William LaRoy, 1919
Higbee, Hugh H., 1828
Higbee, William S., 1883
Higday, Thompkins, 1852
Higgins, Charles B., 1967
Higgins, Eugene Victor, 1942
Higgins, Richard M., 1865
Higgins, Richard T., 1867
Higgins, Samuel J., 1861
Higgins, William F., 1859
Higgs, Thomas F., 1835
High, Bertrand J., II, 1976
High, Carl Milton, 1928
High, David A., 1981
High, Isaac Beidler, 1910
High, John David, 1940
Highsmith, Jacob Franklin, 1889
Highsmith, James DaCosta, 1918
Hight, William Boyd, 1895
Hightower, Charley Counce, 1910
Hilaman, Brad L., 1976
Hilbish, Daniel J., 1847
Hildebrand, Walter Junius, 1896
Hildenbrand, Louis W., 1874
Hilderman, Walter C., Jr., 1942
Hildreth, Eugenius A., 1886
Hildreth, Isaac F., 1856
Hildreth, John A., 1965
Hile, Harry Eugene, Jr., 1943
Hilferty, Daniel Joseph, Jr., 1943
Hill, A. Chandler, 1853
Hill, A. Lewis, 1868
Hill, Alonzo A.F., 1848
Hill, Ambrose B., 1849
Hill, Anthony John, 1896

Hill, Ben Spalding, 1921
Hill, Charles H., 1835
Hill, Cynthia A., 1987
Hill, David I., 1957
Hill, David W., 1984
Hill, Edward Roland, 1924
Hill, Frank P., 1876
Hill, Franklyn C., Jr., 1950
Hill, Franklyn Chapman, 1915
Hill, George, 1838
Hill, George A., 1870
Hill, George Wright, 1906
Hill, Gideon D., III, 1983
Hill, Horace G., 1882
Hill, Howard Henry, 1867
Hill, J. Mark, 1948
Hill, J. Ward, 1857
Hill, J. Willis, 1881
Hill, Jacob F., 1885
Hill, James S., 1844
Hill, James W., 1878
Hill, John Boadley, 1887
Hill, John Bostwick, Jr., 1910
Hill, John Edwin, 1845
Hill, John Emmett, 1897
Hill, John Sturgeon, 1896
Hill, John, 1856
Hill, John, 1866
Hill, Joseph, 1855
Hill, Kenneth O., 1983
Hill, Lafayette, 1854
Hill, Lauriston H., 1861
Hill, Luther L., 1882
Hill, Richard J., 1875
Hill, Richard W., 1953
Hill, Robert G., Jr., 1980
Hill, Robert T., 1865
Hill, Russell S., 1883
Hill, T. Benton, 1875
Hill, W. B., 1869
Hill, Walter B., 1864
Hill, Walter de la M., 1900
Hill, William Adam, 1919
Hill, William Henry, 1845
Hill, William Reed, 1952
Hill, William, 1856
Hillard, James Pearse, 1903
Hilleary, John W., 1854
Hillegass, Eugene Z., 1880
Hillemeyer, William Anton, 1896
Hiller, Tyrie L. J., 1980
Hiller, W. D. B., 1981
Hilliard, Charles Eugene, 1888
Hilliard, G. Himes, 1872
Hilliard, Walter Lewis, 1895
Hilliard, William D., 1878
Hillig, John Edward, Jr., 1962
Hillis, William J., 1868

Hillman Richard E., 1849
Hillsman, George Albert, 1888
Hillsman, John A., 1859
Hillsman, William H., 1848
Hilly, Joseph Francis, 1910
Hillyard, Raymond W., Jr., 1981
Hillyer, Eben, 1854
Hilt, William, 1884
Hilton, E. Bruce, 1973
Hiltz, Deborah J., 1977
Himes, Bower Edwin, 1895
Himes, Ralph F., Jr., 1954
Himes, Ralph Francis, 1923
Himmelwright, Francis E., 1878
Hinchman, B., 1855
Hinckle, Millard Goodrich, 1896
Hinckley, Livingston S., 1921
Hinckley, Walter F., 1877
Hindle, Frank Lawton, Jr., 1937
Hindle, Joseph A., 1940
Hindman, Charles C., 1876
Hinds, S. Houston, 1860
Hine, Francis W., 1836
Hine, Marks Priestly, 1888
Hine, Thomas C., 1839
Hinebaugh, Mahlon Carleton, Jr., 1928
Hiner, Fred T., 1877
Hines, Andrew J., 1853
Hines, Eben P., 1874
Hines, Harvey L., 1859
Hines, William H., 1859
Hinkel, William Henry, 1908
Hinkle, James E., 1967
Hinkley, Seth Bradbury, 1890
Hinks, Robert P., 1982
Hinkson, John F., 1856
Hinkson, William James, 1932
Hinman, Louis Franklin, 1938
Hinrichs, Robert A., 1954
Hinton, Rufus K., 1852
Hipple, Percy, Jr., 1933
Hipps, Allen G. H., 1916
Hirokawa, Ronald H., 1971
Hirons, Robert S. Warren, 1857
Hirsch, Charles Sol, 1901
Hirsch, Henry Leon, 1906
Hirsch, Leon, 1896
Hirsch, Nathan B., 1965
Hirschfield, Bernard, A., 1926
Hirschy, James C., 1964
Hirsh, A. Bern, 1882
Hirsh, Philip R., Jr., 1964
Hirshland, Harold, 1919
Hirst, Cyrus J., 1850
Hirst, Ernest Reed, 1918
Hirst, Jesse Watson, 1893
Hirst, Levi Brook, 1894
Hislop, John, 1892

Hitch, John W., 1854
Hitch, Victor Elmer, 1896
Hitch, William S., 1861
Hitchcock, Alfred 1845
Hitchcock, Enos P., 1835
Hitchens, Elethea Marion, 1966
Hitchner, Charles F., 1867
Hitchner, James C., 1951
Hite, Benjamin H., 1859
Hitt, Willis M., 1855
Hittell, Randolph S., 1870
Hittle, Benjamin F., 1864
Hixson, George William, 1903
Hlavac, Cheryl A., 1984
Hneleski, Ignatius S., Jr., 1964
Hneleski, Ignatius Stanley, 1928
Ho, Albert Kam Tai, 1942
Hoadley, Robert, 1865
Hoag, Harry Martin, 1894
Hoagland, Garret G., 1884
Hoagland, George Bradford, 1895
Hoard, Robert L., 1859
Hoban, Henry, 1838
Hoban, James John, 1907
Hobaugh, David C., 1877
Hobbs, Barbara A., 1979
Hobbs, Harry Kane, 1917
Hobbs, Joseph H., 1956
Hobbs, Robert E., 1931
Hobbs, Robert E., 1974
Hoberman, Edward, 1934
Hoberman, Louis Karl, 1929
Hoberman, Maury, 1960
Hobgood, James Edward, 1907
Hobson, George Fearn, 1856
Hobson, Richard B., 1836
Hobson, Samuel A., 1848
Hobson, William Heverin, 1895
Hoch, Bradley R., 1974
Hoch, John J., 1955
Hoch, John R., II, , 1983
Hock, Howard E., 1960
Hockaday, William L., 1866
Hocutt, John E., Jr., 1975
Hodas, Sidney M., 1936
Hodes, Barton L., 1966
Hodge, Beth Orringer, 1977
Hodge, James R., 1950
Hodge, Joseph, 1952
Hodge, Thomas Ashton, 1954
Hodgens, Isaac Walter, 1894
Hodgens, Samuel G., 1866
Hodges, John H., 1939
Hodges, Wyllys Royce, III, 1966
Hodges, Wyllys Royce, Jr., 1931
Hodgson, Michael Aloysius, 1920
Hoellein, Kenneth D., 1978
Hoerner, Kathleen M., 1984

Hoerner, Oscar G., 1952
Hoerner, Ralph W., 1935
Hoey, James W., 1856
Hofer, Clarence Andreas, 1899
Hofer, Clarence John M., 1928
Hofer, William Robb, 1934
Hoff, Alexander Henry, 1845
Hoff, William S., 1986
Hoffa, Jacob P., 1876
Hoffecker, Robert Crockett, 1894
Hoffman, Arthur F., 1941
Hoffman, Charles I., 1870
Hoffman, Charles S., 1877
Hoffman, Charles W., 1935
Hoffman, Charles Wilbur, 1903
Hoffman, Christian N., 1862
Hoffman, Clarence, 1906
Hoffman, David F., 1990
Hoffman, David, 1932
Hoffman, Edward Almond, 1896
Hoffman, Elmer, E. M., 1892
Hoffman, George Llewellyn, 1904
Hoffman, Gilbert M., 1948
Hoffman, Glen H., 1954
Hoffman, Gregory A., 1977
Hoffman, Harry H., Jr., 1952
Hoffman, J. David, 1956
Hoffman, J. M., 1858
Hoffman, J. R., 1858
Hoffman, Jacob, 1925
Hoffman, James A., 1881
Hoffman, Jamie L., 1981
Hoffman, Jeffrey Mark, 1990
Hoffman, John Hugo, 1881
Hoffman, John Y., 1880
Hoffman, Joseph Francis, 1932
Hoffman, Lewis Albert, Jr., 1943
Hoffman, Olin Huntley, 1891
Hoffman, Philip C., 1972
Hoffman, Richards Holmes, 1928
Hoffman, Ripley C., 1883
Hoffman, Robert H., 1859
Hoffman, Ronald A., 1971
Hoffman, Susan D., 1989
Hoffman, Walter J., 1866
Hoffman, William F., 1854
Hoffman, William Wallace, 1895
Hoffmann, Joseph H., 1883
Hoffmaster, Alfred L., 1936
Hofford, James M., 1952
Hofmann, Kurt P., 1986
Hofmann, Lawrence V., 1968
Hofmann, Michael P., 1977
Hofmann, Oscar Elmer, 1891
Hogan, Henry William, Jr., 1946
Hogdon, Richard L., 1852
Hoge, Arthur Kenworthy, 1914
Hoge, Thomas Rogers, 1923

Hoge, Vane Morgan, 1928
Hogendobler, Israel, 1864
Hogg, Thomas D., 1847
Hogsett, Robert Fuller, 1927
Hogue, Davis A., 1875
Hogue, John Daniel, 1905
Hogue, Rebecca Manning, 1990
Hohl, Joseph C., 1963
Hohman, George Charles, 1932
Hoidal, Charles R., 1982
Hoke, Augustus D., 1857
Hoke, Martin, 1881
Holbert, Walter W., 1882
Holbrook, Arthur Gilbert, 1899
Holbrook, Charles N., 1871
Holbrook, Clark Bates, 1905
Holbrook, William S., 1851
Holcomb, Charles Milo, 1887
Holcomb, Guy Carleton, 1887
Holcomb, Joel Theodore, 1909
Holcombe, Charles Haight, 1901
Holcombe, Hugh W., 1846
Holdcraft, John W., 1956
Holdcraft-Sherrard, Suzanne, 1983
Holden, Newell E., 1883
Holden, William Benjamin, 1945
Holder, Charles Adams, 1897
Holderman, Herbert Helmuth, 1916
Holdsworth, Charles M., 1980
Holland, Daniel J., 1876
Holland, Ebe, 1890
Holland, Edward F., 1953
Holland, Eugene Amos, 1929
Holland, George, 1886
Holland, James W., 1868
Holland, Lemuel C., 1836
Holland, Robert H., S1944
Holland, Thomas Walter, 1857
Holland, Timothy W., 1979
Holland, William T., Jr., 1955
Hollander, Arnold I., 1962
Hollander, George, 1939
Hollander, Irwin J., 1972
Holleman, Charles Edward, Jr., 1932
Hollenbach, Theodore F., 1866
Hollenback, David S., 1882
Hollenback, Jacob S., 1874
Hollendonner, Werner J., 1953
Holley, Chesterfield James, 1922
Holliday, John Wesley, 1892
Hollifield, Horatis N., 1854
Hollingsworth, Edwin F., 1857
Hollingsworth, John B., 1880
Hollingsworth, Robert B., 1902
Hollinsworth, Joseph, 1847
Hollinsworth, William R., 1867
Holloway, Anita M., 1986
Holloway, Thomas P., 1859

Hollywood, James Leonard, 1929
Holm, Alf Justin, 1924
Holman, Albert, 1881
Holman, Charles Sherman, 1919
Holman, Henry W., 1855
Holman, J. C., 1856
Holman, James A., 1879
Holman, John N., 1858
Holman, Paul D., 1968
Holman, Theodore Long, 1945
Holman, Wilgus Alexander, 1923
Holman, William A., 1857
Holman, William B., 1950
Holman, William P., 1854
Holmberg, Carl Edward, 1908
Holmes, Andrew Byron, 1910
Holmes, Arthur E., 1933
Holmes, Benjamin Henry, 1894
Holmes, Henry J., 1854
Holmes, J., 1869
Holmes, John Williams, 1908
Holmes, Joses B.S., 1877
Holmes, R. S., 1838
Holmes, Thomas M., 1882
Holmes, William E., 1879
Holmes, William F., 1968
Holmes, William Frederick, Jr., 1930
Holsburg, Daniel B., 1878
Holshue, Charles Raymond, 1891
Holsinger, Paul G., 1928
Holstein, James J., 1967
Holsten, Steven B., 1967
Holston, John G.F., Jr., 1867
Holston, John George F., Jr., 1903
Holt, Alfred C., 1842
Holt, Camillus I., 1885
Holt, Cicero 1850
Holt, Duncan Waldo, 1918
Holt, Hiram Allen, 1896
Holt, Lloyd Mott, 1911
Holt, M. Quincy, 1849
Holt, Mathew S., 1877
Holt, William F., 1857
Holt, William Preston, 1895
Holt, William Preston, Jr., 1926
Holterman, Robert K., 1983
Holton, Henry C., 1883
Holtz, Kenneth Jastram, 1912
Holverson, Harmon E., 1953
Holzman, Jerome Leopold, 1921
Holzsager, David J., 1971
Homan, John C., 1854
Homel, Steven R., 1961
Homer, Robert W., 1951
Homet, Volney, 1856
Honigman, Joseph, 1962
Honsberg, Angelica E., 1989
Hoobler, Randall J., 1985

Hood, Arch John, 1918
Hood, Christopher K., 1954
Hood, George B., 1939
Hood, Henry H., Jr., 1966
Hood, Humphrey H., 1851
Hood, John Sidney, 1907
Hood, Joseph Turner, 1865
Hood, Renwick C., 1981
Hood, Richard French, 1865
Hood, S. W., 1830
Hood, Thomas C., 1884
Hood, Thomas M., 1880
Hook, William F., 1961
Hoon, Anthony Wilber, 1902
Hooper, Donald, 1960
Hooper, Fred Badman, 1937
Hooper, John W., 1884
Hooper, Joseph Roberts, 1966
Hooper, Philo O., 1856
Hoopes, Charles Wilson, 1893
Hoopes, Timothy G., 1988
Hoopingarner, George P., 1888
Hoover, Alan D., 1973
Hoover, Albert M., 1874
Hoover, Albert, 1884
Hoover, Andrew Jefferson, 1887
Hoover, Andrew S., 1854
Hoover, Daniel Henry, 1888
Hoover, David W., 1860
Hoover, George J., 1849
Hoover, George W., 1858
Hoover, Nicholas M., 1865
Hoover, Percy Linn, 1895
Hoover, Todd A., 1984
Hope, Jesse P., 1851
Hope, John F., 1852
Hope, John Ferguson, 1904
Hope, Walter Geddes, 1886
Hopen, Joseph M., 1949
Hopen, Gary R., 1977
Hopen, Joseph M., 1949
Hopkins, Abram C., 1879
Hopkins, B. Scott, 1853
Hopkins, Benjamin C., 1855
Hopkins, Benjamin F., 1855
Hopkins, Benjamin T., 1981
Hopkins, Ellwood E., 1870
Hopkins, Frederick Miller, 1909
Hopkins, Howard H., 1837
Hopkins, Howard R., 1882
Hopkins, James A., 1859
Hopkins, James Alfred, 1858
Hopkins, James T., 1980
Hopkins, Joseph, 1843
Hopkins, Maurice Albert, 1926
Hopkins, Robert Black, 1887
Hopkins, Scott Bruce, 1897
Hopkins, Thomas B., 1854

Hopkins, Wallace Eckley, 1930
Hopper, Bruce D., 1965
Hopper, Gayle A., 1985
Hopper, Harry C., 1879
Hopper, Thomas Thompson, 1889
Hoppin, Samuel B., 1852
Hopping, Daniel S., 1852
Hopson, Joseph, 1870
Hopwood, George Black, 1906
Hopwood, Herbert G., Jr., 1958
Hopwood, Lucius Locke, 1904
Hopwood, William H., 1877
Hopwood, William Hudson, 1906
Horan, Austin Joseph, 1942
Hore, Walter, 1848
Horewitz, James S., 1961
Horgan, Kelly A., 1987
Horger, Ulrich Peter, 1916
Horhovitz, George Isaac, 1935
Horine, Arlington Grove, 1890
Horine, Dewey Grove, 1921
Horinstein, Joseph Benjamin, 1901
Horn, Edward T., 1940
Horn, George Frederick, 1914
Horn, Harry Y., 1879
Horn, Leonard, 1932
Horn, Paul C., 1956
Horn, Wallace Lincoln, 1895
Hornback, William, 1860
Horne, Benjamin W., 1901
Horne, John H., 1891
Horne, Smith Hamill, 1901
Horner, Daniel W., Jr., 1963
Horner, Earl Hartle, 1902
Horner, James Wallace, 1877
Horner, Myers Worman, 1896
Horner, S. H., 1858
Horner, William R., 1967
Hornick, Leo William, 1912
Horning, Frank, 1896
Horning, Samuel B., 1884
Horning, William H., 1902
Hornor, Caleb W., 1849
Hornor, Joseph H., 1866
Horovitz, Morris Thomas, 1932
Horowitz, Glenn D., 1979
Horowitz, Sandra W., 1976
Horowitz, Steven L., 1975
Horrigan, Arthur Joseph, 1916
Horst, H. Mathilda, 1974
Horstmann, Joseph P., 1972
Hort, William M.W., 1835
Horting, Levi W., 1886
Horton, David J., 1988
Horton, George Ralph, 1915
Horton, Harry M., 1835
Horton, Park Martin, 1932
Horton, Samuel M., 1861

Horton, Terry L., 1987
Horton, Vern H., 1964
Horvath, David Addis, 1990
Horvath, Ronald J., 1964
Horvick, David, 1982
Horwell, Richard J., 1931
Horwitz, Lloyd N., 1882
Horwitz, Louis, 1906
Horwitz, Orville, 1883
Horwitz, Theodore, 1876
Hosack, John P., 1849
Hosack, William, 1874
Hosay, John J., 1943
Hosford-Skapof, Martha A., 1984
Hoskins, John R., 1844
Hoskins, John R., III, J1944
Hoskins, John Robinson, 1905
Hoskins, Percy C., 1875
Hoskins, William, 1855
Hoss, Archibald C., 1875
Hostetter, Abram M., 1957
Hostetter, H. Glenn, 1960
Hostetter, Herman H., 1923
Hostetter, Robert Davis, 1916
Hotchkiss, Sterne, 1842
Hottenstein, Austin C.L., 1871
Hottenstein, Charles Augustus, 1895
Hottenstein, Cyrus D., 1848
Hottenstein, Edward, 1853
Hottenstein, Edward Lewis, 1886
Hottenstein, Elmer K., 1883
Hottenstein, H. Percival, 1845
Hottenstein, William Jacob, 1889
Hottle, Edwin B., 1874
Houck, Earl E., Jr., 1938
Houck, George William, 1943
Houck, Oscar, 1896
Houck, Virgil Lydic, 1952
Hough, Charles B., 1878
Hough, Charles E., S1944
Hough, Charles L., 1883
Hough, De Witt C., 1847
Hough, Douglas R., 1979
Hough, Frank P., 1884
Hough, H. Page, 1878
Hough, Ralph C., 1920
Hough, Thomas A., 1879
Hough, Thomas L., 1856
House, Wooster Hassell, 1915
Householder, Merchant C., 1888
Housekeeper, Philip B., 1868
Housel, Edmund Llewellyn, 1935
Houseman, William W., 1875
Houser, Angela Grace, 1990
Houser, Ben P., Jr., 1963
Houser, Benjamin P., 1934
Houser, Cyrus G., 1964
Houser, James J., 1964

Housman, J. Harold, 1956
Housman, Nathan Samuel, 1919
Houston, Armstrong P., 1854
Houston, Bernard John, 1938
Houston, David Henry, 1842
Houston, Isaac N., 1880
Houston, John, 1855
Houston, Joseph Willis, 1857
Houston, Robert Alexander, 1929
Houston, Robert R., 1942
Houston, Robert R., Jr., 1975
Houston, Vernon Frederick, 1924
Houston, William M., Jr., 1984
Houts, John A., 1871
Houtz, Abraham, 1848
Houtz, Daniel, 1834
Houtz, Henry, 1840
Howaley, William M., 1887
Howanitz, E. Paul, 1978
Howanitz, Emil, S1944
Howard, Edward Stephen, 1896
Howard, Edward W. S., 1894
Howard, Harold Melnotte, 1905
Howard, James David, 1920
Howard, James Harold, 1910
Howard, James T., Jr., 1959
Howard, John E., 1843
Howard, John Edgar, 1901
Howard, Lawrence J., 1972
Howard, LeRoy Downey, 1906
Howard, LeRoy Spangler, 1910
Howard, M., 1869
Howard, Nelson W., 1848
Howard, Randolph N., 1879
Howard, Robert G., 1857
Howard, Stephen, 1966
Howard, Thomas Henry, 1861
Howard, Thomas K., 1960
Howard, William A., 1854
Howard, William H., 1837
Howard, William Travis, 1844
Howd, Salmon Giddings, 1883
Howden, Richard F., 1960
Howe, Barbara Jeanne, 1986
Howe, Jesse Burket, 1907
Howe, John K., Jr., 1964
Howe, Llewellyn Oscar, 1898
Howe, Robert Gerard, 1943
Howe, William L., 1956
Howe, William L., 1982
Howe, William R., 1856
Howell, A. Alexander, 1841
Howell, Aaron, 1887
Howell, Andrew Rufus, 1887
Howell, Elmer Ellsworth, 1889
Howell, George H., 1848
Howell, John T., 1881
Howell, Park, 1898

Howell, Richard L., 1879
Howell, Samuel McKeehan, 1903
Howell, Samuel T., 1871
Howell, Thomas W., 1937
Howell, William Harrison, 1867
Howell, William Murdock, 1932
Howells, Thomas J., 1910
Howerton, William H., 1857
Howes, Daniel L., 1864
Howeth, V. A., 1873
Howitt, John, 1851
Howitt, William H., 1870
Howland, David R., 1846
Howze, Henry Y., 1853
Hoy, William S., 1879
Hoyer, Paul J., 1976
Hoyle, Harry French, 1915
Hoyt, Augustus B., 1852
Hoyt, Dorsey Raymond, 1934
Hoyt, Francis Russell, 1915
Hoyt, John Jay, 1846
Hoyt, Moses C., 1850
Hoyt, Ralph C., 1933
Hoyt, Theodore E., 1879
Hoyt, William D., 1854
Hresko, Michael B., 1960
Hryshko, Frank G., 1972
Hu, Da-Shih, 1980
Huang, Janice, 1986
Huang, Marian M., 1982
Hubbard, Charles Calvin, 1888
Hubbard, Charles Crow, 1930
Hubbard, Frederick Cecil, 1918
Hubbard, J. Clark, 1880
Hubbard, John Parkinson, Jr., 1893
Hubbard, Lex Walter, 1911
Hubbard, Russell B., 1827
Hubbell, S. J., 1856
Huber, Harry Jonas, 1909
Huber, Levi, 1884
Huber, Richard Lumley, 1948
Huber, Samuel Senseny, 1865
Hudacek, Albert Andrew, 1924
Huddell, Benjamin Raymond, 1961
Hudders, Alva Lorraine, 1886
Hudders, Clarence, 1880
Hudders, George W., 1856
Hudders, James W., 1841
Hudders, John S., 1879
Hudelson, Lucius Rollin, 1896
Hudgens, Thomas A., 1859
Hudgings, John C., 1874
Hudock, George E., Jr., 1958
Hudock, Jude A., 1988
Hudson, Clement L., 1852
Hudson, Elmer Alexander, 1888
Hudson, Floyd Isaac, 1932
Hudson, Gilbert L., 1859

Hudson, Harry, Jr., 1903
Hudson, James A, 1830
Hudson, Joseph Charles, 1929
Hudson, Leonard A., 1885
Hudson, Lyell E., 1878
Hudson, Mark E., 1988
Hudson, Robert B., 1850
Hudson, Robert J., 1940
Hudson, William Evans, 1930
Hudson, William M., 1855
Huebener, Walter A.M., 1870
Huebner, Dewees A.W., 1886
Huebner, George William, 1893
Huey, George B., 1853
Huey, James E., 1846
Huff, Charles W., 1949
Huff, Isaac, 1863
Huff, John Melville, 1917
Huff, John Thompson, 1894
Huff, Junius K., 1894
Huff, Scott M., 1893
Huffard, Robert S., 1984
Huffman, Charles R., 1951
Huffman, D. Clark, 1866
Huffman, Frederick, 1868
Huffman, George W., 1894
Huffman, John M., 1870
Huffman, Lucius D., 1885
Huffman, Obad. Layton, 1894
Huffman, William Veloss, 1887
Huffnagle, Frederic T., 1961
Huffnagle, Milford J., II, 1989
Huffnagle, Vera Hentosh, 1989
Hufnal-Miller, Carrie A., 1984
Hug, Edward Victor, 1893
Hug, John Joseph, 1890
Hugg, Arthur A., 1883
Hugg, Joseph, 1861
Huggins, George A., 1852
Huggins, Hermon H., 1852
Hughes, Brady Alexander, 1927
Hughes, Brice M., 1868
Hughes, Dan E., 1878
Hughes, David P., 1972
Hughes, Edgar Lee, 1909
Hughes, Ephraim Georgia, 1907
Hughes, Eugene P., 1948
Hughes, Eugene P., Jr., 1975
Hughes, George H., 1967
Hughes, George W., 1845
Hughes, Harry F., 1987
Hughes, Henry A., 1881
Hughes, Herman Clyde, 1912
Hughes, Howard G., 1974
Hughes, Isaac, 1839
Hughes, James T., 1960
Hughes, Jay M., 1958
Hughes, John C., 1871

Hughes, John Edward, 1948
Hughes, John G., 1853
Hughes, Joseph F., 1935
Hughes, Joseph, 1910
Hughes, Lee Westlake, 1916
Hughes, Louie B., 1902
Hughes, M. B., 1869
Hughes, Michael J., 1883
Hughes, Philip C., 1958
Hughes, R., 1869
Hughes, Roger Lott, 1942
Hughes, Samuel C., Jr., 1975
Hughes, Thomas I., 1850
Hughes, Vincent C., 1924
Hughes, W. Eugene, 1878
Hughes, William F., 1948
Hughes, William Lloyd, 1932
Hughson, Walter, 1846
Huhn, Wolfgang A., 1972
Hulick, Peter R., 1973
Hulick, Peter Vaughn, 1936
Hulkower, Stephen D., 1981
Hull, A. P., 1873
Hull, Elmer S., 1884
Hull, Howard Lane, 1908
Hull, John A., 1859
Hull, Levi, 1833
Hull, Paul J., 1963
Hull, Robert Lord, 1902
Hull, Thomas R., 1838
Hullihen, M. F., 1870
Hulse, John I., 1859
Hulshizer, Allen H., 1878
Hulsizer, Green Robbins, 1887
Hultsch-Smith, Sara E., 1984
Hume, Douglas P., 1980
Hume, Evan Borroum, 1929
Hume, Quintus R., 1855
Hume, William, 1851
Hume., Charles E., 1849
Humes, James J., 1948
Hummel, C. Carroll, 1877
Hummel, Mark J., 1985
Hummel, Merwin Lester, 1925
Hummer, Charles D., III, 1989
Humphrey, Henry Moore, 1842
Humphrey, Isaac, 1926
Humphrey, John B., Jr., 1968
Humphrey, Walter Newton, 1893
Humphrey, William F., 1854
Humphreys, Benjamin W., 1848
Humphreys, George H., 1856
Humphreys, George L., 1874
Humphreys, James P., 1856
Humphreys, John Charles, 1910
Humphreys, Joseph D., 1846
Humphries, S. Osceola, 1885
Hundley, John M., 1849

Hunker, Susan L., 1978
Hunn, Richard Hayes, 1990
Hunsberger, William E., 1867
Hunsberger, William Henry, 1893
Hunsicker, Charles Heil, 1900
Hunsicker, Philip M., 1954
Hunsicker, Sarah, 1904
Hunsinger, David A., 1983
Hunt, Clifton H., 1974
Hunt, Daniel, 1912
Hunt, David G., 1855
Hunt, E. K., 1838
Hunt, J. Spofford, 1856
Hunt, James G., 1871
Hunt, James Lemoin, 1882
Hunt, John T., 1857
Hunt, L. C., 1871
Hunt, Melvin Mundy, 1915
Hunt, Sylvester H., 1865
Hunt, Thomas W., 1894
Hunt, William Henry, 1855
Hunt, William T., Jr., 1927
Hunter, Allen De Turk, 1884
Hunter, Cassius F., 1871
Hunter, Charles J., 1860
Hunter, David, 1878
Hunter, Duke W., 1854
Hunter, George Baxter, 1851
Hunter, George W., 1860
Hunter, Herbert Kingsley, 1893
Hunter, Herbert S., S1944
Hunter, Horatio D., 1859
Hunter, James M., 1953
Hunter, John C., 1853
Hunter, John C., 1868
Hunter, John Pullen, 1919
Hunter, Joseph William, 1893
Hunter, Marcus Catlin, 1892
Hunter, R. P., 1869
Hunter, Randal R., 1876
Hunter, Robert G., 1950
Hunter, Samuel B., 1855
Hunter, Samuel M., 1853
Hunter, Stephen A., 1878
Hunter, Terry W., 1987
Hunter, Theophilus W., 1876
Hunter, Thomas S., 1866
Hunter, W. G., 1870
Hunter, William, 1836
Hunter, William L., 1868
Hunter, William M., 1837
Hunter, William R., 1848
Hunter, Winfield S., 1883
Huntington, Christopher Fell, 1990
Huntington, Park W. Jr., 1949
Huntington, T. Roomeyn, 1851
Huntington, William Dresser, 1886
Huntley, Arthur C., Jr., 1955

Huntley, Oscar Hamilton, 1856
Hunton, George W., 1847
Huntsman, Edwin S., 1886
Hupp, John C., 1847
Hurd, Frank H., 1885
Hurd, Michael E., 1883
Hurdle, Samuel Walker, 1914
Hurff, J. Wallace, 1913
Hurff, Joseph E., 1881
Hurford, William D., 1878
Hurley, Harry J. Jr., 1949
Hurley, Michael Joseph, Jr., 1931
Hurlock, Frank I., 1881
Hurowitz, Bertram D., 1958
Hurowitz, Gerald I., 1984
Hursh, Alexander Miller W., 1923
Hursh, Dale K., 1989
Hursh, George R., 1857
Hurst, Denison A., 1878
Hurst, Lloyd, 1921
Hurst, N. N., 1873
Hurt, Ira Huff, 1919
Hurt, Munford B., 1854
Hurt, P. L., 1867
Hurtt, Mark R., 1981
Hurvitz, Lawrence M., 1975
Hurwitz, Abraham, 1938
Hurwitz, Herbert I., 1988
Hurwitz, Isadore, 1920
Hurwitz, Nathaniel, 1925
Huselton, Elmer C., 1884
Hushion, William F., 1960
Husler, Edward G., 1881
Hussey, Howard S., Jr., 1942
Hussong, Wallace B., S1944
Hustead, Ashbel F., 1885
Hustead, Frank Humbert, 1911
Husted, Francis B., 1886
Huston, Charles, 1842
Huston, Frank Brady, 1891
Huston, James M., 1851
Huston, John M., 1863
Huston, Joseph H., 1866
Huston, Robert M., 1854
Huston, Samuel Wesley, 1917
Hutchins, Adrian Albertus, 1893
Hutchins, Edward R., 1866
Hutchins, Theophilus S., 1832
Hutchinson, Douglas T., 1984
Hutchinson, Howard G., 1987
Hutchinson, James B., 1837
Hutchinson, James H.S., 1878
Hutchinson, Thomas A., 1978
Hutchinson, Thomas D., 1847
Hutchinson, William James, 1929
Hutchison, James C., 1952
Hutchison, Lloyd Snyder, 1930
Hutchison, Wilber Laurin, 1891

Hutchison, Wilber Laurin, 1923
Huttenlock, Robert Edelman, 1906
Hutzel, Oliver L., 1903
Hutzell, Jacob C., 1877
Huxster, Howard Knight, 1952
Huxster, Robert H., 1978
Huyett, Herman J., 1885
Huyett, Robert P.R., 1878
Huzza, Thomas Harry, 1887
Hyatt, Frederick Carlyle, 1907
Hyatt, Glenn A., 1978
Hyde, John H., 1850
Hyde, Nathan D., 1877
Hyde, Patrice, M., 1980
Hyde, William J., 1972
Hydrick, John Lee, 1915
Hyer, Grainger, 1876
Hyett, Joseph, 1843
Hyett, Marvin R., 1963
Hyland, Bernard V., 1950
Hyman, Isaac Charles, 1926
Hyman, Jacob George, 1934
Hyman, Paul S., 1962
Hymovich, Leo, 1929
Hyndman, Samuel E., 1866
Hynson, Garrett Lee, 1911
Hyskell, William Emory, 1903

~ I ~

Iacuzzo, John C., 1971
Iames, William P., 1954
Iannone, Angelo B., 1938
Iannotta, Patricia N., 1989
Iannuzzi, Peter J., 1937
Ibach, Frederick G., 1879
Ickes, George Albert, 1886
Ifft, F. Nicholas, 1969
Ike, Edgar Milton, 1888
Illions, Edward H., 1981
Ilyus, Edmund B., 1882
Imbesi, Steven G., 1989
Imboden, Harry Miles, 1903
Imhoff, Joseph Bloss, 1891
Imhoff, Robert Ernst, 1927
Imlay, John H., 1830
Imler, Daniel Canning, 1927
Imler, Robert L., Jr., 1945
Ingalls, P. P., 1860
Ingenito, Gary G., 1983
Ingerman, Mark J., 1981
Ingersoll, Charles J., Jr., 1858
Ingham, John L., 1934
Inghram, John Garrett, 1951
Inglesby, William G., 1854
Inglis, William D., 1957
Ingraham, Arthur 1849
Ingraham, Norman Reeh, 1902

Ingraham, Samuel Cooke, 1886
Ingram, Charles Braxton, 1886
Ingram, Frank Welton, 1922
Ingram, James M., 1854
Ingram, S. L., 1855
Ingram, Theodore E., 1885
Ingram, Thomas D., 1875
Ingram, William A., 1860
Inguito, Galicano Fernando, Jr., 1990
Ingwer, Irwin, 1970
Inkrote, Warren Webster, 1913
Inman, Mark G., 1989
Insel, Richard A., 1969
Interdonato, Anthony M., 1972
Inverso, Nicholas Anthony, 1990
Inverso-Kirkland, Michele R., 1984
Iobst, William F., 1982
Ioffreda, Michael David, 1990
Ioffreda, Pasqualino, 1959
Ioffreda, Richard E., 1987
Iozzi, Louis, 1949
Irby, John W., 1842
Irby, Moreland R., 1908
Irby, W. C.M., 1870
Iredale, Thomas A., 1836
Ireland, Andrew B., 1885
Ireland, Frederick W., 1903
Ireland, John, 1840
Ireland, Merritte Weber, 1891
Ireland, Milton Stanton, 1902
Irion, John W., 1883
Irish, William Beckford, 1894
Irland, William P., 1840
Irons, William R., 1890
Irvan, Hardin Davenport, Jr., 1909
Irvin, Edgar Harland, 1899
Irvin, George, 1855
Irvin, John Wesley, 1886
Irvin, William, 1855
Irvine, John D., 1840
Irvine, Patrick C., 1851
Irwin, Crawford, 1847
Irwin, George Middleton, 1933
Irwin, James Alexander, 1891
Irwin, James Kennedy, 1888
Irwin, Jos. W., 1873
Irwin, Joseph C., 1886
Irwin, Samuel B., 1844
Irwin, Thaddeus S., 1887
Irwin, William B., 1879
Irwin, William Underwood, 1891
Irwin, William, 1897
Isaac, Leon A. C., 1985
Isaacs, Herman R., 1964
Isaacson, Howard, 1946
Isaacson, Steven R., 1973
Isajiw, George, 1970
Isbell, Abner C., 1848

Ischler, George Herman, 1886
Ise, Charleen L., 1988
Isenberg, Chester L., 1934
Isenberg, Joseph Lloyd, 1893
Isett, Frederick S., 1876
Ishii, Clyde H., 1934
Ishii, Cylde H., Jr., 1978
Ishler, H. Richard, 1936
Ishler, Harold L., 1931
Ishler, Harold L., Jr., 1967
Ishmael, J. W., 1872
Ishman, Raymond M., 1981
Islenberg, Alfred Percy, 1906
Isom, Thomas D., 1839
Israel, George Irving, 1920
Israel, Harold L., 1934
Isserman, Mark S., 1977
Iszard, Reeves H., 1884
Iszard, W. H., 1870
Ito, Mari B., 1986
Ives, Charles L., 1854
Ives, Harold Augustus, 1907
Ivey, Hubert Turner, 1922
Ivins, George, 1874
Ivker, Milton, 1955
Ivker, Miton, 1954
Izenberg, David, 1929
Izes, Betsy A., 1987
Izes, Joseph K., 1986
Izlar, William H., 1929

~ J ~

Jablon, Norman C., 1959
Jack, George A., 1958
Jack, Gregory M., 1981
Jack, James Renwick, 1896
Jack, William, 1864
Jackson, Alexander W., 1878
Jackson, Algernon Brashaer, 1901
Jackson, C. Robert, 1956
Jackson, Charles Ellworth, 1899
Jackson, Chevalier Q., 1886
Jackson, Clarence Cecil R., 1928
Jackson, Craven, 1868
Jackson, Darryl B., 1988
Jackson, Edward A., 1982
Jackson, G. A., 1860
Jackson, George F., 1853
Jackson, George L., 1884
Jackson, Homer, 1876
Jackson, Ion A., 1897
Jackson, Isaac, 1847
Jackson, James Allen, 1906
Jackson, James C., 1847
Jackson, John Osborne, 1909
Jackson, John R., 1951
Jackson, John S., 1855

Jackson, John W., 1859
Jackson, John, 1864
Jackson, John, Jr., 1877
Jackson, L. D., 1859
Jackson, LaFayette, 1858
Jackson, R.M.S., 1838
Jackson, Rice Robinson, 1905
Jackson, Richard S., Jr., 1975
Jackson, Richard Stuart, 1943
Jackson, Robert George, 1905
Jackson, Robert, Jr., 1896
Jackson, Samuel, 1848
Jackson, Shirls Byzantine, 1890
Jackson, Sumner Waldron, 1914
Jackson, Thomas H., 1853
Jackson, Thomas J., 1964
Jackson, Thomas L., 1859
Jackson, Thomas Wright, 1892
Jackson, Thomas, Jr., 1926
Jackson, William F., 1849
Jackson, William Long, 1910
Jackson, William M., 1866
Jackson, Winslow, 1851
Jacob, Albert Nicholas, 1888
Jacob, Harry, 1879
Jacob, James Francis, 1893
Jacob, S. Sprigg, III, 1935
Jacob, Thomas C., Jr., 1985
Jacob, Thomas Charles, 1954
Jacobs, Donald Ray, 1924
Jacobs, Irvin, 1953
Jacobs, Irwin Seymour, 1953
Jacobs, Ivan H., 1973
Jacobs, Jeffrey M., 1985
Jacobs, Jill E., 1985
Jacobs, Joseph A., 1973
Jacobs, Leopold Max, 1911
Jacobs, Louis C., 1931
Jacobs, Louis, 1936
Jacobs, Robert A., 1968
Jacobs, Robert A., 1972
Jacobs, Stanley R., 1972
Jacobs, William Harold, 1956
Jacobs, William Robert, 1954
Jacobson, Barry J., 1980
Jacobson, Bert P., J1944
Jacobson, Edward H., 1854
Jacobson, Frank Jay, 1928
Jacobson, Harry Jacob, 1920
Jacobson, Joseph, 1923
Jacobson, Milton B., 1936
Jacobson, Nathan A., 1975
Jacobson, Nathan Barnet, 1913
Jacobson, Robert E., 1969
Jacobson, Robert Morris, 1936
Jacoby, Aaron Peter, 1887
Jacoby, Charles Wesley, 1898
Jacoby, David A., 1973

Jacoby, James H., 1968
Jacoby, Richard A., 1976
Jacoby, William J., Jr., 1950
Jacoby, William Jerome, 1919
Jacques, Richard H., 1938
Jaeger, Eugene A., 1953
Jaeger, Scott H., 1972
Jaffe, David, 1950
Jaffe, Jonathan S., 1984
Jaffe, Kenneth E., 1974
Jaffe, Marvin E., 1960
Jaffe, Richard L., 1974
Jaffurs, William J., 1952
Jahnig, Richard Paul, 1931
Jahnke, Edward J., 1948
Jahnke, Edward J., 1980
Jahnke, Eric W., 1978
Jahnle, Richard L., 1982
Jalali, Shailen, 1985
Jamack, John August, 1928
Jambro, Robert D., 1971
James, Albert Warren, 1918
James, Alfred Elmore, 1932
James, Carol Jean, 1990
James, Charles Emera, 1911
James, David, 1828
James, H. C., 1870
James, Herbert Halpenny, 1918
James, J. Sexton, 1846
James, James Edward, 1917
James, Jerry M., 1918
James, Jesse Y., 1856
James, John Warren, 1895
James, Joseph M., 1937
James, Martin L., 1852
James, Maurice Clayton, 1914
James, Nathan, 1851
James, Oliver P., 1840
James, Richard Forrest, 1908
James, Robert E., 1834
James, Samuel E., 1877
James, William Daniel, 1908
James, Wilson L., 1859
Jameson, Patrick H., 1849
Jameson, Samuel D.M., 1847
Jamison, Alfred R., Jr., 1951
Jamison, James Braden, II, 1950
Jamison, James L., 1882
Jamison, John McFarland, 1918
Jamison, William A., 1879
Janblatte, Prince Nasib, 1906
Janerich, Albert D., 1977
Janney, Josiah J., 1837
Janney, William S., 1880
Jansen, John T., 1838
Janss, John, 1884
Jarka, Casimir Joseph, 1924
Jarmoszuk, Nicholas, 1972

Jarrell, Bruce E., 1973
Jarrell, Henry J., 1875
Jarrett, George G., 1870
Jarrett, Harry, 1887
Jarvis, Cecil C., 1902
Jarvis, James Fletcher, 1891
Jarvis, James M., 1852
Jaslow, Robert I., 1947
Jasper, Edward H., 1980
Jastram, George Berlin, 1939
Jasty, Murali J., 1977
Jaudon, Benjamin A., 1853
Jauss, Christian E., 1882
Jaworski, Felix Andrew, 1918
Jaxheimer, Eric C., 1977
Jayne, Calvin K., 1879
Jayson, Maury Alan, 1990
Jefferies, George E., III, 1968
Jefferies, John A., 1968
Jefferis, T. Norval, 1876
Jefferson, James, 1904
Jeffery, James C., 1853
Jeffrey, R. Brooke, Jr., 1974
Jeffrey, Robert Brooke, 1945
Jeffrey, Robert Harrison, 1912
Jeffrey, William L., 1955
Jenkin, Michael A., 1966
Jenkins, Cecil G., 1955
Jenkins, David W., 1966
Jenkins, Edward John, 1933
Jenkins, John F., 1856
Jenkins, John R., Jr., 1946
Jenkins, Paul F., 1848
Jenkins, Robert C., 1848
Jenkins, William A., 1851
Jenkins, William F., 1916
Jenkins, William H., 1846
Jenkins, William Sellman, 1890
Jenkins, William T., 1835
Jennings, Alvan J.E., 1850
Jennings, Charles Hinchman, 1889
Jennings, John B., 1836
Jennings, John C., 1849
Jennings, Joseph A., 1896
Jennings, Lewis A., 1849
Jennings, Napoleon B., 1856
Jennings, Olin Henry, 1916
Jennings, Peter E.L., 1853
Jennings, Robert B., 1855
Jennings, Samuel D., 1868
Jennings, William Browning, 1888
Jennings, William K., 1857
Jenofsky, Jack, 1965
Jens, Kurtis D., 1976
Jensen, Ernest Harry, 1950
Jenson, James J., 1987
Jenson, James Lloyd, 1912
Jenson, William K., 1953

Jeppson, John Rufus, 1923
Jepson, Wilhelm, 1891
Jermane, Percy Lee, 1892
Jernigan, Charles H., 1855
Jernstrom, Charles L., 1951
Jernstrom, Paul H., 1947
Jeryan, Edward M., 1974
Jessop, Charles J., 1874
Jessop, Roland, 1892
Jessup, John J., 1848
Jessup, Robert B., 1853
Jessup, Samuel A.S., 1879
Jeter, John W., 1848
Jett, Richard Lawrence, 1907
Jewell, Kathleen T., 1979
Jewett, Theodore H., 1840
Jezyk, David S., 1975
Jimenez, J. M., 1869
Jimenez, Jose Miguel, 1922
Jimenez, Juan Maria, 1917
Jimenez, Luis Paulino, 1900
Jimenez, Saturninus M., 1878
Joaquin, Plana, 1854
Jodzis, Frank Joseph, 1925
Johansen, Erneste Augustus, 1892
John, Brinley, 1924
John, Harry N., 1965
John, Jacob Stacey, 1896
John, Joseph James, 1950
John, Joseph R., 1955
Johnes, Harvey C., 1844
Johnkins, Edmund A., 1951
Johnkins, Roland, 1949
Johns, A. Benning, Jr., 1857
Johns, Christian Rohrer, 1890
Johns, Jacob Rohrer, 1889
Johns, Lynch D., 1856
Johns, Milton W., 1953
Johns, S. P., 1873
Johnson, Albert Sidney, Jr., 1941
Johnson, Alexander, 1836
Johnson, Alf Cornelius, 1925
Johnson, Bertram L., Jr., 1970
Johnson, Bruce L., 1960
Johnson, Charles H., 1884
Johnson, Charles M., 1863
Johnson, Charles Munich, 1889
Johnson, Charles T., Jr., 1953
Johnson, Charles Thomas, 1920
Johnson, Charles W., 1872
Johnson, Cherie J., 1986
Johnson, Crowell W., 1868
Johnson, David J., 1849
Johnson, David M., 1987
Johnson, David Morrison, 1922
Johnson, David O., 1942
Johnson, David S., 1972
Johnson, E. Newton, 1883

Johnson, Edgar N., 1942
Johnson, Edward L., 1875
Johnson, Edward Snyder, 1886
Johnson, Emmanuel H., 1851
Johnson, Eric G., 1977
Johnson, Erwin T., 1883
Johnson, F. F., 1860
Johnson, F. H., 1869
Johnson, Frederick Charles, 1900
Johnson, Gale D., J1944
Johnson, Gaston Frank, 1934
Johnson, George D., 1934
Johnson, George F., 1870
Johnson, Harold Virgil, 1909
Johnson, Harris P., 1883
Johnson, Henry W., 1842
Johnson, Henry W., 1883
Johnson, Howard A., 1931
Johnson, Howard K., Jr., 1958
Johnson, J. Thomas, 1909
Johnson, Jacob D., 1868
Johnson, James H., 1956
Johnson, James Joseph, 1946
Johnson, James S., 1853
Johnson, James W., 1854
Johnson, Jesse W., 1857
Johnson, Joan E., 1983
Johnson, Joe H., 1856
Johnson, John D., 1856
Johnson, John Huston, 1907
Johnson, John S., 1853
Johnson, John Samuel, 1929
Johnson, Joseph Lewis, 1926
Johnson, Joseph M., 1963
Johnson, Karen A., 1981
Johnson, Kenneth P., Jr., 1959
Johnson, Lawrence Carl, 1929
Johnson, Lee, 1911
Johnson, Livingston Franklin, 1905
Johnson, Margaret Mary, 1990
Johnson, Mark E., 1895
Johnson, Matthew E., 1949
Johnson, Melford I., S1944
Johnson, Monroe M., 1853
Johnson, Paul Churchill, 1940
Johnson, Robert G., 1949
Johnson, Robert M., 1974
Johnson, Robert Mandis, 1945
Johnson, Robert P., 1970
Johnson, Sally A., 1976
Johnson, Samuel C., 1879
Johnson, Samuel, Jr., 1894
Johnson, Steven C., 1975
Johnson, Syvert H., 1897
Johnson, Theodore Martin, 1919
Johnson, Thomas J., 1837
Johnson, Tillman D., 1938
Johnson, Vivian Earl, 1920

Johnson, Walter Frederick, 1924
Johnson, Wesley, 1836
Johnson, William, 1826
Johnson, William A., 1882
Johnson, William Charles, 1917
Johnson, William G., S1944
Johnson, William H., 1836
Johnson, William L., 1857
Johnson, William M., 1851
Johnson, William, 1868
Johnson, Wingate Memory, 1908
Johnston, A. Russell, 1881
Johnston, A. Warriston, 1875
Johnston, Charles W., 1875
Johnston, Dale E., 1979
Johnston, David Anderson, 1928
Johnston, Edmund Burke, 1892
Johnston, Frank B., 1943
Johnston, Frank Elmer, 1888
Johnston, George B., 1945
Johnston, George Frear, 1887
Johnston, J. Clark, 1875
Johnston, James, 1855
Johnston, John P., 1879
Johnston, John Waddell, 1888
Johnston, Joseph R., 1846
Johnston, Marion A., 1881
Johnston, Robert W., 1876
Johnston, Russell G., 1971
Johnston, Russell Willhide, 1910
Johnston, Samuel, 1870
Johnston, Sjanna, 1978
Johnston, Thomas W., 1859
Johnston, Thomas, 1854
Johnston, W. A., 1876
Johnston, Walter, 1887
Johnston, Warren Herbert, 1913
Johnston, William F., 1854
Johnston, William McDowell, 1907
Johnston, William R., 1844
Johnston, Wirt, 1868
Joiner, Charles J., 1857
Jolley, William Albert, 1896
Jolly, M. A., 1859
Jonas, Stephen Alphonse, 1934
Jones, A. M., 1869
Jones, Adna Sawyer, 1908
Jones, Albert R., Jr., 1947
Jones, Alexander 1845
Jones, Alexander J., 1837
Jones, Alexander T., 1853
Jones, Allen W., 1946
Jones, Anderson Wilmer, 1890
Jones, Anson, 1827
Jones, Archbold M., Jr., 1959
Jones, Arthur E., 1884
Jones, Arthur Lane, 1919
Jones, Arthur Willis, 1896

Jones, Benjamin Franklin, 1888
Jones, Benjamin R., 1836
Jones, Beverly, 1838
Jones, Callom B., 1836
Jones, Carey Celester, 1920
Jones, Carl White, 1937
Jones, Charles P., 1849
Jones, Daniel Chandler, 1857
Jones, Daniel W., 1848
Jones, David G., 1965
Jones, David J., III, 1958
Jones, David T., 1881
Jones, David W., 1971
Jones, Denwood T., 1855
Jones, E. R., 1840
Jones, E. W., 1861
Jones, Edgar Clyde, 1906
Jones, Edmund Lloyd, 1919
Jones, Edward Hallaran, 1912
Jones, Edwin A., 1846
Jones, Edwin B., 1845
Jones, Emery G., 1884
Jones, Emlyn, 1900
Jones, Emmett Lee, Jr., 1926
Jones, Erasmus D., 1838
Jones, Ernest Price, Jr., 1990
Jones, Eurfryn, 1929
Jones, Florentine Barker, Jr., 1918
Jones, Frank Allen, 1937
Jones, G. P., 1869
Jones, George C., 1842
Jones, George Howard, Jr., J1944
Jones, George M., 1874
Jones, Harold Walter, 1917
Jones, Harry Bradford, 1909
Jones, Henry Orendorf, 1905
Jones, Horace L., 1884
Jones, Hugh McKinsey, 1839
Jones, James M., 1975
Jones, James Y., 1855
Jones, James, 1864
Jones, John Arthur, 1890
Jones, John Bayley, 1903
Jones, John Comer, 1897
Jones, John F. X., 1910
Jones, John Gulick, 1948
Jones, John H., 1846
Jones, John M., 1860
Jones, John P., 1868
Jones, John Paul, 1912
Jones, John T., 1850
Jones, John W., 1836
Jones, John W., 1873
Jones, Joseph Addison, 1855
Jones, Joseph B., 1837
Jones, La Fayette J., 1861
Jones, Leighton Wherry, 1897
Jones, Lewis Edward, 1947

Jones, Luther M., 1849
Jones, Meredith D., 1870
Jones, Montfort, 1860
Jones, Parrish Vernon, 1852
Jones, Paul B., 1965
Jones, Paul Erastus, Jr., S1944
Jones, Paul, 1875
Jones, R. Augustus, 1855
Jones, R. R., 1856
Jones, Ralph Richards, 1896
Jones, Raymond R., 1978
Jones, Richard Wayland, 1935
Jones, Robert E., 1870
Jones, Robert E., 1955
Jones, Robert LeRoy, 1910
Jones, Robert Lewis, 1848
Jones, Robert Turner, 1937
Jones, Russell C., 1977
Jones, S. Willard, 1873
Jones, Samuel, 1843
Jones, Seth M., 1986
Jones, Thomas Edward, 1892
Jones, Thomas J., 1873
Jones, Thomas K., 1978
Jones, U. R., 1856
Jones, W. Brook, 1841
Jones, Ward L., 1965
Jones, William B., 1887
Jones, William D., III, 1966
Jones, William E., 1877
Jones, William Gwillym, 1911
Jones, William Roberts, 1834
Jones, William S., 1878
Jones, William Thomas, 1883
Jones, William Thomas, 1904
Jones, William W., 1854
Jones, William W., 1855
Jones, Z. B. Vance, 1920
Jordan, Andrea G., 1981
Jordan, David A., 1853
Jordan, David B., 1885
Jordan, H. Frank, 1882
Jordan, Herbert V., Jr., 1946
Jordan, J. C., 1857
Jordan, James Shannon, 1930
Jordan, Jerome W., 1971
Jordan, John A., 1837
Jordan, John Alfred, Jr., 1946
Jordan, John Brogan, Jr., 1929
Jordan, M. D.L., 1857
Jordan, Marshall C., 1981
Jordan, Peter Andrew, 1901
Jordan, R. D., 1836
Jordan, Reuben Elm, 1859
Jordan, Richard W., 1852
Jordan, W. A., 1873
Jordan, W. Edward, 1949
Jordan, W. Edward, III, 1976

Jordan, Watson P., 1848
Jordan, William F., 1856
Jordan, William Francis, 1909
Jordy, George H., 1864
Jordy, Louis, 1892
Joselson, Howard, 1949
Joselson, Rae A., 1980
Joseph, Lester George, 1939
Joseph, Louis, 1904
Josephs, Allen S., 1978
Josephs, Mark, 1972
Josephson, Lisa Dawn, 1990
Josloff, Robert K., 1989
Joss, Chester Earle, 1910
Josselson, Alan S., 1973
Jovanovich, Veda Louise, 1990
Joy, Henry L., 1849
Joy, Horatio N., 1847
Joy, Percy Clark, 1915
Joy, William A., 1950
Joyce, Michael F., 1955
Joyce, William Michael, 1917
Joyner, Claudius Cameron, 1899
Jubelirer, Isaac Harold, 1924
Judd, James Frederick, 1895
Judd, Leonardo D., 1877
Judge, Francis Patrick, 1924
Judge, Hugh L., 1889
Judge, Robert Barr, 1887
Judkins, George B., 1860
Judson, Adoniram B., 1865
Judson, Andrew Rice, 1885
Judson, G. Vernon, 1938
Judson, James N., 1966
Judson, Oliver A., 1851
Judson, Susan C., 1972
Judson, William H., 1878
Judson, William W., 1970
Juett, David P., 1857
Juhasz, Alex B., 1972
Julian, Joseph, Jr., 1971
Jumblatt, Albert Fuad, 1924
Junkin, J. Miller, 1845
Jurist, Louis, 1880
Jurkowski, Paul M., 1982
Jurnovoy, Joel B., 1967
Justin, Peter A., 1931

~ K ~

Kaan, Kenneth T., 1979
Kaar, Richard C., 1940
Kabler, Ronald L., 1972
Kachik, Larry J., 1979
Kaczynski, Stanley Bernard, 1938
Kagey, Thomas J., 1904
Kahler, John Alexander, 1920
Kahn, Alexander, 1881

Kahn, Charles B., 1963
Kahn, Eric M., 1961
Kahn, Harry A., 1989
Kahn, Hyman R., 1956
Kahn, Joel A., 1987
Kahn, Leo, 1931
Kahn, Louis DeBarth, 1855
Kahn, Mark B., 1983
Kahn, Murray, 1948
Kahn, Roberta C., 1973
Kahng, Kim U., 1979
Kaigh, Irvin, 1954
Kaighn, Charles Butcher, 1914
Kain, Eugene H., S1944
Kain, John H., 1837
Kain, John Rennett, 1871
Kain, Thomas M., III, 1969
Kain, Thomas Michael, 1912
Kain, Thomas Michael, Jr., 1943
Kain, William Wilkins, 1893
Kairys, John C., 1988
Kaiser, Paul K., 1988
Kajencki, S. Paul, 1983
Kalb, George Bigham, 1886
Kalbach, Isaac Irwin, 1893
Kalchman, Steven H., 1985
Kale, Milton P., 1971
Kalett, Joseph, 1928
Kalez, Marion Michael, 1928
Kalin, Ned H., 1976
Kalinowski, Joseph E., Jr., 1989
Kalish, Robert W., 1964
Kallay, Michael C., 1976
Kallick, Charles J., 1958
Kallish, Marvin, 1958
Kalloch, Parker C., 1881
Kalteyer, Frederick John, Jr., 1899
Kambe, Joseph C., 1971
Kamerer, Joseph W.B., 1871
Kamerling, Joseph M., 1989
Kamsler, David M., 1975
Kandle, Roscoe Peacock, 1934
Kane, Anthony M., 1985
Kane, Clinton Austin, 1903
Kane, Evan O., 1884
Kane, Gregory C., 1987
Kane, Henry A., 1953
Kane, James A., 1938
Kane, James J., 1892
Kane, John J., 1876
Kane, John K., 1855
Kane, Joseph C.M., 1837
Kane, Leo Anthony, 1914
Kane, Michael A. C., 1984
Kane, Robert C., 1970
Kane, Thomas L., 1886
Kane, William M., 1946
Kane, Wilton R., 1956

Kanefield, Jeffrey K., 1986
Kanenson, William L., 1955
Kaneshiro, Francis T., 1940
Kanner, Harry Hamilton, 1950
Kanner, Harry Mitchell, 1919
Kanofsky, Jacob D., 1974
Kanter, Earl, 1951
Kantner, Franklin Jacob, 1888
Kanwal, Neeraj K., 1980
Kao, Yi How, 1976
Kapcar, Albert D., S1944
Kapcar, Andrew J., 1955
Kapeghian, Edward, S1944
Kaplan, Albert Jordan, 1938
Kaplan, Bertram D., 1974
Kaplan, Eliah, 1913
Kaplan, Eliot F., 1980
Kaplan, Gerald F., 1968
Kaplan, Harry Aaron, 1951
Kaplan, Herbert, 1931
Kaplan, Joel A., 1968
Kaplan, Jonathan S., 1969
Kaplan, Louis, 1938
Kaplan, Seth A., 1989
Kaplan, Susan G., 1980
Kaplow, Gwen H. K., 1966
Kapoor, Deepak A., 1984
Kapp, Carl Gailard, 1928
Kapp, Henry Hermann, 1901
Kappes, David A., 1884
Karabell, Sheldon I., 1967
Karam, Joseph A., 1987
Karaman, Boris A., 1983
Karasick, David, 1974
Karasick, Stephen, 1974
Kardos, Joseph A., 1951
Kareha, Louis G., 1943
Karl, Laurie A., 1988
Karlavage, John J., 1974
Karlik, Paul, Jr., J1944
Karns, Robert Earl, 1950
Karp, Louis A., 1965
Karp, Robert J., 1967
Karpeles, Maurice Joseph, 1896
Karpinski, Felix E., Jr., S1944
Karr, David Bernard, 1930
Karr, George Muster, 1894
Karr, Howard Harris, 1932
Karsch, Daniel N., 1967
Karshmer, Ernest Emil, 1935
Karsner, Charles W., 1878
Karsner, Charles, 1859
Karsner, Daniel, 1865
Karsner, James H.M., 1868
Karsner, William C., 1853
Karterman, William D., 1889
Kasarda, Lynnanne, 1987
Kashoff, Robert Leonard, 1957

Kashyap, Vikram Shantaram, 1990
Kaskey, Gary B., 1974
Kasper, Kelvin A., 1926
Kasten, William Henry, 1893
Kastner, Richard H., 1956
Kastner, Scott Meyers, 1976
Katchman, Jerome J., 1960
Kates, Jonathan L., 1975
Kates, Malcolm, 1959
Kates, Michael B., 1984
Katherman, Frank Clark, 1901
Katlan, Michael George, 1990
Katz, Barbara L., 1976
Katz, David A., 1987
Katz, David J., 1969
Katz, Gabriel Henry, 1932
Katz, Harry Kolman, 1924
Katz, Harry R., 1973
Katz, James K., 1981
Katz, Martin Edwin, 1931
Katz, Meyer Joseph, 1903
Katz, Richard B., 1973
Katz, Robert Edward, 1952
Katz, Stephen K., 1976
Katz, Steven A., 1984
Katz, Warren A., 1961
Katzen, Brett W., 1988
Katzman, Harold, 1959
Katzman, Merle H., 1954
Katzman, Samuel Sidney, 1921
Katzman, Scott S., 1989
Kauders, James T., 1962
Kauffman, Emanuel, 1889
Kauffman, John William, 1896
Kauffman, Louis John, 1910
Kauffman, Lyman Greenleaf, 1924
Kauffman, Mark S., 1959
Kauffman, Stephen C., 1964
Kauffman, Walter L., 1885
Kaufman, Abraham, 1931
Kaufman, Alexander Spencer, 1904
Kaufman, Charles, 1919
Kaufman, David, 1908
Kaufman, Edward, 1960
Kaufman, H. Calvin, 1958
Kaufman, Irwin Leonard, 1935
Kaufman, James Nelson, 1957
Kaufman, Jerold, 1968
Kaufman, Kimball C., Jr., 1950
Kaufman, Samuel Russel, 1932
Kaufmann, Samuel Benjamin, 1912
Kaulback, Kyle R., 1988
Kaupp, Albert Theodore, 1891
Kautz, Paul D., 1970
Kavalier, Morton A., 1969
Kavanagh, James K., 1984
Kavanagh, John J., J1944
Kavanagh, John J., Jr., 1975

Kavanaugh, Myles Thomas, 1933
Kavchok, Jospeh, Jr., 1979
Kay, Isaac F., 1855
Kay, James, 1914
Kay, Jonathan, 1975
Kay, Marilyn C., 1975
Kay, Thomas R., 1970
Kazal, Louis A., Jr., 1984
Kazenoff, Steven, 1979
Kazmier, Francis J., 1959
Keaggy, John B., 1875
Keagy, Frank, 1904
Keagy, R. Marvel, 1935
Kealing, Otho Granville, 1912
Kean, Joseph Walter, 1906
Kean, Otho W., 1836
Keane, John F. M., 1920
Kearney, Donald Joseph, 1966
Kearney, James John, 1990
Kearney, Paul A., 1943
Kearney, Paul A., Jr., 1980
Kearney, Robert E., 1983
Kearns, William, 1896
Keates, Edwin U., 1957
Keates, Richard H., 1957
Keath, James W., 1914
Keating, Charles Albert, Jr., 1902
Keating, Charles Vincent, 1909
Keating, Howard Francis, 1916
Keating, John Francis, 1929
Keating, John L., 1856
Keating, William P. S., 1899
Kebabian, Hrand Krecor, 1891
Keck, David John, 1949
Keck, George Osmon, 1900
Keck, William Frederick, 1920
Keefe, John P., 1961
Keeffe, Patrick Eugene, 1910
Keel, Willaim A., Jr., 1970
Keeler, Joseph Clarence, 1896
Keeler, Joseph P., 1880
Keeler, Louis L., III, 1986
Keeler, William A.T., 1873
Keeley, Ellen Catherine, 1990
Keeley, Jerome, 1864
Keelor, Reinard S., 1875
Keelor, Reinhard K., 1852
Keelor, Vincent Z., 1880
Keely, Henry Edgar, 1908
Keely, John, 1901
Keely, Robert N., Jr., 1882
Keely, Thomas J., 1861
Keen, Alfred W., 1884
Keen, William W., Jr., 1862
Keenan, Andrew Joseph, Jr., 1912
Keenan, Francis Edward, 1910
Keenan, Gerald R., 1960
Keenan, Isaac W., 1895

Keenan, Jeffrey A., 1983
Keenan, Lynn M., 1987
Keenan, Paul C., 1945
Keene, Benjamin F., 1847
Keene, Christopher D., 1883
Keene, Richard R., 1971
Keene, Robert Wilson, 1861
Keene, Walter Bullock, 1891
Keeney, Gilbert, 1986
Keeney, Homer Isaac, 1901
Keeney, Jackson P., 1847
Keeney, Madison J., 1900
Keenon, John G., 1851
Keesal, Richard W., 1964
Keesal, Solomon, 1938
Keesee, John J., 1877
Keeton, Theodore A., 1876
Keever, Adolphus P., 1882
Keever, Kenneth William, 1934
Keffer, Julius A., 1833
Kegaries, Donald Luther, 1929
Kegel, Daniel P., 1978
Kegel, Eugene E., 1952
Kegel, Jeffrey G., 1987
Kegel, Mary F., 1982
Kehm, Henry, 1871
Kehm, Ray W., 1940
Kehm, Robert F., 1976
Kehm, Vincent A., J1944
Kehoe, James S., 1868
Kehres, Henry Nathan, 1932
Keidel, Victor, 1906
Keily, James William, 1888
Keim, Ambrose M., 1877
Keim, Ivan N., 1911
Keim, Peter Sloan, 1896
Keisel, James Henry, 1887
Keiser, Frank Martin, 1923
Keiser, Lester, 1950
Keiser, Roland Roderic, 1923
Keiserman, Wayne M., 1970
Keister, Simon W., 1868
Keith, Elvin W., 1913
Keith, Ezekiel, 1865
Keith, N. C., 1859
Keithan, John F., 1934
Kell, Ralph Chester, 1905
Kellam, Frederick C.A., 1837
Kelleher, John C., J1944
Kelleher, Robert C., 1953
Kelleman, John J., 1977
Keller, Anthony, 1883
Keller, Augustis Herman, 1896
Keller, Eli Jeremiah, 1931
Keller, Franklin B., 1874
Keller, Frederick Eugene, 1917
Keller, Henry D., 1870
Keller, I. Basil, 1964
Keller, John Jacob, 1890

Keller, John M., 1946
Keller, Paul, 1917
Keller, Peter Martin, 1899
Keller, Roy L. G., 1920
Keller, William McConkey, 1939
Kelley, Charles R., 1964
Kelley, Daniel Joseph, 1902
Kelley, Edward B.P., 1887
Kelley, Eugene Michael, 1929
Kelley, Harold Charles, 1918
Kelley, Thomas, Jr., 1952
Kelley, William I., 1860
Kellog, Oliver W., 1842
Kellogg, William Ardrey, 1897
Kells, Louis, 1849
Kelly, Arthur M., 1890
Kelly, Charles B.P., 1850
Kelly, Daniel J., 1966
Kelly, Edward A., 1947
Kelly, Edward A., Jr., 1973
Kelly, Elbridge Gerry 1838
Kelly, Francis Joseph, Jr., 1894
Kelly, Frank P., 1881
Kelly, George M., 1875
Kelly, Herbert T., 1925
Kelly, Hiram N., 1857
Kelly, James J., 1939
Kelly, John B., 1859
Kelly, John E., 1959
Kelly, John J., III, 1984
Kelly, John J., Jr., 1954
Kelly, Joseph V., 1868
Kelly, Louis A., 1878
Kelly, M. A., 1876
Kelly, Mark F., 1985
Kelly, Patrick, 1827
Kelly, Richard Sterling, Jr., 1945
Kelly, Rupert Emery, 1940
Kelly, Samuel H., 1851
Kelly, William D., 1887
Kelly, William John, 1891
Kelly, William R., 1863
Kelsey, Arthur Louis, 1888
Kelsey, Charles T., 1852
Kelsey, William L. 1876
Kelso, Samuel M., 1868
Kelso, Thomas, 1960
Kelton, Franklin C., Jr., 1974
Kelton, Melanie Sharon, 1990
Kemble, Charles Cochran, 1897
Kemble, Charles, 1888
Kemble, Harvey C., 1878
Kemble, John W., 1933
Kemble, Robert Penn, 1933
Kemner, Edgar William, 1917
Kemps, Anton P., 1973
Kempton, Augustus, 1880
Kempton, Thomas D., 1852

Kenagy, David N., 1981
Kenan, Frederick M., 1937
Kendall, Eugene Elmer, 1887
Kendall, Henry W., 1870
Kendall, William S., 1852
Kendig, Harry Charles, 1930
Kendig, James W., 1970
Kendig, Jerome Stauffer, 1889
Kendig, Newton E., II, 1984
Kendig, Newton Emerson, 1954
Kendra, Stephen J., 1957
Kendrick, John Fox, 1914
Kendrick, Oscar C., 1848
Kendrick, William M., 1983
Keneagy, Samuel, 1844
Kenna, Denise M., 1982
Kenna, Joseph P., 1948
Kennamer, Samuel R., 1945
Kennard, John F., 1957
Kennedy, Burwell M., 1952
Kennedy, Clempson B., 1870
Kennedy, David Francis, 1953
Kennedy, David Ross, 1921
Kennedy, David, 1867
Kennedy, Edwin Russell, 1899
Kennedy, Finley A., 1929
Kennedy, George W., 1981
Kennedy, James S., 1880
Kennedy, James William, 1899
Kennedy, John Pressly, 1915
Kennedy, Joseph P., 1900
Kennedy, Kathleen Ann, 1979
Kennedy, Leon Toland, 1935
Kennedy, Maxwell, 1855
Kennedy, Patrick J., 1930
Kennedy, Paul A., 1939
Kennedy, Robert F., 1837
Kennedy, Robert S., 1866
Kennedy, Scott M., 1981
Kennedy, Stewart, 1854
Kennedy, Susan Lucille, 1990
Kennedy, Thomas J., 1866
Kennedy, Thomas J., 1946
Kennedy, William B., 1853
Kennedy, William McLane, 1928
Kennedy, William Morton, 1904
Kenner, George R., Jr., 1978
Kenning, James A., 1974
Kenny, Rose M., 1970
Kensinger, William Henry, 1889
Kent, Alfred A., 1885
Kent, Alfred Abraham, Jr., 1931
Kent, Jeffrey D., 1989
Kent, John D., 1854
Kent, Joseph W., 1858
Kenworthy, William Parke, Jr., 1934
Kenyon, Charles Lewis, 1894
Keohane, Richard B., 1967

Kerchner, Benjamin L., 1871
Kerfoot, George B., 1830
Kerley, R. M., 1869
Kerling, George A., 1887
Kermon, Louis T., 1950
Kern, George W., IV, 1970
Kern, Jay A., 1958
Kern, Josiah, 1846
Kern, Palmer M., 1876
Kern, Robert C., 1985
Kern, Stanley R., 1954
Kernan, Thomas H., 1873
Kernish, Alexander I., 1935
Kernish, Richard C., 1976
Kerns, George M., 1860
Kerns, Samuel Proctor, 1892
Kerr, Boyle, 1854
Kerr, Harvey, 1857
Kerr, John G., 1847
Kerr, John W., 1876
Kerr, Joseph T., 1935
Kerr, Mark G., 1838
Kerr, Robert M., S1944
Kerr, Thomas K., 1837
Kerr, William Edmunds, 1903
Kerr, William R., 1843
Kerr, William, 1858
Kerrigan, James J., 1984
Kerry, Marshall, 1929
Kerschbaum, Wesley E., 1975
Kershaw, George Henry, 1920
Kershbaum, Kenneth L., 1967
Kershner, George H., 1970
Kershner, Marilyn S. P., 1970
Kerstein, Louis Norton, 1934
Kerstetter, Paul Franklin, 1914
Kesilman, Morris, 1930
Kesler, Byron Linzie, 1904
Kesling, Otho G., 1912
Kessel, Charles Royall, 1921
Kessel, Clark, 1933
Kessel, James S., 1948
Kessel, James W., 1974
Kessel, Ray M., 1955
Kessel, Russel, 1925
Kesselman, Russell H., 1949
Kesselring, Joseph J., 1985
Kesselring, William T., Jr., 1979
Kessler, Carl Conrad, 1940
Kessler, Carl P., 1961
Kessler, Dan D., 1986
Kessler, David J., 1989
Kessler, Eileen S., 1988
Kessler, Frank J., 1956
Kessler, Frank J., Jr., 1983
Kessler, Harry Tay, 1931
Kessler, Murray A., 1950
Kessler, Paul Rudolph, 1957
Kessler, Samuel Fritz, 1889

Kessler, William Coward, 1913
Kessler, William Frederic, 1934
Kester, Kent E., 1986
Kester, Richard Joseph, 1951
Kester, Robert R., 1981
Kestner, Joseph F., Jr., 1968
Ketchie, James Meredith, 1922
Ketchum, Robert Dickerson, 1930
Keveney, John J., Jr., 1969
Keveney, John Joseph, 1936
Kevin, Robert O., 1882
Key, Albert Z., 1883
Key, Richard S., 1837
Key, Thomas T., 1856
Keyes, Baldwin L., 1917
Keyes, John W., 1942
Keylor, Henry E., 1878
Keys, John, 1851
Keys, Joseph W., 1853
Keyser, Alfred, 1839
Keyser, Bruce J., 1986
Khalil, Cindy L., 1989
Kibbe, John Halbert, 1922
Kibelbek, Michael J., 1979
Kibler, Benjamin H., 1856
Kice, Luther Holden, 1908
Kidder, Lincoln Ellsworth, 1896
Kidder, Richard Francis, 1949
Kiddoo, S. R., 1876
Kidney, James Jordan, 1943
Kiebler, George M., S1944
Kiefer, Raymond Arndt, 1903
Kieffer, Charles Clifford, 1888
Kieffer, Charles Ferdinand, 1891
Kieffer, George C., 1900
Kieffer, Jesse, 1933
Kieffer, Robert A., 1961
Kieffer, Uldrick McLaws, 1914
Kiefner, Robert S., 1980
Kielar, Joseph Romuald, 1920
Kielty, John Thomas, 1925
Kienhofer, Robert F., 1950
Kienzle, G. Edward, 1962
Kiernan, James O'H., 1881
Kiester, D. Milton, 1875
Kifer, Logan M., 1878
Kilborn, Harvey B., 1879
Kilborn, Melville Graves, 1930
Kilburn, Frank, 1879
Kilby, John T., 1847
Kilcheski, Thomas S., 1976
Kilcullen, Michael J., 1975
Kilduff, Charles J., Jr., 1945
Kilduffe, Robert, 1830
Kilduffe, Robert O., 1881
Kiley, Frank Love, 1893
Kiley, Robert William, S1944
Kilfeather, John E., 1961

Kilgus, Harry E., 1904
Kilker, John J. B., 1939
Killian, Caleb L., III, 1953
Killian, Frederick William, 1905
Killips, Thomas Allen, 1908
Kilmer, John H., 1935
Kim, Chang H., 1941
Kim, Edward C., 1989
Kim, Edward, 1988
Kim, John H., 1989
Kim, Ronald C., 1965
Kim, Sanghoon, 1990
Kimbley, John F., 1849
Kimbrough, Andrew H., 1858
Kimbrough, G. William, 1853
Kimbrough, Locket M., 1859
Kimmel, Edmund M., 1850
Kimmel, Judson Howard, 1968
Kimmell, Harry S., 1880
Kimmelman, David B., 1937
Kimmelman, Simon, 1902
Kinard, George W., 1887
Kincaid, John, 1847
Kinderman, Harold Wade, 1915
Kindig, Rudolph, 1887
Kindleberger, David, 1858
Kindrick, Cyrus Jr., 1850
Kine, Garrett D., 1982
King, A. M., 1858
King, Albert Hazlett, 1894
King, Alden P., 1924
King, Alfred T., 1836
King, Benjamin B., 1834
King, Brinsfield, 1913
King, Charles P., 1867
King, Cyrus B., 1862
King, David, 1834
King, David E., 1983
King, Douglas R., 1984
King, E. C., 1858
King, Edward Sandling, 1927
King, Ernest Harold, 1914
King, Eugene P., 1880
King, George A., 1866
King, George M., 1859
King, George P., 1879
King, Harry B., 1883
King, Harry Brown, 1895
King, Harry Howard, 1904
King, Henry H., 1844
King, Hiram Orville, 1893
King, Jack Austin C., 1945
King, James E., 1850
King, James T., 1858
King, John F. W., 1940
King, John F., 1855
King, John W., 1875
King, John Wesley, 1889

King, Joseph J., 1973
King, Joseph J., 1973
King, Joyce R., 1978
King, Orville Carrier, 1927
King, Richard A., 1965
King, Richard G., 1837
King, Richard Morrison, 1903
King, Robert M., 1867
King, S. Victor, 1947
King, T. Starke, 1858
King, W. Norvel, 1858
King, Weir L., 1950
King, William Coffield, 1861
King, William H., 1853
King, William H., 1870
King, William Howard, 1894
King, William M., 1858
King, William, Jr., 1860
Kingma, Douglas W., 1987
Kingsley, Charles, 1891
Kinlaw W. Bernard Jr., 1949
Kinnaird, Virgil Gibney, 1913
Kinnaman, Chauncey Howard, 1886
Kinnaman, Horace A., 1884
Kinnard, George Potts, 1922
Kinnard, Michael C., 1854
Kinnear, Claude Hamilton, 1889
Kinney, Albert Girton, 1928
Kinney, Willard Heil, 1906
Kinnier, Robert Gray, 1880
Kinsey, Frank Robb, 1943
Kinsey, Irwin Zepp, 1926
Kinsey, John, 1827
Kinsey, M. Dean, 1969
Kinsley, Edward William, 1892
Kinsloe, Lemuel, 1839
Kinstlick, Emanuel, 1966
Kinter, John Henry, 1907
Kints, Geerfruida, 1986
Kipa, S. George, 1980
Kipp, Charles M., 1958
Kiproff, Paul M., 1984
Kirby, Frank Brennand, 1902
Kirchner, Henry Stanley, 1915
Kirchner, Richard G., 1947
Kirk, Albert Charles, 1935
Kirk, Clair Bishop, 1908
Kirk, David John, 1929
Kirk, Edward, 1888
Kirk, Grant Elmer, 1891
Kirk, James Newton, 1889
Kirk, Lewis R., 1853
Kirk, Marvin Edward, 1926
Kirk, Norris Jacob, 1929
Kirk, Richmond M., 1865
Kirke, Henry M., 1853
Kirkhuff, A. Lewis, 1875
Kirkland, John A., 1885

Kirkland, Matt L., 1952
Kirkland, Matt L., III, 1983
Kirkpatrick, Andrew B., 1884
Kirkpatrick, Joseph T., 1877
Kirkpatrick, M. Baldwin, 1879
Kirkpatrick, William Burke, 1902
Kirksey, E. Jehu, 1858
Kirkwood, H., 1859
Kirkwood, Robert Carnahan, 1908
Kirkwood, Tom, 1912
Kirkwood, William, 1835
Kirschbaum, Jodi Ann, 1981
Kirschner, Harry Edward, 1902
Kirschner, Robert H., 1966
Kirschner, Robert J., 1957
Kirshbaum, Bernard A., 1950
Kirshner, Drew L., 1984
Kirshner, Jacob J., 1933
Kirshner, Lewis A., 1965
Kissinger, A. H., 1871
Kissinger, Walter Cealey, 1903
Kistler, Alvin Jacob, 1902
Kistler, Chester K., 1897
Kistler, Dominick A., 1989
Kistler, Jacob K., 1875
Kistler, James K., 1879
Kistler, Jonas M., 1883
Kistler, Oliver Franklin, 1887
Kistler, Priscilla J., 1973
Kistler, Sarah E., 1986
Kistler, William S., 1939
Kitchen, Harrison Allen, 1890
Kitchen, Joseph Samuel, 1906
Kitchin, Jesse Walton, 1933
Kitchin, Thurman Delna, 1908
Kitchin, William W., 1940
Kitei, Milton N., S1944
Kitei, Robert A., 1989
Kitei, William J., 1975
Kiteley, William Ellis, 1893
Kitrinos, Nicholas Peter, 1951
Kittle, Chris A., 1978
Kittleberger, William C., Jr., 1948
Kittredge, Thomas, 1837
Kivell, Howard N., 1982
Klacsmann, Peter G., 1975
Klapp, John R., 1831
Klapp, Joseph, 1889
Kleber, Herbert David, 1960
Kleckner, James F., 1948
Kleeberg, Felix, 1899
Kleiman, M. Leonard, 1969
Klein, Adam Raymond, 1904
Klein, Arno, 1911
Klein, Arthur L., 1964
Klein, Barry R., 1971
Klein, Gerald M., 1971
Klein, Howard S., 1978

Klein, Isadore, 1927
Klein, Jack J., 1961
Klein, Jacob, 1968
Klein, Kenneth I., 1976
Klein, Larry H., 1972
Klein, Natalie C., 1979
Klein, Raymond A., 1976
Klein, Sheldon, 1966
Klein, Steven A., 1970
Klein, Warren F., 1887
Kleinbart, Morris, 1925
Kleinman, Herman, 1929
Kleinstuber, William George, 1893
Kleinstuber, William Oscar, 1916
Kleintob, Freas Benjamin, 1916
Klemek, Joseph S., 1967
Klemet, John, 1883
Klemm, Adam, 1891
Klemmer, Herbert, 1937
Klemmer, William Nickolaus, 1893
Klempner, Paul, 1932
Klenk, James Monroe, 1911
Klepser, Marian B., 1978
Klick, James M., 1970
Klieman, Charles H., 1967
Klimowicz, Maryida, 1984
Kline, Antonie D., 1986
Kline, Ben, 1955
Kline, David Frank, 1888
Kline, Edgar W., 1935
Kline, Edmund James, 1889
Kline, Effenger R., 1882
Kline, Gerard L., 1989
Kline, Harvey Winfield, 1912
Kline, Isaac, 1827
Kline, John A., 1970
Kline, John Edward, 1882
Kline, Joseph J., 1938
Kline, Kathy T., 1976
Kline, Luther B., 1867
Kline, Luther Henry, 1926
Kline, Meyer A., 1919
Kline, Michael A., 1990
Kline, Oram R., Jr., 1945
Kline, Oram Roscoe, 1917
Kline, Richard J., 1961
Kline, Robert M., 1955
Kline, Willard Daniel, 1901
Klingensmith, I. Putnam, 1875
Klingensmith, Theodore P., 1866
Klingensmith, William Roger, 1913
Klinger, Frank A., 1977
Klinges, Henry George, Jr., 1955
Klinges, Karl, G., 1956
Klinghoffer, Leonard, 1953
Klinman, Jerome J., 1961
Klinman, Norman R., 1962
Klinman, Steven W., 1971

Klinzing, Gerard F., 1980
Klinzing, Henry, 1908
Klipstein, George T., 1880
Klopp, Edward J., Jr., 1947
Klopp, Edward Jonathan, 1906
Klopp, Eli Leinbach, 1889
Klopp, Peter Paul, 1890
Kloss, Robert A., 1976
Klotz, Edgar J., 1886
Klotz, Robert Bertram, 1893
Klotz, Thomas A., 1974
Kluchinski, Barbara J., 1974
Klufas, Roman A., 1988
Klugh, Oliver Ringwalt, 1889
Klugh, Walter Gray, 1918
Klump, Thomas E., 1963
Klutz, Austin Flint, 1917
Kmonicek, Joseph M., 1978
Knapp, Don B., II, 1964
Knapp, Franklin A., 1848
Knapp, M. L., 1826
Knapp, Thomas Sheridan, 1945
Knapp, Warren A. Bickel, 1893
Knappenberger, Fred Charles, 1928
Knecht, Charles L., III, 1957
Knecht, Cyrus, 1880
Kneedler, William L., 1879
Kneeland, John B., 1978
Kneibert, Fred Louis, 1927
Knepley, David W., 1961
Knepp, Mary E., 1965
Knerr, Edgar D., Jr., J1944
Kniazer, Barry, 1968
Knickerbocker, Boliver, 1860
Knight, Alfred John, 1906
Knight, Guy Augustus, 1905
Knight, Henry S., 1878
Knight, John, 1866
Knight, Robert B., 1875
Knight, William L., 1837
Knipe, Francis M., 1857
Knipe, Jacob O., 1862
Knipe, Jay Clarence, 1890
Knipe, Septimus A., 1866
Knipe, William Henry, 1894
Kniseley, Joseph Harry, 1933
Knode, Oliver B., 1845
Knoll, Frederick William, 1914
Knoll, George Gustavus, 1908
Knoll, George M., 1939
Knopf, Carl Ludwig, 1942
Knorr, John K., III, 1942
Knorr, John K., Jr., 1867
Knorr, Matthias, 1859
Knott, Thomas M., 1861
Knowles, Charles Arthur, 1946
Knowles, Harry J., 1942
Knowles, Harry J., Jr., 1977

Knowles, Henry B., 1880
Knowles, Willard E., 1940
Knowlton, Charles L., 1845
Knox, Earl Ross, 1931
Knox, H. Donald, 1957
Knox, Harry Edward, 1915
Knox, Henry, 1890
Knox, James D., Jr., 1986
Knox, Kenneth R., 1946
Knox, Robert Arthur, 1916
Knox, Samuel D., 1879
Knox, William A., 1854
Knupp, Melvin L., 1945
Kobb, Harold J., 1960
Kobialka, Walter M., 1974
Kobler, George H., 1877
Kobrin, Lowell E., 1971
Koch, Alvin Adam, 1896
Koch, Frederick J., 1968
Koch, Frederick W., 1866
Koch, Gary D., 1982
Koch, John G., 1865
Koch, Joseph C., 1945
Koch, Josiah A., 1874
Kochenderfer, Thomas Taylor, 1935
Kocher, Jacob John, 1907
Kocher, William D., 1981
Kocot, Stanley L., 1957
Kocot, Wenceslaus V., 1945
Koder, Charles A., 1882
Kodroff, Kurt S., 1989
Kodroff, Michael B., 1967
Koegel, William F. H., 1906
Koehl, C. Warren, Jr., 1956
Koehl, Jeremiah, 1868
Koenig, Carl Eugene, 1908
Koerth, Charles John, 1921
Koffler, Arthur, 1936
Koffler, Jeffrey M., 1977
Kogut, Kathleen Marie, 1977
Kohl, John Michael, 1948
Kohl, Sarah Elizabeth, 1986
Kohler, Frederick W., 1882
Kohler, William Henry, 1887
Kohn, Jeffrey K., 1974
Koizumi, Bradley H., 1973
Kolarsick, Albert J., 1943
Kolb, Isadore, 1895
Kolchins, Milton L., 1959
Kolecki, Richard S., 1959
Kolecki, Richard S., 1988
Kolecki, Robert V., 1989
Kolker, James D., 1981
Kolker, Steven A., 1975
Kollock, Harry G.M., 1872
Kolmer, John, 1894
Koltes, John A., Jr., 1947
Konchar, William C., 1977

Kong, Albert Y. Tau, Jr., 1959
Konhaus, Carol H., S1944
Koniver, Garth A., 1968
Konkle, W. Bastian, 1884
Konlian, Donna M., 1989
Kontrick, Andrew J., 1971
Konzelmann, Frank W., 1919
Koogler, M. A., 1874
Koons, John H., 1881
Koons, Oliver H., 1883
Koons, Philip R., 1879
Koontz, David Michael, 1889
Koontz, George H.H., 1848
Koontz, John W., 1880
Kopack, Francis M., 1954
Kopelman, Nathan Austin, 1921
Kopetschny, Ottocar E., 1876
Koplin, A. Herman, 1937
Koplin, Nathaniel Hawthorne, 1909
Koppel, Alexander, 1928
Koppel, Max M., 1957
Koppisch de Cardona, Enrique, 1927
Korbonits, C. William, Jr.,,1973
Korbonits, Charles W., 1946
Koretsky, Irving Bennett, 1954
Koretsky, Leo, 1933
Koretsky, Sidney, 1946
Korey, Joseph J., Jr., 1975
Korhnak, August Joseph, 1896
Korinchak, Jerome L., 1980
Korman, Michael J., 1981
Korn, Laurence, 1960
Korn, Robert L., 1989
Korn, Scott H., 1981
Kornblith, Paul L., 1962
Korneluk-Reilly, Theresa, 1977
Kornfield, Harry, 1940
Kornhauser, Michael S., 1980
Korns, Charles Byron, Jr., 1937
Korson, Roy, 1947
Korvick, Joyce A., 1980
Kosanovic, Frederick, 1934
Kosar, Erol M., 1989
Koser, Martin Luther, 1903
Kosoy, Jerome, 1964
Kostello, Robert T., 1961
Kostelnik, Francis V., 1958
Kostianovsky, Deborah J., 1988
Kostinas, John E., 1958
Kostrzewa, Raymond M., 1956
Kostyla, Edward Andrew, 1938
Kotalik, Frederick, 1988
Kotanchik, Walter E., 1933
Kotchick, E. Donald, 1963
Kotin, Edward Howard, 1930
Kotler, Barry M., 1961
Kottcamp, Edward Charles, 1901
Kottcamp, Edward Charles, Jr., 1936

Kottenhahn, Renee Kathrin, 1990
Kotz, Adam L., 1881
Kough, Othello S., 1931
Koury, James Solomon, Jr., 1953
Koutcher, Martin E., 1967
Kovach, Richard C., 1982
Koval, John M., 1947
Kovalsky, Kenneth, 1978
Kovatich, Audrey M. W., 1979
Kowal, Vladimir, 1920
Kowaleski, Joseph S., 1907
Kozak, John Matthew, 1990
Kozielski, Joseph W., 1971
Kozlek, Thomas F., 1966
Kozloff, Stephen R., 1968
Krabill, Willard S., 1953
Kradin, Richard L., 1976
Kraemer, Richard Joseph, 1935
Kraemer, William Henry, 1906
Krafft, Rudolph M., 1978
Kraft, Albert J., Jr., 1947
Kraft, William F., 1950
Krain, Laurence S., 1983
Krain, Samuel, 1961
Krall, Michael L., 1980
Krall, Robert A., 1976
Krall, Robert P., J1944
Kram, George W., 1879
Kramen, S. Victor, 1936
Kramer, Daniel William, 1913
Kramer, David J., 1983
Kramer, David, 1912
Kramer, Donald L., 1981
Kramer, Edward Raymond, 1910
Kramer, Frederick Herman, 1930
Kramer, Frederick L., 1973
Kramer, Herbert, 1947
Kramer, Naomi R., 1987
Kramer, Norman J., 1965
Kramer, Sherri Lynn, 1990
Kramer, Stephen I., 1978
Krape, Joseph Harman, 1894
Krasney, Robert Louis, 1953
Kratzinger, Stephen Francis, Jr., 1962
Kraus, Gabriel Joseph, 1912
Kraus, Theodore J., S1944
Krause, Katherine C., 1978
Krause, William, 1884
Krauss, George, 1896
Krauss, Jack, 1961
Krauss, Maurice Daniel, 1931
Krauss, Walter Raymond, 1913
Kravatz, Arnold S., 1961
Kravis, Thomas C., 1968
Kravitz, Alan E., 1969
Kravitz, Daniel B., 1984
Kravitz, Morton Atherton, 1938
Kravitz, Simon, 1957

Lasichak, Lydia M., 1976
Laska, Edward M., 1970
Laskas, John J., Jr., 1972
Lasker, Halette, R., 1985
Laskin, Isadore, 1935
Laskin, William B., 1979
Lasky, Lester, 1930
Lasner, Jay E., 1981
Lasota, George L., 1962
Lassiter, Chester Lawrence, 1915
Lassiter, Henry Grady, 1918
Lassiter, James Alexander, 1953
Latham, Claude Aubra, 1922
Latham, James C., 1874
Latham, Joseph Roscoe, 1917
Lathrop, Horace, Jr., 1852
Latimer, Joseph T., 1849
Latshaw, John H., 1883
Latzo, John, 1931
Lau, Mark T., 1989
Lau, Robert E., 1942
Lau, Robert Edmund, 1909
Lau, Scott Wolford, 1899
Laub, Allen S., 1965
Laub, Ronald M., 1977
Laubach, Sherri J., 1977
Laucius, J. Frederick, 1967
Laucks, Samuel S., II, 1981
Lauer, Kurt E., 1952
Laufersweiler, Leonard Frank, 1907
Laughlin, Herbert A., 1945
Laughlin, J. H., 1856
Laughlin, Van Sanford, 1914
Laughrey, John Brooks, 1908
Laurelli, Henry E., 1965
Laurence, William R., Jr., 1982
Lauria, Michael David, 1970
Lauria, Michael H., 1940
Lauricella, John P., 1954
Laurie, Robert Edward, 1954
Laury, William, L., 1974
Lauster, Carl Franz, 1928
Lauter, M. David, 1978
Lauter, O. Scott, 1982
Lautt, Marvin E., 1960
LaVan, Marthe Adler, 1987
Lavanier, Gregory L., 1987
Lavanier, Jeffrey A., 1986
Lavell, Meyer Quintin, 1928
Lavell, Michael, 1853
Lavelle, Harry Minhern, 1900
Lavelle, James P., 1979
Lavelle, Patrick J., Jr., 1945
Lavelle, Paul Edmund, 1922
Laverty, D.W. Clinton, 1877
Laverty, George Lauman, 1912
Laverty, Theodore C., 1854
Lavigne, A. W., 1869

Lavin, David M., 1978
Lavin, John Leonard, 1915
Lavine, Barney Doibe, 1914
Lavine, Harris, 1954
LaVoice, H. Edward, Jr., 1951
Law, George E., 1883
Law, H. L., 1869
Law, Harold William, 1936
Law, Kenneth Alexander, 1937
Law, Samuel B., 1853
Lawhead, James H., 1886
Lawler, Robert A., 1980
Lawless, Stephen J., 1981
Lawlis, John F., III, 1982
Lawlor, John Martin, 1939
Lawlor, Robert J., 1977
Lawrance, Edward Stuart, 1879
Lawrance, Josiah Randall, 1882
Lawrence, Benjamin J., Jr., 1947
Lawrence, Benjamin Jones, 1918
Lawrence, Charles Thomas, Jr., 1934
Lawrence, Charlie W., 1873
Lawrence, Gary W., 1977
Lawrence, Henry Roscoe, 1881
Lawrence, Lillian, 1902
Lawrence, Steven J., 1987
Lawrence, Steven P., 1986
Lawrence, William B., 1877
Lawrence, William B., 1884
Lawrence, William C., 1837
Lawrence, William D., 1974
Laws, James, 1854
Lawson, H. M., 1856
Lawson, J. Columbus, 1883
Lawson, John Alexander, 1895
Lawson, Scott R., 1981
Lawson, T. Chalmers, 1871
Lawson, Thomas Adam, 1906
Lawyer, Fletcher C., 1873
Layden, Paul W., 1950
Layton, Bradley W., 1981
Layton, Joseph, 1851
Layton, Robert Reese, Jr., 1932
Layton, Thomas R., 1973
Lazar, Allan W., 1957
Lazar, Richard J., 1978
Lazarchick, John, 1968
Lazarus, Sanderson, 1868
Lazarus, Solomon D., 1883
Lazer, Edwin, 1832
Lazier, Henry B., 1853
Lazzaro, Orlando Anthony, 1928
Lazzell, James M., 1856
Le Grand, Cecil W., 1877
Le Winn, Edward Bernard, 1929
Le, Daniel Dung Quoc, 1989
Lea, John G., 1861
Lea, Joseph Addison, 1910

Leach, Alonzo L., 1868
Leach, Christopher L., 1973
Leach, E. Clements, 1914
Leach, Edwin M., 1942
Leach, Gary R., 1966
Leach, John Edward, 1933
Leach, Lois Marie, 1984
Leach, William Thomas, 1918
Leaff, Louis A., 1965
Leahy, Jeremiah Emmet, 1896
Leahy, John Francis, 1929
Leahy, Michael M., 1883
Leake, Virginius, 1848
Leal, Pedro Noriega, 1889
Leal-Bliss, Mary Ann E., 1983
Leaman, Brainerd, 1864
Leaman, Henry, 1864
Leaman, John, 1837
Leaman, Rosh, 1882
Leaming, J. Furman, 1846
Leaming, Robert H., 1945
Leaming, Walter S., 1882
Leamon, George Pawling, 1887
Learn, Blair George, 1920
Leary, William B., 1859
Leas, Thomas B., 1878
Leasum, Charles, 1918
Leasum, Robert N., 1954
Leasum, Robert Nels, 1918
Leasure, Daniel, 1846
Leath, MacLean Bacon, Jr., 1933
Leatherbury, Edward R., 1848
Leathers, Douglass A., 1886
Leavitt, Richard M., 1962
Leavitt, Thomas J., 1964
LeBar, Amzi, 1867
Lebcher, Chester, 1874
Leberknight, Adam K., 1878
Leberknight, Daniel C., 1880
Leberknight, F. B., 1874
Lebo, William, 1872
Lebovitz, Edward, 1923
Lebovitz, Jerome J., 1952
Lebovitz, Mark A., 1979
LeCates, Charles Asbury, 1896
Lechman, Joseph Francis, 1932
Lechman, Michael J., 1971
Lechmanick, Eugene A., 1977
Lechner, Frederic C., 1946
Lechner, Frederic Clemons, 1919
Lechner, LeRoy Yohn, 1895
Lechner, Ralph Yahn, 1890
Lecklitner, Myron DeVoy, 1934
Lecklitner, Paul R., 1925
Lecrone, Harris R., 1885
Lecrone, Israel Philip, 1871
Ledbetter, Penlie Briscoe, 1908
Ledden, John V., 1930

Leddy, Joseph P., 1965
Lederman, Ivan I., 1958
Lederman, Jeffrey A., 1988
LeDonne, Anthony T., 1958
LeDonne, Karen A., 1986
Lee, Alfred H., 1839
Lee, Allen H., 1946
Lee, Alvin Craig, 1899
Lee, Arthur B., 1957
Lee, Bernard R., 1879
Lee, Frank Alexander, 1894
Lee, Harry Wooten, 1922
Lee, Jaeho, 1989
Lee, James B., 1956
Lee, James C., 1841
Lee, James H., Jr., 1945
Lee, James M., 1867
Lee, Jeremiah F., 1947
Lee, John G., 1878
Lee, Paul C., 1858
Lee, Robert C., Jr., 1954
Lee, Robert Edward, 1939
Lee, Thomas Benjamin, 1905
Leech, J. Stuart, 1841
Leech, Thomas F., 1866
Leech, William W., 1880
Leedom, John, 1828
Leedom, S. K., 1839
Leeds, William Stuart, Jr., 1965
Leenay, Mark, 1987
Lees, Michael E., 1988
Leete, Edward Don, 1915
LeFavor, Dean Hart, 1924
Lefcowitch, Charles Henry, 1897
LeFerte, Daniel, 1871
LeFever, Charles Wesley, 1897
LeFever, Harry E., Jr., 1958
LeFever, Harry Everett, 1925
Lefevre, John Daniel, 1937
Lefevre, Joseph H., 1845
Lefevre, Rufus Eshbach, 1900
Lefevre, William B., 1838
Leff, Ronald A., 1970
Leffman, H., Jr., 1869
Lefkowitz, Ilene B., 1982
Lefrak, Steven L., 1968
Lefton, Harvey B., 1970
Leftwich, John W., 1850
Legg, Albert Neil, 1908
Legge, Josiah H., 1858
Leggett, Hechaliah H., 1832
Leggett, Leverett L., 1870
Leh, David W., Jr., 1989
Leh, Homer Deems, 1911
LeHardy de Beaulieu, J. C., 1856
Lehman, Asa M., 1915
Lehman, Charles Albert, 1905
Lehman, Edward Dennis, 1951

Lehman, Edwin F., 1884
Lehman, Jacob R., 1882
Lehman, James A., Jr., 1961
Lehman, James Alphonsus, 1928
Lehman, John Foster, 1935
Lehman, Joseph Davis, 1902
Lehman, Matthew H., 1981
Lehman, Robert D., Jr., 1980
Lehman, Robert F., 1964
Lehman, Thomas J. A., 1974
Lehman, Thomas P., 1980
Lehman, William F., 1883
Lehmann, David C., 1983
Lehnkering, Charles F., 1895
Lehr, Cynthia D., 1971
Lehr, George Y., 1863
Lehr, Monroe D., 1884
Lehrer, Lewis, 1939
Lehrer, Luisa E., 1986
Lehrman, Bruce J., 1985
Leib, Owen D., 1836
Leib, Pamela L., 1981
Leibold, Herbert Henry, 1909
Leibowitz, Helen A., 1972
Leiby, Lewis James, 1933
Leiby, Raymond Aaron, 1920
Leichner, Thomas J., Jr., 1965
Leichner, Thomas Joseph, 1933
Leicht, John P., 1981
Leicht, Paul Franklin, 1951
Leichter, Larry R., 1974
Leidich, Barbara Pittner, 1979
Leidich, Raymond B., 1978
Leidy, Edwin D., 1885
Leidy, Ralph Ellis, 1914
Leidy, T. H., 1869
Leigh, John Randolph, 1850
Leigh, William Frederick, Jr., 1916
Leighton, Barbara Mary, 1990
Leighton, Walter H., 1864
Leinaweaver, George, 1846
Leinbach, Benjamin S., 1851
Leinberry, Charles F., Jr., 1984
Leinweber, Bruce K., 1963
Leipold, Bert Eugene, 1896
Leipold, Robert A., 1976
Leis, Dean J., 1973
Leisawitz, Elliott G., 1973
Leisawitz, Paul A., 1937
Leisner, William R., 1980
Leister, Howard A., 1959
Leitch, J. Lewis, 1855
Leitzell, Charles B., 1877
Leitzell, P. Wilson, 1896
Leivy, David M., 1960
Leivy, Frank Edward, 1924
Leivy, Sander W., 1987
Lejarza, Jose Dolores, 1882

Lekawa, Michael Edward, 1990
Leland, John Augustine, Jr., 1936
Leland, William A., 1843
Lemmon, Gamewell A., Jr., 1946
Lemmon, Junius Mayes, 1930
Lemmon, William T., Jr., 1960
Lemmon, William Thomas, 1921
Lemmon, William, 1851
Lemp, Rolf W., 1963
Lempke, Richard Joseph, S1944
Lenahan, Paul John, J1944
Lenahan, Terrence P., 1987
Lenehan, J. Richard, 1937
Lenetsky, Allan M., 1972
Lenker, David Edward, 1888
Lenker, Robert Willis, 1908
Lennard, Joseph M., 1854
Lennon, John, 1857
Lenoir, Benjamin B., 1846
Lenow, James H., 1872
Lenox, Robert J., 1976
Lent, Williard George, 1891
Lentini, Joseph A., 1951
Lentz, Conrad L., 1960
Lentz, Edmund Tutay, 1926
Lentz, John Amandus, 1920
Lentz, Mark R., 1985
Lentz, Ronald J., 1961
Lentz, Sylvester Eugene, 1930
Lenyo, George E., 1955
Leo, Michael C., 1974
Leonard, Arthur, 1964
Leonard, Charles Forrest, 1908
Leonard, Daniel James, III, 1990
Leonard, Edward C., Jr., 1964
Leonard, Glenn R., 1951
Leonard, Jacob C., Jr., 1928
Leonard, James B., J1944
Leonard, John Jr., 1831
Leonard, W. L., 1874
Leone, Michael R., 1967
Leone, Peter Pascal, 1936
Leonhardt, Samuel Chester, 1889
Leopold, Howard Charles, 1932
Leopold, Ronald S., 1984
LePar, Edwin, 1957
Lepie, Richard M., 1969
Lepoff, Norman J., 1977
Lerch, Charles Edmund, 1905
Lerch, Thomas Van Reed, 1937
LerMan, Robert H., 1966
Lermann, William Walsh, 1916
Lerner, Helen B., 1981
Lerner, Joseph, 1934
Lerner, Lori A., 1984
Lerner, Macy Levi, 1914
Lerner, Sidney Simon, 1947
Lerner, William D., 1966

LeRoy, Pierre L., 1956
Lerro, Furey A., 1969
Lescher, Edwin R., 1908
Lescher, Lyell J., 1877
Leschey, William H., Jr., 1963
Leschingski, Robert F., 1987
Lesh, Vincent O., 1932
Lesher, David T., 1880
Lesko, Samuel M., 1977
Leslie, LeRoy K., 1889
Leslie, Warren Deck, 1943
Lesniak, John P., 1961
Lesnow, Jack M., 1931
Lesse, Henry, 1950
Lesse, S. Michael, 1935
Lesse, Stanley, 1945
Lessey, Arthur Gerald, 1940
Lessey, Davis S., 1853
Lessig, Harry C., 1878
Lester, James D., 1852
Lester, James R., 1860
LeStrange, Thomas A., J1944
Letcher, Charles W., 1930
Lethiecq, Joseph Albert, 1894
Letson, James A., Jr., 1966
Letterman, Jonathan, 1849
Leute, Millard S., 1952
Leute, William R., Jr., S1944
Lev, Ian M., 1968
Lev, Ralph, 1948
Levan, Daniel Henry, 1866
LeVan, Gerald W., 1921
Levan, Walter Adam, 1890
Levenberg, Steven, 1979
Levengood, Brooklyn B., 1889
Levenson, Morton W., 1937
Leventhal, Gottlieb Samuel, 1927
Leventhal, Janet B., 1979
Leventhal, Louis, 1939
Leventhal, Nathan Lewis, 1904
Lever, John D. F., 1860
Levering, Joseph H., 1839
Levi, Leo Meyer, 1927
Levick, Alfred David, 1933
Levick, Leonard J., 1946
Levick, Stanley Nelson, 1954
Levien, David Arnold, 1901
Levin, Alex V., 1982
Levin, Andrew J., 1976
Levin, David W., 1947
Levin, Ellis R., 1975
Levin, Gary J., 1973
Levin, Gene D., 1967
Levin, Harvey A., 1964
Levin, Harvey M., 1960
Levin, Israel, 1924
Levin, Kenneth, 1977
Levin, Louis, 1919

Levin, Matthew W., 1985
Levin, Moses Jordan, 1919
Levin, Norman P., 1976
Levin, Raphael A., 1939
Levin, Robert M., 1977
Levin, Stephen A., 1967
Levin, Steven P., 1986
Levin, Warren M., 1956
Levine, Arnold Sidney, 1937
Levine, Marc Jason, 1990
Levine, Raphael K., 1965
Levine, Sidney Charles, 1916
Levinsky, Joseph J., 1972
Levinson, John M., 1953
Levinson, Louis E., 1962
Levinson, Nat E., 1978
Levinson, Sander J., 1969
Levinson, Stuart A., 1965
Levinson, William D., 1945
Levintow, Leon, 1946
Levis, Mahlon M., 1833
Levis, Richard J., 1848
Levitsky, David A., 1951
Levitt, Donald G., 1956
Levitt, Michael Lewis, 1906
Levitt, Richard L., 1965
Levitt, Robert S., 1963
Levy, Alan B., 1964
Levy, Alfred E., 1978
Levy, Charles P., 1870
Levy, Charles, 1928
Levy, Edwin J., 1943
Levy, Jacob Julius, 1928
Levy, Jacob, 1908
Levy, Michael H., 1976
Lewbart, Marvin L., 1957
Lewellyn, John S., Jr., 1852
LeWinn, Emmanuel Sigmund, 1937
LeWinn, Laurence R., 1966
Lewis, Albert Gamaliel, Jr., 1945
Lewis, Arthur Kenneth, 1924
Lewis, Benjamin Sykes, 1888
Lewis, Charles I., 1858
Lewis, Cyril Ettrick, 1904
Lewis, Daniel W., 1860
Lewis, Daniel W., 1909
Lewis, Daniel W., J1944
Lewis, David H., 1877
Lewis, David William, 1846
Lewis, Donald Burns, 1950
Lewis, Earl T., 1954
Lewis, Edmund Henry, 1887
Lewis, Edward C., 1862
Lewis, Estell Budd, 1899
Lewis, Eugene R., 1874
Lewis, Fielding Otis, 1906
Lewis, Francis West, 1846
Lewis, George H., 1830

Lewis, George R., 1857
Lewis, George Walter, 1917
Lewis, Gregory L., 1975
Lewis, Isaiah M., 1858
Lewis, Ivor F., 1976
Lewis, J. Henry, 1851
Lewis, James E., 1855
Lewis, James M., 1850
Lewis, James S., 1982
Lewis, James, 1868
Lewis, John E., 1931
Lewis, John Henry, 1878
Lewis, John S., 1868
Lewis, John Saunders, Jr., 1914
Lewis, Joseph Addison, 1847
Lewis, Joseph G., 1986
Lewis, Kenneth S., 1974
Lewis, Le Roy, 1878
Lewis, Magnus M., 1846
Lewis, Major G., 1840
Lewis, Marvin O., 1946
Lewis, Maurice J., 1961
Lewis, Michael R., 1972
Lewis, Milton L., 1950
Lewis, Norman, 1897
Lewis, Richard E., 1850
Lewis, Robert Edward, Jr., S1944
Lewis, Robert S., 1856
Lewis, Thomas M., 1857
Lewis, W. H.A., 1869
Lewis, William E., 1878
Lewis, William H., 1888
Lewis, William H., 1893
Lewis, William J., 1970
Lewis, William M., 1837
Lewis, Willis Gaylord, 1890
Lewis, Zachary, 1834
LeWitt, Michael H., 1974
Lewitt, William, 1855
Lewkowicz, Charles John, 1972
Leyburn, John, 1858
Leyda, Paul Leighton, 1909
Leydic, Cyrus Clark, 1908
Leydic, Cyrus Clark, Jr., 1941
Leymeister, Martin Luther, 1935
Leytze, Frank Cornelius, 1904
Li, Benjamin Luka, 1929
Li, Gail Gar Lyai, 1947
Li, John C., 1987
Li, Min Hin, 1922
Li-Ma, Gaylyn G. L., 1978
Liao, Jeanne, Min-Li, 1987
Liberace, Ettore Valentino, 1932
Liberman, Miryam, 1979
Liberman, Orlin M., 1982
Libonati, Margaret M., 1965
Lichliter, David C., 1879
Lichstein, Jacob, 1932

Lichtenfeld, Karen M., 1972
Lichtenstein, Mark D., 1976
Lichtenstein, Stephen B., 1974
Lichtmann, Manfred W., 1963
Lichty, Samuel M., 1886
Liddy, Thomas J., 1959
Lide, Lewis Maxwell, 1921
Lide, William R., 1859
Lieber, Marshall Max, 1930
Lieberman, David J., 1950
Lieberman, Joseph A., III, 1964
Liebman, Irvin M., 1961
Liebreich, Mark E., 1987
Liekweg, William G., Jr., 1970
Lien, Jean M., 1984
Ligato, Vincent Anthony, 1977
Liggett, Caleb, 1845
Liggett, Charles L., S1944
Liggett, Charles L., Jr., 1973
Liggett, John S., 1942
Liggett, John S., Jr., 1976
Liggett, Samuel J., 1878
Liggett, Scott P., 1977
Light, Harry G., 1955
Light, John H., 1943
Light, Lincoln Reigel, 1892
Light, Wilma C., 1971
Lightcap, Clement A., 1941
Lightfoot, Gross R., 1877
Lighthizer, Charles William, 1928
Lightner, Samuel B., 1863
Lihn, Henry, 1938
Lilien, Otto M., 1949
Lilla, Robert Stephen, 1925
Lilli, Elmo J., 1958
Lillibridge, Byron J., 1883
Lillington, George, 1850
Lim, John P., 1934
Lim, Nyok K., 1980
Limberg, F. A., 1875
Limeres, Jose R., 1950
Limeres-Jimenez, Jose Rafael, 1950
Limquico, Jose D., 1918
Lin, Angela E., 1980
Lin, Dennis S., 1987
Lin, Rosina P., 1990
Lin, Sheldon S., 1989
Linard, Donald Herbert, 1926
Lincoff, Milton H., 1949
Lincoff, William, 1949
Lincoln, George W., 1902
Lincoln, James B., 1883
Lincoln, James, 1878
Lind, John Y., 1841
Lindell, Marvin M., 1949
Lindeman, Adam, 1884
Lindemuth, Edmund K., Jr., 1953
Lindenheim, Norman, Jr., 1962

Lindenmuth, Norman W., 1972
Lindenmuth, Woodrow Wilson, 1938
Lindes, Conrad, 1974
Lindes, DeArmond, 1946
Lindley, Alfred H., 1850
Lindley, Don Carlos, 1901
Lindley, Henry S., 1866
Lindley, Horace S., 1849
Lindley, Lutellus W., 1873
Lindley, Samuel H., 1875
Lindner, Henry H., 1984
Lindquist, Charles Ariel, 1923
Lindquist, John N., 1943
Lindsay, Andrew, 1855
Lindsay, Bruce D., 1977
Lindsay, Horace F., 1847
Lindsay, James E., 1859
Lindsay, John, 1890
Lindsay, Reuben, 1850
Lindsay, Robert Boyd, 1940
Lindsay, Thomas Edgar, 1929
Lindsey, Beth H., 1979
Lindsey, Hugh N., 1848
Lindsey, James W., 1886
Line, William M., 1851
Lineaweaver, George P., 1852
Lineaweaver, John K., 1861
Lineaweaver, Simeon T., 1864
Linebaugh, Harry W., 1876
Linebaugh, Joseph T., 1873
Lineberry, William T., Jr., 1945
Lineberry, William Taylor, 1915
Ling, Henry T., 1986
Lingo, Douglass, 1846
Link, William, 1850
Linn, Alexander, 1836
Linn, Alexander E., 1847
Linn, G. A., 1869
Linn, Theodore A., 1850
Linn, William H., 1848
Linsz, Henri Philip, 1894
Lintgen, Arthur B., 1966
Lintgen, Isidor Charles, 1925
Linthicum, Richard Lee, 1887
Linthicum, Rufus, Jr., 1859
Linton, Dale, 1975
Linton, Jay Dever, 1902
Linton, Thomas P., 1838
Linton, William B., 1886
Lintz, David I., 1970
Lintz, Robert M., 1978
Linville, Montgomery, 1873
Lipinski, Joseph F., Jr., 1966
Lipinski, Joseph Floyd, 1937
Lipkin, Philip, 1965
Lipp, Edward B., Jr., 1960
Lippe, Richard D., 1963
Lippincott, Ahab Haines, 1892

Lippincott, DeWitt G., 1883
Lippincott, Franklin B., 1864
Lippincott, George C., 1875
Lippincott, Henry, 1864
Lippincott, J. A., 1873
Lippincott, Jesse Diverty, 1894
Lippitt, William F., 1853
Lippman, Nathan Louis, 1939
Lippy, George Dewey, 1924
Lipschultz, Sandor F., 1963
Lipschutz, Harold, 1954
Lipshutz, Benjamin, 1912
Lipshutz, Herbert, S1944
Lipsitz, Hyman David, 1975
Lipson, Richard L., 1956
Lipton, Jeffrey F., 1987
Lisehora, George B., 1984
Lisle, James W., 1842
Lisle, Justin D., 1882
Liss, Henry R., 1948
Lissner, Arthur Bart, 1955
Lista, William A., 1955
Litch, Wilbur F., 1865
Litchfield, Paul Nathan, 1895
Littell, Norval W., 1853
Litten, Frank, 1887
Little, Edwin P., 1980
Little, J. Warren, 1883
Little, Jehu, 1877
Little, John Forsyth, 1904
Little, Joseph Rice, 1942
Little, Lonnie M., 1925
Little, Nancy A., 1983
Little, Robert G., Jr., 1967
Little, William Seely, 1877
Littlepage, George C., 1877
Littleton, Henry Ward, 1915
Litz, Jefferson, 1862
Liu Foo-Sen, Arthur, 1934
Liu, Curtis R., 1978
Liu, Donald Chua, 1990
Liu, Ellen A., 1987
Liu, Evan Y., 1984
Liu, Gordon Foo-Hin, 1948
Liu, Jeffrey E., 1987
Liu, Randal J., 1987
Livesay, Susan, 1989
Livezey, Abraham, 1845
Livingood, Horace F., 1882
Livingood, John Elias, 1913
Livingood, Louis A., 1854
Livingood, Louis J., 1917
Livingood, Michael T., 1849
Livingston, Elizabeth R., 1989
Livingston, Paul, 1910
Livingston, Walter Raleigh, 1917
Lizerbram, Frances W., 1989
Lizerbram, Martin H., 1965

Lloyd, David Corey, 1867
Lloyd, Edward Morris, 1886
Lloyd, John Hepburn, 1896
Lloyd, Thomas V., III, 1966
Lloyd, William E., 1878
Lo, Alan Yung-Tsu, 1990
Lo, Theodore C. M., 1970
Lober, William N., 1920
Loberant, Norman G., 1970
Lochhead, Harris Burton, 1902
Lock, John H., 1883
Lockard, Daniel H., 1880
Lockard, James W., Jr., 1980
Locke, Charles J., 1972
Locke, Samuel T., 1847
Locke, W. H., 1840
Lockett, William Robert, 1899
Lockhart, Wilson, 1853
Lockwood, George A., 1870
Lockwood, George Bertrand, 1897
Lockwood, James Harrison, 1941
Lockwood, John S., 1874
Lockwood, N. S., 1858
Lockwood, Timothy T., 1835
Locuson, Joseph S., 1853
Loder, Earl Samuel, 1933
Loder, John L., 1968
Loder, N. Sherman, 1884
Loder, Percival E., 1875
Lodise, Raymond J., 1959
Loeb, Louis, 1895
Loeb, Ludwig, 1890
Loeliger, William N., 1980
Loeling, Gerhard, 1874
Loewenberg, Leopold S., 1956
Loewy, Ignatz David, 1903
Lofland, Mark Greer, 1852
Loftin, James Merrill, 1860
Loftus, James B., 1948
Loftus, John Edward, 1916
Loftus, Joseph A., 1945
Loftus, Thomas J., 1977
Loftus, Thomas M., J1944
Logan John Adams, 1916
Logan, Edward Johnson, 1903
Logan, John Bronson, 1948
Logan, John E., 1859
Logan, Matthew D., 1850
Logan, P. W., 1861
Logan, Samuel Gilmore, 1901
Logan, Samuel, 1855
Logan, Thomas Megowan, 1927
Logan, William E., 1968
Logue, John G., 1842
Loh, Gary T., 1980
Lohman, James W., 1965
Lohmann, John, Jr., 1934
Lohnes, James, Jr., 1934

Lohr, Dermot, 1934
Lohrmann, Henry, 1900
Loken, Susan C., 1980
Loller, William B., 1863
Loman, Matthew F., 1880
Lomax, Joseph, 1932
Lombardi, Anthony C., 1971
Lombardo, Joseph A., 1978
Lomison, Henry G., 1852
Londergan, Thomas A., 1988
London, Elizabeth Ann, 1971
Long, Andrew, 1852
Long, Charles, 1882
Long, Delbert E., Jr., 1955
Long, H. Horace, 1868
Long, J. Stephen, 1985
Long, John Wesley, 1848
Long, Joseph P., 1939
Long, Kimberly R., 1978
Long, Lemuel L., 1883
Long, Melville Hammond, 1914
Long, Miguel Andres, 1919
Long, Paul R., 1976
Long, Reuben K., 1848
Long, Richard H., Jr., 1986
Long, Robert P., 1878
Long, Robert Schofield, 1940
Long, Robert W., 1866
Long, Ronald A., 1983
Long, Roy Hamilton, 1916
Long, Samuel H., 1849
Long, Sarah S., 1970
Long, Solomon, 1856
Long, William Fegely, 1902
Long, William Henry, Jr., 1896
Long, William Hillwell, Jr., 1892
Longacre, Aaron M., 1961
Longacre, Frederick W., 1877
Longaker, George M., Jr., 1938
Longaker, Horace G., 1915
Longanecker, William A., 1876
Longenbach, Eric W., 1981
Longenecker Benjamin E., 1949
Longenecker, David F., 1876
Longenecker, John Henry, 1846
Longfellow, Austin Harris, 1889
Longfellow, Charles Fay, 1904
Longfellow, Jacob Winslow, 1899
Longino, Thomas Dick, 1882
Longnecker, Benjamin F., 1859
Longnecker, Robert E., 1965
Longo, James Augustus, 1912
Longo, Santo, 1963
Longsdorf, W. Harry, 1856
Longshaw, Thomas Elmer, 1901
Longshore, Ashbel B., 1846
Longshore, William Allen, Jr., 1941
Longstreth, Morris, 1876

Longwill, Robert L., 1863
Loomis, Charles Hepford, 1948
Loomis, James W., 1956
Loos, Isaac B., 1888
Loper, James, 1836
Loper, John C., 1903
Loper, William F., 1863
Lopes, John David, 1950
Lopez, Bernard L., 1986
Lopez, Joseph H., 1876
Lopez-Garcia, Ana Maria, 1988
Loprest, Lorraine Jo, 1986
Lorah, Kevin N., 1985
Lord, Simon L., 1875
Lore, Andrew Provost, 1906
Lore, Harry Elmer, 1905
Lorentz, William B., Jr., 1963
Lorraine, Richard S., 1982
Lorry, Ralph W., 1926
Lort, Joseph, 1870
Lothrop, James E., 1848
Lott, Harry Hunter, 1907
Lott, J. Howard, 1878
Loucks, Charles Edward, 1891
Loucks, James Howe, 1956
Loud, Watson, 1833
Louder, Austin J., 1872
Loughead, John R., Jr., 1954
Loughlin, Dennis J., 1881
Loughlin, James Eneu, 1868
Loughran, James Joseph, 1909
Loughran, James P., 1985
Loughran, Terence, 1834
Loughridge, Samuel O., 1866
Loughridge, Samuel Steen, 1890
Loux, Hiram R., 1882
Love, Carol A., 1978
Love, Frank Seymour, 1887
Love, Harry M. P., 1966
Love, Jack W., Jr., 1962
Love, John King, 1897
Love, John S., 1856
Love, Louis F., 1881
Love, Walter Standlee, 1921
Lovejoy, James W.H., 1851
Lovelace, Lemuel M., 1868
Lovelace, Roger David, 1953
Lovell, Albert G., 1865
Loveren, George Stillman, 1907
Lovett, Henry, 1888
Lovett, Joseph Cook, 1911
Lovett, William J., 1980
Loving, Joseph F., 1853
Lovrinic, Daniel, F., 1966
Lovrinic, William S., 1963
Low, Chin Wen, 1918
Lowber, Alexander, 1882
Lowe, Clement Belton, 1887

Lowe, David Earl, 1912
Lowell, Francis Carroll, 1913
Lowell, Paul, 1913
Lowengrund, Lee, 1878
Lowenstein, Edward Howard, 1975
Lowentrout, Oscar B., 1895
Lowerison Ellmore H., 1883
Lowery, Welles James, 1882
Lowman, Alonzo, 1881
Lowman, John, 1850
Lowman, John Bodine, 1895
Lowman, Webster B., 1867
Lowman, William G., 1855
Lowndes, Charles T., 1864
Lownes, John Barton, 1906
Lowrie, James A., 1831
Lowright, J. Harvey, 1881
Lowry, Forrest Ellsworth, 1931
Lowry, James L., 1878
Lowry, Jonathan C., 1989
Lowry, Silvanus Todd, 1867
Lowry, Squire M., 1861
Lowry, Welles Norwood, Jr., 1957
Lozman, Harvey, 1962
Lubat, Edward, 1982
Lubicky, John P., 1974
Lubin, Jack, 1959
Lubin, Jeffrey H., 1980
Lubkin, Cary L., 1982
Lublin, Fred D., 1972
Lucarella, Joseph Anthony, 1957
Lucarella, Vanessa J., 1983
Lucas, George Lee, Jr., 1852
Lucas, Robert Sloan, 1927
Lucas, Walter Scott, 1910
Lucas, William Frederick, 1930
Lucchesi, Pascal Francis, 1926
Luck, Benjamin D., 1903
Luckett, Charles Davis, 1889
Luckett, Charles Luther, 1928
Luckett, Francis E., 1851
Luckett, George T., 1853
Luckey, Paul David, 1926
Luckner, Wendelin George, 1938
Luczynski, Edward W., Jr., 1956
Luders, John Amandus, 1935
Ludwig, David Boyd, 1911
Ludwig, Peter W.B., 1868
Luff, Jefferson M., 1881
Luffbary, M. Jones, 1884
Luft, Friedrich C., 1968
Lugenbeel, James W., 1850
Luhr, Alfred Francis, 1905
Luhr, Augustine Charles, 1908
Luhr, John Paul, 1946
Lukehart, Joseph Madison, 1910
Lukens, Isaiah, 1890
Lukens, Robert McDowell, 1912

Lukens, Robert W., Jr., 1955
Lull, Clifford Bell, 1915
Lull, Clifford Bell, Jr., 1948
Lull, George Fairless, 1909
Lull, George Fairless, Jr., 1940
Luman, Clark McEwen, 1904
Lumish, Robert M., 1970
Lummis, Frederick Rice, 1913
Lumpkin, Bryan H., 1952
Lumpkin, Forrest E., Jr., 1946
Lumpkin, James M., 1856
Lumpkin, Samuel P., 1855
Lund, Oliver Pancoast, 1886
Lundberg, George A. F., 1919
Lundberg, George A. F., Jr., 1953
Lundgren, Eric C., 1986
Lundgren, Wilbert G., 1956
Lungerhausen, Carl Oscar, 1928
Lungren, Samuel S., 1850
Lunn, Lewis Thomas, 1856
Luongo, Peter A., 1989
Luongo, Romeo A., 1954
Lupfer, Samuel P., 1865
Lupin, Gordon W., 1951
Lupo, Deonis M., 1931
Lupold, Georgetta D., 1974
Lupton, Albert Marsee, 1939
Lupu, Janice, 1978
Luschinskey, Walter, 1920
Luscombe, Herbert A., 1940
Luscombe, Herbert J., 1968
Luscombe, Susan, 1975
Lushbough, Bruce C., 1958
Lussier, George A., 1964
Lussier, Raphael Andre, 1935
Lussy, William J., 1947
Lustberg, Sam R., 1919
Luster, George Edgar, 1893
Lustig, Melvin, 1938
Lustig, Robert A., 1969
Luther, Martin, 1848
Lutterloh, I. Hayden, 1952
Lutterloh, Isaac Hayden, 1921
Lutton, Charles E., 1961
Lutz, Edgar H., 1936
Lutz, Francis Creveling, 1923
Lutz, R. Bruce, III, 1982
Lutz, R. Bruce, Jr., 1951
Lutz, William Miller, 1936
Luzenberg, Charles A., 1827
Lybbert, Glen D., 1986
Lychak, John C., 1950
Lyerly, James Miller, 1931
Lyle, James Nathaniel, 1867
Lyle, John W., 1882
Lyman, Andrew B., 1852
Lyman, J. Baldwin, 1857
Lyman, James Francis, 1933

Lyman, Joseph W., 1849
Lynch, David J., 1984
Lynch, Edward Thomas, 1931
Lynch, George Michael, 1978
Lynch, John Edward, 1935
Lynch, John F., Jr., J1944
Lynch, Marjorie P., 1980
Lynch, Robert E., 1957
Lynch, Samuel Edward, 1887
Lynch, Thomas James, 1910
Lynch, Thomas Sturgis, 1952
Lynch, Vincent Aloysius, 1938
Lynch, William F., 1952
Lynd, Clifford W., Jr., 1971
Lynde, Uri Colvin, 1866
Lynn, B. W., 1855
Lynn, John T., 1953
Lynn, Walter Leonard, 1916
Lynott, Paul J., 1986
Lyon, Charles L., 1842
Lyon, Emory, 1847
Lyon, George B., 1884
Lyon, Richard Henry, 1909
Lyon, Thayer Claude, 1923
Lyon, Thomas, 1833
Lyon, Thomas, 1838
Lyon, William Reynolds, 1895
Lyons, Fowler, 1891
Lyons, James Chalmers, 1909
Lyons, Lawrence H., Jr., 1976
Lyons, Ralph, 1932
Lystash, John C., 1982
Lytel, Frederick, 1955
Lytle, Carl S., 1932
Lytle, Creighton L., 1948
Lytle, George E., 1877
Lytle, Nelson K., 1976
Lytle, Ralph McKay, 1912

~ M ~

Ma Koon Tuck, 1949
Maas, James C., 1971
Mabey, Orson H., Jr., 1951
Mabey, Orson Henry, 1919
Mabey, Rex G., 1956
Mabey, Rex G., Jr., 1985
Mabon, Thomas, 1852
Mabry, James F., 1852
Mabry, Lucien L., 1857
MacAndrew, Raymond N., 1947
MacAndrew, Vincent I., 1945
MacAndrew, Vincent I., Jr., 1984
Macaulay, George, Jr., 1886
Macauley, C. N.B., 1882
Macbeth, L. Craig, 1949
MacCallum, Wallace Peter, 1904
MacCarroll, D. Randall, 1901

MacConkey, Harmar Hendrix, 1934
MacConnell, William G., 1876
MacCord, George Thornton, 1879
MacDonald, Alden B., 1904
MacDonald, Gerard L., 1965
MacDonald, John, 1879
MacDonald, Warren F., Jr., 1972
MacDowell, Samuel Ira, 1897
Mace, Henry Fancher, 1899
Mace, Lloyd Russell, 1905
Mace, William G., 1860
MacElree, George Anderson, 1894
Macfarland, Burr W., 1888
MacFarlane, A. Radford, 1982
MacFarlane, James P., 1905
Macfarlane, Menzies J., 1913
MacGaughey, James David, Jr., 1910
Machete, Frank, 1898
Machiko, Gregory G., 1985
Machle, Edward Charles, 1889
MacIndoe, John H., 1969
MacIntosh, James William, 1898
Mack, Charles Beaver, 1910
Mackall, James I., 1960
MacKay, Gregory D., 1985
MacKelcan, Douglas W., 1945
Mackell, James V., 1946
Mackell, James V., Jr., 1969
Mackell, Thomas E., 1972
Mackenzie, Egbert Gray, 1905
Mackenzie, Thomas G., 1848
Mackey, Alexander S., 1855
Mackey, James G., Jr., 1955
Mackey, James Howard, 1851
Mackey, James W., 1863
Mackie John Howell, 1850
Mackie, Benjamin S., 1866
Mackie, John Alfred, 1923
Mackin, Glenn A., 1983
Mackle, Edward Joseph, 1990
Mackler, Louis, 1917
Mackmull, M. Gulden, 1925
MacKnight, Richard Patton, 1914
Mackowiak, Robert Carl, 1964
Mackowski, Herbert William, 1933
Mackrell, William P., 1957
Maclay, Archibald I., 1874
Maclay, John, 1882
Maclay, Joseph Alan, 1902
MacMillan, Robert M., 1969
MacMoran, Jay W., 1950
MacMurdy, Carlyle Kedzie, 1908
Macneill, Norman Merle, 1916
MacNichol, Bernard W., 1884
MacOdrum, Angus, 1900
Macom, Vorrie B., 1962
Macon, Roland Bain, 1901
Macones, Alexnader J., Jr., 1984

Macones, George A., 1988
Macpherson, William, 1866
Macri, Anthony J., 1962
Macy, Philip A., III, 1971
Madara, Glenn S., 1983
Madara, James W., 1876
Madara, John S., 1945
Madden, Charles D., 1871
Madden, Edmund H., 1866
Madden, Francis P., 1967
Madden, W. Scott, 1876
Maddock, Louis, 1893
Maddox, John Dayton, 1889
Maddox, John Z., 1855
Maddox, William R., 1877
Maddrey, Milner Crocker, 1931
Maddux, James Tolbert, Jr., 1957
Madeira, James Y. D., 1883
Madigan, Robert R., 1967
Madill, Thomas F., 1855
Madison, Charles P., 1858
Madison, James A., 1850
Madison, Robert L., 1851
Madonick, Harvey L., 1985
Madura, Joseph R., 1952
Maerz, John C., 1951
Maerz, John C., Jr., 1979
Maeso, Manuel M., 1921
Magargee, Edward M., 1964
Magargee, Edward R., 1986
Magee, James Carre, 1905
Magee, John C., 1988
Magee, John T., 1957
Magee, Richard Samuel, 1916
Magee, T. James, 1866
Magen, Andrea B., 1986
Magenheim, Herbert G., 1959
Maghee, William H., 1881
Magill, Hugh R., 1904
Magill, Ian D., 1984
Magill, Thomas, 1855
Magilner, Arthur D., 1963
Magley, R. Scott, 1982
Magley, Robert C., 1956
Magnus, E. R. Max, 1888
Magrath, Joseph L., Jr., 1956
Magrath, Joseph Leo, 1927
Magraw, George Thomas, 1897
Magruder, Archibald S., 1838
Magruder, George W., 1859
Maguda, Thomas A., 1939
Maguire, David P., 1982
Maguire, Joseph I., 1955
Maguire, Joseph I., 1983
Maguire, Leo J., III, 1980
Maguire, Leo J., Jr., 1952
Maguire, Randall F., 1975
Mahan, John M., 1877

Mahan, Robert G., 1967
Maher, Paul J., 1966
Mahla, Michael E., 1979
Maholtz, Michele S., 1985
Mahon, Alfred Neale, 1897
Mahon, John B., 1882
Mahon, Ormsby S., 1849
Mahon, William T., 1883
Mahoney, Jack L., 1952
Mahoney, James W., 1972
Mahoney, John Edwin, 1906
Mahoney, John T., 1965
Mahoney, Michael, 1839
Mahood, William H., 1960
Maier, Ernest George, 1905
Maier, Frederick Hurst, 1894
Maiese, Russell L., 1988
Maillard, Philogene P., 1828
Mailman, Wendy R., 1985
Main, Elijah W., 1859
Maines, Robert G., 1863
Mainker, William S., 1963
Mainzer, Francis S., 1926
Mainzer, Peter George, 1926
Mainzer, Thomas R., 1957
Maioriello, Richard P., 1964
Mairs, Atlee, 1910
Mairs, John C., 1852
Maisel, Albert Lloyd, 1939
Maitin, Ian B., 1989
Majeski, Henry John, 1929
Make, Barry J., 1970
Makowski, Israel, 1930
Makuen, George Hudson, 1889
Malachesky, Thomas Michael, 1975
Malatesta, Joseph Mark, 1886
Malcarney, Courtney M., 1962
Malcolm, John A., Jr., 1959
Maldonado, Ferdinand Nicholas, 1891
Malech, Herman F., 1876
Maleson, Franklin G., 1965
Maletta, Karen A., 1987
Maletz, Frank W., 1978
Malfara, Joseph Francis, 1956
Malia, Edward Regis, 1950
Malia, Joseph Eugene, 1940
Malin, Seth A., 1970
Malin, Thomas H., 1965
Malit, Lee A., 1969
Maliver, Leonard E., 1980
Mallek, Anthony Stephen, 1920
Malleus, Stephanie, 1980
Malley, William L., 1941
Mallory, Edwin H., 1891
Mally, S. Stuart, 1949
Malone, G. Dwight, 1976
Malone, Joseph H., 1856
Maloney, Francis Dunn, 1932

Maloney, Maurice, 1897
Maloney, Richard M., 1875
Malovany, Robert John, 1970
Malster, John Charles, 1896
Malyk, Bohdan, 1968
Mambu, Joseph F., 1973
Mamo, George J., 1986
Mamourian, Alexander C., 1978
Manahan, Charles Albert, 1909
Manahan, Valentine, 1850
Manashil, Gordon B., 1966
Mancini, Joseph A., 1989
Mancino, Peter J., 1958
Mancoll, Morris Max, 1928
Mancoll, William, 1960
Mandalaskas, Nicholas J., 1985
Mandel, Harold, 1981
Mandel, Harvey I., 1955
Mandel, Martin M., 1947
Mandel, Richard J., 1976
Mandel, Sheldon R., 1971
Mandelberg, Charles A., 1982
Mandell, Gerald A., 1969
Mandell, Herbert E., 1975
Maness, Archibald Kelly, 1928
Maney, Samuel B., 1859
Manfredi, John A., 1966
Mang, Justin, 1969
Manganiello, Paul D., 1973
Manges, John P., 1936
Manges, John P., Jr., 1968
Manges, Krista A., 1988
Manges, Lewis C., 1932
Manges, W. Bosley, S1944
Manges, Willis Edmund, 1942
Manges, Willis Fastnacht 1903
Mangum, Charles Preston, 1918
Mangum, Charles Stapler, 1894
Mangus, Julian Edward, 1940
Manin, Gordon Charles, 1990
Manion, James Lorne, 1910
Manley, James S., 1986
Manley, John Edward, 1928
Manley, John Gerard, 1926
Mann, Abraham Leon, 1912
Mann, Augustine, A., 1860
Mann, C. Regulus, 1868
Mann, Charles H., 1874
Mann, George Wagner, 1882
Mann, Harold J., 1951
Mann, Hillard, S1944
Mann, I. Thurman, 1912
Mann, James Packard, 1887
Mann, Joseph B., 1845
Mann, Joseph Jacob, 1955
Mann, Lester, 1947
Mann, Lowell D., 1957
Mann, Robert J., 1981

Mann, Stephen C., 1973
Mann, William B., 1843
Mannella, Randall G., 1985
Mannes, Harvey A., 1968
Manning, Charles Jacob, 1889
Manning, Charles LaForge, 1903
Manning, David Franklin, 1889
Manning, Harrison Martin, 1912
Manning, John H., 1835
Manning, Richard G., 1983
Manning, William J., 1895
Mannino, David M., III, 1981
Manser, Jeannne I., 1975
Mansfield, James Albert, 1896
Mansfield, Lyndon E., 1968
Mansfield, Paul F., 1983
Mansfield, Richard S., 1853
Mansker, Joseph Solomon, 1935
Mansmann, Herbert C., Jr., 1951
Mansmann, James Andrew, 1934
Mansmann, Kevin A., 1981
Mansmann, Paris T., 1984
Mantz, Herbert Leslie, 1920
Many, Harry Crawford, 1897
Manz, Donald L., 1955
Manz, John Henry, 1887
Mapow, Larry S., 1974
Mapp, John L., 1860
Marable, George B., 1846
Marable, Henry H., 1836
Marable, John H., 1837
Marable, Joseph E., 1853
Maraskco, Richard M., 1961
Maravich, Nick, Jr., 1989
Marbarger, George S., 1894
Marbourg, Edgar Marcella, 1888
Marbourg, Frank Bower, 1888
Marbourg, H. W., 1858
Marbourg, J. L., 1856
Marbourg, Jeremiah L., 1888
Marbourg, M., 1859
Marcelli, Gene A., Jr., 1980
Marcello, Richard P., 1975
Marcello, Robert S., 1979
March, Conrad Francis, 1949
March, Linton Ellsworth, 1934
March, Noreen Marie, 1967
Marchand Thomas S., 1843
Marchand, Gilles A., 1964
Marchand, James I., 1862
Marchand, Victor H., 1884
Marchand, William King, 1862
Marchant, DeForrest W., 1985
Marchesani, John A., 1955
Marchlewski, Walter F., Jr., 1980
Marcil, George Edward, 1926
Marcks, Kerwin Mathias, 1930
Marcum, Stephen C., 1981

Marcus, Edwin Murray, 1959
Marcus, Jospeh Harvey, 1914
Marcy, Erastus E., 1837
Marder, Carey M., 1972
Marencik, James G., 1974
Marenus, Edward Benjamin, 1938
Margiotta, Michael S., 1987
Margolies, Richard P., 1980
Margolis, Eric J., 1980
Margolis, Mitchell L., 1977
Margolis, Stephen H., 1971
Margossian, Arshag Der, 1901
Margulies, Kenneth B., 1986
Margulies, Michael C., 1971
Marinari, Rosalie K., 1972
Marine, Robert M., 1953
Marino, Dante E., 1947
Marino, Joseph N., 1942
Marino, Kathleen M., 1988
Marino, Ralph J., 1982
Mariotti, Joseph R., 1964
Maris, Edward, 1855
Mark, James B., 1986
Markel, Henry Clayton, 1902
Markel, Isaiah F., 1876
Markel, Joseph, 1931
Markel, Maurice, 1929
Markiewitz, Andrew D., 1989
Markind, Samuel H., 1983
Markind, Simon, 1949
Markle, John Gideon, 1855
Markley, Ralph, 1931
Markmann, Daniel Paul, 1990
Markoe, James C., 1882
Markosi, Charles, Jr., 1963
Markowitz, Harry, 1924
Markowitz, Julius Leonard, 1955
Markowitz, Laurie E., 1984
Markowski, William J., 1988
Marks, Gerald, 1949
Marks, John H., 1989
Marks, Julian C., 1850
Marks, Myer, 1931
Marks, Richard M., 1988
Markunas, Francis B., 1940
Marley, H. B., 1861
Marlier, Bertrand Joseph, Jr., 1963
Marlin, T. J., 1873
Marlow, Nicholas P., 1859
Marlowe, William Anderson, 1919
Marnell, Joseph Vincente, 1936
Marnie, James G., 1945
Maro, Robert J., 1956
Maro, Robert J., Jr., 1980
Marone, Michael L., 1968
Marone, Phillip J., 1957
Maroney, Jane W., 1985
Maroney, John W., Jr., 1986

INDEX

McBride, James G., 1971
McBride, Mark J., 1987
McBride, Robert E., 1964
McBride, Thomas Elliott, 1925
McBride, Thomas J., 1948
McBride, Thomas K., 1871
McBride, Thomas Sutch, 1910
McBride, William G., 1837
McBride, William W., 1951
McBryar, William Lyle, 1886
McBurney, Charles Fred, 1897
McCaa, David J., 1867
McCabe, Edward Burnard, J1944
McCabe, James L., III, 1988
McCabe, James L., Jr., 1959
McCabe, Paul H., 1987
McCadden, Joseph A., 1956
McCafferty, John P., 1943
McCaffrey, Hugh Edward, 1905
McCahey, James Francis, 1921
McCahey, Peter, 1885
McCain, Hugh White, 1909
McCain, Walkup Kennard, 1929
McCairns, Robert G., Jr., 1976
McCall, Douglas S., 1962
McCall, J. Harvey, 1910
McCall, Jane, 1980
McCall, Robert E., 1936
McCallion, Luther Layton, 1942
McCallister, Charles H., 1879
McCallmont, Henry, 1836
McCallum, Arthur Storey, 1922
McCallum, Chester Harold, 1905
McCallum, Donald, 1872
McCallum, James A., 1959
McCamant, Thomas J., 1827
McCandless, A. W., 1870
McCandless, Garrett C., 1928
McCandless, Jas. Newton, 1863
McCandless, Josiah G., 1863
McCandless, Morris D., 1878
McCandless, William C., 1881
McCandlish, Mitch, 1986
McCandliss, Henry M., 1885
McCandliss, William L., 1877
McCann Robert C., 1858
McCann, E. W., 1873
McCann, James P., 1976
McCann, Julia A., 1989
McCann, William D., 1961
McCanna, John Milton, 1905
McCants, W. J., 1858
McCarrell, James R., 1883
McCarron, Joseph Patrick, 1939
McCarten, Robert Emmett, 1910
McCarter, Joseph D., 1883
McCarter, Robert H., 1942
McCarthy, Frank Peter, 1901

McCarthy, George E., Jr., 1962
McCarthy, George Logan, 1928
McCarthy, Henry C., 1874
McCarthy, John A., 1955
McCarthy, Justin A., 1918
McCarthy, Patrick Andrew, 1908
McCarthy, Samuel L., 1870
McCarthy, Samuel Lloyd, 1905
McCartney, J. S., 1856
McCarty, David Wilson, 1892
McCarty, James B., 1849
McCarty, Rufus H., 1875
McCarty, Thomas I., 1870
McCaskey, George W., 1877
McCaughan, James S., Jr., 1956
McCauley, Francis Joseph, 1916
McCauley, Francis P., 1929
McCay, Robert Burns, 1900
McCelvey, John Samuel, 1894
McChesney, Alexander G., 1852
McChesney, C. Thomas, Jr., 1947
McChesney, Franklin Sayre, 1888
McChesney, Robert Aurel, 1856
McChesney, William S., 1847
McClain, Harry C., 1931
McClain, S. W., 1869
McClanahan, Harry M., 1878
McClanahan, John P., 1854
McClanahan, Rice Kemper, 1898
McClarty, Hugh G., 1861
McClean, William J., 1865
McCleery, Edward Heber, 1891
McCleery, James P., 1857
McCleery, Samuel B., 1871
McCleery, William, 1827
McClellan, Ely, 1856
McClellan, Freeman, 1855
McClellan, George, 1870
McClellan, John, 1836
McClellan, R. Miller, 1879
McClellan, Robert Price, Jr., 1888
McClellan, Samuel R., 1839
McClellan, Wallace Roy, 1912
McClelland, Cochran, 1873
McClelland, James, 1837
McClelland, William F., 1849
McClements, William M., 1935
McClenahan, Thomas J., 1847
McClenathan, John C., 1881
McClendon, Joseph W., 1888
McClintic, H. D., 1856
McClintock, James, 1829
McClintock, John Laughlin, 1938
McClintock, Walter Lowrie, 1932
McClintock, Will H., 1882
McClinton, Cedric W., 1974
McCloskey, Edwin Michael, 1951
McCloskey, John R., 1970

McCloskey, Joseph Francis, 1943
McCloskey, Michael D., 1981
McCloskey, Sister Ann M., 1977
McClowry, James T., 1951
McCloy, Merritt J., 1935
McCluney, J. F., 1858
McClung, John A., 1851
McClung, Leigh, 1862
McClung, Samuel H., 1877
McClure, A. T., 1869
McClure, Frank E., 1879
McClure, Henry, 1848
McClure, James D., 1853
McClure, Joseph M., 1844
McClure, Samuel, 1846
McClure, Samuel C., 1878
McClure, William Wallace, 1864
McClurg, John R., 1846
McClurg, Walter A., 1872
McCluskey, Harry B., 1935
McClusky, Henry Lincoln, 1896
McColgan, James, 1889
McColgan, Robert, 1888
McCollester, John Q.A., 1856
McCollin, S. Mason, 1878
McCollough, A. M.F., 1877
McCollum, Ephraim J., 1853
McColly, Marst M., 1870
McComb, James, 1865
McComb, Samuel F., 1879
McCombs, William, Jr., 1882
McConaghy, Edward James, 1911
McConaughey, James Collier, 1914
McConaughy, D. W., 1858
McConaughy, Francis M., 1846
McConaughy, James, 1845
McConaughy, Robert, 1850
McConaughy, Robert, 1875
McCondichie, Wiley G., 1859
McConeghy, Robert Keating, 1908
McConihay, Clarence William, 1910
McConkey, Frank Vance, 1909
McConnell, David B., 1969
McConnell, Edward Fraser, 1897
McConnell, Edward J., III, 1976
McConnell, Edward L., Jr., S1944
McConnell, Irvin Waldo, 1934
McConnell, J. C., 1869
McConnell, Jeffrey R., 1985
McConnell, John B., 1875
McConnell, Thomas William, 1920
McConnell, Walker W., 1898
McConnell, Walter L., 1959
McConnell, William L. H., 1857
McConville, Edward B., S1944
McCool, Stanley Gaylord, 1934
McCord, Eugene Woodworth, 1890
McCord, James Robert, 1909

McCord, John Price, 1871
McCorkle, Frank White, 1917
McCorkle, J. Macon, 1881
McCorkle, John R., 1851
McCorkle, Matthew Locke, 1917
McCorkle, William A., 1855
McCorkle, William Pyles, 1897
McCorkle, William Pyles, Jr., 1933
McCormack, Condon Carleton, 1904
McCormack, John L., 1948
McCormack, Patricia A., 1986
McCormack, Raymond A., Jr., J1944
McCormick, A. Y., 1866
McCormick, Arthur Foster, 1903
McCormick, Charles, 1858
McCormick, Daniel R., 1882
McCormick, Donald John, 1922
McCormick, Horace G., 1874
McCormick, J. C., 1869
McCormick, J. F., 1864
McCormick, John Aloysius, 1897
McCormick, John Aloysius, 1935
McCormick, John F., 1970
McCormick, John, 1854
McCormick, John, 1899
McCormick, John, 1946
McCormick, Louis Provance, 1891
McCormick, S. Carson, 1862
McCormick, William H., 1854
McCormick, William Milton, 1931
McCorvey, Roosevelt, 1973
McCosh, Samuel A., 1874
McCoy, Ambrose, 1888
McCoy, Charles Wayne, 1889
McCoy, Clayton Lloyd, 1915
McCoy, Edwin Richard, 1940
McCoy, Henry W., 1864
McCoy, James Edward, 1902
McCoy, James Edward, Jr., 1936
McCoy, Robert W., Jr., 1948
McCoy, William A., 1884
McCoy, William H., III, 1972
McCranor, Charles D., 1882
McCrary, Elisha W., 1853
McCraw, Ernest Joseph, 1950
McCrea, C. S.A., 1875
McCrea, Lowrain E., 1919
McCready, James Homer, 1906
McCready, Paul J., 1980
McCready, Robert Purdon, 1905
McCrearey, J. K., 1872
McCreary, Henry, 1875
McCreery, John, 1841
McCreery, Rolla Lewis, 1895
McCrone, Elcinda L., 1983
McCrory, W. F., 1873
McCrystle, John, 1875
McCulloch, James T., 1877

McCulloch, Thomas C., 1853
McCulloch, Thomas J., 1857
McCulloch, William P., 1850
McCulloh, Samuel, 1833
McCullough Thomas P., 1847
McCullough, Adam H., 1875
McCullough, Alexander Roscoe, 1938
McCullough, Francis Joseph, 1905
McCullough, Joseph, W., 1860
McCullough, Walter James, 1918
McCullough, William Earl, 1921
McCullough, William John L., 1905
McCune, David M., 1868
McCune, Samuel R. W., 1906
McCunney, Robert J., 1976
McCurdy, Horace G., 1877
McCurdy, John M., 1859
McCurdy, Richard R. P., 1972
McCurdy, Robert S., 1947
McCurdy, William H., 1881
McCuskey, Bradford M., 1955
McCuskey, William Cecil D., 1928
McCutcheon, Royal Howard, 1915
McDade, Robert E., 1929
McDaniel, Edward Bruce, 1893
McDaniel, John R., 1867
McDaniel, Joseph Stites, 1918
McDaniel, Joseph Stites, Jr., 1939
McDaniel, William J., 1883
McDermott, Vincent T., Jr., 1960
McDermott, Vincent Thomas, 1926
McDevitt, Gordon R., Jr., 1986
McDonald, Brown, Jr., 1943
McDonald, Charles D., 1875
McDonald, David R., 1977
McDonald, Donald, 1853
McDonald, Donald J., 1948
McDonald, Edward H., 1854
McDonald, Edward Paul, 1926
McDonald, G., 1870
McDonald, John Angus, 1886
McDonald, John M., 1885
McDonald, Lester Bowman, 1924
McDonald, M. Gay, 1877
McDonald, Marilyn Manco, 1974
McDonald, Michael M., 1983
McDonald, Nesbit, 1850
McDonald, Otis, 1837
McDonald, William Stephen, 1888
McDonnel, Gerald E., 1951
McDonnel, Gerald Ellsworth, 1923
McDonnel, James K., 1983
McDonnell, Robert R., 1945
McDonnell, William V., 1947
McDonough, Gerard A., Jr., 1959
McDonough, Gilbert L., 1960
McDonough, James B., 1854
McDonough, James, 1863

McDonough, Paul G., 1956
McDougall, Charles S., 1885
McDowell, Charles L., 1959
McDowell, George M., 1855
McDowell, Harold Clyde, 1931
McDowell, James Edward, 1910
McDowell, James W., 1866
McDowell, John M., 1883
McDowell, Ralph Walker, 1905
McDowell, Samuel B., 1876
McDowell, Samuel W., 1884
McDowell, William J., 1884
McDowell, William K., 1931
McDuffie, Hector, 1854
McDyer, John Francis, 1990
McEachin, John E., 1852
McElhinney, P. P. Bliss, 1920
McElrath, James B., 1871
McElrath, Robert, 1842
McElree, Frank E., Jr., 1950
McElree, James, 1943
McElroy, Ervin, 1922
McElroy, James F., 1866
McElroy, Robert Clifton, 1937
McElwain, Guy E., Jr., 1976
McElwee, Andrew, 1849
McElwee, Henry W., 1885
McEntire, Oscar Williams, 1891
McEvilly, James Patrick, 1941
McEwan, Christopher, 1855
McEwan, Joseph W., 1859
McEwen, Charles M., 1879
McEwen, William, 1835
McEwen, William, 1852
McFadden, Denise C., 1982
McFadden, James Andrew, Jr., 1953
McFadden, John Francis, 1934
McFadden, John Joseph, 1888
McFadden, Patrick John, 1925
McFadden, Will Gasten, 1870
McFadden, William, Jr., 1876
McFadyen, A. R., 1859
McFadyen, William, 1838
McFall, David M., 1857
McFarland, Henderson, 1849
McFarland, John, 1846
McFarland, John A., 1837
McFarland, John P., 1868
McFarland, Paul E., 1936
McFarland, R. W., 1858
McFarland, Thomas, 1841
McFerran, Joseph A., 1847
McGarry, Thomas F., 1958
McGarry, Thomas F., Jr., 1985
McGarvey, John F., 1883
McGarvey, William C., 1989
McGary, Robert M., 1884
McGaughey, J. David, III, S1944

McGaughey, James D., 1870
McGeary, Francis J., 1926
McGeary, James E., 1975
McGeary, Lester E., 1951
McGee, Donald H., 1947
McGee, J. P., 1861
McGee, James McMeekin, 1893
McGee, Joseph P., Jr., 1947
McGee, Leonard Joseph, 1943
McGee, Michael J., 1984
McGeehan, John T., S1944
McGeehan, Paul A., 1982
McGeehan, Stanley M., 1919
McGehee, Daniel M., 1879
McGehee, David M., 1836
McGehee, Edward H., 1945
McGehee, John M., 1952
McGettigan, Manus John, 1948
McGettigan, Marie C., 1986
McGhee, Harrison John, 1915
McGhee, Saylor John, 1898
McGill, Daniel, 1837
McGinley, David B., 1839
McGinley, Jeremiah, 1867
McGinnis, Edward J., 1980
McGinnis, George Edward, 1911
McGinnis, Russell Smith, 1921
McGintie, Edward, 1839
McGinty, John Francis, Jr., 1943
McGlade, Thomas Henry, 1932
McGlaughlin, Charles C., 1856
McGlaughlin, Michael J., 1979
McGlenn, J. Averill, 1885
McGlynn, Eileen T., 1988
McGlynn, Thomas J., Jr., 1969
McGogney, Samuel, 1879
McGourty, David Philip, 1927
McGovern, Edward W., Jr., 1969
McGovern, Edwin Andrew, 1946
McGovern, James B., Jr., 1970
McGovern, Lawrence O., 1965
McGovern, Leonard F., 1928
McGowan, John M., 1975
McGowan, John Patrick, 1954
McGowan, William 1836
McGrail, William T., Jr., 1986
McGrath, Francis A., 1892
McGrath, James E., 1958
McGrath, Kenneth J., 1956
McGrath, Robert M., 1836
McGraw, James J., Jr., 1973
McGraw, Patrick J., 1976
McGregor, Andrew, 1893
McGrigor, Thompson L., 1851
McGroarty, Raymond J., 1964
McGruder, Zachariah S., 1849
McGuigan, Ignatius, 1868
McGuigan, James A., 1862

McGuigan, John D., Jr., 1950
McGuigan, John Ignatius, 1887
McGuigan, William W., 1847
McGuinness, Robert Jones, 1920
McGuire, Burruss Boyd, 1918
McGuire, Elizabeth A., 1980
McGuire, John G., 1851
McGuire, Patricia M., 1979
McGuire, Thomas E., 1982
McGuire, William J., 1908
McGurrin, Mark A., 1982
McHale, Donald Gareth, 1935
McHatton, A. H., 1860
McHenry, Donald Barton, 1915
McHenry, George M., 1873
McHenry, Thomas, 1862
McHugh, John Joseph, 1908
McHugh, Joseph John, 1943
McHugh, Patrick Francis, 1911
McHugh, Thomas Francis, 1930
McIlhaney, William H., 1885
McIlvaine, Paul William, 1952
McIlvaine, Robert H., 1848
McIlvaine, William Earle, 1914
McIlwaine, R. Emmett, 1870
McIlwaine, Richard, 1919
McIntosh, John P., 1827
McIntosh, John, 1866
McIntosh, Richard, 1837
McIntyre, De Witt C., 1851
McIntyre, James, 1840
McIntyre, John H., 1864
McIntyre, Stephen, 1928
McIver, Robert Boyd, 1916
McJunkin, Cheryl L., 1975
McKay, Alexander P., 1881
McKay, Donald MacGregor, 1896
McKay, Haden E., 1854
McKay, Hamilton W., 1910
McKay, Isaiah R., 1836
McKay, Robert D., 1972
McKea, Carlisle Emerson, 1906
McKeag, Kathleen A., 1973
McKean, William, 1867
McKee, Edward Thomas, Jr., 1943
McKee, Frank William, 1894
McKee, Harry Wright, 1887
McKee, Joseph Allen, 1896
McKee, Louis Edwin, 1908
McKee, Violet J., 1981
McKeever, Clark D., 1962
McKeever, Grant R., 1962
McKeever, John Beaumont, 1945
McKeever, John D., 1965
McKeigue, John E., 1942
McKellar, Harry Rex, 1910
McKelvey, Charles E., 1857
McKelvey, John N., 1868

McKelway, Alexander J., 1835
McKelway, George Irvin, 1893
McKemy, John William, 1903
McKenna, Donald E., 1916
McKenna, Ernest L., Jr., 1955
McKenna, Patrick J., Jr., 1958
McKenna, William Bernard, 1905
McKenney, Jackson L., 1847
McKennie, Marcellus, 1846
McKennon, Archibald M., 1874
McKenzie, Benjamin W., 1916
McKenzie, George I., 1864
McKenzie, John C., 1878
McKenzie, William White, 1893
McKeon, Frank Anthony, Jr., 1954
McKeown, John J., Jr., 1947
McKethan, J. C., 1856
McKibben, Alpheus, 1897
McKim, Charles Palmer, 1935
McKim, Menzie, Jr., 1947
McKim, Robert M., 1964
McKinley, Andrew Stuart, 1906
McKinley, Charles A., 1859
McKinley, Lucien, 1880
McKinley, Oscar Vincent, 1941
McKinley, Robert A., 1951
McKinney, David, 1860
McKinney, J. Edward, 1948
McKinney, J. W., 1855
McKinnie, Lewis Hugh, 1902
McKneely, J. F., 1856
McKnight, Adam S., 1888
McKnight, John Roy, 1906
McKnight, William J., 1884
McKnight, William Patton, 1933
McLain, John Hillman, 1913
McLanahan, Johnston, 1865
McLane, Charles Francis, Jr., 1935
McLane, Robert A., Jr., 1935
McLane, Rogers D., 1970
McLane, William Leonard, J1944
McLatchy, Harris O., 1854
McLaughlin, A. J., 1873
McLaughlin, Catherine, 1987
McLaughlin, Charles Michael, 1889
McLaughlin, Charles Molten, 1904
McLaughlin, David B., 1962
McLaughlin, Edward D., 1956
McLaughlin, Elgie R., 1985
McLaughlin, F. Wendle, J1944
McLaughlin, Guy W., Jr., 1959
McLaughlin, Howard Elliott, 1923
McLaughlin, James A., 1864
McLaughlin, James C., 1951
McLaughlin, James Stephen, Jr., 1920
McLaughlin, John Joseph, 1891
McLaughlin, Margaret L., 1980
McLaughlin, Mark A., 1976

McLaughlin, Randall M., 1946
McLaughlin, Raymond S., 1980
McLaughlin, Robert E., 1961
McLaughlin, Robert J., 1885
McLaughlin, Robert W., 1951
McLaughlin, Thomas Finley, 1932
McLaughlin, Thomas W., 1977
McLaughlin, William J., 1953
McLavery, Bernard J., 1950
McLean, Daniel, 1873
McLean, David William, 1942
McLean, E. P., 1870
McLean, Hugh, 1854
McLean, John, 1881
McLean, Lois G., 1973
McLean, McCormick Earle, 1904
McLean, Robert 1837
McLean, William S., 1852
McLeary, Samuel Bismarck, 1889
McLeary, William T., 1853
McLees, Joseph H., 1859
McLellan, J. Densmore, 1965
McLelland, John Rockwell, 1945
McLelland, William Davies, 1913
McLemore, Robert A., J1944
McLemore, William E., 1980
McLennan, Alexander, 1874
McLeod, Alexander, 1856
McLeod, James P., 1857
McLeod, John, 1855
McLernon, John, 1892
McLoone, John Cornelius, 1952
McMackin, Edward, 1834
McMahan, Joseph N., 1941
McMahan, R. W., 1856
McMahan, William, 1830
McMahon, James Jerome, 1927
McMahon, James Joseph, 1927
McMahon, John, 1881
McMahon, Thomas P., 1969
McManigle, John E., 1980
McMannen, Charles T., 1854
McMartin, William Joseph, 1931
McMaster, Gilbert Totten, 1898
McMaster, James, 1859
McMicken, Thomas E., 1963
McMicken, William H., 1958
McMillan, John D., 1876
McMillan, William Thomas, 1897
McMillen, Leander, 1871
McMonagle, John H., 1878
McMorris, David L., 1954
McMorris, Marc S., 1985
McMullen, Elias Hale, 1845
McMullen, John C., 1879
McMullen, Uriah H., 1898
McMullin, Andrew, 1892
McMullin, Francis Aloysius, 1901

McMullin, James, 1855
McMullin, John Francis, 1934
McMullin, Joseph J.A., 1908
McMullin, Thomas, 1856
McMunn, John C., 1866
McMurran, Robert Lowry, 1890
McMurray, Andrew S., 1842
McMurray, Gerald Joseph, 1894
McMurry, Avery W., 1945
McNail, Thomas A., 1848
McNair, Alexander H., 1834
McNair, F. L., 1856
McNair, James B., 1829
McNair, Neill, 1839
McNair, Robert H., 1890
McNair, Stirling Sharp, 1929
McNair, William Righter, 1899
McNall, James Morgan, 1890
McNally, John, 1833
McNally, John B., 1939
McNally, Michael J., 1955
McNamara, Frank Wallace, 1911
McNamara, Kevin P., 1982
McNamara, Robert M., 1982
McNamee, William B., 1950
McNamee, William B., Jr., 1977
McNary, Hugh Allison, 1877
McNary, Oliver C., 1882
McNary, Robert B., 1867
McNaul, Caleb Gleni, 1890
McNaul, William John, 1894
McNeal, Samuel W., 1925
McNeil, Bernard A., 1856
McNeil, George W., 1874
McNeil, John, 1853
McNelis, Francis L., 1945
McNelis, Thomas, 1913
McNemar, M. R., 1858
McNerney, Aloysius Francis, 1907
McNerney, John C., 1927
McNichol, Edgar, 1879
McNicholas, Edward Martin, 1942
McNicholas, Edward Thomas, 1929
McNicholas, Kathleen W., 1973
McNickle, Jerry Hal, 1941
McNierney, Bronson J., 1957
McNite, William P., 1860
McNutt, James R., 1963
McNutt, Robert, 1851
McNutt, Samuel D., 1853
McOscar, Edward J., 1884
McPeak, Vincent J., Jr., 1951
McPherson, George E., 1855
McPherson, John H., 1855
McPherson, Sidney R., J1944
McQueen, Charles A.S., 1882
McQueen, S. F., 1858
McQuesten, E. Forrest, 1866

McQuiddy, Robert S., 1854
McQuillen, John H., 1852
McReynolds, Hugh L., 1871
McReynolds, John F., 1839
McReynolds, John O., 1849
McReynolds, William T., 1854
McShane, Elizabeth, 1983
McSorley, John, 1878
McSteen, Arthur Joseph, 1934
McStravog, Joseph Lawrence, 1945
McSwiggan, Kathleen C., 1969
McTague, William Francis, 1917
McTear, Thomas Francis, Jr., 1940
McTiernan, Eugene J., 1986
McVeigh, William H., 1850
McVicker, James P., 1866
McWeeney, James M., 1981
McWhinney, Arthur, 1851
McWilliam, John Forsythe, 1884
McWilliams, Charles Earle, 1920
McWilliams, Fred D., 1949
McWilliams, Harold L., Jr., 1961
McWilliams, John C., 1843
McWilliams, Kimber C., 1884
Meachem, Thomas J., 1851
Mead, Harry Burton, 1902
Mead, Michelle A., 1986
Mead, Robert J., Jr., 1978
Mead, Robert M., 1953
Meade, Theresa A., 1990
Meade, Thomas D., 1983
Meadowcroft, James A., 1968
Meadows, Abraham, 1836
Meagher, Angus Campbell, 1930
Meals, Charles Atlee, 1895
Meals, I. J., 1872
Meals, Melvin John, J1944
Means, Charles S., 1883
Means, L. Brown, 1883
Means, Paul Barringer, 1914
Means, Robert Markle, 1893
Means, William B., 1878
Means, William Horace, 1915
Meares, John L., 1846
Meares, William B., 1849
Mears, Benjamin Jr., 1829
Mears, Daniel W., 1885
Mears, Elmer E., 1952
Mears, George V., 1878
Mears, George Washington, 1827
Mears, James Ewing, 1865
Mears, Juan B., 1867
Mears, William W., 1960
Mease, Levi A., 1856
Mebane, Thomas S., III, 1971
Mecca, James John, 1928
Mech, John J., 1968
Mechanik, Harvey Kenneth, 1940

Mechem, C. Crawford, 1988
Mechling, John, 1859
Meck, Pearson A., 1884
Meckel, Louis Oliver, 1917
Meckelnburg, Robert L., 1956
Meckler, David, 1959
Meckstroth, Henry Louis, 1908
Meckstroth, Herman Franklin, 1932
Medd, Henry, 1896
Meddaugh, Fred W., 1909
Medford, William L., Jr., 1968
Medoff, Joseph, 1939
Medve, Robert A., 1989
Medway, Marc J., 1977
Meehan, Edward Joseph, 1947
Meehan, John J., 1947
Meehan, William Francis, Jr., 1937
Meek, Francis Joseph, 1892
Meek, Grover Cleveland, 1906
Meek, James A., 1881
Meeteer, William H., 1847
Megivern, Daniel G., 1984
Megna, Salvatore, 1922
Megowan, Robert, 1932
Mehard, George H., 1882
Mehard, Jas. W., 1872
Mehard, Samuel S., 1847
Meier, George M., 1951
Meier, William Ulysses, 1915
Meiere, William S., 1846
Meigs, James Aitken, 1851
Meigs, Joe Vincent, 1889
Meihofer, Mary A., 1989
Meikle, Charles E., 1960
Meikle, George C., 1985
Meikle, George Charles, 1936
Meikle, Grover Andrew, 1922
Meikle, Robert W., 1984
Meikle, Thomas Harry, 1926
Meinhard, Bruce P., 1974
Meisenhelder, Edmund W., 1868
Meisenhelder, Robert N., 1871
Meisenhelder, Samuel, 1851
Meiser, Edgar William, 1935
Meisle, Frederick Aaron, 1904
Meitzner, Max, 1907
Meixell, Edwin Wesley, 1893
Melanson, Scott W., 1987
Melchonian, A. John, 1882
Mele, Frank E., Jr., 1956
Melhorn, David H., 1882
Melick, Daniel Ramsey, 1865
Mella, Gordon W., 1956
Mellen, Arthur W., IV, 1980
Mellen, George F., 1851
Mellinger, David H., 1832
Mellinger, Henry S., 1845
Mellk, Harlan M., 1965

Mellon, Lawrence J., Jr., 1959
Mellor, John Oliver, 1910
Mellor, Thomas, 1894
Mellor, Wendell John, 1940
Mellus, Edward L., 1878
Melmed, Ronald M., 1956
Melnick, Irving, 1960
Melnick, Joseph L., 1946
Meloni, Michael A., Jr., 1976
Meloy, Albert Parke, 1867
Meloy, John Harold, 1967
Meloy, Thomas R., 1959
Melsheimer, John A., 1883
Melton, John T., 1853
Melton, Robert D., 1854
Melton, Susan M., 1986
Meltzer, Eli O., 1964
Melvin, Alexis Merritt, 1904
Memolo, Mark W., 1987
Menard, Oliver Joseph, 1926
Mench, John Rishel, 1924
Mendel, James Harold, 1918
Mendelsohn, David Henry, 1910
Mendelsohn, Jay S., 1977
Mendelsohn, Steven L., 1979
Mendelssohn, Saul, 1961
Mendenhall, Elliott Marion, 1923
Mendenhall, Nereus, 1845
Mendenhall, Thomas J., 1849
Mendez, Armando A., 1985
Menegas, Jacinto John, 1935
Mengel, John S., 1887
Mengel, Sterling Frederic, 1926
Mengle, Isaac L., 1866
Mensch, Harvey George, 1926
Mensch, William H., 1868
Mentzer, John F., 1882
Meranda, Isaac, 1850
Meranse, Theodore, 1932
Meranze, David Raymond, 1927
Meranze, Steven G., 1979
Mercado, Heriberto, 1920
Mercer, Clarence Mavel, 1907
Mercer, William T., 1835
Mercur, John D., 1878
Meredith, Arch F., Jr., 1960
Meredith, Charles F., 1831
Meredith, Guy Irving, 1923
Meredith, J. Rodney, 1953
Meredith, Joseph S., 1858
Meredith, Samuel Carlisle, 1888
Meredith, William H., 1866
Merendino, Anthony Girard, 1929
Mergenthaler, Dean D., 1960
Merinar, William H., 1848
Meringolo, Robert D., 1969
Meriweather, Tyler, 1899
Meriwether, John H., 1850

Meriwether, William H., 1837
Merkel, Ralph Henry, 1919
Merkin, Alvin, 1952
Merli, Geno J., 1975
Merlino, Anthony F., 1956
Merlino, William A., 1963
Mermon, Michael S., 1933
Merrell, Raymond W., 1974
Merrick, Frederick T., 1888
Merrick, Thomas Dudley, 1888
Merrill, Byrd Farmer, S1944
Merrill, Frank B., 1852
Merrill, Horace, 1908
Merrill, S. Randolph, 1854
Merriman, W. H., 1858
Merritt, Arthur F., 1881
Merritt, Daniel R., Jr., 1859
Merritt, Thomas Edwin, 1937
Merritt, William, 1851
Merryman, John Whitfield, 1899
Merscher, Harry Leonard, 1910
Mersky, Martin R., 1975
Mersky, Steven A., 1970
Merves, Louis, 1937
Mervine, Charles K., III, 1956
Mervine, Graydon Duncan, 1904
Mervine, Ned Dewar, 1936
Mervine, Robert Batten, 1903
Mervine, Thomas B., 1940
Mesropian, Messiah, 1894
Messerschmidt, William H., 1979
Messersmith, John K., 1966
Messersmith, John S., 1833
Messinger, Otis Guy, 1901
Messmer, Anthony Conrad, 1920
Messmore, Isaac Lindsey, 1940
Messori, Divo A., 1957
Mest, John S., 1957
Metcalf, Elliott Harrison, 1914
Metcalf, William A., 1884
Metcalfe, Thomas Norris, 1865
Metheny, David Gregg, 1896
Metheny, David, 1861
Metheny, David, 1923
Metheny, John E., 1953
Metheny, Samuel A. S., 1894
Metkus, Francis M., 1978
Metkus, Thomas S., 1978
Mettauer, Edward M., 1850
Mettler, Dallas E., 1953
Mettler, Fred A., Jr., 1970
Mettler, L. Harrison, 1886
Metz, Albert H., 1868
Metz, Albert V., Jr., 1969
Metz, Charles Oliver, 1929
Metz, Glen W., 1968
Metz, Harry William, 1886
Metz, Jacob K., 1852

Metz, John Pancoast, 1893
Metz, Joseph Arthur, 1901
Metz, Samuel Franklin, 1912
Metzgar, Marshall Rinker, 1922
Metzgar, Thomas I., 1928
Metzger, Carl D., 1968
Metzger, Carl Henry, 1908
Metzger, George S., 1836
Metzger, Harry, 1920
Metzger, M. Diana, 1980
Metzger, Walter S., 1964
Metzler, Erich G., 1988
Metzler, Gottfried, Jr., 1928
Metzler, Victor Wade, 1898
Meunier, Paul A., 1963
Mevshon, R. B., 1839
Meyer, Allen E., 1974
Meyer, Arthur N., 1961
Meyer, Carl A., Jr., 1960
Meyer, Charles A., Jr., 1967
Meyer, Fred H., III, 1967
Meyer, George Phillip, 1916
Meyer, Harold, 1946
Meyer, John Hermann, 1901
Meyer, Joseph John, 1915
Meyer, Julian Erdrich, 1917
Meyer, Kathryn J., 1989
Meyer, L. George, 1874
Meyer, Maurice Mark, Jr., 1952
Meyer, Monica Ann, 1990
Meyer, Thomas J., 1986
Meyer, Willaim A., Jr., 1974
Meyer, William H., 1974
Meyers, Arlen D., 1972
Meyers, Donald I., 1950
Meyers, Donald Irwin, 1950
Meyers, Elmer Llewellyn, 1901
Meyers, Joel S., 1985
Meyers, Max Irving, 1929
Meyers, Melvin Miller, 1935
Meyers, Michael B., 1973
Meyerson, Sheldon B., 1956
Meza, Manuel P., 1985
Mezey, Alan L., 1989
Mhley, Cornelius Michael, 1928
Miceli, Silvio, 1927
Michael Robert L., 1949
Michael Thomas D., 1949
Michael, Douglas W., 1979
Michael, Eric J., 1978
Michael, Herman J., Jr., 1984
Michaelson, Robert I., 1976
Michals, Timothy J., 1966
Michalski, John A., 1985
Michelson, Alan L., 1948
Michelson, Joseph Percy, 1927
Michelson, Peter H., 1983
Michener, Evan W., 1899

Michie, John Augustus, 1850
Michler, William H.H., 1861
Mickley, Howard Peter, 1889
Middlebrook, Robert, Jr., 1912
Middlebrooks, John Raymond, 1915
Middlekauff, Casper Joseph, 1917
Middleton, William J., 1879
Midence, Juan B., 1881
Midgley, Harry St. John, 1902
Midura, Alan T., 1982
Midura, Peter P., S1944
Miel, George W., 1883
Mielcarek, Leon M., Jr., 1962
Miele, Michael Anthony, 1915
Mierau, Ernest W., 1911
Mihalick, Ann L., 1981
Mihalick, Peter John, 1941
Mihalsky, Stephen W., 1986
Mika, John J., Jr., 1959
Mike, Joseph J., Jr., 1986
Mike, Margaret E., 1986
Mikowski, I. Edmund, 1940
Miksch, Carl Edward, 1923
Mikuliak, Helen J., 1967
Milam, Benjamin J., 1877
Milander, John H., 1972
Milani, Frank A., 1959
Miles, B. Fullerton, 1852
Miles, Charles A., 1876
Miles, J. Hunter, 1872
Miles, Robert G., 1895
Miles, William Thomas, 1888
Milewski, Julia A., 1985
Miley, Weir Mitchell, 1910
Milham, Claude Gilbert, Jr., 1927
Millard, Benjamin Joshua, 1892
Millard, Edward M., 1836
Millard, Frederick E., 1980
Millard, Joseph Delcamp, 1928
Millard, Justin, 1839
Millard, Oscar Benjamin, 1928
Millberg, Richard S., 1954
Millberg, William Burkley, 1953
Millberg, William, 1925
Millener, Frederick Hoyer, 1894
Miller, Aaron Gable, 1894
Miller, Albert J., 1883
Miller, Albert L., 1884
Miller, Albertus A., 1868
Miller, Alfred B., 1878
Miller, Alfred Benjamin, 1937
Miller, Allen Erskine, 1887
Miller, Andrew, 1846
Miller, Armand Jones, 1926
Miller, Benjamin F., 1853
Miller, Bernard J., 1943
Miller, Bernard J., 1966
Miller, C. Joseph, 1934

Miller, Carl S., J1944
Miller, Carol A., 1965
Miller, Celeste June, 1985
Miller, Charles Alexander, Jr., 1949
Miller, Charles D., 1884
Miller, Charles E., 1947
Miller, Charles Robert, Jr., 1921
Miller, Charles William, 1889
Miller, Charles William, 1940
Miller, Clarence M., Jr., 1946
Miller, Claude J., 1959
Miller, Clinton R. DeWitt, 1889
Miller, Connell Hutchison, 1933
Miller, D. Rentch, 1874
Miller, D. Warren, 1880
Miller, David H., 1850
Miller, David H., 1967
Miller, David P., 1864
Miller, Donald G., 1955
Miller, Edwin Barclay, 1906
Miller, Edwin John, 1896
Miller, Edwin M., 1890
Miller, Elmer Clare, 1892
Miller, Elmer Harry, 1938
Miller, Emery, 1894
Miller, Eugenia M., 1973
Miller, Francis Grove, 1929
Miller, Frank Henry, 1929
Miller, Fred H., 1975
Miller, Fred John, 1927
Miller, G. Geoffrey, 1977
Miller, Gary A., 1977
Miller, George W., 1854
Miller, George W., 1884
Miller, George William, III, 1939
Miller, George William, Jr., 1906
Miller, Grace, 1904
Miller, Hal Curtis, 1909
Miller, Harold Attig, 1914
Miller, Harold, Baughman, 1890
Miller, Henry B., 1885
Miller, Henry Ernest, 1903
Miller, Horace G., 1925
Miller, Horatio Brown, 1938
Miller, J. Edwin, 1870
Miller, J. K., 1870
Miller, J. Witmer, 1836
Miller, Jacob M., 1862
Miller, James Calvin, 1885
Miller, James Daniel, 1901
Miller, James Henry, 1941
Miller, James L., 1847
Miller, James M., 1868
Miller, James Morgan, 1902
Miller, James S., 1855
Miller, James Wesley, 1923
Miller, Jesse C., 1886
Miller, Joanna, 1976

Miller, John A., 1865
Miller, John Barton, 1901
Miller, John Charles, 1909
Miller, John E., 1942
Miller, John F., 1837
Miller, John F., 1844
Miller, John F., 1858
Miller, John H., 1842
Miller, John Hancock, 1889
Miller, John Harvey, 1896
Miller, John Hume, 1903
Miller, John J., 1854
Miller, John J., Jr., 1972
Miller, John N., 1884
Miller, John P., 1870
Miller, John Sebastian, 1882
Miller, John Veil, 1931
Miller, John W., 1882
Miller, John W., Jr., 1962
Miller, Joseph A., 1955
Miller, Joseph A., 1970
Miller, Joseph Elias, 1886
Miller, Joseph H., 1964
Miller, Joseph T., 1871
Miller, Joseph W., 1867
Miller, Langdon, 1847
Miller, Laurence J., 1973
Miller, Lawrence S., 1970
Miller, Lawrence S., 1979
Miller, Lawson E., Jr., 1934
Miller, Leon, 1933
Miller, Leroy Bernhardt, 1906
Miller, Lloyd T., 1864
Miller, Luther M., 1854
Miller, Martin L., 1874
Miller, Matthew, 1845
Miller, Matthew C., 1981
Miller, Maurice E., 1895
Miller, Merle Middour, 1930
Miller, Michael Kenneth, 1990
Miller, Morrow A., 1883
Miller, Ned David, 1916
Miller, Oliver Joseph, 1905
Miller, Oliver L., 1863
Miller, Pamela J., 1988
Miller, Paul O., 1915
Miller, Randolph J., 1984
Miller, Richard Hagan, 1913
Miller, Richard Oliver, 1903
Miller, Robert Hamilton, 1896
Miller, Robert J., 1977
Miller, Robert Lee, 1917
Miller, Robert V., 1965
Miller, Robert, 1864
Miller, Roger M., 1963
Miller, Samuel Huston, 1917
Miller, Samuel P.H., 1856
Miller, Samuel S., 1876

Miller, Samuel Warren, 1884
Miller, Sanford M., 1957
Miller, Simon, 1830
Miller, Solomon Metz, 1902
Miller, Stanley, 1943
Miller, Stanton B., 1980
Miller, Thomas Benton, 1910
Miller, Thomas M., 1857
Miller, Thomas W., 1859
Miller, Victor Davis, 1861
Miller, Wallace T., 1956
Miller, Walter Marion, 1903
Miller, Warren A., 1947
Miller, Warren Jacob, 1901
Miller, Wayne, 1983
Miller, Wesley Shaffer, 1922
Miller, Wilbur H., Jr., 1955
Miller, Wilbur Hobson, 1926
Miller, William Adam, 1888
Miller, William D., 1978
Miller, William E., 1963
Miller, William H., 1857
Miller, William Haman, 1893
Miller, William I., 1974
Miller, William Ischee, 1889
Miller, William Lamech, 1851
Miller, William McAlevy, 1889
Miller, William Newlon, 1852
Miller, William Robards, 1851
Miller, William S., 1979
Miller, William W., 1854
Miller, William, 1882
Millhoff, Clarence Beacom, 1897
Millhon, Judson S., 1955
Millhon, Myron Eli, 1923
Millhon, William A., 1955
Millick, Howard Collins, 1908
Milligan, Francis H., 1851
Milligan, James R., 1950
Milligan, Robert Sylvester, 1918
Milligan, Robert, 1896
Millikan, Robert H., 1864
Milliken, James Shepard, 1915
Milliken, Lorenzo Fremont, 1905
Milliken, William, 1895
Millikin, John Lindsey, 1878
Millikin, Thomas N., 1885
Millington, J. Thomas, 1936
Millington, J. Thomas, Jr., 1969
Millington, John, 1838
Million, Edward A., 1881
Millner, Jesse L., 1847
Milloy, John, 1861
Millrood, Bernard, 1957
Mills, Arthur, 1914
Mills, Charles S., 1836
Mills, Frederick Hubbell, 1894
Mills, John E., 1949

Mills, John Herman, 1895
Mills, Nathaniel J., 1855
Mills, Samuel R., 1850
Mills, William L., J1944
Milner, Amor C., 1846
Milner, James S., 1850
Milnor, Mahlon T., 1883
Milnor, Robert Hanna, 1896
Milroth, William L., 1964
Milson, Thomas J., 1943
Miltenberger, Arthur, 1912
Milton, Harvey Oliver, 1855
Mimm, Charles Oliver, 1952
Min, Thomas S., 1942
Minassian, Shahab S., 1980
Minde, George Francis, 1946
Mindil, H. W., 1873
Minehan, Kathryn Ann, 1986
Mineo, Cyrus Louis, 1962
Miner, A. G., 1873
Miner, James, 1861
Miner, Philip T., 1970
Mines Godfrey, James H., 1906
Mines, Marcus Keen, 1892
Minford, Wilbur Henry, 1909
Mingey, John R., 1985
Mingle, Daniel B., 1980
Mingle, David H., 1871
Mingos, Jay DePue, 1912
Minich, A. K., 1870
Minicozzi, William P., 1965
Minier, Carl Louis, 1929
Minier, Edward L., 1956
Mink, Arthur DeWitt, 1887
Minner, Louis Augustus, 1900
Minner, Roger Jonas, 1937
Minnich, Philip H., S1944
Minor, Austin Joseph, 1918
Minor, J. Gilmer, 1854
Minteer, Jeffrey F., 1977
Mintek, Rian D. C., 1977
Mintell, David F., 1964
Minter, Donald L., 1954
Minthorn, Henry J., 1877
Minton, Henry McKee, 1906
Mintz, Alfred M., 1947
Mintzer, David M., 1977
Mintzer, Leonidas H.C., 1898
Mira, Joseph Anthony, 1939
Mirabile, Robert J., 1981
Mirbach, Sidney Hershel, 1937
Mirenda, William M., Jr., 1975
Mirman, Joseph M., 1916
Mironoff, Leon, 1961
Mitchell, A. B., 1872
Mitchell, Atlee David, 1904
Mitchell, B. R., 1877
Mitchell, Benjamin W., 1857

Mitchell, Bradford K., 1987
Mitchell, C. B., 1836
Mitchell, Carol G., 1985
Mitchell, Charles L., 1880
Mitchell, Edmund H., 1879
Mitchell, Edmund Mansfield, 1990
Mitchell, Edward Kirkwood, 1906
Mitchell, Elmer Wesley, 1905
Mitchell, Franklin Theodore, 1889
Mitchell, G. W., 1860
Mitchell, George H., 1844
Mitchell, George V., 1834
Mitchell, Gurney Talmage, 1927
Mitchell, H. Hedge, 1862
Mitchell, Henry Chalmers, 1903
Mitchell, Horace Erwin, 1912
Mitchell, J. W., 1856
Mitchell, James Aloysius, 1925
Mitchell, Jessie, 1905
Mitchell, John A., 1877
Mitchell, John P., 1858
Mitchell, John R., 1870
Mitchell, John T., 1880
Mitchell, John William, 1877
Mitchell, John Willis, 1889
Mitchell, Joseph, 1833
Mitchell, Paul L., 1960
Mitchell, Perry L., 1974
Mitchell, R. Pinckney, 1854
Mitchell, R. V., 1858
Mitchell, Robert J., 1979
Mitchell, S. Weir, 1850
Mitchell, Taylor S., 1875
Mitchell, William Albert, 1897
Mitchell, William Cottonham, 1893
Mitchell, William, 1859
Mitchell, William, G., 1859
Mitchener, Calvin C., 1949
Mittower, Abraham, 1835
Mizak, Daniel J., 1968
Mizes, Craig B., 1984
Mizianty, Thomas J., 1975
Mlynarczyk, Francis A., 1966
Mlynarczyk, Peter J., 1969
Mobilio, Joseph A., 1927
Mobley, Samuel Goode, 1856
Mock, Gregory D., 1984
Mockaitis, Martina M., 1968
Moenig, Joseph August, 1896
Mofenson, Howard C., 1951
Moffet, David, 1881
Moffet, John, 1892
Moffet, William, 1875
Moffett, Charles J., 1856
Moffett, Morrow M., 1871
Moffitt, John S., 1949
Moffitt, John J., 1988
Moffitt, William J., 1860

Mogan, Christopher Joseph, 1929
Mogul, Robert S., 1978
Mohan, Francis P., 1981
Moheny, Irvin R., 1905
Mohler, Henry Keller, 1912
Mohler, Roy W., 1921
Mohn, James Oliver, 1894
Mohney, Fred Curtis, 1921
Mohr, Eugene H., 1881
Mohr, Gary A., 1979
Mohr, Henry C., 1871
Mohr, Jacob Eugene, 1888
Moir, John A., 1940
Mokrynski, Gregory, 1986
Mokychic, Walter E., 1956
Moldovan, Stanton I., 1967
Moliken, Murray H., 1963
Molina, Ramon B., 1959
Molinari, William J., Jr., 1968
Molinaro, Anthony D., Jr., 1974
Molino, Robert D., 1978
Moll, Francis K., Jr., 1958
Moll, Francis Keiter, 1928
Moll, Joseph H., 1957
Moll, Thomas B., 1966
Mollen, Martin D., 1974
Moloney, David, 1915
Molumphy, David James, 1906
Monaco, Dean D., 1958
Monaghan, James M., III, 1950
Monahan, Frank Henry, 1892
Monahan, James Joseph, 1916
Monahan, Stanley Theobald, 1920
Monahan, Thomas Aloysius, 1905
Monath, James R., 1989
Money, Philip Monroe, 1888
Mong, Elmer E., 1885
Monie, David McDonald, 1897
Monihan, James M., 1984
Monihan, Richard M., 1961
Monk, John S., S1944
Monk, John S., Jr., 1982
Monk, Susan Marie, 1971
Monkowski, Alfred M., 1970
Monroe, Daniel Geddie, 1939
Monroe, John B., 1970
Monroe, John Joseph, Jr., 1990
Montague, George B., 1852
Montague, James W., 1958
Montague, Samuel Spurgeon, 1910
Monte, Steven A., 1982
Montealegre, Edgar, 1908
Monteiro, Aristides, 1852
Monteiro, Dennis T., 1981
Monteith, William H., 1859
Monteleone, Gaetano P., Jr., 1990
Montelius, Ralph W., 1876
Montella, Joseph M., 1984

Montella, Michael K., 1986
Montemuro, Anthony J., 1989
Montfort, William J., 1859
Montgomery, Bruce B., 1960
Montgomery, Catherine J. Piecyk, 1990
Montgomery, Daniel Cameron, 1910
Montgomery, David Earl, 1914
Montgomery, Edmund B., 1878
Montgomery, Edward E., 1874
Montgomery, Ernest J., 1961
Montgomery, George A., Jr., 1955
Montgomery, James E., 1879
Montgomery, James McKay, 1897
Montgomery, James R., 1880
Montgomery, James Robert, 1915
Montgomery, John Barrick, 1926
Montgomery, John, 1858
Montgomery, Karyn, 1987
Montgomery, Thaddeus L., 1920
Montigney, Paul W., 1978
Montini, John, 1986
Montique, Frank, Jr., 1976
Montmollin, James M., 1862
Monzon, Gary R., 1987
Moodey, Joseph H., 1851
Moody, B., 1869
Moody, David J., 1849
Moody, J. Monroe, 1858
Moody, Milus W., 1855
Moody, Thomas H., 1851
Moog, Charles R., 1942
Mooman, James P., 1858
Moon, Alexander Charles, 1916
Moon, Paul O., 1987
Moon, Robert Charles, 1886
Mooney, Charles S., 1964
Mooney, Jane M., 1980
Moore, Albert Harrison, 1896
Moore, Alexander P., 1855
Moore, Allen Hoyt, 1916
Moore, Bird, 1847
Moore, Brutus Caesar, 1886
Moore, Carl Sinclair, 1913
Moore, Charles Edward, 1907
Moore, D. Forrest, 1925
Moore, Daniel Paul, 1990
Moore, Darius Carrier, 1903
Moore, David H., 1975
Moore, David K., 1982
Moore, Davis Lee, 1936
Moore, Donald B., 1953
Moore, Dunkin D., 1854
Moore, E. D., 1858
Moore, Edward E., 1887
Moore, Edward John, 1934
Moore, Edward Joseph, Jr., 1934
Moore, Edward Lane, 1911
Moore, Eli H., 1840

Moore, Eugene Aloysius, 1908
Moore, Franklin Thomas, 1897
Moore, George Cooper, 1899
Moore, Harmar D., 1873
Moore, Harry Beaumont, 1913
Moore, Henry Blanchard, 1920
Moore, Henry Boynton, 1886
Moore, Henry Dare, 1887
Moore, Ira L., 1851
Moore, Isaac H., 1866
Moore, J. A., 1858
Moore, J. Boardman, 1856
Moore, James A., 1853
Moore, James E., 1849
Moore, James L., J1944
Moore, Jason H., 1882
Moore, John A., 1855
Moore, John Burleson, Jr., 1927
Moore, John C., 1878
Moore, John C., 1881
Moore, John E., 1844
Moore, John Edward, 1890
Moore, John R., 1847
Moore, John R., 1854
Moore, John W. F., 1894
Moore, Joseph Aloysius, 1902
Moore, Joseph, 1852
Moore, LeRoy E., 1955
Moore, Lynford Lardner, 1893
Moore, Matthew S., 1851
Moore, Maurice A., 1851
Moore, Maurice Gardner, 1894
Moore, Merle Wayland, 1924
Moore, Neal Richard, 1926
Moore, Nicholas Gibbon, 1891
Moore, Philip Henry, 1902
Moore, Pierre Albert, 1895
Moore, Richard Dixon, J1944
Moore, Ronald Conrad, 1919
Moore, Samuel Grant, 1865
Moore, Thomas A., II, 1984
Moore, Thomas Kenney, 1899
Moore, Thomas Scott, 1932
Moore, Walter W., 1947
Moore, William G., 1875
Moore, William Houston, 1910
Moore, William I., 1848
Moore, William J., 1874
Moore, William R., Jr., 1955
Moore, Wilson McKenevy, 1904
Moorman, Albert John, 1907
Morales, Jose M., 1880
Morales, Marcos Delio, 1900
Morales, Thomas G., 1989
Moran, John J., 1952
Moran, Patrick, 1830
Moran, Thomas W., Jr., 1947
Moran, Thomas Wesley, 1899

Morehead, John Ellwood, 1953
Morehead, Robert P., 1936
Morehouse, George R., 1850
Morel, Henri Auguste, 1907
Moreland, Isaac J.T., 1871
Moretti, Everett A., 1961
Moretti, John Joseph, 1928
Morey, Andrew C., 1857
Morgan, Arthur Elwood, 1929
Morgan, Benjamin Franklin, 1914
Morgan, D. Porter, 1876
Morgan, David Reynolds, 1916
Morgan, David William, 1908
Morgan, Ellington J., 1860
Morgan, Isaiah C., 1915
Morgan, J. C., 1869
Morgan, James, 1828
Morgan, James Hamilton, 1889
Morgan, James, 1855
Morgan, Leslie Emanuel, 1931
Morgan, Louis Schubert, 1921
Morgan, Marshall Blair, 1915
Morgan, Philip J., Jr., 1961
Morgan, Philip John, 1928
Morgan, Richard J., 1890
Morgan, Richard William, 1933
Morgan, Thomas Rogers, 1916
Morgan, Walter R., 1957
Morgenstern, Bruce Z., 1978
Morgese, Albert Nicholas, 1957
Mori, Gino, 1958
Mori, Hugo, 1962
Morian, Clarence Herbert, 1912
Moriarty, Charles Albert, 1910
Moriarty, John Francis, 1924
Morioka, Wilfred T., 1963
Morison, J. Louis D., 1891
Morison, James H.S., 1853
Morita, Eugene T., 1962
Moritz, Howard A., 1982
Morley, J. R., 1861
Morley, Wynne A., 1989
Morman, Manuel R., 1976
Morningstar, Carol A., 1975
Morningstar, Phyllis Jane, 1975
Morosco, Samuel G., 1960
Morosini, Charles J., 1960
Morosini, Charles Joseph, 1925
Morrell, William R., 1837
Morret, Henry Eckert, 1903
Morris, A. Jesse, III, 1976
Morris, Charles C., 1876
Morris, Florance K., 1876
Morris, George W., 1851
Morris, Henry, 1878
Morris, James Aloysius, Jr., 1953
Morris, Jenkin W., 1845
Morris, John Knox, 1894

Morris, John Louis, 1896
Morris, John, 1861
Morris, Joseph B., 1886
Morris, Joseph, 1896
Morris, Kathryn E., 1981
Morris, Morrill Justin, 1915
Morris, Rae H., 1929
Morris, Sheldon L., 1962
Morris, Spencer, 1872
Morris, Truman Nicholas, 1927
Morris, Wayne S., 1975
Morris, William Francis, 1900
Morris, William Wade, 1860
Morrison, A. J., 1858
Morrison, Archibald, 1925
Morrison, Donald Allan R., 1932
Morrison, Edward Lloyd, 1905
Morrison, George Brooks, 1921
Morrison, George W., 1883
Morrison, James, 1849
Morrison, John A., 1837
Morrison, John B.G., 1863
Morrison, John Huff, 1940
Morrison, Joseph B., 1861
Morrison, M. Porter, 1851
Morrison, N. B., 1857
Morrison, Robert Raymond, 1919
Morrison, Robert, 1883
Morrison, William Brian, 1990
Morrison, William Byrne, 1922
Morrison, William Francis, 1896
Morrow, Francis Gayley, 1872
Morrow, J. Wilson, 1875
Morrow, James Robert, 1914
Morrow, John Riddle, 1888
Morrow, John W., 1873
Morrow, Monica, 1976
Morrow, Nancy B., 1980
Morrow, Robert E., 1955
Morrow, Thomas F., 1959
Morrow, Thomas J., 1977
Morrow, Todd A., 1986
Morrow, William, 1850
Morrow, William Boyd, 1891
Morrow, William Howard, 1886
Morrow, William L., 1855
Morse, Edwin W., 1908
Mortimer, John F., 1840
Morton, Alexander R., 1886
Morton, Charles B., 1860
Morton, Charles William, 1915
Morton, Francis Knoy, 1832
Morton, George R., 1827
Morton, John P., 1974
Morton, Paul Harry, 1938
Morton, Samuel Williams, 1887
Morton, Thomas J., 1885
Morton, Tower D., 1865

Morton, William A., Jr., S1944
Morton, William J., 1849
Morton, William Thomas, 1891
Mory, J. J., 1869
Mory, Stephen C., 1975
Moscarella, Alfred Savino, 1932
Moseley, Dan Parrott, 1949
Moseley, Daniel Willis, 1850
Moseley, George M., 1845
Moseley, Lloyd W., 1967
Moselle, Herbert I., 1961
Moser, George P., 1931
Moser, Howard F. D., 1937
Moser, Ira D., 1880
Moser, Raymond Anson, 1903
Moses, Brett L., 1987
Moses, George P., 1962
Moses, Melvin L., 1962
Moses, Thomas Freeman, 1861
Mosier, George W., 1886
Mosier, Laurance A., 1947
Moskievitz, Max, 1890
Moskovich, Myer Norman, 1919
Mosley, Benjamin J., 1861
Moss, G. W., 1870
Moss, George W., 1848
Moss, Harry Joseph, 1906
Moss, John Hunton, 1914
Moss, John T., 1908
Moss, Morris Israel, 1911
Moss, Obadiah C.G., 1852
Moss, Robert E., 1883
Moss, Samuel, 1909
Moss, Steven H., 1972
Moss, William Finley, 1891
Moss, William, 1855
Mossbrook, Sandra Slade, 1972
Mosser, E. Neff, 1870
Mosser, M. Breneman, 1862
Motley, John F., 1971
Motley, Robert J., 1985
Motsay, Dominic Sylvester, 1938
Mott, Armistead Randolph, 1845
Mott, Edwin Leland, 1918
Mott, Eugene K., 1868
Moukaddim, Hammond, 1893
Moul, Judd W., 1982
Moulton, Percy Daniel, 1907
Moultrie, Alonzo C., 1848
Mountain, John Henry, 1896
Mountain, Walter S., Jr., 1925
Mourat, Constantine, 1949
Mourat, Stephen, S1944
Moury, Nelson F., Jr., 1954
Movelle, John B., J1944
Mowery, Jacob L., 1878
Mowry, Harry Dale, 1926
Mowry, John N., 1850

Mowry, Robert B., 1836
Moy, James Thomas, 1940
Moy, Jin Fuey, 1890
Moyar, Charles Clinton, 1905
Moye, Elbert Alfred, Jr., 1895
Moyer, Adam J., 1877
Moyer, David S., 1878
Moyer, Donald Grosch, 1917
Moyer, Earl S., 1948
Moyer, George Alfred F., 1925
Moyer, Jacob Donelson, 1886
Moyer, John L.S., 1885
Moyer, Joseph, 1844
Moyer, LeRoy M., 1936
Moyer, Ralph D., Jr., 1950
Moyer, Robert A., 1984
Moyer, Rodney D., 1956
Mozdy, Lauren M., 1986
Mozes, Edward, 1935
Mszanowski, Edwin M., 1947
Muangman, Debhanom, 1962
Muangman, Pyn Noyes, 1926
Mucha, Theodore F., 1964
Mudd, John James, 1890
Mudd, Joseph P., Jr., 1946
Mudge, William S., 1877
Muehlhauser, William O., 1946
Muelheims, Robert, 1880
Mueller, Henry, 1866
Mueller, Thomas C., 1986
Muenter, Henry L., 1884
Muetterties, Craig L., 1975
Muffly, Harry Mac, 1953
Muffly, James T., 1978
Muhlfelder, Thomas William, 1966
Mujica, Jorge A., 1988
Mujica-Dueno, Augustin, 1919
Mulford, Francis D., 1851
Mulford, Leslie Frank, 1911
Mulford, William C., 1830
Mulhallon, J. I., 1838
Mulhallon, William E., 1841
Mulholland, David, 1860
Mull, William D., 1868
Mull, William Peter, 1916
Mullahey, Leo Thomas, 1914
Mullan, Eugene A., 1874
Mullen, Andrew J., 1952
Mullen, Carroll Richard, 1926
Mullen, Edward Andrew, 1917
Mullen, Henry, 1864
Mullen, Joseph Aloysius, 1893
Mullen, Joseph P., III, 1973
Mullen, Mark J., 1987
Mullen, Thomas Francis, 1912
Mullen, Thomas J., 1867
Muller, Carl Louis, 1888
Muller, Rodolph Emile, 1893

Muller, Stephen P., 1973
Mullhaupt, Alfred, 1884
Mulligan, Peter Burrill, 1916
Mulligan, Robert L., 1951
Mulligan, Wallace J., 1961
Mullikin, Louis Wagner, 1892
Mullin, Charles Elmer, 1912
Mullin, John H., 1867
Mullin, William J., 1968
Mullins, James C., 1851
Mullins, Thomas F., III, 1971
Mullison, Edwin D. S., 1904
Mullowny, Stephen D., 1840
Mulveny, Carl P., 1967
Mulvey, John R., 1986
Mumford, Ander M., 1941
Mummaw, Lisa A., 1988
Mundhenk, Herbert Conner, 1902
Mundorff, E. A., 1872
Munford, Samuel Archer, 1905
Munford, Samuel E., 1861
Munger, Erastus, A., 1835
Mungle, Earl William, 1919
Munin, Michael C., 1988
Munn, Charles W., 1866
Munroe, Henry Stokes, 1903
Munsch, Augustin Philip, 1903
Munson, Charles Leith, 1930
Munson, Harry G., 1892
Munzer, Steven J., 1963
Murata, James J., 1964
Murchison, Kenneth B., 1854
Murdoch, Andrew C., 1847
Murdoch, James Hutton, 1893
Murdoch, John Floyd, 1893
Murdoch, Winslow W., 1986
Murdock, John N., 1849
Murdock, John Robinson, 1926
Murdock, John S., 1827
Murfree, James B., 1859
Murphy, Albert Thomas, 1915
Murphy, Bernard Patrick, 1895
Murphy, Charles Michael, 1926
Murphy, Cornelius T., 1848
Murphy, Daniel, 1859
Murphy, Edward J., Jr., J1944
Murphy, Edward Joseph, 1906
Murphy, Eugene Francis, 1904
Murphy, Felix Aloysius, 1901
Murphy, Francis Aloysius, 1903
Murphy, Franics John, 1945
Murphy, Henry Cloyd, 1886
Murphy, Herschel Stratton, 1928
Murphy, James F. M., 1909
Murphy, James Paul, 1935
Murphy, John A., 1848
Murphy, John Thomas, 1931
Murphy, Joseph T., 1913

Murphy, Leo J., 1935
Murphy, Margaret G., 1980
Murphy, Michael A., 1980
Murphy, Michael F., 1988
Murphy, Michael Joseph, 1953
Murphy, Myles Joseph, 1932
Murphy, Robert A., 1946
Murphy, Robert M. J., 1951
Murphy, Robert Matthew, 1892
Murphy, Samuel M., 1863
Murphy, Thomas Francis, 1933
Murray, Alexander, 1892
Murray, Austin P., 1958
Murray, Bayard, 1886
Murray, Edward Francis, 1942
Murray, Edwin, 1933
Murray, F. Marion, 1877
Murray, Frank, 1881
Murray, Harry Wallace, 1901
Murray, Henry D., 1937
Murray, Henry Joseph, Jr., 1916
Murray, James A., 1955
Murray, John Allen, 1931
Murray, John Arthur, 1893
Murray, John C., 1837
Murray, John P., 1957
Murray, John Thomas, 1960
Murray, Joseph Edward, 1955
Murray, Kenneth Joseph, 1941
Murray, Lewis R., 1892
Murray, R. J., 1867
Murray, Ralph Vorhees, 1904
Murray, Ransom N., 1866
Murray, Richard C., 1942
Murray, Robert D., 1871
Murray, Roger, 1925
Murray, Stephen R., 1959
Murray, Thomas Elwin, 1908
Murray, Thomas J., 1879
Murray, Thomas Walker, 1885
Murray, Uriah B., 1883
Murray, William Archibald, 1929
Murray, William E., 1953
Murray, William J. C., 1932
Murray, William John, 1920
Murray, William M., 1970
Murrin, Connell Edward, 1904
Murry, Charles M., S1944
Murry, Charles Miller, 1890
Murry, John Y., 1855
Murtland, Albert M., 1950
Murtland, Richard L., 1950
Musa, Agha B., 1916
Musante, Adloph Joseph, 1923
Muschett, James M.A., 1841
Muschlitz, Charles Henry, 1904
Muschlitz, Frederick Allen, 1911
Muschlitz, Robert Roper, 1937

Muse, William H., 1837
Musgrove, Charles W., 1879
Musselman, Isaac, 1838
Musser, Benjamin, 1846
Musser, C. Sumner, 1880
Musser, F. M., 1870
Musser, Guy Musselman, 1910
Musser, Guy R., 1953
Musser, Harry E., 1875
Musser, John Henry, 1866
Musser, Milton B., 1868
Musser, Philip T., 1853
Musser, Urias S., 1878
Musser, Walter Scott, 1895
Musser, William Franklin, 1892
Mustin, Andrew J., 1988
Muta, Samuel A., 1904
Mutchler, J. Pace, 1875
Muthart, Lewis James, 1906
Mutschler, Louis H., Jr., 1965
Muzquiz, Juan Long, 1894
Myer, E. C., 1836
Myers, Alfred, 1875
Myers, Asa Lee, 1918
Myers, B., 1869
Myers, Carl B., 1953
Myers, Donald L., 1975
Myers, Edmund, 1908
Myers, Edward Ralph, 1903
Myers, Herschel S., 1880
Myers, Isaac N., 1862
Myers, Jacob S., 1853
Myers, John Milton, 1882
Myers, Larry S., 1970
Myers, Norman VanSant, 1933
Myers, Samuel Zigman, 1914
Myers, T. D., 1868
Myers, Virginia C., 1976
Myers, W. H., 1855
Mykrantz, Howard B., 1885
Myler, William F., 1867
Mylin, Walter Franklin, 1903
Myrick, Steven R., 1981

~ N ~

Nabity, Stanley F., 1949
Nadel, Jay A., 1953
Naden, Randall Stedman, Jr., 1953
Nadle, Isidor M., 1896
Naef, Richard W., 1953
Naegele, Karl Theodore, 1983
Nagel, David B., 1980
Nagle, Barton 1832
Nagle, H. M., 1857
Nagle, John A., 1955
Nahirniak-Kaufman, Laryssa, 1976
Naide, William, 1965

Naidoff, David, 1936
Nair, Suresh G., 1984
Nale, Thomas William, Jr., 1924
Nall, Burr F., 1861
Nall, Joseph A. F., 1920
Nalle, William Theodore, 1889
Nance, George B., 1885
Nancrede, Charles B., 1883
Nangle, Walter 1838
Nannelee, Virgil T., 1859
Nansteel, John F., Jr., 1975
Napheys, George H., 1866
Naples, Anthony F., 1977
Nappi, Dominic F., 1958
Nard, James A., III, 1984
Nardella, Guy M., Jr., 1974
Nardi, David A., 1985
Nardi, Michael Emil, 1950
Nardone, Donald T., 1985
Narducci, Anthony E., 1929
Narkevic, Carol A., 1979
Narzikul, Gregory T., 1988
Nasca, Leonardo S., Jr., 1983
Nasca, Thomas J., 1975
Nash, Francis J., 1954
Nash, J., 1856
Nash, John W., 1848
Nash, Joseph D., 1865
Nash, Miles H., 1855
Nash, Shepard K., 1852
Nason, Laurentius, 1884
Nassau, Charles Francis, 1906
Nassef, George J., 1948
Nast, Hugo, 1875
Naudain, Andrew, 1835
Naugle, William M., 1876
Naulty, Cheryl M., 1972
Naulty, John S., 1972
Navarrete, Ricardo J., 1982
Navas-Torres, Antonio, 1920
Nayfield, Romald Cornelius, 1936
Nayowith, Bruce E., 1978
Neal, B. T., 1839
Neal, Benjamin T., Jr., 1841
Neal, Harrison, 1859
Neal, Thomas W., 1837
Neale, Henry M., 1880
Neall, Charles H.M., 1889
Nealon, Thomas F., Jr., S1944
Nealon, William H., 1979
Neare, Clifford Reno, 1899
Neary, Edward R., 1937
Nebeker, Henry, 1876
Nebinger, A. R., 1856
Nebinger, Rankin A., 1929
Nebinger, William P., 1854
Neblett, Henry M., 1862
Neblett, Sterling Jr., 1848

Nedeljkovic, Srdjan S., 1987
Nee, Martin P., Jr., 1978
Needham, William C.H., 1868
Neel, George Pressley, 1888
Neel, James D., 1859
Neel, Vern Arguile, 1920
Neely, A. F., 1870
Neely, Henderson J., 1881
Neely, James W., 1875
Neff, Allan J., 1975
Neff, Benjamin 1847
Neff, Charles, 1852
Neff, Francis Felix, 1887
Neff, George W., Jr., 1870
Neff, Henry K., 1851
Neff, Isaac P., 1859
Neff, Jacob K., 1834
Neff, James Woodbury, 1888
Neff, Joseph S., 1875
Neff, Peter D., 1848
Neff, Walter S., 1932
Negendank, William G., III,,1969
Negly, Eliab, 1846
Neifeld, Kenneth A., 1978
Neifeld, Lise Moore, 1979
Neil, Thomas Franklin, 1903
Neilson, Clarence Jamie, 1911
Neilson, Robert, 1850
Neiman, Howard George, 1906
Neiman, Howard Y., 1879
Nellas, Alex L., 1963
Nellas, Constantine L., 1956
Nelms, Homer Leroy, 1923
Nelson Mortimer T., 1949
Nelson, Andrew J., 1852
Nelson, Arthur Braxton, 1890
Nelson, Audley, Emmet, 1897
Nelson, Francis B., 1943
Nelson, Frank W., 1880
Nelson, George W., 1864
Nelson, Guy Maurice, 1928
Nelson, H. W., 1880
Nelson, Jean M., 1988
Nelson, John A., 1858
Nelson, John I., 1838
Nelson, John R., III, 1954
Nelson, John, 1920
Nelson, Joseph Eugene, 1945
Nelson, Leroy John, 1969
Nelson, Lyle Milton, Jr., 1925
Nelson, Parley, 1908
Nelson, Paul I., 1959
Nelson, Robert B., 1846
Nelson, Robert E., 1838
Nelson, Robert M., 1946
Nelson, Robert William, 1846
Nelson, Thomas W., 1860
Nelson, W. H., 1869

Nelson, Will N., 1872
Nelson, William H., 1988
Nelson, William J., 1942
Nelson, William W., 1860
Nemiroff, Richard L., 1970
Neptune, Norman William, 1903
Nes, Henry, 1879
Nesbit, Andrew David, 1887
Nesbit, Dean Abbott, 1914
Nesbit, William Wesley, 1926
Nesbitt, Richard A., 1982
Nespoli, Anthony M., 1972
Nessa, William T., 1976
Nestor, Hubert Richard, 1956
Netherton, Samuel Oliver, 1894
Netscher, Charles Edward, 1883
Netzel, Charles Frederick, 1916
Neubeck, James M., 1970
Neupauer, M. G. Adolph, 1921
Nevara, John B., 1960
Neves, Edmund Fraga, 1942
Neves, Juan Carlos, 1845
Neviaser, Robert J., 1962
Nevin, Janice E., 1987
Nevin, Walter Charles, 1890
Nevin, William W., 1846
Nevins, John C., 1874
Nevins, William, 1882
Nevulis, John J., 1976
Newbaker, John B., 1852
Newbaker, P. E., 1869
Newberry, Thomas L., 1866
Newbill, Alexander M., 1834
Newbold, William Augustus, 1910
Newby, George Edgar, 1900
Newcomb, Andrew Purefoy, Jr., 1922
Newcomb, Charles L., 1884
Newcomb, Marcus Ward, 1903
Newcomer, David, 1859
Newcomer, Frank Sherick, 1888
Newcomer, Irving, 1896
Newcomer, John, 1852
Newcomer, Joseph W., 1864
Newell, David S., 1837
Newell, John H., 1835
Newell, Joseph B., 1859
Newell, Paul M., 1981
Newell, William L., 1859
Newell, William M., 1866
Newgarden, George Joseph, 1889
Newhouse, John Edward, 1916
Newitt, Thomas R., 1949
Newland, J. Oscar, 1857
Newman, Charles, 1868
Newman, George S., 1840
Newman, Henry E., 1966
Newman, L. Roy, 1949
Newman, Louis E., 1883

Newman, Philip Floyd, 1921
Newman, Schuyler, 1985
Newman, William H., 1855
Newman, William H., III, 1961
Newman, William Harris, 1896
Newman, William Harris, Jr., 1931
Newmark, Abe A., 1934
Newnam, Henry Joseph E., 1905
Newson, Albertus, 1902
Newton, Charles T., 1960
Newton, Edwin D., 1859
Newton, Francis Janvier, 1891
Newton, Frederick G., 1880
Newton, James C., 1957
Newton, James F., 1854
Newton, John Search, 1867
Newton, Luke V., 1837
Newton, P. C., 1866
Newton, Zachariah B., III, 1962
Nguyenpho, Hoa T., 1984
Niblock, William G., 1846
Niccolls, Robert, 1849
Nice, Benjamin H., 1877
Nice, Curtis J., 1854
Nice, Franklin B., 1851
Nice, Franklin Mickley, 1901
Nice, George W., 1851
Nice, Harry George, 1883
Nichol, John, 1855
Nicholas, John Thomas, 1848
Nicholls, B. Frank, 1875
Nicholls, James Calvin, 1899
Nicholls, Richard B., 1930
Nicholls, Robert Delmer, 1899
Nichols, Ace Elliott, 1929
Nichols, Austin W., 1853
Nichols, Benjamin R., 1827
Nichols, Bradley Gibson, 1990
Nichols, Charles W., 1964
Nichols, Harold, 1926
Nichols, Henry Hessin, 1896
Nichols, L. C., 1867
Nichols, Pennock J., 1860
Nichols, Robert A., 1960
Nichols, Thomas G., 1846
Nichols, Warren W., 1954
Nicholson, Charles E., Jr., 1959
Nicholson, George L., 1837
Nicholson, Hugh W., 1860
Nicholson, John C., 1855
Nicholson, John, 1861
Nicholson, Malcolm J., 1859
Nickel, James Edward, 1903
Nickel, Minna, 1905
Nickeson, David C., 1977
Nicklas, Donald A., 1973
Nicklas, Floyd W., J1944
Nicklin, John, 1880

Nicodemus, Bryce Elton, 1935
Nicodemus, Edwin Arthur, 1898
Nicodemus, John D., 1879
Nicodemus, Roy Elvin, 1927
Nicoll, G. Stephens, 1962
Nicolo, Anthony, 1936
Niebel, Benjamin Earl, 1912
Niehls, Beverly, 1983
Nielsen, Marvin E., Jr., 1974
Niemeyer, Richard, 1972
Niemtzow, Frank, 1928
Nierle, Richard Hugh, 1953
Nies, Gerald F., 1958
Nifong, Frank M., 1943
Nightingale, Arthur B., 1932
Nightingale, Henry B., 1850
Nightingale, Henry B., 1876
Nightingale, Louis M., 1930
Niklewski, Edmund V., 1956
Niles, John S., 1891
Niles, William Gordon, 1904
Nimoityn, Benjamin Solomon, 1936
Nimoityn, Philip, 1976
Niple, Dio Maine, 1906
Nipple, Henry M., 1871
Nipple, Henry Newton, 1898
Nipple, John O., 1873
Nipple, Vincent Clayton, 1931
Nirosky, Joseph Anthony, 1936
Nisbet, John T., 1847
Nisbet, Joseph A., 1857
Nisbet, Richard H., 1853
Nisbet, William M., 1857
Nisbett, James Menior, 1922
Nishijima, Randal A., 1941
Nishijima, Satoru, 1938
Nissenbaum, Mark, 1969
Nissler, Christian William, 1919
Nitowski, Leonard A., 1982
Nitschke, Ernest Joseph, 1916
Nittoli, Rocco Marion, 1916
Nitzberg, Jerome, 1961
Nix, James Elmer, 1956
Nix, William Henry, 1905
Nixon, Holbert James, 1914
Nixon, Oliver W., 1854
Nixon, Samuel, 1834
Nixon, Warford L., 1889
Noal, John Jeanette, 1917
Nobel, Joel J., 1963
Noble, Angus, 1868
Noble, Charles M., 1876
Noble, Ellis Leo, 1924
Noble, Harvey Read, 1888
Noble, James D., 1861
Noble, John E., 1870
Noble, Nathan Morton, 1931
Noble, S. Ross, 1986

Noble, W. P., 1869
Nobles, Joseph Everett, 1899
Nobles, William H., 1857
Nock, Thomas Oliver, 1886
Nocon, James J., 1971
Noel, George Thompson, Jr., 1938
Noel, Joseph Roberts, 1894
Nofer, George Hancock, 1902
Nofsinger, William R., 1849
Nogi, Jay, 1971
Nogueras, Juan J., 1982
Nolan, J. Philip, 1955
Nolan, James Onslow, 1921
Nolan, John P., Jr., 1982
Nolan, John Thomas, 1908
Nolan, Michael McCormack, 1912
Nolan, Thomas Francis, 1907
Noll, Franklin, Jr., 1892
Noll, Norman Beard, 1902
Noller, William E., 1970
Nolte, Harry Frederick, 1920
Nonamaker, Noah S., 1879
Noome, Andrew Joseph, 1900
Noone, Ernest L., 1923
Noone, James P., 1971
Norcross, J. N., 1872
Nordberg, E. David, 1960
Nordmann, L. E., 1858
Noreika, Joseph C., 1976
Norelli, Charles C., 1983
Norman, John P., 1861
Norment, Benjamin C., 1853
Norment, William Blount, 1922
Norred, Charles Henry, 1886
Norris, Alonzo, 1860
Norris, Elmer Patterson, 1896
Norris, Henry L., 1881
Norris, J. W. Stump, 1859
Norris, James T., 1852
Norris, John Clements, 1862
Norris, John W., 1853
Norris, Leonard Edward, 1907
Norris, Mark C., 1980
Norris, William J., 1882
Norstedt, Gustaf Lewis, 1916
North, Edward, 1868
North, Harry Ross, 1904
North, Henry Urban, 1903
North, J. H., Jr., 1869
North, James, 1880
North, William McK. 1883
Northington, S. Sterling, 1881
Northington, William H., 1849
Northrop, Robert Arthur, 1932
Norton, Andrew J., 1982
Norton, Edward A., 1943
Norton, James F., 1945
Norton, Joseph Glen, 1939

Norton, Roy Roscoe, 1907
Norton, Thomas Joseph, 1905
Norwood, John, 1859
Nosal, Joseph Louis, 1941
Nosheny, Stanley Z., 1966
Nosher, John L., 1971
Noss, John Cyrus, 1920
Nothnagel, Frank Richard, 1910
Notson, William, 1846
Notson, William Morrow, 1861
Nottingham, C. Bell, 1840
Nottingham, Severn P., 1861
Nottingham, Southey S., 1856
Novack, Harry Jacob, 1906
Novicki, Zenon Francis, 1925
Novielli, Karen D., 1987
Novinger, Q. Thomas, 1977
Nowicki, Edward Richard, 1966
Nowinski, Thaddeus S., 1980
Nowlin, John B. W., 1857
Nowotarski, Peter J., 1988
Noyes, Brent R., 1978
Noyes, Franklin L., 1925
Noyes, James 1846
Noyes, Kenneth Eugene, 1927
Noyes, Willard Stover, 1990
Nukes, Theodore A., 1989
Numbers, William W., 1884
Nunan, William Lawrence, 1894
Nungesser, Raymond F., 1980
Nunn, John M., 1842
Nunn, Leslie L., 1925
Nunn, William C., 1856
Nurkiewicz, Stephen A., 1986
Nusbaum, David Hamilton, 1888
Nuss, Robert C., 1962
Nussbaum, Herman, 1939
Nute, William G., 1846
Nutt, James N., III, 1970
Nutter, David E., 1976
Nutter, Phosa David, 1935
Nutting, George Kegley, 1916
Nye, Glenn C., 1972
Nye, Howard Holland, 1921
Nye, Robert Bruce, 1927
Nye, Willard W., 1877

~ O ~

O'Brasky, George Harry, 1920
O'Brasky, Louis, 1922
O'Briant, Albert Lee, 1920
O'Brien, Caleb Stanton, 1890
O'Brien, David William, 1925
O'Brien, Frank Thomas, 1942
O'Brien, George W., 1950
O'Brien, James J., 1960
O'Brien, Jeremiah F., 1980

O'Brien, John Daniel, 1903
O'Brien, John M., 1854
O'Brien, John Patrick, 1935
O'Brien, John R., 1941
O'Brien, John S., II, 1979
O'Brien, Joseph Elmer, 1920
O'Brien, Lynn Murphy, 1983
O'Brien, Michael Gerald, 1925
O'Brien, Patrick Moffit, 1842
O'Brien, Richard Francis, 1958
O'Brien, Robert Faulkner, 1895
O'Brien, Theo Wallace, 1913
O'Brien, Thomas E., 1961
O'Brien, Thomas Gore, 1956
O'Brien, Thomas M., 1985
O'Brien, Timothy James, 1990
O'Brien, Walter M., 1983
O'Brien, William H., 1960
O'Brien, William R., 1943
O'Bryan, William R., 1861
O'Byrne, Brian E., 1979
O'Callaghan, Daniel, 1882
O'Connell, Austin, 1897
O'Connell, Brent J., 1967
O'Connell, Joseph P., 1955
O'Connell, William Aloysius, 1946
O'Conner, Nancy K., 1971
O'Connor, Carolyn B., 1989
O'Connor, Dennis Stephen, 1954
O'Connor, Harry R., 1875
O'Connor, James J., III, 1988
O'Connor, James J., Jr., 1948
O'Connor, James Joseph, 1916
O'Connor, John Hugh, 1888
O'Connor, John P., 1942
O'Connor, Mary E., 1977
O'Connor, Robert L., III, 1986
O'Connor, Stefan S., 1988
O'Daniel, A. Allison, 1884
O'Doherty, Desmond S., 1945
O'Donnel, Hugh Boyle, 1893
O'Donnell, Alan Edward, 1930
O'Donnell, Charles Hugh, 1939
O'Donnell, Dominick A., 1833
O'Donnell, Francis T., 1922
O'Donnell, George J., 1948
O'Donnell, John Anthony, 1920
O'Donnell, Leo Day, 1921
O'Donnell, Michael J., 1986
O'Donnell, Michael P., 1964
O'Donnell, Philip H., 1988
O'Donnell, Ward J., 1988
O'Donnell, William, 1848
O'Farrell, Henry T., 1847
O'Ferrall, Frank, 1878
O'Flaherty, Thomas J., 1828
O'Hanlan, J. Treacy, J1944
O'Hara, Brian J., 1988

O'Hara, James P., 1967
O'Hara, Robert H., 1865
O'Hara, Warren Thomas, 1913
O'Hurley, John George, 1952
O'Keefe, John Joseph, 1937
O'Leary, Arthur, 1866
O'Leary, James J., 1940
O'Leary, James Michael, 1946
O'Leary, Michael P., 1981
O'Leary, Thomas Francis, 1931
O'Looney, John Joseph, Jr., 1945
O'Malley, Eugene John, 1920
O'Malley, John, 1884
O'Malley, Thomas F., Jr., 1981
O'Neil, Ann, 1969
O'Neil, Jack D., 1961
O'Neil, Kevin, 1983
O'Neil, Michael Joseph, 1903
O'Neill, John J., 1949
O'Neill, Chrysostom A., 1899
O'Neill, Daniel K., 1989
O'Neill, James F., 1936
O'Neill, Owen, 1904
O'Neill, Patrick Joseph, 1889
O'Neill, Rodger P., 1883
O'Reilly, Harry Matthew, 1896
O'Reilly, Robert Carlos, 1990
O'Reilly, Thomas W., 1892
O'Riordan, Martin J., 1987
O'Rorke, James, 1847
O'Rourke, Jeremiah Francis, 1897
O'Rourke, Terence L., 1960
O'Rourke, Terence Leonard, 1990
O'Shaughnessy, Nicholas J., Jr.,,1972
O'Toole, Thomas F., 1952
O'Toole, Thomas Henry, 1897
Oaks, Lewis Weston, 1919
Oaks, Lloyd Edress, 1930
Oaks, Samuel, 1851
Oatman, Daniel L.F., 1844
Oatman, James J., 1867
Oberholtzer, John C., M.D.1984
Oblazney, Ludwig John, 1935
Oburn, Albert Sidney, 1896
Ochitill, Herbert N., 1972
Odbert, Frank N., 1880
Oddi, Bernard D., 1975
Oddy, J., 1869
Odell, James Marge, 1917
Oden, Beverly J., 1851
Odorisio, Lynne A., 1987
Oelke, Emil Heinrich, 1904
Oelschlegel, Herbert Charles, 1911
Oesau, Harold Thomas, 1926
Oesau, Harold Thomas, Jr., 1962
Oesterling, Everett F., Jr., 1961
Ogburn, John F., 1855
Ogburn, Lundie C., 1928

Ogden, Andrew Edman, 1927
Ogden, P. B., 1867
Ogilvie, Roy K., 1903
Ogle, H. O., 1869
Ogle, William Matthews, 1882
Ogleby, James, 1868
Oglevee, Thomas Edison, 1903
Ogrodnick, John P., 1989
Oh, Min C., 1986
Ohannesian, Frank, 1918
Ohl, Josiah G., 1855
Okie, Allen, 1969
Okie, William T., 1862
Okulski, Thomas A., 1969
Okun, Milton R., 1954
Olash, F. Albert, 1945
Oldham, Robert H., 1848
Oldham, William H., 1829
Oldmixon, George Scott, 1861
Oldshue, James A., 1881
Olewiler, Dean B., 1951
Olewnik, Ann B., 1983
Olitsky, Scott E., 1988
Oliva, Vincent S., 1956
Oliver, Adlai S., 1914
Oliver, Adlai Stevenson, Jr., 1940
Oliver, Andres Gilberto, 1931
Oliver, David H., 1888
Oliver, Frederic W., 1878
Oliver, Howard M., J1944
Oliver, James E., 1951
Oliver, James G., 1828
Oliver, James W., 1858
Oliver, Jim Upton, 1947
Oliver, John Edward, 1885
Oliver, John G., J1944
Oliver, Richard Loomis, 1942
Oliver, Samuel P., 1843
Oliver-Smith, Richard W., 1953
Olivere, Robert F., 1977
Olivieri, Marie V., 1970
Olivieri, Suzanne P., 1988
Olley, James Francis, 1945
Olney, William Bert, 1974
Olsen, Jean E., 1967
Olsen, Lawrence C., 1972
Olsen, Norman Alma, 1924
Olsho, Sidney Lessing, 1907
Olson, David A., 1976
Onan, Dennis, 1874
Ono, Jo, 1928
Ono, Shunji, 1880
Onufrey, Victor G., 1981
Oppermann, Ralph Clifford, 1923
Oppermann, Richard F.W., 1881
Oram, Joseph Hubbhrd, 1899
Orbock, Jacob A., 1962
Orchow, Harold S., 1957

Ord, James Lycurgus, 1846
Oreamuno-Flores, Alberto, 1929
Orenstein, Alexander Jeremiah, 1905
Oriente, Michael A., 1957
Orlady, George B., 1872
Orlick, Arnold H., 1953
Orlick, Martin E., 1984
Orlidge, Arthur E., 1949
Ormond, Allison Lee, 1930
Ormsbee, Richard S., 1880
Orndoff, Hersey Elroy, 1910
Orndorf, Thomas P., 1985
Orner, Charles T., 1867
Ornston, Darius Gray, 1928
Orocofsky, Morris L., 1968
Orr, A. G., 1869
Orr, Adrian V., 1909
Orr, Adrian V.B., 1844
Orr, Charles Albert, 1901
Orr, Daniel G., 1983
Orr, Gabriel P.N., 1852
Orr, Henry B., 1883
Orr, Joseph D., 1885
Orr, Porter Bynum, 1901
Orr, Samuel M., 1879
Orr, Sidney H., 1946
Orr, Wilson J., 1873
Orris, John Andrew, 1924
Orth, Edward L., 1834
Orth, William M., 1867
Orton, George Lee, 1909
Orton, Henry Boylan, 1908
Orton, Henry, 1857
Orton, Stuart, 1942
Orvald, Todd Busse, 1971
Orvis, Charles, 1866
Orwig, George A., 1876
Osborn, Edward George, 1940
Osborne, Edward A., 1848
Osborne, John Andrew, 1990
Osborne, John M., 1896
Osborne, William E., 1846
Osburn, Curran D., 1886
Oscar, Alvin D., 1964
Oschell, William J., 1954
Osei-Tutu, Ernest P., 1984
Osenbach, Richard K., 1983
Osgood, Carroll P., Jr., 1965
Osgood, Hamilton, 1870
Osgood, William, 1855
Oshrin, Harvey W., 1960
Oskin, Hilbert E., 1958
Osler, Owen, 1846
Osmun, Milton Mackey, 1894
Osmun, William Finley H., 1889
Ost, David Edward, 1990
Osterberg, Eric Runo, S1944
Osterhout, Franklin Farnham, 1928

Osterhout, Paul, 1887
Ostrander, William Alonzo, 1899
Ostrow, Arnold, 1963
Ostrow, David E., 1964
Ostrum, Gordon J., Jr., 1976
Oswald, C. A. Morris, 1871
Otey, Paul H., 1846
Otis, Ashbel R., 1867
Otis, William Henry, 1891
Ott, Brian R., 1979
Ott, Charles Henry, 1883
Ott, Charles Henry, 1920
Ott, Gary Y., 1983
Ott, Lambert, 1878
Ott, Lyman E., 1882
Ott, Susan E. Werhun, 1987
Ottinger, Samuel Joseph, 1892
Otto, Calvin J., 1884
Otto, Ralph N., 1963
Otway, David B., 1879
Ours, Lester, 1922
Ousler, George W., Jr., 1965
Outerson, Andrew Mansergh, 1906
Outerson, Richard Ambrose, 1902
Outhit, George Edward, 1845
Over, Stuart B., Jr., 1941
Overall, George W., 1875
Overbeck, Michael D., 1979
Overend, Edmund J., 1884
Overmiller, Carl L., 1986
Overton, Joe, 1890
Overton, William M., 1851
Overton, William S., 1855
Owen, A. M., 1869
Owen, Edward, 1848
Owen, George A., 1860
Owen, George F., S1944
Owen, John Fletcher, 1920
Owen, John J., 1943
Owen, John Jones, 1878
Owen, Joseph D., 1850
Owen, Joshua, 1840
Owen, Richard D., 1951
Owen, Richard, 1916
Owen, Thomas J., 1844
Owen, W. R., 1869
Owen, W. T., 1860
Owen, William Llewellyn, 1889
Owens, Basil Tabor, 1919
Owens, Benjamin F., 1866
Owens, Bennett G., 1851
Owens, Cleon Clinton, 1887
Owens, Creston Linwood, 1920
Owens, Gary M., 1975
Owens, Harry, 1896
Owens, John Edward, 1862
Owens, Joseph L., Jr., 1953
Owens, Thomas A., 1980

Owens, Thomas Charles, 1952
Owings, Capers Baxter, 1923
Oxamendi, Pedro F., 1870
Oyer, Harry Willrich, 1893
Oyer, William Collins, 1889
Oyster, Joseph, 1841
Ozias, Herman W., 1865

~ P ~

Pacanowski, John P., 1966
Pace, Charles T., 1949
Pace, Karl B., Jr., 1947
Pace, Karl Busbee, 1914
Pace, Samuel Eugene, 1932
Pachtman, Allen H., 1979
Pacifico, Daniel Scott, 1990
Packer, Elmer Benjamin, 1899
Packer, George L., J194
Packer, Milton, 1973
Packer, Robert M., S194
Packer, Susan B., 1980
Packman, Barry E., 1978
Pacropis, Richard F., 1982
Paddock, Richard Bolles, 1957
Paden, Norton Crane, 1941
Padgett, Charles King, 1930
Padilla, Alfonso, 1914
Padnes, Stephen C., 1966
Padula, Anthony M., 1967
Padula, Richard T., 1961
Paffrath, Jeffrey A., 1989
Page, Arthur L., 1907
Page, Claude Weston, 1907
Page, Dudley L., 1879
Page, Edward J., 1883
Page, Harlan Myron, 1892
Page, James H., 1849
Page, John J., 1854
Page, John T., 1849
Page, William G., 1939
Pai, Eun Chan S., 1981
Paige, Harris Lee, 1896
Paine, A. B., 1858
Paine, Robert, 1917
Paine, William A., 1879
Painter, Alonzo Potter N., 1890
Painter, Robert H., 1950
Painter, Theodore P., 1887
Painter, William Isaac, 1894
Painter, William P., 1875
Paist, Stanley S., III, 1975
Palace, William G., 1975
Palascak, Joseph E., 1968
Palchanis, William Theodore, 1916
Palena, Peter V., 1963
Palermo, Francis A., 1984
Palermo, Louis M., 1973
Palm, Howard F., 1881

Palm, James P., 1849
Palm, Philip R., 1846
Palmer, Archibald W., 1853
Palmer, Charles, 1848
Palmer, Charles Walter, 1902
Palmer, Craig M., 1983
Palmer, Daniel B., 1883
Palmer, David, 1873
Palmer, Elton J., 1878
Palmer, Frank Cameron, 1946
Palmer, Isaac S., 1832
Palmer, Joseph Bell, 1901
Palmer, Kathleen M., 1989
Palmer, Louis H., Jr., 1943
Palmer, Robert Maffet, 1913
Palmer, Rufus Edward, III, 1941
Palmer, Thomas D., 1882
Palmer, Thomas Dade, 1871
Palmer, Thomas P., 1876
Palmer, U. Grant, III, J1944
Palmer, Valentine Jackson, 1858
Palmer, William L., 1884
Palmer, William Main, 1890
Palmieri, Julio, 1920
Palmieri, Ronald J., 1970
Palmisano, Vincent S., 1941
Palmore, Charles R., 1850
Palos, Lorraine C., 1982
Paluso, Arthur Albert, 1924
Paluso, Arthur K., 1959
Paluzzi, Michael W., 1986
Panasuk, David B., 1982
Pancerev, C. Paul, 1975
Pancoast, George L. A., 1859
Pancoast, George R., 1884
Pancoast, Richard Montgomery, 1845
Pancoast, William H., 1856
Pandolfo, Harry, 1933
Pang, Meredith K. L., 1969
Panitch, Deborah, 1984
Panitch, Victor, 1958
Pansick, Bob Lee, 1978
Paoletti, Michael A., 1956
Paolino, James S., 1966
Papin, F. Sidney, 1881
Pappas, George, 1959
Paradee, Benjamin R., 1951
Paradowski, Frank W., 1937
Parberry, William, 1858
Parent, F. Noel, III, 1982
Parent, Fernand N., Jr., 1957
Parent, Fernand Noel, 1926
Parent, John Wilfrid, 1924
Parent, Kevin, 1965
Parente, John Peter, Jr., 1990
Parente, Maria G., 1988
Parenteau, Roger E., 1955
Parfitt, Oliver A., 1915

Parham, Frederick L., 1843
Parham, R. J., 1860
Parish, Asbury, 1875
Parish, William H., 1870
Park, Cecil Richard, 1921
Park, Emory Robert, 1909
Park, Frank, 1856
Park, George H., 1840
Park, George, 1928
Park, Grace Eunhye, 1990
Park, John Fish, 1914
Park, John W., 1878
Park, Pauline K., 1982
Park, Richard C., 1962
Park, Thomas Creigh, 1905
Park, Wesley, 1873
Park, William H., 1855
Parke, Benjamin R., 1870
Parke, Clifford D., 1850
Parke, DeLos Hetrick, 1916
Parker, Alan Phares, 1923
Parker, D. Reid, 1861
Parker, Edward H., 1848
Parker, Eustace W., 1840
Parker, George W., 1857
Parker, Gerald B., III, 1988
Parker, Gilbert L., 1874
Parker, Henry Clinton, 1838
Parker, Henry Francis, 1883
Parker, Jabez K., 1852
Parker, James, Jr., 1849
Parker, James Pleasant, 1886
Parker, John L., 1906
Parker, John R., 1857
Parker, Oscar F., 1851
Parker, P. James, 1871
Parker, Pamela Dorothea, 1990
Parker, Philip John, 1942
Parker, Samuel H., 1870
Parker, Talbot F., Jr., 1951
Parker, Theodore, 1849
Parker, Thomas S., 1852
Parker, Victor H., 1876
Parker, William H.H., 1861
Parker, William R., 1853
Parker, William S., 1864
Parkes, A. H., 1859
Parkes, Olyn Floyd, 1919
Parkhill, Clayton, 1883
Parkhurst, Leonard Woods, 1936
Parkhurst, Russel, 1838
Parkinson, Edwin B., 1945
Parkison, John A., 1868
Parks, Clarence Carson, 1906
Parks, Colby R., 1959
Parks, Donald B., 1978
Parks, Edward L., 1874
Parks, Elijah M., 1849

Parks, Gilbert R., 1973
Parks, Harold Darby, 1931
Parks, Hugh, 1921
Parks, L. Raymond. Jr., 1945
Parks, Richard Hill, 1937
Parlavecchio, Joseph G., 1979
Parmelee, Elmer Stuart, 1889
Parmet, David Harris, 1909
Parmet, Morris, 1939
Paronish, William J., 1982
Parr, Richard C., 1853
Parr, Shelley J., 1975
Parr, William P., 1859
Parramore, Edward Lyttleton, 1891
Parramore, William R., 1853
Parris, Herman Morris, 1926
Parris, Ted M., 1976
Parrish, Edward, 1844
Parrish, Joseph Andrew, 1929
Parrish, Robert Eunice, 1914
Parrott, Malcolm Ethan, 1883
Parry, Carolyn E., 1965
Parry, Charles, 1843
Parry, Ely, 1837
Parry, George W., 1875
Parry, Rhinard D., 1943
Parry, William C., 1872
Parshall, Robert Vincent, 1892
Parson, John S., 1873
Parson, Russel Cisney, 1914
Parsons, James M., 1835
Parsons, John M., 1964
Parsons, Sidney Alfred, Jr., 1961
Parsons, Willard Herring, 1920
Partridge, Conrad L., 1874
Partyka, Leo C., 1952
Parvin, Noble Butler, 1891
Parvis, George W., 1853
Pascal, Mark S., 1973
Paschal, George W., Jr., 1931
Paschall, D. A., 1872
Paschall, Gideon W., 1854
Paschall, N. J., 1869
Pascucci, Stephen E., 1948
Pascucci, Stephen E., Jr., 1983
Pashman, David R., 1970
Pashuck, Eugene T., S194
Paskert, James P., 1980
Paskin, David L., 1964
Pasley, E. C., 1858
Pasquarette, Mark M., 1988
Pasquariello, Patrick S., 1929
Pasquariello, Patrick S., 1956
Pass, James H., S194
Pastor, Jose Rodriguez, 1921
Pastor, Larry H., 1984
Pastras, Thomas, 1946
Patchen, Patrick N., Jr., 1989

Patella, Eugene Michael, 1931
Paterson, Alexander G., 1975
Paterson, William D., 1982
Pathroff, Robert, 1955
Patlovich, Mark F., 1979
Patrick, Herbert, 1977
Patrick, Nathan Edward, 1891
Patrick, Nicholas Emil, 1939
Patrick, Theodore E., 1948
Patrick, Thomas E., 1946
Patricoski, Thomas S., 1963
Patten, Clarence Anderson, 1916
Patten, Newton N., 1873
Patten, Robert Swift, 1901
Patterson, Arthur, 1853
Patterson, Arthur J., Jr., 1978
Patterson, Ashmore P., 1847
Patterson, Charles F., 1878
Patterson, Cornelius D., 1849
Patterson, Duncan N., 1854
Patterson, Edwin S., 1866
Patterson, Francis Denison, 1904
Patterson, Frank Iams, 1896
Patterson, Fred Lyle, 1907
Patterson, Howard, 1874
Patterson, J. E., 1869
Patterson, James A., 1882
Patterson, James B., 1862
Patterson, James V., 1846
Patterson, John C., 1942
Patterson, John Gordon, 1908
Patterson, John Kinnier, 1868
Patterson, John M., 1954
Patterson, John P., 1870
Patterson, John R., 1954
Patterson, John W., 1978
Patterson, Joseph Flanner, 1906
Patterson, Robert Lewis, 1935
Patterson, Robert M., 1847
Patterson, Robert Mehard, 1903
Patterson, Robert N., 1854
Patterson, Ronald J., 1974
Patterson, Ross Vernet, 1904
Patterson, Samuel D., 1856
Patterson, Theophilus, 1848
Patterson, Walter Scott, 1901
Patterson, William Stuart, 1888
Patti, Michael J., 1985
Patti, Richard B., 1985
Pattishall, Daniel, 1857
Patton, Abram B., 1877
Patton, Frederick H., 1866
Patton, George E., 1858
Patton, Gideon Harmer, 1902
Patton, Gordie C., 1915
Patton, Howard R., Jr., 1933
Patton, Joseph C., 1850
Patton, Noah Woodrow, 1884

Patton, Thomas, 1847
Patton, Thomas Bustard, 1941
Patton, Thomas, 1855
Patty, Louis Greenlee, 1893
Patzki, Julius H.A., 1867
Paul, Artie Blair, 1924
Paul, Carey B., Jr., 1954
Paul, David B., 1965
Paul, David H., 1973
Paul, James Hale, 1911
Paul, John D., Jr., 1949
Paul, John H., 1846
Paul, Seth B., 1981
Paul, Stuart R., 1976
Paules, William Rumbaugh, 1890
Paullin, Lewis, 1843
Paulson, Andrew James, 1904
Paulus, George Ervin, 1952
Pavich, Rudolph William, 1957
Pavlikowski, Fred Lewis, Jr., 1978
Pavlinko-Ghosh, Jody, 1989
Pawlikowski, Sigismond Bernard, 1917
Paxson, Chauncey G., Jr., 1950
Paxson, Edwin M., 1954
Paxson, Oric H., 1882
Paxton, William B., 1844
Payn, Frederick G., 1856
Payne, Benjamin F., 1852
Payne, Carl Forsythe, 1888
Payne, Edward D., 1857
Payne, Frank Irvin, 1900
Payne, George H., 1828
Payne, John, 1886
Payne, Lewis Banks, 1917
Payne, Marshall John, 1893
Payne, Mosby Hale, 1918
Payne, Philander W., 1858
Payne, R. L., 1857
Payne, Robert Lee, Jr., 1881
Payne, Walter A., Jr., 1943
Payne, William A., 1877
Payzant, Elias N., 1855
Pazner, Sherman S., 1966
Peabody, Chas. A., 1873
Peacock, Arthur Bigelow, 1931
Peacock, Howell, 1920
Peacock, Jay A., 1977
Peacock, John L. C., 1859
Peairs, Elisha P., 1879
Peake, Humphrey, 1857
Pearah, Jeremiah Baba, 1925
Pearce, Claude Melvin, 1899
Pearce, Enoch, Jr., 1854
Pearce, James F., 1857
Pearce, John F., 1883
Pearce, William H., 1845
Pearcy, Cornell, 1983
Pearis, Robert A., 1846

Pearl, Burton W., 1965
Pearl, Frank J., 1974
Pearl, Morton S., 1936
Pearl, Robert M., 1956
Pearlman, Mark A., 1974
Pearlman, Samuel, 1960
Pearson, Albert, 1844
Pearson, Benjamin F., 1881
Pearson, Edward James, 1893
Pearson, Eugene Oscar, 1900
Pearson, Julius R., 1932
Pearson, Manuel Malcolm, 1936
Pearson, Seba A., 1831
Pearson, Steven W., 1982
Pease, Frank David, 1893
Pease, Loren H., 1861
Pease, Walter C., 1873
Peat, Edward, 1881
Pechin, Edward Charles, 1902
Pechin, Sergius, 1940
Pechstein, George R., 1948
Pechstein, Henry, 1945
Peck, Alexander L., 1866
Peck, Barnard S., 1872
Peck, Earle Curtiss, 1914
Peck, F. Bruce, Jr., 1952
Peck, Franklin Bruce, 1923
Peck, Henry T., 1881
Peck, Macie, 1902
Peck, Ronald Alan, 1990
Peck, William J., 1977
Pedicino, Alexander R., 1975
Peditto, Joseph J., 1960
Pedlow, Edward B., 1923
Pedrotty, Francis W., Jr., 1952
Pedrotty, John C., 1984
Peebles, J. H., 1857
Peebles, John H.M., 1850
Peede, Alvin Wortham, 1930
Peek-Ball, Cheryl E., 1986
Peeper, James R., 1857
Peeper, John G., 1857
Peeples, James A., 1868
Peeples, P. W., 1855
Peffer, Ambrose, 1887
Pegau, Paul McDowell, 1925
Peiffer, Charles Oscar, 1904
Peikin, Steven R., 1974
Peirce, Isaac, 1888
Pekala, Raymond T., 1978
Pelczar, Brian T., 1988
Pelczar, Eugene W., 1962
Pelensky, Jeanne M., 1975
Pelham, Atkinson, 1826
Pelham, James Wardlaw, 1888
Pell, Edward N., III, 1966
Pell, Edward N., Jr., 1927
Pellegrini, Daniel P., 1990

Pellegrini, Ronald V., 1963
Pellegrini, Vincent A., 1974
Pellicane, Anthony J., 1933
Pellicane, Anthony J., Jr., 1958
Pello, Mark J., 1975
Pelot, J. Crews, 1858
Pelot, James Decatur, 1836
Pelouze, Percy Starr, 1902
Peltz, Philip Malcolm, 1903
Pemberton, Charles, 1882
Pemberton, Clifford H., 1978
Pemberton, Harry H., 1872
Penater, Frank R., 1975
Penchansky, Barry H., 1971
Pender, John R., III, 1947
Pendleton, Andrew L., 1884
Pendleton, David H., 1852
Pendleton, Edmund S., 1854
Pendleton, Philip Barbour, 1845
Pendleton, Samuel H., 1847
Peniston, Thomas, 1835
Pennes, Alexander E., 1936
Pennes, Edward Lewis, 1950
Pennings, Simon P., 1981
Pennington, James F., 1912
Pennington, Byron C., 1881
Pennington, Charles Arthur, 1889
Pennington, George Powell, 1909
Pennington, Henry Vincent, 1900
Pennington, Howard L. J., 1943
Pennington, John, 1916
Pennisi, Alfio K., 1979
Pennsyl, Philip H., 1864
Penny, Stephen F., 1984
Penrod, Harry Hartzell, 1904
Penrose, Thomas William, 1906
Penta, John Joseph, 1929
Penta, John M., 1969
Penta, Michael, 1922
Pentecost, Milton Irving, 1908
Penton, Frank Vincent, 1897
Penton, Jose Luis, 1906
Pentz, Clarence Rolland, 1932
Pentz, Paul G., 1961
Peoples, Claude Theodore, 1945
Peoples, Harry Joseph, 1930
Peoples, Richard B., 1954
Peoples, Samuel Sterrett, 1941
Pepe, Rosalie, 1986
Pepino, Alfred T., 1962
Pepper, C. T., 1869
Pepper, James J., 1964
Pepper, L. Douglas, 1975
Pepper, Marshall A., 1959
Pepper, Max, 1931
Pepper, Wilbur Lee, 1892
Peralta, Jose Maria, 1893
Peralta, Maximiliano, 1894

Perch, Gerald A., 1959
Perch, Robert B., 1955
Perchment, Albert H., 1860
Perchment, John, Jr., 1857
Perchment, Peter D., 1865
Percy, H. T., 1873
Pergam, Carl J., 1968
Pergola, Richard M., 1977
Peril, Hyman Harry, 1917
Peril, Jack Jerome, 1956
Perilstein, Michael D., 1975
Perilstein, Paul K., 1942
Peris, Leon Abraham, 1955
Perkins, Arthur H., 1923
Perkins, Benjamin B., 1877
Perkins, Benjamin S., 1946
Perkins, Charles W., 1847
Perkins, David S., 1883
Perkins, Finis M., 1866
Perkins, Henry, 1877
Perkins, Joseph B., 1851
Perkins, Lewis W., 1851
Perkins, Thomas H., 1846
Perkins, William Harry, 1917
Perkins, Willis M., 1854
Perlin, Elliott, 1961
Perlman, Abraham, 1949
Perlman, Claire Bertha, 1990
Perlman, Henry H., 1918
Perlman, Herbert Charles, 1962
Perlmutter, Irving Kenneth, 1939
Perlmutter, Mark N., 1987
Perloff, Milton Max, 1952
Perr, Hilary A., 1981
Perr, Irwin N., 1950
Perrault, Leo Thomas, 1908
Perri, Angelo Marco, 1925
Perri, Ernest L., 1921
Perrige, John Joseph, 1951
Perrige, William Michael, 1953
Perrine, Cornelius C., 1932
Perrine, Edmund Kirby, 1886
Perrine, Robert Gordon, 1966
Perrl, Frank Adrian, 1939
Perry, Henry M., 1949
Perry, Daniel G., 1849
Perry, David Russell, 1919
Perry, Frank Leslie, 1924
Perry, George H., 1834
Perry, Hext. M., 1872
Perry, John F., 1970
Perry, Joseph W., 1856
Perry, Marshall S., 1862
Perry, Matthias Rizer, 1866
Perry, Richard J., 1980
Perry, Russell E., 1973
Perry, Samuel Wesley, 1899
Perry, Turner Hunt, 1859

Perry, Van Lear, 1859
Perry, Van Lear, 1892
Perry, Warren, 1891
Perry, Wendell Holmes, 1919
Pershing, Frank S., 1879
Pershing, Hugh S., 1955
Pershing, Paul Frederick, 1910
Persing, Amos Vastine, 1893
Person, John Adam, 1888
Person, O. F., 1872
Person, Russell Harrison, 1914
Person, Sylvanus, 1882
Person, William Cortlandt, 1911
Person, William H., 1877
Peruzzi, Robert V., Jr., 1974
Perzley, Richard I., 1973
Peskind, Arnold, 1887
Pessolano, Joseph Anthony, 1915
Peter, Alexander Monroe, 1924
Peter, Irvin Rue, 1891
Peter, Robert, 1881
Peter, Walter P., Jr., 1951
Peters, Barbara D., 1988
Peters, Benjamin B., 1884
Peters, Clyde Ammon, 1916
Peters, David A., 1951
Peters, Gerard Joseph, 1950
Peters, Harold E., 1951
Peters, Jacob Markwood, 1886
Peters, Joel Monroe, 1889
Peters, John W., 1977
Peters, Johna H., 1981
Peters, Penington L., 1854
Peters, Robert H., III, 1978
Peters, Robert H., Jr., 1941
Peters, Samuel Adams, 1848
Peters, Stanley F., 1962
Peters, Stanley W., 1978
Peters, Thomas G., 1960
Peters, William J., 1970
Peterson, Albert Alonzo, 1901
Peterson, Albert H., 1981
Peterson, Bowman H., 1851
Peterson, Gary Ragner, 1967
Peterson, Henry B., 1866
Peterson, Hirman Dewey, 1899
Peterson, Robert D., 1976
Peterson, William Elmer, 1948
Petitjean, John William, 1903
Petre, John H., Jr., 1946
Petree, Paul Augustus, 1914
Petrie, Herbert L., 1873
Petriken, William H., 1835
Petrillo, Raymond J., 1984
Petrone, Carol T., 1979
Petrone, Louis R., 1987
Petrovich, Frank P., 1963
Petrozza, Joseph A., 1978

Petrucci, Ralph Joseph, 1929
Pettibone, Charles Frederick, 1889
Pettigrew, James William, 1909
Pettigrew, S. H., 1872
Pettit, Albert, 1884
Pettit, Joseph, 1890
Pettit, Paul H., 1941
Pettus, Luther C., 1848
Petty, Orlando H., 1904
Pewterbaugh, David Chester, 1933
Peyton, Edwin O., 1859
Peyton, John C., 1866
Peyton, Lawrence R., 1858
Pezzi, Christpher M., 1982
Pezzuti, Hamil Ralph, 1933
Pfaff, Donna M., 1980
Pfefferle, Oscar, 1919
Pfeiffer, Theodore P.F., 1888
Pfister, Benjamin, Jr., 1856
Pfister, John A., 1942
Pfister, Joseph Charles, 1948
Pflueger, C. F., 1872
Pflug, Ferdinand James, 1914
Pfost, Donald Monroe, 1922
Pfupajena, Howard T., 1972
Phalen, Thomas H., 1935
Pharr, Alexander F., 1853
Pharr, William F., 1965
Phelan, Clause Aloysius, 1908
Phelan, Thomas I., 1974
Phelps, Frederick R., 1853
Phelps, George Floyd, 1907
Phelps, John Mahlon, 1932
Phelps, Robert A., 1844
Pherson, Frank James, 1908
Phiambolis, Thomas P., 1979
Phifer, Frank Marion, 1908
Phifer, Joe Carl, 1954
Phifer, William F., 1986
Philbrick, Kemuel L., 1983
Philbrick, Samuel R., 1848
Philip, George, 1985
Phillips, B. L., 1837
Phillips, Charles Hayden, 1914
Phillips, Chas. Montague, 1886
Phillips, Clarence Eugene, 1933
Phillips, Clarence Reynolds, 1897
Phillips, Dinwiddle B., 1846
Phillips, Earl S., 1924
Phillips, Edward B., 1966
Phillips, Edward Milliken, 1911
Phillips, Edward Stephens, 1938
Phillips, Edwin F., 1871
Phillips, Edwin, 1864
Phillips, Eliot Earle, 1906
Phillips, Ellis, 1867
Phillips, Eric D., 1984
Phillips, Frederic A., 1959

Phillips, George S., 1880
Phillips, Gordon R., III, 1986
Phillips, Herman P., 1962
Phillips, Howard Troy, Jr., 1945
Phillips, Irene, 1983
Phillips, James, 1853
Phillips, James Wendell, 1915
Phillips, John D., 1927
Phillips, John L., 1883
Phillips, Lewis Oliver, 1885
Phillips, N. D., 1860
Phillips, P. Sanford, 1858
Phillips, Richard J., 1883
Phillips, Robert H. C., 1896
Phillips, Robert Lewis, 1952
Phillips, Thomas A., 1848
Phillips, Thomas H., 1864
Phillips, Todd E., 1988
Phillips, Vernon R., 1942
Phillips, W. E. T., 1857
Phillips, Warren C., Jr., 1968
Phillips, Warren Charles, 1934
Phillips, William A., 1947
Phillips, William D., 1866
Phillips, William Greaves, 1909
Phillips, William W. L., 1851
Phillipy, William Tell, 1884
Philson, C. F., 1856
Philson, John R., 1960
Phoebus, Clifford Preston, 1936
Pholeric, John F., Jr., 1974
Piatt, John E., III, 1977
Piatt, William A., 1851
Picard, Harry Leon, 1896
Piccini, Paul A., 1975
Picciochi, Joseph Michael, 1937
Pick, Theodore, 1926
Pickens, Winfield S., 1882
Pickett, Clifford, Jr., 1984
Pickett, William Clendeni, 1895
Pickford, William H., 1881
Picot, Louis Julien, 1873
Picot, Mitchell H., 1861
Piekenbrock, Thomas C., 1949
Pier, Walter B., 1884
Pierce, Amos M., 1876
Pierce, Azel, 1891
Pierce, Carl G., Jr., 1950
Pierce, George L., 1879
Piercy, Elizabeth A., 1983
Pierotti, Richard J., 1976
Pierson, Howard Wilson, Jr., J1944
Pierucci, Louis, Jr., 1955
Pietaro, Michael James, 1925
Pietragallo, Louis D., 1972
Pigall, Joseph Smith, 1892
Piggott, William M., 1850
Pigman, Samuel C., 1879

Pigott, Charles J., 1863
Pihoker, Catherine M., 1984
Pilchard, Sewell Norris, 1910
Pilewski, Robert M., 1965
Pilgram, Paul E., 1978
Pilla, Thomas E., S194
Pilla, Timothy S., 1982
Pilling, George Platt, Jr., 1903
Pillmore, George Utley, 1917
Pillow, Anthony L., 1845
Pillow, Raymond H., 1876
Pilsbury, John Milton, 1865
Pim, Louis T., 1856
Pinckney, Ninian, 1833
Pincus, Frances Ellen, 1966
Pincus, Irwin J., 1937
Pinizzotto, Marie E., 1988
Pinkard, H. M., 1855
Pinner, Warren Elias, 1928
Pinsk, Stephen H., 1967
Pinsky, Carl M., 1964
Pinson, Washington S., 1855
Pintimalli, Joseph T., 1960
Pious, William L., 1932
Piovanetti, Simon, 1951
Piper, Charles Eugene, 1893
Piper, Edward W., 1884
Piper, Milton A., 1871
Piper, Oliver Perry, 1872
Piper, William A., 1844
Pirigyi, Paul R., 1975
Pisor, Oliver P., 1881
Pisula, Vincent Paul, Jr., 1953
Pitcher, Stewart C., 1864
Pitchon, Howard E., 1972
Pitone, A. Joseph, 1938
Pitone, Randall E., 1975
Pitt, Michael Jerome, 1963
Pittelli, Joseph J., 1962
Pittis, Thomas, 1894
Pittman, John H., 1887
Pittman, Malory Alfred, 1921
Pittman, Raymond Lupton, 1910
Pitts, Francis M., 1849
Pitts, Francis M., Jr., 1881
Pitts, Hillary, 1837
Pizzutillo, Peter D., 1970
Place, E. Raymond, 1934
Place, Robert A., 1971
Plaisted, E. Freeman, 1855
Plana, Guillermo Machado, 1876
Plank, Edward H., 1870
Plank, John Ransom, 1896
Plant, Edgar Bossett, 1895
Plass, Charles F.W., 1886
Plastino, John E., 1976
Platko, William P., Jr., 1982
Platt, Edward V., 1938

Platt, Howard A., 1961
Platt, Michael, 1917
Platt, Thomas Heritage, Jr., 1903
Playfoot, Donald E., 1977
Pleible, Eugene Theodore, 1896
Pletcher, Henry William, 1954
Plimpton, Albert F., 1859
Pliskin, Mark, 1962
Plonk, George W., J1944
Plotnick, Marc P., 1987
Plotzker, Edward D., 1985
Plumb, James D., 1974
Plumb, Laurence R., 1975
Plummer, Amos Weston, 1880
Plummer, Gardiner H., 1855
Plummer, Harold B., 1935
Plummer, Lloyd G., 1958
Plummer, Orlando P. S., 1857
Plumstead, Matthew Woodbury, 1887
Pluto, Christine M., 1989
Plymire, Isaac Swartz, 1903
Pobirs, Frederick Walter, 1938
Podboy, August J., 1932
Podgorski, Edward M., 1954
Podgorski, Edward M., Jr., 1983
Podlasky, Harry Bernard, 1909
Podolnick, Nelson, 1939
Podolsky, Michael L., 1974
Podrasky, David F., 1980
Poffenberger, Albert T., 1879
Poffenberger, Joseph Cummings, 1912
Pohl, Charles A., 1987
Pohl, Donald Robert, 1955
Pohl, Henry, 1923
Pohl, William Frederick, 1923
Pohowsky, Alex, Jr., 1942
Poichet, Alphonse T., 1877
Poindexter, Edward H., 1851
Poinsard, Paul J., 1941
Poitiaux, Michael Benedict, 1845
Polacheck, William J., Jr., 1980
Polan, Ruth L., 1976
Polan, William S., 1965
Poland, George Alec, 1925
Poland, Joseph, 1907
Poland, Ronald L., 1965
Pole, William Edward, 1900
Poley, Cyrus S., 1870
Poley, Francis B., 1844
Polin, David G., 1984
Polin, Gerald M., 1961
Polischuk, Wasyl James, 1942
Polk, Alexander Murdoch, 1887
Polk, John L., 1868
Polk, Thomas G., 1847
Pollack, Lee S., 1987
Pollack, Robert B., 1988
Pollard, Augustus T., 1883

Pollard, George F., 1836
Pollard, Leonidas C., 1854
Pollard, William M., 1882
Pollock, Charles H., 1878
Pollock, Isador Ira, 1929
Pollock, James Kells, 1928
Pollock, Morris A., 1969
Pollock, Raymond, 1899
Pollock, Stephen D., 1880
Pollock, William L., 1871
Pollock, William, 1854
Polsky, Harry S., 1970
Pomerantz, Philip A., 1971
Pomerene, Harry Piersol, 1890
Pomerene, Joel, 1858
Pomerene, Peter P., 1861
Pomerleau, Ovid Felix, 1934
Pompey, Daniel T., 1958
Pompey, Daniel T., Jr., 1985
Pomroy, Charles G., 1851
Ponchak, Stephen F., Jr., 1982
Pons, Carlos A., 1920
Pons, Juan Antonio, 1928
Pontell, Jonathan, 1989
Pontius, Nevin Driesbach, 1897
Pool, Bennette Baucom, 1923
Poole, Charles H., Jr., 1937
Poole, Charles Henry, 1907
Poole, Edward K., 1959
Poole, Ernest Frederick, 1925
Poole, Louis Eben, 1902
Poole, R. D'Orsay, 1857
Poole, Robert, 1953
Pope, Chandler M., 1855
Pope, D. Strother, 1875
Pope, Edward Sutphen, 1905
Pope, Irvine Clarendon, 1888
Pope, J. W., 1875
Pope, Mardelle Yates, 1893
Pope, Sampson, 1858
Pope, Willis, 1855
Pophal, Mahlon J., S194
Popolow, Michael L., 1966
Popowich, John G., 1958
Popp, George, 1949
Porch, Albert, 1867
Porch, George B., 1871
Porreca, George A., 1932
Porteous, Edward Johnston, 1904
Porter, Benjamin F., 1855
Porter, Charles A., Jr., 1966
Porter, Clifford Charles, 1888
Porter, Gabriel Ellis, 1853
Porter, George Cooper, 1890
Porter, George L., 1862
Porter, I. Stanley, 1976
Porter, J. Elmer, 1886
Porter, John Henning, 1922

Porter, John, 1885
Porter, Joseph Yates, 1870
Porter, Lynne E., 1973
Porter, Richard Arnold, J1944
Porter, Samuel C., 1958
Porter, William T., 1867
Porter, William, 1872
Porterfield, H. William, 1955
Porterfield, Hubert Lester, 1925
Porterfield, Robert Allen, J1944
Portfolio, Almerindo G., Jr., 1978
Portz, Robert A., 1987
Posatko, Robert J., 1957
Posey, Mordecai A., 1882
Posey, Silas Robert, 1911
Posner, Mark A., 1971
Possanza, Carl J., 1984
Possner, Howard Edmond, Jr., 1941
Post, Albert Todd, 1896
Post, Charles A. H., 1899
Post, Donald Francis, 1965
Post, Sidney Haymond, 1901
Post, Silas B., 1882
Post, William Glenn, Jr., 1921
Postlethwaite, Samuel, 1846
Postlewait, John A., 1878
Poston, James Lewis, 1922
Potash, Irwin M., 1953
Poteat, Robert M., Jr., 1940
Potelunas, Clement B., 1938
Potocki, Peter P., 1952
Potsdamer, Joseph B., 1879
Pottash, Ruben R., 1939
Pottberg, Charles, 1883
Potteiger, George Frederick, 1890
Potteiger, Jonathan B., 1859
Potter, H. Phelps, Jr., 1949
Potter, Charles Wilbur, Jr., S1944
Potter, Elias, 1853
Potter, George Walter, 1902
Potter, Jeffrey N., 1979
Potter, Leonard LeGrande, 1937
Potter, Lloyd G., Jr., 1951
Potter, Richard Joseph, 1948
Potter, Samuel B., 1854
Potter, Samuel Otway, 1882
Potter, Thomas R., 1845
Potter, Thompson E., 1875
Potter, Walter Hubert, 1910
Potts, Donald E., 1955
Potts, George W., 1884
Potts, James F., 1865
Potts, Morris Leroy, 1912
Poupko, Gary G., 1969
Poust, George Alvin, 1895
Poux, George Adrian, 1915
Powell, Alfred H., 1853
Powell, Barton Jerome, 1894

Powell, Belitha, 1853
Powell, Charles H., 1954
Powell, Claudius W., 1853
Powell, Clermont S., 1948
Powell, Craig C., 1986
Powell, Frederick Adams, 1891
Powell, George Perry, 1893
Powell, Grover Cleveland, Jr., 1941
Powell, H. B., 1861
Powell, H. Brooke, 1850
Powell, John S., 1853
Powell, James R., 1982
Powell, James, 1870
Powell, Oscar Littleton, 1900
Powell, Philip, 1959
Powell, Raymond Knight, 1930
Powell, Sydney Joseph, Jr., 1937
Powell, Thomas B., 1844
Powell, Thurston G., 1939
Powell, W. Ernest, 1950
Powell, William J., 1859
Powell, William Niles, 1882
Powell, William R., 1877
Powell, William S., 1874
Power, Edward S., 1882
Power, R. Henry, 1845
Powers, Bruce R., 1934
Powers, Donald V., 1955
Powers, Everett, 1896
Powers, John C., 1957
Powers, Marion Henderson, 1907
Powers, Northern Leslie, Jr., 1949
Pownall, Howard W., 1879
Powne, Norman Groves, 1891
Prabhu, Sumanth D., 1985
Praeger, Hubert F., 1878
Pragheimer, Jacob S., 1888
Prahar, Temple F., 1958
Praiss, Donald E., 1958
Prall, Claudius R., 1856
Prata, James M., 1983
Prather, C. W., 1839
Prather, Richard C., Jr., 1875
Pratt, Arthur G., 1932
Pratt, Bryce M., 1847
Pratt, Charles, 1881
Pratt, D. Leonard, 1875
Pratt, Gerald Edward, 1926
Pratt, J., Richmond, 1851
Pratt, John Lynn, 1894
Pratt, John Perkins, 1900
Pratt, Lester C., 1883
Pratt, Lindsay L., 1953
Pratt, Malcolm Lewis, 1914
Pratt, Robert Boyd, 1910
Pratt, Stephen G., 1975
Pratt, William B., 1961
Praver, Louis L., 1931

Preas, James Henry, 1886
Prebola, William R., Jr., 1988
Prehatny, John Richard, 1957
Preletz, Rudolph J., Jr., 1963
Prendergast, Michael J., 1962
Prendergast, Patrick J., 1873
Prendergast, William, 1883
Prentis, William T., 1844
Prentiss, John Hart, 1859
Prescott, Paul T., 1850
Pressly, David L., 1942
Pressly, George W. L., 1892
Pressly, James Lowry, 1923
Pressly, Joseph L., 1852
Pressman, Mark J., 1987
Presson, William F., 1849
Prestipino, Anthony J., 1983
Preston, Alexander R., 1848
Preston, Benjamin W., 1868
Preston, Robert P., 1883
Preston, Samuel Pleasant, 1887
Preston, William B., 1882
Pretell, Judith O., 1989
Prettyman, G. W., 1873
Prevost, Clarence Worrel, 1894
Prewitt, J. B., 1859
Price, Albert C., 1959
Price, Alison Howe, 1938
Price, Allen D., 1879
Price, Charles Eli, 1900
Price, Daniel T., 1866
Price, David E., 1853
Price, Donna B., 1983
Price, Frederick Fraley, 1891
Price, Frederick Kirker, 1894
Price, Henry S., 1938
Price, Jacob, 1850
Price, James, 1963
Price, Joseph H., 1879
Price, Joyce E., 1965
Price, Raphael I. M., 1962
Price, Richard N., 1853
Price, Richard Taylor, 1956
Price, Robert A., 1855
Price, Thomas H., 1876
Price, Thomas Horner, 1920
Price, Thomas K., 1843
Price, Walter Samuel, 1939
Price, William B., 1857
Price, William Frederick, 1861
Price, William H., 1864
Pricer, William E., 1879
Prichard, Karl Campbell, 1906
Prichard, William Clarence, 1906
Pridgen, Claude Leonard, 1901
Priebe, Carl William, Jr., 1957
Priem, Robert W., 1985
Priest, Albert G., 1852

Prigger, Edward Reuben, 1910
Prime, Elon G., 1870
Primrose, Harry C., 1854
Prince, Francis M., 1849
Prince, Josiah E. Duke, 1852
Prince, Leon Nathaniel, 1933
Prince, Linnaeus Hodgson, 1900
Prince, Robert L., 1963
Prince, Thomas H., 1857
Prince, William E., 1848
Pringle, William W., 1879
Prioletti, John P., 1923
Pritchard, Arthur Thomas, 1905
Pritchard, Enoch T., 1876
Pritchard, Frederick Morris, 1904
Pritchett, James W., 1864
Probst, Charles E., Jr., 1968
Probst, Theodore G., 1971
Proctor, David Green, 1875
Proctor, Francis Edward, 1921
Proctor, Pelatiah R., 1851
Proctor, Stephen, 1842
Promin, David, 1927
Promin, Richard E., 1961
Pronesti, George R., 1985
Pronko, Cynthia M., 1981
Propert, David B., 1958
Prorok, Joseph J., 1963
Prosapio, Philip L., 1986
Prosperi, Aldo J., 1984
Prosser, Stephen Sanford, 1896
Prothero, Harold Ney, 1903
Proulx, J.T. Phileas, 1843
Province, Clarence, 1895
Provisor, Benjamin, 1932
Prowell, George F., 1871
Prowell, William R., 1876
Proy, Bernard C., Jr., 1980
Prunk, Byron Fletcher, 1896
Prunty, Francis Crandall, 1931
Pryce, Richard W., 1868
Pryharski, Andrew J., 1967
Pryor, Charles Allen, 1915
Pryor, Wilbur Michael, 1971
Pryor, William T., 1856
Przybylski, Gregory J., 1987
Puff, Robert C., 1945
Pugh, Edward H., 1849
Pugh, Holly P., 1986
Pugh, John M., 1831
Pugh, V. Watson, 1953
Pugh, Vernon W., 1986
Pugh, Winfield Scott, Jr., 1901
Puhalla, Cyril M. J., 1973
Puleo, Joseph Salvatore, 1946
Puleo, Samuel M., 1978
Pulliam, Benjamin E., 1928
Pulliam, John D., 1861

Pulliam, John M., Jr., S1944
Pulsifer, Horatio B., 1863
Pumphrey, Gordon H., 1934
Pumphrey, Josiah Merton, 1904
Punderson, John O., Jr., 1976
Pupi, Paul A., 1966
Purcell, Edward Francis, 1949
Purcell, George William, 1916
Purcell, James Bernard, 1926
Purcell, Wallace M., 1862
Purdon, James, 1897
Purdue, Gary F., 1976
Purdue, John H., 1829
Purdy, John, 1896
Purefoy, George W., Jr., 1876
Purificato, Alfred Thomas, 1925
Purifoy, John H., 1859
Purman, John, 1881
Purnell, Howard Garrett, 1892
Purnell, John S., Jr., 1954
Purnell, John Straw, 1927
Purnell, Robert F., 1836
Purpura, Anthony J., 1927
Pursel, W. Wilson, 1874
Pursell, John C., 1882
Purser, Thomas, Jr., 1928
Purviance, George, 1867
Purviance, William Emmet, 1889
Purvine, Ralph Emerson, 1935
Purvis, Joseph D., 1976
Purvis, W. I., 1869
Purvis, William Reginald, 1886
Puryear, Richard R., 1848
Puschak, Christine E., 1987
Pusey, David C., 1854
Pusey, Robert B., 1860
Putman, Billie H., 1954
Putnam, Samuel G., III, 1986
Putnam, William Frederick, 1934
Putney, F. Johnson, 1934
Putzel, Charles L., Jr., J194
Pyatt, K. A., 1861
Pyfer, Howard F., 1897
Pyle, Jerome L., 1885
Pyles, John Wylie, 1926
Pyles, Newton C., 1860
Pynchon, Lewis Charlton, 1852

~ Q ~

Quackenbos, Harrie Maxwell, 1914
Quaglieri, Charles E., 1970
Quail, William, 1853
Quarles, Mercer W., 1850
Quarterman, Keith A., 1861
Quesada-Guardia, Roberto A., 1951
Quesenberry, Vevion, 1854
Quick, Jacques Voorhees, 1886

Quick, Lavington, 1850
Quigg, Robert M., 1875
Quilez, Joaquin M., 1868
Quinan, John R., 1844
Quinby, Watson F., 1847
Quiney, James J., 1903
Quiney, James J., Jr., 1939
Quinlan, James William, 1934
Quinlan, Michael F., 1973
Quinn, Edward J., 1965
Quinn, Everett Roy, 1927
Quinn, Frank M., 1962
Quinn, Gerald J., 1962
Quinn, James Joseph, 1940
Quinn, John H., 1855
Quinn, John Lawrence, 1931
Quinn, John P., 1859
Quinn, Michael Henry, 1896
Quinn, Milton James, 1919
Quinn, Norman J., Jr., 1948
Quinn, Norman James, 1913
Quinn, Sidney Augustus, 1911
Quinn, Thomas Ryan, 1919
Quinn, William Russell, 1922
Quinones, Edgardo, 1916

~ R ~

Raban, Reginald J., 1946
Rabe, John Howard, 1894
Rabethge, Charles Arman, 1894
Rabinovitz, Isaac, 1934
Rabinowitch, Bonnie L., 1988
Race, Henry H., 1876
Rach, Joel F., 1983
Racho, George J., 1961
Rachunis, Michael Lewis, 1936
Raczkowski, Wanda T., 1980
Radasch, Henry Erdman, 1901
Radcliffe, Glen J., J1944
Radcliffe, William Mann, 1889
Rader, George Andrew, 1937
Rader, Major H. C., 1963
Radin, Sherwin S., 1951
Radom, Myron M., 1925
Radomski, John S., 1981
Radomski, Theodore J., 1958
Rados, Walter T., 1951
Raessler, Rufus Raymond, 1892
Rafal, Robert D., 1973
Raff, Alexander Berkley, 1905
Raffensperger, Bruce W., 1951
Rafferty, Benjamin F., 1886
Rafferty, Francis Brai, 1928
Rafferty, Herbert Nowell, 1899
Rafter, James J., 1949
Ragan, Patrick J., 1876
Rager, Samuel E., 1915

Ragland, Joseph A., 1836
Ragsdale, Edward, 1868
Ragsdale, Joseph, 1861
Ragsdale, William R., 1849
Rahauser, George G., 1866
Rahn, Norman H., 1901
Rahter, Paul D., 1951
Raiber, Richard, 1956
Raiford, John W., 1955
Raine, John R., 1857
Rainear, A. Rusling, 1882
Rains, Jesse Lewis, 1905
Raisis, Leonidas W., 1983
Raken, William Elkin, 1908
Raker, Frederick D., 1881
Raker, Henry M., 1862
Raker, Ned T., 1935
Rakoff, Abraham Edward, 1937
Rakoff, Jeffrey S., 1971
Ralph, Jonathan D., 1976
Ralph, Leland Paul, 1927
Ralph, Nathan, 1931
Ralston, George Foster, 1886
Ralston, Hugh Evans, 1920
Ralston, James Curtis, 1903
Ralston, James G., 1929
Ralston, James Hamilton, 1901
Ralston, Joseph Alexander, 1937
Ralston, Robert G., 1860
Ralston, Samuel Elmer, 1889
Ralston, William James, 1902
Ramani, Tushar M., 1987
Rambler, Robert A., 1883
Rambo, Harold Shaner, 1920
Rambo, Samuel M., 1879
Ramel, William Joseph, 1945
Ramirez, Leopolde M., 1893
Ramos, Theodore, 1985
Ramos-Barroso, Antonio R., 1956
Ramos-Oller Antonio, 1936
Ramos-Umpierre, Antonio, 1965
Rampona, James Raymond, 1929
Ramsaur, G. Alexander, 1880
Ramsay, Andrew M., 1868
Ramsay, G. Randolph, 1848
Ramsay, George M., 1852
Ramsay, James Graham, 1848
Ramsay, John W., 1853
Ramsay, Robert Hudson, 1897
Ramsay, Robert Warren, 1886
Ramser, James Richard, 1960
Ramsey, Alexander, 1831
Ramsey, Clarence Scott, 1900
Ramsey, Harry E., Jr., 1968
Ramsey, Robert W., 1874
Ramsey, Russell Wiest, 1934
Ramsey, Samuel J., 1840
Ramsey, William George, 1893

Ramsey, William P., 1855
Ramsey, Wilson C., 1855
Ranck, John Milton, 1928
Rand, Howard B., 1848
Randal, Harry Lee, 1901
Randall, Hiram, 1916
Randall, Thomas Anthony, 1954
Randall, William Herdic, 1878
Randall, William, 1858
Randazzo, Vincent T., 1969
Randell, Asher, 1935
Randell, David J., 1970
Randle, Charles C., 1875
Randle, T. S., 1869
Randle, William H., 1878
Randles, Herbert, 1907
Randolph, Lewis C., 1859
Randolph, Tucker Lucas, 1916
Rangatore, Joseph Samuel, 1945
Range, Irving, 1924
Ranish, Deborah A., 1981
Rank, Dale C., 1953
Rank, Harry Phillip, 1897
Ranke, John W. H., 1896
Rankin, A. H., 1858
Rankin, Charles A., 1954
Rankin, Charles Albert, 1926
Rankin, Clarke D., 1850
Rankin, D. Nevin, 1854
Rankin, E. Davidson, 1851
Rankin, James A., 1883
Rankin, John Oliver, 1922
Rankin, Lynn M., 1921
Rankin, Samuel Wharton, 1912
Rankin, Stewart L., 1930
Rankin, William M., 1851
Rannels, Darwin W., 1955
Ransberry, John, Jr., 1855
Ransom, Frederick Page, 1904
Ransom, Matthias Lent, 1902
Ranson, John L., Jr., 1942
Ranson, William A., 1948
Ranyon, Thomas H., 1855
Rapaport, Marvin J., 1962
Raper, Thomas J., 1854
Raper, Thomas Walter, 1897
Rappaccioli, Buenaventura, 1926
Rappaport, Myron E., 1955
Rappaport, Steven H., 1984
Rarig, Howard Raymond, 1913
Raring, Linus Maurice, 1915
Rasmussen, Hans, 1896
Ratchford, Isaac Newton, 1915
Ratchford, W. Buckley, 1971
Ratcliffe, Charles T., 1853
Rathbone, F. Wait, 1883
Rathbun, Frank D., 1878
Rathmell, Thomas Kessinger, 1931

Ratico, Helen L., 1973
Ratke, Henry V., 1941
Ratliff, Charles C., 1855
Ratner, Irving P., 1963
Raub, Michael, W., 1865
Raub, Richard Vaux, 1896
Raudenbush, Abraham S., 1864
Rauth, John D., Jr., 1975
Ravenscraft, William H., 1857
Ravin, Joseph P., 1956
Ravit, George Jonathan, 1931
Rawley, Clarence G., J1944
Rawlins, John W., 1845
Rawls, Elijah H., 1855
Rawls, John E., 1954
Rawls, John Lewis, 1917
Ray, Ethelbert Sheb, 1890
Rayfield, Elliot J., 1967
Rayfield, Morton M., 1972
Raymond, Eugene Edward, 1933
Raymond, Joseph C., 1952
Raymond, Paul A., 1971
Raymond, Roger D., 1966
Raymond, Walter Clemens, 1906
Raynak, Jan T., 1969
Rayner, Mark E., 1975
Rayner, Richard M., 1987
Raynes, Stanton M., 1969
Rea, Alexander M., 1865
Rea, Benjamin F., 1842
Rea, Charles T. I., 1859
Rea, Clarence Galleher, 1904
Rea, James L., 1876
Read, Albert N., 1846
Read, Alfred Hurst, 1897
Read, Clement H., 1859
Read, Edward J., Jr., 1977
Read, Frederick B., 1867
Read, Hilton Shreve, 1923
Read, J. Harleston, 1971
Read, John T., 1853
Read, Josephus D., 1874
Read, Randolph Alexander, 1971
Read, William Parsons, 1896
Reade, Edwin Godwin, 1916
Reading, George Evans, 1885
Reading, John R., 1847
Reagan, Robert S., 1880
Reale, Frank R., 1971
Ream, John, 1828
Ream, Robert S., 1986
Reams, Carl L., 1966
Reardon, James J., 1937
Reardon, Lawrence Craig, 1990
Reath, Joseph Pancoast, 1937
Reber, Charles T., 1856
Reber, Conrad Samuel, 1903
Reber, Howard F., J1944

Reber, John W.H., 1867
Reber, William M., 1863
Reber, William, 1854
Reberdy, George Kanter, 1946
Rebhoun, Earl Herb, 1915
Rebman, Lawrence S., 1866
Reckefus, Charles Halwadt, Jr., 1893
Rector, Robert D., 1948
Red, G. J., 1873
Red, Samuel Clark, 1887
Redd, John T., 1859
Redd, Thomas M., 1854
Redd, Thomas Minor, 1887
Reddan, Martin W. P., 1900
Redden, Joseph W., 1857
Reddick, Samuel T., 1851
Reddish, Thompson K., 1859
Redeker, F. William, 1878
Redelin, Albert Augustus, 1893
Redelin, Albert Norman, 1917
Redfield, J. Ralph L., 1919
Redfield, John, 1852
Redfield, Ronald Laverne, 1934
Redka, James Wilson, 1972
Redland, Arthur John, 1926
Redman, Spence, 1883
Redmond, John L., 1946
Rednor, Daniel Jay, 1938
Redo, Frank L., 1972
Redpath, Nathaniel J., 1887
Redpath, Nathaniel James, 1935
Reed, Anderson F., 1885
Reed, C. Richmond, 1853
Reed, Charles Edgar, 1895
Reed, Charles, 1880
Reed, Crystal D., 1989
Reed, David M., 1978
Reed, Edwin B., 1884
Reed, Elmer M., 1936
Reed, Eugene Lewis, 1884
Reed, Franklin L., Jr., 1943
Reed, George, 1836
Reed, George K., 1874
Reed, H. Allan, 1876
Reed, Harold R., 1915
Reed, Harry Wilson, 1942
Reed, Henry David, 1903
Reed, I. Bebout, 1886
Reed, J. Farley, 1862
Reed, Jacob, Jr., 1866
Reed, James Craig, 1907
Reed, James L., 1837
Reed, James Madison, Jr., 1920
Reed, Jesse J., 1866
Reed, John, 1853
Reed, John Orlando, 1893
Reed, Joseph A., 1847
Reed, Leo Buckley, 1920

Reed, Louis Thompson, 1884
Reed, Marvin Warren, 1903
Reed, T. J., 1864
Reed, Thomas B., 1859
Reed, Thomas Godfrey, 1926
Reed, Thomas Sydenham, 1846
Reed, William, 1853
Reed, William E., 1880
Reed, Willoughby H., 1882
Reedman, Gail A., 1984
Reedy, Walter Joseph, 1933
Reedy, Walter Marion, 1892
Reedy, William J., S1944
Reef, James S., 1958
Reef, Thomas Cline, 1961
Reeme, Elias W., 1849
Reemsnyder, Henry G., 1881
Rees, Edwin, 1835
Rees, Frederic A., 1843
Rees, Glenys S., 1983
Rees, Jerome R., 1964
Rees, William Thomas, 1908
Reese, Beverly P., 1851
Reese, Charles E., 1855
Reese, Charles L., IV, 1978
Reese, Charles Lee, III, 1958
Reese, John Davies, 1925
Reese, Lewis Samuel, Jr., 1921
Reese, Lewis, 1899
Reese, Warren Snyder, 1915
Reeser, Howard S., 1867
Reeser, Richard, 1896
Reeser, T. Howard, 1874
Reeve, Isaac, 1840
Reeve, James T., 1855
Reeve, John Charles, 1886
Reeve, Stephen S., 1858
Reeves, Julius Norman, 1930
Reeves, M. W., 1870
Reeves, Raymond W., 1933
Reeves, Robert H., 1883
Reeves, Samuel, 1856
Reeves, W. Brian, 1979
Reeves, William H., 1862
Refowich, Richard S., J1944
Regan, James R., 1956
Regan, Joseph James, 1941
Reganis, John S., S1944
Reger, Alfred G., 1877
Reger, Robert A., 1880
Regester, Robert Pierson, 1916
Register, H. C., 1874
Rehanek, Dale Charles, 1953
Rehbein, Louis William, 1901
Rehfuss, Kathleen Louise, 1984
Rehm, Victor G.R.J., 1884
Rehr, Eric L., 1987
Reiber, E. William, II, 1965

Reiber, William F., 1858
Reich, Alice, 1990
Reich, David L., 1982
Reichard, Morris, 1905
Reichard, Noah W., 1887
Reichard, Philip L., 1865
Reichard, V. Milton, 1882
Reichel, John, III, 1970
Reichling, George H., 1957
Reichman, Robert T., 1979
Reid, Alexander, 1838
Reid, Christopher J., 1989
Reid, Hugh, 1882
Reid, James H., III, 1983
Reid, James William, 1908
Reid, John Reid, 1847
Reid, Neville C., 1840
Reid, Russell Alexander, 1901
Reidt, William U., 1947
Reidy, John Aloysius, 1903
Reier, Charles E., 1963
Reiff, Rankin, 1907
Reifsnyder, Joseph Calvin, 1888
Reifsnyder, William H., III, 1951
Reigart, Paul M., 1930
Reigle, Erasmus Lear, 1889
Reihard, Kathryn A., 1985
Reilly, Ann E., 1978
Reilly, Eugene Crowell, 1901
Reilly, Francis St. Clair, 1909
Reilly, James F., 1989
Reilly, Patrick M., 1987
Reilly, Paul Jones, 1848
Reilly, Peter Charles, 1890
Reilly, Philip, 1875
Reimer, Charles James, Jr., 1911
Reinemund, Charles Adam, 1904
Reinhard, Harold J., 1953
Reinhard, Warren J., 1951
Reinhard, Wilson J., 1885
Reinhardt, David Jones, III, 1951
Reinhardt, George Robert, 1947
Reinhardt, John F., 1980
Reinhart, Harry A., 1943
Reinhart, J. Crawford, 1882
Reinholdt, John B., 1862
Reis, Paul B., 1931
Reisinger, Paul Bryson, 1918
Reisman, Barry M., 1968
Reisman, Henry Allen, 1922
Reiss, Suzanne E., 1988
Reiter, Martin D., 1945
Reiter, William C., 1839
Reith, Emil, 1891
Reitz, Melvin L., 1946
Relfe, Conyers Blakely, S1944
Remetz, Michael S., 1981
Remig, John Henry, 1891

Remington, Neil D., 1979
Remley, Luke Kinsel, 1938
Remley, Stuart K., 1953
Remondino, Peter Charles, 1865
Remsburg, Stacia T., 1988
Rendleman, James Walter, 1894
Rendleman, John J., 1886
Renfro, C. J., 1867
Renn, Carl Grover, 1915
Renn, Roy Herman, 1906
Reno, Joseph David, 1957
Renquest, Edward Allan, 1954
Rensimer, Wayne T., 1972
Rentschler, Harry Fleisher, 1893
Rentschler, John Horace, 1942
Renzulli, William F., 1965
Repa, Joseph John, 1929
Repici, Anthony J., 1939
Repka, Mark L., 1981
Repka, Michael X., 1979
Repman, Harry Joseph, 1900
Repman, Harry Joseph, Jr., 1941
Repta, Stephen, Jr., 1939
Resch, Frederick A., S1944
Reser, William Marven, 1903
Resnik, Alan M., 1973
Ressetar, Michael J., 1942
Ressler, George W., 1884
Ressler, Joel G., 1870
Ressler, Vincent Roland, 1947
Restaino, Charles Frederick, 1923
Restrepo, Delfin F., 1887
Rether, Clarence S., 1884
Reuben, Mark S., 1973
Reuling, James Risley, Jr., 1914
Reum, Charles George, 1893
Reuss, Mary Lynne, 1973
Reutter, Harry Daniel, 1884
Revelli, Robert J., J1944
Revercomb, Jacob R., 1852
Revere, Seth Dustin, 1935
Rex, George P., 1834
Rex, Oliver P., 1867
Reyes de los, Joseph M., 1928
Reyes, Salvador, 1920
Reynard, Kenneth B., 1968
Reynolds, Bradley P., 1984
Reynolds, Edward S., 1877
Reynolds, H. V.H., 1869
Reynolds, Hammon, 1915
Reynolds, Harvey M., 1852
Reynolds, Jacob E., 1854
Reynolds, John M.C., 1879
Reynolds, John R., 1947
Reynolds, John W., 1988
Reynolds, Kenneth Earl, 1933
Reynolds, Oscar Lloyd, 1936
Reynolds, Samuel K., 1857

Reynolds, Samuel, 1865
Reynolds, V. Karen A., 1984
Reynolds, Victor M., 1905
Reynolds, Walter Forbyce, 1894
Reynolds, Walter J., III, 1967
Reynolds, William Wilson, 1891
Rhea, Edwin Bruce, 1913
Rhea, Edwin Wilson, 1901
Rhea, Robert M., 1868
Rhee, John W., 1984
Rhees, Morgan J., 1846
Rhinehart, Alexander K., 1861
Rhinehart, Solomon E., 1850
Rhoads, Alfred Lawrence, 1910
Rhoads, Edward Elliott, 1905
Rhoads, George H., 1879
Rhoads, George W., 1866
Rhoads, J. Neely, 1885
Rhoads, John, 1902
Rhoads, Michael Albert, 1868
Rhoads, Reuben B., 1857
Rhoads, Thomas J. B., 1861
Rhoads, Thomas Leidy, 1893
Rhoda, Robert Gordon, 1947
Rhode, Marvin C., 1947
Rhode, Solon L., III,,1964
Rhode, Solon Lafayette, 1916
Rhodes, Charles E., 1972
Rhodes, Henry F., 1883
Rhodes, John Frederick, 1942
Rhodes, Samuel T., 1838
Ribeiro, Jeronymo Dias, 1890
Ricchiuti, A. George, 1932
Ricchiuti, Joseph F., 1930
Ricciardi, Susan L., 1985
Rice, Albert R., 1861
Rice, Archibald A., 1853
Rice, Charles Samuel, 1891
Rice, Francis E., 1852
Rice, Frederick Whitney, 1889
Rice, Harrison J., 1849
Rice, Thomas C., 1858
Rice, Wilkie Benjamin, 1910
Rice, William R., 1854
Rice, William Thomas, 1932
Rich, Edward Antoine, 1901
Rich, Edward Israel, 1893
Rich, Ezra Clark, 1894
Rich, Guy C., 1885
Rich, J. Bartlett, 1874
Rich, John T., Jr., 1988
Rich, Joseph R., 1943
Rich, Lorin Farr, 1906
Rich, Richard Innis, 1940
Rich, Robert D., 1966
Rich, Robert E., S1944
Rich, Samuel, 1910
Rich, Thomas C., 1878

Richard, Irving Etienne, 1916
Richards, Arthur Charles, Jr., 1943
Richards, Buchan, 1846
Richards, Charles A.L., 1852
Richards, Charles Egbert, 1887
Richards, Charles F., 1942
Richards, Clayton W., 1878
Richards, Daniel W., 1863
Richards, Davis Bruce, 1896
Richards, James L., 1916
Richards, John C., 1865
Richards, John David, 1897
Richards, Milton S., 1867
Richards, Robert Wayne, 1913
Richards, Thomas J., 1868
Richards, Thomas, 1926
Richards, William Evans, 1895
Richardson, Claude Ervin, 1930
Richardson, Cleves, 1913
Richardson, David R., 1859
Richardson, Davis H., 1885
Richardson, Ernest C., Jr., 1943
Richardson, Fred MacDonald, 1935
Richardson, George A., 1923
Richardson, George B., 1951
Richardson, George N., 1852
Richardson, Harry Tompkins, 1900
Richardson, James, 1885
Richardson, John, 1847
Richardson, John B., 1865
Richardson, John M., 1856
Richardson, Marcus F., 1872
Richardson, Moses, 1856
Richardson, Newton M., 1864
Richardson, Nicholas D., 1853
Richardson, Ross B., 1837
Richardson, Ross E., 1951
Richardson, Waldo, 1909
Richardson, William James, 1886
Richardson, William L., 1848
Richardson, William M., 1854
Richardson, William, 1864
Richeson, Ittacus L., 1853
Richey, James A., 1861
Richie, Robert W., 1852
Richlin, Padie, 1938
Richman, Alan V., 1968
Richman, Craig G., 1988
Richman, Elijah B., 1842
Richman, Kenneth Charles, 1911
Richman, Suzanne, 1988
Richmond, Allen C., 1970
Richmond, John B., 1852
Richmond, John P., 1834
Richter, Douglas M., 1989
Richter, Henry Carl, 1906
Richter, Howard S., 1957
Richter, Julius S., 1962

Ricker, Charles Thorne, 1933
Ricketts, Edward A., 1941
Ricketts, Edward A., Jr., 1969
Ricketts, George Allen, 1908
Ricketts, Gerard C., 1850
Ricketts, John G., 1910
Ricks, Fabius S., 1858
Ricks, Henry C., Jr., J1944
Riddle, A., A.J., 1843
Riddle, Alfonso Ricardo, 1929
Riddle, J. R., 1869
Riddle, Lindsay R., 1940
Riddle, N. Watkins, 1844
Riddle, Norman Clayton, 1919
Riddle, Ransford John, 1935
Ridge, Samuel LeRoy, 1907
Ridgill, Henry L., 1851
Ridgway, Charles 1845
Ridgway, Eli Chester, Jr., 1933
Ridgway, Thomas Edwin, 1864
Ridgway, William Frederick, 1904
Ridgway, William G., 1942
Ridilla, Leonard V., Jr., 1989
Ridley, R. B., 1869
Ridpath, Paul Cole, 1900
Riecker, George A., 1865
Ried, J. H., 1872
Riedy, Melissa Jane, 1976
Riegel, George E., 1951
Riegel, Henry H., 1857
Riegel, Thomas Francis, 1901
Rieger, Francis A. A. T., 1857
Riegert, Louis C., 1939
Riely, John D., 1847
Rifat, Mansur Mustafa, 1907
Riff, Dennis S., 1971
Riffert, Paul M., 1935
Riffle, George N., II, 1960
Riffle, George Newcomer, 1922
Riffle, John E., 1964
Rigg, W. Cochrane, 1859
Riggins, Hazel McLeod, 1924
Riggins, John Carlton, 1929
Riggle, Paul Phillips, 1930
Riggs, David W., 1861
Riggs, E. S., 1869
Riggs, Edward Elder, 1886
Riggs, Lindus La Rell, 1905
Riggs, W. Judson, 1872
Righter, Harvey Mitchell, 1896
Righter, Washington, 1866
Righter, William H., 1879
Righter, William W., 1838
Rightmyer, Eugene, 1955
Rightmyer, John N., 1963
Rightor, John T., 1958
Rihl, Henry W., 1849
Rihl, Jacob L., 1856

Roos, Leon, 1937
Roose, Arthur Eugene, 1895
Root, Douglas C., 1987
Roper, Daniel W., 1851
Roperti, Karen Ann, 1990
Roque, Richard M., 1947
Rorabaugh, James Douglas, 1990
Rosales, Nicasio, 1891
Rosania, B. Hoagland, 1963
Rosati, Vincent Fortunato, 1923
Rosato, Ernest Lancelot, 1990
Rosch, Jeffrey M., 1972
Rosch, Julius C., S1944
Roscoe, Constantine R., 1938
Roscoe, Diane L., 1983
Rose, Abraham Hewitt, 1906
Rose, Algernon H., 1852
Rose, Archimedes, 1879
Rose, Christopher C., 1970
Rose, Clarence Atwood, 1913
Rose, David, 1892
Rose, David, 1924
Rose, Erasmus T., 1835
Rose, Francis Leland, 1943
Rose, Horace Lewis, 1903
Rose, Isadore, 1946
Rose, Latinus Irvine, 1851
Rose, Robert M., 1979
Rose, Samuel J., 1912
Rose, Thurman Hubert, 1929
Rose, Walter C., Jr., 1959
Rose, William W., 1852
Roseman, Milo A. J., 1925
Rosen, Barry A., 1973
Rosen, Bruce J., 1976
Rosen, Harel D., 1989
Rosen, Jay S., 1973
Rosen, Joseph H., 1961
Rosen, Leonard E., 1952
Rosen, Leonard P., 1947
Rosen, Lionel W., 1965
Rosen, Mayer, 1897
Rosenbaum, Arnold S., 1966
Rosenbaum, Jerald Manuel, 1962
Rosenbaum, Leon, S1944
Rosenberg, Anne L., 1981
Rosenberg, Dale J., 1985
Rosenberg, Edward Frank, 1934
Rosenberg, Jack N., 1954
Rosenberg, Kenneth C., 1978
Rosenberg, Leon, 1937
Rosenberg, Louis, 1926
Rosenberg, Paul E., 1964
Rosenberg, Paul J., 1969
Rosenberg, Ronald J., 1971
Rosenberger, Edmund S., 1878
Rosenberger, John Ashby, 1894
Rosenberger, Randle Crater, 1894

Rosenberry, Benjamin F. L., 1932
Rosenberry, Edward Shimer, 1895
Rosenblatt, Alfred A., 1955
Rosenblatt, Elwood C., 1955
Rosenblatt, Harold S., 1925
Rosenblatt, Michael S., 1984
Rosenblatt, Morton A., 1951
Rosenblatt, Sidney, 1918
Rosenblatt, Stanley A., 1962
Rosenblatt, Stanley G., 1965
Rosenblum, Benjamin A., 1984
Rosenblum, Bret Abraham, 1990
Rosenblum, Fred A., 1973
Rosenblum, Harry M., 1978
Rosenblum, Norman G., 1978
Rosenbluth, Sidney B., 1932
Rosenfeld, David Hiram, 1910
Rosenfeld, Edward J., 1987
Rosenfeld, Joel C., 1974
Rosenfeld, Maurice Harry, 1924
Rosenfeld, Myron E., 1960
Rosenfeld, Philip A., 1967
Rosenheim, Gustav E., 1945
Rosenman, David E., 1968
Rosenschein, Serl E., 1976
Rosenshein, Marc S., 1973
Rosenstein, Jerome H., 1981
Rosenstock, Henry, 1896
Rosenthal, Aaron, 1950
Rosenthal, David E., 1962
Rosenthal, Edwin, 1880
Rosenthal, Gary I., 1975
Rosenthal, Herbert A., 1956
Rosenthal, Jacob, 1888
Rosenthal, Joseph Morris, 1910
Rosenthal, Norman R., 1978
Rosenthal, Simon Harry, 1913
Rosenzweig, Maurice, 1923
Rosenzweig, Max, 1936
Rosenzweig, Stanley C., 1957
Rosier, John Bruner, 1900
Rosko, Christopher J., 1981
Rosner, Michael S., 1985
Rosner, William F., 1975
Rosof, Edward, 1971
Ross, D. Gwendolyn, 1980
Ross, Daniel Curley, 1907
Ross, Donald Price, 1927
Ross, Earl Blan, 1921
Ross, Elijah W., 1861
Ross, Ellen I., 1984
Ross, Frank Marcellus, 1874
Ross, George, 1849
Ross, Helen L., 1990
Ross, Hendric Arnold, 1912
Ross, James, 1852
Ross, James Brice, 1866
Ross, James Thweatt, 1885

Ross, John Kirkland, 1907
Ross, Joseph Herman, 1894
Ross, Lewis Rex, 1916
Ross, Matthew Wilkinson, 1889
Ross, Nathaniel, 1892
Ross, Richard Hawthorne, S1944
Ross, Samuel M., 1850
Ross, Steven E., 1976
Ross, Terence C., 1981
Ross, Thomas Wallace, 1927
Ross, Wayne K., 1983
Ross, William Fay, 1905
Ross, William L., Jr., 1945
Rosser, John C., 1867
Rosset, Ephriam Manuel, 1938
Rossien, Ahbrohm Xerxes, 1925
Rossiter, Henry James, 1891
Rossman, Bernard Schecter, 1943
Rossman, Milton D., 1970
Rossy, Evariste A., 1852
Rote, William H., 1890
Roth, Helen, 1905
Roth, James, P., 1915
Roth, Jerry M., 1982
Roth, Michael S., 1972
Roth, Theodore Irving, 1923
Roth, Theodore, 1865
Rothenberger, Marvin K., 1924
Rothenberger, Rodger F., 1986
Rothermel, Franklin J., 1967
Rothermel, John Keim, 1932
Rothermel, William S., S1944
Rothermel, Wilson H., 1894
Rothfeld, Donald, 1963
Rothfeld, Edwin L., 1956
Rothfeld, Laura N., 1987
Rothman, Gerson B., 1966
Rothong, Carole L., 1987
Rothrock, Gilmore M., 1958
Rothrock, John Henry, 1845
Rothrock, William P., 1842
Rothstein, Marianne S., 1981
Rothwell, William J., 1873
Rotko, Bernard Benjamin, 1935
Rotman, Marvin Z., 1958
Rott, Otto Mathias, 1908
Rottner, Charles Selmar, 1891
Rotz, C. Theodore, Jr., 1957
Rouanet, William, 1847
Roumm, Alan D., 1977
Round, Frederick Lutwyche, 1902
Rourk, William Asbury, Jr., 1924
Rouse, Howard, 1917
Rouse, John, Jr., 1904
Rouse, Paul V., 1943
Rouse, William Isaac, 1909
Roussell, Albert E., 1882
Rovit, Richard L., 1950

Rovner, Harold, 1949
Rovner, Barry W., 1980
Rovno, Philip, 1894
Rowan, Charles, 1896
Rowand, Randall W., 1978
Rowand, Robert E., 1945
Rowe, Daniel Mannix, 1926
Rowe, Daniel S., 1948
Rowe, Daniel S., Jr., 1979
Rowe, Hezekiah J., 1876
Rowe, J. Wesley, 1871
Rowe, Joseph J., 1950
Rowe, Thomas, 1859
Rowell, E. H., 1860
Rowland, Francis F., 1873
Rowland, John G., 1853
Rowland, N. Dean, Jr., 1951
Rowland, Robert B., Jr., 1985
Rowland, William A., 1855
Rowley, Quintin John, 1884
Rowley, Samuel D., 1946
Roy, Gustavus G., 1857
Roy, Robert H., 1946
Royal, Benjamin Franklin, 1909
Royce, Charles Clifton, 1899
Royer, B. Franklin, 1899
Royer, Daniel F., 1875
Royer, Franklin B., 1847
Royer, Jacob Weaver, 1892
Royster, James Hunt, 1917
Rozelle, Carlos C., 1907
Rozick, Mark S., 1983
Rozploch, Albin, 1917
Rozycki, Grace F., 1980
Rubel, Martin, 1959
Ruben, Benjamin D., 1913
Rubenfeld, Gordon D., 1987
Rubens, Alan Bruce, 1962
Rubenstein, Myer W., 1923
Rubenstone, Abraham Isadore, 1912
Rubin, Allen W., 1967
Rubin, Harry, 1924
Rubin, Jack D., 1956
Rubin, Jeffry F., 1971
Rubin, Mark G., 1981
Rubin, Morton L., 1967
Rubin, Robert J., 1953
Rubin, S. Bruce, 1964
Rubinstein, Mark I., 1983
Ruby, Cyrus B., 1851
Ruby, Edward B., 1971
Ruby, Samuel R., 1976
Ruby, Victor Mordecai, 1945
Ruch, Charles Frank, 1891
Ruch, William Starick, 1888
Rucker, Ellis D., 1980
Rucker, William P., 1855
Rudansky, Sheldon, 1949

Rudansky, Max C., 1979
Rudisill, Benjamin F., 1860
Rudisill, Hillyer, Jr., 1924
Rudnitzky, Jerome, 1962
Rudolph, Burton M., 1953
Rudolph, Eugene, 1963
Rudolph, Herman Louis, 1935
Rudolph, Jack Arthur, 1928
Rudolph, John P., 1939
Rudolph, Samuel F., Jr., 1958
Rueckel, Mary E., 1985
Ruetschlin, James H., 1939
Rufe, John Johnson, 1902
Ruffin, John M., 1845
Ruffini, Christopher P., 1988
Ruffini, John A., 1958
Ruffini, John J., 1983
Ruffini, Robert A., 1984
Ruffner, Samuel Allemong, 1890
Rugeley, Henry L., 1861
Ruger, Henry H., 1865
Ruggeri, Anthony Joseph, 1973
Ruggiero, Nicholas J., 1966
Rugh, Carroll B., 1885
Rugh, Jacob W., 1851
Rugh, James Torrence, 1892
Ruhl, Levi Albertus, 1905
Ruht, Joseph C., 1946
Ruiz, Jesus, 1889
Rumbaugh, James Howard, 1964
Rumbaugh, James O., Jr., 1954
Rumbaugh, Marshall C., 1908
Rumbaugh, Ulrich David, 1923
Rumbaugh, William P., 1986
Rumbold, F. Frazier, 1862
Rumer, George Francis, 1943
Rummell, Russell William, 1929
Rumph, Sterling Price, 1905
Runcie, John W., 1871
Rundio, Peter C., 1852
Runkle, Stuart Calvin, 1888
Runkle, Stuart Calvin, Jr., 1932
Runkle, William V., 1874
Runowicz, Carolyn D., 1977
Ruof, Andrew C., III, 1943
Rupert, Elon, Sargent, 1887
Rupp, James P., 1980
Rupp, Joseph J., 1942
Rupp, Michael J., 1984
Ruppersberg, Anthony, Jr., 1933
Ruschak, Paul J., 1975
Rush, David G., 1857
Rush, E. W., 1873
Rush, Eugene, 1914
Rush, George Blackmore, 1926
Rush, Irving Arnold, 1934
Rush, Warren Blachley, 1893
Rushing, Greenwood, 1860

Rushmore, Edward, 1872
Rushton, Harold W., 1953
Rushton, John R., III, 1948
Rushton, Percy Hartley, 1908
Rusling, Robert S., 1921
Russ, Heidi R., 1989
Russell G. T., 1870
Russell, B. Royce, Jr., 1976
Russell, Edward R., 1972
Russell, Ephraim P., 1866
Russell, Evans Dounton, 1911
Russell, Ezra R., 1866
Russell, George B., 1836
Russell, John W., 1827
Russell, Joseph William, 1907
Russell, Leonidas, 1855
Russell, Preston W., 1851
Russell, Scott S., 1912
Russell, Thomas Hendrick, 1908
Russell, W. Randall, 1983
Russell, Walter Judson, 1889
Russell, William, 1847
Russell, William M.N., 1850
Russo, James M., Jr., 1968
Russo, James, J1944
Russo, Joseph Romeo, 1924
Russo, Joseph, 1928
Russo, Marc S., 1988
Russo, Michael P., 1978
Rust, Bushrod, 1845
Rust, Emery Andrew, 1904
Rust, George W., 1846
Rutenberg, Joel M., 1975
Ruth, Chauncey Elwood, 1927
Ruth, Corey K., 1981
Ruth, Daniel G., 1857
Ruth, Edwin Z., 1909
Ruth, John A., Jr., 1984
Ruth, John Francis, 1943
Ruthardt, Frederick W., Jr., 1983
Rutherford, Alexander D., 1856
Rutherford, Hiram, 1838
Rutherford, William W., 1832
Rutledge, Albert Thompson, 1889
Rutledge, Jacob I., 1855
Rutledge, Shallus R., 1870
Rutstein, Eric Stephen, 1990
Rutstein, Harvey R., 1960
Rutt, Wilmer M., 1960
Rutter, John R. Barton, 1847
Rutter, William Albert, 1957
Ruzbarsky, Joseph J., 1977
Ruzbarsky, Philip J., 1984
Ruzich, Andrew H., 1987
Ryall, Thomas M., 1883
Ryan, Adam W. T., 1906
Ryan, Charles Calvin, 1912
Ryan, Charles H., 1968

Ryan, Charles S., 1948
Ryan, Earl Francis, 1919
Ryan, Eugene J., S1944
Ryan, James John, 1934
Ryan, James Joseph, 1942
Ryan, James M., 1972
Ryan, John Timothy, 1905
Ryan, Laurence Reginald, 1888
Ryan, Michael C., 1888
Ryan, Randall W., 1982
Ryan, Thomas J., 1836
Ryan, Timothy M., 1978
Ryan, William E., 1959
Ryan, William Francis, 1911
Rybarczyk, Richard M., 1981
Ryder, Blair L., 1958
Ryder, William Harold, 1920
Rykiel, Frank K., 1960
Rynard, John A., 1872
Rynkiewicz, Felix S., 1917

~ S ~

Saalfrank, Charles W., 1886
Sabarra, Howard N., 1968
Sabatini, John R., 1973
Sabatino, Nathan Andrew, 1933
Sabine, Andrew, 1856
Sable, Carole A., 1987
Sabo, Jack C., 1961
Sabo, Robert Alan, 1990
Sabol, Jennifer Lane, 1990
Sabol, John R., 1957
Sabow, J. David, 1967
Sacharok, Cynthia A., 1988
Sack, David M., 1981
Sack, John T., 1966
Sackner, Jonathan D., 1987
Sackner, Marvin A., 1957
Sackrider, Charles, II, . 1863
Sacoolidge, John C., 1979
Saenz-Cuadra, Rafael, 1925
Safir, Donald, 1964
Sage, Abner Potts H., 1913
Sage, Bernard, 1935
Sager, Washington Budd, 1908
Sageser, Joseph Smiley, 1883
Sahelian, Ray R., 1984
Sahm, William K.T., 1877
Sailer, Dale W., 1983
Sailer, Thomas, 1830
Sajer, Susan A., 1985
Sajons, Charles E.L., 1878
Sakulsky, Stephen Barry, 1961
Sala-Diaz, Miguel E., 1924
Salas, Juan Francisco, 1889
Salasin, Robert I., 1970
Salasin, Robert, S1944

Salazar, Andres M., 1968
Sale, John Alexander, 1860
Sale, Richard A., 1835
Saleeby, Ameen Mittry, 1906
Saleeby, Eli R., 1981
Saleeby, Eli Richard, 1922
Saleeby, Richard G., 1946
Salen, Gerald, 1961
Salen, Samuel, 1965
Salerno, Merle S., 1965
Salerno, Nicholas R., 1964
Sales, Irving J., 1940
Sales, Phoenix M., 1934
Salgado, Edward M., 1967
Salinger, Julius Lincoln, 1886
Salisbury, Edward Irving, 1915
Salisbury, Edward M., 1954
Salkin, Marshall A., 1972
Salko, Gregory J., 1971
Salkowe, Jerry, 1975
Sall, David L., 1967
Sallade, Frank Reed, 1893
Sallade, Franklin L., 1866
Sallee William T., 1949
Sallee, Kent A., 1976
Saller, Deveraux N., Jr., 1982
Salmon, Duncan, 1978
Salmon, James Marvin, 1896
Salter, H. B., 1838
Salter, James W., 1830
Salter, William H., 1837
Saltzman Edward J., 1949
Saltzman, Bruce S., 1972
Saltzman, Herbert A., 1952
Saltzman, Louis Andrew, 1902
Saltzman, Maurice, 1922
Salvati, Catherine R., 1989
Salvatore, Joseph Thomas, 1939
Salverian, George A., 1957
Salvin, Monte, 1928
Salvo, John P., 1961
Salwen, Jay K., 1963
Samms, John M., 1977
Sample, Adrian Moore, 1928
Sample, George W., 1872
Sample, John, 1848
Sample, Joseph E., 1853
Sample, Nathaniel W., Jr., 1839
Sample, Samuel R., 1857
Sampsel, D. S., Jr., 1874
Sampsel, James W., 1878
Sampsel, John J., 1953
Sampsel, William H., 1876
Sampsell, Charles Paul, 1888
Sampsell, J. Vinten, 1877
Sams, James M., 1941
Samuel, Edmund W., 1880
Samuel, William Charles, 1894

Samuels, Bernard, 1907
Samuels, Bruce Steven, 1967
Samuels, Melvin L., 1947
Samuels, Pierce D., 1954
Samuels, Sidney Solomon, 1936
Sanabria, Arturo E., 1952
Sanabria, John F., 1952
Sanabria, Nicholas, 1912
Sanchez-Longo, Luis P., 1951
Sanchez-Vigil, Augustin, 1919
Sandberg, Ronald K., 1965
Sanders, William H., 1861
Sanderson, E. L., 1857
Sanderson, Vincent R. A., 1964
Sandford, Joseph K., 1854
Sandford, Leonard J., 1854
Sandhaus, Julius L., 1936
Sandler, Isadore Lewis, 1926
Sandler, Jerome L., 1958
Sandler, Steven C., 1965
Sandrowicz, Richard R., 1980
Sands, Charles Turner, 1907
Sands, J. Seldon, 1882
Sands, Jeffrey J., 1976
Sands, Milton J., 1964
Sanford, James L., 1852
Sanford, James, 1857
Sanford, John W., Jr., 1857
Sanford, Karl Thomas, 1925
Sanford, Robert J., 1851
Sanford, S. W., 1872
Sanger, Eugene F., 1853
Sangimino, Mark Joseph, 1990
Sangimino, Ursula Ripepi, 1990
Sankey, J. W., 1856
Sanner, John C., 1945
Sanstead, John K., 1976
Santaella, Luis R., 1963
Santarlas, John T., 1975
Santee, Andrew Curtin, 1886
Santee, E. A., 1869
Santee, George Oliver O., 1897
Santiago-Rivera, Fernando, 1963
Santibanez, Ramon Ramirez, 1916
Santoro, Thomas Amerigo, 1934
Sapiro, Howard Marshall, 1934
Sapp, Luther Lafayette, 1889
Sappington, John, Jr., 1868
Sarfati, Mark R., 1989
Sargent, Albert Alonzo, 1893
Sargent, John H., 1876
Sargent, John P., 1950
Sargent, Willard Snow, 1920
Sariakusi, Ibrahim Mohammed, 1906
Sariego, Joaquin, Jr.,,1983
Sarmousakis, Constance G., 1979
Sarnowski, Robert J., 1964
Sartschev, Caroline A., 1987

Sarver, William, 1855
Sasaki, Anna W., 1974
Saska, August, 1917
Sasken, Harvey F., 1971
Saslaw, Lewis Benjamin, 1930
Sass, Donald K., 1950
Sass, Franklin Edgar, 1910
Sass, Robert E., 1946
Sassani, Joseph W., 1973
Sasso, Philip J., 1988
Sastic, Jonathan W., 1979
Sastic, Lois M., 1979
Sataloff, Robert T., 1975
Satinsky, Victor P., 1938
Sattel, Andrew B., 1983
Sattel, Leonard, 1951
Satterfield, Benjamin F., 1861
Satur, Nancy M., 1976
Sauer, Emil, 1903
Sauerwine, Scott A., 1989
Saukkonen, Jussi J., 1985
Saukkonen, Kai D. J., 1988
Saul, Robert J., 1943
Saulsberry, Charles Emmet, 1894
Saulsberry, William, 1891
Saulsbury, James K., 1886
Saunders, Charles L., Jr., 1950
Saunders, Christopher J., 1988
Saunders, John B., 1861
Saunders, John Welcome, 1894
Saunders, Orris William, 1898
Saunders, Reuben, 1836
Saunders, Richard Hoskins, 1940
Saunders, Robert Ritchie, 1892
Saunders, Robert Rogers, 1897
Saunders, Samuel A., 1860
Saunders, Samuel, 1851
Saunders, Sheldon Asa, 1914
Saunders, William M., 1854
Savacool, J. Woodrow, 1938
Savage, Albert Lytleton, 1887
Savage, Donald J., 1977
Savage, G. C., 1878
Savage, Kenneth L., 1974
Savage, Michael P., 1980
Savage, Nephi Henry, 1924
Savage, Peter J., 1945
Savage, Robert C., 1977
Savage, William E.F., 1861
Savidge, Aaron Raker, 1856
Savitsky, Joseph Adam, 1893
Savopoulos, Sotiere E., 1989
Savran, Stephen V., 1968
Sawhill, William F., 1882
Sawicki, Anthony Maryan, 1916
Sawin, Robert V., 1885
Sawula, Boris J., 1978
Sawyer, Alton, 1878

Sawyer, Blackwell, 1924
Sawyer, Blackwell, Jr., 1956
Sawyer, Charles Milton, 1872
Sawyer, David T., 1989
Sawyer, R. P., 1873
Sawyer, Waldo Fitch, 1890
Saxanoff, Seymour, 1963
Saxe, Earl I., 1934
Saxe, Jonathan C., 1984
Saxe, LeRoy Hallowell, 1905
Saxon, C. A., 1856
Saxton, Silas Warren, 1903
Say, Eli J., 1863
Sayers, Warren A., 1881
Sayle, Robert, 1856
Sayles, Charles E., 1874
Saylor, Blair W., 1940
Saylor, Clyde Llewellyn, 1937
Saylor, Lloyd Elwood, 1932
Saylor, Melvin A., 1915
Saylor, Obadiah L., 1853
Saylor, Richard F., 1973
Sayre, Jeremiah E., 1883
Sayre, Rodger C., 1983
Sayre, William Douglas, 1908
Scalera, John F., 1940
Scales, James M.A., 1854
Scales, James T., 1846
Scales, Jefferson, 1867
Scales, Samuel W., 1857
Scammon, Franklin 1844
Scanlan, James William, 1829
Scanlon, James Patrick, 1940
Scanlon, M. D., 1869
Scarano, Joseph Albert, 1928
Scarano, Joseph J., 1959
Scarano, Victor R., 1961
Scarborough, Charles F., Jr., 1946
Scarburgh, George T., 1858
Scarcella, James V., 1958
Scariato, Albert F., 1980
Scates, Dan W., 1879
Scavone, Jerome G., 1978
Scearce, J. B., 1858
Schackleton, John Henry, Jr., 1943
Schadt, Mark E., 1985
Schadt, Oliver S., Jr., 1941
Schaebler, David L., 1988
Schaebler, M. Lee, 1957
Schaedler, Russell W., 1953
Schaefer, Patricia K., 1977
Schaefer, Robert M., 1980
Schaefer, William L., Jr., 1942
Schaeffer, Alan M., 1940
Schaeffer, Jackson, 1842
Schaeffer, Scott J., 1985
Schaeffer, Uriah R., 1879
Schaefgen, Madalyn, 1982

Schafer, Earl W., Jr., 1941
Schaffer, Burton, 1955
Schaffer, Edward D., 1941
Schaffer, Harry Abraham, 1904
Schaffer, Michael A., 1988
Schaffner, Boyd Willamber, 1902
Schaffner, Meade Daniel, 1925
Schaffzin, Elliott A., 1967
Schaffzin, Lawrence S., 1972
Schall, David Horace, Jr., 1901
Schall, Harry Mayer, 1887
Schall, LeRoy, 1917
Schall, Robert S., 1965
Schapiro, Gregory David, 1990
Scharadin, Nelson S., 1939
Scharff, Norbert D., 1975
Scharmann, Frank George, 1914
Schatz, Arthur J., 1966
Schatz, Francis J., 1909
Schaub, John J., 1933
Schaubel, Charles Wesley, 1904
Schaudt, Deborah A., 1981
Schauer, Edward A., 1949
Schauer, Andrea J., 1988
Schauer, Joseph W., III, 1981
Schauer, Joseph W., Jr., 1955
Schaufelberger, Franklin, 1894
Schaufelberger, Frederick J., 1884
Schaul, Otho Daniel, 1892
Schechter, David C., 1956
Schecter, Benjamin C., 1966
Scheetz, Herbert Nichols, 1905
Scheffey, Lewis Cass, 1920
Scheifly, John Edward, 1897
Schein, Alan L., 1969
Schell, Donald Edmond, 1930
Schell, Roxie Ann, 1978
Schellenger, Edward A. Y., 1929
Scheller, Christian R., 1883
Schellinger, Clarence M., 1879
Schelpert, John W., III, 1955
Schemm, George Christoph, 1887
Schenck, Daniel Scott, 1903
Schenck, Dodson R., 1883
Schenck, J. H., Jr., 1869
Schenkel, Nickolaus, 1878
Schepps, Donald E., 1975
Scherer, Bernard C., 1980
Scherer, Thomas A., 1883
Scherma, Angelo Salvatore, 1924
Scherr, Stuart A., 1971
Schetman, William R., 1986
Schickling, Leonard F., 1969
Schiffer, Stanton, 1964
Schiffman, Raymond Jack, 1959
Schildnecht, Page Milburn, 1928
Schill, Francis George, Jr., 1897
Schiller, Lawrence R., 1972

Schilling, Francis Marion, 1909
Schilling, Jane, 1966
Schilling, John F., 1981
Schimmel, Nelson H., 1948
Schinfeld, Jay S., 1974
Schinfeld, Louis H., 1939
Schiowitz, Albert, 1939
Schiowitz, Mark F., 1978
Schiowitz, Robert F., 1982
Schiro, John C., 1969
Schisler, Milton Moody, 1925
Schively, George P., 1856
Schively, George Singer, 1851
Schlachter, Frank, 1924
Schlaff, Zachary, 1975
Schlechter, Charles Francis, 1939
Schlechter, William G., 1975
Schleifer, Charles R., 1970
Schlein, Allen P., 1965
Schlemm, Horace Edmund, 1886
Schlesinger, Robert B., 1982
Schlesinger, Samuel, 1938
Schless, Guy L., 1955
Schless, Robert Avrom, 1916
Schlezinger, Nathan S., 1932
Schlindwein, George William, 1904
Schlitt, Mark G., 1989
Schlitt, Michael T., 1987
Schloss, C. David, 1958
Schloss, C. Kenneth, 1928
Schloss, Eugene Mathias, 1928
Schlossbach, Theodore, 1933
Schlosser, David E., 1943
Schlosser, Ralph J., 1948
Schmalhausen, Henry, 1867
Schmehl, Seymour Trout, 1891
Schmeltzer, George Jr., 1846
Schmerin, Michael J., 1973
Schmidt, Edgar T., 1876
Schmidt, H. William, 1950
Schmidt, Henry, 1874
Schmidt, William Clark, 1952
Schminkey, Gurney M., 1884
Schmitt, Philip, 1883
Schmitz, Henry Charles, 1912
Schmoele, H. W., 1839
Schmoele, William F., 1870
Schmoele, William, Jr., 1867
Schmouder, Robert L., 1984
Schnader, Amos Bowman, 1903
Schnall, Sandra F., 1979
Schneeberg, J. Myron, 1958
Schneideman, Theodore B., 1883
Schneider, Bernard, 1960
Schneider, Charles Joseph, 1896
Schneider, Chester L., 1947
Schneider, Emil Sebastian, 1905
Schneider, George Louis, 1911

Schneider, Glenn D., 1970
Schneider, Lynda C., 1983
Schneider, Myles S., 1971
Schneider, Paul J., 1960
Schneider, Peter J., 1987
Schneider, Stanley S., 1953
Schneider, Thomas J., 1965
Schneyer, Barton L., 1972
Schneyer, Julius, 1909
Schnorr, Alphonse Marie, 1908
Schoedler, Scott James, 1990
Schoen, Michael I., 1984
Schoenburn, Marc J., 1977
Schoener, F. D.H., 1869
Schoenfeld, Larry, 1977
Schoenheit, Edward William, 1920
Schoening, John Jacob, 1906
Schoffstall, Joseph W., 1902
Schofield, John L., 1852
Schofield, R. Alan, 1948
Scholfield, David Thorburn, 1865
Scholfield, Nathan M., 1839
Scholl, Alfred K., 1885
Scholl, Benjamin Franklin, 1886
Scholl, Catherine M., 1979
Scholl, Harvey Frederick, 1893
Scholl, Harvey W., 1937
Scholl, Harvey W., Jr., 1967
Scholl, Henry Nathanie, 1907
Scholten, Roger A., 1937
Schonauer, Thomas D., 1966
Schonholz, David H., 1954
Schonwald, John DeWitt, 1909
Schooley, A. Miles, 1871
Schooley, Sherman Richards, 1925
Schoolman, Noah, 1903
Schoonmaker, Irving R., 1884
Schopbach, Robert R., S1944
Schorn, Victor G., 1955
Schorr, Neal A., 1982
Schott, Arnold, 1868
Schrack, David, 1865
Schrack, John, Jr., 1842
Schrader, Herman Frederick, 1910
Schraeder, Paul Louis, 1966
Schrager, Randall E., 1988
Schramm, Francis M. B., 1909
Schramm, Frank E., Jr., 1946
Schran, Albert G., 1947
Schreiner, Herman Michael, 1932
Schriver, Albert, 1850
Schriver, Franklin, 1870
Schroeder, Elizabeth Ann, 1969
Schroy, Paul C., 1957
Schroy, Paul C., III, 1981
Schubb, Thomas, 1914
Schubert, John J., 1959
Schucker, Charles L., 1941

Schuelke, Julius Albert, 1897
Schuessler, Paul W., S1944
Schug, George F., 1904
Schulman, Edward S., 1975
Schulman, Jesse, 1945
Schulman, William M., 1974
Schultheis, Carl F., Jr., 1959
Schultz, J. Donald, 1955
Schultz, Merritt Campbell, 1930
Schultz, Robert Richie, 1925
Schultz, Samuel Karl, 1934
Schultz, William Clyde, 1895
Schultz, William Clyde, Jr., 1926
Schultz-Ross, Roy A., 1987
Schultze, Charles F., 1955
Schultze, Frederic Pitt, 1902
Schulz, Robert E., 1949
Schulze, Henry Louis, 1886
Schulze, Rudolph B., 1883
Schuman, Robert J., 1984
Schussler, Charles, 1837
Schuster, Bruno Lyonel, 1898
Schuster, Lawrence E., 1931
Schuster, Stephen J., 1981
Schutzman, David L., 1978
Schwab, John E., 1938
Schwab, Robert H., 1957
Schwabe, Karl G., 1984
Schwaemmle, Charles Henry, 1890
Schwalb, Neil S., 1969
Schwam, Brian Lewis, 1990
Schwarcz, Harriet B., 1979
Schwartz, Abraham Irving, 1920
Schwartz, Albert Morton, 1936
Schwartz, Augustin J., III, 1971
Schwartz, Bernard, 1908
Schwartz, Burton W., 1967
Schwartz, Charles E., 1933
Schwartz, Daniel J., 1973
Schwartz, David S., 1973
Schwartz, Edward, 1934
Schwartz, Francis R., 1948
Schwartz, Frederick, 1888
Schwartz, George Jacob, 1900
Schwartz, George Jacob, Jr., 1933
Schwartz, Henry Clay, 1924
Schwartz, Ira, 1974
Schwartz, John T., 1955
Schwartz, Judith P., 1970
Schwartz, Lorraine L., 1903
Schwartz, Louis Winn, 1967
Schwartz, Louis, 1905
Schwartz, Martin, 1968
Schwartz, Marvin N., 1959
Schwartz, Melvin Leslie, 1948
Schwartz, Morris R., 1907
Schwartz, Myron E., 1976
Schwartz, Philip S., 1989

Seipel, Wayne D., 1965
Seitz, Frederick, 1886
Seitz, John L., 1882
Sekerak, Albert John, 1928
Selen, Swen Gideon, 1928
Selfon, Paul M., 1955
Selfridge, James N., 1856
Seligman, Abram Pott, 1892
Seligman, Randolph V., 1940
Selinkoff, Paul M., 1970
Sell, Byron Monroe, 1924
Sell, Ronald J., 1984
Sellards, A. G., 1872
Seller, Michael S., 1984
Seller, Theophilus S., 1850
Sellers, Charles, 1840
Sellers, Hiram F., 1860
Sellew, Philip Hamilton, 1890
Sellitto, Anthony M., 1933
Sellmeyer, Bernardo Leo, 1912
Sells, Deshler F., 1908
Selman, David, 1855
Seltzer, Alan M., 1984
Seltzer, Benjamin P., 1969
Seltzer, John H., 1878
Seltzer, John Horace, 1848
Seltzer, Joseph L., 1971
Seltzer, Joseph P., 1937
Seltzer, Leonard H., 1967
Seltzer, Mitchell, 1927
Semans, T. B., 1873
Semans, William R., 1866
Semisch, Charles William, III, 1933
Semple, James, 1856
Semple, Samuel P., 1845
Senape, Saverio J., 1965
Sencindiver, Lewis M., 1858
Sencindiver, Paige Victor, 1952
Sender, Arthur Charles, 1909
Senderling, W. H., 1869
Senecal, Keith E., 1979
Senft, Robert A., 1960
Senior, Robert J., 1955
Senita, G. Robert, 1946
Senn, Francis E., Jr., 1956
Senor, Samuel Earl, 1925
Senseman, Hiram, 1849
Senseman, John, 1864
Senseny, Abraham H., 1835
Senseny, Edgar N., 1870
Senseny, William D., 1861
Sentner, Charles Sylvester, 1929
Sepich, Rodney Milan, 1990
Serafin, Frank J., 1923
Seraly, Mark Patrick, 1990
Seres, David S., 1985
Seres, Joel L., 1958
Serfas, Lee S., 1948

Sergeant, Spencer, 1846
Seright, Thomas Clinton, 1889
Serino, Gerard S., 1932
Sernyak, Michael J., Jr., 1987
Serota, Roger Gene, 1963
Serota, Ronald D., 1968
Serra, Arthur Alves, 1889
Serra, Norberto Alves, 1889
Service, Charles A., 1882
Service, John Haymaker, 1889
Service, Lecky M., 1848
Servoss, Archibald Gooding, 1886
Setzkorn, Ronald K., 1982
Severs, George Harvey, 1905
Sevier, Daniel Edward, 1895
Sevier, Joseph Thomas, 1895
Sewall, Arthur D., 1940
Sewall, Millard Freeman, 1903
Sewell, Myron L., 1981
Sexton, Darryl M., 1975
Sexton, George L., Jr., 1953
Seybert, Frank T., 1881
Seydel, Arthur, 1860
Seymour, Edward W., 1858
Seymour, Parker M., 1970
Seymour, Stuart Howard, 1887
Seymour, William J., 1846
Shaar, Camille M., 1916
Shaar, Richard Thomas, 1947
Shack, Robert P., 1969
Shackelford, Edmond D., 1846
Shackelford, John L., 1839
Shackelford, William, 1861
Shackleford, James, 1861
Shade, Nevin B., 1878
Shadle, Jacob E., 1881
Shaeffer, Brett Randolph, 1866
Shaen, Edward, 1939
Shafer, Albert Henry, 1925
Shafer, Edward A., J1944
Shafer, Frederick William, 1908
Shafer, James A., 1950
Shafer, William, 1884
Shaffer, Charles Porter, 1895
Shaffer, Cornelius Thaddeus, 1888
Shaffer, Eugene M., 1973
Shaffer, Foster Clarke, 1925
Shaffer, George Emery, 1911
Shaffer, Howard L., 1948
Shaffer, Irvin G., 1940
Shaffer, Jerome D., S1944
Shaffer, John F., 1860
Shaffer, John F., 1940
Shaffer, Lawrence A., 1979
Shaffer, Orr Hilemann, 1896
Shaffer, Phineas Jenks, 1909
Shaffrey, Thomas A., 1943
Shafritz, Randy, 1990

Shaham, Simon, 1901
Shain, Francis W., 1882
Shalanta, Vladimir Alexis, 1915
Shallcross, William Gooding, 1897
Shallenberger, Aaron T., 1846
Shallenberger, H. M., 1876
Shallow, Thomas Aloysius, 1911
Shammo, Isaac R., 1852
Shander, Ernest G., 1948
Shands, Aurelius R., 1846
Shands, Thomas E., 1859
Shanfeld, Norman M., 1973
Shanholtz, Carl B., 1983
Shankland, William L., 1865
Shankle, E. A., 1861
Shanks, Frederick Hastings, 1891
Shanks, Harold Jackson, 1934
Shanno, Ralph Leopold, 1927
Shannon, Charles Emery G., 1902
Shannon, Daniel, 1887
Shannon, Francis Patrick, 1911
Shannon, Frank J., Jr., 1946
Shannon, Gerard Michael, 1949
Shannon, James H., 1884
Shannon, Peter, 1827
Shannon, Richard D., 1868
Shannon, Samuel H., 1836
Shannon, T. Jefferson, 1857
Shannon, William A., 1892
Shapera, William, 1921
Shapiro, A. Alver, 1925
Shapiro, Bennett M., 1964
Shapiro, Bertram H., 1956
Shapiro, Jacob, 1926
Shapiro, Jacob, 1931
Shapiro, Jeryl R., 1974
Shapiro, Joan H., 1972
Shapiro, Leonard, 1922
Shapiro, Marc Wells, 1972
Shapiro, Morris E. L., 1917
Shapiro, Morris J., 1938
Shapiro, Morris Samuel, 1912
Shapiro, Richard D., 1964
Shapiro, Samuel S., 1924
Shapiro, Sigmond Joseph, 1925
Shapiro, Stephen J., 1967
Share, Edward J., 1974
Share, William Lionel, 1936
Sharkey, Thomas G., 1977
Sharp, Alexander Jr., 1849
Sharp, Alexander E., 1850
Sharp, Charles Edward, 1914
Sharp, Edward Smith, 1896
Sharp, Eugene B., 1898
Sharp, Francis Alex, 1872
Sharp, Ira R., 1979
Sharp, J. Steward, 1890
Sharp, Norman Wallace, 1902

Sharp, Oliver Ledbetter, 1922
Sharp, Robert C., 1881
Sharp, Samuel C., Jr., 1857
Sharp, Samuel F., 1870
Sharp, William T., 1859
Sharp, William Thomas, 1933
Sharpe, Abraham Maxwell, 1916
Sharpe, Charles Ray, 1914
Sharpe, William, 1829
Sharpe, William R., 1851
Sharples, Abram, 1864
Sharpless, B. Frank, 1880
Sharpnack, T. H., 1872
Sharpnack, William Forrest, 1902
Sharps, Lewis S., 1975
Shartle, J. Miller, 1884
Shartle, John, 1895
Shastid, William Edwards, 1886
Shaub, A. Paul, 1928
Shaub, Howard G., 1946
Shaw, Alexander, 1849
Shaw, Angus G., 1852
Shaw, Arthur Ernest, 1905
Shaw, Benjamin, 1826
Shaw, Byron Earl, 1917
Shaw, Daniel, 1853
Shaw, Daniel, 1856
Shaw, Daniel L., Jr., 1948
Shaw, Daniel W., 1860
Shaw, Ernest Irwin, 1929
Shaw, Frank L., 1887
Shaw, John Harvey, 1909
Shaw, John W., 1952
Shaw, Jonathan K., 1966
Shaw, Joseph Bowen, 1960
Shaw, Katherine, 1905
Shaw, Robert T., 1877
Shaw, Walter Corson, 1906
Shaw, Wilfred McLaurin, 1919
Shaw, William Alger, 1911
Shawaluk, Paul D., Jr., 1968
Shea, David S., 1977
Shea, Peter Champ, 1960
Shea, Thomas Emmet, 1905
Sheaff, Charles G., 1880
Sheaff, Philip Atlee, 1902
Sheaffer, Harold Clement, 1961
Sheaffer, Peter F., 1881
Sheardown, T. Winton, 1879
Shearer, Donald E., 1963
Shearer, James, 1862
Shearer, Oliver F., 1883
Shedden, Arthur H., 1980
Sheeder, Benjamin Franklin, 1893
Sheehe, Dennis M., 1983
Sheehy, Eileen T., 1987
Sheely, William E., 1948
Sheets, Abraham, 1858

Sheets, Everett W., 1885
Sheets, H. W., 1869
Sheets, Joseph, 1849
Sheilds, Edgar A., 1880
Sheldon, Benjamin, 1829
Sheldon, Jonathan, 1831
Shellenberger, J. E., 1869
Shellenberger, Lewis C., 1933
Shelley, Aaron F., 1850
Shelley, Benneville Y., 1846
Shelley, Jay Warren, 1906
Shelley, Mark H., 1982
Shelley, Penn P., 1957
Shelley, Penrose Herr, 1911
Shellman, Alexander, 1928
Shelly, Albert, 1895
Shelly, Mark A., 1986
Shelly, Walter M., 1959
Shelman, Keith B., 1983
Shelmerdine, Robert Q., 1847
Shelton, Edwin Bryant L., 1889
Shelton, Hanson Penn, 1897
Shelton, Thomas W., 1842
Shemanski, Henry Leopold, 1930
Shen, Jane, 1986
Shenberger, William Jacob, 1904
Shenk, George Rigler, 1889
Shenkin, Henry A., 1939
Shepard, Cassius Marion, 1899
Shepard, Ernest Newton, 1895
Shepard, George Andrew, 1888
Shepard, Harvey E., 1988
Shepard, W. E.W., 1868
Shepherd, Francis C., 1854
Shepherd, James B., 1855
Shepherd, Richard Cotton, 1906
Shepherd, Warren S., 1938
Shepherd, Warren, 1910
Shepler, Norman Bruce, 1910
Shepler, Robert McMurran, 1902
Shepp, Margaret A., 1971
Sheppard, Charles Woodruff, 1906
Sheppard, James L., 1859
Sheppard, Leauder W., 1854
Sheppard, Lisa M., 1987
Sheppard, Robert Lester, 1912
Sheppard, Thomas D., 1965
Sheppard, William P., 1840
Sheppey, John V., 1885
Sherard, Jerome A., 1981
Sherer, Bernard D., 1946
Sherer, Jacob, 1827
Sherger, John Adam, 1903
Sherger, John Chalmers, 1935
Sheridan, Campbell, 1849
Sheridan, Lawrence Aloysius, 1903
Sheridan, William F., 1871
Sheridan, William Martin, 1921

Sherk, Abraham Lincoln, 1923
Sherk, Harry Huber, 1886
Sherk, Henry H., 1956
Sherk, Henry Howard, 1887
Sherman, Austin B., 1865
Sherman, Bernard Israel, 1935
Sherman, Craig H., 1982
Sherman, Fred P., 1969
Sherman, Fuller G., 1930
Sherman, George Howard, 1891
Sherman, Harry Ulysses, 1892
Sherman, Henry Arthur, 1888
Sherman, James S., 1880
Sherman, Linda Ann, 1979
Sherman, Nancy H., 1978
Sherman, Virica J., 1975
Sherman, William H., 1969
Sherman, William Sprague, 1888
Sherrell, Joseph L., 1850
Sherrick, Earl Cleveland, 1908
Sherrill, Wade Hampton, 1916
Sherrod, John H., 1965
Sherrod, John I., 1855
Shershin, Peter H., 1947
Sherwood, Norman S., 1957
Sherwood, William C., 1959
Shew, Abraham Marvin, 1864
Shewalter, George William, 1850
Shick, William Binder, 1907
Shickman, Martin D., 1954
Shields, Alexander McMakin, 1889
Shields, Daniel R., Jr., S1944
Shields, Hubert L., 1951
Shields, James M., 1912
Shields, Marshall Francis, 1933
Shields, William Peter, 1934
Shields, William W., 1852
Shigeoka, John W., 1969
Shih, Henry Han-Liang, 1989
Shih, Richard D., 1988
Shilen, Thomas, 1959
Shillingford, Robert P., 1958
Shillito, George M., 1868
Shillott, Charles Joseph, 1915
Shimavonian, Samuel, 1885
Shimmin, James, 1881
Shimoon, Joseph, 1903
Shimp, Archie Joseph, 1888
Shimwell, Benjamin T., 1875
Shinaberry, Rollen Lemuel, 1910
Shinabery, Lawerence, 1924
Shinbach, Kent D., 1963
Shindel, Isaac N., 1846
Shingle, John Delroy, 1906
Shipley, John Thomas, 1929
Shipman, Azariah B., 1844
Shipman, William, 1836
Shipp, Milford B., 1883

Shipp, Milford Bard, 1891
Shipps, Hammell Pierce, 1926
Shirey, Harlan M., 1904
Shirey, John L., 1939
Shirey, Pamela S., 1984
Shirk, John K., 1879
Shirk, Paul Kuhlmann, 1930
Shiroff, Robert A., 1972
Shisler, Frederick H., 1960
Shivelhood, David Kalbach, 1933
Shively, George G., 1878
Shively, James Buchanan, 1887
Shively, Wyant J., 1954
Shivers, C. Hendry, 1872
Shlomchik, Seymour, 1960
Shmokler, Leon, 1951
Shmokler, Mitchell F., 1979
Shmookler, Henry Bernard, 1897
Shoaff, Paris A., III, 1955
Shoaff, Paris Alexander, 1918
Shock, Jacob G., 1827
Shoemaker, B. Dawson, 1963
Shoemaker, David M., 1951
Shoemaker, George Eichholtz, 1886
Shoemaker, George Elmer, 1906
Shoemaker, Henry Keen, 1949
Shoemaker, John V., 1874
Shoemaker, Michael Elias, 1979
Shoener, John A., 1955
Shoenfelt, James Whitaker, Jr., 1939
Shoenthal, Harry Irvin, 1906
Shoenthal, W. James, 1938
Shoff, John Frank, J1944
Shollenberger, Charles F., 1885
Shook, James Curry, 1891
Shope, Abraham Lincoln, 1890
Shope, Charles Edgar, 1922
Shope, Elias Lincoln, 1889
Shope, Jacob W., 1880
Shope, William B., 1948
Shorb, Stanley R., 1966
Shore, David, 1973
Shore, Dean C., 1953
Shore, Ernest Luke, 1925
Shorkley, Thornton Moore, 1906
Short, James C., 1882
Short, James W., 1871
Short, Wesley, 1861
Shortt, William H., 1904
Shotwell, Barbara A., 1989
Shotwell, C. H., 1858
Shotwell, Randolph, 1827
Shoun, Alexander Nelson, 1932
Shoup, Jesse J., 1891
Shoupe, Branden A., 1983
Shovlin, J. Michael, 1970
Shovlin, John Patrick, 1934
Showalter Henry C.W., 1883

Shoyer, Charles C., 1850
Shrader, Edwin Elmer, 1893
Shrader, W. Eric, 1983
Shrawder, John S., 1865
Shreiner, David P., 1964
Shreve, J. Ridgway, 1855
Shriner, Charles H., 1879
Shriner, Howard Martin, 1896
Shriner, Thomas, 1869
Shriver, Colley, 1875
Shriver, J. Milton, 1880
Shrom, Howard Kenneth, 1924
Shrom, Ralph Edwin, 1904
Shrom, Stanley H., 1974
Shropshire, James W., 1857
Shucker, Mark A., 1976
Shue, Spurgeon Theodore, 1931
Shue, William M., 1961
Shuford, Quincy A., 1849
Shugar, Gary L., 1974
Shugart, Richard Tatum, 1946
Shull, Stewart D., 1968
Shull, William H., J1944
Shull, William Milton, 1885
Shulman, Nathan L., 1923
Shultz, Abner W., 1870
Shultz, B. Franklin, 1854
Shultz, Cameron, 1892
Shultz, David L., 1875
Shultz, Peter H., 1868
Shumaker, Luther M., 1889
Shumaker, Scott D., 1978
Shuman, Bernard J., 1945
Shuman, George Ario, 1917
Shuman, Jacob L., 1876
Shuman, John Clinton, 1890
Shuman, Marc A., 1967
Shunk, Francis R., 1846
Shuptar, Daniel, 1955
Shurlock, William C., 1858
Shurtleff, Benjamin, 1866
Shusman, Robert S., 1981
Shuster, Eugene, 1961
Shuster, Patricia A., 1986
Shuster, Samuel A., 1937
Shusterman, Neil H., 1978
Shuttleworth, Benjamin F., 1905
Shuttleworth, William Blair, 1887
Siatkowski, Raymond M., 1987
Sibbald, James, 1881
Sibbald, John, 1875
Sibley, Edward Rufus, 1906
Sica, Leon Samuel, 1909
Sica, Paul A., Jr., 1967
Sica, Paul Anthony, 1931
Sickler, John R., 1829
Siddall, John Richard, 1937
Sidebotham, Henry Larned, 1886

Sides, Benjamin F., 1846
Sides, Benjamin F., 1871
Sidlich, David Mitchell, 1917
Sidor, Carolyn F., 1982
Sidwell, Reuben, 1846
Sieber, Grafton F., 1957
Sieber, Isaac Grafton, 1902
Sieber, Paul Eugene, 1945
Siegel, Alvin Erdreich, 1910
Siegel, Ayn D., 1984
Siegel, Christopher T., 1989
Siegel, Dolores A., 1981
Siegel, Eric J., 1988
Siegel, Everett R., 1980
Siegel, John Morris, 1938
Siegel, Joseph F., 1938
Siegel, Linda Beth, 1990
Sieger, David D., 1984
Siegfried, Chas. A., 1872
Siegfried, Cyrus Sylvester, 1891
Siegfried, Edward G., 1937
Siegle, John C., Jr., 1981
Siegler, Lewis Franklin, 1886
Sienknecht, Henry, 1868
Sifre, Santiago, 1846
Sigal, Robert K., 1985
Siggins, George, 1905
Sigler, Allison J., 1987
Siglinger, Charles Jacob, 1890
Signorella, Albert M., 1982
Sikes, Charles Henry, 1931
Silberg, Samuel J., 1949
Silberman, Carl M., 1972
Silberman, Charles G., 1950
Silberman, Ellis L., 1948
Silberman, Howard, 1966
Silbernagel, Wynne Metcalf, 1930
Silbert, Paul J., 1971
Silenskey, John J., 1940
Silfen, Sheryl L., 1975
Silk, Raymond E., 1948
Silko, Gary J., 1980
Sill, Blin S., 1837
Sill, Thomas M., 1875
Silliman, James E., 1874
Silliman, Warren B., 1946
Silodor, Scott Wayne, 1990
Silva, Joseph C.P., 1880
Silvara, Joseph W., 1874
Silver, Barry A., 1967
Silver, Bruce G., 1974
Silver, David R., 1868
Silver, Frank, 1961
Silver, George A., 1938
Silver, Harris S., 1987
Silver, Harvey D., 1960
Silver, Israel Oscar, 1934
Silver, Joel S., 1984

Silver, Lawrence B., 1966
Silver, Morris Alvin, 1932
Silver, Richard C., 1981
Silver, Stephen C., 1971
Silverman, Daniel, 1937
Silverman, Edward J., 1981
Silverman, Howard S., 1983
Silverman, Lee D., 1988
Silverman, Maurice, 1924
Silverman, Paul B., 1967
Silverman, Stephen D., 1964
Silverstein, Murray N., 1954
Silverstein, Nathan, 1909
Silverstine, Randy J., 1979
Silvey, James, 1845
Silvis, Charles Harrold, 1923
Silvis, George W., 1860
Silvis, John Steele, Jr., 1924
Sim, J. Thomas, 1860
Simkins, Daniel, 1906
Simkins, Raymond, 1915
Simkovich, Alexandra H., 1987
Simmermon, Gerald Fletcher, 1950
Simmonds, James, 1834
Simmons, Agnes H., 1977
Simmons, Alexander Wingate, 1939
Simmons, Allen J., 1851
Simmons, Charles Columbus, 1894
Simmons, Cheston, Jr., 1987
Simmons, Howard Jackson, 1911
Simmons, John F., 1865
Simmons, Richard Gordon, 1889
Simmons, T. J., 1875
Simmons, Thomas W., 1861
Simmons, W. A., 1855
Simms, Benjamin B., 1885
Simms, H. C., 1855
Simon, John L., 1940
Simon, Lincoln G., 1895
Simon, T. Wallace, 1877
Simon, William I., 1864
Simoncelli, Leonard Robert, 1946
Simonian, Thomas M., 1986
Simonis, Arthur Elmer, 1908
Simons, Arthur J., 1885
Simons, Carl I., 1959
Simons, David G., 1946
Simons, John Shirk, 1923
Simons, Samuel Shirk, 1923
Simpkins, Albert, Jr., 1980
Simpson, Edward Percy, 1895
Simpson, Eugene Robbins, 1919
Simpson, Fred Pratt, 1910
Simpson, George B., 1871
Simpson, George W., 1857
Simpson, George W., 1876
Simpson, J. Patillo, 1871
Simpson, James F., 1846

Simpson, James, 1865
Simpson, Joan W., 1975
Simpson, John Reid, 1905
Simpson, Jonathan Chauncey, 1895
Simpson, Joseph Hawkins, 1861
Simpson, Joseph W., 1953
Simpson, Joseph, 1854
Simpson, Moses S., 1883
Simpson, Robert I., 1853
Simpson, Roy W., 1951
Simpson, Thomas W., 1856
Simpson, W. L., 1869
Sims, Amy Louise, 1983
Sims, Arthur I., 1939
Sims, Frederick H., 1853
Sims, James L., 1840
Sims, Joseph Addison, 1849
Sims, Joseph B., 1855
Sims, Marion J., 1835
Sims, Richard H., 1867
Sims, W. Caldwell, 1963
Sims, William B., 1858
Simsohn, Joseph S., 1874
Sinclair, John, 1854
Sinex, William G., 1847
Sinexon, Justus, 1884
Singer, Alvin, 1955
Singer, Arnold, 1958
Singer, James J., 1871
Singer, Jerome, 1966
Singer, Jodi S., 1987
Singer, Lewis U., 1881
Singer, Ronald, 1966
Singer, Samuel, 1915
Singer, Stuart J., 1982
Singh, Ajay B., 1983
Singh, Amitabh, 1990
Singh-Janda, Gurbachan, 1934
Singleton, James A., 1955
Singleton, William McCormick, 1921
Singley, Charles C., 1881
Singley, Harry Paul, 1936
Singley, Thomas L., III, 1957
Sinha, Christopher K., 1988
Sinha, Raj K., 1989
Sinks, Lucius F., 1957
Sinne, Hans H., 1887
Sinnickson, John J., 1832
Sinquest, Noah C., 1835
Sipes, Earl K., 1946
Sippel, George Richard, 1922
Sipple, Katharyn Marie, 1978
Sipski, Marca Leonise, 1983
Sirlin, Nelson, 1968
Sirotnak, Andrew P., 1989
Sirotnak, John J., 1988
Sirotnak, John J., Jr., 1959
Sitelman, Arthur, 1975

Sites, Charles J., 1940
Sitkoff, Malcolm, 1956
Sittler, Albert Monroe, 1886
Sittler, Warren Clement, 1893
Sivalingam, Jocelyn J., 1987
Sizer, George D., 1849
Sizer, James Jr., 1849
Skeel, David A., 1961
Skeen, Andrew M., 1884
Skeist, Barry P., 1972
Skelly, Charles Jackson, 1889
Skelton, Charles, 1837
Skelton, O. P., 1840
Skibber, John M., 1981
Skibber, Sharon A., 1985
Skilling, John, 1878
Skilling, M. J., 1873
Skinner, Richard W., 1948
Skinner, William Francis, 1890
Sklar, Leslie Ann, 1990
Sklaroff, Robert B., 1974
Skloff, David Samuel, 1956
Skloff, Samuel Harry, 1938
Skoloff, Joseph, 1970
Skowronski, Theodore J., 1968
Skreczko, Charles K., 1937
Skrenta, Allan W., 1968
Skurkay, John Bernard, 1924
Skutches, Joseph M., 1957
Skvara, Frederick C., 1970
Skversky, Norman J., 1939
Skyler, Jay S., 1969
Skypala, Patricia L., 1985
Slachta, Gregory A., 1968
Slack, Clarence M., 1865
Slack, James W., 1984
Slagle, David C., 1981
Slagle, William Lister, 1924
Slahter, Edward, 1832
Slasor, William Johnson, 1936
Slater, George Wishart, 1889
Slater, Harvey, 1965
Slater, Lindsey M., 1987
Slater, Ralph Lewis, 1921
Slaughter, James, 1828
Slaughter, Thomas G., 1859
Slavens, Timothy E., 1988
Slawek, Paul P., 1967
Slayden, J. D., 1869
Slayden, William M., 1881
Slaymaker, John M., 1883
Slease, Cyrus B., 1937
Sledge, John G., 1839
Slemmer, J. Ross, 1986
Slenker, Kevin F., 1983
Slezak, Joseph A., 1963
Slicer, J. Edwin, 1854
Slick, Gregory D., 1981

Slifer, Frank Sebring, 1888
Slifer, George Baringer, 1894
Slifer, Walter Levi, 1903
Slimak, Grace G., 1985
Slimak, Randall E., 1984
Sliwkowski, Joseph J., Jr., 1988
Sloan, Dean A., 1983
Sloan, Elmer M., 1884
Sloan, George W., 1876
Sloan, William J., 1836
Sloanaker, Lewis M., 1846
Sloane, Paul, 1925
Slocum, Charles E., 1876
Slocum, Morris Abel, 1914
Slogoff, Stephen, 1967
Slompak, Carol A., 1982
Slonimsky, I. Paul, 1925
Sloop, Eustace Henry, 1908
Sloss, James Olson, 1941
Sloss, Joseph H., 1952
Slota, Paul A., 1988
Sloterbeck, Edgar Blackburn, 1907
Slotkin, Herman Bennett, 1925
Slotnick, Victor B., 1965
Slough, Evan, 1835
Slough, G. B., 1861
Slovin, Isadore, 1939
Slovin, Susan Faith, 1990
Slye, Thomas B., 1840
Small, Edward Lester, 1921
Small, Edwin M., 1871
Small, George A., 1988
Small, John A., 1874
Small, Louis, 1936
Small, Michael L., 1961
Small, Richard H., 1951
Small, Thomas Winn, 1900
Smalley, John K., 1887
Smallwood, John T., 1973
Smarr, Erwin R., 1949
Smarr, Joseph G., 1853
Smart, D. S., 1870
Smathers, Frank Clifford, 1905
Smathers, W. J., 1873
Smeal, Brian C., 1989
Smethers, Gary D., 1979
Smey, Paul, 1973
Smigelsky, Isadore Edward, 1917
Smigelsky, Richard G., 1947
Smiley, Edwin R., 1881
Smiley, Howard Miles, 1897
Smiley, Joseph W., 1965
Smink, Alfred Harrison, 1894
Smith, A. Harvey, 1859
Smith, Addison Whittaker, 1891
Smith, Adin Louis, 1896
Smith, Albert D., 1851
Smith, Albert M., 1870

Smith, Albert S., 1876
Smith, Alfred, 1836
Smith, Alvin H., 1952
Smith, Amos H., 1878
Smith, Amos Vastine, Jr., 1950
Smith, Andrew K., 1849
Smith, Andrew Milliken, 1923
Smith, Angus L., 1915
Smith, Arthur K., 1971
Smith, Augustus Edwin, 1911
Smith, Austin Thomas, 1922
Smith, Barney Barr, 1917
Smith, Barry S., 1969
Smith, Bart M., 1851
Smith, Benjamin, 1842
Smith, Benjamin Franklin, 1896
Smith, Bernard Herman, 1921
Smith, Bernard Reid, 1911
Smith, Brian S., 1986
Smith, Burgess A., 1949
Smith, Calvin, Jr., 1835
Smith, Charles, 1853
Smith, Charles B., 1884
Smith, Charles C., 1884
Smith, Charles Galen, 1897
Smith, Charles S., 1879
Smith, Charles W., 1878
Smith, Chauncey H., 1871
Smith, Chauncey M., 1855
Smith, Clarence Daniel, 1907
Smith, Claude A., 1953
Smith, Clyde Francis, 1921
Smith, Crawford C., 1975
Smith, D. M., 1858
Smith, Daniel, 1852
Smith, David A., 1984
Smith, David D., 1878
Smith, David P., 1853
Smith, David S., 1836
Smith, Delos DeWitt, 1894
Smith, Dennis F., 1881
Smith, Domer Gheen, 1890
Smith, Donald C., 1931
Smith, Donald H., 1965
Smith, Donald L., 1958
Smith, Dudley Almonte, 1900
Smith, Duncan, 1853
Smith, Edgar C., 1947
Smith, Edmund Howard, 1915
Smith, Edward C., 1949
Smith, Edward Hamilton, 1882
Smith, Edward Lincoln, 1887
Smith, Edward M., 1846
Smith, Edward Michael, 1912
Smith, Edwin Glenn, 1888
Smith, Elias Ely, 1847
Smith, Ellen K., 1978
Smith, Ellery P., 1853

Smith, Elliott Iverson, 1848
Smith, Ernest Elmer, 1914
Smith, Ernest Gerard, 1930
Smith, Etley Price, 1909
Smith, F. A.A., 1873
Smith, Floyd Wilbert, 1900
Smith, Forrest Fullerton, 1935
Smith, Francis F., 1854
Smith, Frank H., 1870
Smith, Frank Ira, 1889
Smith, Frank Quincy, 1896
Smith, Franklin Calton, 1921
Smith, Frederick Charles, 1903
Smith, Frederick Forbes, 1895
Smith, Frisby T., 1850
Smith, G. Albert, 1873
Smith, G. Selden, 1856
Smith, Gail B., 1979
Smith, George C., 1876
Smith, George Calvin, 1891
Smith, George F., Jr., 1982
Smith, George Hartford, 1893
Smith, George J., 1978
Smith, George King, 1844
Smith, George L., 1850
Smith, George William, 1965
Smith, Gerald Barcroft, 1919
Smith, Gregory T., 1982
Smith, H. Alexander, Jr., 1954
Smith, H. Lawrence, 1940
Smith, H. Rufus, 1877
Smith, H. Winchel, 1885
Smith, Harmony A., 1838
Smith, Harold C., 1934
Smith, Harris K., 1879
Smith, Harry A., 1915
Smith, Harry C., 1946
Smith, Harry F., 1965
Smith, Harry Martin, 1887
Smith, Henry A.M., 1864
Smith, Henry F., 1963
Smith, Henry Francis, Jr., 1983
Smith, Henry H., 1877
Smith, Henry Harrison, 1887
Smith, Henry J., 1865
Smith, Henry Stephen, 1899
Smith, Hiram J., 1878
Smith, Hosea H., 1855
Smith, Howard B., 1943
Smith, Howard Sedgwick, 1903
Smith, Hugh C., 1853
Smith, Hugh G., 1856
Smith, Ira U., 1978
Smith, Irving W., 1875
Smith, Irwin S., 1949
Smith, Isaac Robert, 1929
Smith, J. Anson, 1897
Smith, J. F., 1869

Snow, William J., 1924
Snowball, James William, 1891
Snowden, Benjamin C., 1845
Snowden, Charles C., 1882
Snowden, Harold, 1858
Snowden, Arthur, 1883
Snyder, Allen M., 1949
Snyder, Abram Elias, 1889
Snyder, Alan I., 1959
Snyder, Albert Joseph, 1941
Snyder, Alva Earl, 1894
Snyder, Barry J., 1980
Snyder, Cecil Dawson, 1929
Snyder, Charles P., 1902
Snyder, Charles P., Jr., 1935
Snyder, Charles Reif, 1914
Snyder, Charles W., 1968
Snyder, Claude Edwin, 1912
Snyder, Emanuel Walton, 1889
Snyder, George A., 1928
Snyder, Gordon Elias, 1938
Snyder, H. Martin, 1956
Snyder, Harry D., 1958
Snyder, Harry Minis, 1926
Snyder, Herbert D., 1979
Snyder, Howard Errol, 1927
Snyder, Howard Lincoln, 1904
Snyder, Howard McCrum, 1905
Snyder, Jacob F. M., 1911
Snyder, James L., 1961
Snyder, James Victor, 1966
Snyder, Jeffrey C., 1985
Snyder, John R. T., 1915
Snyder, Joseph, 1962
Snyder, Lawrence K., 1968
Snyder, Lincoln M., 1984
Snyder, M. Wilson, 1937
Snyder, Marion D., 1896
Snyder, Mark H., 1979
Snyder, Marvin C. G., 1953
Snyder, Michael C., 1966
Snyder, Morgan, 1833
Snyder, Otto Kerr, 1902
Snyder, Peter C., 1862
Snyder, Robert C., 1971
Snyder, Robert J., 1980
Snyder, Thomas, 1898
Snyder, W. Fife, 1884
Snyder, Wayne Lawson, 1905
Snyder, William V., 1845
Snyderman, Deborah A., 1986
Sobelman, Paul B., 1976
Sobie, Pincus, 1938
Sobie, Stephen R., 1982
Soble, Toby Kleiner, 1990
Sockman, Henry A., 1880
Sodroski, Joseph G., 1980
Sohn, Sae H., 1988

Sokas, Patrick, 1980
Sokol, Joel H., 1975
Sokoloff, Bruce H., 1986
Sokoloff, Martin Joseph, 1920
Sokoloff, Norman F., 1969
Sokolowski, Joseph W., Jr., 1962
Solan, James A., 1979
Sole, Sidney W., 1838
Solenski, Nina J., 1989
Solinsky, Stanley P., 1977
Solis-Cohen, Leon, 1912
Solit, Robert W., 1961
Soll, Charles Harold, 1908
Soll, Kenneth H., 1956
Sollenberger, Franklin Samuel, 1934
Solliday, B. F., 1865
Solliday, Edwin S., 1857
Solliday, Monroe Holben, 1901
Solnick, Bennett L., 1986
Solo, David Howard, 1924
Soloman, Milton Bennet, 1936
Solomon, Dean, 1976
Solomon, Henry Doyle, 1922
Solomon, Ira S., 1982
Solomon, Lynn, 1986
Solomon, Macy B., 1954
Solomon, Robert A., 1986
Solorzano, Enrique, 1890
Solow, Edward A., 1973
Soltero, Armando Garcia, 1916
Soltz, Thomas, 1911
Sombart, John E., 1881
Somers, Debra Lynn, 1989
Somers, Herbert J., 1959
Somers, Job Braddock, 1859
Somers, Lewis F., 1939
Somers, Myer, 1927
Somers, Robert G., 1958
Somers, Russell E., 1981
Somerville, Beverly R., 1876
Somerville, George Wallace, 1894
Somerville, William Joseph, 1941
Sommer, Daniel G., 1971
Sommer, Ferdinand Comfort, 1929
Sommer, Henry, Jr., 1893
Sommers, George A., 1852
Sommers, Raymond Lock, 1917
Sommerville, Kenneth W., 1976
Sonda, Lewis Paul, 1919
Songer, John E., 1982
Sonne, Clarence Melvin, 1920
Sonneborn, George, 1905
Sonsini, Gregg A., 1985
Sonstein, Allen, 1972
Sonwers, George F., 1877
Sooy, John Milton, 1885
Sophocles, Aris M., 1950
Sophocles, Aris M., Jr., 1970

Soraruf, L. Peter, IV, 1974
Sorensen, Maryanne, 1982
Sorensen, Robert J., 1954
Sorenson, George D., Jr., 1954
Sorenson, Julie D., 1982
Sorenson, Soren, 1893
Soricelli, Richard R., 1960
Sorin, Herman Mitchell, 1902
Sorokanich, Stephen, 1981
Soronkanich, Stephen, S1944
Sorr, Edward M., 1967
Sorrell, Furman Yates, 1930
Sortman, Harold P., 1936
Sosnowski, John Joseph, Jr., 1911
Soss, Sheldon B., 1964
Sostok, Michael A., 1984
Sostowski, Richard M., 1973
Souder, Elmer Nicholas, 1895
Souder, Lewis Reed, 1887
Souder, Ronald L., 1973
Sour, Stephen A.D., 1891
Sourbeer, Jay C., 1985
Sourbeer, John N., 1955
Southard, Durward W., J1944
Southrn, Frank L., 1889
Southwick, Edward W., 1844
Southwick, Harry Holmes, 1910
Southwick, Samuel G., 1954
Sowash, Millard, 1874
Sowden, Edgar Lentz, 1911
Sowden, Frederic D., 1883
Sowden, Richard G., Jr.,,1970
Sowers, John W., 1935
Spackman, James Paul, 1896
Spackman, Reuben V., 1870
Spady, Thomas, F., 1840
Spagna, Francis, 1924
Spagnoli, Bernita M., 1987
Spagnoli, Marie V., 1980
Spagnoli, Robert C., 1955
Spahr, Robert C., 1969
Spaide, Richard F., 1981
Spalding, A. Eugene, 1874
Spalding, Andrew J., 1849
Spalding, Francis J., 1873
Spalding, Jennifer Anne, 1990
Spalletta, Camillus Henry, 1932
Spandorfer, John M., 1989
Spang, Frederick K., 1860
Spangler Ford C. 1949
Spangler, Benjamin F., 1868
Spangler, Charles F., 1881
Spangler, Clyde Mitchell, 1925
Spangler, Jacob Benson, 1886
Spangler, Jacob R., 1874
Spanich, Christopher G., 1989
Spann, James T., 1854
Spar, Ellen, 1987

Sparks, Charles E., 1968
Sparks, George W., 1865
Sparks, Samuel M., 1927
Speace, George F., II, 1972
Speacht, Clarence Franklin, 1925
Spear, Owen Crow, 1906
Spear, Raymond, 1895
Spearman, Alfred S., 1852
Spears, Abraham Kellar, 1855
Spears, Brent Wood, 1971
Spears, Joseph H., 1853
Spears, Thomas M., 1847
Speas, Julius L., 1877
Spechler, Floyd F., 1971
Speck, George McClellan, 1888
Speck, Julius Caesar, 1919
Speck, Moses Henry, 1920
Spedding, Robert D., 1881
Speed, Joseph Anderson, 1914
Speer, Alexander M., 1853
Speer, Henry Newton, 1893
Speer, William Louis, 1912
Speight, Joseph Powell, 1906
Speir, William, 1852
Speirs, Alfred C., 1959
Speirs, Harold Archer, 1955
Spellman, James E., Jr., 1984
Spelsberg, Walter T., 1957
Spence, David Walter, 1888
Spence, George Sigars, 1905
Spence, William Bayne, 1889
Spence, William Edwin, 1891
Spencer, Boyd Cook, 1889
Spencer, Cadwallader C., 1855
Spencer, Charles W., 1857
Spencer, George Francis, 1920
Spencer, George Wicks, 1892
Spencer, H. Gordon P., 1846
Spencer, James L., 1847
Spencer, James T., S1944
Spencer, John E., 1870
Spencer, Leonard Everett, 1896
Spencer, R. M., 1859
Spencer, W., 1856
Spencer, William Canfield, 1861
Spencer, William Gardner, 1873
Spencer, William Henry, 1916
Spencer, William Oliver, 1891
Spengler, Gideon D., 1878
Sperandio, Peter G., 1989
Sperry, Edward L., 1882
Sperry, Willis C., 1877
Sphar, Raymond L., Jr., 1961
Spicer, John Daniel, 1859
Spiegel, Joseph R., 1979
Spiegel, Richard H., 1985
Spiegelman, David M., 1970
Spiegleman, Arthur M., 1958

Spielman, Ronald L., 1961
Spielman, Sheryl B., 1983
Spielman, Stanley L., 1959
Spigel, G. Thomas, 1971
Spigel, James H., 1980
Spikes, Norman Owen, 1924
Spikol, Lorraine C., 1986
Spikol, Louis E., 1984
Spilka, George Martin, 1938
Spindle, Thomas G., 1846
Spindler, Alva Reed, 1921
Spinner, Jesse F., 1852
Spinuzza, Thomas J., 1983
Spitko, Jane A., 1986
Spitz, Louis, 1902
Spivack, Alfred P., 1954
Spivack, Jerome, 1961
Spivak, Charles D., 1890
Spivak, Louis Joseph, 1906
Spock, Nicholas, 1957
Spohn, William A., 1975
Sponaugle, H. Dale, 1961
Spong, George R., 1949
Sponsler, Rodney L., 1962
Spooner, Edward A., 1854
Spotts, Ricke L., 1976
Spotts, Samuel Dale, 1922
Spotz, Gladfelter Emanuel, 1897
Spragg, Charles William, 1897
Spragg, Sylvanus L.S., 1879
Sprague, Albert G., Jr., 1859
Sprague, Charles Henry, 1914
Sprague, Frank Marion, 1907
Sprague, George Percy, 1890
Sprague, Hugh Boleyn, 1905
Sprague, Rollin, 1829
Sprague, Thomas H., 1975
Sprague, William L., 1988
Sprankle, Paul Darling, 1904
Spratlin, William M., 1876
Spratt, Charles Brewster, 1897
Spratt, John B., 1857
Spratt, Napoleon B., 1868
Sprecher, Omer D., Jr., 1941
Sprenkel, Vaughan Leroy, 1931
Sprenkle, J. Edwin, 1884
Spriggs, John S., 1844
Spriggs, Lem Walter, 1904
Springel, Ronald D., 1978
Springer, James C., 1982
Springer, Joseph Vincent, 1923
Springer, Suzanne R., 1969
Sprinkle, Charles Nichols, 1910
Sprinkle, Lawrence T., 1945
Sprissler, Oscar, 1892
Sproch, Richard M., 1947
Sproch, Thomas M., J1944
Sproul, Samuel M., 1855

Sprowls, Isaac Newton, 1879
Sprowls, John N., 1877
Sprowls, Lee M., 1882
Spruance, Henry Roche, 1892
Spruance, Horace Evans, 1915
Spruance, James Harvey, 1899
Spruill, George E., 1851
Spurgeon, Lincoln, 1968
Spurlock, John W., 1984
Squadrito, James F., Jr., 1980
Squibb, Edward R., 1845
Squiers, Elizabeth C., 1983
Squire, William H., 1851
Squires, Claude Babington, 1919
Squires, Leslie S., 1981
Squires, Walter Howland, 1899
St. Andre, Arthur C., 1975
St. Clair, Charles M., 1878
St. Clair, Frank Earle E., 1904
St. Clair, James Roy, 1912
St. Clair, Jesse W., III, 1979
St. Clair, Thomas, 1847
St. Clair, W. P., 1856
St. John, Thomas Arthur, Jr., 1974
Staas, William E., Jr., 1962
Staats, Enoch Dwight, 1929
Staats, Roydice, 1928
Stabinski, Elizabeth Marie, 1969
Stabler, Craig L., 1981
Stabnick, Joseph Sigmund, 1934
Stack, John M., 1968
Stack, William T., 1952
Stackhouse, H. W., 1837
Stacks, Jacob C., Jr., 1954
Stacy, R. O., 1858
Stader, Richard Otto, 1953
Stadiger, J. Frederick, 1826
Stadulis, I. Martin, 1924
Stadulis, Jerome M., 1952
Staffaroni, Mark A., 1981
Staffen, Robert N., 1988
Stafford, C. T., 1869
Stafford, James Frederick, 1906
Stafford, Marshall William, 1990
Stage, Jacob Samuel, 1900
Stahl, Charles J., III, 1956
Stahl, Lloyd Alva, 1932
Stailey, Henry David, 1930
Staiman, Keith M., 1975
Stair, John G., 1878
Stallings, C. H., 1859
Stambaugh, Ervin Luther, 1927
Stambaugh, John E., Jr., 1966
Stampien, Ted Michael, 1990
Stamps, George Ruffin, 1929
Stanberry, Wellington, 1837
Stancil, James R., 1940
Stander, Paul E., 1980

Stanford, H. K., 1840
Stanford, Louis W., 1877
Stang, Robert B., 1983
Stanger, Samuel F., 1875
Staniels, Susan Edwards, 1972
Stanilla, Joseph K., 1981
Stanitski, Carl L., 1967
Stankard, William F., 1938
Stanley, Augustin O., 1856
Stanley, Christine L., 1988
Stanley, Eugene Arthur, 1904
Stansbury, Robert Mott, 1834
Stanton, Edward Vincent, 1937
Stanton, James G., 1881
Stanton, James Justice, 1905
Stanton, James N., 1905
Stanton, John J., Jr., 1943
Stanton, John Joseph, 1903
Stapinski, Cyril Charles, 1942
Stapinski, Stanley Michael, 1933
Stapp, James T., 1879
Stapp, M. Robertson, 1889
Starcher, Richard Camden, 1935
Starck, Albert A.G., 1883
Starer, Larry J., 1951
Stark, Daniel P., 1857
Stark, Edwin A., 1857
Stark, Horatio, 1847
Stark, Jesse D., 1925
Stark, Robert E., 1949
Stark, Theodore F., 1877
Starke, Richard T., 1987
Starkey, Richard S., 1895
Starks, Gregory C., 1973
Starnes, E. Clingman, 1888
Starr, Edison Burns, 1905
Starr, Henry F., Jr., 1948
Starr, Henry Frank, Jr., 1916
Starr, John G., 1961
Starr, Robert R., 1940
Starrels, Michael E., 1971
Starry, John D., 1847
Starsnic, Janice, 1978
Starsnic-Resnik, Mary Ann, 1973
Starynski, John R., 1980
Starz, Kenneth E., 1970
Starz, Terence W., 1971
Starz, Walter Earl, 1937
Stashak, Frank J., Jr., S1944
Statler, Emanuel J.B., 1868
Statler, Frank B., 1889
Statler, Samuel G., 1851
Statten, Milton, 1852
Staub, Carl Aloysius, 1914
Staub, Carl Aloysius, Jr., 1953
Staub, Franklin N., 1874
Stauber, Gerson, 1976
Stauffer, Daniel J., 1982

Stauffer, Harry J., 1895
Stauffer, Nathan P., 1901
Stauffer, Ralph Stanley, 1916
Stauffer, Stanely Sell, 1953
Stavely, William R., 1855
Stayer, A. S., 1873
Stayer, Morrison Clay, 1906
Stayman, J. Webster, III, 1970
Stayman, Joseph W., Jr., 1942
Steadman, Henry Ree, 1914
Stealey, Jeremiah H., 1882
Steans, John C., 1876
Stearnes, James D., 1881
Stearns, John W., Jr., 1837
Stec, Eugene G., 1954
Stec, Michael John, 1925
Stecher, William A. R., 1929
Stecher, William A., 1958
Steck, Charles G., 1955
Steck, John M., 1880
Steck, Michael, 1842
Steckel, Alfred P., 1864
Steckel, Edmund F., 1862
Steckman, Philip McClellan, 1889
Stedem, Joseph P. H., 1888
Stedge, Rodney Luther, 1925
Stedman, Clarence C., 1871
Steel, John Mattern, 1906
Steel, Maxwell W., III, 1976
Steel, Maxwell W., Jr., J1944
Steele, A. J., 1859
Steele, Ernest Richmond, 1901
Steele, Francis J., 1839
Steele, Frederic Hohman, 1934
Steele, James McLeod, 1933
Steele, John, 1831
Steele, John E., 1964
Steele, John T., 1955
Steele, John Ward, 1902
Steele, R. Edward, 1939
Steele, Robert, 1933
Steele, Willard H., 1911
Steely, Oscar Baker, 1891
Steen, J. Dennis, 1965
Stees, Abiram C., 1838
Stees, John I., 1875
Stefanelli, James L., 1985
Stefans, Vikki A., 1979
Steffens, Arnold O., 1964
Steffey, John Llewellyn, 1868
Stehley, Martin L., 1874
Stehlik, John M., 1963
Stehman, Harry B., 1877
Stein, Barry S., 1974
Stein, Bernard Benjamin, 1927
Stein, David, 1924
Stein, Donald Beuchler, Jr., 1953
Stein, Elliott M., 1964

Stein, George N., 1942
Stein, George W., 1891
Stein, Gerald Bernard, 1940
Stein, Hymen D., 1939
Stein, Irvin, 1930
Stein, Louis H., 1951
Stein, Mark R., 1968
Stein, Robert A., 1970
Stein, Robert M., 1968
Stein, Robert S., 1950
Stein, Samuel Charles, 1937
Stein, Samuel H., 1933
Stein, Scott C., 1967
Steinbach, Lewis W., 1880
Steinbach, William Alexander, 1959
Steinberg, Amber Lynne B., 1990
Steinberg, Arthur, 1950
Steinberg, Harvey, 1962
Steinberg, Michael B., 1970
Steinberg, Saul, 1931
Steinberg, Stanford M., 1962
Steinberg, William J., 1977
Steinberg, William, 1924
Steindel, Carl R., 1966
Steiner, Edwin, 1901
Steiner, John C., 1965
Steiner, John Martin, 1906
Steiner, Josephus M., 1846
Steiner, Robert M., 1964
Steinmetz, Charles G., III, 1948
Steinmeyer, Harry H., Jr., 1951
Steinour, William J., 1979
Steinwandel, John Anthony, 1890
Steitz, J. Arthur, 1942
Stell, W. W., 1857
Stella, Joseph H., 1982
Stello, Brian, 1988
Stellwagen, Thomas Cook, Jr., 1903
Stelzer, Leo, Jr.,,1973
Stem, Frank Ott, 1891
Stembler, Harry Abraham, 1904
Stenberg, Edwin S., 1917
Stenger, Leo E., 1923
Stenhouse, Henry M., Jr., 1948
Stennis, William Hardy, Jr., 1956
Stepansky, David W., 1978
Stepansky, William, 1952
Stephan, George Louis, 1912
Stephen, John Michael, 1887
Stephens, Edward B., 1883
Stephens, James G., 1876
Stephens, James T., 1880
Stephens, James T., 1937
Stephenson, Daniel H., 1935
Stephenson, J. Thomas, 1858
Stephenson, James William, 1846
Stephenson, John Edward, 1927
Stephenson, Marcus P., 1857

Stubbs, Jeremiah B., 1827
Stubbs, Joseph H., 1862
Stubbs, Slater B., 1842
Stubbs, Walter P., 1873
Stubenrauch, Walter Herman, 1926
Stuck, Craig A., 1982
Stucke, Edmund Conrad, 1910
Stuckert, Harry, 1907
Stuckslager, Cyrus R., 1856
Stull, Clark Deakyne, 1916
Stull, James R., 1957
Stull, Mark W., 1982
Stulpin, Michael D., 1979
Stumacher, Russell J., 1968
Stump, Wayne George, 1929
Sturdevant, S. Burton, 1856
Sturdivant, Marcus, 1850
Sturgeon, Eli, 1849
Sturgeon, John D., Jr., 1920
Sturges, William Warren, 1887
Sturr, Robert Porch, 1916
Sturr, Robert Porch, Jr., 1948
Stutzman, Charles D., 1978
Stybr, Charles Joseph, 1900
Styer, Albanus, 1849
Styer, Daniel Webster, 1888
Suarez del Villar, Jose R., 1881
Suarez, Paul A., 1981
Subin, David K., 1961
Subin, Harry, 1924
Suchman, James Frederick, 1974
Suckow, Lowell C., 1963
Sudler, Arthur E., Jr., 1859
Sudler, Stephen A., 1981
Sudler, William J., 1847
Sudler, William T., 1864
Suenaga, Howard James, 1936
Suermann, John E., 1945
Suesserott, Jacob L., 1851
Suffoletta, Daniel Benedict, 1931
Sufrin, Emanuel, 1935
Sugar, Alan M., 1977
Sugarman, Kate S., 1988
Sugden, William A., 1961
Sugerman, Harvey J., 1966
Sugg, William C., 1953
Sugint, Felix Peter, 1936
Sukati, Amy M., 1976
Sullivan, Arthur F., Jr., 1942
Sullivan, Arthur James J., 1912
Sullivan, Daniel R., 1976
Sullivan, Frederick Jeremiah, Jr., 1939
Sullivan, Howard E., Jr., 1954
Sullivan, John James, 1923
Sullivan, John M., 1856
Sullivan, Robert J., 1946
Sullivan, Thomas E., 1969
Sullivan, Timothy Daniel, 1905

Sullivan, William Martin, Jr., 1929
Sullum, Stanford N., 1973
Sumerson, James M., 1967
Sumfest, Jill M., 1978
Sumfest, Joel M., 1982
Summers, Alan L., 1971
Summers, Rowland T., 1857
Summers, William Herbert, 1920
Summersgill, R. Blair, 1978
Summerville, Gregg Paul, 1990
Summey, Thomas Johnson, 1915
Summy, David R., 1883
Sumner, George, Jr., 1853
Sumner, Howard Leon, 1926
Sumner, Ossian, 1842
Sumner, Robert Ernest, J1944
Sumner, Thomas Woodfin, 1910
Sumney, Herbert Clayton, 1890
Sunada, Kayo, 1954
Sunday, Michael L., 1988
Sunder, Theodore R., 1972
Sunderland, William P., 1844
Sunderman, F. William, Jr., 1955
Sundheim, John M., 1973
Sundheim, Suzanne T., 1988
Sundt, Linda M., 1974
Sunnergren, Kenneth P., 1983
Sunshine, Jeffrey A., 1979
Sunstein, Noah, 1902
Suntharalingam, Mohan, 1990
Superdock, Keith R., 1986
Supowitz, Saul, 1936
Supple, Leonard Keating, 1938
Surkin, Marc Ivan, 1978
Surkosky, John Joseph, 1927
Surles, Junius Boyette, 1909
Surmonte, John A., 1947
Surver, James Miller, 1929
Suseri, Caesar William, 1919
Susman, Michael, 1908
Sussman, Marcel S., 1936
Sussman, Nathan, 1935
Sussman, Robert L., 1971
Sussman, Walter, 1926
Suter, Harry F., 1931
Suter, Stanley C., 1936
Suter, William B., 1943
Sutherland, Charles, 1849
Sutherland, Robert Clive, 1916
Sutherland, Roderick, 1849
Sutter, Frederick T., 1981
Suttles, Charles M., J1944
Sutton, Douglas C., 1989
Sutton, George S., 1883
Sutton, Harley H., 1877
Sutton, James L., 1848
Sutton, Lewis, 1848
Sutton, Roger D., 1960

Sutton, William Gordon, 1889
Sutula, John Vincent, 1933
Sutula, Stanley J., Jr., 1965
Sutula, Stanley Joseph, 1934
Sutyak, John P., 1983
Swab, Robert Dubs, 1908
Swaby, William A., 1849
Swallow, Edward E., 1880
Swallow, Frank W., 1906
Swan Reyer O., 1949
Swan, Barbara E., 1981
Swan, David M., 1981
Swan, James, 1826
Swan, James Hayes, 1903
Swan, James R., 1941
Swan, John C., 1876
Swan, Samuel M., 1854
Swan, Walter Sidney, 1877
Swank, Ralph L., II, 1963
Swanker, Wilson A., 1934
Swartley, Robert Norman, 1947
Swartz, Curtis H., 1948
Swartz, Edward F., 1960
Swartz, Edward Philip, 1930
Swartz, George W., 1876
Swartz, Harry M., 1956
Swartz, Joseph, 1857
Swartzlander, Fred, 1872
Swartzwelder, James Sherman, 1892
Swarzlander, Joseph Rankin, 1897
Swavely, Samuel B., 1877
Swayne, Howard Roeder, 1889
Swayze, Burton Willis, 1891
Swayze, George B. H., 1859
Swearingen, A. William, 1888
Swearingen, Robert Goodwin, 1934
Sweat, William W., 1842
Sweeney, Alvin Randolph, 1908
Sweeney, Edgar C., 1949
Sweeney, Edward Joseph, 1907
Sweeney, Frank J., Jr., 1951
Sweeney, Joseph John, 1911
Sweeney, Joseph Patrick, 1920
Sweet, John Larydon, 1836
Sweet, Paul Williams, 1908
Sweet, William Merrick, 1886
Sweetser, Arthur Atkins, Jr., 1945
Sweier, William A., 1883
Sweitzer, Lewis H., 1849
Swenson, John A., 1957
Sweringen, Hiram V., 1876
Swern, Nathan, 1922
Sweterlitsch, Eric M., 1989
Sweterlitsch, Louis H., Jr., 1960
Sweterlitsch, Louis Henry, 1927
Sweterlitsch, Paul R., 1961
Swett, Chester Parker, 1925
Swett, Samuel B., 1834

Swift, Coe T., 1937
Swift, D. D., 1855
Swift, Joanne Hummel, 1986
Swiler, Robert David, 1889
Swiler, William E., 1857
Swindell, Orval Fisher, 1926
Swindells, Walton Creadick, 1900
Swisher, David Falls, 1892
Swisher, John W., 1989
Swisher, Kyle Young, 1921
Swisher, Louis Bush, Jr., 1959
Swygert, Sanders L., 1885
Sygenda, James Thomas, 1983
Sylvis, William Martin, 1908
Symmers, Douglas, 1901
Syms, Charles A., III, 1985
Syms, Charles A., Jr., 1952
Synnott, Myles, 1831
Synott, Martin S., 1839
Syracuse, Victor R., 1923
Syrek, Susan J., 1968
Szabo, Dennis Eugene, 1916
Szabo, Ladislas Thomas, 1929
Szarko, Frank J., 1966
Szawlewicz, Stephen A., 1970
Szeremeta, Wasyl, 1989
Szgalsky, Joseph B., 1985
Szlachetka, Vincent Edward, 1924
Szucs, Richard A., 1982
Szydlowski, Thaddeus R., 1972

~ T ~

Tabas, Janet H., 1984
Tabasco, Joseph F., 1950
Tabb, John P., 1844
Tachmes, Leonard, 1986
Taddonio, William S., 1986
Taft, George H., 1941
Taft, William C., 1940
Taggart, Charles, 1854
Taggart, Horace D., 1874
Taggart, John F., 1860
Taggart, Thomas Dartnell, 1896
Taggart, Tina S., 1989
Taggart, William Graham, 1933
Tai, En Shui, 1928
Tai, George M., 1966
Tait, G. G., 1836
Tait, Thomas Walker, 1888
Takash, Thomas J., 1987
Talacki, Carol Ann, 1972
Talamo, Robert J., 1983
Talamo, Thomas S., 1978
Talbot, Ashton Buchanan, 1888
Talbot, John A., 1831
Talbot, Patrick, 1836
Taliaferro, David M., 1853

Taliaferro, Frank, 1875
Taliaferro, Landon, 1840
Taliaferro, Philip A., 1850
Taliaferro, Robert H., 1839
Taliaferro, Thomas J., 1853
Tallant, Edward James, 1939
Talley, Lewis Robert, 1907
Tallmadge, William Henry, Jr., 1905
Tallman, Edwin H., 1941
Tallman, William, 1852
Tally, Bailey T., 1921
Talmage, Edwin S., 1876
Talmage, Samuel B., 1878
Tam, Felix K., 1981
Tambascia, John Joseph, 1959
Taminosian, Timotheus, 1895
Tan, Clinson B., 1988
Tananis, Anthony Adam, 1943
Tananis, Leonard J., 1954
Tananis, Leonard J., Jr., 1989
Tandowsky, Ralph Myron, 1922
Tandy, Thomas K., III, 1986
Tankersley, James William, 1906
Tannebaum, Ira R., 1968
Tannenbaum, Gerald, 1954
Tanner, Leonard M., 1949
Tantum, Percy L., 1886
Taraska, Gregory J., 1989
Taraska, John J., 1963
Targett, Archibald Frederick, 1893
Tarrant, James Wyatte, Jr., 1928
Tartaglia, Louis, Jr., 1967
Tarver, Samuel, 1849
Tatarian, Gabriel, 1952
Tatarko, Michael, 1989
Tate, Alexander C.H., 1838
Tate, James H., 1926
Tate, John M., 1855
Tate, Robert H., 1849
Tate, Thomas J., 1860
Tatnall, Phillip R., 1973
Tattersall, Harold A., 1940
Tatu, William F., 1976
Tatum, B. Harris, 1852
Tatum, Harry Erskine, 1900
Tatum, Roy C., 1919
Tatum, Walter Low, 1922
Tawil, Albert, 1962
Taxis, Herbert John, 1889
Taxis, J. B., 1870
Tayler, Thomas George, 1886
Taylor, Alfred, 1843
Taylor, Arthur John, 1890
Taylor, Brent W., 1862
Taylor, Charles Jr., 1839
Taylor, Charles Fleming, J1944
Taylor, Claude L., 1924
Taylor, Daniel M., 1884

Taylor, Daniel W., 1860
Taylor, Edward Winslow, 1881
Taylor, Elmer J., Jr., 1952
Taylor, Francis I., 1929
Taylor, Frank Herbert, 1897
Taylor, Frank M., III, 1973
Taylor, Frederick S., 1860
Taylor, George T., 1848
Taylor, Hamilton, 1829
Taylor, Herbert Leonel, 1902
Taylor, Hugh L., 1881
Taylor, J. Marcus, 1851
Taylor, J. Richard, 1870
Taylor, J. Zack, 1875
Taylor, Jackson, 1904
Taylor, James H., 1849
Taylor, James M., 1848
Taylor, James Thomas, 1890
Taylor, James W., 1854
Taylor, James, 1851
Taylor, James, 1865
Taylor, John Dempster, 1891
Taylor, John H., 1859
Taylor, John O., Jr., 1965
Taylor, John Y., 1852
Taylor, Joseph M., 1885
Taylor, Joseph Sheppard, 1856
Taylor, Joseph W., 1878
Taylor, Julian, 1851
Taylor, Julius S., 1835
Taylor, Leonidas C., 1848
Taylor, Mervyn Ross F., 1900
Taylor, Parran, 1849
Taylor, Paul James, 1906
Taylor, Philip H., 1955
Taylor, Raymond A., 1931
Taylor, Richard F., 1905
Taylor, Robert Alexander, 1886
Taylor, Robert F. C., Jr., 1970
Taylor, Robert W., 1864
Taylor, Robert Watson, 1949
Taylor, S. W., 1870
Taylor, Samuel Banks, 1895
Taylor, Samuel M., 1881
Taylor, Sarah, 1905
Taylor, Thomas J., 1934
Taylor, Thomas W., 1850
Taylor, Thompson J., 1874
Taylor, Thos. A., 1872
Taylor, Vernon W., Jr., 1938
Taylor, W. G., 1873
Taylor, W. S., 1873
Taylor, W. Scott, 1961
Taylor, W. V.M., 1873
Taylor, Walter Albert, 1904
Taylor, Wilfred Jerrold, 1900
Taylor, William B., 1849
Taylor, William C., 1853

Taylor, William H., 1859
Taylor, William H., 1954
Taylor, William I., Jr., 1941
Taylor, William S., 1874
Taylor, Zebulon Scriven, 1895
Teagarden, James Warren, 1891
Teague, Thomas J., 1854
Tebbs, Robert H., 1833
Tebbs, Thomas C., 1837
Tedeschi, Luke G., 1960
Tedesco, Louis J., 1985
Tedesco, Orlando P., 1953
Teed, John Francis, 1886
Teeter, Edwin Conrad, 1854
Teichman, Fred, 1978
Teitelman, Edward A., 1963
Tempesto, Joseph Anthony, 1913
Temple, H. Thomas, 1986
Temple, James D.W., 1874
Temple, Joel R., 1960
Temple, Robert, 1836
Temple, Thomas P., 1850
Templeton, Charles Love, 1906
Templeton, E. W., 1915
Templeton, John Y., III, 1941
Templeton, John Young, Jr., 1913
Templeton, Thomas B., 1955
Templin, Theodore, B., 1904
Tems, Sandra J., 1977
Ten Brook, John, 1838
Tenaglia, Nicholas C., 1964
Tenbrook, Andrew, 1876
Tenikat, Gail A., 1972
Tenn, David T., 1982
Tenn, Gordon K., 1967
Tenn, Patricia F., 1977
Tenn, Richard S., 1950
Tennent, John C., 1873
Tenney, Barbara L., 1971
Tenney, John A., 1883
Tepe, Nicholas A., 1980
Terheyden, William A., Jr., 1947
Terhune, Archibald A., 1848
Terhune, Archibald Alexander, 1888
Terkelsen, Kenneth G., 1969
Terrell, J. E.G., 1856
Terrell, John J., 1853
Terry, George H. B., 1895
Terry, Henry R., 1863
Terry, Roger L., 1970
Terzis, Julia K., 1970
Tesh, Robert B., 1961
Teters, Benjamin Franklin, 1886
Teufen Henry J., 1949
Tevis, Samuel, 1888
Thacher, James M., 1849
Thackeray, William T., 1866
Thaimann, William Gregory, Jr., 1937

Tharp, Jonathan, 1848
Tharp, William H., 1848
Tharp, William S., 1879
Thatcher, Charles A., 1834
Thatcher, Henry K., 1881
Thatcher, Jeffrey D., 1983
Thatcher, John P., 1858
Thaxton, Benjamin Adams, 1914
Thaxton, Joseph A., 1840
Thayer, David O., 1975
Thayer, Royal Westcott, 1897
Theriault, Louis Leo, 1918
Thierman, Ernest Julius, 1904
Thies, Wilheim, 1877
Thigpen, Frank Lafayette, 1917
Thigpen, Harry Gordon, 1917
Thigpen, William Jordan, 1900
Thilo, Elizabeth H., 1976
Thistle, Joseph Long, 1886
Thistlethwaite, Alan J., 1982
Thom, Allan C., 1847
Thom, J. Pembroke, 1851
Thoma, Theodore Benjamin, 1950
Thomas, Albert M., 1915
Thomas, Alfred N., 1859
Thomas, Andrew J., 1867
Thomas, Balorus Arby, 1897
Thomas, Barton Kathcart, 1913
Thomas, Carlyle Milton, 1926
Thomas, Carlyle Milton, Jr., 1956
Thomas, Carole Ellen, 1990
Thomas, Charles Daniel, 1957
Thomas, Charles E., 1857
Thomas, Charles Meade, 1910
Thomas, Charles Wallace, 1892
Thomas, Cynthia, 1982
Thomas, Daniel, 1837
Thomas, Daniel J., 1963
Thomas, David B., 1855
Thomas, David W., Jr., 1948
Thomas, Densmore, 1937
Thomas, Eb. W., 1897
Thomas, Edward L. C., 1926
Thomas, Edwin R., 1881
Thomas, Eli J., 1878
Thomas, F. Ardell, 1967
Thomas, Francis Xavier, 1947
Thomas, Frank B., III, 1957
Thomas, G. L., 1869
Thomas, George Carroll, 1906
Thomas, George Clair, 1924
Thomas, George D., 1890
Thomas, George Norfleet, 1923
Thomas, George Perce, 1888
Thomas, George S., 1837
Thomas, Harry Burger, 1929
Thomas, Harry Leedon, 1893
Thomas, Hayward Glazier, 1887

Thomas, Herbert C., 1915
Thomas, Howard Jones, 1923
Thomas, Irving Oakley, 1927
Thomas, James A., Jr., 1960
Thomas, James Anthony, 1928
Thomas, James H., 1953
Thomas, James William, 1903
Thomas, Jerome B., 1858
Thomas, John C., 1846
Thomas, John E., 1958
Thomas, John Henry, 1935
Thomas, John J., 1881
Thomas, John R., 1848
Thomas, Joseph R., Jr., 1973
Thomas, L. Martha A., 1976
Thomas, Llewelyn Ivor, 1912
Thomas, Nathan O., 1970
Thomas, Nathanael Ross, 1939
Thomas, Norman A., 1896
Thomas, Pernett, 1837
Thomas, Richard C., 1861
Thomas, Robert F., Jr., 1980
Thomas, Robert W., 1851
Thomas, Robert Y.H., 1855
Thomas, Roger B., 1940
Thomas, Samuel B., 1911
Thomas, Stephen Jay, 1968
Thomas, Terrence J., 1959
Thomas, Vernon D., 1896
Thomas, Victor J., 1979
Thomas, William A., 1878
Thomas, William J., 1958
Thomas, William J., Jr., 1972
Thomas, William T., 1860
Thomason, George W., 1899
Thomason, William Paul Owen, 1897
Thome, William McKee, 1897
Thomison, Harry Elijah, 1918
Thompkins, Leonard Joseph, 1960
Thompson, Andrew D., 1877
Thompson, Anne M., 1967
Thompson, Charles E., 1981
Thompson, Charles M., 1875
Thompson, Charles O., 1964
Thompson, Davis, 1860
Thompson, Ebenezer, 1862
Thompson, George E., 1856
Thompson, George W., 1854
Thompson, Harry H., 1889
Thompson, Harvey Johnston, Jr., 1945
Thompson, Henry Merrill, 1906
Thompson, Herbert Henry, 1909
Thompson, James A., 1878
Thompson, James Buell, 1889
Thompson, James D., 1878
Thompson, James F., 1864
Thompson, James L., 1845
Thompson, James M., 1952

INDEX

Tomasello, Donald N., 1969
Tomaseski, William Henry, 1932
Tomassene, Raymond Albert, 1916
Tomassetti, Bernard A., 1945
Tomb, Henson, F., 1887
Tomb, Robert Johnson, 1854
Tomichek, Richard C., 1974
Tomkins, Gustavus A., 1837
Tomlinson, Charles O., 1970
Tomlinson, Edwin, 1872
Tomlinson, George Milton, 1908
Tomlinson, J. Wesley, 1927
Tomlinson, John, 1841
Tomlinson, John W., 1962
Tomlinson, Peter W., 1878
Tomlinson, Robert Williams, 1912
Tomlinson, Thomas C., 1879
Tomlinson, Winfield Hibbs, 1903
Tompkins, Alexander C., 1853
Tompkins, Donald R., 1931
Tompkins, Kenneth J., 1982
Tompkins, Samuel W., 1852
Toner, Joseph M., 1853
Toner, Mark Ferdinand, 1893
Toney, David M., 1965
Tong, Fook Hing, 1930
Tonken, Heidi P., 1988
Tonrey, Francis G., 1924
Tonrey, Francis Gerald, 1824
Toof, Richard S., 1980
Toombs, Robert E., 1848
Topham, Bertram Everett, 1906
Topilow, Edmund C., 1978
Topp, Edwin Mitchell, Jr., 1947
Topper, John Albert, 1904
Topper, William H., 1971
Topping, George G., 1872
Torbert, Enos G., 1879
Torbert, John S., 1881
Torbet, George A., 1856
Toreki, William, 1963
Torkington, Joseph, 1885
Torna, Patricia Ann, 1990
Tornay, Anthony S., Jr., 1969
Tornay, Anthony Stephen, 1931
Torrence, D. Rogers, 1879
Torrence, J. M., 1873
Torrence, James Monroe, Jr., 1913
Torrey, Eugene Weiss, 1917
Torrey, Noah, 1847
Toth, George, 1924
Totino, Joseph A., 1957
Totten, John Baldwin, 1861
Touhey, J. Manning, 1926
Tourangeau, Pierre G., 1841
Tourish, William Joseph, 1928
Towle, Clarence Clark, 1904
Towle, Samuel Knapp, 1858

Towler, Harold Hunt, 1907
Towles, Thomas T., 1840
Town, Arno Emerson, 1926
Town, Edwin C., 1873
Townend, Stephen C., 1975
Townes, Isaac Johnson, 1889
Townes, Lafayette, 1852
Townsend, A. R.P., 1855
Townsend, Charles Rees, 1895
Townsend, Charles W., 1849
Townsend, Ellis P., 1863
Townsend, George F., 1858
Townsend, James W., Jr., 1969
Townsend, Jay A., 1968
Townsend, Milton Banes, 1894
Townsend, Morris W., 1853
Townsend, Ralph M., 1866
Townsend, Stephen, 1865
Townsend, William T., 1835
Townsend, William W., 1844
Toy, Frederick J., 1964
Toy, Stephanie M., 1988
Tozer, Richard C., 1945
Trabert, J. W., 1870
Trabin, Jay R., 1974
Trabulsi, L. Richard, 1964
Tracey, George Thomas, 1898
Tracey, Kevin T., 1973
Tracey, Martin L., 1936
Trachtenberg, Eric L., 1989
Trachtenberg, Jacob, 1971
Trachtenberg, Stanford B., 1964
Trachtman, William M., 1989
Tracy, George D., 1859
Tracy, Henry Miron, 1927
Trader, J. Lindsay, 1871
Trafton, Charles T., 1847
Traiman, Harris I., 1964
Traiman, Richard G., 1967
Trainor, Charles Edwin, 1902
Trainor, Joseph Patrick, 1891
Trammell, Appling D., 1847
Trammell, Francis A., 1850
Tran, Michael S., 1985
Tran, Nho Van, 1985
Trauffer, Patrice Lamb, 1986
Traugh, John Calvin, 1824
Traugh, John Calvin, 1924
Traum, Ronald E., 1957
Traupman, Arnold F., 1973
Travaline, John M., Jr., 1988
Traver, D. B., 1869
Traver, Samuel Nisley, 1897
Travitz, Ronald P., 1985
Traynham, William B., 1838
Treacy, Denis J., 1867
Treacy, Edward Aloysius, 1913
Treadwell, Passmore, 1862

Treadwell, Robert O., 1846
Treat, Albert Miller, 1910
Treat, Ernest, 1904
Treat, Michael E., 1940
Treat, Michael R., 1976
Treat, William, 1838
Tredick, John Jr., 1867
Trego, Albert, 1861
Trego, Alfred, 1836
Trego, Joseph H., 1849
Treible, William Henry, 1896
Treichler, A. C., 1869
Treichler, Vere, 1905
Treiman, Arthur Mark, 1990
Trellis, Emil S., 1957
Tren, Aaron, 1886
Trenchard, Albert, 1870
Trenchard, C. M., 1873
Trenchard, Franklin J., 1847
Trent, P. G., 1867
Tressan, Elliott R., 1966
Tressler, Allene M., 1982
Trevaskis, John Davis, 1925
Trevino, Miguel, 1870
Trexler, Charles Amos, 1892
Trexler, Clifford Hertzog, 1926
Trexler, Horatio D., 1873
Trexler, Jacob Amos, 1901
Trexler, Jacob Franklin, 1894
Trexler, William, 1876
Trezza, Scott A., 1983
Triano, Marla R., 1989
Tribit, Charles Burns, Jr., 1952
Tribou, N. M., Jr., 1858
Trichtinger, Martin D., 1980
Triester, Arthur N., 1965
Trigg, Ross Beckham, 1909
Trilla, Emilio F., S1944
Trimber, Connell James, 1960
Trimble, David, 1837
Trimble, George B., 1852
Trimmer, Luther Epeanetus, 1897
Trimmer, Ralph Waldo, 1919
Trinder, John Holmes, 1904
Triolo, Joseph, 1989
Triolo, Paul, 1989
Triplett, W. H., 1859
Tripp, Edwin P., Jr., 1938
Tripp, Warren H., Jr., 1983
Trippe, Henry W., 1858
Trippe, Morton Fitch, 1940
Trisler, J. William, 1884
Trist, Edwin Allen, 1890
Trist, H. B., 1857
Trites, David T., 1842
Troncelliti, Alfred E., 1929
Troncelliti, Edward A., 1942
Troncelliti, Mario V., 1941

Underwood, Grant, S1944
Underwood, Harry Burnham, 1938
Underwood, I. W., 1869
Underwood, James Harris, 1905
Underwood, Warren J., 1864
Underwood, William H., 1868
Ungar, John, Jr., 1932
Unger, Camill, 1883
Unger, George F., Jr., 1957
Uniacke, Brian M., 1982
Unseld, James T., 1852
Unseld, John H., 1854
Unterberger, Herbert, 1945
Up de Graff, Thad S., Jr., 1883
Upchurch, Robert Theodore, 1908
Updegrove, Robert A., S1944
Updike, Furman T., Jr., 1961
Uppal, Arvinder Singh, 1990
Upshaw, William, 1844
Upshaw, William T., 1855
Upshur, George M., 1852
Upson, Francis W., 1839
Upton, George, 1833
Upton, William A., 1857
Uram, Irving Emanuel, 1942
Urbach, Fredrick, 1946
Urbaitis, John Charles, 1930
Urban, Donald G., 1968
Urban, Joseph T., 1933
Urban, Paul L., 1977
Urbanski, Timothy E., 1971
Urian West, Valerie A., 1976
Urich, Isaac K., 1882
Urich, Thomas K., 1877
Urmann, Susan B., 1973
Urmson, Allan Walker, 1897
Urquhart, George, 1850
Urquhart, Thomas H., 1848
Urtecho, J. Y., 1873
Usala, Anton-Lewis, 1983
Ushinski, Stanley C., 1963
Usilton, C. Alfred, 1882
Usry, Joshua F., 1852
Uttal, Joseph, 1926
Uzzle, Edward Foy, 1916

~ V ~

Vaccaro, Michael, 1934
Vaccaro, Philip F., 1925
Vaccaro, V. Michael, 1958
Vaccaro, Vincent M., 1968
Vagley, Richard T., 1968
Vail, William Carey, 1901
Vaill, Charles H., 1863
Valentin, August Carl, 1914
Valentine, Lee S., 1975
Valerio, James Vincent, Jr., 1943

Valko, George P., 1986
Vallette, William H., 1884
Valloti Joseph M., 1949
Vallow, Morton J., 1955
Valls, Bartholomew, 1886
Van Bavel, James O., 1971
Van Bolden, Vernon, II, 1975
Van Buskirk, Charles, 1877
Van Buskirk, Joseph T., 1860
van der Bie, Roscoe, 1921
Van Derpoel, Samuel Oakley, 1845
Van Dyck, C.V.A., 1839
Van Dyke, George Marion, 1888
Van Gundy, Arthur B., J1944
Van Gundy, Gregory A., 1978
Van Kirk, Theophilus R., 1864
Van Loon, Lawrence Gwyn, 1931
Van Neste, George V., 1883
Van Nuys, John D., 1870
Van Sant, Benjamin, 1890
Van Sciver, Cecil B., 1927
Van Summern, John M., 1975
Van Uitert, Bonnie L., 1977
Van Valzah, Frank H., 1870
Van Valzah, Henry J., 1945
Van Valzah, Robert T., 1871
Van Valzah, William W., 1876
Van Vranken, Bruce H., 1975
Van Vranken, Bruce, 1947
VanAntwerp, Eugene H., 1881
VanArtsdalen, Frank V., 1857
VanBuren, Marmaduke Foster, 1892
VanBuskirk, George, 1846
VanBuskirk, Gordon Parker, J1944
VanBuskirk, Henry F., 1882
VanBuskirk, James, 1868
VanBuskirk, Samuel Levick, 1887
VanBuskirk, William A., 1847
Vance, John C., Jr.,,1959
Vance, John Clair, 1927
Vance, John Harris, 1886
Vance, Ralph B., 1938
Vance, Thomas J., 1858
Vance, William N., 1836
VanCleeff, Sander, 1990
Vander Horck, Max P., 1885
Vander Hulst, John C., 1975
Vanderbeck, C. C., 1872
Vanderbeek, Richard R., 1958
Vanderbeek, Stuart Ward, 1921
Vanderlin, Robert L., 1955
Vanderlin, Robert L., II, 1980
Vandersall, Thornton A., 1954
VanDerwerken, Suzanne Wanlass, 1987
Vandever, John H., 1845
VanDuzer, William Roy, 1912
Vanett, Bruce B., 1974
VanGilder, James Emmett, 1912

Vanhoff, Augustus H., 1836
Vanhook, James D., 1859
VanHorn, John William, 1894
VanHorn, Leon, 1896
VanHorne, Augustus K., 1856
VanKeusen, James, 1830
VanKirk, B. H., 1869
Vankirk, Joel K., 1854
VanKirk, Joseph, 1891
VanKirk, Stephen Campbell, 1901
VanKirk, William F., 1868
VanKirk, William Kirnan, 1873
Vann, Herbert M., 1917
Vann, Julius R., Jr., 1917
Vann, Luther Lee, 1890
Vanneman, Albert Walter, 1897
Vanneman, Walter A. R., 1892
Vanneman, William S., 1831
VanNess, Herbert Roy, 1912
Vannort, Joseph Adams, 1887
Vannucci, Robert C., 1966
Vannuys, D. H., 1864
Vanoni, Frank R., 1958
VanPelt, Joseph T.K., 1854
VanReed, Daniel R., 1868
Vansant, Eugene Larue, 1884
Vansant, John, 1855
Vansant, Joseph B., 1865
VanSciver, John E. L., 1899
VanSickle, Frederick L., 1886
VanSickle, Lewis, 1869
Vanston, Gerald Edward, 1959
VanSweringen, Garrette, 1905
VanValzah, H. B., 1873
Vanvalzah, R. F., 1838
VanValzah, Samuel B., 1854
VanValzah, Thomas 1847
VanVoorhis, John S., 1847
Varano, Lottie A., 1965
Varano, Nicholas R., 1936
Varano, Vincent J., 1967
Vardeman, Thomas B., 1852
Varga, Jeffrey M., 1983
Varner, L. Robert, 1964
Varrel, Frank Martin, 1886
Vary, Clarence Godfrey, 1898
Vasey, Charles Frederick, 1901
Vasey, Wilson P., 1852
Vassallo, Enrique M., 1961
Vassalluzzo, Julio E., 1963
Vassalotti, Stephen B., 1948
Vasso, Stephen G., 1962
Vasta, Alfred G., 1974
Vastine, David W., 1966
Vastine, J. H., 1858
Vastine, J. Robert, 1932
Vastine, John S., 1846
Vastine, P. B., 1838

INDEX

Wailes, Leonard A., 1861
Wain, John C., Jr., 1980
Wainstein, Jeffrey L., 1985
Wakefield, Albert T., 1878
Wakefield, Clark Woodworth, 1917
Wakefield, Frank G., 1970
Wakefield, John R., 1945
Wakefield, Matthew F., 1850
Wakefield, Ralph Waldo, 1902
Walchak, Frank R., 1968
Walcott, Henry Joel, Jr., 1896
Waldman, Joseph, 1930
Waldner, John Louis, 1906
Waldo, Frederick A., 1827
Waldron, George F., 1875
Waldron, Peter E., 1983
Walen, Jacob, 1925
Wales, Edmund L.B., 1827
Wales, Westley Rogers, 1891
Walheim, Jon P., 1970
Walker, Alonzo B., 1881
Walker, Andrew B., 1969
Walker, Benjamin Franklin, 1885
Walker, Benjamin H., 1852
Walker, Bernard H., 1849
Walker, Calvin H., 1847
Walker, Charles, 1828
Walker, Charles Jr., 1853
Walker, Charles W., 1859
Walker, Dale L., 1885
Walker, Delavan N., 1858
Walker, Duncan D., Jr., 1946
Walker, Duncan Devane, 1912
Walker, Fleetwood, 1860
Walker, Frank P., 1878
Walker, Frank, 1860
Walker, George S., 1852
Walker, George S., 1859
Walker, Granville Hunt, 1902
Walker, Harry Lewis, 1889
Walker, Henry Crawford, 1891
Walker, Herman Hervey, 1909
Walker, Herschel C., 1916
Walker, Horace, 1865
Walker, Jacob, 1913
Walker, James A., 1918
Walker, James K., 1870
Walker, James M., 1958
Walker, James N., 1878
Walker, James R., 1850
Walker, James S., 1865
Walker, James W.H., 1893
Walker, James, 1854
Walker, James, 1892
Walker, John S., 1946
Walker, John V.F., 1834
Walker, Joseph P., 1886
Walker, Joseph R., 1854

Walker, Joseph, 1908
Walker, Kathleen A., 1987
Walker, L. Brooke, Jr., 1959
Walker, L. Reed, Jr., 1967
Walker, Lise C., 1982
Walker, Lynn Joseph, 1916
Walker, Mark, 1854
Walker, Michael J., 1988
Walker, Richard P., 1885
Walker, Robert B., 1985
Walker, Robert Latshaw, III, 1940
Walker, Samuel E., 1882
Walker, Stephen R., 1983
Walker, T. F., 1858
Walker, Thatcher V., Jr., 1854
Walker, Thomas Davis, 1887
Walker, Thomas Francis, 1890
Walker, W. M., 1872
Walker, Walter, 1859
Walker, William, 1853
Walker, William A., 1854
Walker, William J., 1860
Walker, William J., III, 1953
Walker, William T., 1849
Walker, Z. J., 1859
Walkling, Adolph Augustus, 1917
Wall, James H., 1927
Wall, James R., 1972
Wall, John G., 1845
Wall, Joseph Amplias, 1912
Wall, Paul M., 1975
Wall, Robert E., 1975
Wall, Roscoe L., Jr., 1940
Wall, Roscoe LeGrand, 1912
Wall, Russell Theodore, 1909
Wall, Walter Z., 1877
Wall, William B., 1853
Wallace, Barnett, 1867
Wallace, Charles Chester, 1910
Wallace, Clarence MacNair, 1934
Wallace, Clayton T., 1878
Wallace, Ellerslie, 1843
Wallace, Ellerslie, Jr., 1879
Wallace, George Sellers, 1897
Wallace, Horatio, 1854
Wallace, Hugh Stanley, 1922
Wallace, I. A., 1869
Wallace, J. C., 1871
Wallace, James J., 1851
Wallace, James P., 1864
Wallace, John P., 1837
Wallace, John R., 1852
Wallace, John S., 1865
Wallace, John W., 1846
Wallace, Jonas C.B., 1854
Wallace, Michael, 1844
Wallace, Nathan C., 1883
Wallace, R. Bruce, 1868

Wallace, R. S., 1855
Wallace, Ray B., 1924
Wallace, Richard P., 1974
Wallace, Robert B., 1848
Wallace, Robert D., 1984
Wallace, Samuel J., 1881
Wallace, William Alexander, 1920
Wallace, William C., 1886
Wallace, William D., Jr., 1953
Wallace, William Davies, 1920
Wallace, William E., 1951
Wallace, William Earl, 1920
Wallace, William P., 1836
Wallace, William Sampson, 1881
Wallace, William Smiley, 1893
Wallace, William, 1894
Wallack, Armand, 1951
Wallen, Albert D., 1934
Wallen, Seely, 1879
Waller, George P., 1877
Waller, Tracy E., 1844
Wallhauser, Henry Andrew, 1916
Wallick, Peter G., 1982
Walling, Willoughby, 1847
Wallingford, Alvin M., 1865
Wallis, Charles, 1918
Wallis, Hugh Maxwell, 1860
Wallis, James C., 1877
Wallis, Robert S., 1860
Wallis, Walter, 1861
Wallop, William J.H., 1847
Walls, Joseph P., 1982
Wallton, James C., 1850
Walmer, Ephraim LeRue, 1891
Waln, J. Ryerss, 1884
Walrath Martin H., III, 1949
Walrond, Benjamin, 1874
Walser, Theodore, 1851
Walsh, Arthur W., 1987
Walsh, Eugenia S., 1989
Walsh, Frank Alfred, 1895
Walsh, Gerald Girard, 1922
Walsh, Harry A., 1921
Walsh, James A., 1925
Walsh, James A., 1961
Walsh, James Joseph, 1911
Walsh, John J., 1934
Walsh, John J., IV, 1989
Walsh, John Joseph, 1886
Walsh, Joseph A., 1979
Walsh, Joseph Michael, 1929
Walsh, Thomas Joseph, 1919
Walsh, Timothy P., 1983
Walsh, William F., 1848
Walsh, William Joseph, Jr., 1927
Walson, Charles Moore, 1906
Waltemeyer, John Tassey, 1887
Walter, Adam V., 1895

INDEX

Watkins, Donald Riegel, 1947
Watkins, Evan Lloyd, 1939
Watkins, Fonso Butler, 1907
Watkins, George Thomas, 1915
Watkins, Harold Ryburn, 1920
Watkins, Henry A., 1847
Watkins, Jack G., 1953
Watkins, Joseph Conrad, Jr., 1926
Watkins, Joseph F., 1858
Watkins, Richard H., 1852
Watkins, Robert Earl, 1917
Watkins, Thomas W., 1950
Watkins, William Merritt, 1923
Watlington, Thomas J., 1857
Watson, Andrew J., 1860
Watson, Charles James, Jr., 1916
Watson, Edward D., 1834
Watson, Edward H., 1847
Watson, Gillet F., 1842
Watson, James M., 1852
Watson, John S., S1944
Watson, John W., 1856
Watson, Joseph Harry, 1915
Watson, Lemuel, 1870
Watson, Maria Jeanette, 1990
Watson, Stephen Sidney, 1894
Watson, Thomas E., 1852
Watson, Ulysses Edward, 1960
Watson, William D., 1853
Watson, William W., 1841
Watt, Harry Calvin, 1889
Watt, James Smith, 1881
Watt, Robert, 1897
Watt, William, 1856
Watterson, Robert Wayne, 1916
Watterson, Samuel G., 1964
Watts, Charles W., 1871
Watts, D. Heather, 1981
Watts, David A., 1860
Watts, David C., 1987
Watts, John S., 1867
Watts, William W., 1843
Waugh, James R., 1859
Waugh, William F., 1871
Wawrose, Stephen F., 1986
Way, Eugene, 1879
Way, George C., 1875
Way, Jacob H., 1866
Way, Julius, 1885
Way, Walter R., 1863
Way, William Henry, 1861
Wayland, Clyde, 1910
Wayland, Raymond Theodore, 1913
Wayman, B. Ralph, Jr., 1963
Wayman, Bernard R., III, 1989
Wayman, Bernard Ralph, 1930
Weakley, Virgil William, 1930
Weakley, William Stair, 1906

Weatherby, Francis Elwood, 1913
Weatherford, John Elwood, 1915
Weatherley, T. Ogden, 1880
Weatherly, W. E., 1856
Weathers, Lucien V., 1866
Weaver, A. S., 1874
Weaver, Abe Kipp, 1917
Weaver, Albert Prince, 1892
Weaver, Amy L., 1985
Weaver, Andrew Albert, 1898
Weaver, Andrew Jackson, 1933
Weaver, Charles H., 1864
Weaver, Charles H., 1889
Weaver, Charles W., 1867
Weaver, Clarence Arlington, 1892
Weaver, Elijah, 1873
Weaver, Gayle Joelene, 1990
Weaver, George W., 1873
Weaver, Harold Johnson, 1925
Weaver, Jacob G., 1865
Weaver, John, 1847
Weaver, John D., 1885
Weaver, John Louis, 1949
Weaver, Joseph K., 1867
Weaver, Junius W., 1857
Weaver, L. F., 1873
Weaver, Martin D., 1988
Weaver, Oscar M., 1948
Weaver, Oscar Montague, 1919
Weaver, S. J., 1872
Weaver, William Abbott, 1925
Weaver, William Amy, Jr., 1913
Weaver, William J., 1847
Weaver, William Jackson, 1898
Weaverling, Eric R., 1982
Webb, Abner, 1896
Webb, Charles E., 1861
Webb, E. Burton, 1937
Webb, Edwin L., 1948
Webb, Fred Leland, 1902
Webb, Henry McCorry, 1892
Webb, Henry Young, 1846
Webb, John W., 1866
Webb, Joseph B., 1858
Webb, Lawrence Clayton, 1954
Webb, Lorenzo Lea, 1890
Webb, Louis Harward, 1910
Webb, Robert T., 1854
Webb, S. V., 1858
Webb, Samuel, 1846
Webb, Walter, 1888
Webb, William, 1849
Webb, William Ezekiel, 1887
Webb, William H., 1866
Webber, Charles E., Jr., 1968
Webber, Edward Everett, 1902
Webber, Edwin Russell, 1914
Webber, Joseph B., 1850

Weber, Charles Z., 1882
Weber, Cynthia Elinor, 1989
Weber, David J., 1971
Weber, Edgar H., 1922
Weber, Francis Charles, 1917
Weber, George L., 1946
Weber, Harry Friedman, 1899
Weber, Henry Meyer, 1824
Weber, Henry Meyer, 1924
Weber, John Malcolm, 1917
Weber, Paul R., 1977
Weber, Raymond Kantner, 1905
Weber, Reinhard H., 1866
Weber, Robert C., II, 1989
Weber, Susan L., 1985
Webster, David K., 1940
Webster, George C., Jr., 1913
Webster, Harry N., Jr., 1941
Webster, James Weldon, S1944
Webster, James Weldon, Jr., 1961
Webster, Jesse Grant, 1914
Webster, John R., 1864
Webster, Lane H., 1951
Webster, Samuel, 1837
Weddell, Oliver S., 1876
Wedge, Dudley O., 1874
Weed, Charles L., 1883
Weed, Mark Dye, 1905
Weed, Melrose Edmund, 1929
Weeks, Albert, 1880
Weeks, Carlile B., 1880
Weeks, Job Harry, 1886
Weeks, John Francis, Jr., 1942
Weeks, Ruthellen D., 1981
Weeks, William C., 1851
Weems, Don B., Jr., 1958
Weems, Don Bright, 1930
Weems, Richard, 1839
Weest, Harry Wolfgang, Jr., 1919
Weever, Charles S., 1844
Weever, George Slocumb, 1897
Weever, John B., 1858
Weggenmann, Edward Earle, 1934
Wehler, Andrew J., 1947
Wehner, Daniel R., 1981
Wehner, William H.E., 1887
Wei, Nathan, 1975
Weibel, David C., 1957
Weida, Charles Benjamin, 1889
Weidaw, Harold R., 1954
Weidenmier, Carl Henry, 1927
Weidler, Isaac C., 1827
Weidner, Donald R., 1974
Weidner, Edward Thomas B., 1908
Weigand, Alan H., 1959
Weigel, Charles F. B., 1928
Weikel, Charles H., 1877
Weil, Burton A., 1919

Weiland, Carl, 1890
Weiland, Carl, Jr., 1908
Weiland, T. Frederick, S1944
Weiler, Howard George, 1927
Weimann, Max Ludwig, 1926
Weimann, Robert B., 1956
Weimar, Russell Conwell, 1920
Wein, Barry K., 1985
Weinberg, Charles Berenda, 1909
Weinberg, Jerome A., 1954
Weinberg, Linda L., 1969
Weinberg, Michael G., 1977
Weinberg, Paul M., 1969
Weinberg, Robert M., 1968
Weiner, Fredric R., 1972
Weiner, Michael D., 1967
Weiner, Michael Z., 1975
Weiner, Simon, 1939
Weinman, David S., 1986
Weinstein, Arnold H., 1960
Weinstein, Jack, 1949
Weinstein, Mitchell A., 1969
Weinstein, Morris Abraham, 1906
Weinstein, Rayford Lee, 1936
Weinstein, Stanley, 1947
Weinstein, Steven H., 1979
Weinstein, Steven L., 1974
Weinstein, Sydney, 1930
Weintraub, Harvey, 1961
Weintraub, Sydney Edward, 1932
Weintraub, William C., 1955
Weintrob, Joseph R., 1937
Weir, Frank L., 1876
Weir, John H., 1842
Weir, John M., 1851
Weir, Mary, 1902
Weirich, Colin R., 1882
Weis, Paul R., 1954
Weis, Walter F., Jr., 1966
Weisberg, Jay G., 1974
Weisberg, Martin, 1972
Weisberger, Calvin L., 1970
Weise, Ellwood C., Jr., 1947
Weise, Ellwood Carl, 1920
Weisel, Adolph, 1880
Weisel, William M., 1976
Weiser, Charles S., 1850
Weiser, Don Coleman, 1967
Weiser, Frank Ressler, 1891
Weiser, George B., 1842
Weiser, George B., 1867
Weiser, George B., Jr., 1879
Weiser, Josiah S., 1855
Weisman, Barrie L., 1964
Weisman, Kenneth M., 1980
Weiss, Benjamin Paul, 1907
Weiss, David L., 1975
Weiss, Edward Hervey, 1927

Weiss, Edward, 1917
Weiss, Harry, 1907
Weiss, Hervey Beale, 1901
Weiss, Janet S., 1979
Weiss, Jeffrey C., 1971
Weiss, Joan, 1977
Weiss, Justin F., 1975
Weiss, Lorenzo E., 1884
Weiss, Louis, 1879
Weiss, Malcolm S., 1968
Weiss, Robert A., 1960
Weiss, Steven J., 1983
Weiss, William Anthony, 1938
Weissberger, Ruth E., 1983
Weissman, Bruce W., 1965
Weissman, Burton E., 1962
Weissman, Mark I., 1975
Weissman, William K., 1956
Weist, J. R., 1861
Weitman, John Lewis, 1890
Weitz, Howard H., 1978
Welborne, W. Pinckney, 1859
Welch, J. Patrick, 1981
Welch, Samuel M., 1855
Welch, Stanton A., 1861
Welch, William Lee, 1941
Welcher, Howard Alfred, 1928
Weldman, J. Clayton, 1882
Weldon, Andrew J., 1860
Welfley, Albert Jonas, 1896
Welgoss, Jeffrey A., 1986
Welkie, John F., 1985
Wellenbach, Burton L., J1944
Weller, C. O., 1869
Weller, Harry W., 1954
Weller, James Edwin, 1901
Weller, Joseph Newton, 1901
Weller, Michael H., 1963
Welling, Joseph C., 1828
Wellner, John Edward, 1904
Wells, Allan B., 1967
Wells, Charles, 1840
Wells, Ebenezer, 1836
Wells, Edgar Kennard, 1907
Wells, Howard, 1870
Wells, J. Ralston, 1855
Wells, Joseph Edgar, 1887
Wells, Joseph M., 1878
Wells, Mortimer H., 1949
Wells, Thomas, 1859
Wells, William Hughes, 1891
Welsby, Claude Bedford, 1916
Welsh, Albert Eugene, Jr., 1940
Welsh, D. Emmett, 1878
Welsh, Elmer E., 1882
Welsh, Horace G., 1880
Welsh, James F., 1954
Welsh, John, 1828

Welsh, Theresa M., 1983
Welsh, William A., 1848
Welsh, William Andrew, 1919
Weltin, Johannes D., 1976
Welton, John Seymour, 1958
Welty, Katherine K., 1985
Wendel, Christopher H., 1978
Wenger, Alvin P., Jr., 1943
Wenger, Christian Showalter, 1940
Weniger, Frederick L., 1937
Wenner, Nadine P., 1976
Wenner, Steven M., 1974
Wennersten, Jack R., 1939
Wenof, Michael, 1974
Wenrich, William H., 1865
Wentworth, George W., 1847
Wentworth, Harry Wilder, 1896
Wentz, Frank Riegel, 1913
Wentz, Henry S., S1944
Wentz, Irl Ziegler, 1920
Wentz, Paul Roop, 1907
Wentz, Thomas H., 1874
Wentz, William J., 1865
Wentzel, George Robert, 1938
Wentzel, Harvey E., Jr., 1960
Wentzel, John H. C., 1938
Wentzell, James Earl, 1937
Wentzler, J. Donald, 1946
Wenzel, David R., 1984
Wenzel, Richard P., 1965
Weres, James, 1932
Werhun, Anthony T., 1983
Werkman, Robert F., 1980
Werley, Charles Daniel, 1889
Werley, Charles W., 1945
Werley, John D., 1954
Werley, Walter William, 1918
Wermuth, Charles R., 1963
Werner, Eric J., 1978
Werner, Julius Leon, 1905
Werner, Siegmund, 1897
Werner, Stephen E., 1968
Wersler, William, 1831
Werst, Nevin Blank, 1902
Wert, John M., 1880
Wertheim, Arthur Robert, 1939
Wertheimer, Marc J., 1975
Wertman, Alvin Andrew, 1889
Wertman, Mahlon Andrew, 1902
Wertman, Samuel Ellsworth, 1889
Wertz, Robert R., 1953
Wertz, Silas Grant, 1895
Wescoat, E. Seymour, 1883
Wescott, William A., 1883
Wesner, Michael A., 1876
Wessell, Rosalie W., 1977
West, C. Forrest, III,1975
West, Calvin, 1853

Williams, Gustavus A., 1835
Williams, Harry, 1929
Williams, Henry L., 1852
Williams, Horace James, 1912
Williams, Howard J., 1881
Williams, J. Franklin, 1885
Williams, J. Harold, 1950
Williams, J. Stewart, 1968
Williams, J. Thomas, Jr., 1963
Williams, Jabez Herring, 1920
Williams, James, 1847
Williams, James Q., 1837
Williams, James Thomas, 1904
Williams, James Thomas, 1931
Williams, James, 1867
Williams, John C., 1845
Williams, John F., 1859
Williams, John Henry, 1893
Williams, John Scott, 1935
Williams, Jonathan L., 1967
Williams, Junius S., 1861
Williams, K., 1857
Williams, Kenan B., S1944
Williams, Langdon T., Jr., 1957
Williams, Lester, 1882
Williams, Lorenzo D., 1850
Williams, Louis Carswell, 1901
Williams, Lynn Ryan, 1988
Williams, Mark L., 1986
Williams, Martin Henry, Jr., 1887
Williams, Neil Saxton, 1949
Williams, Neri Barndt, 1892
Williams, Orlando S., 1852
Williams, Philip Banatyne, 1895
Williams, Ralph H., 1954
Williams, Raymond Matthew, S1944
Williams, Robert H., Jr., 1977
Williams, Robert J., 1893
Williams, Robert Lloyd, 1906
Williams, Robert S., 1849
Williams, Roger, 1877
Williams, Royal William, 1919
Williams, Sidney Hampden, 1846
Williams, Stephen K., 1956
Williams, Thomas B., 1887
Williams, Thomas Elmer, 1905
Williams, Thomas F.J., 1856
Williams, Thomas H., 1872
Williams, Thomas Lamar, 1905
Williams, Thomas M., 1979
Williams, Ulysses, Jr., 1981
Williams, Urbane V., 1858
Williams, Victor Albert, 1914
Williams, W. Scott, 1966
Williams, Walter Edward, 1904
Williams, William Jr., 1848
Williams, William A., 1857
Williams, Willis A., 1847

Williamson, Charles W., 1867
Williamson, Duncan, 1846
Williamson, Ernest Gotshall, 1916
Williamson, Jesse, Jr., 1873
Williamson, John H., 1859
Williamson, Joseph Harper, 1886
Williamson, Lea Z., 1859
Williamson, Marjorie Ann, 1976
Williamson, Robert G., 1943
Williamson, Thomas G., 1835
Williamson, William S., 1889
Williamson, William T., 1856
Williard, George Parker, 1867
Willie, Roy C., Jr., 1948
Willingmyre, Sandra Phyllis, 1979
Willis, Arnold J., 1974
Willis, Carroll Vance, 1934
Willis, David W., 1976
Willis, George G., 1943
Willis, George M., 1855
Willis, Herbert, 1904
Willis, John Mitchell, Jr., 1940
Willis, Samuel W., 1864
Willis, T. Hayward, 1858
Willits, Charles C., 1882
Willits, Isaiah W., 1875
Willoughby, Henry W., 1853
Willoughby, Ralph Ray, 1906
Wills, Alexander F., 1856
Wills, James L., 1856
Wills, Jesse J., 1884
Wills, JoAnne K., 1986
Wills, John S., 1967
Wills, Leon Clifford, 1907
Wills, Reginald D., 1974
Wills, Samuel E., 1844
Willsey, Judson, T., 1888
Willson, David B., 1863
Willson, James F., 1839
Willson, John J., 1831
Willson, John, 1861
Willson, Richard T., 1847
Willson, Samuel, 1831
Willtrout, Irving D., 1878
Willwerth, James W., 1957
Wilner, Daniel, 1937
Wilson, Abram S., 1881
Wilson, Adolphus J., 1859
Wilson, Albert R., 1882
Wilson, Alexander, 1849
Wilson, Andrew J., 1848
Wilson, Brian D., 1984
Wilson, Charles, 1845
Wilson, Charles M., 1865
Wilson, Charles Meigs, 1882
Wilson, Charles P., 1863
Wilson, Charles Wesley, 1890
Wilson, Clarence G., 1873

Wilson, Dale Sloan, 1940
Wilson, David H.H., 1865
Wilson, Donald F., 1979
Wilson, Dwight Elliott, 1930
Wilson, Edward A., 1850
Wilson, Edwin K., 1877
Wilson, Ellwood, 1845
Wilson, Elmer E., 1888
Wilson, Felix Brent, 1915
Wilson, Francis S., 1870
Wilson, Frank E., 1882
Wilson, Frederick S., 1953
Wilson, Furman E., 1849
Wilson, George Brinton, Jr., 1933
Wilson, George M., 1957
Wilson, H. Augustus, 1879
Wilson, Harry M., 1874
Wilson, Harry M., 1877
Wilson, Howard A., 1884
Wilson, Israel Kelly, 1834
Wilson, J. C., 1869
Wilson, J. Moore, 1878
Wilson, Jacquelyn J., 1968
Wilson, James A., 1848
Wilson, James A., II, 1980
Wilson, James Alfred, 1919
Wilson, James E., 1857
Wilson, James E., 1866
Wilson, James H., 1885
Wilson, James Hamilton, 1909
Wilson, James L., 1961
Wilson, James Potter, 1846
Wilson, James R., 1847
Wilson, James W., 1837
Wilson, John, 1846
Wilson, John A., Jr., 1982
Wilson, John B., 1859
Wilson, John C., 1866
Wilson, John David, 1990
Wilson, John Denniston, 1905
Wilson, John Edwin, 1895
Wilson, John F., 1937
Wilson, John F., 1987
Wilson, John G., 1841
Wilson, John K., 1943
Wilson, John R., 1850
Wilson, John S., Jr., 1963
Wilson, John T., 1867
Wilson, John W., 1851
Wilson, John W., 1858
Wilson, Jonathan M., 1989
Wilson, Joseph F., 1852
Wilson, Joseph S., 1920
Wilson, Lawrence Addison, 1924
Wilson, Lester Ramon, 1923
Wilson, Linda C., 1978
Wilson, Louis A., 1961
Wilson, Lucien Strain, 1861

Wilson, Miles A., 1846
Wilson, Myron W., 1841
Wilson, N. M., 1866
Wilson, Norman E., 1971
Wilson, Oscar Hermon, 1906
Wilson, Preston, 1886
Wilson, R. A., 1836
Wilson, Richard C., 1965
Wilson, Robert Henry T., 1886
Wilson, Robert V., 1849
Wilson, S. Howard, 1881
Wilson, Samuel G., 1873
Wilson, T. D. Mutter, 1875
Wilson, Terrence J., 1980
Wilson, Thomas Cooper, 1895
Wilson, Thomas G., 1983
Wilson, Thomas S., 1981
Wilson, Thomas, 1867
Wilson, W. Stockton, 1861
Wilson, Walter H., 1867
Wilson, Walter Howard, 1937
Wilson, William C., 1852
Wilson, William Clarence, 1924
Wilson, William Gilliam, Jr., 1921
Wilson, William L., 1836
Wilson, William M., 1866
Wilson, William Reynolds, 1888
Wilson, William, Jr., S1944
Wilson-King, Genester S., 1982
Wilt, Jeffrey A., 1979
Wilt, John W., 1959
Wilton, Edward Andrew, 1953
Wily, Owen H., 1831
Wimberley, Joseph Powell, 1899
Wimbish, James A., 1848
Wimer, Bruce M., 1946
Wimley, George W., 1847
Wimpelberg, Samuel, 1883
Wimsatt, William Anthony, 1961
Winans, Lewis E., 1971
Winch George A., 1949
Winch, George A., Jr., 1981
Winchell, William H., 1950
Winchester, Edgar, 1856
Winchester, Frank M., 1883
Windbrake, Albert Jefferson, 1899
Winder, Aaron, 1844
Winder, Laurence Johnson, 1893
Winder, W. G., 1869
Windham, John Evans, 1933
Windle, Isaac, 1861
Windley, William Hays, 1932
Windsor, Norman, 1857
Wineburgh, George S., 1971
Winfield, Benjamin F., 1846
Winfield, John Q., 1846
Wingate, Otis Lee, 1904
Wingender, Wendell Phillips, 1893

Winger, Franklin, 1886
Winger, Ira Bitzer, 1921
Wingerd, C. Z., 1874
Wingfield, Alonzo C., 1851
Wingo, Thomas R., 1860
Winham, Arthur Jerome, Jr., 1942
Winheld, Rebecca J., 1986
Winick, William, 1935
Winkler, Jeffrey R., 1985
Winkler, Louis H., Jr., 1940
Winlock, Joseph T., 1867
Winn, David R.E., 1852
Winn, Rodger J., 1963
Winne, Charles K., 1859
Winsborough, Joseph W., 1855
Winship, Herring, 1903
Winslow, Bela Henry, 1892
Winslow, Byron, 1879
Winslow, Dean L., 1976
Winslow, Harrison G.O., 1841
Winslow, John Hayes, 1901
Winslow, John Lang, 1891
Winslow, Phillip H., 1965
Winslow, Richard Chambers, 1871
Winslow, William H., 1871
Winston, Gilbert Isaac, 1914
Winston, Joseph M., 1954
Winston, Julius, 1926
Winston, Maurice Joseph, 1920
Winter, Frank, 1878
Winter, J. W., 1873
Winter, James, 1969
Winter, Robert D., 1984
Winter, Stanley M., 1915
Wintermute, George Preston, 1893
Winters, Barton M., 1877
Winters, D. Nixon, 1873
Winters, Frank Winfield, 1894
Winters, Isaac, 1844
Winters, John Leaman, 1890
Winters, Lewis, 1967
Winters, Sadie, 1904
Winters, William Joseph, 1905
Wintersteen, John Charles, 1886
Winterstine, George W., 1878
Winton, Carol J., 1988
Winton, Henry Nelson, 1889
Winton, Horace, 1865
Wintter, William, 1865
Wirgman, Charles, 1877
Wirth, John C., Jr., 1969
Wirts, C. Wilmer, Jr., 1934
Wirts, Steven B., 1974
Wise, Emery D., 1925
Wise, Kenneth D., 1865
Wise, Ralph C., 1901
Wise, Robert Eric, 1937
Wisehart, Eric Edmound, 1911

Wiseman, William Albert, 1886
Wishard, J. Henry, 1883
Wishard, Walter H., 1917
Wishnev, Martin A., 1963
Wisley, Leonard A., 1859
Wisneski, Leonard A., 1973
Wisniewski, Robert E., 1977
Wiss, Raymond J., 1955
Wistar, Richard M., 1830
Wiswesser, George A., 1966
Withers, James Johnston, 1909
Witherspoon, Ambrose Henry, 1894
Witherspoon, H. F., 1857
Witherspoon, John A., 1852
Witherspoon, Oran H., 1865
Witman, Harrison T., 1864
Witman, Henry O., 1851
Witmer, Abraham H., 1866
Witmer, Cassius M., 1881
Witmer, Dennis R., 1979
Witmer, Donald B., J1944
Witmer, Isaac M., 1881
Witmer, Peter Bachman, 1896
Witt, Eric William, 1927
Witt, Robert L., 1981
Witte, Eric H., 1978
Witthoff, E. Milton, Jr., 1957
Witting, Anthony P., 1879
Wittkamp, Andrew L.V., 1876
Wixted, William M., 1972
Wiza, Edward Joseph, Jr., 1960
Woddrop, Henry, 1850
Woddrop, Robert S., 1842
Woehrle, Nelson Christian, 1930
Wofford, Emily, 1981
Wofford, Jesse Lucius, 1951
Wofford, John D., 1954
Wofford, John D., Jr., 1978
Wohlwend, Fred, 1909
Wojczynski, Leon Joseph, 1911
Wolbach, Albert Bogh, Jr., 1958
Woldoff, Herbert S., 1967
Woldorf, Norman M., 1964
Woldow, Irving, 1937
Wolf, Edward T., 1933
Wolf, Frank A., Jr., 1953
Wolf, Frank Aloysius, 1910
Wolf, Jacob G., 1857
Wolf, John A., 1851
Wolf, Kathleen M., 1989
Wolf, Lisa C., 1984
Wolf, Marie Bush, 1982
Wolf, Melvyn A., 1967
Wolf, Sandra M., 1977
Wolfe, David E., 1855
Wolfe, Dwight D., 1977
Wolfe, Edward Inman, 1917
Wolfe, Eugene Fink, 1932

Wolfe, Isaac Reber, 1895
Wolfe, John Bloss, 1915
Wolfe, R. Vincent, 1911
Wolfe, Robert Morton, 1913
Wolfe, Samuel Melville, 1894
Wolfe, Sidney Maurice, 1947
Wolfe, William E., 1857
Wolfe, William Franklin, 1957
Wolfe, William H., 1839
Wolfe, William S., 1897
Wolfel, Eugene E., 1976
Wolfer, Carl F., 1970
Wolfert, Irwin H., 1984
Wolff, Denis Roscoe, 1918
Wolff, George T., 1952
Wolff, Herbert M., 1936
Wolff, John S., 1853
Wolff, Lawrence, 1880
Wolff, M. L., 1867
Wolff, Theodore, 1966
Wolfgang, Gary L., 1967
Wolfgang, Timothy C., 1972
Wolfinger, Walter L., 1937
Wolford, M. Luther, 1880
Wolford, Robert W., 1941
Wolford, W. Scott, 1873
Wolfrom, Carlos Eugene, 1926
Wolfson, Benjamin, 1961
Wolfson, Julius, 1895
Wolin, David, 1914
Wolitz, Richard A., 1977
Woloshin, Jeffrey, 1987
Wolson, Alan H., 1967
Wolverton, Giles, 1931
Wolverton, Lewis, 1883
Womack, Noel C., Jr., 1947
Womack, Noel Catchings, 1905
Womble, Pembroke, M., 1848
Womer, Frank, 1889
Womer, Henry F., 1878
Wong, Bradley D., 1975
Wong, Edwin H., 1979
Wong, James Sin Fook, 1933
Wong, James T. S., J1944
Wong, James, 1967
Wong, Randall V., 1988
Wong, Randolph W., 1988
Wong, Robert T., 1936
Wong, Sau Ki, 1945
Wong, Stephen W., 1972
Wong, Vernon Genkin, 1958
Wong, Wallace Bow On, 1956
Wonnell, Diane M., 1989
Woo, Victor L., 1975
Wood, Charles S., 1851
Wood, Chester Cameron, 1910
Wood, Clark S., 1908
Wood, Daniel Jones, 1849

Wood, Eason B., 1860
Wood, Edwin N., 1850
Wood, Fred Green, 1895
Wood, George G., 1872
Wood, George H., 1880
Wood, George J., 1859
Wood, George Thomas, Jr., 1928
Wood, Hubert, 1895
Wood, Irving C., 1880
Wood, J. Bestor, 1861
Wood, James William, 1905
Wood, John Dean, 1850
Wood, John William, 1895
Wood, Mabel, 1904
Wood, Marcus M., 1857
Wood, Oran Alphonso, 1890
Wood, Oscar T., Jr., 1934
Wood, Rex, 1907
Wood, Rowland Emery, 1940
Wood, Sherrod N., 1950
Wood, Sidney S., 1855
Wood, Walter Franklin, 1905
Wood, William Alva, 1887
Wood, William B., 1965
Wood, William Charles, 1908
Wood, William E., 1844
Wood-Wagemaker, Madeline S., 1989
Woodard, F. M., 1869
Woodbridge, Timothy, 1835
Woodburn, John M., 1881
Woodburn, Samuel S., 1882
Woodburn, William H., 1868
Woodburn, Wilton Allen, 1902
Woodbury, Frank, 1873
Woodbury, Jonathan, 1850
Woodbury, Malcolm Sumner, 1906
Woodhead, Irving Henry, 1896
Woodhouse, Henry John, 1889
Woodhouse, Lisle William, 1916
Woodhouse, Robert J., 1977
Woodhouse, Samuel William, 1895
Wooding, Nathaniel H., 1857
Woodley, Bruce L., 1970
Woodruff, A. Dickinson, 1844
Woodruff, Charles E., 1886
Woodruff, Charles L., 1966
Woodruff, Elias, 1836
Woodruff, George, 1879
Woodruff, James Lloyd, 1909
Woodruff, John Barnaby, 1896
Woodruff, Marston True, 1930
Woodruff, Ralph D., 1965
Woodruff, Ralph G., 1930
Woodruff, Samuel W., 1876
Woodruff, Stephen M., 1970
Woods, Abraham Lincoln, 1897
Woods, Clarence Hubert, 1896
Woods, Essie J., 1982

Woods, George H., 1875
Woods, Harry Robert, 1904
Woods, Henry Lewis, 1887
Woods, James M.B., 1863
Woods, John F., 1871
Woods, John Franklin, Jr., 1888
Woods, Josiah P., 1841
Woods, Kathleen J., 1982
Woods, Matthew, 1849
Woods, Samuel Albert, 1900
Woods, Walter V., 1877
Woods, William James, 1844
Woods, William S., 1864
Woods, William S., 1934
Woods, William Semple, 1854
Woods, William W., 1877
Woodside, Harry Addison, 1897
Woodside, Horatio Linn, 1908
Woodside, Jack R., 1949
Woodside, Jack R., Jr., 1977
Woodside, James A., 1850
Woodside, John S., 1875
Woodson, Albert P., 1834
Woodson, John C., 1853
Woodson, Lewis Green, Jr., 1920
Woodson, Philip T., 1855
Woodward, Abner, Jr., 1852
Woodward, Charles, 1849
Woodward, Charles E., 1864
Woodward, Hugh B., 1950
Woodward, Richard H., 1854
Woodward, William John, 1947
Woodward, William M., 1946
Woodward, William W., 1855
Woody, William Sterling, 1919
Woog, John J., 1980
Wooldridge, Beverly H., 1834
Woolfolk, William T., 1852
Woolford, Joseph S., 1873
Woollcott, Phillip, Jr., 1954
Woolley, Herbert, 1904
Woolman, Granvill S., 1844
Woolridge, John Hayes, 1916
Woolridge, John Hayes, 1952
Woolsey, William F., 1861
Woolverton, Allen N., 1841
Woomer, Lester Elgin, 1916
Wooten, Floyd Pugh, 1920
Wooten, William Isler, 1920
Wootten, Lucius T., 1837
Wootters, John Smith, 1892
Word, James C., 1860
Wordin, N. E., 1873
Worhacz, Walter, 1974
Work, Robert Anderson, 1892
Workman, Benjamin F., 1854
Workman, William M., 1912
Worl, Eli T., 1850

Young, Elisha, 1859
Young, Elizabeth T., 1981
Young, Ellis William, 1935
Young, George, 1845
Young, George D., 1838
Young, George Kemper, 1858
Young, George W., 1850
Young, George W., 1851
Young, Henry N., 1856
Young, Herbert Keith, 1932
Young, James A., 1836
Young, James L., 1926
Young, James W., 1877
Young, John Simpson, 1906
Young, Junius D., 1882
Young, Keith R., Jr., 1978
Young, Keith, 1951
Young, Linda L., 1989
Young, Lockwood Se-Joong, 1967
Young, Marion M., J1944
Young, Mason Pressly, 1913
Young, Matthew H., 1859
Young, Miller, 1873
Young, Oscar H., 1876
Young, Paul Tidence, 1916
Young, Robert, 1836
Young, Robert C., 1871
Young, Robert W., 1875
Young, Roy Lowry, 1905
Young, S. F., 1859
Young, Thomas J., 1849
Young, Thomas J., 1877
Young, Thomas O., 1880
Young, Thomas R., 1859
Young, Thomas S., 1852
Young, Thomas W., 1840
Young, Walter K. W., 1960
Young, Wesley W. H., 1979
Young, Wesley W., 1854
Young, William B., 1845
Young, William P., 1855
Younger, Joel B., 1978
Younger, Samuel, 1947
Youngman, Charles W., 1883
Youngman, George Andrew, 1941
Youseberg, Louis Israel, 1923
Ytterberg, Karen L., 1977
Ytterberg, Steven R., 1976
Yudis, Melvin, 1963
Yundt, Alfred M., 1881
Yundt, W. Scott, 1866
Yunginger, John W., 1964
Yurick, Bernard S., 1955
Yusuf, Amin Ibrahim, 1898
Yutski, William James, 1913

~ Z ~

Zabielski, Gerald C., 1972
Zacharias, J. Forney, 1860
Zacherle, Otto Frank, 1887

Zachian, Victor A., 1978
Zager, Mark A., 1975
Zagory, Conrad, 1949
Zahn, Samuel Finley, 1910
Zajac, Andrej J., 1981
Zajaczkowski, Marie, 1988
Zakrzewski, Kevin M., 1988
Zakrzewski, Matthew Joseph, 1933
Zale, Anthony G., 1942
Zale, Gregory J. P., 1987
Zaleznik, Elliot, 1959
Zamore, Michael S., 1976
Zamore, Steven M., 1974
Zamostien, Bernard B., 1937
Zamostien, Paul S., 1973
Zangrilli, Alfred A., 1931
Zangrilli, Alfred George, 1955
Zangrilli, James G., 1956
Zangrilli, James G., 1988
Zankman, Nathan, 1961
Zapolin, Carrie J. 1987
Zaragoza, Michael R., 1987
Zaret, Bruce S., 1974
Zaret, Cheryl R., 1972
Zarracino, Ramon D., 1865
Zauner, Robert H., 1885
Zavanelli, Barbara Ann, 1979
Zavod, Robert, 1963
Zavod, William Abraham, 1929
Zavod, William S., 1966
Zavodnick, Jacquelyn M., 1970
Zavodnick, Steven, 1973
Zazow, Paul L., 1976
Zech, Harry W., 1908
Zeeman, Beth A., 1985
Zeeman, Stanley E., 1948
Zegel, Harry G., 1975
Zehner, George D., 1927
Zehner, Richard Franklin, 1946
Zehner, William Henry, 1895
Zeiner, Levi S., 1879
Zeitlin, Mark H., 1966
Zeitzer, Kenneth L., 1988
Zeligman, Harvey D., 1971
Zelinka, Marijo A., 1984
Zelkovic, Mark A., 1988
Zell, Amos B., 1865
Zelle, Oscar Lewis, 1908
Zeller, Donald J., 1983
Zeller, Henry, 1837
Zeller, Raymond Bryant, 1927
Zeller, Theodore Cyril, 1923
Zelt, Leo George, 1937
Zemel, Norman P., 1965
Zemel, Walter G., 1968
Zemo, Peter L., III, 1962
Zemp, Francis Eugene, 1924
Zengerle, Frances Susan, 1968

Zenker, David O., 1955
Zenz, Carl, 1949
Zenz, Carl N., 1978
Zenz, Sonja J., 1979
Zeok, John V., 1967
Zerbe, B. Frank, 1878
Zerby, Glenn A., 1980
Zeve, Herman Sigmund, 1922
Zevely, Augustus T., 1840
Zibelman, Robert S., 1976
Ziccardi, Anthony Vincent, 1937
Zieber, Edward S., 1880
Ziegelman, Edward Frank, 1912
Ziegenfus, William D., 1961
Ziegenfuss, Jay F., Jr., 1967
Ziegenfuss, Nathan, 1892
Ziegler, Alfred Henry, 1906
Ziegler, Charles R., 1874
Ziegler, Fred Jay, 1905
Ziegler, George William, 1887
Ziegler, Jacob L., 1844
Ziegler, Maurice L., Jr., 1960
Ziegler, Richard W., 1979
Ziegler, Samuel P., 1845
Ziegler, Virginia Flory, 1970
Ziegler, William H., 1880
Zielinski, Edmund John, 1929
Zielinski, John B., 1934
Zielinski, Joseph Francis, 1938
Ziemba, Joseph F., 1945
Zientek Leon T. 1949
Zieziula, Ronald F., 1967
Zilber, Claire S., 1988
Zimmer, Louis E., 1943
Zimmer, Michael A., 1989
Zimmerman, Coler, 1931
Zimmerman, Cyrus Becker, 1919
Zimmerman, Edward L., 1912
Zimmerman, Frank D., 1907
Zimmerman, Franklin D., Jr., 1943
Zimmerman, G. P., 1870
Zimmerman, Levi, 1883
Zimmerman, Lorenzo Burton, 1894
Zimmerman, Neal J., 1978
Zimmerman, Pius, 1883
Zimmerman, Randall, 1904
Zimmerman, Reuben P., 1848
Zimmermann, George Luther, 1889
Zimskind, Joshua Norman, 1927
Zimskind, Paul Donald, 1957
Zionts, Martin Arnold, 1937
Zipin, David, 1930
Zlupko, George M., 1972
Zolnick, Mark R., 1982
Zon, Leonard I., 1983
Zook, Eli J., 1878
Zook, Henry, 1828
Zorch, Michael J., 1982

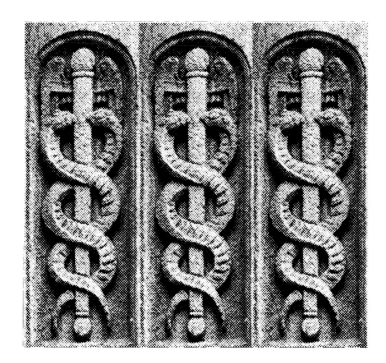

Detail from the College Building

Part II

Honorary Medical College Alumni

The Presidential Badge

JEFFERSON MEDICAL COLLEGE · 1824 ·

~ HONORARY MEDICAL ALUMNI ~

The early Constitution and By-laws of the Jefferson Medical College Alumni Association provided for active and honorary memberships. The By-laws further provided that Trustees of the College and graduates of other recognized medical institutions were eligible for this latter category. Curiously, honorary alumni had not been named until the Executive Committee meeting of November 26, 1929, on which occasion Dr. Ross V. Patterson (JMC, '04) moved that Dr. George Leete, an 1877 graduate of Dartmouth Medical School be made an honorary member. This action had been suggested by his son, Dr. Edward D. Leete (JMC, '15), of New Hampshire. The motion was seconded by Dr. Edward J. Klopp (JMC, '06) and carried.

The following year, four distinguished members of the faculty who were non-graduates of Jefferson were elected, and in 1936 the first member from the Board of Trustees.

The current By-laws state that: "Honorary Membership shall consist of persons not eligible for Active Membership, Trustees of the College, graduates of other accredited medical institutions who have particularly honored Jefferson, non-medical graduates who may be serving the College as Chairmen of Departments, or persons who have given exceptional service to or have singularly honored Jefferson."

The list of honorary members from 1930 to 1990 is as follows:

HONORARY ALUMNI

Year Appointed	Full Name	Year Appointed	Full Name
1930	George Leete, M.D.	1942	William Potter Wear
1931	Joseph O. Crider, M.D.	1949	Heinrich Brieger, M.D.
1931	Nicholas A. Michels, D.Sc.	1949	J. Rudolph Jaeger, M.D.
1931	Virgil Holland Moon, M.D.	1949	James L. Kauffman, Vice Admiral, U.S.N. (Ret.)
1931	J. Earl Thomas, M.D.		
1932	George Russell Bancroft, Ph.D.	1949	Arthur J. Wagers, M.D.
1933	Charles M. Gruber, M.D.	1966	Richard G. Berry, M.D.
1935	David M. Davis, M.D.	1966	Robert L. Brent, M.D.
1936	J. Howard Pew	1966	Floyd S. Cornelison, Jr., M.D.
1937	Brandon Barringer	1966	Thomas David Duane, M.D.
1937	Franklin Spencer Edmonds	1966	Allan Jacob Erslev, M.D.
1937	George P. Muller, M.D.	1966	William C. Frayer, M.D.
1937	Hobart A. Reimann, M.D.	1966	Roy Richard Greening, M.D.
1938	S. M. D. Clapper	1966	George A. Hahn, M.D.
1938	Karl Kornblum, M.D.	1966	Franz X. Hausberger, M.D.
1938	Norris W. Vaux, M.D.	1966	W. Paul Havens, Jr., M.D.
1939	Bernard J. Alpers, M.D.	1966	E. Harold Hinman, M.D.
1939	Horace P. Liversidge	1966	Roy G. Holly, M.D.
1940	Thomas D. M. Cardeza	1966	Robert Love, M.D.
1941	Van Horn Ely, Jr.	1966	Theodore T. Tsaltas, M.D.

Honorary Alumni

Part III

Postgraduate Alumni

Winged Ox Column

Thomas Jefferson Statue

The term "resident" and its counterpart "residency" have undergone major modifications in meaning and function during the past century. As originally used in the last quarter of the nineteenth century it applied to a graduate physician who chose to serve in a hospital and thereby gain clinical experience not provided during medical college. This was a voluntary act on the part of the relatively few graduates who were inclined to pursue academic careers in medicine. Thus, the first residents of Jefferson Medical College Hospital were Jefferson graduates who lived in and served in the 1877 Hospital. There was no requirement for internship at this time and physicians were on their own to gain postgraduate clinical experience. What later became required internships were still often referred to as "residencies." Until the turn of the century most medical students in the United States saw few patients and were expected to gain their clinical experience after receiving the M.D. degree.

INTERNSHIP

The term "intern" was first introduced in the United States in 1897 to describe the graduates of Johns Hopkins Medical School who sought hospital positions. By 1905 the Council on Medical Education of the American Medical Association recommended that all medical school graduates take one year of internship, which was considered as important to the general practitioner as well as the specialist. By 1910 approximately 70 percent of medical school graduates obtained hospital internships which at that time consisted of rotation through the main clinical services. The majority of hospitals, however, had no association with medical schools. The quality of education they offered varied greatly. Also, later, a straight internship became available in which the experience would be entirely in a single one of the major clinical specialties.

By 1914 the state medical boards began to require an internship for licensure and requested that internship be approved by the Council on Medical Education. The CME in that year published the first list of Hospitals with approved internships. In 1919 it issued standards for internship and urged the medical schools to adopt them. This was difficult to implement since most internships were in hospitals having little or no association with medical schools.

During the next three decades there was much variability in the quality of the internship programs. Various organizations concerned with improving and standardizing the internship formed an Internship Review Committee. It consisted of the Academy of General Practice, the American Association of Medical Colleges, the American Hospital Association, the Council on Medical Education, and the Federation of State Medical Boards. They developed *The Essentials for an Approved Internship* according to which internship could be approved, provisionally approved, or placed on probation. After mid-century, the medical schools began to discontinue the internship in their teaching hospitals, but the licensing bodies continued to require them. Thus the number of interns became reduced in the teaching hospitals but maintained in the community hospitals.

In 1965 the American Medical Association sponsored a Report of the Citizens Commission on Graduate Medical Education, *The Graduate Education of Physicians*, which recommended the internship be abandoned in favor of combining with the residency. By 1990 this had virtually happened.

RESIDENCY

In 1897 when the term "internship" was introduced at the Johns Hopkins Hospital, the "residency" system was also introduced there. It was designated as a period of specialty and academic training following the internship. The early residencies were mainly associated with university affiliated hospitals and were sought by those interested in teaching or research.

In 1916 the first specialty board, the American

Board of Ophthalmology, was founded. It established standards for practice and examined the candidates, but did not have authority for licensure. By the third and fourth decades of the twentieth century most specialties had developed formal residencies. The major teaching hospitals along the Eastern seaboard in Boston, New York City, Philadelphia, Baltimore and Washington that were affiliated with prestigious medical schools provided the programs. In the ensuing years a very complex and sophisticated system for training in the specialties and subspecialties developed.

The Directory of Graduate Medical Education Programs for 1987/88 lists 6,332 accredited graduate programs in medical education as of December, 1986. The projection of positions for July, 1987 was 79,854. This did not include physicians in 586 programs accredited too late to be included in the survey. In 1986 more than one fourth of the residents were women, and 38% of these were training either in internal medicine or pediatrics. The proportion of all residents who reported their race as black has remained at 4.5 percent.

FELLOWSHIP

The term "fellowship" in American medicine appeared at the beginning of the twentieth century and was applied to those physicians who were funded to do research, usually for a year or more, and to publish at least one paper embodying the results of their work. As time went on, especially from the 1940s, a fellowship could be counted as part of the time during the residency when some research would be conducted. As applied today a fellowship is generally an optional education program following the formal residency in which a subspecialty is pursued. It may or may not involve a period of research.

The first fellowship at Jefferson was established in 1905 by a gift of $5,000 from the Professor of Surgery, W. W. Keen (JMC, 1862), as a memorial to Mrs. Keen. Whenever the accumulated income amounted to $1,000 a fellowship was awarded by the Trustees to a graduate of Jefferson Medical College of not less than one, nor more than ten years, upon condition of spending at least one year in medical research in a subject approved by the Faculty and upon pub-

lishing the results as the Corinna Borden Keen Fellow. The First Fellow was Aller G. Ellis (JMC, 1900) who in 1907 and 1908 was enabled to study in Germany. It is historically interesting that in 1917 Ellis made a trip to Lancaster, Pennsylvania, to perform an autopsy upon the subject of the first successful removal of a brain tumor in the United States by Professor Keen, the patient having survived for 30 years. The Keen Fellowship is still in existence in support of research by a graduate of Jefferson for a period of one year in Europe, America or elsewhere as recommended by the Faculty.

In 1929 Mrs. John C. Martin established a yearly research grant, the recipient of which was known as the Martin Research Fellow in Pathology. The purpose was to determine what part, if any, was played by infections in certain chronic diseases such as nephritis, cirrhosis, Banti's disease, and others. The first Fellow was Harold L. Stewart (JMC, '26). After teaching for some years in Jefferson's Faculty, he went on to a distinguished career in the National Cancer Institute and received Jefferson's Alumni Achievement Award in 1966. The Fellowship was discontinued in 1936.

The Isidore P. Strittmatter Research Fund was established in 1928. Strittmatter (JMC, 1881) was a leader in organized medicine. The income yielded enough to support one Fellow in 1931. It was thereafter discontinued.

The J. Ewing Mears Training and Research Fellowship was established in May, 1930, by bequest of J. Ewing Mears (JMC, 1865). The income from the fund is used "to defray the expenses of a course of study on conditions that may better the physical and moral qualities of future generations, reserving to the College the right to determine the particular aspects of the science taught." Dr. Karl E. Paschkis, a Viennese physician who opposed the Nazi occupation of Austria, escaped to the United States in 1939. He was appointed to the Mears Fellowship in 1940 and subsequently joined the Jefferson Faculty in which he achieved distinction in endocrine and cancer research.

The Ross V. Patterson Fellowships were established in May, 1938, by bequest of Ross V. Patterson (JMC, '04), the Dean of Jefferson Medical College from 1916 to 1938. The income from the

Fund is used for fellowships to promote the welfare and knowledge of promising graduates, and for payment of salaries to fulltime teachers in the Training School for Nurses. Some of the early Ross V. Patterson Fellows were as follows: C. Wilmer Wirts, Jr. (JMC, '34) in 1939 and J. Edward Berk (JMC, '36) in 1940 (Gastroenterology); Joseph P. Seltzer (JMC, '37) in 1939 (Pathology); Nathan S. Schlezinger (JMC, '32) in 1939 (Neurology); John M. Flumerfelt (JMC, '37) in 1940 (Psychiatry); Earl R. Knox (JMC, '31) in 1940 (Anatomy); Alison H. Price (JMC, '38) in 1940 (Medicine); and Frederick B. Wagner, Jr. (JMC, '41) in 1945 (Surgery).

The Arthur H. Lea Fellowship in Bacteriology and Chemistry was established with appointment of Mr. A. Proskouriakoff in 1939. A Fellowship in Endocrinological Research in the Department of Gynecology was served by Jacob Hoffman (JMC, '25) in 1939. The Thomas McCrae Fellowship in Therapeutics was served by Louis Merves (JMC, '37) in 1939. Evan B. Hume (JMC, '29) was the Fellow in Dermatology in 1940. Welland A. Hause (JMC, '38) served a Hematology Fellowship in 1939. The Joseph V. Horn Fellows in Medicine, Department for Diseases of the Chest, were Robert K. Charr (JMC, '31) in 1939 and J. Woodrow Savacool (JMC, '38) in 1940.

EARLY JEFFERSON RESIDENTS

In 1937 the Emeritus Professor of Obstetrics, P. Brooke Bland (JMC, '01) established two residencies in Obstetrics. Preference in appointment is given to those who have served as interns in Jefferson Hospital. The original residents in this Department were John A. McCormack (JMC, '35) and Joseph L. Finn (JMC, '35), both in 1937. Residents in Roentgenology were Stephen Casper and Louis Buzaid in 1938, and George R. Kennedy in 1939. W. Paul Havens, Jr. was the first Resident in Medicine in 1938. Ned T. Raker (JMC, '35) was the first Resident on Surgery "A" in 1938 and James F. O'Neill (JMC, '36) the first on Surgery "B" in 1939. Oliver W. Suchs was the first in Otolaryngology in 1938, Herbert S. Gaskill in Neurology in 1939, and John W. Hauser the first in Urology in 1939.

JEFFERSON RESIDENTS BECOME ALUMNI MEMBERS (1990)

At the start of the Residency Programs in 1937 and for many years thereafter the training was mainly as "hands on" experience by service in the Hospital. The residents became increasingly involved in the teaching of medical students, sporadically did research, and participated in improving education programs. As chairmen and faculty members became increasingly fulltime, the education of the residents assumed greater academic importance. It also became apparent that a more unified and academically controlled system was really a function of the Medical College, which in July, 1984, assumed this responsibility. Dr. Joseph F. Rodgers (JMC, '57), Clinical Professor of Medicine, was appointed Associate Dean for Affiliations and Residency Programs. Thus, under the aegis of the College, residencies have been educationally improved and balanced with the clinical programs. The success rate in many of the board certification examinations reached as high as 95 percent.

It became recognized that Jefferson residents, whether or not they had received their M.D. degrees from Jefferson Medical College, served for four or five years, - just as long as the four years of Medical College. They were indeed postgraduate alumni under the administration of the College. In 1989, an Ad Hoc Committee of the Alumni Association was formed to consider the pros and cons of a new category of alumni composed of past residents, and decided that it should be known as "Postgraduate Alumni". The proposal was voted upon and passed at the February 22, 1990, Annual Dinner of the Alumni Association.

The Postgraduate Alumni thus become active members by virtue of having completed house staff training sufficient for board certification in a specialty or an approved subspecialty at Thomas Jefferson University Hospital (or its predecessor, Jefferson Medical College Hospital). An appropriate certificate of membership is issued at completion of the house staff training program. The said residents become active members with the right to vote and may become eligible for office.

THE AMERICAN SPECIALTY BOARDS

The advancement of medical science leading to improvements in delivery of health care since the turn of the century led to a proliferation of specialties. Initially there was no system to assure the public that a physician who claimed special expertise was actually qualified. The concept of a specialty Board was first voiced in 1908 at a meeting of the American Academy of Ophthalmology and Otolaryngology. In 1916 the American Board of Ophthalmic Examinations became the first specialty Board. In 1933 its name was changed to the American Board of Ophthalmology.

In 1924 the second specialty Board, The American Board of Otolaryngology, was incorporated. The American Board of Obstetrics and Gynecology became the third in 1930 and the American Board of Dermatology and Syphilology became the fourth in 1932. In 1933 a conference attended by representatives of the four existing boards resulted in creation of the Advisory Board for Medical Specialties. In 1948 a Liaison Committee for Specialty Boards was established accompanied by the publication of the *Essentials for Approval of Examining Boards in Medical Specialties.*

By 1949, according to the *Annual Report and Reference Handbook of the American Board of Medical Specialties* (1990), 14 new specialty Boards had been approved, bringing the total by that time to 18. The additional ones were:

Orthopaedic Surgery, 1935
Pediatrics, 1935
Psychiatry and Neurology, 1935
Radiology, 1935
Urology, 1935
Internal Medicine, 1936
Pathology, 1936
Surgery, 1937
Neurological Surgery, 1940
Plastic Surgery, 1941
Anesthesiology, 1941
Physical Medicine and Rehabilitation, 1947
Colon and Rectal Surgery, 1949
Preventive Medicine, 1949

Between 1949 and 1969 no new Boards were approved by the Liaison Committee for Specialty Boards.

Between 1969 and 1979 the five remaining specialty Boards were approved, bringing the total to 23. They were as follows:
Family Practice, 1969
Thoracic Surgery, 1970
Nuclear Medicine, 1971
Allergy and Immunology, 1972
Emergency Medicine, 1979

Dr. James Surver) (left) conducts tumor clinic for staff and residents (ca. 1950).

Margaret R. Albanese
Georgetown

Clement Au
Temple

Valerie Arkoosh
Nebraska

Christopher H. Anthony
Jefferson

John D. Angstadt
Jefferson

Robert J. Andrews
S.U.N.Y. Upstate

Robin L. Albert
Penn State

Halette L. Anderson
Jefferson

Charles L.V. Anderson
Indiana

Jandel T. Allen-Davis
Dartmouth

David A. Allan
Jefferson

Laila Alidina
Med. Col. Penna

Postgraduate Alumni

Name	Med School	R Specialty	R Year	F Specialty	F Year
Abboud, Elias M.	State Univ. Liege (Belgium)	Pediatrics	1987	Allergy and Immun	1989
Abdel-Misih, Mona	Assuit Univ. (Egypt)	Anesthesiology	1983		
Abell, Charles F., Jr.	Jefferson	Ob/Gyn	1961		
Abkar, Kevork B.	Univ. Damascus	Internal Medicine	1975		
Abramowitz, Jodi S.	N.J. Sch. Osteo. Med.	Internal Medicine	1986		
Abramowitz, Richard P.	Jefferson			Cardiovas Dis	1983
Abrams, Jeffrey S.	S.U.N.Y., Upstate	Orthop Surg	1985		
Abrams, Jerome	Jefferson	Ob/Gyn	1958		
Abrams, Peggy L.	Med. Coll. Pennsylvania	Phys Med/Rehab	1985		
Aceto, Thomas, Jr.	Jefferson	Pediatrics	1956		
Acharya, Ranjit V.	Municipal Med. Coll. (India)	Neurology	1977		
Adams, George H.N.	Med. Univ. South Carolina	Psychiatry	1968		
Adams, Laurence J.	Georgetown Univ.	Neuro Surg	1959		
Adle, Emir H.	Univ. Paris			Endocrinology	1957
Adleman, Ronald W.	Pennsylvania State Univ.			Diag Rad	1985
Adler, Alan G.	Tufts Univ.	Internal Medicine	1979		
Adlesic, Edward C.	Pittsburgh Dental Sch.	Oral & Max Surg	1984		
Adom, Edwin A.	Meharry Med. Coll.	Psychiatry	1972		
Agarwal, Ramesh C.	S.N. Med. Coll. (India)	Internal Medicine	1968		
Agris, Joseph	Albany Med. Coll.	General Surgery	1974		
Agro, Angelo S.	Jefferson	Otolaryngology	1980		
Aikey, Barry R.	Jefferson	Pathology	1969		
Alavi, Freydoun	Univ. Teheran	Internal Medicine	1967		
Albanese, Margaret R.	Georgetown Univ.	Orthop Surg	1982		
Albert, Robin L.	Pennsylvania State Univ.	Radiology	1984		
Albert, Susan J.	Philadelphia Coll. Osteo. Med.	Anesthesiology	1982		
Alderfer, Henry H.	Jefferson	Internal Medicine	1947		
Alegria, Daniel S.	Univ. California, San Diego	Family Practice	1979		
Alessi, Paul J.	Univ. Osteo. Med., Des Moines			Infectious Diseases	1984
Alexander, Edward J.	Cornell Univ.	Phys Med/Rehab	1987		
Alfred, Harry C.	Univ. Tennessee	Radiology	1955		
Alidina, Laila	Med. Coll. Pennsylvania			Pediatric Allergy	1981
Allan, David A.	Jefferson	Internal Medicine	1979		
Allen, Amy J.	Jefferson	Pediatrics	1988		
Allen, James E.	Jefferson	Urological Surgery	1990		
Allen, Lisa S.	Hahnemann Univ.			Rheumatology	1988
Allen-Davis, Jandel T.	Dartmouth Med. Sch.	Ob/Gyn	1988		
Alliegro, George M.	E. Virginia Med. Sch.	Internal Medicine	1986		
Aloia, John F.	Creighton Univ.			Diabetes	1969
Altamirano, Hugo G.	Nat. Univ. Cordoba (Argentina)	Pediatrics	1976	Pediatric Allergy	1978
Altemus, L. Reed, Jr.	Jefferson	Radiology	1962		
Altman, Mark P.	Albert Einstein Coll. Med.			Hand Surgery	1989
Altman, Wayne J.	Rutgers Med. Coll.			Hand Surgery	1984
Altschuler, Robert G.	Jefferson	Internal Medicine	1972		
Amadeo, Jose H.	Jefferson	General Surgery	1957		
Amadio, Peter	Jefferson			Hand Surgery	1981
Amoroso, Michael L.	New Jersey Coll. Med.	Anesthesiology	1984		
Amsel, Sheldon	Jefferson	Internal Medicine	1964		
Amsterdam, Jay D.	Jefferson	Psychiatry	1977		
Anderson, Charles L.V.	Indiana Univ.			Pulm Dis	1985
Anderson, David J.	S.U.N.Y., Upstate	Family Practice	1987		
Anderson, Dudley B.	Univ. Virginia			Hematology	1971
Anderson, Gustav W.	Jefferson	Neurology	1952		

Name	Med School	R Specialty	R Year	F Specialty	F Year
Anderson, Halette L.	Jefferson	Pediatrics	1988		
Anderson, Kenneth F.	Harvard Med. Sch.	Internal Medicine	1960		
Anderson, William J.	Univ. Texas, Galveston			Hand Surgery	1983
Andracchio, Vincent C.	Jefferson	Anesthesiology	1964		
Andrews, Robert J.	S.U.N.Y., Upstate	Internal Medicine	1979		
Angelides, Angelo P.	Long Island Sch. Med.	Internal Medicine	1950		
Angstadt, John D.	Jefferson	General Surgery	1986	Transpl Surg	1987
Annos, Thomas	George Washington Univ.	Ob/Gyn	1976		
Anson, Peter M.	Jefferson	Orthop Surg	1977		
Anthony, Christopher H.	Jefferson	Pathology	1979		
Anticaglia, Joseph R.	Univ. Bologna (Italy)	Otolaryngology	1974		
Anzalone, Deborah A.	Hahnemann Univ.			Nephrology	1989
Aponte, Gonzalo E.	Jefferson	Pathology	1957		
Arena, Mario J.	Georgetown Univ.	Orthop Surg	1984		
Arenas, Apollo M.	Univ. St. Tomas (Philippines)			Neurology	1986
Arger, Peter H.	Univ. Illinois	Radiology	1966		
Arias, Lorraine M.	Virginia Commonwealth Univ.	Anesthesiology	1987		
Arkoosh, Valerie	Univ. Nebraska	Anesthesiology	1990		
Arlinghaus, Frank H., Jr.	Columbia Univ., Coll. P. & S.	Internal Medicine	1983		
Armenti, Frederick	New Jersey Coll. Med.	General Surgery	1989		
Armenti, Vincent T.	Jefferson			Transpl Surg	1990
Armstrong, James S.	Queen's Univ., Belfast			Anesthesiology	1962
Armstrong, Thomas S., Jr.	Jefferson	Orthop Surg	1949		
Aronson, Suellen	S.U.N.Y., Downstate			Neurology	1983
Asbell, Sucha, .	Woman's Med. Coll.	Rad Oncol	1971		
Ashman, Fred C.	Univ. Maryland			Diag Rad	1980
Ashmore, Hugh W.	Jefferson	Pathology	1961		
Asvanitchya, Pensri	Univ. Med. Sc. (Thailand)	Pediatrics	1962		
Athani, Vijay S.	L.T. Municipal Med. Coll. (India)	Urological Surgery	1980		
Athavethi, Emon	Chulalongkorn Univ. (Thailand)	Pediatrics	1967		
Atichartakarn, Vichai	Fac. Med. Siriraj (Thailand)	Internal Medicine	1973		
Atkinson, George W.	Ohio State Univ.	Internal Medicine	1967	Pulm Dis	1970
Atkinson, Gerald R.	Jefferson	Internal Medicine	1959		
Atkinson, John B.	Jefferson	Internal Medicine	1953	Hematology	1954
Au, Clement	Temple Univ.	Family Practice	1985		
Aulicino, Pat L.	New York Med. Coll.			Hand Surgery	1981
Auritt, William A.	Jefferson	Pediatrics	1978	Pediatric Allergy	1980
Azimi, Farhad	Albert Ludwigs Univ. (Germany)	Radiology	1973		
Azzato, John A.	Jefferson	Orthop Surg	1975		

You must always be students, learning and unlearning till your life's end, and if you are not prepared to follow your profession in this spirit, I implore you to leave its ranks and betake yourself to some third-class trade.

Joseph, Lord Lister (1827–1912)

Harvey S. Brodovsky
Manitoba

Leigh Baltuch
Jefferson

Beth Barnet
George Washington

Ronald E. Ballek
Temple

Ronald B. Barnett
Emory

Susan K. Ball
Univ. Pennsylvania

David J. Becker
New Jersey Col. Med.

Peter W. Bauer
Univ. Pennsylvania

Nancy Beggs
Temple

Frederick L. Becker
Jefferson

John H. Benner, IV
Jefferson

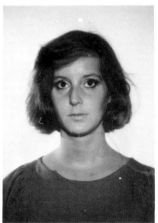

Carole G. Ben-Maimon
Jefferson

Name	Med School	R Specialty	R Year	F Specialty	F Year
Babaria, Ashokkumar R.	B.J. Med. Coll. (India)	Diag Rad	1985		
Babigian, Armen T.	UMDNJ, NJ Med. Sch.	Neurology	1988		
Babitt, Henry I.	Jefferson	Internal Medicine	1967		
Bacevich, Bernard B.	Univ. Cincinnati	Orthop Surg	1972		
Bacharach, Benjamin	Jefferson	General Surgery	1963		
Bacharach, Herbert J.	Jefferson	Ophthalmology	1955		
Bae, Sung Ho	Seoul Nat. Univ.	Neurology	1979		
Bagby, Ramon	Jefferson	Orthop Surg	1978		
Bai, Penugonda Dwaraki	Andhra Univ. (India)	Pediatrics	1971		
Baird, James W.	Johns Hopkins Univ.	Phys Med/Rehab	1980		
Baker, Robert L.	Univ. Pennsylvania	Anesthesiology	1975		
Baker, Wilmoth H., III	Univ. Miami	Anesthesiology	1988		
Balchandani, Rajkumari	Univ. of the Philippines			Rad Oncol	1979
Ball, David S.	Philadelphia Coll. Osteo. Med.			Diag Rad	1987
Ball, Roberta R.	Philadelphia Coll. Osteo. Med.	Psychiatry	1984		
Ball, Susan K.	Univ. Pennsylvania	Psychiatry	1985		
Ballas, Samir K.	American Univ. (Lebanon)			Hematology	1972
Ballek, Ronald E.	Temple Univ.	Internal Medicine	1976	Hematology	1978
Balogh, Robert J., Jr.	Hahnemann Univ.	Emerg Med	1987		
Balshi, Stephen F.	Jefferson	Otolaryngology	1959		
Baltarowich, Oksana	Wayne State Univ.			Diag Rad	1981
Baltuch, Leigh	Jefferson	Psychiatry	1986		
Baltzell, William H.	Jefferson	Otolaryngology	1953		
Banas, Eby L.	Far Eastern Univ. (Philippines)	Neurology	1978		
Bancks, Nicholas H.	Jefferson			Diag Rad	1979
Banner, Marc P.	Jefferson	Radiology	1975		
Bapat, Ashok R.	Univ. Bombay			Blood Banking	1986
Barakat, Adel R.	Cairo Univ.			Hand Surgery	1971
Baran, James J.	Jefferson	General Surgery	1990		
Baranski, Edward J.	Jefferson	General Surgery	1964		
Baraz, Lory E.	UMDNJ-Rutgers	Internal Medicine	1988		
Barlee, Amnat	Chulalongkorn Univ.(Thailand)	Pediatrics	1969		
Barnet, Beth	George Washington Univ.	Family Practice	1988		
Barnett, Ronald B.	Emory Univ.	Internal Medicine	1987	Pulm Dis	1989
Barnhart, Jay S., Jr.	Jefferson	Pathology	1983		
Barringer, Lydia C.R.	Univ. St. Tomas (Philippines)			Anesthesiology	1969
Barth, Klemens H.	Albert Ludwigs Univ. (Germany)	Radiology	1973		
Barto, Robert E., Jr.	Jefferson	General Surgery	1952		
Bartolanzo, Robert A.	New York Med. Coll.	Pediatrics	1986		
Barton, Hugh T.	Med. Coll. South Carolina	Internal Medicine	1954		
Bartone, Francis F.	Jefferson	Urological Surgery	1963		
Bartuska, Doris G.	Woman's Med. Coll.			Endocrinology	1958
Basavanand, Nirmala	Univ. Calcutta			Pediatric Allergy	1976
Basile, Myrtha E.	Univ. Pittsburgh			Hematology	1988
Bator, Susan	UMDNJ, NJ Med. Sch.			Blood Banking	1990
Batuman, Olcay	Hacettepe Univ. (Turkey)			Hematology	1983
Bauer, Francis X.	Jefferson	General Surgery	1946		
Bauer, Harold E.	Jefferson	Pathology	1964		
Bauer, Peter W.	Univ. Pennsylvania	Family Practice	1982		
Bauer, Richard D.	Jefferson	Internal Medicine	1949		
Bauman, John M.	Philadelphia Coll. Osteo. Med.	Anesthesiology	1987		
Bautista, Eliseo M.	Far Eastern Univ. (Philippines)	Internal Medicine	1968		
Baxt, Jan L.	Philadelphia Coll. Osteo. Med.	Neurology	1975		

Name	Med School	R Specialty	R Year	F Specialty	F Year
Bayer, Arnold S.	Temple Univ.	Internal Medicine	1973		
Baylis, John C.	Jefferson	Pathology	1973		
Bazinet, Pauline	Univ. Ottawa			Nephrology	1970
Beasley, Barbara L.	Woman's Med. Coll.	Neurology	1971		
Beatty, Albert C.	Hahnemann Univ.			Cardiothor Surgery	1973
Beatty, Susan E.	Jefferson	Internal Medicine	1976	Pulm Dis	1978
Beaubien, Richard W.	Tufts Univ.	Oral & Max Surg	1967		
Beaumont, Pierre H.	Laval Univ. (Canada)			Hand Surgery	1977
Becker, Andrea J.	Jefferson	Internal Medicine	1983		
Becker, David J.	New Jersey Coll. Med.	Internal Medicine	1986		
Becker, Edward F.	Jefferson	Ophthalmology	1961		
Becker, Francis E.	Georgetown Univ.	Internal Medicine	1985		
Becker, Frederick L.	Jefferson	Psychiatry	1984		
Becker, Gary L.	Jefferson	Dermatology	1979		
Becker, Joseph D.	Philadelphia Coll. Osteo. Med.	Pediatrics	1984		
Beddings, Alejandro	Univ. Chile			Hand Surgery	1982
Beetel, Christopher J.	Jefferson	General Surgery	1965		
Beggs, David W.	Jefferson	Dermatology	1965		
Beggs, Nancy	Temple Univ.	Internal Medicine	1989		
Beggs, Robert A.	Jefferson			Pulm Dis	1969
Behnam, Kazem	Univ. Teheran			Gyn Oncol	1978
Behringer, W. Hayman	Temple Univ.	Otolaryngology	1974		
Beil, Susan J.	S.U.N.Y., Stony Brook	Ob/Gyn	1989		
Bein, Norman N.	Hahnemann Univ.	General Surgery	1977		
Belafsky, Mark L.	Chicago Med. Sch.	Otolaryngology	1971		
Belafsky, Robert B.	S.U.N.Y., Downstate	Otolaryngology	1977		
Belfar, Hanae	New Jersey Coll. Med.			Diag Rad	1986
Bell, Joseph S., III	Med. Coll. Virginia	Internal Medicine	1979		
Bell, Thomas G.	Jefferson	Internal Medicine	1962		
Bellin, Bruce D.	Med. Coll. Wisconsin	Ophthalmology	1976		
Bellin, Harvey J.	Jefferson	Pathology	1972		
Belmont, Ernesto	Nat. Univ. Mexico			Repro Endo	1955
Ben Kinney, James A.	Hahnemann Univ.	Emerg Med	1988		
Ben-Maimon, Carole G.	Jefferson	Internal Medicine	1988	Nephrology	1990
Ben-Menachem, Yoram	Hebrew Univ. (Israel)	Radiology	1972	Radiology	1971
Benchakanchana, Vilai	Univ. Med. Sc. (Thailand)			Repro Endo	1956
Bender, Bruce R.	Jefferson			Rheumatology	1985
Beneski, Daniel A.	Jefferson	Anesthesiology	1987		
Benfield, Thomas C.	Jefferson	Psychiatry	1981		
Benitez, Rolando	Univ. Zulia (Venezuela)			Endocrinology	1960
Benjamin, Alvin D.	Yale Univ.	Radiology	1963		
Benjamin, Sanford H.	Univ. Connecticut	Internal Medicine	1984	Gastroenterology	1987
Benner, John H., IV	Jefferson	Orthop Surg	1978		
Bennett, William W.	Med. Coll Wisconsin	Orthop Surg	1982		
Benovitz, Burton S.	Jefferson	Ob/Gyn	1960		
Berenholz, Leonard P.	Hahnemann Univ.	Otolaryngology	1988		
Berg, Paul K.	Univ. Michigan	Radiology	1964		
Berger, Mark S.	Univ. Virginia	Internal Medicine	1984		
Bergfield, Thomas G.	Creighton Univ.			Hand Surgery	1987
Bergquist, Erick J.	Jefferson	Internal Medicine	1976		
Berguson, Paul D.	Jefferson	Anesthesiology	1978		
Berk, Theodore	Jefferson	Internal Medicine	1982	Gastroenterology	1985
Berlinerblau, Michele M.	Ross Univ. (Dominica)	Psychiatry	1990		

Name	Med School	R Specialty	R Year	F Specialty	F Year
Berman, Jacob H.	Rutgers Med. Coll.	Psychiatry	1987		
Bernstein, Larry N.	S.U.N.Y., Syracuse	Phys Med/Rehab	1987		
Bernstine, Richard T.	Jefferson	Ob/Gyn	1966		
Berrettini, Wade H.	Jefferson	Psychiatry	1980		
Berry, Craig C.	Rutgers Med. Coll.			Cardiovas Dis	1988
Berry, Gerard T.	Jefferson	Pediatrics	1978		
Bertolette, Richard D.	Jefferson	Psychiatry	1964		
Bertoli, Carol L.	Hahnemann Univ.	Radiology	1986		
Berwind, Robert T.	Jefferson	Urological Surgery	1970		
Bhatt, Nayan	Univ. Sheffield (U.K.)	Internal Medicine	1988		
Bickerton, Michael W.	Jefferson	Urological Surgery	1984		
Biddle, Theodore L.	Temple Univ.	Internal Medicine	1970		
Bidot, Pascual	Univ. Puerto Rico	Internal Medicine	1975		
Bidula, Maureen M.	Temple Univ.			Diag Rad	1984
Biermann, William A.	Jefferson	Internal Medicine	1978		
Bigelow, Karen S.	Hahnemann Univ.	Pediatrics	1990		
Billings, William E., Jr.	Boston Univ.			Hand Surgery	1973
Binns, Carl B., Jr.	Jefferson	Radiology	1974		
Birch, Paul K.	Univ. Buffalo			Ob/Gyn	1949
Blake, Thomas D.	Univ. Virginia	Family Practice	1982		
Blanch, Joseph J.	Jefferson	Urological Surgery	1954		
Bland, C. Brinley	Jefferson	Ob/Gyn	1950		
Blatt, Herbert L.	Temple Univ.	Ophthalmology	1977		
Blaum, Louis C., Jr.	Jefferson	General Surgery	1977	Cardiothor Surg	1979
Blewitt, George A.	Jefferson			Nephrology	1967
Blizzard, John J.	Jefferson	Internal Medicine	1958		
Block, Robert A.	Jefferson	Ob/Gyn	1973		
Blomain, Eric W.	Jefferson	General Surgery	1978		
Bloom, Beatrice F.	Albany Med. Coll.	Rad Oncol	1984		
Bloomgarden, Raphael T.	Wayne State Univ.	Internal Medicine	1984		
Blum, Larry W.	Howard Univ.	Neurology	1985	Neurology	1986
Blum, Matthew D.	George Washington Univ.	Otolaryngology	1974		
Blumberg, David L.	Univ. Guadalajara (Mexico)	Anesthesiology	1985		
Blumberg, Kalman D.	Univ. Miami			Orthop Surg	1990
Bodi, Tibor	Pazmany Univ. (Hungary)			Gastroenterology	1957
Boger, Amy S.	Univ. Pennsylvania	Pediatrics	1984		
Bogran, Marco A.	Fac. Medicina (Honduras)	Internal Medicine	1971		
Bolamperti, Richard A.	Creighton Univ.	Radiology	1964		
Bolten, Karl A.	Univ. Jena (Germany)			Repro Endo	1954
Bonatti, William D.	Jefferson	Ophthalmology	1963		
Bonner, Dennis J.	Jefferson	Phys Med/Rehab	1979		
Bonner, Gregory F.	Univ. Pittsburgh	Internal Medicine	1987		
Booth, Kevin R.	Univ. Michigan	Neurology	1989	Neurology	1990
Boova, Robert S.	Jefferson	General Surgery	1982	Cardiothor Surg	1985
Boran, Robert P., Jr.	Jefferson	Orthop Surg	1983		
Boreen, Stuart M.	Jefferson	Anesthesiology	1990		
Borgelt, Bruce B.	Jefferson	Rad Oncol	1979		
Borghesan, Claudio	Univ. Palermo (Italy)	Otolaryngology	1976		
Borkowski, Bernard B.	Jefferson	General Surgery	1959		
Borkowski, Teresa Ann	Jefferson	Dermatology	1989		
Borkowski, Winslow J.	Jefferson	Neurology	1946		
Borofsky, Michael A.	Univ. Pittsburgh	Internal Medicine	1987		
Borthwick, Thomas R.	Jefferson	Internal Medicine	1976	Gastroenterology	1978

Name	Med School	R Specialty	R Year	F Specialty	F Year
Bose, Bikash	Maulana Azad Med. Coll. (India)	Neuro Surg	1984		
Botvin, Julie G.	Woman's Med. Coll.	Phys Med/Rehab	1973		
Bowen, Anne C.	Univ. Pittsburgh	Internal Medicine	1988		
Bowens, Christopher A.	Rutgers Med. Coll.	Internal Medicine	1985	Cardiovas Dis	1987
Bower, Edward B.	Jefferson	General Surgery	1975		
Bower, John R.	Jefferson	Ob/Gyn	1970		
Bowman, Herbert S.	Jefferson	Internal Medicine	1951	Hematology	1954
Bowman, Michael W.	Univ. Cincinnati			Hand Surgery	1986
Bowman, Warren D., Jr.	Univ. Pennsylvania			Hematology	1960
Boyd, Robert L.	Jefferson	Internal Medicine	1979	Hematology	1982
Boyle, Grace K.	Med. Coll. Pennsylvania			Diag Rad	1985
Boysen, Theophilus H., III	Jefferson	Ob/Gyn	1948		
Brace, Frederick H.	Univ. Pennsylvania			Child Psychiatry	1987
Bradley, Earl B.	Temple Univ.	Pediatrics	1986		
Brady, Luther W., Jr.	George Washington Univ.	Radiology	1955		
Bragonier, J. Robert	Univ. Nebraska	Ob/Gyn	1968		
Braid, Stanton M.	Temple Univ.	Oral & Max Surg	1976		
Brajer, Jason H.	Hahnemann Univ.	Anesthesiology	1985		
Branch, Homer M.	Wayne State Univ.			Diag Rad	1985
Brandau, A. Gordon, Jr.	Jefferson	Internal Medicine	1971	Jefferson	
Brandfass, Robert T.	Jefferson	Ob/Gyn	1956		
Brau, Alan S.	Mount Sinai Sch. Med.	Internal Medicine	1989		
Braun, Armand	Inst. Med. Bucharest	Psychiatry	1986		
Brazina, Gary E.	Temple Univ.	Orthop Surg	1979		
Breecker, Steven W.	Tufts Univ.			Cardiovas Dis	1988
Brennan, James E.	Jefferson	Otolaryngology	1957		
Brennan, Martin T.	Jefferson	Otolaryngology	1965		
Brennan, Richard E.	Jefferson	Radiology	1976		
Brent, Lawrence	Jefferson	Internal Medicine	1982	Rheumatology	1984
Bresler, Priscilla A.	S.U.N.Y., Buffalo	Internal Medicine	1987		
Bridenbaugh, G. Alan	Jefferson	Internal Medicine	1982	Cardiovas Dis	1984
Brier, Jonathan A.	S.U.N.Y., Syracuse	Internal Medicine	1990		
Briones, Jose C., Jr.	Univ. St. Tomas (Philippines)	Ophthalmology	1974		
Broad, Louis T.	Jefferson	Internal Medicine	1977	Gastroenterology	1979
Broad, Todd H.	Jefferson	Anesthesiology	1985		
Brodovsky, Harvey S.	Univ. Manitoba	Internal Medicine	1961		
Brodsky, Stuart L.	Jefferson	Urological Surgery	1975		
Brody, Leonard A.	Temple Univ.			Hand Surgery	1985
Brogadir, Stuart P.	Cornell Univ.			Gastroenterology	1983
Bronstein, Merrill H.	Chicago Med.Sch.	General Surgery	1971		
Brooks, Charles M.	Jefferson	Internal Medicine	1971		
Brooks, Ronald J.	Hahnemann Univ.	Internal Medicine	1980		
Brosbe, Donna L.	Temple Univ.	Pediatrics	1983		
Brosbe, Robert J.	Med. Coll. Pennsylvania	Internal Medicine	1982		
Browder, Joe H.	Univ. Tennessee	Anesthesiology	1985		
Brown, Christopher L.	Jefferson	Radiology	1976		
Brown, Earl R.	Temple Univ.	Family Practice	1980		
Brown, Joseph S.	Jefferson	Internal Medicine	1952		
Brown, Leonard R.	S.U.N.Y., Downstate	Internal Medicine	1978		
Brown, Marion L.	Philadelphia Coll. Osteo. Med.	Ob/Gyn	1982		
Brown, Mark D.	Jefferson	Orthop Surg	1971		
Brown, Patti J.	Jefferson	Phys Med/Rehab	1990		
Brown, Richard S.	Jefferson	General Surgery	1957		

Name	Med School	R Specialty	R Year	F Specialty	F Year
Brown, Sheila	Temple Univ.	Anesthesiology	1974		
Brown, Stuart B.	Jefferson	Neurology	1963		
Brown, Sylvan	Jefferson	Internal Medicine	1974	Rheumatology	1976
Brownstein, P. Kenneth	Hahnemann Univ.	Urological Surgery	1976		
Brumback, Robert J.	Univ. Maryland	Orthop Surg	1982		
Brummett, Richard R.	Univ. Kansas	Anesthesiology	1990		
Brunet, Jacques	Laval Univ. (Canada)			Endocrinology	1956
Bryan, J. Elder, Jr.	Jefferson	Urological Surgery	1953		
Bryant, James D.	Vanderbilt Univ.	Family Practice	1982		
Budiamal, Lita R.	Gadjah Mada Univ. (Indonesia)	Anesthesiology	1981		
Buelow, Robert G.	Temple Univ.	Internal Medicine	1971	Gastroenterology	1973
Bulova, Stephen I.	Harvard Univ.			Hematology	1971
Bunyor, Agnes K.	Budapest	Ophthalmology	1968		
Buranasiri, Punya	Univ. Med. Sc. (Thailand)	Neurology	1972		
Burke, Bernard S.	Jefferson	Internal Medicine	1982		
Burke, Gerald V.	Hahnemann Univ.	Ob/Gyn	1983	Repro Endo	1985
Burke, James F., Jr.	Jefferson	Internal Medicine	1971	Nephrology	1972
Burkhard, Edward J.	Georgetown Univ.	Pathology	1967		
Burris, Alfred C.	Howard Univ.			Cardiovas Dis	1979
Burt, Theresa A.	Jefferson	General Surgery	1977		
Busch, Scott L.	N.J. Sch. Osteo. Med.	Otolaryngology	1984		
Butler, Herbert H., Jr.	Jefferson	Internal Medicine	1965		
Butler, Michael J.	Ohio State Univ.	Otolaryngology	1975		
Butt, Muhammed T.	King Edward Med. Coll. (Pakistan)	Internal Medicine	1975	Gastroenterology	1976
Buxbaum, Michael	Univ. London	Psychiatry	1984		
Byrne, Jessica P.	Georgetown Univ.	Psychiatry	1983		
Byrne, Kevin J.	Georgetown Univ.	Radiology	1983	Radiology	1984
Byrnes, Christine A.	Jefferson	Internal Medicine	1981		

John R. Prehatny (surgical resident, 1964, left) oversees work in Dr. Gibbon's laboratory

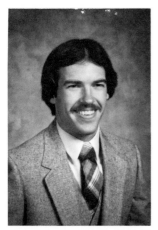

Wayne N. Campbell
Georgetown

Mary F. Callahan
Temple

Laura A. Cannavo
Med. Col. Penna

Jose F. Caro
Montevideo

Mary Ann P. Casey
Temple

Kevin P. Caputo
S.U.N.Y., Syracuse

Ronald Carabelli
Georgetown

Vivian Charneco
Ponce Sch. Med.

Frank D. Caporusso
Georgetown

Gabriel Ceron
Nat. Univ. Colombia

Htesook Chang
Seoul National

John V. Cattie
Jefferson

Name	Med School	R Specialty	R Year	F Specialty	F Year
Cable, Joseph A.	Philadelphia Coll. Osteo. Med.			Pulm Dis	1983
Cahn, Edward L.	Jefferson	Internal Medicine	1965	Medical Oncology	1966
Caicedo-Cuellar, Jorge E.	Univ. Central Venezuela			Repro Endo	1959
Calabrese, Anthony J.	Jefferson			Gastroenterology	1977
Callahan, Clara A.	Med. Coll. Pennsylvania	Pediatrics	1980	Pediatrics	1982
Callahan, Mary F.	Temple Univ.	Family Practice	1988		
Callery, Gerald E.	Jefferson	Orthop Surg	1952		
Calloway, Daniel M.	Univ. So. Florida	General Surgery	1990		
Calmes, Robert L.	Baylor Coll. Med.	Neurology	1969		
Cameron, Roger W.	Coll. Osteo. Med., Kansas City			Hand Surgery	1983
Camishion, Rudolph C.	Jefferson	General Surgery	1959		
Campbell, Kevin M.	Jefferson	Anesthesiology	1986		
Campbell, Wayne N.	Georgetown Univ.	Internal Medicine	1984		
Campbell, William J.	Hahnemann Univ.	Dermatology	1950		
Campo, Martin-del Enrique	Nat. Univ. Mexico	Child Psychiatry	1980		
Campos, Rigoberto	Univ. Barcelona	Neurology	1959		
Canale, S. Terry	Univ. Tennessee	Orthop Surg	1973		
Candia, Andrea	Hahnemann Univ.	Diag Rad	1984		
Cannavo, Laura A.	Med. Coll. Pennsylvania	Ophthalmology	1978		
Cantillo, Joaquin	Univ. Puerto Rico	Anesthesiology	1988		
Cantor, Ronald I.	Temple Univ.	Internal Medicine	1973	Medical Oncology	1975
Cantor, William L.	Seton Hall	Otolaryngology	1970		
Canty, Thomas P.	Jefferson	Rad Oncol	1989		
Capelli, John P.	Jefferson	Internal Medicine	1965	Nephrology	1968
Capetanakis, Nicholas	Univ. Athens			Gyn Oncol	1965
Caplan, Howard J.	Jefferson	Neurology	1979		
Caplan, Howard S.	Univ. Maryland			Hand Surgery	1973
Caplan, Lawrence H.	Northwestern Univ.	Radiology	1963		
Caplan, Stephen R.	Univ. Virginia	Internal Medicine	1969		
Capone, Gaetano J.	Jefferson	Internal Medicine	1982		
Caporusso, Frank D.	Georgetown Univ.	Internal Medicine	1981		
Capriotti, Robert J.	Hahnemann Univ.	Otolaryngology	1970		
Caputo, Kevin P.	S.U.N.Y., Syracuse	Psychiatry	1989		
Carabasi, R. Anthony, III	Jefferson	General Surgery	1982		
Carabelli, Ronald	Georgetown Univ.	Internal Medicine	1982		
Carapellotti, Richard A.	Jefferson	Ob/Gyn	1983		
Carden, Edward T.	Jefferson	Otolaryngology	1971		
Carlucci, Ronald J.	Creighton Univ.	General Surgery	1965		
Carmany, Thomas B.	Jefferson	Pathology	1967		
Carnabuci, Guy	Jefferson	Dermatology	1963		
Caro, Jaime	Univ. Chile			Hematology	1979
Caro, Jose F.	Fac. Med. Montevideo	Internal Medicine	1977	Internal Medicine	1978
Carrig, Thomas F.	Jefferson	Anesthesiology	1972		
Carroll, James F.	Jefferson	Urological Surgery	1958		
Carroll, John F.	S.U.N.Y., Downstate	Pediatrics	1975		
Carroll, Joseph L.	Jefferson	Internal Medicine	1953	Gastroenterology	1951
Carroll, Robert T.	Jefferson	Internal Medicine	1954	Hematology	1956
Carroll, Stanton F.	Temple Univ.	General Surgery	1976		
Carson, John N., III	Jefferson	Internal Medicine	1975	Nephrology	1977
Carter, Debbie R.	Jefferson	Child Psychiatry	1988		
Carter, Kenneth G.	Louisiana State Univ.	Radiology	1972		
Carunchio, Michael J.	Jefferson	Neurology	1980	Neurology	1981
Caruso, Anthony P.	Jefferson	Otolaryngology	1979		

Name	Med School	R Specialty	R Year	F Specialty	F Year
Caruso, Vincent G.	Jefferson	Otolaryngology	1972		
Casey, Anne M.	Temple Univ.			Diag Rad	1990
Casey, Mary Ann P.	Temple Univ.	Pediatrics	1989		
Caskey, William B.	Columbia Univ., Coll. P. & S.	Internal Medicine	1968	Diabetes	1969
Cassidy, Robert H.	Oregon Health Sci. Univ.	Anesthesiology	1985		
Casta, Aurora M.	Univ. Puerto Rico	Child Psychiatry	1988		
Castells, Salvador	Univ. Barcelona	Pediatrics	1966		
Castro, Jaime H.	Univ. San Marcos (Peru)			Endocrinology	1979
Castro, Jennie	Univ. Salamanca (Spain)	Psychiatry	1973		
Castro, Rosella D.	Manila Central Univ.	Pediatrics	1973	Pediatrics	1974
Catalano, Patricia M.	Albany Med. Coll.			Hematology	1977
Cates, Haynes B., Jr.	Jefferson	Urological Surgery	1985		
Cattie, John V.	Jefferson	General Surgery	1979		
Cautilli, Richard A., Jr.	Jefferson	Orthop Surg	1990		
Cautilli, Richard A.	Jefferson	Orthop Surg	1963		
Cavalieri, Thomas A.	Univ. Osteo. Med., Des Moines	Internal Medicine	1980		
Cawley, Noel S.	Med. Coll. Pennsylvania	Pathology	1977		
Cech, Rosanne	Hahnemann Univ.			Allergy and Immun	1984
Celano, Paul	Mt. Sinai Sch. Med.	Internal Medicine	1984		
Cenedese, Luis A.	S.U.N.Y., Downstate			Hand Surgery	1989
Center, Sol	Univ. Minnesota			Diag Rad	1981
Cera, Peter J., Jr.	Jefferson	Pathology	1966		
Ceron, Gabriel	Nat. Univ. Colombia	Radiology	1980		
Certa, Kenneth M.	Jefferson	Psychiatry	1983		
Cerza, Paul F.	Jefferson	Phys Med/Rehab	1978		
Cestero, Rafael V.M.	Univ. Puerto Rico			Nephrology	1968
Chain, Jeffrey R.	Jefferson	Orthop Surg	1988		
Chakravarty, Mira	Univ. Calcutta			Diag Rad	1980
Chalfant, Richard S.	Jefferson	Ob/Gyn	1977		
Chalfin, Lenn J.	Jefferson	General Surgery	1981		
Chambers, Christopher V.	Duke Univ.	Family Practice	1983		
Chan, Asteria C.	Univ. of the Philippines			Ped Hema-Oncol	1960
Chan, Tak-Sek	Nat. Taiwan Univ.			Ped Cardi	1967
Chandler, Allen E.	Jefferson	Pediatrics	1964		
Chang, Hyesook	Seoul Nat. Univ.	Rad Oncol	1980		
Chang, Thomas S.	Washington Univ.	Radiology	1990		
Chaplin, Stanley S.	Jefferson	Ob/Gyn	1970	Repro Endo	1969
Chappell, Thomas E.	Tulane Univ.	Internal Medicine	1985		
Charneco, Vivian	Ponce Sch. Med.	Child Psychiatry	1986		
Chase, Jeffrey S.	Med. Coll. Pennsylvania	Ob/Gyn	1980		
Chase, William V.	Jefferson	General Surgery	1971		
Chatzinoff, Martin	UMDNJ, Newark	Internal Medicine	1985	Gastroenterology	1987
Chatzkel, Sherrie L.	Temple Univ.			Diag Rad	1981
Chavarria-Bonequi, Cesar	Univ. Mexico			Endocrinology	1957
Chawla, Shanta	Maulana Azad Med. Coll. (India)	Internal Medicine	1977		
Cheah, Beng-hong	Temple Univ.	Diag Rad	1982		
Check, Jerome H.	Hahnemann Univ.			Repro Endo	1975
Cheli, David J.	Med. Coll. Pennsylvania	Family Practice	1977		
Chen, Cheng-Hsiung	Nat. Taiwan Univ.	General Surgery	1975		
Chen, Wei-Fan	Nat. Taiwan Univ.	General Surgery	1974		
Chen, Yuh Teh	Nat. Taiwan Univ.	Phys Med/Rehab	1976		
Cheney, Maryalice	Chicago Med. Sch.	General Surgery	1986	Colon and Rec Surg	1987
Cheng, Ping Nan	Taipei Med. Coll.	Neuro Surg	1979		

Name	Med School	R Specialty	R Year	F Specialty	F Year
Cherner, Rachmel	Jefferson	Internal Medicine	1959		
Chernow, Susan	Albert Einstein Coll. Med.	Psychiatry	1981		
Cherry, Kenneth L.	Jefferson	Orthop Surg	1990		
Cheung, Lily So-King	McGill Univ.	Internal Medicine	1967	Hematology	1977
Childs, Julian H.	Howard Univ.	Medical Oncology	1951	Medical Oncology	1952
Chilton, Mark D.	Jefferson	Orthop Surg	1986		
Ching, Nathaniel P.H.	Jefferson	General Surgery	1964		
Chiriboga, Augusto	Catholic Univ. (Ecuador)	Anesthesiology	1981		
Chirife, Ana Maria	Univ. Buenos Aires			Pathology	1977
Chitale, Vidyadhar	Univ. Bombay	Neuro Surg	1986		
Cho, Inwha	Yonsei Univ. (S. Korea)	Neurology	1985		
Chodoff, Paul	Jefferson	Neurology	1943		
Chodosh, Bruce T.	Univ. Virginia	Internal Medicine	1968	Hematology	1969
Chodroff, Paul H.	Jefferson	Neuro Surg	1968		
Chohan, Mohammad A.	King Edward Med. Coll. (Pakistan)	Anesthesiology	1968		
Choi, Heung J.	Severance Med. Coll. (Korea)			Gastroenterology	1964
Choi, Hong Yul	Yonsei Univ. (Korea)	Pathology	1979		
Chollak, William L.	Jefferson	Orthop Surg	1977		
Chotiner, Harold C.	S.U.N.Y., Downstate			Repro Endo	1975
Christopher, Theodore tA.	Mt. Sinai Sch. Med.	Emerg Med	1986		
Christy, Michael G.	Jefferson	General Surgery	1962		
Chu, Elsie Wing-Suen	Univ. Saskatchewan			Pediatrics	1965
Chu, Mu Tek	Univ. Singapore	Dermatology	1983		
Chu, Philip B.T.	St. John's Univ. (China)			Pathology	1949
Chumdermpadetsuk, Saowani	Chulalongkorn Univ. (Thailand)	Pediatrics	1962		
Chung, Chan Kook	Yonsei Univ. (S. Korea)	Rad Oncol	1975		
Chung, Linda C.	Jefferson	Internal Medicine	1990		
Cimoch, Paul J.	Jefferson			Gastroenterology	1955
Ciruffo, Ronaldo F.	Univ. Minas Gerais (Brazil)			Hematology	1962
Clark, Donald L.	Jefferson	Anesthesiology	1962		
Clark, Gary S.	Jefferson	Phys Med/Rehab	1978		
Clark, James E.	Jefferson	Internal Medicine	1956		
Clark, Max A.	Coll. Osteo. Med., Kansas City			Gyn Oncol	1983
Clark, Myles H.	Howard Univ.	Pediatrics	1968		
Clark, Scott K.	Hahnemann Univ.	Anesthesiology	1988		
Clarke, Ellen M.	Georgetown Univ.	Internal Medicine	1990		
Clarke, William F.	Univ. Wisconsin	Emerg Med	1988		
Clauhs, Ronald P.	Temple Univ.	Ob/Gyn	1981		
Clayman, Loren Z.	Tufts Univ.	Otolaryngology	1972		
Clayman, Paul F.	Georgetown Univ.	Orthop Surg	1974		
Clayton, John S.	Philadelphia Coll. Osteo. Med.	Psychiatry	1983		
Clearfield, Ronald J.	Hahnemann Univ.	Radiology	1963		
Clement, John A.	Jefferson	Rad Oncol	1974		
Clemmer, Richard I., Jr.	Jefferson	Orthop Surg	1977		
Clemmer, Virginia B.	Jefferson	General Surgery	1976		
Closkey, Gregory M.	Georgetown Univ.	·		Nephrology	1985
Cloud, Laurence P.	Jefferson	Internal Medicine	1956	Endocrinology	1954
Clouse, Roy	Ohio State Univ.	Psychiatry	1975		
Coapman, Rebecca A.	Univ. Rochester	Pathology	1984		
Cobanoglu, Mustafa A.	Ankara Univ.	General Surgery	1979	Cardiothor Surg	1981
Cochran, Terence A.	Ohio State Univ.	General Surgery	1976		
Codispoti, Joseph R.	Jefferson	Internal Medicine	1983		
Coghlan, William P.	Jefferson	General Surgery	1956		

Name	Med School	R Specialty	R Year	F Specialty	F Year
Cohan, Michael R.	UMDNJ Osteo.	Internal Medicine	1987		
Cohen, David L.	Temple Univ.	Orthop Surg	1979		
Cohen, Eric B.	State Univ. Liege (Belgium)	Psychiatry	1986	Child Psychiatry	1988
Cohen, Pamela E.	Temple Univ.	Phys Med/Rehab	1986		
Cohen, Paul S.	Jefferson	Internal Medicine	1975	Pulm Dis	1977
Cohen, Richard I.	Jefferson			Pediatrics	1972
Cohen, Robert M.	Jefferson	Neuro Surg	1971		
Cohen, Steven M.	New York Med. Coll.			Diag Rad	1989
Cohler, Alan	Univ. Pennsylvania	Rad Oncol	1975		
Cohn, C. Harold	Jefferson	General Surgery	1956		
Cohn, David B.	Jefferson	Internal Medicine	1989		
Cohn, Herbert E.	Jefferson	General Surgery	1962		
Cohn, John R.	Jefferson	Internal Medicine	1979		
Coia, Lawrence R.	Temple Univ.	Rad Oncol	1982		
Colbourn, Arthur W.	Jefferson	Internal Medicine	1976	Cardiovas Dis	1978
Colcher, Robert E.	Jefferson	General Surgery	1955		
Cole, Daniel J.	Jefferson	Urological Surgery	1990		
Cole, Frederick L.	Philadelphia Coll. Osteo. Med.	Orthop Surg	1977		
Coleman, John A., Jr.	Tulane Univ.	Otolaryngology	1968		
Coleman-Miller, Beverly	Temple Univ.	Internal Medicine	1984		
Colen, Helen Sass	New York Univ.	Pediatrics	1974		
Coletta, Anthony V.	Jefferson	General Surgery	1984		
Colkitt, Douglas R.	Univ. Pennsylvania	Rad Oncol	1983		
Collins, Michael F.	Univ. Connecticut	Phys Med/Rehab	1985		
Collura, Paul T.	Georgetown Univ.	Radiology	1975		
Colon-deMarti, Luz	Univ. Puerto Rico			Child Psychiatry	1985
Columbus, Karen Schatz	Albert Einstein Coll. Med.	General Surgery	1990		
Columbus, Michael J.	Jefferson	General Surgery	1990		
Comfort, Joseph A., Jr.	Jefferson	Anesthesiology	1974		
Comiter, Donald	Pritzker Sch. Med.	Urological Surgery	1965		
Connelly, Mary Elizabeth	Jefferson	Psychiatry	1977		
Connelly, Thomas J.	Philadelphia Coll. Osteo. Med.	Dermatology	1985		
Conner, J. Hubert	Jefferson	Orthop Surg	1960		
Connerton, George E.	Jefferson	Pathology	1981		
Connolly, Joanna L. M.	Jefferson	Ob/Gyn	1979		
Connor, Anne E.	Jefferson	Phys Med/Rehab	1984		
Conrady, William E.	Jefferson	Radiology	1952		
Conroy, Joseph V.	Jefferson	Neuro Surg	1986		
Conti, Joseph D.	Jefferson	Urological Surgery	1981		
Contrucci, Robert B.	Philadelphia Coll. Osteo. Med.	Otolaryngology	1985		
Cook, Jerome I.	Jefferson	Orthop Surg	1959		
Cook, John F., Jr.	New Jersey Med. Sch.			Hand Surgery	1980
Cook, John J.	Med. Coll. Pennsylvania	Anesthesiology	1986		
Cook, Richard T., Jr.	Jefferson	Emerg Med	1987		
Cook, Rosemary A.	Med. Coll. Virginia	Internal Medicine	1990		
Cooke, Alfred J.	Jefferson	Orthop Surg	1969		
Cooney, David P.	Northwestern Univ.			Hematology	1958
Cooper, David R.	Jefferson	Orthop Surg	1976		
Cooper, Mark W.	Jefferson	Radiology	1981		
Cooper, Shelby O.	Indiana Univ.	Ob/Gyn	1975		
Cooper, Stephen G.	Temple Univ.	Otolaryngology	1982		
Cooperman, Harry	Med. Coll. Pennsylvania	Radiology	1985		
Coren, Gary S.	Jefferson	Radiology	1973		

Name	Med School	R Specialty	R Year	F Specialty	F Year
Corin, Morton S.	S.U.N.Y., Downstate	Neurology	1969		
Cornell-Murphy, Dianna S.	Univ. Rochester	Pathology	1983		
Corrales, Carlos F.	Univ. Miami Osteo.			Pulm Dis	1974
Corse, Steven K.	Jefferson	Internal Medicine	1984		
Corson, Joseph K.	Univ. Pennsylvania	Dermatology	1951		
Cossrow, Joel I.	Jefferson	Radiology	1976		
Cotler, Howard B.	Jefferson	Orthop Surg	1984		
Cotler, Jerome M.	Jefferson	Orthop Surg	1957		
Cotler, Marc D.	Med. Coll. Pennsylvania			Allergy and Immun	1983
Cottone, Robert N.	Jefferson	Urological Surgery	1961		
Counts, Robert W.	Jefferson	Radiology	1955		
Coven, Roger A.	New Jersey Med. Coll.	Ob/Gyn	1984		
Cowan, George S. M., Jr.	Univ. Aberdeen	General Surgery	1970		
Cowchock, F. Susan	Jefferson	Internal Medicine	1973		
Cox, Fred Ward, III	Temple Univ.	Internal Medicine	1982		
Cox, Jonathan M.	Jefferson	Internal Medicine	1983		
Cox, Robert W.	Jefferson	Nephrology	1977		
Coyle, William A.	Jefferson	Orthop Surg	1963		
Cozzolino, Harlow J.	Jefferson	Internal Medicine	1961	Gastroenterology	1963
Cracco, Joan B.	Seton Hall	Neurology	1969		
Craig, Richard A.	Jefferson	Anesthesiology	1980		
Cristoffanini-Trucco, Alberto	Univ. of Chile			Hematology	1959
Crouse, Farrell R.	Jefferson	Psychiatry	1962		
Crozier, Kelly S.	Hahnemann Univ.	Phys Med/Rehab	1989		
Crumrine, Richard S.	Jefferson	Otolaryngology	1967		
Cruz, Richard L.	Jefferson			Child Psychiatry	1984
Cucinotta, Anthony J.	Temple Univ.			Rheumatology	1970
Cuddy, Vincent D.	Jefferson	General Surgery	1962		
Cudemo, Regina M.	Jefferson	Child Psychiatry	1983		
Cuffia, Blanca L.	Univ. Cordoba (Argentina)	Pediatrics	1969		
Cullen, Chester F.	Jefferson	Neurology	1952		
Cunneff, Raymond L., Jr.	Jefferson	Otolaryngology	1954		
Cunningham, J. David	Jefferson	Otolaryngology	1984		
Cunningham, William S.	Med. Coll. Virginia			Diag Rad	1986
Cupic, Zoran	Univ. Cath. Louvain (Belgium)	Orthop Surg	1970		
Curchin, Thomas J.	Univ. Vermont	Family Practice	1989		
Currie, Violante	Univ. Illinois			Medical Oncology	1972
Curti, Joseph T.	Jefferson	Internal Medicine	1966	Endocrinology	1968
Curtin, Charles T.	Jefferson	Pathology	1973		
Curtis, Danny Lee	Wayne State Univ.	Rad Oncol	1990		
Curtis, John A.	Columbia Univ., Coll. of P.& S.	Radiology	1976		
Czernobilsky, Helen	Univ. Lausanne (Switzerland)			Hematology	1961

John J. Dagianis
Cincinnati

John R. Dalton
Univ. London

Maurice Daniels
S.U.N.Y, Syracuse

Steven Jon Daniels
Chicago Med. Sch.

Spencer I. Danto
S.U.N.Y., Downstate

Sanford H. Davne
Temple

Robert A. Dein
Pennsylvania

Mark De Laurentis
Jefferson

Miguel L. deLeon
Philippines

Leopoldo E. DeLucca
Cincinnati

Frank A. DeLucia
Georgetown

Rudolph T. DePersia
Jefferson

Name	Med School	R Specialty	R Year	F Specialty	F Year
D'Andrea, Linda M.	Jefferson				
D'Elia, Frank L.	Univ. Guadalajara (Mexico)	Internal Medicine	1984	Cardiovas Dis	1986
D'Silva, Henry I.	Univ. Bombay	Urological Surgery	1984		
Dabezies, Marta A.	Univ. Pennsylvania	Internal Medicine	1977	Nephrology	1981
DaCosta, Paulo B.	Univ. Parana (Brazil)	Internal Medicine	1982		
DaCosta, Theodore A.	Seton Hall			Hematology	1959
Dadash-Zadeh, Mahboubeh	Univ. Teheran			Gastroenterology	1964
Dagianis, John J.	Univ. Cincinnati	Pediatrics	1973		
Dalburg, Lewis A., Jr.	New York Med. Coll.	Ophthalmology	1980		
Dalsey, Robert M.	Temple Univ.	Ophthalmology	1962		
Dalton, John R.	Univ. London			Hand Surgery	1989
Dalton, Matthew L.	Jefferson	Urological Surgery	1977		
Daly, James W.	Jefferson	Anesthesiology	1989		
Danaie, Jamshid	Univ. Teheran	Internal Medicine	1953	Cardiovas Dis	1954
Danesh, Irving S.	Univ. Noreste (Mexico)			Rad Oncol	1978
Daniels, Maurice N.	S.U.N.Y., Syracuse	Emerg Med	1986		
Daniels, Steven J.	Chicago Med. Sch.	Pediatrics	1986		
Danis, Christopher J.	Wright State Univ.	Internal Medicine	1980		
Danoff, Barbara F.	Jefferson			Hand Surgery	1988
Dansby, Thomas J.	Univ. Texas			Rad Oncol	1977
Danto, Spencer I.	S.U.N.Y., Downstate	Otolaryngology	1981		
Danyo, John J.	Jefferson	Internal Medicine	1987		
Dardick, Lawrence R.	Univ. Missouri, Columbia	Orthop Surg	1966		
Dasch, Frederick W.	Univ. Pennsylvania	Rad Oncol	1987		
Dash, Lamarr A.	S.U.N.Y., Downstate	General Surgery	1949		
Dave, Rajesh J.	Univ. Bombay	Ob/Gyn	1977		
Davies, Allen L.	Jefferson			Neo- Perinatal Med	1979
Davies, Barbara L.	Jefferson	General Surgery	1966		
Davis, Allen B.	Jefferson	General Surgery	1988		
Davis, Dwight G., Jr.	Jefferson	General Surgery	1975		
Davis, George H.	Texas Coll. Osteo. Med.	General Surgery	1959		
Davis, Harry E., II	West Virginia Univ.			Mater/Fetal Med	1985
Davis, J. Wallace	Jefferson	Internal Medicine	1969		
Davis, Jonathan E.	New York Med. Coll.	Plastic Surgery	1949		
Davis, Paul S.	S.U.N.Y., Syracuse			Diag Rad	1986
Davison, William R.	Jefferson	Radiology	1989		
Davne, Sanford	Temple Univ.	Orthop Surg	1957		
de Andino, Agustin M., Jr.	Jefferson	Orthop Surg	1981		
de la Cruz, Angelina	Univ. of the Philippines	Internal Medicine	1950	Endocrinology	1951
de la Rosa, Jose P.	Univ. St. Tomas (Philippines)	Anesthesiology	1970		
De Laurentis, Mark	Jefferson			Nephrology	1983
De Maria, Peter A.	Jefferson	Radiology	1990		
De Santis, Joseph	Yale Univ.	Psychiatry	1988		
Deardorff, Charles L.	Jefferson	General Surgery	1989		
Dearolf, Walter W., III	Jefferson	General Surgery	1966		
DeBenedictis, Thomas J.	Georgetown Univ.	General Surgery	1987		
DeBerardinis, Camillo	Univ. Pennsylvania	Urological Surgery	1973		
DeCaestecker, Jacques	Univ. Ghent (Belgium)	Gastroenterology	1949		
DeCarlo, John, Jr.	Jefferson	Urological Surgery	1970		
DeCaro, Matthew V.	Jefferson	Radiology	1950		
Deenadayalan, Chitrakootam V.	Madras Med. Coll. (India)	Internal Medicine	1985	Cardiovas Dis	1987
DeEugenio, Lewis J., Jr.	UMDNJ, Newark	Neurology	1981		
DeFelice, Stephen L.	Jefferson	Internal Medicine	1979	Endocrinology	1964

Name	Med School	R Specialty	R Year	F Specialty	F Year
DeFusco, Carmine J.	Univ. Guadalajara (Mexico)			Pediatric Allergy	1980
Deglin, Stuart M.	Jefferson	Internal Medicine	1975	Cardiovas Dis	1976
Deibert, Glenn A.	Jefferson	Orthop Surg	1950		
Dein, Robert A.	Univ. Pennsylvania	Ob/Gyn	1987		
Dekret, Jeffrey J.	Jefferson	Psychiatry	1976		
Del Valle, Rene C.	Univ. Miami	Ob/Gyn	1986		
Delaney, William E., III	Jefferson	Pathology	1958		
DeLano, Margaret W.	Yale Univ.	Pediatrics	1972	Pediatric Allergy	1973
Delaplane, James M.	Jefferson	Psychiatry	1968		
deLeon, Miguel L.	Univ. of the Philippines	Orthop Surg	1982		
DelGiorno, John T.	Jefferson	Pediatrics	1972		
Della Badia, Carl R.	Kirksville Coll. of Osteo. Med.	Ob/Gyn	1978		
DeLong, Philip L.	Univ. Pennsylvania			Anesthesiology	1965
Delrossi, Anthony J.	Jefferson	General Surgery	1974		
DeLuca, Debra	Univ. Cincinnati	Neurology	1985		
DeLucca, Leopoldo E.	Jefferson	Otolaryngology	1981		
DeLucia, Frank A.	Georgetown Univ.	Orthop Surg	1986		
DelValle, John	Univ. Puerto Rico	Internal Medicine	1983		
DeMare, Paul A.	S.U.N.Y., Upstate	Rad Oncol	1972		
DeMeo, Daniel R.	Jefferson	Orthop Surg	1959		
Demmy, Merlyn R.	Jefferson	Psychiatry	1966		
dePaula, Belces	Univ. Minas Gerais (Brazil)			Endocrinology	1960
dePaula, Carl J.	S.U.N.Y., Buffalo	Orthop Surg	1974		
DePersia, Rudolph T., Jr.	Jefferson	Internal Medicine	1984		
DePrisco, John	Philadelphia Coll. Osteo. Med.	Phys Med/Rehab	1975		
Derdel, Jerome D.	Univ. Bologna (Italy)	Rad Oncol	1982		
Derkrikorian, Hagop L.	American Univ. Beirut	Neuro Surg	1981		
Derrick, George R.	Univ. South Carolina	Emerg Med	1988		
Dershaw, D. David	Jefferson	Diag Rad	1979		
Dershaw, Stuart Z.	Hahnemann	Ob/Gyn	1978		
Desai, Hemant J.	Baroda Univ. (India)			Neo-Perinatal Med	1977
Desai, Shobhana A.	Gujarat Univ.			Neo-Perinatal Med	1980
Deshmukh, Kalpana S.	Andhra Univ. (India)			Diag Rad	1982
Desimone, Cheryl A.	S.U.N.Y., Syracuse	Anesthesiology	1987		
Dessen, Edgar L.	Univ. Pennsylvania	Radiology	1941		
Dethoff, John C.	Jefferson	Orthop Surg	1983		
Dettmer, Cornelia M.	Univ. Cincinnati	Rad Oncol	1969		
Dettweiler, Vera E.	Woman's Med. Coll.			Pediatrics	1955
DeTuerk, John J.	Jefferson	General Surgery	1948		
Diamond, Paul H.	Vanderbilt Univ.	Internal Medicine	1963	Pulm Dis	1964
Diamond, Steven M.	Chicago Coll. of Osteo. Med.	Pathology	1975		
Diaz, Rita Maria	Univ. Salamanca (Spain)			Pediatric Allergy	1975
Dick, Bradley W.	Georgetown Univ.	Radiology	1988		
Dickensheets, James G.	Jefferson	Internal Medicine	1954		
Dickerman, Diane E.	Jefferson	Emerg Med	1986		
Dickerson, Gregg A.	Indiana Univ.	Rad Oncol	1988		
Dickerson, Reginald P.	Hahnemann Univ.	Internal Medicine	1980		
DiConcetto, Joseph A.	Hahnemann Univ.			Allergy and Immun	1983
DiFiglia, Marion T.	Woman's Med. Coll.			Nephrology	1969
DiGeorge, Angelo M.	Temple Univ.			Endocrinology	1953
DiGregorio, Vincent R.	Albany Med. Coll.	General Surgery	1974		
DiLeonardo, Mario	Hahnemann Univ.	Dermatology	1989		
Dilks, Robert H.	St. Louis Univ.	Ob/Gyn	1978		

Name	Med School	R Specialty	R Year	F Specialty	F Year
DiRago, George J.	Georgetown Univ.	Anesthesiology	1975		
Dittrich, Richard J.	Univ. Osteo. Med., Des Moines	Ob/Gyn	1977		
Djergaian, Robert S.	Jefferson	Phys Med/Rehab	1982		
Doan, Huynh Trieu	Univ. Hue (Viet Nam)			Radiology	1983
Doane, Stephen H.	Univ. Illinois	Internal Medicine	1976		
Dobelbower, Ralph R.	Jefferson	Rad Oncol	1974		
Dobell, Anthony R.	McGill Univ.	General Surgery	1956		
Dobies, Richard J.	Univ. Pittsburgh	Ophthalmology	1965		
Dobish, Mark P.	Georgetown Univ.	Internal Medicine	1985		
Dodd, Gerald D.	Jefferson	Radiology	1950		
Doenlen, Henry A.	Jefferson	Child Psychiatry	1985		
Doghramji, Karl	Jefferson	Psychiatry	1984		
Doherty, Michael J.	Jefferson	Anesthesiology	1989		
Donahue, Francis I.	Philadelphia Coll. Osteo. Med.			Radiology	1989
Donahue, John R.	Jefferson	Orthop Surg	1981		
Donahue, Michael J.	Creighton Univ.	Dermatology	1970		
Donovan, Althea A.	Univ. Noreste (Mexico)	Psychiatry	1988		
Donovan, Mary	Phiadelphia Coll. Osteo. Med.	Internal Medicine	1982		
Dorn, John M.	Univ. South Carolina	Psychiatry	1985		
Dorsey, Philip W.	Univ. Syracuse	Radiology	1948		
Dorwitt, Deborah I.	S.U.N.Y., Syracuse	Ob/Gyn	1987		
Doto, Joseph B., Jr.	Jefferson	Anesthesiology	1971		
Dougherty, Frances E.	UMDNJ, Newark	Pediatrics	1990		
Dougherty, Miriam T.	Jefferson	Ophthalmology	1980		
Douglas, Thomas E., Jr.	Jefferson	Otolaryngology	1952		
Dovarganes, Rafael	Univ. Mexico City	Neuro Surg	1964		
Dowling, John J.	Jefferson	Orthop Surg	1955		
Doyle, Colin S.	Univ. Illinois	Otolaryngology	1973		
Drake, Willard M.	Jefferson	Urological Surgery	1950	Urological Surgery	1947
Drickman, Arthur	New York Univ.	Pathology	1962		
Drosnes, Dean L.	Temple Univ.	Otolaryngology	1990		
Dryjski, Maciej L.	Medical Academy, Warsaw	General Surgery	1989		
Duara, Ranjan	Christian Med. Coll. (India)	Neurology	1980		
Dubin, Andrew H.	Albany Med. Coll.	Phys Med/Rehab	1990		
Dubin, William R.	Univ. South Carolina	Psychiatry	1977		
DuBreuil, Anne L.	Univ. Pennsylvania	Family Practice	1980		
Duca, Peter R.	Georgetown Univ.	Internal Medicine	1970	Cardiovas Dis	1972
Duchin, Jeffrey S.	UMDNJ, Rutgers	Internal Medicine	1988		
Dugan, Philip J.	St. Louis Univ.			Rad Oncol	1970
Dumont, Jacques	Laval Univ. (Canada)			Hand Surgery	1972
Duncan, John J.	Jefferson	Plastic Surgery	1948		
Dunn, Jerome	Temple Univ.			Pediatric Allergy	1973
Dunnington, William G.	Univ. Oklahoma	Internal Medicine	1952	Hematology	1953
DuPont, John F., Jr.	Georgetown Univ.	Oral & Max Surg	1969		
Durlofsky, Larry	Univ. Osteo. Med., Des Moines	Psychiatry	1988		
Dusitsin, Nikorn	Chulalongkorn Univ. (Thailand)			Repro Endo	1963
Dutch, Stephen J., Jr.	Univ. of Pennsylvania	Neurology	1956		
Dvorkin, Daniel	Univ. Pittsburgh	Internal Medicine	1969		
Dworkin, Gerald E.	Philadelphia Coll. Osteo. Med.	Phys Med/Rehab	1985		
Dyer, Richard H., Jr.	Cornell Univ.	Orthop Surg	1971		

Paul M. Eberts, II
Jefferson

Ellin B. Effinger
Med. Coll. Ohio

Marc T. Edwards
Colorado

Lokeswara R. Edara
Guntur Med. Coll. (India)

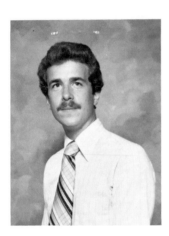

Cliffor Ehrlich
New York Med. Coll.

David S. Eingorn
Temple

Stuart L. Eisenberg
Albert Einstein Coll. Med.

E. Susanna Eisenhower (Turner)
Jefferson

David J. Ellis
Jefferson

Magda S. Elraheb
Cairo

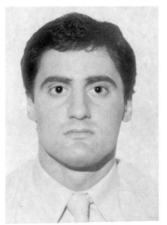

William D. Emper
Harvard

Erich A. Everts
Jefferson

Name	Med School	R Specialty	R Year	F Specialty	F Year
Easler, Richard E.	Jefferson	Pathology	1962		
Ebel, Marc S.	Jefferson			Gastroenterology	1974
Eberts, Paul M., II	Jefferson	Family Practice	1987		
Ebron, Rosita P.	Univ. St. Tomas (Philippines)	Pediatrics	1977		
Echenique, L. Ignacio	Univ. Puerto Rico			Colon and Rec Surg	1986
Eckley, Robert	Jefferson	Ophthalmology	1948		
Edara, Lokeswara R.	Guntur Med. Coll. (India)			Pediatric Allergy	1990
Edelman, Meyer	Jefferson	Anesthesiology	1957		
Edwards, Gary A.	Jefferson	Ophthalmology	1974		
Edwards, Marc T.	Univ. Colorado	Family Practice	1978		
Effat, Mahmoud K.	Cairo Univ.			Pediatric Allergy	1990
Effinger, Ellin B.	Med. Coll. Ohio	Ophthalmology	1979		
Eftimiades, George S.	Univ. Athens	Urological Surgery	1957		
Egert, Joseph	Univ. Maryland	Internal Medicine	1975		
Egloff, Allen C.	Univ. Maryland	Orthop Surg	1976		
Ehrlich, Clifford	New York Med. Coll.	Internal Medicine	1984		
Ehrlich, Dion R.	George Washington Univ.	Ophthalmology	1977		
Eingorn, David S.	Temple Univ.	Orthop Surg	1984		
Eisenberg, Stuart L.	Albert Einstein Coll. Med.	Internal Medicine	1988	Gastroenterology	1990
Eisenberg, Theodore S.	Philadelphia Coll. Osteo. Med.	Orthop Surg	1980	Hand Surgery	1982
Eisenhower-Turner, E. Susanna	Jefferson	Psychiatry	1982		
Eisenstat, Theodore E.	New York Med. Coll.	General Surgery	1971		
El Raheb, Magda S.	Cairo Univ.	Otolaryngology	1984		
El Sawah, M. Shawky	Fac. Med. Alexandria	Orthop Surg	1973		
El-Bakri, Younes N.	Univ. Alexandria			Gyn Oncol	1981
Elanchenny, Indranee	Univ. Ceylon			Family Practice	1983
Eliades, William	Jefferson	Internal Medicine	1963		
Ellis, Carl F.	Temple Univ.	Oral & Max Surg	1971		
Ellis, David J.	Jefferson	Urological Surgery	1987		
Ellis, Ralph Waldo	New York Med. Coll.	Ob/Gyn	1952		
Elsten, Jane L.	Med. Coll Pennsylvania	Anesthesiology	1980		
Elvey, Sharon M.	Med. Coll. Pennsylvania			Allergy and Immun	1986
Emerine, Sally	Woman's Med. Coll.	Anesthesiology	1972		
Emmett, Gary A.	Jefferson	Pediatrics	1979		
Emper, William D.	Harvard Univ.	Orthop Surg	1986		
Englert, Christopher	Univ. Cincinnati	Ob/Gyn	1989		
English, George W.	Nicolaus Copernicus Med. Acad. (Poland)	Pathology	1987		
Enker, Irwin P.	Univ. Ottawa			Hand Surgery	1983
Ente, Philip	Univ. Paris (Pitie-Salpetriere)			Neurology	1984
Epple, Walter D.	Jefferson	Neuro Surg	1976		
Epstein, Byron D.	Univ. Tennessee	Internal Medicine	1952		
Epstein, David E.	Albert Einstein Coll. Med.	Family Practice	1982		
Eraso, Antonio E.	Nat. Univ. Colombia	General Surgery	1960		
Erbaugh, John K.	Univ. Michigan	Ophthalmology	1953		
Ersner, Arthur R.	Temple Univ	Internal Medicine	1979		
Escobar, Lidia Victoria	Univ. El Salvador	Pediatrics	1971		
Eshbach, Richard E.	Jefferson			Pulm Dis	1963
Eskey, Chester W.	Jefferson	Orthop Surg	1956		
Estanol, Bruno V.	Nat. Univ. Mexico	Neurology	1973		
Evans, Bradley D.	Jefferson	Psychiatry	1979		
Evans, Robert L.	Jefferson	Internal Medicine	1955	Cardiovas Dis	1956
Evantash, Alan B.	Temple Univ.	Radiology	1975		

Name	Med School	R Specialty	R Year	F Specialty	F Year
Everhart, Francis J.	Univ. Pennsylvania	Internal Medicine	1965		
Everleth, Wendy	Chicago Coll. Osteo. Med.	Anesthesiology	1990		
Everts, Erich A., Jr.	Jefferson	Anesthesiology	1985		
Eyyunni, Uma	Osmania Univ. (India)	Otolaryngology	1985		

Dr. Willis C. Maddrey (Magee Prof. of Medicine) on rounds with residents (1987).

Charles S. Fineberg
Hahnemann

Daniel P. Ferrick
Maryland

Steven A. Feinstein
Washington

Frederick M. Fellin
Jefferson

Stephen H. Fehnel
Jefferson

Michael J. Fazio
Creighton

Cynthia A. Farrell
Phila. Coll. Osteo. Med.

Harold F. Farber
Albany Med. Coll.

Judith A. Farley
Hahnemann

Christopher M. Frauenhoffer
Jefferson

Michael G. Faust
Pittsburgh

Pantaleon L. Fagel
St. Tomas (Philippines)

Postgraduate Alumni

Name	Med School	R Specialty	R Year	F Specialty	F Year
Faber, K. Kalman	Univ. Toronto	Pediatrics	1949		
Fabi, Mark B.	Jefferson	Psychiatry	1989		
Fabric, Robert K.	Univ. Miami	General Surgery	1973		
Fagel, Pantaleon L.	Univ. St. Tomas (Philippines)	Pathology	1990		
Fakharzadeh Frederick	Columbia Univ., Coll. P. & S.			Hand Surgery	1986
Falkenstein, Sheldon J.	Temple Univ.	Anesthesiology	1975		
Falkner, Bonita E.	Univ. Minnesota			Nephrology	1971
Fallon, Joseph J., Jr.	Chicago Med. Sch.			Endocrinology	1984
Farano, Peter J.	Hahnemann Univ.	Pathology	1987		
Farb, Stanley	Univ. Maryland	Otolaryngology	1963		
Farber, Barry M.	Hahnemann Univ.	Psychiatry	1980		
Farber, Harold F.	Albany Med. Coll.	Dermatology	1987		
Farley, Judith A.	Hahnemann Univ.	Anesthesiology	1984		
Farmer, Peter M.	Jefferson	Neurology	1973		
Farmer, Rodney A.	Jefferson	Neurology	1948		
Farrell, Cynthia A.	Philadelphia Coll. Osteo. Med.	Phys Med/Rehab	1986		
Faust, Michael G.	Univ. Pittsburgh	Ob/Gyn	1987		
Favino, C. James	Jefferson	Pathology	1968		
Favis, Edward A.	Univ. Philippines	Internal Medicine	1957		
Fazio, Michael J.	Creighton Univ.	Dermatology	1990		
Feder, Michael J.	Univ. Missouri	Emerg Med	1990		
Federman, Jay L.	Tufts Univ.	Ophthalmology	1970		
Fedorchak, Arlene M.	Ohio State Univ.	Internal Medicine	1990		
Fehnel, Stephen H.	Jefferson	Ob/Gyn	1981		
Feig, Howard I.	Univ. Illinois	Oral & Max Surg	1968		
Feinstein, Steven A.	Washington Univ.	Internal Medicine	1986		
Feinstein, Theodore A.	Jefferson	Ob/Gyn	1979		
Feit, Elliot S.	Univ. Vermont	Pediatrics	1978		
Feld, Ricky I.	Mt. Sinai Sch. Med.			Diag Rad	1988
Felderman, Eugene S.	Jefferson	Urological Surgery	1956		
Feldman, Ellen K.	Jefferson			Child Psychiatry	1989
Feldman, Julian D.	Jefferson	Ob/Gyn	1963		
Feldman, Marc D.	S.U.N.Y., Syracuse	Otolaryngology	1987		
Feldman, Martin H.	Univ. Utah	Neurology	1966		
Fellin, Frederick M.	Jefferson	Internal Medicine	1983	Hematol/Oncol	1989
Fencil, Ellen L.	Med. Coll. Pennsylvania			Allergy and Immun	1983
Fenlin, John M., Jr.	Jefferson	Orthop Surg	1968		
Ferguson, John B., III	Jefferson	Ophthalmology	1975		
Ferguson, Ronney Lynn	Univ. Texas	Orthop Surg	1978		
Fernandez, Celia M.	Ponce Sch. Med.			Rheumatology	1987
Fernandez, Louis A.V.	Univ. Karachi	Internal Medicine	1970	Hematology	1972
Ferreira, Arturo J.	Catholic Univ. Cordoba (Argentina)	Internal Medicine	1972		
Ferrick, Daniel P.	Univ. Maryland	Family Practice	1984		
Fiastro, James F.	Univ. Maryland	Internal Medicine	1983		
Fidler, Harry E.	Jefferson	Otolaryngology	1956		
Field, Howard L.	Jefferson	Psychiatry	1960		
Fietti, Vincent G.	Boston Univ.			Hand Surgery	1978
Filer, Robert B.	Hahnemann Univ.			Repro Endo	1987
Filip, Zbigniew J.	Med. Acad. Lodz (Poland)	Internal Medicine	1970		
Filomena, Carol A.	Hahnemann Univ.	Pathology	1988	Cytopathology	1990
Findley-Christian, Gertrude	Univ. Liberia			Nephrology	1990
Fineberg, Charles	Hahnemann Univ.	General Surgery	1955		

Name	Med School	R Specialty	R Year	F Specialty	F Year
Fineman, Sanford	Temple Univ.	Neuro Surg	1981		
Finestone, Alvin W.	Temple Univ.	Radiology	1954		
Fink, Jack W.	Jefferson	Ob/Gyn	1960		
Fink, Louis I.	Univ. Pennsylvania			Cardiovas Dis	1987
Finke, James S.	Hahnemann Univ.	Pediatrics	1989		
Finkelstein, Barney	Univ. Pennsylvania	Radiology	1965		
Finkelstein, Ben Ami	Univ. Zurich	Psychiatry	1965		
Finley, Robert K., Jr.	Jefferson	General Surgery	1954		
Finn, Joseph L.	Jefferson	Ob/Gyn	1940		
Fiol-Silva, Zoraida	Univ. Puerto Rico	Ophthalmology	1982		
First, Howard E.	Univ. Pennsylvania	Ob/Gyn	1955		
Firth, Joanna M.	Jefferson			Pediatric Allergy	1979
Fisch, Irwin R.	Jefferson	Internal Medicine	1962		
Fischer, Michael E.	Jefferson	Radiology	1981		
Fischer, Richard L.	Univ. Pennsylvania	Ob/Gyn	1987	Mater/Fetal Med	1989
Fishburn, Mary Jo	Med. Coll. Pennsylvania	Phys Med/Rehab	1989		
Fishburn, Robert I.	Univ. California	Rad Oncol	1974		
Fisher, Andrew W.	Univ. Rochester	Internal Medicine	1984		
Fisher, Gary A.	Philadelphia Coll. Osteo. Med.	Rad Oncol	1980		
Fisher, George R.	Columbia Univ., Coll. P. & S.			Endocrinology	1951
Fisher, Herbert M.	Jefferson	Internal Medicine	1967		
Fisher, Joseph S.	Jefferson	Internal Medicine	1973		
Fishman , Noel H.	UCLA	General Surgery	1965		
Fitzig, Sanford	Jefferson	Urological Surgery	1977		
Fitzpatrick, Ruth Ann P.	Woman's Med. Coll.			Diabetes	1972
Fitzsimmons, John M.	Hahnemann Univ.			Mater/Fetal Med	1981
Fjeld, George C.	Univ. Vermont	Family Practice	1984		
Flaherty, Lisa	Philadelphia Coll. Osteo. Med.	Pediatrics	1984		
Flanders, Adam E.	Rush Med. Coll.			Diag Rad	1989
Flegel, Ernest E.	Jefferson	Internal Medicine	1971	Cardiovas Dis	1973
Fleischer, Leslie R.	Creighton Univ.	Internal Medicine	1978		
Fleishman, Ervin S.	Jefferson	Internal Medicine	1974		
Fleishman, Martin J.	Jefferson	General Surgery	1977		
Fleming, John H.	Univ. Witwatersrand (South Africa)			Hand Surgery	1974
Flick, John B., Jr.	Univ. Rochester	General Surgery	1951		
Flick, Lawrence F., III	Jefferson	General Surgery	1947		
Flickinger, Haviland	Jefferson	Anesthesiology	1960		
Flinker, David	Univ. Pennsylvania			Hematology	1961
Flint, John S.	Tufts Uiv.	Internal Medicine	1952	Hematology	1953
Flis, Raymond S.	Kirksville Coll. Osteo. Med.			Nephrology	1975
Fluellen, Judith H.	Jefferson	Anesthesiology	1985		
Flynn, Joseph C.	Jefferson	Orthop Surg	1958		
Flynn, Paul M.	Univ. Detroit	Oral & Max Surg	1978		
Flynn-Rodden, Karin	Jefferson	Internal Medicine	1988	Allergy and Immun	1990
Fong, Bernard W.D.	Jefferson			Cardiovas Dis	1956
Fontanetta, John A.	Cornell Univ.	Internal Medicine	1986		
Fonte, Donald A.	Louisiana State Univ.	Orthop Surg	1970		
Forbes, William I., III	Jefferson	Otolaryngology	1977		
Forchetti, Concetta	Univ. dell'Aquila (Italy)	Neurology	1988		
Ford, Susan E.	Univ. Maryland			Family Practice	1980
Forde, David L.	Jefferson	Internal Medicine	1966		
Foris, Nicholas P.	Univ. Athens			General Surgery	1959
Forker, Thomas	Jefferson	Orthop Surg	1955		

Name	Med School	R Specialty	R Year	F Specialty	F Year
Formal, Christopher S.	Univ. Maryland	Phys Med/Rehab	1982		
Forman, Harris	Jefferson	Internal Medicine	1964		
Forman, John W.	Univ. Kansas	Internal Medicine	1977		
Forrest, Leonard E.	Hahnemann Univ.	Phys Med/Rehab	1987		
Fort, John G.	Univ. Valencia (Spain)			Rheumatology	1986
Fortin, Benoit	Laval Univ. (Canada)	Radiology	1969		
Foster, Charles G.	Jefferson	Hematology	1950		
Fouts, David W.	Univ. Illinois	Gen Prev Med	1972		
Fowler, William P.	Georgetown Univ.	Psychiatry	1985		
Fox, Henry B.	Stanford Univ.	Internal Medicine	1981		
Fox, J. Robert	Jefferson	Otolaryngology	1947		
Fox, James W., IV	Jefferson	General Surgery	1974		
Fragos, George	Univ. Athens	General Surgery	1975		
Franco, Frank A.	Hahnemann Univ.	Internal Medicine	1957		
Francos, George C.	Jefferson			Nephrology	1983
Frank, Leonard A.	Hahnemann Univ.	Urological Surgery	1968		
Frankel, Kalman	Jefferson	Neurology	1949		
Franklin, John B.	Vanderbilt Univ.	Ob/Gyn	1963		
Franks, Bryan D.	Univ. Maryland	Internal Medicine	1983		
Franzke, Ronald O.	Loma Linda Univ.	Otolaryngology	1968		
Frauenhoffer, Christopher M.	Jefferson	Pathology	1980		
Frauenhoffer, Suzanne M.	Jefferson	Pathology	1982		
Freed, Gary E.	Univ. Osteo. Med., Des Moines	Pediatrics	1976		
Freedman, Allan P.	Jefferson	Internal Medicine	1975		
Freedman, Arthur M.	S.U.N.Y., Downstate			Diag Rad	1988
Freedman, Mitchell K.	Philadelphia Coll. Osteo. Med.	Phys Med/Rehab	1986		
Freimuth, Erich J.	Temple Univ.	Neurology	1964		
Freundlich, Irwin M.	Duke Univ.	Radiology	1964		
Frey, Charles D.	Jefferson	Radiology	1952	Radiology	1953
Fricchione, Patrick J.	Temple Univ.	Emerg Med	1989		
Fried, Guy W.	Yale Univ.	Phys Med/Rehab	1989		
Fried, Paul H.	Jefferson			Ob/Gyn	1947
Fried, Scott M.	New York Coll. Osteo. Med.			Hand Surgery	1987
Friedman, Alan L.	Hahnemann Univ.			Hematology	1981
Friedman, Michael P.	Univ. Maryland			Hematology	1970
Friedman, Oren L.	Rush Med. Coll.			Cardiovas Dis	1986
Friedman, Shlomo	Univ. Jerusalem	Pediatrics	1970	Ped Hema-Oncol	1972
Friedman, Steven A.	Jefferson	Internal Medicine	1972		
Frieman, Barbara G.	Jefferson	Orthop Surg	1985		
Frohner, Richard N.	Jefferson	Internal Medicine	1951		
Frommelt, John C.	Jefferson	Ob/Gyn	1954		
Fronefield, Helen P.	Temple Univ.	Anesthesiology	1971		
Fruncillo, Richard J.	Hahnemann Univ.			Clin Pharmacol	1983
Frye, Joyce C.	Univ. Osteo. Med., Des Moines	Ob/Gyn	1983		
Fu, Remedios T.	Univ. Philippines	Pediatrics	1974		
Fuller, Raymond L.	Philadelphia Coll. Osteo. Med.			Pulm Dis	1978
Fuller, Virginia S.	Med. Coll. Pennsylvania	Anesthesiology	1975		
Funt, Mark J.	Univ. Pennsylvania	Oral & Max Surg	1980		
Furia, Frederick A.	Univ. Pennsylvania	Internal Medicine	1974	Cardiovas Dis	1976
Furnary, Anthony P.	Jefferson	General Surgery	1989		
Fuzesi, Laszlo	Cornell Univ.	General Surgery	1987		

Marcy A. Glinsky
Rutgers

John T. Gallagher
Hahnemann

Leonald G. Gehl
New Jersey Med. Sch.

Steven Georgeson
New York Med. Coll.

Arthur M. Gershkoff
Yale

Giselle J. Geddes
Temple

James K. Gerstley
Tulane

Jeffrey T. Gibson
Temple

Joseph B. Giletto
Jefferson

M. Giudica
Iowa

Diane Gillum
Jefferson

Angust T. Gillis
Jefferson

Name	Med School	R Specialty	R Year	F Specialty	F Year
Gabos, Paul E.	Univ. Pittsburgh	Ob/Gyn	1966	Repro Endo	1967
Gacso, William J.	Tufts Univ.	Anesthesiology	1967		
Gadomski, Stephen P.	Jefferson	Otolaryngology	1986		
Gailliot, Robert V.	Jefferson	Pathology	1965		
Galinat, Brian J.	Virginia Commonwealth Univ.	Orthop Surg	1988		
Galinsky, Marcy A.	New Jersey Rutgers	Family Practice	1985		
Gallagher, Hugh S.	Univ. Pennsylvania			Cardiovas Dis	1970
Gallagher, James J.	Jefferson	Urological Surgery	1957		
Gallagher, John T.	Hahnemann Univ.	Otolaryngology	1987		
Gallagher, Joseph C., Jr.	Phila. Coll. Osteo. Med.	Orthop Surg	1978		
Gallant, Milton	George Washington Univ.	Radiology	1966		
Galler-Rimm, Gabrielle	Univ. Puerto Rico	Pediatrics	1990		
Gammell, Edwin B.	Univ. Vermont	Otolaryngology	1948		
Garber, Mark W.	Univ. Auto Cuidad Juarez (Mexico)	Emerg Med	1986		
Garcia, Lorenzo M.	Univ. St. Tomas (Philippines)	Anesthesiology	1973		
Garg, Rakesh K.	Dayanand Med. Coll. (India)	Neurology	1981		
Garofola, John H.	New Jersey Med. Sch.	Radiology	1975		
Gartland, John J., Jr.	Jefferson	Orthop Surg	1949		
Gary, Gerald L.	Jefferson	Pediatrics	1981		
Gatti, Eugene A.	Georgetown Univ.	Pediatrics	1985	Allergy and Immun	1987
Gaughan, William J.	Hahneman Univ.			Nephrology	1988
Gawchik, Sandra M.	Kansas City Osteo.			Pediatric Allergy	1977
Geddes, Giselle J.	Temple Univ.	Internal Medicine	1990		
Geetter, Philip H.	Jefferson	Ophthalmology	1974		
Gehl, Leonard G.	New Jersey Med. Sch.	Internal Medicine	1979		
Geiger, Leonard R.	Albany Med. Coll.	Neurology	1970		
Geimeier, William J.	Univ. Kentucky			Pediatric Allergy	1979
Gelb, Robert I.	New York Med. Coll.			Hand Surgery	1986
Gelman, Martin Israel	Temple Univ.	Radiology	1971		
Gensemer, George John	Jefferson	General Surgery	1953		
Gentlesk, Michael J.	Georgetown Univ.			Pediatric Allergy	1972
Georgeson, Steven E.	New York Med. Coll.	Internal Medicine	1989		
Gergerian, Edmund L.	Cairo Univ.	Psychiatry	1973		
Gersh, Douglas B.	Jefferson	Neurology	1980		
Gershkoff, Arthur M.	Yale Univ.	Phys Med/Rehab	1982		
Gerstley, James K.	Tulane Univ.	Internal Medicine	1985		
Getz, Donald D.	Jefferson	Orthop Surg	1974		
Getz, Harry D.	Kirksville Coll. Osteo.	Pediatrics	1974		
Getzoff, Charles G.	Temple Univ.	Oral & Max Surg	1965		
Giammattei, Frank P.	Univ. Cincinnati	Orthop Surg	1985		
Gibson, Jeffrey T.	Temple Univ.	Ob/Gyn	1984		
Gigliotti, Lawrence George	Jefferson	Orthop Surg	1962		
Giletto, Joseph B.	Jefferson	Otolaryngology	1982		
Gilgore, Sheldon G.	Jefferson	Internal Medicine	1959	Endocrinology	1961
Gill, Frances McNeill	Pritzker Sch. Med.			Ped Hema-Oncol	1972
Gillis, Angus T.	Jefferson	Anesthesiology	1989		
Gillum, Diane R.	Jefferson	General Surgery	1986		
Gilman, Paul B.	Jefferson			Hematology	1981
Gilmore, Frederick Richard	Harvard Med. Sch.	Radiology	1950		
Ginieczki, Michael J.	Jefferson	Urological Surgery	1974		
Ginsberg, David K.	George Washington Univ.	Internal Medicine	1959	Gastroenterology	1960
Ginsburg, Burt A.	Univ. Tennessee	Ophthalmology	1980		
Girardo, Salvatore P.	Jefferson	Internal Medicine	1972		

Name	Med School	R Specialty	R Year	F Specialty	F Year
Girone, Joseph F.	UMDNJ, Newark	Internal Medicine	1986	Nephrology	1988
Gitlin, Melvin C.	Univ. Pennsylvania	Anesthesiology	1984		
Gittlen, Stanford D.	Jefferson	Internal Medicine	1986		
Giudici, Michael C.	Univ. Iowa	Internal Medicine	1986	Cardiovas Dis	1988
Giudici, Paula A.	Univ. Iowa	Dermatology	1988		
Giuliano, Vincent J., Jr.	Univ. Pennsylvania	Internal Medicine	1968	Rheumatology	1969
Given, Kenneth M.	Jefferson	Internal Medicine	1964	Hematology	1966
Glaser, Arthur H.	Jefferson	Internal Medicine	1974		
Glasofer, Eric D.	Jefferson	Pediatrics	1981	Allergy and Immun	1983
Glass, Phillip	Jefferson	Ob/Gyn	1975		
Glass, Steven J.	Jefferson	Psychiatry	1980		
Glassberg, Edward	U.S.C. Los Angeles	Dermatology	1990		
Glassman, Leonard M.	Jefferson	Radiology	1973		
Glauser, Terry A.	Jefferson	Emerg Med	1986		
Glazer, Alan U.	Chicago Med. Sch.			Diag Rad	1989
Gleason, James Andrew	Univ. Pittsburgh	Internal Medicine	1978		
Gleichauf, John G.	S.U.N.Y., Buffalo	Ophthalmology	1967		
Glenn, Gladys M.	Univ. Pennsylvania	Internal Medicine	1982		
Glickman, Murray R.	Jefferson	Orthop Surg	1956		
Glor, Daniel R.	Johns Hopkins Univ.	Internal Medicine	1987		
Go, Ruby T.	Univ. Philippines			Endocrinology	1986
Gocial, Benjamin	Temple Univ.	Ob/Gyn	1982	Repro Endo	1984
Godwin, Bernard W., Jr.	Jefferson	Pediatrics	1958		
Goepp, Carla E.	Georgetown Univ.	Internal Medicine	1969	Medical Oncology	1967
Goffe, Keith A.	Univ. West Indies	Psychiatry	1977		
Gohel, Vijaysinh K.	Univ. Bombay	Radiology	1961		
Gold, Allan	Jefferson	Otolaryngology	1968		
Goldberg, Andrew G.	UMDNJ, Newark	General Surgery	1989		
Goldberg, Jay A.	Univ. Pittsburgh	General Surgery	1987		
Goldberg, Larry H.	Hahnemann Univ.	Internal Medicine	1981		
Goldberg, Louis	Jefferson	Ophthalmology	1953		
Goldberg, Michael E.	Jefferson	Anesthesiology	1986		
Goldberg, Paul M.	New York Coll. Osteo. Med.			Allergy and Immun	1985
Goldburgh, Warren Pearlman	Jefferson	Internal Medicine	1957		
Golden, Kenneth H.	Southwestern University			Child Psychiatry	1989
Goldenberg, Marc	Jefferson			Cardiov Surg	1983
Goldfarb Alvin F.	Vanderbilt Univ.			Repro Endo	1950
Goldfischer, Mindy Ann	New York Univ.			Diag Rad	1988
Goldin, Nathan P.	Univ. Virginia	Urological Surgery	1983		
Goldman, Arnold M.	Jefferson	Radiology	1965		
Goldman, Arthur J.	Jefferson	Anesthesiology	1979		
Goldman, Avra L.	Albert Einstein College	Family Practice	1989		
Goldman, Scott M.	Jefferson	General Surgery	1981	Cardiov Surg	1983
Goldschmidt, Joseph C.	Jefferson	Internal Medicine	1988		
Goldstein, Gary Neil	Univ. Pennsylvania	Internal Medicine	1979		
Goldstein, Melvyn E.	Univ. Pittsburgh	Anesthesiology	1971		
Golia, John K.	Univ. Bologna (Italy)	Anesthesiology	1984		
Goll, Stephen R.	Jefferson			Orthop Surg	1987
Gomez, Jairo	National Univ. Colombia	Psychiatry	1973		
Gongsakdi, Doung Deun	Univ. Med. Sc. (Thailand)			Repro Endo	1960
Gonyea, Edward F.	Georgetown Univ.	Neurology	1965		
Gonzales, Jorge M.	Univ. San Marcos (Peru)	Urological Surgery	1969		
Gonzalez, Eric H.	Jefferson	Emerg Med	1987		

Name	Med School	R Specialty	R Year	F Specialty	F Year
Gooberman, Marcia Ann	Univ. of Juarez (Mexico)	Rad Oncol	1985		
Good, Robert P.	Jefferson	Orthop Surg	1978		
Goodman, Bruce	Jefferson	Orthop Surg	1959		
Goodman, David A.	Jefferson	Anesthesiology	1987		
Goodman, Elliott L.	Univ. Western Ontario	Internal Medicine	1953	Cardiovas Dis	1955
Goodman, Michael S.	Jefferson	Urological Surgery	1982		
Goodner, David M.	Duke Univ.	Ob/Gyn	1972		
Goodrick, James E.	Jefferson	Anesthesiology	1972		
Goody, Howard E.	Jefferson	Dermatology	1978		
Gorab, Lawrence N.	Georgetown Univ.	Urological Surgery	1971		
Goracci, Armando Frank	St. Louis Univ.	General Surgery	1952		
Gordon, Donald R.	Fairleigh Dickinson	Oral & Max Surg	1975		
Gordon, Keith L.	Hahnemann Univ.	Psychiatry	1987		
Gordon, Stuart L.	Jefferson	General Surgery	1983	Orthop Surg	1987
Gordon, Susan Joan	Jefferson	Internal Medicine	1969	Gastroenterology	1971
Gorham, William K., III	Univ. Pennsylvania	General Surgery	1958		
Gorman, Robert M.	Univ. Pennsylvania	Anesthesiology	1987		
Gorsen, Robert M.	Jefferson	Neuro Surg	1988		
Gorsuch, Paul LeRoy	Jefferson	Neuro Surg	1987		
Gosin, Stephen	Jefferson	General Surgery	1967		
Gosnell, Kermit B.	Jefferson	Ob/Gyn	1969		
Gottesfeld, Peter M.	UMDNJ Rutgers	Family Practice	1988		
Gottlieb, Ronald S.	Univ. Pennsylvania	Internal Medicine	1967	Cardiovas Dis	1973
Gould, Daniel B.	Jefferson			Nephrology	1975
Gove, Ronald C.	Temple Univ.	Internal Medicine	1977		
Goyal, Sudhir	Maulana Azad (India)	Internal Medicine	1987	Nephrology	1986
Grabske, Charles F., Jr.	Univ. Kansas	Otolaryngology	1950		
Grad, L. Christine	Jefferson	Internal Medicine	1981		
Graham, John E., III	Univ. Minnesota	Psychiatry	1972		
Graham, Mark G.	Univ. Connecticut	Internal Medicine	1981		
Graham, Timothy S.	Tulane Univ.	Orthop Surg	1987		
Granite, Edwin L.	Temple Univ.	Oral & Max Surg	1962		
Graves, Lynda C.S.	Univ. Massachusetts	Family Practice	1981		
Gray, Lewis W.	Jefferson	Internal Medicine	1976	Cardiovas Dis	1978
Graziani, Virginia	Jefferson	Phys Med/Rehab	1990		
Graziano, Linda M.	Hahnemann Univ.			Pediatric Allergy	1989
Greco, Richard J.	Jefferson	General Surgery	1988		
Greco, Victor F.	Jefferson	General Surgery	1956		
Green, David	Jefferson	Internal Medicine	1963	Hematology	1964
Green, Howard A.	Boston Univ.	Internal Medicine	1988		
Green, Lawrence	Jefferson	Neurology	1968		
Green, Linda D.	Jefferson	Pediatrics	1979	Pediatric Allergy	1981
Green, Steven J.	Temple Univ.	Otolaryngology	1986		
Green, Steven M.	Albert Einstein Coll.			Hand Surgery	1978
Green, Thomas J.	Jefferson	Orthop Surg	1974		
Greenawald, Kenneth A.	Jefferson	Orthop Surg	1964		
Greenbank, Robert K.	Med. Coll. of Va.	Psychiatry	1955		
Greenberg, Alan	Univ. Pittsburgh	Internal Medicine	1980		
Greenberg, Allan M.	S.U.N.Y., Downstate	Ophthalmology	1971		
Greenberg, Bram	Hahnemann Univ.	Pediatrics	1984		
Greenberg, Stewart Bruce	Hahnemann Univ.	Radiology	1987		
Greenblatt, Jeff M.	Hahnemann	Internal Medicine	1990		
Greenspan, Gail S.	Jefferson	Psychiatry	1984		

Name	Med School	R Specialty	R Year	F Specialty	F Year
Greenspan, Mitchell	Jefferson	Internal Medicine	1977		
Greenwald, Jeffrey R.	Jefferson	Pediatrics	1986		
Griffith, John Richard	Jefferson	Internal Medicine	1952	Cardiovas Dis	1953
Griffith, Vincent Anthony, Jr.	West Virginia Univ.	Ob/Gyn	1980		
Griffiths, Chester F.	Univ. del Este (Dominican Republic) Otolaryngology		1989		
Grimm, Ian S.	Jefferson	Internal Medicine	1987	Gastroenterology	1989
Grizos, William T.	Jefferson	Internal Medicine	1984	Rad Oncol	1988
Groll, Michael	Univ. Pennsylvania			Repro Endo	1972
Groppe, Carl W., Jr.	Univ. Pittsburgh	Internal Medicine	1965	Medical Oncology	1964
Grosky, Murray B.	Jefferson			Endocrinology	1966
Gross, Mitchell J.	UMDNJ, Newark			Neurology	1988
Grossman, Cindy B.	Univ. Osteo. Med., Des Moines	Pediatrics	1983		
Grossman, Jay R.	Chicago Med. Sch.	Anesthesiology	1987		
Grosso, Joseph X.	Jefferson	Psychiatry	1971		
Grover, Joseph G.	Jefferson	Ob/Gyn	1984		
Gruber, Charles Michael, Jr.	Jefferson			Hematology	1948
Grunewald, Karl E.	Michigan State Univ.			Cardiothor Surg	1988
Guardiani, Mary J.	Jefferson	Pathology	1985		
Guarino, Julius M.	Jefferson			Gastroenterology	1986
Guenther, Donna Baillere	Temple Univ.			Pediatric Allergy	1971
Guenther, Wolfgang	Univ. Frankfurt	Internal Medicine	1973		
Guevarra, Andres T.	Univ. St. Tomas (Philippines)	Pediatrics	1986		
Guevarra, Jesusita H.	Univ. St. Tomas (Philippines)	Pediatrics	1986		
Guidon, Marietta	Jefferson	Internal Medicine	1977		
Guillermo, Reinaldo	Havana Univ. Med. Sch.	Colon and Rec Surg	1953		
Guirgius, Samir M.	Ain Shams Univ. (Egypt)	Psychiatry	1975		
Gullotti, Michael J.	Jefferson	Internal Medicine	1977	Cardiovas Dis	1979
Gumnit, Robert Yale	Jefferson	Anesthesiology	1979		
Gurijala, Lalitha	Andhra Univ. (India)	Psychiatry	1980		
Gurland, Mark A.	New York Univ.			Hand Surgery	1985
Gutierrez, Emmeline P.	Univ. Philippines	Phys Med/Rehab	1974		
Gutierrez, Guillermo	Univ. Guadalajara			Neo- Perinatal Med	1975
Gutmann, Rebecca M.	Case Western Reserve Univ.	Phys Med/Rehab	1989		
Gutowicz, Marcia	Temple Univ.	General Surgery	1982		
Guttin, Enrique	Univ. Mexico	General Surgery	1982		
Guttman, Michael	Hahnemann Univ.	Internal Medicine	1981		
Gzesh, Dan J.	Jefferson	Neurology	1989		

To gather knowledge and to find out new knowledge is the noblest occupation of the physician. To apply that knowledge . . . with sympathy born of understanding, to the relief of human suffering, is his loveliest occupation.

Edward Archibald (1872–1945)

Janet L. Haas
Hahnemann

Alex D. Hart
West Indies

Mohammad Abne Hasan
Dow Med. Coll. (Pakistan)

Gwyn Harrison
S.U.N.Y, Downstate

George K. Hanson
Virginia Commonwealth

Linwood R. Haith
Harvard

Rudolph H. Hecksher, Jr
Jefferson

Malcolm S. Harris
Pennsylvania

Deborah H. Hannan
UMDNJ, Newark

Eric Hume
S.U.N.Y., Syracuse

Canaan L. Harris
Georgetown

Elaine R. Haltman
Temple

Postgraduate Alumni

Name	Med School	R Specialty	R Year	F Specialty	F Year
Haas, Alexander Z.	Med. Coll. Zagreb (Yugoslavia)			Rad Oncol	1973
Haas, Janet F.	Hahnemann Univ.	Phys Med/Rehab	1980		
Habermel, John F.	Univ. Louisville			Nephrology	1966
Haddad, Fuad Salim	Univ. Istanbul (Turkey)	Anesthesiology	1960		
Haddad, Marun S.	Amer. Univ. Beirut	Internal Medicine	1974	Cardiovas Dis	1976
Haddad, Nazih M.	French Fac. (Lebanon)	Otolaryngology	1974		
Hadeed, Adnan Joseph	Damascus Univ. (Syria)	Otolaryngology	1978		
Hagan, Ralph E.	Boston Univ.	Neuro Surg	1968		
Haghbin, Mahroo	Univ. Teheran	Rad Oncol	1984		
Hagopian, Edward R.	Jefferson	General Surgery	1961		
Haidet, Keith R.	Penn State Univ.			Diag Rad	1990
Haimowitz, Bernard	Jefferson	Internal Medicine	1988		
Haimowitz, Daniel	Jefferson	Internal Medicine	1986		
Haith, Linwood R., Jr.	Harvard Univ.	General Surgery	1981		
Halka, Kathleen	Creighton Univ.			Hematology	1986
Hallstrom, Judith	Univ. Dominica	Psychiatry	1984		
Haltman, Elaine R.	Temple Univ.	Anesthesiology	1983		
Hamburger, Richard J.	Jefferson	Internal Medicine	1965	Nephrology	1966
Hamilton, Robert W.	Ohio State Univ.			Hematology	1970
Hamilton, William C.	Jefferson	Orthop Surg	1976		
Hammond, N. LeRoy, III	Jefferson	Orthop Surg	1973		
Hananian, Juliet, C.	Univ. Teheran	Pediatrics	1960	Pediatrics	1961
Handler, Jay J.	Univ. Pittsburgh	Urological Surgery	1975		
Hankin, Fred	Univ. Michigan			Hand Surgery	1984
Hannan, Deborah J.	UMDNJ, Newark	Internal Medicine	1988		
Hanney, Dennis E.	Kirksville Coll. Osteo.			Cardiovas Dis	1981
Hanson, George K.	Virginia Commonwealth Univ.	Anesthesiology	1980		
Hanson, Peggy Ann	Johns Hopkins Univ.	Neurology	1966		
Haq, Muhammad I.	King Edward Med. Coll. (Pakistan)			Diag Rad	1981
Hargreaves, William J.	Jefferson	Ob/Gyn	1950		
Harkness, Thomas T.	Yale Univ.	Anesthesiology	1958		
Harmelin, Michael C.	Phila. Coll. Osteo. Med.	Anesthesiology	1983		
Harmon, Sandra Rhoads	Temple Univ.	Family Practice	1977		
Harned, E. Michael	Jefferson	Radiology	1990		
Harris, Canaan L.	Georgetown Univ.	Otolaryngology	1980		
Harris, Kevin R.	Jefferson	Pediatrics	1982		
Harris, Malcolm Stuart	Univ. Pennsylvania	Family Practice	1979		
Harrison, Gwyn	S.U.N.Y., Downstate	Ob/Gyn	1986		
Hart, Alex D.	Univ. West Indies	Anesthesiology	1983		
Hart, Bruce	Jefferson	Internal Medicine	1984		
Hart, Gerard T.	Rutgers Univ.	Family Practice	1986		
Hasan, Mohammad Abne	Dow Med. Coll. (Pakistan)	Rad Oncol	1990		
Hatot, Brian A.	Univ. Pennsylvania	Anesthesiology	1987		
Hatti, Shivkumar S.	Univ. Bombay	Psychiatry	1980		
Haupt, George John	Jefferson	General Surgery	1956		
Haurani, Farid I. Der	Amer. Univ. Beirut	Internal Medicine	1956	Hematology	1957
Hausman, Cheryl L.	New York Univ.			Pediatrics	1987
Haver, Kenan	New York Med. Coll.			Pediatrics	1988
Haycook, William M.	Univ. Cath. Louvain (Belgium)	Neurology	1968		
Hayden, Charles H.	Northwestern Univ.			Hand Surgery	1988

Name	Med School	R Specialty	R Year	F Specialty	F Year
Hayek, Deborah A.	ALbany Med. Coll.	Internal Medicine	1984		
Hayman, Harry Blake	Jefferson	Ob/Gyn	1953		
Haynicz, Peter	Jefferson	Radiology	1969		
Hayward, Catherine Z.	Jefferson	General Surgery	1984		
Heard, Wilbur Don	Univ. Arkansas			Pulm Dis	1975
Heath, Alfred O.	Jefferson	General Surgery	1965		
Hecksher, Rudolph Herman	Jefferson	General Surgery	1951		
Heffron, John J.	Univ. Maryland Dental	Oral & Max Surg	1972		
Hegde, Sunil K.	Kasturba Med. Coll. (India)	Phys Med/Rehab	1988		
Heim, William J.	Jefferson	Internal Medicine	1972		
Heimberg, Florence Jean	S.U.N.Y., Upstate	Diag Rad	1980		
Heine, Marylin J.	Rutgers Univ.	Internal Medicine	1985	Hematology	1988
Helinek, Gerard L.	Temple Univ.			Diag Rad	1990
Hench, Anne	Jefferson	Pediatrics	1978		
Henderson, Janet L.	E. Virginia Med. Sch.	Emerg Med	1988		
Henderson, Mark H., Jr.	Virginia Commonwealth Univ.	Orthop Surg	1990		
Hendler, Steven L.	Univ. Southern California	Phys Med/Rehab	1987		
Hendricks, Pamela J.	Med. Univ. South Carolina	Radiology	1989		
Hendrickson, Frank Rogers	Jefferson	Radiology	1955		
Henning, James	Univ. British Columbia			Hematology	1961
Henry, Norman W.	Jefferson	Pathology	1956		
Henson, David J.	UMDNJ, Newark	Internal Medicine	1982		
Herbert, Walter William	Long Island Coll. Med.	Radiology	1953		
Herbst, Vincent P.	Jefferson	Dermatology	1986		
Hering, Norton	Jefferson	General Surgery	1960		
Herman, Steven	Temple Univ.			Diag Rad	1988
Herman, Walter M.	Univ. Pennsylvania	Internal Medicine	1967		
Hernandez-Ortiz, Jorge	Univ. Guadalajara	Radiology	1970		
Herr, George R.	Temple Univ.	Anesthesiology	1985		
Herrick, Wayne C.	Jefferson	Orthop Surg	1986		
Herring, Malcolm Bell	Indiana Univ.	General Surgery	1976		
Herschmann, Elias M.	S.U.N.Y., Downstate			Gastroenterology	1968
Herskowitz, Lee J.	Phila. Coll. Osteo. Med.	Pediatrics	1981		
Hertzberg, Barbara S.	Duke Univ.			Diag Rad	1986
Hervada, Arturo R.	Univ. Salamanca (Spain)	Pediatrics	1958		
Heslep, J. Haynes	Univ. Mississippi	Radiology	1966		
Hess, John M.	Jefferson	Anesthesiology	1964		
Hessen, Scott E.	Jefferson	Internal Medicine	1986	Cardiovas Dis	1989
Heymach, George John, III	Jefferson	Internal Medicine	1979		
Higgins, Joseph M.	UMDNJ, Newark	Internal Medicine	1990		
High, David A.	Jefferson	Dermatology	1986		
Hill, Franklyn C., Jr.	Jefferson	Neurology	1957		
Hill, Russell R.	Univ. Minnesota			Gyn Oncol	1985
Hillig, John E., Jr.	Jefferson	Ob/Gyn	1969		
Hiltz, Deborah Jane	Jefferson	Pediatrics	1980		
Himelfarb, Terren M.	Univ. Maryland	Urological Surgery	1972		
Himes, Ralph F., Jr.	Jefferson	Ophthalmology	1958		
Hirsch, Jonathan D.	Med. Coll. PA	Internal Medicine	1980		
Hneleski, Ignatius S., Jr.	Jefferson	Ophthalmology	1971		
Hoch, John R.	Jefferson	General Surgery	1989		

Name	Med School	R Specialty	R Year	F Specialty	F Year
Hodes, Barton L.	Jefferson	Ophthalmology	1970		
Hodge, Joseph	Jefferson	General Surgery	1958		
Hodson, Anita Hollmer	Tufts Univ.			Medical Oncology	1974
Hoffman, Joel D.	Jefferson	Orthop Surg	1961		
Hoffman, Morton	Univ. Pennsylvania			Nephrology	1967
Hofford, James M.	Jefferson	Internal Medicine	1955		
Hogan, Thomas F.	Virginia Commonwealth Univ.	Internal Medicine	1975		
Holder, Thomas Martin	Bowman Gray Sch. Med.	General Surgery	1960		
Hollander, Irwin J.	Jefferson	Pathology	1979		
Holloway-Helem, Linda M.	Meharry Med. Coll.	Pathology	1984		
Holman, David P.	Yale Univ.	Internal Medicine	1956	Cardiovas Dis	1957
Holmes, William F.	Jefferson	Otolaryngology	1973		
Holmes-Siedle, Monica	Trinity Coll., (Ireland)	Pediatrics	1970		
Holsten, Steven B.	Jefferson	Orthop Surg	1974		
Homel, Steven R.	Jefferson	Pediatrics	1964		
Honebrink, Ann L.	Medical Coll. Pennsylvania	Ob/Gyn	1985		
Hongsanandana, Chusri	Chulalongkorn Univ. (Thailand)			Repro Endo	1959
Hopkins, James T.	Jefferson	Internal Medicine	1984	Cardiovas Dis	1987
Hopper, Bruce D.	Jefferson	Ob/Gyn	1981		
Horensten, Mayer Lee	Coll. Osteo Med., Des Moines			Nephrology	1971
Horn, Harold Russell, Jr.	Univ. Pennsylvania	Orthop Surg	1954		
Horn, Michael D.	S.U.N.Y., Upstate	Ob/Gyn	1974		
Horstmann, Eckhard R.	Munich Univ.	Internal Medicine	1970		
Horstmann, Helen Meeks	Med. Coll. Pennsylvania	Orthop Surg	1977		
Horstmann, Joseph Patrick	Jefferson	Pathology	1976		
Horvath, Ronald J.	Jefferson	Orthop Surg	1969		
Horvick, David	Jefferson	Internal Medicine	1985		
Horwitz, Brett R.	Temple Univ.	Orthop Surg	1990		
Hourigan Matthias	Univ. Pittsburgh	Oral & Max Surg	1961		
Houseknecht, Thomas R.	Univ. Pennsylvania	Psychiatry	1963		
Housman, John H.	Jefferson	Ophthalmology	1975		
Houston, Robert Ross	Jefferson	Internal Medicine	1978		
Howanitz, E. Paul	Jefferson	General Surgery	1983		
Howell, Stephen M.	Northwestern Univ.	Orthop Surg	1986		
Hoyer, Paul J.	Jefferson	Pathology	1980		
Hsieh, Edmond Wei-dean	Nat. Def. Med. Coll. (Taiwan)	Pathology	1976		
Huang, Peter Sheng-Hsiong	Taipei Med. Coll. (Tiawan)	Neuro Surg	1977		
Hubbard, F. Alan	Med. Coll. Virginia	General Surgery	1988		
Huber, Irving P.	S.U.N.Y., Upstate	Internal Medicine	1979		
Huddell, Benjamin R.	Jefferson	Psychiatry	1970		
Hufty, Mary Page	U.C., San Diego	Family Practice	1979		
Hughes, Eugene Patrick, Jr.	Jefferson	General Surgery	1980		
Hulkower, Stephen	Jefferson	Family Practice	1984		
Hultin, Mae H.	Hahnemann Univ.			Hematology	1976
Hume, Eric L.	S.U.N.Y., Syracuse	Orthop Surg	1983		
Humeniuk, Harry M.	Med. Coll. Ohio	Dermatology	1990		
Hummer, Charles D., Jr.	Hahnemann Univ.	Orthop Surg	1972		
Hunka, Larry E.	Univ. Alberta (Canada)			Hand Surgery	1980
Hunt, Sean E.	Univ. Maryland	Internal Medicine	1988		
Hunter, James M.	Jefferson	Orthop Surg	1958		

Name	Med School	R Specialty	R Year	F Specialty	F Year
Hur, Gham	Korea Univ.	Diag Rad	1979		
Hurvitz, Lawrence M.	Jefferson	Ophthalmology	1979		
Husain, Azam	Univ. Osmania (India)			Cardiovas Dis	1965
Hutchinson, Douglas T.	Jefferson	Orthop Surg	1989		
Hutt, Gordon H.	New York Med. Coll.			Cardiovas Dis	1985
Hux, Charles H.	Case Western	Ob/Gyn	1985	Mater/Fetal Med	1987
Huxster, Robert H.	Jefferson	Orthop Surg	1983	Hand Surgery	1984
Hwang, George S. W.	Univ. New S. Wales	Pediatrics	1977		
Hyde, William J.	Jefferson	General Surgery	1977		
Hyett, Marvin R.	Jefferson	Ob/Gyn	1968		
Hyland, Bernard V.	Jefferson	Radiology	1957		

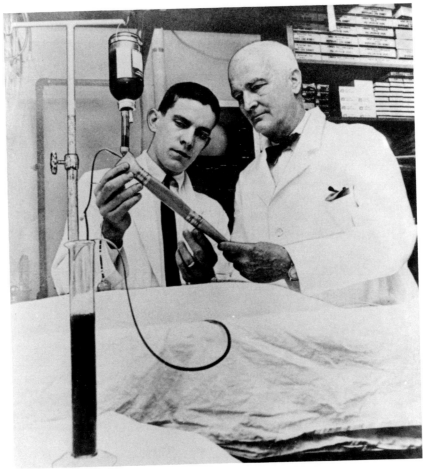

Dr. William T. Lemmon, Jr. (surgical resident, 1967) discusses blood transfusion experiment with Dr. Gibbon.

Vartan Igiobashian
Phila. Coll. Osteo. Med.

Beno U. Ihle
Melbourne

Albert M. Imobersteg
New York Med. Coll.

Anthony Infantolino
UMDNJ, Rutgers

Charles M. Intenzo
Hahnemann

Anthony M. Interdonato
Jefferson

Carmen P. Irizarry
Puerto Rico

Name	Med School	R Specialty	R Year	F Specialty	F Year
Ifarraguerri, Agustin	Central Univ. Madrid	Psychiatry	1964		
Igarashi, Makoto	Keio Univ. (Japan)			Otolaryngology	1960
Igidbashian, Vartan	Phila. Coll. Osteo. Med.			Diag Rad	1988
Ihle, Benno U.	Univ. Melbourne			Nephrology	1978
Ikeda, Satoshi	Keio Univ. (Japan)			Cardiothor Surg	1976
Imobersteg, A. Michael	New York Med. Coll.	Orthop Surg	1986		
Infantolino, Anthony	UMDNJ, Rutgers	Internal Medicine	1988		
Inghram, John Garrett	Jefferson	General Surgery	1956		
Intenzo, Charles M.	Hahnemann Univ.	Rad Oncol	1986		
Interdonato, Anthony Michael	Jefferson	Ophthalmology	1978		
Iossifides, Ioulios	Aristotelian Univ. (Greece)	Pathology	1960		
Irizarry, Carmen P.	Univ. Puerto Rico	Psychiatry	1988		
Isenberg, Gerald	Mt. Sinai Sch. Med.			Colon and Rec Surg	1988
Ishkhanian, Hagop M.	Amer. Univ. Beirut	Orthop Surg	1977		
Isserman, Mark S.	Jefferson	Internal Medicine	1980	Cardiovas Dis	1983
Ivins, J. Leonard	Middlesex Univ. ***	Psychiatry	1966		
Ivker, Milton	Jefferson	General Surgery	1957		
Ivker, Morris	Temple Univ.	Medical Oncology	1949	Medical Oncology	1950

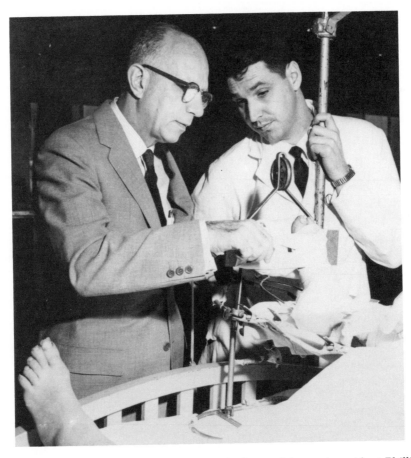

Dr. Anthony F. DePalma (James Edwards Prof. of Orthopaedic Surgery) instructs resident Phillip J. Marone (1963).

Victor S.B. Jorden
S.U.N.Y., Downstate

Barry J. Jacobson
Jefferson

G. Whitfield James
Bowman Gray

Joseph M. Janowicz
Temple

Albert D. Janerich
Jefferson

Rehana A. Jan
Khyber Med. Coll. (Pakistan)

Harish S. Jhaveri
Baroda (India)

Anthony Johnson
West Virginia Osteo. Med.

Eric G. Johnson
Jefferson

Mark W. Johnson
Tennessee

Jeffrey I. Joseph
Phila. Coll. Osteo. Med.

John P.S. Janda
Aberdeen

Name	Med School	R Specialty	R Year	F Specialty	F Year
Jabourian, Zaven	American Univ. Beirut	Otolaryngology	1985		
Jackson, Laird G.	Univ. Cincinnati	Internal Medicine	1962		
Jackson, Paul W.	Coll. Med. Evangelists	Otolaryngology	1965		
Jacobs, Stanley R.	Jefferson	Phys Med/Rehab	1976		
Jacobson, Arnold	New York Univ.	Ob/Gyn	1969		
Jacobson, Barry J.	Jefferson	Ob/Gyn	1984		
Jacoby, William J., Jr.	Jefferson	Internal Medicine	1956	Cardiovas Dis	1957
Jaeger, Edward A.	Univ. Pittsburgh	Ophthalmology	1964		
Jaeger, Scott H.	Jefferson	Orthop Surg	1977		
Jafari, Nercy	Univ. Teheran			Cardiothor Surg	1977
Jaffe, David J.	Temple Univ.	Pediatrics	1990		
Jaffe, Marvin E.	Jefferson	Urological Surgery	1967		
Jafri, Mumtaz	Univ. Dacca (Bangladesh)	Internal Medicine	1973		
Jain, Surendra V.	Univ. Bombay	Internal Medicine	1981		
James, G. Whitfield	Bowman Gray	Internal Medicine	1990		
James, Urmila	Univ. Osmania Med. (India)	Ob/Gyn	1967		
Jan, Rehana A.	Khyber Med. Coll. (Pakistan)	Anesthesiology	1979		
Janda, John P.S.	Univ. Aberdeen	Orthop Surg	1982		
Janerich, Albert D.	Jefferson	Phys Med/Rehab	1980		
Janowicz, Joseph M.	Temple Univ.	Oral & Max Surg	1986		
Jarmoszuk, Nicholas	Jefferson	Med. Genetics	1975	Gastroenterology	1977
Jasper, Edward H.	Jefferson	Internal Medicine	1983		
Jawad, Khalil	Baghdad Coll. Med.	Neuro Surg	1967		
Jayanti, Subbarao	Andhra Univ. (India)	Anesthesiology	1980		
Jeffrey, Robert Brooke	Jefferson	Radiology	1953		
Jernstrom, Paul Herbert	Jefferson	Pathology	1950		
Jhaveri, Harish S.	Baroda Univ. (India)			Diag Rad	1982
Johnson, Anthony	West Virginia Osteo. Med.			Internal Medicine	1989
Johnson, Bertram Lee,, Jr.	Jefferson	Internal Medicine	1978		
Johnson, Eric G.	Jefferson	Family Practice	1980		
Johnson, James J.	Jefferson			Cardiov Dis	1953
Johnson, Mark, W.	Univ. Tennessee	Oral & Max Surg	1989		
Johnson, Robert G.	Jefferson	General Surgery	1955		
Johnson, Ronald	Cornell Univ.	Ophthalmology	1981		
Johnson, Samuel C., III	Univ. Pittsburgh	Oral & Max Surg	1960		
Johnson, William G.	Jefferson	Radiology	1950	Pathology	1948
Johnston, Patricia A.	Hahnemann Univ.	Pediatrics	1974		
Johnston, Terry A.	Tufts Univ.	Radiology	1970		
Jones, A. Alexander	Univ. Virginia			Orthop Surg	1988
Jones, Marion K.	Loma Linda Univ.	Psychiatry	1970		
Jorden, Victor S.B.	S.U.N.Y., Downstate			Anesthesiology	1988
Joseph, Jeffrey I.	Phila. Coll. Osteo. Med.	Anesthesiology	1988		
Joseph, Raymond E.	George Washington Univ.	Internal Medicine	1977	Gastroenterology	1979
Joseph, Sunny V.	Univ. Juarez (Mexico)	Psychiatry	1990		
Joshi, Prakashchandra	Gvant Med. Sch. (India)			Pulm Dis	1966
Joson, Raymond M.	Georgetown Univ.	Neuro Surg	1961		
Josselson, Alan S.	Jefferson	Pulm Dis	1978		
Joyce, Michael F.	Jefferson	Orthop Surg	1960		
Judd, James Malcolm	Harvard Univ.	General Surgery	1952		
Judge, Sheila	Med. Coll. Pennsylvania			Child Psychiatry	1989
Judson, James N.	Jefferson	Orthop Surg	1971		
Jumbala, Puangkaeo	Univ. Med. Sciences (Thailand)	Dermatology	1957		

Zain Kadri
Madras (India)

Vivian B. Kane
S.U.N.Y., Downstate

Samuel Kahnowitz
New York Med. Coll.

Marc S. Kallins
Guadalajara

Louis L. Keeler, Jr.
Univ. Pennsylvania

Eliot F. Kaplan
Jefferson

Susan Kaplan
Jefferson

David Karasick
Jefferson

Susan R. Kassutto
Tel Aviv

Das C.L. Kareti
Andhra (India)

Mitchell Karten
Albany Med. Coll.

Stephen Karasick
Jefferson

Name	Med School	R Specialty	R Year	F Specialty	F Year
Kachel, Richard G.	Columbia Univ., Coll. P. & S.	Internal Medicine	1976		
Kadri, Zain Ud-din	Univ. Madras (India)	Otolaryngology	1978		
Kahn, Hyman R.	Jefferson	Internal Medicine	1959	Cardiovas Dis	1960
Kahnowitz, Samuel David	New York Med. Coll.	Internal Medicine	1979		
Kain, Thomas M., III	Jefferson	Orthop Surg	1978		
Kain, Thomas Michael, Jr.	Jefferson			Cardiovas Dis	1951
Kaiser, James	Albert Einstein Med. Coll.	Internal Medicine	1989		
Kallins, Marc S.	Univ. Guadalajara	Phys Med/Rehab	1982		
Kaloustian, Harry D.	American Univ. Bierut	Internal Medicine	1961		
Kaltenbach, James Lee	Temple Univ.	Pediatrics	1978		
Kamel, Hany T.	Ain Shams Univ. (Egypt)			Blood Banking	1987
Kane, Bruce I.	Temple Univ.	Pathology	1986		
Kane, Henry A.	Jefferson	Pediatrics	1956		
Kane, Michael J.	UMDNJ, Newark	Internal Medicine	1986		
Kane, Vivian B.	S.U.N.Y., Downstate	Emerg Med	1988		
Kane, Vivien G.	Stony Brook	Radiology	1984		
Kang, Yoo Goo	Seoul Nat. Univ.	Anesthesiology	1978		
Kansu, Emin	Hacettepe Univ. (Turkey)	Internal Medicine	1974	Hematology	1978
Kapadia, Dilip	Karnatak Univ. (India)			Nuclear Medicine	1982
Kapcar, Andrew J., Jr.	Jefferson	Pathology	1960		
Kaplan, Eliot F.	Jefferson	Psychiatry	1984		
Kaplan, Richard H.	Hahnemann Univ.	Phys Med/Rehab	1976		
Kaplan, Stephen M.	Univ. Pennsylvania			Gastroenterology	1969
Kaplan, Susan G.	Jefferson	Anesthesiology	1988		
Kaplow, Gwen Katz	Jefferson	Ob/Gyn	1973		
Karasick, David	Jefferson	Radiology	1978		
Karasick, Stephen	Jefferson	Radiology	1978		
Kareti, Das C. L.	Andhra Univ. (India)	Neurology	1984		
Karim, Mahmudul	Dhaka Med. Coll. (Bangladesh)	Pediatrics	1962		
Kariman, Khalil	Meshed Univ. (Iran)	Internal Medicine	1975		
Karmazin, Nelly	State Med. Inst. Kishinev (USSR)	Pathology	1984		
Karpuzoglu, Tuncer	Istanbul Univ.	General Surgery	1974		
Karten, Mitchell K.	Albany Med. Coll.	Internal Medicine	1983		
Kashdan, Bennett	Stony Brook			Radiology	1989
Kass, Younis	Univ. Hamburg			Cardiovas Dis	1962
Kassell, Martin B.	Hahnemann Univ.	Psychiatry	1971		
Kassutto, Susan R.	Tel Aviv Univ.	Pediatrics	1990		
Kaswan, Moises	Univ. Central Venezuela			Oral & Max Surg	1962
Katchman, Jerome J.	Jefferson	Dermatology	1974		
Kates, Malcolm	Jefferson	Internal Medicine	1964		
Katz, Harry R.	Jefferson	Rad Oncol	1977		
Katz, Leonard	Univ. Cath. Louvain (Belgium)	Neurology	1969		
Katz, Sheila Sue	Duke Univ.	Pathology	1973		
Katz, Shelly A.	Univ. CETEC (Dominican Republic)			Endocrinology	1987
Kauffman, James M.	Phila. Coll. Osteo. Med.			Endocrinology	1982
Kauffman, Randi L.	Med. Coll. Pennsylvania	Radiology	1987		
Kaufman, Harvey L.	Med. Coll. Pennsylvania	Family Practice	1980		
Kaufman, Larry J.	Med. Coll. Pennsylvania	Ob/Gyn	1988		
Kaufman, Laryssa Nahirniak	Jefferson	Internal Medicine	1979		
Kaufman, Susan I.	Phila. Coll. Osteo. Med.	Ob/Gyn	1986		
Kauh, Young Chai	Yonsei Univ. (Korea)	Dermatology	1971		
Kavagul, Muenchai	Univ. Med. Sciences (Thailand)	Pediatrics	1961		

Name	Med School	R Specialty	R Year	F Specialty	F Year
Kavandi, Abdol-Hossein	Univ. Teheran			Gastroenterology	1960
Kawamura, Junichiro	Kyoto Univ.	Neurology	1970		
Kay, Patricia A.J.	Univ. Glasgow	Psychiatry	1980		
Kazal, Henry Lawrence	Georgetown Univ.	Pathology	1955		
Kazanski, Mary Beth	Michigan State Univ.	Ob/Gyn	1987		
Kazmi, Najam-ul-Hassan	Nishtar Med. Coll.	Neuro Surg	1979		
Kazmi, Surayya J.	Punjab Univ. Pakistan	Anesthesiology	1980		
Kean, Herbert	Hahnemann Univ.	Otolaryngology	1960		
Kearney, Paul A., Jr.	Jefferson	General Surgery	1983		
Keefe, Bernadette	Columbia Univ., Coll. P. & S.			Diag Rad	1987
Keefe, John P.	Jefferson	Ob/Gyn	1966		
Keeler, Louis L., Jr.	Univ. Pennsylvania	Urological Surgery	1967		
Keeley, Francis X.	Hahnemann Univ.	Internal Medicine	1960		
Keitel, Norma Blickfelt	Columbia Univ., Coll. P. & S.			Psychiatry	1959
Keith, Michael W.	Ohio State Univ.			Hand Surgery	1979
Keller, Irvin B.	Jefferson	Neuro Surg	1970		
Kelley, Kristine	Univ. Texas	General Surgery	1988		
Kelly, James D.	Georgetown Univ.	Radiology	1968		
Kelly, John J., Jr.	Jefferson	Internal Medicine	1957	Cardiovas Dis	1960
Kelly, Mark F.	Jefferson	Otolaryngology	1990		
Kelsey, David M.	Univ. Pennsylvania	Urological Surgery	1973		
Kelton, Franklin C., Jr.	Jefferson	Family Practice	1977		
Kempf, Charles T.	S.U.N.Y., Downstate	Radiology	1981		
Kemps, Anton Peter	Jefferson	Internal Medicine	1979		
Kendall, Benjamin	Temple Univ.	Ob/Gyn	1962		
Kenner, George R., Jr.	Jefferson	Otolaryngology	1983		
Kenton, Edgar J., III	Cornell Univ.	Neurology	1970		
Keohane, Richard B.	Jefferson	Radiology	1972		
Kern, Jay A.	Jefferson	Internal Medicine	1961	Gastroenterology	1962
Kerrigan, James J.	Jefferson	Neurology	1989		
Kersten, Gunther H.	Univ. Cologne Med. Sch. (Germany)	Internal Medicine	1962	Cardiovas Dis	1961
Kerut, Timothy P.	Univ. Mississippi			Pediatric Allergy	1990
Kessler, Seymour	Phila. Coll. Osteo Med.	Ophthalmology	1975		
Kestner, Joseph F., Jr.	Jefferson	Internal Medicinet	1973		
Keveney, John J., Jr.	Jefferson	Internal Medicine	1972	Nephrology	1980
Khajavi, Abolghassem	Univ. Teheran	Radiology	1961		
Khan, Meher S.	Fatima Jinnah Med. Coll. (Pakistan)			Pediatric Allergy	1988
Khouri, Margaret	Univ. Vermont	Internal Medicine	1985		
Kiernan, Thomas W.	New Jersey Coll. Med.	Internal Medicine	1972		
Kilcullen, Michael J.	Jefferson	Pediatrics	1977		
Kim, Achin	Korea Univ.			Pediatric Allergy	1977
Kim, Chang Hwan	Yonsei Univ. (Korea)	Pediatrics	1966		
Kim, Dong-Sun	Med. Coll. Chuhdm Korea	Psychiatry	1973		
Kim, Hyun Jung	Yonsei Univ. Korea	Pathology	1974		
Kim, Joseph J.	Univ. Maryland	Internal Medicine	1989		
Kim, Sung M.	Yonsei Univ. (Korea)	Rad Oncol	1988		
Kim, Yong Mook	Yonsei Univ. (Korea)			Diag Rad	1979
Kim, Young Bai	Yonsei Univ. (Korea)			Diag Rad	1981
Kim, Young Jin	Yonsei Univ. (Korea)	Pediatrics	1967		
Kim, Yung Sup	Seoul Univ. (Korea)	Internal Medicine	1957		
Kimmel, Murray Harris	Temple Univ.	Urological Surgery	1959		

Name	Med School	R Specialty	R Year	F Specialty	F Year
King, Lorraine C.	Med. Coll. Pennsylvania	Ob/Gyn	1975	Repro Endo	1976
King, Melissa B.	Johns Hopkins Univ.			Pulm Dis	1990
King, Richard S.	Albany Med. Coll.	Family Practice	1980		
Kinney, Carolyn L.	Boston Univ.	Phys Med/Rehab	1984		
Kinori, Ilan	Rush Med. Coll.	Radiology	1989		
Kinsey, Frank R.	Jefferson	Radiology	1948		
Kinsey, M. Dean	Jefferson	Internal Medicine	1972	Gastroenterology	1973
Kirkland, Michele R.	Jefferson	Anesthesiology	1988		
Kirkpatrick, William H.	Univ. Cincinnati			Hand Surgery	1988
Kitchin, Llewellyn	Univ. Virginia			Gastroenterology	1990
Kittleberger, W. Clark, Jr.	Jefferson	Ob/Gyn	1954		
Klein, Edward M.	Temple Univ.	Ob/Gyn	1982		
Klein, Murray	Phila. Coll. Osteo. Med.	Phys Med/Rehab	1981		
Klein, Stephen V.	Albert Einstein Coll. Med.			Radiology	1989
Klemek, Joseph S.	Jefferson	Orthop Surg	1972		
Klevan, Judy L.	S.U.N.Y., Buffalo			Pediatrics	1989
Klick, Warren E.	S.U.N.Y., Syracuse	Emerg Med	1990		
Klim, Gerald V.	Jefferson	Phys Med/Rehab	1983		
Klinman, Steven W.	Jefferson	Internal Medicine	1974		
Kmonicek, Joseph M.	Jefferson	Internal Medicine	1982	Cardiovas Dis	1984
Knapp, Stephanie A.	Ohio Univ.			Pediatric Allergy	1987
Knepp, Mary Elizabeth	Jefferson	Dermatology	1976		
Knowles, Harry Joseph	Jefferson	General Surgery	1947		
Knowles, William O.	Hahnemann Univ.			Pediatric Allergy	1982
Kobialka, Walter M.	Jefferson	Internal Medicine	1977	Nephrology	1978
Kobus, Raymond J.	Wright State Univ.			Hand Surgery	1990
Kocher, William D.	Jefferson	Pathology	1985		
Kodroff, Michael B.	Jefferson	Radiology	1984		
Koehler, Jan O.	Penn. State Univ.	Internal Medicine	1978		
Koenigsberg, Bess A.	UMDNJ, Newark	Internal Medicine	1987		
Koffler, Howard B.	Temple Univ.	Internal Medicine	1974	Pulm Dis	1976
Kogan, Allan Jay	Baylor Coll. Med.	Family Practice	1977		
Kohl, John Michael	Jefferson	Radiology	1954		
Kokolis, Panagis S.	Athens Univ. (Greece)	Internal Medicine	1963		
Kolberg, Heidi L.	Johns Hopkins Univ.			Diag Rad	1990
Komarnicky, Lydia T.	Med. Coll. Pennsylvania	Rad Oncol	1986	Rad Oncol	1987
Kondreddy, Bharathi D.	Andhra Univ. (India)	Neurology	1984		
Kong, Albert Yin Tau, Jr.	Jefferson	Orthop Surg	1964		
Koniges, Frank C.	Univ. Texas	General Surgery	1986		
Koniver, Garth A.	Jefferson	Radiology	1972		
Kono, Chikao	Nagoya Univ. (Japan)	Neurology	1967		
Konwinski, Marian	Med. Coll. Warsaw			Hematology	1983
Koo, Kim Eng	Temple Univ.	Neuro Surg	1988		
Kopp, Lizabeth A.	Univ. Virginia	Ob/Gyn	1990		
Koppel, Max M.	Jefferson	Urological Surgery	1965		
Korman, Michael J.	Jefferson	Internal Medicine	1984	Pulm Dis	1986
Korneluk, Theresa J.	Jefferson	Ophthalmology	1981		
Kornhauser, Michael S.	Jefferson	Pediatrics	1983	Neo- Perinatal Med	1986
Koshar, Mark I.	New Jersey Med. Coll.	Internal Medicine	1977		
Kosoy, Jerome	Jefferson	Otolaryngology	1968		
Kostelnik, Elizabeth V.	Woman's Med. Coll.			Radiology	1965
Kostelnik, Francis V.	Jefferson	Pathology	1965		
Kostinas, John E.	Jefferson			Hematology	1963

Name	Med School	R Specialty	R Year	F Specialty	F Year
Kothari, Mayank Kantilal	Baroda Univ. (India)			Medical Oncology	1977
Kovach, Coleman William	George Washington Univ.			Psychiatry	1951
Kovach, Richard C.	Jefferson	Internal Medicine	1985	Cardiovas Dis	1988
Kowalske, Karen J.	Univ. Florida	Phys Med/Rehab	1990		
Kozielski, Joseph W.	Jefferson	Orthop Surg	1976		
Krain, Laurence S.	Jefferson	Neurology	1987		
Krain, Samuel	Jefferson	Radiology	1966		
Krakovitz, Mark R.	Med. Coll. Pennsylvania			Rad Oncol	1988
Krall, Michael L.	Jefferson	Pediatrics	1983	Allergy and Immun	1985
Krall, Robert A.	Jefferson	Pathology	1980		
Kramer, David J.	Jefferson	Internal Medicine	1986		
Kramer, Frederick L.	Jefferson	Radiology	1978		
Kramer, Neil R.	Temple Univ.	Radiology	1985		
Krasner, Paul P.	Hahnemann Univ.			Nephrology	1970
Krasney, Robert L.	Jefferson			Gastroenterology	1957
Krasnow, Steven H.	Stritch Sch. Med.			Hematology	1979
Kratz, Christa Charlotte	Univ. Erlangen (Germany)	Pediatrics	1961		
Kravitz, Elaine K.	Mt. Sinai Sch. Med.			Allergy and Immun	1987
Kravitz, Stuart A.	Temple Univ.			Pediatric Allergy	1981
Krell, Stephen P.	Hahnemann Univ.	Ob/Gyn	1982		
Kremer, Frederic B.	Jefferson	Ophthalmology	1980		
Kresovich, Kimberly A.	Hahnemann Univ.	Emerg Med	1988		
Kron, Kenneth M.	Jefferson	Psychiatry	1969		
Krop, Paul N.	Georgetown Univ.			Orthop Surg	1981
Krotec, Joseph William	Hahnemann Univ.	Ob/Gyn	1980		
Kruper, John S.	Jefferson	Orthop Surg	1963		
Kucer, Kathleen Ann	Jefferson	Dermatology	1980		
Kumar, Parvesh	Univ. Kansas	Diag Rad	1990		
Kuperman, Julio Luis	Buenos Aires State Univ.	Neurology	1971		
Kuperstein, Arthur S.	Temple Univ.	Oral & Max Surg	1977		
Kurey, Robert John	Univ. Pittsburgh	Psychiatry	1960		
Kurtz, Alfred B.	Stanford Univ.			Diag Rad	1978
Kushner, Bertrand	Jefferson	Internal Medicine	1959	Gastroenterology	1960
Kyriazis, Aikaterini	Aristotelian Univ. (Greece)	Pathology	1968		

It is a matter of primary importance in the cultivation of those sciences, in which truth is discoverable by the human intellect, that the investigator should be free, independent, unshackled in his movements; that he should be allowed and enabled to fix his mind intently, nay exclusively, on his special object.

John Henry, Cardinal Newman (1801–1890)

Maria L. Labi
S.U.N.Y., Buffalo

John W. Lace
Pittsburgh

Charles J. Lamb
Jefferson

Rick O. Lambert
New York Univ.

Richard E. Landau
George Washington

Jeanne LaMont
Med. Col. Penna

Deana M. Lazaro
New York Univ.

José R. Landron
Puerto Rico

Jane N. Laeger
Tufts

Joseph H. Lanzillo
Univ. Florida

Domingo A. Lara
El Salvador

Jean Lee
UMDNJ, Newark

Name	Med School	R Specialty	R Year	F Specialty	F Year
Laauwe, Roger Clive	Jefferson	Ophthalmology	1959		
Labi, Maria L.	S.U.N.Y., Buffalo	Phys Med/Rehab	1989		
Laboda, Gerald	Temple Univ.	Oral & Max Surg	1963		
Lace, John W.	Univ. Pittsburgh	Internal Medicine	1989		
Lachenal-Santos, Estela, N.	Univ. St. Tomas (Philippines)	Anesthesiology	1981		
Lachman, Martin J.	Temple Univ.			Diag Rad	1983
Lackay, R. Howard	Jefferson	Internal Medicine	1949		
Laeger, Jane N.	Tufts Univ.	Ob/Gyn	1983		
Lafsky, Robert D.	Univ. Pennsylvania	Internal Medicine	1978		
Lai, Ka-Siu	Albert Einstein Coll. Med.	Phys Med/Rehab	1988		
Laicha, Patricia A.	Woman's Med. Coll.	Pediatrics	1972	Pediatric Allergy	1976
Laigon, Eugene E., Jr.	George Washington Univ.	Otolaryngology	1979		
Lally, James F.	Jefferson	Radiology	1972		
Lamb, Charles J.	Jefferson	General Surgery	1985		
Lambert, Edward H.N.	Queen's Univ. (Canada)	Anesthesiology	1968		
Lambert, Rick O.	New York Univ.	Internal Medicine	1987		
Lambright, Warren Dean	Jefferson	Internal Medicine	1974		
LaMont, Jeanne	Med. Coll. Pennsylvania	Ob/Gyn	1984		
Lampert, Scott	Jefferson	Ophthalmology	1979		
Landau, Richard E.	George Washington Univ.	Urological Surgery	1989		
Landin, Peter D.	Jefferson	Orthop Surg	1987		
Landron, Jose R.	Univ. Puerto Rico ('57)	Radiology	1964		
Landron, Jose R.	Univ. Puerto Rico ('78)	Diag Rad	1982		
Landsberg, Marc Alan	Temple Univ.	Ob/Gyn	1979		
Lane, Jane Lindsey	Oxford Univ.	Pediatrics	1982		
Lane, Thomas A.	Jefferson			Hematology	1975
Lang, Albert A.	Tulane Univ.	Internal Medicine	1959		
Lang, John B.	Phila. Coll. Osteo. Med.	Anesthesiology	1984		
Lang, Warren Reichert	Jefferson	Pathology	1970		
Lange, Eva	Academy of Med. Warsaw	Internal Medicine	1983		
Lantos, Raymond Jay	Jefferson	Internal Medicine	1954	Cardiovas Dis	1955
Lanzillo, Joseph H.	Univ. Florida	Rad Oncol	1986		
Laogan, Evelina C.	Univ. St. Tomas (Philippines)	Pediatrics	1962		
Lara, Domingo	Univ. El Salvador	Neurology	1983		
Larner, James M.	Univ. Virginia	Rad Oncol	1989		
Larrieu, Alberto J.	Univ. San Juan	General Surgery	1983		
Larson, John	Jefferson	Anesthesiology	1990		
Latham, Phillip T.	Ohio State	Oral & Max Surg	1973		
Lattimer, Gary L.	Temple Univ.	Internal Medicine	1972		
Laucius, J. Frederick	Jefferson	Internal Medicine	1973	Medical Oncology	1972
Lazaro, Deana M.	New York Univ.	Internal Medicine	1989		
Lazaro, Ma Thelma	Univ. Philippines	Pediatrics	1972	Pediatrics	1973
Lazovitz, David A.	New York Med. Coll.	Pediatrics	1974		
Le, Nguyen	Univ. Saigon			Cardiovas Dis	1982
Leaming, Robert H.	Jefferson	Radiology	1950	Radiology	1951
Leavitt, Ronald J.	Columbia Univ., Coll. P. & S.			Hand Surgery	1979
Lebeau, Jack	Case Western Reserve Univ.	Internal Medicine	1969		
Lebenthal, Mark J.	Univ. Guadalajara			Cardiovas Dis	1982
Lebowitz, Alan	Hahnemann Univ.	Internal Medicine	1969	Hematology	1970
Lederman, Sandra D.	Woman's Med. Coll.	Anesthesiology	1961		
Lee, Arthur B.H.	Jefferson	Ob/Gyn	1962		
Lee, Doris Chan	Inst. Med. Rangoon (Burma)	Anesthesiology	1982		
Lee, Jean	UMDNJ, Newark	Internal Medicine	1984	Nephrology	1986

Name	Med School	R Specialty	R Year	F Specialty	F Year
Lee, Joon Jae	Korea Univ.	Radiology	1974		
Lee, Kyu Hwan	Yonsei Univ. (Korea)	Radiology	1959		
Lee, Seung Ho	Yonsei Univ. (Korea)	Radiology	1967		
Lee, Yon Hee	Yonsei Univ. (Korea)	Ob/Gyn	1968		
Lefkowitz, Ilene B.	Jefferson	Pediatrics	1985		
Leftenant, Samuel G.	S.U.N.Y., Downstate	Anesthesiology	1986		
Lehman, Thomas P.	Jefferson	Urological Surgery	1986		
Lehrer, Luisa E.	Jefferson	Anesthesiology	1990		
Leib, Pamela L.	Jefferson	Psychiatry	1985		
Leichner, Thomas J.	Jefferson	General Surgery	1970		
Leicht, Paul Franklin	Jefferson	Pathology	1968		
Leinberry, Charles F.	Jefferson	Orthop Surg	1989	Hand Surgery	1990
Leitch, Jennifer L.	New York Med. Coll.	Psychiatry	1987		
Lele, Bramod	Univ. Bombay	Internal Medicine	1984	Nephrology	1985
Lemmon, William T., Jr.	Jefferson	General Surgery	1967		
Lenahan, Terrence P.	Jefferson	Internal Medicine	1990		
Lenchner, Gregory S.	Columbia Univ. Coll. P. & S.	Internal Medicine	1978	Pulm Dis	1980
Lenehan, Peter F.	S.U.N.Y., Downstate	Internal Medicine	1987		
Leonard, Edward C., Jr.	Jefferson	Psychiatry	1968		
Lesorgen, Philip R.	Boston Univ.			Repro Endo	1988
LeStrange, Thomas A.	Jefferson	Pathology	1947		
Letteri, Joseph M.	Georgetown Univ.			Nephrology	1963
Lev-Toaff, Anna	New York Univ.	Radiology	1985		
Levenberg, Steven	Jefferson	Internal Medicine	1982		
Levette, Andrew R.	Howard Univ.	Anesthesiology	1987		
Levin, Ellis R.	Jefferson	Family Practice	1978		
Levin, Eric M.	Univ. Lille (France)	Psychiatry	1984		
Levin, Gary Jan	Jefferson	Ophthalmology	1977		
Levin, Gene D.	Jefferson	Orthop Surg	1974		
LeVine, Jerome Edward	Hahnemann Univ.	Ophthalmology	1954		
Levine, Jonathan K.	Univ. North Carolina	Internal Medicine	1989		
Levine, Laurie J.	S.U.N.Y., Stony Brook	Dermatology	1988		
Levinson, John M.	Jefferson			Ob/Gyn	1955
Levinson, Sander J.	Jefferson	Internal Medicine	1972	Pulm Dis	1974
Levitsky, Carl M.	Hahnemann Univ.	Internal Medicine	1977		
Levitt, Richard L.	Jefferson	Orthop Surg	1972		
Levy, David B.	Temple Univ.			Family Practice	1988
Lewis, Daniel W.	Jefferson			Cardiovas Dis	1952
Lewis, Errol	Univ. Witwatersrand			Diag Rad	1981
Lewis, Gregory Lee	Jefferson	Internal Medicine	1978		
Lewis, William J.	Jefferson	Otolaryngology	1975		
Lewy, Robert I.	Univ Pennsylvania			Hematology	1979
Lex, Joseph R., Jr.	Univ. Texas	Emerg Med	1989		
Liao, Margaret K.	Brown Univ.	Psychiatry	1990		
Libshitz, Herman I.	Hahnemann Univ.	Radiology	1970		
Lieber, Claude	Univ. Cath. Louvain (Belgium)	General Surgery	1980		
Lieber-Seinige, Ursula	Med. Coll. Pennsylvania	General Surgery	1983		
Lieberman, Mark E.	Univ. Miami	Emerg Med	1989		
Lieberman, Steven L.	UMDNJ, Newark	Internal Medicine	1990		
Liebman, Irvin M.	Jefferson	Internal Medicine	1964		
Liggett, Charles L.	Jefferson	General Surgery	1946		
Lightsey, Judith L.	Howard Univ.	Rad Oncol	1990		
Lima, Jose Araujo	Univ. Fed. Rio de Janeiro	Otolaryngology	1978		

Postgraduate Alumni

Name	Med School	R Specialty	R Year	F Specialty	F Year
Lima, Sergio Santos	Univ. Fed. Parana (Brazil)			Radiology	1972
Limberakis, Anthony J.	Duke Univ.	Radiology	1983		
Lin, Shu Ren	Kaohsiung Med. Coll. (Taiwan)	Radiology	1970	Radiology	1971
Linares-Cruz, Hector	Fac. Med.			Cardiovas Dis	1971
Lindell, Marvin M., Jr.	Jefferson	Radiology	1955		
Lindquist, John Norman	Jefferson	Internal Medicine	1951		
Lindsey, Beth H.	Jefferson	Psychiatry	1982		
Lipshutz, Herbert	Jefferson			General Surgery	1949
Lister, Leonard M.	Univ. Maryland			Endocrinology	1956
Litch, Melvin, Jr.	Duke Univ.	Ophthalmology	1966		
Litzenblatt, Ira M.	Univ. Michigan	Internal Medicine	1978		
Liu, Ellen A.	Jefferson	Pediatrics	1990		
Lo Grasso, Paul P.	New York Coll. Osteo Med.	Pathology	1989		
Loewenberg, Leopold S.	Jefferson	Ob/Gyn	1961		
Logan, William E.	Jefferson	Neurology	1970		
Lohman, James W.	Jefferson	Ob/Gyn	1971		
Lohmuller, Herbert W.	Ohio State Univ.			Hematology	1958
Lombardi, Anthony C.	Jefferson	Internal Medicine	1974		
Long, Kimberly R.	Jefferson	Psychiatry	1982		
Long, William B.	Univ. Pennsylvania	Internal Medicine	1969	Gastroenterology	1971
Loose, Jeffrey H.	Hahnemann Univ.	Pathology	1988		
Lopatin, Mark A.	Med. Coll. Pennsylvania			Rheumatology	1989
Lopez, Bernard L.	Jefferson	Emerg Med	1989		
Lorber, Morris L.	Univ. Colorado	Neurology	1967		
Loretto Pleet, Jacqueline	Mt. Sinai Sch. Med.	Pediatrics	1984		
Loriz-Vega, Mark F.	Ponce Sch. Med. (Puerto Rico)	Anesthesiology	1985		
Loucks, James H.	Jefferson	Internal Medicine	1963		
Loughran, Thomas P.	Hahnemann Univ.	Internal Medicine	1982		
Love, Carol A.	Jefferson	Family Practice	1981		
Lovett, Howard A., Jr.	Temple Univ.	Psychiatry	1970		
Lovingood, Frank Smith	Hematology	1947			
Lowy, Joan F.	Case Western Reserve Univ.	Internal Medicine	1968	Gastroenterology	1970
Luberti, Anthony A.	Univ. Pennsylvania			Pediatrics	1988
Lubin, Nathan	State Univ. Iowa	Urological Surgery	1948		
Lucas, Oscar Nestor	Univ. Buenos Aires	Oral & Max Surg	1962		
Lucas, Richard M.	Albert Einstein Coll. Med.	Emerg Med	1987		
Luchaco, Anne L.	Univ. Guadalajara	Pediatrics	1985		
Ludmir, Abraham	San Fernando Med. Fac. (Peru)	Ob/Gyn	1958		
Ludwig, Karl D.	Univ. Pittsburgh	Psychiatry	1966		
Lui, Angela W.K.	Hahnemann Univ.	Internal Medicine	1989		
Luscombe, Herbert Alfred	Jefferson	Dermatology	1948		
Lustig, Robert A.	Jefferson	Rad Oncol	1976		
Lutes, Richard A.	Univ. Illinois	Internal Medicine	1972	Hematology	1974
Luzzi, Carol D.	Hahnemann Univ.			Neo- Perinatal Med	1985

Edward F. McClay
Temple

Marc Manzione
Georgetown

Caròl S. Marshall
Maryland

Raymond J. Marotta, Jr.
UMDNJ, Newark

Patrice Marchand
Connecticut

Tai Joon Moon
Seoul

Frank C. Messina
Mt. Sinai Sch. Med.

Melissa A. McDiarmid
Maryland

Alberto Millos
Uruguay

Melissa A. Markopolos
Maryland

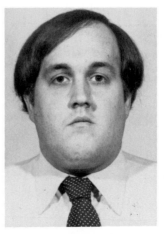

Joseph F. Majdan
Guadalajara

John L. McCormick
Jefferson

Name	Med School	R Specialty	R Year	F Specialty	F Year
MacAndrew, Vincent I.	Jefferson	Orthop Surg	1989		
Macht, Stanley H.	Univ. Virginia	Radiology	1944		
Mack, David A.	Albany Med. Coll.	Internal Medicine	1984		
Mackall, Samuel James	Temple Univ.	Neuro Surg	1963		
Mackell, James V., Jr.	Jefferson	Orthop Surg	1975		
Mackell, James Valentine	Jefferson	Pediatrics	1951		
Mackell, Thomas Edward	Jefferson	Orthop Surg	1978		
Mackessy, Richard P.	UMDNJ, Newark			Hand Surgery	1984
Macklis, Mark A.	Penn State Univ.	Ob/Gyn	1983		
Madan, Vijay	Univ. Delhi (India)	Radiology	1978		
Maehara, Katsuya	Juntendo Univ. (Japan)	Neurology	1977		
Maerz, John C.	Jefferson	Pediatrics	1982		
Maffei, Michael J.	Hahnemann Univ.	Ophthalmology	1975		
Magargal, Larry E.	Temple Univ.	Ophthalmology	1973		
Magargee, Edward M.	Jefferson	Pathology	1969		
Magargee, Susan P.	Phila. Coll. Osteo. Med.	Pediatrics	1989		
Magee, Delors E., Jr.	Meharry Med. Coll.	Ophthalmology	1972		
Magee, Joni L.	Woman's Med. Coll.	Ob/Gyn	1976		
Magill, Ian D.	Jefferson	Psychiatry	1988		
Maguire, David P.	Jefferson	Anesthesiology	1987		
Maguire, Randall Flynn	Jefferson	Pathology	1979		
Mahboubi, Soroosh	Univ. Tehran	Radiology	1973		
Maher, Patricia M.	Phila. Coll. Osteo. Med.	Anesthesiology	1981		
Mahon, John H.	Columbia Univ., Coll. P. & S.	Hand Surgery	1990		
Mahood, William H.	Jefferson	Internal Medicine	1963		
Maiatico, Marc A.	UMDNJ, Newark	General Surgery	1978		
Maier, Donald B.	Hahnemann Univ.	Ob/Gyn	1982		
Mailman, Wendy R.	Jefferson	Anesthesiology	1989		
Maioriello, Richard P.	Jefferson	Otolaryngology	1973		
Majdan, Joseph F.	Univ. Guadalajara			Cardiovas Dis	1981
Majid, Naweed	King Edward Med. Coll. (Pakistan)			Cardiothor Surg	1976
Makary, Rafik Zaky	Ain Shams Univ. (Egypt)	Psychiatry	1973		
Malaspina, Spiros A.	Emory Univ.	Psychiatry	1990		
Malcarney, Courtney M.	Jefferson	Ob/Gyn	1967		
Maldonado, Ruben	Univ. Mexico	Pediatrics	1961		
Malick, Gerald	Temple Univ.	Repro Endo	1970		
Malik, Imtiaz A.	King Edward Med. Coll. (Pakistan)			Hematology	1983
Malis, Helen	Woman's Med. Coll.	Pediatrics	1964		
Malone, Bert H.	Louisiana State Univ.	Radiology	1949		
Malouf, Jamil	Boston Univ.	Internal Medicine	1982		
Malyk, Bohdan	Jefferson	Ob/Gyn	1972	Ob/Gyn	1972
Mandel, Martin Milton	Jefferson	Neurology	1952		
Mandell, Gerald A.	Jefferson	Radiology	1974		
Manfrey, Frank J.	Phila. Coll. Osteo Med.	Ob/Gyn	1979		
Manganiello, Paul D.	Jefferson	Ob/Gyn	1977		
Manges, William Bosley	Jefferson	General Surgery	1948	General Surgery	1950
Manges, Willis Edmund	Jefferson	Radiology	1948		
Mangino, William, II	Univ. Zaragoza (Spain)	Anesthesiology	1982		
Mangione, Maria	Univ. Padua	Neurology	1987		
Manko, Michael A.	Temple Univ.	Infectious Diseases	1964		
Mann, Stephan C.	Jefferson	Psychiatry	1977		
Mannes, Harvey A.	Jefferson	Urological Surgery	1974		
Manser, Jeanne I.	Jefferson	Anesthesiology	1987		

Name	Med School	R Specialty	R Year	F Specialty	F Year
Mansfield, Carl M.	Howard Univ.	Radiology	1961	Rad Oncol	1963
Manus, Stephen C.	Temple Univ.	Internal Medicine	1975	Cardiovas Dis	1977
Manyam, N. V.	Bangalore Med. Coll. (India)	Neurology	1975		
Manzione, Marc	Georgetown Univ.	Orthop Surg	1982		
Mapow, Larry Steven	Jefferson	Pathology	1978		
Marcello, Robert S.	Jefferson	Psychiatry	1984		
March, David E.	Albert Einstein Coll. Med.	Radiology	1989		
Marchand, Patrice M.	Univ. Connecticut	Ob/Gyn	1989		
Marcial, Raul	Univ. Puerto Rico	Radiology	1983		
Marcos, Cecilia Salting	Univ. St. Tomas (Philippines)	Pediatrics	1973		
Mardayat, Maulana	Univ. Indonesia	Neuro Surg	1983		
Margasahayam, Jayanthi N.	Bangalore Univ. (India)	Pediatric Allergy	1988		
Margolis, Eric J.	Jefferson	Pediatrics	1983	Neo- Perinatal Med	1985
Margolis, Mary Ann	Indiana Univ.	Internal Medicine	1976	Nephrology	1977
Margolis, Mitchell L.	Jefferson	Pulm Dis	1982		
Marinkovic, Milos	Belgrade Univ. (Yugoslavia)	Hematology	1971		
Marino, Ralph J.	Jefferson	Phys Med/Rehab	1987		
Markham, Fred William, Jr.	Dartmouth Univ.	Family Practice	1979		
Markind, Samual H.	Jefferson	Neurology	1988	Neuropathology	1989
Markmann, William J.	Temple Univ.	Orthop Surg	1979		
Markoff, Michael J.	Fairleigh Dickinson Univ.	Oral & Max Surg	1985		
Markopolos, Melissa A.	Univ. Maryland	Family Practice	1986		
Marks, Gerald	Jefferson	General Surgery	1957		
Marlowe, Sarah K.	Med. Coll. Penna.	Family Practice	1990		
Marone, Phillip J.	Jefferson	Orthop Surg	1963		
Marotta, Raymond J., Jr.	UMDNJ, Newark	Family Practice	1986		
Marotta, Ruggero C.	Univ. Naples	Hematology	1949		
Marsh, Peter K.	Jefferson	Internal Medicine	1979		
Marshall, Carol S.	Univ. Maryland	Pathology	1986		
Martin, Gerald B.	Jefferson	Internal Medicine	1978	Nephrology	1980
Martin, Gilbert A., Jr.	Jefferson	General Surgery	1958		
Martin, John A., Jr.	Jefferson	Orthop Surg	1990		
Martin, Judith	Univ. Pennsylvania	Family Practice	1978		
Martin, William P.	Jefferson	Radiology	1950		
Martinez, Elba J.	Univ. Puerto Rico			Hematology	1964
Martinez, Jose	Madrid Sch. Med.	Hematology	1969		
Martinez, Marcial	Univ. Santo Domingo	General Surgery	1955		
Martinez-Tapia, Antonio C.	Havana Univ. Med. Sch.	Ophthalmology	1951		
Martino, Christopher J.	New Jersey Coll. Osteo. Med.	Neurology	1986		
Martynowicz, Ted	New York Coll. Osteo Med.	Infectious Diseases	1990		
Marvel, James P., Jr.	Jefferson	Orthop Surg	1968		
Marx, Halvey Edward	Jefferson	Pathology	1949		
Mason, Jeannette C.	Hahnemann Univ.	Pediatrics	1974		
Massoumi, Massoud G.	Univ. Tehran	Hand Surgery	1974		
Master, Herbert	Univ. Bologna (Italy)	Internal Medicine	1974		
Mastrangelo, Michael J.	Johns Hopkins Univ.	Internal Medicine	1969	Medical Oncology	1971
Matlack, Eileen	Hahnemann Univ.	Anesthesiology	1984		
Matouk, Riad G.	Syrian Univ.	Ophthalmology	1960		
Matsko, Janine Ann	Jefferson	Ophthalmology	1979		
Matsui, Takeshi	Shinshu Univ.	Hand Surgery	1977		
Matteo, Anthony J.	Penn State Univ.	Ob/Gyn	1986		
Matteucci, Barbara M.	Jefferson	Internal Medicine	1981		
Matthews, Martha S.	Jefferson	General Surgery	1986		

Name	Med School	R Specialty	R Year	F Specialty	F Year
Matulewski, Thomas J.	Jefferson	General Surgery	1979		
Mauler, G. Gregg	Jefferson	Orthop Surg	1965		
Mauriello, Alfred J., II	Jefferson	Otolaryngology	1974		
Maxwell, Robert Allan, Jr.	Univ. Louisville	Internal Medicine	1962	Hematology	1963
Mayes, Richard L.	Jefferson	Ob/Gyn	1972		
Mayhew, David E.	Univ. Florida	Hand Surgery	1984		
Mayo, James P.	Wayne State Univ.	General Surgery	1974		
Mazdisnian, Fariborz	Med. Coll. Wisconsin	Ob/Gyn	1990		
Mazer, Elliot E.	Univ. Pittsburgh	Internal Medicine	1973		
Mazmanian, Joseph	Jefferson	Pathology	1950		
Mazur, Edward F.	Jefferson	Endocrinology	1953		
McCairns, Robert Gray, Jr.	Jefferson	General Surgery	1981		
McCarthy, John J.	Georgetown Univ.	Hand Surgery	1988		
McClay, Edward Francis	Temple Univ.	Internal Medicine	1983	Medical Oncology	1986
McCloskey, Joseph F.	Jefferson	Pathology	1948		
McCloskey, Sister Ann M.	Jefferson	Pathology	1981		
McCormick, John A.	Jefferson	Ob/Gyn	1940		
McCormick, John F.	Jefferson	Pathology	1975		
McCormick, John Lawrence	Jefferson	General Surgery	1952		
McCormick, Richard C.	West Virginia Sch. Osteo. Med.	Anesthesiology	1988		
McCoy-White, Roslind I.	Univ. Mississippi	Diag Rad	1984		
McCune, Wallace G.	Pritzker Sch. Med.	Internal Medicine	1949		
McCurdy, Donna K.	Tulane Univ.	Internal Medicine	1962		
McCurdy, Jole C.	Univ. Bari (Italy)	Psychiatry	1981		
McCurdy, Richard Ross	Jefferson	Internal Medicine	1975		
McCuskey, Bradford Mann	Jefferson	Urological Surgery	1960		
McDay, John B.	Temple Univ.	Rad Oncol	1980		
McDevitt, John J., IV	Temple Univ.	Internal Medicine	1972		
McDiarmid, Melissa A.	Univ. Maryland	Internal Medicine	1982		
McDonald, John W.	Georgetown Univ.	Dermatology	1982		
McDowell, Charles Lindsay	Jefferson	Orthop Surg	1964		
McDowell, Lucy Jane	Indiana Univ.	Allergy and Immun	1985		
McEntyre, James M.	Med. Coll. Georgia	Ophthalmology	1966		
McFarland, Henry F.	Univ. Colorado	Neurology	1970		
McFarland, Joseph Peter	Stritch Sch. Med.	Dermatology	1977		
McGeary, Lester Ellsworth	Jefferson	Pediatrics	1976		
McGehee, Edward H.	Jefferson	Pathology	1949		
McGinley, Edward J.	Univ. Pittsburgh	Internal Medicine	1976		
McGoff, John P.	Indiana Univ.	Emerg Med	1987		
McGroarty, David John	Georgetown Univ.	Internal Medicine	1979		
McGuire, John Francis	Georgetown Univ.	Neuro Surg	1953		
McGuire, Patricia M.	Jefferson	Psychiatry	1982		
McGurrin, Mark A.	Jefferson	General Surgery	1987		
McJunkin, James E.	West Virginia Univ.	Pediatrics	1980		
McJunkin, Mary Han Lee	West Virginia Univ.	Radiology	1982		
McKeag, Kathleen A.	Jefferson	Ob/Gyn	1978		
McKeen, William Breadner	McGill Univ.	Orthop Surg	1964		
McKeever, Clark D.	Jefferson	Orthop Surg	1968		
McKeever, Grant R.	Jefferson	Orthop Surg	1968		
McKenna, James J., III	Univ. Osteo. Med., Des Moines	Family Practice	1988		
McKenna, Marc	Georgetown Univ.	Family Practice	1981		
McKenna, Patrick J.	Jefferson	Hematology	1962		
McKeon, Francis Anthony, Jr.	Jefferson	Pathology	1957		

Name	Med School	R Specialty	R Year	F Specialty	F Year
McKeown, John Joseph, Jr.	Jefferson	General Surgery	1954		
McLaughlin, Edward D.	Jefferson	General Surgery	1964		
McLaughlin, Guy W., Jr.	Jefferson	Pediatrics	1964		
McLellan, Toni L.	Univ. Texas	Neurology	1985	Neuropathology	1987
McLin, Ronald W.	Marquette Univ.	Anesthesiology	1966		
McMahon, Patrick	Temple Univ.	Pediatrics	1972		
McNelis, Francis L.	Jefferson	Otolaryngology	1951		
McNierney, Bronson J.	Jefferson	Internal Medicine	1960	Gastroenterology	1961
McNulty, Stephen E.	Phila. Coll. Osteo. Med.	Anesthesiology	1985		
McPeak, Vincent Joseph, Jr.	Jefferson	Ob/Gyn	1958		
McQueen, Jerome E.	U.C. San Diego	Anesthesiology	1986	Anesthesiology	1987
McShane, Robert B.	Northwestern Univ.	Orthop Surg	1989		
McWhorter, John E., IV	New Jersey Med. Coll.	Internal Medicine	1970		
Mead, Robert J., Jr.	Jefferson	Pediatric Allergy	1982		
Meade, Thomas D.	Jefferson	Orthop Surg	1988		
Meadowcroft, James A.	Jefferson	Orthop Surg	1973		
Measley, Robert E.	Univ. Massachusetts	Internal Medicine	1987		
Mecca, Donato D.	Temple Univ.	Ophthalmology	1973		
Medellin, Lastra Hector	Nat. Univ. Mexico	Radiology	1966		
Mederos, Rafael M.	Havana Univ. Med. Sch.	Hematology	1966		
Medford, William L., Jr.	Jefferson	Otolaryngology	1973		
Medinilla, Otto Raul	Univ. San Carlos (Guatemala)	Neuro Surg	1978		
Meduri, Anne M.	S.U.N.Y., Syracuse	Pediatrics	1990		
Medway, Marc J.	Jefferson	Phys Med/Rehab	1980		
Mehandru, Sushil Kumar	Christian Med. Coll. (India)	Nephrology	1976		
Mehandru, Urmila	Christian Med. Coll. (India)	Psychiatry	1976		
Mehran, Reza M.	Univ. Tehran	Otolaryngology	1975		
Mehta, Govindram K.	Baroda Univ. (India)	Otolaryngology	1983		
Mehta, Nalini B.	Univ. Bombay	Rad Oncol	1978		
Mellon, Lawrence J.	Jefferson	Gen Prev Med	1972		
Melman, Daniel A.	New York Med. Coll.	Internal Medicine	1980		
Melnick, Howard B.	Med. Coll. Pennsylvania	Otolaryngology	1987		
Melnicoff, Edward N.	Hahnemann Univ.	Anesthesiology	1957		
Melton, Susan M.	Jefferson	Internal Medicine	1989		
Meltz, Richard C.	Phila. Coll. Osteo. Med.	Ob/Gyn	1976		
Memon, Nazir A.	Liaquat Med. Coll. (Pakistan)	Internal Medicine	1975	Pulm Dis	1977
Mendelsohn, Kevin Bruce	Sydney University	Otolaryngology	1977		
Menghetti, Richard A.	Univ. Maryland	Radiology	1987		
Merewitz, Glenn S.	Univ. Maryland	Internal Medicine	1980		
Merion, Judith A.	Hahnemann Univ.	Child Psychiatry	1990		
Merli, Geno J.	Jefferson	Internal Medicine	1980		
Mervine, Thomas Burritt	Jefferson	General Surgery	1949		
Messerschmidt, William H.	Jefferson	General Surgery	1984	Cardiothor Surg	1987
Messina, Frank C.	Mt. Sinai Sch. Med.	Internal Medicine	1990		
Messori, Divo A.	Jefferson	Gastroenterology	1964		
Metry, Nawal G.	Ain Shams Univ. (Egypt)	Pediatric Allergy	1987		
Metz, Albert V., Jr.	Jefferson	Neuro Surg	1976		
Metzgar, Marshall T.	New York Med. Coll.	Anesthesiology	1961		
Meusburger, Charles E.	Univ. Rome	Psychiatry	1990		
Meyerdierks, Elizabeth M.	Tulane Univ.	Hand Surgery	1987		
Mezitis, Nicholas H.E.	Univ. Heidelberg	Internal Medicine	1983		
Mezzanotte, William S.	Univ. Pennsylvania	Internal Medicine	1988		
Michael, Eric J.	Jefferson	Pediatrics	1981	Neo- Perinatal Med	1983

Name	Med School	R Specialty	R Year	F Specialty	F Year
Michael, Herman J., Jr.	Jefferson	Internal Medicine	1987	Nephrology	1989
Michals, Timothy J.	Jefferson	Psychiatry	1973		
Michon, Catherine A.	Woman's Med. Coll.	Ophthalmology	1969		
Migasena, Sricharoen	Siriraj Hosp. (Thailand)			Gastroenterology	1965
Mikhail, Michael G.	Univ. Michigan	Emerg Med	1990		
Millberg, William B.	Jefferson	General Surgery	1959		
Miller, Bernard Joseph	Jefferson	General Surgery	1950		
Miller, Cynthia L.	Med. Coll. Pennsylvania	Radiology	1983	Diag Rad	1985
Miller, David Lee	Ohio State Univ.	Pediatrics	1969		
Miller, Jacqueline L.	Temple Univ.	Ob/Gyn	1971		
Miller, Jeffrey K.	Univ. Pittsburgh	Hand Surgery	1987		
Miller, Joseph H.	Jefferson	Internal Medicine	1968		
Miller, Karen Boudreau	Boston Univ.	Family Practice	1989		
Miller, Lawrence S.	Jefferson	Phys Med/Rehab	1975		
Miller, Lawrence S.	Jefferson	Orthop Surg	1984		
Miller, Linda R.	George Washington Univ.	Internal Medicine	1987		
Miller, Mark D.	Univ. Pittsburgh	Psychiatry	1985		
Miller, Robert A.	Temple Univ.	Otolaryngology	1986		
Miller, Roger M.	Jefferson	Internal Medicine	1965		
Miller, Sanford M.	Jefferson	Anesthesiology	1960		
Miller, Stanton B.	Jefferson	General Surgery	1986		
Millin, Joseph C.	UMDNJ, Sch. Osteo. Med.	Rad Oncol	1990		
Millos, Alberto	Univ. Uruguay	Pathology	1990		
Minassian, Shahab S.	Jefferson	Repro Endo	1986		
Minehart, Charles R.	Temple Univ.			Cardiovas Dis	1980
Mingey, Deborah L.	Hahnemann Univ.	Anesthesiology	1989		
Minkow, Frederick V.	Univ. Michigan	Hand Surgery	1970		
Mintzer, David M.	Jefferson			Hematology	1982
Mirabelli, Richard P.	Univ. Naples	Pediatrics	1963		
Mirenda, William M.	Jefferson	Orthop Surg	1981		
Mirow, Arvin L.	Tel Aviv Univ.	Psychiatry	1988		
Misanik, Lawrence F.	Stritch Sch. Med.	Pathology	1958		
Mitchell, David R.	Univ. Oklahoma	Psychiatry	1988		
Mitchell, Dora S.	Havana Univ. Med. Sch.	Child Psychiatry	1982		
Mitz, Richard B.	Marquette Univ.	Oral & Max Surg	1981		
Miyaji, Naotsune	Univ. Tokyo	Hand Surgery	1975		
Mizak, Daniel J.	Jefferson	Internal Medicine	1970	Cardiovas Dis	1971
Moawad, Atef H.	Cairo Univ. Sch. Med.	Ob/Gyn	1964	Repro Endo	1961
Mobley, Sylvester L.	Hahnemann	Pediatric Allergy	1975		
Mody, Satish K.	Univ. Bombay	Anesthesiology	1974		
Mohan, Kuppa Krishna	Christian Med. Coll. (India)	Internal Medicine	1977	Pulm Dis	1979
Mohiuddin, Mohammed	Osmania Med. Coll. (India)	Rad Oncol	1976		
Mohsenifar, Zabiollah	Univ. Tehran	Internal Medicine	1977		
Mokrynski, Gregory	Jefferson	Internal Medicine	1989		
Molina, Leticia K.	Univ. St. Tomas (Philippines)	Pediatrics	1976		
Molina, Sylvia V.	Univ. St. Tomas (Philippines)	Pediatrics	1959		
Molinari, William J.	Jefferson	Anesthesiology	1971		
Molino, Richard	Tufts Univ.	Internal Medicine	1977		
Molony, Terence James	Royal Coll. Surgeons (Ireland)	Otolaryngology	1953		
Monighetti, Robert A.	Univ. Connecticut	Phys Med/Rehab	1986		
Monroe, Matthew	Wroclaw Sch. Med. (Poland)	Cardiovas Dis	1975		
Monte, Steven A.	Jefferson	Pathology	1986		
Montella, Joseph M.	Jefferson	Ob/Gyn	1988		

Name	Med School	R Specialty	R Year	F Specialty	F Year
Montgomery, Bruce B.	Jefferson	Ob/Gyn	1965		
Montgomery, Owen C.	Hahnemann Univ.	Ob/Gyn	1985		
Montoya, Roberto	Univ. Javeniana (Colombia)	General Surgery	1973		
Moon, Hyung Ro	Seoul Univ.	Pediatrics	1959		
Moon, Tai Joon	Seoul Univ.	Neuro Surg	1957		
Moore, Charles Balcom	Johns Hopkins	Urological Surgery	1946		
Moore, David H.	Jefferson	Internal Medicine	1978	Gastroenterology	1980
Moore, John H., Jr.	Univ. Virginia	General Surgery	1985		
Moore, Michael M.	Univ. Wisconsin	Family Practice	1989		
Moore, Stephen A.	Chicago Med. Sch.	Ophthalmology	1974		
Mooreville, Michael	Penn State Univ.	Urological Surgery	1983		
Mooreville, Ruth	Hadassah Med. Sch. (Israel)	Pediatrics	1983		
Morales, Antonio	Univ. Puerto Rico	Repro Endo	1967		
Morales-Non, Priscilla S.	Univ. Philippines	Pediatrics	1974		
Moreno, Leonel Tirado	Univ. Venezuela	Repro Endo	1958		
Moreno, Tracey J.	Albany Med. Coll.	Internal Medicine	1983		
Morinigo-Mestre, Gladys Stella	Univ. Asuncion (Paraguay)	Pathology	1972		
Moritz, Howard A.	Jefferson	Anesthesiology	1988		
Moritz, Michael J.	Univ. Maryland	General Surgery	1985	Trans Surg	1986
Morone, Teresa M.	Phila. Coll. Osteo. Med.	Nephrology	1984		
Morowitz, William Allen	Univ. Illinois	Internal Medicine	1975	Pulm Dis	1977
Morris, Kathryn E.	Jefferson	Internal Medicine	1985		
Morris, Michele I.	Med. Coll. Pennsylvania	Internal Medicine	1987		
Morris, Patricia A.	Hahnemann Univ.	Anesthesiology	1984		
Morrow, Robert E.	UMDNJ, Newark	Psychiatry	1987		
Moselle, Herbert I.	Jefferson	Otolaryngology	1968		
Moser, Edgar S.	Med. Coll. Virginia	Radiology	1989		
Moses, Melvin L.	Jefferson	General Surgery	1967	Cardiov. Surg.	1970
Mosier, Laurance A.	Jefferson	General Surgery	1955		
Moskowitz, Harold	New York Coll. Med.	Radiology	1964		
Moss, David R.	Temple Univ.	Psychiatry	1984		
Motley, Robert J.	Jefferson	Family Practice	1988		
Moxley, T. Wayne	Med. Coll. Virginia	Ob/Gyn	1984		
Moylan, David J.	Georgetown Univ.	Rad Oncol	1982		
Mueller, John C.	Tufts Univ.	Internal Medicine	1970	Endocrinology	1971
Mueller, Thomas C.	Jefferson	Neurology	1990		
Muench, Peter J.	Temple Univ.	Urological Surgery	1988		
Muetterties, Craig L.	Jefferson	Anesthesiology	1978		
Muffly, Harry M.	Jefferson	Ob/Gyn	1957		
Mujumdar, Suhas P.	Nagpur Univ. (India)	Urological Surgery	1978		
Mulay, Soudamini	Univ. Bombay	General Surgery	1978		
Mundenar, Michael J.	Univ. Pittsburgh	Oral & Max Surg	1990		
Munoz, Santiago J.	Univ. Chile	Internal Medicine	1985	Gastroenterology	1988
Munroe, Donald H.	Queens Univ. (Canada)	Urological Surgery	1952		
Munzer, Steven J.	Jefferson	Radiology	1968		
Murdock, Morton G.	Univ. Pennsylvania	Radiology	1964		
Murphy, Edward J.	Jefferson	Ob/Gyn	1948		
Murphy, Michael J.	Med. Coll. Georgia	Ophthalmology	1973		
Murphy, Nancy G.	S.U.N.Y., Buffalo	Internal Medicine	1985		
Murray, Austin Paul	Jefferson	Ophthalmology	1963		
Musser, Guy R.	Jefferson	Ob/Gyn	1958		
Mussio, John A.	New York Med. Coll.	Neuro Surg	1969		
Myers, Donald L.	Jefferson	Neuro Surg	1980		

Lawrence J. Naame
Georgetown

Farzad Namdaran
Pahlavi

Henry P. Nagelberg
S.U.N.Y., Syracuse

Kazuko Nitta
Nagasaki

Kenneth Neuburger
Albany Med. Col.

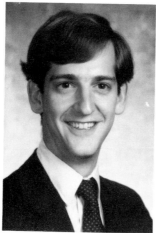
Paul Nyirjesy
Georgetown

Richard Neill
Kentucky

Lawrence J. Nardozzi
Georgetown

Sharon E. Neibel-Pondek
UMDNJ, Rutgers

David E. Nicklin
Pennsylvania

Paul Nakazato
Hahnemann

Phong Nguyen
Med. Col. Virginia

Postgraduate Alumni

Name	Med School	R Specialty	R Year	F Specialty	F Year
Noble, Paul H.	Chicago Med. Sch.	General Surgery	1970	Cardiov Surg	1972
Noble, S. Ross	Jefferson	Phys Med/Rehab	1990		
Nocon, James J.	Jefferson	Ob/Gyn	1975		
Noll, Kathleen R.	Univ. Pennsylvania	Anesthesiology	1986		
Non, Diosdado P.	Univ. St. Tomas (Philippines)	Pathology	1975		
Norelli, Charles C.	Jefferson	Phys Med/Rehab	1986		
Norris, Tom R.	Columbia Univ., Coll. P. & S.			Hand Surgery	1976
Novacek, Paul J.	Marquette Univ.	Anesthesiology	1967		
Nowroozi, Khosrow	Univ. Teheran			Repro Endo	1978
Noyes, Brent R.	Jefferson	Orthop Surg	1983		
Nulty, William Edward, Jr.	New York Med. Coll.	Radiology	1955		
Nwokeji, Peter-Paul	Am. Univ. Caribbean (Monteserrat)	Pediatrics	1988		
Nyirjesy, Paul	Georgetown Univ.	Ob/Gyn	1989		

"Rib Crackers" banquet at the Franklin Inn (1954). These Residents had all trained under Dr. Gibbon, and many more were to follow. Seated from right to left: Drs. Thomas F. Nealon, Jr., John Y. Templeton III, John H. Gibbon, Jr., John J. DeTuerk, J. Louis Wilkerson, and John J. McKeown, Jr.

Victor G. Onufrey
Jefferson

Carlos M. Oliveira
Guadalajara

Arie Oren
Riszkij Med. Inst. USSR

Thomas F. O'Malley, Jr.
Jefferson

Alan E. Ottenstein
Hahnemann

Christine S. O'Donnell
Temple

Kathleen S. O'Banion
Southwestern

Timothy Orphanides
New York

Gary Y. Ott
Jefferson

Patrick M. O'Brien
Georgetown

Lawrence C. Olsen
Jefferson

Roger A. Orsini
Med. Col. Penna

Postgraduate Alumni

Name	Med School	R Specialty	R Year	F Specialty	F Year
O'Banion, Kathleen	Southwestern University	Ob/Gyn	1985		
O'Brien, Kevin F.	New York Med. Coll.			Hematology	1972
O'Brien, Patrick M.	Georgetown Univ.	Emerg Med	1986		
O'Connor, Dennis Stephen	Jefferson	Pathology	1961		
O'Connor, Ellen Callahan	Emory Univ.	Internal Medicine	1990		
O'Connor, Kathryn M.	Jefferson	Pediatrics	1989		
O'Donnell, Christine S.	Temple Univ.	Orthop Surg	1988		
O'Hanlan, Katherine	Med. Coll. Virginia			Gyn Oncol	1986
O'Mahony, Lisa	Med. Coll. Pennsylvania	Pediatrics	1984		
O'Malley, Thomas F., Jr.	Jefferson	Ob/Gyn	1985		
O'Mara, Ellen M.	UMDNJ, Sch. Osteo. Med.			Diag Rad	1990
O'Neal, John R.	Hahnemann Univ.	Ob/Gyn	1975		
O'Neil, James P.	Univ. Kansas	Internal Medicine	1974	Cardiovas Dis	1976
O'Neill, Hugh A.	St. Louis Univ.	Radiology	1948		
O'Neill, Mark F.X.	Georgetown Univ.	General Surgery	1973		
Ocampo-Pineda, Lourdes F.	Univ. St. Tomas (Philippines)	Pediatrics	1971	Pediatrics	1973
Ochiai, Naoyuki	Tokyo Univ.			Hand Surgery	1978
Oesterling, Everett F.	Jefferson	Pathology	1966		
Okie, Allen	Jefferson			Pediatric Allergy	1974
Olaciregui, Andres	Pontificia Univ. Javeriana (Col.)	Psychiatry	1973		
Oline, Jonathan P.	Phila. Coll. Osteo. Med.			Cardiovas Dis	1989
Oliva, Luis Aristides	Univ. Santo Domingo	Neuro Surg	1959		
Oliveira, Carlos M.	Univ. Guadalajara	Ob/Gyn	1981		
Olsen, Jean E.	Jefferson	Radiology	1972		
Olsen, Lawrence C.	Jefferson	Internal Medicine	1975		
Olympia, Manuel B.	Univ. East Philippines	Anesthesiology	1973		
Onufrey, Victor G.	Jefferson	Rad Oncol	1985		
Ordinario, Anacleto T.	Univ. St. Tomas (Philippines)	Internal Medicine	1974	Nephrology	1976
Oren, Arie	Riszkij Med. Inst. (USSR)			Nephrology	1986
Oren-Weiss, Reva	Univ. Bologna (Italy)	Rad Oncol	1977		
Orocofsky, Morris Lee	Jefferson	Internal Medicine	1975		
Orocofsky, Vasantha C.	Christian Med. Coll. (India)	Psychiatry	1980		
Orphanides, Timothy	New York Univ.	Internal Medicine	1986		
Orsini, Roger A.	Med. Coll. Pennsylvania	General Surgery	1983		
Ortiz, Neftali	Univ. Puerto Rico	Psychiatry	1986		
Ortiz, Ramon Z.	Univ. St. Tomas (Philippines)	Anesthesiology	1975		
Orvell, Barry	S.U.N.Y.,			Nephrology	1972
Orzechowska, Eduvigia T.	Univ. Buenos Aires	Dermatology	1966		
Ostrow, Arnold	Jefferson	Internal Medicine	1966	Pulm Dis	1967
Osuna, J. Alfonso	Univ. Buenos Aires			Endocrinology	1967
Ott, Gary Y.	Jefferson	General Surgery	1988		
Ottenstein, Alan E.	Hahnemann Univ.	Neurology	1988		
Otto, Nancy R.	Columbia Univ., Coll. P. & S.			Hand Surgery	1983
Ouano, Romeo C.	Univ. St. Tomas (Philippines)			Rad Oncol	1977
Ousler, George W., Jr.	Jefferson	Orthop Surg	1970		
Overstreet, Arthur Evan	Univ. Louisville	Internal Medicine	1960	Gastroenterology	1961
Overton, Deborah S.	Temple Univ.	Pediatrics	1972		

Sonia M. Padget
Temple

Edward E. Packer
Phila. Col. Osteo. Med.

David P. Perkins
Jefferson

Naomi Parish
Temple

James G. Paraskevas
Washington

John C. Patterson
Johns Hopkins

Herbert Patrick
Jefferson

David B. Panasuk
Jefferson

Vrunda Patel
S.U.N.Y., Syracuse

David P. Perkins
Ohio State

Robert J. Perin
Gudalajara

Pauline K. Park
Jefferson

Name	Med School	R Specialty	R Year	F Specialty	F Year
Pacheco, Susan Monk	Jefferson	Pediatrics	1974		
Pack, Michael A.	Univ. Washington	Internal Medicine	1989		
Packer, Edward E.	Phila. Coll. Osteo. Med.	Pediatrics	1980		
Packin, Gary S.	Phila. Coll. Osteo. Med.			Repro Endo	1976
Paddison, Richard M.	Duke University	Neurology	1951		
Padget, Sonia M.	Temple Univ.	Dermatology	1983		
Padow, Walter D.	Med. Coll. Virginia			Gastroenterology	1970
Padula, Anthony M.	Jefferson	General Surgery	1972	Hand Surgery	1975
Padula, Richard T.	Jefferson	General Surgery	1966		
Paige, Cathy McPherson	Dartmouth Med. Sch.	Anesthesiology	1985		
Palaniswamy, Alagiri	Madras Med. Coll. (India)			Nephrology	1975
Palascak, Joseph E.	Jefferson	Internal Medicine	1971	Hematology	1976
Palena, Peter V.	Jefferson	Ophthalmology	1969		
Palermo, Louis M.	Jefferson	Urological Surgery	1977		
Palmer, Craig M.	Jefferson	Anesthesiology	1988		
Palmer, Timothy W.	Hahnemann Univ.	Pediatrics	1987		
Palos, Lorraine C.	Jefferson	Pediatrics	1985		
Paluzzi, Richard G.	New York Univ.	Internal Medicine	1987		
Pan, Edward Ledesma	Far Eastern Univ. (Philippines)	Orthop Surg	1975		
Panasuk, D. Bruce	Jefferson	General Surgery	1987	Cardiothor Surg	1990
Pancerev, Clifford P.	Jefferson	Anesthesiology	1978		
Pandelidis, Pandelis K.	Univ. Athens	Psychiatry	1962		
Pandya, Pradeep Kumar	M.G.M. Med. Coll. (India)	Urological Surgery	1979		
Paniagua, Cecilio	Univ. Madrid	Psychiatry	1973		
Pao, David S.C.	Columbia Univ., Coll. P. & S.	Ophthalmology	1973		
Papa, Louis A.	Phila. Coll. Osteo. Med.			Cardiovas Dis	1975
Paquet, Jean Pierre	Laval Univ. (Canada)	Urological Surgery	1965		
Paraskevas, James G.	Washington Univ.	Family Practice	1984		
Parish, Naomi	Temple Univ.	Psychiatry	1982		
Park, Chan Hee	Yonsei Univ. (Korea)	Rad Oncol	1970	Nuclear Med.	1971
Park, Chanhi	Albert Einstein Coll. Med.			Diag Rad	1990
Park, Hong Youl	Catholic Med. Coll. (Korea)	Neurology	1976		
Park, Pauline K.	Jefferson	General Surgery	1987		
Parry, Carolyn E.	Jefferson	Rad Oncol	1970		
Parsons, Sidney A., Jr.	Jefferson	Pediatrics	1964		
Pascual, Alfonso M.	Madrid Univ.	Neuro Surg	1975		
Pascual, Eliseo	Univ. Madrid	Internal Medicine	1973		
Pashman, David Roy	Jefferson	Orthop Surg	1975		
Pasto, Matthew E.	Univ. Guadalajara			Diag Rad	1981
Paston, Carrie Z.	Jefferson	Emerg Med	1990		
Patel, Jehangir J.	Albert Einstein Coll. Med.			Diag Rad	1988
Patel, Vrunda	S.U.N.Y., Syracuse	Ob/Gyn	1989		
Patel, Yogishchandra A.	Univ. Bombay			Medical Oncology	1976
Paterson, William D.	Jefferson	Anesthesiology	1985		
Patrick, Herbert	Jefferson	Internal Medicine	1981		
Patterson, John C.	Johns Hopkins Univ.	Internal Medicine	1979		
Patterson, John R.	Jefferson	Internal Medicine	1961		
Patterson, John W.	Jefferson	Internal Medicine	1981		
Paul, Anthony R.	Univ. Sri Lanka, Colombo	Internal Medicine	1976		
Paul, Sindy M.	Temple Univ.	General Surgery	1987		
Payne, George R.	Univ. Virginia			Orthop Surg	1989
Payne, John B.	Univ. Osteo. Med., Des Moines	Neuro Surg	1985		
Peacock, Jay A.	Jefferson	Pathology	1981		

Name	Med School	R Specialty	R Year	F Specialty	F Year
Pearl, Frank J.	Jefferson			Cardiovas Dis	1978
Pearlman, Samuel	Jefferson			Endocrinology	1964
Peck, Marc R.	Univ. Pennsylvania	Radiology	1968		
Pedorosa, Cesar S.	Univ. Madrid	Radiology	1962		
Peinado, Sandra C.	Columbia Univ., Coll. P. & S.			Family Practice	1988
Pelensky, Jeanne M.	Jefferson	Phys Med/Rehab	1981		
Penalver, Jorge Alberto	Univ. Buenos Aires			Hematology	1957
Pennell, Rebecca G.	Med. Coll. Pennsylvania			Diag Rad	1985
Pennington, Howard L.V.	Jefferson	Ob/Gyn	1952		
Penrod, Louis E.	Univ. Pittsburgh	Phys Med/Rehab	1988		
Pepper, Larry	Univ. Pennsylvania	Oral & Max Surg	1982		
Perez, Jose A.	Havana Univ. Med. Sch.	Urological Surgery	1961		
Perez, Raymond J.	Phila. Coll. Osteo. Med.			Diag Rad	1985
Perin, Robert Jean	Univ. Guadalajara	Pediatrics	1979	Pediatric Allergy	1981
Peris, Leon A.	Jefferson	Ob/Gyn	1960		
Perkel, Robert L.	Albert Einstein Coll. Med.	Family Practice	1981		
Perkins, David P.	Ohio State Univ.	Internal Medicine	1990		
Perlman, Herbert C.	Jefferson	Radiology	1969		
Perlow, Lawrence S.	Georgetown Univ.	Internal Medicine	1981		
Perrige, Michael L.	Univ. Pittsburgh	Oral & Max Surg	1970		
Perrige, William M.	Jefferson	General Surgery	1958		
Peters, John W.	Jefferson			Pulm Dis	1982
Peters, Thomas G.	Jefferson	General Surgery	1964		
Peters, William J.	Jefferson	Ob/Gyn	1974		
Peterson, Judith R.	Cornell Univ.	Phys Med/Rehab	1990		
Peterson, Paul, III	N.J. Coll. Osteo. Med.			Nephrology	1985
Petrauski, Gary T.	Temple Univ.			Rad Oncol	1983
Petrone, Carol T.	Jefferson	Psychiatry	1983		
Petrone, Louis R.	Jefferson	Family Practice	1990		
Petrucelli, Robert C.	Hahnemann Univ.	Orthop Surg	1981		
Pham, Doanh	Univ. Nebraska	Urological Surgery	1980		
Phaosawasdi, Buppha	Ramathibodi Hosp. (Thailand)	Pediatrics	1979		
Phaosawasdi, Kamthorn	Ramathibodi Hosp. (Thailand)	Internal Medicine	1976		
Phillips, Frederic A.	Jefferson	Pediatrics	1964		
Phillips, Lawrence D.	Hahneman Univ.	Internal Medicine	1967	Gastroenterology	1969
Phillips, Raymond W.	Washington Univ.	Internal Medicine	1985		
Phung, Tri Minh	Saigon Univ.	Pathology	1981		
Piazza, Michael R.	Pennsylvania State Univ.	Orthop Surg	1988	Orthop Surg	1989
Piccini, Paul A.	Jefferson	Internal Medicine	1978		
Piccoli, Catherine W.	Harvard Univ.	Radiology	1988	Diag Rad	1989
Piccuta, Michael J.	Hahnemann Univ.	Dermatology	1972		
Pierotti, Richard John	Jefferson	Family Practice	1979		
Pierucci, Louis, Jr.	Jefferson	General Surgery	1962		
Pinault, William N.	Tufts Univ.	Ob/Gyn	1970		
Pincus, Frances E.	Jefferson	Pathology	1971		
Pinkus, Harry E.	S.U.N.Y., Buffalo			Diag Rad	1990
Pinski, Gabriel	Univ. Juarez (Mexico)	Psychiatry	1986		
Piotrowski, Joseph C.	New York Univ.	Oral & Max Surg	1988		
Piovanetti, Simon	Jefferson	Pediatrics	1954		
Pirela-Cruz, Miguel	Temple Univ.			Hand Surgery	1987
Piroso, Ettore	Univ. Buenos Aires			Hematology	1990
Pisera, Donna M.	Hahnemann Univ.	Anesthesiology	1985		
Pitt, Michael J.	Jefferson	Radiology	1971		

Name	Med School	R Specialty	R Year	F Specialty	F Year
Pittman, Roy C.	Med. Univ. South Carolina	Neuro Surg	1962		
Pizzano, Joseph A.	UMDNJ, Newark	Ophthalmology	1976		
Pizzica, Albert L.	Univ. Osteo. Med., Des Moines	Pediatrics	1978		
Pizzutillo, Peter D.	Jefferson	Orthop Surg	1975		
Plante, Michael T.	UMDNJ, Newark	Ob/Gyn	1974		
Plaster, Ernest Leslie	Univ. Manitoba			Repro Endo 1972	
Platzek, Bruce E.	Univ. Ghent	Neurology	1976		
Pliskin, Mark	Jefferson	Radiology	1969		
Plumb, James David	Jefferson	Family Practice	1977		
Podgorski, Edward M.	Jefferson	Ob/Gyn	1959		
Podgorski, Edward M., Jr.	Jefferson			Diag Rad	1988
Podolnick, Marvin S.	Univ. Pennsylvania	Radiology	1965		
Podolsky, Michael L.	Jefferson	Ob/Gyn	1978	Gyn Oncol	1979
Polacheck, William J.	Jefferson	Orthop Surg	1985		
Pollicina, Federico	Univ. Venezuela	Internal Medicine	1970		
Pollio, Frank V.	Univ. Pennsylvania	Internal Medicine	1985		
Polsky, Harry S.	Jefferson	General Surgery	1975		
Pomerantz, Philip A.	Jefferson			Nephrology	1977
Pomeranz, Mark	New York Coll. Osteo. Med.	Anesthesiology	1990		
Pompey, Daniel T., Jr.	Jefferson	Anesthesiology	1989		
Pontarelli, William R.	Hahnemann Univ.	Orthop Surg	1980		
Poole, Robert G.	Fairleigh Dickinson Univ.	Oral & Max Surg	1970		
Pope, Alan R.	Univ. Connecticut	Internal Medicine	1983		
Porte, Deanna L.	Temple Univ.			Medical Oncology	1978
Porter, Jon K.	Univ. Washington	Family Practice	1985		
Porter, Leslie D.	Univ. Texas	Phys Med/Rehab	1987		
Possanza, Carl J.	Jefferson	Anesthesiology	1987		
Potok, Julian W.	Phila. Coll. Osteo Med.	Pathology	1974		
Powell, James S.	Univ. Maryland	Neuro Surg	1987		
Pozza, Nicholas J.	Temple Univ.	General Surgery	1960		
Prabhakar, Mahaveer P.	R.G. Kar Med. Coll. (Calcutta)	Orthop Surg	1969		
Prahar, Temple F.	Jefferson	Neuro Surg	1963		
Praiss, Donald E.	Jefferson	Urological Surgery	1966		
Prakash, Manoj	Univ. Bombay	Internal Medicine	1980	Pulm Dis	1982
Pratt, Melody H.	Univ. Cincinnati			Infectious Diseases	1990
Prazak, Ladislao M.	Univ. Peruana (Peru)	Ob/Gyn	1973		
Prefer, Audrey I.	S.U.N.Y., Downstate	Ob/Gyn	1987		
Prehatny, John R.	Jefferson	General Surgery	1964		
Premkumar, Arcot S.	Bangalore Med. Coll. (India)			Pulm Dis	1981
Prestipino, Anthony J.	Jefferson	Pathology	1987		
Price, Donna B.	Jefferson	Otolaryngology	1989		
Price, James L., Jr.	Univ. South Carolina			Hand Surgery	1985
Price, Joyce E.	Jefferson			Cardiov Surg	1971
Priebe, Carl W., Jr.	Jefferson	Psychiatry	1967		
Priolo, Dennis L.	UMDNJ, Rutgers			Diag Rad	1988
Pripstein, Stephen	Temple Univ.	Radiology	1974		
Prizant, Ronald J.	Temple Univ.	Anesthesiology	1990		
Probst, C. E., Jr.	Jefferson	Orthop Surg	1975		
Prontnicki, Janice	New York Univ.	Pediatrics	1988		
Prorok, Joseph J.	Jefferson	General Surgery	1968		
Prosswimmer, Geralyn M.	UMDNJ, Rutgers	Pediatrics	1987		
Protonotarios, Peter D.	Univ. Athens			Repro Endo	1965
Pugh, Vernon W., Jr.	Jefferson	Pediatrics	1956		

Name	Med School	R Specialty	R Year	F Specialty	F Year
Puhalla, Cyril M.J.	Jefferson	Child Psychiatry	1981		
Pulido, David R.	Univ. Manila	General Surgery	1972		
Pupi, Paul A.	Jefferson	General Surgery	1971		
Purdum, Preston P., III	Med. Coll. Virginia	Internal Medicine	1987		
Purohit, Girdhari S.	Sardar Patel Med. Coll. (India)	Urological Surgery	1981		

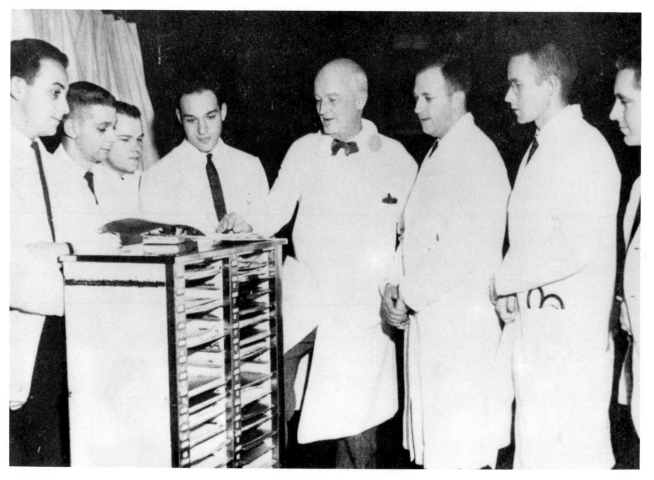

Dr. Gibbon on ward rounds (Dr. Herbert Cohn to the right), 1962.

Dianne M. Quinn
Duke

William Quinones-Baldrich
Puerto Rico

George N. Queen
Hahnemann

Shaukat Qureshi
Nishtar Med. Col. (Pakistan)

Dorothy Quail
UMDNH, Rutgers

Name	Med School	R Specialty	R Year	F Specialty	F Year
Quail, Dorothy M.	UMDNJ, Rutgers	Family Practice	1986		
Queen, George N.	Hahnemann Univ.	Anesthesiology	1989		
Quinn, Dianne McDonald	Duke Univ.	Pathology	1977		
Quinn, Gerald J.	Jefferson	Neurology	1966		
Quinones-Alamo, Benny G.	Univ. del Este (Dom. Rep.)	Anesthesiology	1982		
Quinones-Baldrich, William J.	Univ. Puerto Rico	General Surgery	1982		
Quintero, George A.	Columbia Univ., Coll. P. & S.	Internal Medicine	1953	Gastroenterology	1950
Qureshi, Shaukat M.	Nishtar Med. Coll. (Pakistan)	Urological Surgery	1982		

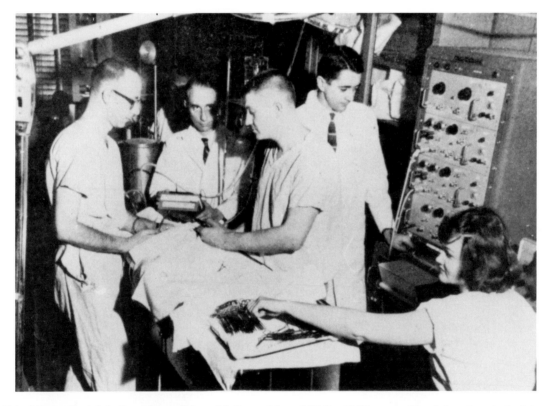

Dr. Leon Scicchitano, Rudolph Camishion, Edward J. Baranski, and Walter Ballinger, with a laboratory technician, studying the effect of the denervation of a lung (1964).

Mark A. Resciniti
Hahnemann

B. Denise Raynor
Jefferson

Randolph H. Renzi
Georgetown

Paul M. Reiter
Albert Einstein Col. Med.

Vicki E. Raab
Texas Med. Sch.

John S. Radomski
Jefferson

Carol R. Reed
Rush Med. Col.

Stanley Rapoport
Emory

Pamela J. Reinhardt
S.U.N.Y., Upstate

Alan Resnik
Jefferson

Elaine L. Reed
Illinois

Name	Med School	R Specialty	R Year	F Specialty	F Year
Raab, Vicki E.	Univ. Texas Med. Sch., San An.	Neurology	1988	Neurology	1989
Rabelo, Alvaro Alves, Jr.	Univ. Fed. Bahia (Brazil)	General Surgery	1973		
Rabinowitz, Lea B.	Albert Einstein Coll. Med.	Pediatrics	1974		
Rabuzzi, Daniel D.	Univ. Pennsylvania	Otolaryngology	1966		
Radomski, John S.	Jefferson	General Surgery	1987		
Ragsdale, Thomas H.	Univ. Tennessee	Hand Surgery	1990		
Raisis, Irene P.	Jefferson	Radiology	1988		
Raja, Mukund C.	Gvant Med. Sch. (India)	Otolaryngology	1983		
Raker, Ned Tyson	Jefferson	General Surgery	1941		
Rakinic, Jan	Tulane Univ.			Colon and Rec Surg	1990
Rakow, Joel I.	Albert Einstein Coll. Med.			Diag Rad	1987
Ralph, Jonathan D.	Jefferson	Ob/Gyn	1980		
Ramirez-Irizarry, Angela A.	Univ. Puerto Rico	General Surgery	1965		
Rancier, Lee F.	S.U.N.Y., Syracuse	Radiology	1974		
Randazzo, Vincent T.	Jefferson	Internal Medicine	1972		
Range, Charles L.	Stritch Sch. Med.			Internal Medicine	1960
Rankin, Joel S.	Boston Univ.			Endocrinology	1966
Rao, Angara Koneti	All India Inst. Med. Sci.	Internal Medicine	1977	Hematology	1979
Rao, Kishan Battu	Gandhi Med. Coll. (India)	Pediatrics	1968		
Rapaport, Jeffrey A.	Emory Univ.	Dermatology	1982		
Rapoport, Stanley	Univ. Witwatersrand	Diag Rad	1981		
Raso, Louis J.	UMDNJ, Rutgers	Anesthesiology	1990		
Ratanatharathorn, Voravit	Mahidol Univ. (Thailand)	Internal Medicine	1975		
Ratchford, W. Buckley	Jefferson	Pediatrics	1974		
Rayner, Mark	Jefferson	General Surgery	1980		
Raynor, B. Denise	Vanderbilt Univ.	Ob/Gyn	1988		
Recine, Carl A.	Temple Univ.			Diag Rad	1982
Reddy, Kuraparti Nirmala	Guntur Med. Coll. (India)	Anesthesiology	1980		
Reddy, Ramachandra	Madras Med. Coll. (India)			Urological Surgery	1961
Reddy, Varadareddy T.	Madras Med. Coll. (India)			Radiology	1980
Reed, Carol R.	Rush Med. Coll.	Internal Medicine	1988		
Reed, David Pardee	Yale Univ.	Internal Medicine	1962		
Reed, Elaine L.	Univ. Illinois	Family Practice	1987		
Reed, Nancy Roberts	Jefferson	Ob/Gyn	1980		
Reese, Charles L., III	Jefferson	Neurology	1963		
Regan, James R.	Jefferson	Internal Medicine	1963	Hematology	1964
Reich, Sanford M.	Albany Med. Coll.	Internal Medicine	1968		
Reichman, Robert T.	Jefferson	General Surgery	1984		
Reinhardt, Pamela J.	S.U.N.Y., Upstate	Orthop Surg	1989		
Reisch, Joanne C.	New York Univ.	Internal Medicine	1989		
Reiter, Paul M.	Albert Einstein Coll. Med.			Cardiovas Dis	1982
Reme, Gerard Julien	Univ. de Haiti			Repro Endo	1971
Renny, Andrew	UMDNJ, Newark	Internal Medicine	1983		
Renzi, Emanuel M.	Univ. Pennsylvania	Radiology	1960		
Renzi, Randolph H.	Georgetown Univ.	Internal Medicine	1985		
Resciniti, Mark A.	Hahnemann Univ.	Anesthesiology	1989		
Resnik, Alan M.	Jefferson	General Surgery	1978		
Reuter, Victor E.	Univ. Natl. P.H. Urena (Dom. R.)	Pathology	1983		
Revanasiddaiah, Madaiah	Mysore Med. Coll. (India)	Internal Medicine	1976		
Reynolds, Ferman R.	Univ. Arkansas	Emerg Med	1990		
Reynolds, Jane E.	Med. Coll. Pennsylvania	Pediatrics	1975		
Reynolds, Judith U.	Univ. S. Florida	Family Practice	1980		
Rhee, Jin Hong	Seoul Nat. Univ.	Orthop Surg	1974		

Name	Med School	R Specialty	R Year	F Specialty	F Year
Rich, Dean C.	Univ. Oregon	Neuro Surg	1973		
Richie, Emily L.	Univ. Pennsylvania	Family Practice	1981		
Rico, Guillermo	Nat. Univ. Colombia	Anesthesiology	1967		
Riffle, George N.	Jefferson	Urological Surgery	1967		
Riffle, John E.	Jefferson	Ophthalmology	1970		
Riggs, Joseph A.	Georgetown Univ.	Ob/Gyn	1964		
Riley, Jean Gale	Jefferson	Pediatrics	1981		
Rimm, Michael L.	Univ. Puerto Rico	Psychiatry	1990		
Ringold, Joel	Temple Univ.			Endocrinology	1968
Riordan, Derle R.	Hahnemann Univ.	Otolaryngology	1963		
Ripepi, Antoinette	Woman's Med. Coll.	General Surgery	1966		
Ripepi, James D.	Jefferson	Neurology	1958		
Rippa, Diane C.	Univ. Vermont	Family Practice	1985		
Risch, Victor R.	Hahnemann Univ.	Internal Medicine	1983		
Riser, Sharon J.	New York Univ.	Psychiatry	1987		
Rissmiller, Richard W.	Phila. Coll Osteo. Med.	Pediatrics	1976		
Ritsema, Rita	Boston Univ.	Internal Medicine	1986	Gastroenterology	1989
Ritsick, Joseph A.	Hahnemann Univ.	Phys Med/Rehab	1974		
Rittenberg, Michael H.	Jefferson	Urological Surgery	1987		
Ritter, Deborah E.	Med. Coll. Pennsylvania	Anesthesiology	1977		
Rivera, Gerant M.	Univ. St. Louis	Radiology	1958		
Rizvi, Masood A.	King George (India)	Internal Medicine	1975		
Rizzo, Albert A.	Jefferson	Internal Medicine	1981		
Rizzo, Karen Ann	Temple Univ.	Otolaryngology	1990		
Robbins, Laurence Jay	Univ. Rochester	Internal Medicine	1978		
Robbins, Terrence E.	Univ. Pennsylvania	Oral & Max Surg	1970		
Roben, George Brock	Med. Coll. Pennsylvania			Child Psychiatry	1987
Roberts, Jay D.	Univ. St. Tomas (Philippines)	Phys Med/Rehab	1979		
Roberts, Keith A.	Jefferson	Neurology	1967		
Robertson, Bruce	Univ. London	Pediatrics	1965		
Robertson, David	Univ. Mexico	General Surgery	1972		
Robin, Howard Steven	Jefferson	Pathology	1976		
Robinson, Alan S.	Cornell Univ.	Internal Medicine	1955		
Robinson, Nancy Beth	Boston Univ.	Pediatrics	1984	Neo- Perinatal Med	1987
Robinson, Norman R.	Jefferson	Otolaryngology	1966		
Robinson, Richard W.	Jefferson	Internal Medicine	1981		
Robles, Emma Enid	Temple Univ.	Pediatrics	1961		
Robzyk, Phillip H.	Hahnemann Univ.	Internal Medicine	1988		
Rockowitz, Neal L.	McGill Univ.			Orthop Surg	1988
Rodgers, Carla	Rush Med. Coll.	Psychiatry	1990		
Rodgers, David M.	Jefferson	Internal Medicine	1980		
Rodgers, Joseph F.	Jefferson	Internal Medicine	1962	Infectious Diseases	1960
Rodham, Russell David	Jefferson	Ob/Gyn	1945		
Rodriguez, Annabelle	UMDNJ, Newark	Internal Medicine	1987		
Rodriguez, Raymond	Georgetown Univ.	Internal Medicine	1986	Cardiovas Dis	1988
Rodriguez, Remy	St. Louis Univ.	Hematology	1952		
Roeloffs, Susan A.	UMDNJ, Rutgers	Pediatrics	1987		
Roeshman, Robert M.	Phila. Coll. Osteo. Med.	Neurology	1981		
Rogalski, Cynthia	Jefferson	Anesthesiology	1987		
Rogers, Jonathan J.	Jefferson	Orthop Surg	1979		
Rogers, Kenneth H.	New York Coll. Osteo. Med.	Anesthesiology	1990		
Rogers, Pamela Young	Temple Univ.	Pediatrics	1978		
Rogers, William H.	Jefferson	General Surgery	1972		

Name	Med School	R Specialty	R Year	F Specialty	F Year
Rollins, Stacy L., Jr.	Jefferson	Neuro Surg	1950		
Romanow, Peter W.	Temple Univ.	Orthop Surg	1954		
Romanzo, George M.	Jefferson	Family Practice	1978		
Roncace, Emilio A.	Jefferson	Otolaryngology	1968		
Ronkin, Shelia L.	UMDNJ, Newark			Mater/Fetal Med	1988
Rooklin, Anthony R.	Jefferson			Pediatric Allergy	1978
Roque, Clemente T.	Univ. Philippines			Diag Rad	1984
Rosales, Remedios K.	Univ. St. Tomas (Philippines)			Neurology	1963
Roscoe, Constantine R.	Jefferson	Pediatrics	1950		
Roscoe, Diane L.	Jefferson	Internal Medicine	1986		
Rose, Fred	Med. Coll. Georgia	Internal Medicine	1969		
Rose, Jacqueline E.	Univ. Maryland	Anesthesiology	1989		
Rose, Lewis J.	Harvard Univ.	Internal Medicine	1981		
Rosen, Amy B.	Hahnemann Univ.	Anesthesiology	1985		
Rosenberg, Ann L.	Jefferson	General Surgery	1986		
Rosenberg, Dale J.	Jefferson	Internal Medicine	1989		
Rosenberg, Franklin I.	Univ. Guadalajara	Anesthesiology	1985		
Rosenberg, Kenneth C.	Jefferson	Internal Medicine	1981		
Rosenberg, Mark M.	Hahnemann Univ.	Psychiatry	1982		
Rosenberg, Paul E.	Jefferson	Dermatology	1967		
Rosenblum, Fred A.	Jefferson	Anesthesiology	1985		
Rosenblum, Harry M.	Jefferson	General Surgery	1983		
Rosenblum, Jay A.	Bowman Gray Sch. Med.	Neurology	1963		
Rosenfeld, David J.	Univ. Buffalo	Otolaryngology	1988		
Rosenfeld, Jane S.	UMDNJ, Rutgers	Internal Medicine	1984		
Rosenfeld, Philip A.	Jefferson	Otolaryngology	1972		
Rosenfeld, Raymond	Paris Fac. Med.			Diag Rad	1984
Rosenstein, Roger G.	Columbia Univ., Coll. P. & S.			Hand Surgery	1981
Rosensweig, Robert A.	Hahnemann Univ.			Diag Rad	1980
Rosenthal, Erik A.	Cornell Univ.			Hand Surgery	1974
Rosenthal, George	Chicago Med. Sch.	Internal Medicine	1968		
Rosenthal, Michael P.	UMDNJ, Rutgers	Family Practice	1984		
Rosenwald, Seth R.	Phila. Coll. Osteo. Med.	Psychiatry	1988		
Rosenzweig, Abraham H.	UMDNJ, Newark	Orthop Surg	1981		
Rosenzweig, Steven	Univ. Pennsylvania	Emerg Med	1989		
Rosky, Lee P.	Univ. Pennsylvania			Gastroenterology	1966
Rosman, Gary A.	New York Med. Coll.	Internal Medicine	1985		
Ross, David Bennett	George Washington Univ.	Rad Oncol	1978		
Ross, Ellen I.	Jefferson	Pediatrics	1987		
Ross, R. Douglas	Hahnemann Univ.	Ob/Gyn	1978	Mater/Fetal Med	1980
Roth, Karl S.	Bowman Gray Sch. Med.			Pediatrics	1972
Rothermel, Franklin J.	Jefferson	Radiology	1972		
Rothfarb, Steven Howard	S.U.N.Y, Upstate	Diag Rad	1980		
Rothman, Marc I.	S.U.N.Y., Upstate	Psychiatry	1980		
Rothman, Richard H.	Jefferson	Orthop Surg	1968		
Rotondo Michael F.	Georgetown Univ.	General Surgery	1989		
Rotz, Clifford T., Jr.	Jefferson	Radiology	1965		
Rouby, Elida	Univ. Cordoba (Argentina)	Rad Oncol	1977	Rad Oncol	1978
Rovner, Harold	Jefferson	General Surgery	1956		
Rowe, Daniel S., Jr.	Jefferson	Anesthesiology	1986		
Rowson, Harold T.	Temple Univ.	Anesthesiology	1989		
Roy, Bhaskar Kumar	All India Inst. Med. Sci.	Internal Medicine	1977		
Roy, John	Univ. Miami	Anesthesiology	1990		

Name	Med School	R Specialty	R Year	F Specialty	F Year
Rozanski, Lawrence T.	Georgetown Univ.	Internal Medicine	1983		
Rubenfeld, Ira G.	S.U.N.Y.	Internal Medicine	1983		
Rubens, Alan	Jefferson	Neurology	1966		
Rubenstein, James B.	New York Med. Coll.			Diag Rad	1983
Rubin, Bernard R.	Chicago Coll. Osteo. Med.			Rheumatology	1982
Rubin, Joyce R.	New York Univ.	Internal Medicine	1984	Infectious Diseases	1986
Rubin, Morton L.	Jefferson	Orthop Surg	1973		
Rubin, Ronald Neal	Temple Univ.			Hematology	1977
Rubino, John J.	Temple Univ.	Ob/Gyn	1981		
Rubinstein, Leonard A.	Med. Coll. Pennsylvania	Otolaryngology	1984		
Rubinstein, Morton F.	Hahnemann Univ.	Pediatrics	1964		
Ruby, Marianne	Emory Univ.	Ob/Gyn	1979	Repro Endo	1981
Ruby, Samuel R.	Jefferson	Internal Medicine	1980		
Ruggeri, Anthony J.	Jefferson	Psychiatry	1978		
Ruggiero, Francesca	Univ. Conneticut	Pathology	1986	Pathology	1987
Ruggiero, Nicholas J.	Jefferson	Internal Medicine	1972	Cardiovas Dis	1974
Rukskul, Arthit	Siriraj Hosp. (Thailand)	General Surgery	1971		
Rumbaugh, William P.	Jefferson	Ob/Gyn	1990		
Rupp, Joseph John	Jefferson	Internal Medicine	1949	Endocrinology	1951
Rupp, Michael J.	Jefferson	Pathology	1988	Cytopathology	1989
Ruschak, Paul J.	Jefferson	Dermatology	1981		
Russell, Bertram Royce	Jefferson			Rad Oncol	1980
Russell, Sudha S.	Med. Coll. Pennsylvania			Allergy and Immun	1984
Russman, France-Helene Marina	Temple Univ.	Anesthesiology	1990		
Rutenberg, Joel M.	Jefferson	Internal Medicine	1978		
Ruth, Corey	Jefferson	Orthop Surg	1986		
Rutkowski, Mark G.	Hahnemann Univ.	Anesthesiology	1989		
Ruttenberg, Norman F.	Phila. Coll. Osteo Med.	Radiology	1972		
Rutter, William A.	Jefferson	Psychiatry	1961		
Ryan, Charles B.	Syracuse Univ.	Thoracic Surgery	1955		
Ryan, John J.	Hahnemann Univ.			Pulm Dis	1971
Ryan, Timothy M.	Jefferson	Pediatrics	1981		
Ryan, William E.	Jefferson	Internal Medicine	1969		

The cure of many diseases is unknown to the physicians of Hellas, because they are ignorant of the whole, which should be treated also; for the part can never be well unless the whole is well. . . . This . . . is the great error of our day in the treatment of the human body, that the physicians separate the soul from the body.

Plato (427?–347 B.C.)

Joseph J. Savon
UMDNJ, R.W. Johnson

Edward L. Schacht
Virginia

Harry J. Sacks
Albert Einstein Col. Med.

William H. Saye, Jr.
Penn State

Dale M. Schaefer
Howard

Jean L. Santo
Hahnemann

Richard S. Schafer
UMDNJ, Rutgers

David L. Smith
Pennsylvania

Alan L. Schuricht
South Carolina

Ronald M. Schlansky
Cornell

Harriet Schanzer
Med. Col. Virginia

Postgraduate Alumni

Name	Med School	R Specialty	R Year	F Specialty	F Year
Sacks, Harry J.	Albert Einstein Coll. Med.	Pediatrics	1989		
Sadeghian, Mohammad R.	Teheran Univ.	Rheumatology	1978		
Sadhu, Vijay K.	All India Inst. Med. Sci.	Radiology	1978		
Sadowski, Robert H.	Hahnemann Univ.	Pediatrics	1989		
Sagalow, Barry R.	UMDNJ, Newark	Radiology	1986		
Saia, John A.	Phila. Col. Osteo. Med.			Cardiovas Dis	1980
Sakarin, Saovakon	Univ. Med. Sciences (Thailand)	Pediatrics	1966		
Sakurai, Kuniteru	Nagoya Univ. (Japan)	Radiology	1968		
Salcedo, Wilfredo G.	Far Eastern Univ. (Philippines)	Pathology	1973		
Salem, Anthony W.	Temple Univ.	Orthop Surg	1969		
Salen, Gerald	Jefferson	Internal Medicine	1964	Gastroenterology	1966
Salerno, Nicholas R.	Jefferson	Radiology	1969		
Salisbury, Roger E.	Albert Einstein Coll. Med.	General Surgery	1971		
Salkowe, Jerry Bruce	Jefferson	Family Practice	1983		
Salvo, John P.	Jefferson	Orthop Surg	1983		
Salzman, Alan S.	Albert Einstein Coll. Med.	Internal Medicine	1990		
Samalio, Justo R., Jr.	Manila Ctrl. Univ.	Anesthesiology	1974		
Samuels, Bruce S.	Jefferson	Internal Medicine	1972		
Sanchez, Ramon M.	Univ. Miami	Neurology	1985		
Sanchez-Longo, Luis P.	Jefferson	Neurology	1953		
Sandberg, Ronald K.	Jefferson	Otolaryngology	1970		
Sandel, M. Elizabeth	Med. Coll. Pennsylvania	Phys Med/Rehab	1984		
Sandler, Carl M.	Tufts Univ.	Radiology	1975		
Sandler, Jerome Lewis	Jefferson	General Surgery	1963		
Sandler, Mitchell S.	Hahnemann Univ.	Diag Rad	1982		
Sandler, Steven C.	Jefferson	General Surgery	1970		
Sands, Milton J., Jr.	Jefferson	Internal Medicine	1969		
Santangelo, Samuel Charles	Temple Univ.	Pathology	1957		
Santo, Jean L.	Hahnemann Univ.	Anesthesiology	1989		
Saraclar, Yildiz	Univ. Istanbul (Turkey)			Pediatric Allergy	1975
Sarfraz, Jamil	King Edward Med. Coll. (Pakistan)			Diag Rad	1980
Sarnoff, Jeffrey	Univ. Genova	Psychiatry	1987		
Sarnowski, Robert J.	Jefferson	Neuro Surg	1973		
Sassani, Sohrab A.	Teheran Univ.	Pediatrics	1961		
Sastre, Marcos	Univ. Buenos Aires	Pathology	1977		
Sattel, Andrew B.	Jefferson			Hand Surgery	1990
Sattel, Leonard	Jefferson	Psychiatry	1964		
Saull, Fredric Rick	Hahnemann Univ.	Orthop Surg	1974		
Savage, Michael P.	Jefferson			Cardiovas Dis	1986
Savon, Joseph J.	UMDNJ, R.W. Johnson	Internal Medicine	1990		
Sawhney, Kewal K.	S.M.S. Med. Coll.	Anesthesiology	1976		
Sawwaf, Ziyad W.	Syrian Univ.	Radiology	1968	Radiology	1976
Sawyer, Blackwell, Jr.	Jefferson	Orthop Surg	1963		
Saye, William Henry, Jr.	Penn State Univ.	Dermatology	1979		
Scariato, Albert F.	Jefferson	Rad Oncol	1982		
Schacherer, Timothy G.	Med. Coll. Virginia			Hand Surgery	1986
Schacht, Edward L.	Univ. Virginia	Psychiatry	1988		
Schaefer, Dale M.	Howard Univ.	Neuro Surg	1990		
Schafer, R. Scott	UMDNJ, Rutgers	Internal Medicine	1987	Cardiovas Dis	1990
Schanzer, Harriet	Med. Coll. Virginia	Family Practice	1986		
Scharoun, Jacques	Univ. Haiti	Pediatrics	1966		
Schatz, John W.	Hahnemann Univ.			Cardiovas Dis	1972
Schatz, Norman J.	Hahnemann Univ.	Neurology	1965		

Name	Med School	R Specialty	R Year	F Specialty	F Year
Schechter, David C.	Jefferson	General Surgery	1958		
Scherer, Henry	St. George's Hospital	Internal Medicine	1976		
Scherr, Stuart A.	Jefferson	Otolaryngology	1976		
Schetman, Anna	UMDNJ, Newark	Pediatrics	1989		
Schiff, David C.	Univ. Florida	Orthop Surg	1975		
Schiffer, Charles F.	Univ. Cincinnati	Internal Medicine	1975	Nephrology	1976
Schilling, John F.	Jefferson	Radiology	1985		
Schillizzi, William	UMDNJ, Rutgers	Internal Medicine	1988		
Schlansky, Ronald M.	Cornell Univ.	Internal Medicine	1978	Rheumatology	1980
Schlesinger, Robert B.	Jefferson	Internal Medicine	1985		
Schlitt, Ludwig E.	Univ. Frankfurt	Pediatrics	1958	Pediatrics	1960
Schmidt, Evelyn D.	Duke Univ.	Pediatrics	1954		
Schmitz, Thomas J.	Penn State Univ.	Anesthesiology	1990		
Schnall, Sandra F.	Jefferson	Internal Medicine	1982		
Schnapf, Donald J.	Phila. Coll. Osteo. Med.			Radiology	1978
Schneiman, Maurice H.	Univ. Maryland	Psychiatry	1966		
Schnoll, Sidney H.	UMDNJ, Newark	Neurology	1971		
Schonholz, Lyris A.	Mt. Sinai Sch. Med.			Diag Rad	1988
Schreml, Wolfgang	Munich Univ.			Hematology	1968
Schucker, Charles L.	Jefferson	Ob/Gyn	1956		
Schuricht, Alan L.	Univ. South Carolina	General Surgery	1990		
Schuster, Stephen J.	Jefferson			Hematology	1988
Schutzman, David Louis	Jefferson	Pediatrics	1981	Neo- Perinatal Med	1983
Schwab, John E.	Jefferson	Neuro Surg	1947		
Schwab, Richard J.	Univ. Pennsylvania	Internal Medicine	1986		
Schwab, Robert H.	Jefferson	Internal Medicine	1961		
Schwabe, Karl G.	Jefferson	Internal Medicine	1987		
Schwandt, Hugo B.	Temple Univ.	Ophthalmology	1972		
Schwartz, Andrew E.	New York Med. Coll.	Internal Medicine	1987		
Schwartz, Burton	Jefferson	Pediatrics	1971		
Schwartz, Gayle S.	Northwestern Univ.	Phys Med/Rehab	1989		
Schwartz, Irving R.	State Univ. New York			Hematology	1957
Schwartz, Marc Lee	Temple Univ.	Internal Medicine	1981		
Schwartz, Martin	Jefferson	Ob/Gyn	1972		
Schwarz, Richard A.	Albert Einstein Coll. Med.			Allergy and Immun	1986
Schwarzschild, Walter	Univ. Zurich			Rheumatology	1969
Sciara, Christine M.	Temple Univ.	Dermatology	1982		
Scicchitano, Leon Pasqual	Jefferson	General Surgery	1963		
Scimeca, Margaret Riley	Albany Med. Coll.	Psychiatry	1978		
Scola, David A.	Temple Univ.	Psychiatry	1984		
Scoles, Karen S.	UMDNJ, Rutgers	Internal Medicine	1986		
Sconzo, Frank T.	New York Med. Coll.			Colon and Rec Surg	1989
Scott, Malcolm P.	Tulane Univ.	Urological Surgery	1972		
Scott, Margery A.	Meharry Med. Coll.	Dermatology	1975		
Scott, Richard D.	Jefferson	Pathology	1989		
Scott, S. David, Jr.	Jefferson	Internal Medicine	1980		
Scott, Thomas H.	Meharry Med. Coll.	Internal Medicine	1974	Pulm Dis	1975
Scott, Timothy Van	Meharry Med. Coll.	Ophthalmology	1972		
Scott, William Eric Bruneton	Queens Univ. (Belfast)			Anesthesiology	1963
Scotti, Daniel Mark	Jefferson			Radiology	1977
Scotti, Thomas M.	Jefferson			Pathology	1944
Sebring, Heatly D.	Univ. Pennsylvania			Pediatric Allergy	1980
Seeger, A. Randall	Jefferson	Urological Surgery	1988		

Name	Med School	R Specialty	R Year	F Specialty	F Year
Segal, Barry G.	Univ. Witwatersrand			Family Practice	1988
Segal, Sharon R.	Phila. Coll. Osteo. Med.			Diag Rad	1987
Segovia, Eva M.	Univ. Hawaii	Anesthesiology	1987		
Segovia, Ignacio M.	Univ. Vanlencia (Spain)			Anesthesiology	1960
Seguin, Hermas	Univ. Montreal			Repro Endo	961
Seidel, Rhonwyn S.	Hahnemann Univ.	Anesthesiology	1983		
Seifert, Raymond D.	Phila. Coll. Osteo. Med.	Anesthesiology	1985		
Seinsheimer, Frank, III	Harvard Univ.			Hand Surgery	1980
Selinger, Howard Andrew	Univ. Pennsylvania	Family Practice	1986		
Seltzer, Joseph L.	Jefferson	Anesthesiology	1975		
Seltzer, Leonard H.	Jefferson			Pediatric Allergy	1973
Sencindiver, Paige Victor	Jefferson	General Surgery	1959		
Serby, Charles W.	SUNY, Syracuse	Pediatrics	1962		
Serota, Ronald D.	Jefferson	Psychiatry	1981		
Sethi, Baljeet S.	Meerut Univ. (India)	Neurology	1983		
Shaber, Gary S.	Ohio State Univ.	Radiology	1966		
Shah, Bipin C.	B.J. Med. Coll. (India)	Neuro Surg	1977		
Shah, Kokila Doshi	Lokmanya Tilak Muni. Med. (India)	Anesthesiology	1979		
Shah, Nasim	Fatima Jinnah Med. Coll. (Pakistan)	Ob/Gyn	1961	Repro Endo	1960
Shah, Surekha U.	B.J. Med. Coll. (India)	Ophthalmology	1981		
Shaikh, Bahu Sultan	Dow Medical Coll. (Pakistan)	Internal Medicine	1972	Hematology	1974
Shaiman, Alan M.	Med. Coll. Pennsylvania	Rad Oncol	1982		
Shalan, Kamal I.	Cairo Univ.	Rad Oncol	1979		
Shallcross, David L.	West Virginia Univ.	Phys Med/Rehab	1990		
Shanfeld, Norman M.	Jefferson	Psychiatry	1976		
Shanker, Kasturi G.	Madras Univ. (India)	Urological Surgery	1976		
Shannon, John J.	Univ. Miami			Cardiothor Surg	1989
Shansky, Martin	Temple Univ.	Internal Medicine	1977		
Shapeero, Lorraine G.	Univ. California, San Francisco	Internal Medicine	1970		
Shapero, Paul A.	Tufts Univ.			Pediatric Allergy	1982
Shapiro, Jon A.	Univ. Pennsylvania	Internal Medicine	1985		
Shapiro, Mark T.	Ohio State Univ.	Ophthalmology	1976		
Shapiro, Myron J.	Univ. Toronto	Otolaryngology	1949		
Shapiro, Richard D.	Jefferson	Ophthalmology	1968		
Sharafabadi, Cyrus	Univ. Tehran	Anesthesiology	1968		
Sharifi-Azad, Said	Univ. Tehran	Anesthesiology	1977		
Sharkey, Peter F.	S.U.N.Y., Upstate	Orthop Surg	1989	Orthop Surg	1990
Sharma, Meera V.	Univ. Bombay	Internal Medicine	1977		
Sharma, Prithvi Raj All	India Inst. Med. Sci.			Cardiovas Dis	1979
Sharma, Raj Kumar	Univ. Allahabad (India)			Neo- Perinatal Med	1982
Sharps, Lewis S.L.	Jefferson	Orthop Surg	1980		
Shavelson, Robert W.	Harvard Univ.			Endocrinology	1962
Shaw, Ellen W.	Hahnemann Univ.			Gastroenterology	1985
Shaw, Linda L.	Med. Coll. Pennsylvania	Pediatrics	1977		
Shaw, Wendy M.	Case Western Reserve Univ.			Diag Rad	1982
Shawaluk, Paul D.	Jefferson	Ophthalmology	1972		
Sheer, George W.	UMDNJ, Newark	Radiology	1974		
Sheft, Douglas J.	Harvard Univ.	Radiology	1965		
Shelton, Barbara	Med. College Pennsylvania	Phys Med/Rehab	1984		
Shepp, Ellen	Burnett Univ. Kentucky	Ob/Gyn	1989		
Sherk, Henry H.	Jefferson	Orthop Surg	1961		

Name	Med School	R Specialty	R Year	F Specialty	F Year
Sherman, Brock V.	Tufts Univ.			Pediatric Allergy	1978
Sherman, Nancy H.	Jefferson	Diag Rad	1982		
Sherwood, William C.	Jefferson	Internal Medicine	1962	Hematology	1963
Sherwyn, Jonathan H.	Chicago Med. Sch.			Hand Surgery	1990
Sheth, Arun V.	Univ. Bombay			Hematology	1990
Sheth, Rajendra D.	Gujarut Univ. (India)	Urological Surgery	1974		
Shimer, Judith	Stringfield Med. Coll. Pennsylvania	Family Practice	1983		
Shin, Myung Hi	Seoul Nat. Univ.	Pediatrics	1966		
Shin, Yongshik	Ewha Women's Univ. (Korea)	Psychiatry	1975		
Shlansky-Goldberg, Richard D.	Univ. Rochester	Radiology	1989		
Shoemaker, Henry K.	Jefferson	Neuro Surg	1954		
Shoemaker, Patricia L.	Temple Univ.	Pediatrics	1983		
Shofstall, William H.	Univ. Oklahoma	Otolaryngology	1949		
Sholes, Dillard McCary, Jr.,	Med. Coll. Virginia			Repro Endo	1953
Sholevar, Farhad	Univ. Tehran	Psychiatry	1988		
Shonnard, Neal H.	Univ. Nevada			Orthop Surg	1990
Shore, Michael W.	Temple Univ.	Psychiatry	1984		
Short, Glenn M.	Hahnemann Univ.	Internal Medicine	1982		
Shortridge, Beth A.	Duke Univ.	Pediatrics	1988	Pediatrics	1990
Shovlin, Patricia M.	Univ. California, Davis	Family Practice	1985		
Shrager, Morton W.	Univ. Pennsylvania	Neurology	1959		
Shreiner, David P.	Jefferson	Internal Medicine	1966		
Shrier, Peter R.	Univ. Vermont	Ob/Gyn	1972		
Shull Stewart, D.	Jefferson	Internal Medicine	1973		
Shupp, David L.	Penn State Univ.	Internal Medicine	1983		
Shusterman, Richard D.	Med. Coll. Pennsylvania			Pulm Dis	1989
Shutack, John G.	Phila. Coll. Osteo. Med.			Neo- Perinatal Med	1977
Shute, Howard E.	Univ. Pennsylvania			Hematology	1967
Sicilia, Ronald F.	Temple Univ.	Oral & Max Surg	1974		
Siegel, Howard I.	UMDNJ, Rutgers	Internal Medicine	1988		
Siegel, Jamie	Med. Coll. Pennsylvania			Hematology	1982
Siegfried, Jay W.	Univ. Cincinnati	Phys Med/Rehab	1981		
Sieper, William J.	Kirksville Coll. tOsteo. Med.	Rad Oncol	1977		
Sigler, Miles H.	Cornell Univ.	Internal Medicine	1958		
Silber, Tomas Jose	Univ. Buenos Aires			Pediatrics	1973
Silberman, Isaac Nathaniel	St. Louis Univ.	Neurology	1953		
Silberstein, Charles Elliot	Univ. Maryland	Orthop Surg	1963		
Silfen, Sheryl L.	Jefferson	Ob/Gyn	1979	Mater/Fetal Med	1981
Silver, Harold M.	Columbia Univ., Coll. P. & S.			Cardiovas Dis	1955
Silver, Michael M.	S.U.N.Y., Downstate	Internal Medicine	1980		
Silverman, Lewis D.	Univ. Miami	Internal Medicine	1975		
Silverman, Neil S.	Univ. Pennsylvania			Mater/Fetal Med	1990
Silverman, Norman R.	Univ. Pennsylvania	Radiology	1969		
Silverman, Paul B.	Jefferson	Anesthesiology	1970		
Silverman, Richard B.	Far Eastern Univ. (Phillipines)	Psychiatry	1989		
Simerman, Lee P.	Albert Einstein Coll. Med.	Radiology	1987		
Simmonds, Mary A.	Med. Coll. Pennsylvania			Hematology	1980
Simmons, Juliana	Indiana Univ.	Rad Oncol	1971		
Simon, David G.	New York Univ.	Internal Medicine	1977		
Simon, Erich H.W.	Westfalische Univ. (Germany)	Neurology	1963		
Simone, Darrell N.	Med. Coll. Ohio	Anesthesiology	1987		
Simonian, Simon K.	Am. Univ. Beirut	Otolaryngology	1980		

Name	Med School	R Specialty	R Year	F Specialty	F Year
Simpson, Joan W.	Jefferson	Ob/Gyn	1979		
Sinclair, Sigmund Robert	Univ. Buffalo	Otolaryngology	1961		
Singer, Daniel I.	Boston Univ.			Hand Surgery	1985
Singh, Sudeep	Univ. Lucknow (India)	Pediatrics	1987		
Sipski, Marcalee	Jefferson	Phys Med/Rehab	1986		
Siripoonya, Praputt	Univ. Med. Sc. (Thailand)	Pediatrics	1968		
Sirlin, Nelson	Jefferson	Ob/Gyn	1972		
Sirotnak, John J.	Jefferson	General Surgery	1990		
Skeist, Barry P.	Jefferson	Radiology	1976		
Sklar, Nathan Robert	Temple Univ.	Diag Rad	1977		
Skolnik, Neil S.	Emory Univ.	Family Practice	1987		
Skvara, Frederick C.	Jefferson	Pathology	1975		
Skypala, Patricia Lynn	Jefferson	Pathology	1990		
Slemmer, James Ross	Jefferson	Pathology	1989		
Slimak, Grace G.	Jefferson	Internal Medicine	1988		
Slimak, Randall E.	Jefferson	Internal Medicine	1987		
Slipyan, Philip	New York Med. Coll.			Repro Endo	1973
Sloan, Frederick W.	S.U.N.Y., Upstate	Internal Medicine	1978		
Slogoff, Stephen	Jefferson	Anesthesiology	1971		
Slota, Paul A.	Jefferson	Phys Med/Rehab	1990		
Slotnick, Edward A.	Phila. Coll. Osteo. Med.			Ob/Gyn	1971
Slotoroff, Howard	Chicago Med. Sch.	General Surgery	1970		
Slysh, Sonya J.	Univ. Pennsylvania	Internal Medicine	1983	Cardiovas Dis	1985
Smeltzer, Kenneth L.	Temple Univ.			Nephrology	1968
Smith, Alvin H.	Jefferson	Ophthalmology	1956		
Smith, Burgess A.	Jefferson	General Surgery			
Smith, C. Richard	Phila. Coll. Osteo. Med.	Internal Medicine	1975		
Smith, C.	Ross Esc. Cent. America (Costa Rica)	Pediatrics	1986		
Smith, David L.	Univ. Pennsylvania			Cardiovas Dis	1990
Smith, Ellen K.	Jefferson	Internal Medicine	1981		
Smith, J. Stanley	Jefferson	Dermatology			
Smith, Jeanene A.	Oregon Health Sciences Univ.	Family Practice	1987		
Smith, John W., II,	Jefferson	Internal Medicine	1984		
Smith, Kevin L.	East Virginia Med. Sch.	General Surgery	1984	Hand Surgery	1985
Smith, Matthew H.	Univ. Pittsburgh	Internal Medicine	1981		
Smith, Quintin J.	Univ. Texas	Ophthalmology	1971		
Smith, Richard T.	Jefferson			Internal Medicine	1950
Smith, Robert V.	Penn State Univ.	Family Practice	1978		
Smith, Steven Phila.	Coll. Osteo. Med.	Radiology	1984		
Smith, T. Burton	Univ. Southern California	Urological Surgery	1949		
Smith, Tamara Lee	Univ. Louisville			Child Psychiatry	1982
Smith, Thomas Timothy	Creighton Univ.	Otolaryngology	1943		
Smullens, Stanton N.	Jefferson	General Surgery	1965	General Surgery	1969
Smythe, Vernon L.	Univ. Colorado	Orthop Surg	1962		
Snedden, Hal Edward	Jefferson	Orthop Surg	1956		
Snedden, Michael H.	Jefferson	Orthop Surg	1984		
Snipes, Edward R.	Jefferson	Internal Medicine	1987		
Snyder, Alan I.	Jefferson	Urological Surgery	1964		
Snyder, Howard M.	Jefferson	General Surgery	1963		
Snyder, Joseph	Jefferson	Internal Medicine	1964		
Snyder, Randall W., Jr.,	Univ. Virginia	Internal Medicine	1971	Gastroenterology	1972
Snyder, Walter H., Jr.,	Phila. Coll. Osteo. Med.			Pulm Dis	1976

Name	Med School	R Specialty	R Year	F Specialty	F Year
Soffen, Deborah Singer	New York Univ.	Pediatrics	1988		
Sokol, Donald Z.	Tufts Univ.	Otolaryngology	1965		
Solan, Merrill J.	Albany Med. Coll.	Rad Oncol	1986		
Solberg, Byrne L.	Temple Univ.	Phys Med/Rehab	1984		
Soliman, Manal D.	Alexandria Univ.	General Surgery	1973		
Solin, Lawrence J.	Brown Univ.	Surgery/Rad Oncol	1982		
Solit, Robert W.	Jefferson	General Surgery	1966	General Surgery	1969
Sollenberger, Stanton E.	Philadelphia Coll. Osteo. Med.	Neurology	1989	Neurology	1990
Solof, Arnold J.	Hahnemann Univ.	Pediatrics	1979		
Solomon, Mark P.	New York Univ.	General Surgery	1983		
Solow, Edward A.	Jefferson	Internal Medicine	1976	Cardiovas Dis	1977
Solz, Heidi	UMDNJ, Rutgers	Family Practice	1983		
Sommerville, Kenneth W.	Jefferson	Neurology	1980		
Sonsini, Gregg A.	Jefferson	Pediatrics	1988		
Sonstein, Allen	Jefferson	Internal Medicine	1974		
Sood, Sanjiv	Univ. Maryland	Internal Medicine	1987		
Sorensen, Maryanne	Jefferson	Anesthesiology	1988		
Soricelli, Richard R.	Jefferson	Internal Medicine	1966	Nephrology	1965
Sosnowski, John R.	Univ. South Carolina			Repro Endo	1952
Soss, Sheldon B.	Jefferson	Otolaryngology	1969		
Sotelo, Augusto	Nat. Univ. Bogota	Otolaryngology	1971		
Soulen, Renate L.	Woman's Med. Coll.	Radiology	1963		
Souri, Mahadev K.	Kurnool Med. Coll. (India)	Neuro Surg	1984		
Spaar, Joseph L.	Temple Univ.	Internal Medicine	1979	Gastroenterology	1981
Speace, George F., II,	Jefferson	General Surgery	1977		
Spechler, Floyd F.	Jefferson	Ophthalmology	1978		
Spector, Howard L.	Univ. Osteo. Med., Des Moines			Rad Oncol	1982
Spencer, James T., Jr.,	Jefferson	Otolaryngology	1948		
Spiegel, William A.	Temple Univ.			Pediatric Allergy	1988
Spill, Ira L.	New York Univ.	Anesthesiology	1984		
Spiro, Arthur W.	Philadelphia Coll. Osteo. Med.	Anesthesiology	1978		
Spitz, Deborah F.	Brown Univ.	Internal Medicine	1980		
Spitzer, Ira E.	Philadelphia Coll. Osteo. Med.			Pediatric Allergy	1983
Sprandio, John D.	Temple Univ.			Hematol/Oncol	1988
Sprecher, Omar D.	Jefferson	General Surgery	1949		
Squadrito, James F.	Jefferson	Urological Surgery	1985		
Squires, Leslie S.	Jefferson	Internal Medicine	1984	Cardiovas Dis	1986
Srinivas, Usha	Bangalore Univ. (India)	Anesthesiology	1983		
St. Laurent, Jean-Yves	Laval Univ. (Canada)			Hand Surgery	1984
Staab, James A.	Univ. Florida	Emerg Med	1987		
Stacks, Jacob C., Jr.,	Jefferson	Psychiatry	1965		
Stambaugh, John E., Jr.,	Jefferson	Internal Medicine	1971	Medical Oncology	1972
Stampfl, David A.	Boston Univ.			Gastroenterology	1990
Stanch, James Univ.	Puerto Rico	Psychiatry	1985		
Stark, Bruce	Univ. Michigan	Ophthalmology	1982		
Stark, James P.	Univ. New Mexico	Otolaryngology	1989		
Starsnic, Mary Ann	Jefferson	Anesthesiology	1977		
Stassi, John	Univ. Pennsylvania	Radiology	1987		
Stavem, Per J.	Univ. Oslo	Internal Medicine	1955		
Stayman, Joseph W., Jr.,	Jefferson	General Surgery	1948		
Stecyk, Markian D.	Tufts Univ.	Orthop Surg	1990		
Steel, Ann E.	Univ. Genova (Italy)	Psychiatry	1988		
Stehlik, John M.	Jefferson	Otolaryngology	1968		

Name	Med School	R Specialty	R Year	F Specialty	F Year
Stein, Ann P.	UMDNJ, Rutgers			Hand Surgery	1989
Stein, Daniel	S.U.N.Y., Downstate	Internal Medicine	1985		
Stein, David K.	New York Med. Coll.	Internal Medicine	1987		
Stein, Scott C.	Jefferson	Anesthesiology	1970		
Steinbach, Alan	Mt. Sinai Sch. Med.	Internal Medicine	1987		
Steinberg, Dean A.	Temple Univ.	Anesthesiology	1985		
Steinberg, Stanford M.	Jefferson	Internal Medicine	1968		
Steinberg, William J.	Jefferson	Rad Oncol	1979		
Steindel, Carl R.	Jefferson	Orthop Surg	1973		
Steinfield, Paul H.	Hahnemann Univ.			Hand Surgery	1988
Stella, Joseph G.	Temple Univ.	Rad Oncol	1969		
Stephenson, Daniel H.	Jefferson			Psychiatry	1949
Sterling, Francis H.	Jefferson			Endocrinology	1965
Stern, Alan L.	Jefferson	Ophthalmology	1978		
Sterner, Todd M.	Temple Univ.	Pediatrics	1982		
Stevenson, Susan M.	Jefferson	Pediatrics	1977		
Steward, Robert E.	Jefferson	Pediatrics	1947	Ob/Gyn	1948
Stewart, Michael P.	Jefferson	General Surgery	1980		
Stewart, Wayne T.	Univ. Central del Este (Dom. Rep.)			Diag Rad	1986
Stiner, Allan E.	Jefferson	Anesthesiology	1985		
Stockwell, Margaret Kathleen F.	Univ. Nebraska	Family Practice	1977		
Stofman, Guy M.	Jefferson	Otolaryngology	1989		
Stofman, Henry C.	Emory Univ.	General Surgery	1958		
Stokes, Thomas L.	Jefferson	General Surgery	1954	General Surgery	1949
Stolberg-Acosta, Robert A.	Univ. Maryland	Psychiatry	1971		
Stoll, David B.	Med. Coll. Ohio	Internal Medicine	1981	Hematology	1983
Stoloff, Irwin L.	Jefferson	Internal Medicine	1953	Internal Medicine	1958
Storfer, Stephen P.	Med. Univ. South Carolina	Internal Medicine	1989		
Stose, Willis G.	Jefferson	Orthop Surg	1963		
Stratt, Bruce J.	Jefferson	Radiology	1979		
Strause, Harold L., Jr.,	Jefferson	Ophthalmology	1955		
Streets, Gerald M.	Meharry Med. Coll.	Psychiatry	1990		
Streletz, Leopold J.	Temple Univ.	Neurology	1973		
Streletz, Patricia M.	Jefferson	Pediatrics	1976		
Stricker, Heinz	Univ. Innsbruck (Austria)	Pediatrics	1967		
Stringfield, John W.	Duke Univ.	Family Practice	1983		
Strong, Michael D., III,	Jefferson	General Surgery	1973		
Stuchin, Steven A.	Columbia Univ., Coll. P. & S.			Hand Surgery	1982
Stumpo, Patrick P.	Philadelphia Coll. Osteo. Med.	Psychiatry	1987		
Styles, Michael J.	Med. Coll. Pennsylvania	Anesthesiology	1989		
Subin, David K.	Jefferson	Orthop Surg	1966		
Suehs, Oliver W.	Univ. Texas	Otolaryngology	1941		
Suh, Jung Ho	Yonsei Univ. (Korea)			Diag Rad	1977
Sukprasith, Ubol	Siriraj Hosp. (Thailand)	Anesthesiology	1969		
Sulit, Armando M.	Manila Cent. Univ.	General Surgery	1974		
Sullivan, Gregory B.	George Washington Univ.	Psychiatry	1989		
Sullivan, James J.	Wayne State Univ.	Radiology	1962		
Sullivan, John L.	Georgetown Univ.			Repro Endo	1966
Sullivan, Kevin L.	UMDNJ, Rutgers	Radiology	1986		
Sultana, Carmen J.	New York Univ.	Ob/Gyn	1990		
Sumawong, Varavudh	Siriraj Hosp. (Thailand)			Repro Endo	1961
Sumerson, James M.	Jefferson	Otolaryngology	1972		
Sun, Lucille Chin Yun	Univ. St. John's (China)			Repro Endo	1956

Name	Med School	R Specialty	R Year	F Specialty	F Year
Sunderman, F. William, Jr.,	Jefferson			Clinical Pathology	1958
Sundheim, John Martin	Jefferson	Internal Medicine	1976		
Sundt, Linda M.	Jefferson	Anesthesiology	1978		
Surgent, Richard E.	UMDNJ, Newark	Orthop Surg	1971		
Suris, Juan E.	Univ. Puerto Rico	General Surgery	1978		
Sussman, Neil Mark	New York Med. Coll.	Neurology	1977		
Sutaputra, Kalaya	Chulalongkorn Univ. (Thailand)	Pediatrics	1965		
Sutter, Francis P.	Philadelphia Coll. Osteo. Med.	General Surgery	1983	Cardiothor Surg	1986
Sweeney, Francis J., Jr.,	Jefferson	Internal Medicine	1958		
Sweterlitsch, Louis H.	Jefferson	Ophthalmology	1964		
Swiecicki, Martin	Hahnemann Univ.	Neuro Surg	1965		
Sypher, Robert V., Jr.,	S.U.N.Y., Upstate			Hand Surgery	1983
Szabo, Joanne S. E.	Virginia Med. Sch.	Pediatrics	1982		

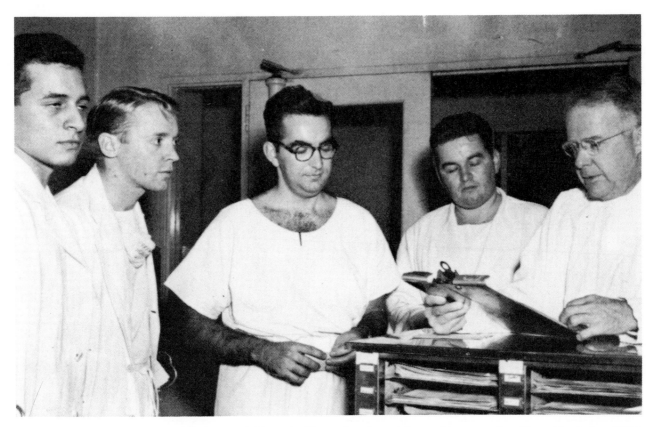

Dr. Thaddeus L. Montgomery (Chairman of Obstetrics/Gynecology) on right, making rounds with residents (ca. 1958).

Postgraduate Alumni

Kenneth A. Tolep
S.U.N.Y., Syracuse

David S. Tabby
Phila Coll. Osteo. Med.

Suzanne Topalian
Tufts

Gerardo Torres
Univ. Puerto Rico

John Y. Templeton, III
Jefferson

Samuel Tarantino
UMDNJ, Rutgers

Luiz C. Toledo
San Carlos (Guatemala)

Robert F. Traflet
UMDNJ, Rutgers

Nguyen D. Tri
Saigon

Karen J. Trygg
UMDNJ, Newark

William O. Thompson
Jefferson

John S. Tavenner
Eastern Virginia

Name	Med School	R Specialty	R Year	F Specialty	F Year
Tabby, David S.	Philadelphia Coll. Osteo. Med.	Neurology	1988		
Taddonio, William S.	Jefferson	Family Practice	1989		
Tadduni, Gregory T.	Albert Einstein Coll. Med.			Orthop Surg	1989
Takeda, Misao	Yokohama Univ.	Pathology	1961		
Talacki, Carol A.	Jefferson			Hematology	1989
Tallant, Edward J.	Jefferson			Gastroenterology	1948
Tallia, Alfred F.	UMDNJ, Rutgers	Family Practice	1982		
Tamaki, Hitoshi Tom	Boston Univ.	Pathology	1948		
Tambe, Aaly	St. Joseph's Univ. (Lebanon)			Cardiovas Dis	1963
Tan, Josefina S.	Univ. St. Tomas (Philippines)	Pediatrics	1962		
Tandhanand, Sunthorn	Univ. Med. Sci. (Thailand)			Endocrinology	1953
Tannebaum, Ira Roy	Jefferson	General Surgery	1973		
Tanyol, Hasib	Istanbul Univ.			Gastroenterology	1954
Tarantino, Samuel	UMDNJ, Rutgers	Ob/Gyn	1989		
Tase, Douglas S.	Temple Univ.	Orthop Surg	1987		
Tatarian, Gabriel	Jefferson	Ob/Gyn	1957		
Tatu, William Francis	Jefferson	Diag Rad	1980		
Taubin, Joel M.	Univ. Virginia	Internal Medicine	1972		
Tavenner, John S. E.	Eastern Virginia	Psychiatry	1984		
Taylor, James A.	Hahnemann Univ.	Psychiatry	1975		
Tchourumoff, Nime	Univ. of Paris	Pathology	1971		
Teitelman, Edward A.	Jefferson	Psychiatry	1969		
Templeton, John Young, III,	Jefferson	General Surgery	1950		
Terracciano, Gina J.	Coll. Osteo. Med., Kansas City			Pediatrics	1985
Terranova, Robert J.	Philadelphia Coll. Osteo. Med.	Neurology	1973		
Terrero, Romulo A.	Univ. Central Venezuela	Neurology	1970		
Thoder, Joseph J.	Temple Univ.			Hand Surgery	1988
Thomas, Gary K.	Northwestern Univ.	Otolaryngology	1966		
Thomas, Gregory M.	Univ. Illinois	Phys Med/Rehab	1978		
Thomas, John E.	Jefferson	Anesthesiology	1961		
Thomas, John L.	Univ. Virginia	Diag Rad	1979		
Thomas, Joseph Raker	Jefferson	Orthop Surg	1978		
Thomasi, Doris A.H.	Univ. Colorado	Psychiatry	1969		
Thompkins, Leonard J.	Jefferson	Pathology	1965		
Thompson, Harvey J., Jr.,	Jefferson	Radiology	1951		
Thompson, Joan Carol	Howard Univ.	Pathology	1975		
Thompson, Noble L., Jr.,	Jefferson	Radiology	1975		
Thompson, Richard A.	Case Western Reserve Univ.	Neurology	1965		
Thompson, William O.	Jefferson	Family Practice	1990		
Thomson, George W.	Univ. Chicago			Pulm Dis	1956
Thornton, James J.	Temple Univ.	Internal Medicine	1969	Gastroenterology	1972
Tibbens, George F.	Jefferson	Ophthalmology	1951		
Tieff, Michael W.	Philadelphia Coll. Osteo. Med.			Diag Rad	1983
Tiffany, Marla S.	UMDNJ, Rutgers			Pediatric Allergy	1987
Tilton, Donald Clarke	Philadelphia Coll. Osteo. Med.	Rad Oncol	1974		
Ting, Rosalind Y.	Nat. Med. Coll. Shanghai			Pediatrics	1960
Tisnado, Jaime	Nat. Univ. San Marcos (Peru)	Radiology	1971	Radiology	1972
Toland, Joseph C.	Hahnemann Univ.	Ophthalmology	1967		
Toldeo, Luiz	Carlos de Campinas (Brazil)	Orthop Surg	1979		
Toledo, Francisco L.	Univ. San Carlos (Guatemala)	Internal Medicine	1977		
Tolep, Kenneth A.	S.U.N.Y., Syracuse	Internal Medicine	1989		
Tolia, Bhupendra	Baroda Univ. (India)	Urological Surgery	1971		
Toll. Norma S.	Temple Univ.	Psychiatry	1987		

Name	Med School	R Specialty	R Year	F Specialty	F Year
Tom. Carol Mei Lin	Hahnemann Univ.	Anesthesiology	1988		
Tomashefski. Joseph F.	Hahnemann Univ.	Pulm Dis	1950		
Tomei. Ralph Paul	Philadelphia Coll. Osteo. Med.	Psychiatry	1981		
Tomichek. Richard C.	Jefferson	General Surgery	1977		
Toohey. Michael R.	Univ. Pennsylvania	Oral & Max Surg	1987		
Topalian, Suzanne	Tufts Univ.	General Surgery	1985		
Toro, Clara	Temple	Univ. Pediatrics	1979		
Torres, Carolina	Univ. St. Tomas (Philippines)	Anesthesiology	1973		
Torres, Jorge L.	Central Univ. Sch. Med. (P.R.)	Diag Rad	1990		
Torres-Feliciano, Gerardo R.	Univ. Puerto Rico	Neurology	1985		
Toton, John F.	Temple Univ.	Orthop Surg	1972		
Townend, Stephen C.	Jefferson	Pediatrics	1978		
Tozer, Richard Charles	Jefferson	Neuro Surg	1950		
Traflet, Robert F.	UMDNJ, Rutgers	Radiology	1989		
Tragoon, Steve	Ramathibodi Hosp. (Thailand)	Internal Medicine	1974		
Trattler, Henry L.	Univ. Maryland	Ophthalmology	1970		
Traum, Ronald E.	Jefferson	Ob/Gyn	1964		
Traupman, Arnold Frank	Jefferson	Ophthalmology	1977		
Travagline, Dominic J.	UMDNJ, Newark	Orthop Surg	1967		
Tri, Nguyen	Univ. Saigon	Rad Oncol	1979		
Triester, Arthur N.	Jefferson	Internal Medicine	1970	Cardiovas Dis	1972
Trigos, Gaston Germain	Univ. of Mexico	Psychiatry	1959	Psychiatry	1960
Trocki, Ira Mark	Stritch Sch. Med.	Otolaryngology	1979		
Troll, Victor	New York Univ.	Pediatrics	1984		
Trollinger, Robert J.	Hahnemann Univ.	Pathology	1963		
Trought, William S.	Tufts Univ.	Radiology	1973		
Trouillot, Jacqueline	Univ. Haiti	Pediatrics	1959		
Troy, Alan D.	Univ. Pennsylvania	Internal Medicine	1980		
Troy, Shoshana	Hahnemann Univ.			Pediatrics	1987
Trygg, Karen J.	UMDNJ, Newark	Internal Medicine	1987		
Tsai, Fong-Yong	Taipei Med. Coll. (Taiwan)			Radiology	1973
Tsay, Chi L.	Nat. Taiwan Univ.	Anesthesiology	1980		
Tuchinda, Jalit	Kyoto Univ.	Internal Medicine	1975	Cardiovas Dis	1977
Tucker, Dale C.	Jefferson	Ob/Gyn	1982		
Tucker, Harvey M.	Jefferson	Otolaryngology	1969		
Tucker, Weir M.	Univ. Virginia	Neurology	1949		
Tupchong, Leslie	Univ. Capetown			Rad Oncol	1984
Turakhia, Bharati V.	Univ. Calcutta			Radiology	1983
Turalba, Cornelius I.C.	Univ. Philippines	Rad Oncol	1977	Rad Oncol	1978
Turchin, Louise H.	Jefferson	Anesthesiology	1985		
Turner, James W.	UMDNJ, Rutgers	Neuro Surg	1989		
Tymeson, Glenn W.	Jefferson	Internal Medicine	1946		
Tytler, Neil B., Jr.,	Philadelphia Coll. Osteo. Med.			Cardiovas Dis	1979

Dona J. Upson
Med. Coll. Wisconsin

Carlos O. Urrutia
George Washington

Martin Uram
Hahnemann

Rebecca C. Ursua
St. Tomas (Philippines)

Paul L. Urban
Jefferson

Andrew J. Uri
Pennsylvania

Name	Med School	R Specialty	R Year	F Specialty	F Year
Uhl, Richard L.	Jefferson			Hand Surgery	1990
Ukawa, Shiro Nmi	Univ. Tokyo	Anesthesiology	1960		
Upson, Dona J.	Med. Coll. Wisconsin	Internal Medicine	1986		
Uram, Martin	Hahnemann Univ.	Ophthalmology	1981		
Urban, Maria D.	Med. Coll. Pennsylvania	Pediatrics	1975		
Urban, Paul L.	Jefferson			Cardiovas Dis	1983
Uri, Andrew J.	Univ. Pennsylvania	Internal Medicine	1985	Pulm Dis	1987
Urrutia-S., Carlos Orlando	George Washington Univ.			Cardiothor Surg	1978
Ursua, Rebecca C.	Univ. St. Tomas (Philippines)	Pediatrics	1985		

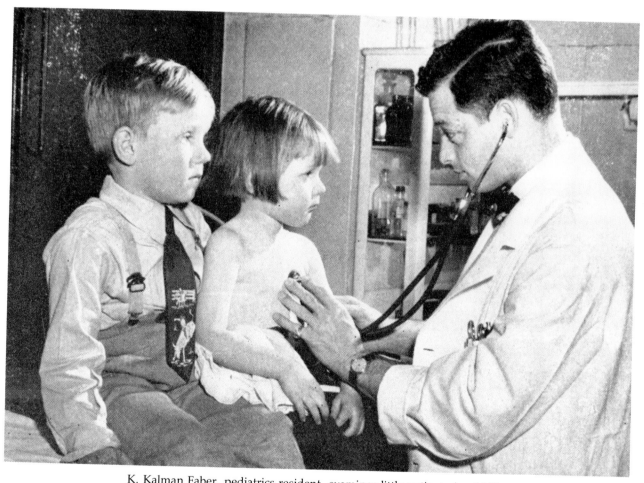

K. Kalman Faber, pediatrics resident, examines little patients (ca. 1949).

Mary Ann Venezia
UMDNJ, Rutgers

George P. Valko
Jefferson

Maria Vilaro
Puerto Rico

Reynaldo Velasco
UMDNJ, Newark

George A. Vaida
Columbia

Cynthia D. Villasis
St. Tomas (Philippines)

Edwin A. Valdiserri
Temple

Anne A. Vetto
Oregon Hlth. Sci.

Amarjit Virk
Punjab

Michael S. Verhille
Illinois

Name	Med School	R Specialty	R Year	F Specialty	F Year
Vahid, Khosro	Univ. Tehran	Pediatrics	1966		
Vaida, George A.	Columbia Univ. Coll. P. & S.	Internal Medicine	1980		
Vaisman, Isaac	Univ. Cent. Venezuela	Rad Oncol	1976		
Valdiserri, Edwin V.	Temple Univ.	Psychiatry	1982		
Valentine, Lee S.	Jefferson	Internal Medicine	1978		
Valko, George P.	Jefferson	Family Practice	1989		
Valle, Edgar	Univ. of the East (Philippines)	General Surgery	1988		
Vallejo, Alvaro	Univ. Valle (Colombia)	Rad Oncol	1973		
Van Ostrand, James R.	Cornell Univ.	Ob/Gyn	1964		
Vanna, Stephen C.	UMDNJ, Newark	Neurology	1971		
Vanston, Gerald E.	Jefferson	Pathology	1964		
Varano, Nicholas R.	Jefferson	Urological Surgery	1955		
Vasso, Stephen G.	Jefferson			Hematology	1968
Vaswani, Ramesh M.	Nagpur Univ. (India)	Pediatrics	1965		
Vegari, Matt M.	Pahlavi Univ. (Iran)	Neurology	1986	Neurology	1987
Velasco, Reynaldo	UMDNJ, Newark	Pediatrics	1985		
Veloso, Nenita G.	Univ. St. Tomas (Philippines)			Pediatrics	1974
Venezia, Mary Ann	UMDNJ, Rutgers	Psychiatry	1985		
Venier, Leon H.	Jefferson	Phys Med/Rehab	1972		
Verhille, Michael S.	Univ. Illinois			Gastroenterology	1990
Vernace, Joseph V.	Jefferson	Orthop Surg	1987	Orthop Surg	1988
Vetto, Anne A.	Oregon Hlth. Sci. Univ.	Internal Medicine	1987		
Vicens, Enrique A.	Univ. Maryland	Otolaryngology	1956		
Vick, James W.	Jefferson	Family Practice	1982		
Vieira, Elio Fernandes	Univ. Porto (Portugal)			Rad Oncol	1972
Vieira, Luciano L.	Univ. Fed. Ceara (Brazil)			Radiology	1971
Vieira, Filho Arthur E.	Univ. Fed. Ceara (Brazil)	Radiology	1971		
Vilaro, Maria	Univ. Puerto Rico	Radiology	1986		
Villanueva, Ma Thelma	Lazaro Univ. Philippines	Pediatrics	1972	Neo- Perinatal Med	1973
Villasis, Cynthia D.	Univ. St. Tomas (Philippines)			Neo- Perinatal Med	1981
Vincent, Lyle D., Jr.,	Jefferson	Internal Medicine	1956		
Virk, Amarjit S.	Punjab Univ. (India)	Anesthesiology	1982		
Viscomi, Vincent A.	Jefferson	Internal Medicine	1984		
Vivacqua, Raymond J.	Jefferson			Hematology	1966
Vlahides, George Dean	New York Med. Coll.			Hematology	1956
Vollenweider, Heinz Emil	Univ. Zurich	General Surgery	1961		
Volosin, Kent J.	Bowman Gray Sch. Med.	Internal Medicine	1983	Cardiovas Dis	1986
Voorhees, Ellen Sher	Georgetown Univ.	Internal Medicine	1989	Pulm Dis	1990
Votta, Richard P.	Univ. Nebraska	Pediatrics	1982		
Vranian, George, Jr.,	Virginia C'wealth Univ.	Internal Medicine	1986	Gastroenterology	1988

Marcia Kass Waitzman
Mount Sinai Sch. Med.

Shimon S. Waldfogel
Ben Gurion (Israel)

Robert L. Wang
St. John's (China)

Wendy B. Warren
Tennessee

Stephen R. Walker
Duke

Jacqueline D. Washburne
Temple

Margaret E. Walker
Hahnemann

Ethel M. Weinberg
Hahnemann

Sharon M. Weiner
Jefferson

Brian K. Walker
Cornell

Howard Weitz
Jefferson

D. Heather Watts
Jefferson

Postgraduate Alumni

Name	Med School	R Specialty	R Year	F Specialty	F Year
Wachman, Amnon	S.U.N.Y., Downstate	Internal Medicine	1966		
Waciega, Mark	Jefferson	Anesthesiology	1986		
Wagman, Albert D.	Univ. Pennsylvania	Neurology	1960		
Wagner, Frederick B., Jr.,	Jefferson	General Surgery	1945	General Surgery	1946
Wagner, Seymour	Hahnemann Univ.	Otolaryngology	1962		
Waitzman, Marcia Kass	Mount Sinai Sch. Med.	Ob/Gyn	1983		
Wald, Leonard A.	Albert Einstein Coll. Med.			Diag Rad	1986
Waldfogel, Shimon S.	Ben Gurion Univ. (Israel)	Psychiatry	1989		
Walker, Ann G.	Duke Univ.	Internal Medicine	1990		
Walker, Brian Keith	Cornell Univ.			Hematology	1978
Walker, Joseph R.	Creighton Univ.	General Surgery	1970		
Walker, Lewis H.	Indiana Univ.			Pediatric Allergy	1971
Walker, Margaret E.	Hahnemann Univ.	Internal Medicine	1980		
Walker, Stephen R.	Jefferson	Urological Surgery	1989		
Wallace, Craig K.	New York Med. Coll.	Internal Medicine	1960		
Wallace, Sidney	Temple Univ.	Radiology	1963		
Walls, Theresa Ann	Philadelphia Coll. Osteo. Med.	Psychiatry	1982		
Walsh, Paul J.P.	Univ. West. Ontario	Ophthalmology	1962		
Walter, Henry A., Jr.,	Tufts Univ.	General Surgery	1971		
Wang, George Chiao-chi	St. John's Univ. (China)	Internal Medicine	1953	Cardiovas Dis	1954
Wang, Robert L.	Mt. Sinai Sch. Med.	Internal Medicine	1986		
Ward, Michael J.A.	Jefferson	Orthop Surg	1983		
Ward, Susan B.	Jefferson			Rheumatology	1990
Warmbrod, James G.	Univ. Tennessee	General Surgery	1970		
Warren, Kenneth C.	Univ. Tennessee	Urological Surgery	1955		
Warren, Ralph E.	Queen's Univ. (Canada)			Gastroenterology	1968
Warren, Wendy B.	Cornell Univ.	Ob/Gyn	1986		
Warren, William J.	Jefferson	Pathology	1963		
Washburne, Jacqueline Denise	Temple Univ.	Internal Medicine	1976	Pulm Dis	1978
Wasser, Samuel H.	George Washington Univ.	General Surgery	1985		
Wasserman, Louis A.	Georgetown Univ.	Internal Medicine	1977		
Wasserman, Robert L.	Albert Einstein Coll. Med.	Ophthalmology	1969		
Wasserman, Theodore W.	Jefferson	Psychiatry	1969		
Watkins, Donald Riegel	Jefferson	General Surgery	1952		
Watson, John Samuel	Jefferson	Internal Medicine	1949	Internal Medicine	1950
Watts, Diane Heather	Jefferson	Ob/Gyn	1985		
Watts, Helena Bollers	Harvard Univ.	Internal Medicine	1989		
Weaver, Oscar	Jefferson	Radiology	1953		
Webber, Carol P.	Woman's Med. Coll.	Ob/Gyn	1970		
Webber, Charles E., Jr.,	Jefferson	General Surgery	1970		
Weber, Fred	UMDNJ, Newark	General Surgery	1979		
Webster, James W.	Jefferson	Ob/Gyn	1947		
Wecsler, Petre I.	Inst. Med. si Farm. (Romania)			Rad Oncol	1980
Wehbe, Marwan	American Univ. Beirut			Hand Surgery	1982
Weibel, Donald E.	Univ. Bologna	Neuro Surg	1978		
Weiland, Theodore Frederick, Jr.,	Jefferson	Radiology	1952		
Weinberg, Ethel M.	Hahnemann Univ.	Anesthesiology	1975		
Weinberg, Linda L.	Jefferson	Pediatrics	1971		
Weinberg, Robert Bruce	Philadelphia Coll. Osteo. Med.			Pulm Dis	1975
Weiner, Michael D.	Jefferson	Ob/Gyn	1971		
Weiner, Sharon M.	UMDNJ, Camden	Internal Medicine	1988		
Weinstein, Allen J.	Univ. Osteo. Med., Des Moines	Radiology	1975		
Weintraub, Harvey	Jefferson			Child Psychiatry	1984

| --- | --- | --- | --- | --- | --- |
Weisberg, Martin	Jefferson	Ob/Gyn	1976		
Weisberg, Paul B.	Temple Univ.	Internal Medicine	1974		
Weisberger, Calvin L.	Jefferson	Internal Medicine	1973	Cardiovas Dis	1975
Weisman, Kenneth M.	Jefferson	Urological Surgery	1986		
Weiss, Arthur J.	Univ. Pennsylvania	Internal Medicine	1953	Hematology	1957
Weiss, David Lawrence	Jefferson	Radiology	1979		
Weiss, Edward D.	Temple Univ.	Colon and Rec Surg	1950		
Weiss, Jeffrey	New York Coll. Osteo. Med.	Anesthesiology	1990		
Weiss, Jeffrey C.	Jefferson	Pediatrics	1976		
Weiss, Richard S.	Philadelphia Coll. Osteo. Med.	Family Practice	1983		
Weiss, Stephen M.	Temple Univ.	General Surgery	1979		
Weitz, Howard H.	Jefferson	Internal Medicine	1982	Cardiovas Dis	1984
Wellenbach, Burton L.	Jefferson	Ob/Gyn	1952		
Weller, Michael H.	Jefferson	Radiology	1968		
Wells, Harriet	Boston Univ.	Neurology	1966		
Wells, William W.	Univ. Syracuse	Dermatology	1949		
Welsh, Douglas V.	Univ. Nebraska			Cardiovas Dis	1990
Welsh, John W.	Philadelphia Coll. Osteo. Med.	Pediatrics	1972		
Welsh, Louis W.	Hahnemann Univ.	Otolaryngology	1958		
Weltin, Johannes D.	Jefferson			Family Practice	1980
Wender, Richard C.	Univ. Pennsylvania	Family Practice	1982		
Wenger, Jeffrey S.	Med. Coll. Pennsylvania	Rad Oncol	1984		
Wenger, Susan Robbins	Temple Univ.	Pediatrics	1980		
Wenner, Steven M.	Jefferson	General Surgery	1976		
Werdiger, Norman S.	Cornell Univ.	Internal Medicine	1979		
Werley, Charles W.	Jefferson	Radiology	1951		
Werner, Sarah S.	Loma Linda Univ.	Neurology	1972		
Werner, Stephen E.	Jefferson			Hand Surgery	1975
Wershba, Martin S.	Georgetown Univ.	Radiology	1975		
Wesley, Barbara D.	Howard Univ.			Mater/Fetal Med	1983
Wester, Suzanne B.	Med. Coll. Pennsylvania	Ob/Gyn	1988		
Westphal, Thomas R.	Jefferson	Orthop Surg	1987		
Whelan, Thomas P.	Univ. Vermont	Internal Medicine	1986		
Wherley, Robert F.	Tufts Univ.	Oral & Max Surg	1983		
White, John Benson, Jr.,	Jefferson	Orthop Surg	1951		
White, Joseph C.	Jefferson	Neurology	1958		
White, Kathlene	Med. Coll. Pennsylvania			Hand Surgery	1979
White, Sno Ellen	Jefferson	Pediatrics	1979		
Whiteley, William Henry, III,	Jefferson	Neuro Surg	1947	Neuro Surg	1949
Whitenack, Stephan H.	Jefferson	General Surgery	1978	Cardiothor Surg	1980
Whitman, Mason	Cornell Univ.	Radiology	1954		
Whitman, Randal L.	Temple Univ.	Pediatrics	1982		
Whitmore, Mason	Cornell Univ.	Radiology	1954		
Whittington, Richard	Jefferson	Rad Oncol	1982		
Wichman, Beth A.	UMDNJ, Rutgers	Family Practice	1981		
Widelitz, Martin M.	Univ. Lausanne (Switzerland)	Internal Medicine	1960	Endocrinology	1961
Widger, John E.	Jefferson	General Surgery	1985		
Wigh, Russell	Harvard Univ.	Radiology	1948		
Wilkerson, Joseph L.	Bowman Gray Med. Sch.	Urological Surgery	1951		
Wilkins, Charles E.	Jefferson	Orthop Surg	1973		
Williams, Barbara Kluchinski	Jefferson	Psychiatry	1977		
Williams, Burton Lamar	Jefferson	Radiology	1944		
Williams, Claude M.	Jefferson			Repro Endo	1963

Name	Med School	R Specialty	R Year	F Specialty	F Year
Williams, Ernest R.	Howard Univ.			Pediatrics	1972
Williams, Glenn L.	Jefferson	Ob/Gyn	1949		
Williams, James	Howard Univ.	Internal Medicine	1969		
Williams, James Robert	Howard Univ. Internal	Medicine	1983	Infectious Diseases	1988
Williams, James Thomas, Jr.,	Jefferson	Orthop Surg	1968		
Wills, Richard B.	Univ. Liege (Belgium)			Infectious Diseases	1981
Wilner, Daniel	Jefferson	Radiology	1949		
Wilson, Earl	Howard Univ.	Anesthesiology	1990		
Wilson, John Dennis Handy	Johns Hopkins Univ.	Radiology	1951	Radiology	1954
Wilson, Louis A.	Jefferson	Ophthalmology	1965		
Wilson-King, Genester S.	Jefferson	Ob/Gyn	1986		
Wiltshire, David Grant	Univ. Toronto			Hand Surgery	1977
Wimer, Bruce Meade	Jefferson	Hematology	1951		
Winkler, Jeffrey R.	Jefferson	Anesthesiology	1989		
Winn, Rodger J.	Jefferson	Internal Medicine	1966		
Winters, Lewis	Jefferson	Anesthesiology	1970		
Wirth, Barbara S.	McGill Univ.			Pediatrics	1990
Wisniewski, Mary L.	Brown Univ.	Pediatrics	1982		
Witkowski, Thomas A.	Hahnemann Univ.	Anesthesiology	1990		
Wixted, William M.	Jefferson	Urological Surgery	1978		
Wohar, Robert M.	Univ. Pennsylvania	Oral & Max Surg	1979		
Woldow, Irving	Jefferson			Hematology	1947
Wolf, Laurence R.	Harvard Univ.			Orthop Surg	1990
Wolf, Ralph S.	Philadelphia Coll. Osteo. Med.	Psychiatry	1986		
Wolf, Sandra M.	Jefferson	Ob/Gyn	1981		
Wolfe, Sidney Maurice	Jefferson	Internal Medicine	1951	Endocrinology	1954
Wolfson, Allan B.	Univ. Pennsylvania			Nephrology	1979
Wolk, Daniel L.	Tufts Univ.	Family Practice	1984		
Wolson, Alan H.	Jefferson	Radiology	1972		
Wong, Fue Lun	Temple Univ.	Pediatrics	1961		
Wong, James T.S.	Jefferson	Ob/Gyn	1950		
Wong, Richard H.	UMDNJ, Newark	Internal Medicine	1982		
Woo, Robert	Univ. Pennsylvania	Anesthesiology	1984		
Woods, Michael W.	Univ. New Mexico	Orthop Surg	1985		
Woody, Daniel J.	Temple Univ.	General Surgery	1981		
Woomer, Dennis J.	Univ. Guadalajara	Anesthesiology	1983		
Wu, Chung-Hsiu	Nat. Taiwan Univ. Coll. Med.	Ob/Gyn	1970		
Wulfestieg, Carl W.	U.C.L.A.	Otolaryngology	1975		
Wutanasupta, Ratanaporn	Siriraj Hosp. (Thailand)	Pediatrics	1968		

You are privileged to walk through the vale of misery and to make it a well of mercy.

George W. Corner (1889–1981)

Mary Yankaskas
UMDNJ, Rutgers

Horatio Yeung
Washington

Deborah Young
UMDNJ, Rutgers

Eric B. Yoss
New York Med. Coll.

Albert T. Yenchick
Med. Coll. Penn

Richard M. Yelovich
Jefferson

Rhinee Yeung-Walter
Ohio State

Sophia Chan Yeung
Jefferson

Kenneth A. Yamamoto
Jefferson

Shuin-Lin Yang
Taipei Med. Coll.

Yung-Fong Yang
Kaoshsiung Med. Coll. (Taiwan)

Name	Med School	R Specialty	R Year	F Specialty	F Year
Yadav, Vasant G.	Nagpur Univ. (India)	Pediatrics	1961		
Yaghmai, Farivar	Univ. Tehran	Pathology	1969		
Yamada, Hideo	Nagoya Univ. (Japan)			Hematology	1971
Yamamoto, Kenneth A.	Jefferson	Internal Medicine	1985		
Yanez, Rafael	Univ. Natl. Colombia	Neuro Surg	1972		
Yang, Shuin-Lin	Taipei Med. Coll.			Trans Surg	1986
Yang, Un Taek	Seoul Nat. Univ.	Anesthesiology	1972		
Yang, Yung-Fong	Kaoshsiung Med. Coll. (Taiwan)	Neurology	1982		
Yankaskas, Mary C.	UMDNJ, Rutgers	Ob/Gyn	1990		
Yantes, Herbert Arthur	Jefferson	Internal Medicine	1954	Gastroenterology	1952
Yardumian, John	Philadelphia Coll. Osteo. Med.	Psychiatry	1975		
Yelovich, Richard M.	Jefferson	Rad Oncol	1987		
Yen, Wang	Nat. Taiwan Univ.	Radiology	1960		
Yenal, Affan S.	Univ. Istanbul	Radiology	1958		
Yenchick, Albert Thomas	Med. Coll. Pennsylvania	Family Practice	1979		
Yeroushalmi, Parviz	Pahlavi Univ. (Iran)	Child Psychiatry	1985		
Yeung, Horatio	Washington Univ.	Radiology	1988		
Yeung, Sophia Chan	Jefferson	Radiology	1985		
Yeung-Walter, Rhinee Wei-Fang	Ohio State Univ.	Family Practice	1978		
Yoo, Dal	Seoul Nat. Univ.	Internal Medicine	1970		
Yoss, Eric B.	New York Med. Coll.	Internal Medicine	1986	Pulm Dis	1988
Young, Deborah A.	UMDNJ, Rutgers	Family Practice	1985		
Young, In Min	Yonsei Univ. (Korea)			Otolaryngology	1961
Ytterberg, Steven Ralph	Jefferson	Internal Medicine	1980		
Yunen, Jose Rafael	Univ. Santo Domingo	Urological Surgery	1962		
Yut, Joseph P.	George Washington Univ.	Otolaryngology	1968		

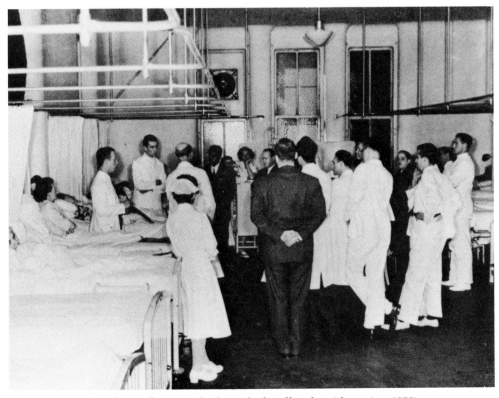

Grand rounds on medical ward of staff and residents (ca. 1950).

Isam Zakhour
American Univ. Beirut

Susan R. Zelitch
Pennsylvania

Ruth Zodkevitch
S.U.N.Y., Syracuse

Joseph B. Zehner
Temple

Richard W. Ziegler
Jefferson

John H. Zoller, III
Med. Coll. Ohio

Gilbert L. Zuckerman
Hahnemann

Barry S. Ziring
Albany Med. Coll.

Marc S. Zimmerman
Med. Coll. Penn

Robert M. Zuckerman
Ross Univ.

Janis Zvargulis
Johns Hopkins

Wayne C. Zwick
Tulane

Postgraduate Alumni

Name	Med School	R Specialty	R Year	F Specialty	F Year
Zacarias, Jose	Univ. Chile	Pediatrics	1959		
Zackai, A. Hertsel	Stritch Sch. Med.			Cardiovas Dis	1974
Zager, Ruth P.	Univ. Texas	Pediatrics	1955		
Zagerman, Abraham J.	Temple Univ.			Endocrinology	1957
Zaid, Gerald	Univ. Pennsylvania	Internal Medicine	1965		
Zakhour, Isam J.	American Univ. Beirut	Ophthalmology	1980		
Zalewski, Andrew P.	Medical Academy, Warsaw	Internal Medicine	1984		
Zankman, Nathan	Jefferson	Pediatrics	1964		
Zarutskie, Susan E.	Duke Univ.	Pediatrics	1975	Ped Hema-Oncol	1976
Zavodnick, Steven	Jefferson	Psychiatry	1977		
Zegel, Harry G.	Jefferson			Diag Rad	1980
Zehner, Joseph B.	Temple Univ.	Orthop Surg	1981		
Zeit, Robert M.	Tufts Univ.	Radiology	1973		
Zelitch, Susan R.	Univ. Pennsylvania	Family Practice	1988		
Zemel, Walter G.	Jefferson	Otolaryngology	1976		
Zemo, Peter L.	Jefferson	Otolaryngology	1969		
Zenouzi, Sirus	Univ. Heidelberg	Anesthesiology	1963		
Zeok, John V.	Jefferson	General Surgery	1972		
Zeok, Suzanne Springer	Jefferson	Anesthesiology	1972		
Zerne, Gustave Edward	Loma Linda Univ.	Otolaryngology	1953		
Zibelman, Robert S.	Jefferson			Child Psychiatry	1980
Ziegenfus, William D.	Jefferson	Urological Surgery	1968		
Ziegenfuss, Jay F., Jr.,	Jefferson			Medical Oncology	1974
Ziegler, Richard W.	Jefferson	Orthop Surg	1984		
Zimmerman, Marc Steven	Med. Coll. Pennsylvania	Orthop Surg	1980		
Zimskind, Paul D.	Jefferson	Urological Surgery	1962		
Zinsenheim, Joyce R.	Ross Univ. (Dominica)	Psychiatry	1990		
Ziring, Barry S.	Albany Med. Coll.	Internal Medicine	1988		
Ziskin, Leah Zoole	Temple Univ.	Gen Prev Med	1972		
Zodkevitch, Ruth	S.U.N.Y., Syracuse			Diag Rad	1989
Zoennchen, Bernhard U.	Univ. Munchen (Germany)	Internal Medicine	1973		
Zoller, John H., III,	Med. Coll. Ohio	Orthop Surg	1988		
Zorita, Manuel D.	Univ. Salamanca (Spain)	Neurology	1972		
Zuckerman, Gilbert Leonard	Hahnemann Univ.	Internal Medicine	1976	Cardiovas Dis	1977
Zuckerman, Robert M.	Ross Univ. (Dominica)			Pediatric Allergy	1988
Zvargulis, Janis	Johns Hopkins Univ.	Anesthesiology	1983		
Zwick, Wayne C.	Tulane Univ.			Family Practice	1986

"Roundabout" landscape at entrance to Bluemle Life Sciences Building.

Part IV

College of Graduate Studies

Bluemle Building (Architects' drawing) 1989

Fig. 1   Philip B. Hawk, Ph.D., Professor of Physiological Chemistry (1912-22), initiated the first courses leading to masters and doctoral degrees at Jefferson.

Prior to 1912 the educational activities at Jefferson were devoted solely to medical and nursing students. Research was of a clinical nature with little of consequence in the basic sciences. In this year Philip B. Hawk, Ph.D. (Fig 1.) succeeded James W. Holland as Head of the Department of Physiological Chemistry. His previous experience at Illinois and the University of Pennsylvania had included courses leading to masters and doctoral degrees in physiological chemistry. Hawk proposed to the Jefferson Faculty that such courses be initiated. This was approved by the Faculty and the Board of Trustees under the provisions of the University Charter granted in 1838.

Rules and regulations for the program were established as well as a five-member Committee of Postgraduate Education. The document stipulated the requirements for residency on the campus, tuition, and an examination by an appropriate committee before the degree could be conferred by the Board of Trustees. Fifteen degrees (eight M.S., four Ph.D. and three Sc.D.) were awarded during the next ten years.

In December, 1922, the administrators of the Medical College received an alert from alumni that the name of Jefferson Medical College and some of its faculty were being used by Dr. Hawk in advertisements for certain well known products as Postum and Fleishman's Yeast. Although the funds were used to support the research in his Department, the Faculty and Board of Trustees considered this practice to be unethical. On December 18, 1922, Dr. Hawk was dismissed and the graduate program ceased until revived in 1949.

GRADUATE DEGREES PRIOR TO 1950

1914

Ph.D — Olaf Bergeim, B.S., South Dakota State College 1908; Univ. of Illinois 1912.

M.S. — James Tiffany Leary, Ph.B., Yale Univ. 1911.

M.S. — Clarence Albert Smith, B.S. Massachusetts Agricultural College, 1911.

1915

Ph.D — Chester Charles Fowler; B.S. Univ. of Illinois, 1909; M.D. Univ. of Illinois, 1913.

Ph.D. — John Oliver Halverson, B.A., Univ. of Minnesota, 1906; B.S., Univ. of Minnesota, 1907; M.A., Univ. of Missouri, 1913.

M.S. — H. Rodell Fishback, A.B., Univ. of Illinois, 1912.

1916

Ph.D.   Clarence Albert Smith, B.S., Massachusetts Agricultural College, 1911; M.S. Jefferson Medical College, 1914

M.S.   Raymond J. Miller, B.S., Pennsylvania State College, 1914.

M.S.   James Alexander Clarke, Jr., A.B., (Fig. 2) Haverford College 1911. (Obtained Jefferson M.D. also in 1916).

1917

D.Sc. in Medicine   H. Rodell Fishback, A.B., University of Illinois, 1912; M.S., Jefferson Medical College, 1915; M.D., Jefferson Medical College, 1916.

1918

D.Sc.   Robert A. Lichtenthaeler, B.Sc. University of North Carolina, 1902; M.S., 1904.

D.Sc.   Raymond J. Miller, B.Sc. Th Pennsylvania State College, 1914; M.S., Jefferson Medical College, 1916.

M.S.   Harry L. Fowler, Babcock Institute of Pharmacy, 1912; B.A., Morningside College, 1916.

1919

D.Sc.   Duncan L. Despard, M.D., (Fig. 3) Jefferson Medical College, 1901.

1923

M.S. in Chemistry   Earl Altemus Shrader.

Fig. 2 James Alexander Clarke, Jr., M.S. (1916), M.D. (1916), early Chief of Jefferson Allergy Clinic (1921).

Fig. 3   Duncan I. Despard, D.Sc. (1919), M.D. (1901), taught in Jefferson's Surgical Department.

At a January 31, 1949, meeting of the faculty, chaired by J. Earl Thomas, Chairman of the Department of Physiology from 1927 to 1955, a recommendation was approved in support of Jefferson offering graduate training leading to the degrees of master of science and doctor of philosophy for qualified students in the basic medical sciences. Thomas then appointed a faculty committee, composed of the chairmen of the basic science departments, to draw up the plans for the reinstitution of graduate education at Jefferson after the 20-year hiatus. In 1952, the first degree was awarded from the new graduate program in physiology. Among the faculty at the time were M.H.F. Friedman, Ph.D., who would later become the Department's Chairman, and Eugene Aserinsky, Ph.D., the discoverer of rapid eye movement.

The Department of Pharmacology was founded in 1932 and programs leading to master of science and doctor of philosophy degrees were added in 1949. The graduate programs soon became a substantial component of the Department. From 1949 until 1953, when the Department Chairman Charles M. Gruber retired, three Ph.D. and two M.S. degrees were granted. Three other graduate students had completed most of their requirements for the Ph.D. degree and one for the M.S. degree. It speaks well for the high standards of the original selection of these students that they all completed their degree requirements by 1956. Julius M. Coon, Ph.D., M.D., was named Chairman of the Department in 1953.

The research program in the Department of Microbiology was built upon Kenneth Goodner's activities in the international field of infectious diseases, most notably, cholera and plague. Dr. Goodner (Fig. 4), who was the Chairman of the Department from 1946 to 1967, played a key role in the development of graduate programs leading toward the Ph.D. degree in the department and in the Medical College. This early period of the graduate program was a time of trial and error. Training started with preceptorships and,

later, courses were added. Lolita Parnell, Ph.D., was recruited in 1950 as Assistant Professor of Bacteriology and Immunology. She was the first woman to be a full-time Professor at Jefferson. Other appointments that year designed to enhance the graduate programs were: Bernard Kroft, Ph.D., Henry Stempen, Ph.D., and Robert J. Mandle, Ph.D. Dr. Mandle remained at Jefferson, advancing to the position of Professor in 1965, and retiring in 1986 as Emeritus Professor. Dr. William G. Sawitz, Associate Professor, published the book *Medical Parasitology* and served as the first Secretary of the Board for the Regulation of Graduate Studies until his death in 1957.

Fig. 4   Kenneth Goodner, Ph.D., Professor of Bacteriology and Immunology (1946-67), played a key role in revival of the postgraduate programs in 1949.

The first two students to enter the Ph.D. program in bacteriology were Keith Jensen and Russell Miller, who joined the staff as assistants and went on to receive their degrees. During this time, a master's degree was required for Ph.D. candidates.

George Allen Bennett, M.D., Sc.D., was Chairman of the Department of Anatomy and Director of the Daniel Baugh Institute of Anatomy from 1948 until his death in 1958. His major scientific contributions were the experimental analysis of the action of mammalian tongue musculature (with Dr. Andrew J. Ramsay), heterochromia in relation to autonomic innervation, and variational anatomy of the shoulder joint. Jefferson's first electron microscope was obtained by Dr. Ramsay in 1952. In 1950, Franz X. Hausberger joined the Department. His research in experimental diabetes and related fat metabolic disorders resulted in his being honored as "The Father of Adipose Tissue Research" by the *Handbook of Physiology* in 1965. Other faculty members to join the Department at this time included James O. Brown, Ph.D., John E. Healy, M.D., Robert J. Merklin, Ph.D., Charles G. Rosa, Ph.D., and Sigfrid Zitzlsperger, D.M.

Abraham Cantarow, M.D., who was Chairman of the Department of Biochemistry from 1945 to 1966, had begun the task of "modernizing" the department. In 1949-1950 the Department announced that it would accept graduate students. He transformed the Department from its European format of teaching to a newer format in which the Department Head shared lectures with several staff members, who in turn might be carrying out independent research. Among the faculty members that he recruited were Bernard Schepartz, Ph.D., Milton Toporek, Ph.D., and Arthur Allen, Ph.D. Drs. Cantarow and Schepartz published the first edition of their textbook *Biochemistry* in 1954.

Microbiology Alumni

Anthony V. Marturano, M.S., D.O., M.D., (1954), went on to a D.O. degree in 1957 and the M.D. degree in 1962. He has specialized in orthopedics, trauma, industrial medicine and hand surgery. He has served as a medical consultant to the State of California Department of Justice, the Los Angeles City Attorney's Office and the County of Los Angeles. He became a Fellow of the American Academy of Neurological and Orthopedic Surgeons, and the American Board of Medical-Legal Analysts in Medicine and Surgery.

Pharmacology Alumni

Julian L. Ambrus, M.D., Ph.D., (1954), had earned his medical degree at the University of Zurich, Switzerland, in 1949. He was named Principal Research Scientist, and then Director of Cancer Research for the New York State Department of Health. He has also held the position of Professor and Chairman of the Department of Experimental Pathology at the Roswell Park Division of SUNY/Buffalo. Dr. Ambrus has co-authored nearly 500 publications in biochemistry, physiology and pharmacology of cancer, and the blood coagulation cascade. He has been a member of over 50 professional organizations and has served on numerous medical and scientific advisory groups including the Food and Drug Administration, the National Heart Institute and the World Health Organization. He has served as editor-in-chief of both the *Journal of Medicine* and *Reviews in Hematology* and as a member of the editorial boards of *Folia Angiologica* and *Haemostais*. In recognition of his scientific accomplishments, he received the College of Graduate Studies 1990 Distinguished Alumnus Award (Fig. 5).

Melvyn Gluckman, Ph.D., (1953, Fig. 6), joined the Parke Davis-Warner Lambert Laboratories in Ann Arbor, Michigan, where he organized a prominent research laboratory and group of investigators. He was elevated to the position of Vice President for Research from which he retired in 1990. During his career he distinguished himself with research in the fields of neuropharmacology and neurophysiology.

Fredric Rieders, Ph.D., (1952, Fig. 7), remained at Jefferson as an Assistant Professor of Pharmacology until 1956 when he was promoted to Associate Professor. He was named Professor of Pharmacology and Toxicology in 1969. He served as Chief Toxicologist in the Office of the Medical Examiner and Director of the Poison Information Center for the City of Philadelphia from 1956 until 1970 when he established National Medical Services, Incorporated, and assumed the positions of President and Laboratory Director. He became a Diplomate in Toxicological Chemistry and in Forensic Toxicology and was certified as a Laboratory Director by the U.S. Public Health Service. A Fellow of the American Academy of Forensic Sciences, he has served as the Chairman of its Toxicology Section and as a representative to the National Library of Medicine's Committee on Toxicology Terminology. Among his numerous professional associations was charter membership in the International Association of Forensic Toxicologists. A long-time supporter of Jefferson, Dr. Rieders was elected to the College of Graduate Studies Alumni Association Board of Directors in 1982 and served as its President from 1986 to 1988.

ALUMNI

1950   Schorr, Sonia, M.S., Microbiology

1951   Bartell, Pasquale, M.S., Microbiology
        Cohen, Burton R., M.S., Anatomy
        DeSanctis, Armand N., M.S., Microbiology
        Fasciana, Michael, M.S., Anatomy
        Kety, Edwin M., M.S., Pharmacology
        Miller, Russell, Jr., Ph.D., Microbiology
        Siegel, Albert N., M.S., Anatomy

1952   Heinrich, Max, Ph.D., Pharmacology
        Jenson, Keith, Ph.D., Microbiology
        Polish, Edwin, M.S., Physiology
        Rieders, Fredric, Ph.D., Pharmacology

1953   Baker, Walter W., Ph.D., Pharmacology
        Gluckman, Melvyn I., Ph.D., Pharmacology
        Morrison, John H., M.S., Microbiology
        Rockford, Emeric J., M.S., Microbiology

1954   Ambrus, Julian L., M.D., Pharmacology
        Davar, Phiroza S., M.S., Anatomy
        Gollub, Seymour, Ph.D., Physiology
        Inashima, Osamu J., Ph.D., Pharmacology
        Marturano, Anthony V., M.S., Microbiology
        Rothstein, Edward L., M.S., Microbiology
        Schroy, Paul C., M.D., Anatomy

Fig. 5.   Julian L. Ambrus, M.D., Ph.D. (Pharmacology, 1954) receives the 1990 Distinguished Alumnus Award from Richard Steelman, Ph.D. (Pharmacology, 1977) President of College of Graduate Studies Alumni Association (right).

Fig. 6. Melvyn Gluckman, Ph.D., Vice President for Research, Parke Davis-Warner Lambert Laboratories.

Fig. 7. Fredric Rieders, Ph.D., President of College of Graduate Studies Alumni Association Board of Directors.

Andrew J. Ramsay (Fig. 8) was named Chairman of the Department of Anatomy and Director of the Daniel Baugh Institute of Anatomy in 1958. He would hold this position until 1972. Upon assuming the chair, his objectives were to strengthen the teaching programs, to foster research of a diversified nature to reflect the skills and interests of the faculty, and to maintain Jefferson's traditional excellence in anatomy. Paul C. Schroy (Fig. 9), the first Ph.D. graduate of the Department (1954), also a J.M.C. graduate (1957), joined the faculty and studied the anatomy of the liver. Albert W. Sedar, Ph.D., joined the Department in 1955 and his research centered on

cytophysiology of cell types aimed at correlating fine cell structure with functional activity.

In the Department of Microbiology, research focus was expanded when Dr. Goodner's involvement with the plague in Madagascar expanded to a life-long interest in cholera and he was subsequently named to the Cholera Committee of the National Institutes of Health. In 1958 the South-East Asia Cholera Research Laboratory was established in Dacca, Pakistan, providing a regional facility for Committee activities which Dr. Goodner visited throughout his lifetime. Harry L. Smith, Jr., Ph.D., (1955), appointed as Instructor in 1957, became involved in the

Fig. 8.   Andrew J. Ramsay, Ph.D., Chairman of Anatomy (1958-72), fostered research of a diversified nature.

Fig. 9.   Paul C. Schroy, Ph.D. (1954), M.D. (1957), first Ph.D. graduate in anatomy, conducted significant research on anatomy of the liver.

investigations with Dr. Goodner on the bacteriology and the epidemiology of cholera. Drs. Frank F. Katz and Rolf Freter were also appointed to the faculty as Assistant Professors. Dr. Katz had experience in teaching parasitology and took over the responsibilities left behind by Dr. Sawitz. Having gone through several changes in name and orientation since its inception in 1909, the designation of the Department was officially changed to Microbiology in 1959. That same year, members of the Department were invited to Bangkok by Pyn Muangman, a 1926 graduate of Jefferson Medical College, to study the cholera epidemic in that country.

When Dr. Coon (Fig. 10) came to Jefferson to head the Department of Pharmacology his research activities in the preceding 12 years had been exclusively in toxicology. Though he continued his own interests and research efforts in this area, no major increase in the emphasis of toxicology in the research and teaching programs of the Department immediately resulted. Through the succeeding years, however, toxicological issues became a substantial part of the research and graduate training activities. During Dr. Coon's tenure as Chairman, approximately half of the faculty and graduate student research activities involved toxicological issues, which were well supported by research and training grants from the National Institutes of Health and other governmental agencies.

After serving as Acting Chairman since 1955 when Dr. Thomas retired, Dr. Friedman (Fig. 11) was named Chairman of the Department of Physiology in 1957. On assuming the chair, Dr. Friedman abolished Saturday classes and mandatory attendance for medical students. His first academic appointments were Drs. Louis Kazal

Fig. 10. Julius M. Coon, Ph.D., M.D., Chairman of Pharmacology (1953-76), introduced toxicology as a branch of Pharmacology.

Fig. 11. M.F.H. Friedman, Ph.D., Chairman of Physiology (1955-74), ushered in cellular physiology and biophysics.

as Assistant Professor and Domenic A. DeBias as instructor. Dr. Kazal also served as the associate director of the Cardeza Foundation from 1960 to 1978. Dr. DeBias, a 1956 graduate, was the first graduate student of the department to assume a staff position at Jefferson. In response to the increasing importance of cellular physiology and biophysics, June N. Barker, Ph.D., was appointed instructor in 1958.

Biochemistry Alumni

Seymour W. Milstein, Ph.D., M.D., (1955), went on to Research Assistant Professor at Hahnemann University, then to Chief of Biochemistry in the U.S. Army Surgical Research Unit at Brooke Army Medical Center, Texas. He earned his M.D. degree at Hahnemann in 1962 and taught Family Medicine and Biochemistry there. He became a Diplomate in Family Medicine and in Quality Assurance and Utilization Review.

Microbiology Alumni

Harry Smith, Ph.D., (1957), was appointed as an instructor in microbiology upon graduation, earning a place among the first and most durable of the Jefferson faculty appointments from the Graduate School. He advanced to full Professor in 1973. During the 1960s the World Health Organization and the National Institutes of Health sent him to study cholera epidemics throughout southeast Asia and during the 1970s he ran an active research program in the area of cholera and diarrheal diseases. Since 1981, Dr. Smith's interests were in computerized aids in teaching, especially in relation to diagnosis of infectious diseases. He developed a computer-assisted teaching program which generated fictional patients from disease models. Housed in the Department of Microbiology, the program has been used extensively by medical students. In recognition of his teaching accomplishments, he was honored by the Jefferson Medical College Class of 1988 with the presentation of his portrait to the University (Fig. 12). Active in numerous University and College committees, he was also instrumental in starting the College of Graduate Studies Alumni Association and was its first president.

Pharmacology Alumni

Clara M. Ambrus, M.D., Ph.D., (1955), had earned her M.D. degree at the University of Zurich, Switzerland, in 1949. She was named Senior Cancer Research Scientist at the Roswell Park Memorial Institute and Associate Research Professor at the State University of New York/Buffalo Graduate School in 1955. She later accepted the additional positions of Assistant Research Professor of Pediatrics in 1959 and, in 1983, Research Professor of Gynecology/Obstetrics at the SUNY/Buffalo Medical School. She served as a member of the International Fellowship Review Committee at the Fogarty Center of the NIH from 1972 to 1975 and as a consultant to the Microcirculatory and Thrombosis Tasks Groups of the NIH from 1972. An expert in the areas of fibrinolysis-blood clotting, thrombosis, neonatal and adult respiratory distress syndrome, and insolubilized enzymes and antidotes, Dr. Ambrus has had over 200 publications.

Joseph Borzelleca, Ph.D., (1956), spent a few years at the Medical College of Pennsylvania as an instructor in pharmacology and then moved to Richmond where he has been a professor in the department of pharmacology and toxicology since 1967, also heading the division of toxicology. His research has included drug movement across bladder, gastrointestinal and salivary membranes, drug metabolism, and toxicological

Fig. 12.   Harry Smith, Ph.D. (Pharmacology, 1957) at Medical College Class Portrait Presentation (1988).

studies using *in vivo* and *in vitro* systems. In the early 1960s he worked with the U.S. Navy to develop a method to stop unprovoked shark attacks. He served as chairman of the National Academy of Sciences Committee on Safe Drinking Water and Committee on Toxicology and has served as a member of the Food Protection Committee. He was the recipient of the U.S. Army's Chemical Research, Development and Engineering Center's Distinguished Service Award. His scientific achievements were recognized by the College of Graduate Studies with its Distinguished Alumnus Award in 1987 (Fig. 13).

Philip Rosenberg, Ph.D., (1957), served for one year as an instructor in Jefferson's Department of Pharmacology and then became research assistant in the College of Physicians and Surgeons at Columbia University, where he advanced to Research Associate and Assistant Professor in 1963. In 1968 he became Chairman and Professor, Section of Pharmacology and Toxicology at

the University of Connecticut, School of Pharmacy. Dr. Rosenberg has been recognized by the U.S. Public Health Service with its Career Development Award and he received the Redi Award for outstanding contributions to the field of toxicology at the World Congress on Animal, Plant and Microbial Toxins. In 1987 he received a Jacob Javits Neuroscience Investigators Award of more than $1.3 million for the period 1987 to 1994 from the National Institutes of Health. He served as president of the International Society of Toxicology and as editor of the journal *Toxicon*. His accomplishments earned him the College of Graduate Studies Distinguished Alumnus Award in 1989.

Sydney Spector, Ph.D., (1957), served for five years, as a pharmacologist in the Laboratory of Chemical Pharmacology at the NIH National Heart Institute. He was then named Head of the Section on Pharmacology in the Experimental Therapeutics Branch there, a position he held until

Fig. 13.   Joseph Borzelleca, Ph.D. (Pharmacology, 1956), receives 1987 Distinguished Alumnus Award from Fredric Rieders, Ph.D. (Pharmacology, 1952), President of CGS Alumni Association Board of Directors (right).

1968. He then accepted the position of Full Member and Section Chief in the Department of Physiological Chemistry at the Roche Institute of Molecular Biology in Nutley, New Jersey, where he was promoted to Department Head in 1977. In 1985 he was named Laboratory Head in the Institute's Department of Neurosciences. He served as a visiting professor in the Department of Pharmacology at Stanford University in 1969 and has served since 1968 as an adjunct professor of pharmacology at New York Medical College. Since 1971 he has been adjunct professor of pharmacology and anesthesiology at Columbia University. In 1970 he also was named a member of the Preclinical Psychopharmacology Research Review Committee of the National Institute of Mental Health. He has served on the editorial boards of a number of publications, including *European Journal of Pharmacology, Immunopharmacology,* and *Circulation Research*. Through his research he has published 79 abstracts, nearly 200 papers and has obtained 13 patents. He was president of the Catecholamine Club in 1972 and president of the American Society of Pharmacology and Experimental Therapeutics in 1979. Dr. Spector was the recipient of the Paul K. Smith

Award from George Washington University School of Medicine and was the 1989 Sterling Lecturer at the University of Michigan, Ann Arbor. In recognition of his accomplishments, in 1983, he was also the first-ever recipient of the College of Graduate Studies Distinguished Alumnus Award (Fig. 14).

Physiology Alumni

Domenic A. DeBias, Ph.D., (1956), was a postdoctoral fellow in the Division of Endocrine Cancer Research at Jefferson Medical College for one year and then was named an instructor in the Department of Physiology. He advanced to the rank of Professor in 1969. In 1975 he was named Professor and Chairman of the Department of Physiology/Pharmacology at the Philadelphia College of Osteopathic Medicine. He was also Assistant Dean of Basic Sciences there in 1979. He served as a consultant for the National Board of Osteopathic Medical Examiners, the National Research Council and the National Library of Medicine's Toxicology Information Program. Through his research, largely in the areas of endocrine physiology, cardiopulmonary physiology and environmental physiology, he has published 58 papers and 46 abstracts of his work.

ALUMNI

1955	Ambrus, Clara M., Ph.D., Pharmacology
	Matthews, Richard J., Ph.D., Pharmacology
	Milstein, Seymour W., Ph.D., Biochemistry
	Rutman, Julia Z., M.S., Physiology
1956	Aschner, Thomas C., M.S., Pharmacology
	Balotin, Nahum M., Ph.D., Pharmacology
	Borzelleca, Joseph F., Ph.D., Pharmacology
	DeBias, Domenic A., Ph.D., Physiology
	Gorby, Charles K., Ph.D., Pharmacology
1957	Begany, Albert J., M.S., Physiology
	Hanes, Robert B., Ph.D., Physiology

	Rosenberg, Philip, Ph.D., Pharmacology
	Smith, Harry L., Jr., Ph.D., Microbiology
	Spector, Sydney, Ph.D., Pharmacology
1958	Gans, Joseph H., Ph.D., Physiology
1959	Appert, Hubert E., Ph.D., Physiology
	DeMartinis, Frederick D., Ph.D., Physiology
	Goldberg, Albert, M.S., Microbiology
	Koff, Gilbert Y., Ph.D., Pharmacology
	LaBelle, Charles W., Ph.D., Pharmacology
	Thind, Khushdarshan S., Ph.D., Microbiology

Fig. 14. Sydney Spector, Ph.D. (Pharmacology, 1957), received the first CGS Distinguished Alumnus Award in 1983.

First five presidents of CGS Alumni Association: (left to right) Ronald Jensh, Harry Smith, Georganne Buescher, Frederic Rieders, and Gerald McGarrity.

To vitalize the course in neuroanatomy, and to initiate basic neuroanatomic research, Dr. Norman Moskowitz was called from Columbia University College of Physicians and Surgeons to Jefferson's Department of Anatomy in 1962. The first significant award for neuroanatomical research in the Department was granted to Dr. Moskowitz in 1963 from the National Institutes of Health, under which he made major contributions to the knowledge of the primate auditory pathways, using the monkey as his normal and experimentally altered research model.

In the Department of Microbiology, the subject of virology was receiving increasing attention at this time. In 1960, Paul B. Johnson, Ph.D., was recruited to the faculty. He was the co-discoverer of the Simian Foamy Agent and he continued his studies at Jefferson with an NIH grant. In 1963, Eileen Randall, Ph.D., received appointment as Assistant Professor of Pathology as well as Microbiology. At this time the Department became involved in the training of foreign students under an NIH teaching grant. Members of the Department also traveled to the Philippines in 1961 and Bangladesh in 1962 to study the cholera epidemics there.

During his tenure as Chairman of the Department of Pharmacology, Dr. Coon recruited a number of faculty members who served the Department well for many years. Those who served on a full-time basis were Drs. R. Snyder, M. S. Silver, J. J. Kocsis (Fig. 15), T. A. Hare (Fig. 16), R. W. Manthei (Fig. 17), and W. H. Vogel (Fig. 18). Also serving the Department for many years was Anthony J. Triolo, Ph.D., a 1964 graduate.

To further enhance the Department of Physiology's work in biophysics, Daniel L. Gilbert, Ph.D. was appointed assistant professor in 1960. Donald B. Doemling, Ph.D. was named instructor in 1961 to further enhance the Department's strong gastrointestinal base. The era of organ system specialization was begun when Dr. Friedman appointed Sheldon F. Gottlieb as Assistant Professor. The second graduate student from the department to be appointed to a faculty position was Leonard M. Rosenfeld (Fig. 19), Ph.D., who in 1964 was named instructor.

Anatomy Alumni

Padmanabhan Siddharth, M.D., Ph.D., (1963), received his M.D. from Madras Medical College of the University of Madras, India, in 1958. He became a Clinical Professor of Surgery at the State University of New York at Stonybrook and Chief of Surgery at the Veterans Administration Medical Center in Northport, New York.

Microbiology Alumni

Eileen L. Randall, Ph.D., (1960), had begun her teaching career at Jefferson as a graduate assistant, and when she left 23 years later, she held the position of associate professor in the Departments of Microbiology and Pathology. From 1955 to 1973 she was also a clinical microbiologist

Fig. 15. James J. Kocsis, Ph.D., Professor of Pharmacology at Jefferson.

at Thomas Jefferson University Hospital. She played an instrumental role in the establishment of the master's degree program in clinical microbiology at Jefferson. In 1973 she became Director of the Division of Microbiology in the Department of Pathology and Laboratory Medicine at Evanston Hospital in Illinois and Associate Professor of Clinical Pathology at Northwestern University Medical School. Her research interests were in parasitology, nosocomial infections and hospital epidemiology, mycology, bacteremia, perinatal infections, automation in microbiology, streptococci and diarrhea. She was a Diplomate of the American Board of Medical Microbiology and a Fellow in the American Academy of Microbiology. She received the Outstanding Contributor to Clinical Microbiology Award from the South Central Association for Clinical Microbiology. In October 1990 the Illinois Society for Microbiology honored her with the Pasteur Award in recognition of her outstanding contribution to the science of microbiology. She was also the recipient of the 1984 College of Graduate Studies

Fig. 17. Roland W. Manthei, Ph.D., Professor of Pharmacology at Jefferson.

Fig. 16. Theodore A. Hare, Ph.D., Professor of Pharmacology at Jefferson.

Fig. 18. Wolfgang H. Vogel, Ph.D., Professor of Pharmacology at Jefferson

Distinguished Alumnus Award (Fig. 20). Dr. Randall died in December of 1990.

Pharmacology Alumni

Harvey J. Sugarman, M.S., (1963), **M.D.,** went on to Jefferson Medical College to earn his M.D. degree in 1966. He became the David Hume Professor of Surgery and Vice-Chairman of the Department of Surgery at the Medical College of Virginia with research interests in the area of sepsis syndrome and gastrointestinal surgery (Fig. 21).

Anthony J. Triolo, Ph.D., (1964), upon graduation was named an instructor in pharmacology at Jefferson where he advanced to full Professor in 1978 (Fig. 22). Since 1987 he also served as Adjunct Professor of Pharmaceutics at the Philadelphia College of Pharmacy and Science. Throughout his career at Jefferson, he has served on numerous University and Department of Pharmacology committees and has served as the graduate student research thesis advisor to 12

students. Through his research, largely in the area of environmental toxicology, he has published 22 papers and 22 abstracts of his work.

Physiology Alumni

Martin F. Tansy, Ph.D., (1964), served as an instructor in physiology at Temple University School of Dentistry from 1962 and was promoted to Assistant Professor in 1964. In 1967 he was appointed Associate Professor and Chairman of the Department of Physiology and Biophysics, and in 1972 promoted to Professor, at the dental school. In 1979 he was named Coordinator of the Basic Science Departments and in 1986 Professor of Physiology and Dean of the Temple University Dental School. He has served as a reviewer for a number of publications, including *Science, American Journal of Physiology* and *Teratology*. He has also served the American Dental Association as a consultant in the basic sciences for numerous dental school accreditation site visits. Dr. Tansy has co-authored eight book chapters,

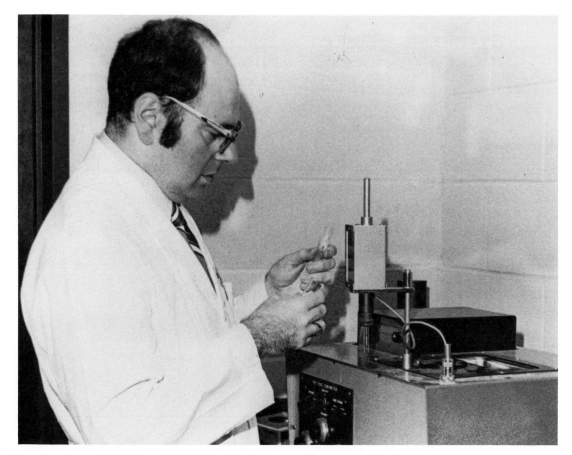

Fig. 19.   Leonard M. Rosenfeld, Ph.D. (Physiology, 1964), Assistant Professor of Physiology at Jefferson.

over 90 scientific papers and over 100 abstracts of his work which focused on the areas of gastrointestinal function and inhalation toxicology.

Henry H. Sherk, M.S., M.D., (1961), was a 1956 graduate of Jefferson Medical College who earned his M.S. in Orthopaedics after residency. He became Professor of Surgery and Chief of the Division of Orthopaedics and Rehabilitation at the Medical College of Pennsylvania.

Paul D. Zimskind, M.D., Ph.D., (1964), earned his M.D. degree at Jefferson in 1957. After an internship, residency in general surgery for one year and then residency for three years in urology, he was awarded an NIH postdoctoral fellowship and went on to earn his Ph.D. from the Department of Physiology. He was then appointed Assistant Professor and in charge of the Urology Research Laboratories at Jefferson. In 1967, at the death of Theodore R. Fetter, Dr. Zimskind was appointed the sixth Chairman of the Department of Urology (Fig. 23). His Urodynamics Laboratory had an international reputation for its productivity and excellence. He led studies on the dynamics of normal and abnormal urinary conduction using pressure recordings and fluoroscopic motion pictures of urinary tract activity. He evaluated the various laboratory, radiographic, and clinical features in patients with renovascular hypertension in an effort to establish firm criteria for differentiating potentially correctable versus noncorrectable cases. He also designed projects to discover means of enhancing the preservation of functional renal and ureteral tissues for future organ transplantation. By the time of his sudden death at age 44, he had written 43 scientific papers and made 77 presentations worldwide. Family, colleagues and friends presented his portrait to the College on April 15, 1983.

Leonard M. Rosenfeld, Ph.D., a graduate of

Fig. 20. Eileen L. Randall, Ph.D. (Microbiology, 1960) receives the Distinguished Alumnus Award (1984), presented by the President of College of Graduate Studies Alumni Association Georganne Buescher, M.S., (Clinical Microbiology, 1974) Ed.D. (left).

the University of Pennsylvania, took post-baccalaureate training in Cellular Physiology at Temple University and earned a Ph.D. in Physiology from Jefferson Medical College in 1964 (Fig. 19). At Jefferson he has held faculty appointments in Physiology in the Medical College, College of Graduate Studies and the College of Allied Health Sciences. He has published articles pertaining to gastrointestinal function, radiobiology, nutrition, hemorrhagic shock, carbon monoxide poisoning, myocardial infarction, history of science, and medical education. Dr. Rosenfeld has been Recording Secretary and in 1991 was President-Elect of the Pennsylvania Academy of Science. He has also served as an Associate Editor of the Academy's *Journal*.

1960 Narasimhula, Shankunthala V., Ph.D., Biochemistry
   Randall, Eileen L., Ph.D., Microbiology
   Smith, Phyllis N., M.S., Physiology

1961 Chan, Asteria C., Ph.D., Pathology/Pediatrics
   Rosen, Lionel, M.S., Physiology
   Sherk, Henry H., M.S.
   Shirakawa, Alice, M.S., Microbiology

1962 Bender, A. Douglas, Ph.D., Physiology
   Kostos, Vincent, M.S., Pharmacology
   Levine, Stanley, Ph.D., Microbiology
   Lipkin, Saul, M.S., Microbiology
   Ma., Pearl, Ph.D., Microbiology
   Nahhas, Laila A., M.S., Microbiology
   Welch, Richard M., Ph.D., Pharmacology
   Wurst, Richard P., M.S., Microbiology

1963 Ch'en, Philip C., M.S., Microbiology
   Coppola, John A., Ph.D., Pharmacology
   Dickerson, Kenneth H., M.S., Physiology
   Ghosh, Gopi M., M.S., Anatomy
   Holburn, Ruth R., Ph.D., Physiology

   McPhillips, Joseph J., Ph.D., Pharmacology
   Messer, James W., Ph.D., Microbiology
   Moawad, Atef H., M.S., (Medicine) OBG
   Schlosser, Walter, Ph.D., Pharmacology
   Schwartz, Edward, Ph.D., Pharmacology
   Siddharth, Padmanabhan, Ph.D., Anatomy
   Sugarman, Harvey, M.S., Pharmacology
   Sullivan, Francis J., Ph.D., Physiology
   Zawoiski, Eugene, Ph.D., Physiology

1964 Clark, Allen M., Ph.D., Pathology
   Gabriel, Karl L., Ph.D., Pharmacology
   Greenwald, Kenneth, Ph.D., Pathology
   Horn, Robert S., Ph.D., Pharmacology
   Hosko, Michael J., Ph.D., Pharmacology
   Kilmore, Mearl A., Ph.D., Physiology
   Lutton, Charles E., Ph.D., Pathology
   Maylock, John H., M.S., Physiology
   Rosenfeld, Leonard M., Ph.D., Physiology
   Siegel, Edward T., Ph.D., Physiology
   Silberstein, Charles E., M.S., Anatomy
   Tansy, Martin F., Ph.D., Physiology
   Tressan, Elliot R., Ph.D., Pathology
   Triolo, Anthony J., Ph.D., Pharmacology
   Zimskind, Paul, Ph.D., Physiology

Anthony J. Triolo (Ph.D., 1964), Professor of Pharmacology, teaching Jefferson student nurses.

Fig. 21. Harvey J. Sugarman, M.S., M.D., Professor of Surgery at the Medical College of Virginia.

Fig. 22. Anthony J. Triolo, Ph.D., Professor of Pharmacology at Jefferson.

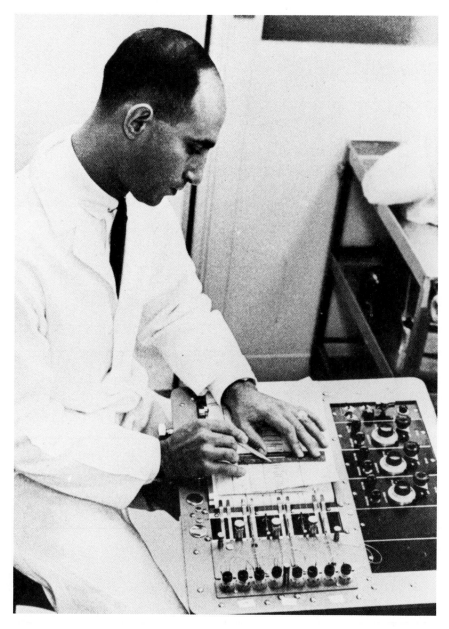

Fig. 23.   Paul D. Zimskind, M.D., Ph.D., Chairman of Urology at Jefferson (1967-76).

1960-64

In 1969, when Thomas Jefferson University was established, the College of Graduate Studies replaced the Board for the Regulation of Graduate Studies. Dr. Robert C. Baldridge (Fig. 24) was named the first Dean of the College and undertook the responsibility of having the new College recognized as an accredited Graduate School.

During this time the graduate program in the Department of Microbiology received a boost from the THEMIS grant from the Department of Defense. This interdepartmental grant supported research in the Departments of Microbiology, Preventive Medicine and Gastroenterology for the study of diarrheal diseases and was instrumental in supporting faculty and students at the time.

In 1965, Dr. George Royal was appointed Assistant Professor, the first African-American to hold a full-time professorial position at Jefferson. That same year, Dr. George Warren returned to the faculty as Professor of Microbiology. Dr. Warren had been a faculty member in the 1940s and then moved to Wyeth Laboratories where he served as Head of the Department of Microbiology. Members of the department traveled to Costa Rica in 1965 to study the infantile diarrhea epidemic. Dr. Goodner retired in June of 1967. Russell W. Schaedler, M.D., (JMC, '53) was appointed the new Chairman in January of 1968 (Fig. 25). The first academic appointee of the new Chairman was Jussi J. Saukkonen, M.D., who would later become Dean of the College of Graduate Studies. Dr. Junius Clark joined the Department in 1969 to develop the study and teaching of cellular immunology.

The graduate programs in the Department of Physiology continued to mature and in this period 23 master's and doctoral degrees were awarded in physiology, more than in all of the previous years combined. Another graduate of the program was appointed instructor. Eugene J. Zawoiski, Ph.D., a 1963 graduate, taught renal physiology and pursued teratological research as well as studies on central nervous system involvement in gastrointestinal function. In recognition of the need to better understand smooth muscle function, Marion J. Siegman, Ph.D., was appointed instructor in 1967. In 1977 Dr. Siegman was the first woman to be named a professor of physiology at Jefferson. In 1968, Chandra M. Banerjee was named Assistant Professor to replace Sheldon Gottlieb.

Paul H. Maurer, Ph.D., was named Chairman of the Department of Biochemistry in 1966 (Fig. 26). With his accession to the Chair, the Department underwent a marked change in character.

Fig. 24. Robert C. Baldridge, Ph.D., first Dean (1970-81).

Because his major interest was immunochemistry, many of the additional staff members appointed were immunochemists. On the average, the staff in subsequent years consisted of immunochemists and traditional biochemists, including "molecular biologists," in about equal proportions. This hybrid character also was reflected in the various areas of teaching and research.

August Epple, Ph.D. was appointed to the faculty in the Department of Anatomy in 1967 and has stood at the forefront of research into the comparative structure and function of the pancreas and its islets throughout phylogeny of the animal kingdom. Upon receiving his degree from Jefferson, Ronald Jensh, Ph.D. was named to the faculty as its first teratologist. The Department moved its new facilities to the fifth floor of Jefferson Alumni Hall in 1968.

Fig. 25.   Russell W. Schaedler, M.D., Chairman of Microbiology (1968-91).

In 1965 a "Graduate Training Program in Public Health" grant was made to the Department of Preventive Medicine with Dr. E. Harold Hinman (Fig. 27) as Project Director and Dr. C. Earl Albrecht as Supporting Director. The experience gained in this graduate training program served as the base for the approval of a three-year residency program in General Preventive Medicine awarded to the Department. This program was designed to train physicians destined for academic appointment in preventive medicine, community medicine, or those interested in associating themselves with administrative responsibility for clinical programs with national, state, or metropolitan health departments. This was a unique program in that it offered variable opportunities for training both in the basic sciences related to preventive medicine such as epidemiology, biostatistics, occupational medicine and nutrition, and in clinical responsibilities. Those completing the program, prepared acceptable theses and passed the examination, earned master of science degrees and became board certified in General Preventive Medicine and/or Occupational Medicine.

Anatomy Alumni

Richard H. Rothman, M.D., Ph.D., (1965), had previously earned his M.D. degree from the University of Pennsylvania and took his surgical training at Jefferson under Anthony F. DePalma, M.D., (JMC, '29). Since January 1986, Dr. Rothman has served as the James Edwards Professor of Orthopaedic Surgery and chairman of the department at Jefferson Medical College. He also became the director of the Rothman Institute at Pennsylvania Hospital, the largest and best recognized facility in the Delaware Valley for orthopaedic implant and reconstructive surgery of the spine and soft tissues surrounding joints. He also opened the city's first Foot Center which complemented Jefferson's already renowned Hand Center. In 1988 he established the Orthopaedic Research Laboratory at Jefferson which was funded by research grants from the National Institutes of Health and the March of Dimes Birth Defects Foundation. He is the author of eight major textbooks and over 100 scientific papers on joint surgery. For his accomplishments, he was awarded the College of Graduate Studies 1988 Distinguished Alumnus Award (Fig. 28).

Ronald P. Jensh, Ph.D., (1966), has served on the faculty at Jefferson Medical College since 1966 and on the graduate faculty of the College of Graduate Studies since 1970 (Fig. 29). He was named Associate Professor of Radiology in 1974 and Professor of Anatomy in 1982. He has also been Section Chief of Microscopic Anatomy since 1988 and Vice Chairman of the Department of Anatomy since 1984. He was the recipient of the Christian R. and Mary F. Lindback Award for Distinguished Teaching in 1973. A consultant to several private companies, he has also been a member of the Embryology and Human Development Study Section of the NIH. A member of numerous professional societies, he served as president of the Behavioral Teratology Society. He was also a member of the College of Graduate Studies Alumni Association Board of Directors, serving as its president in 1982 -1984. Dr. Jensh has published more than 100 papers and abstracts in the field of behavioral and radiation teratology and his research concentrates on the effects of prenatal stressors on young adult animals. He has also been active in developing educational computer programs. An accomplished photographer, he has shown his work at a number of photographic art exhibits and won several awards, including one sponsored by the U.S. Department of the Interior and the Minolta Corporation.

Biochemistry Alumni

Richard J. Cenedella, Ph.D., (1966), did post-doctoral work as a Research Associate in Pharmacology at West Virginia University where he was named Senior Research Pharmacologist in 1967 and advanced to Professor of Pharmacology in 1976. Then he accepted the position of Professor and Chairman of Biochemistry at Kirks-

Fig. 26. Paul H. Maurer, Ph.D., Chairman of Biochemistry (1966-85).

ville College of Osteopathic Medicine in Kirksville, Missouri. He was a Visiting Research Fellow at the University of Melbourne, Australia, and named a Fogarty International Senior Scholar of the NIH in 1989. In 1990 he received the Gutensohn/Denslow Award for Research and Teaching from the American Osteopathic Association. Through his research, most recently in the area of lens cholesterol metabolism and lens protein structural changes, he has co-authored 67 articles in refereed journals, two books and chapters in four books.

John J. Ch'ih, Ph.D., (1968), was named Senior Instructor of Biological Chemistry at Hahnemann University in 1969 and advanced to Professor in 1981. He has served as advisor to numerous master's and Ph.D. recipients. For his teaching accomplishments, he was honored with the 1991 Faculty Teaching Award of the Graduate

Fig. 27. E. Harold Hinman, Ph.D., M.D., Chairman of Preventive Medicine (1962-69).

Student Society of Hahnemann. In 1978 he was named a U.S. Public Health Service Senior International Fellow which took him to Taiwan for eight months where he served as Visiting Professor and Scientist. He also served as a Visiting Professor in China for one month in 1987. Dr. Ch'ih's research has focused on the activation, detoxication and translocation of chemical carcinogens in mammalian tissues and cells, and alterations in gene expression during the initiation of chemical carcinogenesis. He also has studied the mechanism of tumor-modulatory agents on the formation of AFB_1-DNA, RNA and protein adducts. Through his research he has co-authored 28 papers and 33 abstracts.

Marianne L. Egan, Ph.D., (1969), was the recipient of the Biochemistry Department's Paul Pinchuk Memorial Award. She was an Assistant Research Scientist in the Department of Immunology at the City of Hope National Medical Center in Duarte, California, until 1977 when she became Research Assistant Professor of Microbiology at the University of Alabama at Birmingham. She served as Scientist in UAB's Comprehensive Cancer Center, later in the Multipurpose Arthritis Center, and in 1981 on the Graduate Faculty in the Molecular Cell Biology Program. In 1984 she was promoted to Research Associate Professor in the Department of Microbiology and in 1987 in the Division of Clinical Immunology and Rheumatology. She served as Chairperson of the Diagnosis and Treatment Working Group of the Breast Cancer Task Force of the National Cancer Institute from 1980 to 1984. Dr. Egan has co-authored 37 publications and three book chapters relating to her work.

Microbiology Alumni

Vu Qui Dai, M.D., Ph.D., (1965), had earned his M.D. in 1959 from the University of Saigon and then was selected to study abroad in a Vietnamese government program designed to replace the country's largely French-national teachers with Vietnamese. He served as a research fellow in virology at the University of Alabama Medical Center for one year and then came to Jefferson. Upon graduation he returned to Vietnam to teach at the University of Saigon Medical School, serving as Professor and Chairman of the Department of Microbiology and, later, as Dean of the School of Medicine in 1974-75. Later in 1975 he was held for six month in a communist "re-education" camp. He emigrated to the United States as a refugee in 1982 and completed all examinations and retraining necessary for licensure in this country. Since then he has been a staff physician at Agnews Developmental Center in San Jose, California.

Robert G. Stockmal, Ph.D., D.O., (1969), went on to a D.O. degree at the Philadelphia College of Osteopathic Medicine. From 1968 until 1978 he served as Chairman of the Department of Microbiology and Public Health at the same college. He then joined the Ohio University College of Osteopathic Medicine's Department of Family Medicine as Associate Professor. Since 1982 he has also served in the U.S. Army Reserve Medical Corps as a Lieutenant Colonel. He has held the positions of Staff Flight Surgeon in the 83rd U.S. Army Reserve Command and Officer in Charge of the Cardiology Team for the 2291st U.S. Army Hospital.

Pharmacology Alumni

William T. Lynch, Ph.D., (1967), worked at Lederle Laboratories from 1966 to 1977 in toxicology, conducting studies required to obtain registration of pharmaceuticals. He then moved to Rohm and Haas Company where he managed toxicology programs for agricultural chemicals.

John E. Stambaugh, Jr., M.D., Ph.D., (1968), was a 1966 graduate of Jefferson Medical College and received his Ph.D. in Pharmacology. He served his residency in medicine at Jefferson and an oncology fellowship at the National Cancer Institute Training Center. He remained at Jefferson, serving in the Department of Pharmacology and rose to full Professor by 1982 (Fig. 30). He also served as Assistant Professor of Medicine from 1976. He has held staff appointments at

Fig. 28.   Richard H. Rothman, M.D., Ph.D. (Anatomy, 1965), Chairman of Orthopaedics (1986-), receives Distinguished Alumnus Award (1988) from Gerard McGarrity, Ph.D., President of the CGS Alumni Association.

Cooper Hospital, Underwood Memorial Hospital, West Jersey Health System and Our Lady of Lourdes Hospital. Through his research, he has published 57 articles and 44 abstracts of his work.

Physiology Alumni

Allen Cymerman, Ph.D., (1968), served as a Research Physiologist for the US Army Research Institute of Environmental Medicine (USARIEM) in the Biochemistry and Pharmacology Division until 1972, in the Military Stress Division until 1975 and then in the Altitude Research Division, advancing to Director. In 1990 he became Director of the Altitude Physiology and Medicine Division at USARIEM. He has co-authored over 70 articles, book chapters and technical reports and has made 122 abstracts and presentations to medical and scientific communities. His work has been in the area of environmental physiology, stress, and physical and mental performance with particular emphasis on performance at high terrestrial elevations.

Eli Fromm, Ph.D., (1967), had earned both baccalaureate and master's degrees in engineering at Drexel University and returned there upon graduation from Jefferson to hold a series of academic appointments that involved him in teaching, research, administration and grants management. He was named Professor of Biomedical Sciences in 1980 and then Professor of Electrical and Computer Engineering in 1983. He was Interim Dean of Drexel's College of Engineering in 1989 and then Vice Provost for Research and Graduate Studies in 1990. In 1980 through 1981 he also served on the U.S. House of Representatives Committee on Science and Technology as a Congressional Science and Engineering Fellow where he participated in policy formation and legislative committee activity. He also served as

Fig. 29. Ronald P. Jensh, Ph.D. (Anatomy, 1966), Professor of Anatomy at Jefferson.

Fig. 30. John E. Stambaugh, Jr., M.D., Ph.D. became a full Professor of Pharmacology at Jefferson.

the Director of the Bioengineering Program of the National Science Foundation in 1983 and 1984. He has published more than 50 scientific/technical publications relating to fields of research thrusts in physiology, bioengineering, electronics and engineering education, plus congressional documents relating to the FDA approval process, authorization of NSF, National Technologic Foundation, Innovation and Productivity, reindustrialization and economic competitiveness, export control and biotechnology.

Mary D. Osbakken Holmes, M.D., Ph.D., (1969), went on to earn a master's degree in biomedical engineering from Drexel University and then an M.D. degree from Temple University Medical School. She completed her internship and residency in internal medicine at Pennsylvania Hospital in 1977 and then served three fellowships in cardiology, at Temple University Hospital, the University of Pennsylvania and Massachusetts General Hospital. She served as Assistant Professor in the Department of Medicine and Radiology and as an internist and cardiologist at the Milton S. Hershey Medical Center from 1980 to 1985. She then returned to the University of Pennsylvania as Assistant Professor of Anesthesia and Biochemistry/Biophysics. In 1988, she was also named Assistant Professor of Medicine at the Hospital of the University of Pennsylvania. Among numerous editorial appointments, she served as a referee to *American Journal of Cardiology* and the *Journal of Magnetic Resonance in Medicine,* a reviewer to *Journal of Clinical Investigation*, and on the editorial board of *Cardiology.* Through her research, largely in the area of cardiology, she has published 52 papers, two books and 86 abstracts.

Melvin A. Johnson, Ph.D., (1969), had previously taught biology at Central State University in Wilberforce, Ohio. Upon graduation from Jefferson, he became Chairman of the Department of Biology there. He was later promoted to Professor. He also served as Professor of Physiology at Wright State University School of Medicine from 1974 to 1985 and in 1985 he was named Dean of the College of Arts and Sciences at Central State. Active in the American Heart Association, he was also appointed to the Heart Association's national level Committee on Minority

Involvement. He is a charter member of the National Minority Health Affairs Association and the Wright State University Academy of Medicine. Dr. Johnson was elected to the Board of Directors of the College of Graduate Studies Alumni Association in 1983. As a board member he outlined recruitment strategies for the College to attract and recruit minority graduate students and made available information about the Minority Access to Research Careers program. In addition to his responsibilities in academic administration, Dr. Johnson continued to conduct research in the area of cardiovascular physiology and published 17 papers in that area (Fig. 31).

David S. Marsden, Ph.D., (1968), has since 1968 been employed at The Roosevelt Hospital, New York, in the Department of Radiology, recently as Director of the Medical Physics and Radioisotope Laboratories. He has had responsibility for training residents and technicians, and also acts as hospital radiation safety officer and supervisor of the isotope laboratory. He conducted research on the use of radio-isotopes in the diagnosis of gastrointestinal disorders. He was certified by the American Board of Radiology as a Radiological Physicist. Dr. Marsden has also served as Assistant Professor of Radiology at Columbia University and as Chairman of the Roosevelt Hospital Radiation Safety Committee. Active in the National and New York Clinical Radioassay Societies, he has been president and treasurer of both.

Zalmon Pober, Ph.D., (1968), served as a physiologist at the Food Science Laboratory at the U.S. Army Natick Research and Development Command in Massachusetts from 1968 to 1976 where, among other responsibilities, he planned and conducted research programs in nutrition, nutritional physiology and gastrointestinal physiology. In 1976 he was named Assistant Professor of Physiology and Pharmacology at Massachusetts College of Pharmacy and Allied Health Sciences where he was promoted to Associate Professor in 1981. Since 1983 he has also served as Adjunct Instructor in Biomedical Materials at Western New England College's School of Engineering. He earned his M.B.A. degree in 1984 and, since 1985, he has been a consultant to Continuing Professional Education Services where he is responsible for design, accreditation and marketing of continuing education programs for health care professionals. Among his gastro-intestinal function research accomplishments are the establishment of the presence of enterogas-tric reflexes in the intestinal phase of gastric secretion, characterization of factors that make protein a stimulus for the intestinal phase of gastric secretion and determination of the effects of topical anesthetics on intestinal receptors controlling food intake.

Margaret Johnson Roach, Ph.D., (1968), while at Jefferson, studied in the Cardeza Foundation for Hematologic Research. Upon graduation she joined the Medical Center of Delaware to establish its Coagulation Laboratory of which she was Scientific Director. Her publications have centered around qualitative platelet structural and functional abnormalities. These studies were performed on two families who live near Wilmington, Delaware who have very rare and different platelet disorders. The platelets from these families have been studied by many national and international investigators. Dr. Johnson has served as protocol coordinator for the medical center's Research and Human Rights Committee and coordinator of the Institutional Review Board. For six years she lectured nationally and regionally on coagulation for the American Society of Clinical Pathologists. Dr. Johnson was a volunteer for Immaculata College, her undergraduate institution, serving as President of its Alumni Association and Chairman of the President's Council. In 1989 she was honored with the Immaculata Medal, the College's highest award to an alumnus. In 1990 she was appointed to the Jefferson College of Graduate Studies Alumni Association Board of Directors and served as Chairman of its Fund Raising Committee.

In Min Young, M.S., M.D., (1966) had earned his M.D. degree in 1948 from Yonsei University College of Medicine in Seoul, Korea. He came to Jefferson in 1960 as a research associate in otolaryngology and rose to full Professor of Otolar-

Fig. 31.   Melvin A. Johnson, Ph.D. (right) with Leonard M. Rosenfeld, Ph.D. on Alumni Day (1984).

1965-69

yngology (Audiology) in 1972. Additionally, he served as a research audiologist from 1965 to 1972 on an NIH training grant for the College. He has also served as training supervisor for the audiology practicum for Temple University and as a lecturer in audiology at the Naval Regional Medical Center. He was appointed Visiting Professor of Yonsei University College of Medicine in 1986. Through his research, he has published over 60 articles and 90 abstracts.

Pathology Alumni

Mark D. Brown, M.D., Ph.D., (1969), received his M.D. degree in 1965 from Jefferson. Upon graduation he served as an instructor in Orthopaedics until 1971. He was then appointed Staff Orthopaedic Surgeon at the Bethesda Naval Hospital until 1973. He subsequently held several academic positions at the University of Miami School of Medicine. Beginning as a fulltime faculty member, he advanced to Professor of Orthopaedics and Rehabilitation in 1982 and was named Chairman in 1986 (Fig. 32). He has also been Associate Director of the Tissue Bank since 1979. In 1981 he conducted research in the Departments of Orthopaedics and Anatomy at the University of Goteborg in Sweden. A national expert on diseases of the spine and treatment of spinal disorders by surgical modalities and enzyme injections, he has held two patents, and has authored 59 papers, one text book, and chapters in eight texts. He served as Associate Editor for *Clinical Orthopaedics and Related Research* and on the editorial board for *Spine*. Dr. Brown was the 1989 recipient of the Eastern Orthopaedic Association Award for Spinal Research.

William Lawrence Drew, M.D., Ph.D., (1966), was a 1962 graduate of Jefferson Medical College. He completed an Assistant Residency in Medicine at the University of California Hospital, San Francisco, in 1968 and then was an NIH Fellow in Clinical Microbiology at the University of

Washington in Seattle. Since 1969 he has been Director of the Clinical Microbiology and Virology Laboratory, and in charge of infectious diseases at Mount Zion Medical Center at UCSF. In 1985 he was named Associate Professor of Laboratory Medicine and Medicine (Fig. 33). He was also made Director of the Biskind Pathology Research Laboratory in 1980 and Director of AIDS Services in 1988. He has spoken extensively at national and international meetings and published more than 75 papers, most recently in the areas of viral and infectious diseases and AIDS.

Fig. 32. Mark D. Brown, M.D., Ph.D., Professor of Orthopaedics and Rehabilitation, University of Miami School of Medicine.

1965 Dhamabutra, Narathorn, M.D.,
Microbiology
Do, Nhaun Thi, M.S., Microbiology
Lectura, Felix V., M.S., Anatomy
Pant, Keshab D., Ph.D., Microbiology
Rahman, Mohammad A., Ph.D.,
Microbiology
Rothman, Richard H., Ph.D., Anatomy
Vu, Dai Qui, Ph.D., Microbiology

1966 Cenedella, Richard J., Ph.D., Biochemistry
Daley, Daniel J., Jr. M.S., Physiology
Drew, William L., Ph.D., Pathology
Hasan, Syed I., M.S., Microbiology
Jensh, Ronald P., Ph.D., Anatomy
Rioux, Ernest, Ph.D., Physiology

Fig. 33. William L. Drew, M.D., Ph.D., Associate Professor of Laboratory Medicine and Medicine, University of California (San Francisco).

Tri, Le Minh, Ph.D., Physiology
Vipatapatya, Vimonvan, M.S., Physiology
Young, In Min, M.S., Physiology

1967 Cady, William, M.S., Physiology
Freundlich, Jerome J., Ph.D., Physiology
Fromm, Eli, Ph.D., Physiology
Gold, Alan, M.S., Preventive Medicine
Hartman, Herbert H., M.S., Pharmacology
Huang, Joseph C., M.S., Pharmacology
Husain, Azam, M.S., Physiology
Joshi, Prakashchanda C., M.S., Physiology
Lynch, William T., Ph.D., Pharmacology
Miller, Neil, Ph.D., Physiology
Moreno, Oscarr M., Ph.D., Pharmacology
Neff, Ray A., M.S., Pharmacology
Spears, Ruth Ann, Ph.D., Microbiology
Woo, Chi Yuan, M.S., Physiology

1968 Ambromovage, Anne M., Ph.D.,
Physiology
Ch'Ih, John Juwei, Ph.D., Biochemistry
Cinti, Dominick L., Ph.D., Physiology
Cymerman, Allen, Ph.D., Physiology
Drezner, Allen D., Ph.D., Pathology
Fonte, Donald A., Ph.D., Anatomy
Johnson Roach, Margaret M., Ph.D.,
Physiology
Kim, Nam H. Lee, Ph.D., Pharmacology
Kyriazis, Andrew P., Ph.D., Pathology
Marsden, David S., Ph.D., Physiology
McAlack, Robert F., Ph.D., Microbiology
Pober, Zalmon, Ph.D., Physiology
Rhode, Solon L., III, Ph.D., Pathology
Salam, Syed A., Ph.D., Microbiology
Stambaugh, John E., Jr., Ph.D.,
Pharmacology

1969 Brown, Mark D., Ph.D., Pathology
Cramer, Eva Brown, Ph.D., Anatomy
Dettmer, Cornelia M., Ph.D., Physiology
Egan, Marianne L., Ph.D., Biochemistry
Holmes, Mary Osbakken, Ph.D.,
Physiology
Johnson, Melvin A., Ph.D., Physiology
Lambert, William C., Ph.D., Pathology
Laxon, Jaclynne Horn, M.S., Physiology
Leung, Christopher K., Ph.D., Anatomy
Msuya, Philemon M., Ph.D., Biochemistry
Pierce, Lauretta, Ph.D., Physiology
Stockmal, Robert G., Ph.D., Microbiology
Vukovich, Robert A., Ph.D., Pharmacology

Dr. E. Marshall Johnson (Fig. 34) succeeded Dr. Andrew J. Ramsay as Chairman of the Department of Anatomy and Director of the Daniel Baugh Institute in the fall of 1972. A goal of Dr. Johnson on assuming the post was to use the umbrella of the Daniel Baugh Institute to develop an interdisciplinary program consistent with contemporary modes for organization of academic research-educational units. This was to be achieved by recruiting new faculty in the area of developmental biology-teratology to build a critical mass of research expertise that would be nationally and internationally competitive for extramural research support and also be a point

Fig. 34. E. Marshall Johnson, Ph.D., Chairman of Anatomy (1972-   ).

of recognition for the University. A second goal was to enhance the neurobiology component of the Department to begin development of contemporary expertise in cellular biology.

The Clinical Microbiology master's degree program was launched in 1972 with 15 students enrolled. In response to the need for advanced training for medical technologists, the program was spearheaded by Dr. Randall, who was Chief of the Microbiological Laboratories, and Dr. Mandle. In 1971, Dr. E. Frederick Wheelock was appointed Professor of Microbiology. Other appointments during this period included Stephen Toy, Ph.D., and Preston Marx, Ph.D.

In the Department of Pharmacology, substantial research programs other than in toxicology were also being pursued at this time. In psychopharmacology and neuropharmacology, research was directed toward the relationship between both normal and abnormal brain and nerve chemistry on the one hand, and the action and metabolism of drugs on the other hand, with the hope of revealing information leading to improvements in the drug treatment of diseases affecting the brain and nervous system. Other research involved the micro-injection of psychoactive drugs into specific sites of the brain and the recording of the electrical activity from those and related brain centers, to better understand the biochemical basis for neuropsychiatric disorders and provide a basis for more effective drug therapy. Also, an extensive investigation was carried out on the function and importance of taurine in the central nervous system, the eye, and the heart of different species of animals. Other research involved studies of the roles of arachidonic acid and the prostaglandins in relation to platelet aggregation and the use of aspirin and modification of the diet to reduce platelet aggregation.

Dr. Friedman retired as Chairman of the Department of Physiology in June of 1974 and was succeeded by Allan M. Lefer, Ph.D. (Fig. 35). Dr. Lefer came to Jefferson and turned the

Department's research focus from gastrointestinal to cardiovascular. He also established international relationships that would result in a continuing series of visits to the Department of both junior and mature scientists. The first such visitor was Dr. Minuro Okuda, an academic clinician from Japan, who served as visiting associate professor and research associate from 1974 to 1976. Dr. Lefer also appointed two new faculty members, Drs. Michael J. Rovetto and James A. Spath, Jr.

Although no Department of Physics existed at the College, arrangements were made with the Bartol Research Foundation of the Franklin Institute Department of Physics to have it recognized as the Department of Physics at Jefferson. This provided a mechanism for this group to offer a graduate program, the degrees being granted by Jefferson under the regulations established for the basic science departments. The program received approval in 1968 and continued until 1977 when Bartol moved from its original location in Swarthmore to the University of Delaware. In all, Jefferson awarded seven Ph.D. degrees and two M.S. degrees in physics during the program's existence.

Anatomy Alumni

Thomas L. Lewis, O.D., Ph.D., (1974), held a postdoctoral position at Washington University School of Medicine in the Department of Ophthalmology and in 1976 was named Director of the Division of Biological Sciences at the Pennsylvania College of Optometry. In 1978 he was named Chief of the Professional Staff of the Eye Institute at the College. He was named Dean of Academic Affairs and Associate Professor of Anatomy in 1979. In 1989 he was named President of the Pennsylvania College of Optometry. He has served as Chairman of the Section on Anatomy and Pathology and for the Examination Council of the National Board of Examiners in Optometry. He has also served on the review board of *Journal of Optometric Education* and on the editorial council for the *American Journal of Optometry and Physiological Optics*.

Biochemistry Alumni

Samuel G. Franklin, Ph.D., (1973), was the winner of the Department's Paul Pinchuck Memorial Prize for Outstanding Biochemistry Student. He was an NIH postdoctoral fellow at the Institute for Cancer Research in Philadelphia where he was promoted to Research Associate in 1976 and Senior Research Associate in 1981. His research there focused on the purification and characterization of Hepatitis B Virus Binding Substance (IgM) by immunochemical and biochemical techniques. In 1983 he became Senior Research Biochemist at Revlon Health Care Group in New York. He held that position until 1985 when he moved to Smith Kline and French Laboratories as Senior Investigator. In 1988 he was promoted to Assistant Director of the Protein Isolation Group where he has been involved in the design of protein isolation and purification procedures for novel (third generation) thrombolytics, human immunodifficiency virus and related

Fig. 35. Allen M. Lefer, Ph.D., Chairman of Physiology (1974-   ).

and other recombinant proteins. He has published 15 articles.

Lorraine Haeffner-Gormley, Ph.D., (1971), had worked with Dr. O. Dhodanand Kowlessar in various medical college-related laboratories conducting gastroenterology research since 1957. In 1970 she was named an instructor in the department of medicine, division of gastroenterology at Jefferson. In 1975 she accepted a position as Associate Director of the Steroid Research Laboratory at Crozer-Chester Medical Center. In 1978 she moved to the University of Delaware to serve as Research Associate in the department of chemistry. She has published 19 articles relating to her work which is in the area of protein/peptide biochemistry on function/structure relationships.

Yu Chen Lin, Ph.D., (1971), was named an Instructor in the Department of Biochemistry at the Philadelphia College of Osteopathic Medicine where she was later elevated to full Professor of Biochemistry. In 1980 she was awarded the Christian R. and Mary F. Lindback Foundation Award for Distinguished Teaching. She has served on the College's Research, Appeals, Honors and Awards, and Academic Standing Committees. She has published nine articles, 17 abstracts and nine sponsored publications.

Glenn Charles Van Tuyle, Ph.D., (1972), won Biochemistry's Paul Pinchuk Memorial Award for Outstanding Research. He received a postdoctoral appointment in in the Department of Biochemistry at the State University of New York, Stony Brook, where he stayed until 1974. He then was appointed Assistant Professor of Biochemistry at Virginia Commonwealth University and promoted to Associate Professor in 1980. In 1983-84 he was a visiting scientist at the Swiss Institute for Experimental Cancer Research in Lausanne, Switzerland. He has published 14 papers and 16 abstracts of his work, most of it in the area of mitochondrial DNA.

Microbiology Alumni

Frederick C. Blank, M.S., (1974), prior to attending Jefferson, had earned a bachelor's degree in Dairy Husbandry at Delaware Valley College and then began post graduate studies at the University of Maryland while working at the U.S.D.A. Agricultural Research Center. He was then drafted for service in the Vietnam War for five years and served as a Clinical Laboratory Officer at Army Hospitals where he became familiar with malaria and meningococcal meningitis, among other tropical diseases. At his last duty station in Fort Dix, New Jersey, he became familiar with Malcolm Artenstein, who eventually developed the Adeno and Rhino virus vaccines, and who provided Mr. Blank with an introduction to medical research methodologies. Following his discharge, he became an Assistant Microbiologist with E.G. Scott at the Wilmington Medical Center who sent him to study anaerobic bacteriology at the Mayo Clinic and encouraged him to enroll in Jefferson's clinical microbiology program. After graduation he accepted a position as Senior Microbiologist at Crozer-Chester Medical Center. After five years he resigned to embark on an entirely new career as a restauranteur.

Georganne Kretschman Buescher, M.S., Ed.D., (1974), in 1976 was named Assistant Professor in the Department of Medical Technology at Jefferson's College of Allied Health Sciences where she advanced to Associate Professor in 1980. She served as Acting Chairman of that Department from June 1980 to June 1981 and from June 1987 to September 1987. She served on numerous College Committees and was Chairman of the Faculty Committee on Appointment, Promotion and Tenure and the Faculty Affairs Committee. She earned her doctorate in education at Temple University in 1984 and in 1988 she was named an Instructor in the Department of Microbiology and Immunology at Jefferson Medical College and Director of the "Masters in Microbiology" Program for the College of Graduate Studies. She also served as the Coordinator of the Master of Science Program in Biomedical Chemistry which was begun in 1990. She was appointed as Director of the Basic Science M.S. Programs for the College of Graduate Studies as she continued to hold the position of Instructor in Microbiology for the Medical College. Among her many activities at Jefferson, she was President of the Faculty Club in 1986-1987 and President of the College of Graduate Studies Alumni Association from 1984 to 1986 (Fig. 20). Dr. Buescher has served on the

Advisory Boards for the Medical Laboratory Technician Programs at Manor Junior College and Montgomery County Community College as well as Guest Lecturer for the Medical Technology program at the University of Delaware. She has made numerous presentations of her research, which recently focused on borderline oxacillin-resistant Staphylococcus aureus, at meetings of the American Society of Microbiology. She has authored five publications.

Diane Blechman Feik, M.S., (1974), went on to serve as Supervisor of the Clinical Microbiology Laboratory at Albert Einstein Medical Center until 1987. She then accepted a position as Laboratory Testing Supervisor in the Microbiological Testing Laboratory at the University of Pennsylvania School of Dental Medicine in periodontology and oral microbiology. She has presented her work at the 1988 and 1989 national American Society of Microbiology meetings. Mrs. Feik was one of the founding members of the Clinical Microbiology Alumni Group, serving through the years on its board and as president.

Prabhavathi B. Fernandes, Ph.D., (1974), accepted a postdoctoral position at Jefferson in the laboratory of Dr. Charles Panos where she studied the chemistry of lipids. She then moved on to further postdoctoral work at the Institute for Cancer Research at Fox Chase Cancer Center and then at Temple University as a research assistant professor. In 1980 she became Senior Research Microbiologist in In Vivo Microbiology at the Squibb Institute for Medical Research. She moved on to Abbott Laboratories as Project Leader in General Microbiology in 1983 but returned to Squibb as Director of Microbial Genetics and Biochemistry in 1988. For genetics, she has been responsible for heterologous expression in yeast and bacteria and also for developing screens using novel targets for therapeutic agents in the area of antibacterials, antivirals, biosynthesis of cholesterol, oncogenes and cardiovascular areas. In biochemistry, she has been responsible for identifying novel targets for therapeutic agents and determining the selectivity of novel compounds for these targets. She has published over 50 articles and presented her work at more than 70 national and international meetings.

Robert G. Lahita, M.D., Ph.D., (1973), completed the combined M.D./Ph.D. program in microbiology. He finished his postgraduate training in internal medicine at New York Hospital—Memorial Hospital for Cancer and Allied Diseases until 1976 and then served as research associate and postdoctoral fellow in immunology at Rockefeller University. He held numerous academic positions in medicine and in clinical pharmacology at New York Hospital-Cornell University, at Rockefeller University Hospital for Special Surgery, and Columbia University College of Physicians and Surgeons with the rank of Associate Professor. He has also been Senior Attending Physician at Rockefeller University Hospital, Hospital for Joint Diseases, Beth Israel Medical Center, New York Hospital and St. Luke's Roosevelt Medical Center. In 1990 he was appointed Chief of Rheumatology and Connective Tissue Diseases at St. Luke's. He has published 60 articles and 38 abstracts of his work. Dr. Lahita became Chairman of the Board of Directors for the Lupus Foundation of America and has served on the editorial boards for *Clinical and Experimental Rheumatology* and *Journal of NIH Research*.

Susan M. Luscombe, M.S., (1972), **M.D.,** (1975), went on to Jefferson Medical College for her M.D. in 1975. She completed an internship at Jefferson in 1976 and served her residency in ophthalmology at Temple University Hospital in 1979. This was followed by a one-year fellowship in anterior segment surgery at Bascom Palmer Eye Institute. Working in private practice, she has been an international consultant on modern microsurgical cataract procedures, laser surgery and glaucoma surgery.

Gerard J. McGarrity, Ph.D., (M.S. 1964), Ph.D., (1970), in 1965 began his association with the Coriell Institute for Medical Research as a Research Associate and advanced to Head of the Department of Microbiology, Vice President for Scientific Affairs and President in 1986. He served as a Clinical Instructor in the Department of Surgery at the University of Pennsylvania School of Medicine from 1970 to 1975. He has also been Adjunct Professor of Microbiology at Robert Wood Johnson Medical School since 1985, Adjunct Faculty in Cell Biology at the State University of New York, Plattsburgh, since 1984, and Adjunct Professor of Microbiology at Jefferson Medical College since 1984. He was on the NIH Recombinant DNA Advisory Committee and later served as its Chairman. He was an exchange Visitor from the National Academy of Sciences to the Czechoslovakian Academy of Sciences, and President of the Board of Directors of the International Association for Cell Culture. Dr. McGarrity served as a member of the College of Graduate Studies Alumni Association Board of Directors from 1984 to 1990 and as its president from 1988 to 1990. In 1986 he won the College's Distinguished Alumnus Award. He was elected to the Thomas Jefferson University Board of Trustees in 1989, the first College of Graduate Studies Alumnus to hold a University Board position (Fig. 36). He has over 90 scientific publications, largely in the areas of mycoplasma, cell culture techniques and environmental mutagenesis.

David H. Much, Ph.D. (1971), completed an

Fig. 36.   Gerard J. McGarrity, Ph.D., Adjunct Professor of Microbiology and member of Jefferson's Board of Trustees.

NIH postdoctoral fellowship at New York University Medical School and then held academic positions at Princeton University, Franklin and Marshall College and Texas Wesleyan College. He became Associate Professor of Biology and Microbiology and Immunology at Muhlenberg College in Allentown, Pennsylvania. From his research, largely in the area of sexually transmitted diseases, he has published 13 articles and made nine presentations at professional meetings.

Roger P. Orcutt, Ph.D., (1972), assumed a position as Director of Quality Control at the Charles River Breeding Laboratories where he was promoted to Director of Research and Development in 1979. He served as Director of the Animal Health Diagnostic Laboratory at the National Cancer Institute's Frederick Cancer Research Facility in 1981/82. In 1978 he was requested by the National Cancer Institute to develop standard microflora for all NCI nucleus stock animals. This was subsequently adopted by major suppliers, not only for their isolator animals, but for all of their barrier-reared animals as well. Dr. Orcutt has been past president of the Association for Gnotobiotics and became an internationally recognized authority on infectious diseases in laboratory animals.

John F. Salventi, Ph.D., (1974), worked as a clinical microbiologist at Allentown and Sacred Heart Hospital Center (which later became Lehigh Valley Hospital Center) until 1981. He then served as a consulting clinical microbiologist and was promoted to Director of the Clinical Laboratories at Lehigh Valley Hospital Center in 1981. After an interval, he returned to the Allentown Hospital—Lehigh Valley Hospital Center as Vice President of Operations in 1987. His responsibilities have included operations of clinical support services, implementation of the quality improvement process and oversight of the consolidation of the Allentown Hospital and the Lehigh Valley Hospital Center.

Owen S. Weislow, Ph.D., (1971), was a postdoctoral fellow in immunology at the University of South Florida College of Medicine until 1971 and then in immuno-virology with Dr. E. Frederick Wheelock at Jefferson until 1973. He was then named an instructor in Jefferson's Department of Microbiology. In 1974 he became Associate Foundation Scientist at the Southwest Foundation for Research and Education in San Antonio. In 1976 he was named Head of the Support of Developmental Biology and Biochemistry Section at Litton Bionetics. Inc. and Program Resources, Inc. in Frederick, Maryland where he was named Head of the Technical Support Group and Monoclonal Antibody Working Group in the Biological Products Laboratory in 1984. In 1987 he was named Head of their Anti-AIDS Virus Drug Screening Laboratory. Through his current research, in the area of AIDS antiviral chemotherapy, he developed laboratory and high capacity cytoprotection assays used to screen in excess of 30,000 natural products and synthetics per year against the AIDS virus. He has published 35 papers and made numerous presentations.

Loretta F. Rocco, M.S., (1974), was Supervisor in Jefferson's School of Medical Technology from 1965 to 1968. She then served as Supervisor of the Microbiology and Immunoserology Laboratories from 1970 to 1979 at Methodist Hospital where she also served on the Infection Control Committee. In 1979 she was named a Surveyor for the Joint Commission for Accreditation of Hospitals and in 1981 she accepted the position of Infection Control Practitioner at Pennsylvania Hospital. In 1982 she returned to teaching as Medical Technology Teaching Coordinator at Hahnemann University School of Allied Health Sciences. Miss Rocco passed away in November of 1983. In her memory, her family established the Loretta Rocco Memorial Award, an annual scholarship given to outstanding students studying for the master of science degree in microbiology.

Pathology Alumni

Richard H. Conklin, M.D., Ph.D., (1970), studied at Jefferson from 1963 to 1966 and then entered medical school at Upstate Medical Center of the State University of New York where he earned his M.D. degree in 1969. Following training in pathology and infectious diseases (virology and immunology) he became Associate Professor of Pathology and Laboratory Medicine at the University of Texas Medical School, Hous-

ton. Dr. Conklin served as a consultant for water quality on the space shuttle for NASA, for the Rift Valley Fever Vaccine for the U.S. Army, and for the Marine Animal Resource Center in Seattle, Washington.

Pharmacology Alumni

Steven W. Bass, Ph.D., (1970), studied cardiovascular and pulmonary pharmacology as a postdoctoral fellow in the Department of Pharmacology at the University of Pennsylvania Medical School. He then moved to the pharmaceutical industry and held several positions which included responsibility for drug safety assessment, research and development, marketing, and legal, regulatory and scientific affairs. He served at Wyeth Laboratories, Eastman Pharmaceuticals/Sterling Drug, and later at Bristol-Myers Squibb where in 1990 he was named Director, Planning and Coordination in World Wide Regulatory Affairs. Dr. Bass has been a member of the Drug Information Association and the Regulatory Affairs Professional Society. He has also served on the Editorial Board for the *Drug Information Journal* and on the Board of Directors of the College of Graduate Studies Alumni Association.

Irving Cohen, Ph.D., (1973), accepted a postdoctoral position at New York University where he studied the biochemistry of mental disease and developed methods to quantitate enzyme activities in brain areas of animals and blood of humans. In 1975 he moved to I.C.I. Americas where he studied Pharmacokinetics/Pharmacodymanics Atenolol, H2-Receptor Antagonists and Aldose Reductase Inhibitors. In 1988 he became Clinical Scientist at DuPont Merck Pharmaceutical Company in the Medical Products Department (Fig. 37). His research has been in cardiology, hypertension and anti-arrhythmic agents.

Bruce P. Greenberg, Ph.D., (1972), from 1971 until 1973 served as Assistant Professor of Clinical Pharmacology at the University of Cincinnati College of Medicine and as a Cardiovascular Pharmacologist at the May Institute in Cincinnati. In 1973 he became Clinical Research Associate at Lederle Laboratories. He subsequently moved to American Cyanamid Company where he served in several positions, including Manager of International Drug Surveillance and Director of Scientific and Medical Services. He later accepted the position of Vice President of Clinical and Scientific Affairs at MEDED in Wilton, Connecticut. He also served as Visiting Clinical Associate Professor of Pharmacology/Toxicology at New York College of Osteopathic Medicine (Fig. 38). He has published 24 articles on his work.

Robert E. Mancini, Ph.D., D.O., (1973), went on to a D.O. degree from the Philadelphia College of Osteopathic Medicine in 1977. Following residency he was a Fellow in Clinical Pharmacology at Children's Hospital of Philadelphia. In 1980 he became Associate Professor and Chairman of Pharmacology, Toxicology and Experimental Therapeutics at New York College of Osteopathic Medicine, later advancing to Professor of Pharmacology and Toxicology (Fig. 39).

Dr. Mancini, a Fellow of the College of Physicians of Philadelphia, became a member of the National Board of Osteopathic Medical Examiners in 1983 and later served as its President. He has made over 200 educational presentations at meetings throughout the country and has authored 24 publications.

William M. Troetel, Ph.D., (1972), from 1971 to 1973 served as an instructor in pharmacology for Jefferson Medical College. In 1973 he became Division Director of Regulatory Affairs at USV/Revlon Health Care Group, later moving to the position of Senior Vice President at Oxford Research International Corporation. In this position he served as a regulatory consultant to American, European and Japanese health care companies. After a brief interval with Yamanouchi U.K. Limited, he returned to Oxford Research as Chief Executive Officer (Fig. 40). In

Fig. 37. Irving Cohen, Ph.D. Clinical Scientist at DuPont Merck Company.

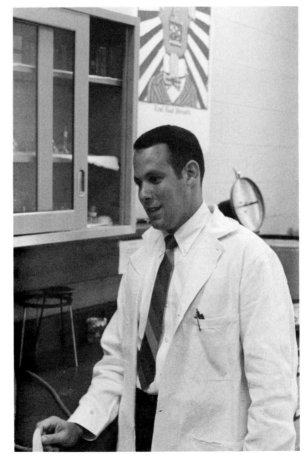

Fig. 38. Bruce P. Greenberg, Ph.D. research scientist in pharmacology/toxicology.

1989 he became Adjunct Assistant Professor at the Arnold and Marie Schwartz College of Pharmacy, Long Island University.

Physiology Alumni

William I. Forbes, III, M.D., Ph.D., (1972), received his M.D. from Jefferson in 1973. He served a general surgery residency at Abington Memorial Hospital in 1973 and then was a resident in otolaryngology at Jefferson under Dr. Lindsay Pratt until 1977. From 1978 to 1988 he was Chief of Maxillofacial Surgery at General Hospital of Saranac Lake in Saranac Lake, New York. He also served as Chief of Otolaryngology for the 1980 Winter Olympics held in Lake Placid,

New York. He has served as a consultant in otolaryngology to a number of hospitals and since 1988 he has held staff appointments in three New York hospitals.

Lewis F. McLean, Ph.D., (1974), became an Associate in clinical research at Merck Sharp & Dohme Research Laboratories where he monitored clinical drug trials. In 1981 he was promoted to Assistant Director of Clinical Neuroscience where he was involved in planning, protocol design, recruitment of investigators, and monitoring of clinical trial programs.

Preventive Medicine Alumni

Lawrence J. Mellon, M.S., M.D., (1972), had

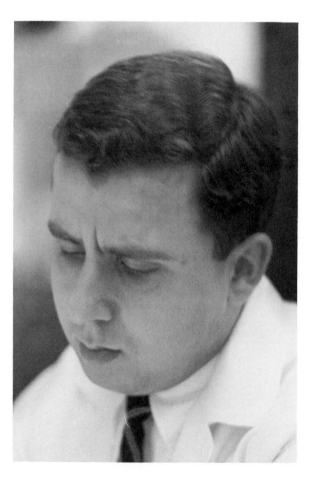

Fig. 39. Robert E. Mancini, Ph.D., D.O., Professor and Chairman of Pharmacology and Toxicology, Assistant Dean for Clinical Sciences, New York College of Osteopathic Medicine.

Fig. 40. William M. Troetel, Ph.D., Chief Executive Officer, Oxford Research International.

1970-74

earned his M.D. degree in 1959 from Jefferson. From 1966 to 1978 he was Medical Director at Boeing Vertol Company in Philadelphia. He became certified by the American Board of Preventive Medicine in Occupational Medicine in 1975. In 1978 he was named Vice President of Health, Safety and Environmental Affairs at CertainTeed Corporation in Valley Forge. He is a Fellow of the American Academy of Occupational Medicine and Past President of the Industrial Medical Association of Philadelphia. He has also served as Adjunct Clinical Assistant Professor of Preventive Medicine at Jefferson Medical College.

Leah Z. Ziskin, M.S., M.D., (1973), had earned her M.D. degree from Temple School of Medicine in 1962. In 1966 she joined the United States Air Force as an Occupational Health Officer. In 1968 she became a public health physician for the Camden City Health Department and in 1974 Chief of the Communicable Disease Program for the New Jersey State Department of Health. She continued with the Department of Health in various capacities including Acting State Commissioner of Health and then Acting Deputy Commissioner. Dr. Ziskin served as Vice-Chairperson of the 1988 Task Force which reported on Adolescent Pregnancy in New Jersey and also served on the Governor's Council on the Prevention of Mental Retardation. Through her research, mostly in the areas of preventive medicine and public health, she has authored 12 articles and made ten major addresses at national meetings.

Physics Alumni

Panayotis A. Assimakopoulos, Ph.D., (1971), was a research physicist with the Nuclear Research Centre Democritos in Athens, Greece, before coming to the United States to earn a master's degree in physics from Rutgers University. He served as a research fellow at the Bartol Research Foundation of the Franklin Institute while earning his Ph.D. at Jefferson. He then returned to Greece to serve as Senior Research Physicist at the NRC Democritos until 1977. During that time he also served as Adjunct Assistant Professor of Physics at the Chair of Nuclear Physics at the University of Ioannina, Greece. In 1977 he was named Professor of Physics. In 1983 he was promoted to Chairman of the Department of Physics, and in 1989 Director of the Division of Atomic, Molecular, Nuclear and High Energy Physics at the University. In 1984 he took a sabbatical and served as Visiting Professor of Physics in the Department of Radiology at the University of California at San Francisco School of Medicine. He has written eight books and more than 39 publications in the areas of physics and chemistry, electromagnetic measurements, nuclear physics and NMR imaging.

ALUMNI

1970 Bass, Steven W., Ph.D., Pharmacology
Callahan, Hugh J., Ph.D., Biochemistry
Conklin, Richard H., Ph.D., Pathology
Fried, Dennis A., M.S., Anatomy
Grosso, Louis S., Ph.D., Pharmacology
Hospador, Michael A., Ph.D., Pharmacology
Lee, Eun Woo, Ph.D., Pharmacology
McGarrity, Gerard J., Ph.D., Microbiology
Rubin, Benjamin D., M.S., Anatomy
Saito, Fumike U., Ph.D., Pharmacology
Summers, Alan L., Ph.D., Physiology
Weinberg, Martin, Ph.D., Physiology

1971 Assimakopoulos, Panayotis A., Ph.D., Physiology
Forbes, Barbara F., Ph.D., Anatomy
Freedburg, Paul S., M.S., Physics
Gonasun, Leonard M., Ph.D., Pharmacology

Haeffner-Gormley, Lorraine, Ph.D., Biochemistry
Hefton, John M., Ph.D., Anatomy
Lin, Yu Chen, Ph.D., Biochemistry
Smyth, Robert D., Ph.D., Biochemistry
Weislow, Owen S., Ph.D., Microbiology

1972 Abaidoo, Kodwo J., Ph.D., Physiology
Belej, Miroslaw A., Ph.D., Pharmacology
Castingnano, Dominic E., Ph.D., Physiology
Forbes, William I., III, Ph.D., Physiology
Fouts, David W., M.S., Preventive Medicine
Greenberg, Bruce P., Ph.D., Pharmacology
Hoffman, Stanley A., M.S., Physiology
Hollshwandner, Caroline H., Ph.D., Physiology
Koepke, Uwe C., Ph.D., Pharmacology
Luscombe, Susan, M.S., Microbiology

Mellon, Lawrence J., M.S., Preventive
Medicine
Much, David H., Ph.D., Microbiology
Orcutt, Roger P., Ph.D., Microbiology
Phelan, Thomas I., M.S., Anatomy
Schlesinger, Harvey R., Ph.D.,
Microbiology
Scott, Carolyn M., M.S., Anatomy
Troetel, William M., Ph.D., Pharmacology
Van Tuyle, Glenn, Ph.D. Biochemistry
Wa Kimani, Steven N., Ph.D., Physiology
Whitenack, Stephen H., Ph.D., Anatomy

1973   Borgelt, Bruce E., Ph.D., Pathology
Brownstein, Stanley S., M.S., Preventive
Medicine
Buchbinder, Dale, M.S., Anatomy
Cohen, Irving, Ph.D., Pharmacology
Dickman, Michael D., Ph.D., Microbiology
Franklin, Samuel G., Ph.D., Biochemistry
Goody, Howard E., Ph.D., Pathology
Lahita, Robert G., Ph.D., Microbiology
Lang, Armand F., Ph.D., Biochemistry
Malish, Steven L., Ph.D., Pharmacology
Mancini, Robert E., Ph.D., Pharmacology
Martin, John S., Ph.D., Physiology
Papageorgopoulos, Christos A., Ph.D.,
Physics
Scott, Samuel D., Ph.D., Physiology
Wessell, Rosalie W., Ph.D., Physiology
Wighton, Robert, Ph.D., Physiology
Ziskin, Leah Z., M.S., Preventive Medicine

1974   Adolphe, Allen B., Ph.D., Pharmacology
Blank, Frederick C., M.S., Clinical
Microbiology
Bower, John R., Ph.D., Physics

Buescher, Georganne K., M.S., Clinical
Microbiology
Cohn, Richard D., Ph.D., Pharmacology
D'Agostino, Maria A., Ph.D., Biochemistry
Dombkoski, Frank P., Ph.D., Physiology
Elkins, Marsha E., M.S., Clinical
Microbiology
Erickson, Lance, M.S., Clinical Microbiology
Feik, Diane Blechman, M.S., Clinical
Microbiology
Gadarowski, John J., Ph.D., Physiology
Greene, Charlotte H., Ph.D., Physiology
Grego, Nicholas J., Ph.D., Physiology
Hami, Dvora, Ph.D., Physiology
Kobrin, Lowell, Ph.D., Anatomy
Mackowiak, Elaine D., Ph.D.,
Pharmacology
McLean, Lewis F., Ph.D., Physiology
Murphy, Christine V., M.S., Clinical
Microbiology
Noble, Clifford, J., Ph.D., Physics
Ohashi, David K., M.S., Clinical
Microbiology
Papanicolaou, Basil G., M.S., Physics
Poupard, James A., M.S., Clinical
Microbiology
Rocco, Loretta, M.S., Clinical Microbiology
Rowan, Regina, M.S., Clinical Microbiology
Salventi, John F., Ph.D., Microbiology
Schebalin, Margarete, Ph.D., Physiology
Stipcevich, Jane E., M.S., Clinical
Microbiology
Wade, Thomas J., Ph.D., Microbiology
Weber, Paul R., Ph.D., Pharmacology
West, Norman R., Ph.D., Pharmacology

Speakers at 1990 Career Opportunities Symposium: (left to right) Martin L. Ogletree, Physiology, '78; Gloria G. Post, Pharmacology, '83; Elise A. Triano, Pharmacology, '83; and Arlene A. McLean, Physiology, '76.

After 23 years as Chairman of the Department of Pharmacology, Dr. Coon retired in 1976 and was named Professor Emeritus. The new Chairman, effective July 1, 1976 was Carmine Paul Bianchi, Ph.D. (Fig. 41). Toxicology continued as an important part of the research program, although under Dr. Bianchi's direction, the major emphasis in research became redirected toward the general areas of cell pharmacology and neuropharmacology.

Two of the Department of Physiology's support facilities were added during this period, an electronic laboratory for design and maintenance and a photographic laboratory for assistance in presentations and publications. Active recruitment resulted in the appointments of Drs. Marlys H. Gee and Anatole Besarab as assistant professors. During 1976/77, another major departmental support facility was developed, an electron microscopy suite. Further recruitment resulted in the 1976 appointments of Drs. Thomas M. Butler, John T. Flynn and Joseph R. Sherwin. In 1977, Paul S. Blum, Ph.D., was named Assis-

Fig. 41.   Carmine P. Bianchi, Ph.D., Chairman of Pharmacology (1976-86).

tant Professor. A growing research interest developed with emphasis on metabolic, hemodynamic, and pathophysiological aspects of myocardial ischemia and circulatory shock. The main focus of such activities was within the Department of Physiology, with significant additional interest in the Departments of Pharmacology, Medicine and Surgery. Collaborative research projects developed, and out of this interaction the Ischemia-Shock Research Center was established in 1977.

Among the new faculty members in the Department of Anatomy at the time were Drs. Devendra J. Kochhar and Kenneth P. Chepenik, developmental biologists who were trained in anatomy departments and were competitive at the National Institutes of Health for extramural funding. Both later rose to the rank of full Professor. Drs. Richard R. Schmidt and Robert M. Greene were also recruited at this time. Both were gross anatomists with potential for significant additional development. Dr. Greene went on to obtain a Research Career Development Award, a highly useful avenue for enhancing the growth of young faculty.

Dr. Charles Panos was appointed Professor of Microbiology in 1975. His experience in research and teaching in the area of microbial pathogenesis was needed to expand the Department's work in this area. Dr. Donald Lee Jungkind replaced Dr. Randall as Director of the Clinical Microbiology Laboratory. Dr. Clark also left Jefferson in 1977 and Catherine E. Calkins, Ph.D. was appointed to maintain the program in immunology. In 1978 Dr. Thomas MacDonald was appointed to complement Dr. Calkin's immunology program.

Anatomy Alumni

Vincent T. Armenti, M.D., Ph.D., (1979), earned his M.D. degree at Jefferson. He completed residency and fellowship training at St. Vincent's Hospital and Medical Center of New York after which he served as a Clinical Instructor in General Surgery at New York University and New York Medical College. In 1988 he returned to Jefferson as a clinical transplant fellow in renal and hepatic transplantation and Instructor in Surgery. He was then named attending surgeon on the University Surgical Service and Trauma Division. His clinical responsibilities included co-directorship of the Nutrition Support Service. He was also designated principal investigator on the National Database for Pregnancy Outcome in Transplant Recipients, which is funded by Sandoz Pharmaceuticals. Through his research, he co-authored and published six articles, nine abstracts and three book chapters.

Mildred Stoehr Christian, Ph.D., (1979), from 1967 to 1979 held various positions at McNeil Laboratories including Research Associate in Psychopharmacology, Pathology/Toxicology, Senior Scientist in Reproductive Pathology, and Group Leader in General Toxicology. In 1979 she joined Argus Research as Director of Research and was promoted to President in 1981, then named President of Argus International in 1982 (Fig. 42). She was responsible for supervision and conduct of activities performed by the company as consultants in reproductive, develop-

Fig. 42. Mildred S. Christian, Ph.D., President of Argus International.

mental and general toxicology and in quality assurance procedures to private corporations and governmental regulatory agencies. She was also named a Faculty Member of the INTOX Division Faculty in the Interdisciplinary Toxicology Graduate Program at the University of Arkansas. She has co-authored 33 papers and 41 abstracts in her field. In 1988 Dr. Christian was elected to the College of Graduate Studies Alumni Association Board of Directors and served as its Secretary.

Norman Rosenblum, Ph.D., M.D., (1975), earned his M.D. degree at Jefferson. Following residency and a fellowship in gynecologic oncology at the Hospital of the University of Pennsylvania he advanced to attending physician in 1985. He served as Clinical Assistant Professor of Obstetrics and Gynecology at the Medical College of Pennsylvania and also held appointments at Jefferson and at Temple University School of Medicine. He has been an attending physician at Lankenau Hospital and on staff at Fox Chase Cancer Center and Jeanes Hospital. A fellow of the American College of Obstetricians and Gynecologists, Dr. Rosenblum has authored 16 publications and made over 30 invited lectures in the area of gynecologic oncology.

Biochemistry Alumni

Lewis J. Klunk, Ph.D., (1976), received the Department's Paul Pinchuck Award for Outstanding Student in Biochemistry. While working toward his degree, he served as Senior Biochemist in the Biochemical Pharmacology Group at William H. Rorer, Inc. In 1976 he became Section Head in the Metabolism and Methods Development Section of the Drug Disposition Department of Revlon Health Care Research in Tuckahoe, New York. He was responsible for all aspects of pre-clinical and certain clinical drug metabolism studies carried out on novel drug molecules during their discovery and development. In 1986 Dr. Klunk moved on to Bristol-Myers Squibb Company where he served as Associate Director of Metabolism and Pharmacokinetics until 1990 when he was promoted to Director. He has co-authored 39 publications and presentations of his work.

Microbiology Alumni

Kathleen Meehan Arias, M.S., (1979), was supervisor of the microbiology laboratory at

Frankford Hospital in Philadelphia until 1980 and then was named infection control coordinator. In 1990 she became hospital epidemiologist at Hahnemann University. She received certification as a Specialist in Public Health and Medical Laboratory Microbiology from the American Academy of Microbiology in 1981 and in Infection Control from the Certification Board of Infection Control in 1984. She testified before the Pennsylvania Environmental Quality Board on the proposed Pennsylvania Infectious and Chemotherapeutic Waste Regulations and before the Occupational Safety and Health Administration on its proposed regulations on prevention of transmission of bloodborne pathogens in the workplace. As a member of the faculty at the Pennsylvania State University, she has taught infectious disease concepts to educators whose backgrounds may not be in the healthcare field. An active member of Jefferson's Clinical Microbiology Alumni Group, Mrs. Arias is also active in the American Society for Microbiology and the Association for Practitioners in Infection Control.

Walter P. Carney, Ph.D., (1978), completed a postdoctoral Research Fellowship at Massachusetts General Hospital, Harvard Medical School in 1982 and became Principal Scientist at New England Nuclear/E.I. DuPont. He was promoted to Supervisor of Oncogene Research in 1983 and then Research Associate/Supervisor of the Oncogene Research Program in 1987. He was also named Assistant Clinical Professor in the Department of Pathology at Tufts New England Medical Center in Boston in 1985. As part of a joint venture, Dr. Carney was responsible for the discovery and development of the Neu Oncogene ELISA, an immunoassay, to be utilized in evaluating human breast tissue and blood samples for the detection and quantitation of the Neu Oncogene protein. He has published 45 papers and 85 abstracts of his work.

Eugene V. Genovesi, Ph.D., (1979), was an NIH Postdoctoral Trainee in Viral Oncology in the Tumor Virus Laboratory at Duke University Medical Center and later became a Research Associate there. In 1981 he became a Resident Research Associate of the National Research Council at the U.S. Army Medical Research Institute of Infectious Diseases. He then went on to serve in various capacities at the Plum Island Animal Disease Center, including Research Microbiologist and Acting Chief of the Microbiology Laboratory. He has published 29 papers and 28 abstracts of his work. His research has involved the immunobiology and pathogenesis of host/ -virus, -tumor, and -microbial diseases, and the immunobiologic regulation of virus-encoded and cellular-encoded functions.

Thomas J. Harkins, M.S., (1979), has been employed at Southeast Regional Medical Center in Petersburg, Virginia as Chief Technologist in Microbiology. In his work, he developed a screening test for Yersinia on CIN agar.

Michael H. Levy, M.D., Ph.D., (1976), was trained in the combined M.D./Ph.D. program. During his third year he became involved with Ars Morendi, a group of health care professionals concerned with the needs and care of the dying. His interest in terminal care continued throughout his training and led to his position as a medical oncologist at Fox Chase Cancer Center (Fig. 43). He formed and directed the Center's Palliative Care Service, an inpatient consultation and home-care hospice program and was also medical director of home health services. He has served on the Board of Directors of the National Hospice Organization.

Valerie Mowrer Linter, M.S., (1978), was employed until 1981 as a clinical microbiologist at J.C. Blair Memorial Hospital. In 1981 she accepted a position as Veterinary Clinical Microbiologist at the Pennsylvania State University where she worked until 1988 when she became Adjunct Instructor in Biology at Juniata College in Huntingdon, Pennsylvania.

Barbara Sawyer Lowry, M.D., M.S., M.P.H., (1977), had previously earned her M.D. at Temple Medical School and, after Jefferson, went on to earn an M.P.H. degree at Johns Hopkins University School of Hygiene and Public Health. A Lieutenant Colonel in the United States Army Medical Corps, she worked as a Research Scientist at the U.S. Army Medical Research Institute of Infectious Diseases in the Bacteriology Division and served as its Assistant Chief from 1980 to 1985. She was a Visiting Assistant Professor of Pathology at the Medical College of Pennsylvania from 1968 to 1978 and an Instructor in Pathology at Jefferson Medical College from 1974 to 1978. She became a Consultant in Hospital Epidemiology with expertise in Infection Control, Pathology, Clinical Microbiology, Eldercare and Clinical Trials.

Jeri L. deTurck May, M.S., (1979), became a Microbiologist at Wyeth Laboratories and was promoted to Supervisor of the Microbiology Monitoring Group in Quality Assurance in 1980. In 1984 she took a position with ICI Pharmaceuticals, a division of ICI Americas, as Developmental Microbiologist in the Methods Development Services Group where she was promoted to Group Leader in 1986.

Elcinda McCrone, M.S., M.D., (1977), went on to her M.D. from Jefferson in 1983. From 1977 to 1979 she was Division Head of Microbiology at Allentown Hospital in Allentown, Pennsylvania. She was a resident in Medicine at Boston City Hospital and then served as a Clinical Fellow in the Infectious Disease Departments of Beth Israel Hospital, Brigham & Women's Hospital and Dana Farber Cancer Institute in Boston. From 1987 to 1989 she was a Research Fellow in Infectious Diseases at Beth Israel Hospital. Since 1989 she has been Assistant Professor of Medicine at Boston University School of Medicine, Staff Physician and Director of the Infection Control Unit at Boston University Hospital, and Staff Physician in the Department of Medicine at Boston City Hospital. In her positions, Dr. McCrone has been involved in several clinical drug trials.

Karin L. McGowan, M.S., (1977), **Ph.D.**, received her degree in clinical microbiology at Jefferson and went on to earn a Ph.D. in Microbiology and Immunology at Temple University in 1984. From 1984 to 1986 she served as Assistant Professor in the Department of Pediatrics at Temple Medical School and Director of the Microbiology Laboratory at St. Christopher's Hospital for Children in Philadelphia. In 1986 she was appointed Assistant Professor in the Depart-

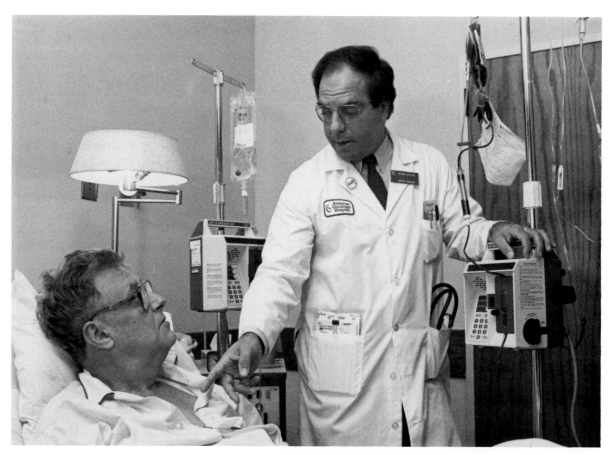

Fig. 43.   Michael H. Levy, M.D., Ph.D., medical oncologist, Fox Chase Cancer Center, and Board Member, National Hospice Organization.

1975-79

ment of Pediatrics at the University of Pennsylvania School of Medicine and Director of the Microbiology Laboratory at Children's Hospital of Philadelphia. Since 1988 Dr. McGowan has also served as a consultant in laboratory medicine at the American Research Hospital for Children in Krakow, Poland, through PROJECT HOPE. She has published 13 papers and 11 abstracts on her work in infectious diseases.

Gail Schwarz, M.S., (1979), **Ph.D.**, worked as the Supervisor of Microbiology at Frankford Hospital until 1984 when she was named Director of Infection Control at Our Lady of Lourdes Hospital in Camden, New Jersey. She earned her Ph.D. degree from the University of Pennsylvania in the area of Science Education/Infection Control in 1986. She became the Program Director at Medisys, Incorporated, an infection control consulting firm, and then in 1989 the Administrative Director of Infection Control at Cooper Hospital in Camden. In 1990 she was named Chairperson of the Camden County Rabies Task Force for the State of New Jersey Department of Health. Also in that year she was named a part-time faculty member in Jefferson's master of science program in microbiology where she presents the course in Epidemiology and Infection Control. An active member of Jefferson's Clinical Microbiology Alumni Group, she served as its president in 1981-1983.

Ostein Barnes Truitt, M.S., (1975), worked as a medical technologist at Lankenau Hospital until 1976 and then became Education Coordinator/Instructor of Medical Laboratory at Marymount College of Virginia. In 1980 she was appointed instructor of clinical microbiology in the medical technology program at the University of Maryland. In 1989 she went on to Assistant Professor in the medical laboratory technology program at Montgomery College in Takoma Park, Maryland.

Linda P. Villazon, M.S., (1978), enrolled in the Ed.D. degree program in Education Administration at Temple University. She served as Program Director of Medical Laboratory Technology at Gwynedd-Mercy College until 1985 and then as Educational Coordinator of the Allied Health Division of Manor Junior College until 1986. She was an instructor of science at Montgomery County Community College in 1989-1990 and then returned to Gwynedd-Mercy to serve as Chairperson of the Allied Health Division.

Kent J. Weinhold, M.S., Ph.D., (1979), had previously earned his master's degree in clinical microbiology from Jefferson in 1974. He served as a postdoctoral research associate in the laboratory of Dr. E.F. Wheelock at Jefferson and then went to Duke University Medical Center for continued postdoctoral training in the Division of Immunology. He remained at Duke, holding the positions of Associate in the Department of Surgery until 1982 and Assistant Medical Research Professor until 1989. He was named Project Leader of Pre-Clinical Studies on Prevention and Intervention in AIDS and Chief Retrovirologist in Duke's National Cooperative Drug Discovery Group in 1986. In 1987 he became Chief Cellular Immunologist and Chief Retrovirologist in the AIDS Treatment Evaluation Unit there and in 1989 he was named Associate Professor of Experimental Surgery at Duke University Medical Center and Director of the Cellular Immunology Program at the Duke Center for AIDS Research (Fig. 44). He was also named Co-Chairman of the Immune Based Therapies Committee of the AIDS Clinical Trial Group, Vice-Chairman of the Immunology Core Committee of the AIDS Clinical Trials Group and Chief Cellular Immunolo-

Fig. 44. Kent J. Weinhold, Ph.D., Associate Professor of Experimental Surgery and Director of Cellular Immunology Program, Duke University.

gist of the AIDS Vaccine Evaluation Group at NIAID/NIH. Dr. Weinhold has co-authored 83 publications in his areas of expertise—human retrovirology, human cellular immunology and immunotherapy.

Pharmacology Alumni

Wade H. Berrettini, M.D., Ph.D., (1979), had earned his M.D. from Jefferson Medical College in 1977. Following residency in the Department of Psychiatry and Human Behavior at Jefferson he was appointed Clinical Associate in the Biological Psychiatry Branch of the National Institutes of Mental Health. In 1982, Dr. Berrettini became Senior Surgeon/Senior Clinical Associate at the United States Public Health Service Clinical Neurogenetics Branch of the NIMH and also Adjunct Assistant Professor of Psychiatry and Human Behavior and Pharmacology at Jefferson Medical College. In addition to these positions, in 1986 he became Chief of the Outpatient Clinic in the Division of Intramural Research Programs at NIMH. His research is in the area of molecular genetics of manic-depressive illness and schizophrenia and cerebrospinal fluid studies of neuropsychiatric diseases. He has published 79 papers in his field (Fig. 66).

Eric Glasofer, Ph.D., (1975), following graduation earned an M.D. degree at Jefferson in 1978. He completed a residency in pediatrics in 1981 and then a fellowship in allergy and clinical immunology in 1983 at Jefferson. He received NIH funding for three years to study the disposition of theophylline in asthmatic children and later was in the private practice of allergy and clinical immunology (Fig. 45).

Richard D. Pinder, Ph.D., (1978), worked as a forensic toxicologist in the Office of the Medical Examiner of Philadelphia from 1973 to 1978. In 1979 he became Director of the Toxicology Laboratory in the Office of the Chief Medical Examiner for the State of Connecticut. In 1988 he was also named Forensic Laboratory Inspector for the National Laboratory Certification Program of the National Institute on Drug Abuse and in 1989 he was also named Clinical Instructor in the Department of Laboratory Medicine at the University of Connecticut Health Center.

Walter C. Prozialeck, Ph.D., (1978), com-
pleted his postdoctoral work in the Departments of Pharmacology and Anatomy at the Medical College of Pennsylvania. In 1980 he became Assistant Professor of Pharmacology at the Philadelphia College of Osteopathic Medicine where he advanced to Professor in 1989 (Fig. 46). In 1986 he was also appointed Adjunct Associate Professor of Pharmacology at the Medical College of Pennsylvania. He received the Christian R. and Mary F. Lindback Foundation Award for Distinguished Teaching in 1989. His research has been in toxicology and biochemical pharmacology. He has published 37 articles.

Sidney H. Schnoll, Ph.D., (1976), progressed to Professor of Internal Medicine and Psychiatry at the Medical College of Virginia/Virginia Commonwealth University.

Richard L. Steelman, Ph.D., (1977), held numerous positions beginning in 1954 at Smith Kline and French Laboratories as a junior phar-

Fig. 45. Eric Glasofer, Ph.D., M.D. Professor of Pharmacology at College of Osteopathic Medicine in Chicago.

macologist and worked up to Group Leader of Toxicology. He joined McNeil Pharmaceutical in 1968 as Head-Toxicology Section, was appointed Acting Director of Pathology/Toxicology in 1969 and Director of Drug Safety Evaluation until 1988. From 1988 to 1990 he was Group Director of Drug Safety Evaluation for RWJ Pharmaceutical Research Institute. In 1990 he became President of Concord Consultants, Inc. Dr. Steelman is a Diplomate of the American Board of Toxicology and has served on the Board of Governors of the American College of Toxicology. He joined the Board of Directors of the College of Graduate Studies Alumni Association in 1988 and became its president in 1990.

Physiology Alumni

Michael S. Blank, Ph.D., (1976), accepted a postdoctoral position in physiology and endocrinology at the University of Manitoba Faculty

Fig. 46.   Walter C. Prozialeck, Ph.D., Professor of Pharmacology, Philadelphia College of Osteopathic Medicine.

of Medicine in Winnipeg. In 1978 he moved on to Yerkes Regional Primate Research Center at Emory University as Assistant Research Professor and Chief of the Radioimmunoassay Laboratory and, later, Associate Research Professor. He also became Assistant Professor of Anatomy and Cell Biology at Emory School of Medicine. He received a one year sabbatical in 1983 and served as an Expert in the Section on Molecular Endocrinology, Endocrinology and Reproduction Research for the National Institute of Child Health & Human Development at the National Institutes of Health. In 1985, Dr. Blank moved on to Hazleton Biotechnologies Company as a Senior Staff Scientist and Senior Project Administrator and later Laboratory Director. In 1988 he was named Principal Scientist and Group Leader at R.W. Johnson Pharmaceutical Research Institute. His work involves the oversight of eight scientists involved in analytical method development and implementation for support of pharmacokinetic trials of organic protein therapeutic agents. As a result of his work, he has published 35 papers in his field (Fig. 47).

James E. Foley, Jr., Ph.D., (1976), completed his postdoctoral work at Tulane University School of Medicine where he studied renal pharmacology, hematopharmacology and erythropoietin. In 1977 he joined the Squibb Institute for Medical Research where his field was cardiovascular pharmacology. In April of 1989 he moved to the Squibb Corporation where he assumed the position of Director, Scientific Liaison—Japan. In October of that year he was named Director of Worldwide Licensing for Bristol-Myers Squibb Company. His office, located in Tokyo, is involved in licensing and strategic research alliances.

Patricia A. Gwirtz, Ph.D., (1978), accepted a postdoctoral position in cardiovascular physiology at the University of Oklahoma where she was named instructor of physiology in 1980. She then served for one year as a Research Assistant Professor at the Dalton Research Center and Department of Physiology at the University of Missouri. In 1982 she was named Assistant Professor in the Department of Physiology at Texas College of Osteopathic Medicine where she was promoted to Associate Professor in 1988. She has served as a reviewer for such journals as the

American Journal of Physiology, Circulation Research and *Journal of Applied Physiology*. She has also served as a grant reviewer for the Texas Affiliate of the American Heart Association, the Veterans Administration and the NIH Respiratory and Applied Physiology Study Section. Through her research, emphasizing sympathetic neural control of myocardial contractile function and coronary blood flow, she has published 31 papers and 53 abstracts.

Arlene Andrews McLean, Ph.D., (1976), began her career in 1962 at Wyeth Laboratories as a Research Assistant. In 1966 she became Junior Statistician at Merck Sharp & Dohme Research

Fig. 47. Michael S. Blank, Ph.D., research pharmaceutical scientist.

Laboratories and worked her way through numerous positions in Analytic Virus and Cell Biology Research to Senior Director of Special Projects. In 1986 she moved on to Centocor, Inc. in Malvern, Pennsylvania as Director of Biomedical Operations in the Research and Development Division. In 1987 she was advanced to Director of U.S. Regulatory Affairs and in 1988 was named Vice President. She has co-authored 60 publications.

Diane Reibel-Shinfeld, Ph.D., (1978), received postdoctoral training in the department of physiology at the Milton S. Hershey Medical Center in Hershey, Pennsylvania and at Temple University School of Medicine in the Department of Medicine, Cardiology Section. In 1981 she returned to Jefferson as a Research Associate in the Department of Physiology, where she was named Assistant Professor in 1982 and Research Associate Professor in 1988. She was the recipient of the NIH Individual National Research Award and an American Heart Association Fellowship in 1981 for her work in lipid metabolism in cardiac hypertrophy and failure. Dr. Reibel-Shinfeld has authored 26 papers and 32 abstracts.

Kenneth P. Sunnergren, M.D., Ph.D., (1979), subsequently earned his M.D. degree at Jefferson in 1983. He completed a residency at the Medical College of Virginia in 1986 and then went to the University of Texas Southwestern Medical Center in Dallas to serve as the Bugher Fellow in Molecular Cardiology. In 1990 he was named Assistant Professor of Medicine at Cooper Hospital/University Medical Center in Camden, New Jersey.

George J. Trachte, Ph.D., (1979), became Associate Professor of Pharmacology at the University of Minnesota-Duluth (Fig. 48). His work involved study of two hormones—angiotensin and thromboxane—to try to determine how they affect nerve activity. He has published over 40 articles. Dr. Trachte has also received Honorable Mention for the Basic Science Teacher of the Year at UMD School of Medicine.

1975 Dobelbower, Ralph, Ph.D., Physiology
Fernandes, Prabhavathi B., Ph.D., Microbiology
Fugo, Richard J., Ph.D., Physiology
Gilson, Barbara E., Ph.D., Anatomy
Glasofer, Eric D., Ph.D., Pharmacology
Glaudel, Ursula A., M.S., Clinical Microbiology
Koplovitz, Irwin, Ph.D., Physiology
Lewis, Sandra, M.S., Pharmacology
Lewis, Thomas L., Ph.D., Anatomy
Neilsen, Erling W., Ph.D., Physics
Rosenblum, Norman Ph.D., Anatomy
Schlesinger, Diana M., Ph.D., Anatomy
Sternberg, Arieh, Ph.D., Physiology
Temcharoen, Prasong, M.S., Microbiology
Truitt, Osteen, M.S., Clinical Microbiology
Wentzel, H. Earl, M.S., Preventive Medicine

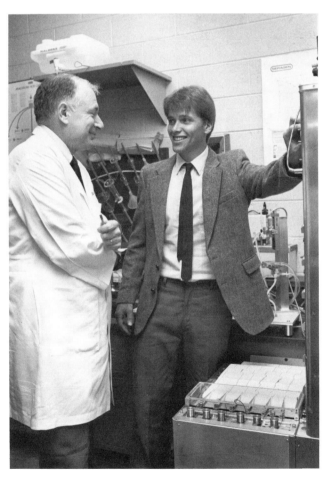

Fig. 48. George J. Trachte, Ph.D., Associate Professor of Pharmacology, University of Minnesota-Duluth with Dr. Allan M. Lefer (left).

1976 Andrews, Larry S., Ph.D., Pharmacology
Axman, Dennis J., M.S., Clinical Microbiology
Bergquist, Joanne R., M.S., Clinical Microbiology
Blank, Michael S., Ph.D., Physiology
Bridenbaugh, G. Alan, Ph.D., Physiology
Buch, Judith E., M.S., Clinical Microbiology
Foley, James E., Jr., Ph.D., Physiology
George, Wendy S., M.S., Clinical Microbiology
Hassan, Joseph R., Ph.D., Physiology
Hoops, Carol V., Ph.D., Anatomy
Klunk, Lewis K., Jr., Ph.D., Biochemistry
Lai, Chang-Hai, Ph.D., Biochemistry
Levy, Michael H., Ph.D., Microbiology
Lim, Vincente N., M.S., Clinical Microbiology
McLean, Arlene A., Ph.D., Physiology
Parrish, Christine M., M.S., Clinical Microbiology
Pottgen, Paul A., Ph.D., Pathology
Rosenberg Silverman, Bonita S., M.S., Clinical Microbiology

1977 Becker, Roger J., Ph.D., Physics
Bills, Thomas K., Ph.D., Pharmacology
Blume, Wendy M., M.S., Clinical Microbiology
Carlson, Richard P., Ph.D., Physiology
Cole, Mercedes T., M.S., Clinical Microbiology
DeMesquita, Susan, Ph.D., Physiology
East, James M., Ph.D., Anatomy
Faricelli, Jack A., M.S., Clinical Microbiology
Fow, Mark I., Ph.D., Pharmacology
Hall, Reginald, Ph.D., Pharmacology
Irwin, Maureen Hiser, M.S., Clinical Microbiology
Jenckes, George A., III, M.S., Clinical Microbiology
Lowry, Barbara Sawyer, M.S., Clinical Microbiology
McCrone, Elcinda L., M.S., Clinical Microbiology
McGowan Karin L., M.S., Clinical Microbiology
Paul, Stephen M., Ph.D., Biochemistry
Rosco, Diane L., M.S., Clinical Microbiology
Rosen, Arye, M.S., Physiology
Rudolph, Paul G., Ph.D., Physics

Schnoll, Sidney, H., Ph.D., Pharmacology
Shearman, Clyde W., Ph.D., Biochemistry
Sheretta, Annemarie D., M.S., Clinical
Microbiology
Steelman, Richard L., Ph.D., Pharmacology
Weeks, Susan A., M.S., Clinical
Microbiology
Wilson, Maria Theodos, M.S., Clinical
Microbiology
Young, Janice, M.S., Clinical Microbiology
Zdetsis, Aristides D., Ph.D., Physiology

1978   Balla, Pearl E., M.S., Clinical Microbiology
Bondi, James M., M.S., Clinical
Microbiology
Cancro, Jamie A., M.S., Clinical
Microbiology
Carney, Walter P., Ph.D., Microbiology
Colasante, Georgia, M.S., Clinical
Microbiology
Connor, Christine Carson, M.S., Clinical
Microbiology
Cowardin, Barbara Mitchell, M.S., Clinical
Microbiology
Dougherty, Thomas J., Ph.D., Microbiology
Francis, Elaine Z., Ph.D., Anatomy
Frankel, Mark S., Ph.D., Biochemistry
Glaeser, Bruce S., Ph.D., Pharmacology
Gwirtz, Patricia A., Ph.D., Physiology
Herr, Daniel L., M.S., Pharmacology
Himmelreich, Carol M.S., Clinical
Microbiology
Lintner, Valerie Mowrer, M.S., Clinical
Microbiology
Miller, Patricia A., M.S., Microbiology
Ogletree, Martin L., Ph.D., Physiology
Ostrawski, Stanley M., M.S., Clinical
Microbiology
Pinder, Richard D., Ph.D., Pharmacology
Prozialeck, Walter C., Ph.D., Pharmacology
Reibel-Shinfeld, Diane K., Ph.D.,
Physiology
Sonk, Joseph S., Ph.D., Microbiology
Tanaka, Hiroko, M.S., Clinical Microbiology
Villazon, Linda P., M.S., Clinical
Microbiology

1979   Adams, Kathleen O'Looney, M.S., Clinical
Microbiology
Armenti, Vincent T., Ph.D., Anatomy
Bentsen, Christopher, M.S., Clinical
Microbiology
Berrettini, Wade H., Ph.D., Pharmacology
Bjorensen, Jean Young, Ph.D., Anatomy
Callahan, Rosemary M., Ph.D.,
Microbiology
Christian, Mildred S., Ph.D., Anatomy
Churchill, Judy R., Ph.D., Microbiology
Earle, Roberta, M.S., Clinical Microbiology
Fitzpatrick, Jean Hirsekorn, Ph.D.,
Anatomy
Genovesi, Eugene V., Ph.D., Microbiology
Golash, Roman, G., M.S., Clinical
Microbiology
Grossman, Mark, H., Ph.D., Pharmacology
Harkins, Thomas J., M.S., Clinical
Microbiology
Hinkle, Anne M., M.S., Clinical
Microbiology
Hulkower, Christine Wier, M.S., Clinical
Microbiology
Lincoln, Marcia L., M.S., Clinical
Microbiology
Mabrouk, Fadia M., M.S., Preventive
Medicine
Meehan Arias, Kathleen, I., M.S., Clinical
Microbiology
Pashko, Steven, Ph.D., Pharmacology
Ross, Sherril, M.S., Clinical Microbiology
Sagemuehl May, Jeri L., M.S., Clinical
Microbiology
Schoemaker, Joyce, Ph.D., Microbiology
Schwartz, Ira, Ph.D., Pharmacology
Schwarz, Gail H., M.S., Clinical
Microbiology
Sunnergren, Kenneth P., M.S., Physiology
Trachte, George J., Ph.D., Physiology
Tutlane, Victoria, M.S., Clinical
Microbiology
Warnick, Michael R., M.S., Physiology
Watson Griffey, Vivi-Anne, M.S., Clinical
Microbiology
Weinhold, Kent J., Ph.D., Microbiology
Wirth, Julia J., Ph.D., Microbiology

After more than a decade of fruitful service, Dean Robert C. Baldridge resigned in 1981 to pursue his earlier interest in teaching and research. He was succeeded by Jussi J. Saukkonen, M.D. who had come to Jefferson in 1969 as Associate Professor of Microbiology, rising to full Professor in 1972. Dr. Saukkonen, a native of Finland, had an extensive background in research, teaching and editorial work which qualified him well for the Deanship (Fig. 49).

During the early 1980s, the explosion of biological knowledge of the previous two decades required further expansion of the Microbiology Department for the extensive teaching and research programs. In 1980, Joye E. Jones, Ph.D.,

Fig. 49. Jussi J. Saukkonen, Dean of the College of Graduate Studies (1981 -).

was appointed Assistant Professor to further promote the area of immunology and to renew the area of investigative parasitology. Alumnus Thomas J. Wade, Ph.D., was also named Assistant Professor. The Department had been reorganized during this period along three separate but interrelated groups: immunology, molecular genetics, and virology, with pathogenesis of infectious diseases at the molecular level.

The hybrid nature of the Department of Biochemistry was recognized formally in 1983/84 when two separate programs of graduate study were listed: Biochemical Approach to Immunology, and Molecular and Developmental Biochemistry. These graduate programs reflected also the divergent research interests of the two groups within the Department.

In 1979 the Department of Pharmacology was awarded a training grant in Industrial and Environmental Toxicology by the National Institute of Environmental Health Sciences. The purpose of this award was to provide postdoctoral training in toxicology for individuals who had previously received their Ph.D. degrees in other sciences. Ten M.S. degrees were subsequently awarded in this program between 1981 and 1986.

In April of 1980, the Ischemia-Shock Research Center of the Department of Physiology sponsored a minisymposium on shock. Stuart K. Williams, II was appointed Assistant Professor of Physiology in 1981. His research interests were in microcirculation and the role of micropinocytosis in capillary endothelium. In 1980, Dr. Joseph R. Sherwin was named coordinator of the first-year course in medical physiology. He was later named Associate Dean of the College of Graduate Studies and Director of the University Office of Research Administration.

Warren R. Lang, M.D., (Fig. 50) became Acting Chairman of the Department of Pathology in 1979, following the sudden death of Dr. Aponte. He was named the seventh Chairman and first Gonzalo E. Aponte Professor of Pathology in 1983. By 1963, Dr. Lang had risen to prominence in his specialty of Obstetrics and Gynecology, cooperating with Drs. Lewis Scheffey (JMC, '20) and Abraham Rakoff (JMC, '37) in the early development of gynecologic cytology. It surprised many of his colleagues when he decided in 1968 to make his career change to pathology.

The Faculty in the Department of Anatomy at the time included neuroscientists Drs. Leonard M. Eisenman, Daniel Goldwitz, Gerald Grunwald and Kevin S. Lee. As research programs in the individual laboratories developed momentum, it became increasingly easy to recruit additional young people to the faculty because they sought the ferment and interaction available from a group of individuals working in the related areas of developmental biology from the viewpoint of teratogenesis or of neurosciences.

Fig. 50. Warren R. Lang, M.D., Chairman of Pathology (1979-86).

Anatomy Alumni

Mindy George-Weinstein, Ph.D., (1984), was a postdoctoral fellow in the Department of Biochemistry and Biophysics at the University of Pennsylvania from 1984 to 1987 and in the Department of Microbiology until 1988. Her postdoctoral work was supported by NIH and Muscular Dystrophy Association grants. From there she became Assistant Professor of Anatomy at the Philadelphia College of Osteopathic Medicine. Dr. George-Weinstein's work again received NIH support for her research on the commitment and development of somatic myoblasts. She has published 13 papers on her work.

Thomas B. Knudsen, Ph.D., (1981), upon graduation worked as a Research Scholar in Cell Biology at the Children's Hospital Research Foundation Institute of Developmental Research in Cincinnati. In 1982 he was appointed as NIH Postdoctoral Fellow in Biology at Emory University where he advanced to Assistant Professor of Biology in 1986. He later became Assistant Professor of Anatomy at East Tennessee State University. In 1990 he returned to Jefferson as Assistant Professor of Anatomy and continued research in the area of mechanisms of abnormal embryonic development. Dr. Knudsen has been Associate Editor of *Teratology* and a Special Reviewer for Study Sections of the NIH. He has published 16 papers.

Scott A. Waldman, M.D., Ph.D., (1980), became a postdoctoral fellow at the University of Virginia in the Department of Medicine, Division of Clinical Pharmacology where his research involved purification and characterization of soluble and particulate guanylate cyclase from mammalian tissue. He continued these studies during a second postdoctoral fellowship at Stanford University. His research there was expanded and included transmembrane signalling pathways underlying stimulus-response coupling in systems sensitive to atrial natriuretic peptides. He also attended Stanford's School of Medicine, earned his M.D. degree in 1987, and served his residency in internal medicine at Stanford. In 1990, he was appointed Assistant Professor of Medicine and Pharmacology and Chief of the Laboratory for Signal Transduction Research at Jefferson. He was also named Director of Jefferson's Laboratory of Investigative Medicine and Interim Medical Director of the Clinical Research Unit. He was the recipient of the Pharmaceutical Manufacturer's Association Foundation Research Starter Grant and Faculty Development Award in Basic Pharmacology. He also served as Teaching Coordinator for the Division of Clinical Pharmacology and Coordinator for the Jefferson-French Binational Cooperative Training Program. Dr. Waldman has published nearly 100 papers, chapters, reviews and abstracts.

Biochemistry Alumni

Steven R. Per, Ph.D., (1984), served a postdoctoral position at the Wistar Institute of Anatomy and Biology where he researched the molecular cloning of human RNA polymerase genes as a means to study transcriptional control of gene expression. In 1986 he became a Postdoctoral Associate at Smith, Kline and French Laboratories in Philadelphia where he studied the biochemical mechanisms of topoisomerase enzymes and the functional relationship between gene structure, enzyme pharmacology and drug resistance. In 1988 he moved to Quality Biotech, Inc. in Camden, New Jersey as a Senior Scientist. There Dr. Per has been accountable for the management, planning and implementation of assays related to safety testing for biological products. He also designed test systems for detection of residual DNA, oncogenes and retroviruses. He has published nine papers and 13 abstracts.

Thomas H. Rushmore, Ph.D., (1983), served a postdoctoral fellowship in the Department of Pathology at the University of Toronto where he worked with Dr. Emmanuel Farber until 1987. He had received a National Research Service Award Fellowship from the NIH for the term of 1985 to 1987. He was then awarded a second postdoctoral fellowship at Merck Sharp and Dohme Research Laboratories which he held until 1991 when he accepted the position of Senior Research Molecular Biologist at Merck Frosst Center for Therapeutic Research in Kirkland, Quebec. His research interests included mechanisms of carcinogenesis, carcinogenesis and gene regulation, interaction of carcinogens and activated xenobiotics with RNA and DNA, mechanisms of cell death, and benzene metabolism and

toxicity. He has co-authored 25 publications and 24 abstracts.

Robert L. Siegel, Ph.D., (1982), was the winner of the Paul Pinchuk Award for Outstanding Biochemistry Student. He served as an instructor in biochemistry at LaSalle University until 1982 when he became Research Chemist at E.I. DuPont de Nemours & Company, where he had research and development responsibilities for fluorochemical and antimicrobial based fiber products. He was promoted to Patent Specialist in 1986 and was named Group Leader in the Patent Division in 1989. Later that year he became Manager of the Organizational Development Group and Technical Group Manager in the Pioneering Research Laboratory with responsibility for the synthetic polymer R&D group involved in development of new synthetic polymers. Dr. Siegel served as Secretary of the College of Graduate Studies Alumni Association Board of Directors from 1984 to 1989 (Fig. 51).

Microbiology Alumni

Jerome G. Buescher, Ph.D., (1981), was appointed Instructor in the Department of Medical Technology at Jefferson's College of Allied Health Sciences in 1980 and advanced to Assistant Professor in 1982. After the Department was merged in 1987 he was named Assistant Professor in the Department of Laboratory Sciences and Assistant Program Director in medical technology. He was later named Acting Program Director. Since 1984, he has lectured on TOGA, Bunyamwera, and Arena Viruses and on Spirochetes in Jefferson's Department of Microbiology. He has also served as a Portfolio Assessor since 1984 for Thomas A. Edison State College in Trenton, New Jersey. He was Consulting Editor for *Clinical Laboratory Science* in 1989 and was named Coordinating Editor of the *Microbiology in Practice* section of that publication in 1990. His research, since 1987, on borderline semisynthetic penicillin resistance and on methicillin resistance has been conducted in the Department of Medicine, Division of Infectious Diseases at Jefferson (Fig. 52).

Susan Croushore, M.S., M.B.A., (1982), served as the Laboratory Manager at Metropolitan Hospital in Philadelphia from 1982 to 1986. In 1983 she earned a master's degree in business administration from LaSalle University and in 1986 moved to Hahnemann University Hospital where she served as Laboratory Administrator until 1989. In 1989 she became Assistant Vice President-Ancillary Services at the Medical College of Pennsylvania Hospital. Ms. Croushore, an active member of Jefferson's Clinical Microbiology Alumni Group, was elected to the Board of Directors of the College of Graduate Studies Alumni Association in 1990.

Marilyn Chesler Hailperin, M.S., (1980), served as Supervisor of the Microbiology Laboratory at the Hospital of the University of Pennsylvania until 1981 when she joined Shared Medical Systems and held multiple positions, progressing to Manager of the Systems Analysis Department. In 1988 she became Assistant Vice President for Management Information Systems at West Jersey Health System where she has been responsible for strategic planning.

Bernardine Basquil Maloney, M.S., (1981), worked as a Senior Technologist at the Lahey Clinic from 1980 to 1984. From there she went on to the University of California at San Diego Medical Center where she has been a Clinical Microbiology Technologist Specialist since 1984.

Mark T. LaRocco, Ph.D., (1984), went on to a postdoctoral position at the University of Texas Medical School/Baylor College of Medicine in Medical Laboratory and Public Health Microbiology. In 1986 he became Assistant Professor of Pathology and Laboratory Medicine at the University of Texas Medical School. In 1989 he was appointed Section Chief of the Clinical Microbiology Laboratory at Hermann Hospital. He has published 26 abstracts and 30 articles.

Fig. 51. Robert L. Siegel, Ph.D. DuPont research chemist and member of CGS Alumni Association Board of Directors.

Fig. 52. Jerome G. Buescher, Ph.D. conducted research on antibiotic resistance.

1980-84

Mark A. Marsili, M.D., Ph.D., (1981), following a postdoctoral fellowship at New York University Medical Center, earned his M.D. degree at Jefferson in 1988. After a one-year internship at Jefferson, in 1989 he began a residency in dermatology at the University of Texas Southwestern Medical Center at Dallas. His clinical interests have been in cutaneous laser surgery and general dermatology. He has published eight papers and five abstracts.

Rita L. Rhoads, M.S., (1980), was employed in the clinical laboratory of Allentown Hospital until 1982 and then at Bionics, Inc. and Cooper Biomedical, two biotechnology companies, until 1986. Since then she has served as a Senior Clinical Research Associate at McNeil Consumer Products Company where she has conducted clinical studies for new and marketed products and for FDA approvals.

Karen Plummer Sawyer, M.S., (1982), worked in clinical microbiology at Crozer-Chester Medical Center in Chester, Pennsylvania. In 1985 she assumed the position of Technical Supervisor of Microbiology in the Department of Pathology and Laboratory Medicine at the Hospital of the University of Pennsylvania. An active member of Jefferson's Clinical Microbiology Alumni Group, she was elected its President in 1990.

Keith H. St. John, M.S., (1984), served as Director of Infection Control and Clinical Microbiologist at the Alfred I. DuPont Institute in Wilmington, Delaware. While there he also coordinated the conference *Pediatric Infections: Perspectives 1989* and then again in *1990*. He also developed a student affiliate program at A.I. DuPont for master's graduate students at Jefferson. He then transferred to Sacred Heart Medical Center in Chester, Pennsylvania, as Director of Infection Control and Employee Health. An active member of Jefferson's Clinical Microbiology Alumni Group, Mr. St. John served as its president from 1986 to 1988 and was appointed to the College of Graduate Studies Alumni Association Board of Directors in 1987.

Richard B. Thomson, Jr., Ph.D. (1981), served a postdoctoral year in Clinical Microbiology and Public Health at the Mayo Clinic in Rochester, Minnesota. In 1982 he was named Director of Clinical Virology at Children's Hospital Medical Center and Director of Clinical Microbiology at Akron City Hospital in Akron, Ohio. He subsequently became Director of Microbiology and Virology at Evanston Hospital in Evanston, Illinois. From 1983 he served as Associate Professor of Clinical Microbiology in Pathology and also, from 1984, Associate Professor of Microbiology/Immunology at Northeastern Ohio Universities College of Medicine. He served on the American Academy of Microbiology Committee on Postdoctoral Educational Programs from 1988 and was editor of the microbiology section of the *American Society of Clinical Pathologist Tech Sample* from 1989. He has published 24 articles and made over 40 scientific presentations.

Karen Fisher Tyszka, M.S., (1983), while a student, received the Jane Stepcevitch Award for Research in Clinical Microbiology. Since 1982, she has been the Department Head of the Clinical Microbiology Laboratory at Atlantic City Medical Center.

Pathology Alumni

William J. Adams, Jr., Ph.D., (1980), also earned his M.S. degree in toxicology in 1981. He held the position of Assistant Professor of Toxicology at the Philadelphia College of Pharmacy and Science from 1981 to 1986. In 1983, he joined the U.S. Army Reserve as a Captain in the Medical Service Corps and in 1986 entered Officer Indoctrination School at the Naval Education and Training Command in Newport, Rhode Island. Dr. Adams served as a Research Biochemist in the Radioprotection Division at the Armed Forces Radiobiology Research Institute from 1986 to 1989. In 1989 he was named Lieutenant Commander and Radiation Health Officer aboard the U.S.S. Fulton AS-11, an auxillary submarine tender.

Pharmacology Alumni

Nancy J. Lawrie Esterline, M.S., (1983), became a Laboratory Technician at the University of Medicine and Dentistry of New Jersey/Robert Wood Johnson Medical School in 1983 and was promoted to Research/Teaching Specialist in 1984. In 1987 she became Senior Research Pharmacologist at Nova Pharmaceutical Corporation in Baltimore and was promoted to Project Manager in 1988. In 1989 she accepted the position of Associate Scientist at Rhone-Poulenc Rorer. She has co-authored three publications and nine abstracts.

Kathryn Hill DeTurck, Ph.D., (1983), V.M.D., served a postdoctoral position at Rutgers University Center of Alcohol Studies where she studied short and long term effects of ethanol on rats' behavior and cardiac enzymes. Through this work she published ten papers and two abstracts. She then received her V.M.D. degree from the University of Pennsylvania School of Veterinary Medicine in 1989. In 1990, Dr. DeTurck became Senior Staff Veterinarian and Assistant Professor at the University of Medicine and Dentistry of New Jersey/Robert Wood Johnson Medical School (Fig. 53). Her area of research has been in animal models of human disease and comparative laboratory animal medicine.

Kim D. Lamon, M.D., Ph.D., (1980), went on to his M.D. degree from Jefferson in 1981. He received postdoctoral training in biochemical pharmacology at Jefferson in 1979/80 and then served an internal medicine internship at Jefferson until 1982. He then joined William H. Rorer Company as Assistant Director of Clinical Research and advanced to Director in 1985. After a company merger, he was appointed Director of Clinical Research at Rorer Central Research. In 1987 he was named Vice President of Medical Affairs and his responsibilities included worldwide clinical research and development programs for all investigated drugs. After another company merger, he was named Senior Vice President of Clinical Research and Regulatory Affairs at Rhone-Poulenc-Rorer Central Research

Fig. 53. Kathryn H. DeTurck, Ph.D., V.M.D., Senior Staff Veterinarian and Assistant Professor, University of Medicine and Dentistry, New Jersey.

Fig. 54. Kim D. Lamon, M.D., Ph.D., Senior Vice President of Clinical Research, Rhone-Poulenc-Rorer.

1980-84

in 1990 (Fig. 54). Since 1989 he also served as Adjunct Assistant Professor of Pharmacology at Jefferson. He has co-authored 23 publications, mainly in the area of drug effects.

Stephen L. Longacre, Ph.D., (1980), served in a postdoctoral position in Biochemical Toxicology in the Department of Pharmacology at the Medical University of South Carolina. In 1982 he was appointed Study Director of Biochemical Toxicology in the Toxicology Department of Rohm and Haas Company in Spring House, Pennsylvania. In 1985 he was promoted to Group Leader of that area where he coordinated the overall scientific and administrative activities of the group. In 1989, Dr. Longacre was promoted to Toxicology Program Manager at Rohm and Haas, where he has been responsible for programs in developmental and commercial products, risk assessments, and corporate toxicology issues. He has co-authored 16 papers and five abstracts.

David Sammett, Ph.D., (1982), was a postdoctoral fellow in the Department of Pediatrics at New York Hospital of Cornell Medical Center until 1983 and then in the Department of Medicine at Columbia University College of Physicians and Surgeons until 1985. Following these experiences he went on to Mount Sinai School of Medicine where he earned his M.D. degree in 1989. He has co-authored six papers and three abstracts.

Joel E. Shaffer, Ph.D., (1980), has served as Head of the Department of Drug Evaluation at Glaxo Incorporated in Research Triangle Park, North Carolina.

John C. Shryock, Ph.D., (1982), served postdoctoral fellowships at the University of Virginia where he studied cultured endothelial cell adenosine metabolism. In 1988 he accepted a position as Research Scientist at the University of Florida in Gainesville. His studies there focused on cardiac actions of adenosine.

Toni L. Stanton, Ph.D., (1981), began her career as a nurse and then received a bachelor's degree in zoology and a master's degree in physiology before coming to Jefferson. She accepted a postdoctoral position at the Alfred I. DuPont Institute as a Research Assistant until 1982 and then as a Research Neuroscientist until 1986. She also served as an Associate Scientist at the School of Life and Health Sciences at the University of Delaware until 1985 and Associate Professor of Nursing at the College of Nursing. In 1986 she received the Excellence in Teaching Award at the University of Delaware. In 1987 she became Associate Professor of Anatomy and Physiology and Women's Studies at California State University at Long Beach (Fig. 55). Her research is in the area of CNS mechanisms involved in the control of brain arousal level; physiological, biochemical and behavioral aspects of TRH action in mammalian CNS and melatonin action in the mammalian CNS. She has published 20 papers and 16 abstracts.

Theodore J. Taylor, Ph.D., (1981), received his master's degree in toxicology from Jefferson in 1976. He was the state of North Carolina's first government environmental toxicologist and a proponent of environmental protection (Fig. 56). In 1983 he confirmed that conversion of peat to methanol had the potential to produce methyl-

Fig. 55. Toni L. Stanton, Ph.D. Associate Professor of Anatomy and Physiology, California State University (Long Beach).

mercury, a highly neurotoxic chemical causally associated with birth defects. His findings stopped a private company from mining and processing peat in eastern North Carolina. In his position, he also undertook the task of risk assessment and risk communication related to exposure to toxic chemicals. He evaluated risks associated with hundreds of chemical contamination problems in North Carolina including leaking underground storage tanks, drinking water supplies contaminated with heavy metals, pesticides and organic chemicals, abandoned waste sites and municipal toxic landfills. Dr. Taylor also catalyzed the formation of the Air Toxics Panel of the State Academy of Sciences and provided valuable input for the panel's derivation of acceptable levels from approximately 100 previously unregulated toxic air pollutants. Dr. Taylor died in April of 1990 of a rare form of liver cancer.

Elise Ann Triano, Ph.D., (1983), completed her postdoctoral work as an Instructor in the Department of Neurosurgery at Jefferson. In September 1984, she accepted a position as Assistant Professor of Biology at Gettysburg College. In 1985 she became Assistant Professor of Biology at West Chester University where she was promoted to the rank of Associate Professor in 1990 (Fig. 57). She also served as Visiting Assistant Professor of Pharmacology at the Pennsylvania College of Optometry from 1986 to 1989. Dr. Triano has published nine articles. Her subsequent studies involved membrane abnormalities that cause predisposition to alcoholism.

Carol M. Ingerman Wojenski, Ph.D., (1981), served her postdoctoral studies at the Cardeza Foundation for Hematologic Research at Jefferson where she was also an Instructor in the Department of Pharmacology. In 1985 she was promoted to Assistant Professor. Dr. Wojenski has co-authored 37 articles and 15 book chapters

Fig. 56. Theodore J. Taylor, Ph.D., environmental toxicologist for State of North Carolina.

Fig. 57. Elise A. Triano, Ph.D., Associate Professor of Biology, West Chester University.

1980-84

and review articles. Her research, in collaboration with Paul K. Schick, M.D., was in the area of fatty acid uptake, synthesis and metabolism in guinea pig megakaryocytes at different stages of maturation, with emphasis on the effect of dietary fatty acids on megakaryocyte and platelet phospholipid composition and adenine nucleotide synthesis and development of dense bodies in megakaryocytes at different stages of maturation. In 1987, she was elected to the College of Graduate Studies Alumni Association Board of Directors where she later served as Treasurer.

Physiology Alumni

Sandra E. Burke, Ph.D., (1983), was the winner of the Alumni Research Award for the best doctoral dissertation (Fig. 58). She served a post-doctoral fellowship at the Robert Wood Johnson Cardiovascular Research Institute at the Deborah Heart and Lung Center. In 1984 she became a Senior Scientist at Warner-Lambert Company. While supervising three associate scientists, they

conducted hemodynamic evaluation of cardiotonic agents, the cardiovascular risk assessment of lead compounds and special studies in myocardial infarct models. In 1987 she was named Senior Research Pharmacologist at Abbott Laboratories where she has been responsible for all in vivo studies on thrombolytic agents. In addition, her staff has studied platelet function and myocardial infarct size after coronary artery occlusion and reperfusion. Dr. Burke has served as a lecturer on antithrombotic/thrombolytic agents at the University of Illinois at Rockford and on the Council on Thrombosis for the American Heart Association. She has published 25 papers and 19 abstracts.

Edward F. Smith, III, Ph.D., (1981), won the Alumni Research Award in 1981 and was a finalist in the Council of Graduate Schools University Microfilms International Award. Upon graduation, he was also awarded a Humboldt Research Fellowship of the Alexander von Humboldt Foundation in Bonn, West Germany, and stud-

Fig. 58. Sandra E. Burke, Ph.D. receives Alumni Research Award for best doctoral dissertation from Dean Saukkonen (1983).

ied at the Institute of Pharmacology at the University of Cologne, West Germany, until 1983. Upon his return to the United States, Dr. Smith became postdoctoral fellow at the Medical University of South Carolina in the Departments of Physiology and Pharmacology. In 1984 he became a Senior Scientist in Cardiopulmonary Research at Ciba-Geigy Pharmaceuticals where he was promoted to Senior Research Scientist in 1985. In 1986 he was appointed Senior Investigator in Cardiovascular Pharmacology at Smith, Kline and French Laboratories. He was promoted to Assistant Director of Cardiovascular Pharmacology in 1988. Since 1989 he has also served as a Lecturer in Medical Physiology at Jefferson and on the Board of Directors of the Graduate School Alumni Association. He has published 60 abstracts and 86 papers.

Chen-Tung Yen, Ph.D., (1982), was a Guest Researcher in the Department of Physiology at the University of North Carolina at Chapel Hill, studying intracellular staining of raphe-spinal neurons. He then took the position as Research Associate at Washington University School of Medicine in the Department of Neurosurgery. In 1983 he was appointed Visiting Associate Professor in the Department of Zoology at National Taiwan University, where he advanced to Professor in 1990. He was named an NIH Fogarty Fellow in 1988 and spent one year studying the spinothalamic input to the thalamus at the University of California, California College of Medicine in the Department of Anatomy and Neurobiology. Through his research, largely in the area of neurophysiology, he has published 16 papers and 19 abstracts.

Ira Mills, Ph.D., (1981), was a postdoctoral trainee at Brown University from 1981 to 1985 and then a postdoctoral fellow at Brigham and Women's Hospital at Harvard Medical School. He was appointed Assistant Professor of Medicine at Rhode Island Hospital-Brown University in 1987, and later he became Associate Research Scientist at Yale University School of Medicine in the Division of Vascular Surgery. Through his research, most recently in the area of coronary artery vascular smooth muscle, he has published 18 papers and 15 abstracts.

ALUMNI

1980   Adams, William J., Jr., M.S., Pathology
        Cerwinka, Paul L., M.S., Clinical Microbiology
        DiGiovanni Barnshaw, Margaret L., M.S., Clinical Microbiology
        Faone-Harhay, Fiorina, M.S., Clinical Microbiology
        Fischman, Gary J., M.S., Pathology
        Gerber, Joseph C., III, Ph.D., Pharmacology
        Gorsen, Robert M., M.S., Pharmacology
        Haenick, David H., Ph.D., Pharmacology
        Hailperin, Marilyn C., M.S., Clinical Microbiology
        Lamon, Kim D., Ph.D., Pharmacology
        Lebman, Deborah A., M.S., Microbiology
        Longacre, Stephen L., Ph.D., Pharmacology
        Machuga, Stephen J., M.S., Clinical Microbiology
        McGregor Stong, Anne, M.S., Microbiology
        Metz, Jeffrey A., M.S., Pathology
        Moyer, Robert A., M.S., Clinical Microbiology
        Paynton, Barbara V., Ph.D., Anatomy
        Pentella, Michael A., M.S., Clinical Microbiology

        Provencher, Robert A., M.S., Clinical Microbiology
        Rhoads, Rita L., M.S., Clinical Microbiology
        Robison, Steven H., Ph.D., Pathology
        Ruane, Mildred V., M.S., Clinical Microbiology
        Shaffer, Joel E., Ph.D., Pharmacology
        Siegl, Adelaide M., Ph.D., Pharmacology
        Swanson, John W., Ph.D., Physiology
        Waldman, Scott A., Ph.D., Anatomy
        Watts, Linda L., M.S., Clinical Microbiology
        Weidmann Landin, Cecilia, M.S., Clinical Microbiology

1981   Basquil, Bernadine, M.S., Clinical Microbiology
        Buescher, Jerome G., Ph.D., Microbiology
        Cooper, Keith R., M.S., Toxicology
        Fauver, Patricia A., M.S., Clinical Microbiology
        Heltzel, Joann M., Ph.D., Pharmacology
        Ingerman Wojenski, Carol M., Ph.D., Pharmacology
        Knudsen, Thomas B., Ph.D., Anatomy

Kohl, M. Pauline, M.S., Clinical
    Microbiology
LaVelle, James M., M.S., Toxicology
Levich, Judith P., Ph.D., Microbiology
Lorr, Nancy A., M.S., Toxicology
Marsili, Mark A., Ph.D., Microbiology
Master, Ronald N., M.S., Clinical
    Microbiology
McCarthy, William V., M.S., Clinical
    Microbiology
Palombo, Sandra S., M.S., Clinical
    Microbiology
Smith, Edward F., III, Ph.D., Physiology
Taylor, Theodore J., Ph.D., Pharmacology
Thomson, Richard B., Jr., Ph.D.,
    Microbiology
Williams, David O., III, Ph.D., Physiology
Wright, Marguerite L., M.S., Clinical
    Microbiology

1982   Aharony, David, Ph.D., Pharmacology
Barsotti, Robert J., Ph.D., Physiology
Bashore, Marion M., M.S., Clinical
    Microbiology
Beckman Stanton, Toni L., Ph.D.,
    Pharmacology
Bossard Hoffert, Margaret, M.S., Clinical
    Microbiology
Child, Jeffrey, M.S., Clinical Microbiology
Chisom, Josephine, M.S., Clinical
    Microbiology
Croushore, Susan, M.S., Clinical
    Microbiology
Curtis, Mark T., Ph.D., Physiology
Dashow, Larry J., Ph.D., Anatomy
Eberly, Virginia S., M.S., Clinical
    Microbiology
Ebersole, Lonnie L., M.S., Clinical
    Microbiology
Goldschmidt, Joseph C., Jr., Ph.D.,
    Microbiology
Kroft, Charlotte, M.S., Clinical Microbiology
McDonough, Pauline M., M.S., Clinical
    Microbiology
Mills, Ira, Ph.D., Physiology
Osbahr, Carol, M.S., Clinical Microbiology
Plummer Sawyer, Karen M., M.S., Clinical
    Microbiology
Sammett, David, Ph.D., Pharmacology
Shryock, John C., Ph.D., Pharmacology
Siegel, Robert L., Ph.D., Biochemistry

Sredy, Janet, Ph.D., Microbiology
Sternberg, Edmund, M.S., Biochemistry
Theis, Deborah S., M.S., Clinical
    Microbiology
Weiss, Stephen A., M.S., Pharmacology
Yen, Chen-Tung, Ph.D., Physiology

1983   Burke, Sandra E., Ph.D., Physiology
Chiger, Judith L., Ph.D., Pharmacology
Clark DeMeis, Anne F., M.S., Clinical
    Microbiology
DeTurck, Kathryn Hill, Ph.D.,
    Pharmacology
Ellis, John S., Ph.D., Biochemistry
Fisher, Karen A., M.S., Clinical
    Microbiology
Goldman, Patricia R., M.S., Pharmacology
Ho, Wenshe, Ph.D., Anatomy
Ingenito, Gary O., Ph.D., Microbiology
Krieger, Jeffrey I., Ph.D., Biochemistry
Lawrie Esterline, Nancy J., M.S.,
    Pharmacology
Leibowitz, Robert, M.S., Clinical
    Microbiology
Ling, Henry T., Ph.D., Microbiology
Post, Gloria B., Ph.D., Pharmacology
Renzi, Alfred A., Jr., M.S., Microbiology
Rushmore, Thomas H., Ph.D., Biochemistry
Triano, Elise A., Ph.D., Pharmacology

1984   Bell, Marilyn R., M.S., Clinical Microbiology
Boreas, Rosann, M.S., Clinical Microbiology
Brandt, Mary E., Ph.D., Clinical
    Microbiology
Fusco, Joanne Damiani, M.S., Clinical
    Microbiology
George-Weinstein, Mindy E., Ph.D.,
    Anatomy
Gray, Mark S., Ph.D., Pathology
Havill, Andrew M., Ph.D., Physiology
LaRocco, Mark T., Ph.D., Microbiology
Moore, Jonni S., Ph.D., Microbiology
Per, Steven R., Ph.D., Biochemistry
Roth, David, Ph.D., Physiology
Shannahan, Barbara E., M.S., Clinical
    Microbiology
Simpson, Janell Broussard, M.S., Toxicology
St. John, Keith H., M.S., Clinical
    Microbiology
Tsay, Bee-Lin, Ph.D., Biochemistry
Vollberg, Thomas, Ph.D., Pathology

The College of Graduate Studies celebrated the 20th anniversary of its establishment and the 40th anniversary of graduate education at Jefferson on May 4, 1990, at its annual Alumni Day dinner. It was also the tenth anniversary of the Alumni Association. As part of the celebration, the College hosted a symposium, *Graduate Education and Research in the 1990's*, at which Anthony Demsey, Ph.D., associate director for referral and review in the NIH Division of Research Grants, and Jules B. LaPidus, Ph.D., president of the Council of Graduate Schools, were the featured speakers. At the Alumni Dinner later in the evening, the first-ever College of Graduate Studies Medals were awarded by Dean Jussi J. Saukkonen to Robert Baldridge, Ph.D., the College's first dean, R. William Manthei, Ph.D., retired professor of pharmacology, and Andrew Ramsay, Ph.D., former chairman and emeritus professor of anatomy. Also, Lewis W. Bluemle, M.D., President of Thomas Jefferson University, was awarded Honorary Life Membership in the CGS Alumni Association for his "outstanding contributions and continuing support of graduate education at Thomas Jefferson University."

Through an interdisciplinary program, the Department of Anatomy faculty took the leadership and was awarded both a pre- and post-doctoral training grant in developmental biology-teratology by the Child Health and Human Development section of the National Institutes of Health. This is the only grant of this type by the NIH and is now a degree-granting program. The first pre-doctoral student studying for the Ph.D. degree in Developmental Biology-Teratology started shortly before funding for the program began on October 1, 1986. The Department had the largest, best trained group of investigators in the country studying questions dealing with abnormal development, from pre-implantation biology to post-natal behavioral deficits and all areas in between.

On July 1, 1985, Dr. Maurer resigned as Chairman of the Department of Biochemistry and Dr. Robert C. Baldridge was appointed Acting Chairman. Dr. Baldridge had been appointed Profes-

sor of Biochemistry and Dean of the Graduate College in 1970, serving as Dean until 1981. Dr. Baldridge's major research interest centered on amino acid metabolism, particularly in genetic disorders such as histidinemia. On July 22, 1985, Darwin J. Prockop, M.D., Ph.D. (Fig. 59) was appointed Chairman and also named Director of the newly formed Jefferson Institute of Molecular Medicine. Dr. Prockop's major research centered on the metabolism of collagen and other constituents of connective tissue. The Institute's research drew on the newly-developed technology of recombinant DNA (gene splicing) with a goal of eliminating genetic diseases or altering

Fig. 59. Darwin J. Prockop, M.D., Ph.D., Chairman of Biochemistry and Molecular Biology, and Director of Jefferson's Institute of Molecular Medicine (1986-   ).

their course. In June of 1986, the Department sponsored a three-day conference, *Molecular Biology and Pathology of Matrix*, which attracted 176 of the most eminent scientists from around the world.

The Department of Pathology was renamed the Department of Pathology and Cell Biology when Emanuel Rubin, M.D. (Fig. 60), was named its Chairman in 1986, succeeding Dr. Lang. He is one of the world's leading experts on alcohol-induced diseases. The change in name of the Department reflected Rubin's belief that the boundaries between traditional pathology and biochemistry, cell physiology, and molecular pharmacology are disappearing - in the research laboratory at the moment but in routine practice in the near future. Dr. Rubin brought to Jefferson a staff of 54, including five pathologists, eight investigators with Ph.D.s, and more than $3.5 million per year in research grants.

In 1986 Dr. Bianchi resigned as Chairman of Pharmacology and remained as Professor to pursue his research interests more actively. Dr. Wolfgang H. Vogel, Professor of Pharmacology, then was named Acting Chairman of the Department. Dr. Vogel's primary research and teaching interests have been in the areas of psycho- and neuropharmacology. Graduate training leading to the Ph.D. degree in pharmacology has been a major and continuous program of the Department since its official inception in 1949. The Department takes pride in its achievements in this respect. It is interesting to note that of the 343 Ph.D. degrees awarded at Jefferson commencements through 1990, there were 101 Ph.D.s in Pharmacology.

In 1985, the Department of Physiology received a five-year predoctoral training grant from the National Heart, Lung and Blood Institute to study cardiovascular regulation and performance. The funds supported three students each year. The Department continued its success in attracting quality international visitors and in the participation of staff members in international meetings and symposia, giving scientists all over the world exposure to the work being done at Jefferson. The Department was also active in forging joint ventures, both with outside institutions and other Jefferson departments. Within Jefferson, fruitful collaborations existed with the Department of Medicine (divisions of cardiology, pulmonary diseases, clinical pharmacology, and toxicology),

Surgery, Anesthesia, Pathology, Radiology and Anatomy. Marion J. Siegman, Ph.D., professor of physiology, received the Burlington Northern Foundation Faculty Achievement Award for excellence in teaching in 1986 and Thomas Butler, Ph.D., professor of physiology, received the award in 1988.

Robert Grafstrom, Ph.D., was appointed Assistant Professor in the Department of Microbiology in 1985 to head the DNA laboratory and develop the area of molecular genetics. Other recent appointees included Richard Peluso, Ph.D., a virologist engaged with replication of the RNA genome of the vesicular stomatitis virus, and Timothy Block, Ph.D., who studied Marek's Disease virus genes and the molecular details of the killing of cells by the Herpes virus. In 1987 Dr. Robert Korngold, a specialist in graft-versus-host disease problems, was appointed Associate Professor.

The master of science in nursing program was begun in 1987 in cooperation with the Department of Baccalaureate Nursing in Jefferson's College of Allied Health Sciences. After a comprehensive assessment uncovered a critical need for more highly educated nurses in four areas—adult rehabilitation, pediatric rehabilitation, critical care/trauma and home health care—four tracks of study were designed. Each track is specifically geared toward implementing and evaluating intervention based on conceptual models, utilizing relevant theories and technologies, improving the

Fig. 60. Emanuel Rubin, M.D., Chairman of Pathology and Cell Biology (1986-).

delivery of health care, evaluating the changing roles and responsibilities of health care providers, and developing leaders who will ultimately influence health care policy and the health care system.

A master's degree program in occupational therapy was also begun in 1987 in conjunction with the College of Allied Health Sciences's Department of Occupational Therapy. The program was established in response to the profession's encouragement of therapists to have more advanced degrees. Students in the program may study in depth the problems they have identified in clinical practice, or gear their program toward occupational therapy research or management.

A unique program for so-called Gibbon scholars was initiated in 1985 in which students could enter directly into a combined M.D./Ph.D. program under the joint auspices of the Medical College and the College of Graduate Studies. The first year was spent in the College of Graduate Studies, and then in a total of six or seven years a goal in clinical and research work could be pursued. A somewhat similar course in which the first two years were spent in the Medical School and then followed in combined M.D./Ph.D. work had been in progress since 1970 and was renamed Dunglison in 1985. Gibbon and Dunglison Scholars were aided financially by stipends and fellowships. By 1990, twenty-five such students had participated in the combined programs.

Anatomy Alumni

Charles B. Hathaway, Ph.D., (1990), after completing his studies in August of 1989, accepted a postdoctoral position at the University of North Carolina at Chapel Hill. There he studied the monoaminergic control of development in the tobacco hornworm. He later took a position as a Research Assistant at the Bowman Gray School of Medicine of Wake Forest University. His work, in the Department of Medicine/Endocrinology, involves reverse cholesterol transport.

Pierette M. Shipman-Appasamy, Ph.D., (1987), studied in the interdepartmental Developmental Biology program. She did her postdoctoral work in the laboratory of Michael B. Prystowsky, M.D., Ph.D. in the Department of Pathology and Laboratory Medicine at the University of Pennsylvania where she studied the Regulation of T-Lymphocyte Proliferation and Differentiation. She

became an Instructor at the Pittsburgh Cancer Institute/University of Pittsburgh, Department of Pathology. Her work was funded by the National Leukemia Association.

Biochemistry and Molecular Biology Alumni

James W. Karaszkiewicz, Ph.D., (1990), took a postdoctoral position as a Biotechnology Fellow in the Laboratory of Cellular Oncology at the National Cancer Institute of the National Institutes of Health (Fig. 61). As a student, he was active in the Graduate Student Association, serving as its President in 1985.

Fredda London, Ph.D., (1987), won the 1987 Alumni Research Award (Fig. 62). Dr. London earned a bachelor's degree in English and a master's degree in comparative literature and taught English composition before even considering science as a career. Following her graduation from Jefferson, she accepted a postdoctoral position at the University of Pennsylvania Connective Tissue Research Institute where her research was in the cardio-vascular area. In 1989 she became Research Assistant Professor at the Temple University School of Medicine, with research in the area of coagulation.

Mary Hinzman Whitman, Ph.D., (1986), received a postdoctoral appointment as a research associate professor at the University of Maryland School of Medicine. In 1987 she was awarded a

Fig. 61. James W. Karaszkiewicz, Ph.D., cellular biologist, National Cancer Institute.

fellowship as a Visiting Scientist at the National Cancer Institute of the National Institutes of Health where she studied the role of fecapentaenes in colon carcinogenesis. In 1988 she accepted the position of manager, Regulatory Submissions at Wyeth-Ayerst Research in Clinical Research and Development. In 1990 she also assumed a part-time faculty position in the department of chemistry at Villanova University. A former Rhodes Scholarship finalist, Dr. Whitman is a member of the Sigma Delta Epsilon Graduate Women in Science honor society. In 1990 she served the College of Graduate Studies on its Distinguished Alumnus Award Committee.

Microbiology and Immunology Alumni

Troy L. Couch, Ph.D., (1988), became a medical microbiologist with particular expertise in general and molecular bacteriology. His research expertise has been in the areas of anaerobic bacteriology, cell culture and fermentation microbiology. Dr. Couch began a postdoctoral research fellowship in 1987 in which he studied prokaryotic molecular biology at Lederle Laboratories. Following his fellowship, he remained at Lederle as a research microbiologist in the Sexually Transmitted Disease Group, Bacterial Vaccine Research and Development Department, of which he became Group Leader in 1990.

Thomas Day, M.S., (1989), was the student recipient of the Loretta Rocco Memorial Award, which is presented in recognition of academic achievement. Mr. Day was appointed Supervisor of Microbiology at Lankenau Hospital in Philadelphia in 1990.

Susan B. Dillon, Ph.D., (1985), received a postdoctoral position in the Department of Medicine, Division of Rheumatology and Immunology at Duke University where her research focused on signal transduction mechanisms in leukocytes. In 1987 she was appointed Research Associate and Instructor in the Department of Neurology at Temple University. There her research centered on human T-cell responses in multiple sclerosis. In 1988 she moved to Smith Kline Beecham Pharmaceuticals as Associate Senior Investigator in the Department of Immunology and was promoted to Senior Investigator in 1989. Dr. Dillon has co-authored 16 articles and ten abstracts.

Judy Earl, M.S., (1985), worked as Laboratory Supervisor at the Memorial Hospital of Burlington County in New Jersey and Adjunct Professor at Burlington County College School of Science, Mathematics and Technology until 1989. She was then appointed Supervisor of Microbiology, Virology and Serology at Pennsylvania Hospital in Philadelphia while also serving as Microbiology Lecturer at Jefferson's College of Allied Health Sciences. She became a member of the American Society of Microbiology and was certified by the American Society of Clinical Pathology.

Tessa Rappaport Freeman, M.S., (1987), had received her bachelor of science degree in medical technology from Jefferson's College of Allied Health Sciences. She worked as a medical technologist until 1988 when she was named Education Coordinator at Northeastern Hospital in Philadelphia. In 1990 she became Supervisor of the Microbiology Laboratory at St. Agnes Medical Center in Philadelphia. From 1987 she also

Fig. 62. Fredda London, Ph.D., Research Assistant Professor, Temple University.

served as a parttime instructor in microbiology at Manor Junior College in Jenkintown. She became a member of the Eastern Pennsylvania Branch of the American Society of Microbiology, the American Society of Clinical Pathologists and the Association of Practitioners in Infection Control.

Gerald E. Hancock, Ph.D., (1986), won the Alumni Research Award for his doctoral dissertation. His work also won him first place at the Sigma Xi Research Day. He accepted a position as a postdoctoral fellow in the Laboratory of Cellular Physiology and Immunology at Rockefeller University in New York. There he investigated cellular interactions in cell-mediated immunity in humans.

Jennifer A. Lata, Ph.D., (1988), served as postdoctoral fellow in the Department of Medicine at Jefferson in the laboratory of J. Bruce Smith, M.D., where she studied reproductive immunology and rheumatology. She received the Finkelstein Memorial Award in May 1990 for excellence in rheumatological postdoctoral research. She subsequently was appointed Director of Immunology at Greenwich Pharmaceuticals in Fort Washington, Pennsylvania.

Robert D. Miller, Ph.D., (1987), went on to a postdoctoral position in the Division of Molecular Biology of the Medical Biology Institute in LaJolla, California. Through his graduate and postgraduate work, he co-authored nine papers and six abstracts. His work also earned him a Juvenile Diabetes Foundation International Fellowship.

Elaine Starr, M.S., (1990), became a Clinical Scientist at Wyeth-Ayerst Research in the Rhesus Rotavirus Vaccine Department. Prior to this position she was Chief Supervisor in the Clinical Microbiology Laboratory at Temple University Hospital.

Pathology and Cell Biology Alumni

LiLi Hsiao, Ph.D., (1989), was the recipient of the Alumni Research Award for her dissertation entitled, *Modification of Host Cell Membrane Lipids During the Intraerythrocyctic Maturation of Human Malarial Parasite P. falciparum* (Fig. 63). She accepted a postdoctoral position in Jefferson's Department of Dermatology doing basic research on keloid, an acquired cutaneous lesion with a strong genetic predisposition with blacks and orientals,

and neurofibroma, a genetic nerve disorder. In 1990 she enrolled in Jefferson Medical College while continuing her research.

Marcela Jensen, Ph.D., (1990), received her master's degree in pathology from Jefferson and the same year received her Ph.D. in Chemistry from Commenius University in Bratislava, Czechoslovakia. She has served as Assistant Professor in the Department of Pediatrics at Jefferson and Director of the Monoclonal Antibody Laboratory in the Division of Developmental Biology at the Alfred I. DuPont Institute in Wilmington, Delaware. She had begun at Jefferson in 1969 as a research assistant in the Department of Pediatrics. Her areas of expertise are monoclonal antibody technique, flourescent antibody technique, histochemistry, protein chemistry, teratology, immunology of fetal development and embryonic nutrition. She has co-authored more than 50 articles in these areas.

Fig. 63. LiLi Hsiao, Ph.D. conducted research in dermatology before entering Jefferson Medical College.

Pharmacology Alumni

Ragunath Appasamy, M.D., Ph.D. (1987), received his M.D. from the Bangalore Medical College of India and then came to Jefferson to study for his Ph.D. After graduation, he was an intern in internal medicine at Jefferson and later at Cooper Hospital/University Medical Center in Camden, NJ. He then went to Presbyterian Hospital at the University of Pittsburgh for a Gastroenterology Fellowship.

Thomas N. Ferraro, Ph.D., (1985), went on to a postdoctoral position in the Department of Neurology at Jefferson as a Research Associate. He became an Instructor and then Assistant Professor in the Department of Neurology. He has served as a course coordinator and lecturer for advanced neurosciences, pharmacology, toxicology, and neuroanatomy. He has also been on the Neurosciences Teaching Committee and the Gibbons Scholar Program Committee. He was a Research Consultant to the Department of Veteran's Affairs in Coatesville, Pennsylvania. He subsequently advanced to Assistant Professor of Psychiatry and Human Behavior and Pharmacology at Jefferson. Through his research he has co-authored 29 articles, five book chapters and 46 abstracts.

Peter A. Glascott, Jr., Ph.D., (1990), took a postdoctoral position in the laboratory of John Farber, M.D., in the Jefferson Department of Pathology (Fig. 64). There he studied the mechanisms of cell toxicity and the metabolism of Vitamin E and Vitamin C during oxidative stress.

Joanne M. Miller, Ph.D., (1990), pursued her postdoctoral education as a research fellow in neurology at the Massachusetts General Hospital in Boston (Fig. 65).

Robert B. Raffa, Ph.D., M.S., (1986), earned his Ph.D. in pharmacology at Temple University and then came to Jefferson for his master's degree in toxicology. He co-authored one book, *Principles in General Pharmacology*, 46 manuscripts, and 31 abstracts. In 1990 he accepted a position of Senior Scientist, CNS Research at R.W. Johnson Pharmaceutical Research Institute. Dr. Raffa is the founder and co-editor of *Pharmacology Letters* (Life Sciences) and the winner of National Research Service Awards in 1983 and 1984.

Physiology Alumni

Mark Brezinski, M.D., Ph.D., (1988), a Dunglison Scholar, studied under the direction of Alan M. Lefer, Ph.D. at Jefferson. Dr. Brezinski was the 1988 winner of the Alumni Research Award for the most outstanding doctoral dissertation. Having earned his M.D. and Ph.D. simultaneously at Jefferson, he was enrolled in a Research Residency program at Brigham and Women's Hospital to work jointly in his residency in internal medicine and his postdoctoral work in the division of hematology at Harvard Medical School. Through his research at Jefferson and in his postdoctoral work, Dr. Brezinski has co-authored 15 papers, six abstracts and one book chapter.

Karen A. Foster, Ph.D., (1987), accepted a postdoctoral position at the Weis Center for Research at the Geisinger Clinic. There she worked on the identification, expression and function of

Fig. 64. Peter A. Glascott, Jr., Ph.D., pursued postdoctoral studies in Jefferson's Department of Pathology.

cardiac G proteins. Through her work, as a research technician, a student at Jefferson and in post-graduate research, she has co-authored 11 publications and nine abstracts.

Donna J. Price, Ph.D., (1988), while a student, co-authored seven papers in the area of thyroid iodination with her advisor, Joseph Sherwin, Ph.D. In 1990, she became Assistant Professor of Biology at St. Thomas University in the Department of Mathematics and Science.

Maria Ann Rupnick, Ph.D., (1988), **M.D.**, at the completion of her graduate work enrolled in Jefferson Medical College and began work toward the M.D. degree which she subsequently finished at Harvard Medical School. She then was accepted into the Research Residency Program in internal medicine at Brigham and Women's Hospital, having been awarded an Andrus Research Fellowship in 1990. She also received the Jefferson Medical College Clinical Research Award from the Department of Surgery, Transplantation Division in 1990 following her work with that group. Through her research at Jefferson and postdoctoral work, Dr. Rupnick has co-authored nine publications and seven abstracts.

Gregory L. Stahl, Ph.D., (1988), became a Research Fellow of the American Heart Associ-ation at the University of California at Davis, Division of Cardiovascular Medicine. He has co-authored 23 articles in the areas of the mechanisms of cardiovascular reflexes originating from visceral organs, the role of humoral mediators in myocardial ischemia and circulatory shock, and the interrelationship among humoral mediators including platelet activating factor, the complement system and eicosanoids in the regulation of coronary circulation during physiologic and pathophysiologic conditions. With his advisor, Allan M. Lefer, Ph.D., Dr. Stahl also co-authored a book chapter in 1989.

Nursing Alumni

Barbara E. Drake, M.S.N., (1989), was in the first class of graduates of the Master of Science in Nursing program. She has been a Rehabilitation Clinical Specialist at Methodist Hospital in Philadelphia, providing care to patients with ostomies, pressure sores, diabetes, and rehabilitation needs. She has also engaged in nursing research and in service as a clinical preceptor for students.

Melissa Ann Krauss, M.S.N., (1989), has been

Fig. 65. Joanne M. Miller, Ph.D., Research Fellow in Neurology, Massachusetts General Hospital.

Fig. 66. Wade H. Berrettini, M.D., Ph.D., became Professor of Psychiatry and Human Behavior and Pharmacology at Jefferson in 1990.

employed as a Clinical Nurse Specialist at the A.I. DuPont Institute in Wilmington, Delaware in the area of pediatric rehabilitation nursing.

Diane J. Lavallee, M.S.N., (1989), specialized in rehabilitation nursing and has been serving as clinical nurse specialist and nursing practice coordinator for The Rehabilitation Center of the Royal Ottawa Health Care Group. She received the Jeanne Ann Clery Memorial Fellowship while a student at Jefferson. In November 1990, she was appointed to the Ontario Ministry of Health Advisory Committee on Rehabilitation.

Nancy Tomaselli, M.S.N., (1988), became an Enterostomal Therapy Clincial Nurse Specialist at Jefferson Hospital. She has authored two articles in the *Journal of Enterostomal Therapy* and 14 patient education publications. Ms. Tomaselli has also made numerous presentations in the areas of Ostonomy and Wound Care and Patient Education.

ALUMNI

1985
Barrueco, Jose, Ph.D., Pharmacology
Blum, Lee M., Ph.D., Pharmacology
Bower, Eric, Ph.D., Pharmacology
Dillon, Susan, Ph.D., Microbiology
Earl, Judy, M.S., Clinical Microbiology
Ferraro, Thomas N., Ph.D., Pharmacology
Hann, Linda J., M.S., Clinical Microbiology
Hoffmann, Barbara E., M.S., Clinical Microbiology
Huss, Harry, M.S., Clinical Microbiology
Lander, David W., M.S., Clinical Microbiology
Munley, Ingrid A., M.S., Clinical Microbiology
Perkowski, Sandra Z., Ph.D., Physiology
Pisano, M. Michele, Ph.D., Anatomy
Rieders, Michael F., Ph.D., Pharmacology
Rothermel, Annette, Ph.D., Microbiology
Tellone, Carmella, Ph.D., Anatomy
Van Wagoner, David R., Ph.D., Pharmacology
Weidner, Mary Ann, M.S., Clinical Microbiology
Wu, Jiunn-Jong, M.S., Clinical Microbiology
Yander, Gail, M.S., Toxicology

1986
Blatt, Gene J., Ph.D., Anatomy
Chabot, Marie C., Ph.D., Anatomy
Conahan, Shawn T., Ph.D., Pharmacology
Glick, David L., Ph.D., Microbiology
Hancock, Gerald E., Ph.D., Microbiology
Hinzman, Mary J., Ph.D., Biochemistry
Korn, Robert L., Ph.D., Physiology
Kyle, Marlene, Ph.D., Pharmacology
Raffa, Robert, M.S., Toxicology
Reichwein, Barbara A., M.S., Clinical Microbiology
Shinkarow, Jane, M.S., Clinical Microbiology
Smith, Martin J., M.S., Pharmacology
Warren, Thomas, M.S., Physiology

1987
Badiavas, Evangelos V., Ph.D., Pharmacology
Foster, Karen, A., Ph.D., Physiology
Fritch, Dean F., Ph.D., Pharmacology
Gould, Susan S., M.S., Clinical Microbiology
Grim, Diane, M.S., Clinical Microbiology
Jones, Jolynda, Ph.D., Anatomy
Lagunowich, Laura P., Ph.D., Pathology
London, Fredda S., Ph.D., Biochemistry
Rappaport, Tessa, M.S., Clinical Microbiology
Sparrow, Marta Graffy, Ph.D., Pharmacology

1988
Appasamy, Ragunath, Ph.D., Pharmacology
Brezinski, Mark E., Ph.D., Physiology
Couch, Troy L., Ph.D., Microbiology
Crochelt, Robert F., Ph.D., Pharmacology
Dansky, Linda A., M.S., Anatomy
Jaweed, M. Mazher, Ph.D., Pharmacology
Lata, Jennifer A., Ph.D., Microbiology
Mandelbaum, Isabel L., M.S., Environmental Toxicology
Messler, Carol J., M.S., Clinical Microbiology
Miller, Robert D., Ph.D., Microbiology
Mirakhur, Beloo, Ph.D. Microbiology
Pellicore, Linda S., Ph.D., Pharmacology
Pimental, Christine M., M.S., Clinical Microbiology
Price, Donna J., Ph.D., Physiology
Rupnick, Maria A., Ph.D., Physiology
Satischandran, Vilas, M.S., Clinical Microbiology
Shipman Appasamy, Pierette M., Ph.D., Anatomy
Stahl, Gregory L., Ph.D., Physiology
Yen, Yun, Ph.D., Pathology

1989   Beach, Jeffrey, M.S., Nursing Masters
        Program
        Bower, David Ph.D., Pharmacology
        Cardonick, Cynthia, M.S., Nursing Masters
        Program
        Day, Thomas E., M.S., Microbiology
        Dowzicky, Michael J., M.S., Microbiology
        Drake, Barbara E., M.S., Nursing Masters
        Program
        Durkee, Karen M., M.S., Nursing Masters
        Program
        Gawel-Thompson, Kathleen J., Ph.D.,
        Anatomy
        Glavey Dowhy, Catherine M., M.S.,
        Nursing Masters Program
        Grubb, John D., Ph.D., Biochemistry
        Hagen, Edna F., M.S., Nursing Masters
        Program
        Hoshowsky, Victoria M., M.S., Nursing
        Masters Program
        Hsiao, Li Li, Ph.D., Pathology
        Jefferies, Lynn S., M.S., Nursing Masters
        Program
        Jin, Shan, Ph.D., Pathology
        Karaszkiewicz, James, Ph.D., Biochemistry
        Mitchell, Kathleen Luba, M.S., Nursing
        Masters Program
        Newman, Deborah A., M.S., Nursing
        Masters Program
        Orso, Jeanmarie, M.S., Nursing Masters
        Program
        Peck, Nancy L., M.S., Nursing Masters
        Program
        Picarello, Nancy J., M.S., Nursing Masters
        Program
        Pittius Innes, Christine, M.S., Nursing
        Masters Program
        Scerrato, Sharon, M.S., Nursing Masters
        Program
        Speicher, Lisa, Ph.D., Physiology
        Tomaselli, Nancy Hass, M.S., Nursing
        Masters Program
        Weikel, Catherine M., M.S., Nursing
        Masters Program
        Yerardi Woodford, Diane, M.S., Nursing
        Masters Program

1990   Bobbie, Mary E., M.S.N., Nursing Masters
        Program
        Cerasoli, Frank, Ph.D., Physiology
        Considine, Robert V., Ph.D., Physiology

Davis, Annette L., M.S.O.T, Occupational
Therapy
Dorando-Unkle, Margaret M.,, M.S.O.T,
Occupational Therapy
Fabiszewski, Rosemary R., M.S.N., Nursing
Masters Program
Frazer, Glenn D., Ph.D., Pharmacology
Glascott, Peter A., Ph.D., Pharmacology
Halal-Szoke, Ann Marie, M.S.N., Nursing
Masters Program
Hathaway, Charles B., Ph.D., Anatomy
Herman, Frances M., M.S.N., Nursing
Masters Program
Hershock, Diane M., Ph.D., Pharmacology
Hines, Judith A., M.S.N., Nursing Masters
Program
Jensen, Marcela. M.S.. Pathology & Cell
Biology
Khetarpal, Vinod, M.S., Envir. Medicine &
Toxicology
Krauss, Melissa A., M.S.N., Nursing
Masters Program
Lavallee, Diane J., M.S.N., Nursing Masters
Program
Learn, Brian A., Ph.D., Microbiology &
Immunology
Liu, Donald C., Ph.D., Pharmacology
Miller, Joanne M., Ph.D., Pharmacology
O'Rourke, Brian Ph.D., Physiology
Osborne, John A., Ph.D., Physiology
Pollock, John V., Ph.D., Physiology
Riesdorph-Ostrow, Wendi, M.S.N., Nursing
Masters Program
Roark, Eileen F., Ph.D., Anatomy
Rooney, John E., Ph.D., Biochemistry &
Molecular Biology
Satre, Michael A., Ph.D., Anatomy
Smeyne, Richard J., Ph.D., Anatomy
Smith, Donna P., M.S.N., Nursing Masters
Program
Starr, Elaine G., M.S., Clinical Microbiology
Vause-Earland Tracey L., M.S.O.T,
Occupational Therapy
Wang, Yu Mei, M.S., Biochemistry &
Molecular Biology
Zhao Mijin, M.S., Biochemistry & Molecular
Biology

~ A ~

Abaidoo, Kodwo J., 1972
Adams, Kathleen O'Looney, 1979
Adams, William J., Jr., 1980
Adolphe, Allen B., 1974
Aharony, David, 1982
Ambromovage, Anne M., 1968
Ambrus, Clara M., 1955
Ambrus, Julian L., 1954
Andrews, Larry S., 1976
Appasamy, Ragunath, 1988
Appert, Hubert E., 1959
Armenti, Vincent T., 1979
Aschner, Thomas C., 1956
Assimakopoulos, Panayotis A., 1971
Axman, Dennis J., 1976

~ B ~

Badiavas, Evangelos V., 1987
Baker, Walter W., 1953
Balla, Pearl E., 1978
Balotin, Nahum M., 1956
Barrueco, Jose, 1985
Barsotti, Robert J., 1982
Bartell, Pasquale, 1951
Bashore, Marion M., 1982
Basquil, Bernadine, 1981
Bass, Steven W., 1970
Beach, Jeffrey, 1989
Becker, Roger J., 1977
Beckman Stanton, Toni L., 1982
Begany, Albert J., 1957
Belej, Miroslaw A., 1972
Bell, Marilyn R., 1984
Bender, A. Douglas, 1962
Bentsen, Christopher, 1979
Berguist, Joanne R., 1976
Berrettini, Wade H., 1979
Bills, Thomas K., 1977
Bjorensen, Jean Young, 1979
Blank, Frederick C., 1974
Blank, Michael S., 1976
Blatt, Gene J., 1986
Blum, Lee M., 1985
Blume, Wendy M., 1977
Bobbie, Mary E., 1990
Bondi, James M., 1978
Boreas, Rosann, 1984
Borgelt, Bruce E., 1973
Borzelleca, Joseph F., 1956

Bossard Hoffert, Margaret, 1982
Bower, David, 1989
Bower, Eric, 1985
Bower, John R., 1974
Brandt, Mary E., 1984
Brezinski, Mark E., 1988
Bridenbaugh, G. Alan, 1976
Brown, Mark D., 1969
Brownstein, Stanley S., 1973
Buch, Judith E., 1976
Buchbinder, Dale, 1973
Buescher, Georganne K., 1974
Buescher, Jerome G., 1981
Burke, Sandra E., 1983

~ C ~

Cady, William, 1967
Callahan, Hugh J., 1970
Callahan, Rosemary M., 1979
Cancro, Jamie A., 1978
Cardonick, Cynthia, 1989
Carlson, Richard P., 1977
Carney, Walter P., 1978
Castingnano, Dominic E., 1972
Cenedella, Richard J., 1966
Cerasoli, Frank 1990
Cerwinka, Paul L., 1980
Ch'en, Philip C., 1963
Ch'Ih, John Juwei, 1968
Chabot, Marie C., 1986
Chan, Asteria C., 1961
Chiger, Judith L., 1983
Child, Jeffrey, 1982
Chisom, Josephine, 1982
Christian, Mildred S., 1979
Churchill, Judy R., 1979
Cinti, Dominick L., 1968
Clark DeMeis, Anne F., 1983
Clark, Allen M., 1964
Cohen, Burton R., 1951
Cohen, Irving, 1973
Cohn, Richard D., 1974
Colasante, Georgia, 1978
Cole, Mercedes T., 1977
Conahan, Shawn T., 1986
Conklin, Richard H., 1970
Connor, Christine Carson, 1978
Considine, Robert V., 1990
Cooper, Keith R., 1981
Coppola, John A., 1963
Couch, Troy L., 1988

Cowardin, Barbara Mitchell, 1978
Cramer, Eva Brown, 1969
Crochelt, Robert F., 1988
Croushore, Susan, 1982
Curtis, Mark T., 1982
Cymerman, Allen, 1968

~ D ~

D'Agostino, Maria A., 1974
Daley, Daniel J., Jr., 1966
Dansky, Linda A., 1988
Dashow, Larry J., 1982
Davar, Phiroza S., 1954
Davis, Annette L., 1990
Day, Thomas E., 1989
DeBias, Domenic A., 1956
DeMartinis, Frederick D., 1959
DeMesquita, Susan, 1977
DeSanctis, Armand N., 1951
Dettmer, Cornelia M., 1969
DeTurck, Kathryn Hill, 1983
Dhamabutra, Narathorn, 1965
Dickerson, Kenneth H., 1963
Dickman, Michael D., 1973
DiGiovanni Barnshaw, Margaret L., 1980
Dillon, Susan, 1985
Do, Nhaun Thi, 1965
Dobelbower, Ralph, 1975
Dombkoski, Frank P., 1974
Dorando-Unkle, Margaret M., 1990
Dougherty, Thomas J., 1978
Dowzicky, Michael J., 1989
Drake, Barbara E., 1989
Drew, William L., 1966
Drezner, Allen D., 1968
Durkee, Karen M., 1989

~ E ~

Earl, Judy, 1985
Earle, Roberta, 1979
East, James M., 1977
Eberly, Virginia S., 1982
Ebersole, Lonnie L., 1982
Egan, Marianne L., 1969
Elkins, Marsha E., 1974
Ellis, John S., 1983
Erickson, Lance, 1974

~ F ~

Fabiszewski, Rosemary R., 1990
Faone-Harhay, Fiorina, 1980
Faricelli, Jack A., 1977

Fasciana, Michael, 1951
Fauver, Patricia A., 1981
Feik, Diane Blechman, 1974
Fernandes, Prabhavathi B., 1975
Ferraro, Thomas N., 1985
Fischman, Gary J., 1980
Fisher, Karen A., 1983
Fitzpatrick, Jean Hirsekorn, 1979
Foley, James E., Jr., 1976
Fonte, Donald A., 1968
Forbes, Barbara F., 1971
Forbes, William I., III, 1972
Foster, Karen A., 1987
Fouts, David W., 1972
Fow, Mark I., 1977
Francis, Elaine Z., 1978
Frankel, Mark S., 1978
Franklin, Samuel G., 1973
Frazer, Glenn D., 1990
Freedburg, Paul S., 1971
Freundlich, Jerome J., 1967
Fried, Dennis A., 1970
Fritch, Dean F., 1987
Fromm, Eli, 1967
Fugo, Richard J., 1975
Fusco, Joanne Damiani, 1984

~ G ~

Gabriel, Karl L., 1964
Gadarowski, John J., 1974
Gans, Joseph H., 1958
Gawel-Thompson, Kathleen J., 1989
Genovesi, Eugene V., 1979
George, Wendy S., 1976
George-Weinstein, Mindy E., 1984
Gerber, Joseph C., III, 1980
Ghosh, Gopi M., 1963
Gilson, Barbara E., 1975
Glaeser, Bruce S., 1978
Glascott, Peter A., 1990
Glasofer, Eric D., 1975
Glaudel, Ursula A., 1975
Glavey Dowhy, Catherine M., 1989
Glick, David L., 1986
Gluckman, Melvyn I., 1953
Golash, Roman, G., 1979
Gold, Alan, 1967
Goldberg, Albert, 1959
Goldman, Patricia R., 1983
Goldschmidt, Joseph C., Jr., 1982
Gollub, Seymour, 1954
Gonasun, Leonard M., 1971
Goody, Howard E., 1973
Gorby, Charles K., 1956
Gorsen, Robert M., 1980
Gould, Susan S., 1987
Gray, Mark S., 1984

Greenberg, Bruce P., 1972
Greene, Charlotte H., 1974
Greenwald, Kenneth, 1964
Grego, Nicholas J., 1974
Grim, Diane, 1987
Grossman, Mark, H., 1979
Grosso, Louis S., 1970
Grubb, John D., 1989
Gwirtz, Patricia A., 1978

~ H ~

Haeffner-Gormley, Lorraine, 1971
Haenick, David H., 1980
Hagen, Edna F., 1989
Hailperin, Marilyn C., 1980
Halal-Szoke, Ann Marie, 1990
Hall, Reginald, 1977
Hami, Dvora, 1974
Hancock, Gerald E., 1986
Hanes, Robert B., 1957
Hann, Linda J., 1985
Harkins, Thomas J., 1979
Hartman, Herbert H., 1967
Hasan, Syed I., 1966
Hassan, Joseph R., 1976
Hathaway, Charles B., 1990
Havill, Andrew M., 1984
Hefton, John M., 1971
Heinrich, Max, 1952
Heltzel, Joann M., 1981
Herman, Frances M., 1990
Herr, Daniel L., 1978
Hershock, Diane M., 1990
Himmelreich, Carol, 1978
Hines, Judith A., 1990
Hinkle, Anne M., 1979
Hinzman, Mary J., 1986
Ho, Wenshe, 1983
Hoffman, Stanley A., 1972
Hoffmann, Barbara E., 1985
Holburn, Ruth R., 1963
Hollshwandner, Caroline H., 1972
Holmes, Mary Osbakken, 1969
Hoops, Carol V., 1976
Horn, Robert S., 1964
Hoshowsky, Victoria M., 1989
Hosko, Michael J., 1964
Hospador, Michael A., 1970
Hsiao, Li Li, 1989
Huang, Joseph C., 1967
Hulkower, Christine Wier, 1979
Husain, Azam, 1967
Huss, Harry, 1985

~ I ~

Inashima, Osamu J., 1954
Ingenito, Gary O., 1983

Ingerman Wojenski, Carol M., 1981
Irwin, Maureen Hiser, 1977

~ J ~

Jaweed, M. Mazher, 1988
Jefferies, Lynn S., 1989
Jenckes, George A., III, 1977
Jensen, Marcela, 1990
Jensh, Ronald P., 1966
Jenson, Keith, 1952
Jin, Shan, 1989
Johnson Roach, Margaret M., 1968
Johnson, Melvin A., 1969
Jones, Jolynda, 1987
Joshi, Prakashchanda C., 1967

~ K ~

Karaszkiewicz, James, 1989
Kety, Edwin M., 1951
Khetarpal, Vinod 1990
Kilmore, Mearl A., 1964
Kim, Nam H. Lee, 1968
Klunk, Lewis K., Jr., 1976
Knudsen, Thomas B., 1981
Kobrin, Lowell, 1974
Koepke, Uwe C., 1972
Koff, Gilbert Y., 1959
Kohl, M. Pauline, 1981
Koplovitz, Irwin, 1975
Korn, Robert L., 1986
Kostos, Vincent, 1962
Krauss, Melissa A., 1990
Krieger, Jeffrey I., 1983
Kroft, Charlotte, 1982
Kyle, Marlene, 1986
Kyriazis, Andrew P., 1968

~ L ~

LaBelle, Charles W., 1959
Lagunowich, Laura P., 1987
Lahita, Robert G., 1973
Lai, Chang-Hai, 1976
Lambert, William C., 1969
Lamon, Kim D., 1980
Lander, David W., 1985
Lang, Armand F., 1973
LaRocco, Mark T., 1984
Lata, Jennifer A., 1988
Lavallee, Diane J., 1990
LaVelle, James M., 1981
Lawrie Esterline, Nancy J., 1983
Laxon, Jaclynne Horn, 1969
Learn, Brian A., 1990
Lebman, Deborah A., 1980
Lectura, Felix V., 1965

Lee, Eun Woo, 1970
Leibowitz, Robert, 1983
Leung, Christopher K., 1969
Levich, Judith P., 1981
Levine, Stanley, 1962
Levy, Michael H., 1976
Lewis, Sandra, 1975
Lewis, Thomas L., 1975
Lim, Vincente N., 1976
Lin, Yu Chen, 1971
Lincoln, Marcia L., 1979
Ling, Henry T., 1983
Lintner, Valerie Mowrer, 1978
Lipkin, Saul, 1962
Liu, Donald C., 1990
London, Fredda S., 1987
Longacre, Stephen L., 1980
Lorr, Nancy A., 1981
Lowry, Barbara Sawyer, 1977
Luscombe, Susan, 1972
Lutton, Charles E., 1964
Lynch, William T., 1967

~ M ~

Ma, Pearl, 1962
Mabrouk, Fadia M., 1979
Machuga, Stephen J., 1980
Mackowiak, Elaine D., 1974
Malish, Steven L., 1973
Mancini, Robert E., 1973
Mandelbaum, Isabel L., 1988
Marsden, David S., 1968
Marsili, Mark A., 1981
Martin, John S., 1973
Marturano, Anthony V., 1954
Master, Ronald N., 1981
Matthews, Richard J., 1955
Maybock, John H., 1964
McAlack, Robert F., 1968
McCarthy, William V., 1981
McCrone, Elcinda L., 1977
McDonough, Pauline M., 1982
McGarrity, Gerard J., 1970
McGowan, Karin L., 1977
McGregor Stong, Anne, 1980
McLean, Arlene A., 1976
McLean, Lewis F., 1974
McPhillips, Joseph J., 1963
Meehan Arias, Kathleen, I., 1979
Mellon, Lawrence J., 1972
Messer, James W., 1963
Messler, Carol J., 1988
Metz, Jeffrey A., 1980
Miller, Joanne M., 1990
Miller, Neil, 1967
Miller, Patricia A., 1978
Miller, Robert D., 1988

Miller, Russell, Jr., 1951
Mills, Ira, 1982
Milstein, Seymour W., 1955
Mirakhur, Beloo, 1988
Mitchell, Kathleen Luba, 1989
Moawad, Atef H., 1963
Moore, Jonni S., 1984
Moreno, Oscarr M., 1967
Morrison, John H., 1953
Moyer, Robert A., 1980
Msuya, Philemon M., 1969
Much, David H., 1972
Munley, Ingrid A., 1985
Murphy, Christine V., 1974

~ N ~

Nahhas, Laila A., 1962
Narasimhula, Shankunthala V., 1960
Neff, Ray A., 1967
Neilsen, Erling W., 1975
Newman, Deborah A., 1989
Noble, Clifford, J., 1974

~ O ~

O'Rourke, Brian, 1990
Ogletree, Martin L., 1978
Ohashi, David K., 1974
Orcutt, Roger P., 1972
Orso, Jeanmarie, 1989
Osbahr, Carol, 1982
Osborne, John A., 1990
Ostrawski, Stanley M., 1978

~ P ~

Palombo, Sandra S., 1981
Pant, Keshab D., 1965
Papageorgopoulos, Christos A., 1973
Papanicolaou, Basil G., 1974
Parrish, Christine M., 1976
Pashko, Steven, 1979
Paul, Stephen M., 1977
Paynton, Barbara V., 1980
Peck, Nancy L., 1989
Pellicore, Linda S., 1988
Pentella, Michael A., 1980
Per, Steven R., 1984
Perkowski, Sandra Z., 1985
Phelan, Thomas I., 1972
Picarello, Nancy J., 1989
Pierce, Lauretta, 1969
Pimental, Christine M., 1988
Pinder, Richard D., 1978
Pisano, M. Michele, 1985
Pittius Innes, Christine, 1989
Plummer Sawyer, Karen M., 1982

Pober, Zalmon, 1968
Polish, Edwin, 1952
Pollock, John V., 1990
Post, Gloria B., 1983
Pottgen, Paul A., 1976
Poupard, James A., 1974
Price, Donna J., 1988
Provencher, Robert A., 1980
Prozialeck, Walter C., 1978

~ R ~

Raffa, Robert, 1986
Rahman, Mohammad A., 1965
Randall, Eileen L., 1960
Rappaport, Tessa, 1987
Reibel-Shinfeld, Diane K., 1978
Reichwein, Barbara A., 1986
Renzi, Alfred A., Jr., 1983
Rhoads, Rita L., 1980
Rhode, Solon L., III, 1968
Rieders, Fredric, 1952
Rieders, Michael F., 1985
Riesdorph-Ostrow, Wendi, 1990
Rioux, Ernest, 1966
Roark, Eileen F., 1990
Robison, Steven H., 1980
Rocco, Loretta, 1974
Rockford, Emeric J., 1953
Rooney, John E., 1990
Rosco, Diane L., 1977
Rosen, Arye, 1977
Rosen, Lionel, 1961
Rosenberg Silverman, Bonita S., 1976
Rosenberg, Philip, 1957
Rosenblum, Norman, 1975
Rosenfeld, Leonard M., 1964
Ross, Sherril, 1979
Roth, David, 1984
Rothermel, Annette, 1985
Rothman, Richard H., 1965
Rothstein, Edward L., 1954
Rowan, Regina, 1974
Ruane, Mildred V., 1980
Rubin, Benjamin D., 1970
Rudolph, Paul G., 1977
Rupnick, Maria A., 1988
Rushmore, Thomas H., 1983
Rutman, Julia Z., 1955

~ S ~

Sagemuehl May, Jeri L., 1979
Saito, Fumike U., 1970
Salam, Syed A., 1968
Salventi, John F., 1974
Sammett, David, 1982
Satischandran, Vilas, 1988

Part V

The School of Nursing

Statue of Athena, Goddess of Wisdom and the Healing Arts (ca. 2nd century A.D.)

A Clinic in the "Pit" of the 1877 Hospital (ca. 1900).

~ SCHOOL OF NURSING ~

The efforts of Florence Nightingale after her experiences in 1854 in the Crimean War focused attention on the necessity for nurses and an educational system to prepare them. The American Civil War additionally accentuated this need both militarily and in civilian life. Jefferson's Professor of Surgery, Samuel D. Gross, who was President of the American Medical Association in 1868, stated at its meeting that year:

"It seems to me to be just as necessary to have well-trained, instructed nurses, as to have intelligent and skillful physicians. I have long been of the opinion that there ought to be in all the principal towns and cities of the Union, institutions for the education of persons whose duty it is to take care of the sick." The following year Dr. Gross was Chairman of a Committee of the American Medical Association on the training of nurses and stated in his report:

"There is marked diminution of mortality in hospitals where nursing is done by trained women, a decided decrease in expenditures and a general improvement in the moral character of the inmates." The Committee recommended that district schools for training of nurses be formed under the guidance of the County Medical Societies. As enlightening as these recommendations seemed to be, they were not adopted.

Dr. Gross did not live to see the establishment of a School of Nursing at Jefferson, but as late as 1883, one year before his death, his continued interest was manifested by an article entitled "The Best Means of Training Nurses for Rural Districts."

When Jefferson Medical College Hospital was opened on September 17, 1877, it had no trained nurses. This building at 1020 Sansom Street provided beds for 125 patients. During the first year 441 patients were admitted , 621 the second year and 890 the third year. The purpose of the hospital was not only to care for the sick but to provide clinical experience for the medical students.

America's first trained nurse was Melinda Ann Richards who graduated from the New England Hospital for Women and Children in Boston on October 1, 1873. At this time the principles of surgical antisepsis as advocated by Joseph Lister in 1867 had not been accepted, as witnessed by the Thomas Eakins painting of the *Gross Clinic* (1875) in which the great surgeon in street clothes is operating with bare hands. The science of bacteriology would not even begin until around 1880.

It would take 14 years for the 1877 Jefferson Medical College Hospital to open its School of Nursing in 1891. During that time the nursing care was given by unskilled and untrained attendants. Women took care of women patients, and men took care of men. They had little or no knowledge of drugs. Important symptoms could pass unnoticed. A clinical assistant might be assigned by the surgeon to sit by the patient's bedside during emergence from ether anesthesia to maneuver the best position for vomiting. Unconscious or paralyzed patients risked being burned by hot water bags. Many of these undesirable conditions would be ameliorated during the last decade of the 19th century with the establishment of the School of Nursing.

"I salute Jefferson nurses, past and present. For their outstanding contributions to nursing education and patient care and for upholding the highest standards of the nursing profession, they deserve accolades of praise."

Paul C. Brucker, M.D.
President, Thomas Jefferson University

The training school for nurses was established at Jefferson in connection with the Hospital. There were three nurse supervisors for the first 13 students who enrolled. The age requirement was from 21 to 35. The course of instruction covered two years and the students worked 14 hours a day. Miss Ella Benson, the first Directress of Nurses, was assisted in the teaching by members of the Attending Hospital Staff who gave a prescribed course of lectures.

Initially it was necessary to retain many of the former untrained attendants, but the old and new mix did not blend well. Dissensions erupted. Some conservative members of the Staff opposed the trainees as a step toward "chaos and destruction." Within a few months, however, the improvements in nursing service were so obvious that accord ensued.

In the Crimean War (1853-1856), Florence Nightingale was superintendent of nurses in Turkey. The training school for nurses that she established in England in 1860 became a model for early nursing schools in the States. (Courtesy of *Commitment to Excellence*, 1982, p. 7.)

The Maternity Department which had opened in 1886 in cramped quarters of the hospital was moved to a rented Building at 327 Pine Street. The Hospital Trustees provided for fuel, light, medical supplies and part of the nursing salary cost. A Board of Lady Managers, in later years to become the Women's Board, formed a Maternity Committee of which Mrs. E. D. Gillespie was the President. This Committee paid for the rent of the Maternity Building, the food, domestic services and part of the salary of the Head Nurse. The latter had just graduated this year from the Philadelphia (General) Hospital. Dr. Edward P. Davis, destined to become Jefferson's first Chairman of Obstetrics (1898-1925), was made the Director of the Maternity Department.

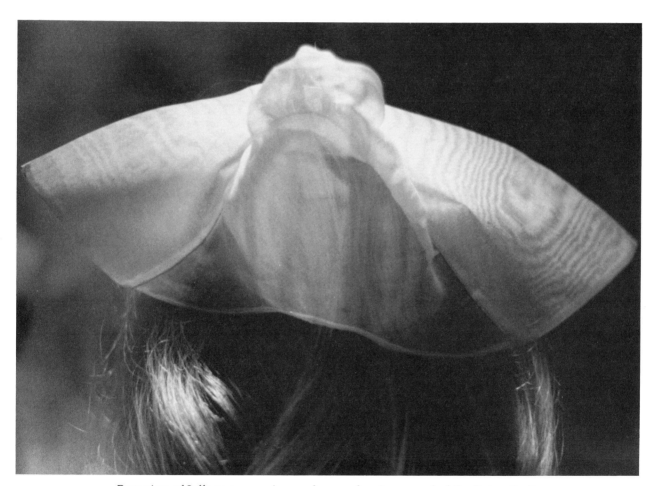

Rear view of Jefferson nurses' organdy cap, showing spread of the "wing tips".

In this year the course of instruction was lengthened to three years. A stipend of $6.00 per month was paid to students of the first year in addition to board, lodging and laundry. Tuition was free. There was a vacation period of two weeks a year and hospital care for illness. The monthly stipend was $7.00 per month for the second year and $8.00 for the third.

In May the first Nurses' Home was formally opened at 518 Spruce Street. The previous lodging had been in cramped quarters on the upper floors of the hospital.

Miss Benson, who remained as Directress but a short time, was succeeded this year by Miss Katherine ("Effie") Darling (Fig. 1). During the latter's tenure (1893/94) the first graduation exercises (Fig. 2) were held on November 23 in the clinical amphitheater ("pit") of the Hospital. Five nurses were awarded the Diploma of the Training School. The graduates were:

CLASS OF 1893

Armstrong, Mary
Bear, Carrie
Bower, Sara Brook
Howell, Georgianna
Martin, Sara Elizabeth

Fig. 1.   Katherine ("Effie") Darling, Directress of Nursing (1893/94).

The trained nurse has become one of the great blessings of humanity, taking a place beside the physician and the priest, and not inferior to either in her mission.

Sir William Osler (1849–1919)

Fig. 2.   Graduating Class of 1893/94.

There is probably no ten-year span in nursings' history during which so many important events or so many fateful decisions were made than in the period between 1890 and 1900. It was a time of unprecedented growth in American nursing, a period of emergence of several of our most important nursing leaders, an era of tremendous proloferation of schools of nursing, and the decade of the greatest organizational strides for the fledgling profession.

Theresa E. Christy

1893

In this year Miss Darling resigned as Directress to accept a position in Denver, Colorado. She was succeeded by Miss Susan C. Hearle, who would serve effectively for the next 14 years (Fig. 3). She was an English woman who had received early training in Great Britain under Florence Nightingale and subsequently graduated from the Philadelphia (General) Hospital in 1890.

The Maternity Department at 327 Pine street was moved under the auspices of the Board of Lady Managers to a house at 224 South Seventh Street on Washington Square (Fig.4). The Ladies paid the annual rent of $1,000 and continued to defray the cost of food, domestic services and a part of the nurses' salaries. The day cost for a patient was 26 cents or $7 a month. Two of the pupil nurses were on duty at a time for instruction in obstetric nursing. Postgraduate instruction was also given to nurses who graduated from other schools and in this way adequate personnel was obtained.

The enrollment had increased to 30 students but the Class of 1894 records only one graduate:

Fig. 3.   Susan C. Hearle, Directress of Nursing (1894-1908).

CLASS OF 1894

Walker, Margaret (Logan)

Nursing in its highest form is now classed with the professions, since it has professional characteristics—long, difficult preparation, work which is primarily for humanity rather than for oneself, compensation that is more in satisfaction than in money or prestige.

Quoted from Minnie Goodnow, R.N.: *Nursing History in Brief,*
W.B. Saunders Co., Philadelphia, London, 1950.

Fig. 4.   Maternity Facility at 224 West Washington Square, established in 1894 for patient care and student instruction.

An outstanding event of this year was the founding of the Jefferson Nurses Alumnae Association by Miss Hearle, who became the first President. As in the Medical College, this organization throughout the years would greatly aid the welfare of the School of Nursing by its Annual Bulletin, Nosokomos Year Book, scholarships, awards, sick benefits and reunions.

Another improvement was the moving of the nurses' quarters to 226 South Seventh Street, adjacent to the building for the Maternity Department (Fig. 4 and 5). The students could thus get their obstetrical training next door.

The Maternity Department treated 82 women this year of whom 23 were married and 59 single. A few years later this proportion was reversed.

The Annual Report of the School this year revealed 110 applications of which 44 were appointed. The active enrollment reached a high of 35 students with four probationers. More than 70 lectures were delivered to 62 class sessions on Anatomy and Physiology; Obstetrical and Gynecological Nursing; Diseases of Children; Diseases of the Eye and Ear; and Therapeutics, Bandaging and Massage.

The fifteen graduates were as follows:

Fig. 5.   Sitting room in Nurses' Home.

Dinkle, Clara, VA
Funk, Mary
Harris, Margaret
Kendig, Laura
Laughlin, Emma (Grove)
Lemmon, Mary, NJ (Hammersty)
Martin, Grace
Monaghan, Katherine (Trieber)

Orchard, Mary A., CA
Ramsey, Mamie, CA
Schneider, Pena
Thompson, Coe
Thompson, Elizabeth, PA
Thompson, Nellie (Wiley)
Zetterland, Anna

Private floor reception room in 1877 hospital.

1895

After the first year of instruction the pupil nurses were farmed out to care for the sick in their homes. This was under the Supervision of the attending physician who assumed full responsibility for his patient and the nurse. The Hospital charged for the service of the student nurse as follows: $10 per week for general nursing and $12 per week for contagious disease care. The daily rates were $2, or $3 with massage. The patient paid for travel and laundry expenses of the nurse. If the patient's condition permitted, the nurse was allowed one half hour each day for out door exercise, plus time for sufficient sleep. The nurse's time limit in a single case was eight weeks. The charges were due at the end of service and a blank had to be filled out as to whether the care was satisfactory or not. This practice was maintained until 1905.

In 1897 a teaching kitchen for pupil nurses was established (Fig. 6).

In the records of the Nursing School, the 5 graduates of 1896 and 1897 are combined together as follows:

Fig. 6. Teaching kitchen for pupil nurses.

Aikens, Bessie
Egden, Ada
Krause, Henrietta
Lane, Lottie, OR (Thorne)
Lester, Mame, CA
Milburg, Maude
Myers, Lena L., OH
Rothwell, Nellie

Shook, Elizabeth, PA (Brenholtz)
Smith, Sarah
Stiebler, Mary
Strohmaier, Katherine
Trigg, Lucy
Walters, Dora
Zook, Menta

Turn of the century orthopaedic dispensary. Note nurse on duty (right).

After the first year of instruction the pupil nurses were farmed out to care for the sick in their homes. This was under the Supervision of the attending physician who assumed full responsibility for his patient and the nurse. The Hospital charged for the service of the student nurse as follows: $10 per week for general nursing and $12 per week for contagious disease care. The daily rates were $2, or $3 with massage. The patient paid for travel and laundry expenses of the nurse. If the patient's condition permitted, the nurse was allowed one half hour each day for out door exercise, plus time for sufficient sleep. The nurse's time limit in a single case was eight weeks. The charges were due at the end of service and a blank had to be filled out as to whether the care was satisfactory or not. This practice was maintained until 1905.

In 1897 a teaching kitchen for pupil nurses was established (Fig. 6).

In the records of the Nursing School, the 15 graduates of 1896 and 1897 are combined together as follows:

CLASS OF 1897

Aikens, Bessie
Egden, Ada
Krause, Henrietta
Lane, Lottie, OR (Thorne)
Lester, Mame, CA
Milburg, Maude
Myers, Lena L., OH
Rothwell, Nellie

Shook, Elizabeth, PA (Brenholtz)
Smith, Sarah
Stiebler, Mary
Strohmaier, Katherine
Trigg, Lucy
Walters, Dora
Zook, Menta

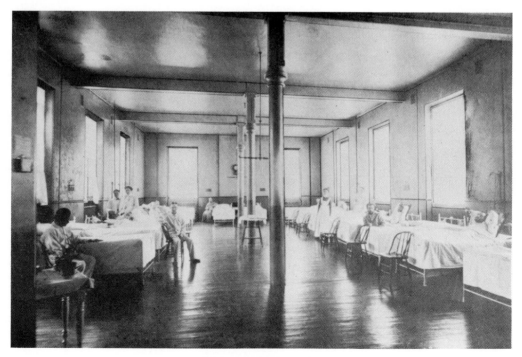

Men's medical ward.

1897

During the Spanish-American War the mortality in the American troops was high due to typhoid fever and inadequately trained nursing personnel. Two Jefferson nurses, Katherine Baker (1898) and Adelaide O'Laughlin (1899) were assigned to "train service." This entailed traveling by service train to camp Fernandina, Florida, and returning with 50 very ill soldiers. There was one death in transit. Some additional Jefferson graduates volunteered their services without remuneration.

Lectures and practical training during these early years accounted for a full 14-hour day. Mealtimes provided welcome relief from this arduous routine (Fig. 7).

The 10 graduates of the Class were:

CLASS OF 1898

Baker, Katherine, PA
Brown, Margaret, AL
Clark, Catherine
Cumminskey, Nellie, PA
Graham, Adelaide

King, Ella
Major, Olive (Anderson)
Nolan, Anna, PA (Butler)
Reed, Mary E., PA (Butler)
Segsworth, Laura

Fig. 7.   Student nurses and their supervisors at dinner.

By the last year of this decade the School of Nursing had established a secure identity. There was an adequate and increasing enrollment; the curriculum was updated and expanded; lodging was improved; and good working relationships had developed with the attending physicians and students. The scientific era in medicine was now well under way, with the role of the nursing profession more clearly defined (Fig. 8).

There were 18 graduates in this class as follows:

CLASS OF 1899

Biswanger, Frieda
Boyer, Esther (Sipler)
Brooke, Mary (St. Clair)
Clement, Jane (Hazlett)
Clewes, Marcella (Cocoa)
Dom, Addie
Graham, Jessie
Hammer, Signe
Hildebrant, May

Hurley, Jeanette, OR (Pierce)
Mannon, Etta
O'Laughlin, Adelaide
Pie, Emma
Pie, Rosalie
Rogers, Katherine, PA
Scherf, Catherine, PA
Segsworth, Evelyn, MO (Brown)
Zeisser, Kate, PA

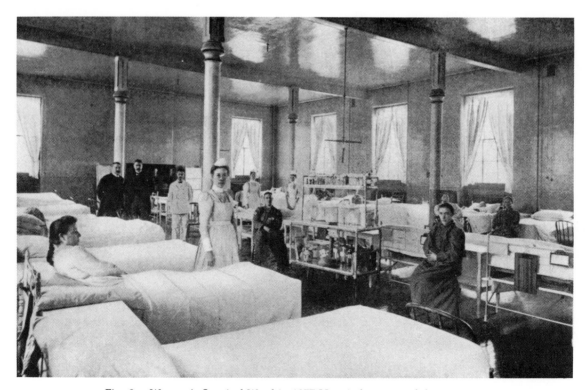

Fig. 8. Women's Surgical Ward in 1877 Hospital at turn of the century.

The turn of the century was marked by a public recognition of the need for trained nurses. This need was highlighted when a group of Jefferson nurses was dispatched to Galveston, Texas, to aid the victims of a devastating flood.

The seven graduates of this class are listed:

CLASS OF 1900

Craft, Mabel, NC (Harley)
Haldeman, Florence (Hood)
Krause, Harriet R., PA
Martin, Sara Jane

Rogers, Elizabeth
Synnamon, Anna, PA
Witmer, Susan, PA

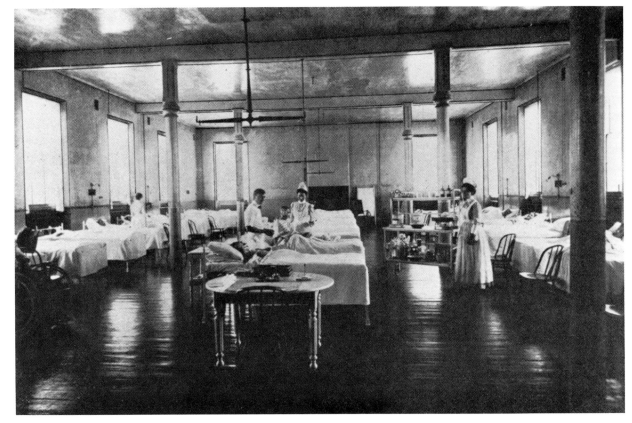

Men's Surgical Ward.

Scientific medicine had not yet significantly altered the ravages of infectious diseases such as diphtheria, scarlet fever, tuberculosis, pneumonia, typhoid and other enteric diseases. Life expectancy was approximately 46 years. By this time 500 nursing schools in the country had around 10,000 graduates. In this process the Jefferson School of Nursing had attained a reputation for excellence. The teaching Medical School Clinics at this time usually required the presence of a nurse (Fig. 9).

The five graduates of 1901 were:

CLASS OF 1901

Carey, Lucy
Mahoney, Mary, PA
Morrow, Helen, CT

Roe, Margaret
Spangler, Katie

Fig. 9.   Clinic in "pit" of 1877 Hospital (ca. 1903). Note nurse at entrance.

During this period *The Jeffersonian* (the medical student publication) highlighted the fact that few hospitals compared in excellence with the clinical instruction the Jefferson student nurses received. This was especially true in surgery and obstetrics in which the wealth of clinical material and large physician staff was particularly effective. Miss Hearle was complimented for the leadership and thoroughness of her teaching program.

The 20 graduates of 1902 were:

CLASS OF 1902

Bland, Rachel, PA (Campbell)
Boehme, Louise (Ellis)
Chrisholm, Margaret
Cooley, Mildred, NY (Oliver)
Cross, Jennie, PA (Irick)
Cushen, Mary
DeChaney, Emily, PA
DeSanto, Emelia, COSTA RICA
Ditto, Caroline, PA
Downes, Katherine, PA

Glouner, Anna
Koser, Emily, PA (Henry)
Lawrence, Lillian
Mccomber, Olive, TX (Roundtree)
McCombes, Anna, IL (Boyajian)
McPherson, Edith, PA
Peck, Macie, OH
Pfau, Emma (Brallier)
Weir, Mary
Wolfe, Mary, DE (Richter)

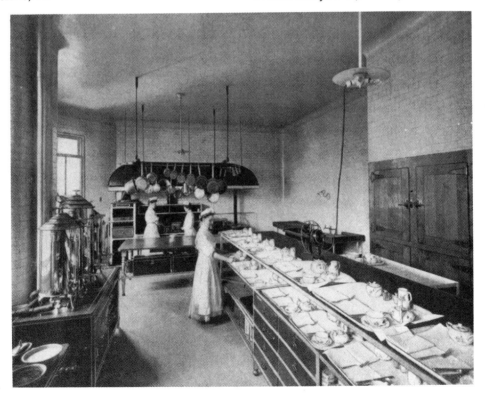

Nurses in diet kitchen of 1877 hospital.

There was a call from Butler, Pennsylvania, for nurses to care for the victims of a severe epidemic of typhoid fever. Four Jefferson pupil nurses from the class of 1905 were detailed for this emergency, namely Margaret Hicks, Jessie Mitchell, Katharine Shaw, and Elizabeth Supplee. Charlotte Lane, Assistant Directress of nurses, was in charge.

The 12 graduates of 1903 are listed.

CLASS OF 1903

Brown, Violet
Clippinger, Jessie, PA (Fraser)
George, Bertha H., PA
Graham, Catherine (Gillam)
Jamieson, Mary A., OH
Keigley, Sadie, PA (Conklin)

MacMahon, Margaret, PA
McKean, Mary, PA
Murphy, Emily, NY (O'Donnell)
Patterson, Katherine, DC (Alexander)
Strohmaier, Bertha, PA (Spencer)
Stute, Wilhelmina

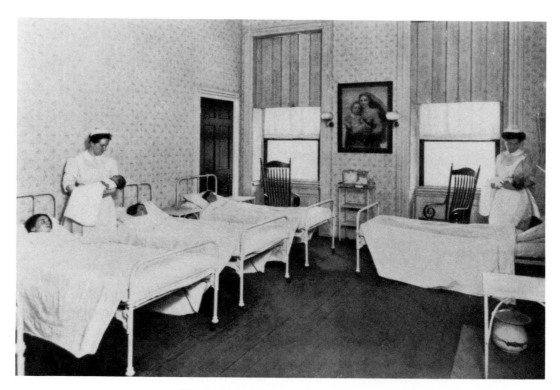

Maternity Ward, turn of the century.

In this year a Constitution and By-Laws of the Nurses Alumnae Association were formally adopted.

Since 1892 the Board of Lady Managers had given both moral and financial support to the Maternity Department. This contributed significantly to the high standard of maternity care at Jefferson for the beginning of the twentieth century which benefited not only the patients but the educational program for the nurses. The application of Listerian principles of antisepsis and asepsis as taught and practiced in this Department led to improved rates of maternal and infant mortality (Fig. 10).

There were 17 graduates in this year's Class as follows:

CLASS OF 1904

Allison, Virginia (Shipe)
Brazanson, Almira
Cannon, Nellie
Clippinger, Maude, PA (Faust)
Detterer, Nellie
Folwell, Lydia (Dexter)
Hanson, Etta, NJ (Surtees)
Hunsicker, Sarah, PA
Lichty, Blanche, PA (Barnard)

Loveren, Gertrude, MA
Miller, Grace
Mollenkoff, Amanda, PA (DeLaney)
Read, Ella, TX (Ward)
Richards, Mary, PA (Ginder)
Simmonds, J. Ellen, NJ (Welsh)
Winters, Sadie
Wood, Mabel

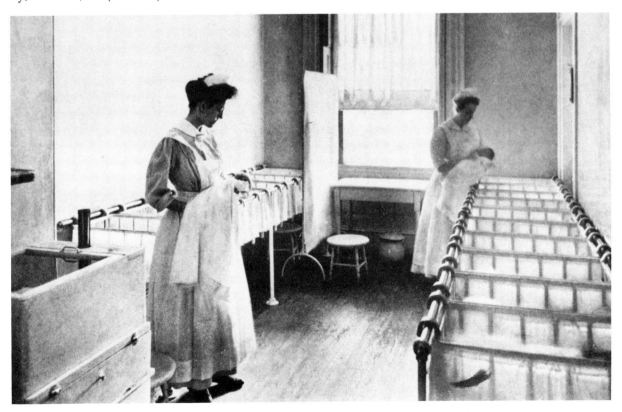

Fig. 10.   Maternity Ward and Nursery (early 1900s).

~ 1905 ~

The regular minutes of the Alumnae Association meetings were first recorded in this year.

Plans for the 1907 Hospital, which were already under way during this period, included an upgrading of facilities for the care of children (Fig. 11).

There were 15 graduates in the Class.

Colette, Laura
Comstock, Susie, PA
DaCosta, Clara
Detwiler, Elizabeth
Harris, Charlotte, PA (Jenkins)
Hicks, Margaret
Knight, Anna, PA (Hill)
Mitchell, Jessie

Nelson, Iowa C., CA (Morris)
Nickel, Minna
Roth, Helen
Shaw, Katherine
Supplee, Elizabeth
Taylor, Sarah, NJ
Vogt, Josephine (Ingold)

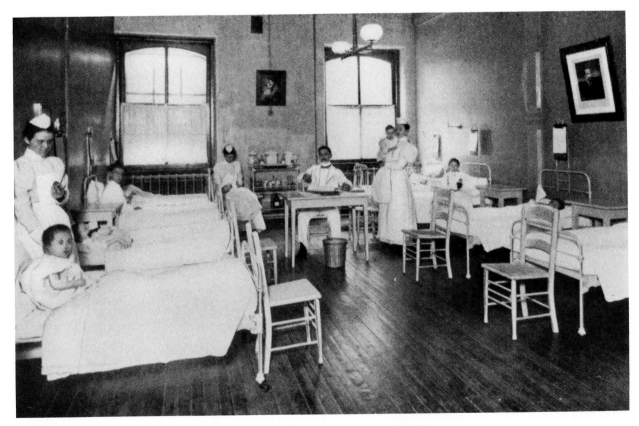

Fig. 11.   Children's Ward in 1877 Hospital.

This was the last year in which the first Hospital built in 1877 would serve inpatients (Fig. 12). In nearly 30 years 148 nurses were trained; 5,000 doctors emanated from its halls; 2,000,000 patients were cared for in wards and dispensaries; and nearly 50,000 accident cases were treated.

The clinical amphitheater ("pit") of this hospital would be maintained for teaching purposes through 1923, while the vacated portion would be used for lodging and classrooms of the nurses.

The class consisted of 14 graduates.

CLASS OF 1906

Carnahan, Florence, PA
Ely, Ida, PA (Norton)
Fair, Florence (Feilis)
Gumpert, Anna, CO (Laughlin)
Howe, Elizabeth, PA (Frowert)
Hower, Martha (Dunn)
Laughlin, Anna

Morgan, Rebecca, NJ (Ritter)
Reisler, Leila, PA (Kirshbaum)
Rich, Jennie, NH
Risser, Phoebe, NJ (Haldman)
Schindel, Anna, MD
Smith, Mary
Williams, Mary, MD (Biddle)

Fig. 12.   Nurses' drug station on fifth floor of 1877 Hospital.

Increasing demands were placed upon the School of Nursing with the opening on June 8 of the new Hospital at Tenth and Sansom Streets (now called "Old Main"), adjoining the 1877 Building on the east. There were now a Directress of Nurses, an Assistant Directress, and 13 Supervisors. Ninety-three student nurses were enrolled. This ample Hospital was the most modern for its time and could vie with the best in the country. It provided 300 beds (Fig. 13).

The graduates of this Class numbered eight.

CLASS OF 1907

Allen, Mary, CA
Conran, Anna, PA
Doxrud, Olivia, PA
Morgan, Margaret, CANADA
Prime, Mary, CANADA
Tipping, Kate Dolan, LA
Voorhees, Georgianna, NY (Wolfe)
Wadsworth, Anna, DC (Lynch)

Fig. 13. "Old Main Hospital" (1907).

Miss Hearle, Directress of Nurses, resigned this year and was succeeded by Miss Anna E. Laughlin (Fig. 14). The latter, from the Class of 1906, was the first Jefferson graduate to assume this post. One of her improvements was the adoption of "hands on" experience in pediatrics, maternity, medicine and surgery. In addition, a Training School Committee of the Medical Staff composed of five members formulated the curriculum and assigned the instructors for the various subjects. Miss Laughlin served faithfully for seven years.

There were 16 graduates this year.

CLASS OF 1908

Bennett, Evalyn C., PA
Campbell, Katherine
Creig, Mary (Hepler)
Dickinson, Pamela (Briggs)
Doan, Evelyn, NJ (Supplee)
Dougherty, Elizabeth, NJ
Heater, Alice, CA (Morse)
Kreider, Ida

Lynn, Rose, NC
Ossenbeck, Margaret, MA
Patterson, Margaret, OR (Reeves)
Reeves, Jean, NY (Noland)
Shoemaker, Nora E., PA
Stansbury, Ann, MA
Swager, Clara, PA (Sweeney)
Viles, Emily, ID (Stewart)

Fig. 14.   Anna E. Laughlin ('06), first Jefferson Training School Nurse to become Directress (1908-15).

~ 1909 ~

This year marked passage by the Pennsylvania State Legislature of the first bill for regulation of the practice of nursing. A Board of Examiners, consisting of five professional nurses, was appointed to oversee the measures. This represented an early attempt on the part of government to assure the public of safe and competent care.

Members of this class were the first to receive a school pin in addition to the diploma. This original gold pin bore a replica of the head of Florence Nightingale surrounded by the name of the school (Fig. 15).

The Class consisted of 21 graduates.

CLASS OF 1909

Angle, Nell
Brooke, Martha, PA (Watkins)
Bruch, Florence, PA
Colebaugh, Effie
Dague, Anna, PA
Dinsmore, Hattie, OH (Stockdale)
Disher, Grace
Gass, Violet, CA
Grier, Lucy (Carrington)
Hickman, Mary, PA
Lingo, Harriet, DE (Cannon)

McElwain, Laura, CA (Overman)
Patton, Anna, FL (Webster)
Pearson, Charlotte (Smith)
Robinson, Mary, PA (Godfrey)
Rohde, Helen, NJ
Scattergood, Katherine
Smaling, Emily, PA
Strunk, Daisy, PA
Yates, Mary, NC (Woodlief)
Zeller, Eva, DC

We need to realize and to affirm anew that nursing is one of the most difficult of arts. Compassion may provide the motive, but knowledge is our only working power. Perhaps, too, we need to remember that growth in our work must be preceded by ideas, and that any conditions which suppress thought, must retard growth. Surely we will not be satisfied in perpetuating methods and traditions. Surely we shall wish to be more and more occupied with creating them.

M. Adelaide Nutting (1858-1948).
Professor of Nursing, Teachers' College,
Columbia University, First in the World.

Fig. 15.   First school pin (1909).

We have strived here to avoid the sin which tends to beset all institutions, that is to become impersonal and mechanized. At the head of every department has been placed a mature and sympathetic nurse with the desire to appreciate that sick people are not numbered individuals and just cold medical problems, one with whom patients can become acquainted and to whom they can turn for information, direction and sympathy at the time of their visits.

Frank H. Lahey (1880-1953).

The members of this class preferred a new design to the school pin. An entirely new seal was made with a gold scroll, containing a blue cross, surrounded by black enamel and lettered with the name of the institution (Fig. 16). These pins were first presented in 1910 to each member of the graduating class by Dr. William M. L. Coplin as the personal gift of the Board of Trustees of the Hospital. This practice was continued at each graduation until the closing of the School of Nursing in 1982.

The student's dress uniform that would prevail until 1915 is represented by Elizabeth Morrill of this class (Fig. 17). It was of pink color, floor length, with buttons down the front, and accommodated a high bishop's collar that buttoned on the back. Balloon sleeves fastened tightly at the wrists; bib and apron adorned the front; and the cap consisted of a wide band turned back with a ruffle on the edge.

This class had 37 graduates, the highest number thus far.

Fig. 16.   Second school pin (1910).

Antes, Alvirda, FL (Taylor)
Baker, Cora, PA
Baker, Myrtle, NY (Bendt)
Barcalow, Mary, PA (Mullin)
Bowen, Ruth B., PA (Pardee)
Bray, Ruth, NJ
Brenneman, Blanche, MA (Fielding)
Bush, Lemos, CO (Warne)
Campbell, Mary (Rogers)
Carpenter, Evelyn, PA
Carson, Bertha (Simpson)
Clark, Maude (Hill)
DeLouzanne, Adelaide, PA
Dow, Mayfair, FL (Gillingham)
Fulford, Bettie, NC
Gardner, Naomi, PA
Gibbs, Jean
Gorman, Helen

Grimm, Emily, WI (Storey)
Haas, Essie, PA (Wolfe)
Hazel, Bessie, PA (Campbell)
Holdern, Rose, IN (Daft)
Hough, Irene, PA (Lobb)
Ivory, Margaret, PA (Keating)
Kehoe, Sarah, AUSTRALIA (Murphy)
Melville, Clara
Morrill, Elizabeth
Neff, Sarah (Ransom)
Ohland, Eda, CA
Parsons, Anna, CA (Johnson)
Richards, Lavina, CANADA
Scudder, Jessie, CA (Fisher)
Shafer, Anna, PA
Smith, Helen
Squire, Emily (Beath)
Toddings, Dorothy, NJ (Rehm)
White, Arline (Buckley)

Fig. 17.   Elizabeth Morrill ('10) wearing student uniform of the period.

Nursing is an art; and if it is to be made an art, it requires as exclusive a devotion, as hard a preparation, as any painter's or sculptor's work; for what is the having to do with dead canvas or cold marble, compared with having to do with the living body— the temple of God's spirit? It is one of the Fine Arts; I had almost said the finest of the Fine Arts.

Florence Nightingale (1820-1910).

This marked the 20th year of founding of the School of Nursing. Jefferson's educational and practical instruction in nursing had proven itself to be effective. The hospital staff physicians did most of the teaching of basic subjects. The Directress and head nurses gave the bedside instruction. Whenever a graduate nurse was not available, a senior student would be placed in charge of a ward and would help in instruction of the less advanced students. Classes were held wherever space could be found near the wards. Oral examinations of the students by the physicians were usually conducted in their offices.

There were 24 graduates this year.

CLASS OF 1911

Armstrong, Gertrude, NY
Boyer, Amanda, IL (Bolger)
Calhoun, Mary, PA (McNitt)
Casperson, Elsie M., NJ
Daly, Rhoda (Smith)
Danser, Virginia, PA (Scattergood)
Dickey, Nelle, PA (Wilson)
Herrman, Emilie, CA
Hill, Jessie
Jackson, Edna, NH (Noyes)
Jones, Elizabeth, PA
Jordan, Margaret

Minnier, Ellen, PA (Gift)
Morgan, Alberta, MN (Hall)
Moser, Bertha, PA (Price)
Moser, Esther, PA
Oburn, Minnie, PA (Adams)
Pullen, Laura, NJ
Smith, Eleanore, CA (Spear)
Sudo, Maya
Swentzel, Marguerite, PA (Evans)
Terrill, Beatrice (Zinn)
VanWinkle, Bessie, VT (Perley)
Weems, Mary

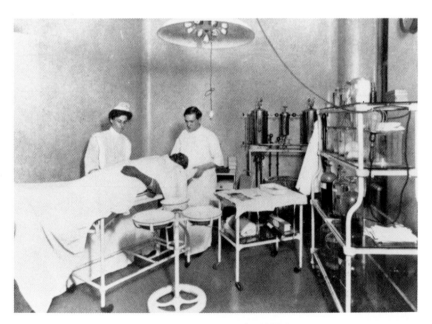

Emergency room (early 1900s).

The Jefferson Nurses' Alumnae Association Relief Fund was established this year.

There were 12 graduates.

CLASS OF 1912

Bechtel, Emma, PA
Buckman, Leila, PA (Kesslinger)
Good, Gail, PA (Boyd)
Greig, Jessie, PA (Hicks)
Klink, Helen, PA (Pollack)
Morgan, Mary, PA (Ford)

Shearer, Nora, PA (Parsons)
Shively, Elizabeth, PA (Wilfong)
Stalford, Bessie, PA
Thrasher, Belle, IL (Carr)
Vernon, Dorothy, PA (Wayland)
Waller, Leona, DE (Drumm)

Nurses' reception room in 1877 Hospital Building.

~ 1913 ~

Plans were developed this year for a Department for Diseases of the Chest at 236-238 Pine Street, a facility that would aid the prevention and treatment of tuberculosis as well as provide additional nursing experience for the students.

The 25 graduates were as follows:

Bartley, Mary, IRELAND
Bateman, Helen, PA
Bush, Margaret, PA
Christensen, Olga, DENMARK
Conrad, Margaret, PA (Weaver)
Delker, Linda, PA
Detwiler, Sara, PA
Emmert, Mae, MD (Seibert)
Gibb, Helen C., PA
High, Carrie, PA (Campbell)
Kendall, K. Ella, PA
Lomison, Edith, PA

Luman, Myrtle, PA (Shallow)
MacAdams, Marian, NY (Thompson)
Mann, Christine, PA (Butler)
Meisenhelder, Mabel, PA (Dyson)
Orr, Margaret, PA (Lull)
Schwab, Anna, PA
Snyder, Anna, PA (MacMurray)
Snyder, Minnie (Dean)
Staub, Harriet, PA (Chambers)
Swank, Effie, PA
Waters, Essie, DE (Spooner)
Welker, Ada, PA
Zimmerman, Ada, PA

Practically there should be for each of you a busy, useful, and happy life; more you cannot expect; a greater blessing the world cannot bestow. Busy you will certainly be, as the demand is great, both in private and public, for women with your training. Useful your lives must be, as you will care for those who cannot care for themselves, and who need about them, in the day of tribulation, gentle hands and tender hearts. And happy lives shall be yours, because busy and useful; having been initiated into the great secret—that happiness lies in the absorption in some vocation which satisfies the soul; that we have here to add what we can to, not to get what we can *from* life.

William Osler: Doctor and Nurse. Address, Johns Hopkins Hospital, 1891.

The opening of the Department for Diseases of the Chest, as planned during 1913, occurred in April of this year (Fig. 18). Good nursing care had become a very important aspect in the treatment of tuberculosis at this time and would be so for the next three decades.

This Class numbered 38 graduates.

CLASS OF 1914

Adams, Martha, MD (Stubblefield)
Barnett, Marguerite, PA
Bergey, Sara R., PA
Boller, Mabel G., PA
Brown, Clara
Call, Mary, OH (Hilbish)
Cribbs, Bertha (Vauclain)
Crouse, Mary, PA (Bancroft)
Davies, Annie, PA (Barnhard)
Dolan, Ethel, PA
Girton, Ethel M., PA
Grosch, Helen, PA
Hallman, Mary, OH (Lindsey)
Herring, Effie, PA
Hill, Nellie G., PA
Hobbs, Ellen, WV
Homewood, Mary, MD (Gary)
Knock, Emma, DE
Lane, Cora, WV (Osterblom)

Lesser, E. Irene, PA (Hindle)
Lewis, Gwendolyn, PA (Mann)
Libengood, Stella, CA (Brenner)
Logue, Katherine
Love, Jessica, KY
McNulty, Rose, NY (Graham)
Miller, Mabel B., PA
Ott, Effie, PA (Hivner)
Potticher, Druce, DC (Slye)
Rodgers, Mary, OH (Knarr)
Sprenkle, Myrtle (Ake)
Stager, Lettie
Sturgeon, Jane S., ENGLAND
Trumbauer, Matilda, PA (Knerr)
Turriff, Marion
Weisenberg, Melanie
Witmer, Katherine, NY (Adolph)
Womer, Kathryn, GA (Harris)
Wood, Martha, PA (Baker)

Fig. 18.   Department for Diseases of the Chest (1914) at 236-238 Pine Street.

Outpatient Department for Diseases of the Chest at 236-238 Pine Street.

There is a dread disease which so prepares its victim, as it were, for death; which so refines it of its grosser aspect, and throws around familiar looks, unearthly indications of the coming change—a dread disease, in which the struggle between soul and body is so gradual, quiet, and solemn, and the result so sure, that day by day, and grain by grain, the mortal part wastes and withers away, so that the spirit grows light and sanguine with its lightening load, and, feeling immortality at hand, deems it but a new term of mortal life—a disease in which death and life are so strangely blended, that death takes the glow and hue of life, and life the gaunt and grisly form of death— a disease which medicine never cured, wealth warded off, or poverty could boast exemption from—which sometimes moves in giant strides, and sometimes at a tardy sluggish pace, but, slow or quick, is ever sure and certain.

Reflections of Charles Dickens (1812-1870)
in *Nicholas Nickelby*, regarding tuberculosis (consumption),
the leading cause of death during the nineteenth century.

~ 1915 ~

Miss Clara E. ("Tillie") Melville, from the Class of 1910, who had been the assistant to Miss Laughlin, became the Directress this year (Fig. 19). She would serve in this capacity until her death in 1937. In accord with the times, she was a strict disciplinarian. As a legendary figure, she contributed greatly to the welfare and progress of the School.

The Class graduates numberd 20.

CLASS OF 1915

Allen, Mattie, PA (Turner)
Butz, Ada, IL (Arsentos)
Cassel, Carrie, CA (Coffman)
Dorsey, Margaret, PA
Faubel, Eleanor, PA
Gonder, Sara, PA
Heaton, Elizabeth T., PA
James, Mary (Short)
Kassabian, Virginia (Bohjelian)
Lewis, Adele M., PA

Litter, Jeanette, OH
Martin, Nora, PA (Charlton)
Mathews, Dorothy, DE
Owens, Mary A.
Peters, Minerva (Bilger)
Rorabaugh, Jessie, DE (Hearn)
Smith, Ethel, PA (Genzmer)
Warren, Ann, NY (Howard)
Warren, Dorothy, MS (Brown)
Yochim, Margaret

Fig. 19.   Clara E. Melville ('10), Directress (1915-37).

~ 1916 ~

The Women's Auxiliary formed the Nurses' Home Committee. This activity provided residential comforts and recreational facilities that softened the hard features of student life. Concern over the War in Europe had little impact on the curriculum in this pre-War year.

There were 24 graduates.

CLASS OF 1916

Black, Lydia Ann, DE (Cannon)
Brewer, Myrtle, NJ (Thrasher)
Browning, Florence J., MD
Butler, Frances, PA (Pangburn)
Campbell, Edna, PA (Boar)
Crossley, Mabel, PA
Daxter, Flora, PA
Day, Loleta, PA (Steen)
Depp, Martha, PA (Templeton)
Dillon, Gertrude, ME (Brown)
Duke, Mary, MO (Holton)
Guerin, Agnes C.A., 86

Heverly, Mary, PA (Moore)
Hodler, Adele, PA (Connell)
Hughes, Marie, PA (Byrne)
Jackson, Mildred, PA (Pillmore)
Morgan, Jane, PA (Morgan)
Musser, Mary E., PA
Myers, Wilona, PA (Rollwitz)
Rowe, Effie, CANADA (Billingsley)
Shoemaker, Ella, PA
Troester, Christine (Fellows)
Williams, Mae, PA
Witmer, Laura, PA

Remember that for doctors and nurses, the most important canal in the world is not the Panama, the Suez, the Soo, the Kiel, or any other of the great geographical canals of the world, but, as has been well said, the alimentary. Watch, therefore, with scrupulous care everything that enters it. Learn how to cook the little appetizing bonnes bouches *and (do not forget this) to serve them with the daintiness which stimulates or even evokes an appetite, just as slovenliness dulls or even destroys it.*

W.W Keen, M.D. (1837-1932)
Address to the Graduating Class of Nurses,
Allentown Hospital, May 27, 1915.

~ 1917 ~

In World War I, Jefferson formed a Base Hospital #38 in which 100 nurses, organized by Miss Clara Melville as Chief Nurse, comprised a Unit stationed in Nantes, France (Fig. 20). Under the command of Dr. William M.L. Coplin, Professor of Pathology, they rendered care in the 1,000-bed hospital. Miss Adele M. Lewis (Fig. 21), Class of 1915, subsequently served for three more decades as Head Nurse in the "Old Main" Hospital.

There were 36 graduates in the Class.

CLASS OF 1917

Badorf, Myra, PA
Black, Mabel, PA
Bowen, Lillian E., PA (Plumb)
Dietrich, Minnie, PA (Gregory)
Eby, Virginia, PA (Lee)
Eppler, Edith, PA
Faust, Ethel, PA
Fordyce, Pearl, PA (English)
Grove, Frances M., PA
Haag, Irene, PA (Beck)
Hagey, Vera, PA (Brouillet)
Hollenbaugh, Pearl, PA
Hollman, Mary A., PA
Huey, Caddie G., PA (Fleming)
Iles, Sara, KY (Paynter)
Jones, Fannie M., PA (McAleer)
Jones, Florence M., PA
Kirby, Hilda, DE

Knerr, Carrie E., PA
Lane, Ida E.
Lloyd, Maggie N., PA (Clark)
Longacre, Mary, PA (Grim)
McLean, Margaret, PA (Jones)
Miller, Elsie J., PA
Miller, Nellie V., PA (Mehler)
Paulson, Erma R., PA
Rogers, Anna, PA (Cannon)
Serfass, Sallie, A., PA
Shea, Winifred D., PA
Smith, Marion E., PA (Lauffer)
Stephens, Anna, DE (Griffin)
Temple, Lillian, PA (Faggart)
Vaughn, Alice, PA (Lucas)
Young, Ada, PA (McNeal)
Ziegler, Amy F., PA (Ide)
Zudrell, Jennie, PA (Levy)

Fig. 20.   Jefferson's Base Hospital #38 in World War I, established in Nantes, France.

Fig. 21. Adele M. Lewis ('15) in World War I Base Hospital #38. She served as Head Nurse for more than three decades in "Old Main Hospital."

The trained nurse has given nursing the human or shall we say, the divine touch, and made the hospital desirable for patients with serious ailments regardless of their home advantages.

Charles H. Mayo (1865-1939).

In the absence of Miss Melville who was on active duty as Chief Nurse at Base Hospital #38 in Nantes, France, Miss Nora E. Shoemaker acted as Directress of Nurses.

In the autumn of this year there broke out the worst pandemic of influenza on record. In the United States alone there were more than 4,000 new cases a day. All hospitals, including Jefferson, were loaded beyond capacity. Provision of adequate nursing care was impossible. Many of the nurses fell ill and five of the students died.

The first list of approved Nursing Schools in Pennsylvania was published this year. Jefferson's School promptly was among them.

The 27 graduates were:

CLASS OF 1918

Bitner, Effie, PA (Girton)
Brechin, Mae, PA (Boyle)
Craig, Ada, NY (Falkingham)
Darone, Verna
Davis, Helen, PA (Livingston)
Dunn, Elsie E., AL
Goupp, Lydia, MI (Gray)
Gurd, Verna, OK (Taylor)
Hardy, Rose
Huff, Grace, PA (MacDonald)
Johnson, Anna, PA (Brumbaugh)
Keiffer, Blanche (String)
Koons, Gertrude, NC (Blalock)

McCormack, Marion, PA
Moss, Naomi, PA
O'Neill, Mary, PA (Ellies)
Pilling, Charlotte (Dotson)
Plummer, Helen R., (Terrell)
Schoen, Elva, PA
Shawfield, Cora
Smith, Elizabeth P., NY
Sykes, Amanda 86 (Nicholson)
Talley, Nanne, CA
Tomlin, Elsie, NY
Webster, Dorothy, PA (Taggart)
Wheildon, Lillian
Woods, Margaret, NY

S.S. "Nopatin," transport ship to Base Hospital #38.

During World War I, 69 Jefferson nurses served with the Red Cross. This was in addition to the 100 stationed in France. In this year and for several following, the Nurses Alumnae Association donated $200 to the Red Cross.

The graduates numbered 33.

CLASS OF 1919

Alexander, Ida M., NC
Bishop, Esther, PA (McConnell)
Bostic, India, PA (Collins)
Brown, Evelyn, PA (Hanst)
Dwyer, Nora B., PA
Elliott, Velma, OH (Musser)
Fitzgerald, Anna, MD (Nissler)
Fortner, Helen M., PA
Goodyear, Mildred, PA (Wismer)
Hillyer, Lucy M.E., PA
Hinderliter, Emma, PA (Snyder)
Hovis, Mabel, PA (Grove)
Jobson, Clara E., PA
Johnson, Adelaide G., PA
Johnson, Zayda B., NY
Lawrence, Ethel, PA (Hannon)

Lingo, Miriam, DE (MacGinnis)
MacGinness, Anna, PA (Wible)
McCullough, Eliza, PA (Williams)
McNerney, Hazel E., MA
Melander, Anna M., PA
Myers, Effie, PA
Neely, Margaret, PA (Boston)
Rice, A. Irene, PA (Paist)
Ricker, Blanche M., PA
Satterlee, Bernice, PA (Ross)
Silbermann, Hilda, PA (Cole)
Swisher, Ida, PA (O'Hara)
Warner, Bertha, PA (Koons)
Wary, Cora M., PA (Staggs)
Williams, Hattie, PA (Book)
Williams, Sadie, PA (Long)
Worthington, Alice L., PA

Receiving ward of Base Hospital #38.

The post-War curriculum was expanded to include numerous courses beyond the basic ones previously taught. The courses consisted of anatomy, chemistry, bacteriology, medical nursing, drugs and solutions, hygiene, dietetics, orthopaedics, pediatrics, nursing ethics, bandaging and massage.

Louise Graves, of this class, became a pioneer nurse anesthetist.

There were 36 graduates.

CLASS OF 1920

Bennett, Dorothy, PA (Fitzgerald)
Bigney, Henrietta, ME
Bohlin, Helen, PA (Price)
Campbell, Anna, PA (Trego)
Cecil, Leona, MT (Duran)
Cleaves, Olive J., ME
Connell, Margaret A., MD
Crouse, Ada Kathryn, PA
Cuthbert, Margaret, NY (Laughlin)
Cypher, Edith V., PA
Dewitt, Ann V., PA
Goodwin, Olive, NC
Graves, M. Louise, PA
Griffin, Sara, VA (Turner)
Hafler, Viola, PA (Shafer)
Hartman, Francis Ida, PA
Heritage, Mae Dare, NJ (Williamson)
Howard, Ethel Irene, PA (Marsh)

Lewdrop, Estelle M., NJ (Fleming)
Neibert, Alice, PA (Fulmer)
Neifert, Blanche Edna, PA
Owl, Agnes, NC (Madrano)
Rainey, Carolyn Evelyn, PA
Ramey, Edith, PA (Harr)
Reimer, Myrtle Pearl, PA
Schmucker, Carrie Katharine, PA
Scott, Sarah Virginia, VA
Smith, Bernice Leona, PA (Zeigler)
Steigerwalt, Viola E., PA (Irsic)
Strouse, Florence Ellen, PA (Speigelmire)
Tegge, Olga Rosalyn, PA (Higgins)
Thomas, Rhoda Rebecca, PA (Guertin)
Wilson, Ann, DE (Hall)
Winner, Johanna Kathleen, PA
Woods, Pauline, PA (Montgomery)
Zufall, Nora Llewellyn, PA

Now that man has harnessed nature's forces, speeds messages through space, rides the air, travels under the sea, and calls the universe his own, is it not possible to possess his very soul, encourage humane creative thought and strangle the demons that have grown great and insolent within him? Dare not the still small voices of conscience rise to thunder tones that shall awaken nations from the lethargy of myth and tradition that makes war glorious and calls warriors heroes? Can't its needless horrors be impressed upon mankind and its pettiness and futility be made obvious? If, through the aeons man has failed, and apparently he has, then, "Woman, where art thou?" Page woman.

W.M.L. Coplin, M.D. (1864-1928)
Director, U.S. Army Base Hospital #38.

~ 1921 ~

There was a growing appreciation of nursing care and Jefferson graduate nurses found many employment opportunities. They filled responsible positions in every field of nursing.

The Class, the largest thus far, consisted of 43 graduates.

Arthur, Elizabeth J., PA
Clendenin, Frances, MD (Platt)
Dienstel, Nellie, PA (Crandall)
Dupay, Elizabeth R., NJ
Enck, Miriam, PA (MacFarland)
Fitzgerald, Henrietta, MD (Spruance)
Fitzkee, Effie, PA (Furey)
Flickinger, Katherine, PA (Aagaard)
Fuller, Maude, NY (Spencer)
Garner, Elizabeth, PA (Miller)
Gillespie, Emma, DE (Frigar)
Henry, Genevieve A., FL
Hunt, Ethel M., SCOTLAND
Irwin, Frances, PA (Heess)
Keller, Verna, PA (Roberts)
Kirk, Florence D., NJ
Klipple, Arlene, PA (Reed)
Kuller, Agnes, PANAMA (Reeves)
Kutz, Alma, PA (Kaufman)
Kutz, Jennie E., PA
Lee, Rhea H., FL (Neylon)

Maling, Laura, ME
Malloy, Anna, PA (Craver)
Maull, Ethyl S., DE
McGowan, Ruth, PA (Davis)
Noonan, Lena, PA (Davis)
Osbaugh, Sue A., PA
Parsons, Anne, NC (Weaver)
Peterman, Della (Speidel)
Peterson, Mildred, PA (Reese)
Prophet, Nancy, OK (Roche)
Purcell, Katharine, PA (Smock)
Purinton, Ruth, NJ
Rhule, Almira, PA (Kutz)
Roller, Venone Grace, PA
Skelton, M. May, PA (Roth)
Steinbock, Freda, PA
Swaar, Effie, PA (Lehmann)
VannAuker, Priscilla, PA (Danforth)
Weaver, Ruth, PA (Hartman)
Wilkinson, Florence A., ENGLAND
Williams, Helen, PA (Niles)
Wolf, Jennetta, PA

The newcomers were young ladies with high ideals and earnest purposes. They were ruled by conscience. They were educated, were being carefully taught their profession, were dainty, tender, and charming. They worked rapidly and certainly, without noise or hurry. They knew what was wanted and how to have it ready. They worked not only with their hands but also with their brains and hearts. They watched their patients through the long hours with the calm self-reliance and confidence which bore a message of hope, with the knowledge that at once detected a change for the better or for the worse, with a tenderness that helped to blunt the very arrows of anguish.

John Chalmers DaCosta, M.D. (1863-1933)
From his *Papers and Speeches.*

Demolition of the 1877 Hospital at 1020 Sansom Street was started this year, requiring new facilities to lodge the nurses. On August 14, some newly acquired houses at 1012, 1014, and 1016 Spruce Street were opened for occupancy by the nurses (Fig. 22). The yard space in the back of these buildings was approved for construction of new lodging facilities, scheduled for 1925.

There were 26 graduates.

Fig. 22. Nurses' residence entrance at 1014 Spruce Street (1922).

Artley, Mary, PA (Tully)
Berlin, Elizabeth, PA (Kidney)
Boggess, Flora M., WV (Burg)
Cope, Florence, PA (Garner)
Emig, Viletta, PA (May)
Gonder, Anna, PA (Ward)
Harp, Elizabeth, MD (Wilson)
Jones, Frances H., PA (Sturgeon)
Lawson, Lois, CANADA
Long, Iva M., PA (Heilman)
Maybee, Grace, PA (Troutman)
Neibert, Jessie, PA (Fletcher)
Phillips, Ruth E., PA

Piquenais, Angele, FRANCE
Reamy, Mary A., PA
Rowe, Sarah E., MD
Schoch, Agnes S., PA
Sheffler, Emma B., PA (Turton)
Sorden, Sylvia A., PA (Lambdin)
Starr, Claudia, WV (Wiedlund)
Strunk, Frances M., PA (Gleoggler)
Swanson, Esther M., NY (Schubert)
Uhler, Hannah, PA (Buffington)
Weber, Helene, PA
Welsh, Mary Pierce, VA
Wood, Carrie, PA (Pollock)

Ever since Blockley (Philadelphia General Hospital) days my respect for the trained nurse and my confidence in her have increased. She is an absolutely necessary part of a hospital. You can't run a hospital without her. An institution with a training school has given bonds to have first-class nurses. I do not dare to stand here and counsel the young ladies of the training school. I no more dare to do so than I would dare, stained as I am with worldly contact, to go into a fairy garden and admonish the lilies to be fair and bid the violets to be true. But I do bow in respectful admiration to those who devote their lives to this most useful calling.

John Chalmers DaCosta, M.D. (1863-1933)
From his *Papers and Speeches.*

Facilities for teaching were once more upgraded with additional classroom space to accommodate the increasing number of students. Two more laboratories were added within the 1907 Hospital, one for dietetics and one for chemistry (Fig. 23).

The Class consisted of 40 graduates.

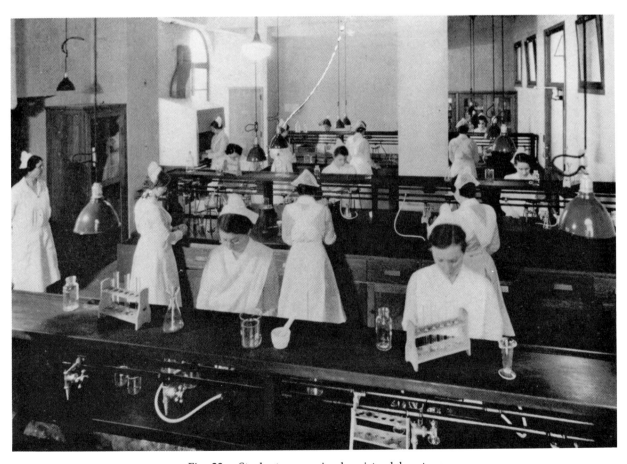

Fig. 23.   Student nurses in chemistry laboratory.

Beck, Mary, PA (Hinkel)
Beyer, Edith, PA (Lyall)
Blevins, Rachel, NC (Marshbourn)
Botdorf, Esther, PA (Sickler)
Bowser, Mary Esther, PABenton
Brunner, Clara M., PA
Cornelius, Zelma, PA (Brennan)
Dailey, Miriam A., TN
Dewitt, Lulu, PA (Hunsinger)
Diseroad, Rosa B., PA
Donaldson, C. Margaret, PA
Doxtator, Elizabeth, KS
Glenn, Martha, PA
Herrity, Sarah, PA (Corson)
Hill, Laura, PA
Hook, Grace, PA (Woltersdorf)
Kauffman, Florence, PA
Kelly, Emily, PA
Kline, Maude, PA (Steiner)
Knoll, Matilda, NJ (Petersen)

Knoll, Ruth, NJ (Thompson)
Lauer, Gertrude M., PA
MacDonough, Jennie, PA
Malsbury, S. Elizabeth, NJ (Roark)
McGinnis, Roxie, WV (Smith)
McLaughlin, Catherine, NC
Moser, Pearl, PA (Shappell)
Nonnemacher, Eva L., PA
Orr, Mae, PA
Powell, Alice, PA (Faries)
Reed, Helen B., PA (Noffin)
Roberts, Ruth, PA
Rue, Gladys C.
Sanders, Marie, PA (Sanders)
Shambach, Anna, PA (Hopkins)
Strunk, Jessie, PA (Reed)
VanSant, Evelyn, PA (Whitfield)
White, Rena L., PA
Wrights, Grace, PA
Yingst, Clara, PA

Student nurses in diet kitchen

Returning from Red Cross duty, Miss Nora E. Shoemaker (Fig. 24) was appointed the first Directress of Nursing Education under Nursing Directress Clara E. Melville. The Samuel Gustine Thompson Annex, Jefferson's new 16-story modern hospital building on Sansom Street between Tenth and Eleventh was opened November 1, further increasing the total bed capacity and requiring larger numbers of nurses (Fig. 25).

The graduates numbered 28.

Fig. 24. Nora E. Shoemaker, first Directress of Nursing Education in 1924 and Directress of the School (1937-43).

CLASS OF 1924

Bakkelid, Johanna, PA (Campbell)
Blessing, Helen K., 87 (Sniscak)
Clarke, Lillian A., MD (Weber)
Dougherty, Cecelia M., PA (Unkle)
Eavenson, Sara M., PA (Yocum)
Edler, G. Altha, PA
Felter, Mildred, PA (Semler)
Ganster, Julia, PA

Greenwalt, Kathryn, PA (Wilson)
Harley, Lillian M., PA (Pratt)
Hasenfuss, Helen, PA (Beale)
Hepler, Hilda, PA (Griffith)
Hopkins, Nina Lee, DE
Johnson, Hilda, PA (Edholm)
LaMure, Ethel, FRANCE (Muchnick)
Larson, Lillian E., PA (Hudson)

Lucas, Josephine R.
McCloskey, Genevieve, PA (Lewis)
Moseman, Lydia E., PA (Griffith)
Owens, Veronica C., PA
Randels, Lulu R., PA (Kuntz)
Reinhard, Catherine, PA (Gregory)

Rowles, Evelyn L., PA (Fore)
Steigerwalt, Estelle, PA (Taylor)
Tash, Kathryn L., PA
Uffelman, Mary E., DE
Wasilko, Jeannette, PA (Phillips)
Welker, Mary A., PA (O'Connor)

Fig. 25.   Thompson Annex (1924).

The new nurses' home in the rear of 1014 Spruce Street was occupied May 15. It provided single rooms for 90 nurses on six floors. In 1926 two floors were added to increase the total rooms to 120 (Fig. 26).

The gradual change in the style of nurses' uniforms caused a shortening this year of skirts to five inches from floor level (Fig. 27).

An outstanding member of this class was Nora I. Smith ('25), an operating room nurse supervisor who was seen regularly in Dr. Shallow's Wednesday surgical clinics (Fig. 28).

There were 43 graduates.

Fig. 26.   Architect's sketch of proposed new Nurses' Home.

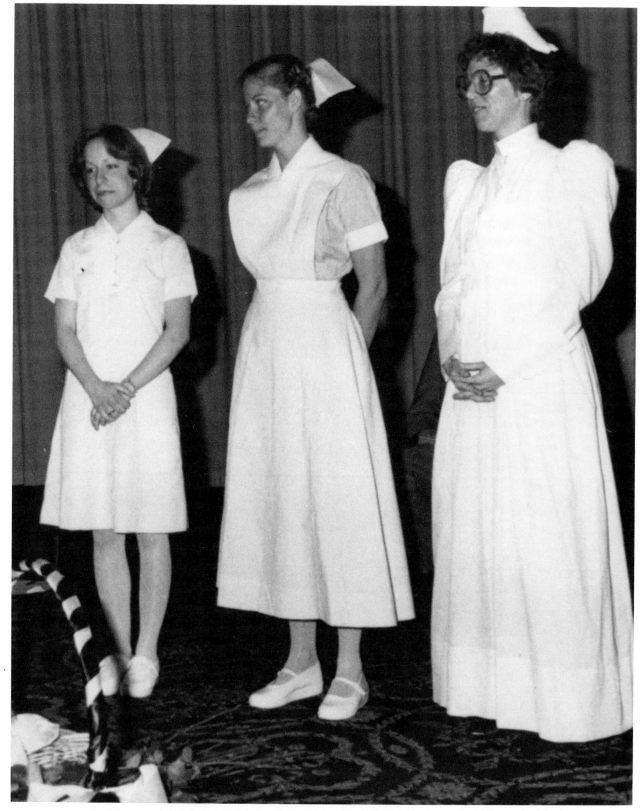

Fig. 27. Changes in nurses' uniforms: 1894-1925 (right); 1925-59 (middle); 1959-82 (left).

1925

Albright, Mary E., PA
Barnhart, Bernice, PA (Pfeiffer)
Bashore, Edith (Ogder)
Bergner, Anne, PA (Newhouse)
Bratton, Anne L., PA
Callahan, Gladys, PA (Floyd)
Carpenter, Ethyle G., PA
Dilliard, Lillie, PA (Hartman)
Duffy, Hazel M., PA
Farquhar, Elizabeth, PA (Jones)
Gantz, Maud W., PA (Busch)
George, Elizabeth C., PA (Lewis)
Gilbert, Helen E., PA (Haas)
Gilbert, Sara E., PA (Conrad)
Goldberg, Myrtle, PA (Frank)
Haines, Alverta, PA (Kaufmann)
Hammond, Mildred G., PA
Hauck, Elsie, PA
Hendricks, Deliah T., PA (Lloyd)
Howeter, Anna, PA (Hildebrand)
Kelly, Alice P., PA

Kimble, Mary A., PA
Knapp, A. Pauline, PA (Shallcross)
Kroupa, Mildred, PA (Okunishi)
Lloyd, Ethel, PA (Grove)
Luchsinger, Clara I., PA
MacDonald, Margaret Mary, PA (Staples)
MacGregor, Margaret, CANADA (Lehman)
Marquardt, Mafalda G., PA (Ziegler)
McCoy, Barbara M., PA (Mcguigan)
McKinstry, Mary A., PA
Owens, Della I., PA
Robinson, Marian L., PA (Briggs)
Scanlin, Mary A., PA (Harrar)
Scotton, E. Elizabeth, (Poore)
Secor, Marjorie J., PA (Cameron)
Shearer, Pleasant H., PA (Larchuk)
Smith, Nora I., PA (Fry)
Stewart, Elizabeth, PA (Ewing)
Styver, Marian H., PA (Carey)
Wetmore, Rowena E., PA (Vickerman)
Yocum, M. Elizabeth, MD (Sieling)
Yoder, Mabel C., PA (Kreiger)

Fig. 28.   Nora Smith ('25), supervisor of operating rooms.

~ 1926 ~

The Sesqui-Centennial Exposition of the United States opened in Philadelphia for six months this year and drew more than six million visitors. The Delaware River Bridge, later renamed the Benjamin Franklin, also opened. Although the School of Nursing did not celebrate the 35 years since the founding, it nevertheless had much for which to be proud.

The Class was the largest thus far, numbering 52.

CLASS OF 1926

Akers, Martha C. (Boyd)
Anthony, Blanche M., PA (Chedester)
Bixler, Beatrice H., PA
Bonenberger, Mary E., PA
Bray, Martha R., PA (Clark)
Breth, Mary C., PA
Bryan, A. Lucille, PA (Spangler)
Buxton, Margaret A., PA (Pinkerton)
Casper, Alice W., PA (Wright)
Deitrich, Laura V., (Gross)
Doran, Elsie M., PA (Chase)
Durovick, Agnes, PA (Tomasula)
Engle, Dorothy P., PA (Daniels)
Finn, C. Eleanor, PA (Stewart)
Fisher, L. Ruth, PA
Fitz, Phoebe E., PA (McCleaf)
Foulk, Marion, PA (Reighard)
Fowler, Isabel, PA (Diezel)
Fruehan, Mayda L., PA (Maxwell)
Frye, Kathryn M., PA
Getz, Agnes L., PA (Milham)
Ginn, Camille R., DE (Insolo)
Godshalk, Gwendolyn I., PA (Cressman)
Greenlee, Mary C., (Patterson)
Grundkovski, Ernestine M., NY (Rowe)
Grundkovski, Freida A., NY (Wood)

Gustitis, Adele I., PA (Ruppersburg)
Hatfield, Mildred L., DEMowry
Howard, Elizabeth W., PA (Farmer)
Lamon, Mary J., PA (Roller)
Lanks, Mary E., PA (Peterson)
Lightner, Adda R., PA (Stambaugh)
Malone, Mildred M., PA (Bein)
McDevitt, Jane A., IA (Seddon)
McKinney, Margot, PA (Cassaday)
Miles, Josephine C., PA (Dickerson)
Radar, Marion S., PA (Buchanan)
Recklitis, Anna M., PA
Regnier, Kathryn M., IA (Sidewell)
Riggs, Anna H., VA (Ricketson)
Schaefer, Emma, DE (Reinhart)
Shermer, Nellie M., PA (Waterman)
Sickler, Anna F., PA (Polk)
Smith, Ruth E., PA (Davis)
Stewen-Steinheil, Dagmar, FINLAND (Boton)
Thomas, Margaret E., PA (Newhall)
Wall, Pauline K., PA (Still)
Waltman, Grace E., PA (Kuhns)
West, India A., PA (Feller)
Wilkinson, Mary I., ENGLAND
Workinger, Marjorie E., PA
Worthing, Ruby E., PA

I know that much disquietude, if not unhappiness, has been felt by students, and especially by the best informed and best disposed, when, at the entrance of their profession, they have been met by obstacles which seem insurmountable.

Peter Mere Latham (1789-1875)

Although only indirectly related to the School of Nursing, a campaign goal of $2 million for public solicitation was launched this year. Plans called for a new Medical College Building to be erected at 1025 Walnut Street. The existing College Building at Tenth and Walnut Streets was to be altered for outpatient departments and nursing education. As events turned out, the latter building was replaced by the Curtis Clinic.

There were 35 graduates this year.

CLASS OF 1927

Acheson, Viola, PA (Hayes)
Austin, Hazel E., PA
Baker, Frances A., PA (Crossan)
Bishop, Viola M., PA (Kane)
Brinkman, Anna C., PA (Faust)
Carey, Margaret A., DE
Collins, Alice J., DE (McManus)
Dreisbach, Pauline H., PA (Crown)
Duncan, Lorelle B., PA (Benner)
Fairlamb, Orpha, PA (Lucas)
Freudenberger, Bernice, PA (Collins)
Gerber, Clara I., PAHardy
Greathouse, Carolyn, KY (Miller)
Hawk, Florence S., NJ
Hibbard, Anna G., PADunlap
Kevel, Isabella R., PA (Heverly)
Klingeman, Mildred R., PA (Sellers)

Knoll, Lorraine M., PA (Mayers)
McElwee, Pauline M., PA (Gillen)
Mertz, Lillian M., PA
Meyer, Marie, GERMANY
Minner, Urieta M., DE (Coakly)
Pfaltzgraff, Sara E., PA (Barrick)
Phillips, Anne H., PA
Pletcher, Lillian M., PA (Holter)
Riden, Edna M.
Riland, Martha E., PA
Roesch, Mary, PA (McLaughlin)
Saylor, Helen E., PA (Amelia)
Sickler, Bella E., NJ (Dunn)
Stickler, Myrtle L., PA (Clough-Lee)
Tiracchia, Filomema R., PA (Doherty)
Watkins, Frances S., PA (Polm)
Weiss, Esther M., (Wilson)
White, Myra E., DE (Hayes)

Staff nurses in library of Thompson Building.

In this year an affiliation was established between the Pennsylvania Hospital for Nervous and Mental Diseases and the Jefferson Nursing School to train male nurses for a period of 11 months in surgery, medicine, urology, the operating room and dispensary. Male nurses, however, would not be accepted into the training program at Jefferson itself until 1973.

Despite the rigors of the training program, the morale in the school remained high and applications were increasing (Fig. 29).

Dr. Harvey M. Righter, a graduate of Jefferson Medical College (1896), member of the surgical faculty, and much admired friend of the nurses, presented a long stemmed red rose to each member of the class at graduation this year. This impressive gesture was continued at successive graduations and led to the tradition of the "Rose Arch" under which each graduate would pass to receive her diploma (Fig. 31).

The graduating Class numbered 56.

Fig. 29.   Probationers (1928).

Angwin, Lillian, PA (Nigh)
Bargar, Margery E., PA
Bartlett, Helen G., PA (Brophy)
Benninger, Ruth M., PA (Coover)
Bevan, Mary E., PA (Luckett)
Bingel, Esther A., PA
Black, Lavina A., PA (Ralston)
Bowers, Marion E., PA
Breunig, Grace E., (Meikle)
Carey, Lena, PA (Davis)
Carleton, Laura A., PA (Short)
Cartwright, Clara J., PA (Boyles)
Chubb, Hazel M., PA
Clarkson, Lydia L., PA
Currie, Mhora S., NJ (Newsom)
Derr, Myrtle I., PA (Hess)
Ellis, Grace C., DE (Nauman)
Fleck, Katherine S., PA (Saunders)
Goldberg, Louise E., PA
Gouker, Emma L., PA (Naugle)
Henderson, V. Mae, PA (Shindel)
Herrman, Adda I., PA
Hess, Frances M., PA (Currie)

Hudkins, Winifred E., PA (Gleitz)
Jensen, Elvira 87 (Herb)
Jerrett, L. Marion, NEWFOUNDLAND (Bartlett)
Kahler, Margart F., PA (Baldwin)
Kinkead, Adalyne, PA (Casper)
Kreiser, Viola A., PA (Tredick)
Lanning, Ruth L., NJ (McCarter)
MacArthur, Gertrude K., PA (Deiber)
Malone, Marguerite G., PA (Peters)
Martin, Margaret E., PA (Lauchle)
Neely, S. Elizabeth, PA (Joy)
Noll, Beatrice E., PA (Smith)
Phetteplace, Doris G., MD (Wise)
Pierson, Frances, FL (Wolf)
Rebert, Ellen L., PA (Evey)
Rebert, Helen (Murray)
Roth, Ethel L., PA (Groundwater)
Rougeau, Amelie, NJ (Jaspers)
Roush, Alma E., PA (Ross)
Scott, Edna W., PA
Shearer, Edna A., PA (Richards)
Smith, Dorothy E., PA (Bennett)
Smith, Phoebe E., (Martin)

Fig. 30.   Harvey M. Righter (JMC, 1896), surgical faculty member, started the tradition of the "Rose Arch".

Fig. 31.   The "Rose Arch" at graduation.

Stauffer, Mary A., PA (Malick)
Stoner, Elizabeth M., PA (Davidson)
Warner, Marion F., PA (Scarlet)
Welsko, Anna L., PA (Billie)
Wertman, Hannah E., PA (Umpstead)

Whitmore, Katherine E., PA (Heath)
Wilson, Esther M., PA (Knoll)
Wilson, Margaret N., NJ (Kenerup)
Worman, Ruth M., MD (Bowers)
Yergy, Lelia E., PA

Playroom for children in "Old Main Hospital."

The onset of the economic depression had little immediate impact on the School of Nursing. In fact, in the next few years enrollment and the number of graduates actually increased despite discontinuation of the small monthly stipend provided for students. The daily census in the hospital exceeded 500 patients and gradually more staff nurses were employed.

Mabel C. Prevost, a 1929 graduate, joined the teaching staff, advancing to Directress of Nursing from 1953 to 1958 and then on to Assistant Hospital Director until 1974 (Fig. 32).

Ruth Jeffries Koch (Fig. 33) of this class was the granddaughter of the world renowned discoverer of the tubercle vacillus, Robert Koch.

There were 50 graduates.

CLASS OF 1929

Alston, Mary Louise, NJ (Hoenes)
Badorf, Florence L., PA (Williams)
Baer, C. Thelma, PA (Dunkleberger)
Bauder, Mary E., PA (Beard)
Becker, Pearl B., PA (Ankeny)
Besecker, Hazel B., PA (Beach)
Boyer, Evelyn G., PA (McIntyre)
Burkhalter, Helen I., PA (Andrews)
Cool, Lillian, PA (Wells)
Cooper, Dorothy A., PA (Gilmore)
Daniels, Alice A., NJ (Embree)
Deans, Marion I., PA (Crystal)
Dewitt, Catherine C., PA (Smith)
Frantz, Joyce M., PA
Frendak, Verna M., PA
Glenn, Georgina, IRELAND
Hart, Neta Y., PA (Anderson)
Higgins, Gladys E., PA (Parsons)
Kauffman, Ruth M., (Schuler)
Kissinger, Edith S., PA (Neille)

Koch, Ruth J., PA
Lansberry, Arlene R., PA (Maurer)
Manewal, Jane A., PA
Metz, Blanche E., PA (Henderson)
Miller, Josephine, PA (Minnich)
Moore, Charlotte D., NJ (Burt)
Nunemaker, Fern, PA (Lapniewski)
Nutter, Mabel P., NJ
Prevost, Mabel C., PA
Pyle, Florence D., NJ (McCarty)
Reighard, Frances M., PA (Hellreigel)
Rowe, Zelda K., PA (Mencer)
Shearer, Margaret L., PA (Gile)
Shera, Gertrude M., PA (Tscharner)
Shoemaker, Nora A., PA (Ehrig)
Snodderly, Evelyn C., PA (Smith)
Steele, Kathryn R., PA (Shaffer)
Stepp, M. Elizabeth, PA (Lewis)
Vancavage, Mary E., PA (Neds)
VanHorn, Lois C., MD (Dawson)

Fig. 32. Mabel C. Prevost ('29), Directress of Nursing (1953-58) and Assistant Hospital Director (1958-74).

Weiss, Verna R., PA (Herber)
Wheeler, Frances E., PA (Babb)
Wildonger, Francis K., PA
Wilhelm, M. Ella, DE
Williams, Ann, PA (Candler)

Wolford, Grace G., PA (Eichelberger)
Wright, Mary E., DE
Yonson, Jean, PA (Nordness)
Young, Barbara A., PA (Cornell)
Zeitler, Phyllis S., PA

Fig. 33. Ruth Jeffries Koch ('29), granddaughter of first German bacteriologist, Robert Koch.

Nature and kind nursing save a much greater proportion in our plain way, at a smaller expense, and with less abuse.

Thomas Jefferson (1743-1826)

The modernization program which had been in the planning stages for Jefferson during recent years forged ahead in spite of the adverse economic condition. The Curtis Clinic was now under construction on the Tenth and Walnut Street site of the old College Building and would provide greatly improved teaching facilities for the School of Nursing.

The graduates numbered 67.

CLASS OF 1930

Akers, Mary A., PA (Andrews)
Avery, Virginia S., PA
Balavage, Teresa E., PA (Sweeney)
Blanche, R. Emaline, DE
Bless, Cecelia E., PA
Botz, Mildred M., PA (Zook)
Bowlby, Alice M., NJ (Brummell)
Campbell, Agnes, PA (Downs)
Chafe, Dorothy S., NEWFOUNDLAND (Guyer)
Confer, Dorothy V., PA (Stephens)
Denny, Vernita L., PA (Folkdal)
Diedel, Elsie K., PA (McElvoy)
Duckworth, Helen I., NJ (Tiger)
Engel, Ella R., AL (Kelsh)
Fesmier, Thelma A., PA (Edson)
Frauenfelder, Ruth D., PA (Heisey)
Gambal, Anna E., PA
Geist, Gertrude I., (Evans)
Hancock, Ruth E., PA (Hughes)
Hannon, Edna W., PA (Peters)
Hendricks, Ethel C., PA (Krugler)
Hussey, Violet T., DE (Newmeyer)
Irvin, Nina H., PA (Studebaker)
Kline, Lillian C., PA (Ernst)
Kuehn, Myrtle L., PA (Shuman)
Kupple, Lillian M., AZ (Nelson)
Lane, Edith Scott, MD
Lentz, Minerva M., PA (Welch)
Lewis, Clara E., PA (Lyons)
Lewis, Marion D., PA (Petrosky)
Marquette, Lucille M., PA (Clow)
Mattern, Gladys A., PA (James)
Maus, Emma H., PA (Smeck)

McArthur, Thelma P., PA (Wolford)
McNeish, Mabel L., PA (Young)
Meighan, Katherine E., PA (Witherbee)
Metzer, Mary L., PA
Miller, Virginia, PA (Bruner)
Moffett, Annetta M., PA (Whitehead)
Murray, J. Serena, PA (Eshelman)
Oaks, E. Isabelle, PA (Widing)
Oberdorf, Hazel V., PA
Parker, M. Pauline, DE (Siegle)
Rakestraw, M. Frances, PA (Eutermarks)
Rauenzahn, Myra J., PA (Martin)
Reed, Josephine E., (Bailey)
Reeder, Marion B., PA
Sachs, Elmina C., PA (Hanges)
Schenck, Dorothy, PA (Ragan)
Sealer, Elizabeth F., PA (Weiss)
Sellers, Emma R., PA (Johnson)
Sheriff, M. Elizabeth, PA (Angier)
Shontz, Vera E., PA
Skane, Dabaniam (Zarrilli)
Souder, Minnie S., PA (Ruh)
Spatz, Margaret H., PA (Gauger)
Stevens, Muriel, NY (Canis)
Stott, Frances T., PA (Hayes)
Tebbs, Edith M., PA
Umholtz, Ada M., PA (Daley)
Underkoffler, Minnie M., PA (Humphrey)
Wamsher, Edythe G., PA (Care)
Whitesell, Grace E., PA (Schmidt)
Williams, Dorothy M., PA (Derk)
Wills, Thelma J., PA (Laird)
Winslow, Sara M., PA (Helm)
Woomer, Mary E., PA (Boyd)

The Curtis Clinic Building at 1015 Walnut Street was completed, providing much needed space for the School of Nursing (Fig. 34). There was a classroom on the tenth floor for theoretical and practical nursing, a dietectic laboratory with food preparation facilities, as well as a reference library and study room. The 11th floor contained a science laboratory for teaching of chemistry and

Fig. 34.   Curtis Clinic (1931).

bacteriology, and a demonstration room with beds, bedside tables, an infant and model bathroom, and other appurtenances. On the 12th floor there was an assembly room with a 175 seating capacity, a motion picture booth, blackboards, and an adjoining anatomy and physiology laboratory.

By the end of 1931, the fortieth year since its founding, the Training School had graduated 1,031 nurses. Many of these joined the staff of the Jefferson Hospital.

There were 74 graduates, the largest Class to date.

CLASS OF 1931

Alder, Willie L., MD (Hamilton)
Anstine, Dorcas R., PA (Ward)
Bahner, Emma M., PA
Bell, Bertha A., PA (McCloskey)
Bell, Hilda, ENGLAND
Benedict, Augusta, PA (Owen)
Besecker, Janet C., PA (Willett)
Blanche, T., PA (Ford)
Brendle, Minerva A., PA (Hickman)
Brubaker, Marion E., PA (Stephens)
Brumbaugh, Ruth, PA (Gunnett)
Buck, Blanche E., PA (Sherky)
Bundy, M. Grace, PA (Rogers)
Burggraf, Harriet S., PA (Goff)
Chamberlain, Mary J., NJ (Bonk)
Clegg, Pearl, PA (Shellenberger)
Cowen, Esther, PA (Huntsberger)
Curtin, Hannetta E., PA (Hoffner)
Delancey, Mary L., MD (Bouchelle)
Eckert, Pauline M., PA (Mebane)
Emmert, Doris V., MD (Leo)
English, Mildred, PA (Hively)
English, Ruth A., AZ (Whitley)
Everett, Susie B., MD (Wentworth)
Fannin, Mary M., PA (McMahon)
Foster, Anna M., PA (Atkinson)
Goodnow, Bernice S., (Cottrell)
Greenly, Helen A., PA (Hileman)
Griffiths, Hannah L., PA (Connor)
Guyer, Esther, PA (Lentz)
Haines, Nellie, PA (Humphrey)
Heiss, Emma M., PA (Iannuzzi)
Hood, Olive M., PA (Hale)
Hoover, Edith N., PA (Frizell)
Horner, Marion R., PA (Brady)
Huff, Blanche B., PA (Huckaby)
Johnson, Agnes D., PA (Gaffney)

Jones, Irene R., PA
Kalbach, Mary E., PA (Bistline)
Kevel, Agnes M., PA (Henry)
Kutz, Mary E.P., PA
Lentz, Genevieve A., PA (Harmon)
Lucas, Anna V., NJ
MacFarlane, Olive, PA
Mann, Eleanor C., PA (Voorhies)
Martin, Grace J., PA (Werner)
Martin, Isabelle C., PA (Gehr)
Meyers, Edith (Hunter)
Parker, Laura A., MD (Matthews)
Peterson, Dorothy T., PA
Petrikin, Lucille, PA (Slavik)
Pusey, Alice M., DE (Hammond)
Reeser, Evelyn B., PA (Arnold)
Reimel, Madelyn P., PA (Knapp)
Rhyne, Grace, NC (Clay)
Richards, Dorothy, DE (Ratledge)
Rodewig, Helen C., PA
Schoch, Mildred E., PA (McGee)
Shaffer, Annabelle, PA
Shellenberger, Bertha M., PA (Stover)
Singer, Cathleen J., PA (Boyd)
Snoddy, Hermorene, VA (Brubaker)
Spangenberg, Mildred, PA (Nason)
Stair, Nellie A., PA (Teller)
Stonehill, Edna M., PA (Dutill)
Taylor, Mary A., PA (Lawley)
Tufenkian, Yeprakse, TURKEY (Kounjian)
Ulsh, Ruth I., PA (Menicon)
Walp, Eleanor K., PA (Hager)
Ward, Harriet W., PA
Watt, Eleanor K., PA
Webner, Mildred N., PA (Witmyer)
Williams, Sue E., PA (Wells)
Youngblood, Elizabeth W., NJ (Gaul)

The opening of the Curtis Clinic provided new opportunities for recent nursing graduates with the need for staffing in all clinical areas as the depression increased the demand for services in the various clinics (Fig. 35). Among the graduates of 1932 was Thelma M. Showers (Morris) who was recruited for the Pediatric Outpatient Clinic (Fig. 36). She was later Supervising Nurse in the Department for Diseases of the Chest (Pine Street and Barton Memorial).

Marie Scherer (Maxwell) became an obstetric supervisor at Jefferson Medical College Hospital. She saw wartime service with the Jefferson Unit, advancing to Assistant Chief Nurse and later took her B.S. degree at the University of Pennsylvania. She was maternity supervisor at Cooper Hospital, Camden, for ten years and then Director of practical Nursing at Camden County Vocational School until retirement in 1977.

Elizabeth Ent began her operating room career as head nurse in the ground floor ENT clinic, then moved to the eighth floor operating room as head nurse. From 1939 to 1941 she was in charge of all operating rooms at Jefferson but resigned then to go to Taylor Hospital, Ridley Park, in the same capacity. In 1953 she was placed in charge of the operating rooms at Hunterdon Medical Center, Flemington, New Jersey.

The Nurses' Alumni Prize was awarded for the first time. The Prize was specified for the member of the graduating class who attained the highest average during the three-year course of study.

There were 55 graduates.

CLASS OF 1932

Adams, Dora, NM (Reynolds)
Andrews, Alma I., PA (Johnson)
Arnold, Gladys N., PA (Blue)
Bates, Dorothy V., PA (Young)
Bucher, Mildred, PA (Price)
Bulette, Dorothea, PA (Watson)
Clineberg, Gladys, PA (Anderson)
Cole, Sylvia A., PA (Vlam)
Collins, Mildred S., MD (Getz)
Cooper, Julia E., PA (Wellensiek)
Coulbourne, Ellen I., DE (Wise)
Coup, Erma N., PA (Painter)
DeGroft, Naomi, PA (Price)
Detwiler, F. Lenore, PA (Hammond)
DeWitt, Laura S., PA
Dubler, Helen R., PA (Hendrickson)
Dundore, Dorothy E., PA (Williams)
Ent, Elizabeth C., PA
Felker, Emma N., PA (Reinhart)
Fester, Esther M., CANADA (Greth)
Fuller, Virginia M., MD
Garman, Mildred V., PA (Jeffers)
Gonder, Gail C., PA (Willard)
Greger, Hazel, PA (Biddle)
Harpel, Lucille S., PA
Herr, Mary E., PA (Seibert)
Hostetter, Almeda M., PA (Grumbein)

Jones, Carolyn M., PA (Transue)
Kanour, Miriam K., PA
Kern, Dama O., PA (Brobst)
Kester, Dorothy M., PA (Green)
Lilley, Catherine (Wilson)
Lynch, Ethel E., DE (Taylor)
Mangold, Norma A., (Gould)
Miller, Evelyn G., PA (Flickinger)
Moore, S. Evelyn, PA (Larsen)
Myers, Verna M., NJ (Zimmerman)
Ney, Florence E., WV (Singe)
Patchel, Grace E., (Herring)
Phoebus, Emma H., MD (Kelly)
Pie, M. Alice, PA (Bonner)
Pucci, Theresa E., NH (Wakeley)
Raymer, Sara M., PA
Ross, Anne F., DE
Roth, Adeline A., PA (Miller)
Russell, Isabelle D., PA (Lindecamp)
Scherer, Marie, PA (Maxwell)
Schrepple, Miriam M., PA (Reeder)
Selgrath, Rose, PA (Dodson)
Showers, Thelma M., PA (Morris)
Sickler, Norma M., NJ (Bond)
Smith, Mildred E., PA (O'Connor)
Stelzer, Florence A., PA (Brandt)
Thompson, H. Evelyn, PA (Niece)
Welsko, Veronica V., PA

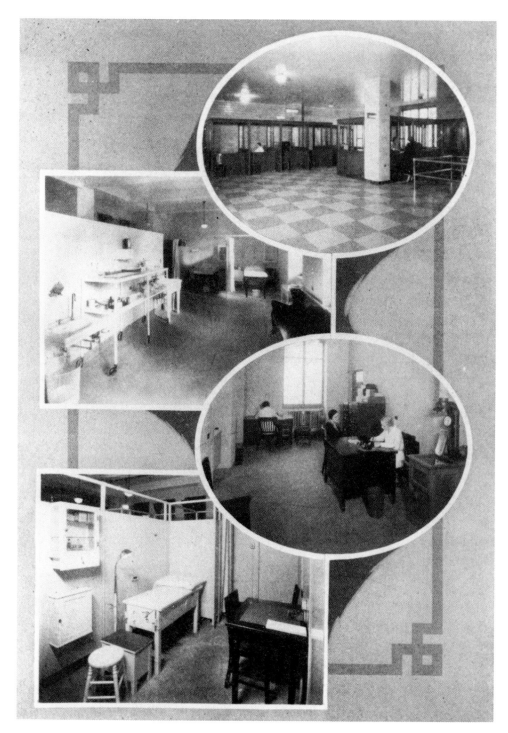

Fig. 35. Curtis Clinic (left upper); Treatment Room (left lower); First Floor Office (right upper); and a Clinic Office (right lower).

Curtis Clinic Nurses

Top: Thelma Showers, Leona Clouser, Rose A. Selgrath, Gladys Arnold.
Bottom: Mildred Smith, Minnie Souder, Marguerite Barnett, Ruth Ulsh, Carolyn Jones.

Fig. 36.   Curtis Clinic Nurses (1932).

The first official Alumnae Day of the School of Nursing was held on April 22 of this year. This became a popular annual event which survived beyond the closing of the School in 1982. Also the student yearbook *Nosokomos* was first published, the term deriving from two Greek words "Noso", the study of the sick and "Komos", a female who attends (Figure 37).

The graduates this year numbered 50.

CLASS OF 1933

Bay, A. Ruth, PA (Fennell)
Blackburn, Sara R., PA (Baxter)
Breisch, Harriet E., PA (March)
Brown, Mildred G., WV (Breisacher)
Bryant, Myrtle I., NC (Loving)
Bumgardner, M. Louise, PA (Steinberg)
Checklinski, Frances M., PA (Rogowicz)
Clouser, Leona R., PA (Gehris)

Cockill, Helen F., PA (Boyd)
Cornell, Ruth M., NJ (Williams)
Culp, Nellie E., PA (Sharrah)
Doutrich, Geneva E., PA (McKee)
Duncan, Margaret, FL (Moscarella)
Fralic, Madalen P., PA (Osborne)
Frendak, Pauline A., PA (McGee)
Frye, Frances B., PA (Kelly)

nosokomos

published by
class of september, 1933
of the
jefferson medical college hospital
school of nursing
philadelphia, pennsylvania

Fig. 37. *Nosokomos* Yearbook (1933).

Gray, Catherine I., PA (Paine)
Gulian, Takouhi, TURKEY (Ishkania)
Heist, Florence G., PA
Helman, Pauline R., PA (Kough)
Hoover, Eugenia Z., PA (Hendricks)
Huber, Mildred C., PA (Bentz)
Kinch, Katherine R., PA (Leach)
King, Isa R., IRELAND
Koon, Margaret J., PA (Lecklitner)
Long, Martha M., NH (Garver)
Lonsbery, Margaret O., PA (Chrisholm)
Mack, Ruth F., PA (Prince)
McCready, Rose H., PA (Miller)
Miller, Marjorie M., NJ (Martin)
Minns, Clara M., PA (Greeman)
Mitchell, Elsie V., PA (Drissel)
Moody, Ethel, NC

Nemshick, Juliana D., PA (Davoney)
Ohler, Ruth V., PA (Amos)
Olsen, Carolyn A., PA (Kaltenstein)
Passmore, Vivian M., PA (Murray)
Piatt, Ellen E., PA (Vetenko)
Pollitt, Marion C., DE (Carey)
Rhoads, Muriel A., PA
Rice, Irene N., PA (Sales)
Romick, Elizabeth H., PA (Cobb)
Ruhle, Kathryn C., PA
Sparks, Ethel, PA (Kates)
Steele, Dorothy M., PA (Norris)
Swisher, Chloe B., PA (Ericksen)
Tryenes Sarah G., PA (Wright)
West, Kathryn M., DE (Magin)
Whitebread, Evelyn E., PA (Demshaw)
Woodring, Anne M., PA (Crofford)

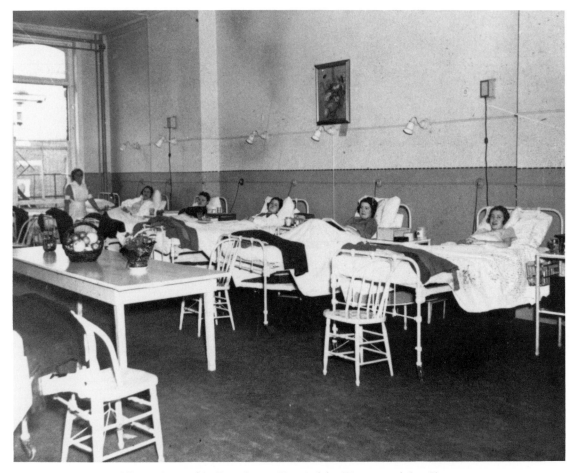

Women's ward in Pine Street Hospital for Diseases of the Chest.

~ 1934 ~

At this time the enrollment in the School of Nursing averaged 240 for the entire three years. There were 35 subjects in a comprehensive curriculum covering the basic sciences and all the branches of practical and specialty nursing. "Hands on" training was experienced in the Main Hospital and the Pine Street Chest Unit. The latter facility had become an important training resource for a large portion of the class.

Elizabeth E. Piersol, a member of this class, went on to an extended Jefferson career beginning as a staff nurse and advancing to Head Nurse in Men's Medical Ward. She was later Supervisor of the entire Medical Floor. Subsequently she was Coordinator of the Exchange Visitor Nurse Program and then of the Home Health Service. In 1985, in retirement, she became Coordinator of the Nurses' Alumni Association (Fig. 38).

The Class numbered 67.

CLASS OF 1934

Adams, Ruth S., PA (Fritch)
Artman, Ethel M., PA
Aumiller, Mildred L., PA (Brown)
Blake, Margaret R., PA
Bowman, Mary Alice, PA (Grazioli)
Bowmaster, Isaphine A., PA (Kasper)
Breinig, Anna E., PA (Hartman)
Carey, Ellyn G., PA (Elstein)
Carr, Donna J., PA (Cornelius)
Clapsaddle, Nellie, PA (Gillis)
Clayton, Margaret E., NJ (Schellenger)
Corson, Helen M., NJ (Smith)
D'Espinosi, M. Catherine, PA (Klein)
Davis, Ruth R., PA (Wolfe)
Dore, Mildred V., PA (Estrada)
Duff, Jessie J., NY (Mulcohy)
Dunkle, Mildred D., PA (Brinkman)
Dunn, Clara B., NJ (Miller)
Engle, Alda M., PA (Brammer)
Fisher, Harriet M., PA (Thompson)
Fleck, M. Hope, PA (Hahn)
Frymire, Lois M., PA (Bastian)
Haller, Enid (Colantino)
Hare, Helen L., PA (Duncan)
Harrison, Wanda L., PA (Sachs)
Hartman, Marian E., PA (Burch)
Hastings, Edna M., PA (Flagens)
Hertzler, Verna M., PA (Diehm)
Hoffman, Kathryn A., PA (Snader)
Hoffman, Marion E., PA (Miller)
Ingraham, Eva M., PA (Grenoble)
Jackson, Elizabeth, PA
Jacoby, Anna M., PA (Gehrke)

Johnston, Frances K., PA (LeFavour)
Jones, Sara I., PA (Ross)
Keene, Marie, PA (Lawton)
Kepner, Pauline, PA (Leary)
Klink, Laura M., NJ (Williams)
Larson, Margaret, NY (Winkler)
Mariano, Margaret E., PA (Pargola)
Martin, Tasamene, PA (Zelt)
Metzger, Maude L., PA
Moore, Marguerite D., NJ (Chew)
Myers, Mildred G., PA (Smith)
Myers, Ruth E., PA (Peterson)
Orner, Rhea M., PA (Kassay)
Piersol, Elizabeth, PA
Raubenhold, Dorothy K., PA
Reimer, Helen V., PA (Motsay)
Rickard, Alice R., PA (James)
Ritchey, Helen M., PA (Frederick)
Robertson, Esther M., PA (Walker)
Roeder, Charlotte E., PA (Jacques)
Sherman, Anna E., PA (Bryan)
Smulling, Catherine, AK (Gair)
Spencer, Ruth V., PA (Dunfee)
Stahle, M. Louise, PA (Adams)
Stuart, Catherine C., PA (Kizink)
Taylor, Elizabeth, MD (Davidson)
Thomason, Grace E., PA (Mitchell)
Tyler, Julia, PA (Kennedy)
Wall Dorothy M., PA (Ghares)
Warner, Kathleen L., PA (Armitage)
Wilson, Evelyn M., PA (Frazier)
Woolsey, Eva, NC (Warren)
Yarnall, Margaret E., PA (Snear)
Ziegler, Harriet E., PA (Mertz)

Fig. 38.   Elizabeth Piersol ('34), career nursing supervisor.

*It is our duty to remember at all times and anew that medicine is not only a
science, but also the art of letting our own individuality interact with the individuality
of the patient.*

Albert Schweitzer (1875-1905)

A highlight of the year was the presentation of the portrait of Miss Clara Melville, Directress of the School of Nursing, by the Nurses' Alumnae Association. Miss Melville (Fig. 19) had served effectively since 1915 and died two years after this well deserved honor. This portrait is highly regarded in Jefferson's art collection.

Another important event in this year was the presentation of a referenced library of 1,200 volumes, cataloged and arranged in mahogany cases, as a gift to the Nurses' Home by Ross V. Patterson, Dean of the Medical College. This was the beginning of a library in two rooms of the residence.

Intermediates

Top: Margaret Pound, La Verne Manges, Marian Smith, Louise Huegel, Malinda Endicott, Elizabeth Wertzberger, Mildred Kalinowski, Ruth Schaum, Louise Evert, Elmetta Yearick.
Bottom: Elizabeth Stephan, Mary Elizabeth Hyatt, Mary Fielden, Helen Miller, Elizabeth Kasales, Myra Snyder, Mary Ann Dauber.

Not on Picture

Dorothy Black, Mildred Cook, Miriam Deatrich, Evelyn Dute, Elinor Farber, Frances Hamilton, Elizabeth Koegel, Margaret MacFarland, Thelma Marks, Janet McIlwain, Inez Olofson, Clara Sweeney, Mary Tananis, Rebecca Thornton, Anna Woodhouse, Lydia Yerkes.

Fig. 39. Intermediate Class (1935).

The Jefferson Choral Club was organized this year and the first Alumnae Bulletin was printed.

A portion of the intermediate class is pictured (Fig. 39). The enhanced recreational facilities in the Nurses' Home are shown in Fig. 40.

There were 66 graduates.

Fig. 40.   Rumpus room in the Nurses Home.

CLASS OF 1935

Ainsworth, Sara L., (O'Malley)	Gilbert, Elizabeth M., PA (Gallagher)
Armstrong, Margaret O., PA (Tunnard)	Gnaw, Inez, PA
Baird, Ruth E., PA (Judd)	Henry, Alice H., PA (Beyer)
Barritt, Ruth, NJ	Henry, Eleanor E., PA (Porter)
Battin, Marian I., PA (Howe)	Herrold, Louise, FL (Dunn)
Biddle, Anna E., MD (Robertson)	Hulgus, Helene, PA
Blacksmith, Anna M., PA	Hyde, Geraldine L., PA (Powers)
Burton, Laura M., DE (McCabe)	Jones, Gertrude M., PA (Saunders)
Campbell, Christella M., PA (Butler)	Kaplan, Rebecca A., PA (Yuninger)
Chaapel, Jean P., PA (Freeman)	Keat, Flora A., PA
Claybaugh, Mary, PA (May)	Keller, Stella, PA (Godshall)
Coldren, Elizabeth S., PA (Hoaglund)	Kelly, Frances L., PA (Fisher)
Coles, Mary W., NJ (Moore)	Kelly, Marie A., PA (Klaus
Crawford, Ellen M., PA (Teague)	Kratzer, Rita (Roeder)
Edmonds, Lucille E., PA (Hand)	Krauser, Irene P., PA (Supple)
Entrikin, Sara W., NJ	Latsha, Esther H., PA (Neidig)
Fehr, LaVere E., NJ (Phillips)	Latsha, M. Pauline, PA (Thorp)

1935

Lee, Irma, NC (Harris)
Lyons, Mildred M., PA (Stouth)
Mackintosh, Margaret W., PA
Martin, Arlene R., PA (Walther)
Massey, Ruth A., DE
McCabe, Ruth C., DE (Cropper)
McCullar, Erma L., PA (O'Donnell)
McCully, Eleanor M., PA (Lau)
McDaniels, Helen F., NJ (Hall)
McMullen, Mary R., PA (Rosnic)
Packer, Dorothy E., PA
Patton, Esther E., PA (Webb)
Rakestraw, Margaret R., PA (Schmitt)
Rolland, Evelyn M., PA (Curran)
Ross, Catherine F., PA (Sullivan)

Rotz, Mary, DE (Evans)
Rushin, Blanche T., PA
Schaeffer, Mary E., PA (Ries)
Sharbaugh, E. Jane, PA (Ryan)
Sipple, Margaret M., PA (Monaghan)
Slaybaugh, Rhoda M., PA (Krumrine)
Snyder, Alma P., PA (Miller)
Steele, Agnes E., PA (Picone)
Stees, Rebecca E., PA (Feltwell)
Swoyer, Gertrude E., PA (Rhoads)
Vanderslice, Priscilla, PA (Margerum)
Waller, Esther L., DE
Weigand, Laverne, PA
Willing, Martha E., PA (King)
Wintermyer, Helen M., PA (Ibaugh)
Zetterlund, S. Georgianna, FL (Kirk)

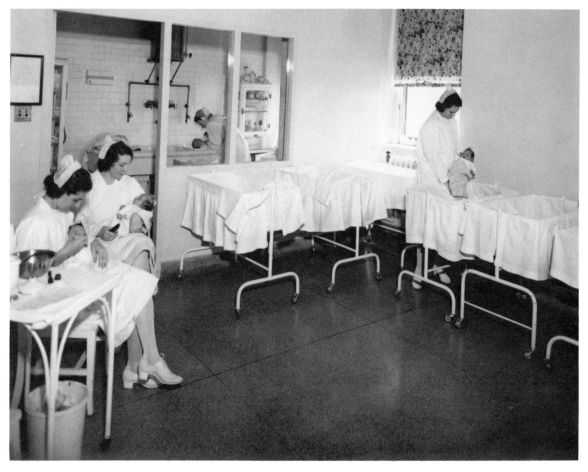

Eleventh floor nursery of Thompson Building.

Carrying forward the gradual decrease in austerity of the nurses' uniforms, this year saw a change to shorter sleeves with separate cuffs. The advanced students were also wearing a solid pink uniform to distinguish them from the pink and white checked ones for the younger trainees. The nurses were also enjoying increased recreational facilities in their quarters (Fig. 41).

In March ten graduating students volunteered their services to aid victims of a disastrous flood in Western Pennsylvania.

The Nurses Alumnae Scholarship Loan Fund was established this year.

During this period the graduates enjoyed op-portunities not only at Jefferson but in the profession at large. Evelyn L. Dute, of this class, went on to lifetime service as a clinical nursing supervisor at Jefferson (Fig. 42).

Mary S. Radel (Menendez) was representative of a number of Jefferson student nurses who came from the anthracite region of Pennsylvania especially during the depression years. She lived in a "Company Town" referred to as a "patch" and her first six years of elementary school were spent in a one-room schoolhouse. She illustrated a group of solid students who found opportunity for a career entry at Jefferson.

There were 50 graduates.

CLASS OF 1936

Anderson, Velma G., DE (Wilson)
Bardo, Grace M., PA (Ruopp)
Bohn, Lillian M., IA (Hawley)
Brede, Dorothy M., PA (Connole)
Cook, Mildred V., PA (Cox)
Daeuber, Maryann, NJ (Lamb)
Davis, Martha C., PA (Kester)

Dieck, Geraldine, PA (Baker)
Dute, Evelyn L., PA
Ely, Virginia K., PA (Schneebury)
Endicott, Malinda S., NJ (Gallagher)
Evert, Louise D., PA (Keich)
Farber, Elinor E., PA (Brosious)
Fawcett, Laura, PA

Fig. 41.   Relaxation in Nurses' quarters (1936).

Fig. 42. Evelyn L. Dute ('36), nursing supervisor at Jefferson.

Fielden, Mary, PA (Wiley)
Hamilton, Frances V., PA (Williams)
Huegel, Louise M., PA (Hafer)
Hyatt, Mary E., NC (Dominich)
Jones, Ethel W., PA (Neiman)
Kalinowski, Mildred V., PA (Smith)
Kasales, Elizabeth E., PA
Koegel, Elizabeth W., PA (Wardell)
Landis, Miriam H., PA
MacFarland, Margaret, FL (Semisch)
Manges, Binnie L., PA
Manier, Juanita, PA (Schettig)
Marks, Thelma M., PA (Saylor)
McIlwain, Janet J., NJ (Cramer)
Miller, Helen E., PA (Harding)
Moore, Mabelle E., PA (Cooke)
Nickel, Jane, PA (Moyer)
Olofson, Inga-Lisa, PA (Wheat)
Painter, Emma, PA (Lanzetta)
Pound, Margaret T., MD (Ransom)
Radel, Mary S., PA (Menendez)
Robinson, Eleanor B., PA
Schaum, Martha R., PA (Goodman)
Smith, Marion E., PA
Snyder, Myra C., PA (Dunkle)
Spangler, Edna M., PA (McAvoy)
Stein, Lois C., PA (Caswell)
Stephan, Elizabeth C., PA (Miller)
Sweeney, Clara N., PA (McArthur)
Tananis, Mary E., PA
Thornton, Rebecca S., VA (Ingling)
Wertzberger, A. Elizabeth, PA (Weiss)
Wilkinson, Catherine V., MA (Meier)
Woodhouse, Anna W., NC (Greene)
Yearick, Elmetta J., PA (Carter)
Yerkes, Lydia K., PA

Make it a rule never to be angry at anything a sick man says or does to you.
Sickness often adds to the natural irritability of the temper. We, therefore, bear the
reproaches of our patients with meekness and silence.

Benjamin Rush (1745-1813)

~ 1937 ~

Upon the death of Miss Melville after 22 years as Directress of the School of Nursing, Miss Nora E. Shoemaker succeeded as Directress (Fig. 24). During her six-year tenure a social sciences course was introduced into the curriculum. A recreational program for the students was also developed.

Rules and Regulations were adopted by the Alumnae Association for the Relief Fund which had been established in 1912.

There were 63 graduates.

CLASS OF 1937

Adams, Kathryn S., PA (Lindemann)
Bickel, H. Virginia, PA (Miller)
Black, Dorothy M., PA (Ruth)
Butler, Ruth E., PA (Sowers)
Cooper, Thelma A., PA (Stock)
Crotty, Catherine L., FL (Keith)
Davis, Pauline, DE (Leager)
Eifert, Henrietta L., NJ (Stetler)
Fagan, Marjorie A., PA (Gold)
Fox, Viola K., PA
Geesey, Margaret M., PA (Pope)
Gilbert, Vivian C., PA
Gregory, Jessie I., PA (Crum)
Groff, Dorothy, PA (Compton)
Haines, Sara, PA (Wolford)
Hall, Alice E., PA
Hardin, Charlotte M., TN (Buxton)
Hatley, Cannie E., NC (Matucci)
Haugh, Gertrude K., PA (Foreaker)
Heake, Eleanor, NJ (Mathews)
Heal, Etta L., NJ (Baker)
Heine, Jeane E., PA (Arnold)
Heisler, Genevieve E., PA (Eubanks)
Henderson, C. Beryl, NJ (Jess)
High, Fern L., PA
Hill, Caroline H., PA (Masuda)
Hoffman, Esther M., PA (Lorenz)
Kenton, Audrey M., MD (Myers)
Kiger, Jane E., PA (Townsend)
Killinger, Elizabeth, PA (Mowday)
Kinney, Bernadine T., NJ

Kipikash, Margaret B., PA (Petrone)
Kline, Dorothy M., PA (Miller)
Landis, Dorothy R., PA
Lane, Myrtle W., NC (Mathews)
Larish, Virginia P., PA (Gingrich)
Leatherman, Alice I., PA (Fulmer)
Long, Helyn R., PA (Romberg)
Markle, Mary V., PA
Marshall, Ethel M., DE (Shannon)
Martinson, Ida E., NJ
Matlack, Areta, NJ (Rule)
Miller, Mary E., PA (Sullivan)
Myers, Lillian A., PA (German)
Nichols, Gertrude G., DE (Sessions)
Rine, Rachel C., PA (Bonham)
Rorabaugh, Kathryn, PA
Saunders, Lillian M., NJ
Seury, Martha (Stanton)
Sheva, Helen T., (Fasy)
Shive, Florence, FL (Kauffman)
Smith, Josephine L., (Snyder)
Smith, June, PA
Smith, Violet, PA (Orland)
Spatig, Harriet R., PA (Zeller)
Taylor, Margaret C., PA
Vinyard, Louise P., NJ (Fisher)
Welty, Gladys M., PA (Reichard)
Wetzel, Dorothy V., PA
Woodhead, Mildred M., PA (Hawkesworth)
Woomer, Alice L., PA (Gallagher)
Wright, Doris T., MD (Wolter)
Zukowski, Laura, NJ (Johnson)

The commencement ceremony was held in the amphitheater of Thompson Annex with President of the Board Robert P. Hooper addressing the graduates (Fig. 43).

At this time Jefferson still maintained an ambulance service (Fig. 44). During the World War II years this function was taken over by police and fire personnel, and still later by regional ambulances.

Madeline M. Ullom joined the United States Army Nurse Corps upon graduation. After two years at Walter Reed Hospital she was assigned to the Philippines where she became a prisoner of war in 1942. Remaining in the army after her release, she advanced to the rank of Lieutenant Colonel and received her M.S. in Nursing Education from Catholic University. After many international experiences her last position was Assistant Chief Nurse and Educational Coordinator at Fitzsimons Army Hospital in Denver. She was listed in *Who's Who of American Women* and *Leaders of American Science*.

Lida P. Pardee (Goodell) entered the United States Navy Nurse Corps in 1943 and served for 20 years, retiring in 1963 with the rank of Lieutenant Commander.

There were 57 graduates this year.

Fig. 43. Graduation exercises (1938).

Bastian, Kathryn V., PA
Beck, Dorothy M., PA (Baker)
Bedford, Jeanette, PA
Benner, Wilma V., PA (Overal)
Borowski, Theophilia A.
T., PA (King)
Boyd, Elsa V., PA (Antal)
Briggs, Margaret L., NC (Batts)
Bryan, Anita, SC (Eisner)
Clark, Emily M., PA (Nichols)
Cooke, Laura J.
L., PA (Lackay)
Cooper, Florence R., DE (Engle)
Cronlund, Elizabeth G., PA (Kern)
Dickinson, Rachael L., NJ
Fleishman, Barbara E., PA (Snape)
Frazier, R. Geraldine, PA
Gendebien, Edith M., PA (Reeves)
Gould, Frances M., PA (Austin)
Greenfield, Jeanne G., PA (Schmidt)
Greenlee, G. Mildred, NJ (Durham)
Greenly, Hazel V., DE (Staub)

Haupt, Dorothy M., PA (Bonsall)
Hughes, Ruth E., PA (Fratini)
Hyde, Doris L., PA
Kelly, Sara E., PA (Little)
Kinter, Virginia B., DC (Hatton)
Kring, Charlotte R., PAEldridge
Lindquist, Linnea N., PA (Casperson)
Maciejewska, Lorraine T., PA (Wallen)
Mann, L. Claire, PA (Schelle)
Mason, Edna F., WV (Stewart)
McCullough, Mildred, PA (Thomas)
Medwid, Eva B., PA
Miller, Charlotte G., PA (Emerson)
Miller, Elinor V., PA (Wentzel)
Morrison, Jessie L., PA (Kerth)
Null, Dorothy I., PA (Drennen)
Nunan, Kathleen D., PA (Lewis)
O'Brien, Mary L., NJ
Owen Margaret, PA (Wert)
Owen, Edith M., PA (McCutcheon)
Pardee, Lida G., DE (Goodell)
Poole, Ruth M., PA (Mclean)
Reeder, Mary K., PA (Copeland)
Richter, Dorothea M., DE (Lewis)
Schilling, Alice I., PA
Sitgreaves, S. Elizabeth, PA (Eichlin)
Smith, Josephine M., PA (McDowell)
Smith, Mary E., PA
Snare, Matilda E., PA (Finn)
Stever, Mildred, PA (Close)
Ullom, Madalyn M., NE
Weidaw, Ruth I., PA (Lorenzo)
Williams, Isabelle E., DE (Snedaker)
Williams, Marion E., PA (Binley)
Willwerth, Ruby L., PA
Winger, Emma R., PA (Steerman)
Wirt, B. Elizabeth, PA (Bailey)

Fig. 44.   Jefferson ambulance (1938).

After all, we are merely the servants of the public, in spite of our M.D.'s and hospital appointments.

Henry Howarth Bashford (1880-1961)

Among the graduates of this class who joined the Jefferson staff were Dorothy B. Ranck (Fig. 45) and Olga H. Dygan (Fig. 46), both of whom later served on Star Floor of Thompson Annex where many members of the medical staff and their families were cared for.

Miss Ranck became a nursing supervisor and went on to appointment as Director of Nursing Education at Jefferson. She later joined the Pennsylvania State Department of Health and Welfare and advanced to Director of the Division of General and Special Hospitals.

Victoria C. Malinowski became an officer in the United States Public Health Service. She received an M.P.H. degree and served as an epidemiologist in the Air Pollution Division, later becoming involved in Community Health Studies (Home Health Agencies). She retired in 1978 as Lieutenant Colonel and in 1983 received the first Victoria Malinowski Award from the Maryland Association of Home Health Agencies.

Barbara G. Schutt pursued a career in nursing education and moved to Connecticut in 1968. She became Director of Nursing at Mohegan Community College, Norwich, and in 1977-79 served as President of the Connecticut Nurses Associ-

Fig. 45. Dorothy B. Ranck ('39), became Head Nurse of Star Floor (Thompson Annex) and Associate Directress of Nurses.

Fig. 46. Olga H. Dygan (Mitchell), Class of '39, well known Staff Nurse for many years.

ation. She was also editor of the *American Journal of Nursing* and received the American Nursing Association's Honorary Award.

Johanna K. Laise (Wagner) joined the Pine Street Staff as operating room nurse but subsequently went on to an M.D. degree from Temple University School of Medicine and entered the private practice of medicine. She was thus the first Jefferson diploma school nurse to graduate in medicine.

There were 73 graduates.

Bathgate, Jessie, PA
Bilancio, Rose, NJ (Bilancio)
Bird, Grace E., NJ (Petersen)
Brunner, Miriam L., PA (Cureton)
Bushek, Josephine M.A., PA (Shuck)
Byerly, Helen F., PA (Coeney)
Castaldi, Mildred, NJ (Waldman)
Cole, Phyllis R., PA (Makurdsik)
Cooper, Marjorie A., NJ (Richter)
Davenport, Charlotte F., NJ
Dygan, Olga H., PA (Mitchell)
Esmond, Josephine M., PA (Iandoli)
Fisher, Mary L., PA (Hill)
Foor, Virginia E., PA
Gans, Thelma L., PA (Beshgetoorian)
Garretson, Edna, PA (Eyler)
Goudie, Lenore, PA (McPherson)
Greulich, Winnie F., PA (Kistler)
Grysewicz, Eleanor, PA (Bobrowski)
Gugliotta, Florence M., NJ (Stolpe)
Harding, Barbara M., PA (Cusano)
Harrison, Harriet, NY
Hill, Blanche E., MD (Wilson)
Hock, Kathleen G., PA (Martin)
Houseal, Helen B., PA (Kunkle)
Howard, Lois O., PA (James)
Hudak, Margaret V., PA (Buckey)
Keehan, Patricia, PA (Mills)
Kellner, Harriet, FL (Mertz)
Kelly, Florence A., PA (Gunster)
Knowles, Elizabeth A., NJ (Kain)
Laise, Johanna K., PA (Wagner)
Lucabaugh, Leah, PA (Stambaugh)
Malinowski, Victoria T., PA
Martin, Elizabeth A., PA (Doyle)
Martinelli, Isabel, PA (Jackson)

May, Kathryn, PA (Silver)
Musial, Stephanie M., PA (Taylor)
Neil, Marian H., PA (Findley)
Nissler, Helen O., PA (Richards)
Nolte, Kathryn M., PA (Lilley)
Patton, Sarah, NC (Saunders)
Pensinger, Lorraine, PA (Phillips)
Pfeiffer, Dorothy L., PA (Lepley)
Ranck, Dorothy B., PA
Roller, Grace A., PA (Castner)
Sayers, Eleanor A., PA (Redenbach)
Schevtchuk, Anne, IN (Taylor)
Schlemme, Ruth, PA (Green)
Schlenker, Beatrice, PA (Uurtamo)
Schropp, Helen M., PA (Daniel)
Schutt, Barbara G., PA
Schwab, Mary M., PA (Gregg)
Scott, Eleanor, NJ (Fetter)
Shearer, Marie, PA (Roche)
Shelly, Mary E., PA (Monk)
Smey, Julia, PA (Kennedy)
Smith, Ada M., PA (Ford)
Smith, Charlotte F., NJ (Stacey)
Smith, Geraldine H., IL (Baechle)
Smith, Ruth E., NJ (Stickles)
Swanson, Ruth E., NY (Penny)
Umberger, Juliet R., PA (Light)
Veet, Angela, PA (Toomey)
Wasitosky, Mary, PA (Coll)
Wentzel, L. Irene, PA (Anslow)
Werkheiser, Eva R., PA (Shook)
Wessells, Marion E., MD
Williams, Catherine A., PA (Stokes)
Williams, E. Elizabeth, NJ (Kochel)
Wilson, Catherine R., PA (Campbell)
Winneshick, Doris, PA (Day)
Winstead, Judith M., PA (Kreemer)

~ 1940 ~

Progress in the general field of nursing was signaled by the major curriculum changes this year to conform with the new "Curriculum Guide for Schools of Nursing" published in 1937 by the National League for Nursing Education.

In the spring of this year, Dr. Baldwin L. Keyes was asked by the Surgeon General of the U.S. Army to recruit doctors and nurses for a 1000-bed General Field Hospital. This mandate to Dr. Keyes was energetically pursued among Jefferson nurse graduates.

The career of Dorothy McComb (Talbot) evolved in Public Health Nursing with major contributions to Public Health Organizations and publications. She received her B.S.N. from Texas Women's University, M.A. from Teacher's College, M.P.H. and Ph.D. from Tulane. She was Public Health Consultant to the United States Army for 10 years. She was President of the Southern Public Health Association, Chairman of the Public Health Nursing Section and Vice-President of the American Public Health Association. In 1984 she retired as Chair of the Department of Public Health Nursing at the University of North Carolina and was named Professor Emeritus.

Norma Ziegler (Smith) served as staff nurse and supervisor on the surgical floor at Jefferson from 1941 to 1943. Thereafter she embarked upon a career in public health nursing, retiring in 1985. She received her B.S. in Nursing from the University of Maryland in 1972 and M. Ed. from Loyola College in 1976. In 1979 she was named Maryland Nurse of the year.

There were 67 graduates this year.

CLASS OF 1940

Armitage, Esther D., PA (Musselman)
Banks, Mary Sue, TN (Dale)
Browning, Rebecca V., MD (O'Hara)
Byers, Goldie, PA (Pringle)
Chambers, Dorothy, NJ (Rounsaville)
Cohick, Dorothy, PA (Rosenberg)
Crafton, Catherine, PA (Lambert)
Dieterle, Doris K., NJ
Eisenbrown, Florence, PA (Corts)
Eisenhart, Mary A., PA (Fleming)
Elliott, Judy J., PA (Kesselring)
Endicott, Ellora W., NJ (Myer)
Falkinburg, T. Virginia, NJ (Ritter)
Fedock, Eva, PA (Swantko)
Fisher, Margaret B., NJ (Reed)
Flyte, Mary E., PA (Rosser)
Foor, Margaret M., PA (Miller)
Fortner, Edna, PAFeloni
Freed, Alice M., PA (Moore)
Garrett, Violet M., PA (Hyman)
Gipe, Helen, PA (Loughry)
Griffiths, Ida Mae, PA (Varga)
Hally, R. Estelle, OH (McGehean)
Hicks, Janet H., TN (Arnold)
Himmelwright, Thelma, PA (Dietz)

Hoffman, Gladys, PA (Brundage)
Hoffman, Helen D., PA (Hermaniferman)
Irwin, Martha H., PA (Reed)
Jedrziewski, Stella B., PA (Wawrynovic)
Job, Helen L., PA (Enterline)
Jones, Marion J., PA (Tracy)
Kemerer, Caroline, PA
Kramer, R. Hope, PA (Mood)
Kustay, Marion, PA (Sobiesiak)
Landis, Hazel R., PA (Knepper)
Lynch, Janet, PA (Plant)
MacDonald, Janet, NC (Coats)
Mannon, Virginia, NJ (Mutschler)
Martin, Mary R., PA (McCoy)
Maxwell, A. Claire, PA (Wallace)
McComb, Dorothy W., LA (Talbot)
McRae, Virginia, PA (Avitable)
Means, Roberta, NY (Cronk)
Metz, Alberta H., PA
Nettles, Ruth, PA (Painter)
Newcomer, Alda, PA (Knodel)
Novak, Marion, PA (Manfredi)
Ott, Virginia, PA (Rowan)
Owens, Jane M., (Goodman)
Packer, Doris M., PA (Engelbrecht)

Paden, Ruth E., PA (Frazer)
Parker, Elizabeth B., NJ (Fuhse)
Racik, Margaret A., PA (Meyers)
Remensnyder, Ellen E., PA (Carlton)
Ritter, Ruth A., PA (Holbrook)
Schanley, Dorothy E., PA (Somerville)
Shaffer, Alma M., PA (Shofstall)
Sherin, Marie R., MA (Maurano)
Stranko, Anna, PA (Russin)

Summerfield, G. Averne, PA (Murphy)
Sutton, Frances R., NC (Weiss)
Vantilberg, Sara E., NJ (Cattermole)
Weaver, Thelma L., PA (Taylor)
Werstler, Sara L., PA
Wigglesworth, Bernice G., NJ (Sprecher)
Yost, Arline, PA (Conn)
Ziegler, Norma N., PA (Smith)

Nurses in clinical conference, Men's Medical Ward.

One of the problems confronting the nursing profession at this time was the necessity of supplying sufficient personnel to care for the needs of both civilian and military hospitals. Jefferson responded by offering refresher courses. In addition, two full-time instructors were appointed and courses in physiology and social problems were initiated.

Plans for organization of General Hospital #38 were well in place for the onset of war which suddenly erupted on December 7 at Pearl Harbor.

Harriet H. Werley ('41) launched her post-graduate career in the U.S. Army Nurse Corps and in 1951 became the Personnel Assignment Officer in the Office of the Surgeon General. She pursued further education leading to a Ph.D. degree in psychology, associated with research, teaching, and publication of more than 100 articles. In 1978 she received the Alumni Achievement Award of Jefferson's College of Allied Health Sciences. She became Distinguished Professor, School of Nursing, University of Wisconsin in 1983. In 1989 she received the honorary degree of Doctor of Science from the University of Illinois (Fig. 47).

Fig. 47. Harriet H. Werley ('41), Ph.D., Sc.D., Distinguished Professor, School of Nursing, University of Wisconsin.

Fig. 48. Margaret Summers ('41), supervisor, and coordinator of Alumni Office.

Margaret Summers ('41), joined the nursing staff, becoming head nurse on the fifth floor. She subsequently progressed to supervisor of the fifth and sixth floors and participated in staff development. She was a member of the medicolegal committee respresenting the nursing service and from 1985 served as coordinator of the Alumnae Office (Fig. 48).

The Commencement was held in the hospital amphitheater at which time 74 graduates received their diplomas.

CLASS OF 1941

Ammerman, Reba E., PA (Flack)
Anderson, Mary Jane, PA
Barbour, Josephine C., NJ (Moellers)
Chamberlain, Geraldine E., NJ (Topping)
Cressman, Lydia M., CANADA
DeRemer, Roberta W., PA (Coble)
DiCrescenzo, Filomena M., PA (Hubsch)
Dietrich, Louise E., PA (Fitzgerald)
Duffy, Kathryn A., NJ (Quackenbush)
Ehrhart, Perma M., PA (Davis)
Elliott, Margaret A. K., PA (Wallett)
Evans, Margaret J., PA (Koehler)
Evans, Rebecca B., PA (Peterson)
Ferg, Anna, PA (Peer)
French, F. Lucille, NJ (Cake)
Frie, Gertrude E., NJ (Riviello)
Gery, Nellie F., PA (Force)
Graf, Augusta R., PA (Waters)
Groman, Dorothy A., PA
Haines, Ann E., MD (Heermans)
Heller, Ethel M., PA (Todaro)
Hemmer, Marie R., PA (Dunn)
Hertzler, Sara J., PA (Harting)
Hinebaugh, Jean W., PA (Nooker)
Holt, Esther J., PA (Martin)
Hummel, Leah M., PA (Edwards)
Huston, Frances L., PA (Rumberger)
James, Margaret, PA (Wager)
John, Margaret, PA
Justice, Winifred M., (Messick)
Karstetter, Cora G., PA
Kiefman, Ruth G., PA (Giletto)
Kishbaugh, Dorothy J., (Freeman)
Leader, Doris L., PA (Miller)
Lehotsky, Helen, PA (Jacobson)
Lindberg, Lillian E., NY

Llewellyn, Dorothy A., PA (Tillman)
Lockwood, Jean E., PA (Wagner)
Matig, Victoria D., PA
McEwen, Sara K., PA (Miller)
Moyer, Martha S., PA (Darnell)
Moyer, Rhea, PA (Johns)
Murray, Janet M., PA (Wooddall)
Pachuta, Mary, PA
Painter, Elizabeth R., NJ (Tighe)
Pfaff, Helen F., PA (Bedner)
Pickens, Sophia K., PA (Driscoll)
Porter, Emily I., PA (Martin)
Rasely, Elizabeth A., PA
Recchiutti, Mary J., PA (Capriotte)
Rich, Mary R., (Saylor)
Robisson, Marion, PA (Barbour)
Roush, Gene, PA (Jerabek)
Samson, Janet M., PA (Polley)
Shaner, Ruth E., PA
Simmons, Grace B., PA (Peacock)
Smith, E. Virginia, PA (Bowman)
Smith, Mary I., PA (Stryker)
Snyder, Clara Mae, PA (Fitts)
Soltys, Frances, PA (Wolicki)
Summers, Margaret L., PA
Swan, Helen W., PA (Joslin)
Taylor, Doris Lee, NC (Ahlsen)
Thomas, Esther L., PA (Watt)
Wampler, Lucille S., PA (Stradley)
Watkins, Melba K., PA (Snyder)
Werley, Harriet H., PA
Williams, Geraldine E., PA (Waters)
Williams, Pearl L., PA (Glover)
Wilson, Eleanor L., PA (Hyatt)
Wippel, Frances M., WV (Masser)
Yoch, Lavinia L., PA (Fuller)
Yuskoski, Martha J., PA (Whitney)
Zoll, Ruth M., PA (Essig)

During this critical year, recruitment of additional student nurses kept pace with the demands of the military. The graduates of this year numbered 75, a record number to date.

On May 15 eighy nurses left Broad Street Station for Camp Bowie, Texas (Fig. 49). After intensive training, the group moved in October to New Brunswick, New Jersey. Ten days later, under cover of night, they boarded ship which took them to their final destination near Cairo, Egypt. Willie L. Alder ('31) was the first Chief Nurse of General Hospital No. 38 (Fig. 50).

The Scholarship Fund was designated the "Clara Melville Scholarship Fund" and made available to graduates of the Nursing School.

Fig. 49. Portion of Jefferson personnel, Camp Bowie, Texas (1942).

CLASS OF 1942

Alexander, Anne, PA (Krall)
Baker, Lillian S., PA (Herring)
Bell, Grace (Heldon)
Bewley, June L., PA (Wall)
Boehret, Alice C., PA
Boschert, Alice J., PA (Phelan)
Bowman, Doris E., PA
Burg, Rhoda A.M., PA (Weisz)
Christian, Laura E., PA (Leeper)
Chronister, Sara M., PA (Mendino)
Cianfrani, Anna F., PA (Harrison)
Clark, Angela D., PA
Cloud, Dorothy A., NJ
Cook, Viola M., PA (Brubaker)
Correll, Janet E., PA (Reinhard)
Dickinson, Margaret, PA (Indrika)
Donovan, Alice, NJ (Massey)
Edgar, Dorothy J., PA (Burns)
Ericson, Anna K., PA (McCormick)

Erway, Frances L., PA (Althouse)
Farnsworth, Sara E., PA (Batchelor)
Fraley, Dorothy E., PA (Templeton)
Fromtling, Mildred L., PA (Dekorte)
Gresh, Doris M., PA (Delong)
Habecker, Nancy S., PA (Maxwell)
Hauser, Virginia M., PA (Heckman)
Hendrickson, Sylvia E., NJ .
Hosterman, Rosalyn R., PA (Boyle)
Jennings, Grace E., PA (Dunkelberger)
Jones, Doris L., PA (Schecter)
Kauffman, Mildred D., PA (Sahms)
Keiper, Gladys D., PA
Kinch, Madeline L., TX (Knight)
Kipp, Eleanor, NJ (Eagan)
Kolodziej, Elizabeth, PA (Kurz)
Lardin, Mary J., PA (Braid)
Lauver, Irene M., PA (Polner)
Longacre, Lois B., PA (Kelly)

Lutz, Virginia M., NJ (Spalding)
Maag, Dorothy M., PA (Frizen)
McClure, Sydney V., PA (Bechtel)
McCurley, Ellen D., PA (Steward)
McHugh, Sally T., PA (Luscombe)
Metzler, Jane C., PA (Flack)
Millard, Elizabeth M., PA (Kerr)
Miller, Jane (Guerin)
Miller, M. Elaine, PA
Miller, Ruth, PA (Tylden)
Moore, Elsie M., PA (Richardson)
Moore, Rebecca M., PA (Wilson)
Moore, Ruth E., PA (Macadam)
Olsson, Sigbrit V. S., PA (Butler)
Paff, Ferne R., PA (Lubin)
Pesci, Rose I., PA (Nicastro)
Potter, Mary E., PA (Wartenburg)
Raub, Beatrice B., PA (Staron)

Rayman, Beatrice L., PA (Snyder)
Reed, Gladys K., PA (White)
Roberts, Madge, PA (Miller)
Rogal, Dorothy E., PA (Nifong)
Rose, Joyce I., PA (Sproch)
Sample, Dolores M., PA (Nelson)
Scott, Eva M., NJ (Blackman)
Selby, Carolyn E., PA (Gebel)
Simpkins, Elizabeth, NJ (Mayhew)
Stone, Gertrude E., PA (Buckey)
Taylor, Myrtle V., NJ (Berman)
Tenari, Anna L., PA (Reganis)
Terrell, Molly Ann, NC (Radcliffe)
Thorp, Ruth E., PA (West)
Tomasso, Kathryn L., NJ (Beitel)
Trimble, Frances L., PA (Barnard)
Williams, Ruth A., PA (Alexis)
Wonder, Georgiana H., PA (Green)
Zelt, Mary R., PA (Wittman)

Fig. 50. Willie L. Alder ('31), first Chief Nurse of General Hospital No. 38.

~ 1943 ~

Miss Ethel Hopkins, who held a B.S. degree from Columbia University and had much prior experience in the middle west, came to Jefferson in 1937 as Educational Director and was advanced to Directress of Nurses in 1943 (Fig. 51).

The decreasing staff of graduate nurses as a result of the war effort encouraged an increase in volunteer workers. Eighteen Gray Ladies were added and courses for an additional 100 were planned. These volunteers provided much needed relief work.

The number of Nurses' Aides was increased and their instruction expanded to include more procedures.

In June of this year the Cadet Nurse Corp was created by Congress as another program for relief of the acute shortage of nurses. Educational expenses were paid and the courses accelerated.

The graduates numbered 64 in this year.

CLASS OF 1943

Abel, Lucy E., MD (Antrim)
Baldwin, Marjorie H., DE (Dore)
Beans, Lois, NJ (Williams)
Benedict, Mary A., CA (Weller)
Blizzard, Mina L., (Birch)
Bowmaster, Edna O., (Wescott)
Boyle, Catherine M., PA (Knapp)
Brainard, Margaret E., PA (Scull)
Burns, Eleanor, NJ (Whelan)
Byrne, Elizabeth E., PA (Kimlin)
Calhoun, Betty L., PA (Suttles)
Claycomb, Evelyn, PA (Long)
Cresswell, Jeanne C., PA (Zukowski)
Dalgleish, Marian, PA (Gabuzda)
Davis, Ann Lois, PA (Cabrey)
Davis, Dolores I., PA (Wilkinson)
Dean, Anna M., WV (Feagens)
Drysdale, Jean D., VA (Warren)
Farrell, Jean G., PA (Kehm)
Fisher, Ruth M., (Dougherty)
Gaugler, Fay, PA (McCune)
Gearhart, Gertrude G., PA (Malloy)
Gray, Theresa (Hart)
Hahn, Marion A., PA (Lash)
Hanes, Betty, PA (McKim)
Hare, Anne C., PA (Inemer)
Hershey, Mary V., PA (Donahey)
Hosterman, Marie, PA (Breon)
Jones, Ruth E., PA (Schmitt)
Keatley, Mary L., PA (Williams)
King, Virginia C., PA (Parry)
Lloyd, Muriel, DE (Peake)

Lovell, Virginia (Hollandsworth)
Machen, Theo (Peterson)
Matrician, Helen, PA
McCready, Anna A., PA (Gallagher)
Metzer, Betty J., PA (Shaw)
Meyle, Elaine A., PA (Trankley)
Milewski, Esther C., PA (Kahn)
Mogck, Anna M., NJ (Whittaker)
Moyer, Vivian I., PA
Neff, Rita A., NM (Schlachter)
Ohler, Audrey E., MD (Zydel)
Painter, Ruth, NJ (Greener)
Ripple, Alice G., PA (Clover)
Robertson, Janet, PA (Gerow)
Rutt, Kathryn S., PA (Combs)
Rutter, Marion, PA (Morris)
Sallinger, Mary F., (Gough)
Schirmer, Nellie M., NJ (Warshaw)
Smith, Amanda L., PA
Snyder, Mildred M., FL (Francis)
Steinmetz, Helen M., PA (Tananis)
Strong, Mary Jo, PA (Lake)
Sullinger, Mary F., PA (Gogh)
Sunderlund, Ruth I., PA
Swirk, Evelyn A., PA (Houck)
Thomas, Helen M., NJ (Reistle)
Thompson, Vera V., PA (Scoggin)
Trostle, Anna L., PA (Miller)
Whitehead, Marjorie E., NJ (Mitchell)
Widmeier, Marie L., NJ (Thompson)
Wittenmyer, Elizabeth S., PA (Lewis)
Workman, Jane E., PA (Pawlak)
Zindel, Vivian, PA (Bowen)

Fig. 51. Miss Ethel Hopkins became Directress of Nurses in 1943.

The Art of Detachment, the Virtue of Method, and the Quality of Thoroughness may make you students, in the true sense of the word. . .but your characters may still lack that which can alone give permanence to power—the Grace of Humility.

Sir William Osler (1849-1919)

~ 1944 ~

A major step forward was the institution of an 8-hour day for all nurses. The increase in the availablity and skills of Gray Ladies, Nurses' Aides and Canteen Workers provided some of the impetus for these improved working conditions.

In November of this year, Miss Margaret M. Jackson, R.N., B.S.,(Fig. 52) succeeded Miss Hopkins as Directress of Nurses.

The largest number of enrolled students reached 350, and the graduates numbered 69.

CLASS OF 1944

Alwine, Virginia E., PA (Sweigart)
Baginski, Bertha J., PA (Walters)
Brown, Lorraine, NJ (Pierce)
Butler, Dorcas L., PA (Revelli)
Byer, Janet B., PA
Campbell, Helen L., PA
Cannon, Marie, PA (Philer)
Cupp, Mary K., PA
Delizier, Norma R., NJ (Schleher)
Dorn, Arlene, PA
Dress, Ardeth A., PA (Weeks)
Eckley, Marie F., PA
Fink, Marjorie E., PA (Searing)
Frampton, Emily A., TN (Donnelson)
Frankenfield, Vivian C., PA (Gragg)
Fritz, Sarah E., PA (Munroe)
Gackenbach, Jean M., PA (Swarte)
Gaston, Mary L., PA (Stewart)
Gates, M. Elizabeth, PA
Gerfin, Emily J., PA (Hewitt)
Gilbert, Mary F., VA (Helden)
Gwynneth, Lewis M., PA
Housenick, Mary C., PA
Kaneshiro, Neddie, NJ (Atchison)
Keeports, Janet V., PA (Kinch)
Keiser, Elaine P., PA (Carol)
Kerr, Virginia V., PA (Allen)
Klockner, Betty L., NJ
(Brower) Kreiser, Sarah J., PA (Harris)
Lambert, Marjorie A., PA (Swindlehurst)
Lee, Betty J., PA (Elliott)
Leigh, Marjorie Y., NJ (Butler)
Little, Grace A., PA (Emery)
Lowe, Ann B., PA (Hornstein)

Lytle, Alfreda, PA (Davis)
McMullen, Jean E., (Koutsouros)
McNitt, Jean C., PA (Middleswarth)
Meenahan, Mary J., PA (Trueheart)
Morgan, Anna P., PA (Rowan)
Myhlertz, Mary Faith, FL (Babcock)
Nash, Mary, PA (Collins)
Naugle, Katherine E., PA (Painter)
Neary, Catherine T., PA (Merkel)
Newman, Joyce E., NY (Purchell)
Overdorff, Janet F., PA (Nachurd)
Peck, Mary K., PA (Brill)
Powell, Lucille M., PA (Dye)
Rhoads, Carol J., PA (Hanford)
Robinson, Emily L., PA (Whiteneck)
Schelhas, Beverly E., PA (Litsinger)
Schell, Anna M., PA (Snyder)
Schreffler, Geraldine, PA (Myer)
Schultz, Betty E., PA (Mair)
Seifris, Rosanne, PA (Gardner)
Sharpless, Maureen O., PA (McCool)
Shore, June E., FL (VanCise)
Showers, Dorothy G., PA (Hoffer)
Smith, Elizabeth W., WV (Alt)
Smith, Rosie M., PA (Jones)
Snook, Mary E., PA (Smolkovic)
Spangler, Elizabeth L., PA
Stover, Charolette, PA (Ellenbogen)
Thomas, Mary E., VA (Dickerson)
Voglarr, Norma A., PA (Falconer)
Wall, Thelma D., PA (Latz)
Williams, Vivian R., CO (Reinhart)
Wilson, June B., PA (Tymeson)
Wilson, Amy E., PA (Allen)
Young, Thelma E., PA (Tojek)

Fig. 52. Miss Margaret M. Jackson, Acting Directress of Nurses (1944).

Thoughtfulness, consideration and kindness, I am sure you have learned, are indispensable qualities of your noble profession. Patience is probably the virtue which you found most difficult to exhibit at times. Patients may be sometimes querulous and thoughtless in their demands. The same individuals when well may be charming, delightful and considerate people; yet fever, pain, malnutrition or other abnormal states altered these natural attributes. With such people, forbearance and patience must be yours in abundance.

John H. Gibbon, Jr., M.D. (JMC, '27)

~ 1945 ~

In this year the Nursing School began participation in the National League of Nursing Education Pre-Nursing and Guidance Test Program.

An improvement in facilities was the increase of complete bedside units to 13 for the teaching of practice procedures. Contrary to former custom the student could now learn to take complete care of a patient by demonstrating to her instructor whether or not she could carry out nursing procedures. In addition, a Procedure book was completed by Janet Correll ('41).

On March 8, the 38th General Hospital was awarded a Meritorius Service Unit Plaque, the highest award which the army services can give to a non-combat unit.

In the Spring Class of 1945 there were 62 grad-uates and in the Fall Class there were 80. These classes resulted from accelerated programs necessitated by the war.

Anna Kuba served at Jefferson on private duty and as instructor in the School of Nursing until 1954 when she assumed teaching positions at the University of Pennsylvania, advancing to Assistant Professor in Nursing, Vice-Chairman of the Graduate Program, and Assistant Dean. In 1965 she held similar positions at Boston University School of Nursing in administration. She was later with the American Nurses' Association as Coordinator and in 1979 she became Executive Director of the North Carolina Board of Nursing. She had numerous publication and organizational positions.

SPRING 1945

Anderson, Mary E., IN (Barrick)
Baird, Martha J., PA (Tomassetti)
Baldwin, Frances L., PA (Kinner)
Barr, Ruth M., PA (Siciliano)
Brady, Lenore I., NJ (Strigari)
Butzer, Beata J., PA (Shaw)
Carlson, Florence M., NJ (Harley)
Chudzinski, Regina A., PA (White)
Covert, Betty K., PA (Rhodes)
Deitzler, Betty J., PA (Heuston)
Diacumakas, Christine, DE (Heckler)
Dickinson, Jacqueline N., NC (Moore)
Druckenmiller, Gladys, PA (DuPell)
Ebert, Ina L., PA (Bonde)
Eisenbrown, Mary C., PA (Bruno)
Eisenhauer, Harrietta E., PA
Fairer, Marjorie A., NJ (Cummins)
Finton, Eleanor L., PA (Young)
Fleck, Lillian H., PA (Baker)
Fleck, Madeline E., PA (Nevins)
Fleegle, Alma J., PA (Williams)
Fowler, Kathryn E., NJ (Hood)
Frohman, Marie R., PA
Greenly, M. Esther, DE (Rothermill)
Gregory, Ruth, PA (Dudley)
Hastings, Margaret C., PA
Heaps, Doris M., PA (Parrish)

Hoyle, Beatrice L., PA (Young-Dean)
Jennings, Pearl M., NJ (Rice)
Kelly, Marian L., DE (Carver)
Knipe, Frances C., PA (Gracy)
Kressler, Alta, PA
Leffler, Anna R., PA (Poole)
Lloyd, Betty J., PA (Wildasin)
Markione, Jean B., (Eveland)
Marocci, Berthe A., PA (Ledet)
McFarland, Miriam E., PA (Raphelson)
Miller, Caroline J., PA (Longsdruff)
Moore, Helen M., PA (Price)
Moyer, Betty G., NJ (Greenwood)
O'Donnell, Mary R., PA (Miller)
Owen, Lorraine L., PA (Imsehwener)
Parkinson, Martha V., PA
Rhoades, Marjorie B., PA (Weyant)
Rickley, Mary A., PA (Gardner)
Riggin, Betty J., MD (Laggner)
Riggin, Ruth L., MA (Corson)
Rohr, Ruth F., PA (Starner)
Shaeff, Eleanor M., PA (Hager)
Sheckler, Gloria A., (Robertson)
Sherick, Evelyn F., PA (Sell)
Shetzley, Thelma L., PA (Fleming)
Shultz, Betty A., PA (Smith)
Stottlemyer, Opal L., PA (Shelley)

Wagoner, Bette, WV (Hudson)
Walker, Kathryn M., PA (Jenkins)
Wallace, Helen M., PA (Bedner)
Williams, Betty J., DE (Knox)

Wilson, Marjorie J., PA
Wingard, Mina A., NJ (Zimmerman)
Woltman, Huldah M., PA
Young, Etna V., GA (Arrington)

FALL 1945

Ace, Dorothy E., PA (Roberts)
Alex, Victoria P., PA (Anzulewicz)
Alexander, Josephine A., PA (Januszkiewicz)
Alisio, Jennie E., PA (Rule)
Auman, Bettyann, PA (Wenbert)
Barnard, Eugenia M., NJ
Barney, Eva, PA (Sheetz)
Bellis, Jane E., NJ (Mack)
Betz, Col Catherine, NJ
Byorick, Byrnice R., PA (Hurt)
Chillem, Nellie M., NJ
Churella, Dorothy M., PA (Adams)
Climenson, Marilyn J., PA (Eubanks)
Cooper, Charlotte A., PA (Phillips)
Crawford, Patricia, PA
Decoursey, Audrie D., PA (Johnson)
Dick, Helen, PA (Anderson)
Dinse, Charlotte A., PA (Fretz)
Dusman, Dorothy, PA (Mowery)
Eshelman, Marylin J., PA (Engel)
Eshleman, Geraldine F., PA (Meryweather)
Everett, Dorothy, PA (Novak)
Fishel, Jean E., PA (Carter)
Fluck, Ida Jean, PA (Bertram)
Freed, Jane, PA (Nyce)
Gaffey, Margaret M., PA (Poole)
Gingrich, Eileen G., PA (Ebling)
Glass, Kathryn L., PA (LeBate)
Grant, Lorraine M., PA (Lubka)
Haleski, Audrey R., NJ (Kahoun)
Halvorsen, Geraldine M., PA (Wagner)
Hankee, Catherine A., PA (Shinton)
Hartzell, Phyllis V., PA (Smith)
Hawk, Janet M., PA (Caldretti)
Hechler, Betty R., PA (Fleming)
Holcomb, Mary J., PA (Trautman)
Hoover, Janet L., PA (Valentine)
Jacobs, June M., PA
Jones, Betty Lou, PA (Jahnke)
Karo, Sarah E., PA (Huston)

Kline, Ada J., PA (Jacoby)
Koch, Shirley M., PA (Alderfer)
Kuba, Anna, PA
Larson, Irene L., PA (Kessler)
Laube, Ruth F., PA (Covell)
Leauber, Ruth S., PA (Vivian)
Lewis, Catherine J., PA
Lindes, Christine W., PA (Park)
Long, Margaret E., PA (Mawhood)
MacHamer, Delphine W., PA (Hale)
Maier, Betty I., PA (Breaw)
Mathuse, Beryl V., NJ (Chipowsky)
McAllonis, Ruth M., NJ (Wainwright)
Miller, Helen E., PA (Hollingsworth)
Mitchell, Eliza J., PA (Kendall)
Morgan, Roberta F., NJ (Vogel)
Mullen, Harriet I., PA (Palmer)
Nash, Margaret, PA (Schulheiscz)
Ocker, Marie P., PA
Overdorf, Vivian H., PA (Wert)
Ozer, Sylvia K., PA (Beck)
Raup, Alice E., PA (Linn)
Roadarmal, Lois S., PA (Rank)
Roberts, Caroline E., PA (King)
Ruble, Jeane V., PA (Visalli)
Schleinkofer, Dorothy W., NJ (Hannaway)
Schmick, Florence L., PA (Howanitz)
Smith, Vivian R., PA (Osborn)
Snyder, Elizabeth L., PA
Sorensen, Bella S., NJ (Martinez)
Thomas, Olive E., PA (Hall)
Umbower, Betty G., PA (Attanasio)
Utterbach, Lillian M., PA (Herrick)
Vandyke, Hanan M., PA (Reynolds)
Vitetta, Rita A., PA (Labate)
Wall, June M., PA (Kyle)
Wenzel, Margaret H., VA (Fansler)
White, Evelyn L., PA (Collett)
Winnick, Eleanor, PA (King)
Zundt, I. Helge, PA (Michael)

The Alumnae Association in this year absorbed the 248 graduates of the White Haven Sanitorium into its organization with full privileges. This coincided with the merger in 1946 of White Haven Sanitorium with Jefferson and the closure of its School of Nursing.

A most important event was the opening of the Barton Memorial Division of Jefferson Medical College Hospital, located at Broad and Fitzwater Streets. It would house the Department for Diseases of the Chest from 1946 to 1961 (Fig. 53).

The Melville Nurses' Scholarship Fund reached $10,000 this year.

There were 75 graduates in this class.

CLASS OF 1946

Albert, Ruth Helen, PA (Super)
Allison, Mae Elizabeth, PA (Koch)
Anderson, Elaine Faithe, PA (Mitchell)
Baer, Jacqueline Kay, PA (Coffroth)
Baker, Marguerite Alice, PA (Baker)
Becker, Gloria LaRaine, PA (Kovack)
Beer, Jane Yingling, PA (Klinger)
Bernd, Jeanne Trappe, PA (Hannigan)
Bowers, Mary Catherine, PA (McKensie)
Brandt, Ruth Elizabeth, PA (Guthrie)
Brodginski, Louise Pauline, PA (McGowan)
Brown, Frances Amy, PA (Saunders)
Butler, Alice E., PA (Reisinger)
Caldwell, Alice Rose, PA (Hornickel)
Cook, Margaret Mary, PA (Biggs)
Dinklocker, Marilyn Jane, PA (Hodge)
Eathorne, Nancy Louise, PA (Seeley)
Ellison, Louise Mae, NC (Eudy)
Fairweather, Ruth Doris, PA (Nemeth) Faust,
Nelmah Florence, PA (Shaffer)
Fessler, Dorothy Ann, PA
Fink, Anita, PA (Shubert)
Gilardone, Esther Dorothy, PA (Strachan)
Gilbert, Jean Katherine, PA (Metzler)
Gourley, Ruth Lee, PA (Gelb)
Handy, Jane Elizabeth, DE (Ward)
Hart, Geraldine, PA (Rockel)
Heishman, Anna K. Heiker, PA (Koert)
Henney, Ruth Elaine, PA (Warnock)
Herr, Jeanne Marie, PA (Burkins)
Holzman, Mary Frances, PA (McQuown)
Hopkins, Muriel Emma, PA (Scott)
Irvin, Dorothy Mae, PA (Fisher)
Jarrett, Jane, PA (Fox)
Kielar, Lorayne M., PA
Kimmel, Betty Marie, PA (Frommelt)

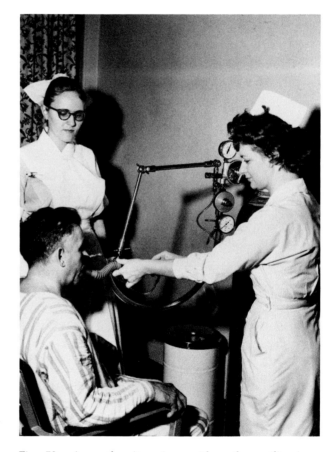

Fig. 53. An anthracite miner with anthracosilicosis receives treatment with intermittent positive pressure breathing from Miss Emma Gallo (right), Barton Supervising Nurse, who is teaching the technique.

Kneebone, Shirley Isabel, PA (Rush)
Kopilchack, Helen, PA
Kowalesky, Miriam Louise, PA (Pursel)
Lebkicker, Jeanne Louise, PA
Maurer, Laura Elizabeth, OH (Pollack)
Morrison, Marilyn Grace, PA (Hecksher)
Morrow, Phyllis Isabelle, PA (Justis)
Mosser, Freida Virginia, PA
Nasveschuk, Emelia Catherine, PA (Hayman)
Nissler, Elizabeth Ann, PA (Black)
Noble, Betty C., PA (Gurewich)
Northey, Sarah Jane, PA (Boysen)
Null, Jeanne Kay, PA (Collevechio)
Patterson, Laura Ruth, PA (Hart)
Pispecky, Josephine, PA (Warner)
Rebert, Vivienne Lorraine, PA (Hatton)
Reeder, Idabelle Lorena, PA (Hartley)
Rowan, Ellen Patricia, PA (Stephens)
Schappet, Elaine Barbara, PA (Hines)

Scholes, Margaret Mae, PA (Schwartz)
Schroy, Ruth Shirley, NJ (Hersey)
Seiple, Nancy Cecile, PA (Stager)
Shoemaker, Helen Suzanne, PA (Crain)
Shottin, Claire Bernice, NJ (Hogue)
Smith, Mary Minerva, PA (Moorehead)
Spalding, June Patricia, PA (Eyerly)
Stong, Elaine Margaret, PA (Kimbel)
Supplee, Jeanne Louise, PA
Swartzlander, Evelyn, PA (Riggin)
Sweeney, Dionysia Mary, PA (Ruht)
Tritt, Helen Marie, PA (Mischitz)
Udicious, Mary Madeline, NY (Weisman)
Vail, Elinor Franklin, WA (deRoulhae)
Varker, Lois Emilyn, PA (Benning)
Watters, Shirley Grace, PA (O'Reilly)
Weldon, Betty Marie, NJ (Saunderlin)
Wiestling, Irene May, PA (Ruhl)
Williams, Margaret Louella, DE (Jones)
Yost, Betty Virginia, PA (Zehner)

WHITE HAVEN

In accord with Jefferson's acquisition of the White Haven Sanatorium, all of the 248 graduates of its School of Nursing became members of the Jefferson Nurses Alumnae Association. The list is as follows:

Abernathy, Gertrude
Alexander, Mary J., (Bain)
Altman, Beatrice
Aschenbrenner, Caroline (MacCallum)
Baker, Helene S., (Saltzer)
Baker, Lillian
Bartash, Minnie, PA
Bashinko, Mary (Nylund)
Beatty, Marie
Beddis, Julia
Bennett, Gladys
Bernauer, Sophie (Levy)
Bitzer, Bertha
Bluitt, Sara (Pollock)
Bobbie, Jennie M.
Boder, Helen (Hvisdas)
Boullier, Annie
Braxton, James
Brinkheide, Margaret (Crane)
Brown, Ella M.
Campbell, Elizabeth
Cardenti, Isabel (Camilli)
Carney, Elizabeth
Cermak, Helen (McGuire)
Chiara, Mary
Chomeszak, Anna

Chomeszak, Eva (Matys)
Chomszak, Olga (Weiss)
Clark, Elizabeth
Collins, May
Coltre, Helen Mary, (Mitchell)
Comsick, Anna (Reinert)
Comsick, Viola
Conaghen, Eleanor (Waiver)
Conley, Alice P., (Tisdale)
Cooper, Betty
Corta, Emily Mary, (Doyle)
Cozza, Angela R., PA
Creasy, Margaret C., (Helms)
Crone, Mildred A.
Cross, Helen
Crowe, Mary, NY (Murtha)
Crowley, Margaret M., (Sokolowski)
Cunningham, Margaret T.
Dalton, Elizabeth (Miller)
Darmobray, Roseanna (Torbick)
Davidson, Hannah Margaret,
Dean, Harriet
Demko, Anna N., PA
Denvers, Nellie (Fitzgerald)
DeVille, Catherine (Hochderfer)
Devlin, Agnes

Dill, Anna M.
Dill, Helen A., NJ (Maddock)
Dipolene, Josephine M.
Disante, Anna, NJ (Fink)
Dixon, Ruth (Griffin)
Doherty, M. Estelle,
Dolan, Thomas J.
Domolavage, Elizabeth A., (Croshaw)
Domolavage, Mary A.
Donohue, Florence M.
Donovan, Catherine A., (Baylis)
Downey, Nora
Doyle, Anna (Clifford)
Drake, Carrie Hieb
Dublin, Eloise (Travers)
Dulian, Ann (Goodman)
Dunker, Ellida
Early, S. Marie
Ehrstein, Mary
Erickson, H. Carl
Ernst, Ida (Teplitz)
Evans, Madeline R.
Faust, Mae (Mitchell)
Ferguson, Marjorie F.
Fisher, Frances A.
Flood, Bertha H.
Foote, Beatrice (O'Hara)
Franklin, Edith (Watterson)
Fulk, Helen M., (Campbell)
Gallagher, Margaret (Crunlish)
Gardiner, Ruth M.
Gebauer, Elsie
Gerista, John
Gilderman, Ida, (Smith)
Gilway, Elizabeth
Gippert, Augusta (Skiener)
Goldsmith, Helen
Greenblatt, Annette
Grohowski, Julia
Groome, Anna
Hall, Carrie M.
Halverson, Eleanor (Ward)
Hampshire, Rosa M., (Tucker)
Hancock, Elinor
Hancock, Mary E., (Dierman)
Hanlon, Margaret
Hanlon, Mary C., (Faulkner)
Hansis, Margaret
Hanzliet, Edith (Morelli)
Harding Lillian (Postell)
Hardy, Anna
Hartburger, Walburga (Callahan)
Hawver, Edna (Lauchlan)
Hayes, M. Camilla, (Hudson)

Healey, Margaret G., (Ruane)
Hemmer, Frances
Henkelman, Frieda M.
Henry, Dorothy, B., NJ (McGlade)
Hoeller, Hermine T., (McBride)
Hopkins, Edna (Dobbs)
Hosage, Marie C., PA (Destafano)
Hottle, Edna
Humenay, Margaret V.
Hurd, Laura (Johnson)
Hurd, Rudelle J.
Isadore, Helen M.
Ischi, Clara
Ives, Dorothy
Jackson, Minnie
Jacobs, Rose
Jensen, Mary
Jeske, Emma P.
Johnson, Jewel
Jones, Ethel M.
Kacala, Anna (Bednash)
Kava, Rose
Kayley, Josephine McKenna
Kelemonick, Anna R., (Bebe)
Kelly, Mary (Brennan)
Kelly, Rosina
King, Helen B., (Healy)
Kiraly, Helen L., NY (Dean)
Kirk, Betty
Kirkpatrick, Elizabeth
Kiss, Miriam M., (Bell)
Kissling, Anna
Koethe, Gladys
Kreider, Susanne
Kubak, Pauline
Kuhn, Anna (Lang)
Kundreskas, Anna
LaMontee, Dircle
Latshew, Mabel C., (Fritsche)
Laudano, Antoinette, CT (Romayne)
Lavelle, Catherine (Sullivan)
LeFevre, Agnes B.
Lenhart, Dorothy A.
Longobardi, Mary S.
Lyons, Hedwig (Wrobley)
Mackewice, Amylia (Plucker)
MacKewice, Julian
Maiorano, Frances, NJ (Cielo)
Malinoski, Marie, PA (Dimarco)
Marrero, Elisa
Martin, Beulah
Martin, Helen (Welch)
Maybin, Mary
McCann, Elizabeth

McCarthy, Anna (Schermerhorn)
McCarthy, Gertrude
McDermott, Elizabeth
McDole, Eleanor (York)
McGeehan, Marie E., (Fripp)
McGlynn, Mary R.
McGowan, Margaret
McGuire, Frances
McGuire, Susan
McHugh, Mary E.
McNevin, Kathryn
Melin, Mildred
Messick, Margaret (Herr)
Metzler, Edith
Milkun, Wilma Dorothea
Miller, Sue N.
Minner, Pauline G.
Minton, Anna (Regalis)
Monka, Cecelia (Blackmore)
Moteyunas, Ann M.
Mulranen, Mary
Munch, Rose
Murphy, Alice
Muskoff, Loretta A., (Mattarella)
Naylor, Daisy
Neely, Catherine
Nelson, Alfreda
Nelson, Alice
Nicholson, Eva (Morrow)
Nick, Catherine
Noone, Lillian (Block)
Novak, Anna (Dutko)
Novak, Helen
O'Connell, Mildred (Hessmer)
O'Neill, Elizabeth
Ott, S. Miriam, (Farrell)
Peat, Marie (Teneyck)
Perry, Ulainee
Phillips, Martha (Strand)
Potoski, Brigid (Lebow)
Potter, Elizabeth (Mald)
Prager, Frances
Pribish, Anna, PA (Miller)
Prohaski, Alvina M.

Purcell, Kathleen (Hewitt)
Quinn, Jane (Field)
Raper, Pansy E.
Rappaport, Elsie
Rashinko, Mary, NY Nylund)
Regnier, Reba
Reilly, Edna (Sanzo)
Rice, Alma K., PA (Kocher)
Rice, Mary G.
Richman, Rose R.
Rock, Florence (Finnegan)
Roos, Katherine C.
Rydall, Frances (Thatcher)
Ryder, Gertrude (O'Dell)
Salmon, Anna (Koerth)
Sankey, Margaret (Wood)
Sauerhoff, Mary (Handy)
Scaga, Anna R., IL (Scanlon)
Scherl, Rose
Schulze, Henrietta
Schumayer, Blanche, (Mcguigan)
Seiler, Rose (Young)
Shaffer, Justyne E.
Sieminski, Mary Ann, (Robertson)
Small, Mary
Smith, Caroline J., (Lief)
Smith, Rose Mary (Schmidt)
Spear, Rose (Berlant)
Stanberger, Eve
Steinerman, Julia (Tobin)
Stenbroner, C. Lucille, (Wilcox)
Stoutenberry, Gretchen L.
Straub, Elinor
Stuart, Hester
Sullivan, Agnes
Thompson, Mildred
Thornton, Marie V.
Tomlinson, Frances
Treffeisen, Emma (Thomas)
VonBeek, Johanna J.
Wilson, Laura
Wilson, Mary P., (Cancellarini)
Zajac, Elizabeth T. K., CA (Sedway)
Zellner, Blanche (Keller)

Miss Katherine Childs became Directress of the School of Nursing and Nursing Service as of July 1 (Fig. 54). During her administration the classes were divided into clinical and academic sections.

As of this year the staff of graduate nurses had markedly increased. The Hospital was now employing 150 graduate nurses.

The Class of 1947 numbered 127 graduates, the largest to date.

CLASS OF 1947

Alexander, Mary Ella, PA (Nida)
Baloga, Marie L., PA (Peters)
Banks, Lucy Emma, PA (Stillings)
Barner, Ann Kay, PA (Wright)
Beattie, LaDean Ruth, PA (Kramp)
Bell, Florence Ann Mae, NJ (Mitchell)
Bielon, Laura Jean, PA (Tobia)
Black, Helen Jane, PA (Guerin)
Buffum, Marie Adeline, NJ (Hunter)
Burd, Mildred Rose, PA (Sterner)
Campbell, Edith Virginia, PA
Carico, Virginia Caroline, DE (DelVecchio)
Chesnulevich, Bernadine Ann, PA (Winchell)
Correnti, Paula Joan, PA (Tyler)
Cossman, Margaret Mary, PA
Craft, Lois Ann, PA (Dunlap)
Crane, Hilda Eloise, PA (Lineweaver)
Davis, Audrey June, PA (Kerber)
Deckard, Barbara Ann, PA (Zigler)
Durr, Helen Jeanne, WV
Eckbod, Verna Mae, NJ (Andreas)
Edgell, Wanda Elizabeth, PA (Kinsey)
Edwards, Janet Elizabeth, PA (Maurer)
Evancho, Irene, PA (Werner)
Fanucci, Flora Frances, PA (Simpson)
Farne, Eugenia D., PA (Purcell)
Feiler, Elizabeth, PA (McNulty)
Feiler, Margaret, PA (Cygan)
Fiebig, Anne Stella, PA (Cloud)
Forrest, Lorena Mae, MD (Hester)
Foster, Audrey Louise, PA (Bearer)
Fox, Ruth, PA (Hallowell)
Gast, Eleanor, PA (Foulke)
Geovanelle, Evelyn Frances, PA
Gilman, Jane Virginia, NJ (Collins)
Gleichert, Emma Belle, PA (Yahres)
Glover, Ann Winifred, PA (Gloser)
Gluck, Clara, PA (Horowitz)
Golden, Elizabeth Marye, PA (Cooper)

Gover, Elaine, PA (Hampton)
Graber, Verna Eileen, IA (Kuehl)
Green, Frances May, MD (Saunders)
Grimm, Evelyn Marie, PA (Smith)
Groves, Ruth, PA (McCormick)
Hambright, Betty M., PA (Wiley)

Fig. 54. Miss Katherine Childs, appointed Directress of the School of Nursing and Nursing Service (1947).

Hamm, Joanne Lorraine, PA (Koelle)
Hangan, Marie Jeanne, NJ
Harding, Dorothy Grace, PA (Kohl)
Harding, Martha, NJ (Boehmler)
Harkins, Mary Edith, PA (Kerr)
Harris, Dorothy A., (VanVranken)
Harter, Irene, PA (Natela)
Hendershot, Barbara Ann, PA (Marks)
Herman, Mildred Eva, PA (Noll)
High, Martha Anna, PA (Hershberger)
Hill, Bobbie Lee, NJ (Davis)
Himes, Evelyn Marie, PA (Lewis)
Hirst, Madeline Rita, PA (Jennis)
Hunsberger, Grace Urffer, PA (Mease)
Hunsicker, Marjorie Viola, PA (Lorah)
Jackson, Elizabeth Baldwin, PA (Watkins)
Jacobs, Lois Jane, PA (Custer)
Jusaitis, Alberta Theresa, PA (Bouyer)
Keller, Iris Patricia, PA (Walters)
Klingerman, Mildred Elaine, PA (Ertwine)
Knerr, Harriet Yvonne, PA (Heffner)
Koerner, Helen Mary, PA (Corrigan)
Kratz, Jay Terese, PA (Jackson)
Kutz, Gene Peters, PA (Fuoti)
Leonard, Marie Margaret, PA (Sabo)
Ludrof, Teresa Josephine, PA (Lewis)
Lutz, Emma Louisa, PA (Subers)
Martin, Elizabeth Ruth, PA (Spencer)
McConnell, Gladys May, PA (Temple)
Mertz, Dorothy Marie, PA (Sturr)
Messa, Josephine Frances, PA (Quinn)
Miller, Anne Daphine, PA (Spohn)
Miller, Arlean Viola, PA Miller,
Beryl Yvonne, PA (Bashore)
Miller, Ruth Dessamond, PA (Downey)
Molitor, Georgianna J., PA (Anderson)
Morrett, Judith Alice, PA (Hess)
Moyer, Duane Stewart, (Summers)
Murphy, Claire Miriam, PA (Boylan)
Murray, Lora May, NJ (Flaherty)
O'Connor, Elizabeth Jane, PA (Oakes)
Oesterle, Marie Theresa, PA (Thiers)

Park, Iona Jean, PA (Ball)
Pavulak, Mary, NY (Swan)
Pennell, Avis Louis, PA (Fetrow)
Pfromm, Doris Emily, PA (Cavanaugh)
Prendergast, Catherine Cecelia, PA
Prisnock, Elizabeth Kathleen, PA
Pyle, Elizabeth Jane, PA (Miller)
Read, Anna Catherine, PA (Olund)
Rhiel, Clara Luella, PA (Bahner)
Roberts, Ruth Marie, PA (Goodin)
Robinson, Constance Mervine, PA (Forker)
Robinson, Jeanne Kathryn, PA (Holback)
Ronco, Grace Inez, PA (Stagaman)
Saltzer, Frances May, PA (Saunders)
Sanders, Maude Reeves, PA (Schwab)
Schuetz, Irma Sophie, NJ (Heller)
Shoup, Mary June, PA (Dove)
Sokodinsky, Josephine, NJ (Laird)
Souders, Mary Carolyn, PA
Stevens, Carol, NJ (Covert)
Steward, Betty Ellen, PA (McConnell)
Stouppe, Gwendolyn Ann, PA (Callis)
Stout, Julia Constance, PA
Striney, Dorothy Josephine, PA (Serosky)
Sturges, Emily Virginia, PA (Lawrence)
Sweyer, Sheila Gene, PA (Bachman)
Taylor, Wahnette Marie, PA (Carosi)
Tice, Muriel Anne, PA (Rotherman)
Trambley, Madge Vivian, PA (Abel)
Treon, Jane Elizabeth, PA (Reitz)
Valohs, Maria Nettie, PA (Menninger)
Vlahos, Marie Nettie, PA (Menninger)
Walk, Helen May, PA (Roth)
Wargo, Mary Jane, PA (Church)
Welliver, Marie E., PA (Smith)
Whysong, Betty Arlene, PA (Mathers)
Wilkinson, Betty Louise, PA (Renn)
Young, Doris Mae, PA (Moore)
Zello, Julia Margaret, PA (King)
Zimmerman, Hazel Ann, PA (Boyer)
Zinni, Florence Anne, NJ (Checchia)
Zipf, Marjorie June, PA (Logan)

I have always loved the way the great English surgeon, Lord Berkeley Moynihan, characterized nursing as the gentlest profession. Men are capable of gentleness, but it is after all a womanly quality, and you will always be rich in your possession of it.

John H. Gibbon, Jr., M.D. (JMC, '27)

~ 1948 ~

The student council, organized in 1945, was effective in persuading the school administration to grant more relief time, more social time, and improved physical amenities. White shoes and stockings replaced the former unpopular black ones. Late passes were liberalized.

Throughout the 1940's the Women's Board provided additional support in the form of decoration of the residences, installation of a modern library, and the refurbishing of a lounge. These improvements provided a setting for more frequent social events, including semi-annual formal dances.

Rose M. Kirshbaumer entered the Medical Mission Sisters, a Roman Catholic Agency, and served in many foreign areas, mainly Africa. She was also a participant and consultant for nursing programs and establishment of hospitals at the University of Nairobi, Kenya and the University of Malawi. She also had major responsibility for planning and implementing workshops and teaching programs in Nursing and Health Education. In 1988 she received the Jefferson Alumni Special Achievement Award from the College of Allied Health Sciences.

Sofia H. Gormish became a member of the United States Navy Nurse Corps and advanced to her final rank as Commander, retiring in 1973. She served in many domestic and foreign assignments, received her B.S.N from the University of Buffalo, and M.S. in Nursing Administration from the University of Minnesota. Her last assignment was Assistant Chief of Nursing Services, U.S. Naval Hospital, Camp Pendleton, California.

There were 109 graduates.

CLASS OF 1948

Albright, Mary Eileen, PA (Olinyk)
Archer, Mary Joanne, NJ (Porter)
Bailey, Barbara Ann, PA (Roach)
Basler, Margaret Mary, PA (Blaine)
Bilger, Lois Marion, CT (Kelley)
Bortner, Margaret Elizabeth, PA (Becker)
Breen, Mercedes Frances, NJ (Christ)
Brokenshire, Mildred, PA (Spencer)
Bullock, Ruth Rilla, PA (Garrett)
Burke, Doris Alice, PA (Hano)
Casaday, Lillian Louise, PA (Bagamery)
Cogan, Ruth Ellen, PA (Courtet)
Cohen, Mildred Abby, PA (Hindman)
Cominsky, Eleanor, PA (Dunkleman)
Cornelius, Inez Elizabeth, PA (Mirenda)
Curts, Gladys Mae, PA (Weaver)
Darling, Shirley May, PA (Horowitz)
Daubert, Bettilou, PA (Brown)
Deiter, Faye Elizabeth, PA (Groff)
Destan, Bertha, PA (Geary)
Diehl, Arlene Royer, PA (Cohen)
Diehl, Dorothy Irene, PA (Dickie)
Dombrosky, Alexa Helen, PA (Seepol)
Dopirak, Nadine, PA (Fetsko)
Drake, Barbara Florence, NY

(Kinkead) Duke, Elinor Louise, PA (Doubet)
Dutton, Laurel Yvonne, FL (Inge)
Exdahl, Carolyn Estelle, PA (Hankins)
Fetsko, Eleanor, PA (Adams)
Fleming, Nita Gray Sterrett, PA (Glennan)
Franks, Mildred Louise, PA (Hines)
Furtaw, Elizabeth Dolores, PA (Logan)
Geil, Mercedes Kathryn, PA (Weber)
Getch, Dorothy Ann, PA (Ryder)
Geyer, Elinor Yvonne, PA (Hays)
Gormish, Sophia Henrietta, PA
Grundon, Norma Eleanor, PA (Bicking)
Guerin, Phyllis Jean, PA (Courtney)
Gustas, Helen M., PA (Hauber)
Hafer, Kathryn, PA (Eyrich)
Haines, Doris Ellen, PA (Stevens)
Hanning, Bette Jayne, PA (Berkley)
Hawk, Joane A., PA (DeRose)
Hawthorne, Anita Florence, PA (Garrett)
Hayes, Anne Marie, NJ (Rahn)
Hershman, Sara Ellen, PA (Leopold)
Hickey, Aileen R., PA (Wapner)
Hopkins, Beverly Jeanne, PA (Isberner)
Irvine, Rachel L., PA (Herbert)
Johns, Betty Lucille, PA (Budrow)

Johnson, Catherine Lillian, NJ (Haas)
Johnson, Dorothy C., NJ (Nelson)
Kapitula, Martha, PA (Hartwell)
Kersbaumer, Rose Mary, PA
Koval, Mary Ann, PA (Buzydlowski)
Kulp, Wanda Patricia, PA (Przywara)
Kunkle, Mae Florence, PA (Remington)
Lentz, Evelyn Louise, PA (Craig)
Long, Joyce Marie, PA (Campbell)
Long, Mary Patricia, PA (Haupt)
Loyd, Gloria Jean, PA (Downey)
Malinoski, Bernadine Marie, PA Maneval,
Ellen Jean, PA (Karvasale)
Martz, Betty R., PA (Muthler)
Maurer, Phyllis A., PA (Matanick)
McDowell, Kathryn Marie, NJ
McMichael, Adele Griffith, PA (Wasson)
Michaels, Doris Lorraine, PA (Weitzman)
Mitstifer, Margaret Ann, PA (Hamill)
Mogle, Dorothy Jean, PA (Forshey)
Morrison, Christine Lowe, NJ (Blasius)
Morton, Joan, PA (Hoffman)
Mullen, Miriam Patricia, PA
Narcowich, Irene Mary, PA (Kaufman)
Newkirk, Sara Elizabeth, PA (Boydelatour)
Olivia, Anne Marie J., PA (Carballo)
Painter, Anna Mae, PA (Chalupa)
Parsons, Betty Lucille, PA (Konjusky)
Peterson, Dorothy Ellen, PA (Turnbow)

Pickell, Dawne Marie, PA (Ferich)
Prim, Sally Anne, PA (Riley)
Pritchard, Jean, PA (Monagham)
Quairiere, Althea Claire, PA (Snow)
Rohman, Vera C., PA (Gordon)
Russell, Phyllis Marie, PA (Szewczak)
Scott, Barbara Ann, MD (Schuler)
Shirey, Jean Elizabeth, PA (Wighaman)
Sickenberger, Helen Jean, PA (Taylor)
Smith, Catherine Helen, PA (Dodson)
Spangler, Joyce Marie, PA (Weik)
Spence, Virginia Mae, PA (McCrone)
Stamm, Jeanne M., PA (Campbell)
Sturgeon, Marian Grace, PA (Hartman)
Swartz, Louise Catherine, PA (Lorah)
Taylor, Helen Cooper, NJ (Currier)
Thorne, Faye Evans, PA (Kaufman)
Towner, Jean Martha, PA (Yarnall)
Towsey, Betty Lois, PA (Daughenbaugh)
Tratch, Helen Mary, NJ (Robinson)
Trimmer, Hazel Viola, PA (Barkdoll)
Vernoy, Lillian N., PA (VanHoy)
Von Franzke, Ruth Ann, PA (Cassidy)
Wandell, Norma Ruth, PA (Board)
Weaver, Dorothy Virginia, PA (Heller)
Weikel, Nancy LaRue, PA (Ritzman)
Widney, Evelyn Mae, PA (McClellan)
Wray, Gloria Elizabeth, PA (Green)
Yohey, Mildred Arlene, PA (Watkins)
Zong, Lois Patricia, PA

A NURSE'S PRAYER

Because the day that stretches out for me
Is full of busy hours, I come to Thee
To ask Thee, Lord, that Thou wilt see me through
The many things that I may have to do
Help me to make my beds the smoothest way.
Help me make more tempting every tray
Help me to sense when pain must have relief.
Help me to deal with those borne down by grief.
Help me to take to every patient's room
The Light of Life to brighten up the gloom.
Help me to bring to every soul in fear

The sure and steadfast thought that Thou art near.
And if today, or, if tonight, maybe
Some patients in my care set out to sea
To face the great adventure we call death,
Sustain them, Father, in their parting breath.
Help me to live throughout this live-long day
As one who loves Thee well, dear Lord, I pray;
And when the day is done, and evening stars
Shine through the dark above the sunset bars,
When weary quite, I turn to seek my rest,
Lord, may I truly know I've done my best.

Ruth Winant Wheeler

This year marked the retirement of Miss Anna Shafer, after an association with Jefferson of 34 years. She graduated from the Nursing School in 1910 and after 1912 served on night duty as supervisor for the remainder of her professional career. She is remembered as a legendary character (Fig. 55).

In this year an 8-hour shift of private duty nursing was compensated by $10 instead of the previous $8.

The Jefferson Hospital Staff Nurses Association was formed this year. Miss Margerie Wilson, Supervisor of the Surgical Floor, was elected President and Mrs. M. Morrison Hecksher, Head Nurse of Women's Medical Ward, was elected Secretary-Treasurer.

There were 74 Graduates in this class.

CLASS OF 1949

Antes, Margaret S., PA (Bathurst)
Augustine, LaVerne Rosalie, PA (Lang)
Ball, Marjorie Maud, NJ (Hoeck)
Beard, Jean Elizabeth, NJ (Davison)
Bechtold, Mary Catherine, PA (French)
Bell, Mary Louise, NJ (Santoro)
Beloff, Bertha Marie, NJ (Batten)
Boczkowski, Irene Agnes, PA (Hunter)
Brown, Barbara Mildred, NJ (Breen)
Bushek, Theresa B., PA (Poli)
Campbell, Jeanne Mae, NJ (Farley)
Cashner, Roberta Pearl, PA (Greiff)
Clarke, Margaret Emily, PA
Daugherty, Helen Estelle, DE (Barrett)
Dawson, Donna Mae, PA (Lewis)
Detrich, Lois Jane, PA (Vahey)
Diehl, Helen J., PA (Ellenberger)
Dietz, Louise Marie, PA (Strayer)
Dowiak, Frances, PA
Duffield, Joanne, PA (O'Brien)
Flavell, Mae Lucille, PA (Henkelmann)
Freed, Mary Elizabeth, PA (Wakely)
Gerber, Nancy Jean, PA (Fager)
Gerngross, Alice Rita, NJ (Perkins)
Glasgow, Mary Joan, PA
Gockley, Josephine Mae, PA (Schriver)
Granger, Anne Elizabeth, PA (Doubet)
Graver, Doris Ann, PA (Schuman)
Groves, Mazie Joy, NJ (Boyd)
Hackerl Margaret Jane, PA (Ponzer)
Hanna, Catherine Allene, PA (Gallagher)
Hansen, Annie Joyce, NJ (Rozynko)
Hassall, Esther Jane, NJ (May)
Johnson, Faye Arlene, PA (Pepperman)

Fig. 55. Anna Shafer ('10), a legendary night supervisor, retired in 1949.

Kauffman, Dorothy Lane, NJ (Miller)
Kautz, Marie Minerva, PA (Larsen)
Kilby, Eleanor Brunton, NJ (Whitehead)
Kissinger, Charmaine L., PA
Koulik, Ursula Mary, PA (Hurley)
Kresge, Ella Priscilla, PA (Nicholson)
Lamson, Dorothy Elizabeth, NJ (Sheets)
Lange, Ruth Edna, DE (Wettig)
Leach, Barbara Faye, PA (Cornelius)
Levinsky, Mary Elizabeth, PA
Loftus, Mary Patricia, PA (O'Riordan)
Logan, Margaret Mary, PA (Casey)
Lundy, Bettie Irene, PA (Poleto)
Magnitsky, Alice Louise, PA (Woodside)
Martin, Helen Marie, PA (Norstedt)
McCormick, Mildred Betty, FL (Galvin)
McGeary, Kathleen Ann, NJ (Tierney)
McKelvey, Patricia Ann, PA
Mease, Jeanne Elizabeth, PA
Mengel, Bette Jane, PA (Borkey)
Milewski, Lorraine Marian (McCall)
Nemshick, Gertrude Ann, PA
Newcomer, Catherine Evelyn, PA (Foreman)
Norstedt, Patricia Jane, PA (Johnson)
Nye, Mary Winifred, PA (Woodwell)

O'Donnell, Elizabeth Ann, NJ (Snell)
Oikawa, Teri, PA (Picante)
Paris, Eleanor Viola, PA (Robinson)
Pennypacker, Lois Mae, PA Prebula,
Pauline Mary, PA (Ronco)
Price, Joyce Evaline, PA
Reed, Peggy Lou, PA (Piekenbrook)
Reeves, Jean Lucy, NJ (Wolfe)
Roche, Lorraine Marie, PA
Sannino, Elizabeth Adele, NJ (Fischer)
Sassaman, June Lucille, PA (Bleam)
Schadel, Phyllis Wanda, PA (Huntzinger)
Schmuck, Wanda Gene, PA (Geesey)
Scian, Mary Jo, NJ (Miller)
Searfoss, Jean Merle, PA (Lamson)
Servello, Florence Marie, PA (McAlpin)
Sheckler, Hazel Elizabeth, PA (Kogler)
Sherlin, Ruth Esther, PA (Godfrey)
Skvir, Elsie Kristine, PA (Nierle)
Snyder, Shirley Rae, PA (Bittner)
Sprenkel, Carolyn Louise, PA (Marchione)
Turner, Marilyn DuBois, PA (O'Brien)
Wargo, Elizabeth Helen, PA (Carrick)
Wilson, Clara Arlene, PA (Seasultz)
Zbuckvich, Helen Penelope, PA (Buckwalter)

Private room in Thompson Annex.

~ 1950 ~

Changes in post-war nursing education included more graduates seeking advanced courses. Those who had been in military service received aid under the G-I Bill of Rights. Scholarships were also available for non-veterans.

The need for counseling of student nurses was recognized this year by the appointment of a full-time counselor, whose responsibilities included extra-curricular activities. A 44-hour week was initiated for students and staff (Fig. 56). The nursing library continued to be updated.

There were 74 graduates in this class.

CLASS OF 1950

Albert, Ann Pauline, PA (Lundgren)
Anderson, Twila Beatrice, PA (Sanborn)
Baran, Ellen Carolyn, PA (Stahl)
Barry, Marion Lorraine, PA (Koerner)
Bauschard, Jeanette Rachel, PA (Kaucher)
Buxton, Marilyn Kathleen, PA (Gould)
Christman, Joan Audrey, PA (Clauss)
Dunkle, Nancy Ann, PA (Konstanzer)
Fisher, Barbara Fair, PA (Ackerman)
Flannery, Mary Theresa, PA (Rotella)
Fleck, Donna Elaine, PA (Gearhart)
Gardner, Ellen, PA (Spuhler)
Glaudel, Rose Marie, PA (Mulligan)
Goff, Agnes Marie, PA (Anderson)
Green, Elizabeth Dorothy, NJ (Wahl)
Gunsallus, Isabelle, PA (Lutterloh)
Harper, Eunice, PA (Shinn)
Heffelfinger, Jane, PA (Whipple)
Henry, Margaret Jane, PA (Jones)
Hoffman, Louise, PA (Douglas)
Hohe, Jean Gloria, PA (Larkin)
Hough, Harriet, NJ (Linnquist)
Hummel, Nancy Virginia, PA (Orsini)
Johnston, Helen, PA (Dowlin)
Koch, Audrey Iris, PA (Wolfberg)
Kowaleski, Eleanor Barbara, PA (Larson)
Krestynick, Rita, PA (Bolinsky)
Kundrat, Ellen B., PA (Clarke)
Laskowski, Elizabeth Eleanor, PA (Greenlee)
Latshaw, Audrey Eileen, NJ (Sutton)
Leidy, Shirley Joan, PA (Edwards)
Lingle, Eleanor Ruth, PA (Sauler)
Lundfelt, Martha Amelia, PA (Peter)
Mackley, Shirley M., PA (Hoffert)
Matsuo, June Matsuno, NJ (Fugita)
Messa, Marie T., PA (Wagner)

Michalski, Helen Bernadine, PA (Hummel)
Moore, Joyce Arlene, PA (Madara)
Moore, Mary Louise, DE (Brumbaugh)
Morrow, Wealthy Ellen, PA (Shutt)
Mosteller, Mary Ann, PA (Stitzer)
Myers, Helen Elizabeth, PA (Rosenrans)
Nash, Emily, PA (Hollenbach)
Opel, Jean Louise, PA (Serena)
Osborne, Mary Louise, PA (Foy-Failla)
Ottoson, L. Irene, NJ (Frett)
Palichka, Agnes Jean, PA (Wess)
Palmer, Diane, PA (Dehuff)
Parcel, Helen, PA (Bowhall)
Pearson, Mary Ann, PA (Calligan)
Richardson, Clara C., PA (Flynn)
Ross, Gerhart Ruth, PA (Nadler)
Satterfield, Elinor V., DE (Lynch)
Schersching, Grace Edna, NJ (Atkinson)
Schorn, Miriam Margaret, NJ (Bower)
Shaver, Joan Louise, PA (Hermann)
Sheriff, Helen Louise, PA (Rightor)
Skubic, Mary Joan, DE (McDowell)
Stauffer, Janet Marie, PA (Mayo)
Stemler, Geraldine Elizabeth, PA (Styre)
Stevens, Nancy Mae, PA
Swinehart, Ruth Frances, PA (Merroth)
Trach, Elizabeth, NJ
Trettis, Josephine Loretta, PA (Kern)
Twaddel, Anna Margretta, NY (Setnicky)
Wachter, Dorothy Marie, NJ (Brett)
Walters, Joyce Larue, PA (Hill)
Wasson, Janet Patricia, PA (Thomas)
Werner, Anne Elizabeth, PA (Breach)
Whiteleather, Marjorie Jane, PA (Schramm)
Yocum, Joan Gertrude, PA
Young, Sara Louise, NJ (Konstanzer)

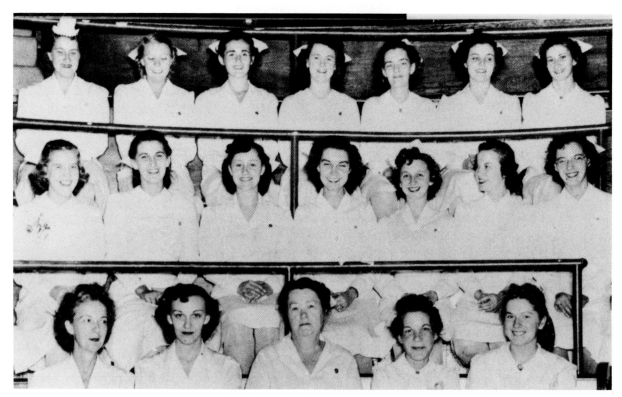

Fig. 56.   A group of Staff Nurses (1950).

Entrance to Thompson Annex.

~ 1951 ~

The education program of the 1950's was improved by better correlation between formal classes and clinical experience (Fig. 57,58). The new "block" type curriculum was adopted under which half of the students attended class for two weeks while the other half was assigned to clinical practice. At the end of the period the groups switched. This system provided a more in-depth approach to both theoretical instruction and "on-the-job" training. The program included a two-week stay at White Haven Sanatorium as a part of the pulmonary disease course which also required a month on duty at the Barton Division.

There were 66 graduates this year.

CLASS OF 1951

Adams, Kathleen Beatrice, NJ (Moody)
Barclay, Mary Elizabeth, PA (Paxson)
Bareuther, June Bertha, NJ (Graf)
Binns, Pearl Jean, PA (Smith)
Bolton, Catherine Louise, PA
Bond, Mary Alice, PA (Romig)
Davis, Nina Elaine, NJ (Weller)
Dewees, Dorothy Theresa, NJ (LoSasso)
DeWitt, Ethel Irene, PA (Gerst)
Donald, Rachael Ann, PA (Catha)
Duckworth, Barbara Elaine, PA (Arkes)
Eberly, H. Joanne, PA (Loose)
Edwards, Barbara, PA (Beam)
Garber, Joanne, PA (Sencindiver)
Gerhard, Phyllis Jean, PA (McClure)
Gieson, Alice Mary, DC (Costello)
Gothie, Nelda Elizabeth, PA (Edson)
Hackett, Martha Jane, PA (Santoro)
Harrington, Janet Marie, DE (Melvin)
Hastings, Elizabeth Wilson, PA (Donald)
Hawk, Jane Elizabeth, PA (Aires)
Hess, Mary Lou, PA
Hoffman, Marian Edith, NJ (Narbuth)
Hoke, D'Etta Anne, PA (Tracy)
Holzbaur, Jeanne V., NJ (McLaughlin)
Hysmith, Colleen R., PA (Winship)
Jeitner, Lorraine Alice, PA
Jones, Norma V., DE (Murray)
Katherman, Nancy Noll, PA (Kohut)
Kehler, Delma Arlene, PA (Oxenrider)
Kostenbauser, Nancy Vogel, PA (Tibbens)
LaLiberte, Jean Andre, CT

Laws, Bettie Jane, PA (Taylor)
Lehr, Grace Margaret, PA (Carleton)
Macinko, Magdaline, PA (Moseley)
Mannino, Eleanora Elvira, PA (Reibel)
Moll, Elizabeth Cora, PA (Chevola)
Morris, Elva H., PA (Cohn)
Morrison, Joan Dolores, PA (Carlin)
Moyer, Elizabeth R., PA (Sproal)
Mumper, Jean Anne, OH (Seibert)
Murray, Irene Elizabeth, PA
Pauster, Dolores Ann, PA (Gorham)
Plasterer, Jeanette, PA
Ramp, Marion J., NJ
Roberts, Audrey Mae, MD (Reynolds)
Rozell, Virginia Lou, PA (Bryant)
Selen, Barbara A., PA (Paul)
Shirk, Elizabeth Louise, PA (Troback)
Shoemaker, Patricia Joanne, PA (Verbinski)
Smith, Isabele Joy, PA (Shaw)
Snook, Ida Jane, NJ (Liebmann)
Sparrow, Marilyn Jean, PA (Marshall)
St. Clair, Shirley M., PA (Weller)
Thompson, Nancy Ellen, NJ (Powell)
Thorp, Florence Marian, PA (Williams)
Troxell, Anna Jeanne, PA (Humphreys)
VanHorn, Claire E., PA (White)
Weber, Mary Kate, PA (Morgan)
Wesley, Virginia Louise, PA (Dorman)
Wheatley, Grace June, PA (Guraughty)
Withka, Janet M., PA (Warden)
Young, Ruth Naomi, PA (Roth)
Zarella, Patricia Ann, PA
Zug, Catharine Louise, PA (Sanders)

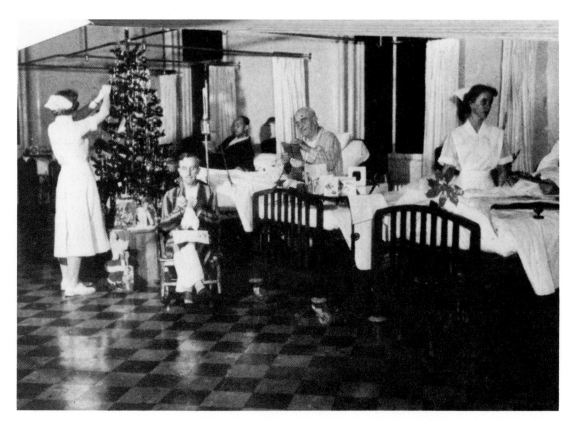

Fig. 57. Clinical experience in the wards (Christmas, 1951).

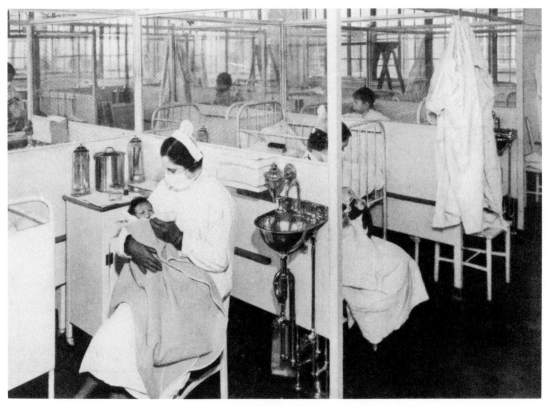

Fig. 58. Nursing in the solarium (Old Main Hospital).

~ 1952 ~

Miss Katherine Childs, Director of the School of Nursing, requested the Women's Board of the Hospital to grant scholarships of $100 to aid students through the first year of training because of economic distress in the upstate mining area from which so many promising applicants came.

The Nurses's Home Committee provided such scholarships in the amount of $800. At the same time, Miss Childs proposed an endowment for the School of Nursing which later was implemented.

There were 75 graduates in this year.

CLASS OF 1952

Anderson, Mary Ann, PA (Waddell)
Beard, Jane Elizabeth, PA (Maxwell)
Bechtel, Elizabeth Ann, PA (Runge)
Beck, Janice Barbara, PA (Pisano)
Bivans, Mary Lois, PA (Doyle)
Blasko, Joan Kathleen, PA (Boruckow)
Bohland, Evelyn Virginia, OH
Cleaver, Anna, PA (Angert)
Craver, Ann Marie, (Andrews)
Creek, Dorothy Mae, NJ (Howley)
Delamater, Alice Louise, NJ (Chase)
DeLuca, Filomena Ida, PA
Domchick, Genevieve Patricia, PA (McTiernan)
Evey, Dolores Nina, PA (Justice)
Faust, Margaret Kathryn, PA (Keates)
Flanagan, Jeanne Therese, PA (Ryan)
Forgione, Rose A., PA (Shambers)
Fox, Rebecca, PA (Cella)
Goff, R. Anita, PA (Partington)
Graves, Joyce Elaine, PA (Lesher)
Greising, Nancy Lee, FL (Wilhelm)
Groh, Nancy Lorraine, PA (Messick)
Haney, Phyllis Marian, PA (Heim)
Hardish, Joan Helen, PA (Reid)
Harris, Helen Rogena, PA (Sampsel)
Hatlem, Phyllis Shirley, FL (Rigano)
Hawthorne, Virginia May, PA (Spangler)
Heim, Phyllis Ethel, PA
Heller, Audrey Elizabeth, PA (Strehl)
Hibner, Nina Ruth, PA (Hoehm)
Hippensteel, Eloise Joan, PA
Hoffer, Joanne J., PA (Graff)
Hurd, Myrtice Gwendolyn, PA (Wilkins)
Jones, Marilyn, PA (Beard)
Kohler, Muriel Jean, NJ (Knerr)
Macks, Eleanor Helen, PA (Donahue)
Malone, Jacqueline LaDune, MD (Kolsher)

Mangle, Joyce Eleanor, NJ (Simpkins)
Mankus, Alice Elizabeth, PA (Bush-Brown)
Matthews, Catherine Woodward, NJ (DeLucca)
McClure, Doris Lou, PA (Givin)
McCoy, Jean Dee, PA (Pachelbel)
McFadden, Lillian Mary, PA (Haeberlein)
Miller, Ada Irene, PA (Matthews)
Oberholtzer, Clara Anne, PA (Brugger)
Ostrosina, Annette Jeanne, PA (Boyer)
Paucke, Dorothy Marie, PA
Pencavage, Delores A., (Schwartz)
Pettebone, Joan Esther, PA (Bucciarelli)
Plaisted, Marilyn Louise, CA (Mirviss)
Powell, Lois Evelyn, PA (Glassgow)
Price, Shirley Jean, PA
Pupo, Edda Helen, PA (Tureo)
Reynolds, Jane Adell, PA (Johnson)
Richard, Grace Clarice, PA
Richardson, Sue Mary, PA (Tanner)
Rittenhouse, Joan Mignon, PA (Roberts)
Roberta, Christine Ann, PA (Germano)
Rowinski, Florence, PA (Fus)
Rugart, Lois Margaret, NJ (Abood)
Savage, Ann Louise, PA (Walters)
Schadel, Barbara Mary, PA
Sentner, Joan Lorraine, PA (Maziarczk)
Stewart, Nancy Lee, PA (Stoicovy)
Summers, Dorothy Ann, PA (Nesbella)
Sweisford, Jean F., PA (Tornetta)
Thorn, Doris Mae, NJ (Suter)
Thumm, Dorothy Mary, NJ (Earle)
Varklet, Marion, PA
Vetro, Albina Marie, PA (Stackhouse)
Wightman, Jeanetta Marian, NJ (Caffey)
Wilhelm, Barbara Ann, NJ (Tichian)
Wilson, Irene Hazel, PA (Flanagan)
Yoder, Mary Ann, PA (Wertmen)
Zechman, Claudette Elizabeth, PA (Strohm)

Miss Mabel C. Prevost, B.S., M.S. ('29, Fig. 32) succeeded Miss Katherine Childs as Director of Nursing. During her administration vigorous recruiting efforts resulted in increased enrollment. Also, a campaign was waged for a modern Nurses' Home, and National League for Nursing accreditation was actively pursued. Classroom and faculty office space were secured in the Hospital. The graduates of this class numbered 56.

CLASS OF 1953

Albright, Nancy, PA (Webster)
Beisel, Claire Adele, PA (Miller)
Boerlin, Paully J., PA (Kreps)
Bowen, Barbara Ann, PA (Lewis)
Boyd, Barbara Anne, PA (Griesmer)
Conway, Patricia Anne, PA (Diehl)
Crandall, Nellie Adelaide, RI (Richards)
Dalton, Cynthia Murray, NJ
Delong, Madelyn Joan, PA (Hanratty)
Deluca, Betty Lillian, PA (Yamrick)
Edwardsen, Janet Christian, NJ (Meredith)
Eyster, Janet Bonita, PA (Hartshorn)
Fitzwater, Emmanuel Faye, WV (Oskin)
Fullerton, Marilyn Fern, PA (Bower)
Gibson, Irene Edith, NJ (O'Brien)
Gieseke, Barbara Ann, NJ (Portelli)
Gration, Lorraine Carolyn, NJ (Goodman)
Halko, Helen Agnes, PA
Hand, Helen Marcia, NJ (Eder)
Haught, Betty Jane, PA (Anderson)
Heist, Thelma Louise, PA (Goodhart)
Horton, Marilyn Louise, NJ (Tilden)
Howerter, Florence Norma, PA (Milbrand)
Hughes, Mildred Mabel, DE (McClellan)
Ilchuck, Irene Mary, PA (Trayer)
Jendrzejewski, Bernardine Marie, PA (Kovaleski)
Kapp, Louise Adele, NJ (Hartman)

Kazmer, Frances Ann, PA (Balistrieri)
King, Joan Marie, PA (Gross)
Kircher, June Marian, PA (Kathan)
Koch, Darthy Mona, PA (Davis)
Lange, Gertrude Anna L., PA (Amend)
Lavelle, Sharon Rita, PA (Kelly)
Lee, Sally Ann, PA
LeVan, Edith Arlene, PA (Swisher)
Margiasso, Cathleen Edith, PA (Keating)
Maurer, Clare Lydia, PA (Martz)
Miller, Dorothy Elizabeth, PA (Matuskevich)
Mowrey, Joan Louise, PA (Kramer)
Orr, Jessie Susann, PA (Carney)
Reimer, Jane, PA (Lemmon)
Rutledge, Helen Marie, PA
Sattazhan, Alma Stowe, PA (Jamison)
Sharp, Florence Corrine, NJ (Scott)
Shonk, Ruth Louise, PA (Trettis)
Sivacek, Lois Marie, FL (Hoerner)
Splett, Dorothy Marie, PA (Webb)
Stank, Margaret Alice, PA (Dombroski)
Symthe, Ruth Adele, PA (Taylor)
Troxell, Carolyn Ruth, PA (Haas)
Umbower, Margaret Marie, PA (Curfman)
Wayne, Donna Jean, PA (Curtis)
Weidner, Joyce Irene, PA (Mest)
Wetzel, Jeanne Estella, PA
Yancoski, Joan Irene, MI (Barry)

All are not equal in ability or attainments. Each, to be successful must develop the philosophy of living and practicing the art of nursing that at the end of each day, you may truthfully answer your most severe critic, your own conscience. Today I have done the best of which I am capable.

Alison H. Price, M.D. (JMC, '38)

The Nurses' Relief Fund in this year reached a total of $40,175. A new Hospital Pavilion for which ground had been broken in 1952 was completed and dedicated on November 8 (Fig. 59). It represented an important period of growth and advancement in the physical facilities of the hospital complex. This ultra-modern addition, at a cost of $7.5 million, added nearly 300 badly needed beds. While the nursing service problems were

Fig. 59. New Hospital Pavilion, Architect's drawing (1954).

many, the gradual opening of the new floors proceeded smoothly.

The need for a new Nursing Home, already under consideration, now loomed with increasing urgency.

The graduates numbered 71.

Alderfer, Geneva Inez, PA (Batten)
Angelo, Rose Marie, PA
Barrett, Phyllis Mae, PA (Ostman)
Billig, Mary Hope, PA (Carter)
Bollinger, Julia Catherine, PA (Becker)
Brock, Joan Marie, PA (McCusker)
Carson, Mary Jane, PA (McCleaf)
Castellano, Christine, PA (Elmer)
Cole, Nancy Louise, PA (Schmidt)
Davis, Loralee Arlene, PA (Carter)
Deardorff, Diane Merle, PA (Fischer)
Esterline, Constance Mae, PA (McSurdy)
Fetsko, Helen Marie, PA (Besecker)
German, Peggy Ann, PA (Gerard)
Glass, Helen Carole, PA (Hammon)
Glaudel, Alice Helen, PA (Kessler)
Graham, Marcia, NJ (Martin)
Gustafson, Anna Marie, PA (Graham)
Hanes, Lois Emilie, PA (McCluskey)
Henninger, Josephine I., PA (Murray)
Henry, Doris Elaine, NJ (Schramm)
Herring, Janet Esther, PA (Oswald)
Hindson, Sally Ann, PA (Wagner)
Horst, Patricia Ann, PA
Hubbs, Jennie Keyes, PA (Jakacki)
Hubiak, Olga, PA
Irwin, Margaret Frances, PA (Riemer)
Kashner, Jean Carol, PA (Olsefsy)
Keelins, Pauline Elaine, DE (Carter)
Korn, Joan Marie, PA (Purnell)
Kuberski, Dolores, PA (Stanley)
Kuklenski, Louise Mary, PA (Schmidt)
Kunkelman, Patricia A., PA (Quinn)
Kuntz, Mary Lu, PA (Stoudt)
Loughran, Anne Marie, PA (Delaney)

Lynch, Barbara Joanne, PA (Hummer)
Manhart, Louisa, PA (Hoch)
Mannix, S. Fame, PA (Ackerman)
May, Noami Marie, PA (Davis)
Mehalko, Ruth E., PA (French)
Melevin, Alice Catherine, NJ (Rosano)
Mengotto, Roberta Eleanore, PA (Smith)
Mishkofski, Rita Ann, PA (Curfman)
Narusiewicz, Patricia Ann, PA
Neff, Mary Jane, PA (Gabriel)
Newcombe, Barbara Ann, NJ
Nichols, Joan Maxine, DE (Davis)
O'Connor, Joan Loretta, PA (Adomines)
Painter, Janet E., PA (Doman)
Pazel, Mary Katherine, PA (Washeleski)
Potoski, Mary Ann, PA (Suhadolnik)
Pottiger, Marilyn Elaine, PA (Andrews)
Reiner, Barbara, PA (Bachman)
Richards, Betty Louise, PA (Stone)
Sauvageot, Rena Virginia, WV (Graham)
Scarlett, Ann Warner, PA (Jordan)
Seckinger, Janet, PA (Marshall)
Snyder, Elisa Beth Ann, PA (Collins)
Snyder, Jane Blanche, DE (Wilgus)
Sode, Joan Phyllis, PA (Broshuis)
Stauffer, Mary Ann, PA
Stoutenburg, Mary Lee, PA (Russell)
Stuart, Carol Alice, PA (Baxter)
Tangye, Jean Ruth, PA (Crummer)
Tomlin, Jean Barbara, NJ (Dempsey)
Urban, Nancy Jane, PA (Schwindt)
Warren, Dorothy G., PA (Biddle)
Wells, Patricia Jean, PA (Steinhagen)
Whitehill, Anne Catherine, NJ (Hoover)
Wise, Elinor Ann, PA (Chermella)
Zartman, Lou Ann Romaine, PA (Craley)

~ 1955 ~

To relieve the immediate increased needs for nursing housing, the Board of Trustees leased the Whittier Hotel at 15th and Cherry Streets as temporary residence. Bus transportation was arranged.

The pediatric teaching this year was expanded to include home visits and observation of nursery school procedures.

Georgene Strazzeri (Callahan), after several appointments as Nursing Supervisor, concentrated on continuing educational projects especially in pharmaceutical fields.

She developed professional education symposia, publications, and audio-visual materials for conventions and training programs.

There were 59 graduates this year.

CLASS OF 1955

Amorose, Doris Dolores, PA (Giardino)
Applebaum, Sydney Marilyn, PA (Cassell)
Bjork, Carol Ruth, PA (Schmidt)
Bonaccurson, Marie Angela, PA (Pancari)
Brown, Dorothy J., PA (Klause)
Brown, Shirley Alice, PA (Blackburn)
Buchanan, Theresa Shirley, PA (Klemovage)
Carissimi, Claire, PA (Iannuci)
Chadwick, Joan Louise, NJ (Cramer)
Clampffer, Katherine Evelyn, PA (Gross)
Clayton, Anita Mary, NJ (Pittola)
Conway, Barbara A., PA (Timson)
Costello, Patricia Jean, PA (Magley)
Culp, Esther Nancy, PA (Scott)
Curcio, Jeanne Marie, NJ (Pelle)
Deitman, Dawn D., PA (John)
DeLong, Nannette Eileen, PA (Smith)
Evans, Rosemary J., PA (Williams)
Feissner, Mary H., PA (Quigley)
Gibney, Mary Joyce, PA
Hancock, Marietta Jane, PA
Heckenberger, Dolores Helen, PA
Hirata, Takako, NJ (Tokumasu)
Hoffman, Charlotte Roberta, PA (Orvis)
Hutzel, Evelyn Joyce, PA (Lewis)
Ingling, Joyce Marlene, PA (Salazar)
Johnson, Jean Blair, NJ (Ann)
Jones, Elizabeth Moses, PA (Hubbs)
Lammie, Sheila Maureen, PA (Baldorf)

Larimer, Gwendolyn A., PA (Reese)
Lucarini, Jean Gladys, PA (Avila)
Marasco, Adrienne Ruth, PA (Rodgers)
McGowan, Mary L., PA (Pettinato)
Meckley, Shirley Ann, PA (Schneider)
Mohler, Patricia Anne, PA (Weinberg)
Murray, Mildred Catherine, PA (Kline)
Nace, Norma Jean, PA (Messer)
Niemczura, Lorraine Jean, NJ
Patten, Elizabeth Jean, NJ (Ward)
Pratt, Marianne Louise, PA (Shinkevich)
Reihart, Hazel Ann, PA (Klein)
Roberts, Marjorie Sue, MD (Boyer)
Romano, Marlyn Mae, PA (Whyte)
Schaeffer, Nancy Louise, PA (Boas)
Schleyer, Margaret Elaine, PA (Deming)
Smith, Barbara Godfrey, PA
Strazzeri, Georgene Barbara, PA (Callahan)
Sweeney, Josephine Marie, DE (McDonough)
Titlow, Audrey Ruth, PA (Priga)
Trettis, Patricia J., PA
Turnbull, Marjorie Ann, PA
Waite, Peggy Jane, PA (Lazar)
Walls, Naomi G., NJ (Wilson)
Watson, Susan, PA (Simoneau)
Widney, Dorothy Jean, PA (Lucas)
Wisotzkey, Dolores Ann, PA (Spirt)
Yablonski, Rosemary Ann, PA (LuLavage)
Yocum, Nancy Louise, PA (Dodson)
Young, Carol, PA (Justice)

The increased need for nurses stimulated vigorous recruiting efforts. Jefferson student nurses suggested nursing careers on television programs in addition to promotion efforts of the Faculty.

This class was the first in ten years to have one hundred percent passing rate on the State Board Examinations.

Joan Halbleib (Bristow) was distinctive in earning her M.A. in Health Care Administration at age 50. She was associated with St. Francis Medical Center, Trenton, New Jersey. Her principal concerns related to Risk Management. In 1988/89 she was included in "Who's Who in American Nursing".

The class numbered 63 graduates.

CLASS OF 1956

Ambrose, Marlene Mary, PA (Mika)
Ambrose, Natalie K., PA (Becker)
Angert, Helen Marie, PA (Allemand)
Arnold, Marjorie E., PA (Cook)
Baird, Dorothy A., PA
Bertolet, Joyce Elaine, NJ (Hutton)
Bias, Dolores Sylvia, PA (Kirby)
Bingman, Betty L., PA (Kendall)
Bonikowski, Leona Marie, MN (Kley)
Bruno, Lorraine Philomena, PA (Arayo)
Caffrey, Margaret Agnes, PA (Lehman)
Clarke, Georgia Marie, PA (Brown)
Cordner, Margaret Myra, NJ (Baker)
Dawson, Norma Jean, PA
Depo, Betty Louise, PA (Miller)
Elbertson, Joan Elizabeth, NJ (McGinnis)
Fellman, Barbara Marcia, PA
Ferry, Carole Mae, PA (Rosle)
Fitzpatrick, Dixie Lee, PA (Robinson)
Fry, Wilhemina Carole, PA (Crawley)
Gherardi, Lorene Kathryn, PA (Witthoff)
Halblieb, Joan B., PA (Bristow)
Handy, Virginia Belle, PA (Putney)
Henningan, Mary Ann, PA (Sherman)
Hung, Gertrude Fong, NJ (Chan)
Johnson, Marguerite Louise, PA (Domenick)
King, Noreen Mary, PA (Poole)
Kneidel, Ann F., PA
Kostrow, Jean, PA (Krosynger)
Krasnisky, Jean, PA (Pike)
Kressly, Lois Mae, PA (Pesaresi)

Malone, Mary Lou, PA (Frank)
Metka, Shirley Ann, PA
Orndorff, Shirley Jeanne, PA (Doernte)
Palmer, Suzanne Marie, PA (Rogers)
Pfleegor, Betty Doane, PA (McElroy)
Plevyak, Catherine R., PA (Fisch)
Pope, Eleanor Lorraine, PA (Baird)
Pope, Lorraine Philomena, PA (Arayo)
Puskar, Dorothy Ann, PA (Lalor)
Rau, Elizabeth Dorothy, PA (Berardi)
Ritter, Suzanne Jean, PA (Daveler)
Robertson, Marilyn Ann, IL (Glauber)
Roche, Florence Ann, PA
Rupp, Beverly Ann, PA
Saunders, Mary Anne, PA (Port)
Saunders, Ruth Ann, PA (Jacobson)
Savidge, Geraldine Ella, NJ (Martin)
Scarlett, Paula Marion, PA (Kenworthy)
Segal, Sandra Lee, NJ (Lord)
Smith, Jacqueline Lee, NJ (Brecker)
Snell, Anne Bradley, WV (Kopple)
Stancavage, Shirley, PA (Gallo)
Stewart, M. Faith, MI (Graham)
Straughen, Jodella Mae, NJ (Ellington)
Taylor, Phyllis Jean, PA (Meadows)
Thomas, Martha E., PA (Rigling)
Toy, Patricia Ann, NJ
Walker, Joan Suzanne, PA (Randolph)
Walters, Myrl Ann, PA
Welsko, Joann Marie, NJ (Odonnell)
Wisniewski, Helen, PA (Hervada)
Wyse, Marguerite Joyce, PA (Hagopian)

In this year the Nurses' Alumnae Association reported a total of $9,500 toward its pledge of $25,000 for the projected new Nurses' Residence. The Association was also able to present two $500 scholarships per annum to eligible nurses seeking aid for the pursuit of further education in the field of nursing.

The first intensive care unit, consisting of nine beds, was opened, allowing closer supervision and nursing care.

The student government continued to function well in its role of promoting the welfare of the group (Fig. 60).

The graduates numbered 68.

CLASS OF 1957

Achenbach, Helen Phoebe, PA (Anthony)
Aliantro, Barbara Louise, NJ (Hamblin)
Angelo, Anne Louise, PA (O'Brien)
Aschenbach, Gretchen Alta, PA (Baker)
Bervinchak, Marion, PA (Leschey)
Blair, Nancy Margaret, PA (D'Angelo)
Bunker, Ruth Sandra, PA (Walsh)
Burrows-Pegg, Margaret, PA (Rodal)
Caputo, Patricia Ann, NJ (Zebrowski)
Carpo, Aleta Bernice, NJ (Scott)

Conley, Anna Patricia, PA
Corrado, Catherine Frances, NJ (Cotter)
Costino, Cleo Jean, PA (Estock)
Crotsley, Donna Lee, PA (Drake)
Daneils, Monica A., PA (Graham)
DiGenova, Benedetta T., PA (Veciferri)
Duckworth, Mary Alice, PA (Bopf)
Dufallo, Arlene Mary, PA (Rayno)
Eckhart, Peggy Lou, PA (Hess)
Eichmann, Mary Catherine, PA (Cowen)

Left to right: D. Crotsley, A. Taylor, B. Aschenbach, Unidentified, J. Preister, P. Wander, M. Milotich, B. Beard, B. Tichy, Unidentified, S. Bunker, R. Robens.

Fig. 60. Student government (1957).

Engel, Irene Joan, PA (DePhillipo)
Everett, Stephanie Rae, PA (Burke)
Fallon, Marjorie Eileen, PA (Smith)
Fernandez, Julia G., PA (Placendo)
Fromuth, Molly A., PA (Hamilton)
Geissler, Marcella Grace, NJ
Genter, Elizabeth J., NJ (Hettel)
Glaudel, Patricia Marie, PA (Aronica)
Griffiths, Mary Katherine, PA (Okavage)
Groat, Dorothy Arlene, NJ
Hamill, Eleanor, PA (Miller)
Hassenplug, Betty Jane, PA (Graham)
Haught, Shirley J., PA (Simmons)
Hyland, Carol Wright, NJ (Gray)
Imler, Shirley Ann, PA (Johns)
Jacobs, Georgann Anita, PA (Miller)
Kepping, Ann Elizabeth, PA (Snyder)
Kostenbauder, Katherine Marilyn, PA (Smith)
Kozura, Marie Ann, PA (Scott)
Laibinis, Elizabeth Ann, PA (Ramakus)
Lampil, Barbara Joan, NJ (McGovern)
Mercer, Beryl J., NJ
Miller, Wilma Mary, PA (Miller)
Milotich, Margaret Lucy, PA (Martin)

Molitoris, Martha, PA (Werler)
Nosek, Marion J., PA (Nimey)
Paxon, Ann Shirley, PA (Ross)
Pollack, Kathleen Marie, PA
Pufnock, Mary Lou, PA
Reginak, June Darlene, NJ (Dupnock)
Risser, Ginette Rae, PA (Garretson)
Schwechler, Margaret Jane, PA (Haines)
Seely, Jeanne Elizabeth, NJ (Abbott)
Shannon, Barbara Ann, NJ (Bellus)
Shinglock, Mary Elizabeth, PA (Gallagher)
Shrupski, Joan Marie, PA (Salve)
Sierant, Constance Theresa, PA (Vetter)
Smith, Grace, PA (Clancy)
Taylor, Audrey Rose, PA (Meunier)
Tenbrook, Jacqueline, NJ (McCall)
Thompson, Mary Patricia, PA
Timony, Tomasello, Rose Marie, NJ
Warthin, Esther Lee, VA (Webb)
Wedge, Colleen Marilyn, PA (Scussa)
Wilson, Gladys May, PA (Kitchen)
York, Ruth Eva, NJ (Robens)
Yuhas, Rose Marie, PA (Dudas)
Zatzariny, Tanya, NJ

Barton Memorial Hospital (Chest Department), 1946–1961.

In this year a change in nursing administration took place. Two departments were formed, - one for service to be headed by Miss Mable C. Prevost ('29, Fig. 32) as Assistant Hospital Director; the other, the School of Nursing under the Directorship of Doris E. Bowman ('42, Fig. 61).

Miss Bowman, directly following graduation, served with the Hospital #38 Unit. After obtaining her Bachelor's and Master's degrees in education she returned to Jefferson as Instructor in Pediatrics in 1954. In 1958 she succeeded Miss Prevost as Director of the School, a post she retained until 1982. The book *Commitment to Excellence*, a history of the School of Nursing, was dedicated to her in 1982. She was designated Emeritus Professor of Nursing and her portrait was presented to the University. She contributed a chapter on the history of the School of Nursing to *Thomas Jefferson University: Tradition and Heritage* (1989).

The 91 graduates reflected the successful recruitment efforts of the previous several years.

CLASS OF 1958

Auman, Linda, PA (Pickering)
Barlieb, Pearl Virginia, PA (Dougherty)
Barrett, Barbara Jane, NJ (Borkowski)
Battram, Audrey Ann, PA (Rhoads)
Beard, Barbara Jane, PA (Garzon)
Beard, Mary Jean, PA (Ecker)
Beard, Nancy Elizabeth, PA (Griggs)
Boeckel, Lois Mae, PA (Toomey)
Brown, Mary Louise, PA
Bushey, Buddy Jeanne, MD (Metz)
Chicote, Katharine Frances, PA (Cole)
Corman, Day Dawn, PA
Countryman, Dolores Catherine, PA (Spong)
Dailey, Elizabeth, PA (Hubbs)
Davies, Deanna Grace, NJ (Schweyer)
Digiondomenico, Barbara Ann, PA (Denney)
Doll, Linda Lee, PA (Eppley)
Duncan, Mary Ellen, NJ (Higgins)
Dutton, Barbara Anne, PA (Kanas)
Endo, Patricia Fusako, PA (Watanabe)
Fetteroff, Elenore Joan, PA
Foster, Yvonne Rose, FL (King)
Freshcoln, Carol Elizabeth, NJ (Gilcher)
Gademan, Doris Margaret, PA (Stephens)
Gasparon, Joan Frances, NJ
Gibbs, Jacquelyne Yvonne, PA (Collis)
Hand, Barbara Jane, NJ (Brodovsky)
Harmer, Joan Carol, PA (Tribolet)
Hashem, Anna Marie, Evans, PA (Gallagher)
Hill, Shirley Rebecca, PA (Walker)
Horn, Jane Ellen, PA (Altmann)
Hornyak, Dolores Eileen, PA (Parisi)
Hunsinger, Geneva Merolene, PA (Bowman)

Fig. 61. Miss Doris E. Bowman ('42), Director of the School of Nursing (1958-82).

Keelins, Mary Jane, DE (Pileggi)
Kistner, Mary Patricia, NY (Gelchrut)
Knaff, Rose Marie Josephine, PA (Glanfield)
Koch, Alice Lorraine, NJ (Zilling)
Kovarie, Mulveena M., PA (Baldauf)
Kuehner, Patricia Joan, NJ
Leach, Carol Jean, NJ (Lyons)
Lentz, Anita Lorene, PA (Arner)
LeVan, Muriel Joan, PA (Keller)
Lockwood, Edna Dolores, PA (Hneleski)
Matircho, Shirley Anne, PA (Campbell)
McClenahan, Margaret Jane, PA
McDonald, Mary Ellen, NJ
McGee, Sonia Lee, PA (Williamson)
McKee, Mary Margaret, PA (Blue)
McNamara, Josephine Ellen, TX (Wheeler)
Moore, Rosemary Elizabeth, PA
Mosely, Joan Marie, NJ (Pesco)
O'Neill, Mary Irene, PA
Pangborne, Patricia Kirchner, PA (Floreck)
Paponi, Margaret Rose, NJ (Shanosky)
Paranzino, Josephine G., NJ (Antolik)
Petrock, Jean, PA
Priester, Janis Maxine, PA (Wilkinson)
Quinn, Dolores Margaret, PA (Atkinson)
Ravicini, Joan C.M., MD (Randles)
Rennebaum, Mabel Elizabeth, NJ (Hollender)
Riccio, Drosalina Mariana, NJ (Riffle)
Rickley, Janet Marie, DE (McQuale)

Rodgers, Christina Louise, PA
Ross, Donna Jane, PA (Wallace)
Roulston, Geraldine, PA (Scott)
Sakella, Annunciata Joan, FL (Daneman)
Sarappa, Marie Lois, NJ (Keenan)
Showers, Bertha Louise, PA (Brown)
Sincavage, Joan Ann, PA (Shimkus)
Skovran, Caroline Esther, NJ
Smith, Barbara Ann, PA
Smith, Inga Jeanne, PA (Scott)
Smith, Joanne Rae, PA
Smith, June Elizabeth, PA
Staley, Constance Dawn, NY (Lish)
Steinmetz, Arlene Elizabeth, PA
Stoudt, Darlene Sylvia, PA (Bleile)
Tanner, Sylvia Yvonne, PA (Lawrence)
Tichey, Bernadine Ann, PA (Gashow)
Timbrell, Bernice Louise, PA (Glad)
Weisel, Susanna M., NJ (Sagi)
West, Patricia C., PA (Coone)
Williams, Louise Cornell, NJ (Dunn)
Wilson, Barbara Louise, DE (Kelso)
Wingate, Edith J., PA (Green)
Witt, Grace Louise, PA (Becker)
Wolfe, Lynne Mary, NJ (Gumina)
Wunder, Sophie Margaret, PA (Wells)
Young, Isabella Margaret, PA (Kelly)
Yurkovich, Mary E., PA
Ziegler, Louise R., PA

You young ladies are fortunate, indeed, for having chosen the nursing profession for your contribution to the assets of humanity. To you is given the opportunity to enjoy the fruits of work twofold, namely, the application of the knowledge and special skill you have acquired in your course of nursing, which you so capably demonstrate at the bedside, and secondly, the contribution of the finer things of life that belong only to womankind.

George J. Willauer, M.D. (JMC, '23)

A long-awaited new Nurses' Residence (The Martin Building) was completed this year with accommodations for 336 student nurses (Fig. 62). This eight-story facility at Eleventh and Walnut Streets was opened in September at a cost of $2 million. A corridor separated the utilities from the bedrooms so that each bedroom allowed greater privacy and quietness for the students. A lounge and kitchen were provided on each floor.

There was a change in the student nurse's uniform this year from the organdy apron and bib to match the cap, long-sleeved dress with separate cuffs, and the disliked black shoes and stockings. It was replaced with a one-piece pink dress with gored skirt and tucked white bib, cuffs, shoes, and stockings. This attire was now considered as modern as the Residence.

The graduates numbered 75.

CLASS OF 1959

Bachers, Arlene Weaver, PA (Baumann)
Berry, Kathryn Cecelia, PA (Stout)
Boyer, Arlene Romaine, PA (Dicken)
Corkery, Carol Ann, PA (Staas)
Corzen, Gloria, PA
Cottringer, Carolyn Mary, NJ (Kong)
Curtis, Diane Marie, PA (Jacobsen)
Davis, Nancy Corrine, CANADA (Crawford)
Davis, Sandra Diane, PA (Marsden)
Delikat, Irene A., DE (Frett)
Gardier, Angelina Patricia, PA (Hagan)
Griff, Bernice Gladys, PA (Catalona)
Hanling, Marylou Ethel, NJ (Vollrath)
Heisey, Patricia Ann, PA (Harzer)
Hertensteiner, Ester Matilda, PA (Barsbher)
Heveran, Alice Anita, PA
Hoerst, Charlotte Edna, NJ
Hoover, Dolores Pauline, PA
Horensky, Eileen Betty, PA (Terlecky)
Houser, Patricia, PA (Johns)
Hudson, Jane Alma, PA
Hughes, Betty Ann, PA (Kosko)
Hunter, Deanna Peggy, PA (Smeck)
Janicek, Bernadine, PA (Plocinik)
Jones, Carol Jean, PA (Stange)
Karnes, Carol Ann, PA (Wenzel)
Keller, Bette Ann, PA (Tindley)
King, Ellen Marie, PA (Herb)
Klinestiver, Janet Carol, PA (Mosley)
Kling, Jeanne Helen, NJ (Farrell)
Knoll, Nancy Ruth, NJ (Viereck)
Koswoski, Josephine Joan, PA
Kowalick, Jean Marie, PA (Konzman)
Kozak, Virginia Ann, PA (Fritz)

Kraus, Pauline Louise, MD (Parsons)
Lesley, Susan, PA (Derrickson)
Little, Sara Ellen, NJ (Danyo)
Longfellow, Joanne, MD (Holder)
Longworth, Marie Aurora, PA (Kostello)
Mackes, Miriam Carrie, PA
Maddams, Nancy Ruth, DE (Keelins)
Maiese, Joan Joyce, NJ (Lucchetti)
Major, Anne Verle, PA (Jones)
McFarland, Marlene Mae, PA (Olivieri)
McQuown, Helen Mae, PA (Cangelosi)
Miller, Marilyn Ann, MN
Mooney, Betty Colleen, PA (Wagner)
Moore, Zelva Ann, DE (Devine)
Morris, Janet Beverly, PA (Renn)
Moser, Mary Lynn, OH (Shonk)
Neuhaus, Marilyn Gene, PA
O'Rourke, Sally Alice, MD
Ossman, Elizabeth Ann, PA
Phelps, Barbara Lynne, PA (Flounders)
Reath, Hazel Marjorie, PA
Reinhart, Nancy May, PA (Wandschneider)
Rockafellow, Betty Rae, NJ (Laird)
Ryan, Jane Patricia, PA (Dietrich)
Sager, Ruth Ann, PA (Simpson)
Sanderson, Marlene Ruth, PA
Sankey, Margaret Patricia, PA (Brown)
Scherer, Joanne Alice, PA (D'Alonzo)
Smith, Barbara Ann, PA (Prendergast)
Stanek, Dolores, PA (Gray)
Stevens, Vera Emilie, PA (Myers)
Stiles, Thelma Sarah, NJ (Malecek)
Tarapchak, Dolores Stephanie, PA (Timko)
Walsh, Jacqueline Martha, NY (Long)

Weiss, June Helen, NJ
Whelan, Stella Reginia, PA
Willey, Jane Eleanor, MO
Wilson, Carolyn Joyce, PA (Dales)

Wisotzsky, Sandra Virginia, PA (Hall)
Wood, Nancy Ann, NJ (Cohen)
Wright, Juanita Ann, PA (Bloes)

Fig. 62.   The James R. Martin Nurses' Residence (1959).

A patient feels the touch of life in the professional nurse and willingly entrusts himself to her knowledge and skill. A complete definition of this ability is not possible. It is most often the result of rich emotional understanding or perhaps better stated the fruit of experience richly shared.

Kenneth E. Fry, M.D. (JMC, '31)

In this year full accreditation was achieved by the School of Nursing from the National League for Nursing, the award having marked the culmination of efforts by the faculty and administration for several years. This approval was renewed at each periodic re-evaluation review in subsequent years.

The decade of the 1960s was perhaps the period of greatest accomplishment in the history of the School. The morale of the students was high, owing largely to their perception of the quality of their education and to improved recreational features. Innovative teaching devices including closed-circuit television were installed.

Carol Baxter (Zeller) went on to teaching of clinical nursing and further education (Jefferson, University of Pennsylvania, and University of California School of Nursing). She developed skills in teaching of Computer Assisted Instruction courses with numerous publications. In 1988/89 she received the Outstanding Faculty Award from Marin Community College School of Registered Nursing.

Alice Bolig (Gahan) was the first editor of the revived school newspaper *Caps N' Capes* in 1958. She went on to graduate work with degrees of B.A. and M.A. She was involved in school nursing programs and active in the National Association of School Nurses.

There were 86 graduates.

CLASS OF 1960

Barton, Dorothea, PA
Baxter, Carol, PA (Zeller)
Bilbrough, Betty, MD (Alexy)
Boehmler, Elizabeth, NJ
Bolig, Alice, PA (Gahan)
Brennan, Patricia, PA (Houtman)
Brittan, Eunice, PA (Yakkel)
Bulkley, Catherine, PA
Burkowski, Ruth, PA (Gavioli)
Cale, Dorothy, NJ (Van Derripe)
Carrozzino, Dolores, PA (Pascoe)
Cella, Alma, NJ (Grieco)
Christian, Virgie, PA (Medley)
Christine, Virginia, NJ
Christner, Sue Ann, WV (Cozzolino)
Coleman, Virginia, PA (Nill)
Connor, Elizabeth, PA (Alexander)
Corson, Claire, NJ (Scott)
Cranmer, Ellen, NJ (Spratt)
Danner, Shelva, PA
Davidson, Caroline, PA
De Angelis, Roseanna, PA
De Turk, Beverly, PA (Wentz)
Driscoll, Joan, PA (Kelley)
Dutton, Jean, PA (Strong)
Emerson, Janet, MD (Lutton)
Estep, Barbara, PA (Nevara)
Farris, Mary, NY (Taylor)

Frank, Mildred, NJ (Arndt)
Frey, Mary, PA (Levengood)
Giorgio, Sally, PA (Harris)
Graham, Heather, PA (Pressler)
Guthrey, Joeann, PA (Taylor)
Haas, Judith, PA (Stauffer)
Haupt, Suzanne, PA (Funke)
Heaps, Barbara, PA (Vitelli)
Henly, Madeline, PA (Glass)
Hill, Ann, MD (Griffaw)
Hom, Loretta, PA (Chin)
Hooks, Janetta, PA (Thomas)
Hurley, Sarah, PA (Conrad)
Isenhour, Judith, MD (Ferraro)
Kost, Helen, PA
Leader, Joanne, PA
Lightner, Marval, PA
Lipan, Sara, PA (Callanen)
Longhitano, Virginia, PA
Mahoney, Jane, FL (Dynan)
Manges, Kathleen, PA (Kleponis)
Mathie, Sandra, PA (Manning)
Mazakas, Patricia, PA (Van Strien)
Metzger, Elva, PA (Helverson)
Mockaitis, Martina, PA (Martin)
Mounce, Jeannette, NJ (Kohler)
Murphy, Roseanne, PA
Naylor, Anna, PA

Noll, Georgia, PA
Ostroski, Loretta, PA (Dempsey)
Parry, Phyllis, PA (Kolander)
Pate, Joan, NJ (Ake)
Raksnis, Irene, PA
Reaver, Bette, PA (Light)
Ressler, Carolyn, PA (Goepfert)
Rickert, Phyllis, PA (Hirst)
Riegel, Carol, PA (Nystrom)
Romack, Judith, MD
Ruebman, Judith, PA (Mearig)
Runyan, Carol, PA (Medsger)
Sampsell, Dorothy, PA
Schniepp, Dottie, PA (Stose)
Schwartz, Florence, NJ

Scott, Carol, NJ
Sell, Carolyn, PA (Iezzi)
Shea, Pauline, PA
Skidmore, Beverly, PA (Young)
Smeltzer, Rhoda, PA (Little)
Smith, Betty, MD (Patterson)
Snellbaker, Sandra, PA (Repman)
Stambaugh, Eileen, PA
Taylor, Nancy, PA
Washburn, Elizabeth, VA
Washburn, Nancy, VA (Noe)
Wolters, Dorothy, PA (Guerra)
Yoo, Jean, PA (Cressman)
Yurkovich, Kathryn, PA (Mihalik)
Zellner, Barbara, PA

Staff Nurse Anesthetists (left to right): *Martin Burke, Kathryn Rowlands, Virginia Anderson, Nellie Maloney, Gwynneth Lewis, Barbara Perkins, Robert Steininger.* (Standing left to right): *Isabelle Widing, Marguerite Mazaleski, Elaine Haidt, Gwendolyn Baxter, Elizabeth Phillips, Jean Taylor, Anne Kandra.*

This class was the last one to graduate in February, as a result of continuing efforts to streamline the academic schedule. Throughout the remainder of the decade and until 1971 the commencements were held in September. In 1971 and thereafter they were held in June.

In this year Margaret C. McClean was appointed the first non-nurse on the full time faculty as a registered dietician (Fig. 63). Several years later she was promoted to Assistant Director of the School.

In February, 1961, a cooperative program between Jefferson Nursing Department and Pennsylvania State University was established. Classes for faculty members, supervisors and head nurses were taught by faculty of Penn State. College credit was granted and 27 persons participated the first year.

Joyce Evaline Price ('49) entered the first class of women matriculants of Jefferson Medical College in this year. She thus became the first Jefferson Diploma Nurse to receive an M.D. degree from Jefferson in 1965.

Among the recreational facilities during this period was a very active student Nurses' Choir which was particularly effective during the Christmas season (Fig. 64). The basketball team was also popular at this time, winning some of the championships (Fig. 65).

There were 75 graduates this year.

Fig. 63. Margaret C. McClean, first non-nurse faculty member, later Assistant Director of the School (1974-82).

CLASS OF 1961

Arnold, Stephanie, PA (Boegly)
Barron, Ann, NJ (McBeth)
Borrell, Barbara, NJ (Fleishman)
Braithwaite, Barbara, NJ (Schwartz)
Brown, Ruth, PA (Bales)
Caldwell, Patricia, MI (Turnbull)
Canal, Barbara, NJ (Obin)
Capolarello, Theresa, PA (Lipinski)
Caponigro, Rosalie, PA (Gee)
Conley, Elizabeth, PA (Bearden)
Coppersmith, Janet, PA (Brechtel)
Craig, Mary, PA

Danch, Mary, NJ (Mascena)
Danisavich, Dorothy, PA (Ward)
Davis, Loretta, NJ (Cunninghame)
Doorly, Carolyn, PA (Vizzard)
Douglas, Jane, PA (Wills)
Eckert, Roberta, PA (Brown)
Elsesser, Jacqulin, PA (Harris)
Faust, Ethel, PA (Bazemore)
Fullerton, Barbara, NJ (Strong)
Gauger, Fay, PA (Wuchter)
Gilmore, Dolores, PA (Dunn)
Girard, Rosalie, NJ (Samet)

Gravish, Mary, PA (Cushing)
Greenawalt, Barbara, PA (Eichhorn)
Gryczko, Adrienne, PA (Boyle)
Hartlaub, Cleopha, NJ (Herzog)
Heilner, Marion, PA (McGarrey)
Hoffman, Beverly, PA (Vart)
Jaszczal, Barbara, PA (Birney)
Jones, Anna, PA
Keller, Shirley, PA (Hermann)
Kemmerer, Ellen, MD (Warren)
Kunzman, Elaine, PA (Griffin)
Lewis, Arlethia, PA (Wright)
Lewis, Patricia, MD (Truitt)
Lutz, Emily, PA (Hogan)
Lynch, Clare, PA
Maule, Edna, PA (Staub)
McQuillen, Elizabeth, PA (Larkin)
Michaels, Patricia, PA (Calhoun)
Miller, Julianne, OH (Wren)
Moser, Christine, OH (Favino)
Mostoller, Emma, PA (Shaffer)
Murdock, Mary, PA (Gilmore)
Mutter, Joan, PA (McBride)
Parman, Gale, PA (Klupt)
Parrish, Mary, PA

Patterson, Patricia, NJ (Hilton)
Pojawis, Mary, PA (Marti)
Potts, Sharon, PA (Sahrage)
Rhoda, Beatrice, NJ (Mull)
Ross, Marjorie, PA (Berrier)
Salter, Joan, PA (Sheahan)
Schafer, Mary, NJ (Cook)
Shaffer, Joyce, PA
Simonson, Betty, PA (Woods)
Simpson, Janet, PA (Rapp)
Smigelski, Elizabeth, NJ (Mungioli)
Smith, Patricia, PA (Richardson)
Sprow, Constance, PA (Abrams)
Steelman, Susan, NJ (Caselli)
Sunday, Jane, PA
Thompson, Patricia, NJ (Black)
Trumbauer, Elaine, PA (Yaich)
Tumolo, Rose, PA (Moyer)
Verdier, Miriam, PA (Wall)
Webb, Carole, PA (Levenson)
Williams, Carolyn, NJ (Richman)
Williams, Susanne, NY (Jacobson)
Wilson, Edrie, PA (Brennan)
Wingert, Minnie, PA (Wright)
Zarella, Margaret, PA
Zettler, Barbara, PA (Hahn)

Fig. 64.   Student Nurses' Choir (1961).

Fig. 65.   Basketball Team.

In July of this year the position of Home Care Coordinator provided for referral of patients to community agencies such as the Community Nursing Service so that a patient's care could be continued after discharge from the hospital. This service became highly successful and was expanded in later years.

In September, Eva Woosley (Warren) from the Class of 1934 gave the graduation address to the fourth class of the Woman's College of the University of North Carolina at Greensboro. She had received Masters degrees from Duke and the University of North Carolina and was serving as Dean of the School of Nursing at East Carolina College.

Corrine R. Kurzen was a staff nurse at Jefferson while pursuing further education. She received a B.S.N. from the University of Pennsylvania in 1967 and Master's degrees from Temple University in 1973 and University of Delaware in 1989. Her book *Contemporary Practical/Vocational Nursing* was published in 1989. She was employed in various capacities by the School District of Philadelphia and active in nursing organizations.

The graduating class numbered 74.

CLASS OF 1962

Arnold, Janet, DE (Hanks)
Aufferman, Carole, PA (Guttschall)
Baxter, Louise, PA (Fox)
Becker, Carol, PA (Meister)
Beiermeister, Elizabeth, PA (Birtwhistle)
Berry, Barbara, PA (Jaczun)
Blumberg, Janet, NJ
Bonner, Margaret, PA (Furey)
Bowen, Joan, NJ (Ronalds)
Boyer, Sally, PA (Johnson)
Boyle, Ellen, PA
Budash, Mary, PA (Smith)
Campbell, Joan, NJ (Moselle)
Cashman, Rosemary, PA (Smith)
Chambers, Leona, NJ (Hansell)
Choinska, Marian, PA (Pell)
Costello, Carole, PA (Tomlinson)
Dennis, Susanne, PA (Dunbrack)
Deshong, Ann, PA (Morgan)
Eckerd, Susan, PA (Leake)
Eich, Karen, PA (Wilson)
Falcone, Frances, PA (Baumgartner)
Fiqueriredo, Terese, PA (Hohl)
Frame, Carol, PA (Green)
Fry, Patricia, PA (Kline)
Gates, Eleanor, PA (Tullos)
Glancy, Ruth, PA (Pankuck)
Glaspey, Ellen, NJ (Willard)
Godwin, Mary, PA (Militello)
Grieshaber, Martha, PA (Moore)

Hansen, Gudrun, NJ (Henderson)
Hartwell, Barbara, NJ (Akeret)
Julius, Barabra, PA (Brooks)
Kania, Arlene, PA (Hillig)
Keen, Elizabeth, PA (Meyer)
Koder, Patricia, PA (Daniels)
Korb, Adelheid, PA (Henson)
Krahling, Marian, PA (Hammond)
Kropnick, Gail, PA (Friedman)
Kurzen, Corrine, OH
Lefchick, Theresa, PA (Lamberth)
Lehman, Sue, PA (Rice)
Liebel, Elizabeth, PA (Stewart)
Linner, Linda, NJ (Neveling)
Long, Judith, NJ (Wagner)
MacArevich, Evelyn, PA (Hoban)
Macknis, Mary, PA (Kolker)
McHugh, Joyce, KY (Kormanis)
McKeith, Edith, FL
McMinn, Sandra, PA (Laudadio)
Moore, Margaret, PA
Moyer, Dolores, PA (Knepp)
Murphy, Barbara, NJ (Fink)
Panick, Janice, PA (Billick)
Paul, Joann, PA (Mussio)
Powell, Janet, PA (Wolf)
Reck, Jessie, NJ (Keith)
Ries, Anita, PA (Dudzek)
Robeson, Billie, NJ (Bradley)
Rongyos, Irene, PA (Markus)

Rumberger, Frances, PA (Carter)
Sahler, Nancy, MD (Ayers)
Saksa, Margaret, PA (Tansy)
Smith, Pamela, PA (Fellencer)
Sode, Carol, AR (Dotts)
Spece, Joan, PA (Yanessa)
Sterner, Patience, PA (McKeever)

Stumb, Ruth, PA (Klawitter)
Sutthill, Phyllis, CT (Johnson)
Swalm, Carolee, PA (Mitchell)
Thomas, Patricia, PA (Goetz)
Weiss, Ruth, PA (Collier)
Welsko, Marian, PA (Ambrose)
Welter, Carolyn, PA (Bewsher)

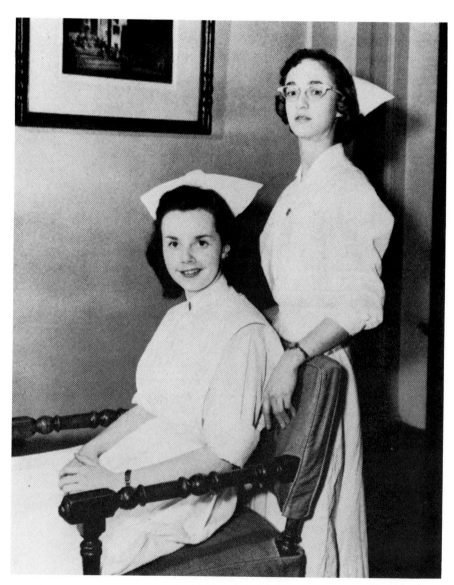

Intravenous Therapy Team. Katherine Clampffer (Jeff., R.N., '55), left
and Nancy Katherman (Jeff., R.N., '51)

The School of Nursing conducted a television program on the University of the Air. In a 17-week course, instructors presented lectures using various visual aids on the subject "Healthful Living in the Community".

The "Miss Jefferson" contest launched in 1962 under the sponsorship of the student newspaper *Caps 'N Capes* became an annual event for eight years. Candidates were judged by the nursing staff, physicians and faculty on the basis of appearance in uniform, nursing care, personality, school spirit, talent and residence department.

The winner received a blue sash emblazoned with the title and year, a gold bracelet with a charm (a disc featuring a caduceus), and a bouquet of roses. The presentation drew an enthusiastic audience from all segments of the School family (Fig. 66).

The funds contributed by the Marjorie Benton Haviland Fund continued to provide instruction for members of the faculty, strengthening their own skills with resultant improvement in the educational programs.

There were 86 graduates in the class.

CLASS OF 1963

Abele, Dianne, NJ (Rehman)
Adams, Emily, DE (Bilton)
Allen, Jean, PA (McConnell)
Ardos, Martha, PA (Zizic)
Barcelou, Carol, PA (Johnson)
Bretschneider, Marie, PA (McGlade)
Bricker, Sharon, PA (Sites)
Brosious, Joann, PA
Brough, Elizabeth, PA
Butler, Judith, PA (Yost)
Camilli, Ann, NJ (Musitano)
Carr, Margaret, PA (Hargrave)
Carroll, Judith, NJ (Cassario)
Cassidy, Maureen, NJ (McKeever)
Caum, Janet, PA (Brandt)
Cimino, Sandra, NJ (Bethanis)
Clymer, Gayla, PA (Shucker)
Cooper, Ann, NJ (Flack)
Cresswell, Jane, PA (Hospador)
Curlee, Geraldine, PA
David, Jo, NJ (McGann)
Dutt, Mary, PA (Vernallis)
Fanelle, Dorothy, NJ (Brown)
Fletcher, Donna, PA (Adams)
Frizell, Judith, PA (Waltman)
Gallagher, Nancy, NJ
Gaston, Maryann, PA (Losik)
Greenwood, Mary, NJ (Schaal)
Grouleff, Mary, NJ (Bond)
Haines, Marjorie, NJ (Powell)
Hannigan, Margaret, NJ (Bethanis)

Hart, Ann, PA (Preston)
Heblich, Janice, NJ (Nadeau)
Herold, Arline, NJ (Geary)
Hyland, Patricia, PA (Gardner)
Jones, Aldwyth, PA (Cunningham)
Keim, Mary, PA (McGinn)
Kingsley, Katherine, PA (Kinsey)
Lammer, Carol, PA (McFarland)
Leitch, Joan, PA (Murray)
Leohner, Mary, PA (Richter)
Levin, Kay, PA (St. Jean)
Lingsch, Nancy, PA (Muschek)
Little, Jean, PA (Macri)
Lonholm, Caryl, PA (Martinchek)
Mackenzie, Margaret, NJ
Mander, Mary, PA (Serfass)
Marat, Shirley, PA (McLemore)
McCall, Geraldine, PA (Pendell)
McCoy, Paula, DE (Jernigan)
McGuire, Maureen, NJ
McKillip, Linda, PA (Ely)
Mitzel, Alisande, PA (Barnes)
Monillas, Myla, PA (Einwechter)
Moore, Virginia, MD (Greenhalgh)
Murphy, Patricia, PA (Holmes)
Perry, Margaret, DE (Friedel)
Rees, Carole, PA (Slonaker)
Regan, Mary, PA (Monaghan)
Rich, Loretta, NJ (Kurland)
Rinehart, Shelva, PA (Walsh)
Robson, Theresa, PA (Cooke)

Royer, Marlene, PA (Harris)
Scriber, Lucille, PA (Ayres)
Shoemaker, Doris, PA (Townsend)
Shuey, Phyllis, PA (Weaver)
Siddall, Virginia, PA (Teitman)
Smart, Miriam A (Kramer)
Smith, Nancy, PA (Hamme)
Speicher, Mary, MD (Gillin)
Spoerl, Mary Louise, PA (Hack)
Stabile, Beatrice, NJ (Ambruso)
Sullivan, Marilyn, PA (Bonatti)
Taylor, Stephanie, NJ (Crisafulli)

Tharp, Frances, DE (McGill)
Thomas, Linda, PA (Jones)
Tiracchia, Mary, PA (Mullin)
Turner, Margaret, PA (Cannon)
Vache, Suzanne, PA (Blackburn)
Wermick, Linda, PA (Gaylor)
Whipple, Malinda, PA (Allen)
Wilhelm, Bonnie, MD (Zaldivar)
Williams, Ann, NJ (Fronduti)
Wilson, Barbara, PA (Starner)
Wilson, Judith, PA (Waltman)
Wolfel, Janet, PA (Newell)

Fig. 66.   Marjorie J. Haines

~ 1964 ~

In this year Eileen Cancelli, a senior student, became president of Area #1 Student Nurses' Association of Pennsylvania. During the 1960s membership in the organization was mandatory for freshman students and optional for the upper classes. Jefferson was host to over 400 student nurses for an evening of entertainment and to select an area member to represent Philadelphia at the State Convention in Pittsburgh. This enterprise was supported by the Alumnae Association.

Student nurses participated in the city-wide campaign to immunize against poliomyelitis.

Basic nursing techniques were first taught through closed-circuit television in 1964. This obviated the need to handle heavy equipment for demonstrations. The Fundamentals Laboratory was thus converted into a TV studio.

The School of Practical Nursing, intended to fill a long perceived need, opened in November, 1964, under the Directorship of Elizabeth J. Sweeney. There were 22 students admitted to the first class.

The graduates numbered 74.

CLASS OF 1964

Axelson, Roanne, NJ (Heise)
Bailey, Carol, PA (Miller)
Benn, Mary, PA (Brooks)
Bregman, Marsha, PA (Seltzer)
Bundens, Mary, NJ (Holverstott)
Burkholder, Elyse, PA (Detwiler)
Cancelli, Eileen, PA (DeSipio)
Capotosto, Jeanetta, PA (Clark)
Chambers, Dorothy, NJ (Ulrich)
Ciabocchi, Barbara, PA (Violanti)
Cone, Linda, NJ (Rupertus)
Cox, Jane, NJ (Gay)
Dahlmann, Margaret, VA (Coopey)
Downing, Judith, NJ (Maloney)
Dvorak, Susanne, PA (Klinger)
Ewing, Sarah, NJ
Ferster, Janet, PA (Losch)
Fesmier, Betty, PA (Davis)
Gardner, Patricia, PA (Marquette)
Gobrecht, Vicki, PA (Armstrong)
Grace, Margaret, PA (David)
Gray, Nancy, PA (Woodruff)
Greene, Grace, PA (Braun)
Hamilton, Ruth, NJ (Harris)
Hedenberg, Barbara, PA (Narehood)
Hendrickson, Nancy, NJ
Hieter, Joyce, PA (Seiple)
Hieter, Joyce, PA (Seiple)
High, Judith, PA
Insley, Patricia, MD (Orr)

Jones, Penelope, PA (McAlees)
Kemmerer, Carol, MD (Clement)
Kemmerer, Dorothy, PA (Cohler)
Kroupa, Isabella, PA (Erb)
Kunzler, Margaret, PA (Leach)
Langan, Kathleen, PA (Jones)
Lee, Lydia, PA
Lenker, Barbara, PA (Tredick)
Lingenbrick, Judith, PA (Linker)
Logue, Josephine, PA
MacKenzie, Gale, NJ
Magee, Virginia, NJ (Wample)
Marasco, Jeraldine, PA (Kohut)
Matz, Rose, PA (Devine)
McMaster, Lynn, PA (Nagatani)
Mead, Vivian, PA (Caceres)
Melfe, Jewell, NJ (Hornyak)
Micale, Patricia, PA (Samuels)
Miller, Marilyn, NJ (Long)
Munz, Joan, PA (Manno)
Nase, Barbara, PA (Anderson)
Nuttall, Dorothy, PA (Stelzner)
O'Donnell, Valerie, PA
Parzniewski, Carol, NJ (Teplick)
Records, Stephanie, NJ (Seipel)
Reed, Elizabeth, NJ
Rinear, Judith, PA (Young)
Rockhill, Donna, NJ (Ruggieri)
Ronalds, Joanne, PA (Miller)
Roth, Linda, PA (Seda)

Sbrolla, Phyllis, NJ (DeJesse)
Scheib, Judith, PA (Witmer)
Shaffer, Faye, NJ (Butzback)
Shearer, Nancy, NJ (Jones)
Tremmel, Gertrude, PA (Clemons)
Wang, Linda, NJ (Pincus)
Welsko, Judith, PA (Lynn)

Wetzel, Alice, PA
White, Patricia, PA (Block)
Woerner, Mary, PA (Schubel)
Wyker, Rebecca, OH (Hawksley)
Yelen, Joan, PA (Kleiman)
Zimmerman, Paulette, TN (Snodgrass)

Jefferson nurse admires *Gross Clinic* outside McClellan Hall.

1964

~ 1965 ~

Five months of preparation culminated in the annual show, "A Musical Mistake", written and produced by the students and directed by class members Dianne Keegan and Judith Snyder. It was one of the most successful of the annual productions which included "Showboat", "A Fair to Remember", and "Fantastic Furlough". Proceeds this year were divided among the three classes and the Student Council.

Mary L. Bennett (Rocheleau) went on to specialized programs in nursing education. Having taken her M.B.A. in administration, she was appointed Nursing Career Programs Representative at the University of Colorado School of Nursing, Denver, in 1977. From 1979 to 1982 she was also Director of Presbyterian/St. Luke's School of Nursing in Denver.

There were 74 graduates this year.

CLASS OF 1965

Abbott, Judith, NJ (Getz)
Ammons, Gail, PA (Kotz)
Bartkowski, Andrea, PA
Bennett, Claudia, DE (Penders)
Bennett, Mary, NJ (Kendrick)
Beyer, Virginia (Ives)
Boyeronus, Sharon, NJ (Ciceria)
Champion, Joyce, NJ
Chinappi, Mary Ann, NJ (Reese)
Ciortan, Patricia, PA (Wilkinson)
Connelly, Julia, PA (Flynn)
Conrad, Elaine, PA (Doyle)
Davis, Barbara, PA (Schraeder)
Ennis, Valerie, PA (Kegelman)
Farber, Kay, NJ (Matejkovic)
Fischer, Margaret, PA (McGroarty)
Graham, Nancy, PA (Heverly)
Green, Darlene, PA (Knight)
Hamilton, Dorothea, PA (Lindberg)
Harbison, Anita, PA (Karpetsky)
Hoaster, Vera, PA (Dengler)
Johnson, Pamela, PA (Drzik)
Jones, Carolyn, PA (Walchak)
Jongenburger, Jenny, NJ (Adams)
Keegan, Dianne, NJ (Aufderheid)
Kessler, Dorothy, PA (Rosencrance)
Kirner, Eunice, MI (Friedman)
Knaur, Cheryl, PA (Weber)
Kopel, Marianne, PA
Krout, Marilyn, PA (Garcia)
Lahti, Diane, PA (Hodges)
Larson, Judith, PA (Moyse)
Lever, Barbara, PA (Rash)
Lowe, Adrienne, NJ (Daughenbaugh)
Lupo, Pauline, PA
Lynch, Karen, PA (Bayers)
Malloy, Alice, PA

Materio, Catherine, NJ (Teti)
Maule, Elizabeth, PA (Zentner)
May, Ellen, PA (Whitehorne)
Maynor, Carolyn, PA (Wing)
McDowell, Carolyn, PA (Yasinski)
McKinstry, Susan, PA
Mickey, Rita, PA (Mendel)
Miles, Lore, NJ (Eichfeld)
Morgan, Joan, PA
Ott, Barbara, PA (Plamondon)
Pratt, Janet, NJ (Sanders)
Russell, Lois, PA (Foxen)
Sandt, Bonnie, PA (Inglis)
Scheingold, Dianna, PA (Ketterer)
Schmidt, Sandra, NJ (Kolodziej)
Schofield, Margaret, PA (Frishmuth)
Schraga, Nancy, PA (Wilson)
Schweitzer, Barbara, PA
Senese, Angelina, NJ
Shockley, Carol, MD (Sowder)
Skillen, Diane, PA (McCarthy)
Slamon, Elizabeth, PA
Sliwinski, Barbara, PA
Smith, Helen, PA
Snyder, Judith, PA (King)
Starry, Cassandra, PA
Steininger, Margaret, PA (Keller)
Stout, Sally, NJ
Swann, Patricia, DE (Baranowski)
Swartz, Sharon, PA (Butler)
Tallman, Nadine, NJ (Hoey)
Walker, Janet, PA (Respess)
Widman, Carolyn, PA (Bohn)
Wilhour, Susan, PA (Smeltz)
Wolfe, Linda, PA (Rogers)
Wright, Gail, NJ (Baker)
Zabelicky, Karen, PA (Meservey)

The 75th Anniversary was celebrated at the Annual ALumnae Luncheon held May 7 in the Crystal Ballroom of the Benjamin Franklin Hotel (Fig. 67). The enthusiasm of the Alumnae was manifested by an attendance of 320.

In this year a "Position Paper", published in December, 1965, by the American Nurses' Association, created concern with respect to recruitment of student nurses and faculty for diploma schools of nursing. The recommendation was that nursing education should be provided in institutions of higher learning (such as Jefferson) and lead to a baccalaureate degree. Since diploma schools were providing 85% of the nation's nurses, the elimination of these schools could result in an even more acute shortage of nurses than already existed.

Bonnie Ann Crofford pursued a career in gerontology and rehabilitation medicine. She took a Master's degree in Gerontology at Case Western Reserve University and published articles on nursing aspects of geriatrics and rehabilitation.

This year's 73 graduates brought the 75th Anniversary total to nearly 4,000. Seven members of the class were commissioned in the Armed Forces.

Fig. 67.   75th Anniversary Luncheon at Benjamin Franklin Hotel (1966).

Allen, Judith, PA (Long)
Allen, Kathleen, PA (Bauman)
Ayres, Nancy, PA (Bowman)
Barclay, Suzanne, PA (Levine)
Bartholomew, Anne, PA
Baublitz, Judy, PA (Mitchell)
Bealer, Maryann, PA (Harvey)
Berkowitz, Susane, NJ (Zamitis)
Brecker, Mary, PA (Butkovich)
Brice, Maureen, PA (McBride)
Burt, Constance, PA (Trudgeon)
Carey, Marion, NJ (Goodwin)
Carlson, Beverly, NJ (Roberts)
Carver, Dorothy, NJ (Petrozzi)
Conboy, Teresa, PA (Tule)
Crevey, Kathleen, PA
Crofford, Bonnie, PA
Denise, Carol, PA (Kolsky)
Downey, Patricia, PA (Houck)
DuCoin, Edna, NJ (Moan)
Edwards, Judith, PA (Hamblen)
Formisano, Carol, NJ (Swendson)
Fullerton, Rebecca (Omerhi)
Gelston, Lauralee, NJ (Williford)
Gosser, Elsa, PA (DeCenzi)
Haffner, Judith, PA (Gries)
Hagelgans, Judith, FL (Hoefle)
Halliwell, Agnes, PA (Kirschner)
Hartman, Judith, PA (Endriss)
Kadushin, Mona, PA (Berch)
Karabasz, Clare, PA
Kavalunis, Sandra, NJ
Kennett, Judith, PA (Tracy)
Kessler, Ruth, NJ (Openlander)
Kinkaid, Janet, PA
Kocher, Donna, NJ (Christensen)

Korosec, Mary, PA (Kearney)
Kramen, Judith, DE (Seltzer)
Kreider, Edith, PA (O'Brien)
Lashinski, Jean, PA (Strelzik)
Lawrence, Judith, PA (Winckles)
Lithgow, Nancy, PA (Pearson)
Lucchesi, Margaret, PA (Connell)
Mentzer, Brenda, PA (Hethcate)
Miller, Terri, PA (Zindell)
Milon, Patricia, OH
Moyer, Judith, PA (Thumme)
Murphy, Jane, PA (Skurecki)
Neis, Judith (Horton)
Novario, Rita, PA
Oakley, Mary, NY (Fusaro)
Paynter, Marilyn, PA (Sharkey)
Piro, Bessie, PA (McGrath)
Reilly, Helen, NJ
Richardson, Patricia, PA
Roe, Martha, PA (Russell)
Rogers, Leslie, NY (Wagner)
Sampson, Joan, DC (Cupic)
Santarone, Claire, PA
Sass, Rosemarie, PA
Schlegal, Anita, PA (Hess)
Scull, Nancy, NJ (Brainard)
Shearer, Karen, PA (Hughes)
Shermer, Barbara, PA (Ruehl)
Shisler, Bonnie, PA
Shuck, Catherine, PA (Heller)
Smith, Mary, NJ (Lebsack)
Steadman, Marilyn, NJ
Stewart, Susan, AR (Porter)
Thompson, Christina, NJ (Ford)
Valentine, Tracy, PA (Booth)
Webb, Mary, PA
Weiner, Lenora, PA (Schwartz)

This is my vow: To pefect my medical art and never to swerve from it so long as God grants me my office, and to oppose all false medicine and teachings. Then, to love the sick, each and all of them, more than if my own body were at stake. Not to judge anything superficially, but by symptoms, not to administer any medicine without understanding.

Paracelsus (1493–1541)

A Conference on Nursing Education was held at Jefferson on April 10, to explore necessary future innovations. Authorities in the field came as guest speakers from Massachusetts, Florida and California.

In this year a School of Allied Health Sciences was founded which incorporated the School of Nursing under its administration. Responsibility for the education of nurses was to be transferred from the Hospital on January 1, 1968. John W. Goldschmidt, M.D. (JMC '54) was appointed the first Dean. Miss Doris Bowman and Miss Mabel Prevost retained their respective positions as Director of the School of Nursing and Assistant Hospital Director.

Orlowitz Residence Hall was opened this year, allowing additional housing for staff nurses.

There were 90 graduates.

CLASS OF 1967

Amabile, Jean, PA (Michiels)
Ashby, Christine, PA (Gerity)
Aubrey, Rosemary, PA (Gamburg)
Baird, Ledjie, PA
Balmer, Joanne, PA
Barbee, Annette, PA (Bunting)
Bartello, Sandra, NJ (Fida)
Bartilucci, Marianne, VA (Gardner)
Beener, Paula, PA (Kelling)
Bender, Jill, PA (Moyer)
Blauvelt, Carole, PA (Reeser)
Brady, Karen, PA (Neubeck)
Breidenthal, Sally, PA (Gilbert)
Buechley, Ellen, PA (Freeze)
Buehler, Virginia, PA (Taylor)
Christie, Amelia, PA (Lyons)
Creamer, Sharon, PA (Murphy)
Dougherty, Geraldine, PA (Popolow)
Engelkraut, Sharon, PA
Fitzsimmons, Denise, PA (McKee)
Fraim, Patricia, PA (Heil)
Gabriel, Anita, PA (Marshall)
Gallihue, Carol, PA (Gross)
Gartland, Ursula, PA
Goldman, Sybil, PA (Leson)
Good, Susan, PA (Jewett)
Goodman, Linda, PA
Gottschall, Ann, PA (Walker)
Gurgul, Cynthia, NJ (Joffe)
Haedel, Rita, NJ (Becchetti)
Hampf, Joan, NJ (Heaton)
Hansen, Marie, NJ (Killough)
Higgins, Patricia, PA (Stewart)
Higham, Sally, PA (Fenlin)
Hollister, Eleanor, PA (Reinhardt)

Jakabcin, Mary, PA (Perkins)
Johnson, Judith, NJ (Hougendobler)
Kazelis, Jane, NJ (Kriebel)
Kurtz, Marcia, PA (Favinger)
Labbe, Doris, PA (Silance)
Lachman, Sue, PA
Laros, Paula, NJ (Rich)
Lawer, Karen, PA (Bedell)
MacDonnell, Marilyn, AL (Hunt)
McCafferty, Jane, PA (Joering)
McCafferty, Verna, PA (Walters)
McKenney, Gail, NJ (Ford)
Miller, Linda, PA (Crouch)
Morgan, Judith, PA
Musser, Dorothy, PA
O'Neill, Jane, PA (Henehan)
Oaster, Dolores, PA (Lingo)
Ortlip, Elizabeth, PA (Robleto)
Osmundson, Susan, PA (Stanley)
Osterhus, Janice, NJ (Shipley)
Park, Jane, MS (Haueisen)
Peters, Cheryl, PA (Markle)
Phillips, Amber, PA (Smith)
Pollock, Laurie, LA (Weisberg)
Posey, Cathie, PA (Wambough)
Prentice, Catherine, PA (Reynolds)
Raab, Kathleen, PA (Fitzgerald)
Rainey, Nancy, NJ (Eagan)
Reed, Joan Ann, PA (Darden)
Reeves, Susan, NJ (LaPlante)
Rennwantz, Alyce, PA (Munson)
Rich, Catherine, NJ (Young)
Rood, Sharon, PA (Rajnic)
Ruble, Marilyn, NJ (Scelba)
Schubele, Christine, PA (Holmberg)

Schwartz, Sheila, PA (Rich)
Senkowsky, Carolyn, NJ (Housman)
Shachter, Elayne, PA (Gould)
Sheaffer, Carol, NJ (McClerkin)
Siegrist, Carol, PA (Woodruff)
Simons, Jacquelin, PA (Alvarez)
Simpson, Jill, PA (Bower)
Sochovka, Carol, PA (Knickerbocker)
Stevens, Suzanne, NJ
Stevenson, Judith, PA (Lagansky)

Strege, Linda, PA (Jones)
Swinand, Frances, PA
Taylor, Eileen, PA (Caravello)
Tootchen, Phyllis, PA
Valentine, Linda, PA (Russell)
Watkins, Deidre, PA (Blank)
Wishart, Kathleen, NJ (Castello)
Wormald, Suzanne, DE (Nolan)
Yingling, Patsy, PA (Braman)
Zerbe, Linda, PA (George)

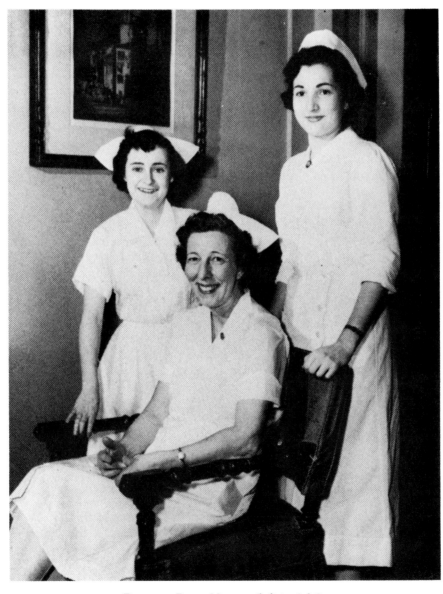

Recovery Room Nurses, (left to right):
Susan Watson (Jeff., R.N., '55), Viola Fox (Jeff., R.N., '37), Renee Weinberg.

Administratively the School of Nursing became part of the newly organized School of Allied Health Sciences.

The academic program was shortened from 36 to 35 months and the following year to 33 months.

In this year an affiliation agreement was signed with the Philadelphia College of Pharmacy and Science whereby Jefferson nursing students could begin work toward a degree with college credit courses as electives. Twenty students enrolled the first year.

Complete block rotation was instituted for the class of 1970, which included courses in psychiatric nursing at Philadelphia State Hospital (Byberry) and Eastern State School for Children. Studies were included in "Student Evaluation of Courses in Nursing Education;" "An Analytical and Comparative Study of the Performance by Jefferson Graduates on State Board Examinations;" "Relation of Psychological Type to Nursing School Success at Jefferson (Class of 1968)."

Linda Meachum (Scheetz) pursued a career in nursing education and research. She received her B.S. in 1977, M.A. (New York University) in 1981 and Ed.D. (Columbia University) in 1988. She served as Chairperson, Division of Nursing, Mt. Saint Mary College, Newburgh, New York, and as consultant in many academic and clinical areas.

College entrance board examinations became an admission requirement.

The Alumni Association presented a check for $22,358 to President Herbut toward the Building Fund (Fig. 68).

There were 62 graduates this year.

CLASS OF 1968

Anglim, Rosemary, PA (Dickson)
Arnold, Eileen, PA (Dietz)
Ball, Janet, NJ (Lyons)
Barnum, Karen, PA (Kushto)
Bozarth, Virginia, NJ (Waldron)
Browne, Margaret, PA (Kern)
Brucker, Suzanne, PA (Merryman)
Burke, Paulette, PA (Krapf)
Buscher, Donna, PA (Libby)
Cohen, Carol, PA (Leventhal)
Crum, Shirley, MD (Radzai)
Crumlish, Dolores, PA (Brown)
Davis, Barbara, PA (Cross)
Dubis, Shirley, PA (Poling)
Feller, Rosalyn, PA
Gannon, Eileen, PA (Fagnani)
Guy, Susan, NJ (Murschell)
Hannah, Katherine, NJ (Haywood)
Inghram, Bonnie, FL (Siegrist)
Johnson, Carol, NJ (Harnish)
Jones, Nancy, NJ (Harrington)
Kane, Jeanne, PA
Kinna, Carolyn, PA (Smith)
Kline, Donna, PA (Miller)
Klinedinst, Nancy, PA (Kerns)
Korin, Beth, PA (Sherr)

Kramer, Roberta, FL
Landi, Joanne, PA
Leight, Margaret, PA (Beckett)
Levine, Paula, NJ
Lubrecht, Maxine, PA (Heller)
Lucas, Catherine, PA
Lugowski, Kathleen, PA (Schade)
Martz, Teresa, PA (Oldroyd)
Masten, Elizabeth, DE (Cahall)
May, Catherine, NJ (Dirr)
Mayse, Linda, PA (Peterson)
McCullough, Judith, PA (Backstrom)
Meachum, Linda, PA (Scheetz)
Moffitt, Patricia, PA (Mueller)
Mohr, Nancy, PA (Scheetz)
Montgomery, Ruth, NJ (Penta)
Neveras, Patricia, PA
Novitsky, Mary, PA (Stanton)
O'Connor, Marcella, PA (Strange)
Paxton, Sharon, NJ (Treaster)
Payne, Sandra, PA (Kenton)
Picard, Joyce, NJ
Piekarska, Halina, TN (Warmbrod)
Powell, Margaret, PA
Price, Sandra, PA
Reichard, Jill, PA (Tropia)

Rittenhouse, Lynn, PA (Allison)
Rosenfeld, Regina, PA (Friedman)
Schleyer, Diane, PA (Berkowitz)
Squires, Mary, PA (Getz)
Stanch, Regina, NJ (Slack)

Strange, Celinda, PA (McGovern)
Suber, Kathleen (Mebus)
Taraskas, Mary, PA (Hammond)
Vogel, Anne, NJ (Clayton)
Wartella, Marie, PA (Skowronski)

Seated, Peter A. Herbut, M.D. *President, Jefferson Medical Center,* Standing left to right: Margaret Cossman, *past President,* Mary Ann Stauffer, *past President,* Glady Keiper, *President,* Perma Davis, *Recording Secretary,* Henrietta Spruance, *Chairman, Building Fund Committee,* Elizabeth Piersol and Margaret Summers, *Members, Building Fund Committee,* Francis J. Sweeney, M.D., *Director, Jefferson Medical College Hospital,* Alma Miller, *past Treasurer,* Mabel Prevost, *Assistant Director, Jefferson Medical College Hospital,* Caroline Masuda, *Treasurer.*

Fig. 68.   Alumni Association presents Building Fund check to President Herbut (1968).

The Jefferson Medical College and Medical Center became Thomas Jefferson University on July 1, 1969. At this transition, the School of Allied Health Sciences became the College of Allied Health Sciences. Nursing students were now able to participate in the elective programs offered by the College of Allied Health Sciences. Beginning in September, sociology and psychology were given as credit courses.

In this year the new facilities of Jefferson Alumni Hall became available to students of nursing. These included a gymnasium, swimming pool, lounges and meeting rooms (Fig. 69). Also, senior class presidents of the School of Nursing served on the Commons Board.

There were 87 members in this class.

CLASS OF 1969

Armstrong, Marie, NJ (Beckerman)
Barbour, Linda, NJ (Borden)
Bardfeld, Alice, NJ
Beatty, Melody, PA (Darrow)
Bergner, Marilyn, PA
Bokal, Barbara, PA (Peroutka)
Brown, Carolyn, PA (Merryman)
Brunt, Caroline, NJ (Moriuchi)
Bugen, Sharon, PA (Greenberg)
Burdett, Deborah, PA (Allen)
Burgess, Kitty, DE
Caprara, Carol, NJ (Mannery)
Carey, Carolyn, PA (Wright)
Clawson, Eleanor, PA (Suback)
Clement, Catherine, PA
Coghlan, Patricia, PA (Stowe)
Colleluori, Rosemarie, PA (Malizia)
Compton, Leslie, NJ (Peddle)
Connolly, Dorothy, PA
Croasdale, Linda, PA (Eickhoff)
Davis, Alberta, NJ
DiBartolomeo, Marie, NJ (Longworth)
Doddy, Lizabeth, NJ (Paxton)
Drennan, Patricia, PA (Bleistine)
Dudash, Sharon, PA (Warycka)
Eldredge, Annie, NJ (Kahn)
Farrell, Roberta, NJ (Klause)
Fewer, Sharon, NJ (Foytlin)
Fox, Kathleen, NJ (Foster)
Fox, Sandra, NJ (Wendel)
Freeman, Marion, PA (Jablonski)
Gansky, Freda, PA (Feldman)
Gartland, Barbara, PA (Chandler)
Gaspari, Marianne, PA (Collins)

Gerstlauer, Donna, PA (Lonie)
Getkin, Dianne, PA (Dixon)
Greenfield, Beth, PA (Getz)
Guidi, Marilyn, NJ (Rourke)
Hancock, Mary, PA (Reede)
Harris, Irene, PA
Hillerstrom, Jean, PA (Rakey)
Hitchens, Kay, DE (Jennings)
Hoffman, Kathleen, PA (Kline)
Huff, Ruth, NJ (Luliano)
Hughes, Dolores, PA
Jones, Daveen, NJ (Edmiston)
Kuehner, Joan, NJ (Munyon)
Lake, Linda, PA (Boyle)
Laury, Laraine, NJ (Labriola)
Loury, Nancy, PA (Argonish)
Macelis, Mary, NJ (Lane)
McGarvey, Jane, PA (Wuerth)
Menendez, Rosalinda, PA (Heayn)
Morris, Virginia, PA (Hunter)
Morrison, Marsha, PA (Perry)
Mount, Mary, PA (Bull)
Mullen, Christine, PA (Fox)
Murray, Mary, NJ (Burkhardt)
Nelson, Susan, PA (Davis)
Nevin, Nancy, PA (McClees)
Norman, Martha, NJ (Schwarz)
Paoletti, Elvira, PA
Pierson, Carol, PA (James)
Pierucci, Susan, PA (Laine)
Preston, Donna, PA (Schmidt)
Ramsey, Sandra, PA (Bauer)
Reed, Elizabeth, NJ (Kirschling)
Reppert, Dawn, PA (Meek)

Russo, Hope, NJ (Schooley)
Schafer, Carol, PA (Hamilton)
Schwarz, Diana, PA (Kawasaki)
Seebaur, Marie, PA (Panebianco-Ford)
Shanahan, Kathleen, NJ (Huffman)
Shannon, Kathleen, PA (Cook)
Sierer, Aleta, PA (Gilmore)
Sloyer, Carol, NJ (Ianoville)
Smith, Anne, NJ (Hennessey)
Smith, Sandra, NJ (Hitchner)

Sovin, Marlene, NJ (Croce)
Tachovsky, Irene, PA (Holly)
Troutman, Diana, CA (Balsiger)
Wallace, Beverly, PA
Watts, Beverly, PA
Wypszinski, Elaine, PA (Musial)
Yahnke, Elizabeth, PA (Tozzini)
Zubatch, Mary, PA (Marchetti)
Zwick, Linda, NJ (Reichel)

Fig. 69.   Jefferson Alumni Hall (1969).

The stresses placed upon the School of Nursing to scale down the Diploma Program in favor of the Baccalaureate Degree resulted in strenuous efforts to obtain more candidates. While concentrating its efforts on top-notch high school graduates, the School did not remain aloof from the social concerns of the times. Accordingly, this summer a remedial program was launched for a group of ten disadvantaged students to assist them in becoming qualified for admission.

The Scott Memorial Library occupied its new building at 1020 Walnut Street (Fig. 70). With four times the previous space, the collections of the Medical School and School of Nursing were integrated. The new facilities included several small rooms for study, numerous carrels and a browsing room for recreational reading.

Commencement exercises were held for 63 graduates at the Sheraton Hotel. The address was delivered by Dr. Ellsworth R. Browneller, former Jefferson Medical College Hospital Director and currently Secretary of the Department of Health of Pennsylvania.

Fig. 70.   Scott Library (1970).

Belmonte, Marie (Pike)
Betz, Janet, PA (Phillips)
Blake, Catherine, PA (Cavanaugh)
Blome, Marion, NJ (Frockowiak)
Boyeronus, Susan (Smolensky)
Burger, Linda, PA (Belis)
Clark, Sandra, MD (Hall)
Cochocki, Elizabeth, PA (Hessenthaler)
Coligan, Alice, NJ (Conte)
Connors, Margaret, CA (Marchant)
Dalgity, Audrey, PA (McCash)
Deal, Patricia, ID (Gallagher)
Dooley, Kathleen, PA (Hyde)
Drigan, Rosemary
Eick, Catherine, PA (Encloe)
Evans, Carol, PA (Phillips)
Fenning, Linda, NJ (Johnson)
Garforth, Lois
Giannini, Domenica, PA (Chromiak)
Gillis, Deborah
Goodman, Tanna, MD (O'Mansky)
Grabowski, Cynthia, PA
Gratzik, Maria, NJ (Marinelli)
Guise, Beverly (Cockerham)
Hom, Helen, NJ (Makowski)
Hook, Linda, NJ (Garbrecht)
Jennis, Stephanie, FL
Johnston, Gail, PA (Gallagher)
Kaempf, Gail
Kelly, Kathleen, PA (Ballek)
Kirlin, Linda, PA (Khadpe)

Lacy, Karen, NJ
Logan, Kathleen, PA (Martin)
Loris, Linda, NY (Hall)
Louderback, Janice
Lukiewski, Nancy, PA (Hagdorn)
MacMillan, Susan, PA
March, Fern, PA
Marcincin, Julianne, PA (Darrow)
Maycott, Constance, NJ (Yood)
McCarthy, Kathleen, PA (Whalen)
Moiso, Barbara
Moore, Linda, PA (Fekete)
Moyer, Gini-Ann, PA (Scott)
Murray, Margaret, PA (Randazzo)
Nice, Phyllis, PA (Anders)
Pasquini, Phyllis, PA (Randazzo)
Peters, Suzanne, PA (McLean)
Randazzo, Catherine, PA
Reed, Christine, NJ (Little)
Roat, Lynne, PA (Juel)
Roberts, Jill, DE (Ferguson)
Schulman, Karen, NJ (Johnston)
Schultz-Pizzutillo, Barbara (Cegles)
Shirey, Cynthia, PA
Slovich, Rosann, PA (Provost)
Stanton, Mary, PA (Sellers)
Stroup, Cynthia, PA (Beal)
Tomaszewski, Barbara, NJ
Valentine, Janice, NJ (Nadeau)
Webster, Donna, PA
Wolfe, Susan, PA (DiSanto)
Ziplow, Judith, VA

One does not ask of one who suffers: What is your country and what is your religion?
One merely says: You suffer, this is enough for me: you belong to me and I shall help you.

Louis Pasteur (1822–1895)

~ 1971 ~

The early 70s constituted a time of philosophical restructuring of concepts relating to various levels of nursing education and service. The American Nursing Association had previously recommended the desirability of baccalaureate degree education. The ultimate thrust of the program was for nurses to obtain college degrees. Jefferson's College of Allied Health Science was planning accordingly for baccalaureate, diploma, and practical nursing.

Commencement exercises were held June 26 in the Sheraton Hotel Ballroom. Dr. Dorothy Novello, Chairman of the State Board of Nurses Examiners and Chairman, Division of Nursing, Villa Maria College in Erie, was the guest speaker.

At this time there were approximately 2700 nurses still living and the graduating class numbered 56.

CLASS OF 1971

Anderson, Louise, PA (Sweeney)
Appell, Patricia, PA (Dunn)
Bartolone, Marianne, NJ (Speno)
Beck, Carol, NY (Cleri)
Blum, Eileen, PA (Moran)
Boothby, Frances, PA (Koniers)
Briley, Patricia, AL (McKay)
Broomall, Lynda, NY (Scazafabo)
Brownstein, Annette, TX
Carlson, Mary
Christianson, Linda, NJ (Gough)
Ciociola, Carol
Denes, Cathleen (Webber)
Dougherty, Denise (Becht)
Dupras, Sally, KS (Blessinger)
Feeney, Mary, PA (Raab)
Fitzhenry, Katharine
Francis, Kathryn, PA
Freeman, Debra (Ulvad)
Furry, Peggy, PA (Kuster)
Gore, Elizabeth, PA (Coughlin)
Goss, Cynthia (Byrd)
Graham, Susan, PA
Hand, Beverly
Heisey, Beth (Riedel)
Hoffman, Ruth, MA (Pearson)
Hudak, Kathryn (Behm)
Jess, Judith, NJ

Johnson, Louise, VA
Jones, Judith
Kramp, Janet, MA
Kubiak, Eileen,
LaFleur, Louise (Giese)
Lease, Jane (O'Hara)
Malek, Carole, NJ (Genello)
Manni, Karen, NJ (McGough)
Mullin, Deidre, FL (Yuknavich)
Newby, Mildred, CA (Riff)
Peterson, Susan, PA (Szymanik)
Powers, Patricia, DE (Pedrick)
Raub, Cynthia, PA (Butterworth)
Reitz, Pamela (Wolfe)
Senderling, Jane (Maggini)
Shreiner, Kathleen, DE (Ely)
Smith, Linda, PA (Korey)
Spena, Grace
Stack, Christine, PA
Steinhagen, Jeanette
Streeper, Lynn, PA
Suber, Loretta, PA (Heyduk)
Terlecki, Adele, PA (Mueller)
Trembach, Carol (Krause)
Van Dyke, Kathryn, VA (Hayes)
Wertz, Susan
Wolfe, Roxanna
Zettler, Ellen

~ 1972 ~

The Baccalaureate program commenced in September with the Admission of 46 students who transferred from other colleges and universities. Charlotte E. Voss Ed.D. was the first Chairman of the Department of Baccalaureate Degree Nursing. She developed a curriculum encompassing a broad base in the natural and social sciences, arts and humanities. Her programs were enhanced by a $94,000 grant which she obtained from the U.S. Department of Health, Education and Welfare.

For the first time the Martin Residence was used as a housing facility for women university students other than nurses. The entire second floor was used for this purpose.

There were 62 graduates this year.

CLASS OF 1972

Adams, Judith, NJ (Lemmerman)
Ammarell, Eileen, NJ (Shelton)
Auerbach, Denise, NJ (Wychowance)
Barfield, Eileen
Baumgartner, Cheryl, PA (Meyer)
Biache, Madeline, NJ (Skarpetowski)
Boyer, Ellen, PA
Braucher, Kathy, PA (Berkebile)
Brewer, Deborah
Cmar, Constance, PA (Brophy)
Coleman, Catherine
Cruice, Elaine, PA (Sein)
Dalton, Mary, PA
Daly, Kathleen Dempsey, Margaret, CA
Derickson, Marie, PA (Flis)
DiGiorgio, Carol, MA (Saul)
DiMarcello, Ann, NJ (Menschner)
DiNubile, Carol, IL
Dougherty, Elizabeth, PA (McGettigan)
Eng, Nancy, NJ (Hom)
Engle, Elizabeth, NJ (Corcory)
Eriksen, Helen, PA
Fisher, Mary, PA (Fish)
Freedman, Anita, PA (Lief)
Furlong, Donna, FL (Miller)
Hancy, Patricia, PA (Hemphill)
Hand, Karen, PA (Matejik)
Hawley, Nancy, FL (Imperiale)
King, Eileen, PA (Vanett)
Konrad, Kathleen, CA

Kugler, Elaine (Kulp)
Lerch, Barbara (McLaughlin)
Lupinacci, Catherine, NJ
Manns, Rose (Kufrovich)
Marshall, Theresa (Plenty)
Monroe, Donna, PA (Phelps)
Mooney, Arlene, PA (McFadden)
Mooty, Ann, PA (Cawley)
Neff, Cheryl, PA
Payne, Joyce, NJ (Blank)
Peffer, Bonnie, PA
Pfeiffer, Irene, PA (Slater)
Philip, Karen
Quinn, Christine, PA (Hodder)
Sachs, Christine, IN (McCann)
Schoeffel, Elizabeth, NJ (Fredrickson)
Scholz, Carol, PA (Carrick)
Scott, Mary Seher, Alrene, NJ
Serchia, Arlene (Seher)
Shaffer, Nancy, NY (Stanton)
Snider, Sandra, PA
St. John, Dorothy, PA (Brennan)
Swartz, Karen, CT (St. Jean)
Van Dyke, Margaret, NJ (Beattie)
Warmlinski, Linda, PA (Belinsky)
Waters, Deborah, CA (Wayne)
Webb, Mary, PA (Hulick)
Welke, Dolores, PA (Obert-Thorn)
Wolk, Helen (Ney)
Wunsch, Donna, NY (Stuurop)
Yeakle, Patricia, MO (Yesenosky)

~ 1973 ~

The Jefferson School of Nursing, in contrast to many other diploma schools, was now able to offer college credit for freshman courses in psychology (3), sociology (3) and microbiology (5). Students desiring additional credit courses had the privilege of enrolling in the College of Allied Health Sciences elective program.

In September the School of Nursing became coeducational with the admission of two male students, although male applicants had been accepted since 1971.

The graduating class numbered 68.

CLASS OF 1973

Aldersley, Mary
Arena, Kim
Aukerman, Catherine, DE (Bostick)
Baals, Karen, PA (Jaxheimer)
Bender, Joanne, NJ
Bouregy, Pamela (Puhalla)
Boyle, Theresa, NJ (Napoli)
Breder, Cheryl, PA (Wenger)
Broadwater, Susan, MD (Franklin)
Brock, Doris (Fagan)
Canney, Helene, PA (Donohue)
Carman, Wendy, CA
Coleman, Christina (Moore)
Corotto, Virginia, PA (Kramer)
Couser, Marie, PA
Dalton, Elizabeth
Denham, Patricia, KS (Howanitz)
Diehl, Anne, PA
Dillon, Marie, PA
Dodson, Margaret, MA
Esten, Bonnie, PA (Zuckerman)
Felix, Kate (Snyder)
Fiorentino, Barbara, FL (Richey)
Giordano, Carmenella, PA
Goldfarb, Eugenie, PA (Green)
Heller, Phyllis, PA (Richman)
Henry, Mary, PA
Heydt, Linda (Quinn)
Hoberman, Shelah, FL (Luber)
Huber, Karen, PA (Ciarrochia)
Jonas, Ellen, CA (Salkin)
Kee, Donna, PA (Townsend)
Kenney, Kathleen, PA (Collura)
Laboda, Constance, PA (Mumper)

Lambert, Marjorie, FL (Gibson)
Loftus, Maureen (Cattie)
Logue, Constance
Malone, Margaret
Mastrovito, Eileen, PA
McAlister, Susan, NJ (Rans)
McDermott, Joan, MA (Sullivan)
McGillin, Mary, PA
McGrory, Anne, PA (Berry)
Mikota, Catherine, NJ (Branton)
Miller, Luann, ENGLAND (Daggett)
Mills, Cathy, PA (Speace)
Morkun, Constance, PA
Morthorst, Margaret, PA
Mrvica, Linda, CT (Lee)
Murphy, Nanette, MD (Beckner)
Ricci, Jean, PA
Ridgway, Cacelia, PA (Bokas)
Roddy, Mary, NY (Puglis)
Romano, Karen
Rose, Christine, PA (Saltzman)
Sabin, Beverly (Debold)
Sawka, Leslie, PA (Hildrew)
Shelgosh, Barbara, PA
Steimer, Cheryl, OH (Sprague)
Sweeney, Mary, FL (MacCrory)
Valent, Helen, PA (Fasy)
Webb, Linda, NJ
Welsh, Janet, CA
Willey, Barbara, AK (Blood)
Wise, Mary (Lynch)
Woltemate, Mary, PA (Stec)
Young, Margaret, MD (Silvester)
Zaiss, Bonnie, CT

The Health Sciences Center (Edison Building) at Ninth and Sansom Streets was opened this year (Fig. 71). It was structured to implement innovative programs in ambulatory care, to provide space for the College of Allied Health Sciences, and to allow offices for Jefferson staff physicians. It would provide much needed space for instruction and student nurses.

At this time students could be married during the programs and live off campus. Of the 273 students, 10 were married and two had children. Night duty was a thing of the past.

There were 68 graduates.

CLASS OF 1974

Bennett, Ann (Townsend)
Birch, Margaret, PA (Ashton)
Bisson, Judith
Bonham, Patricia, NJ (Strosnider)
Boyd, Denise, PA (D'Angelo)
Boyle, Debora, DE (Borkowski)
Callaghan, Kathleen, NY (Nasca)
Crow, Susan (Landes)
D'Angelo, Denise, NJ (Rinehart)
DeBias, Deborah, NJ (Lynch)
Dildine, Maria, PA (Pepper)
Dmytryshak, Patricia, PA
Feher, Pamela, PA
Fernicola, Maureen (Bowe)
Fitzgibbons, Elizabeth
Fox, Sally
Fuhrman, Deborah, PA (Rodkey)
Giardina, Jeanne, PA (Stanton)
Gilmore, Christine, PA
Graf, Barbara, NJ
Gray, Katharine, PA (Pyle)
Hampton, Nancy, NJ (Hilkert)
Haney, Patricia, PA (Lynn)
Heinzelmann, Linda
Holford, Anita
Hunt, Wendy, PA (McCole)
Jacobs, Leslee (Doherty)
James, Cheryl, IL (Hill)
Jennerjahn, Ellen
Jennings, Julie, NJ (Fenimore)
Jinning, Mary, PA (McMullin)
Jones, Patricia, SC (Clark)
Kane, Kathleen, PA (Karlowicz)
Kearney, Frances, PA
Kelly, Maureen, PA (Lefevre)
Konowal, Noelle, PA (Parkin)

Krause, Ruth, NJ (Bunting)
Lloyd, Kathryn, PA (Ozalas)
Margraf, Jeanne, VA (Wagner)
Mayer, Patricia, NJ
McGinley, Patricia (Linton)

Fig. 71. Health Sciences Center (Edison Building).

McHugh, Patricia
McLaughlin, Carol, PA
Obst, Wendy, VT (Manganiello)
Ott, Margaret, TX (Martin)
Paulson, Virginia, NJ (Priory)
Pepper, Elaine, PA
Preiss, Joyanne, NJ (Bodine)
Rocheleau, Eileen (Arsenault)
Rogers, Edith, MA (Coghlan)
Rossetti, Carla, PA (Bolton)
Ruht, Nancy, PA (Gauger)
Sass, Patricia (Hoffman)
Sessions, Lisa (Hoffbauer)

Sheaffer, Susan, PA (Cantwell)
Shelgosh, Donna, PA (Clare)
Shreeves, Diane, NJ (Reiley)
Smith, Hope, PA (McCann)
Smith, Margaret, PA
Steinhagen Theresa, NJ (Grace)
Stockton, Janet, NJ (Ludy)
Strick, Sandra (Larimer)
Styslinger, Jean
Taylor, Patricia, PA
Thomas, Mary, NH (Boyd)
Tomlinson, Mary, MD (Seckinger)
Verdeur, Michele, PA
Wiggins, Susan, PA

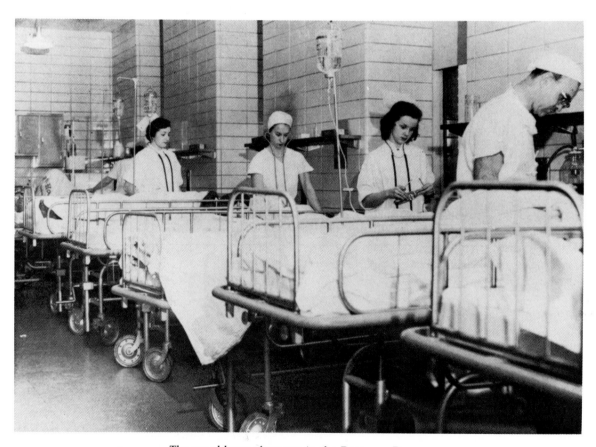

The usual busy afternoon in the Recovery Room

The move into the Health Sciences Center (Edison Building) raised the morale of the School's Asministration Staff and Faculty. It provided spacious offices and ample classrooms (Fig. 72). This vacated three previously occupied floors in the Curtis Building. Students from other programs in the University were now occupying the Martin Residence which on July 1 was transferred to the supervison of the Director of Auxiliary Services of Thomas Jefferson University.

At the 82nd Commencement for the School of Nursing on June 21, 85 students graduated. This brought the total number of graduates to 4,572.

Fig. 72.   Anthony J. Triolo, Ph.D. Department of Pharmacology, teaching student nurses.

CLASS OF 1975

Barraclough, Dale, NJ (Beloff)
Bartoszek, Maryanne, CT
Bauer, Nancy, PA (Schmoyer)
Bertram, Denise, PA (Capaldi)
Bingaman, Linda, PA (Napieralski)
Blubaugh, Diane, WA
Bowes, Mary, IL (Fabrizio)

Boyle, Elizabeth, NJ (Adomanis)
Byrne, Donna, PA (Catrino)
Carberry, Lynda, PA (Kuhar)
Casper, Maria, PA (Whalen)
Christopher, Gloria, GA (Downey)
Costello, Eleanor, VA (Anderson)
Cox, Florence, CA (Zapolski)

Craven, Carol, NJ (Baker)
D'Angelo, Dorothy, VA
Davis, Helen, NJ
Deame, Debra
Di Nardo, Loretta, PA
Dick, Patricia, NJ (Walsh)
Dougherty, Carol Ann, PA (Mashouf)
Dugan, Jane, PA (Vaccaro)
Ellis, Patricia, PA (Pagano)
Ettenger, Joyce, PA (Deffendach)
Ferraro, Judith, NJ (Ryan)
Fitzgerald, Mary, PA (Madaline)
Freiling, Kathleen, PA
Friedman, Debra, MD (Iwanczuk)
Gaymon, Bonnie, GA (Morris)
Gaynor, Kathleen, PA (Keough)
George, Cynthia, PA (Boyle)
Glavey, Catherine, NJ (Dowhy)
Grimmie, Carole, NJ (Gargano)
Hamilton, Barbara, NH (Fox)
Hamlett, Debra, NJ (Reed)
Harrison, Amy, VA
Howell, Mary, DE (Wendel)
Husband, Jane, PA (Mueller)
Johnston, Frances, PA
Keers, Ruth, PA (Eanes)
Kiersnowski, Cynthia, NM
King, Regina, PA (Klinger)
Klekotka, Nancy, PA (Picarello)
Lenhardt, Anne, IL (Cadez)
Lynn, Sherrie, AK (Seward)
Maguire, Marian, PA (Mee)
Margolin, Barbara (Grunes)
Marple, Deborah, PA (O'Connor)
Matthews, June, KY (DeMoya)

McCullough, Susanne, IN (Hoffman)
McLauglin, Joanne (Fornadel)
Moore, Jane, NJ (Glinka)
Mueller, Cheryl, PA (Friedman)
Nimmer, Lee (Smyth)
O'Brien, Theresa, PA (Funt)
Orr, Sue, NJ (Raup)
Owens, Linda, PA (Bicich)
Palczewski, Joyce, PA
Phillips, Beth, PA
Phillips, Judith, NJ (Vadurro)
Plumly, Sarah (Doto)
Ranieri, Donna, PA (Ambrogi)
Reustle, Mary, PA (Eddis)
Rice, Eileen, PA (Pirolli)
Riggin, Susan, DE
Roberts, Ethel, PA (Corley)
Scanlon, Therese, PA (Richmond)
Schmidt, Anna, PA
Scott, Barbara, PA
Scott, Brenda, CA (Goldberg)
Scott, Germaine, TN (George)
Skwarek, Eileen, PA
Smith, Dava (Carlson)
Smith, Deborah, DE (Nelms)
Snyderman, Shelley, PA
Solomon, Rebecca, PA (Brown)
Spohrer, Anne, PA (Woods)
Stockman, Nora, PA (Jens)
Sumner, Sara, PA
Timm, Margaret, PA (Mainwaring)
Triolo, Maria, DE (Glavey)
Tuno, Patricia, UT (Yenchick)
Watters, Honor, PA
Webb, Barbara, PA (Folger)
Worrall, Jill, CA

The physician, the patient, the medicine, and the attendants (nurses) are the four essential factors of a course of medical treatment.

Sushruta (Fifth Century B.C.)

In this year the name of the Alumnae Association was changed to Alumni Association.

An Alumni Student Recognition award of $300 was established to be given to a Junior Student for the highest academic rank, including didactic and clinical experience.

This Bicentennial year was observed at Jefferson with a lecture entitled "Mr. Jefferson and Dr. Dunglison". It took place April 14, the day after Jefferson's actual birthdate. A colonial style reception followed.

The Winged Ox Column honoring 50 world-renowned physicians, including five from Jefferson, was erected adjacent to Orlowitz Hall. Barringer Residence Hall (Fig. 73) opened this year.

Commencement exercises were held June 12 at the Sheraton Hotel for 96 graduates. Dr. Robert I. Wise, Chairman of the Department of Medicine, delivered the address.

CLASS OF 1976

Ankenbrand, Kathryne, PA (Cochlin)
Arnold, Betty, NJ (Lees)
Baldino, Denise (Kelly)
Bankert, Karen

Bille, Sherrie, NJ
Blankemeyer, Anne, PA (McDermott)
Boehly, Cheryl, NJ
Bonder, Susan, PA (Battagliese)

Fig. 73.   Barringer Residence Hall (1976).

Bowler, Patricia, MA
Burke, Joanne, PA (Miccolis)
Carter, Anita, RI (Campbell)
Caruso, Joan, NJ
Critzer, Linda
Davis, Elizabeth
Deitz, Cynthia
Denham, Margaret
Dudek, Carolyn, PA (Leach)
Dugan, Mary, PA (Jordan)
Edger, Nancy
Farley, Joanne, PA
Fink, Cynthia, NV (Runion)
Garrity, Anne, CA (Kuzma)
Getzow, Ellen
Giordano, Theo
Grailey, Dorothy, PA (Medon)
Guida, Karen, PA (Shauger)
Hansell, Eleanor, PA (Cunningham)
Harper, Anne, NJ (Galdo)
Healy, Eileen, PA (Garrity)
Hegarty, Marianne, NJ (Alexander)
Heintz, Barbara (Raymond)
Hills, Kathie, PA (Ida)
Hoesch, Stephanie, GA (Ferguson)
Holliday, Sara, PA (Reese)
Holohan, Elizabeth, NJ (Michael)
Homel, Teresa, UT
Ishuin, Aileen, PA (MacMillan)
Iwasko, Joanne, NJ (Cava)
Jordan, Karen, PA
Keller, Mary, MD (Mitchell)
Kobrynski, Donna, PA (Molyneaux)
Kunkle, Judith, PA
Lenzi, Laura (Lipiccki)
Lyons, Paula, MA (Lichtenstein)
Malloy, Anna, PA (Quinn)
Mancini, Donita, NJ
Marion, Cecelia, NJ (Ellis)

Marriott, Sue, CA (Sauzet-Parini)
May, Leslie, PA (Tahsler)
McAveney, Maureen, PA
McClintic, Joanne, PA
McGrath, Colleen, PA (Kraus)
McLeer, Rosemary, AK (Fennerty)
Mickle, Linda, PA
Mikulski, Karen (Fanelli)
Morrow, Carol (McGair)
Munda, Kathleen, PA (McNamara)
Nickel, Barbara, PA
Nufrio, Susan (Bodman)
O'Neill, Patricia, MN (Trachte)
Orsine, Donna, CT (Simone)
Osborne, Margaret, PA (Montgomery)
Ott, Judith, CA
Parks, Nancy, NJ
Patterson, Karen, PA (Taylor)
Pierce, Barbara, PA
Polesinski, Christine
Preihs, Patricia, NJ
Quigley, Barbara
Richmond, Janice, PA (Malloy)
Schmidt, Claudia, NJ (Dimond)
Sheridan, Susanne, NJ (Starano)
Simpson, Ruth, PA (Snyder)
Snyder, David, PA
Souders, Betsy, PA (Machalette)
Sprague, Valerie, NJ (Reso)
Sutton, Deborah (Allen)
Thomas, Marie (Kmonicek)
Thompson, Linda, PA (Torrens)
Till, Donna, NJ
Tingley, Susan
Tiver, Veronica, PA (Metkus)
Tomlinson, Suzanne, NJ (Kunis)
Trzaska, Linda, NJ (Courant)
Waselus, Andrea, PA (Kaye)
Wheeler, Wendy, MA (Landolfi)

The practice of medicine is an art, not a trade; a calling, not a business; a calling in which your heart will be exercised equally with your head. Often the best part of your work will have nothing to do with potions and powders, but with the exercise of an influence of the strong upon the weak, of the righteous upon the wicked, of the wise upon the foolish.

William Osler (1849–1919)

A major administrative event occurred on August 1 with the arrival of Lewis W. Bluemle, Jr. M.D. as Jefferson's second President of the University (Fig. 74). At this time there were three Nursing School programs, - baccalaureate, diploma and practical, each with its own faculty, facilities and resources. He suggested a unified teaching program fashioned after that of medical education, one school with one administrative structure, one faculty, and one student body, but with a variety of education tracks commensurate with the interests and needs of the students.

The 84th commencement took place on June 21 at the Sheraton Ballroom with 88 students in the graduating class. The Address was delivered by Dr. John W. Goldschmidt, former Dean of Jefferson's College of Allied Health Sciences. In this year Marten M. Kernis, Ph.D. became the new Dean.

CLASS OF 1977

Bachman, Barbara, PA (Symons)
Beck, Betty, PA (Hedges)
Bonnacorsi, Donna, NJ (McKernan)
Brady, Maureen, PA (Fox)
Brooks, Harris, PA
Brown, Cynthia, PA (Panasuk)
Callum, Diane, PA (Buza)
Cameron, Jeffrey
Capritti, Maryann, NJ
Carson, Ann, PA (Bono)
Cheesman, Karen, NJ
Chilandese, Karen, NJ (D'Alonzo)
Cooney, Eileen, PA
Donovan, Nancy, NJ (Cohen)
Doyle, Patricia, PA
Dupont, Janeane, PA (Sloane)
Ficca, Luisa
Fiderer, Paula, PA (Jasionowski)
Fowler, Joan, CA (Book)
Frelond, Joan, PA (Sato)
Gallagher, Mary, PA
Gallagher, Sondra, PA
Gallagher, Susan, PA
Gibney, Laurie
Gloeckler, Doris, PA (DeBias)
Gudknecht, Karen, NJ (Smith)
Haynes, Joy, PA (Bailey)
Hood, Lisa, PA
Kampmeier, Margaret, PA (Sucsy)
Kazokas, Diane, PA
Keiser, Miriam, NC (Michael)
Kline, Cheryl, PA
Kobryn, Nina, PA
Kruszewski, Mary, NJ

Fig. 74. Lewis W. Bluemle, Jr., M.D., second President of Thomas Jefferson University (1977-90).

Lanahan, Susan, NJ (Bowers)
Landherr, Patricia, PA (Thalheimer)
Lasure, Roxanne, PA
Leedom, Barbara, PA (Russ)
Lewis, Nancy, PA (Delozier)
Lomazoff, Arlene, PA
Lotter, Linda, PA (Romano)
Lydon, Jacqueline, PA (Halgash)
Mahon, Julia, NJ
Maro, Patricia, NJ (Sherf)
Martin, Holly (Pistone)
Matthews, Deborah, NJ (Stenton)
Matz, Rae, NJ (Fierro)
Maurer, Luciann, PA (Drinkwater)
Mayne, Terry, GA (Colella)
McCann, Donna, PA
McClellan, Judith, IA (Delucca)
McColgan, Anne, PA (Curry)
McDonald, Clare, NJ (Poplaski)
McFarland, Wendy, PA (Hinsey)
Metzger, Therese, PA
Mirecki, Karen, PA (Webster)
Moretto, Maria
Mulligan, Karen, PA (Robnett)
Mulnick, Debra
Nyce, Deborah, PA (Flanagan)
O'Keefe, Eileen, OH (West)

O'Neill, Beverly, PA (Ashkenase)
Pryor, Patricia, PA
Ribaric, Darlene, PA (Rosendale)
Richard, Karen, PA (Emerle)
Roantree, Eileen, PA
Roberts, Karen, PA (Armstrong)
Rose, Sari, OH (Krafft)
Sawyer, Deborah
Schjavland, Elena, PA
Serbun, Nancy, NC (Cregan)
Sheaffer, Ruth, PA (Lind)
Sheedy, Mary, PA
Sitvarin, Harriet
Smith, Nancy, IL (Clayton)
Solimine, Vera, PA
Spitalniak, Christine
Stevens, Kathleen, DE
Stewart, Susan, PA
Strauss, Mindy, PA
Thompson, Patricia, NJ (Jenkins)
Tursi, Patricia, NJ (Quinn)
Veltry, Josephine (Zapf)
Weisback, Arleen, PA (Black)
Weisner, Patricia
Winnemore, Barbara
Wuebber, Anke, PA (Delone)
Zebrowski, Bonnie

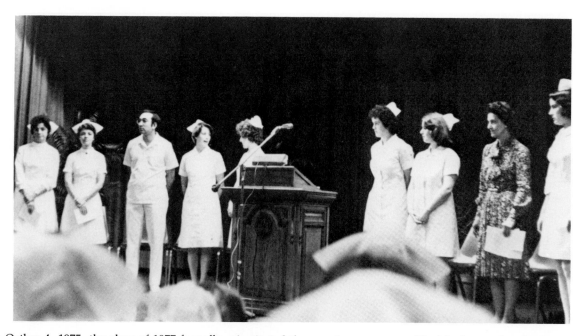

On Octber 4, 1975, the class of 1977 formally reinstituted the capping ceremony. We felt the need to honor our cap because to us it symbolized a life-long dream: to be a Jefferson nurse. Our cap represents a code of honor, pride, and integrity that we strive to maintain throughout our career. Therefore, we unanimously decided to restore this traditional ceremony, so that future nurses could witness this spirit.

The new Thomas Jefferson University Hospital opened in this year (Fig. 75). In providing a single standard of care it eliminated the old hospital wards and the clinics in the Curtis Building. The specialized intensive care units required a more sophisticated level of nursing care.

Harriet H. Werley ('41), Ph.D. received the Alumni Achievement Award of the College of Allied Health Sciences (Fig. 76).

The graduates numbered 84 this year.

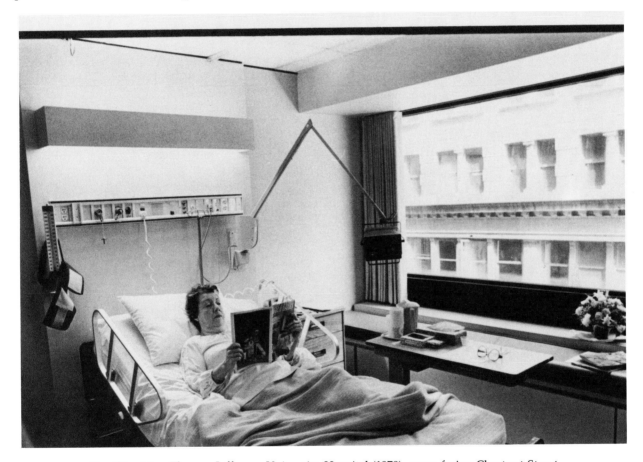

Fig. 75.   New Thomas Jefferson University Hospital (1978), room facing Chestnut Street.

CLASS OF 1978

Aleski, Patricia, NJ
Aspinwall, Linda, PA (Borromeo)
Barboun, Judith, NJ
Bouyer, Barbara (Cornele)
Boyle, Carole, PA (Lynch)
Bradshaw, Carolyn, PA
Budnicki, Barbara, PA
Burrell, Susan, PA (Sawula)

Cammoroto, Joseph
Cohen, Joyce
Conly, Doris, PA (Green)
DiPietro, Lorraine, PA
Eigenbrot, Margaret
Falvey, Mary, NJ
Foltz, Rebecca, NJ (Williams)
Forcina, Linda

Franzone, Theresa, MD (Snell)
Garbus, Suzanne
Goertzen, Jean, PA (Evans)
Gumann, Faith, OH (Collins)
Halpin, Doroth, PA
Healy, Theresa, NJ (Dunford)
Heinold, Linda, PA (Muelenaer)
Hitchens, John, MD
Hojnowski, Lynne, NJ (Vanore)
Holliday, Janet, CT (Reed)
Hubbs, Catherine (Levesque)
Insogna, Regina, NJ (Procopio)
Jenks, Luanne, PA
Jones, Deborah, NH
Kaercher, Ann, PA (Miller)
Keating, Teresa, PA (Sandman)
Kopenhaver, Luann, PA (Vanaman)
Kuser, Linda, NJ
LaFerriere, Cecilia, NJ
Levan, Georgann, PA (Geiser)
Locke, Teresa, PA
Looby, Colleen, PA

Mallee, Maryann, TX (Bowman)
Marvel, Rosemary, PA
Mayo, Deborah, NJ
McChesney, Joni, NJ
McCloskey, Christine
McCullough, Lorraine, NJ (MacFeeters)
McGrenra, Barbara, CA (Doerr)
McKernan, Regina, PA
Meyle, Hedy, PA (DiCola)
Miller, Carol, NJ (Muller)
Miller, Gayle
Minahan, Mary, PA
Muller, Barbara, PA (Gavin)
Murtha, Kathleen, CA (Cardenas)
O'Boyle, Colleen, DE (Smith)
O'Brien, Marjorie
O'Brien, Sharon, VA (Yuras)
Parr, Linda, MD (Southwick)
Patrick, Eileen, PA (Walsh)
Patterson, Janet, NJ (Huplits)
Pfeiffer, Lisa, PA (Parry)
Riesdorph, Heidi, PA (Wright)
Rittle, Jannifer, PA (Cayless)
Rocchio, Janet, PA
Rodden, Ann, PA (Elkind)
Rosen, Sandra, PA (Shlifer)
Rothman, Andrea (Mann)
Sacks, Jeanette, NJ (Kaufman)
Schade, Kathleen, PA (Toomey)
Schwartz, Sheryl, NJ
Scott, Diane, NJ (Ross)
Simmons, Patricia, PA
Spinnraker, Joan, PA
Stasche, Jan, AL (Vanderveer)
Stewart, Rosemarie, PA
Stock, Joanne, WA (Petrelli)
Thompson, Jennifer, PA
Toth, Joanne, PA
Tripple, Kathleen, NC (Holl)
Venzie, Bette, NJ (Reese)
Ward, Mary, IN (Collingwood)
Warden, Diane, PA (Carugno)
Waters, Kathleen, PA (Blake)
Weatherley, Ernest
Wilkinson, Leslie, PA (Stickley)
Wolbert, Joan, NJ (Reimer)

Fig. 76. Harriet H. Werley ('41), Ph.D., receives the Alumni Achievement Award from Drs. Sweeney, Bluemle and Abrams (1978).

~ 1979 ~

The painful acknowledgement that the Diploma School of Nursing had to be phased out was officially stated by Miss Doris Bowman, its Director, in a letter of April 19, to Dr. Abrams, Dean of Allied Health. This indicated that the students admitted this year would be in the last graduating class of the Diploma School. Although many alumni were saddened by this decision, the faculty and administration were in agreement that it was in the best interests of the institution.

Perma Ehrhart (Davis) of the class of 1941 became Alumni President this year and served until 1982 (Fig. 77). Having been connected with the School of Nursing as an instructor for many years, her recent assignment included supervising the health care of the student nurses.

There were 89 graduates this year.

CLASS OF 1979

Alcoy, Kathy, NJ
Anderson, Deborah, PA (Johnson)
Artis, Mary
Barut, Theresa, PA
Baxter, Cynthia, PA (Barrett)
Bellace, Diane, OH (Goll)
Berk, Donna, NJ
Bradbury, Barbara, PA (Stewart)
Brian, Cheryl, SC
Buggy, Christine, NJ (Gross)
Callahan, Donna, PA (Stabler)
Camillo, Cheryl, PA
Cassel, Stacey (Busch)
Cavuto, Judith, NJ
Cooley, Mary, PA
Corn, Mindy
Datz, Mary, MD (Moss)
Devine, Kelly, PA (Hollander)
DiCristofaro, Judy, PA
Dietzler, Maureen (Fitzgerald)
Eltonhead, Karen, PA (Policare)
Evonishon, Debra
Finkelman, Anita, PA (Devlin)
Flynn, Robin, FL (Butto)
Folcarelli, Mary, NJ
Foley, Diane (Osborne)
Freidel, Joyce, PA
Frost, Deborah, NJ (Horowitz)
Ghegan, Kathleen, NJ (D'Alessandro)
Goldberg, Laurel, PA (Gutter)
Grimes, Cherly, PA (Allen)
Harkins, Mary, DE (Lack)
Harle, Alison, TX (Coombs)
Harris, Rebecca, NJ
Hollander, Karen, PA (Bernardini)

Fig. 77. Perma Erhart (Davis), Class of '41, Alumni President (1979-82).

Humphreville, Lynda, NJ (Leisner)
Johnston, Marline, PA
Keegan, Lisa, PA (Sarcewicz)
Kelley, Kathleen, PA
Kresge, Kathleen, WA (Hopkins)
Krol, Jane, PA
Langley, Michelle, PA (Kopicki)
Leisch, Alice, PA (Guarino)
Lyman, Debra
Macelis, Barbara, NJ
Maedel, Linda, NJ (Breve)
McAndrew, Kathleen, NJ (Corse)
McClure, Geraldine, PA (Derkorian)
McGlynn, Theresa, DE (Rupp)
McGrory, Joyce, NJ
Meyle, Lisa, PA
Michaux, Holly, MD (Enders)
Miller, Barbara, PA
Miller, Sharon, PA (Chilton)
Morris, Annamarie, PA (Brown)
Mote, Rhonda (Pierce)
Mullen, Joan
Murphy, Jacqueline
Murray, Beth, PA
O'Connor, Peggy, NJ
O'Donnell, Susan, MN (Hagan)

Peller, Cynthia, PA
Portner, Andrea
Robinson, Linda, NJ
Rose, Janine Russo, Carmen, NJ
Sakosky, Marie, PA
Samuel, Deborah, NJ (Timpano)
Sandell, Kathryn, PA
Sandler, Hope, PA
Schatz, Carol, PA
Schlotterer, Susan, PA
Schwarz, Teresa, FL
Shestakov, Katherine, PA
Sloss, Annamarie, PA (Moritz)
Smith, Sandra, NJ (Scrofani)
Smith, Sharon, NJ
Stair, Helene, NJ
Stites, Terry, NJ (Marren)
Stout, Catherine, PA (Ishman)
Swenk, Diane
Tegethoff, Deborah, NJ
Thomas, Marline, PA (Johnston)
Wagner, Donna, CA
Weiss, Debra (Nesenberg)
Wilson, Sandra, NJ
Wilson, Susan, NJ (Peacock)
Wolvin, Diane, NJ (Hinkel)
Yerardi, Diane, NJ (Woodford)

Miss Patricia McBride, Class Advisor

This class of 1979 would like to extend our genuine appreciation to Patricia McBride, our class advisor. An advisor is defined as someone who gives counsel. We feel that Miss McBride gave us more than advice. She gave willingly of herself to each of us. She was always available to offer support, give encouragement or just to smile and say hello. All of us have benefitted from her ever present support of our class in all our endeavors. We hope to fulfill all her expectations of us.

Commencement was held on June 4 in the Ballroom of the Benjamin Franklin Hotel. Seventy-four students received the diploma and school pin. The portrait of Doris E. Bowman ('42), Director of the School, was unveiled during the ceremonies and later displayed in the Scott Memorial Library (Fig. 78).

Fig. 78.   Doris E. Bowman ('42) at her portrait presentation (1980).

CLASS OF 1980

Albrecht, Susan, PA (Curcio)
Barry, Susan, PA
Bergdoll, Susan, NJ
Borgard, Beth (Bryson)
Brady, Mary, PA (Stephany)
Brennan, Nadine, PA
Bundens, Jeanne, NJ (Rossiter)
Burkeitt, Lisa, NJ (Cangemi)
Burns, Valerie, NJ (DiBartolo)
Collick, Rhoda

Crew, Linda (Semple)
Curcio, Ann, PA
Dance, Constance
Duall, Kathleen, NJ
Dwyer, Patricia, PA (Cappello)
Engel, Barbara, NJ (Kenney)
Fenyus, Margot, PA
Force, Marci, NJ (Green)
Gaughan, Michele, PA
Gillen, Katherine, CT (Leslie)

Golomb, Cynthia
Gramata, Bernadine, PA
Harris, Lea, PA
Hartman, Patricia, NJ (Reilly)
Hillman, Marijo, NJ
Hoshino, Susanne, MD
Hughes, Kathleen, NJ
Katz, Shari, PA (Ellenbogen)
Kennedy, Stacey
Kenney, Susan
Kloss, Donna, VA (Casey)
Kobulsky, Kathleen, PA
Lindenmuth, Donna, PA (Cowhey)
Littlefield, Nancy
Lucas, Tamra, PA (Goldschmidt)
Martens, Katherine, NJ (Schultz)
Maslofsky, Ursula, NJ
Maxwell, Marianne, NJ (Ostrow)
McGee, Mary, NJ
McGrattan, Gail, NJ
McNeil, Carol, PA (Pilla)
Miller, Katherine, PA (Silver)
Mock, Patricia, PA (Clark)
Mood, Gloria, PA (Brumbaugh)
Mullaney, Joanne
Mullen, Margaret, PA (Fortino)
Mullen, Maryann, NJ (Ragone)

Nowak, Linda, NJ
O'Brien, Kathleen, NJ (Shindle)
O'Malley, Anne, NJ (Delengowski)
Olesiewicz, Dianne, NJ (Yasik)
Parisi, Valerie, PA
Perry, Abbey, PA
Petit, Ann, NC (Fariss)
Ravenstahl, Str. Bernadette, PA
Retay, Clare, PA (Ebersole)
Roberts, Donna, NJ
Robinson, Jessica, MD (Ross)
Scheidegg, Karen
Scheidt, Sara, PA
Schieffer, Debra, NJ (Beveridge)
Schreiber, Deborah, PA
Sharpe, Kristen, NJ (Haag)
Strain, James
Sullivan, Susan, PA
Thompson, Stephen Jr., PA
Tragessor, Deborah, NJ (Sharpe)
Troutman, Judith, PA
Urevick, Denise, NJ
Utke, Suzanne
Virelli, Donna, PA
Weippert, Pamela, PA (Goldenberg)
Whelpley, Carole, SC (Foley)
Zampino, Victoria, NJ

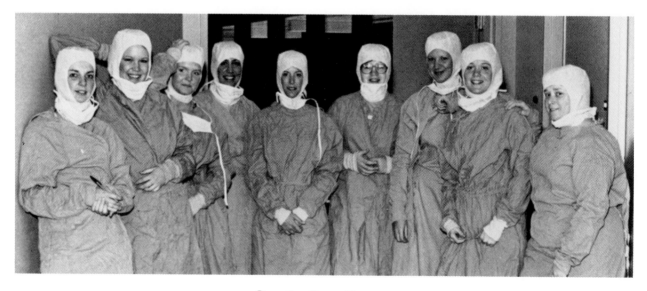

Operating Room Nurses.

One of the projects relating to phasing out of the Diploma School was the converting of previous graduate nurse records to a more compact and efficient microfiche system compatible with that of the College of Allied Health Sciences. This would involve transfer of over 5,000 graduate records into the office of the Registrar of the College of Allied Health Sciences.

At the request of the graduating class, Miss Patricia Zarella ('51) R.N., B.S.N., delivered the Commencement address for the 59 graduates Fig, 79).

Fig. 79.   Graduating Class (1980).

Babins, Irene, MD (Repka)
Bader, Debra, PA
Bonnett, Kimberly, PA (Boyce)
Boylan, Martha, NJ
Bradley, Suzanne, NC
Bressi, Lisa, NJ (Auletta)
Browne, Kathleen, PA (Rodriguez)
Budnick, Karen, PA (Troppman)

Carley, Kathleen
Cooney, Cecilia, PA
Crane, Francine, PA
Donohue, Kathleen
Edick, Raymond, PA
Engel, Joanne, VA (Robinson)
Fisher, Susan
Focht, Barbara, NJ (Hochuli)

Franchetti, Rose, PA (Stapleton)
Gallagher, Nancy, NJ (Smith)
Gallo, Karen, PA
Gordon, Linda, PA (Tucker)
Graham, Debra, PA (McGarry)
Grantham, Linda, OR
Grzywacz, Karen
Hardy, Kimberlin
Hluchy, Gay, NJ
Houghton, Denise, PA
Hoyt, Susan, PA
Kelly, Lisa, PA (Sakser)
Koch, Terri, PA (Martin)
Koehl, Donna
Kopistansky, Christine, PA
Lee, Leisa, PA (Krespan)
Lindenmuth, Patricia, PA (Matlack)
Loux, Melody, PA
Marcolina, Lynn, PA
Marcussen, Kristi, PA
Mihalanas, Angela, PA (Siliani)

Morris, Pamela, PA
Morrow, Paul
Moyer, Suzanna
Pantalone, Marla, DE (Carpenter)
Paul, Laurie, PA (Strassman)
Power, Elizabeth, PA
Pritts, Nancy (Rose)
Ritaldato, Angela (Dages)
Rubin, Debra
Santoro, J., NJ (Stone)
Schmidt, Joanne
Schuster, Madonna
Shaffer, Lori (Wehner)
Sheaffer, Susan, CA (Schwab)
Souder, Sandra (Sisk)
Spaeth, Sylvia, PA (Brayton)
Tichian, Tamara, NJ (Magenta)
Tregear, Kathleen, TX
Welsh, Melinda (Hardy)
White, Rebecca White, Sara, PA
Zlotnik, Barbara

Doris E. Bowman, R.N., M.S.Ed.
Director, School of Nursing

Margaret C. McClean, R.D., M.S.
Assistant Director

Margaret J. MacKenzie, R.N., M.S.
Guidance Counselor

Eloise Hippensteel, R.N., M.S.N.
Asst. Director-Curriculum

During the previous three-year phase-out of the School of Nursing, a loyal Faculty had maintained the same standards of excellence that had characterized the school since its founding in 1891. The last Commencement was held on June 10, at which time the 38 graduates marched under the traditional arch of Roses (Fig. 80).

The last of 5,087 graduates to receive the diploma and pin was Linda M. Yarnall (Fig. 81).

She received the Women's Board Prize for demonstrating the greatest versatility and cooperation in nursing care.

The Address was delivered by Kathleen A. Carlson, R.N. ('68), Assistant Executive Director, Pennsylvania Nurses Association (Fig. 82).

Commitment to Excellence (1982) by Andre W. Shearer chronicled the 91-history of the School.

Fig. 80.   Last walk through the Arch of Roses (Graduation, 1982).

Barna, Karen
Carmody, Suzanne
Carter, Deborah (Roberts)
Cava, Deborah (Frye)
Chialastri, David, PA
Comerford, Dawn, NJ (Kasper)
Dalgliesh, Susan (Keeley)
Farrell, Jacqueline, PA (Jones)
Fink, Theresa, PA (Markert)
Flynn, Patricia, PA (Corey)
Heim, Theresa, NC (Cook)
Heinick, Maryann
Holohan, Ellen
Howie, Anne, PA (Mercede)
Jenkins, Patricia, PA (Barnard)
Kominsky, Barbara, NJ (Leone)
Krebs, Sandra, PA (D'Amelio)
Linardo, Jane, NJ (McClory)
Mayer, Christina

McCarthy, Cheryl, NJ (Furman)
McGarrigle, Theresa, PA (Healy)
Meisner, Carol (Greene)
Mengel, Marie, PA (Mackenzie)
Molineaux, Cheryl (Rahilly)
O'Kane, Margaret, NJ (DeNicola)
Peterson, Catherine, NJ
Pollock, Francine, PA (Miller)
Ramsey, Nona
Santangelo, Kathleen
Solecki, Susan, PA
Stanton, Duane
Stern, Christine
Sylvester, Theresa, PA
Tanner, Karen, MA (Frick)
Waldron, Marie, NC (Hopkins)
Wolf, Lisa, PA (Turco)
Woods, Katherine, NJ (Cava)
Yarnall, Linda, PA (Sohanic)

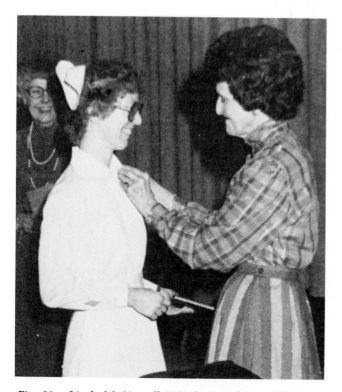

Fig. 81. Linda M. Yarnall ('82), last graduate of Diploma School.

Fig. 82. Kathleen A. Carlson ('68), R.N. delivered the final Commencement Address (1982).

~ A ~

Abbott, Judith Jean, 1965
Abel, Lucy E., 1943
Abele, Dianne Katherine, 1963
Achenbach, Helen Phoebe, 1957
Acheson, Viola, 1927
Adams, Dora, 1932
Adams, Emily May, 1963
Adams, Judith Anne, 1972
Adams, Kathleen Beatrice, 1951
Adams, Kathryn S., 1937
Adams, Martha, 1914
Adams, Ruth S., 1934
Aikens, Bessie, 1896
Ainsworth, Sara L., 1935
Akers, Martha C., 1926
Akers, Mary A., 1930
Albert, Ann Pauline, 1950
Albert, Ruth Helen, 1946
Albrecht, Susan Evelyn, 1980
Albright, Mary E., 1925
Albright, Mary Eileen, 1948
Albright, Nancy, 1953
Alcoy, Kathy Lee, 1979
Alder, Willie L., 1931
Alderfer, Geneva Inez, 1954
Aldersley, Mary Erica, 1973
Aleski, Patricia Ann, 1978
Alexander, Anne, 1942
Alexander, Ida M., 1919
Alexander, Mary Ella, 1947
Aliantro, Barbara Louise, 1957
Allen, Jean Lindsay, 1963
Allen, Judith Carole, 1966
Allen, Kathleen Rae, 1966
Allen, Mary, 1907
Allen, Mattie, 1915
Allison, Mae Elizabeth, 1946
Allison, Virginia, 1904
Alston, Mary Louise, 1929
Alwine, Virginia E., 1944
Amabile, Jean Marie, 1967
Ambrose, Marlene Mary, 1956
Ambrose, Natalie K., 1956
Ammarell, Eileen Louise, 1972
Ammerman, Reba E., 1941
Ammons, Gail Joan, 1965
Amorose, Doris Dolores, 1955
Anderson, Deborah Jean, 1979
Anderson, Elaine Faithe, 1946
Anderson, Louise Marie, 1971
Anderson, Mary Ann, 1952

Anderson, Mary Jane, 1941
Anderson, Twila Beatrice, 1950
Anderson, Velma G., 1936
Andrews, Alma I., 1932
Angelo, Anne Louise, 1957
Angelo, Rose Marie, 1954
Angert, Helen Marie, 1956
Angle, Nell, 1909
Anglim, Rosemary, 1968
Angwin, Lillian, 1928
Ankenbrand, Kathryne Margaret, 1976
Anstine, Dorcas R., 1931
Antes, Alvirda, 1910
Antes, Margaret S., 1949
Anthony, Blanche M., 1926
Appell, Patricia, 1971
Applebaum, Sydney Marilyn, 1955
Archer, Mary Joanne, 1948
Ardos, Martha Anne, 1963
Arena, Kim Veronica, 1973
Armitage, Esther D., 1940
Armstrong, Gertrude, 1911
Armstrong, Margaret O., 1935
Armstrong, Marie, 1969
Armstrong, Mary, 1893
Arnold, Betty Lynn, 1976
Arnold, Eileen Johanna, 1968
Arnold, Gladys N., 1932
Arnold, Janet Lynne, 1962
Arnold, Marjorie E., 1956
Arnold, Stephanie Eleanor, 1961
Arthur, Elizabeth J., 1921
Artis, Mary Catherine, 1979
Artley, Mary, 1922
Artman, Ethel M., 1934
Aschenbach, Gretchen Alta, 1957
Ashby, Christine, 1967
Aspinwall, Linda Lee, 1978
Aubrey, Rosemary, 1967
Auerbach, Denise Lynn, 1972
Aufferman, Carole Orpah, 1962
Augustine, LaVerne Rosalie, 1949
Aukerman, Catherine Harriet, 1973
Auman, Linda, 1958
Aumiller, Mildred L., 1934
Austin, Hazel E., 1927
Avery, Virginia S., 1930
Axelson, Roanne Ingrid, 1964
Ayres, Nancy Welfer, 1966

~ B ~

Baals, Karen Jane, 1973
Babins, Irene Faye, 1981

Bachers, Arlene Weaver, 1959
Bachman, Barbara Ann, 1977
Bader, Debra Ann, 1981
Badorf, Florence L., 1929
Badorf, Myra, 1917
Baer, C. Thelma, 1929
Baer, Jacqueline Kay, 1946
Baginski, Bertha J., 1944
Bahner, Emma M., 1931
Bailey, Barbara Ann, 1948
Bailey, Carol Ann, 1964
Baird, Dorothy A., 1956
Baird, Ledjie Roth, 1967
Baird, Ruth E., 1935
Baker, Cora, 1910
Baker, Frances A., 1927
Baker, Katherine, 1898
Baker, Lillian S., 1942
Baker, Marguerite Alice, 1946
Baker, Myrtle, 1910
Bakkelid, Johanna, 1924
Balavage, Teresa E., 1930
Baldino, Denise, 1976
Baldwin, Marjorie H., 1943
Ball, Janet Elaine, 1968
Ball, Marjorie Maud, 1949
Balmer, Joanne Marie, 1967
Baloga, Marie L., 1947
Bankert, Karen Lynn, 1976
Banks, Lucy Emma, 1947
Banks, Mary Sue, 1940
Baran, Ellen Carolyn, 1950
Barbee, Annette Theresa, 1967
Barboun, Judith Elizabeth, 1978
Barbour, Josephine C., 1941
Barbour, Linda Mae, 1969
Barcalow, Mary, 1910
Barcelou, Carol Ann, 1963
Barclay, Mary Elizabeth, 1951
Barclay, Suzanne Johnston, 1966
Bardfeld, Alice Rebecca, 1969
Bardo, Grace M., 1936
Bareuther, June Bertha, 1951
Barfield, Eileen Edythe, 1972
Bargar, Margery E., 1928
Barlieb, Pearl Virginia, 1958
Barna, Karen Anne, 1982
Barner, Ann Kay, 1947
Barnett, Marguerite, 1914
Barnhart, Bernice, 1925
Barnum, Karen Elizabeth, 1968
Barraclough, Dale Ann, 1975

Borgard, Beth Louise, 1980
Borowski, Theophilia A. T., 1938
Borrell, Barbara Joan, 1961
Bortner, Margaret Elizabeth, 1948
Boschert, Alice J., 1942
Bostic, India, 1919
Botdorf, Esther, 1923
Botz, Mildred M., 1930
Bouregy, Pamela Lynn, 1973
Bouyer, Barbara, 1978
Bowen, Barbara Ann, 1953
Bowen, Joan Elsie, 1962
Bowen, Lillian E., 1917
Bowen, Ruth B., 1910
Bower, Sara Brook, 1893
Bowers, Marion E., 1928
Bowers, Mary Catherine, 1946
Bowes, Mary Josephine, 1975
Bowlby, Alice M., 1930
Bowler, Patricia Anne, 1976
Bowman, Doris E., 1942
Bowman, Mary Alice, 1934
Bowmaster, Edna O., 1943
Bowmaster, Isaphine A., 1934
Bowser, Mary Esther, 1923
Boyd, Barbara Anne, 1953
Boyd, Denise Anne, 1974
Boyd, Elsa V., 1938
Boyer, Amanda, 1911
Boyer, Arlene Romaine, 1959
Boyer, Ellen Kay, 1972
Boyer, Esther, 1899
Boyer, Evelyn G., 1929
Boyer, Sally Elizabeth, 1962
Boyeronus, Sharon Stephanie, 1965
Boyeronus, Susan, 1970
Boylan, Martha, 1981
Boyle, Carole, 1978
Boyle, Catherine M., 1943
Boyle, Debora Kay, 1974
Boyle, Elizabeth, 1975
Boyle, Ellen, 1962
Boyle, Theresa Marie, 1973
Bozarth, Virginia June, 1968
Bradbury, Barbara Jane, 1979
Bradley, Suzanne Fay, 1981
Bradshaw, Carolyn Patricia, 1978
Brady, Karen Anne, 1967
Brady, Mary Ann, 1980
Brady, Maureen Ann, 1977
Brainard, Margaret E., 1943
Braithwaite, Barbara Ann, 1961
Brandt, Ruth Elizabeth, 1946
Bratton, Anne L., 1925
Braucher, Kathy Ann, 1972
Bray, Martha R., 1926
Bray, Ruth, 1910
Brazanson, Almira, 1904

Brechin, Mae, 1918
Brecker, Mary Louise, 1966
Brede, Dorothy M., 1936
Breder, Cheryl Toni, 1973
Breen, Mercedes Frances, 1948
Bregman, Marsha, 1964
Breidenthal, Sally Ann, 1967
Breinig, Anna E., 1934
Breisch, Harriet E., 1933
Brendle, Minerva A., 1931
Brennan, Nadine D., 1980
Brennan, Patricia Ann, 1960
Brenneman, Blanche, 1910
Bressi, Lisa, 1981
Breth, Mary C., 1926
Bretschneider, Marie, 1963
Breunig, Grace E., 1928
Brewer, Deborah Ann, 1972
Brewer, Myrtle, 1916
Brian, Cheryl Lynn, 1979
Brice, Maureen Mary, 1966
Bricker, Sharon Linda, 1963
Briggs, Margaret L., 1938
Briley, Patricia Kay, 1971
Brinkman, Anna C., 1927
Brittan, Eunice Lillian, 1960
Broadwater, Susan Ann, 1973
Brock, Doris Jean, 1973
Brock, Joan Marie, 1954
Brodginski, Louise Pauline, 1946
Brokenshire, Mildred, 1948
Brooke, Martha, 1909
Brooke, Mary, 1899
Brooks, Harris Herbert, 1977
Broomall, Lynda Lee, 1971
Brosious, Joann Ruth, 1963
Brough, Elizabeth Caroline, 1963
Brown, Barbara Mildred, 1949
Brown, Carolyn Ruth, 1969
Brown, Clara, 1914
Brown, Cynthia Barrett, 1977
Brown, Dorothy J., 1955
Brown, Evelyn, 1919
Brown, Frances Amy, 1946
Brown, Lorraine, 1944
Brown, Margaret, 1898
Brown, Mary Louise, 1958
Brown, Mildred G., 1933
Brown, Ruth Ann, 1961
Brown, Shirley Alice, 1955
Brown, Violet, 1903
Browne, Kathleen Nora, 1981
Browne, Margaret Ann, 1968
Browning, Florence J., 1916
Browning, Rebecca V., 1940
Brownstein, Annette, 1971
Brubaker, Marion E., 1931
Bruch, Florence, 1909

Brucker, Suzanne Carol, 1968
Brumbaugh, Ruth, 1931
Brunner, Clara M., 1923
Brunner, Miriam L., 1939
Bruno, Lorraine Philomena, 1956
Brunt, Caroline Janet, 1969
Bryan, A. Lucille, 1926
Bryan, Anita, 1938
Bryant, Myrtle I., 1933
Buchanan, Theresa Shirley, 1955
Bucher, Mildred, 1932
Buck, Blanche E., 1931
Buckman, Leila, 1912
Budash, Mary Margaret, 1962
Budnick, Karen Anita, 1981
Budnicki, Barbara Ann, 1978
Buechley, Ellen Letitia, 1967
Buehler, Virginia May, 1967
Buffum, Marie Adeline, 1947
Bugen, Sharon, 1969
Buggy, Christine Anne, 1979
Bulette, Dorothea, 1932
Bulkley, Catherine Laurel, 1960
Bullock, Ruth Rilla, 1948
Bumgardner, M. Louise, 1933
Bundens, Jeanne Anne, 1980
Bundens, Mary Carol, 1964
Bundy, M. Grace, 1931
Bunker, Ruth Sandra, 1957
Burd, Mildred Rose, 1947
Burdett, Deborah Lee, 1969
Burg, Rhoda A. M., 1942
Burger, Linda Jean, 1970
Burgess, Kitty Louise, 1969
Burggraf, Harriet S., 1931
Burke, Doris Alice, 1948
Burke, Joanne Rosemary, 1976
Burke, Paulette, 1968
Burkeitt, Lisa, 1980
Burkhalter, Helen I., 1929
Burkholder, Elyse Anne, 1964
Burkowski, Ruth, 1960
Burns, Eleanor, 1943
Burns, Valerie C., 1980
Burrell, Susan Anne, 1978
Burrows-Pegg, Margaret, 1957
Burt, Constance, 1966
Burton, Laura M., 1935
Buscher, Donna Lynn, 1968
Bush, Lemos, 1910
Bush, Margaret, 1913
Bushek, Josephine M. A., 1939
Bushek, Theresa B., 1949
Bushey, Buddy Jeanne, 1958
Butler, Alice E., 1946
Butler, Dorcas L., 1944
Butler, Frances, 1916
Butler, Judith Ann, 1963

Butler, Ruth E., 1937
Butz, Ada, 1915
Buxton, Margaret A., 1926
Buxton, Marilyn Kathleen, 1950
Byer, Janet B., 1944
Byerly, Helen F., 1939
Byers, Goldie, 1940
Byrne, Donna, 1975
Byrne, Elizabeth E., 1943

~ C ~

Caffrey, Margaret Agnes, 1956
Caldwell, Alice Rose, 1946
Caldwell, Patricia Ann, 1961
Cale, Dorothy Annette, 1960
Calhoun, Betty L., 1943
Calhoun, Mary, 1911
Call, Mary, 1914
Callaghan, Kathleen Rita, 1974
Callahan, Donna Lynn, 1979
Callahan, Gladys, 1925
Callum, Diane Margaret, 1977
Cameron, Jeffrey, 1977
Camilli, Ann Theresa, 1963
Camillo, Cheryl Maureen, 1979
Cammoroto, Joseph Charles, 1978
Campbell, Agnes, 1930
Campbell, Anna, 1920
Campbell, Christella M., 1935
Campbell, Edith Virginia, 1947
Campbell, Edna, 1916
Campbell, Helen L., 1944
Campbell, Jeanne Mae, 1949
Campbell, Joan Irwin, 1962
Campbell, Katherine, 1908
Campbell, Mary, 1910
Canal, Barbara Joan, 1961
Cancelli, Eileen Rita, 1964
Canney, Helene, 1973
Cannon, Marie, 1944
Cannon, Nellie, 1904
Capolarello, Theresa Barbara, 1961
Caponigro, Rosalie Anne, 1961
Capotosto, Jeanetta Adeline, 1964
Caprara, Carol Ann, 1969
Capritti, Maryann, 1977
Caputo, Patricia Ann, 1957
Carberry, Lynda Ann, 1975
Carey, Carolyn Marie, 1969
Carey, Ellyn G., 1934
Carey, Lena, 1928
Carey, Lucy, 1901
Carey, Margaret A., 1927
Carey, Marion Allaire, 1966
Carico, Virginia Caroline, 1947
Carissimi, Claire, 1955
Carleton, Laura A., 1928

Carley, Kathleen Ann, 1981
Carlson, Beverly Ann, 1966
Carlson, Mary Loretta, 1971
Carman, Wendy Leigh, 1973
Carmody, Suzanne Elizabeth, 1982
Carnahan, Florence, 1906
Carpenter, Ethyle G., 1925
Carpenter, Evelyn, 1910
Carpo, Aleta Bernice, 1957
Carr, Donna J., 1934
Carr, Margaret Ann, 1963
Carroll, Judith Elizabeth, 1963
Carrozzino, Dolores Mary, 1960
Carson, Ann Theresa, 1977
Carson, Bertha, 1910
Carson, Mary Jane, 1954
Carter, Anita Lyn, 1976
Carter, Deborah Lee, 1982
Cartwright, Clara J., 1928
Caruso, Joan, 1976
Carver, Dorothy Bunny, 1966
Casaday, Lillian Louise, 1948
Cashman, Rosemary, 1962
Cashner, Roberta Pearl, 1949
Casper, Alice W., 1926
Casper, Maria Agnes, 1975
Casperson, Elsie M., 1911
Cassel, Carrie, 1915
Cassel, Stacey Francine, 1979
Cassidy, Maureen, 1963
Castaldi, Mildred, 1939
Castellano, Christine, 1954
Caum, Janet Lynne, 1963
Cava, Deborah Ann, 1982
Cavuto, Judith Lee, 1979
Cecil, Leona, 1920
Cella, Alma A., 1960
Chaapel, Jean P., 1935
Chadwick, Joan Louise, 1955
Chafe, Dorothy S., 1930
Chamberlain, Geraldine E., 1941
Chamberlain, Mary J., 1931
Chambers, Dorothy, 1940
Chambers, Dorothy Jane, 1964
Chambers, Leona, 1962
Champion, Joyce, 1965
Checklinski, Frances M., 1933
Cheesman, Karen Louise, 1977
Chesnulevich, Bernadine Ánn, 1947
Chialastri, David A., 1982
Chicote, Katharine Frances, 1958
Chilandese, Karen Therese, 1977
Chinappi, Mary Ann Margaret, 1965
Choinska, Marian Louise, 1962
Chrisholm, Margaret, 1902
Christensen, Olga, 1913
Christian, Laura E., 1942
Christian, Virgie L., 1960

Christianson, Linda Jane, 1971
Christie, Amelia Joanne, 1967
Christine, Virginia C., 1960
Christman, Joan Audrey, 1950
Christner, Sue Ann, 1960
Christopher, Gloria Lynn, 1975
Chronister, Sara M., 1942
Chubb, Hazel M., 1928
Ciabocchi, Barbara Ann, 1964
Cianfrani, Anna F., 1942
Cimino, Sandra Camille, 1963
Ciociola, Carol Ann, 1971
Ciortan, Patricia Ann, 1965
Clampffer, Katherine Evelyn, 1955
Clapsaddle, Nellie, 1934
Clark, Angela D., 1942
Clark, Catherine, 1898
Clark, Emily M., 1938
Clark, Maude, 1910
Clark, Sandra, 1970
Clarke, Georgia Marie, 1956
Clarke, Lillian A., 1924
Clarke, Margaret Emily, 1949
Clarkson, Lydia L., 1928
Clawson, Eleanor Rae, 1969
Claybaugh, Mary, 1935
Claycomb, Evelyn, 1943
Clayton, Margaret E., 1934
Clayton, Anita Mary, 1955
Cleaver, Anna, 1952
Cleaves, Olive J., 1920
Clegg, Pearl, 1931
Clement, Catherine Irma, 1969
Clement, Jane, 1899
Clendenin, Frances, 1921
Clewes, Marcella, 1899
Clineberg, Gladys, 1932
Clippinger, Jessie, 1903
Clippinger, Maude, 1904
Cloud, Dorothy A., 1942
Clouser, Leona R., 1933
Clymer, Gayla Suzanne, 1963
Cmar, Constance Jean, 1972
Cochocki, Elizabeth Anne, 1970
Cockill, Helen F., 1933
Cogan, Ruth Ellen, 1948
Coghlan, Patricia Ann, 1969
Cohen, Carol Ann, 1968
Cohen, Joyce Eleanor, 1978
Cohen, Mildred Abby, 1948
Cohick, Dorothy, 1940
Coldren, Elizabeth S., 1935
Cole, Nancy Louise, 1954
Cole, Phyllis R., 1939
Cole, Sylvia A., 1932
Colebaugh, Effie, 1909
Coleman, Catherine M., 1972
Coleman, Christina, 1973

Coleman, Virginia Grace, 1960
Coles, Mary W., 1935
Colette, Laura, 1905
Coligan, Alice Louise, 1970
Colleluori, Rosemarie, 1969
Collick, Rhoda Franceska, 1980
Collins, Alice J., 1927
Collins, Mildred S., 1932
Comerford, Dawn Patricia, 1982
Cominsky, Eleanor, 1948
Compton, Leslie Ann, 1969
Comstock, Susie, 1905
Conboy, Teresa Marie, 1966
Cone, Linda Mary, 1964
Confer, Dorothy V., 1930
Conley, Anna Patricia, 1957
Conley, Elizabeth Ann, 1961
Conly, Doris Catherine, 1978
Connell, Margaret A., 1920
Connelly, Julia Anne, 1965
Connolly, Dorothy Rose, 1969
Connor, Elizabeth Anne, 1960
Connors, Margaret, 1970
Conrad, Elaine Genevieve, 1965
Conrad, Margaret, 1913
Conran, Anna, 1907
Conway, Barbara A., 1955
Conway, Patricia Anne, 1953
Cook, Margaret Mary, 1946
Cook, Mildred V., 1936
Cook, Viola M., 1942
Cooke, Laura J. L., 1938
Cool, Lillian, 1929
Cooley, Mary Elizabeth, 1979
Cooley, Mildred, 1902
Cooney, Cecilia Theresa, 1981
Cooney, Eileen Marie, 1977
Cooper, Ann Elizabeth, 1963
Cooper, Dorothy A., 1929
Cooper, Florence R., 1938
Cooper, Julia E., 1932
Cooper, Marjorie A., 1939
Cooper, Thelma A., 1937
Cope, Florence, 1922
Coppersmith, Janet Louise, 1961
Cordner, Margaret Myra, 1956
Corkery, Carol Ann, 1959
Corman, Day Dawn, 1958
Corn, Mindy Jo, 1979
Cornelius, Inez Elizabeth, 1948
Cornelius, Zelma, 1923
Cornell, Ruth M., 1933
Corotto, Virginia Lee, 1973
Corrado, Catherine Frances, 1957
Correll, Janet E., 1942
Correnti, Paula Joan, 1947
Corson, Claire Marie, 1960
Corson, Helen M., 1934

Corzen, Gloria, 1959
Cossman, Margaret Mary, 1947
Costello, Carole Anne, 1962
Costello, Eleanor, 1975
Costello, Patricia Jean, 1955
Costino, Cleo Jean, 1957
Cottringer, Carolyn Mary, 1959
Coulbourne, Ellen I., 1932
Countryman, Dolores Catherine, 1958
Coup, Erma N., 1932
Couser, Marie Annette, 1973
Cowen, Esther, 1931
Cox, Florence Louise, 1975
Cox, Jane, 1964
Craft, Lois Ann, 1947
Craft, Mabel, 1900
Crafton, Catherine, 1940
Craig, Ada, 1918
Craig, Mary Elizabeth, 1961
Crandall, Nellie Adelaide, 1953
Crane, Francine Theresa, 1981
Crane, Hilda Eloise, 1947
Cranmer, Ellen Jeanette, 1960
Craven, Carol Jean, 1975
Craver, Ann Marie, 1952
Crawford, Ellen M., 1935
Creamer, Sharon Lea, 1967
Creek, Dorothy Mae, 1952
Creig, Mary, 1908
Cressman, Lydia M., 1941
Cresswell, Jane Marie, 1963
Cresswell, Jeanne C., 1943
Crevey, Kathleen, 1966
Crew, Linda Lee, 1980
Cribbs, Bertha, 1914
Critzer, Linda Sue, 1976
Croasdale, Linda Murray, 1969
Crofford, Bonnie Ann, 1966
Cronlund, Elizabeth G., 1938
Cross, Jennie, 1902
Crossley, Mabel, 1916
Crotsley, Donna Lee, 1957
Crotty, Catherine L., 1937
Crouse, Ada Kathryn, 1920
Crouse, Mary, 1914
Crow, Susan Marie, 1974
Cruice, Elaine, 1972
Crum, Shirley Rebecca, 1968
Crumlish, Dolores Marie, 1968
Culp, Esther Nancy, 1955
Culp, Nellie E., 1933
Cumminskey, Nellie, 1898
Cupp, Mary K., 1944
Curcio, Ann Ruth, 1980
Curcio, Jeanne Marie, 1955
Curlee, Geraldine Valerie, 1963
Currie, Mhora S., 1928
Curtin, Hannetta E., 1931

Curtis, Diane Marie, 1959
Curts, Gladys Mae, 1948
Cushen, Mary, 1902
Cuthbert, Margaret, 1920
Cypher, Edith V., 1920

~ D ~

D'Angelo, Denise Marie, 1974
D'Angelo, Dorothy Marie, 1975
D'Espinosi, M. Catherine, 1934
DaCosta, Clara, 1905
Daeuber, Maryann, 1936
Dague, Anna, 1909
Dahlmann, Margaret Frances, 1964
Dailey, Elizabeth, 1958
Dailey, Miriam A., 1923
Dalgity, Audrey Sharon, 1970
Dalgleish, Marian, 1943
Dalgliesh, Susan, 1982
Dalton, Cynthia Murray, 1953
Dalton, Elizabeth Mary, 1973
Dalton, Mary Patricia, 1972
Daly, Kathleen, 1972
Daly, Rhoda, 1911
Dance, Constance Lynne, 1980
Danch, Mary Jill, 1961
Daneils, Monica A., 1957
Daniels, Alice A., 1929
Danisavich, Dorothy Regina, 1961
Danner, Shelva Jean, 1960
Danser, Virginia, 1911
Darling, Shirley May, 1948
Darone, Verna, 1918
Datz, Mary Agnes, 1979
Daubert, Bettilou, 1948
Daugherty, Helen Estelle, 1949
Davenport, Charlotte F., 1939
David, Jo Anne, 1963
Davidson, Caroline Ann, 1960
Davies, Annie, 1914
Davies, Deanna Grace, 1958
Davis, Alberta Martha, 1969
Davis, Ann Lois, 1943
Davis, Audrey June, 1947
Davis, Barbara Ann, 1965
Davis, Barbara Jean, 1968
Davis, Dolores I., 1943
Davis, Elizabeth Anne, 1976
Davis, Helen, 1918
Davis, Helen Lee, 1975
Davis, Loralee Arlene, 1954
Davis, Loretta Lane, 1961
Davis, Martha C., 1936
Davis, Nancy Corrine, 1959
Davis, Nina Elaine, 1951
Davis, Pauline, 1937
Davis, Ruth R., 1934

Fitzgerald, Mary Genevieve, 1975
Fitzgibbons, Elizabeth, 1974
Fitzhenry, Katharine Marie, 1971
Fitzkee, Effie, 1921
Fitzpatrick, Dixie Lee, 1956
Fitzsimmons, Mary Denise, 1967
Fitzwater, Emmanuel Faye, 1953
Flanagan, Jeanne Therese, 1952
Flannery, Mary Theresa, 1950
Flavell, Mae Lucille, 1949
Fleck, Donna Elaine, 1950
Fleck, Katherine S., 1928
Fleck, M. Hope, 1934
Fleishman, Barbara E., 1938
Fleming, Nita Gray Sterrett, 1948
Fletcher, Donna Lee, 1963
Flickinger, Katherine, 1921
Flynn, Patricia, 1982
Flynn, Robin Linda, 1979
Flyte, Mary E., 1940
Focht, Barbara Claire, 1981
Folcarelli, Mary Ellen, 1979
Foley, Diane, 1979
Foltz, Rebecca Lynn, 1978
Folwell, Lydia, 1904
Foor, Margaret M., 1940
Foor, Virginia E., 1939
Force, Marci Ann, 1980
Forcina, Linda Carolynne, 1978
Fordyce, Pearl, 1917
Forgione, Rose A., 1952
Formisano, Carol Ann, 1966
Forrest, Lorena Mae, 1947
Fortner, Edna, 1940
Fortner, Helen M., 1919
Foster, Anna M., 1931
Foster, Audrey Louise, 1947
Foster, Yvonne Rose, 1958
Foulk, Marion, 1926
Fowler, Isabel, 1926
Fowler, Joan Marie, 1977
Fox, Kathleen, 1969
Fox, Rebecca, 1952
Fox, Ruth, 1947
Fox, Sally Kathleen, 1974
Fox, Sandra Kuuipo, 1969
Fox, Viola K., 1937
Fraim, Patricia Ann, 1967
Fraley, Dorothy E., 1942
Fralic, Madalen P., 1933
Frame, Carol Louise, 1962
Frampton, Emily A., 1944
Franchetti, Rose M., 1981
Francis, Kathryn Marie, 1971
Frank, Mildred Mary, 1960
Frankenfield, Vivian C., 1944
Franks, Mildred Louise, 1948
Frantz, Joyce M., 1929

Franzone, Theresa Anne, 1978
Frauenfelder, Ruth D., 1930
Frazier, R. Geraldine, 1938
Freed, Alice M., 1940
Freed, Mary Elizabeth, 1949
Freedman, Anita Gae, 1972
Freeman, Debra Ann, 1971
Freeman, Marion Arlene, 1969
Freidel, Joyce Ann, 1979
Freiling, Kathleen Ann, 1975
Frelond, Joan, 1977
French, F. Lucille, 1941
Frendak, Pauline A., 1933
Frendak, Verna M., 1929
Freshcoln, Carol Elizabeth, 1958
Freudenberger, Bernice, 1927
Frey, Mary Anna, 1960
Frie, Gertrude E., 1941
Friedman, Debra Ann, 1975
Fritz, Sarah E., 1944
Frizell, Judith Ann, 1963
Fromtling, Mildred L., 1942
Fromuth, Molly A., 1957
Frost, Deborah Lynne, 1979
Fruehan, Mayda L., 1926
Fry, Patricia Darlene, 1962
Fry, Wilhemina Carole, 1956
Frye, Frances B., 1933
Frye, Kathryn M., 1926
Frymire, Lois M., 1934
Fuhrman, Deborah Lee, 1974
Fulford, Bettie, 1910
Fuller, Maude, 1921
Fuller, Virginia M., 1932
Fullerton, Barbara Helen, 1961
Fullerton, Marilyn Fern, 1953
Fullerton, Rebecca Whitman, 1966
Funk, Mary, 1895
Furlong, Donna Maria, 1972
Furry, Peggy Marie, 1971
Furtaw, Elizabeth Dolores, 1948

~ G ~

Gabriel, Anita, 1967
Gackenbach, Jean M., 1944
Gademan, Doris Margaret, 1958
Gallagher, Mary Elizabeth, 1977
Gallagher, Nancy Elizabeth, 1981
Gallagher, Nancy Margaret, 1963
Gallagher, Sondra Lee, 1977
Gallagher, Susan Mary, 1977
Gallihue, Carol Ann, 1967
Gallo, Karen Lynn, 1981
Gambal, Anna E., 1930
Gannon, Eileen Frances, 1968
Gans, Thelma L., 1939
Gansky, Freda Ina, 1969

Ganster, Julia, 1924
Gantz, Maud W., 1925
Garber, Joanne, 1951
Garbus, Suzanne Mary, 1978
Gardier, Angelina Patricia, 1959
Gardner, Ellen, 1950
Gardner, Naomi, 1910
Gardner, Patricia Lee, 1964
Garforth, Lois Anne, 1970
Garman, Mildred V., 1932
Garner, Elizabeth, 1921
Garretson, Edna, 1939
Garrett, Violet M., 1940
Garrity, Anne Marie, 1976
Gartland, Barbara, 1969
Gartland, Ursula Marie, 1967
Gaspari, Marianne Rose, 1969
Gasparon, Joan Frances, 1958
Gass, Violet, 1909
Gast, Eleanor, 1947
Gaston, Mary L., 1944
Gaston, Maryann, 1963
Gates, Eleanor June, 1962
Gates, M. Elizabeth, 1944
Gauger, Fay Hannah, 1961
Gaughan, Michele, 1980
Gaugler, Fay, 1943
Gaymon, Bonnie Michele, 1975
Gaynor, Kathleen, 1975
Gearhart, Gertrude G., 1943
Geesey, Margaret M., 1937
Geil, Mercedes Kathryn, 1948
Geissler, Marcella Grace, 1957
Geist, Gertrude I., 1930
Gelston, Lauralee Ellen, 1966
Gendebien, Edith M., 1938
Genter, Elizabeth J., 1957
George, Bertha H., 1903
George, Cynthia Ann, 1975
George, Elizabeth C., 1925
Geovanelle, Evelyn Frances, 1947
Gerber, Clara I., 1927
Gerber, Nancy Jean, 1949
Gerfin, Emily J., 1944
Gerhard, Phyllis Jean, 1951
German, Peggy Ann, 1954
Gerngross, Alice Rita, 1949
Gerstlauer, Donna Rae, 1969
Gery, Nellie F., 1941
Getch, Dorothy Ann, 1948
Getkin, Dianne Joan, 1969
Getz, Agnes L., 1926
Getzow, Ellen Sue, 1976
Geyer, Elinor Yvonne, 1948
Ghegan, Kathleen Susan, 1979
Gherardi, Lorene Kathryn, 1956
Giannini, Domenica Maria, 1970
Giardina, Jeanne Maria, 1974

Gibb, Helen C., 1913
Gibbs, Jacquelyne Yvonne, 1958
Gibbs, Jean, 1910
Gibney, Laurie Elizabeth, 1977
Gibney, Mary Joyce, 1955
Gibson, Irene Edith, 1953
Gieseke, Barbara Ann, 1953
Gieson, Alice Mary, 1951
Gilardone, Esther Dorothy, 1946
Gilbert, Elizabeth M., 1935
Gilbert, Helen E., 1925
Gilbert, Jean Katherine, 1946
Gilbert, Mary F., 1944
Gilbert, Sara E., 1925
Gilbert, Vivian C., 1937
Gillen, Katherine Loretta, 1980
Gillespie, Emma, 1921
Gillis, Deborah Evelyn, 1970
Gilman, Jane Virginia, 1947
Gilmore, Christine, 1974
Gilmore, Dolores Irma, 1961
Ginn, Camille R., 1926
Giordano, Carmenella, 1973
Giordano, Theo, 1976
Giorgio, Sally Ann, 1960
Gipe, Helen, 1940
Girard, Rosalie M., 1961
Girton, Ethel M., 1914
Glancy, Ruth Ann, 1962
Glasgow, Mary Joan, 1949
Glaspey, Ellen Ruth, 1962
Glass, Helen Carole, 1954
Glaudel, Alice Helen, 1954
Glaudel, Patricia Marie, 1957
Glaudel, Rose Marie, 1950
Glavey, Catherine Mary, 1975
Gleichert, Emma Belle, 1947
Glenn, Georgina, 1929
Glenn, Martha, 1923
Gloeckler, Doris, 1977
Glouner, Anna, 1902
Glover, Ann Winifred, 1947
Gluck, Clara, 1947
Gnaw, Inez, 1935
Gobrecht, Vicki Anne, 1964
Gockley, Josephine Mae, 1949
Godshalk, Gwendolyn I., 1926
Godwin, Mary Josephine Mae, 1949
Godwin, Mary Catherine, 1962
Goertzen, Jean Beverly, 1978
Goff, Agnes Marie, 1950
Goff, R. Anita, 1952
Goldberg, Laurel Anne, 1979
Goldberg, Louise E., 1928
Goldberg, Myrtle, 1925
Golden, Elizabeth Marye, 1947
Goldfarb, Eugenie Joy, 1973
Goldman, Sybil, 1967

Golomb, Cynthia Ellen, 1980
Gonder, Anna, 1922
Gonder, Gail C., 1932
Gonder, Sara, 1915
Good, Gail, 1912
Good, Susan Tucker, 1967
Goodman, Linda Louise, 1967
Goodman, Tanna, 1970
Goodnow, Bernice S., 1931
Goodwin, Olive, 1920
Goodyear, Mildred, 1919
Gordon, Linda, 1981
Gore, Elizabeth Anne, 1971
Gorman, Helen, 1910
Gormish, Sophia Henrietta, 1948
Goss, Cynthia Marie, 1971
Gosser, Elsa Mae, 1966
Gothie, Nelda Elizabeth, 1951
Gottschall, Ann Louise, 1967
Goudie, Lenore, 1939
Gouker, Emma L., 1928
Gould, Frances M., 1938
Goupp, Lydia, 1918
Gourley, Ruth Lee, 1946
Gover, Elaine, 1947
Graber, Verna Eileen, 1947
Grabowski, Cynthia Jane, 1970
Grace, Margaret Mary, 1964
Graf, Augusta R., 1941
Graf, Barbara June, 1974
Graham, Adelaide, 1898
Graham, Catherine, 1903
Graham, Debra Ann, 1981
Graham, Heather Jessie, 1960
Graham, Jessie, 1899
Graham, Marcia, 1954
Graham, Nancy Carol, 1965
Graham, Susan Mary, 1971
Grailey, Dorothy Marie, 1976
Gramata, Bernadine Mary, 1980
Granger, Anne Elizabeth, 1949
Grantham, Linda Christine, 1981
Gration, Lorraine Carolyn, 1953
Gratzik, Maria, 1970
Graver, Doris Ann, 1949
Graves, Joyce Elaine, 1952
Graves, M. Louise, 1920
Gravish, Mary Ann, 1961
Gray, Catherine I., 1933
Gray, Katharine Elizabeth, 1974
Gray, Nancy Blake, 1964
Gray, Theresa, 1943
Greathouse, Carolyn, 1927
Green, Darlene Kay, 1965
Green, Elizabeth Dorothy, 1950
Green, Frances May, 1947
Greenawalt, Barbara Ann, 1961
Greene, Grace Armelda, 1964

Greenfield, Beth Jay, 1969
Greenfield, Jeanne G., 1938
Greenlee, G. Mildred, 1938
Greenlee, Mary C., 1926
Greenly, Hazel V., 1938
Greenly, Helen A., 1931
Greenwalt, Kathryn, 1924
Greenwood, Mary, 1963
Greger, Hazel, 1932
Gregory, Jessie I., 1937
Greig, Jessie, 1912
Greising, Nancy Lee, 1952
Gresh, Doris M., 1942
Greulich, Winnie F., 1939
Grier, Lucy, 1909
Grieshaber, Martha Louise, 1962
Griff, Bernice Gladys, 1959
Griffin, Sara, 1920
Griffiths, Hannah L., 1931
Griffiths, Ida Mae, 1940
Griffiths, Mary Katherine, 1957
Grimes, Cheryl Ann, 1979
Grimm, Emily, 1910
Grimm, Evelyn Marie, 1947
Grimmie, Carole Lynn, 1975
Groat, Dorothy Arlene, 1957
Groff, Dorothy, 1937
Groh, Nancy Lorraine, 1952
Groman, Dorothy A., 1941
Grosch, Helen, 1914
Grouleff, Mary Elizabeth, 1963
Grove, Frances M., 1917
Groves, Mazie Joy, 1949
Groves, Ruth, 1947
Grundkovski, Ernestine M., 1926
Grundkovski, Freida A., 1926
Grundon, Norma Eleanor, 1948
Gryczko, Adrienne Camille, 1961
Grysewicz, Eleanor, 1939
Grzywacz, Karen, 1981
Gudknecht, Karen, 1977
Guerin, Agnes C.A., 1916
Guerin, Phyllis Jean, 1948
Gugliotta, Florence M., 1939
Guida, Karen Corinne, 1976
Guidi, Marilyn Ann, 1969
Guise, Beverly Romaine, 1970
Gulian, Takouhi, 1933
Gumann, Faith Ann, 1978
Gumpert, Anna, 1906
Gunsallus, Isabelle, 1950
Gurd, Verna, 1918
Gurgul, Cynthia Joyce, 1967
Gustafson, Anna Marie, 1954
Gustas, Helen M., 1948
Gustitis, Adele I., 1926
Guthrey, Joeann Leona, 1960
Guy, Susan Louise, 1968

Hunsberger, Grace Urffer, 1947
Hunsicker, Marjorie Viola, 1947
Hunsicker, Sarah, 1904
Hunsinger, Geneva Merolene, 1958
Hunt, Ethel M., 1921
Hunt, Wendy Jo, 1974
Hunter, Deanna Peggy, 1959
Hurd, Myrtice Gwendolyn, 1952
Hurley, Jeanette, 1899
Hurley, Sarah Melissa, 1960
Husband, Jane Elizabeth, 1975
Hussey, Violet T., 1930
Huston, Frances L., 1941
Hutzel, Evelyn Joyce, 1955
Hyatt, Mary E., 1936
Hyde, Doris L., 1938
Hyde, Geraldine L., 1935
Hyland, Carol Wright, 1957
Hyland, Patricia Anne, 1963
Hysmith, Colleen R., 1951

~ I ~

Ilchuck, Irene Mary, 1953
Iles, Sara, 1917
Imler, Shirley Ann, 1957
Inghram, Bonnie Edward, 1968
Ingling, Joyce Marlene, 1955
Ingraham, Eva M., 1934
Insley, Patricia Ann, 1964
Insogna, Regina Theresa, 1978
Irvin, Dorothy Mae, 1946
Irvin, Nina H., 1930
Irvine, Rachel L., 1948
Irwin, Frances, 1921
Irwin, Margaret Frances, 1954
Irwin, Martha H., 1940
Isenhour, Judith Brent, 1960
Ishuin, Aileen, 1976
Ivory, Margaret, 1910
Iwasko, Joanne, 1976

~ J ~

Jackson, Edna, 1911
Jackson, Elizabeth, 1934
Jackson, Elizabeth Baldwin, 1947
Jackson, Mildred, 1916
Jacobs, Georgann Anita, 1957
Jacobs, Leslee Anne, 1974
Jacobs, Lois Jane, 1947
Jacoby, Anna M., 1934
Jakabcin, Mary Diane, 1967
James, Cheryl Suzette, 1974
James, Margaret, 1941
James, Mary, 1915
Jamieson, Mary A., 1903
Janicek, Bernadine, 1959

Jarrett, Jane, 1946
Jaszczal, Barbara Ann, 1961
Jedrziewski, Stella B., 1940
Jeitner, Lorraine Alice, 1951
Jendrzejewski, Bernardine Marie, 1953
Jenkins, Patricia Ann, 1982
Jenks, Luanne Vesta, 1978
Jennerjahn, Ellen Jean, 1974
Jennings, Grace E., 1942
Jennings, Julie Rose, 1974
Jennis, Stephanie Jo, 1970
Jensen, Elvira, 1928
Jerrett, L. Marion, 1928
Jess, Judith Kay, 1971
Jinning, Mary Jo, 1974
Job, Helen L., 1940
Jobson, Clara E., 1919
John, Margaret, 1941
Johns, Betty Lucille, 1948
Johnson, Adelaide G., 1919
Johnson, Agnes D., 1931
Johnson, Anna, 1918
Johnson, Carol Ann, 1968
Johnson, Catherine Lillian, 1948
Johnson, Dorothy C., 1948
Johnson, Faye Arlene, 1949
Johnson, Hilda, 1924
Johnson, Jean Blair, 1955
Johnson, Judith, 1967
Johnson, Louise Ann, 1971
Johnson, Marguerite Louise, 1956
Johnson, Pamela Rose, 1965
Johnson, Zayda B., 1919
Johnston, Frances Ellen, 1975
Johnston, Frances K., 1934
Johnston, Gail Anne, 1970
Johnston, Helen, 1950
Johnston, Marline Thomas, 1979
Jonas, Ellen Lucile, 1973
Jones, Aldwyth Evelyn, 1963
Jones, Anna Mary, 1961
Jones, Carol Jean, 1959
Jones, Carolyn Elizabeth, 1965
Jones, Carolyn M., 1932
Jones, Daveen Kay, 1969
Jones, Deborah Lynn, 1978
Jones, Doris L., 1942
Jones, Elizabeth, 1911
Jones, Elizabeth Moses, 1955
Jones, Ethel W., 1936
Jones, Fannie M., 1917
Jones, Florence M., 1917
Jones, Frances H., 1922
Jones, Gertrude M., 1935
Jones, Irene R., 1931
Jones, Judith Ann, 1971
Jones, Marilyn, 1952
Jones, Marion J., 1940

Jones, Nancy Virginia, 1968
Jones, Norma V., 1951
Jones, Patricia Ann, 1974
Jones, Penelope Ann, 1964
Jones, Ruth E., 1943
Jones, Sara I., 1934
Jongenburger, Jenny Christina, 1965
Jordan, Karen Marie, 1976
Jordan, Margaret, 1911
Julius, Barbara Sue, 1962
Jusaitis, Alberta Theresa, 1947
Justice, Winifred M., 1941

~ K ~

Kadushin, Mona Joyce, 1966
Kaempf, Gail Marie, 1970
Kaercher, Ann, 1978
Kahler, Margart F., 1928
Kalbach, Mary E., 1931
Kalinowski, Mildred V., 1936
Kampmeier, Margaret L., 1977
Kane, Jeanne Marie, 1968
Kane, Kathleen, 1974
Kaneshiro, Neddie, 1944
Kania, Arlene, 1962
Kanour, Miriam K., 1932
Kapitula, Martha, 1948
Kaplan, Rebecca A., 1935
Kapp, Louise Adele, 1953
Karabasz, Clare Marie, 1966
Karnes, Carol Ann, 1959
Karstetter, Cora G., 1941
Kasales, Elizabeth E., 1936
Kashner, Jean Carol, 1954
Kassabian, Virginia, 1915
Katherman, Nancy Noll, 1951
Katz, Shari Lynn, 1980
Kauffman, Dorothy Lane, 1949
Kauffman, Florence, 1923
Kauffman, Mildred D., 1942
Kauffman, Ruth M., 1929
Kautz, Marie Minerva, 1949
Kavalunis, Sandra Joan, 1966
Kazelis, Jane, 1967
Kazmer, Frances Ann, 1953
Kazokas, Diane Marie, 1977
Kearney, Frances Eileen, 1974
Keat, Flora A., 1935
Keating, Teresa Ann, 1978
Keatley, Mary L., 1943
Kee, Donna Clare, 1973
Keegan, Dianne Marie, 1965
Keegan, Lisa Ann, 1979
Keehan, Patricia, 1939
Keelins, Mary Jane, 1958
Keelins, Pauline Elaine, 1954
Keen, Elizabeth, 1962

Keene, Marie, 1934
Keeports, Janet V., 1944
Keers, Ruth Anna, 1975
Kehler, Delma Arlene, 1951
Kehoe, Sarah, 1910
Keiffer, Blanche, 1918
Keigley, Sadie, 1903
Keim, Mary Louise, 1963
Keiper, Gladys D., 1942
Keiser, Elaine P., 1944
Keiser, Miriam Ruth, 1977
Keller, Bette Ann, 1959
Keller, Iris Patricia, 1947
Keller, Mary Agnes, 1976
Keller, Shirley Jean, 1961
Keller, Stella, 1935
Keller, Verna, 1921
Kelley, Kathleen, 1979
Kellner, Harriet, 1939
Kelly, Alice P., 1925
Kelly, Emily, 1923
Kelly, Florence A., 1939
Kelly, Frances L., 1935
Kelly, Kathleen, 1970
Kelly, Lisa Ann, 1981
Kelly, Marie A., 1935
Kelly, Maureen, 1974
Kelly, Sara E., 1938
Kemerer, Caroline, 1940
Kemmerer, Carol Jane, 1964
Kemmerer, Dorothy Esther, 1964
Kemmerer, Ellen Mae, 1961
Kendall, K. Ella, 1913
Kendig, Laura, 1895
Kennedy, Stacey Michelle, 1980
Kennett, Judith Lynn, 1966
Kenney, Kathleen Mary, 1973
Kenney, Susan Anne, 1980
Kenton, Audrey M., 1937
Kepner, Pauline, 1934
Kepping, Ann Elizabeth, 1957
Kern, Dama O., 1932
Kerr, Virginia V., 1944
Kersbaumer, Rose Mary, 1948
Kessler, Dorothy Barbara, 1965
Kessler, Ruth Ellen, 1966
Kester, Dorothy M., 1932
Kevel, Agnes M., 1931
Kevel, Isabella R., 1927
Kiefman, Ruth G., 1941
Kielar, Lorayne M., 1946
Kiersnowski, Cynthia Ann, 1975
Kiger, Jane E., 1937
Kilby, Eleanor Brunton, 1949
Killinger, Elizabeth, 1937
Kimble, Mary A., 1925
Kimmel, Betty Marie, 1946
Kinch, Katherine R., 1933

Kinch, Madeline L., 1942
King, Eileen Margaret, 1972
King, Ella, 1898
King, Ellen Marie, 1959
King, Isa R., 1933
King, Joan Marie, 1953
King, Noreen Mary, 1956
King, Regina Ann, 1975
King, Virginia C., 1943
Kingsley, Katherine Marie, 1963
Kinkaid, Janet Baird, 1966
Kinkead, Adalyne, 1928
Kinna, Carolyn Sue, 1968
Kinney, Bernadine T., 1937
Kinter, Virginia B., 1938
Kipikash, Margaret B., 1937
Kipp, Eleanor, 1942
Kirby, Hilda, 1917
Kircher, June Marian, 1953
Kirk, Florence D., 1921
Kirlin, Linda Louise, 1970
Kirner, Eunice Claire, 1965
Kishbaugh, Dorothy J., 1941
Kissinger, Charmaine L., 1949
Kissinger, Edith S., 1929
Kistner, Mary Patricia, 1958
Klekotka, Nancy, 1975
Kline, Cheryl Lee, 1977
Kline, Donna Jean, 1968
Kline, Dorothy M., 1937
Kline, Lillian C., 1930
Kline, Maude, 1923
Klinedinst, Nancy Ann, 1968
Klinestiver, Janet Carol, 1959
Kling, Jeanne Helen, 1959
Klingeman, Mildred R., 1927
Klingerman, Mildred Elaine, 1947
Klink, Helen, 1912
Klink, Laura M., 1934
Klipple, Arlene, 1921
Klockner, Betty L., 1944
Kloss, Donna Jean, 1980
Knaff, Rose Marie Josephine, 1958
Knapp, A. Pauline, 1925
Knaur, Cheryl Anne, 1965
Kneebone, Shirley Isabel, 1946
Kneidel, Ann F., 1956
Knerr, Carrie E., 1917
Knerr, Harriet Yvonne, 1947
Knight, Anna, 1905
Knock, Emma, 1914
Knoll, Lorraine M., 1927
Knoll, Matilda, 1923
Knoll, Nancy Ruth, 1959
Knoll, Ruth, 1923
Knowles, Elizabeth A., 1939
Kobryn, Nina Veronica, 1977
Kobrynski, Donna Marie, 1976

Kobulsky, Kathleen, 1980
Koch, Alice Lorraine, 1958
Koch, Audrey Iris, 1950
Koch, Darthy Mona, 1953
Koch, Ruth J., 1929
Koch, Terri Beth, 1981
Kocher, Donna Marie, 1966
Koder, Patricia Ann, 1962
Koegel, Elizabeth W., 1936
Koehl, Donna Marie, 1981
Koerner, Helen Mary, 1947
Kohler, Muriel Jean, 1952
Kolodziej, Elizabeth, 1942
Kominsky, Barbara Ann, 1982
Konowal, Noelle Ruth, 1974
Konrad, Kathleen Ann, 1972
Koon, Margaret J., 1933
Koons, Gertrude, 1918
Kopel, Marianne Theresa, 1965
Kopenhaver, Luann Orsola, 1978
Kopilchack, Helen, 1946
Kopistansky, Christine, 1981
Korb, Adelheid, 1962
Korin, Beth Zamira, 1968
Korn, Joan Marie, 1954
Korosec, Mary Kathryn, 1966
Koser, Emily, 1902
Kost, Helen Geraldine, 1960
Kostenbauder, Katherine Marilyn, 1957
Kostenbauser, Nancy Vogel, 1951
Kostrow, Jean, 1956
Koswoski, Josephine Joan, 1959
Koulik, Ursula Mary, 1949
Koval, Mary Ann, 1948
Kovarie, Mulveena M., 1958
Kowaleski, Eleanor Barbara, 1950
Kowalesky, Miriam Louise, 1946
Kowalick, Jean Marie, 1959
Kozak, Virginia Ann, 1959
Kozura, Marie Ann, 1957
Krahling, Marian Louise, 1962
Kramen, Judith Phyllis, 1966
Kramer, R. Hope, 1940
Kramer, Roberta Mary, 1968
Kramp, Janet Michele, 1971
Krasnisky, Jean, 1956
Kratz, Jay Terese, 1947
Kratzer, Rita, 1935
Kraus, Pauline Louise, 1959
Krause, Harriet R., 1900
Krause, Henrietta, 1896
Krause, Ruth Esther, 1974
Krauser, Irene P., 1935
Krebs, Sandra Lynne, 1982
Kreider, Edith May, 1966
Kreider, Ida, 1908
Kreiser, Sarah J., 1944
Kreiser, Viola A., 1928

Kresge, Ella Priscilla, 1949
Kresge, Kathleen, 1979
Kressly, Lois Mae, 1956
Krestynick, Rita, 1950
Kring, Charlotte R., 1938
Krol, Jane Mary, 1979
Kropnick, Gail, 1962
Kroupa, Isabella Jean, 1964
Kroupa, Mildred, 1925
Krout, Marilyn Weisel, 1965
Kruszewski, Mary Ann, 1977
Kuberski, Dolores, 1954
Kubiak, Eileen, 1971
Kuehn, Myrtle L., 1930
Kuehner, Joan Marie, 1969
Kuehner, Patricia Joan, 1958
Kugler, Elaine, 1972
Kuklenski, Louise Mary, 1954
Kuller, Agnes, 1921
Kulp, Wanda Patricia, 1948
Kundrat, Ellen B., 1950
Kunkelman, Patricia A., 1954
Kunkle, Judith Lynn, 1976
Kunkle, Mae Florence, 1948
Kuntz, Mary Lu, 1954
Kunzler, Margaret Andora, 1964
Kunzman, Elaine Marie, 1961
Kupple, Lillian M., 1930
Kurtz, Marcia Lee, 1967
Kurzen, Corrine Rae, 1962
Kuser, Linda Marie, 1978
Kustay, Marion, 1940
Kutz, Alma, 1921
Kutz, Gene Peters, 1947
Kutz, Jennie E., 1921
Kutz, Mary E. P., 1931

~ L ~

Labbe, Doris Clare, 1967
Laboda, Constance Mary, 1973
Lachman, Sue Ann, 1967
Lacy, Karen Lee, 1970
LaFerriere, Cecilia Marie, 1978
LaFleur, Louise Julia, 1971
Lahti, Diane Lynn, 1965
Laibinis, Elizabeth Ann, 1957
Laise, Johanna K., 1939
Lake, Linda R., 1969
LaLiberte, Jean Andre, 1951
Lambert, Marjorie A., 1944
Lambert, Marjorie Dianne, 1973
Lammer, Carol, 1963
Lammie, Sheila Maureen, 1955
Lamon, Mary J., 1926
Lampil, Barbara Joan, 1957
Lamson, Dorothy Elizabeth, 1949
LaMure, Ethel, 1924

Lanahan, Susan Jean, 1977
Landherr, Patricia Esther, 1977
Landi, Joanne, 1968
Landis, Dorothy R., 1937
Landis, Hazel R., 1940
Landis, Miriam H., 1936
Lane, Cora, 1914
Lane, Edith Scott, 1930
Lane, Ida E., 1917
Lane, Lottie, 1896
Lane, Myrtle W., 1937
Langan, Kathleen Alice, 1964
Lange, Gertrude Anna L., 1953
Lange, Ruth Edna, 1949
Langley, Michelle Louise, 1979
Lanks, Mary E., 1926
Lanning, Ruth L., 1928
Lansberry, Arlene R., 1929
Lardin, Mary J., 1942
Larimer, Gwendolyn A., 1955
Larish, Virginia P., 1937
Laros, Paula Jane, 1967
Larson, Judith Ann, 1965
Larson, Lillian E., 1924
Larson, Margaret, 1934
Lashinski, Jean Frances, 1966
Laskowski, Elizabeth Eleanor, 1950
Lasure, Roxanne Lynne, 1977
Latsha, Esther H., 1935
Latsha, M. Pauline, 1935
Latshaw, Audrey Eileen, 1950
Lauer, Gertrude M., 1923
Laughlin, Anna, 1906
Laughlin, Emma, 1895
Laury, Laraine Susan, 1969
Lauver, Irene M., 1942
Lavelle, Sharon Rita, 1953
Lawer, Karen Louise, 1967
Lawrence, Ethel, 1919
Lawrence, Judith Ruth, 1966
Lawrence, Lillian, 1902
Laws, Bettie Jane, 1951
Lawson, Lois, 1922
Leach, Barbara Faye, 1949
Leach, Carol Jean, 1958
Leader, Doris L., 1941
Leader, Joanne Marie, 1960
Lease, Jane Ann, 1971
Leatherman, Alice I., 1937
Lebkicker, Jeanne Louise, 1946
Lee, Betty J., 1944
Lee, Irma, 1935
Lee, Leisa Ellen, 1981
Lee, Lydia Rosamond, 1964
Lee, Rhea H., 1921
Lee, Sally Ann, 1953
Leedom, Barbara Ann, 1977
Lefchick, Theresa, 1962

Lehman, Sue Margaret, 1962
Lehotsky, Helen, 1941
Lehr, Grace Margaret, 1951
Leidy, Shirley Joan, 1950
Leigh, Marjorie Y., 1944
Leight, Margaret Elsie, 1968
Leisch, Alice B., 1979
Leitch, Joan Phyllis, 1963
Lemmon, Mary, 1895
Lenhardt, Anne Marie, 1975
Lenker, Barbara Faye, 1964
Lentz, Anita Lorene, 1958
Lentz, Evelyn Louise, 1948
Lentz, Genevieve A., 1931
Lentz, Minerva M., 1930
Lenzi, Laura Lee, 1976
Leohner, Mary Jane, 1963
Leonard, Marie Margaret, 1947
Lerch, Barbara Ann, 1972
Lesley, Susan, 1959
Lesser, E. Irene, 1914
Lester, Mame, 1896
LeVan, Edith Arlene, 1953
Levan, Georgann Donna, 1978
LeVan, Muriel Joan, 1958
Lever, Barbara Louise, 1965
Levin, Kay Lois, 1963
Levine, Paula Joan, 1968
Levinsky, Mary Elizabeth, 1949
Lewdrop, Estelle M., 1920
Lewis, Adele M., 1915
Lewis, Arlethia Theresa, 1961
Lewis, Clara E., 1930
Lewis, Gwendolyn, 1914
Lewis, Marion D., 1930
Lewis, Nancy Ann, 1977
Lewis, Patricia Ann, 1961
Libengood, Stella, 1914
Lichty, Blanche, 1904
Liebel, Elizabeth Mary L., 1962
Lightner, Adda R., 1926
Lightner, Marval Pearl, 1960
Lilley, Catherine, 1932
Linardo, Jane Frances, 1982
Lindberg, Lillian E., 1941
Lindenmuth, Donna Marie, 1980
Lindenmuth, Patricia, 1981
Lindquist, Linnea N., 1938
Lingenbrick, Judith Gwenn, 1964
Lingle, Eleanor Ruth, 1950
Lingo, Harriet, 1909
Lingo, Miriam, 1919
Lingsch, Nancy Marie, 1963
Linner, Linda Rose, 1962
Lipan, Sara Corrine, 1960
Lithgow, Nancy Lynn, 1966
Litter, Jeanette, 1915
Little, Grace A., 1944

Little, Jean Elizabeth, 1963
Little, Sara Ellen, 1959
Littlefield, Nancy Wick, 1980
Llewellyn, Dorothy A., 1941
Lloyd, Ethel, 1925
Lloyd, Kathryn Agnes, 1974
Lloyd, Maggie N., 1917
Lloyd, Muriel, 1943
Locke, Teresa Ann, 1978
Lockwood, Edna Dolores, 1958
Lockwood, Jean E., 1941
Loftus, Mary Patricia, 1949
Loftus, Maureen Julia, 1973
Logan, Kathleen Ann, 1970
Logan, Margaret Mary, 1949
Logue, Constance Elizabeth, 1973
Logue, Josephine Ellen, 1964
Logue, Katherine, 1914
Lomazoff, Arlene Ellen, 1977
Lomison, Edith, 1913
Long, Helyn R., 1937
Long, Iva M., 1922
Long, Joyce Marie, 1948
Long, Judith Helen, 1962
Long, Martha Mary, 1933
Long, Mary Patricia, 1948
Longacre, Lois B., 1942
Longacre, Mary, 1917
Longfellow, Joanne, 1959
Longhitano, Virginia Marie, 1960
Longworth, Marie Aurora, 1959
Lonholm, Caryl Elizabeth, 1963
Lonsbery, Margaret O., 1933
Looby, Colleen M., 1978
Loris, Linda Anne, 1970
Lotter, Linda Irmgard, 1977
Louderback, Janice Dorothy, 1970
Loughran, Anne Marie, 1954
Loury, Nancy Sharon, 1969
Loux, Melody Mae, 1981
Love, Jessica, 1914
Lovell, Virginia, 1943
Loveren, Gertrude, 1904
Lowe, Adrienne Francine, 1965
Lowe, Ann B., 1944
Loyd, Gloria Jean, 1948
Lubrecht, Maxine Frances, 1968
Lucabaugh, Leah, 1939
Lucarini, Jean Gladys, 1955
Lucas, Anna V., 1931
Lucas, Catherine Malvena, 1968
Lucas, Josephine R., 1924
Lucas, Tamra Ann, 1980
Lucchesi, Margaret, 1966
Luchsinger, Clara I., 1925
Ludrof, Teresa Josephine, 1947
Lugowski, Kathleen, 1968
Lukiewski, Nancy, 1970

Luman, Myrtle, 1913
Lundfelt, Martha Amelia, 1950
Lundy, Bettie Irene, 1949
Lupinacci, Catherine Valerie, 1972
Lupo, Pauline Deatra, 1965
Lutz, Emily Janet, 1961
Lutz, Emma Louisa, 1947
Lutz, Virginia M., 1942
Lydon, Jacqueline M., 1977
Lyman, Debra Kay, 1979
Lynch, Barbara Joanne, 1954
Lynch, Clare Patricia, 1961
Lynch, Ethel E., 1932
Lynch, Janet, 1940
Lynch, Karen Marie, 1965
Lynn, Rose, 1908
Lynn, Sherrie, 1975
Lyons, Mildred M., 1935
Lyons, Paula Jean, 1976
Lytle, Alfreda, 1944

~ M ~

Maag, Dorothy M., 1942
MacAdams, Marian, 1913
MacArevich, Evelyn, 1962
MacArthur, Gertrude K., 1928
MacDonald, Janet, 1940
MacDonald, Margaret Mary, 1925
MacDonnell, Marilyn Louise, 1967
MacDonough, Jennie, 1923
Macelis, Barbara Jean, 1979
Macelis, Mary Anne, 1969
MacFarland, Margaret, 1936
MacFarlane, Olive, 1931
MacGinness, Anna, 1919
MacGregor, Margaret, 1925
Machen, Theo, 1943
Maciejewska, Lorraine T., 1938
Macinko, Magdaline, 1951
Mack, Ruth F., 1933
MacKenzie, Gale Adair, 1964
Mackenzie, Margaret Jean, 1963
Mackes, Miriam Carrie, 1959
Mackintosh, Margaret W., 1935
Mackley, Shirley M., 1950
Macknis, Mary Ann, 1962
Macks, Eleanor Helen, 1952
MacMahon, Margaret, 1903
MacMillan, Susan Lynne, 1970
Maddams, Nancy Ruth, 1959
Maedel, Linda Ruth, 1979
Magee, Virginia May, 1964
Magnitsky, Alice Louise, 1949
Maguire, Marian, 1975
Mahon, Julia Catherine, 1977
Mahoney, Jane Elaine, 1960
Mahoney, Mary, 1901

Maiese, Joan Joyce, 1959
Major, Anne Verle, 1959
Major, Olive, 1898
Malek, Carole Anne, 1971
Maling, Laura, 1921
Malinoski, Bernadine Marie, 1948
Malinowski, Victoria T., 1939
Mallee, Maryann, 1978
Malloy, Alice Patricia, 1965
Malloy, Anna, 1921
Malloy, Anna Marie, 1976
Malone, Jacqueline LaDune, 1952
Malone, Margaret Marie, 1973
Malone, Marguerite G., 1928
Malone, Mary Lou, 1956
Malone, Mildred M., 1926
Malsbury, S. Elizabeth, 1923
Mancini, Donita R., 1976
Mander, Mary Alice, 1963
Maneval, Ellen Jean, 1948
Manewal, Jane A., 1929
Manges, Binnie L., 1936
Manges, Kathleen Ann, 1960
Mangle, Joyce Eleanor, 1952
Mangold, Norma A., 1932
Manhart, Louisa, 1954
Manier, Juanita, 1936
Mankus, Alice Elizabeth, 1952
Mann, Christine, 1913
Mann, Eleanor C., 1931
Mann, L. Claire, 1938
Manni, Karen Ann, 1971
Mannino, Eleanora Elvira, 1951
Mannix, S. Fame, 1954
Mannon, Etta, 1899
Mannon, Virginia, 1940
Manns, Rose Marie, 1972
Marasco, Adrienne Ruth, 1955
Marasco, Jeraldine Joanne, 1964
Marat, Shirley Anne, 1963
March, Fern Carroll, 1970
Marcincin, Julianne Marie, 1970
Marcolina, Lynn, 1981
Marcussen, Kristi Lorraine, 1981
Margiasso, Cathleen Edith, 1953
Margolin, Barbara Gail, 1975
Margraf, Jeanne Marie, 1974
Mariano, Margaret E., 1934
Marion, Cecelia A., 1976
Markle, Mary V., 1937
Marks, Thelma M., 1936
Maro, Patricia Ann, 1977
Marple, Deborah Anne, 1975
Marquardt, Mafalda G., 1925
Marquette, Lucille M., 1930
Marriott, Sue Ellen, 1976
Marshall, Ethel M., 1937
Marshall, Theresa, 1972

Martens, Katherine Elizabeth, 1980
Martin, Arlene R., 1935
Martin, Elizabeth A., 1939
Martin, Elizabeth Ruth, 1947
Martin, Grace, 1895
Martin, Grace J., 1931
Martin, Helen Marie, 1949
Martin, Holly, 1977
Martin, Isabelle C., 1931
Martin, Margaret E., 1928
Martin, Mary R., 1940
Martin, Nora, 1915
Martin, Sara Elizabeth, 1893
Martin, Sara Jane, 1900
Martin, Tasamene, 1934
Martinelli, Isabel, 1939
Martinson, Ida E., 1937
Martz, Betty R., 1948
Martz, Teresa Jean, 1968
Marvel, Rosemary A., 1978
Maslofsky, Ursula Marie, 1980
Mason, Edna F., 1938
Massey, Ruth A., 1935
Masten, Elizabeth Jane, 1968
Mastrovito, Eileen Catherine, 1973
Materio, Catherine Theresa, 1965
Mathews, Dorothy, 1915
Mathie, Sandra Rachael, 1960
Matig, Victoria D., 1941
Matircho, Shirley Anne, 1958
Matlack, Areta, 1937
Matrician, Helen, 1943
Matsuo, June Matsuno, 1950
Mattern, Gladys A., 1930
Matthews, Catherine Woodward, 1952
Matthews, Deborah Louise, 1977
Matthews, June Allyn, 1975
Matz, Rae Andrea, 1977
Matz, Rose Dolores, 1964
Maule, Edna Louise, 1961
Maule, Elizabeth Ann, 1965
Maull, Ethyl S., 1921
Maurer, Clare Lydia, 1953
Maurer, Laura Elizabeth, 1946
Maurer, Luciann Louise, 1977
Maurer, Phyllis A., 1948
Maus, Emma H., 1930
Maxwell, A. Claire, 1940
Maxwell, Marianne, 1980
May, Catherine Mary, 1968
May, Ellen Elizabeth, 1965
May, Kathryn, 1939
May, Leslie Denise, 1976
May, Noami Marie, 1954
Maybee, Grace, 1922
Maycott, Constance Gay, 1970
Mayer, Christina Erika, 1982
Mayer, Patricia, 1974

Mayne, Terry Irene, 1977
Maynor, Carolyn Lynette, 1965
Mayo, Deborah Jean, 1978
Mayse, Linda Lee, 1968
Mazakas, Patricia, 1960
McAlister, Susan Marie, 1973
McAndrew, Kathleen, 1979
McArthur, Thelma P., 1930
McAveney, Maureen, 1976
McCabe, Ruth C., 1935
McCafferty, Jane Marie, 1967
McCafferty, Verna, 1967
McCall, Geraldine Mare, 1963
McCann, Donna Marie, 1977
McCarthy, Cheryl, 1982
McCarthy, Kathleen Marie, 1970
McChesney, Joni Lynn, 1978
McClellan, Judith Lynn, 1977
McClenahan, Margaret Jane, 1958
McClintic, Joanne Margaret, 1976
McCloskey, Christine Marie, 1978
McCloskey, Genevieve, 1924
McClure, Doris Lou, 1952
McClure, Geraldine Frances, 1979
McClure, Sydney V., 1942
McColgan, Anne, 1977
McComb, Dorothy W., 1940
Mccomber, Olive, 1902
McCombes, Anna, 1902
McConnell, Gladys May, 1947
McCormack, Marion, 1918
McCormick, Mildred Betty, 1949
McCoy, Barbara M., 1925
McCoy, Jean Dee, 1952
McCoy, Paula Ann, 1963
McCready, Anna A., 1943
McCready, Rose H., 1933
McCullar, Erma L., 1935
McCullough, Eliza, 1919
McCullough, Judith Lee, 1968
McCullough, Lorraine Jean, 1978
McCullough, Mildred, 1938
McCullough, Susanne, 1975
McCully, Eleanor M., 1935
McCurley, Ellen D., 1942
McDaniels, Helen F., 1935
McDermott, Joan Ellen, 1973
McDevitt, Jane A., 1926
McDonald, Clare, 1977
McDonald, Mary Ellen, 1958
McDowell, Carolyn Patricia, 1965
McDowell, Kathryn Marie, 1948
McElwain, Laura, 1909
McElwee, Pauline M., 1927
McEwen, Sara K., 1941
McFadden, Lillian Mary, 1952
McFarland, Marlene Mae, 1959
McFarland, Wendy Lynn, 1977

McGarrigle, Theresa Ann, 1982
McGarvey, Jane Louise, 1969
McGeary, Kathleen Ann, 1949
McGee, Mary Ellen, 1980
McGee, Sonia Lee, 1958
McGillin, Mary Kathleen, 1973
McGinley, Patricia Ann, 1974
McGinnis, Roxie, 1923
McGlynn, Theresa Marie, 1979
McGowan, Mary L., 1955
McGowan, Ruth, 1921
McGrath, Colleen Patricia, 1976
McGrattan, Gail Elizabeth, 1980
McGrenra, Barbara Ann, 1978
McGrory, Anne Elizabeth, 1973
McGrory, Joyce, 1979
McGuire, Maureen Claire, 1963
McHugh, Joyce Ann, 1962
McHugh, Patricia M., 1974
McHugh, Sally T., 1942
McIlwain, Janet J., 1936
McKean, Mary, 1903
McKee, Mary Margaret, 1958
McKeith, Edith Dorothy, 1962
McKelvey, Patricia Ann, 1949
McKenney, Gail Lee, 1967
McKernan, Regina, 1978
McKillip, Linda Lucille, 1963
McKinney, Margot, 1926
McKinstry, Mary A., 1925
McKinstry, Susan, 1965
McLaughlin, Carol Anne, 1974
McLaughlin, Catherine, 1923
McLauglin, Joanne, 1975
McLean, Margaret, 1917
McLeer, Rosemary, 1976
McMaster, Lynn, 1964
McMichael, Adele Griffith, 1948
McMinn, Sandra Jo, 1962
McMullen, Jean E., 1944
McMullen, Mary R., 1935
McNamara, Josephine Ellen, 1958
McNeil, Carol Ann, 1980
McNeish, Mabel L., 1930
McNerney, Hazel E., 1919
McNitt, Jean C., 1944
McNulty, Rose, 1914
McPherson, Edith, 1902
McQuillen, Elizabeth, 1961
McQuown, Helen Mae, 1959
McRae, Virginia, 1940
Meachum, Linda Jean, 1968
Mead, Vivian Earleen, 1964
Means, Roberta, 1940
Mease, Jeanne Elizabeth, 1949
Meckley, Shirley Ann, 1955
Medwid, Eva B., 1938
Meenahan, Mary J., 1944

Mehalko, Ruth E., 1954
Meighan, Katherine E., 1930
Meisenhelder, Mabel, 1913
Meisner, Carol, 1982
Melander, Anna M., 1919
Melevin, Alice Catherine, 1954
Melfe, Jewell Ann, 1964
Melville, Clara, 1910
Menendez, Rosalinda, 1969
Mengel, Bette Jane, 1949
Mengel, Marie Patricia, 1982
Mengotto, Roberta Eleanore, 1954
Mentzer, Brenda Lee, 1966
Mercer, Beryl J., 1957
Mertz, Dorothy Marie, 1947
Mertz, Lillian M., 1927
Messa, Josephine Frances, 1947
Messa, Marie T., 1950
Metka, Shirley Ann, 1956
Metz, Alberta H., 1940
Metz, Blanche E., 1929
Metzer, Betty J., 1943
Metzer, Mary L., 1930
Metzger, Elva Maria, 1960
Metzger, Maude L., 1934
Metzger, Therese Marie, 1977
Metzler, Jane C., 1942
Meyer, Marie, 1927
Meyers, Edith, 1931
Meyle, Elaine A., 1943
Meyle, Hedy Lynn, 1978
Meyle, Lisa Ann, 1979
Micale, Patricia, 1964
Michaels, Doris Lorraine, 1948
Michaels, Patricia Anne, 1961
Michalski, Helen Bernadine, 1950
Michaux, Holly Ferris, 1979
Mickey, Rita Marie, 1965
Mickle, Linda Ann, 1976
Mihalanas, Angela, 1981
Mikota, Catherine Frances, 1973
Mikulski, Karen Helen, 1976
Milburg, Maude, 1896
Miles, Josephine C., 1926
Miles, Lore Keating, 1965
Milewski, Esther C., 1943
Milewski, Lorraine Marian, 1949
Millard, Elizabeth M., 1942
Miller, Ada Irene, 1952
Miller, Anne Daphine, 1947
Miller, Arlean Viola, 1947
Miller, Barbara Ann, 1979
Miller, Beryl Yvonne, 1947
Miller, Carol Ann, 1978
Miller, Charlotte G., 1938
Miller, Dorothy Elizabeth, 1953
Miller, Elinor V., 1938
Miller, Elsie J., 1917

Miller, Evelyn G., 1932
Miller, Gayle Beth, 1978
Miller, Grace, 1904
Miller, Helen E., 1936
Miller, Jane, 1942
Miller, Josephine, 1929
Miller, Julianne, 1961
Miller, Katherine Elizabeth, 1980
Miller, Linda Elizabeth, 1967
Miller, Luann, 1973
Miller, M. Elaine, 1942
Miller, Mabel B., 1914
Miller, Marilyn Ann, 1959
Miller, Marilyn Lee, 1964
Miller, Marjorie M., 1933
Miller, Mary E., 1937
Miller, Nellie V., 1917
Miller, Ruth, 1942
Miller, Ruth Dessamond, 1947
Miller, Sharon Marie, 1979
Miller, Terri Ann, 1966
Miller, Virginia, 1930
Miller, Wilma Mary, 1957
Mills, Cathy Ann, 1973
Milon, Patricia Ann, 1966
Milotich, Margaret Lucy, 1957
Minahan, Mary Anne, 1978
Minner, Urieta M., 1927
Minnier, Ellen, 1911
Minns, Clara M., 1933
Mirecki, Karen Ann, 1977
Mishkofski, Rita Ann, 1954
Mitchell, Elsie V., 1933
Mitchell, Jessie, 1905
Mitstifer, Margaret Ann, 1948
Mitzel, Alisande Myrta, 1963
Mock, Patricia Ann, 1980
Mockaitis, Martina Mary, 1960
Moffett, Annetta M., 1930
Moffitt, Patricia Annie, 1968
Mogck, Anna M., 1943
Mogle, Dorothy Jean, 1948
Mohler, Patricia Anne, 1955
Mohr, Nancy Lea, 1968
Moiso, Barbara Jo, 1970
Molineaux, Cheryl Ann, 1982
Molitor, Georgianna J., 1947
Molitoris, Martha, 1957
Moll, Elizabeth Cora, 1951
Mollenkoff, Amanda, 1904
Monaghan, Katherine, 1895
Monillas, Myla May, 1963
Monroe, Donna Elizabeth, 1972
Montgomery, Ruth Elaine, 1968
Mood, Gloria Lynne, 1980
Moody, Ethel, 1933
Mooney, Arlene, 1972
Mooney, Betty Colleen, 1959

Moore, Charlotte D., 1929
Moore, Elsie M., 1942
Moore, Jane Elizabeth, 1975
Moore, Joyce Arlene, 1950
Moore, Linda Jean, 1970
Moore, Mabelle E., 1936
Moore, Margaret Jane, 1962
Moore, Marguerite D., 1934
Moore, Mary Louise, 1950
Moore, Rebecca M., 1942
Moore, Rosemary Elizabeth, 1958
Moore, Ruth E., 1942
Moore, S. Evelyn, 1932
Moore, Virginia Sue, 1963
Moore, Zelva Ann, 1959
Mooty, Ann Marie, 1972
Moretto, Maria Frances, 1977
Morgan, Alberta, 1911
Morgan, Anna P., 1944
Morgan, Jane, 1916
Morgan, Joan Ann, 1965
Morgan, Judith, Laura, 1967
Morgan, Margaret, 1907
Morgan, Mary, 1912
Morgan, Rebecca, 1906
Morkun, Constance Helen, 1973
Morrett, Judith Alice, 1947
Morrill, Elizabeth, 1910
Morris, Annamarie, 1979
Morris, Elva H., 1951
Morris, Janet Beverly, 1959
Morris, Pamela Regina, 1981
Morris, Virginia Sue, 1969
Morrison, Christine Lowe, 1948
Morrison, Jessie L., 1938
Morrison, Joan Dolores, 1951
Morrison, Marilyn Grace, 1946
Morrison, Marsha Ann, 1969
Morrow, Carol Ann, 1976
Morrow, Helen, 1901
Morrow, Paul D., 1981
Morrow, Phyllis Isabelle, 1946
Morrow, Wealthy Ellen, 1950
Morthorst, Margaret Anne, 1973
Morton, Joan, 1948
Mosely, Joan Marie, 1958
Moseman, Lydia E., 1924
Moser, Bertha, 1911
Moser, Christine Ann, 1961
Moser, Esther, 1911
Moser, Mary Lynn, 1959
Moser, Pearl, 1923
Moss, Naomi, 1918
Mosser, Freida Virginia, 1946
Mosteller, Mary Ann, 1950
Mostoller, Emma Noreene, 1961
Mote, Rhonda Ann, 1979
Mounce, Jeannette Miriam, 1960

Orndorff, Shirley Jeanne, 1956
Orner, Rhea M., 1934
Orr, Jessie Susann, 1953
Orr, Mae, 1923
Orr, Margaret, 1913
Orr, Sue Ellen, 1975
Orsine, Donna Marie, 1976
Ortlip, Elizabeth, 1967
Osbaugh, Sue A., 1921
Osborne, Margaret Marie, 1976
Osborne, Mary Louise, 1950
Osmundson, Susan, 1967
Ossenbeck, Margaret, 1908
Ossman, Elizabeth Ann, 1959
Osterhus, Janice Lillian, 1967
Ostrosina, Annette Jeanne, 1952
Ostroski, Loretta, 1960
Ott, Barbara Jean, 1965
Ott, Effie, 1914
Ott, Judith Anne, 1976
Ott, Margaret Mary, 1974
Ott, Virginia, 1940
Ottoson, L. Irene, 1950
Overdorff, Janet F., 1944
Owen Margaret, 1938
Owen, Edith M., 1938
Owens, Della I., 1925
Owens, Jane M., 1940
Owens, Linda Jane, 1975
Owens, Mary A., 1915
Owens, Veronica C., 1924
Owl, Agnes, 1920

~ P ~

Pachuta, Mary, 1941
Packer, Doris M., 1940
Packer, Dorothy E., 1935
Paden, Ruth E., 1940
Paff, Ferne R., 1942
Painter, Anna Mae, 1948
Painter, Elizabeth R., 1941
Painter, Emma, 1936
Painter, Janet E., 1954
Painter, Ruth, 1943
Palczewski, Joyce, 1975
Palichka, Agnes Jean, 1950
Palmer, Diane, 1950
Palmer, Suzanne Marie, 1956
Pangborne, Patricia Kirchner, 1958
Panick, Janice Ann, 1962
Pantalone, Marla Ann, 1981
Paoletti, Elvira, 1969
Paponi, Margaret Rose, 1958
Paranzino, Josephine G., 1958
Parcel, Helen, 1950
Pardee, Lida G., 1938
Paris, Eleanor Viola, 1949

Parisi, Valerie Valentine, 1980
Park, Iona Jean, 1947
Park, Jane Abbott, 1967
Parker, Elizabeth B., 1940
Parker, Laura A., 1931
Parker, M. Pauline, 1930
Parks, Nancy Carol, 1976
Parman, Gale Mary, 1961
Parr, Linda Anne, 1978
Parrish, Mary Whittier, 1961
Parry, Phyllis Gale, 1960
Parsons, Anna, 1910
Parsons, Anne, 1921
Parsons, Betty Lucille, 1948
Parzniewski, Carol Edwina, 1964
Pasquini, Phyllis Ann, 1970
Passmore, Vivian M., 1933
Patchel, Grace E., 1932
Pate, Joan Barbara, 1960
Patrick, Eileen, 1978
Patten, Elizabeth Jean, 1955
Patterson, Janet Lynn, 1978
Patterson, Karen Elizabeth, 1976
Patterson, Katherine, 1903
Patterson, Laura Ruth, 1946
Patterson, Margaret, 1908
Patterson, Patricia Lena, 1961
Patton, Anna, 1909
Patton, Esther E., 1935
Patton, Sarah, 1939
Paucke, Dorothy Marie, 1952
Paul, Joann, 1962
Paul, Laurie Anne, 1981
Paulson, Erma R., 1917
Paulson, Virginia Kay, 1974
Pauster, Dolores Ann, 1951
Pavulak, Mary, 1947
Paxon, Ann Shirley, 1957
Paxton, Sharon Elizabeth, 1968
Payne, Joyce Ann, 1972
Payne, Sandra Kay, 1968
Paynter, Marilyn Jean, 1966
Pazel, Mary Katherine, 1954
Pearson, Charlotte, 1909
Pearson, Mary Ann, 1950
Peck, Macie, 1902
Peck, Mary K., 1944
Peffer, Bonnie Rene, 1972
Peller, Cynthia Elizabeth, 1979
Pencavage, Delores A., 1952
Pennell, Avis Louis, 1947
Pennypacker, Lois Mae, 1949
Pensinger, Lorraine, 1939
Pepper, Elaine Barbara, 1974
Perry, Abbey Catherine, 1980
Perry, Margaret Anne, 1963
Pesci, Rose I., 1942
Peterman, Della, 1921

Peters, Cheryl Ann, 1967
Peters, Minerva, 1915
Peters, Suzanne Marie, 1970
Peterson, Catherine Anne, 1982
Peterson, Dorothy Ellen, 1948
Peterson, Dorothy T., 1931
Peterson, Mildred, 1921
Peterson, Susan Elaine, 1971
Petit, Ann Louise, 1980
Petrikin, Lucille, 1931
Petrock, Jean, 1958
Pettebone, Joan Esther, 1952
Pfaff, Helen F., 1941
Pfaltzgraff, Sara E., 1927
Pfau, Emma, 1902
Pfeiffer, Dorothy L., 1939
Pfeiffer, Irene Mary, 1972
Pfeiffer, Lisa Mary, 1978
Pfleegor, Betty Doane, 1956
Pfromm, Doris Emily, 1947
Phelps, Barbara Lynne, 1959
Phetteplace, Doris G., 1928
Philip, Karen Ann, 1972
Phillips, Amber Janet, 1967
Phillips, Anne H., 1927
Phillips, Beth Ann, 1975
Phillips, Judith Ellen, 1975
Phillips, Ruth E., 1922
Phoebus, Emma H., 1932
Piatt, Ellen E., 1933
Picard, Joyce Elaine, 1968
Pickell, Dawne Marie, 1948
Pickens, Sophia K., 1941
Pie, Emma, 1899
Pie, M. Alice, 1932
Pie, Rosalie, 1899
Piekarska, Halina Josefina, 1968
Pierce, Barbara Jean, 1976
Piersol, Elizabeth, 1934
Pierson, Carol Lynn, 1969
Pierson, Frances, 1928
Pierucci, Susan Lee, 1969
Pilling, Charlotte, 1918
Piquenais, Angele, 1922
Piro, Bessie Angela, 1966
Pispecky, Josephine, 1946
Plaisted, Marilyn Louise, 1952
Plasterer, Jeanette, 1951
Pletcher, Lillian M., 1927
Plevyak, Catherine R., 1956
Plumly, Sarah Helene, 1975
Plummer, Helen R., 1918
Pojawis, Mary Ann, 1961
Polesinski, Christine Mary, 1976
Pollack, Kathleen Marie, 1957
Pollitt, Marion C., 1933
Pollock, Francine L., 1982
Pollock, Laurie Michelle, 1967

Poole, Ruth M., 1938
Pope, Eleanor Lorraine, 1956
Pope, Lorraine Philomena, 1956
Porter, Emily I., 1941
Portner, Andrea Patrice, 1979
Posey, Cathie Mae, 1967
Potoski, Mary Ann, 1954
Potter, Mary E., 1942
Potticher, Druce, 1914
Pottiger, Marilyn Elaine, 1954
Potts, Sharon Rae, 1961
Pound, Margaret T., 1936
Powell, Alice, 1923
Powell, Janet Elaine, 1962
Powell, Lois Evelyn, 1952
Powell, Lucille M., 1944
Powell, Margaret Mae, 1968
Power, Elizabeth Ann, 1981
Powers, Patricia Ann, 1971
Pratt, Janet Elaine, 1965
Pratt, Marianne Louise, 1955
Prebula, Pauline Mary, 1949
Preihs, Patricia Ann, 1976
Preiss, Joyanne Ann, 1974
Prendergast, Catherine Cecelia, 1947
Prentice, Catherine Edith, 1967
Preston, Donna Lee, 1969
Prevost, Mabel C., 1929
Price, Joyce Evaline, 1949
Price, Sandra, 1968
Price, Shirley Jean, 1952
Priester, Janis Maxine, 1958
Prim, Sally Anne, 1948
Prime, Mary, 1907
Prisnock, Elizabeth Kathleen, 1947
Pritchard, Jean, 1948
Pritts, Nancy, 1981
Prophet, Nancy, 1921
Pryor, Patricia Ann, 1977
Pucci, Theresa E., 1932
Pufnock, Mary Lou, 1957
Pullen, Laura, 1911
Pupo, Edda Helen, 1952
Purcell, Katharine, 1921
Purinton, Ruth, 1921
Pusey, Alice M., 1931
Puskar, Dorothy Ann, 1956
Pyle, Elizabeth Jane, 1947
Pyle, Florence D., 1929

~ Q ~

Quairiere, Althea Claire, 1948
Quigley, Barbara Sue, 1976
Quinn, Christine Loretta, 1972
Quinn, Dolores Margaret, 1958

~ R ~

Raab, Kathleen Mary, 1967
Racik, Margaret A., 1940
Radar, Marion S., 1926
Radel, Mary S., 1936
Rainey, Carolyn Evelyn, 1920
Rainey, Nancy Jean, 1967
Rakestraw, M. Frances, 1930
Rakestraw, Margaret R., 1935
Raksnis, Irene Alice, 1960
Ramey, Edith, 1920
Ramp, Marion J., 1951
Ramsey, Mamie, 1895
Ramsey, Nona Marie, 1982
Ramsey, Sandra Jane, 1969
Ranck, Dorothy B., 1939
Randazzo, Catherine Murray, 1970
Randels, Lulu R., 1924
Ranieri, Donna Marianna, 1975
Rasely, Elizabeth A., 1941
Rau, Elizabeth Dorothy, 1956
Raub, Beatrice B., 1942
Raub, Cynthia Lou, 1971
Raubenhold, Dorothy K., 1934
Rauenzahn, Myra J., 1930
Ravenstahl, Sr. Bernadette, 1980
Ravicini, Joan C.M., 1958
Rayman, Beatrice L., 1942
Raymer, Sara M., 1932
Read, Anna Catherine, 1947
Read, Ella, 1904
Reamy, Mary A., 1922
Reath, Hazel Marjorie, 1959
Reaver, Bette Louise, 1960
Rebert, Ellen L., 1928
Rebert, Helen, 1928
Rebert, Vivienne Lorraine, 1946
Recchiutti, Mary J., 1941
Reck, Jessie Laverne, 1962
Recklitis, Anna M., 1926
Records, Stephanie Parker, 1964
Reed, Christine Marie, 1970
Reed, Elizabeth Ann, 1964
Reed, Elizabeth Anne, 1969
Reed, Gladys K., 1942
Reed, Helen B., 1923
Reed, Joan Ann, 1967
Reed, Josephine E., 1930
Reed, Mary E., 1898
Reed, Peggy Lou, 1949
Reeder, Idabelle Lorena, 1946
Reeder, Marion B., 1930
Reeder, Mary K., 1938
Rees, Carole Ethel, 1963
Reeser, Evelyn B., 1931
Reeves, Jean, 1908
Reeves, Jean Lucy, 1949
Reeves, Susan Elizabeth, 1967

Regan, Mary Catherine, 1963
Reginak, June Darlene, 1957
Regnier, Kathryn M., 1926
Reichard, Jill Ann, 1968
Reighard, Frances M., 1929
Reihart, Hazel Ann, 1955
Reilly, Helen J., 1966
Reimel, Madelyn P., 1931
Reimer, Helen V., 1934
Reimer, Jane, 1953
Reimer, Myrtle Pearl, 1920
Reiner, Barbara, 1954
Reinhard, Catherine, 1924
Reinhart, Nancy May, 1959
Reisler, Leila, 1906
Reitz, Pamela Jane, 1971
Remensnyder, Ellen E., 1940
Rennebaum, Mabel Elizabeth, 1958
Rennwantz, Alyce Jeanne, 1967
Reppert, Dawn Frances, 1969
Ressler, Carolyn Mae, 1960
Retay, Clare Louise, 1980
Reustle, Mary Elizabeth, 1975
Reynolds, Jane Adell, 1952
Rhiel, Clara Luella, 1947
Rhoads, Carol J., 1944
Rhoads, Muriel A., 1933
Rhoda, Beatrice Ruth, 1961
Rhule, Almira, 1921
Rhyne, Grace, 1931
Ribaric, Darlene Marie, 1977
Ricci, Jean Elaine, 1973
Riccio, Drosalina Mariana, 1958
Rice, A. Irene, 1919
Rice, Eileen, 1975
Rice, Irene N., 1933
Rich, Catherine Cecelia, 1967
Rich, Jennie, 1906
Rich, Loretta, 1963
Rich, Mary R., 1941
Richard, Grace Clarice, 1952
Richard, Karen Louise, 1977
Richards, Betty Louise, 1954
Richards, Dorothy, 1931
Richards, Lavina, 1910
Richards, Mary, 1904
Richardson, Clara C., 1950
Richardson, Patricia Ann, 1966
Richardson, Sue Mary, 1952
Richmond, Janice Eileen, 1976
Richter, Dorothea M., 1938
Rickard, Alice R., 1934
Ricker, Blanche M., 1919
Rickert, Phyllis Marie, 1960
Rickley, Janet Marie, 1958
Riden, Edna M., 1927
Ridgway, Cacelia Orlena, 1973
Riegel, Carol Elaine, 1960

Ries, Anita Marie, 1962
Riesdorph, Heidi Nan, 1978
Riggin, Susan Patricia, 1975
Riggs, Anna H., 1926
Riland, Martha E., 1927
Rine, Rachel C., 1937
Rinear, Judith Mildred, 1964
Rinehart, Shelva Jean, 1963
Ripple, Alice G., 1943
Risser, Ginette Rae, 1957
Risser, Phoebe, 1906
Ritaldato, Angela Celeste, 1981
Ritchey, Helen M., 1934
Rittenhouse, Joan Mignon, 1952
Rittenhouse, Lynn Gundel, 1968
Ritter, Ruth A., 1940
Ritter, Suzanne Jean, 1956
Rittle, Jannifer Ellanore, 1978
Roantree, Eileen, 1977
Roat, Lynne Jo, 1970
Roberta, Christine Ann, 1952
Roberts, Audrey Mae, 1951
Roberts, Donna Marie, 1980
Roberts, Ethel Marie, 1975
Roberts, Jill Ann, 1970
Roberts, Karen Marie, 1977
Roberts, Madge, 1942
Roberts, Marjorie Sue, 1955
Roberts, Ruth, 1923
Roberts, Ruth Marie, 1947
Robertson, Esther M., 1934
Robertson, Janet, 1943
Robertson, Marilyn Ann, 1956
Robeson, Billie Anne, 1962
Robinson, Constance Mervine, 1947
Robinson, Eleanor B., 1936
Robinson, Emily L., 1944
Robinson, Jeanne Kathryn, 1947
Robinson, Jessica Kim, 1980
Robinson, Linda Carol, 1979
Robinson, Marian L., 1925
Robinson, Mary, 1909
Robisson, Marion, 1941
Robson, Theresa, 1963
Rocchio, Janet, 1978
Roche, Florence Ann, 1956
Roche, Lorraine Marie, 1949
Rocheleau, Eileen Rita, 1974
Rockafellow, Betty Rae, 1959
Rockhill, Donna Karen, 1964
Rodden, Ann, 1978
Roddy, Mary Ann, 1973
Rodewig, Helen C., 1931
Rodgers, Christina Louise, 1958
Rodgers, Mary, 1914
Roe, Margaret, 1901
Roe, Martha Ellen, 1966
Roeder, Charlotte E., 1934

Roesch, Mary, 1927
Rogal, Dorothy E., 1942
Rogers, Anna, 1917
Rogers, Edith Grace, 1974
Rogers, Elizabeth, 1900
Rogers, Katherine, 1899
Rogers, Leslie Evelyn, 1966
Rohde, Helen, 1909
Rohman, Vera C., 1948
Rolland, Evelyn M., 1935
Roller, Grace A., 1939
Roller, Venone Grace, 1921
Romack, Judith Ann, 1960
Romano, Karen Joanne, 1973
Romano, Marlyn Mae, 1955
Romick, Elizabeth H., 1933
Ronalds, Joanne Louise, 1964
Ronco, Grace Inez, 1947
Rongyos, Irene, 1962
Rood, Sharon Jane, 1967
Rorabaugh, Jessie, 1915
Rorabaugh, Kathryn, 1937
Rose, Christine, 1973
Rose, Janine M., 1979
Rose, Joyce I., 1942
Rose, Sari Rochelle, 1977
Rosen, Sandra Denise, 1978
Rosenfeld, Regina Susan, 1968
Ross, Anne F., 1932
Ross, Catherine F., 1935
Ross, Donna Jane, 1958
Ross, Gerhart Ruth, 1950
Ross, Marjorie Kay, 1961
Rossetti, Carla Ann, 1974
Roth, Adeline A., 1932
Roth, Ethel L., 1928
Roth, Helen, 1905
Roth, Linda Lee, 1964
Rothman, Andrea Sharon, 1978
Rothwell, Nellie, 1896
Rotz, Mary, 1935
Rougeau, Amelie, 1928
Roulston, Geraldine, 1958
Roush, Alma E., 1928
Roush, Gene, 1941
Rowan, Ellen Patricia, 1946
Rowe, Effie, 1916
Rowe, Sarah E., 1922
Rowe, Zelda K., 1929
Rowinski, Florence, 1952
Rowles, Evelyn L., 1924
Royer, Marlene, 1963
Rozell, Virginia Lou, 1951
Rubin, Debra Joyce, 1981
Ruble, Marilyn, 1967
Rue, Gladys C., 1923
Ruebman, Judith Avous, 1960
Rugart, Lois Margaret, 1952

Ruhle, Kathryn C., 1933
Ruht, Nancy Darice, 1974
Rumberger, Frances Suzanne, 1962
Runyan, Carol Anne, 1960
Rupp, Beverly Ann, 1956
Rushin, Blanche T., 1935
Russell, Isabelle D., 1932
Russell, Lois Gail, 1965
Russell, Phyllis Marie, 1948
Russo, Carmen William, 1979
Russo, Hope Cecelia, 1969
Rutledge, Helen Marie, 1953
Rutt, Kathryn S., 1943
Rutter, Marion, 1943
Ryan, Jane Patricia, 1959

~ S ~

Sabin, Beverly Theresa, 1973
Sachs, Christine Ellen, 1972
Sachs, Elmina C., 1930
Sacks, Jeanette Freda, 1978
Sager, Ruth Ann, 1959
Sahler, Nancy Lee, 1962
Sakella, Annunciata Joan, 1958
Sakosky, Marie Theresa, 1979
Saksa, Margaret Katherine, 1962
Sallinger, Mary F., 1943
Salter, Joan Ann, 1961
Saltzer, Frances May, 1947
Sample, Dolores M., 1942
Sampsell, Dorothy Irene, 1960
Sampson, Joan Cochran, 1966
Samson, Janet M., 1941
Samuel, Deborah May, 1979
Sandell, Kathryn Elizabeth, 1979
Sanders, Marie, 1923
Sanders, Maude Reeves, 1947
Sanderson, Marlene Ruth, 1959
Sandler, Hope Beth, 1979
Sandt, Bonnie Ellis, 1965
Sankey, Margaret Patricia, 1959
Sannino, Elizabeth Adele, 1949
Santangelo, Kathleen Marie, 1982
Santarone, Claire Marie, 1966
Santoro, J. Eileen, 1981
Sarappa, Marie Lois, 1958
Sass, Patricia Ann, 1974
Sass, Rosemarie, 1966
Sassaman, June Lucille, 1949
Sattazhan, Alma Stowe, 1953
Satterfield, Elinor V., 1950
Satterlee, Bernice, 1919
Saunders, Lillian M., 1937
Saunders, Mary Anne, 1956
Saunders, Ruth Ann, 1956
Sauvageot, Rena Virginia, 1954
Savage, Ann Louise, 1952

Shermer, Nellie M., 1926
Shestakov, Katherine, 1979
Sheva, Helen T., 1937
Shinglock, Mary Elizabeth, 1957
Shirey, Cynthia Darlene, 1970
Shirey, Jean Elizabeth, 1948
Shirk, Elizabeth Louise, 1951
Shisler, Bonnie Eileen, 1966
Shive, Florence, 1937
Shively, Elizabeth, 1912
Shockley, Carol Ann, 1965
Shoemaker, Doris Kay, 1963
Shoemaker, Ella, 1916
Shoemaker, Helen Suzanne, 1946
Shoemaker, Nora A., 1929
Shoemaker, Nora E., 1908
Shoemaker, Patricia Joanne, 1951
Shonk, Ruth Louise, 1953
Shontz, Vera E., 1930
Shook, Elizabeth, 1896
Shore, June E., 1944
Shottin, Claire Bernice, 1946
Shoup, Mary June, 1947
Showers, Bertha Louise, 1958
Showers, Dorothy G., 1944
Showers, Thelma M., 1932
Shreeves, Diane Gail, 1974
Shreiner, Kathleen Gareth, 1971
Shrupski, Joan Marie, 1957
Shuck, Catherine Marie, 1966
Shuey, Phyllis Irene, 1963
Sickenberger, Helen Jean, 1948
Sickler, Anna F., 1926
Sickler, Bella E., 1927
Sickler, Norma M., 1932
Siddall, Virginia Anne, 1963
Siegrist, Carol Lynn, 1967
Sierant, Constance Theresa, 1957
Sierer, Aleta Ann, 1969
Silbermann, Hilda, 1919
Simmonds, J. Ellen, 1904
Simmons, Grace B., 1941
Simmons, Patricia Gail, 1978
Simons, Jacquelin Ellen, 1967
Simonson, Betty Lou, 1961
Simpkins, Elizabeth, 1942
Simpson, Janet Joy, 1961
Simpson, Jill Louise, 1967
Simpson, Ruth Elizabeth, 1976
Sincavage, Joan Ann, 1958
Singer, Cathleen J., 1931
Sipple, Margaret M., 1935
Sitgreaves, S. Elizabeth, 1938
Sitvarin, Harriet Gail, 1977
Sivacek, Lois Marie, 1953
Skane, Dabaniam, 1930
Skelton, M. May, 1921
Skidmore, Beverly Jane, 1960

Skillen, Diane Wilson, 1965
Skovran, Caroline Esther, 1958
Skubic, Mary Joan, 1950
Skvir, Elsie Kristine, 1949
Skwarek, Eileen, 1975
Slamon, Elizabeth Ann, 1965
Slaybaugh, Rhoda M., 1935
Sliwinski, Barbara Kathryn, 1965
Sloss, Annamarie, 1979
Slovich, Rosann, 1970
Sloyer, Carol Elizabeth, 1969
Smaling, Emily, 1909
Smart, Miriam, 1963
Smeltzer, Rhoda May, 1960
Smey, Julia, 1939
Smigelski, Elizabeth Ann, 1961
Smith, Ada M., 1939
Smith, Amanda L., 1943
Smith, Anne Kesting, 1969
Smith, Barbara Ann, 1958
Smith, Barbara Ann, 1959
Smith, Barbara Godfrey, 1955
Smith, Bernice Leona, 1920
Smith, Betty Ann, 1960
Smith, Catherine Helen, 1948
Smith, Charlotte F., 1939
Smith, Dava, 1975
Smith, Deborah Ann, 1975
Smith, Dorothy E., 1928
Smith, E. Virginia, 1941
Smith, Eleanore, 1911
Smith, Elizabeth P., 1918
Smith, Elizabeth W., 1944
Smith, Ethel, 1915
Smith, Geraldine H., 1939
Smith, Grace, 1957
Smith, Helen, 1910
Smith, Helen B., 1965
Smith, Hope, 1974
Smith, Inga Jeanne, 1958
Smith, Isabele Joy, 1951
Smith, Jacqueline Lee, 1956
Smith, Joanne Rae, 1958
Smith, Josephine L., 1937
Smith, Josephine M., 1938
Smith, June, 1937
Smith, June Elizabeth, 1958
Smith, Linda Jane, 1971
Smith, Margaret Jane, 1974
Smith, Marion E., 1917
Smith, Marion E., 1936
Smith, Mary, 1906
Smith, Mary E., 1938
Smith, Mary I., 1941
Smith, Mary Louise, 1966
Smith, Mary Minerva, 1946
Smith, Mildred E., 1932
Smith, Nancy Ann, 1963

Smith, Nancy Beth, 1977
Smith, Nora I., 1925
Smith, Pamela Lynne, 1962
Smith, Patricia Marie, 1961
Smith, Phoebe E., 1928
Smith, Rosie M., 1944
Smith, Ruth E., 1926
Smith, Ruth E., 1939
Smith, Sandra Lavon, 1979
Smith, Sandra Rae, 1969
Smith, Sarah, 1896
Smith, Sharon Elizabeth, 1979
Smith, Violet, 1937
Smulling, Catherine, 1934
Snare, Matilda E., 1938
Snell, Anne Bradley, 1956
Snellbaker, Sandra Eileen, 1960
Snider, Sandra Kay, 1972
Snodderly, Evelyn C., 1929
Snoddy, Hermorene, 1931
Snook, Ida Jane, 1951
Snook, Mary E., 1944
Snyder, Alma P., 1935
Snyder, Anna, 1913
Snyder, Clara Mae, 1941
Snyder, David James, 1976
Snyder, Elisa Beth Ann, 1954
Snyder, Jane Blanche, 1954
Snyder, Judith Ann, 1965
Snyder, Mildred M., 1943
Snyder, Minnie, 1913
Snyder, Myra C., 1936
Snyder, Shirley Rae, 1949
Snyderman, Shelley, 1975
Sochovka, Carol Ann, 1967
Sode, Carol Anne, 1962
Sode, Joan Phyllis, 1954
Sokodinsky, Josephine, 1947
Solecki, Susan Marie, 1982
Solimine, Vera, 1977
Solomon, Rebecca Myra, 1975
Soltys, Frances, 1941
Sorden, Sylvia A., 1922
Souder, Minnie S., 1930
Souder, Sandra Ann, 1981
Souders, Betsy Jane, 1976
Souders, Mary Carolyn, 1947
Sovin, Marlene, 1969
Spaeth, Sylvia M., 1981
Spalding, June Patricia, 1946
Spangenberg, Mildred, 1931
Spangler, Edna M., 1936
Spangler, Elizabeth L., 1944
Spangler, Joyce Marie, 1948
Spangler, Katie, 1901
Sparks, Ethel, 1933
Sparrow, Marilyn Jean, 1951
Spatig, Harriet R., 1937

Spatz, Margaret H., 1930
Spece, Joan Anne, 1962
Speicher, Mary Elizabeth, 1963
Spena, Grace Ann, 1971
Spence, Virginia Mae, 1948
Spencer, Ruth V., 1934
Spinnraker, Joan, 1978
Spitalniak, Christine Maria, 1977
Splett, Dorothy Marie, 1953
Spoerl, Mary Louise, 1963
Spohrer, Anne B., 1975
Sprague, Valerie, 1976
Sprenkel, Carolyn Louise, 1949
Sprenkle, Myrtle, 1914
Sprow, Constance Joy, 1961
Squire, Emily, 1910
Squires, Mary Elizabeth, 1968
St. Clair, Shirley M., 1951
St. John, Dorothy, 1972
Stabile, Beatrice Joy, 1963
Stack, Christine Ann, 1971
Stager, Lettie, 1914
Stahle, M. Louise, 1934
Stair, Helene Marie, 1979
Stair, Nellie A., 1931
Staley, Constance Dawn, 1958
Stalford, Bessie, 1912
Stambaugh, Eileen June, 1960
Stamm, Jeanne M., 1948
Stancavage, Shirley, 1956
Stanch, Regina, 1968
Stanek, Dolores, 1959
Stank, Margaret Alice, 1953
Stansbury, Ann, 1908
Stanton, Duane, 1982
Stanton, Mary Ellen, 1970
Starr, Claudia, 1922
Starry, Cassandra, 1965
Stasche, Jan Ellen, 1978
Staub, Harriet, 1913
Stauffer, Janet Marie, 1950
Stauffer, Mary A., 1928
Stauffer, Mary Ann, 1954
Steadman, Marilyn, 1966
Steele, Agnes E., 1935
Steele, Dorothy M., 1933
Steele, Kathryn R., 1929
Steelman, Susan, 1961
Stees, Rebecca E., 1935
Steigerwalt, Estelle, 1924
Steimer, Cheryl Adele, 1973
Stein, Lois C., 1936
Steinbock, Freda, 1921
Steinhagen Theresa Marie, 1974
Steinhagen, Jeanette Marie, 1971
Steininger, Margaret Murray, 1965
Steinmetz, Arlene Elizabeth, 1958
Steinmetz, Helen M., 1943

Stelzer, Florence A., 1932
Stemler, Geraldine Elizabeth, 1950
Steigerwalt, Viola E., 1920
Stephan, Elizabeth C., 1936
Stephens, Anna, 1917
Stepp, M. Elizabeth, 1929
Stern, Christine Kenny, 1982
Sterner, Patience Julie, 1962
Stevens, Carol, 1947
Stevens, Kathleen Mary, 1977
Stevens, Muriel, 1930
Stevens, Nancy Mae, 1950
Stevens, Suzanne Kathleen, 1967
Stevens, Vera Emilie, 1959
Stevenson, Judith Lynn, 1967
Stever, Mildred, 1938
Steward, Betty Ellen, 1947
Stewart, Elizabeth, 1925
Stewart, M. Faith, 1956
Stewart, Nancy Lee, 1952
Stewart, Rosemarie Patricia, 1978
Stewart, Susan Elisabeth, 1977
Stewart, Susan Irene, 1966
Stewen-Steinheil, Dagmar, 1926
Stickler, Myrtle L., 1927
Stiebler, Mary, 1896
Stiles, Thelma Sarah, 1959
Stites, Terry Dee, 1979
Stock, Joanne Marie, 1978
Stockman, Nora Ann, 1975
Stockton, Janet Marie, 1974
Stone, Gertrude E., 1942
Stonehill, Edna M., 1931
Stoner, Elizabeth M., 1928
Stong, Elaine Margaret, 1946
Stott, Frances T., 1930
Stoudt, Darlene Sylvia, 1958
Stouppe, Gwendolyn Ann, 1947
Stout, Catherine Ann, 1979
Stout, Julia Constance, 1947
Stout, Sally Judith, 1965
Stoutenburg, Mary Lee, 1954
Stover, Charolette, 1944
Strain, James E., 1980
Strange, Celinda Lou, 1968
Stranko, Anna, 1940
Straughen, Jodella Mae, 1956
Strauss, Mindy S., 1977
Strazzeri, Georgene Barbara, 1955
Streeper, Lynn Margaret, 1971
Strege, Linda Louise, 1967
Strick, Sandra Marie, 1974
Striney, Dorothy Josephine, 1947
Strohmaier, Bertha, 1903
Strohmaier, Katherine, 1896
Strong, Mary Jo, 1943
Stroup, Cynthia Ann, 1970
Strouse, Florence Ellen, 1920

Strunk, Daisy, 1909
Strunk, Frances M., 1922
Strunk, Jessie, 1923
Stuart, Carol Alice, 1954
Stuart, Catherine C., 1934
Stumb, Ruth Elizabeth, 1962
Sturgeon, Jane S., 1914
Sturgeon, Marian Grace, 1948
Sturges, Emily Virginia, 1947
Stute, Wilhelmina, 1903
Styslinger, Jean Kathleen, 1974
Styver, Marian H., 1925
Suber, Kathleen Ann, 1968
Suber, Loretta Josephine, 1971
Sudo, Maya, 1911
Sullinger, Mary F., 1943
Sullivan, Marilyn Elizabeth, 1963
Sullivan, Susan Joan, 1980
Summerfield, G. Averne, 1940
Summers, Dorothy Ann, 1952
Summers, Margaret L., 1941
Sumner, Sara Ellen, 1975
Sunday, Jane Alice, 1961
Sunderlund, Ruth I., 1943
Supplee, Elizabeth, 1905
Supplee, Jeanne Louise, 1946
Sutthill, Phyllis Shirley, 1962
Sutton, Deborah Ann, 1976
Sutton, Frances R., 1940
Swaar, Effie, 1921
Swager, Clara, 1908
Swalm, Carolee Joyce, 1962
Swan, Helen W., 1941
Swank, Effie, 1913
Swann, Patricia Ann, 1965
Swanson, Esther M., 1922
Swanson, Ruth E., 1939
Swartz, Karen Elise, 1972
Swartz, Louise Catherine, 1948
Swartz, Sharon Louise, 1965
Swartzlander, Evelyn, 1946
Sweeney, Clara N., 1936
Sweeney, Dionysia Mary, 1946
Sweeney, Josephine Marie, 1955
Sweeney, Mary Kathleen, 1973
Sweisford, Jean F., 1952
Swenk, Diane E., 1979
Swentzel, Marguerite, 1911
Sweyer, Sheila Gene, 1947
Swinand, Frances, 1967
Swinehart, Ruth Frances, 1950
Swirk, Evelyn A., 1943
Swisher, Chloe B., 1933
Swisher, Ida, 1919
Swoyer, Gertrude E., 1935
Sykes, Amanda, 1918
Sylvester, Theresa Anne, 1982

Symthe, Ruth Adele, 1953
Synnamon, Anna, 1900

~ T ~

Tachovsky, Irene Kay, 1969
Talley, Nanne, 1918
Tallman, Nadine Louise, 1965
Tananis, Mary E., 1936
Tangye, Jean Ruth, 1954
Tanner, Karen McKee, 1982
Tanner, Sylvia Yvonne, 1958
Tarapchak, Dolores Stephanie, 1959
Taraskas, Mary Ann, 1968
Tash, Kathryn L., 1924
Taylor, Audrey Rose, 1957
Taylor, Doris Lee, 1941
Taylor, Eileen Mary, 1967
Taylor, Elizabeth, 1934
Taylor, Helen Cooper, 1948
Taylor, Margaret C., 1937
Taylor, Mary A., 1931
Taylor, Myrtle V., 1942
Taylor, Nancy Lee, 1960
Taylor, Patricia Rose, 1974
Taylor, Phyllis Jean, 1956
Taylor, Sarah, 1905
Taylor, Stephanie Ruth, 1963
Taylor, Wahnette Marie, 1947
Tebbs, Edith M., 1930
Tegethoff, Deborah Lee, 1979
Tegge, Olga Rosalyn, 1920
Temple, Lillian, 1917
Tenari, Anna L., 1942
Tenbrook, Jacqueline, 1957
Terlecki, Adele Marie, 1971
Terrell, Molly Ann, 1942
Terrill, Beatrice, 1911
Tharp, Frances Elizabeth, 1963
Thomas, Esther L., 1941
Thomas, Helen M., 1943
Thomas, Linda Jane, 1963
Thomas, Margaret E., 1926
Thomas, Marie Grace, 1976
Thomas, Marline, 1979
Thomas, Martha E., 1956
Thomas, Mary E., 1944
Thomas, Mary Lou, 1974
Thomas, Patricia Ann, 1962
Thomas, Rhoda Rebecca, 1920
Thomason, Grace E., 1934
Thompson, Christina Ann, 1966
Thompson, Coe, 1895
Thompson, Elizabeth, 1895
Thompson, H. Evelyn, 1932
Thompson, Jennifer Jean, 1978
Thompson, Linda Ann, 1976
Thompson, Mary Patricia, 1957

Thompson, Nancy Ellen, 1951
Thompson, Nellie, 1895
Thompson, Patricia Ann, 1961
Thompson, Patricia Arlene, 1977
Thompson, Stephen Edgar, Jr. 1980
Thompson, Vera V., 1943
Thorn, Doris Mae, 1952
Thorne, Faye Evans, 1948
Thornton, Rebecca S., 1936
Thorp, Florence Marian, 1951
Thorp, Ruth E., 1942
Thrasher, Belle, 1912
Thumm, Dorothy Mary, 1952
Tice, Muriel Anne, 1947
Tichey, Bernadine Ann, 1958
Tichian, Tamara Lee, 1981
Till, Donna Lee, 1976
Timbrell, Bernice Louise, 1958
Timm, Margaret Rita, 1975
Tingley, Susan Elaine, 1976
Tipping, Kate Dolan, 1907
Tiracchia, Filomema R., 1927
Tiracchia, Mary Frances, 1963
Titlow, Audrey Ruth, 1955
Tiver, Veronica Lee, 1976
Toddings, Dorothy, 1910
Tomasello, Rose Marie, 1957
Tomasso, Kathryn L., 1942
Tomaszewski, Barbara Jean, 1970
Tomlin, Elsie, 1918
Tomlin, Jean Barbara, 1954
Tomlinson, Mary Suzanne, 1974
Tomlinson, Suzanne Mary, 1976
Tootchen, Phyllis Barbara, 1967
Toth, Joanne, 1978
Towner, Jean Martha, 1948
Towsey, Betty Lois, 1948
Toy, Patricia Ann, 1956
Trach, Elizabeth, 1950
Tragessor, Deborah Ann, 1980
Trambley, Madge Vivian, 1947
Tratch, Helen Mary, 1948
Tregear, Kathleen, 1981
Trembach, Carol, 1971
Tremmel, Gertrude, 1964
Treon, Jane Elizabeth, 1947
Trettis, Josephine Loretta, 1950
Trettis, Patricia J., 1955
Trigg, Lucy, 1896
Trimble, Frances L., 1942
Trimmer, Hazel Viola, 1948
Triolo, Maria, 1975
Tripple, Kathleen, 1978
Tritt, Helen Marie, 1946
Troester, Christine, 1916
Trostle, Anna L., 1943
Troutman, Diana Lynn, 1969
Troutman, Judith Lynn, 1980

Troxell, Anna Jeanne, 1951
Troxell, Carolyn Ruth, 1953
Trumbauer, Elaine Gladys, 1961
Trumbauer, Matilda, 1914
Tryenes Sarah G., 1933
Trzaska, Linda Helene, 1976
Tufenkian, Yeprakse, 1931
Tumolo, Rose Anne, 1961
Tuno, Patricia Ann, 1975
Turnbull, Marjorie Ann, 1955
Turner, Margaret Anne, 1963
Turner, Marilyn DuBois, 1949
Turriff, Marion, 1914
Tursi, Patricia, 1977
Twaddel, Anna Margretta, 1950
Tyler, Julia, 1934

~ U ~

Udicious, Mary Madeline, 1946
Uffelman, Mary E., 1924
Uhler, Hannah, 1922
Ullom, Madalyn M., 1938
Ulsh, Ruth I., 1931
Umberger, Juliet R., 1939
Umbower, Margaret Marie, 1953
Umholtz, Ada M., 1930
Underkoffler, Minnie M., 1930
Urban, Nancy Jane, 1954
Urevick, Denise, 1980
Utke, Suzanne Marie, 1980

~ V ~

Vache, Suzanne Elsa, 1963
Vail, Elinor Franklin, 1946
Valent, Helen Theresa, 1973
Valentine, Janice Edith, 1970
Valentine, Linda, 1967
Valentine, Tracy Foulke, 1966
Valohs, Maria Nettie, 1947
Van Dyke, Kathryn Elizabeth, 1971
Van Dyke, Margaret Ethel, 1972
Vancavage, Mary E., 1929
Vanderslice, Priscilla, 1935
VanHorn, Claire E., 1951
VanHorn, Lois C., 1929
VannAuker, Priscilla, 1921
VanSant, Evelyn, 1923
Vantilberg, Sara E., 1940
VanWinkle, Bessie, 1911
Varker, Lois Emilyn, 1946
Varklet, Marion, 1952
Vaughn, Alice, 1917
Veet, Angela, 1939
Veltry, Josephine Marie, 1977
Venzie, Bette Jane, 1978
Verdeur, Michele, 1974

Verdier, Miriam Anne, 1961
Vernon, Dorothy, 1912
Vernoy, Lillian N., 1948
Vetro, Albina Marie, 1952
Viles, Emily, 1908
Vinyard, Louise P., 1937
Virelli, Donna Maria, 1980
Vlahos, Marie Nettie, 1947
Vogel, Anne Marie, 1968
Voglarr, Norma A., 1944
Vogt, Josephine, 1905
Von Franzke, Ruth Ann, 1948
Voorhees, Georgianna, 1907

~ W ~

Wachter, Dorothy Marie, 1950
Wadsworth, Anna, 1907
Wagner, Donna Jean, 1979
Waite, Peggy Jane, 1955
Waldron, Marie Kathryn, 1982
Walk, Helen May, 1947
Walker, Janet Carolyn, 1965
Walker, Joan Suzanne, 1956
Walker, Margaret, 1894
Wall Dorothy M., 1934
Wall, Pauline K., 1926
Wall, Thelma D., 1944
Wallace, Beverly Jane, 1969
Waller, Esther L., 1935
Waller, Leona, 1912
Walls, Naomi G., 1955
Walp, Eleanor K., 1931
Walsh, Jacqueline Martha, 1959
Walters, Dora, 1896
Walters, Joyce Larue, 1950
Walters, Myrl Ann, 1956
Waltman, Grace E., 1926
Wampler, Lucille S., 1941
Wamsher, Edythe G., 1930
Wandell, Norma Ruth, 1948
Wang, Linda Bonnie, 1964
Ward, Harriet W., 1931
Ward, Mary Patricia, 1978
Warden, Diane, 1978
Wargo, Elizabeth Helen, 1949
Wargo, Mary Jane, 1947
Warmlinski, Linda, 1972
Warner, Bertha, 1919
Warner, Kathleen L., 1934
Warner, Marion F., 1928
Warren, Ann, 1915
Warren, Dorothy, 1915
Warren, Dorothy G., 1954
Wartella, Marie Lynda, 1968
Warthin, Esther Lee, 1957
Wary, Cora M., 1919
Waselus, Andrea, 1976

Washburn, Elizabeth Ann, 1960
Washburn, Nancy Lee, 1960
Wasilko, Jeannette, 1924
Wasitosky, Mary, 1939
Wasson, Janet Patricia, 1950
Waters, Deborah Ann, 1972
Waters, Essie, 1913
Waters, Kathleen Marie, 1978
Watkins, Deidre Marion, 1967
Watkins, Frances S., 1927
Watkins, Melba K., 1941
Watson, Susan, 1955
Watt, Eleanor K., 1931
Watters, Honor Jardine, 1975
Watters, Shirley Grace, 1946
Watts, Beverly Ann, 1969
Wayne, Donna Jean, 1953
Weatherley, Ernest Albert, 1978
Weaver, Dorothy Virginia, 1948
Weaver, Ruth, 1921
Weaver, Thelma L., 1940
Webb, Barbara Jean, 1975
Webb, Carole Ann, 1961
Webb, Linda Jane, 1973
Webb, Mary Jo, 1966
Webb, Mary Johanna, 1972
Weber, Helene, 1922
Weber, Mary Kate, 1951
Webner, Mildred N., 1931
Webster, Donna Mae, 1970
Webster, Dorothy, 1918
Wedge, Colleen Marilyn, 1957
Weems, Mary, 1911
Weidaw, Ruth I., 1938
Weidner, Joyce Irene, 1953
Weigand, Laverne, 1935
Weikel, Nancy LaRue, 1948
Weiner, Lenora Esther, 1966
Weippert, Pamela Gail, 1980
Weir, Mary, 1902
Weisback, Arleen, 1977
Weisel, Susanna M., 1958
Weisenberg, Melanie, 1914
Weisner, Patricia Sue Ann, 1977
Weiss, Debra Ellen, 1979
Weiss, Esther M., 1927
Weiss, June Helen, 1959
Weiss, Ruth Leanna, 1962
Weiss, Verna R., 1929
Weldon, Betty Marie, 1946
Welke, Dolores Lynn, 1972
Welker, Ada, 1913
Welker, Mary A., 1924
Welliver, Marie E., 1947
Wells, Patricia Jean, 1954
Welsh, Janet Doris, 1973
Welsh, Mary Pierce, 1922
Welsh, Melinda Anne, 1981

Welsko, Anna L., 1928
Welsko, Joann Marie, 1956
Welsko, Judith Marie, 1964
Welsko, Marian Elaine, 1962
Welsko, Veronica V., 1932
Welter, Carolyn Jean, 1962
Welty, Gladys M., 1937
Wentzel, L. Irene, 1939
Werkheiser, Eva R., 1939
Werley, Harriet H., 1941
Wermick, Linda Jane, 1963
Werner, Anne Elizabeth, 1950
Werstler, Sara L., 1940
Wertman, Hannah E., 1928
Wertz, Susan Marie, 1971
Wertzberger, A. Elizabeth, 1936
Wesley, Virginia Louise, 1951
Wessells, Marion E., 1939
West, India A., 1926
West, Kathryn M., 1933
West, Patricia C., 1958
Wetmore, Rowena E., 1925
Wetzel, Alice Marie, 1964
Wetzel, Dorothy V., 1937
Wetzel, Jeanne Estella, 1953
Wheatley, Grace June, 1951
Wheeler, Frances E., 1929
Wheeler, Wendy Ferree, 1976
Wheildon, Lillian, 1918
Whelan, Stella Reginia, 1959
Whelpley, Carole Anne, 1980
Whipple, Malinda Jane, 1963
White, Arline, 1910
White, Myra E., 1927
White, Patricia Jean, 1964
White, Rebecca Lynn, 1981
White, Rena L., 1923
White, Sara Ann, 1981
Whitebread, Evelyn E., 1933
Whitehead, Marjorie E., 1943
Whitehill, Anne Catherine, 1954
Whiteleather, Marjorie Jane, 1950
Whitesell, Grace E., 1930
Whitmore, Katherine E., 1928
Whysong, Betty Arlene, 1947
Widman, Carolyn Ruth, 1965
Widmeier, Marie L., 1943
Widney, Dorothy Jean, 1955
Widney, Evelyn Mae, 1948
Wiestling, Irene May, 1946
Wiggins, Susan Lynn, 1974
Wigglesworth, Bernice G., 1940
Wightman, Jeanetta Marian, 1952
Wildonger, Francis K., 1929
Wilhelm, Barbara Ann, 1952
Wilhelm, Bonnie Gay, 1963
Wilhelm, M. Ella, 1929
Wilhour, Susan Ann, 1965

We did it!

Part VI

College of Allied Health Sciences

Scott plaza, facing Jefferson Alumni Hall.

A bronze bust of Thomas Jefferson by famed sculptor Rudolph Evans, given to the University by Chairman of the Board of Trustees and his wife, Mr. and Mrs. William W. Bodine, Jr.

INTRODUCTION:
ORIGINS TO 1967

The listings of the College of Allied Health Sciences alumni begin with the graduates of 1968 from what was then called the School of Allied Health Sciences. It was on January 1, 1968, that the hospital-based programs in nursing and allied health were officially transferred to the School of Allied Health Sciences.

One of those programs was the Diploma School of Nursing, which continued to be a part of the newly organized College of Allied Health Sciences until the Diploma School closed in 1982. The long and distinguished history of the Diploma Nursing program and the listings of its alumni appear in a separate chapter.

While the School of Allied Health Sciences, established in 1967, was the immediate precursor to the College of Allied Health Sciences, established in 1969, the roots of the College extended much deeper. Education of nurses at Jefferson, which ultimately would come under the jurisdiction of the College, had begun in 1891. Over the years, the Hospital had been active in training programs in a variety of allied health areas: medical technology since 1929; radiologic technology since 1935; and cytotechnology since 1953.

Plans for the College had their origins in 1952 when key members of the Executive Faculty of Jefferson Medical College discussed the development and expansion of teaching in the paramedical field. In 1953 several members of the Executive Faculty also raised the question of University status, either by affiliation or on its own.

Among those members was Peter A. Herbut, M.D., Professor and Chairman of the Department of Pathology and Director of the Clinical Laboratories, who would later become President of Jefferson Medical College and Medical Center and then of the University in 1969 (Fig. 1).

In April, 1964, a meeting of the Executive Faculty of the Medical College in Hershey, Pennsylvania, identified a need for an academic program in the allied medical fields. By April, 1966, the Special Committee on Paramedical Studies, which had been formed in 1965 and was chaired by Peter A. Herbut, M.D., delivered its report that recommended the establishment of a School of Allied Health Sciences. The recommendation, which noted that it was "a golden opportunity to take the lead in the field of health professions

Fig. 1. Peter A. Herbut, M.D. (1912-76). Third Medical College President (1966-69). First University President (1969-76).

and occupations," was endorsed by the Executive Faculty.

Jefferson's Board of Trustees, on January 9, 1967, established the School of Allied Health Sciences of Jefferson Medical College and appointed John William Goldschmidt, M.D., as the first Dean (Fig. 2).

Dr. Goldschmidt, a Jefferson Medical College graduate of 1954, had joined the Medical Faculty in 1959, became Director of Physical Medicine and Rehabilitation at Jefferson Medical College and had become a nationally recognized leader in the field of rehabilitation medicine. His eight-year tenure as Dean witnessed the evolution of the new Division into an organized, thriving College.

Education in medical technology, in one form or another, had been part of Jefferson since the inception of the Hospital's first laboratories. In 1929, for the first time, students were taught in all disciplines of the Hospital's laboratories. In the early years, the program lasted 12 months and consisted almost entirely of one-on-one instruction by a laboratory technologist. On average, two or three students were accepted into the program at a time.

In September of 1941, the first formal class of four students was accepted at Jefferson. By 1950 the program was accredited for 15 students. The Medical Technology School was reaccredited in 1953 and again in 1963, each time with distinction.

Fig. 2.   John W. Goldschmidt, M.D., First Dean, School of Allied Health Sciences, (1967-1969), and College of Allied Health Sciences (1969-1975).

Introduction

Throughout the years, many of the graduates of the Medical Technology program in the years prior to 1968 remained close to Jefferson. These included: Sara E. Ransom, 1930; Bessie Dellette, 1936, who also served on the College's Alumni Advisory Committee for several years; June B. White (Fig. 3), 1938; Florence Cook, 1945; and Mary Jane Stetser Devitt, 1947.

Also, in the 1950s: Jean S. White, 1950; Doris T. Rowell, 1951; Frances Graupensberger, 1952, who earned a bachelor of science degree from Juniata College and became a Research Biologist at Wyeth-Ayerst Laboratories; Lois Renfer, 1953; Virginia Makarewicz, later Virginia Lyon, 1953, who earned a bachelor of science degree in medical technology from the University of Delaware, became a technical assistant at Memorial Hospital in Burlington County, New Jersey, and whose daughter Maureen Lyon graduated from the College's Medical Technology program in 1982; Mary Joan Robinson, later Mary Joan Robinson Pancoast, 1956, who earned a bachelor of science degree in medical technology at Gwynedd Mercy College, a master's degree from Immaculata College, and who became a therapist at Human Services of Downingtown, in Pennsylvania.

Also, in the 1960s: Carol Mattheiss, 1960; Carol A. Phipps Davis, 1961; Sara K. Davis, 1962, who earned three master of science degrees, in medical technology and in microbiology from Temple University and in library science from Villanova University, and became Manager, Patent Information, Corporate Patents-U.S. for Smith Kline Beecham Pharmaceuticals; Carol A. Vecchione,

later Carol V. Richards, 1962, who began her career in the Clinical Chemistry Laboratory at Jefferson Hospital and became Supervisor during her 16-year tenure.

Others in the 1960s: Gretchen Williams, 1963, who became a nurse at Bethesda Memorial Hospital in Boynton Beach, Florida; H. Louise Watson, 1964; Mary Ann Maier, later Mary Ann Cera, 1965, who became a Research Assistant for the University of Pennsylvania, working on research in cardiology at Geisinger Medical Center in Danville, Pennsylvania; Diane Blechman (Fig. 4), later Diane Feik, 1966, who graduated from Fairleigh Dickinson University and from Jefferson's College of Graduate Studies, became Laboratory Supervisor of the Microbiology Testing Laboratory of the University of Pennsylvania School of Dental Medicine, and co-authored numerous papers in the field of periodontology and microbiology; Ann Patterson Grossman, 1967; and Lynn S. Knestrick, 1967.

In the field of radiologic technology, Jefferson has a long history. The x-ray technician training program founded in the 1930s at Jefferson was one of the first in the United States. Accredited by the American College of Radiology, the program was on that organization's first roster of approved schools. Since that time, Jefferson has continuously featured a fully accredited program of radiologic technology.

Like most hospital-based programs over the next several decades, training was practice-oriented as students became apprentices, serving alongside technicians during the hospital workday. During this time period, Jefferson's graduates were highly successful in their national certifying examinations.

In March of 1966, the American College of Radiology noted that Jefferson had "a general excellent program," and in June of that same year the program received the approval of the Council on Medical Education of the American Medical Association for its 24-month program.

Pre-1968 graduates of the Radiologic Technology program who remained close to the College included: Letitia Mae Dana, later Letitia Dana Tanner, 1958, who began her career in the Radiology Department at Jefferson Hospital and later became an x-ray technician for New Jersey Man-

Fig. 3. June B. White, medical technology, 1938.

ufacturers Insurance Company and Helene Fuld Hospital; Wanda E. Wesolowski, 1958, who earned an associate of science degree at Hahnemann Medical University, a bachelor of arts degree from LaSalle University, and a master of arts degree from Beaver College, and who became Professor/ Chairperson of the Radiologic Technology program at Community College of Philadelphia, while contributing numerous presentations and publications in her field and receiving many honors and awards, including being named a fellow of the American Society of Radiologic Technologists and being presented with the College of Allied Health Sciences' Alumni Special Achievement Award in September, 1981; Seymour Sterling, 1959, who was named a fellow of the American Society of Radiologic Technologists and became Regional Technical Specialist for the Eastman Kodak Company and who returned to

Jefferson periodically to speak to students about career options; Betty Madigan, 1962; and Sarah M. Scharadin, 1963.

In the field of cytotechnology, researchers at Jefferson were studying the potential diagnostic applications of cytology in the 1940s and subsequently began to organize material to be used in training. It was on September 4, 1957 that Norma Ermler, a medical technologist, became the first student in a formal cytology training program at Jefferson.

In the beginning, the one-year program attracted an average of five students per year. In 1960 it acquired accredited status according to requirements established by "The Essentials of an Acceptable School of Cytotechnology," the first set of standards established for cytology schools, which were later accepted by the American Medical Association. Jefferson's program

Fig. 4.   Diane Bleckman, later Diane Feik, left, medical technology, 1966, and College of Graduate Studies, 1974, talks with Loretta Rocca, College of Graduate Studies, 1972, at a Symposium on Clinical Laboratory Management, sponsored by the College's Department of Medical Technology, in 1977.

Introduction

emphasized a student's proficiency in preparing cytologic specimens for microscopic analysis and in distinguishing between benign and malignant cells of the body's systems.

During the 1960s, students spent a total of 40 hours per week in the classroom/laboratory located on the third floor of the Foerderer Pavilion. Philadelphia-area physicians donated specimens from their laboratories, which helped increase the students' practical experience and developed their abilities to make critical differential diagnoses.

The need for cytotechnologists during the 1960s was great, accounting for the fact that the most consistent recruiters for the program were area pathologists who sent members of their technical laboratory staffs to receive cytology training. It was also during this time that cytotechnology began to enhance its professional status nation-

wide and create improved employment opportunities. Among the pre-1968 graduates was Cecile A. Wenker, later Sister M. Zita Wenker, 1966, who became a Roman Catholic nun, entering the Congregation of Jesus Crucified, O.S.B. and residing in Devon, Pennsylvania. She earned a bachelor of arts degree in biology from Salve Regina College and a master of arts degree in theology from St. John's University in Minnesota. She became active in theological scholarship, publishing and presenting papers at national and international conferences.

The School of Practical Nursing, which began in the spring of 1964, was a 12-month certificate program designed to provide more nurses to serve in direct patient care. Enrollments in the program gradually increased, both before and after its official integration into the School of Allied Health Sciences in 1968. When its last class, 66 students,

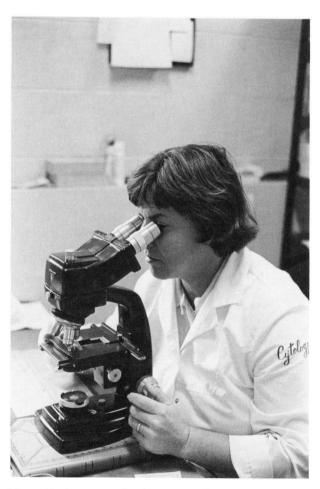

Norma Begley, cytotechnology, 1956, shown screening slides in a Jefferson laboratory in 1975.

Hilda Spence, cytotechnology, 1964, shown in 1975 at work in the Jefferson cytology laboratory.

graduated in 1980, the School of Practical Nursing had contributed 665 nurses to the profession.

By 1967, the foundations of quality education in nursing and the allied health professions at Jefferson had been laid. What happened at the end of the decade of the 1960s was the organization of the separate programs under a single administrative structure, the School of Allied Health Sciences, and later the College of Allied Health Sciences.

The pattern of development in the College at that time was to upgrade certificate programs to baccalaureate degree status, as well as to add new programs at the baccalaureate level. Originating with the vision of Dean John Goldschmidt and continuing under the leadership of Dean Lawrence Abrams, and with the cooperation of the other Divisions of the University, the support of the President and the Board of Trustees, the College of Allied Health Sciences, by the mid 1980s, emerged as a national leader in allied health education.

What follows is a 23-year accounting of the alumni, for whom the College has pride and affection, and of the evolution of the College through 1990.

Miss Carole R. Urban (right) No. 1 student in the 1962 class of the School of Medical Technicians, receives charm bracelet prize August 31 from Dr. Richard C. Taylor, Associate Professor of Pathology, while honor student's mother, Mrs. Austin Hiller, looks proudly on.

Prior to the historic School of Nursing commencement at which the 4,000th diploma was awarded to Miss Marilyn D. Ruble. Front row (l. to r.) Miss Mabel C. Prevost, R.N., B.S., M.S., Hospital assistant director; Mrs. Baldwin L. Keyes, member of Women's Board who presented its awards; Dr. Jane Wilcox, executive secretary, Epidemiology and Disease Control, Division of Research Grants, NIH, who was commencement speaker; Miss Doris E. Bowman, R.N., B.S., M.S., director of School of Nursing. Back row: Dr. John W. Goldschmidt, dean of School of Allied Health Sciences; Trustee Revelle W. Brown, member of Advisory Committee for School of Nursing; Mr. George M. Norwood, Jr., vice president for business-finance (treasurer): Mr. N. Ramsay Pennypacker, vice president for development; Dr. Baldwin L. Keyes, professor of psychiatry emeritus and member of Advisory Committee, School of Nursing; Dr. Peter A. Herbut, president of The Jefferson Medical College and Medical Center; Dr. Francis J. Sweeney, Jr., Hospital director; Dr. William F. Kellow, Jefferson Medical College dean and Rev. Frank M. Brown, D.D., associate pastor, Holy Communion Lutheran Church, and member of Advisory Committee, School of Nursing.

The graduating class of June, 1966, of the Jefferson School of Practical Nursing at the joint exercises June 27, 1967: First row (l. to r.), Elizabeth McGonigle, Carol West, Kathleen Cassell, Ellen Higgins, Barbara Del Villano, Kathy Lynn Smith. Second row (l. to r.), Carole Gardy, Dinah Best, Karen Swindell, Miss Elizabeth J. Sweeney, B.S., N.Ed., M.S.Ed., director of the Practical School of Nursing, Mary Ann Cieslak, Deaconess Hildegard Breves and Desiree Lafferty.

When the 1967/68 academic year began, the School of Allied Health Sciences was only a few months old, and many of the year's important activities involved the establishment of administrative structures and policies necessary for organized growth.

On January 1, 1968, the paramedical training programs of the Hospital were officially transferred to the School of Allied Health Sciences. These programs comprised the Diploma Nursing School with 275 students, the Practical Nursing School with 30 students, three Medical Laboratory programs with a total of 32 students, Radiologic Technology with 34 students, and Pharmacy with five students, for a total enrollment of 376. Faculty and administration numbered 73, and the annual operating costs were $618,000.

On January 8, by an action of the University Board of Trustees, a Trustee Committee for the School of Allied Health Sciences was created. Board Chairman James M. Large appointed Mr. William P. Davis, III (Fig. 5), as Committee Chairman for the affairs of the School. Mr. Davis was aided by six other members of the Board who, with the granting of the Thomas Jefferson University Charter on May 20, 1969, (Fig. 6) functioned subsequently as the Committee for the new College of Allied Health Sciences, officially starting July 1, 1969. The Committee held its first meeting on February 23.

Also in January, at a meeting with a representative from the Middle States Association of Colleges and Secondary Schools, the plans for the School of Allied Health Sciences to seek accreditation received enthusiastic encouragement.

In February, the School established an Office of Program Planning. At the time, the administration comprised three offices: the 1968 Office of the Dean; the Office of Admissions and Records; and the Office of Program Planning.

It was during this time that Lawrence Abrams, a member of the original planning committee for the School, while Coordinator of the Education Office in the Department of Rehabilitation Medicine, became the Coordinator of the Office of Program Planning and Director of Admissions and Registrar. This appointment proved to be the first in a string of promotions and broadening responsibilities that would culminate with his appointment as Dean of the College of Allied Health Sciences in 1978.

The Office of Program Planning and the other administrative offices for the School were established at 1008 Chestnut Street. Its neighbors were the Philadelphia Electric Building at the corner of Tenth and Chestnut Streets with its courtyard on one side and Pearson's Sporting Goods store on the other side.

Fig. 5. William P. Davis, III, Chairman of Board of Trustees Committee on Allied Health Sciences.

The School received a grant in June from the United Health Services and the Heart Association of Southeastern Pennsylvania for "Demonstration of Function and Effectiveness of a Health Careers Guidance Clinic." Working with Lawrence Abrams, Project Coordinator Dorothy Grieb established a program intended to fill gaps in recruiting and counseling services of both the educational and employment systems. The Clinic featured separate programs for guidance counselors, high school students and college students. What ultimately developed was a more than 20-year commitment to a public service activity sponsored by the School, later the College, of Allied Health Sciences.

Another component of the program, the Health Careers Guidance Manual, a reference book with in-depth descriptions of health careers, educational opportunities and related material, was published. Other editions of the *Manual* were published periodically through the years, the ninth edition appearing in 1989.

During the year, the medical technology program was reaccredited with distinction, and the curriculum was revised and divided into two segments. The first was a four-month period, during which students spent their time in lectures and student laboratories. The remaining eight months the students spent "at the bench" of the hospital laboratory for further practical experience.

Fig. 6.   Granting of the Charter to Thomas Jefferson University at City Hall, Philadelphia, May 20, 1969. Left to right: John W. Goldschmidt, M.D. (Dean of College of Allied Health Sciences); Francis J. Sweeney, M.D. (Hospital Director); James M. Large (Chairman of the Board); Judge Vincent Carroll; Peter A. Herbut, M.D. (President); N. Ramsay Pennypacker (Vice President for Development; George M. Norwood (Vice President for Planning); and William F. Kellow, M.D. (Dean).

In addition to 17 medical technology graduates, the Class of 1968 included seven in cytotechnology, 15 in radiologic technology and 28 in practical nursing.

Judy Phillips, radiologic technology, joined the staff of Jefferson Hospital's Department of Radiology.

Carol Chung Guy, radiologic technology, while on the staff of the Jefferson Hospital Department of Radiology, became Chairperson of the Staff Advisory Committee for radiologic technology students in the College of Allied Health Sciences in 1977 (Fig. 7).

Cynthia McCurdy, medical technology, joined the Jefferson Hospital staff in the Chemistry Laboratory. She served as an officer in the Medical Technology Alumni Association during the 1970s (Fig. 8).

Fig. 7. In 1977, Carol Chung Guy, radiologic technology, third from right, was Chairperson of the Staff Advisory Committee of Jefferson Hospital's Department of Radiology, the purpose of which was to give staff technologists a voice in the formation or revision of policies that affect radiologic technology students in the College of Allied Health Sciences during their clinical practicum rotations. Also pictured are, left to right: Tom Edwards, B.S., RT, instructor in the Department of Radiologic Technology; Lana Rau Clark, RT (radiologic technology, 1972); Brenda Thomas, staff technologist; Larry Walker, M.Ed., Acting Chairperson of the Department of Radiologic Technology; Ms. Guy; Barbara Yousaitis (radiologic technology, 1972), and Terry Corrado (radiologic technology, 1974).

1968

CERTIFICATE IN MEDICAL TECHNOLOGY
Barber, Diana, PA
DelValle, Nancy Carolyn, PA
Farrell, Joann M., PA
Fendrich, Cynthia M., PA
Grotzinger, Karen Rose, PA
Irvine, Barbara Kaye, PA
Jankowski, Marie Alice, PA
Klimaytis, Patricia, PA
Kummer, Judith Elizabeth, PA
McCurdy, Cynthia Ann, PA
Neidermyer, Kathleen McCarthy, PA
Ott, Judy Ann, PA
Ponemon, Sandra, PA
Rhein, Eileen P., PA
Smith, Alice Jane, PA
Spivack, Phyllis G., PA
Wantuck, Patricia A., NJ

CERTIFICATE IN CYTOTECHNOLOGY
Churchill, Judy Rae, NJ
Derbes, Jane Agnes, TX
Hoffman, Kathy Louise, PA
Lazow, Ilene Hope, PA
Neiffer, Christine Anne, PA
Ocampo, Ofellia Ong, PA
Salg, Sister Joyce, PA

CERTIFICATE IN RADIOLOGIC TECHNOLOGY
Argondizza, Linda, PA
Chaiken, Iris, PA
Connors, Kathleen, PA
Dixon, Joseph, PA
Doyle, Maryanne, PA
Greenspan, Barbara, PA
Guy, Carol, PA
Lewalski, Frances, PA
Linstrom, George, NJ
Matthews, Dianne, PA
Noble, Barbara, PA
O'Neill, Sallie, PA
Phillips, Judy, NJ
Smith, Rita, PA
Stackhouse, Sandra, PA

CERTIFICATE IN PRACTICAL NURSING
Bonneau, Barbara F., NJ
Cassidy, Eleanor Agnes, PA
Coviello, Helen Catherine, PA
DeYulius, Maria Margaret, NJ
Eustace, Christine, PA
Exum, Jacqueline Joyce, PA
Ford, Judy Lynn, NJ
Grayno, Joyce Ann, PA
Higgins, Winifred Johnson, PA
Hitchins, Daphne Susanna, PA
Jones, Shirley Ann, NJ
Kane, Mary Agnes, PA
Kinzinger, Mary Lou, PA
Mantegna, Jennie Careen, PA
McFarland, Sandra Lea, PA
McHenry, Gemma Charlette, PA
Melton, Barbara Virginia, NJ
Murray, Barbara Jean, NJ
Siems, Stephanie Beth, PA
Simon, Susan Lee, PA
Smalls, Yvonne, PA
Smith, Ann Marie Hancock, PA
Stevenson, Dolores Sallie, PA
Stuart, Susan Marie, PA
Thompson, Lula Mae Hollis, PA
Valentino, Gorgetta Mae, PA
Wiktor, Carol Jean, PA
Wolford, Michele Rogers, PA

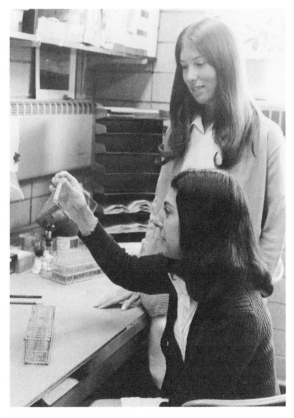

Fig. 8. Cynthia McCurdy, medical technology, standing, is pictured with Carol Tobin (medical technolgy, 1975) doing serial dilutions in serology in a Jefferson laboratory in 1975.

Starting with the 1968/69 academic year, the School of Allied Health Sciences, through the General Studies Program, offered basic college-level courses as an opportunity for students in the School of Nursing and students in other allied health programs to begin or continue working toward an associate or baccalaureate degree. The General Studies Program, which included courses in the humanities, the social sciences, and the natural sciences, was offered in cooperation with the Philadelphia College of Pharmacy and Science. A total of 43 students matriculated in the fall quarter.

In October, 1968, the Health Careers Guidance Clinic conducted the first of its 18 Saturday student clinic sessions and three counselor workshops for the academic year. By May, 1969, more than 500 high school students and 29 school counselors had visited Jefferson.

The School of Practical Nursing completed its fifth year of operation and passed the 100 mark in number of graduates, with 27 finishing the program in 1969.

The School of Radiologic Technology, which completed a two-year reorganization, graduated 13 students. In March, 1969, the Council on Medical Education of the American Medical Association gave unqualified continuing approval to the program and raised the approved number of students to 44. During the year, for the first time, radiologic technology students participated in the student affairs of Jefferson's Commons in order to facilitate more contact with other students. The School's Francis Carey Award, given to the radiologic technology graduating student who most completely combines technical skill with kindness in dealing with patients, went to Harriet Cathcart. The Mallinckrodt Award was won by Deirdre Howard.

The School of Medical Technology expanded its instructional facilities by a partial move to space in the Department of Pathology in Jefferson Alumni Hall, where a laboratory, faculty office, lecture room and conference room were made

available. Ten students graduated in 1969. The record of the School, Dean Goldschmidt noted in a report, is superior with less than 5% attrition and a 98% success in passing the registry (ASCP) examinations.

The Division of Cytology, home of the School of Cytotechnology, was granted independent status within the Clinical Laboratory, and the program's facilities were relocated from the third floor of the Foerderer Pavilion to the second floor of Jefferson Alumni Hall. Eight students earned their certificates in cytotechnology in 1969.

Kathleen M. Koons (Fig. 9), later Kathleen

Fig. 9. Kathleen M. Koons, medical technology, as pictured in a 1976 photograph published in the alumni publication, *Allied Health Review.*

Koons Brown, medical technology, became a medical technologist in the Radio-isotopes Laboratory at Jefferson. She later graduated from West Chester University, majoring in health sciences administration.

Judith A. Scheeler, later Judith A. Wicken, medical technology, became a research technologist in macrophage studies at Duke University Medical Center. She later took a position as a medical technologist with a specialty in immunology at the Maine Medical Center in Portland, Maine. She completed her graduate studies in immunology at the University of Southern Maine in 1988 and received ASCP certification as a specialist in immunology in 1989. She co-authored a research paper on chronic lymphocytic leukemia and worked on a Lyme disease research project on Monhegan Island, Maine.

CLASS OF 1969

CERTIFICATE IN MEDICAL TECHNOLOGY
Dzink, Joann Louise, PA
Heineman, Adele Mary, PA
Koons, Kathleen Mary, PA
McBride, Dianne Leslee, PA
Miller, Rochelle A., PA
Mortensen, Pamela Anne, PA
Nach, Ilene Etta, PA
Pietkutowski, Karen, PA
Sheeler, Judith Ann, PA
Shah, Usha J., NJ

CERTIFICATE IN CYTOTECHNOLOGY
Albert, Margaret Walsh, PA
Bristand, Ifalia I., PA
Madonna, Dorothy, PA
Nadig, Constance, PA
Pienta, Nancy Ann, NJ
Stickle, Donovan, CA
Theodulfa, Sister Mary, PA
Vanore, William, PA

CERTIFICATE IN RADIOLOGIC TECHNOLOGY
Babal, Marlene, PA
Brown, Lynn, NJ
Cathcart, Harriet, PA
Edgar, Lenore, NJ
Howard, Deirdre, PA
Lober, Connie, PA
Margulies, Myra, PA
Masi, Carlotta, PA
Ochitill, Karen, PA

Pish, Christina, PA
Potter, Donna, PA
Sandor, Susan, PA
Stone, Susan, PA

CERTIFICATE IN PRACTICAL NURSING
Alizzi, Lucille Frances, PA
Beausang, Anna Marie, NJ
Bell, Carolyn Elizabeth, PA
Capista, Anne Satoris, PA
Capitanio, Barbara Rose, PA
Conway, Maureen Margaret, PA
Corsey, Florence Lillian, NJ
Doakley, Virginia Ann, NJ
Ferrari, Kathleen Mary, PA
Gillan, Moira Patricia, PA
Hanna, Phoebe Annett, NJ
Harrell, Judith Ann, PA
Hoffman, Carol Ann, PA
Kaiser, Patricia Ann, PA
Larsen, Judith Dane, NJ
Magnotta, Marion Claire, PA
Malone, Mary Eileen, DE
Morgan, Sally Ann, PA
Perkins, Stella, PA
Phillips, Carolyn D'Addarie, PA
Sandom, Alice Irene, PA
Skinner, Vira Mae, PA
Taylor, Joanne Mary, PA
Troutner, Susan Kathleen, PA
Yox, Judith, PA
Zagnojny, Elsie Cecilia, PA
Zwirner, Ellen, NJ

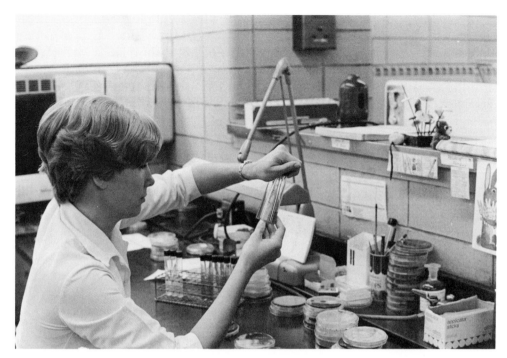

Joann Dzink, medical technology (1969), shown checking biomedical reactions in Jefferson's microbiology laboratory (1975).

Dr. Peter A. Herbut, president of Jefferson Medical College and Medical Center (left, seated), accepts a check from the Merck Company Foundation, which is donating $15,000 toward the planning and founding of Jefferson's School of Allied Health Sciences. Mr. Rolland J. LeTourneau (seated, right) and Mr. Richard E. Kiefner, (center, standing), acted for the Merck Company Foundation. They are field representatives of Merck Sharp & Dohme. Dr. John W. Goldschmidt, dean of the School of Allied Health Sciences and director of the Department of Physical Medicine and Rehabilitation, (left, standing) and Dr. Francis J. Sweeney, Jr., Hospital Director (right, standing) look on.

The 1969/70 fiscal and academic year was a landmark year for Jefferson. Effective July 1, 1969, Thomas Jefferson University and the College of Allied Health Sciences were created by action of The Board of Trustees. The former School of Allied Health Sciences, became the College of Allied Health Sciences under the new University Charter.

The College was joined by the newly named College of Graduate Studies, and by Jefferson Medical College and Jefferson Hospital to form the new University Health Science Center. Each Division was organizationally parallel, with a separate administration directly responsible to the President under the overall control of the Board of Trustees.

During the year, medical technology students were the first accepted into the newly organized College. To reflect this major change in status, the curriculum was redesigned, extended to 24 months, and consisted of courses in each of the content areas that awarded academic credit. To follow in the tradition of practical experience, during one-third of the curriculum, the students worked at the bench in the Hospital laboratory in clinical rotation.

With the approval of the College of Allied Health Sciences Committee of the University Board of Trustees, the College began a program with the Lankenau Hospital School of Nursing, whereby General Studies courses were included in Lankenau's diploma-level curriculum and taught by College faculty. In March, 1970, a similar agreement, to be effective the following academic year, was reached and approved for nursing students at Pennsylvania Hospital.

In its second year of operation, the Health Careers Guidance Clinic workshops for guidance counselors and clinics for high school and college students, included tours of clinical facilities where students could meet health care professionals in their workplace and learn first-hand about specific careers (Fig. 10).

On June 25, 1970, the College of Allied Health Sciences Committee of the Board of Trustees approved implementation of an upper-level (junior and senior years) baccalaureate degree program in medical technology for September, 1970. Graduates awarded certificates included 13 in medical technology, nine in cytotechnology, 16 in radiologic technology and 33 in practical nursing.

Anna M. Romano, later Anna R. Savage, cytotechnology, became a cytotechnologist at Philadelphia Naval Hospital. In 1977, she earned a bachelor of science degree in sociology from St. Joseph's University. She later entered a master's degree program in social work at Rutgers University.

Beverly Werner, later Beverly Werner Volk, medical technology, earned a master's degree in social work.

Susan Parsons, later Susan Parsons Page, medical technology, became an instructor of clinical microbiology in the Medical Technology Department at the University of Vermont. She earned a master of science degree from Ohio State University in 1972.

Gabriel P. Cesare, cytotechnology, became a cytotechnologist for the Upjohn company in King of Prussia, Pennsylvania.

CLASS OF 1970

CERTIFICATE IN MEDICAL TECHNOLOGY
Bingman, Mary Ellen, PA
Braconaro, Diana M., PA
Brown, Joan K., PA
Caplan, Lois, PA
Forman, Anita B., PA
Freedman, Rochelle Edithe, PA

Habazin, Dolores Ann, PA
Himmelwright, Mary Lynn, PA
Johnson, Suzanne, PA
Kavchok, JoAnn, PA
Papier, Susan, PA
Parsons, Susan Dale, NJ
Werner, Beverly Dianne, PA

CERTIFICATE IN CYTOTECHNOLOGY
Cann, Rose, PA
Cesare, Gabriel Patrick, PA
Garcia, Mireya Fortuny, NJ
Levy, Elena Geozon, PA
Lewicki, Stefania Helena, PA
Mann, Dorothy Elizabeth, PA
Meyers, Barbara Rose, PA
Oliver, Bonnie Lee, PA
Romano, Ann Marie, PA

CERTIFICATE IN RADIOLOGIC TECHNOLOGY
Bamford, Barbara, PA
Brody, Teresa, PA
DiMond, Michele, NJ
Forshaw, Diane, NJ
Licardello, Eileen, NJ
Lindahl, Dagmar, PA
Longstretch, Susan, PA
Lynch, Christine, PA
Madden, Mary, NJ
Moss, Janice, PA
Murphy, Beverly, PA
Schlager, Carol, NJ
Simmington, Linda, NJ
Steet, Christine, PA
Vaudreuil, Michele, PA
Wajda, Joan, NJ

CERTIFICATE IN PRACTICAL NURSING
Acquarolo, Mary Anne, NJ
Archut, Linda Denelsbeck, NJ

Blythe, Alice Mae, PA
Branch, Pearl May, NJ
Cesarini, Rosalie Anne, PA
China, Virginia, PA
Costello, Margaret Mary, NJ
Duffy, Cathy Elaine, PA
Dugan, JoAnn Gertrude, PA
Filler, Joann Rose, PA
Forte, Josephine Gerald, PA
Ginyard, Judith Sandra, PA
Hamaniuk, Marianna, PA
Heenan, Elizabeth Anne, PA
Jacobs, Kathleen Rose, PA
Johnson, Portia Keen, NJ
Krywucki, Karen Elizabeth, PA
MacFarland, Cathy Lee, PA
McGroarty, Katherine Ann, PA
Money, Wilhelmina Anna, PA
Patrick, Mylette Alethea, PA
Perrine, Diane Louise, PA
Sawicki, Margot M., PA
Segal, Elise Karen, PA
Sherman, Nancy Jane, PA
Speights, Christine, PA
Terry, Kathleen Anne, PA
Treston, Elizabeth Marie, PA
Tulone, Stephen John, PA
Winnberg, Hannah Mary, NJ
Wollman, Barbara Ann, NJ
Wozniak, Gerri Lynn, PA
Wozny, Rosemary Anne, PA

Fig. 10.   Health Careers Guidance Clinics provide tours for high school and college students.

The 1970/71 academic year was noteworthy in the development of the College. In the fall of 1970, the College admitted its first class of students to seek a baccalaureate degree from Thomas Jefferson University when 10 students entered the medical technology program.

The University Board of Trustees, at a meeting on November 2, 1970, gave its approval for the College to establish a bachelor of science in a nursing degree program. This would complement the two already existing nursing programs, diploma nursing and practical nursing.

During the year, Jefferson's hospital-based cytology program and the College drew closer. Cytology education at Jefferson and elsewhere was on the verge of a major transformation when the United States Public Health Service funds were terminated. Although 13 schools closed, Jefferson's cytology school battled financial difficulties by charging tuition for the first time in its history—$50 per student for the six-month course. This provided funding for the students, but the teaching/supervisory position had lost its support. The program turned to the College of Allied Health Sciences in hope of assistance. Dean Goldschmidt approved transfer of the supervisor's position to the College. Thus the Jefferson program survived the transition in funding sources and grew closer to the goal of becoming fully integrated with the College and enhancing the likelihood of a degree program, which became an actuality a few years later.

By December, 1970, the College's administrative offices had moved from 1008 Chestnut Street to the second floor of Jefferson Alumni Hall (Fig. 11), and the administration had expanded to serve the growing student body. In his 1971 *Plan for the College of Allied Health Sciences*, Dr. Goldschmidt addressed the need for Jefferson to take the initiative in solving the nation's health care crisis, which included serious shortages of health care personnel. He noted too that "health professionals must be educated to be both scientists and humanists."

Graduates of the Class of 1971 included students who earned certificates in medical technology (15), cytotechnology (10), radiologic technology (17) and practical nursing (47).

Dail White, later Dail White Deitrick, medical technology, became chief hematology technologist in the pediatric oncology branch of the National Cancer Institute.

Rhonda Karp, cytotechnology, joined the College's cytotechnology faculty in 1975 after spending three years as a cytotechnologist at Hahnemann Medical College and Hospital and Temple University Hospital and earning a master's degree in pathology from Temple University. First as Education Coordinator and then as Chairman, she converted the hospital-based School of Cytotechnology into the College-based baccalaureate degree program Department of Cytotechnology in 1975 and 1976. In 1977, she was the College's first recipient of its Alumni Special Achievement Award (Fig. 12). She earned an Ed.D. at Temple University in 1978 and continued to chair the department until 1979 when she was appointed Assistant Dean of the College and Professor of Cytotechnology. She became Associate Dean in 1982 (Fig. 13), yet continued to contribute to her field, including editorship of *The Cytotechnologist's Bulletin* from 1981 to 1986 and active participation in the American Society of Cytology, which named her "Cytotechnologist of the Year" in 1987. In 1984, Dr. Karp was awarded a Fulbright Lectureship in Quito, Equador, and named an "Outstanding Young Leader in Allied Health" by the American Society of Allied Health Professions (ASAHP). She was elected to the ASAHP Board of Directors in 1985 and to the Committee on Allied Health Education and Accreditation of the American Medical Association in 1987. She left her position as Associate Dean in 1987 to become Executive Associate to University President Lewis W. Bluemle, Jr., M.D., until June 1990, when she returned to the College as Chairman of the Department of Laboratory Sciences.

CERTIFICATE IN MEDICAL TECHNOLOGY

Bamford, Helen, PA
Cheung, Amy Ping-Lok, PA
Cureton-Freed, Deborah, PA
Gessner, Judith O., PA
Harrington, Jean Elizabeth, PA
Jarmoszuk, Diane, PA
Loveless, Darlene, PA
Meicke, Marian L., CA
Metcalf, Julia, PA
Mueller, Carolyn Ann, PA
Niemeyer, Jean Marie, PA
Schramm, Linda Susan, PA
Smith, Jean Marie, PA
Travia, Maria Ann, PA
White, Dail Charlotte, PA

CERTIFICATE IN CYTOTECHNOLOGY

Boddorff, Elizabeth Anne, DE
Cox, Linda Susan, NJ
Edelstein, Marian Debra, PA
Hwang, Yank Suk, WI
Karp, Rhonda, PA
Loturco, Marie Teresa, PA
McClosky, Sister Ann Margaret, PA
Mitchell, Valerie Lee, PA
Setty, Shantna L., PA
Shearn, Margaretta Ellen, PA

CERTIFICATE IN RADIOLOGIC TECHNOLOGY

Alcaide, Juanito, PA
Fisher, Constance, PA
Gallagher, Theresa, PA
Glovin, Susan, PA
Kaplan, Rita, PA
Labella, Nadia, NJ
LaMere, Denise, NJ
Miller, Joan, PA
Powell, Mary, PA
Rosenblum, Bonnie, MD
Saul, Thomas, PA
Schank, Eileen, PA
Sosnowski, Krystine, PA
Tool, Cheryl, NJ
Vallieu, Marie, NJ
Wapner, Ellen, DE
Wydra, Debra, PA

CERTIFICATE IN PRACTICAL NURSING

Anderson, Eloise, PA
Anderson, Deborah Lucille, NJ
Andrews, Paula Jane, NJ
Barbera, Joan, PA
Becker, Louise Ellen, PA
Brown, Susan Marie, PA
Canter, Dorothy Elizabeth, NJ
Carhart, Cynthia, NJ
Centifonti, Nancy Ruth, NJ
Ciuffetelli, Mary Josephine, PA
Cline, Jacqueline Rita, NJ
Colonna, Elaine Alice, NJ
Dokes, Myrtle Jane, PA
D'Onofrio, Christina Marie, NJ
Ericson, Celine Marie, PA
Esdale, Gwendolyn Joan, NJ
Graefe, DonnaMarie, PA
Hart, Lee, PA
Holley, Constance Teresa, PA
Howard, Patricia Ann, NJ
Johnstone, Brenda Renee, PA
Lyles, Constance Eloise, NJ
Mammele, Patricia Anne, PA
Mathis, Elizabeth R., PA
McLaughlin, Annette Marie, PA
McMahon, Kathryn Lee, PA
Meckley, Martha Gene, PA
Meehan, Marilyn Ann, PA
Mireno, Deborah Mary, PA
Mitchell, Karen Elizabeth, NJ
Parks, Roberta Lee, NJ
Petch, Renee Theresa, PA
Pickett, Dorthea Ahnee, PA
Purnell, Carol Ann, PA
Puzio, Mary Elizabeth, PA
Quigley, Sr. Loretta Mary, PA
Rhone, Sara E., NJ
Rietheimer, Estelle Diane, PA
Schupack, Ilsa, PA
Scott, Doris Elaine, PA
Singletary, Aurora, PA
Spegel, Patricia Jean, NJ
Stith, Deborah Laura, PA
Stone, Sharon Anne, NJ
Wecksler, Linda Michele, PA
Wilson, Walter Ray, PA
Witty, Virginia Adrienne, PA

Fig. 11. Jefferson Alumni Hall became home to the administrative offices of the College of Allied Health Sciences in December, 1970.

Fig. 12. Rhonda Karp, cytotechnology, received the College's first Alumni Achievement Award in 1977 from Marten M. Kernis, Ph.D., Dean.

Fig. 13. Rhonda Karp, Ed.D., cytotechnology, as Associate Dean of the College of Allied Health Sciences.

Fig. 14. Dean John W. Goldschmidt indicates career options in Allied Health.

When the 1971/72 academic year began, the College of Allied Health Sciences comprised four schools: the School of Nursing, a three-year diploma program, with an enrollment of 234 students; the School of Practical Nursing, a one-year certificate program and a 21-month work-study program, with 61 students; the School of Radiologic Technology, a two-year certificate program, with 46 students; and the School of Medical Technology with three programs, a one-year certificate program in histologic technology, with four students, a third-year certificate program in cytotechnology, with six students, and a third- and fourth-year baccalaureate degree program in medical technology, with 39 students.

During the year, the newly formed Department of Baccalaureate Nursing prepared for its first entering class in the fall of 1972 by developing its curriculum, receiving approval of the State Board of Nurse Examiners, recruiting seven faculty members and accepting a class of 46 students.

Also during the year, application was made, a process of self-study was instituted, and site visits were conducted by visiting consulting teams in order to gain accreditation status by the Middle States Association of Colleges and Secondary Schools. On June 23, 1972, the University received notification of acceptance as a recognized candidate for Middle States Accreditation.

Dean Goldschmidt (Fig. 14) wrote in a report: "The development of the College has progressed encouragingly and much valuable groundwork has been laid."

The Merves Distinguished Lecture in the Humanities in Medicine was established in honor of the late Louis Merves, M.D. (Fig. 15), who was associated with Jefferson Medical College from 1933 to 1969, through the generosity of Dr. Merves and many of his friends. The guest lectureship was administered by the Office of Student Affairs and Services.

At Commencement Exercises in June, 1972, four medical technology graduates were awarded the

Fig. 15. Louis Merves, M.D., for whom the College's Distinguished Lecture in the Humanities in Medicine was named.

bachelor of science degree, marking the first time that such degrees were granted by Thomas Jefferson University.

Marilyn J. McHenry, later Marilyn McHenry Pachefsky (Fig. 16), cytotechnology, returned to Jefferson as a faculty member in the cytotechnology program in 1976 after holding a cytotechnology position with Upjohn Laboratory Procedures East in King of Prussia, Pennsylvania. Working with the program's Education Coordinator Rhonda Karp (Fig. 16) (cytotechnology, '71), she was instrumental in the evolution of the School of Cytotechnology into the Department of Cytotechnology in 1976, offering the first two-year, upper-division bachelor's degree program in the nation. She earned a master's degree in health education at Temple University. She served as the Department of Cytotechnology Chairman from 1980 to 1984. After leaving Jefferson, she earned a law degree from Temple University.

Geneva Cook, later Geneva Wiggins-Collins, cytotechnology, pursued her career at Smith Kline Beecham Clinical Laboratories in West Norriton, Pennsylvania, becoming a senior cytotechnologist. She also earned a master of arts degree in theater at Villanova University and worked part-time as a professional actress.

B.S. in MEDICAL TECHNOLOGY
Guerrera, Donna Theresa, PA
Ho, Wendy Wen-In, PA
Hull, Robert Merrill, MD
Shlaifer, M. Edward, PA

CERTIFICATE IN HISTOTECHNOLOGY
Brown, Rochelle F., PA
Krebs, Karen H., PA
Lewis, Joan E., PA
Yonchek, Joan C., PA

CERTIFICATE IN CYTOTECHNOLOGY
Carroll, Anthony Brendan, PA
Chepulis, Margaret Ann, NJ
Cook, Nellmarie Geneva, NJ
Green, Richard Wayne, PA
Kim, Soon-Hi Shin, KOREA
McHenry, Marilyn, PA
Paradis, John J., PA
Raphelson, Nancy, PA
Stavely, Janet Lynn, NJ

CERTIFICATE IN RADIOLOGIC TECHNOLOGY
Andrukitas, Aleta, PA
Bartolomeo, Rita, PA
Britt, Barbara, PA
Callahan, Denise, NJ
Farrell, Linda, PA
Faulkner, Darlene, NJ
Giordano, Donna, PA
Gritton, Patricia, NJ
Hoffman, Marcia, PA
Nardone, Anna, PA
Nicolella, Anna, NY
Pigliacelli, Irene, PA
Pitchon, Lisa, NJ
Prubaker, Prem, PA
Rachover, Michael, PA
Rau, Lana, PA
Raup, Gretchen, NJ

Smith, Jacqueline, PA
Somerset, Catherine, NJ
Weber, Mary, PA
Wehner, Patricia, NJ
Wise, Catherine, PA
Yousaites, Barbara, PA

CERTIFICATE IN PRACTICAL NURSING
Angelo, Darcelle Roslyn, PA
Borochaner, Gail Robin, PA
Buecheler, Mary Elizabeth, PA
Busciacco, Linda Jean, NJ
Carroll, Rosemarie Ann, PA
Chestnut, Ruth Ann, PA
Clews, Margaret Ann, PA
DeCarlo, Denise Ann, Pa
Feldman, Anna Ruth, NJ
Ferguson, Loretta Joanna, PA
Foster, Michelle Ann, PA
Giosa, Rosemary Louise, PA
Graham, Maxine, NJ
Gray, Marjorie Louise, NJ
Guariglia, Eva-Lynn Edith, PA
Jackson, Gwendolyn Zetella, PA
Jonas, Patricia Frances, PA
Kairunas, Nancy Katherine, PA
Kraus, Elsie Katherine, PA
Krylowicz, Donna Ann, PA
Maloney, Karen Ilene, NJ
McGinn, Margaret Anne, PA
McKeough, Valerie Kathleen, PA
Miller, Allison Dowie, MO
Newell, Mary-Frances, NJ
Pernicano, Lucille Mary, PA
Poulos, Margaret Josephine, PA
Quartana, Theresa Ann, PA
Roach, Kathleen Barbara, PA
Shirk, Susan Hall, PA
Sierchio, Karen Ann, PA
Spause, Susan Sophia, PA
Traczuk, Luba, PA
Zalecky, Anne-Marie, PA

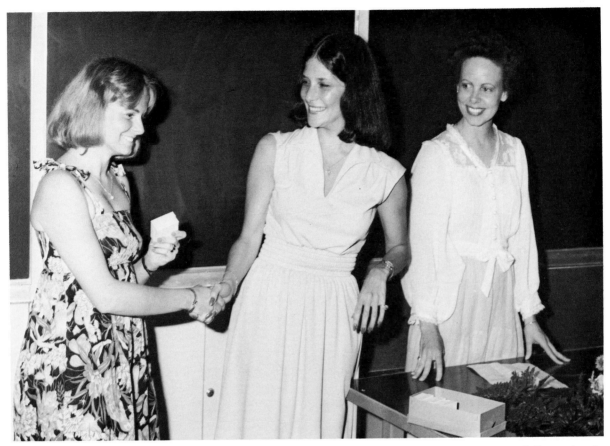

Fig. 16. Marilyn J. McHenry, cytotechnology, right, as an instructor in the College's Department of Cytotechnology in 1978, participates in an awards ceremony with Department Chairman Dr. Rhonda Karp, center.

The natural course of the human mind proceeds from credulity to skepticism.

Thomas Jefferson (1743–1826)

A major milestone in the development of the College was reached during the 1972/73 academic year with the matriculation of the College's first class of baccalaureate degree-seeking nursing students, numbering 46, in September, 1972. The new curriculum, which admitted students at the junior level, when joined to the College's on-going programs in diploma nursing and practical nursing, was seen as broadening the spectrum of opportunity for alternative pathways to a nursing career and providing upward career mobility.

A Special Project Grant from the Division of Nursing, Bureau of Health Manpower, for more than $94,000 was used to help develop the nursing program, its curriculum, faculty offices, learning equipment and materials.

In addition to Thomas Jefferson University Hospital, other sites for clinical learning experiences in nursing were obtained through affiliation agreements with Methodist, Pennsylvania and St. Christopher's Hospitals as well as with the South Philadelphia Neighborhood Health Center and Rebound Health Center.

In the medical technology program, a new curriculum for the senior year was implemented with the incoming class of 1972. The former 12-month apprentice-type instruction in the hospital was converted into an academic nine-month program of three quarters carrying 32 semester credit hours. This curriculum was reviewed and approved with high praise by the American Society of Clinical Pathologists' Board of Schools.

Continuing education programming in medical technology was begun this year with a Workshop on Microscope Maintenance, conducted in March, 1973, which attracted 34 technologists from the clinical laboratories and basic science departments as well as graduate and medical students.

Effective in July, 1972, as part of the institutional fringe benefit program, all fulltime employees of Jefferson became eligible to participate in a tuition reimbursement program for courses taken in the College's Department of General Studies.

The College's Student Activities Committee was formed in the spring of 1973 and was the prime mover in the publication of a Student Handbook and the development of the Orientation Program for incoming students.

A total of 148 students graduated from the six programs of the College at the conclusion of the 1972/73 academic year. At the University's June 8 Commencement Exercises, 15 medical technology students were awarded the bachelor of science degree. Non-degree graduates numbered 133 in the programs of cytotechnology, histologic technology, diploma nursing, practical nursing and radiologic technology.

Vivian D. Fleming, later Vivian F. Christian, medical technology, earned a master of science degree in medical biology with a specialization in clinical hematology from the C.W. Post Center of Long Island University in 1976. During her career, she worked with the three major manufacturers of hematology analysers, Coulter, Technicon and TOA, as a clinical specialist or consultant. She also taught hematology in the medical technology program at Georgia State University. In 1990, living in Decatur, Georgia, she held a position as Hematology Support Specialist for Baxter Healthcare Corporation's Scientific Products Division.

Naomi Bee Culp (Fig. 17 and 18), medical technology, earned a master's degree in biology in 1978 and a doctorate of arts in medical technology in 1983, both from The Catholic University of America. From 1978 to 1980, she was assistant professor of medical technology at Wichita State University. By 1984, she had become a training and applications specialist for Sysmex Hematology Instruments at Baxter Scientific Products in Chicago. In 1989, she was named Manager for the Clinical Applications, Quality Assurance and Regulations Division of TOA Medical Electronics in Los Alamitos, California.

Maria Gloria Theodos (Fig. 18), later Maria

Theodos Wilson, medical technology, earned a master of science degree from Jefferson's College of Graduate Studies.

Edward Pierzynski (Fig. 17 and 18), medical technology, began his career as a Laboratory Technician for Community Clinical Laboratories in Oaklyn, New Jersey, and was subsequently promoted to Laboratory Manager. He moved to BioQuest Company where he was Senior Sales Representative. Continuing his career in sales, he became National Training Manager for BBL Microbiology Systems. He then went to Johnston Laboratories as Industrial Sales Manager and later Marketing Manager. In 1987, he became Director of Sales and Marketing for Helvoet Pharmaceuticals. In 1990, he held the position of Marketing Manager at Thomas Scientific in Swedesboro, New

Jersey. A very active alumnus, Mr. Pierzynski periodically returned to Jefferson to speak to student groups. Over the years since his graduation, he held a variety of alumni positions, including President of the Medical Technology Alumni Association, a member of the College's Alumni Advisory Committee, Chairman of the College's Annual Fund Raising Campaign and member of the Board of Directors of the Alumni Association.

Joanne Beyer Bergquist, medical technology, after pursuing her career in the microbiology laboratory at Jefferson (Fig. 19), went on to service in Latrobe, Pennsylvania. She taught at the community college and served parttime as a histology technologist at Latrobe Area Hospital. She published a paper "Primary Care" in *The Office Laboratory*.

Fig. 17. Medical technology alumni, pictured in 1976, include four members of the Class of '73. Left to right: Stephanie Cole, '74; Arnold Storr, '73, newly elected Vice President of the Medical Technology Alumni Association; Naomi Culp, '73, former Secretary/Treasurer; Edward Pierzynski, '73, President; Harold McClintic, '73, former Vice President, and Cynthia McCurdy, '68, Secretary/Treasurer.

B.S. in MEDICAL TECHNOLOGY

Beyer, Joanne Ruth, PA
Culp, Naomi Bee, NJ
Derham, Patricia Anne, PA
Fleming, Vivian Denise, PA
Lin, Yueh Kuei, NJ
McClintic, Harold Maxwell, Jr., PA
Neill, Suzanne, PA
Noorbakhsh, Parveen Hassan, PA
Pierzynski, Edward J., NJ
Sciole, Marilyn Bernadette, PA
Storr, Arnold C., PA
Strable, Donald L., NJ
Theodos, Maria Gloria, PA
Toth, Valerie Joan, PA

CERTIFICATE IN HISTOLOGIC TECHNOLOGY

Goldie, Lynn Sheryl, PA
Bond, Carole, PA
Goodie, Lucie, PA
Oros, Della, PA

CERTIFICATE IN CYTOTECHNOLOGY

Gifford, Ruth Naomi, PA
Peters, Marina, PA
Sheehan, Jane Katherine, NJ
Singla, Veena, NJ
St. John, Sr. Mary Louise, PA
Young, Maryanne, PA

CERTIFICATE IN RADIOLOGIC TECHNOLOGY

Connor, Carole, PA
Dienno, Maryann, PA
Gilbert, Susan, PA
Hanlin, Joann, PA
Harrigan, James, PA
Jones, Patricia, PA
Kane, Helene, PA
Krier, Nancy, PA
Lalli, Annette, PA
Lampfield, Susan, PA
Lutz, Carol, PA
Marozzi, Adrienne, PA
Pinelli, Mary, PA
Readinger, Margaret, PA

Fig. 18.   Members of the Medical Technology classes of 1972 and 1973 held a tenth-year reunion in June, 1983. Left to right: Maria Theodos Wilson, '73; Arnold Storr, '73; Joanne Beyer Bergquist, '73; Edward Pierzynski, '73; Naomi Culp, '73; Kathleen Meehan Arias, '72; Patricia Derham Hines, '73; and Valerie Toth Call, '73.

1973

Shasanya, Yinka, PA
Vetter, Joann, PA

CERTIFICATE IN PRACTICAL NURSING

Adam, Joanne Marlowe, PA
Albani, Anna Maria, NJ
Baker, Nancy Jean, PA
Bellenghi, Jean Mary, PA
Bratzler, Margaret Mary, PA
Bullock, Joyce, PA
Clayton, Barbara Ann, PA
Curry, Ann Frances, PA
Daransky, Marguerite Elsie, PA
DiFelice, Valorie Ann, PA
DuBois, Patricia Ann, PA
Freedman, Jacqueline, PA
Gusz, Kathryn Ann, NJ
Hall, Suzanne Marple, PA
Harrison, Gayle Ellen, PA
Hemphill, Clare Anne, PA

Higher, Rosetta, PA
Hirschhorn, Dena, NJ
Hochberg, Joyce Alice, PA
Jones, Amye Lee, PA
Kennedy, Francis, Jr., PA
Kenney, Patricia Louise, NJ
Kratky, Sandra Patricia, PA
Krauss, Ruth Mildred, PA
Lehman, Rose Marie, PA
Martinac, Frances Marie, NJ
McCraig, Rita, PA
Nusspickel, Theresa Ann, PA
Page, RoseMarie Ann, NJ
Petta, Anthony Domenic, PA
Pierce, Kathleen Theresa, PA
Sage, Theresa Ann, PA
Savard, Theresa Ann, PA
Schindler, Kathlen Joan, PA
Sherman, Donna Jane, NJ
Tokarski, Mary C., PA
Young, Marsha Louise, PA

Fig. 19. Joanne Beyer Bergquist, medical technology, at work as supervisor, special microbiology laboratory at Jefferson, in 1975.

The 1973/74 academic year was marked by an expansion of the student body, faculty and facilities. Total fulltime enrollment for all classes numbered 551, an increase of more than 90 students from the previous year.

The newly acquired Health Sciences Center, also known as the Edison Building, at 9th and Sansom Streets, made it possible to upgrade facilities for accommodation of diploma and practical nursing faculty as well as students in offices and classrooms (Fig. 20).

Affiliation with Chestnut Hill Hospital, whereby senior medical technology students would rotate through clinical laboratory experiences, was successfully negotiated. This allowed for the expansion of the senior class from 18 to 25 students.

In April, 1974, a team of five College of Allied Health Sciences students entered the Medical Technology Student College Bowl, held at Pennsylvania State University, and placed second in the state competition.

A first major effort in continuing education for allied health personnel, designed to maintain currency of information and skill in proficiencies of professional practice, was launched. As part of Jefferson's Sesquicentennial Celebration, an Interprofessional Symposium featuring concurrent sessions in nursing, medical technology and cancer rehabilitation was attended by more than 400 professionals in May.

The College's Health Careers Guidance Clinic marked its sixth year of operation. The Clinics were over-subscribed, with 237 students from 71 area schools attending seven clinics. In addition, 38 guidance counselors attended the two Counselor Workshops and the fourth edition of the *Health Careers Guidance Manual* was published.

Commencement Exercises were held on Friday, June 7. The bachelor of science degree was conferred on 18 medical technology students and 40 nursing students. This was the first class of baccalaureate degree nursing students in the history of the College. A total of 161 other students graduated from the College's non-degree courses

in cytotechnology, histologic technology, diploma nursing, practical nursing and radiologic technology.

Radiologic technology students receiving awards were: Theresa Joan Corrado, the Frances Carey Award for extraordinary tact and kindness in patient care; Donna Marie Annarelli, the Dean's Award for the academically outstanding gradu-

Fig. 20.   Edison Building (Health Sciences Center).

ate; Michael S. Kuber, the Clinical Award, presented by the Squibb Pharmaceutical Company for outstanding clinical practice; and Jane Elizabeth Storjohann, the Class Award, presented by the Mallinckrodt Company for the student who demonstrated understanding and interest in fellow students.

Thomas Edward Leahey, medical technology, a member of the College's 1974 Medical Technology Student Bowl team that placed second in the state competition, returned to his native Connecticut. He earned a master's degree from Quinnipiac College and became Assistant Director, Laboratory Services, at Griffin Hospital in Derby, Connecticut.

Nancy Meier Calabrese, nursing, became the Medical Director of the Hand Surgery and Rehabilitation Center in Washington, D.C. In 1989, she published an article, "Reconstructive Hand Surgery, Distraction Augmentation Manoplasty" in *Modern Medicine*. She also served on the Board of Directors of Washington, D.C.'s Ronald McDonald House.

Josephine Ann Catanzaro, nursing, became a staff nurse in London, England in 1979/80, was certified in critical care nursing in 1981, and earned a master of science in nursing degree from the University of Pennsylvania in 1986. In 1990, she was Critical Care Clinical Nurse Specialist and Coordinator for the Critical Care Nurse Internship Program at Hahnemann University.

Mary Elizabeth Payne, nursing, became a board certified enterostomal therapist in 1985 and subsequently held the position of Public Health Nurse III/Enterostomal Therapist for the Sussex County Health Unit in Georgetown, Delaware.

Theresa Marie O'Connor, nursing, earned a master of science in nursing degree and subsequently began a private practice in psychotherapy. An active alumnus, she returned to Jefferson periodically to speak to nursing students about career options (Fig. 21).

Leigh Anne Pierson, later Leigh Pierson-Brown, nursing, spent two years at Children's Hospital in Philadelphia before joining Thomas Jefferson University Hospital in 1976. She left Jefferson three years later to enroll in the pediatric nurse practitioner curriculum at Gwynedd-Mercy College. After her graduation in 1980, she decided to work as a pediatric nurse practitioner in Cambodia and Thailand in a program sponsored by the International Health Division of Cornell University and operated under the auspices of the International Rescue Committee (Fig. 22). The program was designed to provide medical care to the thousands of refugees who were fleeing Cambodia. She later returned to the United States, settled in Oakland, California, earned a master's degree in public health and continued to serve refugees through her work in public health.

Beverly Elizabeth Vandergrift, later Beverly Vandergrift Farrar, radiologic technology, became supervisor of Magnetic Resonance Imaging at the Hospital of the University of Pennsylvania.

Nancy Lee Council, later Nancy Council-Maguire, histologic technology, returned to the College to earn a bachelor of science in cytotechnology in 1978. A full description of her career and accomplishments appears in that year's text (Fig. 43).

B.S. in MEDICAL TECHNOLOGY
Branch, Erica Marie, PA
Cole, Stephanie Barbara, PA
Dalal, Asha N., PA
Deitz, Andrea Phyllis, PA
DiBartolomeo, Mona Lisa, NY
Gala, Suresh Gangji, PA
Jacques, Daniel Lee, PA
Joachim, Leonard, PA
Kenis, Marilyn Margaret, PA
Leahey, Thomas Edward, CT
Levy, Claudia Erica, PA
Mancinelli, Joseph J., PA

Roberts, Lauren Sari, NY
Schildhorn, Marsha Wendy, PA
Schottenfeld, Susan, NJ
Schwartz, Donna, NY
Utley, Barbara Lynn, PA
White, Susan Joyce, PA

B.S. in NURSING
Boehm, Deborah Hedy, PA
Bucher, Linda, NJ
Buckman, Jane Lowenthal, NJ
Calabrese, Nancy Meier, NJ
Catanzaro, Josephine Ann, PA

Comeaux, Kathleen Gillard, PA
Conlon, Ruth B., PA
Coyle, Dolores Ann, PA
Davis, Betsy Ann, PA
DeBaun, Janice Gail, FL
Erthal, Mary Ann, PA
Gellar, Ellen Anne, PA
Gordon, Carol Ilene, NY
Gottheim, Merle Schwartz, NJ
Haggerty, Patricia Mary O'Halloran, PA
Hummel, Jane Alice, PA
Hwozdek, Lorraine Monica Mueller, PA
Lazar, Stuart A., PA
Lynch, Judith Ann, PA
Maguire, Patricia Anne, PA
Mannherz, Elaine Carol, PA
Mattera, Nancy Louise, PA
McCormick, Carolyn Jean, PA
McLane, Michael James, PA
Midouhas, Robyn Lynn Gesemyer, PA
Mintz, Lynda G., PA
Nicolo, Donna M., PA
O'Connor, Theresa Marie, PA
Oliver, Elizabeth, PA
O'Neill, Adele Barker, PA

Payne, Mary Elizabeth, PA
Pierson, Leigh Anne, PA
Previti, Marianne, NJ
Sedmak, Judith Anne, PA
Taylor, Sherry Lee, PA
Timmons, Ann Vera, MD
Walter, Valerie, PA
Wejant, Gail Elaine, NJ
Weisburg, Linda Prepstein, VA
Wozny, Rosemary Anne, PA

CERTIFICATE IN HISTOLOGIC TECHNOLOGY
Council, Nancy Lee, PA
Fordyce, Kathleen Ann, PA
Galvin, Denise Jean, PA
Patterson, Pamela Joan, PA

CERTIFICATE IN CYTOTECHNOLOGY
Armento, Janice C., DE
Berg, Ellen D., PA
Conrad, Deborah Joy, NJ
Hogue, Barbara Constance, PA
Masse, Agnes Theresa, PA
Otero, Mary Agnes, PA
Park, Young Sook, PA

Fig. 21.   Theresa Marie O'Connor, nursing (1974), addresses students about career options (1979).

CERTIFICATE IN RADIOLOGIC TECHNOLOGY
Ahlum, Diane, PA
Annarelli, Donna Marie, PA
Corrado, Teresa Joan, PA
Fields, Deborah Jane, PA
Frattali, Elizabeth, PA
Frederick, Martha Adele, PA
Gerhart, Wendy Jo Fluck, PA
Gilmartin, Patricia Anne, PA
Hartman, June Marie, PA
Horvath, Patricia, NJ
Katubi, Mary Margaret, PA
King, Robin, PA
Kneezel, Carol Naomi, PA
Kuber, Michael S., MA
Lavinsky, Joan Ann, PA
Lee, Cheryl, PA
Lusk, Linda Jeanne, PA
Nessel, Debra, PA
Orlando, Antonetta, PA
Simone, Diane, PA
Storjohann, Jane Elizabeth, PA
Szcypiorski, Jennifer J., PA
Tepper, Virginia M., PA
Tyrell, Dorothy Ann, PA
Vandergrift, Beverly Elizabeth, PA
Wilson, Janice Marie, PA

CERTIFICATE IN PRACTICAL NURSING
Adams, James Fletcher, PA
Anderson, Cristina D., NJ

Fig. 22. Leigh Pierson-Brown, nursing, with refugees in Cambodia.

Bennett, Clare Ellen, PA
Bienvenue, Robyn Michele, PA
Boyer, Margaret Elizabeth, PA
Brown, Ethel Mae, PA
Brown, Juanita T., PA
Cadwallader, Judy S., PA
Capron, Faith Irene, PA
Castiglione, Sandra Maria, NJ
Civa, Deborah Ann, PA
Cole, Patricia Elizabeth, PA
Collins, Thomas Francis, PA
Congar, Elizabeth Ann, PA
Conoscento, Martha Ann, PA
Dayen, Renee Gail, PA
DeCecco, Denise Ann, PA
Dilworth, Geraldine F., NJ
Dresner, Judith Gale, PA
Elliott, Nancy Ann, PA
Friedman, Margaret Ruth, PA
Giovanelli, Janice Mary, PA
Hanson, Susan Marie, PA
Harrison, Susan Marie, PA
Hart, Judith Anne, PA
Horgan, Frances Moshinski, PA
Jervis, Patricia Mary, PA
Konieczka, Patricia Ann, PA
Lambertson, Margaret Lesley, PA
Lingenfelter, Patricia Ann, PA
Magee , Marie Quimby, PA
McDaniels, Rosemary, PA
Miller, Loretta Elodia , PA
Mulherin, Elizabeth Ann , NJ
Mulhern, Joanne Marie , PA
Mullen, Pamela Allyson , PA
Niebish, Theresa Louise, PA
Orlando, Mary Katherine , PA
Pastakia, Saroj D., PA
Pastor, Martha Lou, NJ
Pohar , Debora Ann, PA
Pusey , Katheryn Eyer, PA
Ramuno, Debora Ann, PA
Rhock, Gregory Leonard, NJ
Rizzi, Arlene Katherine, PA
Rodriguez, Marican C., PA
Rowell, Jacqueline Lisa, PA
Russell, Christine Caroline, PA
Schwoerer, Diane Marie, PA
Setler, Kathleen Elizabeth, PA
Stens, Diane Carole, NJ
Swan, Michelle Ann, PA
Verdone, Irene Elizabeth, PA
Wedler, Marla Jean, PA
Weiss, Deborah Ray, PA
Whiteleather, Christine Eva, PA
Yates, Ruth Ann, PA

A number of developments in student activities dominated the College's 1974/75 academic year. For the first time, a student directory, organized by program, was produced and made available to students, faculty and administration. A Student Government Association constitution was drafted.

The Student Activities Committee developed a two-day orientation program for the incoming class of 1976, a junior-senior friends program, and a class photography service for graduating seniors. The College's first Parents' Day was held on May 3, 1975, with more than 200 students and parents participating.

Two radiologic technology students, Lori Witten and Nicholas Croce, participated in the Techni-Bowl, a competition among area schools of radiologic technology sponsored by the Philadelphia Society of Radiologic Technologists. In Jefferson's first year of entry, the team finished in second place.

In May, the College co-sponsored a continuing education conference for nurses, along with the School of Nursing and Nursing Service of Jefferson Hospital (Fig. 23). Among the conference attendees were several baccalaureate nursing graduates of 1974: Deborah H. Boehm, Mary Ann Erthal, Carol Gordon, Janice DeBaun Hastings, Elizabeth Oliver and Robyn Midouhas.

Officers of the Medical Technology Alumni Association elected at their May meeting were: Edward J. Pierzynski, '73, President; Arnold Storr, '73, Vice President; and Cynthia McCurdy, '68, Secretary/Treasurer. At the same time, the baccalaureate nursing group of the Alumni Association elected their first officers: President Melanie Reading Pirollo, '75; Vice President Elizabeth Oliver, '74; and Secretary/Treasurer Theresa O'Connor, '74.

University Commencement Exercises were held on June 6 at the traditional site, the Academy of Music (Fig. 24). The College of Allied Health Sciences baccalaureate degree graduates numbered 76, 20 medical technologists and 56 nurses. A dinner preceeding the exercises was held May 28. Graduates were joined by alumni, faculty and administration (Fig. 25).

Separate ceremonies were held in September for students graduating from the radiologic technology and practical nursing programs (Fig. 26 and 27). Among the radiologic technology graduates were: Louann Kindsvater, winner of the Frances Cary Award for extraordinary tact and kindness in daily patient care; Lori Witten, Dean's Award recipient for highest academic average; Nicholas Croce, winner of the Malinckrodt Award for outstanding clinical practice; and Pamela Chmelewski, who received the Class Award, presented by the Squibb Pharmaceutical Company, for the senior who demonstrated the most interest in her fellow students. At the practical nursing ceremony, Judith D. Oliver, President of the class, spoke to the graduates.

Jane Anne Marko, later Jane Marko Carabasi, nursing, earned a master of science degree in health education from St. Joseph's University in 1981 and an Ed.D. in health education from Temple University in 1989. She subsequently was cer-

Fig. 23. Guest speakers at the continuing education conference for nurses: seated, Miriam Lundgren, R.N., M.S., and Clifford Jordan, R.N., Ed.D.; standing, John W. Goldschmidt, M.D., Dean, and Charlotte E. Voss, R.N., Ed.D., Chairman of the Department of Baccalaureate Nursing.

tified as a health education specialist. She was named to the Dean's Council of Overseers for the College of Allied Health Sciences in 1990.

Ruth Davis Craymer, later Ruth E. Gordon, nursing, earned a master of science in nursing degree from the University of Pennsylvania in 1982 and later became certified as an obstetrical/gynecological nurse practitioner. She pursued a career in nursing education, first on the faculty at Holy Family College in Philadelphia from 1983 to 1988 and then at The Pennsylvania State University beginning in 1989. Her volunteer work included service at the Rosebud Indian Reservation in South Dakota, the Keams Canyon Indian Reservation in Arizona, and the Homeless Commission in Philadelphia. She also volun-

teered as an "AIDS Buddy" in Philadelphia. In 1990, she was a doctoral candidate in adult education at Pennsylvania State University.

Mary Bettina McLaughlin, later Tina Kemps, nursing, was President of the Camden County Medical Society Auxiliary in 1987/88. She developed a county-wide Adolescent Health Education Day for all county high schools and junior high schools, a program which was nominated for a national adolescent health award in Washington, D.C.

Constance Ogletree, later Constance O. Kolva, nursing, began her own business, Kolva Consulting, in 1986, serving as President. The company provided consultation and education services to private and public hospitals, universities

Fig. 24.   Attending the College's 1975 Commencement Exercises are, left to right, Dr. Mario J. Saldana, Associate Professor of Pathology; Eva Marie Welcz; Dean John W. Goldschmidt; Gloria Cairns, Educational Coordinator, School of Histologic Technology; and Dr. Gonzalo E. Aponte, Professor of Pathology and Head of the Department.

1975

and agencies. It also sponsored continuing education programs for nurses.

Nancy Redfern, later Nancy Redfern Freedman, nursing, received the Outstanding Orthopaedic Practice Award for 1986 from the National Association of Orthopaedic Nurses.

B.S. in MEDICAL TECHNOLOGY
Andersen, Karen Elizabeth, PA
Cogan, Frances Ann, NJ
Cohen, Shelley, PA
Deverant, Charlene Constance, PA
Earle, Roberta Dian, PA
Fletman, Ricki Lee, PA
Garmat, Diana Rosemarie, MD
Hou, Wen Fan, PA
Ivins, Johanna Marie, NJ
Marsh, Loretta Vivienne, PA
McDonald, David Paul, DE
Petrick, Joanne Marie, NJ
Pinkerton, Judith Ann, PA
Simmendinger, Mary Evelyn, PA
Thompson, Mary Ellen, PA
Tobia, Carol Marie, PA
Tsui, Miriam, PA
Vitale, Joanna Abbattista, NJ
Voltz, Kathryn Jan, PA
Weron, Theodore Francis, PA

B.S. in NURSING
Baker, Susan Marie, PA
Binder, Virginia Ann, PA
Blimegger, Carole Gluch, PA
Boyd, Eugene Ralston, Jr., PA
Brown, Carol Anne, PA
Burke, Laurie Ruth, NJ
Christie, Carol Rae, PA
Cleary, Marialice Joan, PA
Conboy, Victoria Joan, NY
Condike, Barbara Jane, PA
Cornell, Margareta Lynn, PA
Crawford, Lynda Bulach, PA
Craymer, Ruth Davis, PA
Czulada, Roberta Ann, PA
Danley, Ida Elizabeth, NJ
DelVecchio, Marie Theresa, PA
Egan, Virginia Suzanne, PA
Faust, Donna Lee, PA
Green, Suzann Lee, PA
Hayes, Nancy Jean, PA
Heise, Kathleen, PA
Herman, Andrea, PA
Jordan, Janet Lynn, NJ

Kabler, Susan Lynne, PA
Keane, Joanne Elizaebth, NJ
Koski, Rebecca Jane, MN
LeCappelain, Elizabeth Irene, OH
Lohr, Jennifer Curtis, PA
Marko, Jane Anne, NJ
McCausland, Nina Marie, PA
McCubbin, Jane Richey, PA
McIntyre, Patricia Edith, PA
McLaughlin, Mary Bettina, NJ
McPeek, Lynn Jeanette, NJ
Megill, Sharon Jeanne, NJ
Miller, Cheryl Kay, PA
O'Connor, Jean Marie, PA
Ogletree, Constance Christina, PA
O'Hara, Susan Dorothy, PA
Pirollo, Melanie Reading, NJ
Quiring, Ellen Sue, PA
Raney, Deborah Louise, PA
Redfern, Nancy, PA
Rojo, Guia Firmalo, PA
Rosen, Alexa Sandra, PA
Rosen, Sheryl Elaine, PA
Sanders, Julia Floridis, NJ
Sauer, Charolotte Ann, NJ
Scenna, Julie Fitzgibbons, PA
Shepherd, Mary Alice, NJ
Sloan, Stephanie June, PA
Spilman, Ann, NJ
Taylor, Nicki Lou, PA
Ward, Nan Lynne, PA
Wood, Rebecca Bowman, PA
Zimmerman, Peggy Louise, PA

CERTIFICATE IN HISTOTECHNOLOGY
Achenbach, Donna Marie, PA
Meeker, Sally C., NE
Welcz, Eva Marie, PA

CERTIFICATE IN CYTOTECHNOLOGY
Arch, Bonnie Ellen, PA
Finnegan, Patrick Thomas, NJ
Griswold, Diane Louise, PA
Heim, Cheryl Ann, PA
Kelly, Lynda Jo-Anne, PA
McWilliams, June Diane, PA
Mukai, Barbara Anne, PA
Rodia, Francine Marie, PA
Sullivan, John Patrick, PA

Fig. 25.   Allied Health Sciences Dinner held May 28, 1975.

CERTIFICATE IN RADIOLOGIC TECHNOLOGY
Ballezza, Elizabeth Ann, PA
Chmelewski, Pamela Jean, NJ
Ciociola, Anna Theresa, PA
Connor, Maria Angela, NJ
Croce, Nicholas Joseph, PA
Fox, Theresa Mary, PA
Goldstein, Deborah Ann, PA
Harbord, Theresa Frances, PA
Hopkins, Susan Jeanne, PA
Kindsvater, Louann, PA
Lackman, Adrienne Lisa, PA
O'Donnell, Kathleen Elizabeth, PA
Roseman, Lynn Audrey, PA
Solge, Jacqueline Marie, DE
Solof, Shelley Marsha, NJ
Witten, Lori Ilene, PA
Zizzamia, Marie Jean, NJ

CERTIFICATE IN PRACTICAL NURSING
Boone, Marian A. Claude, PA
Boudwin, Susan Anne, PA
Cannariato, Joan A., PA
Carroll, Juanita Naomi, PA
Carrozza, Rosanne Bernidette, PA
Castleberry, Eleanor M., PA
Chantz, Lois Elizabeth, PA
Ciccarelli, Annette Rita, PA
Coleman, Paulette Elaine, PA
Dougherty, Monica Ann, PA
East, Susan, PA
Felice, Margaret Mary, PA
Finnerty, Dorothy Anne, PA
Foley, Christine Marie, PA

Franks, Darlene Bernice, PA
Gerhart, Kathleen Dorthea, PA
Gordon, Helen Mary, PA
Greene, Deborah Anne, PA
Guckin, Margaret Mary, PA
Halter, Pamela Marie, PA
Harper, Patricia Ann, PA
Heininger, Donna Lynn, PA
Heininger, Linda, PA
Holliday, Dorisanne Fielding, PA
Janis, Barbara Ann, NJ
Jones, Valerie Yvette, PA
Kelly, Rosemary Theresa, PA
Margiotta, Anna Lee, PA
McCrossen, Deborahann Patricia, PA
McDermott, Margaret Anna, PA
McGlynn, Eileen Alice, PA
Moore, Barbara Jean, PA
Morrison, Cheryl Lynn, PA
Oliver, Judith Ann, NJ
Reeve, Shirley Bonita, PA
Rhinehart, Margaret, PA
Smith, Delores E., PA
Stevenson, April Jane, PA
Timney, Patricia Aileen, DE
Trudell, Kathleen Patricia, PA
Tusch, Janie, NJ
Vines, Mary Margaret, PA
Vogt, Evelyn Ada, PA
Willis, Ann Morrow, PA
Wyrembek, Benita Marie, PA
Yeager, Diane Marie, NJ
Young, Beverly, PA
Zappala, Josephine Ann, PA

Fig. 26. The Class of 1975, School of Practical Nursing.

Fig. 27. Graduation for the School of Practical Nursing included a candlelight ceremony.

1975

During the 1975/76 academic year, the College continued its steady process of growth and development, both in curricular and extracurricular areas.

The College's first catalog, covering the years 1975-77, was published in October. During the year, the first College yearbook was started by seniors in medical technology and nursing. The yearbook was called *Karyon*, chosen through a name contest. The winning entry was submitted by Susan Barbuto, a junior baccalaureate nursing student. A class ring, designed by senior radiologic technology students, was approved.

After nine years as the first Dean of the College, Dr. John W. Goldschmidt (Fig. 28) resigned, effective December 31, 1975, to accept a new post as Associate Medical Director of the Rehabilitation Institute of Chicago and Professor of Rehabilitation Medicine at Northwestern University. Lawrence Abrams, Associate Dean and Director of Student Affairs, was appointed Acting Dean.

The College, as well as the rest of the University, suffered a loss on March 31, 1976, when University President Peter A. Herbut, M.D. died. Dr. Herbut had been Jefferson's President since 1966 (Fig. 29).

The Department of Baccalaureate Nursing, in cooperation with the Nursing Service Department of Jefferson Hospital, presented a continuing education symposium for nurses, entitled "My Patient Can't Cope: A Seminar in Crisis Intervention." The Department of Medical Technology, in conjunction with the Clinical Laboratories of Jefferson Hospital, presented "A Symposium on Clinical Laboratory Management," also a continuing education program.

The Department of Cytotechnology received a positive summary evaluation after its accreditation visit by the American Society of Cytology in March. The evaluation included a recommendation to the Council on Medical Education of the American Medical Association for five years full accreditation.

The Department of Baccalaureate Nursing received notice of its full accreditation status for the maximum eight years from the National League for Nursing in May.

The end of the academic year also marked the termination of the College's histologic technology program.

At the University's Commencement Exercises on June 11, degrees were awarded to baccalaureate degree graduates of the College, 20 in medical technology and 58 in nursing. In addition, the first two associate of arts degrees, earned through the College's General Studies program, were awarded.

Fig. 28. John W. Goldschmidt, M.D., Dean of the College since its establishment as the School of Allied Health Sciences in 1967, resigned during the year. He is pictured as he appeared in the College's first yearbook, *Karyon*.

Fig. 29. University President Peter A. Herbut, M.D., who died during the year. He is shown in attendance at a 1975 College of Allied Health Sciences dinner chatting with medical technology program alumni, Emira Zamilli, '45, left, and Betty Ransom, '30.

Five honorary degrees were conferred at that ceremony. Marian Anderson, world famous contralto; Dr. Roger W. Heyns, president of the American Council on Education; Arthur C. Kaufmann, former president of Gimbel's, business and civic leader; James A. Michener, Pulitzer prize novelist; and Dr. Jo Ono, Jefferson Medical College graduate, class of 28 and world renowned otolaryngologist, were the recipients.

A few months later, the radiologic technology program graduates included two award winners: Betsy Lynn Hayes, the recipient of both the Frances Cary Award and the Clinical Award, the latter presented by the Mallinckrodt Company; and Viola Louise Harris, the winner of the Class Award, given to the most helpful graduating senior, presented by the Squibb Pharmaceutical Company.

Kathy L. Norris, later Kathy L. Grant, cytotechnology, was a founding member of the Delaware Valley Society of Cytology in 1979 and

President of that organization in 1981 (Fig. 30). She earned a master of science degree from St. Joseph's University in 1986. She became the chief cytologist and anatomic pathology co-ordinator at Mansfield General Hospital in Mansfield, Ohio, as well as a doctoral candidate at the University of Akron, and a member of the Board of Directors of the Wayne County Unit of the American Cancer Society.

Elizabeth A. Celenza, later Elizabeth A. Borowski, medical technology, earned her certification as a specialist in blood banking and became Director of Technical Education at American Red Cross Blood Services in Philadelphia. An active lecturer at many professional meetings, she was also enrolled in a master's degree program at the University of Pennsylvania.

Rachelle A. Alisa, later Rachelle A. Jeannette, radiologic technology, became a radiologic technologist for Bancroft X-Ray, Inc. in Wilmington, Delaware, and earned two academic incentive scholarship awards from Delaware Technical and Community College and an American Chemical Society Scholarship Award.

Nancy Fulginiti, practical nursing, subsequently attended Gloucester County College in New Jersey, where she earned degrees in respiratory therapy in 1979 and nursing in 1985 (Fig. 31). She was on the Licensed Practical Nursing Advisory Committee at Gloucester County Vocational and Technical School. She became a Nurse Recruitment Specialist for Kennedy Memorial Hospitals-University Medical Center.

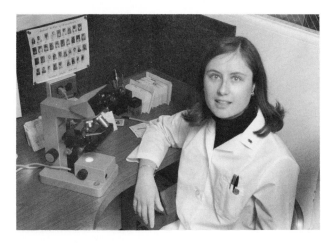

Fig. 30. Kathy Norris-Grant, cytotechnology, a founder and 1981 President of Delaware Valley Society of Cytology.

Susan Werther Cohen, Esq., nursing, went on to a law degree in 1979. That same year she became President of the baccalaureate nurses' Alumni Association (CAHS), and in December was elected to Jefferson's Board of Trustees (Fig. 32). Rachel E. Moore, medical technology, became a specialist in blood banking and embarked on a career that included Hershey Medical Center in Hershey, Pennsylvania, and Johns Hopkins University Hospital in Baltimore. In 1985, she became Coordinator of the Rare Donor Registry and Reference Laboratory Technologist for the American Red Cross National Headquarters in Washington, D.C. After several promotions, she was made Marketing Associate for Plasma Operations.

B.S. in MEDICAL TECHNOLOGY
Allegretto, Carole A., NJ
Basile, Michael Domenick, PA
Burke, Donna Marie, PA
Celenza, Elizabeth Anne, PA
Connell, Mary Jane, PA
Cool, Elizabeth Marie, PA
Denshaw, Mary Theresa, PA
Fajt, Marcia Louise, PA

Fig. 31. Nancy Fulginiti, practical nursing, earned degrees in respiratory therapy and nursing.

Gibbons-Neff, Emily, PA
Haberbusch, Inge Anne Marie, PA
Illuminati, Janice, PA
Kao, Henry Ming, PEOPLE'S REPUBLIC OF CHINA
Kao, Rang Ling, PEOPLE'S REPUBLIC OF CHINA
Kelly, Frank Jay, PA
Loredo, Rosa Marie, PA
Messa, Joanne Germaine, PA
Montgomery, Carole Page, PA
Moore, Rachel Elizabeth, NJ
Siwczak, Patricia Piccolella, NJ
Widmann, Ellen Christine, PA

B.S. in NURSING
Abbruzzo, Frances Maria, PA
Alexander, Saren Kay, PA
Andreola, Saskia Linda, NJ
Beil, Jo Ann, PA
Bender, Alene Sue, PA
Boyle, Maureen Ann, PA
Bozarth, Penelope Elizabeth, NJ
Broad, Bonnie Dale, PA
Buxbaum, Susan Ruth, PA
Callahan, Helen Marie, PA
Callery, Susan Veronica, NJ
Casey, Lynne Susan, NJ
Ciccone, Martha Ann, PA
Conti, Stephanie Marie, PA
Deford, Susan Lynne, PA
DePersia, Cynthia Marie, NJ
Dillon, Diane Deborah, PA
Durgin, Judith Margaret, PA
Eakin, Patricia Murray, PA
Fair, Sheila Marie, PA
Franco, Patricia Marie, PA
Furst, Catherine Mary, PA
Graffy, Susanna Marta, PA
Guberman, Lynn Susan, PA
Holbrook, Phyllis Elizabeth, ME
Holmsten, Holly Lynn, PA
Ippolito, Lucille Kathleen, PA
LaNoce, Virginia Ann, PA

Lee, Beth E., PA
Love, Lynn Kimberly, PA
Magee, Constance Lou, NJ
McCulley, Kathleen Susan, PA
Meeker, Rex Lee, PA
Nires, Caren Levitt, PA
Olszewsky, Patricia J., PA
Parente, Betty Jo, PA
Parker, Catherine M., NJ
Remaly, Rochelle Lisa, PA
Roach, Ruth G., PA
Sapnas, Kathryn G., PA
Scholl, Barbara Ann, PA
Shaffer, Christine Louise, PA
Summers, Susan Gail, PA
Swisher, Margaret Rose, PA
Tarullo, Dorothy Glasgow, PA
Tase, Elizabeth Jean, PA
Thompson, Karen L., NJ
Trofe, Gayle Linda, NJ
Vinson-Ciano, Virginia Wilkinson, PA

Fig. 32. Susan Werther Cohen, Esq., nursing, was named to Jefferson's Board of Trustees in 1979.

Wardius, Sherri Ann, PA
Werther, Susan Carol, PA
Whetstone, Giovina Perotti, PA
Wright-Horan, Deborah Jean, PA
Yarrow, Leanore Rebecca, PA
Yatsko, Faye Ann, PA
Young, Mary Louise, PA
Zabinski, Kathleen M., PA
Zeller, Rita Helene, PA

ASSOCIATE IN ARTS
Miller, Dorothy, PA
Stewart, Geraldine Haly, PA

CERTIFICATE IN HISTOTECHNOLOGY
Coffield, Barbara Jean, PA
Isaacson, Lee Joy, PA
Marino, Karen Marie, PA
Menna, Michelle, PA

CERTIFICATE IN CYTOTECHNOLOGY
Beale, Ellen Marie, DE
Cichonski, Linda Catherine, PA
Duddey, Helena Golla, PA
Estacio, Felomina, CA
Kilstein, Karen Linda, NJ
Leavitt, Arlene Frances, NJ
Norris, Kathy Lynn, NJ
Paul, Elyse R., PA
Shovlin, Marcella V., PA
Sniger, Sherri Lisa, PA
Woolery, Claire Louise, PA
Ysmach, Linda Carol, NY

CERTIFICATE IN RADIOLOGIC TECHNOLOGY
Alisa, Rachelle Ann, DE
Ejsmont, Linda Eileen, PA
Emery, Cynthia Marie, NJ
Harris, Viola Louise, PA
Hayes, Betty Lynne, PA
Irwin, Anne, NJ
Kelly, Bernadette Mary, NJ
Koller, Karen Elizabeth, PA
Linstrom, Joseph H., NJ
Mangano, Mary, PA
Murphy, Margaret Mary, PA
Rambo, Anita Marie, PA
Regosch, Catherine, PA
Santone, Anita Rose Patricia, PA
Scalise, Julia Antoinette, PA
Schwarz, Lauren Marie, PA
Snitzer, Barbera, PA
Vogt, Anna Marie, NJ

CERTIFICATE IN PRACTICAL NURSING

Banks, James Lee, PA
Beach, Kathleen Theresa, PA
Bell, Maryanne Theresa, PA
Bennett, Stephen Edward, PA
Bockle, Joanne Elizabeth, NJ
Bowar, Karlene Marie, PA
Cappelli, Theresa Ann, PA
Carides, Debra Lynn, NJ
Cavicchia, Terry Ann, PA
Chandler, Diane Michele, PA
DeLeo, Jacqueline Ann, PA
Engelbert, Susan Carol, PA
Evans, Karen Ann, PA
Finchen, Valerie Lynn, NJ
Foss, Joan Ursin, PA
Fulginiti, Nancy, NJ
Govan, Beth Anne, PA, PA
Haag, Eileen Marie PA, PA
Hammen, Ann Birmingham, PA
Hosey, Chrisine Vesta, PA
Isaacson, Linda, PA
Jacobson, Rosanne, FL
Jaspersen, Nancy Helen, PA
Kelly, Anne Beatrice, PA
Kenney, Barbara Ann, PA

Kreseskie, Mary Theresa, PA
Lambing, Deborah Patalone, PA
Leppert, Leslie Ellen, PA
Lewis, Bernese Gamble, PA
Malukas, Cynthia Marie, PA
Matsko, Joann Cecelia, PA
Maxwell, Emerson, PA
McBride, Cathie McLean, PA
McDevitt, Julia Ann, FL
McGee, Rose Ann, PA
Mohl, Jill Stacey, PA
Newell, Kathleen Mooney, PA
Owens, Jean Marie, NJ
Pettine, Nicholas Charles, PA
Piernikowski, Diane Katherine, PA
Rider, Gertrude Wilson, PA
Riggin, Mary Elizabeth, PA
Shaw, Deborah Jean, PA
Shivy, Marykay Joyce, PA
Smith, Cheryl Anne, PA
Stevenson, Maisie Moys, PA
Tretter, Denise Ann, PA
Vallieu, Alma Lynn, NJ
Wallace, Judith Ellen, PA
Walz, Charles Maritn, PA
Wright, Elaine Margaret, PA

Parents Day organizers: standing left to right, Mrs. Dorothy Grieb, Assistant Director of Student Affairs and Services; students Mitch Bergman and Rachel Moore; and seated, Ellen Berg and Faye Yatsko.

The 1976/77 academic year was a pivotal one for the College of Allied Health Sciences. Effective July 1, 1976, a number of changes took place that consolidated the allied health professional programs at the baccalaureate level within the College. The School of Radiologic Technology became the Department of Radiologic Technology. The School of Cytotechnology became the Department of Cytotechnology. The final class of 12 cytotechnology certificate students graduated a month later. The Department of Dental Hygiene was officially established.

Marten M. Kernis, Ph.D., assumed the position of Dean of the College of Allied Health Sciences on September 1 (Fig. 33). Dr. Kernis had been Associate Dean of the School of Basic Medical Sciences in the College of Medicine at the University of Illinois, and associate professor of anatomy and obstetrics and gynecology.

A non-traditional interinstitutional academic program (NIAP) in medical technology was planned (Fig. 34). It would admit students two times, in September 1977 and September 1978. A cooperative effort among Jefferson, Temple University and the University of Pennsylvania, the program was supported by a federal grant. The special weekend course of study, spread over three years, provided the third and fourth years of a baccalaureate degree program for clinical laboratory technicians and technologists who were seeking to meet the qualifications set by recent state and federal legislation.

During 1977, the College celebrated the 10th anniversary of its founding as the School of Allied Health Sciences. The University's Interim President, George M. Norwood, Jr., wrote in a letter published in the *Allied Health Review*, the College's alumni periodical, that the College "has successfully met the challenges of the times during the past decade. . . . The growth of the College has been dramatic. . . . On behalf of the University, it is gratifying to commend the College for its emergence as a most vital part of the institution."

In April, 1977, Tenley Albright, M.D., a general surgeon affiliated with New England Baptist Hospital in Boston, a graduate of Harvard Medical School and an Olympic gold medalist figure skating champion in 1956, delivered the College's Merves Lecture. The Merves Lecture, designed to address a topic on the humanities in medicine, was established in 1968 in honor of the late Dr. Louis Merves, an associate professor

Fig. 33. Martin M. Kernis, Ph.D., assumed the position of Dean of the College of Allied Health Sciences on September 1, 1976.

of clinical medicine at Jefferson, whose gift to the College supported the lecture program.

The Department of Radiologic Technology's annual awards included several graduates of 1977. Theresa Ragano won the Frances Cary Award, which recognized the combination of technical expertise with kindness and humanitarian concern for patients. Alma Jean Calcagno won the Mallinckrodt Award, given to the senior who was most helpful to junior students. The Squibb Award for highest overall academic and clinical performance was shared by Alma Jean Calcagno, Joyce Keil and Joanne Landis.

At the University's Commencement Exercises on June 10, the College of Allied Health Sciences awarded bachelor of science degrees to 57 nurses and 24 medical technologists. Separate ceremonies were held for certificate graduates of radiologic technology and practical nursing (Fig. 35 and 36).

Honorary degrees were presented to Derek E. Denny-Brown, M.D., a distinguished neurologist from Harvard Medical School; Dr. Millard E. Gladfelter, Chancellor of Temple University; and

Fig. 34. Planning the curriculum for the Non-traditional Interinstitutional Academic Program (NIAP) in medical technology are, left to right, Alison McPherson, Ph.D., NIAP program administrator; Elizabeth A. Turner, Ph.D., chairperson of the College's Department of Medical Technology; NIAP program director; and Patsy L. Chavles, M.S., Education Coordinator.

Hobart A. Reimann, M.D., Associate Director of Medical Affairs at Hahnemann Hospital.

Carla M. Trautman, medical technology, a summa cum laude graduate and a member of the Medical Technology Student Bowl Team, became Supervisor of Veterinary Services, World Services/Johnson Control.

Theresa M. Poiesz, radiologic technology, continued her education, earning a certificate in radiation oncology from Gwynedd-Mercy College in 1978 and a bachelor of science degree from Neumann College in 1983. She was a Senior Radiation Oncology Technologist at Thomas Jefferson University Hospital.

Mitchell T. Bergmann, nursing, earned a master of science in nursing degree in nursing administration and gerontology from Gwynedd-Mercy College in 1986 and became Administrative Director for Surgery and Anesthesia at Medical College of Pennsylvania. He remained a very active alumnus serving on the College's Alumni Advisory Committee and participating in Career Options programs and other College events.

Hebe Diana Hearn Jungkind, later Hebe Diana Hearn Lutz, nursing, received a master of science in nursing degree from the University of Pennsylvania in 1984 and became an instructor in the Department of Nursing at Eastern Michigan University and a staff nurse at the University of Michigan.

Victoria A. Kolodzey, nursing, became a rehabilitation consultant for Conseruco in Voorhees, New Jersey. She returned to Jefferson as a student in 1990 and enrolled in the master of science in nursing degree program in rehabilitation nursing.

Meri Lynn Wieder, later Meri Wieder Sirkin, nursing, earned a master's degree from Rutgers University and became certified in adolescent and child psychiatric and mental health nursing. She was the Assessment and Treatment Coordinator in the Adolescent Substance Abuse Unit of Fair Oaks Hospital in Summit, New Jersey. She also lectured on cults, satanism, and adolescent substance abuse.

Karen R. Krylowicz, practical nursing, became Clinical Services Coordinator of the Department of Obstetrics and Gynecology, Hospital of the University of Pennsylvania.

B.S. in MEDICAL TECHNOLOGY
Bojanowski, Linda Marie, NJ
Born, Beth Ann, NJ
Bossard, Margaret Rose, PA
Caddy, Patricia Anne, PA
Casey, Maryann C., NJ
Contrisciano, Karen Marie, NJ
Cooper, Laura Anne, NJ
Diloreto, Diane Elizabeth, PA
Gerace, Maria Rita, PA
Giannini, Cynthia Pauline, OH
Gilman, Gary Ellis, OH
Hough, Janet Campbell, NJ
Kelly, Janis Marie, PA
Lesutis, Lorraine Christine, PA
Manshil, Mindy Joan, PA
Margerum, Helene Henry, PA
Miller, Joann Marie, PA
Navatier, LaVanche Marie, NJ
Nenstiel, Lynne Omer, PA
Procino, Janet Katherine, PA

Schrock, Melissa Lee, PA
Tarawaly, Sheik Mahdieu, PA
Trautman, Carla Marie, PA
Woods, Karen Elizabeth, PA

B.S. in NURSING
Aldinger, Kay E., PA
Amritt, H. Denise, PA
Backenstose, Suzanne Nannette, WA
Barbuto, Susan M., PA
Becker, Peggy M., NJ
Bergmann, Mitchell T., PA
Bird, April Lee, NJ
Bohan, Juliane N., DE
Brown, Elizabeth Lynne, PA
Brown, Susan Nancy, NJ
Carter, Cathy Lynn, PA
Charles, Lisa Jean, NJ
Davis, Judith Ann, PA
Drake, Amanda L., PA
Eppley, Mary Susan, OH

Fig. 35.   Graduation for 56 students in the School of Practical Nursing took place on August 31, 1977.

Forster, Anne Abel, PA
Freiberger, April Gillen, NJ
Furlong, Raymond J., Jr., PA
Gardner, Donna Sue, NJ
Glick, Dorina Kandas, CA
Gorodetzer, Michael Steven, NJ
Holmes, Mariellyn J., PA
Hordis, Barbara H., PA
Ingram, Monique Antoinette, PA
Isard, Barbara Lona, PA
Johnson, Diane Catherine, PA
Jungkind, Hebe Diana Hearn, PA
Kolodzey, Victoria Anne, PA
Lodge, Susan Marie, NJ
Loughery, Susan Mary, NJ
Mamalis, Emily Vasille, PA
McCarter, Pamela Young, PA
Moore, Jayne Ellen, PA
Morgan, Ralph Oscar, Jr., PA
Murphy, Jane Margaret, PA
Orkin, Tracy, CT

Orkwiszewski, Monica Mary, PA
Prossack, Cheryl T., PA
Repman, N. Jean, DE
Riley, Timothy W., PA
Rosella, Melanie Martina, PA
Rosenthal, Joy Sandra, PA
Rudolph, Virginia Anne, PA
Sammons, Melanie Ann, DE
Sheinman, Claire Susan, PA
Slouka, Jean Irene, NJ
Smith, Diane Jean, NJ
Snyder, Maragaret Bailey, NJ
Solomon, Muriel Edith, PA
Strese, Lisa Ann, PA
Thompson, Laurie, MD
Treichler, Barbara Jean, PA
Tyrell, Eugenia Ann, PA
Vorberg, Rene Gene, PA
Wieder, Meri Lynn, PA
Wolgin, Frances Ann, PA
Yovanovich, Paula Kathleen, PA
Young, Margaret Ann, PA

Fig. 36.   Elizabeth J. Sweeney, Director of the School of Practical Nursing, "pins" a student of the Class of '77.

At Opening Exercises in September for the 1977/78 academic year, Martin M. Kernis, Ph.D., the Dean of the College, presented the first College of Allied Health Sciences' Achievement Award for Student Life to Bonnie L. Dymek, radiologic technology (Fig. 38). Thereafter, the award was presented annually to the student who had made the most outstanding contribution to student life.

The Opening Exercises were particularly significant for the College and the University as Lewis W. Bluemle, Jr., M.D., was inaugurated University President. Dr. Bluemle, who served as President until his retirement in 1990, proved to be a strong supporter of the College's nursing and allied health programs (Fig. 39).

In September, College students, faculty and administrators joined in the celebration of a milestone in the University's history, the centennial of Thomas Jefferson University Hospital (Fig. 40).

The approval of the Bylaws of the College by the University Board of Trustees in September provided the faculty with a set of guidelines by which participatory governance could be maintained and provided for student representation on seven of the nine College committees.

The incoming class was marked by three firsts: the matriculation of the first class of dental hygiene students (Fig. 41), two classes of radiologic technology baccalaureate degree students after the department phased out its hospital-based certificate program following the summer quarter of 1977, and a group of medical technology

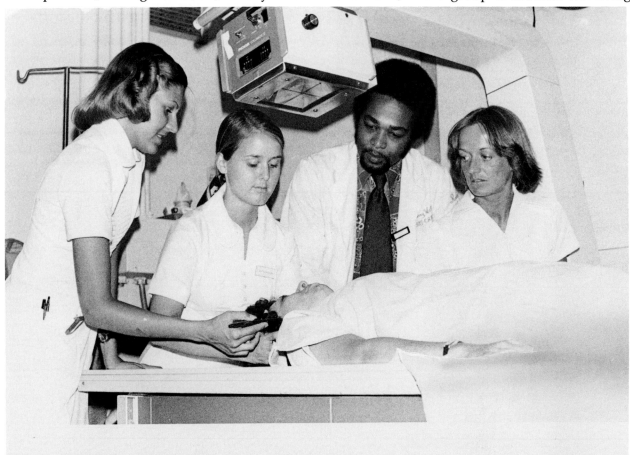

Fig. 38.   Among the radiologic technology students pictured with the department's acting chairperson, Larry Walker, M.Ed., is Bonnie L. Dymek, far left, the recipient of the College's first Achievement Award for Student Life.

students in a non-traditional, weekend program sponsored by a grant from the U.S. Department of Health, Education and Welfare.

At Parents' Day in October, Dean Kernis presented the first College of Allied Health Sciences' Alumni Special Achievement Award to Rhonda Karp, Ed.D., chairman and Associate Professor, Department of Cytotechnology (Fig. 42). This award, given to a graduate in recognition of that person's contribution to his or her profession in the areas of education, research, or community service which reflect on Thomas Jefferson University as that person's alma mater, continued to be awarded annually.

Ribbon-cutting ceremonies for the Department of Dental Hygiene's new clinical facility and administrative offices, located on the 18th and 22nd floor of the Edison Building respectively, were held November 9, 1977.

In the spring, the Department of Radiologic Technology sponsored its first Symposium for Radiologic Technologists. The event was well attended and attracted technologists from Pennsylvania, New Jersey, New York, Maryland, Washington, D.C., and Texas.

Dean Kernis submitted his resignation in March and Lawrence Abrams was appointed by President Bluemle to serve as Dean Pro Tem.

At the June 9 Commencement Exercises, the College graduated 113 students. In addition to graduates in medical technology, nursing and radiologic technology, the Class of '78 included its first group of baccalaureate degree cytotechnologists, 12 in number.

Bonnie L. Dymek (Fig. 38), later Bonnie L. Behm, radiologic technology, the recipient of the College's first Achievement Award for Student Life, for her editorship of the College yearbook and numerous other activities, stayed at the College as an admissions counselor in the Office of Admissions, Records, and Financial Aid. Subsequently, she became Coordinator of Financial Aid, then Director of Financial Aid. An active alumnus who served on the Alumni Advisory Committee, she earned a master's degree in health care administration and held numerous leadership positions in the Pennsylvania Association of Student Financial Aid Administrators.

Phyllis Glantzow, later Phyllis Granados, medical technology, earned a master's degree from the University of Pennsylvania in infection control education. At Roxborough Memorial Hospital, she was Microbiology Supervisor and Infection-Control Practitioner.

Lorraine J. Zwolak, cytotechnology, became an instructor in the College shortly after her graduation. In 1981 she became the Assistant to the Deputy Health Commissioner for the City of Philadelphia and subsequently attended Temple University Law School, graduating in 1985. She later became an Associate Attorney, involved with products liability defense, and insurance coverage analysis.

Nancy Council, later Nancy Council-Maguire, cytotechnology, who had received a diploma in histotechnology from Jefferson in 1974, returned to Jefferson in 1980 as a faculty member in the Department of Cytotechnology. She earned a master of science degree in biomedical sciences from Drexel University in 1984. A summa cum laude graduate and a charter member of the Jef-

Fig. 39.   Lewis W. Bluemle, Jr., M.D., inaugurated as University President in September, 1977.

ferson chapter of the Alpha Eta Society, the national allied health honor society, she continued to serve in leadership roles in that organization. Her research in the areas of immunocytochemistry and cytopathology standards of practice became recognized nationally and internationally. In 1989, she was given the"Cytotechnologist Award" from the American Society of Cytology for her scientific paper on cervical cancer. In the area of Pap smear testing, the outcomes of her studies on interobserver variations in cytopathologic diagnosis have formed the scientific basis for requiring uniform gynecologic cytology reporting systems in federal and state regulations for cytology laboratories. For her many contributions, she was presented with the College's Alumni Special Achievement Award in 1990 (Fig. 43).

Helena Bolton Stewart, nursing, developed the first geriatric floor in an acute care hospital, serving as geriatric coordinator. In 1985, she graduated from St. Joseph's University with a master of science degree in gerontology and became a consultant in elder care.

Barbara D. Herlich, later Barbara D. Moses-Haratz, nursing, organized the first U.S.-Yugoslavia Nursing Conference and presented four papers on cardiovascular nursing in Belgrade and Sarajevo, Yugoslovia, in 1982.

Paul B. Schaeffer, nursing, an asthma and allergy nurse at Kaiser Permanente in San Diego, who also had served in the U.S. Navy, was recalled to active duty for Operation Desert Shield. He was experienced in shipboard and flight nursing.

Susan Romano, later Susan Romano O'Brien, medical technology, authored and presented a paper entitled "Development of the Plasminogen and Alpha 2 Antiplasmin Assays for Evaluating Systemic Fibrinolysis in the Dog" at the 1986 annual meeting of the Society of Toxicology.

Teresa Darden, radiologic technology, earned a master of science degree and became a radiation specialist/health physicist for the Nuclear Regulatory Commission.

CLASS OF 1978

B.S. in MEDICAL TECHNOLOGY
Cappo, Rosemary Elizabeth, NJ
Creany, Consuela Marie, PA
Elwell, Alice Louise, NY
Glantzow, Phyllis Nora, NJ
Hartman, Mary, NJ
Harwood, Marcia Ann, ME
Klemovage, Linda Marie, PA
Luscombe, Jill Ann, PA
Lyman, Beverly Ann, NJ
Merves, Scot Gabriel, PA
Ockenhouse, Ingrid Fischer, PA
Petrylak, Elizabeth Mills, PA
Pulido, Mary Lynn Balinao, MI
Romano, Susan Ann, PA
Salkowe, Andrea Joyce, PA
Twist, Karen Louise, PA
Walthall, Debra May, NJ

B.S. in NURSING
Abrams, Mark M., NJ
Amend, Debra Lynn, PA
Bleile, Regina M., PA
Boyle, Kathleen Regina, PA
Brin, Leslie Ann, NY
Christopher, Bernice Bailey, PA

Coper, Julia Anne, PA
D'Angelo, Laura Louise, PA
Davy, Melody Donna Joy, PA
DeLong, Janet Kelly, PA
Dillon, Patricia Bonnano, PA
Doyle, Frances Elaine, PA
Fitzmyer, Suzanne Marie, PA
Fortune, Adelaide Lucinda, NC
Frank, Donna Wylie, PA
Gallagher, Sharon M., PA
Gambo, Joanne, PA
George, Mindy Ellen, PA
Green, Rhonda Lynn, PA
Handel, Bonnie Silver, NJ
Haney, Susan Lynn, PA
Herlich, Barbara Moses, NJ
Hogeland, Susan Carol, PA
Holzman, Karen Ann, PA
Ingraham, Brenda Ann, NJ
Jadick, Anthony Martin, PA
Kelly, Linda J., PA
Kuber, Frances Anne, PA
Lamont, Patricia Jean, PA
Lampert, Bonni Jill, PA
LeNoir, Michele Jeannette, PA
Linehan, Denise L., NY

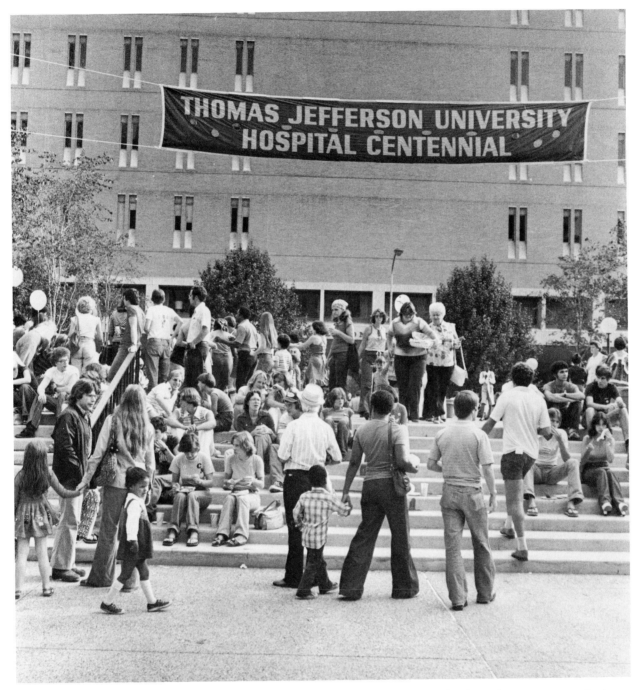

Fig. 40.   The Centennial of Thomas Jefferson University Hospital brought student, faculty, administrators and others out to celebrate on Scott Plaza.

Lorenzon, Lynne Ann, PA
Mann, Carol Jane, PA
Marcucci, Ruth Joette, PA
McClure, Frances Lindquist, PA
McNichol, Susan Marie, PA
Napoletano, Mary Theresa, PA
Ottaway, Sheryl, NJ
Oughton, Elizabeth Robyn, PA
Peterson, Karen ELizabeth, NJ
Prossack, Linda Susan, PA
Querner, Karin Anne, PA
Richter, Susan Helen, PA
Rose, Vicki Joan, PA
Rosen, Joan, PA
Rowand, Janet Lee, NJ
Ruesch, Regina Marie, PA
Sara, Sharon R., NJ
Schaeffer, Paul Bretz, PA
Shanabrook, Jan Ardice, NJ
Sherr, Mona A., PA
Siter, Lester Harold, PA
Slack, Susan Gail, PA
Smethers, Karen McMorris, PA
Stewart, Helena Bolton, PA

Stewart, June Ann, PA
Stoughton, Deborah Ann, PA
Sullivan, Kathleen Hennessy, PA
Sweeney, Marilyn Ann, PA
Tillman, Dorothy Massenburg, PA
Van Name, Jeanne Hinish, NJ
Waldbaum, Lisa A., PA
Whitfield, Darlene Marie, NJ
Woodford, Judith Ann, PA
Yale, Diane Haviland, NJ

B.S. in CYTOTECHNOLOGY
Chen, Jessie Chih Hsien, PA
Council, Nancy Lee, PA
Fernandez, Louise Elaine, NJ
Flanagan, John Jacob, Jr., NJ
Gatta, Patricia Ann, PA
Kreitzer, David Saul, PA
McAnany, Virginia Marie, PA
Micarelli, Catherine Elizabeth, NJ
Midgett, Susan, PA
Moffatt, Tamarah Harkness, NJ
West, Patricia Frances, NJ
Zwolak, Lorraine Julia, PA

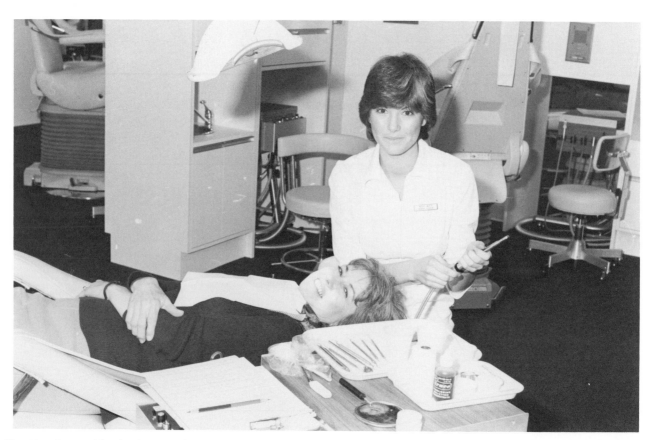

Fig. 41. Scenes like this became familiar as the College's Department of Dental Hygiene opened its new clinical facility on the 18th floor of the Edison Building.

1978

B.S. in RADIOLOGIC TECHNOLOGY

Cheetham, Eric Carl, NJ
Darden, Teresa Hall, PA
Deibler, David Grant, PA
Dymek, Bonnie Lee, PA
Ferry, J. Aifric, PA
Franklin, Harriet, PA
Holst, Rodger Joseph, PA
McGrath, Maureen Sepe, PA
Mulnick, Esther, NJ
Osborne, William Stephen, PA
Pekter, Debra Ann, PA
Price, Thomas Edward, PA
Randall, Roosevelt Iley, PA
Scheflow, Martha Lee, PA
Slothus, Robert John, NJ
Sweitzer, Wilbur Lee, PA
Walsh, Alan Michael, PA
Zdziarski, Catherine Ann, PA

CERTIFICATE IN PRACTICAL NURSING

Anderson, Deborah Joan, PA
Antrim, Ruth Catherine, PA
Atlee, Deborah Ann, PA
Bayliss, Linda Smith, PA
Biurgren, Phyllis Marie, NJ
Bliss, Donna Mary, PA
Borolla, Barbara Dugan, PA
Canavan, Kathleen Jean, PA
Carolan, Jacqueline Eberly, PA
Casey, Catherine Malloy, PA
Chepelevich, Regina Roman, PA
Clark, Gail Perna, PA
Costello, Irene Stevens, PA
Coyne, Cynthia Ann, PA
Coyne, Patricia Lynn, PA
Cusumano, Eileen Marie, PA
Cywinski, Theresa Ann, PA
Dare, Erla Geddis, NJ
Donahue, Patricia Cecelia, PA

Duffin, Regina Mary, PA
Duffy, Patricia Ann, PA
Eschinger, Barbara Therese, PA
Forsythe, Donna Lee, NJ
Golbeski, Nancy Ann, PA
Greenlee, Dawn, PA
Haviland, Patricia Dolores, PA
Helf, Cheryl Ann, PA
Hennessey, Linda Louise, PA
Hennessy, Kathleen Mary, PA
Herman, Gayle Audrey, PA
Horton, Stephen Walter, PA
Hosgood, Margaret Mary, PA
Howarth, Janet Lynne, PA
Jackson, Lillian Collissa, PA
Kessler, Marian-Carol Porter, PA
Konrad, Joseph Matthew, PA
Laub, Betty Smith, PA
Laurie, Gregory G., PA
Linetty, Joanne Patricia, PA
Mannherz, Gertrude Bauknecht, PA
McCullion, Linda Ann, PA
Moore, Dorothy Marie, PA
Moreno, Margarita, PA
Mullen, Kathleen Gallagher, PA
Nolan, Maryellen Theresa, PA
O'Donnell, Deborah Marie, NJ
Prendergast, Karen, PA
Rochow, Joyce Marie, PA
Sampson, Glenda Maurer, PA
Schoenberger, Donna Lynn, PA
Schulle, Rosanna Ashmore, PA
Skutack, Margaret Kolinofsky, PA
Smith, Evette Mary, PA
Stine, Beryl Brucknow, PA
Tannahill, Kathleen Mary, PA
Tobias, Joan Michele, PA
Tomaszewski, Claudia Ann, PA
Walker, Laura Anne, PA
Weston, Cynthia Frances, PA
Whalen, Bernice Ann, PA

Health is a precious thing, and the only one, in truth, which deserves that we employ in its pursuit not only time, sweat, trouble, and worldly goods, but even life; inasmuch as without it life comes to be painful and oppressive to us. . . . As far as I am concerned, no road that would lead us to health is either arduous or expensive.

Michel de Montaigne [1533–1592]

Fig. 42. Rhonda Karp, Ed.D., received the Alumni Special Achievement Award on the occasion of its first presentation (1978).

Fig. 43. Nancy Council-Maguire received the College's Alumni Special Achievement Award from Dean Lawrence Abrams in October, 1990. As Nancy Council, Class of '78, she was a cytotechnology major.

A few months into the 1978/79 academic year, Lawrence Abrams, who had served as Dean Pro Tem since June, was named Dean of the College (Fig. 44). Dr. Abrams had previously served the College in a variety of positions, including Associate Dean and Director of Student Affairs and Services.

The Student Life Award, announced on Parents' Day in October, went to nursing student Diane Hamburg, whose many activities included serving as co-editor of the College's yearbook, *Karyon.*

Five students from the Department of Medical Technology comprised the winning Jefferson team in the Pennsylvania Society of Medical Technology College Bowl Tournament, competing against 21 other teams from the Commonwealth. Jeffer-

Fig. 44. Lawrence Abrams, Ed.D., was named Dean of the College of Allied Health Sciences during the academic year.

son was represented by Kathryn Reihard, Beth Macy, Donna Farber, Theresa Carrigan and Linda Harker.

The addition of new staff positions made it necessary for the College to expand and renovate space in Jefferson Alumni Hall. The changes affected the Office of the Dean, Office of Admissions and the Departments of Cytotechnology and Medical Technology.

The recipient of the Alumni Special Achievement Award was Harriet H. Werley, Ph.D. Dr. Werley, a 1941 nursing graduate, earned a B.S. degree in nursing education at the University of California, a master's degree in nursing service administration at Teachers College of Columbia University, and a Ph.D. in psychology at the University of Utah. An Associate Dean for Research at the College of Nursing, University of Illinois, Dr. Werley's research focused on the social and psychological aspects of health, family planning, and health delivery systems in nursing.

The Department of Dental Hygiene was honored as one of 20 dental auxiliary programs across the country to be selected by the American Dental Association's Commission on Accreditation of Dental and Dental Auxiliary Educational Programs to pilot test the self-study accreditation manual. In addition, the Commission on Accreditation granted full accreditation status to the Department of Dental Hygiene for seven years.

The Class of 1979 included 122 graduates in the degree programs, the largest graduating class in the College's history to this time, with another 86 graduates of the School of Diploma Nursing and 51 graduates of the School of Practical Nursing (Fig. 45).

The year 1979 was the last that the College of Allied Health Sciences graduation exercises were held jointly with those of Jefferson Medical College and the College of Graduate Studies.

Honorary degrees were awarded to W. Edward Chamberlain, M.D., a distinguished radiologist; Jonathan E. Rhoads, M.D., one of the country's leading surgeons; and Jessie M. Scott, assistant surgeon general in the United States

Public Health Service and a national and international authority on nursing.

The Department of Dental Hygiene, the College's most recently established department, graduated its first class in June. All seven graduates successfully passed both the National and the Northeast Regional Board Examinations with scores well above the national and regional averages.

Jeffrey A. Krantz, radiologic technology, who was very involved in student activities including serving as co-editor of the yearbook, earned his M.Ed. degree, also in 1979, from Pennsylvania State University. He subsequently attended the University of Pittsburgh, where he took a master's degree in health administration in 1986. He became Director of Planning for Southeast Missouri Hospital.

Susan Burke, nursing, earned a master of science in nursing degree in 1983 and returned to the College of Allied Health Sciences as a faculty member from 1983 to 1988. In 1990 she was on the nursing faculty at The Catholic University of America where she was also a doctoral candidate in nursing.

Dale Leslie Miller, later Dale Leslie Hopkins, nursing, received a master of science in nursing degree from the University of Pennsylvania in 1986, specializing in perinatal nursing. She developed and implemented comprehensive obstetric and pediatric nursing services at Tempe St. Luke's Hospital in Tempe, Arizona, where she held the position of Director of Women's and Children's Services.

Kyla M. Kraft, later Kyla M. Lester, nursing, embarked on a career as a missionary nurse, first at Turtle Mountain Indian Reservation Hospital from 1979 to 1982. Subsequently, she practiced nursing at a rural mission hospital in Zimbabwe from 1984 to 1986 before moving to The Evangelical Alliance Mission in the Republic of South Africa.

Fig. 45. The Class of 1979, School of Practical Nursing.

Karen Mandzak, later Karen Mandzak-Mc-Carron, nursing, developed a specialty in rehabilitation nursing at Thomas Jefferson University Hospital (Fig. 46). She presented two papers at the national conference of the Association of Rehabilitation Nurses in 1989. She was appointed to the National Certification Board of Rehabilitation Nurses and later became its Chairperson.

Jane Lynch, later Jane Lynch Rozycki, nursing, earned a master of science in nursing degree and became the clinical coordinator of obstetrical/neonatal nursing at the Hospital of the University of Pennsylvania. She served on the College's Alumni Advisory Committee (Fig. 47).

Carolyn Wakefield, later Carolyn Wakefield-

Shank, medical technology, remained close to Jefferson for years, working in the Clinical Laboratories and serving on the College's Alumni Advisory Committee (Fig. 48).

Albert Cadogan (Fig. 49), cytotechnology, held a variety of positions with SmithKline Beecham Pharmaceuticals, eventually becoming a Scientist of Morphological Pathology, Department of Experimental Pathology. He was also an active member of the College's Alumni Advisory Committee.

James E. Weidmann, cytotechnology, was awarded the 1988 Diamond Cover Award from the *Journal of Histotechnology* and Miles Scientific for one of the best published articles in 1988.

Fig. 46. Karen Mandzak McCarron, nursing, received an award for innovation in rehabilitation nursing practice in 1987 from the Greater Philadelphia Chapter of the Association of Rehabilitation Nurses.

Fig. 47. Jane Lynch, nursing, volunteering during the College's Fund-raising Phonathon.

B.S. in MEDICAL TECHNOLOGY

Carrigan, Theresa Marie, PA
Ceperley, James Fairchild, PA
Ceperley, Jeffrey Charles, PA
Demopulos, Nick, PA
Ellis, Rhona Weinrach, PA
Farber, Donna Sue, FL
Flick, Pamela Ann, PA
Goldsmith, Lisa Ida, NJ
Harker, Lynda Marie, NJ
Hugus, Martha Loadholt, PA
Macy, Elizabeth Boots, MD
Moy, Melanie Bick Gin, MD
Patel, Surendrakumar Marghabhai, INDIA
Reihard, Kathryn Anita, NY
Rinker, Margaret Ann, PA
Rivest, Pamela Jean, PA
Sedergran, Deborah Jean, PA
Seigel, Michele Ellyn, PA
Solodar, Louise Rachel, PA
Soly, Raymond Moore, PA

Thibeault, Annette R., PA
Thornton, James Arthur, PA
Trotman, Carol Lee, PA
Wakefield, Carolyn, PA
Ziaie, Hasan, IRAN
Zlupko, Ruth Ann, NJ

B.S. in NURSING

Alberts, Mari Ann Patricia, PA
Alderman, Sue Ellen Silverblatt, PA
Balderston, Philip Alan, PA
Bartlett, Melonie, PA
Binanay, Cynthia Anne, PA
Borsellino, Josephine Teresa, PA
Brennan, Betsy Gamon, NJ
Burke, Susan Maria, PA
Butcher, Howard Karl, PA
Byrd, Thelma Diane, PA
Callan, Mary Joanne, PA
Caruthers, Theresa Ann, PA
Cather, Deborah L., NJ
Chin, Marie Ann, PA

Fig. 48. Carolyn Wakefield, medical technology, spent her early years in the Clinical Laboratories at Thomas Jefferson University Hospital.

Cole, Linda Diane, PA
Csaszar, Thomas Albert, PA
Doordan, Margaret Mary, PA
Fausnacht, Donna J., PA
Finkle, Shelley Nan, PA
Finley, Amy Marie, PA
Forsberg, Sally Anne, PA
Fretz, Nancy Bruzas, PA
Furjanic, Rita Marie, PA
Gerlach, Violet Ann, NJ
Godsey, Judith Gwendolyn, NJ
Goldstein, Lee Alan, NJ
Grant, Rosemary Terry, PA
Gross, Phyllis Jean, PA
Hackman, Julie Ellen, PA
Hamburg, Diane Lynn, PA
Hiserote, Marjorie Garrison, NJ
Kastenhuber, Susan Claire, PA
Kelly, Michele, PA
King, Carol Elizabeth, NJ
Kline, Kathleen Sue, NJ
Korbel, Susan Elizabeth, PA
Kraft, Kyla Marie, NY
Kramer, Elizabeth Marie, PA
Lazarich, Elizabeth Marina, PA
Lynch, Jane Marie, PA
Maier, Vickie Ellen, NJ
Mandzak, Karen Michele, PA
McCloskey, Harry Charles, PA
McGurrin, Mary Eileen Patricia, PA
McNeal, Allen Ira, PA
Miller, Dale Leslie, PA
Niziolek, Nadine Theresa, PA

Phillips, Jane Ann, PA
Potts, Susan Elizabeth, PA
Reville, Patricia Katherine, NY
Rowan, Anita Marie, PA
Sabella, Donna Marie, PA
Schenk, Cathi Lee, PA
Smith, Beth Ann, PA
Sonsino, Renee Michele, PA
Stein, Lori Diane, PA
Sussman, Joan Lori, PA
Szal, Marianne Cathleen, PA
Taylor, Helga Roslyn, PA
Vanderlip, Janice Elaine, PA
Washington, Veronica Marie, PA
Zdzieborski, Krystyna Jacqueline, PA

B.S. in CYTOTECHNOLOGY
Aker, Andrew Hughes, NJ
Andrews, Karen Linda, PA
Baer, Kenneth Howard, PA
Balogh, Drew Gabor, PA
Cadogan, Albert S.A., PA
Carberry, Elizabeth Anne, PA
Garduque, Teresita Yabes, PHILIPPINES
Gluch, Joan Patricia, PA
McGlade, Mary Theresa, NJ
O'Neill, Kathleen M., PA
Weidmann, James Elmer, PA

B.S. in RADIOLOGIC TECHNOLOGY
Blaine, Maryann, PA
Dalton, Matthew Lewis, AUSTRALIA
Denecola, Lynn Kristine, NJ
Finnegan, James Joseph, III, PA
Gambogi, Margaret Helene, NJ
Goldberg, Melody Gail, PA
Hecker, Linda Paula, NJ
Heller, Beverly Jane, PA
Johnson, Darryl Wayne, PA
Krantz, Jeffrey Albert, PA
Paris, Mary Ann, NJ
Vitali, Jane Judith, PA

B.S. in DENTAL HYGIENE
Inderlied, Mary Elizabeth, DE
Lloyd, Carol Anne, PA
Morse, Mishel, VA
Moss, Julia Katherine, NJ
Rubinson, Holly Beth, PA
Snyder, Beth Lynda, NJ
Weller, Robin Sue, MD

Fig. 49. Albert Cadogan, cytotechnology, entered the pharmaceutical field and remained an active alumnus.

ASSOCIATE IN ARTS
Pascetta, Patricia Maria, PA
Swartz, Mary Ann, PA
Wall, Nadine R., PA

ASSOCIATE IN SCIENCE
Tocci, Rita Maria, PA

CERTIFICATE IN PRACTICAL NURSING
Adamczyk, Phyllis Margaret, PA
Allmer, Linda Marie, PA
Anoia, Donna Marie, PA
Berg, Dana Jean, PA
Berringer, Deborah Ann, PA
Bosch, Joanne Elizabeth, PA
Buonasorte, Roberta Diane, PA
Chiaverelli, Patricia Ann, PA
Christmann, Maureen Ann, PA
Dawson, Janet Lynn, NJ
Detweiler, Mary Emily, PA
Dolce, Marie Patricia, NJ
Dwyer, Donna Antoinette, PA
Fillius, Elaine Lockhart, PA
Flaherty, Teresa Joan, PA
Gallagher, Eileen Marie, PA
Gengler, Theresa Ann, PA
Harris, Lynette Michele, NJ
Heim, Linda Tynan, PA
Hertach, Janet Leanne, PA
Kalicki, Lynn Prout, PA

Kenny, Beverly Jean, PA
Kent, Maryanne Ryan, PA
Lardon, Patricia Wyremski, PA
Lehmann, Rosemarie Eileen, PA
Litz, Sharon Ann, PA
Markuszka, Marie Burke, PA
Maxwell, Anne Hamilton, PA
Muller, Diane Wanner, PA
O'Donnell, Karen Hoppe, PA
Rowe, Paula Faith, PA
Rozon, Laura Jean, PA
Sacks, Carole Anne, MD
Schuberg, Teresa Dykes, PA
Searle, Janice Dorothy, PA
Smith, Nancy Joan, NJ
Sobolusky, Barbara Clark, PA
Soda, Marian Goshow, PA
Stimson, Faith Allyne, PA
Swerdel, Robert Howard, NY
Tobin, Kathleen Bridget, PA
Tomlin, Anne Patricia, PA
Traynham, Patricia Ann, PA
Wajda, Terese Marie, NJ
Walsh, Esther A., PA
Wargo, Virginia Dornan, PA
Weiss, Kathleen Ann, NJ
White, Margaret Mary, NJ
Widmeier, Margaret Cunningham, PA
Wilson, Sandra Ann, PA
Ziegler, Sandra Rubinsky, PA

Charlotte E. Voss, right, performs one of her last official duties as Chairperson of the Department of Baccalaureate Nursing, the awarding of class pins. Dr. Voss retired in 1979 and was succeeded by Mary D. Naylor, standing at podium at left.

A Nursing Honor Society was established within the Department of Baccalaureate Nursing in 1979. Inducted that May were front row, left to right, Lee A. Goldstein, Donna M. Sabella, Shelley N. Finkle, Thomas A. Csaszar; middle row, left to right, Julia E. Hackman, Judith G. Godsey, H. Roslyn Taylor, Cynthia A. Binanay, Mary Jo Callan, Dale L. Miller, Kyla M. Kraft, Jo Ann Conry (faculty member); top row, left to right, Sally A. Forsberg, Donna J. Fausnacht, Mari Ann Alberts, Mary Eileen McGurrin, Elizabeth M. Lazarich, Susan E. Korbel, Janice E. Vanderlip, Barbara Oelschlegel. Not pictured: Sue E. Alderman, Melonie P. Bartlett, Lori D. Stein.

Health is not to be purchased by idleness and inactivity, which are the greatest evils attendant on sickness, and the man who thinks to conserve his health by uselessness and ease does not differ from him who guards his eyes by not seeing, and his voice by not speaking. For a man in good health could not devote himself to any better object than to numerous humane activities.

Plutarch [46?–120?]

Despite an overall trend toward decreased federal funding for allied health education, in the 1979/80 academic year the College received four grants. Supported by grants were training workshops on the role of the humanities in allied health education and the management of a radiological quality assurance program. In addition, a dental hygiene grant was awarded to develop an expanded function dental auxiliary training program (Fig. 50), and another went to develop a program for management, supervision and evaluation for dental hygiene educators.

The College's Alumni Special Achievement Award was presented at University Opening Exercises on September 5 to Dolores (Dee) Hughes, a 1969 nursing graduate (Fig. 51). After earning a bachelor's degree from Antioch University and a master's degree from St. Joseph's University, Ms. Hughes developed a specialty in cardiac care, serving as head nurse in Jefferson Hospital's cardiac care unit and later as the unit's Program Coordinator of Health Education.

The year marked the establishment of College chapters of two honor societies. The Beta Omega chapter of the national dental hygiene honor society, Sigma Phi Alpha, was approved in November, and the first Jefferson faculty and students were inducted in April. Also in April, the Jefferson chapter, Delta Rho, of Sigma Theta Tau, the nursing honor society, received its official charter with the induction of 98 undergraduate students, alumni, faculty and community nurses.

The College's first fund-raising Phonathon was held in May, 1980 (Fig. 52).

The College's School of Practical Nursing graduated its last class in August, 1980 (Fig. 53). The class of 66 graduates was the largest in the school's 16-year history and brought the total number of graduates to 665.

At the June 6 Commencement Exercises, the College graduated 197 students. The Commencement speaker was Luther Christman, Ph.D., R.N., vice president for nursing affairs at Rush Presbyterian-St. Luke's Medical Center, who also received an honorary Doctor of Humane Letters degree. John W. Goldschmidt, M.D., President of the American Congress of Rehabilitation Medicine, and founding dean of the College of Allied Health Sciences, was awarded an honorary Doctor of Science degree. An honorary Doctor of Literature degree was awarded to Judge A. Leon Higginbotham Jr., Esq., LLB., a Jefferson trustee.

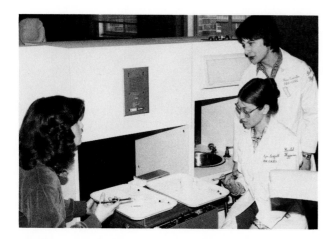

Fig. 50. Under a Department of Health, Education and Welfare grant, the Department of Dental Hygiene developed an Expanded Function Dental Auxiliary (EFDA) Program. Assistant Professor Joan Gluch-Scranton, standing at right, supervises students in the (EFDA Program).

Fig. 51. Dolores Hughes, a 1969 Nursing graduate, accepts the College's Alumni Special Achievement Award from Dean Lawrence Abrams at University Opening Exercises.

Six of the summa cum laude graduates earned perfect 4.0 grade point averages: Bernadine Gramata-Kopicki, Carolyn Mann, April Manzinger-Crawford and Ursula Maslofsky, all nursing. The Student Life Award winner was Patricia Goda, dental hygiene. She was also inducted into the newly formed Sigma Phi Alpha dental hygiene honor society. Later, as Patricia Goda Donahoe, she served as President of the Western Pennsylvania Dental Hygienists Association.

M. Elaine Bower, nursing, received a master of science in nursing degree from Gwynedd-Mercy College and became an assistant professor of nursing at Community College of Philadelphia.

Sandra Kowalski, later Sandra Schwartz, nursing, graduated from Allentown College of St. Francis de Sales with a master of science in nursing degree in 1989. She was Director of Patient Education at The Allentown Hospital-Lehigh Valley Hospital Center.

Faith Joyce, nursing, earned her master of science in nursing degree at the University of Pennsylvania in 1987. She was a geriatric nurse practitioner at the Coatesville Veterans Administration.

Nancy Osinski Cuttic, dental hygiene, subsequently attended West Chester University where in 1985 she took an M.Ed. degree in health. She held positions as an assistant professor of dental hygiene at Montgomery County Community College and at Harcum Junior College.

Karen R. Hammers, medical technology, began her career as a medical technologist in clinical hematology and microbiology laboratories. Subsequently, she earned a master of science degree in biology from Duquesne University in 1984. She then returned to Jefferson as a medical student, graduating from Jefferson Medical College in 1988. By 1990, she was in her second year of her psychiatry residency training program.

Fig. 52. Alumni and student Volunteers enjoyed a supper meeting as they prepared for the College's first Fund-raising Phonathon on May 5, 1980.

B.S. in MEDICAL TECHNOLOGY

Dungan, Kimberly Ruth, PA
Eagan, Marguerite E., PA
Focer, Lucille Patricia, PA
Gabel, Bradley E.G., PA
Gorman, Regina Maria, NJ
Grant, Carson E., PA
Hammers, Karen R., PA
Hoffing, Janis McLaughlin, WA
Jones, Sylvia Marlene, NJ
Kelly, Barbara Ann, NJ
Kostas, Kostantinia, DE
Lewkowicz, Diane Marie, PA
Mooney, Geralyn R., PA
O'Neill, Ellen Frances, NH
Parente, David Michael, NJ
Parker, Ada R., NJ
Przybylowski, EiLeen Elizabeth, PA
Ree, Valli Teresa, PA
Ristine, Carla Mary, PA
Schwartz, Joan Taber, DE
Siegel, Wendy Anne, NJ
Speer, Denyse G., NJ
Stutz, Carol Ann, PA
Swetavage, Susan Anne, PA
Swierzy, Joanne P., PA
Tokarski, Patricia Marie, PA
Wang, Gene Chin-Yeh, TAIWAN
Wearing, Diana Theresa Nash, PA
Welch, Patricia Karen, PA
Zarycranski, Deborah, NJ

B.S. in NURSING

Abrams, Marianne L., NJ
Alpern, Nancy, NJ
Aulenbacher, Richard Harvey, PA
Berlin, Patricia Ruth, PA
Bewsher, Rita A., NJ
Borgard, Kathleen Elizabeth, NJ
Bower, Mary Elaine, NJ
Brent, Deborah Ann, PA
Brown, Jeanne Geiger, NJ
Chang, Heather Ruth, NY
Chung, Jacqueline, PA
Cole, Martha Jemison, NY
Connolly, Patricia Ann, PA
Costa, Margaret Mary Cox, NJ
Crouter, Jennifer Elaine, NJ
Cubler, Amy Jeanette, PA
Ebner, Victoria E., PA
Edwards, William Francis, PA
Elicker, Debra Kay, PA
Embiscuso, Victoria, PA

Farley, Paul, PA
Farwell, Donna Marie, PA
Flynn, Karin, NJ
Fountain, Pamela Joan, PA
Garland, Bettyann Teresa, PA
Giannetti, Rita McConnaghy, PA
Green, Patrice Phyllis, PA
Hauer, Kundry Eileen, PA
Herron, Daniel Ferrell, TN
Hughes, Mary Lee Moffett, PA
Ingram, Ami Marie, PA
Johnson, Shelley Arleen, PA
Joyce, Faith Light Hart, PA
Kowalski, Sandra Rita, NJ
Lamb, Thomas Leonard, NJ
Lorah, Dawn June, PA
Madden, Katherine Anne, PA
Maiatico, Geraldine Joan, NJ

Fig. 53. Elizabeth Sweeney was the Director of the School of Practical Nursing since its inception at Jefferson in 1964. The final class graduated in 1980.

Manzinger, April Ann, PA
McCarrick, Michelle Marie, PA
McHugh, Nancy Elizabeth, NJ
Minter, Margaret Elizabeth, PA
O'Donnell, Maribeth Theresa, PA
Ollivier, Pamela Ann, NJ
Onaro, Ann Marie, PA
Panico, Eleanor Antoinette, NJ
Poklemba, Concetta Mary Magdalene, PA
Redmond, Maryanne Ellen, PA
Richards, Janet Lee, PA
Robertson, Patricia Ann, PA
Robitschek, Judith Irene, E. AFRICA
Roe, Paula Ann, PA
Rosenwald, Beth Joy, PA
Schirn, Jackie Greenleaf, PA
Schoenwalder, Ellen Jean, NJ
Schwiers, Elmslie Anne, NJ
Sempier, Carlyn Ay, PA
Shaffer, Lisa MacNeil, NJ
Short, Paula Marie, NJ
Sigman, Dianne W., PA
Simerson, Mary Anne Teresa, PA
Tryon, Thomas D., NJ
Valentino, Carol Ann, PA
Walter, Eva, PA
Wilcke, Susan M., PA
Zalesky, Carole Ann, PA

B.S. in CYTOTECHNOLOGY
Calafati, Stephanie Anne, PA
DiBartolo, Carol Ann, PA
Donnelly, Christine, PA
Durham, Robert Karl, NJ
Green, Vanessa Helene, PA
Guardiani, John, NJ
Policare, Michael Thomas, PA
Re, Elaine Margaret, NJ
Smith, Mary Austin, PA
Staniszewski, Mary Ann, NJ
Szerbin, Mariann, NJ
Vargas, Geneva Wood, PA

B.S. in RADIOLOGIC TECHNOLOGY
Hall, Kenneth Henry, NJ
Landan, Ivan Ronald, PA
LoMonaco, Rose Amelia, NJ
Maristch, Donna Marie, PA
Shasanya, Oluyinka Christiana, NIGERIA
Wilson, Kimberly Gray, PA
Yorgey, Lauren L., PA

B.S. in DENTAL HYGIENE
Beutel, Kathrin Bettina, PA
Burke, Kathryn Margaret, PA

Comly, Elizabeth Ann, PA
Cuttic, Nancy Osinkski, PA
Goda, Patricia Marie, PA
Kakascik, Donna Marie, NJ
Larsen, Susan Kim, NJ
Littleton, Carol Ann, PA
Pang, Mary, INDONESIA
Preitz, Kathy Ann, PA
Rinaldi, Janice Marie, PA
Rose, Patricia Lynn, PA
Rubsamen, Susan Ruth, NJ
Rudowitz, Wendy Beth, NJ
Silverman, Stacie Terri, MD
Tulskie, Ann Marie, PA

ASSOCIATE IN ARTS
Mulgrew, Linda I., PA

CERTIFICATE IN PRACTICAL NURSING
Alesky, Diane Lynn, PA
Alexander, Clara Gaihring, PA
Bagden, Helen Christene, PA
Barnett, Deborah Anne, PA
Bell, Brenda, NJ
Brander, Gail Mealey, PA
Broomes, Linda Denice, PA
Burke, Lorraine Sherpinsky, PA
Conley, Sharon Kay, NJ
Cunningham, Lisa, PA
D'Agostino, Rita Morabito, PA
Davis, Georgianna Jennifer, NJ
Donovan, Maryann Karnis, PA
Dutch, Kathleen Frances, PA
Feeney, Karen, PA
Foley, Lois Tetor, PA
Gordon, Susan Regina, PA
Gross, Jacqueline Michelle, PA
Hall, Ollie Creecy, PA
Hatala, Sharon Ammons, PA
Hoffman, Linda Sims, PA
Huml, Mary Theresa, PA
Jackmon, Rebecca Ingram, PA
Kelly, Susan May, PA
Lea, Cynthia Gladys, PA
Lee, Jessie Hinson, PA
Madden, Margaret Mary, PA
Mahan, Colleen Frances, PA
Malone, Lisa Marie, PA
Mann, Carolyn Jean, NJ
Marko, Elizabeth Anne, PA
Martin, Susan Christine, PA
Mayer, Joyce Buchannan, PA
McCullough, Margaret Ann, PA
Miller, Annette Marie, PA

Morris, Claire Platus, PA
Moscato, Maryann Elizabeth, PA
Mullen, Irene Quinlan, PA
Octavo, Ruben Bonayon, PA
Oyer, Lynn Carol, PA
Penkala, Loretta Frances, PA
Prelle, Patricia, PA
Purnell, Carol Louise, PA
Richter, Raymond Edward, PA
Romig, Suzanne Elizabeth, PA
Rowland, Valerie Ann, PA
Sacchetti, Mary Rudick, PA
Schad, Catherine Emma, PA
Schultze, Barbara Leibrand, PA
Scott, Lisa Marie, PA

Sharrow, Kathleen Mary, PA
Sibert, Ivonia Lee, PA
Silvestri, Michelle Christine, PA
Sloan, Mary Beth, PA
Smith, Alicia Jonasz, PA
Stroker, Barbara Brown, PA
Tighe, Mary Louise, PA
Tucker, Linda, NJ
Wagner, Jacqueline Alice, PA
Wahl, Lynda Armstrong, PA
White, Kathleen Mary, PA
Wilkie, Stacy Ann, PA
Williamson, Adell Tierney, PA
Wolf, Susan Liebers, PA
Wuchter, Lois Brady, PA
Zaborowski, Kimberly Ann, PA

Senior medical technology students work on their required research projects: (left to right) Carla Ristine, Gene C. Wang and Patty Welch.

The 1980/81 academic year was marked by several achievements and firsts. The College had a successful accreditation by the Commission on Higher Education of the Middle States Association of Colleges and Schools.

The Department of Radiologic Technology's Pilot Project 21, a proposal to institute a four-year study of preparing radiologic technology students in 21 months, rather than 24 months, was given approval by the Joint Review Committee on Education in Radiologic Technology, by the American Medical Association's Committee on Allied Health Education and Accreditation, and by the American Registry of Radiologic Technologists.

A Nurse Scholar Series was established in the Department of Baccalaureate Nursing. Ann Marie Douglas, R.N., Ph.D., was appointed nurse scholar in residence (Fig. 54).

The first class of students in the Post-Certificate Baccalaureate Degree Program in Dental Hygiene matriculated in September. Designed for licensed dental hygienists who had a certificate or associate's degree, the program included elective specialization courses in education, public health and health management.

The Alumni Special Achievement Award for this year was presented to Barbara G. Schutt, R.N., a 1938 graduate of the School of Nursing (Fig. 55). Her career included serving as a lieutenant in the U.S. Army Nurse Corps during World War II in Okinawa, as a director of nursing at Mohegan Community College in Norwich, Connecticut, as executive director of the Pennsylvania Nurses Association and as editor of the *American Journal of Nursing.*

Linda C. Gorham, radiologic technology, received the department's Mallinckrodt Award for the senior giving the most help to juniors (Fig. 56).

The 153 graduates at the June 5 Commencement Exercises included the first class of students from the Advanced Placement Program for Registered Nurses. The Class of '81 heard an address by Karl Danner Clouser, Ph.D., professor of humanities of the College of Medicine, Hershey Medical Center, Pennsylvania State University. Dr. Clouser received an honorary Doctor of Humane Letters degree. In addition, an honorary Doctor of Science degree was awarded to Catherine M. Keebler, R.N., C.T. (ASCP), a leading figure in the field of cytotechnology, nationally and internationally.

Fig. 54.   Ann Marie Douglas, R.N., Ph.D., was named Jefferson's first Nurse Scholar in Residence.

The College's Student Life Award was presented to Donna E. Eckardt (Fig. 57), later Donna E. Budak, cytotechnology, President of the Student Dormitory, who was also Co-Editor-in-Chief of the student yearbook and a representative on the Student Advisory Committee. During her career she became Chief Cytotechnologist at Medical College of Pennsylvania and later Cytology Supervisor at St. Luke's Hospital in Newburgh, New York.

Seven of the summa cum laude graduates earned perfect 4.0 grade point averages: Geraldine Koppenhaver, Helen Charles, Renee Merlino Luchtman and Raymond Miller, all medical technology; Andrea Hein, Elizabeth Torresson and Mary Wood, all nursing.

Nancy Stackhouse, dental hygiene, a magna cum laude graduate who served on the Alumni Advisory Committee, relocated to California, where she held a variety of board positions for the Orange County Dental Hygiene Society beginning in 1982. While continuing her career in a private periodontist practice, she also became a clinical instructor in the Department of Periodontics at the University of Southern California School of Dentistry in 1985.

Marsha Venner, dental hygiene, whose love of animals led her to earn an associate's degree in the veterinary technician program at Harcum Junior College, combined her two degrees to help start a veterinary dentistry practice within the field of veterinary medicine. In 1990, she was performing her dental specialty both on domestic and exotic animals in Houston, Texas.

Valli Meeks, dental hygiene, earned a Doctor of Dental Surgery degree from the University of Maryland Dental School in Baltimore. Since 1985, she continued in private practice as well as serv-

Fig. 55. Barbara G. Schutt, R.N., was the recipient of the College's Alumni Special Achievement Award.

Fig. 56. Linda C. Gorham, radiologic technology, holds the department's Mallinckrodt Award.

ing as clinical coordinator of the University of Maryland Dental School. Dr. Meeks received the Coalition of Minority Professional Students Award for Outstanding Leadership and Service. She also served as a board member of the Rainbow Head-start Program in Philadelphia.

Claire Shaw, medical technology, earned a Doctor of Dental Medicine degree from Temple University in 1987 and a certificate in periodontics, also from Temple, in 1989. By 1990, she was the owner of Doylestown Periodontics and assistant clinical professor in the Department of Graduate Periodontics at Temple.

Gerald Davidson, nursing, became a lieutenant in the United States Navy. In 1989, he received the Navy Commendation Medal from the Secretary of the Navy for meritorious service while assigned to the U.S. Naval Hospital at Subic Bay in the Philippines from 1985 to 1988.

Margaret Gavigan, nursing, began her career at Thomas Jefferson University Hospital as a clinical nurse II in the surgical cardiac care unit, later becoming clinical nurse III, then clinical nurse specialist, then nursing care coordinator in 1985. She earned her Master of Science in Nursing degree from the University of Pennsylvania in 1985. From 1987 to 1989, she was a clinical research nursing manager for Smith Kline Beecham corporation. She became head nurse in the General Surgery and Cardiothoracic Intensive Care Units at the Hospital of the University of Pennsylvania in 1989. The following year she received the Commonwealth Fund Nurse Executive Fellowship.

Marjorie-Linda Zaharfy, nursing, was a very active alumnus, serving on the College's Alumni Advisory Committee. She returned to the College for her nursing degree, having graduated from medical technology in 1976. She became acting nurse supervisor at the Philadelphia Corporation for the Aging in Philadelphia.

Fig. 57. The 1981 Student Life Award winner: Donna E. Eckardt, cytotechnology.

B.S. in MEDICAL TECHNOLOGY
Baldridge, Brian K., MD
Bax, Robert L., PA
Bigley, Frances M., NJ
Camoratto, Joseph John, NJ
Carpenter, Helen Grace, PA
Charles, Helen Claire, IN
Clay, Dorseina, PA
Cramer, Shirley Grace, NJ
Cromie, Elizabeth Marilea, PA
DelPrato, Thomas V., PA
DeSantis, Donna Marie, NJ

Dwyer, Karen Mae, NJ
Flanigan, Maureen Theresa, PA
Fleming, Nancy Leigh, NJ
Flood, Joan Marie Sherno, PA
Gillen, Judith Anne, NJ
Guerrieri, Donna Marie, PA
Kazmierczak, Irene, PA
Klein, Mary, PA
Koppenhaver, Geraldine Minerva, PA
Luchtman, Renee Merlino, NJ
Madorna, Janet Lisa, PA
Miller, Raymond L., NJ

Neuner, Michelle Anne M., PA
Ohanissian, Verjik, PA
Pattison, Cynthia Ann, NJ
Rainey, Kim L., PA
Shaw, Claire Elaine, NJ
Sherno, Marie C., PA
Sninski, Mary Macario, PA
Steel, Janet Lucille, NJ
Wolper, Eileen Marie Genevieve, PA
Yarrick, Kathy Louise, NJ

B.S. in NURSING
Adams, Deborah Lynne, NJ
Alexandrakos, Mary A., PA
Anderson, Elizabeth Burderi, NY
Autenzio, Laura, PA
Blackway, Betsy Lynne, PA
Brostowicz, Karen Ann, NJ
Bushnell, Sandra Sumi, PA
Colavechio, Anna M., PA
Davidson, Gerald Allen, PA
Davis, Jan Noel, PA
Davis-Moon, Linda Joan, NJ
Derkas, Kathy, PA
Destra, Joseph John, PA
Evans, Leslie Carol, PA
Fine, Suzan Weller, PA
Fitzgerald, Kathleen Elaine, PA
Florentine, Paul Edward, PA
Forte, Marcy Sandra, PA
Forward, Christine Cooke, NJ
Friedman, Lee, PA
Gavigan, Margaret Ann, PA
Gdowik, Linda, PA
Goldman, Judy Ann, PA
Goodman, Phyllis Susan, PA
Hax, Stephanie Christine, PA
Hein, Andrea Jean, PA
Holland, Karen Marie, PA
Horner, Maureen Ernwood, PA
Hughes, Ellen Foster, PA
Imber, Arlene Phyllis, PA
Justh, Margaret Ann, PA
Kinney, Katherine Anne, NJ
Kinslow, Cheryl Ann, PA
Kornse, Lisa Diane, NJ
Krafft, Joseph Raymond, Jr., PA
Langendorf, Debbe Lynn, PA
Lees, Gary, PA
Levenson, Carol, PA
Levin, Eileen Cheryl, PA
Lindner, Laverne Joyce, PA
Loredo, Rosa Maria, PA
Marcille, Priscille Anne, ME

May-Hoey, Natalie, NJ
McClain, Anne Elizabeth, PA
Mellon, Mary E., PA
Meshejian, Susan, PA
Miller, Darcie Leanne, CA
Miller, Kathleen Marie, PA
Morris, Marilys Rose, NJ
Musetti, Myrtie Jane, PA
Nappen, Susan Lois, PA
Nasuti, Patricia Ann, PA
Ott, Laurie Ann, PA
Peduto, Sharon Kathryn, PA
Pershing, Pamela, PA
Phelan, Barbara Ann, NJ
Plumb, Patricia Hope, PA
Pressler, Florri Rose, PA
Prossack, Janice Hope, PA
Raiburn, Edward Joseph, PA
Reithmeier, Dolores Ann, PA
Roache, Mary Beth Bernadette, PA
Rost, Joan Marie, PA
Sabol, John Joseph, PA
Schaal, Mary Greenwood, NJ
Schneider, Shelly Robin, NJ
Segal, Perri Lee, PA
Silverthorne, Elizabeth Anne, PA
Spaar, Barbara Demer, PA
Thomas, Joan Settle, PA
Torresson, Elizabeth Lawhon, PA
Vadurro, Judith Phillips, NJ
Volk, Douglas V., PA
Walsh, Michelle Anne, PA
Weiner, Debra Ann, PA
Wiley, Gary Allen, PA
Wolfgang, Cynthia Ann, PA
Wood, Mary Ann Rose, PA
Woodman, Steven R., PA
Zaharfy, Marjorie-Linda, PA
Zehler, Carol Mary, NJ

B.S. in CYTOTECHNOLOGY
Brennan, Gary Hugh, PA
Eckardt, Donna Lynn, NJ
Gibbon, Thomas Michael, PA
Gratch, David Marshall, PA
Harrington, Margaret Ann, NJ
Kent, Suzanne Rita, PA
Lipscomb, Joseph Fennigan, NJ
Rosen, Louis, PA
Santoro, Barbara Ann, NJ
Segal, Susan Elaine, PA
Stahl, Anna Roberta, PA
Waas, John Karl, PA
Weisblatt, Roseann Ellen, PA

B.S. in RADIOLOGIC TECHNOLOGY

DiSarro, Constantina, NJ
Fennie, Regina Ellen, PA
Forman, Tami Beth, PA
Gorham, Linda Cheryl, WV
Halfon, Robyn Lyne, PA
Hepler, Leslie Ann, NJ
Kraushaar, Barbara Teresa, PA
Kutas, Geraldine Ann, PA
O'Connell-Wellman, Deborah Marie, P
Sproch, Pamela Ann, NJ
Stevenson, Kathy Lynn, PA

B.S. in DENTAL HYGIENE

Boorse, Linda Reed, PA
Breon, Gwendolyn Susan, PA

Bowling, Angela Elizabeth, PA
Ehrlich, Trina Jean, PA
Kerstetter, Christine Lee, NJ
Matamoros, Linda Louise, PA
McKenna, Mary Theresa Anne, PA
Meeks, Valli Irene, PA
Parris, Frank Thomas, Jr., PA
Shapiro, Randi Lauren, NJ
Stackhouse, Nancy Joan, NJ
Tashof, Cheryl Lynn, MD
Venner, Marsha Lori, NJ

ASSOCIATE IN ARTS

Neary, Brita Ann, PA

ASSOCIATE IN SCIENCE

Siegel, Mary Lou G., PA

A happy scene from the June 5, 1981 Commencement.

At the University Opening Exercises of the 1981/82 academic year, held on September 9, the College's Alumni Special Achievement Award was presented to Wanda E. Wesolowski, who was coordinator/assistant professor, radiologic technology program at the Community College of Philadelphia (CCP). A 1958 graduate of the School of Radiologic Technology at Jefferson Hospital, Ms. Wesolowski's career was marked by numerous presentations, publications and awards. She was named a fellow of the American Society of Radiologic Technologists. Ms. Wesolowski later became professor/chairperson of the CCP radiologic technology program.

The implementation of the College's Strategic Plan, "A Decade of Planned and Controlled Progress (1982-92)" began during this year. This included the official approval in November by the University Board of Trustees of the Departments of Occupational Therapy and Physical Therapy.

The thirteenth floor of the Edison Building was renovated in order to build the Department of Nursing's Learning Resources Center. The Center was comprised of three clinical simulation areas (Fig. 58), three audiovisual rooms and a reception area. At the same time, the department established a five-year plan to develop and implement computer technology into the nursing curriculum.

On June 11, 221 graduates received their degrees at Commencement Exercises at the Academy of Music. Two honorary degrees were awarded: a Doctor of Science to Patricia Stanton McLean (Fig. 59), a national leader in the field of dental hygiene, and a Doctor of Literature to Edmund D. Pellegrino, M.D. educator and scholar known especially for his studies in medicine and the humanities (Fig. 60).

At the Commencement, the College's Achievement Award for Student Life was presented to Francine Savage, cytotechnology (Fig. 61). Ms. Savage's many activities included being student chairperson of Parents' Day, editor of the Student Life Handbook, and representative on the Student Advisory Council and the Student Affairs and Services Committee. Later, as Francine Savage Kates, she returned to the College as an Admissions Counselor and then Assistant Director of Admissions. She remained an active alumnus, serving on the Alumni Advisory Committee.

Six of the summa cum laude graduates earned perfect 4.0 grade point averages: Matthew Yucis, medical technology; Kathleen King, nursing;

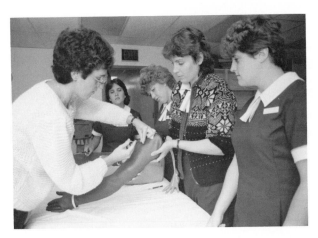

Fig. 58.   Clinical simulation area, Department of Nursing Learning Resources Center.

Fig. 59.   Honorary degree recipient Patricia Stanton McLean (center), with Chairman, Department of Dental Hygiene, Linda Kraemer and Dean Abrams.

Charlene Fenster, Kathleen Frasher-Wirbisky, Jacqueline A. Marcin, and Angela Scarlata-Rom, all dental hygiene.

Karen E. Blumenthal, later Karen E. Fox, cy-totechnology, graduated from Philadelphia College of Osteopathic Medicine in 1987 and became board certified in family practice two years later. She began a practice in Bensalem, Pennsylvania, and was on the staffs of Delaware Valley Medical Center and St. Mary's Hospital in Langhorne.

Jacqueline A. Marcin (Fig. 62), dental hygiene, graduated from Temple University School of Dentistry in 1987, at which time she won numerous awards including the Alpha Omega Scholarship Award for highest scholastic average. After a general practice residency in dentistry at Langley Air Force Base in Hampton, Virginia, she served as a general dental officer, Chief of the Department of Periodontics, with the rank of captain, at McGuire Air Force Base in New Jersey. She subsequently practiced in West Hazelton, Pennsylvania.

Nina Markovic (Fig. 63), dental hygiene, became a senior research coordinator at the Uni-

Fig. 60. Edmund D. Pellegrino, M.D. (center), with Dean Abrams and Thomas K. McElhinney, Ph.D.

Fig. 61. Francine Savage, Cytotechnology, winner of Achievement Award for Student Life.

Fig. 62. Jacqueline A. Marcin, Dental Hygiene, went on to D.D.S., Temple University, 1987.

versity of Pennsylvania School of Dental Medicine. Subsequently, she took a position as a research associate at Columbia University School of Dentistry and Oral Surgery, where she earned a Master of Science degree with honors in 1987. A member of the American Dental Hygienists' Association Council on Research, Ms. Markovic later received a doctoral fellowship in cardio-vas-cular epidemiology in the School of Public Health at the University of Pittsburgh.

Lori Stillerman, later Lori Smith, dental hygiene, began her career as a dental hygienist in Lausanne, Switzerland, treating oral cancer patients among others. She went on to Madrid, Spain, where she established that city's first dental hygiene program. Ms. Smith returned to the United States to become a Provider Network Specialist for Aetna Life and Casualty, setting up a network of dentists for that company's alternative dental plan.

Matthew Yucis, medical technology, graduated from the University of Osteopathic Medicine and Health Sciences in Des Moines, Iowa, in 1988. After an internship at Riverside Hospital in Wilmington, Delaware, he became a resident in psychiatry at Eastern Virginia Graduate School of Medicine.

Laura Chercass, medical technology, began her career as a medical technologist at Jefferson Hospital. She later became a marketing representative for a supplier of health care information systems, and then moved on to IMS America, Ltd., where she was named Product Manager, responsible for the production of pharmaceutical market research reports.

Melinda Mercer, nursing, became the Assistant Director, Congressional and Agency Relations, for the American Nurses' Association.

Jacqueline J. Exum, nursing, went to Liberia, West Africa, where she served as village health nurse and educator.

Michael Gerofsky, radiologic technology, embarked on a varied career as a CAT scan technologist at Wills Eye Hospital in Philadelphia. He returned to the College as Clinical Education Coordinator of the radiography program in the Department of Diagnostic Imaging. Mr. Gerofsky was a very active member of the Alumni Advisory Committee.

Fig. 63. Nina Markovic, Dental Hygiene, pursued research career.

B.S. in MEDICAL TECHNOLOGY
Biasello, Sandra, PA
Blain, Julia Marie, PA
Brown, Hilton, Jr., PA
Cap, Michael, NJ
Chercass, Laura Ilene, PA
Coelho, Eusebio Rodriques, PA
Entenman, Lori Ann, PA
Everson, Dorothy Suszanne, NY
Feder, Marla Joy, PA

Feola, Jo-Ann Marie, NJ
Gill, Sheryl May, PA
Goldsmith, Gail Elaine, PA
Gowan, Patricia Susan, PA
Hippensteel, Leslie Catherine, PA
Hogan, Mary Trapani, NJ
Jackowicz, Donna Holohan, PA
James, Vanessa Miranda, PA
Kessler, Lynn Avis, NJ
Long, Joyce Marie, PA

Lord, Denise Renee, MI
Lyon, Maureen, NJ
Mattei, Yvonne Louise, NJ
McCullough, Mary Ann, PA
O'Bryan, Thomas Anthony, PA
Price, June Lee, PA
Ruff, Kathryn Louise, NJ
Sand, Ellen Mary, NY
Siemon, Margaret Mary, PA
Solen, Venessa Evette, PA
Walker, Bruce, NJ
Yucis, Matthew Joseph, NJ
Zehner, Carol Suzanne, PA

B.S. in NURSING

Adams, James Fletcher, NJ
Aldinger, Leslie Joan, PA
Armstrong, Richard Joseph, PA
Barney, Sharon L., NJ
Becker, Beverly Bond, NJ
Becker, Jill Anne, PA
Bigge, Paula Mae, NJ
Blank, Linda Elizabeth, NJ
Bliss, Donna Mary, PA
Blumenstein, Elizabeth, NJ
Boas, Lyn Denworth, NJ
Bobb, Leslie Enid, PA
Brown, Wanda Frances, PA
Burns, Regina A., PA
Carey, Shavaun Mary, NJ
Cassel, Stacey Francine, PA
Charles, Nancy Anne, PA
Chiaro, Virginia Maisch, NJ
Clark, Michael Thomas, PA
Clark-Evans, Clifford Marion, MI
Cooley, Mary Elizabeth, PA
Corrado, Leigh Ann, PA
Craig, Joan Helen, PA
Cunningham, Lisa Wilson, NJ
Czarnecki, Susan Corine, PA
Davis, Ellen Bennett, PA
DePaul, Debra, PA
Devoy-McDonnell, Patricia, PA
DiMauro, Rosemarie Frances, NJ
DiRocco, Elizabeth Maureth, PA
Draper, Judith L., NJ
Dunkelberger, Donna, PA
D'Entremont, Ann Louise Mary, PA
Egan-Smith, Deborah Anne Marie, NJ
Ewart, Barbara Ann, NJ
Exum, Jacqueline Joyce, PA
Fenton, Jan Ame, NJ
Filbey, Jacquelyn Carol, NJ
Forst-Paulus, Maryellen, PA
Freeman, Deborah Johanne, PA
Gabellini, Kimberly Maria, PA

Gallagher, Linda L., PA
Gallagher, Mary Elizabeth, PA
Gambill, Gail Marie, PA
Garnier, Giby, PA
Gates, Eleanor Martin, PA
Gee, Barbara Kathryn, NJ
George, Nancy Malozzi, PA
Gervase, Theresa Maria, PA
Glickman, Jacqueline Kaye, PA
Godfrey, Mary Flavia, DC
Gorham, John, PA
Gunsallus, Regina Marie, NJ
Hale, Pamela Muschek, PA
Hayes, Sandra Lynn, NJ
Hermann, Debra M., NJ
Hetherington, Terese, PA
Hilferty, Margaret M., PA
Hopchik, Jordan, PA
Hopkins, Claire Linda, NJ
Huber-Edmundowicz, Anne Marie, PA
Humphrey, Jewette Nance, SC
Inzillo, Elena Judith Leamer, NJ
Izes, Sherri Robin, PA
Jabs, Adela Mary, PA
Jefferies, Lynn Susan, NJ
King, Kathleen Mary, NJ
Kleinman, Rita Susan, PA
Krick, Susan Wray, PA
Lane, Lisa Ann, PA
Lawrence, Susan Elizabeth, PA
Layer, Diane Judith, PA
Lee, Denise Marie, PA
Leshner, Beth Randi, PA
Levin, Janet Engle, PA
Litwack, Carol Ann, PA
Loeser, Lisa Marie, NJ
Long-Evans, Susan Barbara, PA
Loomis, Michael Conrad, PA
MacBain, Lisa Karen, PA
Margraff, Donna Lee, PA
Marion, Cathleen Anne, PA
Martin, Diane Patricia, PA
May, Beverly Ann, FL
McConarty, James Paul, PA
McGrenra, Barbara Ann, PA
McVeigh, Kathy Regina, PA
Meaney, Elizabeth Margaret, PA
Mercer, Melinda Elizabeth, PA
Mohl, Karen Irene, PA
Morley, Charlotte, NJ
Moxey, Susan Lynn, PA
Murphy, Judith Ann, PA
Neiburg, Riki Sue, PA
O'Malley, Anne Maureen, PA
O'Toole, Charles Francis, NJ
Ostrum, Linda Gail, PA

Patterson, Margaret Ann, PA
Pezzella, Debbie Anne, NJ
Posmontier, Barbara Elaine, PA
Proud, Kathy Ann, PA
Raphael, Theresa Eileen, PA
Ratka, Rosemarie, PA
Remilev, Carmen, PA
Ricciardi, Sharon Marie, PA
Robinson, Margo Charisse, PA
Roche, Patricia Bernadette, PA
Rosen, Shea Ellen, NJ
Salitsky, Nancy Jean, PA
Sandifer, Sophia, PA
Sass, Rebecca Ann, NJ
Schmid, Carol Lorraine, PA
Schmidt, Marion Bach, NJ
Sears, Sarah Hoy, OH
Shadis, Marilyn, PA
Shaffer, Rose Barbara, PA
Shapiro, Barbara Beth, PA
Sheehan, Lee Ann, CA
Sikina, Heidi Lugosch, NJ
Smeekens, Mary Sue, PA
Spence, Sharon Kay, PA
Spuhler-Gaughan, Mary Jane C., NJ
Sturgeon, Penny Kayoko, NJ
Tannenbaum, Susan Lynn, NJ
Walsh, Eileen Joan, NJ
Warren, Julie Ann, MI
Weir, Michael Joseph, PA
Wentz, Carol Olsavsky, PA
Wilkinson, William Alan, NJ
Yi, Pilsun, NJ

B.S. in CYTOTECHNOLOGY
Blumenthal, Karen Eillen, PA
Carrozza, Michael Joseph, PA
Chianese, David A., PA
DeJohn, Janice Marie, PA
Dixon, Gissele Anitamea, DE
Euperio, Julius Gonzales, PA
Fortino, Martin Robert, PA
Gruber, Ilene Paula, PA
Kerrigan, Vivianne Mastrogiacomo, P
Mainier, Lisa Anne, PA
O'Hara, Brian Jerome, NJ
Rowen, Christine Marie, PA
Savage, Francine Harriet, NJ

B.S. in RADIOLOGIC TECHNOLOGY
Citrino, Sharon Mary, PA
Colbert, Terry Donald, PA

Corma, Amy Kathleen, PA
Gerofsky, Michael David, PA
Kelley, Mary Ovinia, PA
Kelvin, Dianne Elizabeth, PA
Lazar, Wendy Marie, NJ
Ruoff, Richard R., PA
Santoro, Marylou, NJ

B.S. in DENTAL HYGIENE
Bortz, Diane Abby, PA
Callahan, Susan Michele, PA
Champlin, Susan June Hallowell, PA
Collier, Andrea Rachel, PA
Cummings, Catherine Louise, PA
Dawley, Dawn Elizabeth, NJ
Fenster, Charlene Anne, NJ
Frasher, Kathleen Mae, DE
Freedman, Dorothea Beryl, PA
Gurley, Cheryl Lynn, PA
Hickman, Kimberly Ann, DE
Huss, Jayne Naomi, PA
Karow, Lynn Michelle, NY
Kunsman, Kay Ann, PA
Marcin, Jacqueline Ann, PA
Markovic, Nina Marie, DE
Matricciano, Donna Marie, NJ
Mayer, Carol June, NJ
Mullen, Marie Elvira, PA
Orenstein, Lynn Robin, PA
Pollick, Sharon Ann, PA
Price, Janice Marie, PA
Rom, Angela Scarlata, MD
Ruggles, Christy Lynn, PA
Slone, Kathleen Ann, KS
Stewart, Lisa Ann, PA
Stillerman, Lori Ellen, IN
Wyszynski, Susan Elizabeth, PA
Zack, Minnie, NJ
Zerone, Barbara Jean, NJ

ASSOCIATE IN ARTS
Bobbin, Joann Frances, PA
Cannava, Maureen Vivian, NJ
Garwood, Joann Jersey, NJ
McAnally, Theresa Maria, PA

ASSOCIATE IN SCIENCE
Guido, Noreen Ann, PA
Issa, Ali Hussein, NJ
Scarantino, Patricia Lynn M., PA

During the 1982/83 academic year, the proposed new College programs, occupational therapy and physical therapy, took a step closer to reality when their respective Program Planning Consultants, Ruth E. Levine, O.T.R., Ed.D., and Jeffrey Rothman, P.T., Ed.D., were appointed Department Chairmen.

The Chairman of the Department of Baccalaureate Nursing, Mary D. Naylor, R.N., Ph.D., was selected from more than 700 applicants nationwide to receive a three-year W.K. Kellogg Foundation Fellowship grant to pursue a self-designed plan of study focused on leadership skills. Another Jefferson nursing leader, Doris E. Bowman, R.N., M.S. Ed., who had served as Director of the School of Nursing from 1958 to 1982, was appointed College Archivist, the first person to hold that position.

The Alumni Special Achievement Award this year was presented to Jeraldine J. Kohut, R.N., M.A., who earned her diploma in 1964 from the School of Nursing (Fig. 64). Ms. Kohut was an assistant professor of nursing and director of continuing education at the School of Nursing at Tennessee Technological University. Known especially for her work with the elderly, Ms. Kohut was the organizer of the first elderly daycare program established in a private nursing home in Pennsylvania.

Several publications related to the College were completed and distributed during the year. They included the commemorative publication *Thomas Jefferson University School of Nursing 1891-1982: A Commitment to Excellence*; the seventh edition of the *Health Careers Guidance Manual for the Greater Philadelphia Region* (Fig. 65); and *Something More Like a Cathedral, A Report and Analysis of a Nontraditional Interinstitutional Academic Program in Medical Technology*, which was the culmination of a five-year federally funded project and which was distributed to all medical technology programs in the nation.

On June 4, 1983, the College of Allied Health Sciences' new chapter of the Alpha Eta Society, the national honor society for allied health, had its first initiation ceremony. Chapter organizing members were: Lynn Durst, Nancy Council Maguire, Jasbir Sethi, and Joan Gluch-Scranton, the latter of whom was elected President. Four faculty members and eight baccalaureate members were initiated.

The Commencement Exercises for the Class of 1983, numbering 214 graduates, were held on June 10 and featured honorary degrees awarded to Ruth F. Hovde, former President of the American Society for Medical Technology and allied health leader, and to educator Vartan Gregorian, President and Chief Executive Officer of The New York Public Library (Fig. 66).

Fig. 64. Jeraldine J. Kohut, winner of Alumni Special Award shown with Dean Abrams.

Fig. 65.   Dorothy Grieb, co-editor with 7th edition, *Health Careers Guidance Manual*.

Fig. 66.   Vartan Gregorian, honorary degree recipient with Dean Abrams.

Graduate Peter J. Leporati (Fig. 67), a former Philadelphia police officer who decided to change careers to nursing, was the recipient of the Student Life Award. Mr. Leporati was President of the Nursing Student Government and Vice President of Jefferson's chapter of the Student Nurses' Association of Pennsylvania, among his many activities.

Four of the summa cum laude graduates earned perfect 4.0 grade point averages: Grace M. Glowka-Howell, medical technology, who was also inducted into Alpha Eta Honor Society; Rita E. McGinley, nursing; Linda Shegda, nursing; and Jeslyn Farrow, dental hygiene.

Jeslyn C. Farrow (Fig. 68), who also received her department's Achievement Award in Dental Management, became the Office Manager of ProDent, Inc., a management company for corporately owned dental group practices. After serving for a time as Assistant Director, she was

Fig. 67.   Nursing graduate Peter J. Leporati, recipient of Student Life Award.

promoted to Vice President of Operations and a member of the Board of Directors.

Lynn Finocchi, dental hygiene (Fig. 69), who received her Department's Esteemed Colleague Award and Education Award, continued her dental hygiene education at Columbia University, where she earned her master's degree and won the outstanding student award. Ms. Finocchi continued her relationship with Jefferson as an active member of the Alumni Advisory Committee.

Allison Frazier-Hancock, later Allison Cooper, dental hygiene, who was President of Jefferson's Student Dental Hygiene Association, continued her professional leadership activities. While a practicing dental hygienist, Ms. Cooper served in the late '80s as both Vice President and President of the Southern New Jersey Dental Hygienists' Association and as Vice President of the New Jersey Dental Hygienists' Association.

Laura A. Beckman, later Laura A. Berkowitz, dental hygiene, earned a law degree from Georgetown University Law Center in 1987. She practiced law with a Philadelphia firm where she specialized in personal injury, litigation, product liability, general negligence and dental malpractice defense.

Patricia Alexandrowicz, later Patricia Litostansky, cytotechnology, established the cytology laboratory in the Bucks County Women's Diagnostic Center, the first center of its kind in Bucks County, Pennsylvania.

Lynn Bender, later Lynn Rogowicz, medical technology, who earned her Department's Clinical Chemistry Award, began her career as a medical technologist in clinical microbiology at Jefferson Hospital. She later joined the pharmaceutical industry as a research associate in medical microbiology at Bristol-Myers Squibb

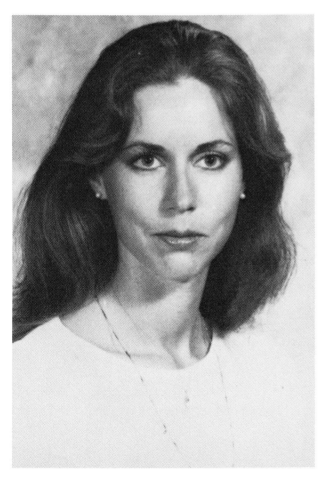

Fig. 68. Jeslyn C. Farrow, dental hygiene, recipient of Departmental Achievement Award in Dental Management.

Fig. 69. Lynn Finocchi, dental hygiene. Esteemed Colleague and Education Award recipient.

Company in Princeton, New Jersey, where she performed preclinical antibiotic research.

Tessa Rappaport, later Tessa Freeman, medical technology, continued her education at Jefferson, graduating from the College of Graduate Studies in 1987 with a master's degree in clinical microbiology and winning the award for best research project presentation. She later became microbiology laboratory supervisor at St. Agnes Medical Center in Philadelphia.

Jiunn-Jong Wu, medical technology (Fig. 70), entered the master of science degree program in clinical microbiology at Jefferson's College of Graduate Studies and graduated in 1985. He earned his Ph.D. from Temple University in 1989 and then became a research fellow at the Research Institute of Scripps Clinic in La Jolla, California.

Irene Jubinsky, later Irene Cardell, nursing, continued her nursing career at Jefferson Hospital following her graduation. She subsequently wrote the script for a videotape designed for patients awaiting surgery for the hospital's educational television channel.

B.S. in MEDICAL TECHNOLOGY
Anderson, Judy Kaye, MD
Arwood, Robert Edward, NJ
Bender, Lynn Carol, NJ
Braun, Leslee Anne, PA
Brennan, Linda M., PA
Caroluzzi, Susan Laura, PA
Cherian, Simon Ooramvelil, PA
Coffee, Deborah, NJ
Fediw, Sonya Berta, PA
Glowka, Grace Mary, PA
Goldman, Ferne Rochelle, PA
Mendoza, Ana Mercedes Gonzalez, PR
Houck, Karen, PA
Khalifa, Samar F., PA
Leskiw, Patricia E., PA
McEvoy, Karen Louise, PA
McGeary, Kathleen Anne, NJ
Moberg, Rebecca Lee, PA
Morris, Sylvia Regina, NJ
Nagel, Mary C., PA
O'Donnell, Robin Michelle, PA
Previte, Catherine, PA
Rappaport, Tessa, PA
Roider, Brian Harold, MO
Sedorvitch, Antonia Lynn, NJ
Smietana, Juanita Marie, PA
Soares, Ilsa Del Carmen, PR
Wu, Jiunn-Jong, TAIWAN

B.S. in NURSING
Anderson, Maxwell Granger, PA
Barry, Christine, NJ
Bechtel, Marlene Ann, PA
Beningo, Linnette Sue, CT
Bilker, Diane Maryland, PA
Blazich, Donna Marie, NJ
Bloom, Debra Ann, PA

Board, Kathy Virlene, PA
Boettger, Diane Osolnick, SC
Bonner, Kathryn Elizabeth, NJ
Bradbury, Linda Marie, NJ
Brown, Denise Rochelle, PA

Fig. 70. Jiunn-Jong Wu, medical technology, went on to M.S. in microbiology at College of Graduate Studies.

Capie, Linda Claire, NJ
Cardonick, Cindy Diane, PA
Carter, Mary Lee, PA
Cassidy, Anne Marie, PA
Cathcart, Tressa Ann, PA
Cavanaugh, Ritanne, NJ
Cenci, Carol Ann, PA
Clydesdale, Gale Adrienne, PA
Cohen, Elizabeth Wilson, PA
Colbert, Theresa Elizabeth, PA
Colladay, Joyce, PA
Collins, John Patrick, PA
Cook, Deborah Lee, NJ
Cordier, Lisa Ann, NJ
Cowden, Wendi Sue, PA
Craig, Christopher , PA
Croce-Burgess, Marlene Catherine, N
Davis, Helen Kline, NJ
Davis, Susan Briggs, NJ
Depman, Ruth Ann, PA
DeStefano, Edward John, Jr., PA
Dixon, Nancy Montgomery, PA
Dorsey, Deirdre Fay, NJ
Driesbach, Regina Hensley, NJ
Ebersole, Joyanne, NJ
Faulk-Bazemore, Ettie Belle, PA
Fee, Dolores C., NJ
Felix, Karen Jeanne, PA
Field, Cynthia Ruth, PA
Fitzpatrick, Kathleen Marie, PA
Fordyce, Barbara Jean, PA
Formeller, Mary Angela Agnes, PA
Franck, Suzanne, PA
Gellman , Cheryl Ann Fleishman, PA
Glosenger, Donna Carol, NJ
Gonzalez, Diane Michelle, PA
Grimmel, Jane Helen, MD
Guiney, Colleen , PA
Haas, Nancy Ann, NJ
Harris, Linda Lee, PA
Hawkshaw, Mary Jean, PA
Heffernan, Matilda Elizabeth, PA
Hillegass, Terri Lynn, PA
Hodorovich, JoEllen Christina, PA
Howarth, Janet Lynne, PA
Hyde, Kathryn Anita, DE
Jones, Susan Marie, NJ
Jones, Susan Traub, NJ
Joseph, Erin Fern, PA
Jubinsky, Irene Catherine, PA
Kanas, Sandra Jean, PA
Keen, Pamela Lee, NJ
Kelly, Kathleen Jean, NJ
Kelly, Marybeth, NY

Kennedy, Maureen A., PA
Kerns, Timothy Joseph, RI
Koller, Hope Beth, PA
Konzelman, James Joseph, PA
Kopistansky, Christine , PA
Kramer, Sharon Leslie, PA
Kreischer, Lisa Ann, PA
Lang, Mary Anne, PA
Latshaw, Louise Lenore, PA
Leporati, Peter Joseph, PA
Levin, Barrie Ruth, PA
Litwinczuk, Lydia Teresa, PA
Margraff, Darlene Ruth, PA
Matalonis, M. Denise, PA
Matalucci, Barbara Patricia, NJ
Mayer, Anne Marie, NJ
McColgan, Margaret Mary, PA
McGinley, Rita Elizabeth, NJ
McKee, Kathleen Regina, PA
McShea, Maureen Theresa, NJ
Meidt, Kathleen Foley, NJ
Meier, Deborah Kathryn, PA
Moffat, Sandra Ann, PA
Montgomery, Carole Page, PA
Noonan, Joseph Michael, PA
O'Brien, Kathleen Marie, NJ
Ochlak, Mary Jo M., PA
Olivet, Dean Carmen, CT
Oxenreider, Joy Louise, PA
Panarella, Dolores Marie, NJ
Pedano, Antonia Marie, NJ
Peetros, Susan Lynn, PA
Penney, Susan L., PA
Piemontese, Marilyn Maureen, PA
Pierson, Roseanne , PA
Quigley, Maureen Jeannette, PA
Read, Alice Jeanne, PA
Rettig, Susan Louise, PA
Ritaldato, Angela Celeste, PA
Rose, Marlyn Jana, PA
Rosenstock, Rachel Jean , PA
Roth, Mavis Leona, PA
Schwartz, Susan, NJ
Seely, Michael Scott, PA
Semanoff, Randi S., PA
Sengin, Kathi Kendall, NJ
Sheehan, Maurice Michael, PA
Shegda, Linda Maria, PA
Shinal, Susan Marie, PA
Smart, Rita Marie Therese, PA
Snyder, Susan Ann, PA
Sparkler, Ilisa Meg, PA
Springstead, Kermit, Jr., NJ
Steed, Carole LaVerne, PA

Steinmetz, Nancy Lowry, PA
Stoltzfus, Cynthia Lee, PA
Strawn, Katherine Anne, PA
Swan, Frances Elizabeth, PA
Swartz, Amy Hope, PA
Swartzlander, Diane Jean, PA
Thompson, Shelvy Jean, PA
Torrillo, Susan Ann, NY
Valentine, Lisa Ann, PA
VanDoren, Laura Ellen, PA
Van Nest, Joann M., NJ
Veon, Judith Thompson, NJ
Wade, Kathleen, PA
Waegerle, John David, PA
Walsh, Patricia Dorothy, NJ
Wargo, Donna Jean, PA
Watson, Wendy Ann, PA
Wechter, Jill Susan, PA
Whelpley, Jack Joseph Daniel, PA
Williams, Betty Jean, PA
Williams, Eileen , PA
Wilson, Kimberly , PA
Wittke, Jill Anne, NJ
Woehr, Nancy Elizabeth, PA
Woodcock, Robert William, PA
Wosiski , Karen Smith, PA
Wright, Katherine, PA
Zarnosky , Linda Marie DiVito, NJ
Zomchick, Mary , PA

B.S. in CYTOTECHNOLOGY
Alexandrowicz, Patricia Sue, PA
Baran, Elizabeth Marie, PA
Hennick, Cynthia Louise, PA
Hidalgo, Margaret Susan, PA
Norwood, Tracy Lee, PA
Salovich, Suzanne Renee, PA
Stewart, Beverly Anita, PA

B.S. in RADIOLOGIC TECHNOLOGY
Byrd, Harold Thomas, NJ
Cox, Sister Mary Elizabeth, WA
De Simone, Debra Norma, PA
Mancinow, Tatyanna , PA
Porpiglia, Mary Ellen, PA
Rainey, Kimberly Ann, DE
Ryles, Darryl Anthony, PA
Sassler, Fredrick Saul, PA

B.S. in DENTAL HYGIENE
Beckman, Laura Ann, PA
Dinan, Mary Clare, PA
Dobbs, Linnette Lilieth, PA
Farrow, Jeslyn Claire, NJ
Finocchi, Lynn Louise, PA
Frazier-Hancock, Allison, NJ
Gaddis, Barbara Eileen, NJ
Gallagher, Michele Frances, PA
Hamilton, Suzanne, PA
LaSassa, Marian Ida, PA
Levin, Nadine Beth, PA
Losty, Susan Joan, CT
Marino, Mary Catherine, PA
Messina, Diane Sarah, NY
Mooney, Lauren E., PA
Nappo, Luisa, NY
O'Brien, Kimberly Irene, CT
Panichi, Karen Marie, PA
Schwartz, Beth Robin, NJ
Uchic, Susan Lorraine, PA

ASSOCIATE in ARTS
Robinson, Linda Carol, NJ

ASSOCIATE in SCIENCE
Wah, Marie Yves, PA

I am in favor of war. I am very much in favor of the kind of war that we are conducting here at Warm Springs, the kind of war that, aided and abetted by what we have been doing at Warm Springs now for fourteen or fifteen years, is spreading all over the country—the war against the crippling of men and women and, especially, of children.

Franklin D. Roosevelt [1882–1945]
Remarks at Warm Springs
Georgia, November 23, 1939

When the 1983/84 academic year began, the College of Allied Health Sciences had approximately 1,000 students in 14 programs in the College's eight departments, marking the enrollment peak in its history to that time.

Contributing to the enrollment were the College's first entering classes in occupational therapy and physical therapy (Fig. 71). In addition, the Department of Nursing introduced two new options designed to allow registered nurses to pursue a baccalaureate degree part-time, one based at Jefferson and the other based in Harrisburg.

At the University's Opening Exercises in September, University President Lewis W. Bluemle, Jr., M.D., presented Dean Lawrence Abrams with a "Citation for Distinguished Service" for his leadership of the College for the past five years (Fig. 72).

During the year, three departments were re-accredited, each for the longest allowable times. The Department of Nursing was re-accredited for eight years, the Department of Medical Tech-

nology and the Department of Radiologic Technology for five years.

In the fall, the College co-hosted the 18th Annual Meeting of the American Society of Allied Health Professions. Later in the year, the Department of Nursing initiated its Visiting Professor of Nursing Seminar Series.

Held at the traditional site, the Academy of Music, the 1984 Commencement Exercises on June 8 featured the awarding of two Honorary Doctor of Science degrees. The recipients were allied health educator Dr. Darrel J. Mase, who was a founder and the first President of the American Society of Allied Health Professions, and Philadelphian Lieutenant Colonel Guion S. Bluford, Jr., an astronaut who served as flight engineer on the eighth Challenger Space Shuttle mission.

Among the 268 graduates was Patricia Ann Paul, nursing, who won the College's Student Life Award (Fig. 73). Her participation and leadership in numerous College activities, including the presidency of the Jefferson chapter of the Student Nurses Association of Pennsylvania,

Fig. 71. The faculty of the College's new Department of Occupational Therapy (left to right): Dawn Papougenis, M.B.A., O.T.R., instructor; Susan C. Merrill, M.A., O.T.R., instructor; Roseann Schaff, M.S., O.T.R., instructor; Ruth E. Levine, O.T.R., Ed.D., professor and chairman; and Ellen Kolodner, M.S.S., F.A.O.T.A., O.T.R., assistant professor.

Fig. 72. At Opening Exercises for the 1983/84 academic year, Dean Lawrence Abrams (left) received a "Citation for Distinguished Service" for his leadership of the College from University President Lewis W. Bluemle, Jr., M.D.

earned her the award. As Patricia Ann Paul-Berkes in 1990, she remained close to Jefferson, holding a Clinical Nurse II position at Jefferson Hospital, where she was chairperson of the nursing department's Retention Advisory Committee (1988-90). In addition, she served as a member of the College's Alumni Advisory Committee.

Four of the summa cum laude graduates earned perfect 4.0 grade point averages: Sandra K. Tran, medical technology; Carol Catalina, Mary Kirk and Denise DiDio-Donar, all nursing.

Ms. DiDio-Donar, who also earned several awards and honors upon graduation, earned a second baccalaureate degree in 1986, in school nursing from Glassboro State College (Fig. 74). She subsequently became a Clinical Nurse Specialist/Nursery Nurse Educator at All Children's Hospital in St. Petersburg, Florida. In 1990, she received her master's degree in public health, with a concentration in maternal and child health, from San Diego State University, graduating summa cum laude.

Edward Joseph Harvilla, nursing, who was President of the Nursing Student Government in his senior year, attended Rutgers University School of Law, graduating with a tax honors certificate in 1987. Entering private practice, he began to explore the uses of computer technology related to law. In 1988, Mr. Harvilla founded Clinical Financial Legal (CFL) Knowledge Systems, Inc., which established trademarks for specific software inventions of his. He also trademarked a telephone computer service that disseminates up-to-the-minute information on changes in federal tax and Medicare regulations.

Jeffrey R. Gusst, nursing, began his nursing career as a trauma staff nurse at Albert Einstein Medical Center in Philadelphia and at Brandy-

Fig. 73. The 1984 Student Life Award recipient: Patricia Ann Paul, nursing.

Fig. 74. Denise DiDio-Donar, after winning awards and honors, became a nurse educator.

wine Hospital as a flight nurse crew chief in a medical evacuation helicopter (Fig. 75). In 1987, he joined Jeanes Hospital in Philadelphia as nurse manager of the Emergency Department. The following year, Mr. Gusst returned to Jefferson as the program coordinator of JeffSTAT, Jefferson Hospital's air and ground emergency transport team. Besides being a licensed R.N. in both Pennsylvania and New Jersey and holding 12 additional certifications, Mr. Gusst held a position as First Lieutenant Flight Nurse Medical Crew Director with the United States Air Force Reserves.

Linda Khalife Baka, dental hygiene, graduated from Case Western Reserve University's School of Dentistry in 1989 and by 1990 was practicing at Jefferson Dental Associates and the Temple University School of Dentistry in Philadelphia.

Ann Eshenaur Spolarich, dental hygiene, a summa cum laude graduate who, as a student,

wrote the oral health care protocol for head and neck cancer patients at Jefferson Hospital, took a teaching and research position at the Dental School of the University of Maryland (Fig. 76). She earned a Master of Science degree from the University of Maryland in 1988. Later that year she returned to Jefferson as a faculty member and senior clinic coordinator in the Department of Dental Hygiene. She was also a teaching associate at the University of Pennsylvania School of Dental Medicine. The recipient of several research grants, Ms. Spolarich presented over 30 papers nationally and internationally by 1990.

Sharon M. Foulds-Coleman, dental hygiene, joined the Delta Dental Plan in Medford, Massachusetts, in 1985 as lead customer service representative, then became assistant supervisor of customer service in 1986, and underwriter in 1987. She earned her M.B.A. from New Hampshire College in 1990.

CLASS OF 1984

B.S. in MEDICAL TECHNOLOGY
Borrelli, Jacqueline Ann, PA
Carlson, Jeffery Glen, MI
DiBattista, Maria Lisa, PA
Fulginiti, Nancyann Maria, PA
Fynan, Susan Clare, NJ
Giampa, Theresa Lynn, PA
Giglio, Joseph Lewis, NJ
Green, Carol Elaine, PA
Gregoire, Todd Philip, PA
Hanges, Lisa Gail, PA
Hasyn, Barbara, PA
Houck, Karen M., PA
Koch, Jean Marie, PA
Laux, Anne Veronica Bridget, PA
Lingappan, Kasturi, NJ
Magee, Deborah Anne, PA
Maialetti, Dina Ann, PA
Matthews, Paula Marie Ann, PA
Molnar, Tina Marie, PA
Mujorra, Silverio E., PA
Myr, Daria Maria, PA
O'Dwyer, Noreen, PA
Poliwoda, Elizabeth Mary, PA
Rugh, Regina Marie, PA
Sand, Margaret Mary, NY
Saulli, Valerie Waltrich, NJ
Sedotti, Grace Mary, NJ
Stroud, Joanne Kay, PA

Tran, Sandra Krick, PA
Versland, Heidi Jean, CT
Young, Shelley Johanna, NJ
Zelikoff, Mindy J., NJ
Zimmerman, Cathleen Marian, PA
Zwysen, Carol Ann, PA

B.S. in NURSING
Abbate, Catherine J., NJ
Ailes, Mary Anne Elizabeth, NJ
Albert, Lori Marie, PA
Albright, Rhonda Faye, PA
Anderson, Linda Merrick, PA
Armstrong, Robert Joseph, PA
Arnold, Kaaren, PA
Babecki, Barbara Ann, NJ
Bahr, Jacqueline T., NJ
Ballistreri, Nancy Lee, NJ
Bates, Susan Karen, PA
Beard, Martha Elizabeth, PA
Beck, Diane Louise, PA
Becker, Donna Renee, PA
Bergmaier, Linda Marie, PA
Blair, Joyce Irene, NJ
Blasciak, Karen Lynn, NJ
Blumenfeld, Susan Joy, PA
Bound, Jessamyn M., PA
Boyle, Gina Marie, PA
Bradley, Gayla Evette, PA

Buonora, John Edward, PA
Burke, Kathleen Patricia, PA
Cable, Barbara, PA
Carlin, Alice Mary, PA
Carney, Bridget Marie, PA
Catalina, Carol Lynne, PA
Chubin, Ronald Scott, PA
Cope, Bethany Sheryn, NJ
Copper, Carol Ann, NJ
Corley, Stephanie , PA
Corse, Kathleen M., NJ
Costello, Lynn Ann, PA
Craik, Alan, NJ
Cronin, Kathleen, PA
Davenport, Amy L., PA
Davies, Nancy Danella, PA
Deakins, Teri Sue, PA
Denham, Margret M., NJ
Dennis, Wendy Hetherington, NJ
DeSilvio, Dennis G., NJ

Devine, Lucy V., PA
Devine-Hollander, Kelly Ann, PA
DeVivo, Denise Diane, PA
Devlin, Joanne Patricia, PA
Dexter, Mary Catherine, PA
DiDio, Denise E., PA
DiGiacomo-Modell, Maureen, NJ
DiLuciano, Marlene Michele, PA
DiNardi, Victoria Ann, PA
Dodd, Deborah Anne, PR
Dodd, Nancy Alberta, NJ
Doney, Susan Johanna, PA
Donohue, Kathleen Mary, PA
Duffy, William John, PA
Dyer, Kathleen McCullough, PA
D'Eramo, Rosanne Marie, NJ
Ehrlich, Karen Louise, PA
Ellingson, Sharon Lynne, PA
Epright, Barbara Ann, NJ
Essner, Barrie Sydelle, PA

Fig. 75. Jeffrey R. Gusst developed skills in emergency services.

Fig. 76. Ann Eshenaur Spolarich, dental hygiene, recipient of research grants and author of numerous articles in dental medicine.

Evans, Marianne T., PA

Evanson, Odette Marina, WEST INDIES

Everett, Cynthia Jane, PA

Farnan, Catharine Maria, PA

Farrell, Patricia Ann, PA

Fiocchi, Julie Frances, NJ

Fish, Merriel Anne, PA

Francis, Andrew Albert, PA

Freedman, Arlene Barbara, PA

Fugaro, Claudia Maria, NJ

Gales, Kimberly Jeanette, PA

Gerace, Maria Rita, PA

Gift, Kathryn Marie, MD

Glowacz, Cynthia Marie, NJ

Goldschmidt, Tamra A., PA

Gordon, Linda , PA

Green, Diane Frances, PA

Green, Linda Frances, PA

Greenberg, Sharon Ellen, PA

Griffith, Denise J., PA

Grimes, Cheryl Ann, NJ

Gusst, Jeffrey Robert, PA

Haines, Mary Jane, PA

Hanna, Pamela Linda, PA

Harms, Jennifer Linnea, NJ

Harris, Mary Frances, SC

Harvilla, Edward Joseph, PA

Hattman, Elizabeth Amelia, MD

Haux, Marianne, PA

Hayne, Dana Masterson, PA

Heath, Annemarie, PA

Hescock, Dianne Plouff, VT

Hoffman, Barbara Ann, PA

Hoffman, Marion Louise, CO

Hogan, Kathleen, NJ

Holm, Ingrid Margareta, NJ

Horowitz, Deborah F., PA

Hosgood, Margaret M., PA

Houghton, Denise Helenmarie, PA

Huggler, Tami Kay, PA

Hvisdas, Robert R., NJ

James, Marcelline Ann, PA

Jerdon, E. Jessica , PA

Johnson, Joyce Ann, NJ

Joos, Carole Ellen, PA

Jugran, Linda Marie, NJ

Keller, Gerhart O., Jr., PA

Kelly, Dena Marie Hartman, PA

Kirby, Jacqueline Lee, PA

Kirk, Mary Ethel, PA

Korn, August Charles, PA

Kory, Donna Elise, FL

Kripke, Rebecca Dotterer, PA

Krus, Carol Ann, NJ

Laube, Bonnie Lynn, NJ

Lauch, Anne Mercedes, PA

LeBlanc, Andrea E., MA

Lee, Kelli A., PA

Leichter, Diane Lora, PA

Lepone, Anna Marie, PA

Levin, Debra Susan, PA

Lindinger, Marybeth, PA

Mackell, MaryAnn, PA

Maguire, Linda Marie, NJ

Marnell, Nancy Marie, PA

Masciantonio, Kathleen, PA

Mattioli, Jodi Susan, PA

McCall, Janice Alethea, PA

McGeehan, Joan Patricia, PA

McPeak, Ursula Marie, PA

Mignona, Frances Mary, PA

Milam, Lynn, NJ

Millett, Stacie Ann, PA

Moore, Patricia Ann, PA

Moulder, Caryl Jean, PA

Nagy, Rose Magdelena, PA

Nasr, Deborah D., PA

Neff, Linda Joyce, NJ

Ney, Elizabeth R. L., NJ

Ngo, Tu Tuyet, PA

Nusca, Esty Carl, PA

O'Neill, Kathleen A., PA

Papa, Andrea Ann, NJ

Parise, Helene Louise, PA

Paul, Patricia Anne, NJ

Phillips, Deborah Ellen, PA

Pickett, Ann Lindsay, NJ

Prince, Vivian, PA

Reffle, Susan Marie, PA

Reyes, Rissa Tolentino, NJ

Rivers, Gertrude Dianne, PA

Rodio, Carol Ann, NJ

Rose, Gilbert Pattison, PA

Sarnacki, Joan D., PA

Sayles, Roy Scott, PA

Schelle, Mary Elizabeth, PA

Schellhammer, Audrey Marie, PA

Schjavland, Elena Theresea, PA

Schmidt, John Frank, PA

Smith, Dianne Marie, PA

Snow, Diane Marie, PA

Sobolewski, Mark Vincent, NJ

Solominsky, Barbara Ruth, PA

Stetto, Jayne Ellen, PA

Symons, Barbara Bachman, PA

Tarquini, Diane Regina, PA

Thomas, Josita Marie, PA

Tipka, Catherine Karen, PA

Trombetta, Karen Lee, NJ
Tully, Kathleen C., NJ
Van Wyk, Susan, FL
Vekkos, Lynda Renee, NJ
Vogler, Robert Charles, Jr., NJ
Vollmer, Kathleen Theresa, PA
Von Wellsheim, Elizabeth, NY
Wagenseller, Toni Helen, NJ
Weill, Susan Lynn, PA
Weiner, Susan Marks, PA
Wilson, Darlene Jacqueline, PA
Winitz, Mindy S., PA
Wolfe, Victoria Leonora, NJ
Wright, Beryl Anne, NJ
Zartarian, Karen Nevart, NJ

B.S. in CYTOTECHNOLGY
Casillas, Johnny, PA
Johnson, Kimberly Annette, PA
Kek, Bronya, MA
Locke, Darron Blaine, PA
Ludin, Claire Debra, PA
McElwee, Joanne, PA
Nowak, Kathleen Mary, PA
Phillips, Pamela Mary, PA
Proulx, James Wesley, PA
Schell, Yvonne Marie, PA
Trubilla, Mary Elizabeth, PA

B.S. in RADIOLOGIC TECHNOLOGY
Abuschinow, Sandsha, PA
Capano, Michele, PA
Cohen, Sheryl, PA
DeMarshall, Deborah Anne, PA
Grande, Petruzza, PA
Hansen, Marcianne, NJ

Harris, Tracey Lee Anne, VA
Kelly, Margaret Mary, PA
McClure, Lisa Dorothy, PA
Otey, Shereen LaVette, PA
Reese, Francesca, PA
Simon, Andree Elisabeth, PA
Skiptunas, Suzanne Marie, PA
Swikart, MaryAnne, NJ
Ward, Linda Darlene, DE
Williams, Doreen Beatrice, PA

B.S. in DENTAL HYGIENE
Asure, Barbara Britton, PA
Bennett-Coccia, Lisa Mary, PA
Capers, Ruth Zoller, NJ
Donatucci, Carol Susan, PA
Eshenaur, Ann Elizabeth, PA
Foulds, Sharon Marie, MA
Grove, Vicki Lynn, PA
Khalife, Linda , PA
Kimmel, Ellen Suzanne, NJ
Kirk, Rosanne, NJ
Levin, Sandra Irene, NJ
Maynor, Michelle D., PA
Mazyck, Jayne, NJ
Murray, Ann Erin, PA
Paroby, Lisa Maria, PA
Peditto, Michele Renee, PA
Studdard, Eletha, TN
Tinsley, Laureen, PA
Wilkoff, Janis Brown, PA

ASSOCIATE in ARTS
Andrew, Carole Lee, MA
Biernbaum, Sandra Helene, PA
Ferreira, Joan, PA
Smiler, Harriet F., PA

The College's "Career Options Program," where alumni return to speak to current students, was in its fifth year in 1984. Speaking on a nursing panel were B.S.N.. graduates: (back row) Jane Marko Carabasi '75, Nancy Redfern Freedman '75, Terry Raphael '82, and Linda Gallagher '82; (front row) Linda Bucher '74, Melanie Pirollo '75, Josephine Borsellino '79 and Lynn Jeffries.

The 1984/85 academic year was a landmark year in the evolution of College programs. The College's newest ones, occupational therapy and physical therapy, received accreditations from their respective professional associations and produced their first graduates. In addition, a program in diagnostic medical sonography (ultrasound) was begun.

During the year, Dean Lawrence Abrams was honored for his contributions to allied health on a national level by being named a Fellow of the American Society of Allied Health Professions. More locally, Dr. Abrams' responsibilities at Jefferson expanded this year as he was appointed Student Affairs Officer for the University.

The June 7 Commencement Exercises were notable by the addition of the first graduates of the occupational therapy and physical therapy programs. In occupational therapy, 15 students received the bachelor of science degree and another 12 received the post-baccalaureate certificate. In physical therapy, 48 students were awarded the bachelor of science degree. In all, the College graduated 318 students.

At the 1985 Commencement ceremony, four honorary degrees were conferred: nurse educator and researcher Virginia Henderson, Doctor of Letters; physical therapy educator and researcher Eugene Michels, Doctor of Letters; occupational therapy researcher and author Wilma L. West (Fig. 77), Doctor of Science; and Superintendent of Philadelphia public schools, Dr. Constance Clayton, Doctor of Science. Dr. Clayton, who also gave the Commencement Address to the graduates, later became a member of the University's Board of Trustees (Fig. 78).

Also at the ceremony, Kurt L. Douglass (Fig. 79), cytotechnology, was recognized as the winner of the 1985 Student Life Award. Following graduation, Mr. Douglass began his career as a staff cytotechnologist at Brigham and Women's Hospital in Boston. By 1990 he had become a scientific programs specialist for the Cytyc Corporation in Marlborough, Massachusetts. He was also a member of the College's Alumni Advisory Committee.

Seven of the 1985 summa cum laude graduates earned perfect 4.0 grade point averages: Francis Marcinowski, III, radiologic technology; George Alber, medical technology; Patricia Brophy, Linda B. Harper, Lori Rosen, Evelyn Sudick and Ellen Vanauken, nursing.

Barbara Warren, dental hygiene, established her own business management and computer

Fig. 77. At Commencement Exercises, Occupational Therapy Department Chairman Ruth E. Levine, Ed.D. (left) reads the honorary degree citation for Wilma L. West (center), occupational therapy researcher and author, as University President Lewis W. Bluemle, M.D., looks on.

Fig. 78. Honorary degrees were presented at the College's Commencement to outstanding individuals in their respective fields, left to right: Eugene Michels, physical therapy; Constance Clayton, education; Virginia Henderson, nursing; and Wilma L. West, occupational therapy.

management consulting firm, Delaware County Consulting.

Cheryl L. Smugar (Fig. 80), radiologic technology, continued her education at the University of Pennsylvania where she earned a Master of Science degree. She returned to the College and became Coordinator of the Radiography Program in 1987. Ms. Smugar Weiss became active in her profession, taking leadership positions in the Philadelphia Society of Radiologic Technologists. In 1990, she was president-elect of the organization. In addition to making presentations at local and state professional meetings, she presented a paper at the First World Congress on Allied Health in Denmark. She was among those named as Outstanding Young Women of America in 1987. Ms. Weiss was an active member of the College's Alumni Advisory Committee.

Lynne M. Brophy, medical technology, began her career at Jefferson Hospital, moved to the Rheumatology Department of the Veteran's Administration Medical Center in Philadelphia, then to the Molecular Pharmacology Department, Smith Kline & French in King of Prussia, Pennsylvania. By 1990, she was a research scientist at Sterling Drug, Inc. in Great Valley, Pennsylvania, where she was working on arthritis research.

Margaret Seiler, physical therapy, became Director of Physical Therapy at Crozer Chester Medical Center where she developed innovative physical therapy practices in burn cases and presented papers at professional meetings on the subject.

Margaret Dorando, occupational therapy, became a therapist and a consultant at a variety of institutions, mostly in New Jersey, including the St. John of God Early Intervention Program in Westville Grove. In addition, she began her own private practice, Therapedics, where she provided consultation and in-service training to special educators. She was an active member of the occupational therapy community in South Jersey. Ms. Dorando-Unkle maintained close ties to Jefferson, returning to earn her master's degree in occupational therapy in 1990, the first graduating class for that program, as well as serving on the College's Alumni Advisory Committee.

David Potena, physical therapy, began his career as a staff physical therapist at St. Mary's Hospital in Langhorne, Pennsylvania. In 1987, he took a position at Good Samaritan Hospital in Lebanon, Pennsylvania, as Supervisor of Rehabilitation Physical Therapy and in 1990 became its Director of Physical Therapy Services. He presented the results of his clinical research at several national conferences. Mr. Potena was an active member of the Alumni Advisory Committee.

Jeanne Fisher Hannum, nursing, started her own marketing business, The Quality Circle, based in Philadelphia.

Donna A. Petti Enrico, nursing, became Manager of the Pediatric Intensive Care Unit at Humana Children's Hospital in Las Vegas, Nevada, where she initiated a critical incident stress management program with emergency team members, police and fire personnel in that city.

Fig. 79. Kurt L. Douglass, cytotechnology major, receives 1985 Achievement Award for Student Life.

B.S. in MEDICAL TECHNOLOGY

Alber, George Charles, NJ
Ardito, Desiree Marie, NJ
Benac, Irene Katherine, NJ
Brophy, Lynne M., PA
Brown, Wayne Darryl, PA
Burcin, Andrea Laura, PA
Davidson, Leo, Jr., PA
Dhanjal, Manmohan, NJ
Fullem, Darlene Carole, PA
Gawin, Gary Paul, NJ
Gill, Ravinder Kaur, PA
Goldner, Paul L., Jr., NJ
Guido, Noreen Ann, PA
Gyasi, Emmanuel Osei, PA
Jarrel, Alexy, PA
Kadukammakal, Joy Augustine, PA
Kessler, Barbara Ann, PA
Long, Dawn Angela, JAMAICA
Mandalia, Kalpana Vinodkumar, PA
Odorisio, Mark David, PA
Pauline, Lucy Ann, PA
Sobuza, Sipho Wigram, PA
Swann, Mary Louise, PA
Voigt, Grace Anne, PA
White, Theresa A., PA
Wisocky, Susan Joanne, PA
Yuhas, Catherine Bernadette, PA

B.S. in NURSING

Albert, Deborah Lynn, PA
Ali, Rebecca Hanifah, PA
Atkinson, Jean Ellen, NJ

Fig. 80. Cheryl L. Smugar (left), radiologic technology, inducted into Alpha Eta Society, the national honor society for allied health, by faculty member Joan G. Scranton, R.D.H., Ed.M.

Aungier, Monica Eileen, PA
Baldassano, Maureen Patricia, PA
Barndt, Janice Ann, NJ
Barrett, Tina Marie, PA
Barron, Diane Melanie, NJ
Batt, Lisa Joanne, PA
Bergdoll, Susan Amy, NJ
Berr, Georgina, NJ
Blankman, Julia Susan, MD
Brady, Karen Ann, NJ
Brophy, Patricia Alice, PA
Browner, Linda Anne, PA
Burton, Wanda Marie, NJ
Clements, Valerie LaVerne, PA
Coia, Theresa Marie, NJ
Collins, Lynda M., NJ
Collins, Sharon Ann, PA
Como, Sandra P., NJ
Cousins, Dorothy Denise, GA
Crane, Francine Theresa, PA
Crowthers, Roberta Lee, NJ
Curcio, Ann Ruth, PA
Davis, Elizabeth Ann, PA
DeLeon, Patricia, PA
DeTitto, Maria, NJ
Diamond, Jacqueline Linda, PA
Dimon, Joanne, NJ
Dougherty, Patricia Anne, NJ
Drumm, Suzanne Debra, NJ
Duchneskie, Michelle Ann, NJ
Dunkle, Karen Ruth, PA
Ehart, Denise Paule, PA
Eissler, Kathryn Mary, NJ
Fassnacht, Kelly Dee, PA
Fedoryka, Alexis Marie, NJ
Ficaro, Jean Rosalie, CT
Floyd, Donna Lynn, PA
Fonseca, Alexis, PA
Frank, Lora Louise, PA
Gallagher, Karen Marie, PA
Giunta, Karen Ann, NJ
Glasbrenner, Erich Heinz, PA
Godshall, Carol Louise, PA
Goetz, Deborah Deming, PA
Goetz, Lisa Kathryn, PA
Green, Donna Jeanne, NJ
Gyger, Deborah Heidi, PA
Hagan, Mary Ellen Elizabeth, PA
Hannum, Jeanne Fisher, OH
Harper, Linda Marie, PA
Harper, Susan Jennifer, PA
Headley, Barbara Jean, NJ

Hewitt, Carol Ann, PA
Hipple, Kimberly Todd, PA
Hirsh, Cheryl Lynne, PA
Hneleski, Janice Anne, PA
Hoser, Donna Cheryl, PA
Jean-Pierre, Nelta Napoleon, NJ
Jenkins, Elaine Catherine, NJ
Johnson, Janice Ruth, PA
Johnson, Ruthann, NJ
Kaplan, Robin Sue, PA
Karpovich, George David, PA
Kasper, Julia Ann, PA
Katz, Ellyn Beverly, PA
Keimes, Janine Lizabeth, NJ
King, Stacey, NJ
Klauder, Betsy Weisel, PA
Klusek, Marianne Martynowski, PA
Kravitz, Paula Anne, PA
Kunz, Elisabeth Ann, PA
Lackman, Lauren Ina, PA
Landau, Susan Them, PA
Langan, Mary Elizabeth , NJ
Laurencio, Rommel Esperanzate, PA
Lee, Cindy Eunmi, PA
Levy, Joanne U., PA
Lewis, Edmond, PA
Lockhead, Margaret Mary, PA
Loevner, Peggy Jan, PA
Looney, Anne Bridget, CT
Lown, Kenneth Joseph Alexander, PA
Maher, Anne Cecilia, PA
Mariner, Elizabeth Marie, PA
Marnell, Nancy, PA
Martin, Patricia Ann, PA
Mau, Linda Joyce, NJ
Maxwell, Saundra Diane, NJ
McBride, H. Michael, NJ
McCash, Edward William, PA
McCormick, Janice Anne, PA
McGinn, Maryellen Patricia, NJ
McGrattan, Gail Elizabeth, NJ
McGuigan, Kathleen Mary, PA
Merola, Teresa Lynn, NJ
Micalizzi, Marlynne, PA
Michael, Elizabeth Holohan, NJ
Mikolosky, Lori Susan, PA
Milici, Maria Lisa, PA
Minisi, Claire Bernadette, PA
Moffatt, Tamarah Harkness, NJ
Murphy, Jacqueline, PA
Nagel, Mary C., PA
Nevins, Nancy Louise, NJ
Nufrio, Susan Marie, PA
Noble, Jeanne Jordan, PA

O'Donnell, Mary Margaret, MD
O'Gorman, Jeri, PA
Ojeda, Casiana, PA
O'Malley, Eileen Frances Maria, PA
Oppenheim, Melissa Carol, NJ
Orth, Linda Leigh, PA
Ostrow, Marianne Kathryn, NJ
Peissner, Theresa Ann, NJ
Perilstein, Robin, PA
Petti, Donna Anela, NJ
Picarello, Nancy Jane, PA
Pilla, Carol Ann McNeil, PA
Pipitone, Debra Lynne, NJ
Quach, Tinh Chi, PA
Raschilla, Joseph Francis, PA
Riesdorph-Ostrow, Wendi Dee, PA
Robinson, Dilara Shelley, PA
Robson, Donna Lynn, PA
Rosen, Lori B., PA
Rue, Michelle Denise, PA
Rump, Nancy Gibson, PA
Sady, Michelle M'Liss, PA
Sargent, Catherine Anne, PA
Schafer, Nancy Jean, PA
Schauder, Patricia Ann, PA
Schellhorn, Barbara Ann, PA
Schoellkopf, Julie A., NJ
Scholl, Deborah Anne, PA
Schraishuhn, Lynn D., PA
Schultz, Jeanne Marie, PA
Scott, Annette Renee, PA
Shanfield, Mollie Michelle, PA
Shaw, Barbara Ellen, PA
Shelly, Kathleen Sue, PA
Shore-Brown, Heidi, PA
Shute, Amy Marie, PA
Smoker, Nancy Phiels, PA
Snider, Sandra Kay, PA
Stair, Helene Marie, NJ
Stallings, Julie Ann, NJ
Stitzer, Nancyanne, NJ
Sudick, Evelyn Beth, PA
Sweda, Joan Marie, PA
Synnestvedt, Ann, PA
Teeter, Jennifer Gray, MD
Tegzes, John Henry, II, PA
Tiger, Elizabeth Louise, PA
Turpin, Julie Lynne, PA
Umar, Tuna, PA
Urbanski, Linda Marie, PA
Van Auken, Ellen Louise, NY
Vandegrift, Michele, NJ
Vora, Charu, NJ
Watts, Jill Leslie, OH

Weil, Carol Ann, NJ
Weinberg, Cynthia Faith, PA
Wenclawiak, Joan Marie, PA
Whitley, Margaret Lynn, PA
Whitman, Marie, PA
Wilkie, Kathy Ann, PA
Williams, Valerie Anne, NJ
Wright, Beryl Anne, NJ
Wychunis, JoElla, PA
Young, Lucia Lim, PA

B.S. in CTYOYECHNOLOGY
Ardekani, Reza Afkhami, PA
Douglass, Kurt Lee, PA
Dressler, Theresa Marie, PA
Henry, Michelle Jennee, PA
Styer, Kelly Anne, PA

B.S. in RADIOLOGIC TECHNOLOGY
Buck, Maria, PA
Coleman, Timothy Laurence, PA
D'Olio, Michael Anthony, NJ
Fogleman, Randy Lee, PA
Gargiulo, Anna Marie, PA
La Russo, Salvatore Anthony, PA
Lebegern, Heidi Marie, PA
Marcinowski, Francis, III, PA
Neff, Holly Anne, PA
Proskauer, Petra Ingrid, FL
Scafidi, Marianne Theresa, PA
Small, Tammy Beth, PA
Smugar, Cheryl Lynne, PA

B.S. in DENTAL HYGIENE
Aaronson, Stefanie A., PA
Aust, Barbara Ann, PA
Bardsley, Marilu, NJ
Boland, Barbara O'Brien, PA
Boyle, Wendy Susan, CT
Corbi, Jean Brimfield, NJ
Frisby-al-Fareed, Ivy L., PA
Gisel, Wendy Ann, PA
Hooper, Marsha Jane, PA
Hudson, Lori Marie, PA
Kellis, Mary, PA
Kiner, Mary Rose, PA
Manzone, Donna Lee, CT
Metzger, Katherina A., NJ
Peters, Aliki, PA
Ronaldson, Julie Sue, PA
Schulam, Valerie Susan, CT
Shapiro-Benoff, Sharon, PA
Sheaffer, Tracey Ann, PA
Sopin, Caren, PA

Strohecker, Sandy Lee, PA
Van Zanten, Sandra R., PA
Warren, Barbara Jean, PA
Zipf, Marcia Karen, PA

B.S. in PHYSICAL THERAPY
Alexander, Deborah Marie, PA
Armstrong, Wendy Sue, PA
Baker, Kathleen Elizabeth, NJ
Campbell, William Leroy, Jr., PA
Campeaux, Suzanne M., LA
Coole, Lorie Lynn, PA
Davidson, Colleen Ann, NJ
Digeser, Susan Karen, NY
Donley, Susan Lynn, PA
Fitzgerald, Anne Mary, PA
Fitzgerald, Robert Brian, PA
Gough, Dorothea Marie, NJ
Griffiths, Tami Lynn, PA
Hamar, Darci Jean, PA
Hill, David Joseph, NJ
Jervis, Robyn Leslie, PA
Johnson, Tararya Lynn, PA
Judd, Michelle Ann, MA
Kleivene, Kenneth, PA
Lime, Debra Ann, NJ
Long, Michael Patrick, NJ
MacNair, Kevin, PA
McCulloh, Jamie Erin, PA
Mickle, Wendy Kay, PA
Mitchell, Miriam Alice, PA
Mitchell, Rebecca Susanne, NY
Morris, Jeanne Marie, NJ
Oruch, Edward Hiram, NJ
Pelczar, Mary Ann, PA
Perkins, Sandra Marie, NJ
Potena, David Peter, PA
Radi, Julianne Andrea, PA
Rasera, Susan E., PA
Regan, Laura Ann, PA
Rombach, Steven Edward, DE
Rosania, Dianne Jean, PA
Rudisill, George Daniel, PA
Sanner, Susan Allegra, PA
Scotton, Linda Cornelous, IL
Seiler, Margaret, NJ
Skripek, Kerri Ann, PA
Smith, Diane Ruth, PA
Suriano, Christine, NJ
Toye, Celeste Arnell, PA
Trachtenberg, Marla Beth, PA
Vaughn, Susan Kay, PA
Verdon, Michael Patrick, PA
Wechsler, Janet Vivian, NJ

B.S. in OCCUPATIONAL THERAPY
Capoccia, Sandra Yuki, NJ
Connelly, John Thomas, PA
Heilig, Linda Ann, PA
Kozlowski, Jane Elizabeth, PA
LeFever, Mark Richard, PA
Marder, Barbara-Lou, NJ
O'Donnell, Deidre Elizabeth, PA
Petrillo, Denise Keegan, NJ
Scott, Robin Renae, NY
Sindoni, Dawn Alice, PA
Stansbury, Susan Louise, PA
Summers, Loretta Dorothy, PA
Weintraub, Renee Iris, PA
Weitzman, Barton Eden, PA
Wiley, Kathy Ann, FL

POST-BACCALAUREATE CERTIFICATE in OCCUPATIONAL THERAPY
Coruzzi, Joanne Theresa, NJ
Cousin, Monique Michelle, PA
Dorando, Margaret Mary, NJ
Freedman, Debbie Sue, PA
Jamme, Elizabeth Ann, PA
Kanemoto, Neil Yoshio, PA
Kinsella, Nancy Elizabeth, MA
Newman, Elizabeth Marie, MD
Shapiro, Harriet, PA
Shiley, Georgena Louise, PA
Singer, Pamela, PA
Yamamoto, Suzanne Yukiji, PA

ASSOCIATE IN ARTS
Powell, Kimberly Tracy, PA

At the annual "Career Day," employers recruit College of Allied Health Sciences' students prior to graduation.

Among the participants at the College's annual Leadership Development Retreat in February were (left to right): Ann Synnestvedt, Ed McCash and John Tegzes, all nursing seniors.

Graduate education in the College of Allied Health Sciences became a reality in the 1985/86 academic year when a master of science in rehabilitation nursing program, to be offered under the auspices of the College of Graduate Studies, was approved by the University Board of Trustees (Fig. 81). Its first students were admitted in September.

The name of the Department of Radiologic Technology was changed to the Department of Diagnostic Imaging to better reflect the direction of the department as the variety of imaging modalities increased. The newly named department also began an advanced placement program for registered radiographers seeking the baccalaureate degree.

The Department of Cytotechnology received funding from the March of Dimes Foundation to plan a cytogenetics technology program. This was subsequently developed and became a regular part of the curriculum.

In the fall of 1985, a dedication ceremony was held in the Edison Building to acknowledge the gift from the Connelly Foundation that provided the resources for the renovations in the Departments of Occupational Therapy, Physical Therapy and Nursing. Many members of the Connelly family attended the ceremony (Fig. 82).

The 1986 Alumni Special Achievement Award was presented to Barbara Davis Schraeder, Ph.D., R.N, a 1965 nursing graduate (Fig. 83). Dr. Schraeder, an associate professor in the Department of Nursing at the College, was recognized for her contributions to nursing education, research and professional excellence. Her special area of research was very low birth weight infants and children.

At Commencement on June 6, honorary degrees were conferred upon Ernest Boyer, Ph.D., (Fig. 84) and Robert Kinsinger, Ed.D., both nationally known educators. The first group of students from the College's nursing program in Harrisburg were among the 355 graduates.

At the ceremony, Teresa Halley, dental hygiene, was presented with the 1986 Student Life Award (Fig. 85). She had already earned an Achievement Award in Education from her department and had been inducted into the Sigma

Fig. 81. Internationally known wheelchair athlete Doug Heir (left) and Jefferson Hospital patient Mike Memmo joined nursing faculty members at a ceremony launching the new master of science in rehabilitation nursing.

Fig. 82. Connelly family members at dedication ceremony of renovations in Departments of Occupational Therapy, Physical Therapy and Nursing by the Connelly Foundation. Left to right: Emily C. Riley and daughter Amelia, Josephine C. Mandeville and daughter Caroline, Christine C. Connelly, and Thomas S. Connelly.

Phi Alpha Honor Society. A member of the College's Alumni Advisory Committee, Theresa Halley O'Connor returned to Jefferson as a speaker at alumni and Career Services Center programs.

Twelve graduates among those receiving summa cum laude recognition earned perfect 4.0 grade point averages: from cytotechnology, Sharyn Healy, who was also inducted into Alpha Eta Honor Society; from dental hygiene, Helen Horan-Bourret, also Alpha Eta and Sigma Phi 6Alpha and an Achievement Award in Hospital Dental Hygiene; and Michelle Peifley, also Alpha Eta and an Achievement Award in Education; from diagnostic imaging, Sandra Smith; from medical technology, Helene M. Cohen, also Alpha Eta, and Jaqueline Little, also Alpha Eta; from nursing, Gail Erhart, Felicia Gonzalez, Lisa Plowfield, Melissa Turner, Jill Zalman-Wilkens, and Bethany Hall-Long.

Following her graduation, Bethany Hall-Long (Fig. 86) continued her nursing education at the Medical University of South Carolina, where she earned her M.S.N., summa cum laude, and received the Outstanding Graduate Student Award, both in 1988. She was selected as a professional staff member for one year for the U.S. Department of Health and Human Services, Secretary's Commission on Nursing. She subsequently entered a doctoral program in nursing administration at George Mason University.

Catherine Anne Losse, nursing, inducted into the Sigma Theta Tau Honor Society while at Jefferson, earned her M.S.N. from the University of Pennsylvania in 1989. She has been named to *Who's Who in American Nursing, Who's Who among Human Service Professionals, Who's Who of Women Executives* and the *National Distinguished Service Registry of Nursing.* In 1990 she was a clinical nurse III in pediatric cardiology at Deborah Heart and Lung Center in Browns Mills, New Jersey.

Sherri Frace-Meyers, dental hygiene, a summa cum laude graduate who was inducted into the Alpha Eta Honor Society and was the recipient of an Achievement Award in Education, became

Fig. 83. Barbara D. Schraeder, Ph.D., R.N., recipient of the 1986 Alumni Special Achievement Award.

an instructor in dental hygiene at Northampton Community College. She also began a master's degree program in dental hygiene at the University of Maryland at Baltimore.

Craig L. Evans, medical technology, became the chief technologist at Evangelical Community Hospital in Lewisburg, Pennsylvania, in 1989. Jacqueline Little, medical technology, spent more than three years as a research specialist in pulmonary immunology at the University of Pennsylvania and then became a pharmacologist at ICI Americas in Wilmington, Delaware, testing drugs for asthma research.

Alison Platt Klein, physical therapy, began her career as a staff physical therapist at the Hospital of the University of Pennsylvania and at Osteopathic Medical Center of Philadelphia, then became Director of Physical Therapy at Berlin (New Jersey) Physical Therapy and Rehabilitation Center. An active alumnus, she was elected to the Board of Directors for the College of Allied Health Sciences Alumni Association in 1990.

Fig. 84. Jefferson Board of Trustees member Constance E. Clayton, Ed.D., Philadelphia's Superintendent of Schools, read the honorary degree citation for Ernest Boyer, Ph.D., at Commencement Exercises (1986).

CLASS OF 1986

B.S. in MEDICAL TECHNOLOGY
Amati, Diane Angela, PA
Azimzadeh, Rita, PA
Banavong, Sakhone, PA
Bynum, Cherlyn Gregory, PA
Cohen, Helene Marilyn, PA
DiFiore, Linda Catherine, PA
Duffin, Laurie Ann, NJ
Elverud, Amy Jo, MN
Evans, Craig LaRue, PA
Gloates, David Michael, CA
Hagan, William David, Jr., PA
Horta, Vanessa De las Mercedes, PR
Kaufman, Nancy Lynn, PA
Little, Jacqueline, NJ
McNeff, Deborah Ann , PA
Newstat, Beth Olivia, PA
Parris, Joseph Henry, III, PA
Ricciuti, Dina Marie, PA
Rodden, Jeanine Marie, PA
Sedor, John Francis, PA
Simmons, Vanessa Lorraine, CT

B.S. in NURSING
Abel, Elizabeth Ann, PA
Adams, Lisa Ann, PA
Adler, Karla, DC
Allen, Amy Jeanne, VT
Andrews, Arlene S., PA
Bader, Debra Ann, NJ
Bath, Dale Charles, NJ
Baxter, Lisa, PA
Beil, Laurie Ann, PA
Beirne, Charlotte Ann, PA
Bender, Kelley, PA
Benson, Joyce Roscoe, PA
Boraski, Patricia Jean, CANADA
Bradley, Judith Elizabeth, PA
Brock, Kathleen Elizabeth, NJ
Bruaw, Lori Ann, PA
Buggy, Christine Anne, NJ
Bur, Anne Forbes, PA
Burcaw, Elizabeth Ann, FL
Butler, Tracey Ellen, PA
Campbell, Sheila Faye, PA

Fig. 85.   Teresa Halley, dental hygiene, displays her 1986 Student Life Award.

Fig. 86.   Bethany Hall-Long, M.S.N., joined the Commission on Nursing, U.S. Department of Health and Human Services.

Campuzano, Maria Louise, PA
Cannon, Susan Elaine, PA
Chalick, Beth Randi, PA
Chandler, Julianne, NJ
Chase, Susan Denise, PA
Christinzio, Janice Marie, PA
Clouse, Donna Jean, PA
Coady, Allison Mary, PA
Coar, Elise Rose, DE
Conover, Constance Joy, PA
Cramer, Jill Patricia, NJ
Dahlquist, Karen Lynn, NJ
Darby, Wanda Marie, PA
De Vecchis, Susan Dea, NJ
DiCristofaro, Judy, PA
Dobrota, Deborah Jane, PA
Donald, Katherine Weidner, NJ
Donati, Mark Joseph, PA
Erhart, Gail Elaine, DE

Eyre, S.A., MA
Fehon, Theresa Jean, NJ
Finkle, Cathy, PA
Fiocco, George Anthony, Jr., PA
Frankenfield, Gay Ellen, PA
Funaro, Kathleen Gloria, PA
Gardner, Pamela R., PA
Gattone, Linda Dierce, PA
Gaughan-Lizzi, Michele, PA
Glaskin, Shari Anne, PA
Goergen-Deal, Carlyn Ramona, NJ
Gonzalez, Felicia Ellen, NJ
Haas, Nancy L., NJ
Hall, Bethany Ann, DE
Hand, Sandy Lee, PA
Harrison, Diane G., PA
Harrison, Susan Caprice, PA
Hellwege, Paula Amanda, PA
Hillerman, Carolyn Joyce, PA

1986

Hinkel, Diane Joyce, NJ
Holbrook, Christine Lynn, PA
Horwitz, Michael, PA
Howe, Donna Joan, PA
Hughes, Kathleen Gail, PA
Hurt, Linda S., OH
Jackson, Tamiko Darcell, PA
Johnson, Janet Bernice, PA
Johnstone, Mary Dolores , PA
Kaden, Maureen McCue, PA
Kazokas, Diane Marie, PA
Kelly, Patricia Dianne, PA
Kennedy, Joseph Xavier, PA
Keun-Allenbach, Alyce Marlene, NJ
Kevorkian, Jeri Deran, PA
Kingston, Richard Raynald, PA
Kinslow, Michael Francis, PA
Kolonich, Janine, PA
Koszick, Darlene, PA
Krauss, Theresa Mary, PA
Krimmel, Wilmagwynn Kathryn, PA
Kuba, Marrisa Shelley, PA
Lara-Anderson, Jacqueline, IN
Laskowski, Laurene Ann Noelle, PA
Latini, Vincent, PA
Levin, Marcia Nan, PA
Lewis, Michele Nash, PA
Lipinski, Janine Francis, PA
Logan-Abrams, Kathleen, NJ
Lorber, Nancy C., PA
Losse, Catherine Ann, NJ
Lowry, Christine Lynne, NJ
Lynch, Joseph D., PA
Mack, Karen Harper, PA
Mangold, Antonia Marie, NJ
Manning, Mary Dolores, PA
McCloskey, Michael Alphonsus, PA
McGeady, Susan, NJ
McGuigan, Jay, PA
Meier, Anne Cecilia, PA
Meliniotis, Christina, NJ
Menerey, Gertrude G., NJ
Mikolosky, Shelley Ann, PA
Miller, Joan Carper, PA
Moses, Jacqueline, NY
Murphy, Diane Elizabeth, NJ
Murphy, Georgeanne, NJ
Myer, Shari Lee, PA
Nappi, Christina Maria, NJ

Newman, Deborah A., NJ
Nicolo, Bernadette Margaret, PA
Oakes, Helene Primich, PA
Olkiewicz, Linda Susan, NJ
O'Brien, Robert, PA
Palmer, Denise Lisa, NJ
Patterson, Felicia Helene, PA
Pellegrino, Victoria Lynn, PA
Perks, Joan Marie, PA
Pittius, Christine Ann, PA
Plowfield, Lisa Ann, PA
Pryzbylkowski, Anne, PA
Pukenas, Barbara Lynn, NJ
Rafa, Lizabeth Jane, PA
Rayner, Leslie Michelle, PA
Reid, Virginia Anne, PA
Reilly, Cheryl, PA
Repko, Marie Perpetua, NJ
Rizzo, Donna Marie, PA
Robertson, Risa Dawn, PA
Roesler, Grant Eugene, WI
Rosenbluth, Denise Rochelle, PA
Rosendale, Robert W., PA
Ross, Catherine, PA
Rossano, Rachel Marie, NJ
Russell, Janet Marie, NJ
Ryder, Sarah, NJ
Salmonsen, Mary Beth, NJ
Salomone, Margherita Irene, PA
Salwocki, Kimberly Ann, CT
Schiding, Dorothy E., PA
Sculli, Gary Laurence, NJ
Seitz, Kathleen Margaret, PA
Serafini, Gregory Joseph, PA
Shanley, Meghan Christina, PA
Sheldon, Susan Jane, PA
Sheppard, Wanda Lynette, NJ
Shore, Patricia Jean, NJ
Shuler, Dell Kirsten, PA
Sitvarin, Gail Harriet, PA
Siwert, Sharin Jean, PA
Slane, Kimberly Lynn, PA
Slivjak, Anne Taylor, PA
Slutz, Sherry Barbara, PA
Smith, Sharon, NJ
Spaeder, Margaret Anne, PA
Studzinski, Ann Katrina, PA
Sullivan, Susan Joan, PA
Swanick, Mary Kathleen, PA

Sweeney, Kathleen Marie, PA
Szlachta, Michael John, PA
Taggart, Ellen Marie, PA
Tagmire, Christine, NJ
Tashof, Tracy Lane, MD
Thomas, Sandra Lorraine, PA
Thompson, Karen Ellen, NJ
Timpano, Deborah May, NJ
Toth, Joanne Mary, PA
Trace, Eileen, NJ
Turner, Melissa, PA
Vo, Trinh Tuyet, PA
Weikel, Catherine M., NJ
Whaley, Lois Michelle-Denise, PA
Wilkens, Jill Carlton, PA
Williams, Kyela Jarett, PA
Williams, Lesley Jane, NJ
Winch, Nancy Elizabeth, PA
Wolf, Susan Louise, PA
Woloszyn, Mary Frances, PA
Yerardi-Woodford, Diane, NJ
Yuckenberg, Susan Loretta, PA
Zataveski, Linda Ann, PA

B.S. in CYTOTECHNOLOGY
Bragg, Allison Elaine, NJ
Bungay, Patricia Marie, PA
Burker, James Francis, PA
Gerstle, Cheryl Lynn, PA
Healy, Sharyn Marie, NJ
Krieble, Tracy Lynn, PA
Lipshaw, Diane Marie, MD
Milligan, Kim M., NJ
Santucci, Deborah S., PA
Underwood, Robert Shawn, PA
Wiggins, Cheryl Marie, NJ
Young, Cheryl Dawn, PA

B.S. in DIAGNOSTIC IMAGING
(Radiography)
Altare, Deborah Ann, PA
Aronica, Joseph Michael, PA
Cinelli, Cynthia Marie, NJ
Dopkowski, Angela Jean, PA
Green, Terri-Lynn Marie, NJ
Hergert, Patricia A., NY
Jacobson, Carolyn Therese, PA
Kendrick, Denise Ann, NJ
McLaughlin, Dennis Gregory, PA
Natale, Peter Mark, PA

Ogren, Kelly Ann, NJ
Scola, Lois Angela, NJ
Williams, Jacinda Lanette, AL

B.S. in DIAGNOSTIC IMAGING
(Diagnostic Medical Sonography)
Bowers, Nadine Francis, PA
Ghilardi, Denise R., PA
Ferraro, Jeffrey J., NY
La Russo, Salvatore Anthony, PA
Smith, Sandra Lee, MD

B.S. in DENTAL HYGIENE
Baggus, Cheryl Lynne, PA
Bilodeau, Diane Louise, CT
Bowman, Donna Marie, PA
Brady, Linda Sue, PA
Christensen, Deborah Lynn, PA
Clark, Crystal Dawn, PA
Deutermann, Bonny Gayle, PA
Fox, Nancy Lois, NY
Frace, Sherri Lynn, PA
Furukawa, Rika, PA
Gleason, Patricia Mary, PA
Green, Jamie Hope, DE
Halley, Teresa Anne, NJ
Hartigan, Kathleen, VT
Horan, Helen Marie, PA
Jackson, Nancy Clare, PA
Kocis, Mary C., PA
La Bruno, Mary Jean, NJ
Lechleitner, Leanne, PA
Murrell, Dean Thornhill, NJ
Nicolini, Christina Lucia, PA
O'Fee, Diane Veronica, PA
Peifley, Michelle Ann, PA
Peters, Lorraine J., NJ
Rogodzinski, Jean, NJ
Safin, Julie Anne, NJ
Sheehan, Cynthia Walsh, PA
Sindoni, Joann Elise, PA
Smith, Nancy Lynn, NJ
Thomas, Julie Louise, PA
Waldo, Patricia June, NY
Wojciechowski, Linda, PA

B.S. IN PHYSICAL THERAPY
Agostini, Margaret Mary, PA
Arena, Janice Marie, PA
Barry, Mary Alice, PA

Beers, Lisa Jane, PA
Bernd, Mary Lynn, PA
Bloch, Jodi F., NJ
Bobrowsky, Roxanne C., PA
Bowers, David Lee, NJ
Brammer, Paula Kay, PA
Brewer, Lynn Biddle, PA
Connelly, Lisa Anne, MD
deMoss, Lisa Eileen, PA
Ferringer, Judith Irene, PA
Fisher, Doreen May, PA
Flinn, Kellie Diane, PA
Gross, Susan Barbara, PA
Hepler, Jeffrey Brian, NJ
Homa, Grace Maria, PA
Horenstein, Penni Rise, NJ
Jackson, Mary Catherine, NJ
Jankiewicz, Diane Stephanie, NJ
Jreige, Nora Antonieta, VENEZUELA
Kaiser, Anne Marie, PA
King, Patricia Ann, NJ
Kiriluk, Tracey Leigh, NY
Kocur, Carol Rose, NJ
Korotkin, Susan Rae, MD
Lasorda, Joseph James, PA
Lorow, Michele Marie, PA
Machek, Michael A., PA

McNelis, Ann Mary, PA
Meyer, Theresa Jean, NJ
Milano, David Joseph, PA
Murphy, Mary Ann, PA
Napolitano, Joseph Vincent, NJ
Norton, Troy G., PA
Ostrowski, Jeffrey R., PA
Patel, Supriya D., NJ
Patterson, Kathleen, PA
Pelura, Donna Wieczorek, NJ
Pickul, Angela Rosemarie, PA
Platt, Alison, NJ
Quirk, James Martin, NJ
Ray, Kris Ellen, PA
Ries, Hildegarde Annemarie, PA
Rodgers, Kathleen Marie, PA
Rubinstein, Ronald Steven, PA
Ruhl, Joseph Thomas, Jr., PA
Schildkraut, Barbara Iana, NJ
Shannon, Margaret Partrick, PA
Silverman, Karen R., PA
Sotnick, Andrea Ann, PA
Theofilos, John Christopher, OH
Tran, Binh Michael, VA
Walther, Robyn Kathleen, NJ
Weiss, Cynthia Ivette, NJ
Wugofski, Barbara Eileen, PA

Physical Therapy students simulated handicaps and went into the community as part of their annual Handicapped and Barrier Awareness Day activities.

B.S. in OCCUPATIONAL THERAPY
Barthelmess, Dawn Michele, PA
Bender, Amy West, PA
Bostel, Lisa Ann, NJ
Clark, Catherine A., PA
Connor, Susan Elaine, PA
Davis, Leigh Ann, PA
Evans, Karin Anne, PA
Flicker, Ann Toby, PA
Flood, Sallieann M., PA
Gambescia, Ann Marie Elizabeth, PA
Goldberg, Jan Susan, PA
Good-deCurnou, Luann, PA
Grzybek, Geralyn Marie, PA
Hand, Selena Anne, PA
Hiller, Debra Ann Silveri, PA
Mueller, Abigail Huntington, PA
Nazareth, Rachel, PA
Richard, Barbara Ann, PA
Spadafora, Barbara Ann, NJ
White, Claire Catherine, PA

POST-BACCALAUREATE CERTIFICATE in OCCUPATIONAL THERAPY

Clifford, Peter, PA
Eisert, Linda Sloan, PA
Feldman, Ruth L., PA
Gallagher, Denise Marie, PA
Griffith, Judith Horner, PA
Herge, E. Adel Casper, PA
Koefoed, B. Susan, NJ

Kriegel, Hinda S., NJ
Landers, Ellen Maureen, PA
Lynch, Lisa Jane, PA
McCairns, Margaret Burtman, PA
Padova, Joseph Richard, PA
Parsons, Shirley Jane, PA
Seygal, Gail Elizabeth, PA
Turzi, Robert J., PA

Philadelphia Mayor W. Wilson Goode was surrounded by students, faculty members and administrators when he brought a proclamation to the College's Department of Dental Hygiene to recognize "National Dental Hygiene Week" in the city.

Every tooth in a man's head is more valuable than a diamond.

Miguel de Cervantes [1547–1616]
Don Quixote, Pt. 1, Bk. 111

The 1986/87 academic year was a year of growth and development for the College of Allied Health Sciences. Graduate education expanded further with the approval of a master's degree program in occupational therapy by the University's Board of Trustees in February for implementation in the fall of 1987.

At the undergraduate level, the Department of Cytotechnology and the Department of Medical Technology were consolidated to form a new Department of Laboratory Sciences. The Department of Diagnostic Imaging developed two new programs: the first university-based, baccalaureate-level, advanced imaging program and the nation's first integrated multicompetency baccalaureate-degree level curriculum in diagnostic imaging.

During the year, the College-sponsored Health Careers Guidance Clinic recognized its 5,000th student participant since 1968 when the program began (Fig. 87).

The College opened its Career Services Center in January, 1987. Believed to be the only such facility in the country at an organized college of allied health, the Center provided career services through programs, presentations and individual appointments for students and alumni.

In the summer of 1987, the College became more geographically consolidated when its administrative offices and the Department of Laboratory Sciences moved from Jefferson Alumni Hall to the Edison Building (Fig. 88).

Deidre Watkins Blank, R.N., D.S.N., a 1967 nursing graduate, was chosen to receive the College's Alumni Special Achievement Award, which was presented at University Opening Exercises in September. Dr. Blank was Chief of the Health Promotion/Disease Prevention Branch of the National Center for Nursing Research, National Institutes of Health (Fig. 89).

At the June 5 Commencement Exercises, 283 graduates of the College witnessed the conferring of an honorary Doctor of Humane Letters degree on distinguished educator Dr. K. Patricia Cross. The Student Life Award was presented to Carla Jane Carbo, cytotechnology (Fig. 90). In 1989 Ms. Carbo earned a master's of health science degree as a pathologist's assistant from Quinnipiac College and married a 1989 graduate of Jefferson Medical College, Christopher Jackson Reid, M.D.

Three of the summa cum laude graduates earned perfect 4.0 grade point averages: Margaret Bonner, Kathleen Hawe-Andjel and Lucille Whisler, all nursing.

Roberta M. Guertin, nursing, began her career at Jefferson Hospital and in 1989 was the first recipient of the Pennsylvania State Nurses Association's Search for Excellence Award.

Linda Carol Robinson, nursing, who had previously earned her diploma in nursing and an associate in arts degree from Jefferson, became the head nurse in the operating room for vascular/transplant surgery and coordinator for vascular research at Jefferson Hospital. She also travelled to Kenya as a member of "Operation Smile" in 1990.

Carla A. Crosby, physical therapy, after taking a specialty apprenticeship in hand therapy, be-

Fig. 87. During this academic year the College sponsored Health Careers Guidance Clinics had served 5,000 students. Dean Abrams and Dorothy Grieb (left) observe the occasion with high school participant Tricia Neal.

came a therapist at Pennsylvania Hand Center and made a presentation at an international hand therapy meeting in Toronto in 1990. Randall K. Cope, physical therapy, became supervisor of outpatient physical therapy at Geisinger Medical Center in Danville, Pennsylvania, and a lecturer for the Arthritis Foundation.

Beth Fisher, occupational therapy, earned her department's academic achievement award for highest grade point average in the class. She was also class valedictorian and was inducted into the Alpha Eta Honor Society. Following graduation, she became a staff therapist for ReMed Recovery Care Centers and subsequently Director of their Community Re-entry Services Program. She developed expertise in head injuries and crisis intervention.

Nancy Brown Rydzewski, diagnostic imaging,

Fig. 89. Deidre W. Blank, R.N., D.S.N., flanked by her husband and Dean Abrams, receives Alumni Special Achievement Award.

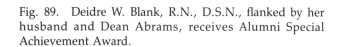

Fig. 88. Ninth Street entrance to Edison Building.

earned the Richard Cage Memorial Award for Academic Excellence in 1989 from Johns Hopkins Hospital where she completed an advanced imaging program. Barbara Price, cytotechnology, won the American Society of Cytology's Award in 1990. Diana Kwasnycky Zawadowycz, dental hygiene, who earned her department's Achievement Award in Education and Clarke J. Hollister Award, and who was also inducted into the Sigma Phi Alpha Honor Society, became a student at the dental school of Temple University.

Rosalie Chillemi-Di Ferdinand, dental hy-

giene, inductee into the Sigma Phi Alpha Honor Society and recipient of many departmental awards, received faculty appointments at Harcum Junior College and the University of Pennsylvania.

In September, 1987, Governor Casey proclaimed National Allied Health Week in Pennsylvania. Dean Abrams and President Blumele display a copy of the proclamation in Figure 91 and the banner was displayed on Walnut Street (Fig. 92).

CLASS OF 1987

B.S. in MEDICAL TECHNOLOGY
Berry, Patricia Anne, PA
Bradley, Donna Lynn, PA
Butash, Michelle Joan, PA
Capobianco, Teresa Maria, PA
Celenza, Elizabeth Ann, PA
Frick, Rodney Ray, PA
Ginn, Dana Jayne, PA
Howlett, Andrew, PA
Kitson, Joanne M., NJ
Kline, Marcy Ellene, PA
Kornafel, Kathryn Ann, NJ
Lahr, Timothy C., PA

Marchese, Marcia, NJ
McCleery, Colleen Marie, NJ
Mitz, Karen Lynn, PA
Nussbaum, Paula, PA
Palagruto, Terri Ann, PA
Wagner, Dianne Marie, PA
Young, Jacqueline Louise, PA

B.S. in NURSING
Adams, Diane, PA
Aldridge, Heather Lynn, NJ
Amoroso, Marykay Bridget, PA
Arcidicono, Patricia Ann, NJ
Argoe, Wendy L., NJ
Armstrong, Kathleen Ann, PA
Barsuglia, Kathleen Bernadette, PA
Beitel, Susan Mary, PA
Blocklinger, Fred L., PA
Bonner, Margaret Mary, PA
Breve, Linda, NJ
Brooks, Audrey Elaine, NJ
Cafagna, Denise Marie, NJ
Cella, Luca R., PA
Cerullo, Mary Martin, PA
Chalk, Carolyn Lee, NJ
Clark, Denise Marie, PA
Comly, Joanne Quatrani, PA
Conant, Ellen Elaine, PA
Cong-Huyen, Emilie Giang, PA
Conley, Cheryl Nelson, NJ
Cooksey, Michael B., NJ
Cooney, J. Dan Joseph, PA
Costello, Todd Carl, PA
Courtright, Louise Grace, PA
D'Arcy, Catherine M., NJ
Davis, Carol Elizabeth, NJ
Dech, Jenene Lynette, OH
Deisroth, Amy Jane, PA

Pamela G. Watson, Sc.D., R.N. Chairman, Department of Nursing and Associate Director, Nursing Service, Thomas Jefferson University Hospital (1987–)

DeJesus, Iris Nereida, PA
Dietz, Ann Elizabeth, PA
Doe, Maria Katherine, PA
Dombrowski, John Charles, Jr., PA
Dwyer, James Thomas, PA
Elder, Bonnie Janet, NJ
Feldman, Anna M., PA
Fernandez, Debra Lynn, NJ
Field, Gregory Arthur, NJ
Gallagher, Deborah, NJ
Gallihue, Deborah, PA
Gaston, Sharon, PA
Germscheid, Gabrielle M., PA
Gernert, Sherry Lynn, PA
Goldberg, Evelyn Kallen, PA
Gormley, Lisa Marie, PA
Gramlich, Lisa Christine, NJ
Greco, Andrea Joan, PA
Greene, Carol M., PA
Grosshauser, Barbara G., PA
Guertin, Roberta Marie, PA
Hart, Ellen M., PA
Hawe, Kathleen Marie, NJ

Fig. 91.   Dean Abrams and President Bluemle display gubernatorial proclamation of National Allied Health Week in Pennsylvania.

Fig. 90.   Carla J. Carbo receives 1987 Student Life Award.

Fig. 92.   Passersby at Eleventh and Walnut Streets observe the University's National Allied Health Week banner.

Healy-Lamb, Anne R., PA
Horswood, Amy Louise, NJ
Howell-Clarke, Charlotte Joan, PA
Ierubino, Jane Robinson, PA
Isherwood, Margaret Magoun, PA
Johnson, Chandel Susan, PA
Johnson, Christine Dellmuth, NJ
Johnson, Martha Anne, NJ
Jonas, Mary Regina, PA
Kaiser, Carole Jeannette, NJ
Kaplan, Lisa, PA
Kazan, Faith Anne, PA
Keegan, Marie Elizabeth, PA
Keenan, Kimberly Ann, PA
Kemmler, Sharon Louise, PA
Kent, Shirley Ann, PA
Kessler, Victoria Grace, PA
Kremp, Jill Aileen, NJ
Kuhn, Joanne Kathryn, NJ
Lee, Therese M., PA
Lehrman, Robert Louis, PA
Longworth, Maria D., NJ
Maley, Peggy Ann, PA
Maloney, Eileen Marie, PA
Maltby, Carol Y., PA
Manno, Ronald John, NJ
Martindale, Margaret Lee, NJ
Matthews, Mary Ellen, NJ
Mazzola, Carmel Marie, NJ
McAlister, Beth Ann, PA
McCarty, Bridget Ryan, PA
McKenna, Margaret Ellen, PA
McLaughlin, Nancy A., PA
Meglino, Pamela, PA
Mehigan, Kelly Marie, NJ
Morgan, Bethann, PA
Mugil, Dawn Marie Alexes, NJ
Mullen-Fortino, Margaret, PA
Myr, Daria Maria, PA
Ortlip, Paul Oliver, NJ
Paroby, Lisa Maria, PA
Pauley, Carol Jill, PA
Petit de Mange, Elizabeth Anne, NJ
Pike, Lori Lynn, NJ
Preole, Margaret Ann, NJ
Price, Katherine Yvonne, PA
Primera, Jacobo Miguel, PA
Radice, Lynda Anne, PA
Rappaport, Judith L., PA
Reiner, Dianne Marie, PA
Rheinheimer, Marjorie Lynne, PA
Rhoads, Elayne B., PA
Richardson, Donna Lee, NJ
Rivera, Lissette, PA

Robinson, Linda Carol, NJ
Rose, Joanne Michele, PA
Rossi, Robert M., PA
Salmonsen, Kristina Marie, PA
Satariano, Joanne Marie, OH
Schreiber, Francine Mitchell, PA
Schultz, Edward J., PA
Schwenker, Diane, PA
Sharpe-Howell, Louise, PA
Shuster, Judy Beth, PA
Slotter, Nancy Susan, PA
Snyder, Barbara Susan, NJ
Spaeth-Brayton, Sylvia Maria, PA
Stacy, Janeen Alicia, PA
Strachan, Brenda Margaret, NJ
Talley, Patricia Ellen, NJ
Thomas, Patricia Pate, PA
Tilton, Lorraine Lois, NJ
Tompkins, Melinda Lynn, NJ
Townsend, Mary Elizabeth, NJ
Wallace, Glenna Jean, PA
Walsh, Kathleen Ann, PA
Watson, Bernadette Marie, NJ
Westervelt, Judith Ann, NJ
Whisler, Lucille Marie, PA
Wild, Nancy Marie, PA
Williams, Mary Ellen, PA
Yusem, Randi Ellen, NJ

B.S. in CYTOTECHNOLOGY
Carbo, Carla Jane, PA
Cassidy, Mary Teresa , PA
Price, Barbara Anne, NJ
Stock, Donna Jean, PA

B.S. in DIAGNOSTIC IMAGING
(Radiography)
Agnew, Christian Scott, NJ
Bernstein, Michael, PA
Brown, Nancy Lee, PA
Flemming, Kristin Eleanor, PA
Gillespie, Mary Susan, PA
Hopkins, Susan, PA
Knecht, Gail Susan, PA
Pascuzzi, Frances Anne, PA
Tuckey, Monique Lenora, PA

B.S. in DIAGNOSTIC IMAGING
(Diagnostic Medical Sonography)
Barcomb, Lynn M., NY
Galbraith, Kenneth Duane, NY
Goldberg, Rick Spencer, FL
Kohn, Michael Dennis, PA

Van Orden, Patricia J., NY
Witlin, Laurie A., PA

B.S. in DENTAL HYGIENE
Alexander, Kristin, MA
Bersani, Theresa Margaret, PA
Binkley, Pamela, PA
Brothers, Samantha Lynn, NY
Chillemi, Rosalie Elaine, PA
Clarke, Jeannine Amy, PA
Collette, Shelly Lynn, PA
Cummings, Mary Frances, PA
Kelley, Theresa Mary, PA
Kwasnycky, Diana E., PA
Paterno, Michele Marie, NJ
Perantoni, Margaret Rose, NY
Rosen, Cheryl Lynne, NJ
Touey, Jean Baptiste, PA
Williams, Carla, OH
Wojtecki, Roberta Levithan, PA
Zweiback, Marcy Beth, PA

B.S. in PHYSICAL THERAPY
Armstrong, Douglas Francis, PA
Armstrong, Mark Joseph, PA
Baggerly, Tracy Lynn, NJ
Basiago, Marlene Marie, PA
Beneck, John Charles, PA
Blitz, Michele Susan, NJ
Buckwalter, Sharon Louise, NJ
Bunting, Barbara Ann, NJ
Caporale, Marilena, VENEZUELA
Cardelli, Maryanne, PA
Cella, Marion Rose, PA
Comisky, Anne Theresa, NJ
Cooley, Brendan Michael, PA
Cope, Randall Kevin, PA
Courtwright, Diane Marie, PA
Crosby, Carla Anna, PA
Daugherty, Lisa Kay, PA
DeHorsey, Kimberly Lyn, PA
Dickstein, Anne Elizabeth, PA
Durrwachter, Kimberly Sue, PA
Egger, Joleen Ann, PA
Franco, Mario Anthony, Jr., NJ
Franz, Lawrence George, PA
Good, Keith Leroy, PA
Halpin, Constance Elizabeth, NJ
Hayes, Christine Frances, PA
Heckler, Marcy L., PA
Heim, Paul, NJ
Hilf, Merrill Jean, NY
Hill, Thomas W., PA
Kelly, Gerald Joseph, PA

Kessler, Carole Ann, PA
Mackin, Kristine, NJ
Markel, Ann Fischer, NJ
Meier, Catherine Marie, PA
Miller, Dianne Mary, NJ
Molas, Geraldine V., NJ
Morris, Robin Marie, PA
Mueller, Elizabeth Marie, PA
Nastasi, Stephen, NJ
Olenginski, Debra J., PA
Orren, Thomas Joseph, PA
Perrucci, Roselle M., NJ
Pettes, Cheryl Ann, TX
Posner, William H., NJ
Quinlisk, Ernest James, PA
Ricker, Claire M., PA
Romano, Kimberley Beatrix, NJ
Rzepka, Carolyn Ann, MI
Schmidt, Matthew Justin, NJ
Sigman, Michele, PA
Smith, Amy Lenore, PA
Vargo, Lynda Marie, NJ
Walsh, Patricia Ann, PA
Wilson, Scott Corcoran, PA
Witkowski, Jay M., PA

B.S. in OCCUPATIONAL THERAPY
Bingaman, Kathleen Diane, PA
Brick, Carol Anne, PA
Broad, Michele Eileen, NJ
Burt, Kathleen Elizabeth, NJ
Coleman, Jean Ann, PA
Dinsdale, Lynne April, PA
DuVerlie, Kareen Elaine, MD
Emerick, Brian Paul, PA
Finkel, Margo Elissa, PA
Fischer, Beth Lee, PA
Goldman, Judith Lisa, NJ
Gorman, Michael James, NJ
Kaul, Cynthia Frances, PA
Kees, Deborah Ann, NJ
Kilgus, Jacqueline Marie, PA
Laky, Laura Balderston, PA
Montefusco, Carman Patricia, PA
Nazarian, Jeanette Sophia, PA
Reed, Laurie Ann, PA
Rhodes, Amy Beth, PA
Smalley, Andrea Marie, PA
Watts, Lizabeth L., NJ
White, Dianne Tracy, PA
Wolfman, Emily J., PA

POST-BACCALAUREATE CERTIFICATE
in OCCUPATIONAL THERAPY
Anelauskas, Kathryn M., PA
Archer, Lynn Gitlow, PA
Cox, Robert Harris Woods, PA
Greiss, Lisa Kay, PA
Hare, Janice Lee, NJ
Mackin, Suzanne Frances, PA
Mulcahey, MaryJane Patricia, PA

Nelson, Charles Dewayne, PA
Powell, Judith Ann, PA
Seiberlich, Ellen Joan, PA

ASSOCIATE IN ARTS
Baker, Kathleen A., PA
Douglas, James Bacon, II, PA
High, Sheryl, PA
Kitchen, Karen Quirple, PA

In January, 1987, physical therapy students sponsored a charity Dance Marathon to benefit the South Jersey Burn Center.

The College's first Grand Marshall Linda G. Kraemer, Ph.D., carries the University Mace at the 1987 Commencement.

This year marked the beginning of the College's efforts to exert influence on the international health scene. The College was involved in the planning for the First World Congress on Allied Health, held in Elsinore, Denmark. The Conference was attended by more than 250 individuals from 26 countries. The College had a significant impact on its success, with 12 members of the faculty and administration presenting papers. Their presentations constituted more than 10% of the scholarly contributions to this assembly. Also on the international scene, Dean Abrams completed a three-week lecture tour of the People's Republic of China as a preliminary to a long-term project that would take shape over the next few years.

Meanwhile, the College was strengthening its academic programs with an eye to the future. The third graduate program in the College, a master of science in physical therapy degree, was approved by the University's Board of Trustees. The three-year program, combining the existing baccalaureate program with the one-year master's component, offered under the auspices of the College of Graduate Studies, would admit its first students in the fall of 1989. The program was designed with a focus on health promotion and disease prevention with a heavy research emphasis.

The College implemented the nation's first integrated multicompetency baccalaureate degree-level curriculum in diagnostic imaging. The program, combining radiography and ultrasound in a concentrated 28-month schedule, would admit its first students in September, 1988. The first class of 14 students graduated in December of 1990. The Department of Nursing expanded its graduate program to include two additional specializations, pediatric rehabilitation and critical care/trauma.

During the year, the College awarded an Alumni Special Achievement Award to Sister Rose Kershbaumer, S.C.M.M., a 1948 graduate of the School of Nursing (Fig. 93). A few years after her graduation and her work at Jefferson Hospital, Sister Rose prepared for nursing as a Medical Mission Sister in newly developing countries. She spent over 30 years in a variety of nursing roles, mostly in Africa, including more than 10 years with the World Health Organization.

On June 10, 328 graduates participated in Commencement Exercises, which featured the awarding of honorary degrees to Dr. Elizabeth J. Yerxa, occupational therapy scholar, and to Dr. Carol Ann Lehmann Lindeman, nurse researcher. Kathleen O'Brien, dental hygiene, who had previously received her department's Pro-

Fig. 93. Rose Kershbaumer (School of Nursing, 1948) received Alumni Special Achievement Award (1988).

fessional Development and Leadership Awards, was presented with the College's Student Life Award at Commencement (Fig. 94).

Twelve graduates earned perfect 4.0 grade point averages: from dental hygiene, Helen Horan-Bourret; Julia Gunn-Hickenbottom, who was also inducted into the Sigma Phi Alpha and Alpha Eta Honor Societies; Diane Indictor-Sandberg, also Alpha Eta, and Bernadette Young, also Alpha Eta and her department's Achievement Award in Education and Esteemed Colleague Award; from diagnostic imaging, Frank Aritz also Alpha Eta; from nursing, Maureen Dimakopoulos; Bonnie Goldberg; Julie Hill; Sally Schell; Diane Schmidt; Barbara Shocker, and Jennie Basiago, who also won the Adeline Potter Memorial Award and entered the Jefferson M.S.N. program while pursuing her nursing career at the Hershey Medical Center.

Louise Clarke, cytotechnology, won the Tony Kostecky Cytotechnology Student of the Year Award, sponsored by the New Jersey Association of Cytology. Jay Field, cytotechnology, who had been a member of the Commons Board and Chairman of the students' United Way Campaign, took a position as a staff cytotechnologist at Fox Chase Cancer Center. He also assisted in student recruitment for the College's Department of Laboratory Sciences and became an active member of the Alumni Advisory Council.

Linda Piccone-Hood, dental hygiene, who was President of the Jefferson Chapter of the Student

Fig. 94. Kathleen O'Brien receives the Student Life Award at graduation.

American Dental Hygienists' Association, won an award from that organization and was also inducted into the Sigma Phi Alpha Honor Society. Joyce Rohn Schaen, dental hygiene, the recipient of a Student American Dental Hygienists' Association Award as well as the department's Esteemed Colleague and Leadership Awards, continued her professional activities as a representative to the American Dental Hygienists' Association and the American Association of Dental Schools.

Daniel A. Merton, diagnostic imaging, an inductee into the Alpha Eta Honor Society, continued his career in the Division of Ultrasound, Department of Radiology of Jefferson Hospital, moving from staff ultrasonographer to ultrasonographer specialist/research sonographer in 1988 when he began working on the development of new applications of medical ultrasound. Between 1988 and 1990, he co-authored more than 10 published articles, had nearly 30 abstracts accepted for presentation, including one at the International Perinatal Doppler Society in Paris, and gave dozens of other lectures at professional meetings throughout the United States. He also began his own business as a private consultant in diagnostic ultrasound.

Elaine M. Venuti (Fig. 95), medical technology, who was inducted into the Alpha Eta Honor Society (Fig. 96), began her career at the Hospital of the University of Pennsylvania as a microbiologist and in 1990 was also a part-time student in the master's degree microbiology program at Jefferson's College of Graduate Studies. She also served on the Alumni Advisory Council.

Kathleen Klein, occupational therapy, a summa cum laude graduate, received three departmental recognitions, the Academic Achievement Award for the highest grade point average, a Meritorious Service Award and Valedictorian of her class (Fig. 97). An inductee in the Alpha Eta Honor Society, she was also a presenter at the 1988 and 1989 national conventions of the American Occupational Therapy Association. In 1989, Ms. Klein returned to Jefferson to pursue a master's degree in occupational therapy, and in 1990 she began her own business, Cape May Therapy Services.

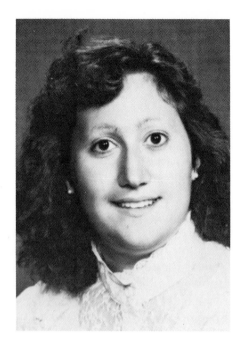

Fig. 95.   Elaine M. Venuti, Medical Technology, Alpha Eta Honor Society inductee.

Fig. 96.   Inductees (1988) of Alpha Eta, the National Honor Society for Allied Health.

Julie Monahan, physical therapy, was inducted into the Alpha Eta Honor Society as well as receiving her department's Faculty Award and Academic Achievement Award for the highest grade point average in her class, graduating summa cum laude (Fig. 98). By 1990 she had become the senior physical therapist at Jefferson Hospital and had made professional presentations for the Pennsylvania chapter of the American Physical Therapy Association and the National Spinal Cord Injury Association.

Maria Mazzitelli, Steven S. Walther and Mary Coleen Sholomisky, nursing, earned their master of science degrees in nurse anesthesiology from Albany Medical College in 1990. Kathleen Carlson, nursing, a graduate of the College's Harrisburg program and a staff member of the Pennsylvania Nurses Association, wrote the Pennsylvania Nurses Practice Act. Diane Gittlemacker, nursing, founded a non-profit organization called Changes, Unlimited, Inc. to help recovering alcoholics and drug addicts.

CLASS OF 1988

B.S. in MEDICAL TECHNOLOGY
Alvarez, Maria Flor, SPAIN
Bautista, Ceasar James, PA
Danenberger, Catherine Ann, PA
Foraker, Marie Anne, PA
Frisbie, Jennifer Lynne, PA
Kearns, Deirdre Ann, PA
Lam, Christine Mary, PA
Ray, Elizabeth J., PA
Rogers, Barbara Ann, PA
Satchmei, Maryam, PA
Schmerfeld, Deborah Rose, PA
Schurer-Pelletier, Ann Margaret, PA
Spalletta, Sherry Ann, NJ
Topeka, Sandra Elaine, NJ
Tortu, Alicia J., PA
Venuti, Elaine Marie, PA
Wheeler, Mary Theresa, PA
Wilson, Kelly Suzanne, NJ

B.S. in NURSING
Abrams, Lori Susan, PA
Adams, Donna Loretta, PA
Agard, Nancy Celia, PA
Algarin-Steinberg, Judith Lillian, PA
Allen, Felicia Lori, NJ
Alves, Kathleen Ippolito, PA
Amodeo, Elisa Ann, NJ
Angelastro, Margaret Ann, NJ
Baker, Karen Beth, PA
Barnard, KC, NJ
Bartoletti, MaryLynn, PA
Basiago, Jennie Lee Harpster, PA
Bateman, Andrea Rose, NJ
Becker, Maureen Patricia, PA
Berger, Lizanne Jaclyn, PA
Bilotta, Christine Patricia, PA
Bobbie, Mary Elizabeth, PA
Bookman, Margaret Michelbacher, PA

Bradway, Terese Marie, NJ
Bratman, Lisa Eileen, PA
Brown, Sharon Davy, PA
Buddy, MaryLynn, PA
Burt, Sharon Lee, PA
Callahan, Kerry Rose, PA
Carl, Deborah Ann, PA
Carlson, Kathleen Ann, PA
Carty, Marguerite Mary, PA
Cava, Deborah Ann, PA
Childress, Sarah Bridget, PA
Cleary, Kathleen, PA
Clement, Joanna U., PA
Cong-Huyen, Theresa Huong, PA
Cooley, Sara Ann, PA
Crawford-Kemp, Lori Jayne, NJ
Cristoforo, Carol Beth, NJ
Cummins, Heather Whaley, NJ
Cunningham, Margaret Ann, PA
Davenport, Shasmay, PA
Davis, Elizabeth Anne, PA
De Jong, Ytje, PA
Dimakopoulos, Maureen Elizabeth, PA
Dolente, Donna Faith, PA
Domanico, Kimberly Ann, PA
Donahue, Gail Denise, NJ
Dougherty, Kathleen Patricia, PA
Egan, Elaine Patricia, PA
Ellingsworth, Diane Madlyn, PA
Elsaesser, Lesley Jo, PA
Erickson, Julie Rae, PA
Fischer, Alyson Beth, PA
Fish, Nancy Eileen, NJ
Fisher, Catherine Claire, PA
Forman, Michelle Jennifer, PA
Formanek, Maria, NJ
Francis, Mary C., NJ
Furst, Ethel Mae, PA
Gillece, Michele Mary, NJ

Giosa, Rosemary, PA
Gittlemacker, Diane Anita, PA
Goldberg, Bonnie Zaiss, NJ
Grau, Anne Marie, PA
Griffiths, Lori J., PA
Grzechowiak, Maria Ann, NJ
Guckin, Anne Marie, PA
Guertin, Frances Marie, PA
Haneiph, Rosanna P., PA
Hardy, Karen Michele, NJ
Hartman, Stephanie Izane, PA
Heinick, Maryann, PA
Heintzelman, Cheryl Ann, PA
Hill, Diana Dee, PA
Hill, Julie A., PA
Hill, Selma Sheryl, PA
Hoffman, Brenda Gelb, PA
Hoffman, Dharla Lynn, PA
Hoffman, Kathleen Mary, PA

Horneff, Joseph Randall, NJ
Huff, Janie Marie, PA
Huynh, Hoa, PA
Jackson, Bernadette Ann, PA
Jewell, Maureen Theresa, PA
Johnson, Sandra Anderson, NJ
Jones, Patricia Marie, PA
Justice, John Wesley, IV, PA
Kaupp, Phyllis Jean, PA
Keeler, Monica Elise, PA
Kelley, Kathleen A., PA
Kelly, Eileen, PA
Kennedy, Lynne Ann, PA
Malessa, Joy Heather, NJ
Mann, Sarah Dorothy, IL
Matthews, Yolande Ingrid, PA
Mazzitelli, Maria, NJ
McConnell, Mary-Rowe, PA
McFadden, Janet Patricia, PA

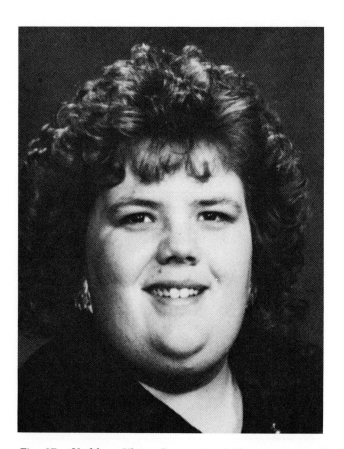

Fig. 97. Kathleen Klein, Occupational Therapy, received Academic Achievement Award for highest grade point average.

Fig. 98. Julie Monahan, Physical Therapy, received Academic Achievement Award in her program.

McGee, Michael Timothy, PA
McGinnis, Kathleen Sweeney, NJ
Mongiello, Donna Marie, NJ
Moorehead, Jon Lee, DC
Morris, Tia Nanette, PA
Mowrey, Janet Elizabeth, PA
Mundth, Jennifer Blanchard, PA
Muskett, Helen Marie, NJ
Odell, Kelly Anne, PA
O'Donnell-Pirog, Joan, PA
Orlando, John Anthony, PA
O'Rourke, Jacquelyn Nicole, PA
Paek, Annie H., CA
Parker, Lisa Beth, PA
Penkal, Irena, PA
Perrotto, Carol Teresa, PA
Pierce, Lorraine, PA
Pierson, Elisia Louise, PA
Poulshock, Sheryl Lynn, PA
Reiley, Jane Dolores, PA
Renna, Russell Johnathen, AZ
Riggs, Kathleen, PA
Rogers, Patricia DeProspero, NJ
Rohne, Barbara Mae, PA
Rosen, Randi Jill, FL
Santanna, Mary Elizabeth, PA
Schaffer, Kathleen Elizabeth, NJ
Schatz, Jill Susan, PA
Schell, Sally Ann, PA
Schmeiss, Andrea Helena, PA
Schmidt, Diane Norlaine, PA
Schulgen, Kimberlee Ann, PA
Schwartz, Abby L., PA
Shocker, Barbara A., PA
Sholomisky, Mary Coleen, NJ
Sieminski, Joanna Beata, PA
Skitzki, Jeanette Patricia, PA
Solnick, Arlene Janet, PA
Sufian, Sureya, NJ
Timpko, Beth Anne, PA
Travitz, Brenda Teresa, PA
Ubaldi-Rosen, Regina Mary, PA
Venney, Roberta, PA
Walther, Steven Stanley, NJ
Wasilewski, Maryann, PA
Waters, Kathleen Marie, PA
Waugaman, Geraldine Miller, NJ
Wilkinson, MaryAnn, NJ
Williams, Ingrid June, DE
Wixted, Patricia Ann, NJ
Wojnar, Anne Gemma, NJ
Wojtelwicz, Sandra, PA
Wolper, Eileen M., PA
Woods, Mary Catherine, NJ

B.S. in CYTOTECHNOLGY
Clarke, Louise D., PA
De Santis, Paula Maria, NJ
Field, Jay Alan, PA
Gravell, Rita Lim, NY
Lattanze, Sandra Marie, PA
Wilson, Wesley Stanley, Jr., PA
Zalewski-Sorling, Anne Frances, PA

POST-BACCALAUREATE CERTIFICATE in CYTOGENETIC TECHNOLOGY
Roche, Melanie Elizabeth, NJ

B.S. in DIAGNOSTIC IMAGING
(Radiography)
Anthony, Damita Jo, PA
Aritz, Frank A., PA
Berkey, Heather Anne, PA
Brauer, Susan Rochelle, PA
Cerrone, Frank Anthony, PA
Derstine, Jill Ann, PA
DiVirgilio, Elizabeth Ann, PA
Jacobs, Joan, NJ
Lichtman, David S., PA
Long, Lisa Marie, PA
Miller, Lynn M., PA
Sapp, Suzanne Denise, PA
Schlenk, Michael Joseph, NJ
Sciochetti, Melissa Ann, PA
Verholy, Karen Louise, PA
Williams, Jacqueline, PA
Yannone, Lisa Marie, PA

B.S. in DIAGNOSTIC IMAGING
(Diagnostic Medical Sonography)
Arnold, Charlene, PA
Austin, Janice Lynn, PA
Beatty, Lisa Danae, PA
Dalton, Thomas James, PA
Dunn, Sandra Louise, PA
Floto, Jennifer Lynn, NY
Hartman, Michael John, PA
Knecht, Gail Susan, PA
Kovach, Carolyn Anne, PA
McDonald, Maureen E., PA
Merton, Daniel Arthur, PA
Moreau, Loretta Mary, RI
Rigefsky, Phyllis, PA
Rupp, LuAnn Lynn , PA
Schmidt, John David, PA
Zawalski, Linda Marie, NY

B.S. in DENTAL HYGIENE
Allen, Karen Marie, MA
Bailey, Sheryl Taylor, PA

Barnes, Diane Irene, PA
Callahan, Lisa Marie, PA
Celli, Marybeth Rita, PA
Clark, Elizabeth Ann, PA
De Mumbrum, Catherine Jean, PA
Gunn, Julia Elizabeth, CA
Indictor, Diane Lynn, PA
Mihalek, Wendy, PA
O'Brien, Kathleen Ann, PA
Pandiscio, Amy Jo, MA
Pencek, Lynn Ann, NY
Perper, Donna Kay, NJ
Piccone, Linda Concetta, PA
Ricefield, Leslie Jane, PA
Rick, Bethanne, PA
Schaen, Joyce Rohn, DE
Schnitzer, Nancy J. Goldstein, PA
Schwarz, Nora M.P., PA
Young, Bernadette Feliciani, PA

B.S. IN PHYSICAL THERAPY

Axner, MaryEllen, PA
Berg, Rachel Karlan, PA
Bialsky, Jay Arnold, NJ
Bowman, Suzanne Lee, PA
Brooks, Kyle Robert, PA
Castiglioni, Michelle, PA
Chamberlain, Melody Joy, NJ
Danusiar, Karen Ann, PA
DeSanto, Donna Ann, PA
Donohoe, Maureen, NJ
Dorak, Beth Ann, PA
Dunn, Kevin Patrick, NJ
Evans, Rebecca L., NJ
Fee, Eileen, NJ
Fitzgerald, Kathleen Patricia, NJ
Flint, Cynthia Nadine, PA
Franceschini, Debbie Marie, NJ
Fredericks, Christine Maria, PA
Galanti, Michele Christina, DC
Harrison, Kristine Sue, PA
Howard, Deborah Jean, NJ
Human, Judith Anne, PA
Jobst, Judith Ann, PA
Kadis, Lori Beth, PA
Kiger, Thomas Patrick, PA
Kozempel, Jean A., PA
Krause, Kevin Walter, PA
Kruczek, Mark James, PA
McCusker, Kathleen Ann, PA
McGowan, Margaret Mary, PA
Megay, Penny Jayne, PA
Mehlman, Constance A., PA
Meyer, Beth A., VA

Mitrovic, John Andre, NJ
Monahan, Julie Katherine, NJ
Money, Sharon Marie, MD
Montemuro, Richard-Alan, PA
Newsome, John Thomas, III, PA
Nolan, Mary Patricia, MD
Oldakowski, Marie Carol, PA
O'Toole, Lucy Ann, NY
Ott, Lisa Marie, PA
Piontek, Carole, PA
Pojunis, Mary Ann , PA
Quarmley, Laura Jean, PA
Reeves, Kathleen Patrice, PA
Schickling, James Michael, Jr., PA
Shearon, Marie Anne, VA
Silverman, Karen Beth, NJ
Weil-Inglas, Wendy, PA
Wellmon, Robert H., Jr., PA
Wenick, Abby Jane, NJ
Will, Joyce Ann, NJ
Wright, Paula Jane, PA
Yocum, Kathleen Mary, NJ
Zimmerman, Jean Ann, PA

B.S. in OCCUPATIONAL THERAPY

Calhoun, Lorraine Barol, PA
Cappelli, Theresa Marie, PA
Carr, Dianna Lynn, PA
Cohen, Debra Nancy, PA
Daniels, Jane Kathleen, PA
Dyer, Lisa Marie, NY
Egan, Ann Louise, NJ
Fisher-Aman, Mary Kathleen, PA
Hackler, Bethany Ann, PA
Hess, Patricia Ann, PA
Howe, Nancy Frances, PA
Katsigiannis, JoAnne S., PA
Kelly, Catharine Elizabeth, PA
Klein, Kathleen, PA
Lane, Diane Marie, PA
Lauer, Adrienne Claudia, FL
Leinmiller, Susan Marie, PA
Lower, Michelle Marie, PA
McCarron, Eileen, PA
Moyer, Janet Lynn, PA
Myers, Cathy Ann, PA
Naughton, Vincent Gregory, PA
Paige, Sonia LuAnne, PA
Patel, Nisha, NJ
Peralta, Virginia Raquel, MD
Prigmore, Rosemary, PA
Quigley, Marie Claire, NJ
Samilenko, Michele Motria, NJ

Shelton, Joyce Mueller, PA
Spellacy, Sandra Therese, PA

POST-BACCALAUREATE CERTIFICATE
in OCCUPATIONAL THERAPY
Bennett, Sally Harriet, PA
DeFero, Tammy Lynn, NJ
Hall, Bernice Davis, NJ
Hershey, H. Peter , PA
Komara, Kathryn Smith, PA
Lister, Sharon Montgomery, PA

Mihoch, Deborah Lee, PA
Vadala, Helen Lorraine, PA

ASSOCIATE IN ARTS
Cherry, Judith Marie, PA
Mills, Renee Andrea, PA
Ruch, Denise Andrea, PA

ASSOCIATE IN SCIENCE
Bass, Queena Rouse, PA
Brophy, Ida, PA

Student Advisory Committee

Back row, left to right: John Meale, Kim Furson, William Thygeson, Karen Kitchen, Cheryl Hunt, Bonnie Lee Behm, Caren Blumenthal, Jacqueline Schuler, Nancy McNamara, Maria Elfreth. Seated: Cindy Benckini, Susan Glenn, Megan Trindle. Not pictured: Lisa Farace, Lynne Brecker.

During the 1988/89 academic year, Dean Lawrence Abrams led a six-person delegation from the College to the People's Republic of China as part of a long-term project to design and establish five colleges of allied health sciences in that country. On the national level, Dean Abrams began a two-year term as President of the American Society of Allied Health Professions. He was installed in November at the organization's 21st Annual Conference in New Orleans (Fig. 99).

The College-sponsored Health Careers Guidance Clinic made significant changes. After 20 years and more than 5,000 students, the Clinic discontinued the student clinic component of the program. However, the Clinic extended its counselor workshop program and published the ninth edition of the *Health Careers Guidance Manual*, co-edited by Dean Abrams and Dorothy Grieb and expanded to include every county in Pennsylvania, New Jersey and Delaware (Fig. 100). In its first national initiative, the Clinic inaugurated a toll-free, nationwide 800 number for health careers information and guidance. The only one of its kind in the country, this National Health Careers Information Hotline proved to be immediately successful, receiving 20,000 calls during

the first year and more than that the following year (Fig. 101).

Faculty in the College's cytotechnology program played a leading role in the national Pap-smear controversy sharing their expertise with Congress and professional organizations about factors that may cause misdiagnosis of Pap smears and how to prevent the potentially deadly errors.

For the first time in the University's history, the College of Allied Health Sciences held its Commencement Exercises on a different day from those of the Medical College and the College of Graduate Studies because the College converted

Fig. 100. Dean Abrams with Ninth Edition of the *Health Careers Guidance Manual*.

Fig. 99. Dean Lawrence Abrams receives Presidential gavel of American Society of Allied Health Professions at Annual Meeting in November, 1988.

its academic schedule from the quarter system to a semester calendar. The ceremony continued to be held at the traditional site, the Academy of Music, but was moved to a Thursday because the Academy was not available on a Friday. The May 11 Commencement featured 305 graduates. Reverend Leon Sullivan, an internationally recognized black social activist, received an honorary degree and gave an inspiring address to the graduates (Fig. 102).

The Student Life Award was won by Amy Beth Cole, physical therapy. She was also inducted into the Alpha Eta Honor Society. Eight graduates earned a perfect 4.0 grade point average: from diagnostic imaging, Frank Aritz and Deborah Dawson Werneburg, who also became the Pennsylvania state representative for the Society of Diagnostic Medical Sonographers and a guest lecturer for the College's Diagnostic Medical Sonography program students; from nursing, Constance Cox, also inducted into the Alpha Eta Honor Society; Elaine Mallios; Irma Neckritz-Yehuda, also Alpha Eta; Barbara Ryley, also Alpha Eta; Joyce Williams, and Joan Zomchick, also Sigma Theta Tau Honor Society.

Maureen Dorsey, dental hygiene, was a scholarship recipient, a winner of departmental and Student American Dental Hygienists' Associa-

Fig. 101. Inauguration of the "National Health Careers Information Hotline." Dean Abrams shown with Hotline Coordinator, Vicki Carto.

tion awards, and an inductee into the Alpha Eta and Sigma Phi Alpha Honor Societies. Lillian J. Feliciani, dental hygiene, earned the department's Professional Achievement Award, earned induction into the Alpha Eta Honor Society and gave numerous professional presentations, locally, regionally and nationally. While continuing her career in a private dental practice, she also taught part time at Jefferson and at Montgomery County Community College. Kristin Flemming, diagnostic imaging, began her own business as President of Radiology Techs, Inc. of Trevose, Pennsylvania. Cheryl Shames, physical therapy, and Susan Edwards, occupational therapy, earned academic achievement awards for the highest grade point averages in their respective programs. Ms. Edwards was also named Valedictorian of the occupational therapy class.

Marcella Dawson, cytotechnology, received the Warren R. Lang Scholarship Award, sponsored by the American Society for Cytotechnology. Clementine Hawthorne, cytotechnology, continued in her position as supervisor of the Cytopathology Department in the Clinical Laboratory of Jefferson Hospital, serving also as clinical laboratory instructor for Jefferson cytotechnology students and as a participant in the Career Options series co-sponsored by the College's Alumni Office and Career Services Center.

M. Ellen Botella, nursing, was the recipient of the 1989 Outstanding Adult Student in Higher Education Award, given by the Pennsylvania Association for Adult Continuing Education (Fig. 103). Judith C. Carrozza, nursing, a scholarship recipient, vice president of student government, Sigma Theta Tau Honor Society inductee, and summa cum laude graduate, began her career at Jefferson Hospital as a registered nurse in the neurosensory care program and later in the pediatric intensive care unit. Sherry Alyse Kaplan, nursing, who was chairman of the College's Orientation Committee in 1989, President of the department's chapter of the Student Nurses Association of Pennsylvania and an inductee into the Sigma Theta Tau Honor Society, also began her career at Jefferson Hospital.

B.S. in MEDICAL TECHNOLOGY
Angelucci, Jennifer Joan, NJ
Brown, Debbie Ann, PA
Ciaverelli, Christine Marie, PA
Fineman, Valerie Jean, PA
Gray, Jacqueline Theresa, NJ
Ladik, Dina M., NJ
McAllister, Karen Jean, NJ
Rucci, Kenneth P., PA
Wagner, Joyce Eileen, PA
Wendt, Karl William, NJ

B.S. in NURSING
Abramson, Cathy Ellen, PA
Adams, Marlene Michele, PA
Alesi, Maria P., PA
Andreacola, Phylis Lynn, NJ
Bardsley, Mark Stuart, PA
Barlow, Frances Mary, PA
Beatty, James D., OH
Bodrog, Patricia, NJ
Botella, M. Ellen, PA
Broadnax, Adwoa, GHANA
Brooks, Cheryl Ann, PA
Brown, Laura Lucille, PA
Bryan, Theresa Lynn, NJ
Burrage, Annette, PA
Carnabuci, Vincent Anthony, PA
Carrozza, Judith Craig, PA
Citerone, Christine Helena, NJ
Cohen, Sara Moljo, PA
Cox, Constance Ann Helena, PA
Craft, Kimberly Lynn, NJ

Creamer, Eunice Marie, NJ
Curcio, Susan Evelyn, PA
Daniels, Jeanmarie Anne, PA
Davis, Pamela Lenora, DE
Davis, Clayton Alphonsol, III, NJ
DePalmer, Jennifer Anne, PA
Diehm, Cheryl L., NJ
DiNatale, Rosemary F., NJ
Dougherty, Kathyanne, PA
Doyle, Susan Patricia, NJ
Dunne-McGurk, Kathleen E., PA
Ertel, Denise Marlene, PA
Falkenberg, Cheryl Lynn, PA
Fallon, Ellen Marie, PA
Felder, Henrietta, PA
Flamini, David, NJ
Flynn, Marie Patricia, PA
Formal, Debra M., PA
Fox, Wanda Lynn, NJ
Frankow, Christine Sophia, PA
Gallo, Karen L., NJ
Giese, Louise Julia, NJ
Gilbert, Rose Ann, NJ
Glassey, Patricia Anne, PA
Golden, Deidre DiCristo, NJ
Goldfrit, Iris N., NJ
Grace, Theresa Marie, NJ
Greenblatt, Sharon Ilene, PA
Haitsch, Patricia Marie, PA
Hartmann, Deborah Ann, PA
Hefty, Deborah Carol, NJ
Henderson, Helen June, PA
Hernando, Maria Erlina, NJ
Hoang, Joann Sung Hoa, PA
Hogan, Diana Marie, NJ
Holohan, Ellen, PA
Hough, Denise Ann Johnstone , PA
Iannotti, Marlene, NJ
Izzi, Maryann Alexis, PA
Jones, Lisa Ellen, NJ
Jordan, Karen Maria, PA
Kapigian, Diane Alice, NJ
Kaplan, Sherry Alyse, PA
Knight, Daniel Joseph, PA
Koppenhaver, Joanne Madeline, PA
Lamelza, Lynn Marie, PA
Lamelza, Marie, PA
Lewis-Jones, Pamela Anita, AL
Lynch, Patricia T., PA
Magenta, Tamara Lee, NJ
Mallios, Elaine, PA
Masino, Deborah Ceceila, PA

Fig. 102. The Rev. Leon Sullivan receives Honorary Degree of Doctor of Literature from President Bluemle. Dr. Kraemer places the hood.

McCall, Barbara H., PA
McGlynn, Barbara Lynn, PA
McGrory, Joyce, PA
McMichael, Marguerite Veronica, NJ
McMillen, Michael Lindsay, PA
Mercer, Carol Margaret, NY
Millaway, Maryellen, PA
Miller, Carolyn Patricia, PA
Minor, Lillian Beth, NJ
Moore, Nancy Aliesa, NJ
Moy, Diane Jane, PA
Notkin, Eric S., MA
Ostra, Marilyn Cowden, PA
Palermo, Maria Elizabeth, PA
Panasosky, Diane Marie, PA
Rabbitt, Colleen M., PA
Reynolds, Renee Ann, PA
Romaine, Dale M., NJ
Rosenberger, Kyna Joy, PA
Rossi, Carol, NJ
Rottmund, Carroll Marie, PA

Rubin, Cheri Ellen, PA
Rumovitz, Dawn Marie Cheryl, PA
Ryley, Barbara Anne, NJ
Santucci, MaryEllen Germaine, PA
Schanne, Linda Catherine, PA
Schlansky, Rita Cohon, PA
Schmidt, Jo Anne, NJ
Schroeder, Kathleen Eva, NJ
Schuck-Choyce, Christina Marie, PA
Sciamanna, Lisa Lorraine, NJ
Segal, Debra Lynn, PA
Seigworth, Cinda Lee, PA
Serlen, Rhoda Lea, PA
Sharpe, Erin Marie, PA
Spangler, Donna L., PA
Specht, Dawn Marie, PA
Sternberg, Caren Hope, PA
Stone, Michelle Elaine, PA
Tremper, Deborah Lynn, NJ
Trouton, Rosemarie Beth, NJ
Tullos, Teresa Ann, PA
Vizzachero, William A., PA
Weimar, Barbara Ann, PA
Weisberg, Robyn Leslie, PA
Welding, Linda Ann, NJ
Wells, Angela Anna, PA
Wenitsky, Dennis Ray, PA
Williams, Joyce Marie, PA
Williams, Wendy Lee, NJ
Wilson, Karen Denise, PA
Worthy, Gloria Ruby, PA
Yehuda, Irma N., PA
Zarraga, Rita T., PA
Zomchick, Joan, PA

B.S. in CYTOTECHNOLOGY
*D'Alessandro, Anita Daria, PA
*Dawson, Marcella Damiana, PA
Donaldson, Marie Anne, NJ
Dunn, William Joseph, PA
Falcon, Karen Marie, PA
Ganguly, Atul Sukhendu, PA
Griffin, Teresa M., PA
Hammud-Dib, Hanan Abdallah, LEBANON
Hawthorne, Clementine Marie, NJ
Hemrick, David E, PA
Kreuzburg, Patricia Ann, PA
*Madara, Elizabeth R., PA
Murphy, Laura Kay, MI
Peloso, Lisa Marie, PA

Fig. 103.   Ellen Botella, B.S.N., recipient of 1989 Outstanding Adult Student in Higher Education Award.

*The four students identified with an asterisk (*) above earned both the B.S. in Cytotechnology Degree and the Post-Baccalaureate Certificate in Cytogenetic Technology.

*Porter, Carol Rae, NJ
Sherwin, Renee Janine, PA
Snyder, Rose Marie, PA

B.S. in DIAGNOSTIC IMAGING
Druckenmiller, Ellen, PA
Mahood, Kevin Wayne, PA
Myers, John Gregory, PA
Rufo, Ann Frances, PA
Snyder, Brian Robert, NJ
Winderl, Fritz K., NY

B.S. in DIAGNOSTIC IMAGING
(Radiography)
Bloom, Kenneth Harold, Jr., CT
Bonsall, Louise C., NJ
Crowthers, Beth Ann, PA
Dompkosky, Robert Anthony, PA
Gerace, Kenneth Anthony, PA
Hill, Bryan John, PA
Huot, Soktha, PA
Joseph, George, PA
Marchetti, Lauren, PA
Mulcahy, Ann Marie, IRELAND
Rake, Randal Carter, PA
Rencevicz, Denise Mary, NJ
Schwarz, Craig Henry, PA
Sgro, Angela Marie, NJ
Vivaldo, Marie Luisa, PA

B.S. in DIAGNOSTIC IMAGING
(Diagnostic Medical Sonography)
Baldwin, Kathleen Kim, MD
Berkey, Heather Anne, PA
Cogar, Laura Anne, DE
Fischer, Jennifer Susan, PA
Micka, Mariann Elizabeth, PA
Nardone, Diane Louise, NJ
Robbins, Karen Lynn, MD
Sciochetti, Melissa Ann, PA
Sprott, Barbara Joanne, PA
Torpey, Janice, PA
Werneburg, Deborah Dawson, PA
Zanin, Linda Madeline, PA

POST-BACCALAUREATE CERTIFICATE
in ADVANCED IMAGING
Aritz, Frank A., PA
Miller, Lynn M., PA
Natale, Peter Mark, PA
Sapp, Suzanne Denise, PA
Williams, Jacqueline, PA

B.S. in DENTAL HYGIENE
Bates, Maureen Kelly, PA
Berk, Joy Lynne, PA
Brophy, Elizabeth Jane, PA
Byington, Debbie Kaye, CA
Conley, Joelle Christeen, NJ
Cooley, Rosemarie Ann, PA
Dorsey, Maureen Ann, PA
Feliciani, Lillian Jessie, PA
Hoffman, Linda Mae, NY
Hottenstein, Amy Beth, PA
Kirk, Bernadette Therese, PA
Matina, Edith Ann, PA
Novak, Annette Marie, PA
Packer, Beth Anne, NY
Palladino, Ronnamarie Gibson, NJ
Perks, Kellyann, PA
Reynolds, Rebecca Ann, PA
Seeley, Connie Marie, NY
Sullivan, Pamela Ann, PA

B.S. in PHYSICAL THERAPY
Allison, Joseph Conrad, PA
Andrews, Michele, NJ
Anselmo, David Brian, NJ
Bixby, Jane Bunting, PA
Blanche, Noelle Yvonne, MD
Bower, Tracey Dee, PA
Brown, Suzanne Ellen, MA
Campbell, Sandra Lee, PA
Cauley, Megan Elizabeth, NJ
Ciavaglia, Troy C., PA
Clements, James Joseph, Jr., NJ
Colasante, Blaise Anthony, PA
Cole, Amy Beth, PA
Collot, Gilbert Georges, Jr., NJ
Cucinotta, Kelly M., PA
Curley, Mary Ellen, NJ
DeLozier, Denise Louise, PA
Devine, Ilise Gwen, NJ
Ellow, Robert John, Jr., PA
Fleck, Ronald Leroy, Jr., PA
Gilhooly, Ann Hull, PA
Ginn, Michael Albert, NJ
Gontarchick, Judith Marie, PA
Grady, Katherine Mary, MD
Haley, Lois Andrea, MD
Heiland, Brenda Sue, PA
Herbster, Christopher James, PA
Jergensen, Lisa Marie, NJ
Kunkle, Brenda Jean, PA
Lavine, Kristen Marie, PA
Longnecker, Jill Marie, NJ
McKenna, Regina Maria, NY

McLaughlin, Nancy Theresa, PA
Mueller, Kris Ann, TX
Murray, Annette Eileen, PA
Myers, Kathleen Sue, NJ
Oiler, Amy Lynn, PA
Pan, Stephanie Lok-Yi, NJ
Prelewicz, Marcy Marie, MD
Prokapus, Mary Elizabeth, NJ
Puleo, Donna Marie, PA
Ravkin, Denise Lyn, PA
Rozhitsky, Yury, NJ
Rudden, Kathryn Teresa, PA
Russell, Margaret Ann, PA
Schuck, Terri Lynn, NJ
Scrabut, Lisa Marie, PA
Shames, Cheryl Lynne, PA
Shepps, Lisa Anne, PA
Shore, Debra, PA
Steinbach, Lore Jeanne, NJ
Timbrook, Katherine Sue, CO
Wallop, John Douglass, MD
Walters, Michael Andrews, PA
Waltz, Daniel Eugene, PA
Whiteside, Elizabeth Anne, PA
Wollman, Bruce Stuart, NJ

B.S. in OCCUPATIONAL THERAPY
Ackerman, Barbara L., PA
Brown, Elizabeth Ellen, NC
Brown, Jennifer Ann, NJ
Burns, Donna Marie, PA
Corda, Karol L., NJ
Currie, Jeanne Marie, PA
Dauerbach, Rosemary Frances, PA

Donnelly, Denise Carol, NJ
Edwards, Susan Lee, PA
Freedman, Sande, PA
Gallagher, Marie Elena, PA
Gillard, Gloria V., PA
Goldberg, Donna Louise, PA
Heinze, Louise Ann, PA
Lipson, Julie, PA
Lodge, Kathryn Ruth, PA
Miller, Kimberly Ann, PA
Modhera, Kalpa R., NJ
Pahlke, Linda Irene, PA
Patel, Sangita, PA
Rule, Patricia Jean, PA
Schulz, Lisa Marie, PA
Slota, Linda Joan, PA
Strine, Carrie Elizabeth, DE
Treacy, MaryBeth, PA

POST-BACCALAUREATE CERTIFICATE in OCCUPATIONAL THERAPY
Dunoff, Beth Hope, NJ
Ellman, Janet Ilyce, PA
Elwood, Marion Hunter, PA
Graff, Janine Ellen, PA
Greene, Barbara Ann, MI
Hann, Brett Stewart, PA
Kallus, Karen Lee, PA
Post, Marian Mulville, PA
Priestley, Deborah Ann, PA
Smyth, Catherine Margaret, PA
Spaeth, Julie A., PA

ASSOCIATE IN ARTS
Wideman, Norman, PA

If any thing is sacred the human body is sacred,
And the glory and sweet of a man is the token of manhood untainted,
And in man or woman a clean, strong, firm-fibred body, is more beautiful than the most beautiful face.

Walt Whitman [1819–1892]
Leaves of Grass,
"I Sing the Body Electric"

The College of Allied Health Sciences celebrated its 20th anniversary during the 1989/90 academic year. At Opening Exercises, an honorary degree was presented to Dr. Edmund J. McTernan (Fig. 104), a nationally known figure in allied health, and a gift of a lectern was presented to the University by the College (Fig. 105). In October, the College sponsored a research day featuring poster presentations by alumni and students, preceded by a speech by Maggie Kuhn, founder of the Gray Panthers. Later in the year, the Scott Memorial Library held an exhibit that focused on the history of the College. In April, a luncheon was held honoring alumni who had been recipients of the Alumni Special Achievement Award or the Achievement Award for Student Life, and plaques to be permanently displayed in the College were dedicated. The culmination of the 20th anniversary celebration was the Alumni Day Cruise, held on the ship "Spirit of Philadelphia" (Fig. 106).

The Report of the Task Force to Plan the Focus of the College of Allied Health Sciences for the 1990s was accepted by the Board of Trustees. One of the major recommendations, the establishment of a Center for Collaborative Research, was implemented.

A Dean's Council of Overseers, representing leaders in the community, business and the health care professions, was formed to bring the College leadership new perspectives, based on broad practical experience. An alumnus of the College's nursing program, Jane Marko Carabasi,

Fig. 105. Dean Abrams presents gift of a lectern from College of Allied Health to the University. President Bluemle and Board Chairman Driscoll on left.

Fig. 104. Dr. Edmund J. McTernan, national figure in allied health, receives honorary degree from President Bluemle (middle). Board Chairman Edward C. Driscoll on left.

Fig. 106. Twentieth Anniversary cake on "Spirit of Philadelphia" cruise ship. Left to right: Bonnie Dymek Behm, '78; Dean Abrams; Maria C. Elfreth, Director of Alumni Programs; and Antonia Mangold, '86.

B.S.N., Ed.D., was among the first members of the Council.

The year was marked also by the master's degree program in nursing receiving its initial accreditation from the National League for Nursing.

The 1990 Commencement, held on May 18, was the last at which President Bluemle would preside before his retirement the following month and the last for Edward C. Driscoll as Chairman of the Board of Trustees before he stepped down from that position at the same time (Fig. 107).

Honorary degrees were presented to Byllye Y. Avery, founder of the National Black Women's Health Project, and to higher education researcher Dr. Alexander W. Astin (Fig. 107).

Among the 287 graduates at the Commencement was Lisa Klinger, dental hygiene, who won the College's Student Life Award (Fig. 108). Ms. Klinger was also elected to the Alpha Eta Honor Society and Sigma Phi Alpha. She received the Student American Dental Hygienists' Association Award, among other honors.

Five graduates earned perfect 4.0 averages: Mary Jo Cosgrove, dental hygiene; Carol Ann Bass, medical technology; and Christine Arnold, Antoinette Falconi and Elizabeth Kempf, nursing.

Holli Sue Pheasant, nursing, who was president of the Student Nurses Association and was inducted into Sigma Theta Tau, the nursing honor society, entered Jefferson Medical College in September, 1990. Mary Ann Albano Sigmund, cytotechnology, received the Warren R. Lang Scholarship Award sponsored by the American Society for Cytotechnology. Lisa Vaughan, dental hygiene, winner of several awards, continued to be involved and to hold leadership roles in both the New Jersey and Southern New Jersey Dental Hygienists Associations.

Maureen A. Fox, nursing, who graduated summa cum laude, was inducted into Sigma Theta Tau Honor Society and named to *Who's Who in American Nursing* among her recognitions (Fig. 109). A clinical nurse II at Jefferson Hospital, Ms. Fox continued her studies in the MSN/MBA dual degree program at Widener University. Raezel Tucker, occupational therapy (OT), earned the highest grade point average in the OT certificate program, graduated summa cum laude, was Valedictorian of her OT class, and was inducted into the Alpha Eta Honor Society. Catherine Miller, physical therapy, earned the department's academic award for highest grade point average in her class.

The nearly 4000 Alumni of the College of Allied Health Sciences have pursued diverse careers. Many have continued their education to masters and doctoral degrees. Others have entered teaching and research. Numerous graduates have been attracted to hospitals, laboratories and the pharmaceutical industry. The disciplines acquired

Fig. 107. Commencement (1990): Board Chairman Edward C. Driscoll, Dr. Alexander W. Astin (honorary degree recipient), Byllye Y. Avery (honorary degree recipient), Dean Abrams, and President Bluemle.

Fig. 108. Lisa Klinger, B.S., Dental Hygiene, receives Student Life Award from William Thygeson, Director of Student Affairs and Services.

during their training have provided a solid background for whatever fields they entered.

The College of Allied Health Sciences has become established as a leading force in the national arena for innovative programs and teaching in this increasingly sophisticated field. Further progress is envisioned with greater emphasis on research. A *Strategic Plan for the Nineties* provides forward-looking guidelines for this effort.

B.S. in LABORATORY, SCIENCES
(Medical Technology)
 Aquilino, Patrick, PA
 Arena, Valerie Lynn, PA
 Bass, Carolann, PA
 Baur, Colleen, PA
 Garner, Michael Anthony, PA
 Glenn, Susan Anne, PA
 Graf, Kelly Ann, VT
 Harkins, Michael J., PA
 Lafferty, Colleen, NJ
 McLaughlin, Bernice Christine, PA
 Monk, Kelly D., PA
 Nabulsi, Deena Sameh, PA
 *Palermo, Colleen Marie, PA
 Phengvath, Chanhpheng, PA
 Rosa, Miguel H., PA
 Schaunt, Michelle, PA

B.S. in LABORATORY SCIENCES
(Cytotechnology)
 Albano, MaryAnna, DE
 *Benckini, Cynthia Marie, PA
 Buniak, Kelly Anne, NJ
 *DeWitt, Catherine Malizia, NJ
 Diaz, Maribel, PA
 Drozd, Kimberly Ann, PA
 Grassia, Raquel Marino, NJ
 Kalnick, Lucinda, PA
 Keehfuss, Linda J., NM
 Kolbenheyer, Kim Anne, NY
 *Mututu, Edwin Kumbirai, ZIMBAB
 Nabulsi, Tesreen Sameh, PA
 *Nfila, Saliwe Busilu, BOTSWANA
 Pirolli, Jennifer Maria, NJ

POST-BACCALAUREATE CERTIFICATE
in CYTOGENETIC TECHNOLOGY
 Golembiewski, Victoria Ann, PA

*The five students identified with an asterisk earned both the B.S. in Laboratory Sciences Degree and the Post-Certificate in Cytogenetic Technology.

B.S. in NURSING
 Adams, Tina Marie, NJ
 Albrecht, Nancy L., NJ
 Allerton, Girten Lee, NC
 Amato, Rita Frances, PA
 Araujo, Aurea F., BRAZIL
 Arnold, Christine D., PA
 Basile, Joanne Catherine, PA
 Beach, Nancy L., PA
 Bendig-Philpott, Denise, PA
 Bennett, Lewis R., PA
 Betzner, Karen J., PA
 Beyer, Carolyn A., NJ
 Blackman-Spears, Patricia Ann, NJ
 Boris, Ann Sophia, PA
 Brady, Pauline Frances, PA

Fig. 109. Maureen A. Fox, R.N., B.S.N., summa cum laude graduate, named in *Who's Who in American Nursing*.

Brennan, Janet L., PA
Briggs, Janet, NJ
Britten, Nancy A., PA
Brophy, Ida, PA
Brown, Linda Marion, PA
Bryan, Kathleen Joan, NJ
Bull, Ann M., NJ
Carugno, Diane Marion, PA
Chandler, Steven, NJ
Cherry-Lamb, Alice Ann, PA
Ciarlante, Judith Anne, NJ
Cini, William, Jr., NJ
Ciorrocco, Nancy J., PA
Colbridge, Colleen Marie, NJ
Dean, Linda Marie, PA
Demchur, Joseph, PA
Dennis, Tania Vanessa, NJ
Dildine, Lorraine S., PA
Dilmar, Rayfield, Sr., PA
Dinofrio, Judy A., PA
DiRuocco, Elizabeth Louise, NJ
Diskin, Peter C., PA
Dissinger, Patricia Kelly, PA
Dlugosz, Joseph, PA
Eastman, Nancy L., PA
Eaves, Margaret Catherine, PA
Eisner-Oakes, Marie, PA
Emrick, Lori Michelle, NJ
Evans, Nancy Marie, NJ
Falconi, Antoinette, NJ
Farace, Lisa Ann, NJ
Ference, Paul Geoffrey, PA
Fisher, Allison Elizabeth, NJ
Fisher, Amy Louise, PA
Flamini, Darlene Joan, NJ
Floyd, Valerie Evette, PA
Fox, Maureen A., PA
Franco, Renee, PA
Fritz, Deborah Louise, NJ
Gallagher, Kathleen Patricia, PA
Gardener, Cheryl Lynn, NJ
Germer, Heidi Lynn, PA
Glenn, Margaret, PA
Good, Margaret Fetter, PA
Gorman, Rosemary Celeste, PA
Hackney, Lisa Jean, PA
Halleck, Lois R., NJ
Harvey, Mark Joseph, PA
Henderson, Lynease Renee, PA
Henning, Shirley Lynne, NJ
Hester, Donna L., PA
Houseal, Sarah J., NJ
Huber, Kathy A., PA
James, Suzanne M., PA

Kane, Maribeth Justine, NJ
Karsnitz, Deborah K., PA
Kelly, Patrick Donald, PA
Kelly, William Thomas, PA
Kempf, Elizabeth Renee, PA
Klink, Denise, PA
Lamar, Bobbi Jean, WI
Lambert, Anne Elizabeth, PA
Leinhauser, Karen Cecile, PA
Lendzinski, William Joseph, PA
Litka, Patti L., PA
Lopacki, Caroline Beth Anne, PA
Lubin, Steven, NJ
Maglaya, Lualhati M., PA
Marion, William G., PA
Martindell, Sherri Lynn Ann, PA
Masek, John Charles, PA
McKenna, Lori C., PA
Mentzer, Lisa Jo, PA
Meyer, Eleanor Christina, NJ
Monzo, David M., PA
Mulholland, Nanci Ann, PA
Mumin, Khadijah, PA
Nevara, Cindy L., CA
Olsack, Andrea N., NJ
Omana, Josephine M., PA
Patel, Bhavna V., NJ
Pheasant, Holli Sue, PA
Phillips, Diane, PA
Pine, Vivian B., PA
Repko, Susan Ann, NJ
Reyes, Rinna Tolentino, NJ
Rivera, Ruth, NJ
Romagano, Linda A., PA
Ruane, Margaret Mary, PA
Schleider, Joanne, NJ
Schmidt, Mark E., NJ
Shewbrooks, Susan L., PA
Short, Melissa Lee, PA
Solomon, Brenda Frances, PA
Sommer, Gay Lauren, NJ
Stafford, Eileen B., NJ
Tague, Ann Marie, PA
Thompson, Marilyn Y., NJ
Ullman, Jane E., PA
Van Stan, Susan Tracy, PA
Vargas, Genalyn P., NJ
Wachlin, Joan G., PA
Wainer, Alice Lynne, PA
Walson, Omana A., PA
Walton, Edward William, PA
Wessner, Natalie Lorraine, PA
Whedbee, Rosann R., NJ
Whittle, Patricia R., NJ

Windfelder, Joyce M., PA
Wise, Wendy Jo, PA
Wisla, Anne Marie B., NJ
Wright, Dominica Felicia, PA
Wright, Edith Louise, PA
Wright, Lesley J., PA

B.S. in DIAGNOSTIC IMAGING
Caccia, Holly C.H., NJ
Capano, Dolores L., PA
Darrow, Donna L., NY
Kueny, Margaret Rose, PA
Leuthner, Bonnie, NJ
Olson, Richard Eric, NJ
Parikh, Sangita Amit, PA
Valosky, Cherylanne Mary, PA

B.S. in DIAGNOSTIC IMAGING
(Diagnostic Medical Sonography)
Coleman, Anorna Apryl, LA
Dlugosz, John Anthony, PA
Fazekas, Constance Karin, PA
Goodman, Haekyong Chang, PA
Innamorato, Denenne M., PA
James, Kathryn Madeline, NJ
Mallon, Joyce E., NJ
Nesbitt, Kimberly Ann, PA
Patel, Alpa S., PA
Sykes, Roberta Jo, NJ

B.S. in DENTAL HYGIENE
Cosgrove, Mary Jo, PA
Dodge, Julie Lyn, NJ
Klinger, Lisa Suzanne, PA
Levin, Nan L., PA
Pacifico, Trina J., PA
Pappelardo, Ann-Marie Frances, MA
Prego, Lisa Maria, NJ
Randolph, Tanya Latisha, PA
Sullivan, Elise Marie, PA
Vaughn, Lisa Diane, NJ
Walter, Sandra Nancy, PA
Walters, Dawn Elizabeth, NJ
Wolfe, Hope L., PA

B.S. IN PHYSICAL THERAPY
Alexander, Michele, PA
Baniewicz, James Matthew, PA
Binns, Kathleen A., PA
Cahoon, Kelly, NJ
Carpenter, Linda Geyelin, PA
Church, Kevin Dee, UT
Clauss, Kerry, PA
Coutts, Darlene Joy, NJ

Doran, Jo Anne, PA
Dougherty, Norma J., PA
Eastlake, Cynthia A., PA
Farmer, Sandra, PA
Ffitch, Mary Elise, PA
Gleason, Juanita Ann, PA
Graham, John W., NJ
Hampton, Tracy, PA
Hehn, Lea Joy, NJ
Hewlett, Susan Lanette, VA
Johns, Gail Ann, PA
Jorgensen, Karen Ann, CA
Karafa, Mark Gregory, PA
Kennedy, Kathleen Susan, PA
Kester, Bethann Elizabeth, PA
Mattocks, Larry Wayne, Jr., PA
McKean, Lois Kathryn, PA
Meehan, Marie Ethel, NJ
Miller, Catherine M., PA
Miller, Susan D., PA
Mitchell, Christine Marie, PA
Moceri, Frank R., Jr., NJ
Moss, Pamela Brooke, VA
Norkitis, Jacqueline Annette, PA
Oie, Carrie-Anne Michie, MD
Opperman, Charles Henry, Jr., PA
Patel, Seema, NJ
Pinto, Cristina Maria, MD
Pullen, William J., NJ
Richert, Tammy Marie, NY
Rome, Christine Kellie, MD
Schuler, Jacqueline Marie, NJ
Shah, Bina, CT
Smith, Kirsten Field, CT
Smyser, Troy Allen, PA
Sorrentino, Vicki Lynn, NJ
Spangler, Noelle J., NJ
Starr, Michael, PA
Steffy, Kim Ann, PA
Teare, Monica L., DE
Thomas, Colleen Wile, PA
Waltz, Norman Brian, PA
Ward, Wendy Denise, NJ
Wollam, Katrina Ann, MA
Wright, Cindy Lynn, NJ

B.S. in OCCUPATIONAL THERAPY
Abel, Donna M., PA
Bauder, Jill Denise, PA
Bazela, Alesia Danielle, DE
Bires, Jeanne Teresa, PA
Bowman, Paula Lee, PA
D'Alessio, Teresanne Rosamund, PA
Davis, Robin P., NJ

Dimenna, Michelle Marie, NJ
Dunne, Elizabeth, M., PA
Durkin, Maria J., PA
Edwardson, Barbara Anne, NJ
Ghergo, Lisa Marie, PA
Gunkel, Wendy S., PA
Johns, Pamalyn A., PA
Jones, Diane Marie, NJ
Klein, Michael Sean, PA
Little, Lisa Renee, PA
Maines, Cherryl Ann, PA
Malandro, Karen, NJ
Napier, Jeanette, PA
Novotny, Mark Anthony, CO
Pelzer-Fenning, Kiz D., PA
Rollins, Janet L., PA
Smith, Leslie Marie, OH
Spotts, Judith A., PA
Sturm, Eileen M., NJ
Topolski, Eileen Elizabeth, DE
Trindle, Meghan Elaine, PA

Veronis, Lisa Rose, PA
Waltman, Sharon Lynn, NJ
White, Wendy Lynn, PA

POST-BACCALAUREATE CERTIFICATE in OCCUPATIONAL THERAPY
Arrell, Patricia Ann, PA
Bride, Elizabeth Lyons, PA
Collier, Gina Fay, PA
Fox, James Leon, Jr., PA
Levin, Debra Jean, NJ
McNamee, Mary Jane, DE
Pichola, Jenifer Marie, PA
Swan, Lynda R., PA
Tucker, Raezel Fonda, NJ

ASSOCIATE IN ARTS
Dolan, Teresa, PA

ASSOCIATE IN SCIENCE
Barranger, Kelly Ann, NJ
Harris, Frank M., ME

Commencement (1990) graduates who chose to start their careers at Jefferson.

Statue of Thomas Jefferson, sculpted by Lloyd Lillie,
donated by
John P. McGovern M.D., Sc.D, LL.D., L.H.D. (Jefferson)

Bahr, Jacqueline T., 1985
Bailey, Sheryl Taylor, 1988
Baker, Karen Beth, 1988
Baker, Kathleen A., 1987
Baker, Kathleen Elizabeth, 1986
Baker, Nancy Jean, 1973
Baker, Susan Marie, 1975
Baldassano, Maureen Patricia, 1986
Balderston, Philip Alan, 1979
Baldridge, Brian K., 1981
Baldwin, Kathleen Kim, 1989
Ballezza, Elizabeth Ann, 1975
Ballistreri, Nancy Lee, 1985
Balogh, Drew Gabor, 1979
Bamford, Barbara, 1970
Bamford, Helen, 1971
Banavong, Sakhone, 1986
Baniewicz, James Matthew, 1990
Banks, James Lee, 1976
Baran, Elizabeth Marie, 1983
Barber, Diana, 1968
Barbera, Joan, 1971
Barbuto, Susan M., 1977
Barcomb, Lynn M., 1987
Bardsley, Marilu, 1986
Bardsley, Mark Stuart, 1989
Barlow, Frances Mary, 1989
Barnard, KC, 1988
Barndt, Janice Ann, 1986
Barnes, Diane Irene, 1988
Barnett, Deborah Anne, 1980
Barney, Sharon L., 1982
Barranger, Kelly Ann, 1990
Barrett, TinaMarie, 1986
Barron, Diane Melanie, 1986
Barry, Christine, 1983
Barry, Mary Alice, 1986
Barsuglia, Kathleen Bernadette, 1987
Barthelmess, Dawn Michele, 1986
Bartlett, Melonie, 1979
Bartoletti, MaryLynn, 1988
Bartolomeo, Rita, 1972
Basiago, Jennie Lee Harpster, 1988
Basiago, Marlene Marie, 1987
Basile, Joanne Catherine, 1990
Basile, Michael Domenick, 1976
Bass, Carolann, 1990
Bass, Queena Rouse, 1988
Bateman, Andrea Rose, 1988
Bates, Maureen Kelly, 1989
Bates, Susan Karen, 1985
Bath, Dale Charles, 1986
Batt, Lisa Joanne, 1986
Bauder, Jill Denise, 1990
Baur, Colleen, 1990
Bautista, Ceasar James, 1988

Bax, Robert L., 1981
Baxter, Lisa, 1986
Bayliss, Linda Smith, 1978
Bazela, Alesia Danielle, 1990
Beach, Kathleen Theresa, 1976
Beach, Nancy L., 1990
Beale, Ellen Marie, 1976
Beard, Martha Elizabeth, 1985
Beatty, James D., 1989
Beatty, Lisa Danae, 1988
Beausang, Anna Marie, 1969
Bechtel, Marlene Ann, 1983
Beck, Diane Louise, 1985
Becker, Beverly Bond, 1982
Becker, Donna Renee, 1985
Becker, Jill Anne, 1982
Becker, Louise Ellen, 1971
Becker, Maureen Patricia, 1988
Becker, Peggy M., 1977
Beckman, Laura Ann, 1983
Beers, Lisa Jane, 1986
Beil, Jo Ann, 1976
Beil, Laurie Ann, 1986
Beirne, Charlotte Ann, 1986
Beitel, Susan Mary, 1987
Bell, Brenda, 1980
Bell, Carolyn Elizabeth, 1969
Bell, Maryanne Theresa, 1976
Bellenghi, Jean Mary, 1973
Benac, Irene Katherine, 1986
Benckini, Cynthia Marie, 1990
Bender, Alene Sue, 1976
Bender, Amy West, 1986
Bender, Kelley, 1986
Bender, Lynn Carol, 1984
Bendig-Philpott, Denise, 1990
Beneck, John Charles, 1987
Beningo, Linnette Sue, 1983
Bennett, Clare Ellen, 1974
Bennett, Lewis R., 1990
Bennett, Sally Harriet, 1988
Bennett, Stephen Edward, 1976
Bennett-Coccia, Lisa Mary, 1985
Benson, Joyce Roscoe, 1986
Berg, Dana Jean, 1979
Berg, Ellen D., 1974
Berg, Rachel Karlan, 1988
Bergdoll, Susan Amy, 1986
Berger, Lizanne Jaclyn, 1988
Bergmaier, Linda Marie, 1985
Bergmann, Mitchell T., 1977
Berk, Joy Lynne, 1989
Berkey, Heather Anne, 1988
Berkey, Heather Anne, 1989
Berlin, Patricia Ruth, 1980
Bernd, Mary Lynn, 1986

Bernstein, Michael, 1987
Berr, Georgina, 1986
Berringer, Deborah Ann, 1979
Berry, Patricia Anne, 1987
Bersani, Theresa Margaret, 1987
Betzner, Karen J., 1990
Beutel, Kathrin Bettina, 1980
Bewsher, Rita A., 1980
Beyer, Carolyn A., 1990
Beyer, Joanne Ruth, 1973
Bialsky, Jay Arnold, 1988
Biasello, Sandra, 1982
Bienvenue, Robyn Michele, 1974
Biernbaum, Sandra Helene, 1985
Bigge, Paula Mae, 1982
Bigley, Frances M., 1981
Bilker, Diane Maryland, 1983
Bilodeau, Diane Louise, 1986
Bilotta, Christine Patricia, 1988
Binanay, Cynthia Anne, 1979
Binder, Virginia Ann, 1975
Bingaman, Kathleen Diane, 1987
Bingman, Mary Ellen, 1970
Binkley, Pamela, 1987
Binns, Kathleen A., 1990
Bird, April Lee, 1977
Bires, Jeanne Teresa, 1990
Biurgren, Phyllis Marie, 1978
Bixby, Jane Bunting, 1989
Blackman-Spears, Patricia Ann, 1990
Blackway, Betsy Lynne, 1981
Blain, Julia Marie, 1982
Blaine, Maryann, 1979
Blair, Joyce Irene, 1985
Blanche, Noelle Yvonne, 1989
Blank, Linda Elizabeth, 1982
Blankman, Julia Susan, 1986
Blasciak, Karen Lynn, 1985
Blazich, Donna Marie, 1983
Bleile, Regina M., 1978
Blimegger, Carole Gluch, 1975
Bliss, Donna Mary, 1978
Bliss, Donna Mary, 1982
Blitz, Michele Susan, 1987
Bloch, Jodi F., 1986
Blocklinger, Fred L., 1987
Bloom, Debra Ann, 1983
Bloom, Kenneth Harold, Jr., 1989
Blumenfeld, Susan Joy, 1985
Blumenstein, Elizabeth, 1982
Blumenthal, Karen Eillen, 1982
Blythe, Alice Mae, 1970
Board, Kathy Virlene, 1983
Boas, Lyn Denworth, 1982
Bobb, Leslie Enid, 1982
Bobbie, Mary Elizabeth, 1988

Caddy, Patricia Anne, 1977
Cadogan, Albert S.A., 1979
Cadwallader, Judy S., 1974
Cafagna, Denise Marie, 1987
Cahoon, Kelly, 1990
Calabrese, Nancy Meier, 1974
Calafati, Stephanie Anne, 1980
Calhoun, Lorraine Barol, 1988
Callahan, Denise, 1972
Callahan, Helen Marie, 1976
Callahan, Kerry Rose, 1988
Callahan, Lisa Marie, 1988
Callahan, Susan Michele, 1982
Callan, Mary Joanne, 1979
Callery, Susan Veronica, 1976
Camoratto, Joseph John, 1981
Campbell, Sandra Lee, 1989
Campbell, Sheila Faye, 1986
Campbell, William Leroy, Jr., 1986
Campeaux, Suzanne M., 1986
Campuzano, Maria Louise, 1986
Canavan, Kathleen Jean, 1978
Cann, Rose, 1970
Cannariato, Joan A., 1975
Cannava, Maureen Vivian, 1982
Cannon, Susan Elaine, 1986
Canter, Dorothy Elizabeth, 1971
Cap, Michael, 1982
Capano, Dolores L., 1990
Capano, Michele, 1985
Capers, Ruth Zoller, 1985
Capie, Linda Claire, 1983
Capista, Anne Satoris, 1969
Capitanio, Barbara Rose, 1969
Caplan, Lois, 1970
Capobianco, Teresa Maria, 1987
Capoccia, Sandra Yuki, 1986
Caporale, Marilena, 1987
Cappelli, Theresa Ann, 1976
Cappelli, Theresa Marie, 1988
Cappo, Rosemary Elizabeth, 1978
Capron, Faith Irene, 1974
Carberry, Elizabeth Anne, 1979
Carbo, Carla Jane, 1987
Cardelli, Maryanne, 1987
Cardonick, Cindy Diane, 1983
Carey, Shavaun Mary, 1982
Carhart, Cynthia, 1971
Carides, Debra Lynn, 1976
Carl, Deborah Ann, 1988
Carlin, Alice Mary, 1985
Carlson, Jeffery Glen, 1985
Carlson, Kathleen Ann, 1988
Carnabuci, Vincent Anthony, 1989
Carney, Bridget Marie, 1985
Carolan, Jacqueline Eberly, 1978

Caroluzzi, Susan Laura, 1984
Carpenter, Helen Grace, 1981
Carpenter, Linda Geyelin, 1990
Carr, Dianna Lynn, 1988
Carrigan, Theresa Marie, 1979
Carroll, Anthony Brendan, 1972
Carroll, Juanita Naomi, 1975
Carroll, Rosemarie Ann, 1972
Carrozza, Judith Craig, 1989
Carrozza, Michael Joseph, 1982
Carrozza, Rosanne Bernidette, 1975
Carter, Cathy Lynn, 1977
Carter, Mary Lee, 1983
Carty, Marguerite Mary, 1988
Carugno, Diane Marion, 1990
Caruthers, Theresa Ann, 1979
Casey, Catherine Malloy, 1978
Casey, Lynne Susan, 1976
Casey, Maryann C., 1977
Casillas, Johnny, 1985
Cassel, Stacey Francine, 1982
Cassidy, Anne Marie, 1983
Cassidy, Eleanor Agnes, 1968
Cassidy, Mary Teresa , 1987
Castiglione, Sandra Maria, 1974
Castiglioni, Michelle, 1988
Castleberry, Eleanor M., 1975
Catalina, Carol Lynne, 1985
Catanzaro, Josephine Ann, 1974
Cathcart, Harriet, 1969
Cathcart, Tressa Ann, 1983
Cather, Deborah L., 1979
Cauley, Megan Elizabeth, 1989
Cava, Deborah Ann, 1988
Cavanaugh, Ritanne, 1983
Cavicchia, Terry Ann, 1976
Celenza, Elizabeth Ann, 1987
Celenza, Elizabeth Anne, 1976
Cella, Luca R., 1987
Cella, Marion Rose, 1987
Celli, Marybeth Rita, 1988
Cenci, Carol Ann, 1983
Centifonti, Nancy Ruth, 1971
Ceperley, James Fairchild, 1979
Ceperley, Jeffrey Charles, 1979
Cerrone, Frank Anthony, 1988
Cerullo, Mary Martin, 1987
Cesare, Gabriel Patrick, 1970
Cesarini, Rosalie Anne, 1970
Chaiken, Iris, 1968
Chalick, Beth Randi, 1986
Chalk, Carolyn Lee, 1987
Chamberlain, Melody Joy, 1988
Champlin, Susan June Hallowell, 1982
Chandler, Diane Michele, 1976
Chandler, Julianne, 1986

Chandler, Steven, 1990
Chang, Heather Ruth, 1980
Chantz, Lois Elizabeth, 1975
Charles, Helen Claire, 1981
Charles, Lisa Jean, 1977
Charles, Nancy Anne, 1982
Chase, Susan Denise, 1986
Cheetham, Eric Carl, 1978
Chen, Jessie Chih Hsien, 1978
Chepelevich, Regina Roman, 1978
Chepulis, Margaret Ann, 1972
Chercass, Laura Ilene, 1982
Cherian, Simon Ooramvelil, 1984
Cherry, Judith Marie, 1988
Cherry-Lamb, Alice Ann, 1990
Chestnut, Ruth Ann, 1972
Cheung, Amy Ping-Lok, 1971
Chianese, David A., 1982
Chiaro, Virginia Maisch, 1982
Chiaverelli, Patricia Ann, 1979
Childress, Sarah Bridget, 1988
Chillemi, Rosalie Elaine, 1987
Chin, Marie Ann, 1979
China, Virginia, 1970
Chmelewski, Pamela Jean, 1975
Christensen, Deborah Lynn, 1986
Christie, Carol Rae, 1975
Christinzio, Janice Marie, 1986
Christmann, Maureen Ann, 1979
Christopher, Bernice Bailey, 1978
Chubin, Ronald Scott, 1985
Chung, Jacqueline, 1980
Church, Kevin Dee, 1990
Churchill, Judy Rae, 1968
Ciarlante, Judith Anne, 1990
Ciavaglia, Troy C., 1989
Ciaverelli, Christine Marie, 1989
Ciccarelli, Annette Rita, 1975
Ciccone, Martha Ann, 1976
Cichonski, Linda Catherine, 1976
Cinelli, Cynthia Marie, 1986
Cini, William, Jr., 1990
Ciociola, Anna Theresa, 1975
Ciorrocco, Nancy J., 1990
Citerone, Christine Helena, 1989
Citrino, Sharon Mary, 1982
Ciuffetelli, Mary Josephine, 1971
Civa, Deborah Ann, 1974
Clark, Catherine A., 1986
Clark, Crystal Dawn, 1986
Clark, Denise Marie, 1987
Clark, Elizabeth Ann, 1988
Clark, Gail Perna, 1978
Clark, Michael Thomas, 1982
Clark-Evans, Clifford Marion, 1982
Clarke, Jeannine Amy, 1987

Clarke, Louise D., 1988
Clauss, Kerry, 1990
Clay, Dorseina, 1981
Clayton, Barbara Ann, 1973
Cleary, Kathleen, 1988
Cleary, Marialice Joan, 1975
Clement, Joanna U., 1988
Clements, James Joseph, Jr., 1989
Clements, Valerie LaVerne, 1986
Clews, Margaret Ann, 1972
Clifford, Peter, 1986
Cline, Jacqueline Rita, 1971
Clouse, Donna Jean, 1986
Clydesdale, Gale Adrienne, 1983
Coady, Allison Mary, 1986
Coar, Elise Rose, 1986
Coelho, Eusebio Rodriques, 1982
Coffee, Deborah, 1984
Coffield, Barbara Jean, 1976
Cogan, Frances Ann, 1975
Cogar, Laura Anne, 1989
Cohen, Debra Nancy, 1988
Cohen, Elizabeth Wilson, 1983
Cohen, Helene Marilyn, 1986
Cohen, Sara Moljo, 1989
Cohen, Shelley, 1975
Cohen, Sheryl, 1985
Coia, Theresa Marie, 1986
Colasante, Blaise Anthony, 1989
Colavechio, Anna M., 1981
Colbert, Terry Donald, 1982
Colbert, Theresa Elizabeth, 1983
Colbridge, Colleen Marie, 1990
Cole, Amy Beth, 1989
Cole, Linda Diane, 1979
Cole, Martha Jemison, 1980
Cole, Patricia Elizabeth, 1974
Cole, Stephanie Barbara, 1974
Coleman, Anorna Apryl, 1990
Coleman, Jean Ann, 1987
Coleman, Paulette Elaine, 1975
Coleman, Timothy Laurence, 1986
Colladay, Joyce, 1983
Collette, Shelly Lynn, 1987
Collier, Andrea Rachel, 1982
Collier, Gina Fay, 1990
Collins, John Patrick, 1983
Collins, Lynda M., 1986
Collins, Sharon Ann, 1986
Collins, Thomas Francis, 1974
Collot, Gilbert Georges, Jr., 1989
Colonna, Elaine Alice, 1971
Comeaux, Kathleen Gillard, 1974
Comisky, Anne Theresa, 1987
Comly, Elizabeth Ann, 1980
Comly, Joanne Quatrani, 1987

Como, Sandra P., 1986
Conant, Ellen Elaine, 1987
Conboy, Victoria Joan, 1975
Condike, Barbara Jane, 1975
Cong-Huyen, Emilie Giang, 1987
Cong-Huyen, Theresa Huong, 1988
Congar, Elizabeth Ann, 1974
Conley, Cheryl Nelson, 1987
Conley, Joelle Christeen, 1989
Conley, Sharon Kay, 1980
Conlon, Ruth B., 1974
Connell, Mary Jane, 1976
Connelly, John Thomas, 1986
Connelly, Lisa Anne, 1986
Connolly, Patricia Ann, 1980
Connor, Carole, 1973
Connor, Maria Angela, 1975
Connor, Susan Elaine, 1986
Connors, Kathleen, 1968
Conoscento, Martha Ann, 1974
Conover, Constance Joy, 1986
Conrad, Deborah Joy, 1974
Conti, Stephanie Marie, 1976
Contrisciano, Karen Marie, 1977
Conway, Maureen Margaret, 1969
Cook, Deborah Lee, 1983
Cook, Geneva, 1972
Cooksey, Michael B., 1987
Cool, Elizabeth Marie, 1976
Coole, Lorie Lynn, 1986
Cooley, Brendan Michael, 1987
Cooley, Mary Elizabeth, 1982
Cooley, Rosemarie Ann, 1989
Cooley, Sara Ann, 1988
Cooney, J. Dan Joseph, 1987
Cooper, Laura Anne, 1977
Cope, Bethany Sheryn, 1985
Cope, Randall Kevin, 1987
Coper, Julia Anne, 1978
Copper, Carol Ann, 1985
Corbi, Jean Brimfield, 1986
Corda, Karol L., 1989
Cordier, Lisa Ann, 1983
Corley, Stephanie , 1985
Corma, Amy Kathleen, 1982
Cornell, Margareta Lynn, 1975
Corrado, Leigh Ann, 1982
Corrado, Teresa Joan, 1974
Corse, Kathleen M., 1985
Corsey, Florence Lillian, 1969
Coruzzi, Joanne Theresa, 1986
Cosgrove, Mary Jo, 1990
Costa, Margaret Mary Cox, 1980
Costello, Irene Stevens, 1978
Costello, Lynn Ann, 1985
Costello, Margaret Mary, 1970

Costello, Todd Carl, 1987
Council, Nancy Lee, 1974
Council, Nancy Lee, 1978
Courtright, Louise Grace, 1987
Courtwright, Diane Marie, 1987
Cousin, Monique Michelle, 1986
Cousins, Dorothy Denise, 1986
Coutts, Darlene Joy, 1990
Coviello, Helen Catherine, 1968
Cowden, Wendi Sue, 1983
Cox, Constance Ann Helena, 1989
Cox, Linda Susan, 1971
Cox, Robert Harris Woods, 1987
Cox, Sister Mary Elizabeth, 1983
Coyle, Dolores Ann, 1974
Coyne, Cynthia Ann, 1978
Coyne, Patricia Lynn, 1978
Craft, Kimberly Lynn, 1989
Craig, Christopher, 1983
Craig, Joan Helen, 1982
Craik, Alan, 1985
Cramer, Jill Patricia, 1986
Cramer, Shirley Grace, 1981
Crane, Francine Theresa, 1986
Crawford, Lynda Bulach, 1975
Crawford-Kemp, Lori Jayne, 1988
Craymer, Ruth Davis, 1975
Creamer, Eunice Marie, 1989
Creany, Consuela Marie, 1978
Cristoforo, Carol Beth, 1988
Croce, Nicholas Joseph, 1975
Croce-Burgess, Marlene Catherine, 1983
Cromie, Elizabeth Marilea, 1981
Cronin, Kathleen, 1985
Crosby, Carla Anna, 1987
Crouter, Jennifer Elaine, 1980
Crowthers, Beth Ann, 1989
Crowthers, Roberta Lee, 1986
Csaszar, Thomas Albert, 1979
Cubler, Amy Jeanette, 1980
Cucinotta, Kelly M., 1989
Culp, Naomi Bee, 1973
Cummings, Catherine Louise, 1982
Cummings, Mary Frances, 1987
Cummins, Heather Whaley, 1988
Cunningham, Lisa Wilson, 1982
Cunningham, Lisa, 1980
Cunningham, Margaret Ann, 1988
Curcio, Ann Ruth, 1986
Curcio, Susan Evelyn, 1989
Cureton-Freed, Deborah, 1971
Curley, Mary Ellen, 1989
Currie, Jeanne Marie, 1989
Curry, Ann Frances, 1973
Cusumano, Eileen Marie, 1978
Cuttic, Nancy Osinkski, 1980

Cywinski, Theresa Ann, 1978
Czarnecki, Susan Corine, 1982
Czulada, Roberta Ann, 1975

~ D ~

D'Agostino, Rita Morabito, 1980
D'Alessandro, Anita Daria, 1989
D'Alessio, Teresanne Rosamund, 1990
D'Angelo, Laura Louise, 1978
D'Arcy, Catherine M., 1987
D'Entremont, Ann Louise Mary, 1982
D'Eramo, Rosanne Marie, 1985
D'Olio, Michael Anthony, 1986
D'Onofrio, Christina Marie, 1971
Dahlquist, Karen Lynn, 1986
Dalal, Asha N., 1974
Dalton, Matthew Lewis, 1979
Dalton, Thomas James, 1988
Danenberger, Catherine Ann, 1988
Daniels, Jane Kathleen, 1988
Daniels, Jeanmarie Anne, 1989
Danley, Ida Elizabeth, 1975
Danusiar, Karen Ann, 1988
Daransky, Marguerite Elsie, 1973
Darby, Wanda Marie, 1986
Darden, Teresa Hall, 1978
Dare, Erla Geddis, 1978
Darrow, Donna L., 1990
Dauerbach, Rosemary Frances, 1989
Daugherty, Lisa Kay, 1987
Davenport, Amy L., 1985
Davenport, Shasmay, 1988
Davidson, Colleen Ann, 1986
Davidson, Gerald Allen, 1981
Davidson, Leo, Jr., 1986
Davies, Nancy Danella, 1985
Davis, Betsy Ann, 1974
Davis, Carol Elizabeth, 1987
Davis, Clayton Alphonsol, III, 1989
Davis, Elizabeth Ann, 1986
Davis, Elizabeth Anne, 1988
Davis, Ellen Bennett, 1982
Davis, Georgianna Jennifer, 1980
Davis, Helen Kline, 1983
Davis, Jan Noel, 1981
Davis, Judith Ann, 1977
Davis, Leigh Ann, 1986
Davis, Pamela Lenora, 1989
Davis, Robin P., 1990
Davis, Susan Briggs, 1983
Davis-Moon, Linda Joan, 1981
Davy, Melody Donna Joy, 1978
Dawley, Dawn Elizabeth, 1982
Dawson, Janet Lynn, 1979
Dawson, Marcella Damiana, 1989

Dayen, Renee Gail, 1974
De Jong, Ytje, 1988
De Mumbrum, Catherine Jean, 1988
De Santis, Paula Maria, 1988
De Simone, Debra Norma, 1983
De Vecchis, Susan Dea, 1986
Deakins, Teri Sue, 1985
Dean, Linda Marie, 1990
DeBaun, Janice Gail, 1974
DeCarlo, Denise Ann, 1972
DeCecco, Denise Ann, 1974
Dech, Jenene Lynette, 1987
DeFero, Tammy Lynn, 1988
Deford, Susan Lynne, 1976
DeHorsey, Kimberly Lyn, 1987
Deibler, David Grant, 1978
Deisroth, Amy Jane, 1987
Deitz, Andrea Phyllis, 1974
DeJesus, Iris Nereida, 1987
DeJohn, Janice Marie, 1982
DeLeo, Jacqueline Ann, 1976
DeLeon, Patricia, 1986
DeLong, Janet Kelly, 1978
DeLozier, Denise Louise, 1989
DelPrato, Thomas V., 1981
DelValle, Nancy Carolyn, 1968
DelVecchio, Marie Theresa, 1975
DeMarshall, Deborah Anne, 1985
Demchur, Joseph, 1990
Demopulos, Nick, 1979
deMoss, Lisa Eileen, 1986
Denecola, Lynn Kristine, 1979
Denham, Margret M., 1985
Dennis, Tania Vanessa, 1990
Dennis, Wendy Hetherington, 1985
Denshaw, Mary Theresa, 1976
DePalmer, Jennifer Anne, 1989
DePaul, Debra, 1982
DePersia, Cynthia Marie, 1976
Depman, Ruth Ann, 1983
Derbes, Jane Agnes, 1968
Derham, Patricia Anne, 1973
Derkas, Kathy, 1981
Derstine, Jill Ann, 1988
DeSantis, Donna Marie, 1981
DeSanto, Donna Ann, 1988
DeSilvio, Dennis G., 1985
DeStefano, Edward John, Jr., 1983
Destra, Joseph John, 1981
DeTitto, Maria, 1986
Detweiler, Mary Emily, 1979
Deutermann, Bonny Gayle, 1986
Deverant, Charlene Constance, 1975
Devine, Ilise Gwen, 1989
Devine, Lucy V., 1985
Devine-Hollander, Kelly Ann, 1985

DeVivo, Denise Diane, 1985
Devlin, Joanne Patricia, 1985
Devoy-McDonnell, Patricia, 1982
DeWitt, Catherine Malizia, 1990
Dexter, Mary Catherine, 1985
DeYulius, Maria Margaret, 1968
Dhanjal, Manmohan, 1986
Diamond, Jacqueline Linda, 1986
Diaz, Maribel, 1990
DiBartolo, Carol Ann, 1980
DiBartolomeo, Mona Lisa, 1974
DiBattista, Maria Lisa, 1985
Dickstein, Anne Elizabeth, 1987
DiCristofaro, Judy, 1986
DiDio, Denise E., 1985
Diehm, Cheryl L., 1989
Dienno, Maryann, 1973
Dietz, Ann Elizabeth, 1987
DiFelice, Valorie Ann, 1973
DiFiore, Linda Catherine, 1986
Digeser, Susan Karen, 1986
DiGiacomo-Modell, Maureen, 1985
Dildine, Lorraine S., 1990
Dillon, Diane Deborah, 1976
Dillon, Patricia Bonnano, 1978
Dilmar, Rayfield, Sr., 1990
Diloreto, Diane Elizabeth, 1977
DiLuciano, Marlene Michele, 1985
Dilworth, Geraldine F., 1974
Dimakopoulos, Maureen E., 1988
DiMauro, Rosemarie Frances, 1982
Dimenna, Michelle Marie, 1990
Dimon, Joanne, 1986
DiMond, Michele, 1970
Dinan, Mary Clare, 1983
DiNardi, Victoria Ann, 1985
DiNatale, Rosemary F., 1989
Dinofrio, Judy A., 1990
Dinsdale, Lynne April, 1987
DiRocco, Elizabeth Maureth, 1982
DiRuocco, Elizabeth Louise, 1990
DiSarro, Constantina, 1981
Diskin, Peter C., 1990
Dissinger, Patricia Kelly, 1990
DiVirgilio, Elizabeth Ann, 1988
Dixon, Gissele Anitamea, 1982
Dixon, Joseph, 1968
Dixon, Nancy Montgomery, 1983
Dlugosz, John Anthony, 1990
Dlugosz, Joseph, 1990
Doakley, Virginia Ann, 1969
Dobbs, Linnette Lilieth, 1983
Dobrota, Deborah Jane, 1986
Dodd, Deborah Anne, 1985
Dodd, Nancy Alberta, 1985
Dodge, Julie Lyn, 1990

INDEX

Fugaro, Claudia Maria, 1985
Fulginiti, Nancy, 1976
Fulginiti, Nancyann Maria, 1985
Fullem, Darlene Carole, 1986
Funaro, Kathleen Gloria, 1986
Furjanic, Rita Marie, 1979
Furlong, Raymond J., Jr., 1977
Furst, Catherine Mary, 1976
Furst, Ethel Mae, 1988
Furukawa, Rika, 1986
Fynan, Susan Clare, 1985

~ G ~

Gabel, Bradley E.G., 1980
Gabellini, Kimberly Maria, 1982
Gaddis, Barbara Eileen, 1983
Gala, Suresh Gangji, 1974
Galanti, Michele Christina, 1988
Galbraith, Kenneth Duane, 1987
Gales, Kimberly Jeanette, 1985
Gallagher, Deborah, 1987
Gallagher, Denise Marie, 1986
Gallagher, Eileen Marie, 1979
Gallagher, Karen Marie, 1986
Gallagher, Kathleen Patricia, 1990
Gallagher, Linda L., 1982
Gallagher, Marie Elena, 1989
Gallagher, Mary Elizabeth, 1982
Gallagher, Michele Frances, 1983
Gallagher, Sharon M., 1978
Gallagher, Theresa, 1971
Gallihue, Deborah, 1987
Gallo, Karen L., 1989
Galvin, Denise Jean, 1974
Gambescia, Ann Marie Elizabeth, 1986
Gambill, Gail Marie, 1982
Gambo, Joanne, 1978
Gambogi, Margaret Helene, 1979
Ganguly, Atul Sukhendu, 1989
Garcia, Mireya Fortuny, 1970
Gardener, Cheryl Lynn, 1990
Gardner, Donna Sue, 1977
Gardner, Pamela R., 1986
Garduque, Teresita Yabes, 1979
Gargiulo, Anna Marie, 1986
Garland, Bettyann Teresa, 1980
Garmat, Diana Rosemarie, 1975
Garner, Michael Anthony, 1990
Garnier, Giby, 1982
Garwood, Joann Jersey, 1982
Gaston, Sharon, 1987
Gates, Eleanor Martin, 1982
Gatta, Patricia Ann, 1978
Gattone, Linda Dierce, 1986
Gaughan-Lizzi, Michele, 1986

Gavigan, Margaret Ann, 1981
Gawin, Gary Paul, 1986
Gdowik, Linda, 1981
Gee, Barbara Kathryn, 1982
Gellar, Ellen Anne, 1974
Gellman, Cheryl Ann F., 1983
Gengler, Theresa Ann, 1979
George, Mindy Ellen, 1978
George, Nancy Malozzi, 1982
Gerace, Kenneth Anthony, 1989
Gerace, Maria Rita, 1977
Gerace, Maria Rita, 1985
Gerhart, Kathleen Dorthea, 1975
Gerhart, Wendy Jo Fluck, 1974
Gerlach, Violet Ann, 1979
Germer, Heidi Lynn, 1990
Germscheid, Gabrielle M., 1987
Gernert, Sherry Lynn, 1987
Gerofsky, Michael David, 1982
Gerstle, Cheryl Lynn, 1986
Gervase, Theresa Maria, 1982
Gessner, Judith O., 1971
Ghergo, Lisa Marie, 1990
Ghilardi, Denise R., 1986
Giampa, Theresa Lynn, 1985
Giannetti, Rita McConnaghy, 1980
Giannini, Cynthia Pauline, 1977
Gibbon, Thomas Michael, 1981
Gibbons-Neff, Emily, 1976
Giese, Louise Julia, 1989
Gifford, Ruth Naomi, 1973
Gift, Kathryn Marie, 1985
Giglio, Joseph Lewis, 1985
Gilbert, Rose Ann, 1989
Gilbert, Susan, 1973
Gilhooly, Ann Hull, 1989
Gill, Ravinder Kaur, 1986
Gill, Sheryl May, 1982
Gillan, Moira Patricia, 1969
Gillard, Gloria V., 1989
Gillece, Michele Mary, 1988
Gillen, Judith Anne, 1981
Gillespie, Mary Susan, 1987
Gilman, Gary Ellis, 1977
Gilmartin, Patricia Anne, 1974
Ginn, Dana Jayne, 1987
Ginn, Michael Albert, 1989
Ginyard, Judith Sandra, 1970
Giordano, Donna, 1972
Giosa, Rosemary Louise, 1972
Giosa, Rosemary, 1988
Giovanelli, Janice Mary, 1974
Gisel, Wendy Ann, 1986
Gittlemacker, Diane Anita, 1988
Giunta, Karen Ann, 1986
Glantzow, Phyllis Nora, 1978

Glasbrenner, Erich Heinz, 1986
Glaskin, Shari Anne, 1986
Glassey, Patricia Anne, 1989
Gleason, Juanita Ann, 1990
Gleason, Patricia Mary, 1986
Glenn, Margaret, 1990
Glenn, Susan Anne, 1990
Glick, Dorina Kandas, 1977
Glickman, Jacqueline Kaye, 1982
Gloates, David Michael, 1986
Glosenger, Donna Carol, 1983
Glovin, Susan, 1971
Glowacz, Cynthia Marie, 1985
Glowka, Grace Mary, 1984
Gluch, Joan Patricia, 1979
Goda, Patricia Marie, 1980
Godfrey, Mary Flavia, 1982
Godsey, Judith Gwendolyn, 1979
Godshall, Carol Louise, 1986
Goergen-Deal, Carlyn Ramona, 1986
Goetz, Deborah Deming, 1986
Goetz, Lisa Kathryn, 1986
Golbeski, Nancy Ann, 1978
Goldberg, Bonnie Zaiss, 1988
Goldberg, Donna Louise, 1989
Goldberg, Evelyn Kallen, 1987
Goldberg, Jan Susan, 1986
Goldberg, Melody Gail, 1979
Goldberg, Rick Spencer, 1987
Golden, Deidre DiCristo, 1989
Goldfrit, Iris N., 1989
Goldie, Lynn Sheryl, 1973
Goldman, Ferne Rochelle, 1984
Goldman, Judith Lisa, 1987
Goldman, Judy Ann, 1981
Goldner, Paul L., Jr., 1986
Goldschmidt, Tamra A., 1985
Goldsmith, Gail Elaine, 1982
Goldsmith, Lisa Ida, 1979
Goldstein, Deborah Ann, 1975
Goldstein, Lee Alan, 1979
Golembiewski, Victoria Ann, 1990
Gontarchick, Judith Marie, 1989
Gonzalez, Diane Michelle, 1983
Gonzalez, Felicia Ellen, 1986
Good, Keith Leroy, 1987
Good, Margaret Fetter, 1990
Good-deCurnou, Luann, 1986
Goodie, Lucie, 1973
Goodman, Haekyong Chang, 1990
Goodman, Phyllis Susan, 1981
Gordon, Carol Ilene, 1974
Gordon, Helen Mary, 1975
Gordon, Linda, 1985
Gordon, Susan Regina, 1980
Gorham, John, 1982

Gorham, Linda Cheryl, 1981
Gorman, Michael James, 1987
Gorman, Regina Maria, 1980
Gorman, Rosemary Celeste, 1990
Gormley, Lisa Marie, 1987
Gorodetzer, Michael Steven, 1977
Gottheim, Merle Schwartz, 1974
Gough, Dorothea Marie, 1986
Govan, Beth Anne, 1976
Gowan, Patricia Susan, 1982
Grace, Theresa Marie, 1989
Grady, Katherine Mary, 1989
Graefe, DonnaMarie, 1971
Graf, Kelly Ann, 1990
Graff, Janine Ellen, 1989
Graffy, Susanna Marta, 1976
Graham, John W., 1990
Graham, Maxine, 1972
Gramlich, Lisa Christine, 1987
Grande, Petruzza, 1985
Grant, Carson E., 1980
Grant, Rosemary Terry, 1979
Grassia, Raquel Marino, 1990
Gratch, David Marshall, 1981
Grau, Anne Marie, 1988
Gravell, Rita Lim, 1988
Gray, Jacqueline Theresa, 1989
Gray, Marjorie Louise, 1972
Grayno, Joyce Ann, 1968
Greco, Andrea Joan, 1987
Green, Carol Elaine, 1985
Green, Diane Frances, 1985
Green, Donna Jeanne, 1986
Green, Jamie Hope , 1986
Green, Linda Frances, 1985
Green, Patrice Phyllis, 1980
Green, Rhonda Lynn, 1978
Green, Richard Wayne, 1972
Green, Suzann Lee, 1975
Green, Terri-Lynn Marie, 1986
Green, Vanessa Helene, 1980
Greenberg, Sharon Ellen, 1985
Greenblatt, Sharon Ilene, 1989
Greene, Barbara Ann, 1989
Greene, Carol M., 1987
Greene, Deborah Anne, 1975
Greenlee, Dawn, 1978
Greenspan, Barbara, 1968
Gregoire, Todd Philip, 1985
Greiss, Lisa Kay, 1987
Griffin, Teresa M., 1989
Griffith, Denise J., 1985
Griffith, Judith Horner, 1986
Griffiths, Lori J., 1988
Griffiths, Tami Lynn, 1986
Grimes, Cheryl Ann, 1985

Grimmel, Jane Helen, 1983
Griswold, Diane Louise, 1975
Gritton, Patricia, 1972
Gross, Jacqueline Michelle, 1980
Gross, Phyllis Jean, 1979
Gross, Susan Barbara, 1986
Grosshauser, Barbara G., 1987
Grotzinger, Karen Rose, 1968
Grove, Vicki Lynn, 1985
Gruber, Ilene Paula, 1982
Grzechowiak, Maria Ann, 1988
Grzybek, Geralyn Marie, 1986
Guardiani, John, 1980
Guariglia, Eva-Lynn Edith, 1972
Guberman, Lynn Susan, 1976
Guckin, Anne Marie, 1988
Guckin, Margaret Mary, 1975
Guerrera, Donna Theresa, 1972
Guerrieri, Donna Marie, 1981
Guertin, Frances Marie, 1988
Guertin, Roberta Marie, 1987
Guido, Noreen Ann, 1982 & 1985
Guiney, Colleen, 1983
Gunkel, Wendy S., 1990
Gunn, Julia Elizabeth, 1988
Gunsallus, Regina Marie, 1982
Gurley, Cheryl Lynn, 1982
Gusst, Jeffrey Robert, 1985
Gusz, Kathryn Ann, 1973
Guy, Carol, 1968
Gyasi, Emmanuel Osei, 1986
Gyger, Deborah Heidi, 1986

~ H ~

Haag, Eileen Marie, 1976
Haas, Nancy Ann, 1983
Haas, Nancy L., 1986
Habazin, Dolores Ann, 1970
Haberbusch, Inge AnneMarie, 1976
Hackler, Bethany Ann, 1988
Hackman, Julie Ellen, 1979
Hackney, Lisa Jean, 1990
Hagan, Mary Ellen Elizabeth, 1986
Hagan, William David, Jr., 1986
Haggerty, Patricia M., 1974
Haines, Mary Jane, 1985
Haitsch, Patricia Marie, 1989
Hale, Pamela Muschek, 1982
Haley, Lois Andrea, 1989
Halfon, Robyn Lyne, 1981
Hall, Bernice Davis, 1988
Hall, Bethany Ann, 1986
Hall, Kenneth Henry, 1980
Hall, Ollie Creecy, 1980
Hall, Suzanne Marple, 1973

Halleck, Lois R., 1990
Halley, Teresa Anne, 1986
Halpin, Constance Elizabeth, 1987
Halter, Pamela Marie, 1975
Hamaniuk, Marianna, 1970
Hamar, Darci Jean, 1986
Hamburg, Diane Lynn, 1979
Hamilton, Suzanne, 1983
Hammen, Ann Birmingham, 1976
Hammers, Karen R., 1980
Hammud-Dib, Hanan Abdallah, 1989
Hampton, Tracy, 1990
Hand, Sandy Lee, 1986
Hand, Selena Anne, 1986
Handel, Bonnie Silver, 1978
Haneiph, Rosanna P., 1988
Haney, Susan Lynn, 1978
Hanges, Lisa Gail, 1985
Hanlin, Joann, 1973
Hann, Brett Stewart, 1989
Hanna, Pamela Linda, 1985
Hanna, Phoebe Annett, 1969
Hannum, Jeanne Fisher, 1986
Hansen, Marcianne, 1985
Hanson, Susan Marie, 1974
Harbord, Theresa Frances, 1975
Hardy, Karen Michele, 1988
Hare, Janice Lee, 1987
Harker, Lynda Marie, 1979
Harkins, Michael J., 1990
Harms, Jennifer Linnea, 1985
Harper, Linda Marie, 1986
Harper, Patricia Ann, 1975
Harper, Susan Jennifer, 1986
Harrell, Judith Ann, 1969
Harrigan, James, 1973
Harrington, Jean Elizabeth, 1971
Harrington, Margaret Ann, 1981
Harris, Frank M., 1990
Harris, Linda Lee, 1983
Harris, Lynette Michele, 1979
Harris, Mary Frances, 1985
Harris, Tracey Lee Anne, 1985
Harris, Viola Louise, 1976
Harrison, Diane G., 1986
Harrison, Gayle Ellen, 1973
Harrison, Kristine Sue, 1988
Harrison, Susan Caprice, 1986
Harrison, Susan Marie, 1974
Hart, Ellen M., 1987
Hart, Judith Anne, 1974
Hart, Lee, 1971
Hartigan, Kathleen, 1986
Hartman, June Marie, 1974
Hartman, Mary, 1978
Hartman, Michael John, 1988

Hartman, Stephanie Izane, 1988
Hartmann, Deborah Ann, 1989
Harvey, Mark Joseph, 1990
Harvilla, Edward Joseph, 1985
Harwood, Marcia Ann, 1978
Hasyn, Barbara, 1985
Hatala, Sharon Ammons, 1980
Hattman, Elizabeth Amelia, 1985
Hauer, Kundry Eileen, 1980
Haux, Marianne, 1985
Haviland, Patricia Dolores, 1978
Hawe, Kathleen Marie, 1987
Hawkshaw, Mary Jean, 1983
Hawthorne, Clementine Marie, 1989
Hax, Stephanie Christine, 1981
Hayes, Betty Lynne, 1976
Hayes, Christine Frances, 1987
Hayes, Nancy Jean, 1975
Hayes, Sandra Lynn, 1982
Hayne, Dana Masterson, 1985
Headley, Barbara Jean, 1986
Healy, Sharyn Marie, 1986
Healy-Lamb, Anne R., 1987
Heath, Annemarie, 1985
Hecker, Linda Paula, 1979
Heckler, Marcy L., 1987
Heenan, Elizabeth Anne, 1970
Heffernan, Matilda Elizabeth, 1983
Hefty, Deborah Carol, 1989
Hehn, Lea Joy, 1990
Heiland, Brenda Sue, 1989
Heilig, Linda Ann, 1986
Heim, Cheryl Ann, 1975
Heim, Linda Tynan, 1979
Heim, Paul, 1987
Hein, Andrea Jean, 1981
Heineman, Adele Mary, 1969
Heinick, Maryann, 1988
Heininger, Donna Lynn, 1975
Heininger, Linda, 1975
Heintzelman, Cheryl Ann, 1988
Heinze, Louise Ann, 1989
Heise, Kathleen, 1975
Helf, Cheryl Ann, 1978
Heller, Beverly Jane, 1979
Hellwege, Paula Amanda, 1986
Hemphill, Clare Anne, 1973
Hemrick, David E, 1989
Henderson, Helen June, 1989
Henderson, Lynease Renee, 1990
Hennessey, Linda Louise, 1978
Hennessy, Kathleen Mary, 1978
Hennick, Cynthia Louise, 1983
Henning, Shirley Lynne, 1990
Henry, Marilyn, 1972
Henry, Michelle Jennee, 1986

Hepler, Jeffrey Brian, 1986
Hepler, Leslie Ann, 1981
Herbster, Christopher James, 1989
Herge, E. Adel Casper, 1986
Hergert, Patricia A., 1986
Herlich, Barbara Moses, 1978
Herman, Andrea, 1975
Herman, Gayle Audrey, 1978
Hermann, Debra M., 1982
Hernando, Maria Erlina, 1989
Herron, Daniel Ferrell, 1980
Hershey, H. Peter , 1988
Hertach, Janet Leanne, 1979
Hescock, Dianne Plouff, 1985
Hess, Patricia Ann, 1988
Hester, Donna L., 1990
Hetherington, Terese, 1982
Hewitt, Carol Ann, 1986
Hewlett, Susan Lanette, 1990
Hickman, Kimberly Ann, 1982
Hidalgo, Margaret Susan, 1983
Higgins, Winifred Johnson, 1968
High, Sheryl, 1987
Highter, Rosetta, 1973
Hilf, Merrill Jean, 1987
Hilferty, Margaret M., 1982
Hill, Bryan John, 1989
Hill, David Joseph, 1986
Hill, Diana Dee, 1988
Hill, Julie A., 1988
Hill, Selma Sheryl, 1988
Hill, Thomas W., 1987
Hillegass, Terri Lynn, 1983
Hiller, Debra Ann Silveri, 1986
Hillerman, Carolyn Joyce, 1986
Himmelwright, Mary Lynn, 1970
Hinkel, Diane Joyce, 1986
Hippensteel, Leslie Catherine, 1982
Hipple, Kimberly Todd, 1986
Hirschhorn, Dena, 1973
Hirsh, Cheryl Lynne, 1986
Hiserote, Marjorie Garrison, 1979
Hitchins, Daphne Susanna, 1968
Hneleski, Janice Anne, 1986
Ho, Wendy Wen-In, 1972
Hoang, Joann Sung Hoa, 1989
Hochberg, Joyce Alice, 1973
Hodorovich, JoEllen Christina, 1983
Hoffing, Janis McLaughlin, 1980
Hoffman, Barbara Ann, 1985
Hoffman, Brenda Gelb, 1988
Hoffman, Carol Ann, 1969
Hoffman, Dharla Lynn, 1988
Hoffman, Kathleen Mary, 1988
Hoffman, Kathy Louise, 1968
Hoffman, Linda Mae, 1989

Hoffman, Linda Sims, 1980
Hoffman, Marcia, 1972
Hoffman, Marion Louise, 1985
Hogan, Diana Marie, 1989
Hogan, Kathleen, 1985
Hogan, Mary Trapani, 1982
Hogeland, Susan Carol, 1978
Hogue, Barbara Constance, 1974
Holbrook, Christine Lynn, 1986
Holbrook, Phyllis Elizabeth, 1976
Holland, Karen Marie, 1981
Holley, Constance Teresa, 1971
Holliday, Dorisanne Fielding, 1975
Holm, Ingrid Margareta, 1985
Holmes, Mariellyn J., 1977
Holmsten, Holly Lynn, 1976
Holohan, Ellen, 1989
Holst, Rodger Joseph, 1978
Holzman, Karen Ann, 1978
Homa, Grace Maria, 1986
Hooper, Marsha Jane, 1986
Hopchik, Jordan, 1982
Hopkins, Claire Linda, 1982
Hopkins, Susan Jeanne, 1975
Hopkins, Susan, 1987
Horan, Helen Marie, 1986
Hordis, Barbara H., 1977
Horenstein, Penni Rise, 1986
Horgan, Frances Moshinski, 1974
Horneff, Joseph Randall, 1988
Horner, Maureen Ernwood, 1981
Horowitz, Deborah F., 1985
Horswood, Amy Louise, 1987
Horta, Vanessa De las Mercedes, 1986
Horton, Stephen Walter, 1978
Horvath, Patricia, 1974
Horwitz, Michael, 1986
Hoser, Donna Cheryl, 1986
Hosey, Chrisine Vesta, 1976
Hosgood, Margaret M., 1985
Hosgood, Margaret Mary, 1978
Hottenstein, Amy Beth, 1989
Hou, Wen Fan, 1975
Houck, Karen M., 1985
Houck, Karen, 1984
Hough, Denise Ann Johnstone , 1989
Hough, Janet Campbell, 1977
Houghton, Denise Helenmarie, 1985
Houseal, Sarah J., 1990
Howard, Deborah Jean, 1988
Howard, Deirdre, 1969
Howard, Patricia Ann, 1971
Howarth, Janet Lynne, 1978
Howarth, Janet Lynne, 1983
Howe, Donna Joan, 1986
Howe, Nancy Frances, 1988

Katubi, Mary Margaret, 1974
Katz, Ellyn Beverly, 1986
Kaufman, Nancy Lynn, 1986
Kaul, Cynthia Frances, 1987
Kaupp, Phyllis Jean, 1988
Kavchok, JoAnn, 1970
Kazan, Faith Anne, 1987
Kazmierczak, Irene, 1981
Kazokas, Diane Marie, 1986
Keane, Joanne Elizaebth, 1975
Kearns, Deirdre Ann, 1988
Keegan, Marie Elizabeth, 1987
Keehfuss, Linda J., 1990
Keeler, Monica Elise, 1988
Keen, Pamela Lee, 1983
Keenan, Kimberly Ann, 1987
Kees, Deborah Ann, 1987
Keimes, Janine Lizabeth, 1986
Kek, Bronya, 1985
Keller, Gerhart O., Jr., 1985
Kelley, Kathleen A., 1988
Kelley, Mary Ovinia, 1982
Kelley, Theresa Mary, 1987
Kellis, Mary, 1986
Kelly, Anne Beatrice, 1976
Kelly, Barbara Ann, 1980
Kelly, Bernadette Mary, 1976
Kelly, Catharine Elizabeth, 1988
Kelly, Dena Marie Hartman, 1985
Kelly, Eileen, 1988
Kelly, Frank Jay, 1976
Kelly, Gerald Joseph, 1987
Kelly, Janis Marie, 1977
Kelly, Kathleen Jean, 1983
Kelly, Linda J., 1978
Kelly, Lynda Jo-Anne, 1975
Kelly, Margaret Mary, 1985
Kelly, Marybeth, 1983
Kelly, Michele, 1979
Kelly, Patricia Dianne, 1986
Kelly, Patrick Donald, 1990
Kelly, Rosemary Theresa, 1975
Kelly, Susan May, 1980
Kelly, William Thomas, 1990
Kelvin, Dianne Elizabeth, 1982
Kemmler, Sharon Louise, 1987
Kempf, Elizabeth Renee, 1990
Kendrick, Denise Ann, 1986
Kenis, Marilyn Margaret, 1974
Kennedy, Francis, Jr., 1973
Kennedy, Joseph Xavier, 1986
Kennedy, Kathleen Susan, 1990
Kennedy, Lynne Ann, 1988
Kennedy, Maureen A., 1983
Kenney, Barbara Ann, 1976
Kenney, Patricia Louise, 1973

Kenny, Beverly Jean, 1979
Kent, Maryanne Ryan, 1979
Kent, Shirley Ann, 1987
Kent, Suzanne Rita, 1981
Kerns, Timothy Joseph, 1983
Kerrigan, Vivianne M., 1982
Kerstetter, Christine Lee, 1981
Kessler, Barbara Ann, 1986
Kessler, Carole Ann, 1987
Kessler, Lynn Avis, 1982
Kessler, Marian-Carol Porter, 1978
Kessler, Victoria Grace, 1987
Kester, Bethann Elizabeth, 1990
Keun-Allenbach, Alyce Marlene, 1986
Kevorkian, Jeri Deran, 1986
Khalifa, Samar F., 1984
Khalife, Linda, 1985
Kiger, Thomas Patrick, 1988
Kilgus, Jacqueline Marie, 1987
Kilstein, Karen Linda, 1976
Kim, Soon-Hi Shin, 1972
Kimmel, Ellen Suzanne, 1985
Kindsvater, Louann, 1975
Kiner, Mary Rose, 1986
King, Carol Elizabeth, 1979
King, Kathleen Mary, 1982
King, Patricia Ann, 1986
King, Robin, 1974
King, Stacey, 1986
Kingston, Richard Raynald, 1986
Kinney, Katherine Anne, 1981
Kinsella, Nancy Elizabeth, 1986
Kinslow, Cheryl Ann, 1981
Kinslow, Michael Francis, 1986
Kinzinger, Mary Lou, 1968
Kirby, Jacqueline Lee, 1985
Kiriluk, Tracey Leigh, 1986
Kirk, Bernadette Therese, 1989
Kirk, Mary Ethel, 1985
Kirk, Rosanne, 1985
Kitchen, Karen Quirple, 1987
Kitson, Joanne M., 1987
Klauder, Betsy Weisel, 1986
Klein, Kathleen, 1988
Klein, Mary, 1981
Klein, Michael Sean, 1990
Kleinman, Rita Susan, 1982
Kleivene, Kenneth, 1986
Klemovage, Linda Marie, 1978
Klimaytis, Patricia, 1968
Kline, Kathleen Sue, 1979
Kline, Marcy Ellene, 1987
Klinger, Lisa Suzanne, 1990
Klink, Denise, 1990
Klusek, Marianne Martynowski, 1986
Knecht, Gail Susan, 1987

Knecht, Gail Susan, 1988
Kneezel, Carol Naomi, 1974
Knight, Daniel Joseph, 1989
Koch, Jean Marie, 1985
Kocis, Mary C., 1986
Kocur, Carol Rose, 1986
Koefoed, B. Susan, 1986
Kohn, Michael Dennis, 1987
Kolbenheyer, Kim Anne, 1990
Koller, Hope Beth, 1983
Koller, Karen Elizabeth, 1976
Kolodzey, Victoria Anne, 1977
Kolonich, Janine, 1986
Komara, Kathryn Smith, 1988
Konieczka, Patricia Ann, 1974
Konrad, Joseph Matthew, 1978
Konzelman, James Joseph, 1983
Koons, Kathleen Mary, 1969
Kopistansky, Christine, 1983
Koppenhaver, Geraldine Minerva, 1981
Koppenhaver, Joanne Madeline, 1989
Korbel, Susan Elizabeth, 1979
Korn, August Charles, 1985
Kornafel, Kathryn Ann, 1987
Kornse, Lisa Diane, 1981
Korotkin, Susan Rae, 1986
Kory, Donna Elise, 1985
Koski, Rebecca Jane, 1975
Kostas, Kostantinia, 1980
Koszick, Darlene, 1986
Kovach, Carolyn Anne, 1988
Kowalski, Sandra Rita, 1980
Kozempel, Jean A., 1988
Kozlowski, Jane Elizabeth, 1986
Krafft, Joseph Raymond, Jr., 1981
Kraft, Kyla Marie, 1979
Kramer, Elizabeth Marie, 1979
Kramer, Sharon Leslie, 1983
Krantz, Jeffrey Albert, 1979
Kratky, Sandra Patricia, 1973
Kraus, Elsie Katherine, 1972
Krause, Kevin Walter, 1988
Kraushaar, Barbara Teresa, 1981
Krauss, Ruth Mildred, 1973
Krauss, Theresa Mary, 1986
Kravitz, Paula Anne, 1986
Krebs, Karen H., 1972
Kreischer, Lisa Ann, 1983
Kreitzer, David Saul, 1978
Kremp, Jill Aileen, 1987
Kreseskie, Mary Theresa, 1976
Kreuzburg, Patricia Ann, 1989
Krick, Susan Wray, 1982
Krieble, Tracy Lynn, 1986
Kriegel, Hinda S., 1986
Krier, Nancy, 1973

INDEX

Long-Evans, Susan Barbara, 1982
Longnecker, Jill Marie, 1989
Longstretch, Susan, 1970
Longworth, Maria D., 1987
Loomis, Michael Conrad, 1982
Looney, Anne Bridget, 1986
Lopacki, Caroline Beth Anne, 1990
Lorah, Dawn June, 1980
Lorber, Nancy C., 1986
Lord, Denise Renee, 1982
Loredo, Rosa Maria, 1981
Loredo, Rosa Marie, 1976
Lorenzon, Lynne Ann, 1978
Lorow, Michele Marie, 1986
Losse, Catherine Ann, 1986
Losty, Susan Joan, 1983
Loturco, Marie Teresa, 1971
Loughery, Susan Mary, 1977
Love, Lynn Kimberly, 1976
Loveless, Darlene, 1971
Lower, Michelle Marie, 1988
Lown, Kenneth Joseph, 1986
Lowry, Christine Lynne, 1986
Lubin, Steven, 1990
Luchtman, Renee Merlino, 1981
Ludin, Claire Debra, 1985
Luscombe, Jill Ann, 1978
Lusk, Linda Jeanne, 1974
Lutz, Carol, 1973
Lyles, Constance Eloise, 1971
Lyman, Beverly Ann, 1978
Lynch, Christine, 1970
Lynch, Jane Marie, 1979
Lynch, Joseph D., 1986
Lynch, Judith Ann, 1974
Lynch, Lisa Jane, 1986
Lynch, Patricia T., 1989
Lyon, Maureen, 1982

~ M ~

MacBain, Lisa Karen, 1982
MacFarland, Cathy Lee, 1970
Machek, Michael A., 1986
Mack, Karen Harper, 1986
Mackell, MaryAnn, 1985
Mackin, Kristine, 1987
Mackin, Suzanne Frances, 1987
MacNair, Kevin, 1986
Macy, Elizabeth Boots, 1979
Madara, Elizabeth R., 1989
Madden, Katherine Anne, 1980
Madden, Margaret Mary, 1980
Madden, Mary, 1970
Madonna, Dorothy, 1969
Madorna, Janet Lisa, 1981

Magee , Marie Quimby, 1974
Magee, Constance Lou, 1976
Magee, Deborah Anne, 1985
Magenta, Tamara Lee, 1989
Maglaya, Lualhati M., 1990
Magnotta, Marion Claire, 1969
Maguire, Linda Marie, 1985
Maguire, Patricia Anne, 1974
Mahan, Colleen Frances, 1980
Maher, Anne Cecilia, 1986
Mahood, Kevin Wayne, 1989
Maialetti, Dina Ann, 1985
Maiatico, Geraldine Joan, 1980
Maier, Vickie Ellen, 1979
Maines, Cherryl Ann, 1990
Mainier, Lisa Anne, 1982
Malandro, Karen, 1990
Malessa, Joy Heather, 1988
Maley, Peggy Ann, 1987
Mallios, Elaine, 1989
Mallon, Joyce E., 1990
Malone, Lisa Marie, 1980
Malone, Mary Eileen, 1969
Maloney, Eileen Marie, 1987
Maloney, Karen Ilene, 1972
Maltby, Carol Y., 1987
Malukas, Cynthia Marie, 1976
Mamalis, Emily Vasille, 1977
Mammele, Patricia Anne, 1971
Mancinelli, Joseph J., 1974
Mancinow, Tatyanna, 1983
Mandalia, Kalpana Vinodkumar, 1986
Mandzak, Karen Michele, 1979
Mangano, Mary, 1976
Mangold, Antonia Marie, 1986
Mann, Carol Jane, 1978
Mann, Carolyn Jean, 1980
Mann, Dorothy Elizabeth, 1970
Mann, Sarah Dorothy, 1988
Mannherz, Elaine Carol, 1974
Mannherz, Gertrude Bauknecht, 1978
Manning, Mary Dolores, 1986
Manno, Ronald John, 1987
Manshil, Mindy Joan, 1977
Mantegna, Jennie Careen, 1968
Manzinger, April Ann, 1980
Manzone, Donna Lee, 1986
Marchese, Marcia, 1987
Marchetti, Lauren, 1989
Marcille, Priscille Anne, 1981
Marcin, Jacqueline Ann, 1982
Marcinowski, Francis, III, 1986
Marcucci, Ruth Joette, 1978
Marder, Barbara-Lou, 1986
Margerum, Helene Henry, 1977
Margiotta, Anna Lee, 1975

Margraff, Darlene Ruth, 1983
Margraff, Donna Lee, 1982
Margulies, Myra, 1969
Mariner, Elizabeth Marie, 1986
Marino, Karen Marie, 1976
Marino, Mary Catherine, 1983
Marion, Cathleen Anne, 1982
Marion, William G., 1990
Maristch, Donna Marie, 1980
Markel, Ann Fischer, 1987
Marko, Elizabeth Anne, 1980
Marko, Jane Anne, 1975
Markovic, Nina Marie, 1982
Markuszka, Marie Burke, 1979
Marnell, Nancy Marie, 1985
Marnell, Nancy, 1986
Marozzi, Adrienne, 1973
Marsh, Loretta Vivienne, 1975
Martin, Diane Patricia, 1982
Martin, Patricia Ann, 1986
Martin, Susan Christine, 1980
Martinac, Frances Marie, 1973
Martindale, Margaret Lee, 1987
Martindell, Sherri Lynn Ann, 1990
Masciantonio, Kathleen, 1985
Masek, John Charles, 1990
Masi, Carlotta, 1969
Masino, Deborah Ceceila, 1989
Masse, Agnes Theresa, 1974
Matalonis, M. Denise, 1983
Matalucci, Barbara Patricia, 1983
Matamoros, Linda Louise, 1981
Mathis, Elizabeth R., 1971
Matina, Edith Ann, 1989
Matricciano, Donna Marie, 1982
Matsko, Joann Cecelia, 1976
Mattei, Yvonne Louise, 1982
Mattera, Nancy Louise, 1974
Matthews, Dianne, 1968
Matthews, Mary Ellen, 1987
Matthews, Paula Marie Ann, 1985
Matthews, Yolande Ingrid, 1988
Mattioli, Jodi Susan, 1985
Mattocks, Larry Wayne, Jr., 1990
Mau, Linda Joyce, 1986
Maxwell, Anne Hamilton, 1979
Maxwell, Emerson, 1976
Maxwell, Saundra Diane, 1986
May, Beverly Ann, 1982
May-Hoey, Natalie, 1981
Mayer, Anne Marie, 1983
Mayer, Carol June, 1982
Mayer, Joyce Buchannan, 1980
Maynor, Michelle D., 1985
Mazyck, Jayne, 1985
Mazzitelli, Maria, 1988

Miller, Loretta Elodia, 1974
Miller, Lynn M., 1988 & 1989
Miller, Raymond L., 1981
Miller, Rochelle A., 1969
Miller, Susan D., 1990
Millett, Stacie Ann, 1985
Milligan, Kim M., 1986
Mills, Renee Andrea, 1988
Minisi, Claire Bernadette, 1986
Minor, Lillian Beth, 1989
Minter, Margaret Elizabeth, 1980
Mintz, Lynda G., 1974
Mireno, Deborah Mary, 1971
Mitchell, Christine Marie, 1990
Mitchell, Karen Elizabeth, 1971
Mitchell, Miriam Alice, 1986
Mitchell, Rebecca Susanne, 1986
Mitchell, Valerie Lee, 1971
Mitrovic, John Andre, 1988
Mitz, Karen Lynn, 1987
Moberg, Rebecca Lee, 1984
Moceri, Frank R., Jr., 1990
Modhera, Kalpa R., 1989
Moffat, Sandra Ann, 1983
Moffatt, Tamarah Harkness, 1978
Moffatt, Tamarah Harkness, 1986
Mohl, Jill Stacey, 1976
Mohl, Karen Irene, 1982
Molas, Geraldine V., 1987
Molnar, Tina Marie, 1985
Monahan, Julie Katherine, 1988
Money, Sharon Marie, 1988
Money, Wilhelmina Anna, 1970
Mongiello, Donna Marie, 1988
Monk, Kelly D., 1990
Montefusco, Carman Patricia, 1987
Montemuro, Richard-Alan, 1988
Montgomery, Carole P., 1976 & 1983
Monzo, David M., 1990
Mooney, Geralyn R., 1980
Mooney, Lauren E., 1983
Moore, Barbara Jean, 1975
Moore, Dorothy Marie, 1978
Moore, Jayne Ellen, 1977
Moore, Nancy Aliesa, 1989
Moore, Patricia Ann, 1985
Moore, Rachel Elizabeth, 1976
Moorehead, Jon Lee, 1988
Moreau, Loretta Mary, 1988
Moreno, Margarita, 1978
Morgan, Bethann, 1987
Morgan, Ralph Oscar, Jr., 1977
Morgan, Sally Ann, 1969
Morley, Charlotte, 1982
Morris, Claire Platus, 1980
Morris, Jeanne Marie, 1986

Morris, Marilys Rose, 1981
Morris, Robin Marie, 1987
Morris, Sylvia Regina, 1984
Morris, Tia Nanette, 1988
Morrison, Cheryl Lynn, 1975
Morse, Mishel, 1979
Mortensen, Pamela Anne, 1969
Moscato, Maryann Elizabeth, 1980
Moses, Jacqueline, 1986
Moss, Janice, 1970
Moss, Julia Katherine, 1979
Moss, Pamela Brooke, 1990
Moulder, Caryl Jean, 1985
Mowrey, Janet Elizabeth, 1988
Moxey, Susan Lynn, 1982
Moy, Diane Jane, 1989
Moy, Melanie Bick Gin, 1979
Moyer, Janet Lynn, 1988
Mueller, Abigail Huntington, 1986
Mueller, Carolyn Ann, 1971
Mueller, Elizabeth Marie, 1987
Mueller, Kris Ann, 1989
Mugil, Dawn Marie Alexes, 1987
Mujorra, Silverio E., 1985
Mukai, Barbara Anne, 1975
Mulcahey, MaryJane Patricia, 1987
Mulcahy, Ann Marie, 1989
Mulgrew, Linda I., 1980
Mulherin, Elizabeth Ann, 1974
Mulhern, Joanne Marie, 1974
Mulholland, Nanci Ann, 1990
Mullen, Irene Quinlan, 1980
Mullen, Kathleen Gallagher, 1978
Mullen, Marie Elvira, 1982
Mullen, Pamela Allyson, 1974
Mullen-Fortino, Margaret, 1987
Muller, Diane Wanner, 1979
Mulnick, Esther, 1978
Mumin, Khadijah, 1990
Mundth, Jennifer Blanchard, 1988
Murphy, Beverly, 1970
Murphy, Diane Elizabeth, 1986
Murphy, Georgeanne, 1986
Murphy, Jacqueline, 1986
Murphy, Jane Margaret, 1977
Murphy, Judith Ann, 1982
Murphy, Laura Kay, 1989
Murphy, Margaret Mary, 1976
Murphy, Mary Ann, 1986
Murray, Ann Erin, 1985
Murray, Annette Eileen, 1989
Murray, Barbara Jean, 1968
Murrell, Dean Thornhill, 1986
Musetti, Myrtie Jane, 1981
Muskett, Helen Marie, 1988
Mututu, Edwin Kumbirai, 1990

Myer, Shari Lee, 1986
Myers, Cathy Ann, 1988
Myers, John Gregory, 1989
Myers, Kathleen Sue, 1989
Myr, Daria Maria, 1984 & 1987

~ N ~

Nabulsi, Deena Sameh, 1990
Nabulsi, Tesreen Sameh, 1990
Nach, Ilene Etta, 1969
Nadig, Constance, 1969
Nagel, Mary C., 1985
Nagy, Rose Magdelena, 1985
Napier, Jeanette, 1990
Napoletano, Mary Theresa, 1978
Napolitano, Joseph Vincent, 1986
Nappen, Susan Lois, 1981
Nappi, Christina Maria, 1986
Nappo, Luisa, 1983
Nardone, Anna, 1972
Nardone, Diane Louise, 1989
Nasr, Deborah D., 1985
Nastasi, Stephen, 1987
Nasuti, Patricia Ann, 1981
Natale, Peter Mark, 1986
Natale, Peter Mark, 1989
Naughton, Vincent Gregory, 1988
Navatier, LaVanche Marie, 1977
Nazareth, Rachel, 1986
Nazarian, Jeanette Sophia, 1987
Neary, Brita Ann, 1981
Neff, Holly Anne, 1986
Neff, Linda Joyce, 1985
Neiburg, Riki Sue, 1982
Neidermyer, Kathleen McCarthy, 1968
Neiffer, Christine Anne, 1968
Neill, Suzanne, 1973
Nelson, Charles Dewayne, 1987
Nenstiel, Lynne Omer, 1977
Nesbitt, Kimberly Ann, 1990
Nessel, Debra, 1974
Neuner, Michelle Anne M., 1981
Nevara, Cindy L., 1990
Nevins, Nancy Louise, 1986
Newell, Kathleen Mooney, 1976
Newell, Mary-Frances, 1972
Newman, Deborah A., 1986
Newman, Elizabeth Marie, 1986
Newsome, John Thomas, III, 1988
Newstat, Beth Olivia, 1986
Ney, Elizabeth R. L., 1985
Nfila, Saliwe Busilu, 1990
Ngo, Tu Tuyet, 1985
Nicolella, Anna, 1972
Nicolini, Christina Lucia, 1986

Patterson, Felicia Helene, 1986
Patterson, Kathleen, 1986
Patterson, Margaret Ann, 1982
Patterson, Pamela Joan, 1974
Pattison, Cynthia Ann, 1981
Paul, Elyse R., 1976
Paul, Patricia Anne, 1985
Pauley, Carol Jill, 1987
Pauline, Lucy Ann, 1986
Payne, Mary Elizabeth, 1974
Pedano, Antonia Marie, 1983
Peditto, Michele Renee, 1985
Peduto, Sharon Kathryn, 1981
Peetros, Susan Lynn, 1983
Peifley, Michelle Ann, 1986
Peissner, Theresa Ann, 1986
Pekter, Debra Ann, 1978
Pelczar, Mary Ann, 1986
Pellegrino, Victoria Lynn, 1986
Peloso, Lisa Marie, 1989
Pelura, Donna Wieczorek, 1986
Pelzer-Fenning, Kiz D., 1990
Pencek, Lynn Ann, 1988
Penkal, Irena, 1988
Penkala, Loretta Frances, 1980
Penney, Susan L., 1983
Peralta, Virginia Raquel, 1988
Perantoni, Margaret Rose, 1987
Perilstein, Robin, 1986
Perkins, Sandra Marie, 1986
Perkins, Stella, 1969
Perks, Joan Marie, 1986
Perks, Kellyann, 1989
Pernicano, Lucille Mary, 1972
Perper, Donna Kay, 1988
Perrine, Diane Louise, 1970
Perrotto, Carol Teresa, 1988
Perrucci, Roselle M., 1987
Pershing, Pamela, 1981
Petch, Renee Theresa, 1971
Peters, Aliki, 1986
Peters, Lorraine J., 1986
Peters, Marina, 1973
Peterson, Karen ELizabeth, 1978
Petit de Mange, Elizabeth Anne,1987
Petrick, Joanne Marie, 1975
Petrillo, Denise Keegan, 1986
Petrylak, Elizabeth Mills, 1978
Petta, Anthony Domenic, 1973
Pettes, Cheryl Ann, 1987
Petti, Donna Anela, 1986
Pettine, Nicholas Charles, 1976
Pezzella, Debbie Anne, 1982
Pheasant, Holli Sue, 1990
Phelan, Barbara Ann, 1981
Phengvath, Chanhpheng, 1990

Phillips, Carolyn D'Addarie, 1969
Phillips, Deborah Ellen, 1985
Phillips, Diane, 1990
Phillips, Jane Ann, 1979
Phillips, Judy, 1968
Phillips, Pamela Mary, 1985
Picarello, Nancy Jane, 1986
Piccone, Linda Concetta, 1988
Pichola, Jenifer Marie, 1990
Pickett, Ann Lindsay, 1985
Pickett, Dorthea Ahnee, 1971
Pickul, Angela Rosemarie, 1986
Piemontese, Marilyn Maureen, 1983
Pienta, Nancy Ann, 1969
Pierce, Kathleen Theresa, 1973
Pierce, Lorraine, 1988
Piernikowski, Diane Katherine, 1976
Pierson, Elisia Louise, 1988
Pierson, Leigh Anne, 1974
Pierson, Roseanne, 1983
Pierzynski, Edward J., 1973
Pietkutowski, Karen, 1969
Pigliacelli, Irene, 1972
Pike, Lori Lynn, 1987
Pilla, Carol Ann McNeil, 1986
Pine, Vivian B., 1990
Pinelli, Mary, 1973
Pinkerton, Judith Ann, 1975
Pinto, Cristina Maria, 1990
Piontek, Carole, 1988
Pipitone, Debra Lynne, 1986
Pirolli, Jennifer Maria, 1990
Pirollo, Melanie Reading, 1975
Pish, Christina, 1969
Pitchon, Lisa, 1972
Pittius, Christine Ann, 1986
Platt, Alison, 1986
Plowfield, Lisa Ann, 1986
Plumb, Patricia Hope, 1981
Pohar , Debora Ann, 1974
Pojunis, Mary Ann , 1988
Poklemba, Concetta Mary M., 1980
Policare, Michael Thomas, 1980
Poliwoda, Elizabeth Mary, 1985
Pollick, Sharon Ann, 1982
Ponemon, Sandra, 1968
Porpiglia, Mary Ellen, 1983
Porter, Carol Rae, 1989
Posmontier, Barbara Elaine, 1982
Posner, William H., 1987
Post, Marian Mulville, 1989
Potena, David Peter, 1986
Potter, Donna, 1969
Potts, Susan Elizabeth, 1979
Poulos, Margaret Josephine, 1972
Poulshock, Sheryl Lynn, 1988

Powell, Judith Ann, 1987
Powell, Kimberly Tracy, 1986
Powell, Mary, 1971
Prego, Lisa Maria, 1990
Preitz, Kathy Ann, 1980
Prelewicz, Marcy Marie, 1989
Prelle, Patricia, 1980
Prendergast, Karen, 1978
Preole, Margaret Ann, 1987
Pressler, Florri Rose, 1981
Previte, Catherine, 1984
Previti, Marianne, 1974
Price, Barbara Anne, 1987
Price, Janice Marie, 1982
Price, June Lee, 1982
Price, Katherine Yvonne, 1987
Price, Thomas Edward, 1978
Priestley, Deborah Ann, 1989
Prigmore, Rosemary, 1988
Primera, Jacobo Miguel, 1987
Prince, Vivian, 1985
Procino, Janet Katherine, 1977
Prokapus, Mary Elizabeth, 1989
Proskauer, Petra Ingrid, 1986
Prossack, Cheryl T., 1977
Prossack, Janice Hope, 1981
Prossack, Linda Susan, 1978
Proud, Kathy Ann, 1982
Proulx, James Wesley, 1985
Prubaker, Prem, 1972
Pryzbylkowski, Anne, 1986
Przybylowski, EiLeen Elizabeth, 1980
Pukenas, Barbara Lynn, 1986
Puleo, Donna Marie, 1989
Pulido, Mary Lynn Balinao, 1978
Pullen, William J., 1990
Purnell, Carol Ann, 1971
Purnell, Carol Louise, 1980
Pusey , Katheryn Eyer, 1974
Puzio, Mary Elizabeth, 1971

~ Q ~

Quach, Tinh Chi, 1986
Quarmley, Laura Jean, 1988
Quartana, Theresa Ann, 1972
Querner, Karin Anne, 1978
Quigley, Marie Claire, 1988
Quigley, Maureen Jeannette, 1983
Quigley, Sr. Loretta Mary, 1971
Quinlisk, Ernest James, 1987
Quiring, Ellen Sue, 1975
Quirk, James Martin, 1986

~ R ~

Rabbitt, Colleen M., 1989
Rachover, Michael, 1972

Radi, Julianne Andrea, 1986
Radice, Lynda Anne, 1987
Rafa, Lizabeth Jane, 1986
Raiburn, Edward Joseph, 1981
Rainey, Kim L., 1981
Rainey, Kimberly Ann, 1983
Rake, Randal Carter, 1989
Rambo, Anita Marie, 1976
Ramuno, Debora Ann, 1974
Randall, Roosevelt Iley, 1978
Randolph, Tanya Latisha, 1990
Raney, Deborah Louise, 1975
Raphael, Theresa Eileen, 1982
Raphelson, Nancy, 1972
Rappaport, Judith L., 1987
Rappaport, Tessa, 1984
Raschilla, Joseph Francis, 1986
Rasera, Susan E., 1986
Ratka, Rosemarie, 1982
Rau, Lana, 1972
Raup, Gretchen, 1972
Ravkin, Denise Lyn, 1989
Ray, Elizabeth J., 1988
Ray, Kris Ellen, 1986
Rayner, Leslie Michelle, 1986
Re, Elaine Margaret, 1980
Read, Alice Jeanne, 1983
Readinger, Margaret, 1973
Redfern, Nancy, 1975
Redmond, Maryanne Ellen, 1980
Ree, Valli Teresa, 1980
Reed, Laurie Ann, 1987
Reese, Francesca, 1985
Reeve, Shirley Bonita, 1975
Reeves, Kathleen Patrice, 1988
Reffle, Susan Marie, 1985
Regan, Laura Ann, 1986
Regosch, Catherine, 1976
Reid, Virginia Anne, 1986
Reihard, Kathryn Anita, 1979
Reiley, Jane Dolores, 1988
Reilly, Cheryl, 1986
Reiner, Dianne Marie, 1987
Reithmeier, Dolores Ann, 1981
Remaly, Rochelle Lisa, 1976
Remilev, Carmen, 1982
Rencevicz, Denise Mary, 1989
Renna, Russell Johnathen, 1988
Repko, Marie Perpetua, 1986
Repko, Susan Ann, 1990
Repman, N. Jean, 1977
Rettig, Susan Louise, 1983
Reville, Patricia Katherine, 1979
Reyes, Rinna Tolentino, 1990
Reyes, Rissa Tolentino, 1985
Reynolds, Rebecca Ann, 1989

Reynolds, Renee Ann, 1989
Rhein, Eileen P., 1968
Rheinheimer, Marjorie Lynne, 1987
Rhinehart, Margaret, 1975
Rhoads, Elayne B., 1987
Rhock, Gregory Leonard, 1974
Rhodes, Amy Beth, 1987
Rhone, Sara E., 1971
Ricciardi, Sharon Marie, 1982
Ricciuti, Dina Marie, 1986
Ricefield, Leslie Jane, 1988
Richard, Barbara Ann, 1986
Richards, Janet Lee, 1980
Richardson, Donna Lee, 1987
Richert, Tammy Marie, 1990
Richter, Raymond Edward, 1980
Richter, Susan Helen, 1978
Rick, Bethanne, 1988
Ricker, Claire M., 1987
Rider, Gertrude Wilson, 1976
Ries, Hildegarde Annemarie, 1986
Riesdorph-Ostrow, Wendi Dee, 1986
Rietheimer, Estelle Diane, 1971
Rigefsky, Phyllis, 1988
Riggin, Mary Elizabeth, 1976
Riggs, Kathleen, 1988
Riley, Timothy W., 1977
Rinaldi, Janice Marie, 1980
Rinker, Margaret Ann, 1979
Ristine, Carla Mary, 1980
Ritaldato, Angela Celeste, 1983
Rivera, Lissette, 1987
Rivera, Ruth, 1990
Rivers, Gertrude Dianne, 1985
Rivest, Pamela Jean, 1979
Rizzi, Arlene Katherine, 1974
Rizzo, Donna Marie, 1986
Roach, Kathleen Barbara, 1972
Roach, Ruth G., 1976
Roache, Mary Beth Bernadette, 1981
Robbins, Karen Lynn, 1989
Roberts, Lauren Sari, 1974
Robertson, Patricia Ann, 1980
Robertson, Risa Dawn, 1986
Robinson, Dilara Shelley, 1986
Robinson, Linda Carol, 1983 & 1987
Robinson, Margo Charisse, 1982
Robitschek, Judith Irene, E., 1980
Robson, Donna Lynn, 1986
Roche, Melanie Elizabeth, 1988
Roche, Patricia Bernadette, 1982
Rochow, Joyce Marie, 1978
Rodden, Jeanine Marie, 1986
Rodgers, Kathleen Marie, 1986
Rodia, Francine Marie, 1975
Rodio, Carol Ann, 1985

Rodriguez, Marican C., 1974
Roe, Paula Ann, 1980
Roesler, Grant Eugene, 1986
Rogers, Barbara Ann, 1988
Rogers, Patricia DeProspero, 1988
Rogodzinski, Jean, 1986
Rohne, Barbara Mae, 1988
Roider, Brian Harold, 1984
Rojo, Guia Firmalo, 1975
Rollins, Janet L., 1990
Rom, Angela Scarlata, 1982
Romagano, Linda A., 1990
Romaine, Dale M., 1989
Romano, Ann Marie, 1970
Romano, Kimberley Beatrix, 1987
Romano, Susan Ann, 1978
Rombach, Steven Edward, 1986
Rome, Christine Kellie, 1990
Romig, Suzanne Elizabeth, 1980
Ronaldson, Julie Sue, 1986
Rosa, Miguel H., 1990
Rosania, Dianne Jean, 1986
Rose, Gilbert Pattison, 1985
Rose, Joanne Michele, 1987
Rose, Marlyn Jana, 1983
Rose, Patricia Lynn, 1980
Rose, Vicki Joan, 1978
Rosella, Melanie Martina, 1977
Roseman, Lynn Audrey, 1975
Rosen, Alexa Sandra, 1975
Rosen, Cheryl Lynne, 1987
Rosen, Joan, 1978
Rosen, Lori B., 1986
Rosen, Louis, 1981
Rosen, Randi Jill, 1988
Rosen, Shea Ellen, 1982
Rosen, Sheryl Elaine, 1975
Rosenberger, Kyna Joy, 1989
Rosenblum, Bonnie, 1971
Rosenbluth, Denise Rochelle, 1986
Rosendale, Robert W., 1986
Rosenstock, Rachel Jean, 1983
Rosenthal, Joy Sandra, 1977
Rosenwald, Beth Joy, 1980
Ross, Catherine, 1986
Rossano, Rachel Marie, 1986
Rossi, Carol, 1989
Rossi, Robert M., 1987
Rost, Joan Marie, 1981
Roth, Mavis Leona, 1983
Rottmund, Carroll Marie, 1989
Rowan, Anita Marie, 1979
Rowand, Janet Lee, 1978
Rowe, Paula Faith, 1979
Rowell, Jacqueline Lisa, 1974
Rowen, Christine Marie, 1982

Rowland, Valerie Ann, 1980
Rozhitsky, Yury, 1989
Rozon, Laura Jean, 1979
Ruane, Margaret Mary, 1990
Rubin, Cheri Ellen, 1989
Rubinson, Holly Beth, 1979
Rubinstein, Ronald Steven, 1986
Rubsamen, Susan Ruth, 1980
Rucci, Kenneth P., 1989
Ruch, Denise Andrea, 1988
Rudden, Kathryn Teresa, 1989
Rudisill, George Daniel, 1986
Rudolph, Virginia Anne, 1977
Rudowitz, Wendy Beth, 1980
Rue, Michelle Denise, 1986
Ruesch, Regina Marie, 1978
Ruff, Kathryn Louise, 1982
Rufo, Ann Frances, 1989
Ruggles, Christy Lynn, 1982
Rugh, Regina Marie, 1985
Ruhl, Joseph Thomas, Jr., 1986
Rule, Patricia Jean, 1989
Rumovitz, Dawn Marie Cheryl, 1989
Rump, Nancy Gibson, 1986
Ruoff, Richard R., 1982
Rupp, LuAnn Lynn , 1988
Russell, Christine Caroline, 1974
Russell, Janet Marie, 1986
Russell, Margaret Ann, 1989
Ryder, Sarah, 1986
Ryles, Darryl Anthony, 1983
Ryley, Barbara Anne, 1989
Rzepka, Carolyn Ann, 1987

~ S ~

Sabella, Donna Marie, 1979
Sabol, John Joseph, 1981
Sacchetti, Mary Rudick, 1980
Sacks, Carole Anne, 1979
Sady, Michelle M'Liss, 1986
Safin, Julie Anne, 1986
Sage, Theresa Ann, 1973
Salg, Sister Joyce, 1968
Salitsky, Nancy Jean, 1982
Salkowe, Andrea Joyce, 1978
Salmonsen, Kristina Marie, 1987
Salmonsen, Mary Beth, 1986
Salomone, Margherita Irene, 1986
Salovich, Suzanne Renee, 1983
Salwocki, Kimberly Ann, 1986
Samilenko, Michele Motria, 1988
Sammons, Melanie Ann, 1977
Sampson, Glenda Maurer, 1978
Sand, Ellen Mary, 1982
Sand, Margaret Mary, 1985

Sanders, Julia Floridis, 1975
Sandifer, Sophia, 1982
Sandom, Alice Irene, 1969
Sandor, Susan, 1969
Sanner, Susan Allegra, 1986
Santanna, Mary Elizabeth, 1988
Santone, Anita Rose Patricia, 1976
Santoro, Barbara Ann, 1981
Santoro, Marylou, 1982
Santucci, Deborah S., 1986
Santucci, MaryEllen Germaine, 1989
Sapnas, Kathryn G., 1976
Sapp, Suzanne Denise, 1988 & 1989
Sara, Sharon R., 1978
Sargent, Catherine Anne, 1986
Sarnacki, Joan D., 1985
Sass, Rebecca Ann, 1982
Sassler, Fredrick Saul, 1983
Satariano, Joanne Marie, 1987
Satchmei, Maryam, 1988
Sauer, Charolotte Ann, 1975
Saul, Thomas, 1971
Saulli, Valerie Waltrich, 1985
Savage, Francine Harriet, 1982
Savard, Theresa Ann, 1973
Sawicki, Margot M., 1970
Sayles, Roy Scott, 1985
Scafidi, Marianne Theresa, 1986
Scalise, Julia Antoinette, 1976
Scarantino, Patricia Lynn M., 1982
Scenna, Julie Fitzgibbons, 1975
Schaal, Mary Greenwood, 1981
Schad, Catherine Emma, 1980
Schaeffer, Paul Bretz, 1978
Schaen, Joyce Rohn, 1988
Schafer, Nancy Jean, 1986
Schaffer, Kathleen Elizabeth, 1988
Schank, Eileen, 1971
Schanne, Linda Catherine, 1989
Schatz, Jill Susan, 1988
Schauder, Patricia Ann, 1986
Schaunt, Michelle, 1990
Scheflow, Martha Lee, 1978
Schell, Sally Ann, 1988
Schell, Yvonne Marie, 1985
Schelle, Mary Elizabeth, 1985
Schellhammer, Audrey Marie, 1985
Schellhorn, Barbara Ann, 1986
Schenk, Cathi Lee, 1979
Schickling, James Michael, Jr., 1988
Schiding, Dorothy E., 1986
Schildhorn, Marsha Wendy, 1974
Schildkraut, Barbara Iana, 1986
Schindler, Kathlen Joan, 1973
Schirn, Jackie Greenleaf, 1980
Schjavland, Elena Theresea, 1985

Schlager, Carol, 1970
Schlansky, Rita Cohon, 1989
Schleider, Joanne, 1990
Schlenk, Michael Joseph, 1988
Schmeiss, Andrea Helena, 1988
Schmerfeld, Deborah Rose, 1988
Schmid, Carol Lorraine, 1982
Schmidt, Diane Norlaine, 1988
Schmidt, Jo Anne, 1989
Schmidt, John David, 1988
Schmidt, John Frank, 1985
Schmidt, Marion Bach, 1982
Schmidt, Mark E., 1990
Schmidt, Matthew Justin, 1987
Schneider, Shelly Robin, 1981
Schnitzer, Nancy J. Goldstein, 1988
Schoellkopf, Julie A., 1986
Schoenberger, Donna Lynn, 1978
Schoenwalder, Ellen Jean, 1980
Scholl, Barbara Ann, 1976
Scholl, Deborah Anne, 1986
Schottenfeld, Susan, 1974
Schraishuhn, Lynn D., 1986
Schramm, Linda Susan, 1971
Schreiber, Francine Mitchell, 1987
Schrock, Melissa Lee, 1977
Schroeder, Kathleen Eva, 1989
Schuberg, Teresa Dykes, 1979
Schuck, Terri Lynn, 1989
Schuck-Choyce, Christina Marie, 1989
Schulam, Valerie Susan, 1986
Schuler, Jacqueline Marie, 1990
Schulgen, Kimberlee Ann, 1988
Schulle, Rosanna Ashmore, 1978
Schultz, Edward J., 1987
Schultz, Jeanne Marie, 1986
Schultze, Barbara Leibrand, 1980
Schulz, Lisa Marie, 1989
Schupack, Ilsa, 1971
Schurer-Pelletier, Ann Margaret, 1988
Schwartz, Abby L., 1988
Schwartz, Beth Robin, 1983
Schwartz, Donna, 1974
Schwartz, Joan Taber, 1980
Schwartz, Susan, 1983
Schwarz, Craig Henry, 1989
Schwarz, Lauren Marie, 1976
Schwarz, Nora M.P., 1988
Schwenker, Diane, 1987
Schwiers, Elmslie Anne, 1980
Schwoerer, Diane Marie, 1974
Sciamanna, Lisa Lorraine, 1989
Sciochetti, Melissa Ann, 1988
Sciochetti, Melissa Ann, 1989
Sciole, Marilyn Bernadette, 1973
Scola, Lois Angela, 1986

INDEX

Smith, Rita, 1968
Smith, Sandra Lee, 1986
Smith, Sharon, 1986
Smoker, Nancy Phiels, 1986
Smugar, Cheryl Lynne, 1986
Smyser, Troy Allen, 1990
Smyth, Catherine Margaret, 1989
Snider, Sandra Kay, 1986
Sniger, Sherri Lisa, 1976
Sninski, Mary Macario, 1981
Snitzer, Barbera, 1976
Snow, Diane Marie, 1985
Snyder, Barbara Susan, 1987
Snyder, Beth Lynda, 1979
Snyder, Brian Robert, 1989
Snyder, Maragaret Bailey, 1977
Snyder, Rose Marie, 1989
Snyder, Susan Ann, 1983
Soares, Ilsa Del Carmen, 1984
Sobolewski, Mark Vincent, 1985
Sobolusky, Barbara Clark, 1979
Sobuza, Sipho Wigram, 1986
Soda, Marian Goshow, 1979
Solen, Venessa Evette, 1982
Solge, Jacqueline Marie, 1975
Solnick, Arlene Janet, 1988
Solodar, Louise Rachel, 1979
Solof, Shelley Marsha, 1975
Solominsky, Barbara Ruth, 1985
Solomon, Brenda Frances, 1990
Solomon, Muriel Edith, 1977
Soly, Raymond Moore, 1979
Somerset, Catherine, 1972
Sommer, Gay Lauren, 1990
Sonsino, Renee Michele, 1979
Sopin, Caren, 1986
Sorrentino, Vicki Lynn, 1990
Sosnowski, Krystine, 1971
Sotnick, Andrea Ann, 1986
Spaar, Barbara Demer, 1981
Spadafora, Barbara Ann, 1986
Spaeder, Margaret Anne, 1986
Spaeth, Julie A., 1989
Spaeth-Brayton, Sylvia Maria, 1987
Spalletta, Sherry Ann, 1988
Spangler, Donna L., 1989
Spangler, Noelle J., 1990
Sparkler, Ilisa Meg, 1983
Spause, Susan Sophia, 1972
Specht, Dawn Marie, 1989
Speer, Denyse G., 1980
Spegel, Patricia Jean, 1971
Speights, Christine, 1970
Spellacy, Sandra Therese, 1988
Spence, Sharon Kay, 1982
Spilman, Ann, 1975

Spivack, Phyllis G., 1968
Spotts, Judith A., 1990
Springstead, Kermit, Jr., 1983
Sproch, Pamela Ann, 1981
Sprott, Barbara Joanne, 1989
Spuhler-Gaughan, Mary Jane C., 1982
St. John, Sr. Mary Louise, 1973
Stackhouse, Nancy Joan, 1981
Stackhouse, Sandra, 1968
Stacy, Janeen Alicia, 1987
Stafford, Eileen B., 1990
Stahl, Anna Roberta, 1981
Stair, Helene Marie, 1986
Stallings, Julie Ann, 1986
Staniszewski, Mary Ann, 1980
Stansbury, Susan Louise, 1986
Starr, Michael, 1990
Stavely, Janet Lynn, 1972
Steed, Carole LaVerne, 1983
Steel, Janet Lucille, 1981
Steet, Christine, 1970
Steffy, Kim Ann, 1990
Stein, Lori Diane, 1979
Steinbach, Lore Jeanne, 1989
Steinmetz, Nancy Lowry, 1983
Stens, Diane Carole, 1974
Sternberg, Caren Hope, 1989
Stetto, Jayne Ellen, 1985
Stevenson, April Jane, 1975
Stevenson, Dolores Sallie, 1968
Stevenson, Kathy Lynn, 1981
Stevenson, Maisie Moys, 1976
Stewart, Beverly Anita, 1983
Stewart, Geraldine Haly, 1976
Stewart, Helena Bolton, 1978
Stewart, June Ann, 1978
Stewart, Lisa Ann, 1982
Stickle, Donovan, 1969
Stillerman, Lori Ellen, 1982
Stimson, Faith Allyne, 1979
Stine, Beryl Brucknow, 1978
Stith, Deborah Laura, 1971
Stitzer, Nancyanne, 1986
Stock, Donna Jean, 1987
Stoltzfus, Cynthia Lee, 1983
Stone, Michelle Elaine, 1989
Stone, Sharon Anne, 1971
Stone, Susan, 1969
Storjohann, Jane Elizabeth, 1974
Storr, Arnold C., 1973
Stoughton, Deborah Ann, 1978
Strable, Donald L., 1973
Strachan, Brenda Margaret, 1987
Strawn, Katherine Anne, 1983
Strese, Lisa Ann, 1977
Strine, Carrie Elizabeth, 1989

Strohecker, Sandy Lee, 1986
Stroker, Barbara Brown, 1980
Stroud, Joanne Kay, 1985
Stuart, Susan Marie, 1968
Studdard, Eletha, 1985
Studzinski, Ann Katrina, 1986
Sturgeon, Penny Kayoko, 1982
Sturm, Eileen M., 1990
Stutz, Carol Ann, 1980
Styer, Kelly Anne, 1986
Sudick, Evelyn Beth, 1986
Sufian, Sureya, 1988
Sullivan, Elise Marie, 1990
Sullivan, John Patrick, 1975
Sullivan, Kathleen Hennessy, 1978
Sullivan, Pamela Ann, 1989
Sullivan, Susan Joan, 1986
Summers, Loretta Dorothy, 1986
Summers, Susan Gail, 1976
Suriano, Christine, 1986
Sussman, Joan Lori, 1979
Swan, Frances Elizabeth, 1983
Swan, Lynda R., 1990
Swan, Michelle Ann, 1974
Swanick, Mary Kathleen, 1986
Swann, Mary Louise, 1986
Swartz, Amy Hope, 1983
Swartz, Mary Ann, 1979
Swartzlander, Diane Jean, 1983
Sweda, Joan Marie, 1986
Sweeney, Kathleen Marie, 1986
Sweeney, Marilyn Ann, 1978
Sweitzer, Wilbur Lee, 1978
Swerdel, Robert Howard, 1979
Swetavage, Susan Anne, 1980
Swierzy, Joanne P., 1980
Swikart, MaryAnne, 1985
Swisher, Margaret Rose, 1976
Sykes, Roberta Jo, 1990
Symons, Barbara Bachman, 1985
Synnestvedt, Ann, 1986
Szal, Marianne Cathleen, 1979
Szcypiorski, Jennifer J., 1974
Szerbin, Mariann, 1980
Szlachta, Michael John, 1986

~ T ~

Taggart, Ellen Marie, 1986
Tagmire, Christine, 1986
Tague, Ann Marie, 1990
Talley, Patricia Ellen, 1987
Tannahill, Kathleen Mary, 1978
Tannenbaum, Susan Lynn, 1982
Tarawaly, Sheik Mahdieu, 1977
Tarquini, Diane Regina, 1985

Tarullo, Dorothy Glasgow, 1976
Tase, Elizabeth Jean, 1976
Tashof, Cheryl Lynn, 1981
Tashof, Tracy Lane, 1986
Taylor, Helga Roslyn, 1979
Taylor, Joanne Mary, 1969
Taylor, Nicki Lou, 1975
Taylor, Sherry Lee, 1974
Teare, Monica L., 1990
Teeter, Jennifer Gray, 1986
Tegzes, John Henry, II, 1986
Tepper, Virginia M., 1974
Terry, Kathleen Anne, 1970
Theodos, Maria Gloria, 1973
Theodulfa, Sister Mary, 1969
Theofilos, John Christopher, 1986
Thibeault, Annette R., 1979
Thomas, Colleen Wile, 1990
Thomas, Joan Settle, 1981
Thomas, Josita Marie, 1985
Thomas, Julie Louise, 1986
Thomas, Patricia Pate, 1987
Thomas, Sandra Lorraine, 1986
Thompson, Karen Ellen, 1986
Thompson, Karen L., 1976
Thompson, Laurie, 1977
Thompson, Lula Mae Hollis, 1968
Thompson, Marilyn Y., 1990
Thompson, Mary Ellen, 1975
Thompson, Shelvy Jean, 1983
Thornton, James Arthur, 1979
Tiger, Elizabeth Louise, 1986
Tighe, Mary Louise, 1980
Tillman, Dorothy Massenburg, 1978
Tilton, Lorraine Lois, 1987
Timbrook, Katherine Sue, 1989
Timmons, Ann Vera, 1974
Timney, Patricia Aileen, 1975
Timpano, Deborah May, 1986
Timpko, Beth Anne, 1988
Tinsley, Laureen, 1985
Tipka, Catherine Karen, 1985
Tobia, Carol Marie, 1975
Tobias, Joan Michele, 1978
Tobin, Kathleen Bridget, 1979
Tocci, Rita Maria, 1979
Tokarski, Mary C., 1973
Tokarski, Patricia Marie, 1980
Tomaszewski, Claudia Ann, 1978
Tomlin, Anne Patricia, 1979
Tompkins, Melinda Lynn, 1987
Tool, Cheryl, 1971
Topeka, Sandra Elaine, 1988
Topolski, Eileen Elizabeth, 1990
Torpey, Janice, 1989
Torresson, Elizabeth Lawhon, 1981

Torrillo, Susan Ann, 1983
Tortu, Alicia J., 1988
Toth, Joanne Mary, 1986
Toth, Valerie Joan, 1973
Touey, Jean Baptiste, 1987
Townsend, Mary Elizabeth, 1987
Toye, Celeste Arnell, 1986
Trace, Eileen, 1986
Trachtenberg, Marla Beth, 1986
Traczuk, Luba, 1972
Tran, Binh Michael, 1986
Tran, Sandra Krick, 1985
Trautman, Carla Marie, 1977
Travia, Maria Ann, 1971
Travitz, Brenda Teresa, 1988
Traynham, Patricia Ann, 1979
Treacy, MaryBeth, 1989
Treichler, Barbara Jean, 1977
Tremper, Deborah Lynn, 1989
Treston, Elizabeth Marie, 1970
Tretter, Denise Ann, 1976
Trindle, Meghan Elaine, 1990
Trofe, Gayle Linda, 1976
Trombetta, Karen Lee, 1985
Trotman, Carol Lee, 1979
Troutner, Susan Kathleen, 1969
Trouton, Rosemarie Beth, 1989
Trubilla, Mary Elizabeth, 1985
Trudell, Kathleen Patricia, 1975
Tryon, Thomas D., 1980
Tsui, Miriam, 1975
Tucker, Linda, 1980
Tucker, Raezel Fonda, 1990
Tuckey, Monique Lenora, 1987
Tullos, Teresa Ann, 1989
Tully, Kathleen C., 1985
Tulone, Stephen John, 1970
Tulskie, Ann Marie, 1980
Turner, Melissa, 1986
Turpin, Julie Lynne, 1986
Turzi, Robert J., 1986
Tusch, Janie, 1975
Twist, Karen Louise, 1978
Tyrell, Dorothy Ann, 1974
Tyrell, Eugenia Ann, 1977

~ U ~

Ubaldi-Rosen, Regina Mary, 1988
Uchic, Susan Lorraine, 1983
Ullman, Jane E., 1990
Umar, Tuna, 1986
Underwood, Robert Shawn, 1986
Urbanski, Linda Marie, 1986
Utley, Barbara Lynn, 1974

~ V ~

Vadala, Helen Lorraine, 1988
Vadurro, Judith Phillips, 1981
Valentine, Lisa Ann, 1983
Valentino, Carol Ann, 1980
Valentino, Gorgetta Mae, 1968
Vallieu, Alma Lynn, 1976
Vallieu, Marie, 1971
Valosky, Cherylanne Mary, 1990
Van Auken, Ellen Louise, 1986
Van Name, Jeanne Hinish, 1978
Van Nest, Joann M., 1983
Van Orden, Patricia J., 1987
Van Stan, Susan Tracy, 1990
Van Wyk, Susan, 1985
Van Zanten, Sandra R., 1986
Vandegrift, Michele, 1986
Vandergrift, Beverly Elizabeth, 1974
Vanderlip, Janice Elaine, 1979
VanDoren, Laura Ellen, 1983
Vanore, William, 1969
Vargas, Genalyn P., 1990
Vargas, Geneva Wood, 1980
Vargo, Lynda Marie, 1987
Vaudreuil, Michele, 1970
Vaughn, Lisa Diane, 1990
Vaughn, Susan Kay, 1986
Vekkos, Lynda Renee, 1985
Venner, Marsha Lori, 1981
Venney, Roberta, 1988
Venuti, Elaine Marie, 1988
Veon, Judith Thompson, 1983
Verdon, Michael Patrick, 1986
Verdone, Irene Elizabeth, 1974
Verholy, Karen Louise, 1988
Veronis, Lisa Rose, 1990
Versland, Heidi Jean, 1985
Vetter, Joann, 1973
Vines, Mary Margaret, 1975
Vinson-Ciano, Virginia Wilkinson, 1976
Vitale, Joanna Abbattista, 1975
Vitali, Jane Judith, 1979
Vivaldo, Marie Luisa, 1989
Vizzachero, William A., 1989
Vo, Trinh Tuyet, 1986
Vogler, Robert Charles, Jr., 1985
Vogt, Anna Marie, 1976
Vogt, Evelyn Ada, 1975
Voigt, Grace Anne, 1986
Volk, Douglas V., 1981
Vollmer, Kathleen Theresa, 1985
Voltz, Kathryn Jan, 1975
Von Wellsheim, Elizabeth, 1985
Vora, Charu, 1986
Vorberg, Rene Gene, 1977

Wilson, Sandra Ann, 1979
Wilson, Scott Corcoran, 1987
Wilson, Walter Ray, 1971
Wilson, Wesley Stanley, Jr., 1988
Winch, Nancy Elizabeth, 1986
Winderl, Fritz K., 1989
Windfelder, Joyce M., 1990
Winitz, Mindy S., 1985
Winnberg, Hannah Mary, 1970
Wise, Catherine, 1972
Wise, Wendy Jo, 1990
Wisla, Anne Marie B., 1990
Wisocky, Susan Joanne, 1986
Witkowski, Jay M., 1987
Witlin, Laurie A., 1987
Witten, Lori Ilene, 1975
Wittke, Jill Anne, 1983
Witty, Virginia Adrienne, 1971
Wixted, Patricia Ann, 1988
Woehr, Nancy Elizabeth, 1983
Wojciechowski, Linda, 1986
Wojnar, Anne Gemma, 1988
Wojtecki, Roberta Levithan, 1987
Wojtelwicz, Sandra, 1988
Wolf, Susan Liebers, 1980
Wolf, Susan Louise, 1986
Wolfe, Hope L., 1990
Wolfe, Victoria Leonora, 1985
Wolfgang, Cynthia Ann, 1981
Wolfman, Emily J., 1987
Wolford, Michele Rogers, 1968
Wolgin, Frances Ann, 1977
Wollam, Katrina Ann, 1990
Wollman, Barbara Ann, 1970
Wollman, Bruce Stuart, 1989
Woloszyn, Mary Frances, 1986
Wolper, Eileen M., 1988
Wolper, Eileen Marie Genevieve, 1981
Wood, Mary Ann Rose, 1981
Wood, Rebecca Bowman, 1975
Woodcock, Robert William, 1983
Woodford, Judith Ann, 1978
Woodman, Steven R., 1981
Woods, Karen Elizabeth, 1977
Woods, Mary Catherine, 1988
Woolery, Claire Louise, 1976
Worthy, Gloria Ruby, 1989
Wosiski, Karen Smith, 1983

Wozniak, Gerri Lynn, 1970
Wozny, Rosemary Anne, 1970
Wozny, Rosemary Anne, 1974
Wright, Beryl Anne, 1985
Wright, Beryl Anne, 1986
Wright, Cindy Lynn, 1990
Wright, Dominica Felicia, 1990
Wright, Edith Louise, 1990
Wright, Elaine Margaret, 1976
Wright, Katherine, 1983
Wright, Lesley J., 1990
Wright, Paula Jane, 1988
Wright-Horan, Deborah Jean, 1976
Wu, Jiunn-Jong, 1984
Wuchter, Lois Brady, 1980
Wugofski, Barbara Eileen, 1986
Wychunis, JoElla, 1986
Wydra, Debra, 1971
Wyrembek, Benita Marie, 1975
Wyszynski, Susan Elizabeth, 1982

~ Y ~

Yale, Diane Haviland, 1978
Yamamoto, Suzanne Yukiji, 1986
Yannone, Lisa Marie, 1988
Yarrick, Kathy Louise, 1981
Yarrow, Leanore Rebecca, 1976
Yates, Ruth Ann, 1974
Yatsko, Faye Ann, 1976
Yeager, Diane Marie, 1975
Yehuda, Irma N., 1989
Yerardi-Woodford, Diane, 1986
Yi, Pilsun, 1982
Yocum, Kathleen Mary, 1988
Yonchek, Joan C., 1972
Yorgey, Lauren L., 1980
Young, Bernadette Feliciani, 1988
Young, Beverly, 1975
Young, Cheryl Dawn, 1986
Young, Jacqueline Louise, 1987
Young, Lucia Lim, 1986
Young, Margaret Ann, 1977
Young, Marsha Louise, 1973
Young, Mary Louise, 1976
Young, Maryanne, 1973
Young, Shelley Johanna, 1985
Yousaites, Barbara, 1972

Yovanovich, Paula Kathleen, 1977
Yox, Judith, 1969
Ysmach, Linda Carol, 1976
Yucis, Matthew Joseph, 1982
Yuckenberg, Susan Loretta, 1986
Yuhas, Catherine Bernadette, 1986
Yusem, Randi Ellen, 1987

~ Z ~

Zabinski, Kathleen M., 1976
Zaborowski, Kimberly Ann, 1980
Zack, Minnie, 1982
Zagnojny, Elsie Cecilia, 1969
Zaharfy, Marjorie-Linda, 1981
Zalecky, Anne-Marie, 1972
Zalesky, Carole Ann, 1980
Zalewski-Sorling, Anne Frances, 1988
Zanin, Linda Madeline, 1989
Zappala, Josephine Ann, 1975
Zarnosky, Linda Marie DiVito, 1983
Zarraga, Rita T., 1989
Zartarian, Karen Nevart, 1985
Zarycranski, Deborah, 1980
Zataveski, Linda Ann, 1986
Zawalski, Linda Marie, 1988
Zdziarski, Catherine Ann, 1978
Zdzieborski, Krystyna Jacqueline, 1979
Zehler, Carol Mary, 1981
Zehner, Carol Suzanne, 1982
Zelikoff, Mindy J., 1985
Zeller, Rita Helene, 1976
Zerone, Barbara Jean, 1982
Ziaie, Hasan, 1979
Ziegler, Sandra Rubinsky, 1979
Zimmerman, Cathleen Marian, 1985
Zimmerman, Jean Ann, 1988
Zimmerman, Peggy Louise, 1975
Zipf, Marcia Karen, 1986
Zizzamia, Marie Jean, 1975
Zlupko, Ruth Ann, 1979
Zomchick, Joan, 1989
Zomchick, Mary, 1983
Zweiback, Marcy Beth, 1987
Zwirner, Ellen, 1969
Zwolak, Lorraine Julia, 1978
Zwysen, Carol Ann, 1985